Biology for AP® Courses

SENIOR CONTRIBUTING AUTHORS
JULIANNE ZEDALIS, BISHOP'S SCHOOL
JOHN EGGEBRECHT, BROOKLYN TECHNICAL HIGH SCHOOL

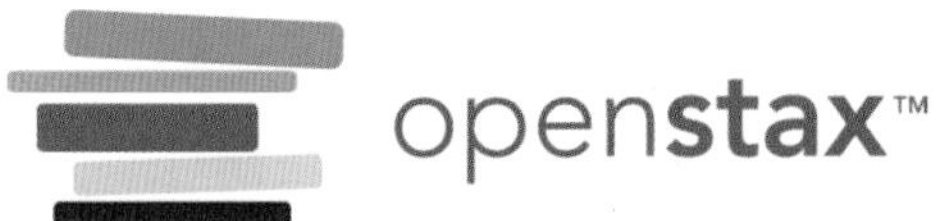

OpenStax
Rice University
6100 Main Street MS-375
Houston, Texas 77005

To learn more about OpenStax, visit https://openstax.org.
Individual print copies and bulk orders can be purchased through our website.

PRINT BOOK ISBN-10	**1-947172-40-9**
PRINT BOOK ISBN-13	**978-1-947172-40-1**
PDF VERSION ISBN-10	**1-947172-41-7**
PDF VERSION ISBN-13	**978-1-947172-41-8**
Revision Number	**APB-2018-001(03/18)-BKB**
Original Publication Year	**2018**

Printed in China

OpenStax

OpenStax provides free, peer-reviewed, openly licensed textbooks for introductory college and Advanced Placement® courses and low-cost, personalized courseware that helps students learn. A nonprofit ed tech initiative based at Rice University, we're committed to helping students access the tools they need to complete their courses and meet their educational goals.

Rice University

OpenStax, OpenStax CNX, and OpenStax Tutor are initiatives of Rice University. As a leading research university with a distinctive commitment to undergraduate education, Rice University aspires to path-breaking research, unsurpassed teaching, and contributions to the betterment of our world. It seeks to fulfill this mission by cultivating a diverse community of learning and discovery that produces leaders across the spectrum of human endeavor.

Foundation Support

OpenStax is grateful for the tremendous support of our sponsors. Without their strong engagement, the goal of free access to high-quality textbooks would remain just a dream.

Laura and John Arnold Foundation (LJAF) actively seeks opportunities to invest in organizations and thought leaders that have a sincere interest in implementing fundamental changes that not only yield immediate gains, but also repair broken systems for future generations. LJAF currently focuses its strategic investments on education, criminal justice, research integrity, and public accountability.

The William and Flora Hewlett Foundation has been making grants since 1967 to help solve social and environmental problems at home and around the world. The Foundation concentrates its resources on activities in education, the environment, global development and population, performing arts, and philanthropy, and makes grants to support disadvantaged communities in the San Francisco Bay Area.

Calvin K. Kazanjian was the founder and president of Peter Paul (Almond Joy), Inc. He firmly believed that the more people understood about basic economics the happier and more prosperous they would be. Accordingly, he established the Calvin K. Kazanjian Economics Foundation Inc, in 1949 as a philanthropic, nonpolitical educational organization to support efforts that enhanced economic understanding.

Guided by the belief that every life has equal value, the Bill & Melinda Gates Foundation works to help all people lead healthy, productive lives. In developing countries, it focuses on improving people's health with vaccines and other life-saving tools and giving them the chance to lift themselves out of hunger and extreme poverty. In the United States, it seeks to significantly improve education so that all young people have the opportunity to reach their full potential. Based in Seattle, Washington, the foundation is led by CEO Jeff Raikes and Co-chair William H. Gates Sr., under the direction of Bill and Melinda Gates and Warren Buffett.

The Maxfield Foundation supports projects with potential for high impact in science, education, sustainability, and other areas of social importance.

Our mission at The Michelson 20MM Foundation is to grow access and success by eliminating unnecessary hurdles to affordability. We support the creation, sharing, and proliferation of more effective, more affordable educational content by leveraging disruptive technologies, open educational resources, and new models for collaboration between for-profit, nonprofit, and public entities.

The Bill and Stephanie Sick Fund supports innovative projects in the areas of Education, Art, Science and Engineering.

Table of Contents

PREFACE

Welcome to *Biology for AP® Courses*, an OpenStax resource. This textbook was written to increase student access to high-quality learning materials, maintaining highest standards of academic rigor at little to no cost.

About OpenStax

OpenStax is a nonprofit based at Rice University, and it's our mission to improve student access to education. Our first openly licensed college textbook was published in 2012, and our library has since scaled to over 25 books for college and AP® courses used by hundreds of thousands of students. OpenStax Tutor, our low-cost personalized learning tool, is being used in college courses throughout the country. Through our partnerships with philanthropic foundations and our alliance with other educational resource organizations, OpenStax is breaking down the most common barriers to learning and empowering students and instructors to succeed.

About OpenStax resources

Customization

Biology for AP® Courses is licensed under a Creative Commons Attribution 4.0 International (CC BY) license, which means that you can distribute, remix, and build upon the content, as long as you provide attribution to OpenStax and its content contributors.

Because our books are openly licensed, you are free to use the entire book or pick and choose the sections that are most relevant to the needs of your course. Feel free to remix the content by assigning your students certain chapters and sections in your syllabus, in the order that you prefer. You can even provide a direct link in your syllabus to the sections in the web view of your book.

Instructors also have the option of creating a customized version of their OpenStax book. The custom version can be made available to students in low-cost print or digital form through their campus bookstore. Visit the Instructor Resources section of your book page on OpenStax.org for information.

Errata

All OpenStax textbooks undergo a rigorous review process. However, like any professional-grade textbook, errors sometimes occur. Since our books are web based, we can make updates periodically when deemed pedagogically necessary. If you have a correction to suggest, submit it through the link on your book page on OpenStax.org. Subject matter experts review all errata suggestions. OpenStax is committed to remaining transparent about all updates, so you will also find a list of past errata changes on your book page on OpenStax.org.

Format

You can access this textbook for free in web view or PDF through OpenStax.org, and for a low cost in print.

About *Biology for AP® Courses*

Biology for AP® Courses covers the scope and sequence requirements of a typical two-semester Advanced Placement® biology course. The text provides comprehensive coverage of core biology concepts and foundational research through an evolutionary lens. *Biology for AP® Courses* was designed to meet and exceed the requirements of the College Board's AP® Biology framework while allowing significant flexibility for instructors. Each section of the book includes an introduction based on the AP® curriculum as well as rich features that engage students in scientific practice and AP® test preparation. It also highlights careers and research opportunities in the biological sciences.

Coverage and scope

In developing *Biology for AP®* Courses, we relied on experts in the goals and approach of the AP® curriculum, carefully considered the AP® framework design, and listened to the advice of hundreds of high school and college biology instructors.

The result is a book that provides excellent coverage of the AP® framework while addressing the sheer breadth of biology topics in the modern age. We provide a thorough treatment of biology's foundational concepts while condensing selected topics. We also strive to make biology, as a discipline, interesting and accessible to students. In addition to a comprehensive coverage of core concepts and foundational research, we have incorporated features that draw learners into the discipline in meaningful ways.

Unit 1: The Chemistry of Life. Our opening unit introduces students to the sciences, including scientific methods and the fundamental concepts of chemistry and physics that provide a framework within which learners comprehend biological processes.

Unit 2: The Cell. Students will gain solid understanding of the structures, functions, and processes of the most basic unit of life: the cell.

Unit 3: Genetics. Our comprehensive genetics unit takes learners from the earliest experiments that revealed the basis of inheritance through the intricacies of DNA's structure, replication, and expression, to current applications in the studies of biotechnology and genomics.

Unit 4: Evolutionary Processes. The core concepts of evolution are discussed in this unit with examples illustrating evolutionary processes. Additionally, the evolutionary basis of biology reappears throughout the textbook in general discussion and is also reinforced through special call-out features highlighting specific topics in evolution.

Unit 5: Biological Diversity. The diversity of life is explored through detailed study of all phyla of organisms as well as discussion of their phylogenetic relationships. The unit begins with viruses and then moves through prokaryotes and eukaryotes, ending with a discussion of vertebrates and, finally, humans.

Unit 6: Plant Structure and Function. Our plant anatomy and physiology unit thoroughly covers the fundamental structure and function of plant cells, tissues, and organs. It also covers important plant physiological functions such as tissue differentiation, material transport, and the roles of plant hormones.

Unit 7: Animal Structure and Function. An introduction to the form and function of the animal body is followed by detailed chapters on specific body systems and their physiological function. This unit touches on the biology of all organisms while maintaining an engaging focus on human anatomy and physiology that helps students connect to the topics.

Unit 8: Ecology. Ecological concepts are broadly covered in this unit, beginning with the small-scale relationships of population ecology and gradually building to the large-scale processes of ecosystem ecology. Localized, real-world issues of conservation and biodiversity are presented at numerous points along the way.

AP® Connections

Every section of the textbook — over 200 total — begins with a "Connection for AP® Courses." Section. Written by Julianne Zedalis, the College Board's AP® Biology Curriculum Committee Co-Chair, these valuable overviews provide meaningful support for students and instructors.

Each Connection highlights the key concepts of the section in the context of the AP® Biology Curriculum Framework and explains their importance in brief, engaging language.

The explanations build upon the knowledge gained in previous sections, reinforcing the most significant concepts and alerting students of the foundational basis of upcoming material. This helps students build a more comprehensive understanding and helps instructors reference prior explanations.

Direct references to the relevant sections of the AP® Curriculum Framework are first explained and then outlined in table format emphasizing their importance and relating them to the overall design of the course. Students and teachers using these reference tables can easily see their progression through and coverage of the required curriculum.

Scientific practices

The AP® Biology Science Practices are presented to students through several active learning features.

Science Practice Connections for AP® Courses provide a context and suggested activity linking the concepts with the relevant science practices. Students are often asked to build representations, undertake brief research, or answer critical thinking questions.

Science Practice Questions, designed and authored by John Eggebrecht and Julianne Zedalis, present a complex scenario or data set and ask students a series of multiple-choice and open-ended questions based on a complex scenario or data set. These robust activities hone students' scientific thinking skills and prepare them for similar questions on the AP® Examination.

Pedagogical foundation and features

Biology for AP® Courses® is grounded in a solid scientific base, with features that engage the students in scientific inquiry:

Evolution Connection features highlight the importance and relevance of evolutionary theory to all biological study. Through discussions like "The Evolution of Metabolic Pathways" and "Algae and Evolutionary Paths to Photosynthesis," the student is able to see how evolution pervades all aspects of biology.

Scientific Methods Connection call-outs walk students through actual or thought experiments that elucidate scientific processes and procedures for a variety of topics. Features include "Determining the Time Spent in Cell Cycle Stages" and "Testing the Hypothesis of Independent Assortment."

Career Connection features present information on a variety of careers in the biological sciences. They are meant to introduce students to professions and day-to-day work related to the current section content. Examples include microbiologist, ecologist, neurologist, and forensic scientist.

Everyday Connection features tie biological concepts to students' everyday lives as well as emerging world issues related to biology. Topics include "Chesapeake Bay" and "Can Snail Venom Be Used as a Pharmacological Pain Killer?"

Illustrations and animations that engage

Illustrations within the book are designed to help students visualize the concepts of biology using figures with simple, clear, designs and color schemes that go side-by-side with vivid photos and micrographs. *Biology for AP® Courses* also incorporates links to relevant animations and interactive exercises that help bring biology to life.

Visual Connection features identify core figures in each chapter for student study. Questions about key figures, including clicker questions that can be used in the classroom, engage students' critical thinking to ensure genuine understanding.

Link to Learning features direct students to online interactive exercises and animations that add greater context to core content.

Additional resources

Student and instructor resources

We''ve compiled additional resources for both students and instructors, including Getting Started Guides, and a teacher''s guide. Instructor resources require a verified instructor account, which you can apply for when you log in or create your account on OpenStax.org. Take advantage of these resources to supplement your OpenStax book.

Community Hubs

Insert paragraph text here.OpenStax partners with the Institute for the Study of Knowledge Management in Education (ISKME) to offer Community Hubs on OER Commons – a platform for instructors to share community-created resources that support OpenStax books, free of charge. Through our Community Hubs, instructors can upload their own materials or download resources to use in their own courses, including additional ancillaries, teaching material, multimedia, and relevant course content. We encourage instructors to join the hubs for the subjects most relevant to your teaching and research as an opportunity both to enrich your courses and to engage with other faculty.

?To reach the Community Hubs, visit **https://www.oercommons.org/hubs/OpenStax (https://www.oercommons.org/hubs/OpenStax)** .

Partner resources

OpenStax Partners are our allies in the mission to make high-quality learning materials affordable and accessible to students and instructors everywhere. Their tools integrate seamlessly with our OpenStax titles at a low cost. To access the partner resources for your text, visit your book page on OpenStax.org.

About the authors

Senior contributing authors

Julianne Zedalis, Bishop's School, La Jolla, California
Julianne Zedalis has taught AP® Biology for over twenty years. She served on the College Board's committee to rewrite and test the revised AP® Curriculum Framework, working with other high school AP® teachers and college faculty as well as the National Science Foundation. She was later selected to chair the College Board's Curriculum Development and

Assessment Committee.

John Eggebrecht

Dr. John Eggebrecht, Brooklyn Technical High School (retired), Brooklyn, New York
John Eggebrecht taught AP® Physics and Biology courses for over thirty years. He was instrumental in the development and revision of various AP® curriculum frameworks over an extended collaboration with the College Board and other educational organizations. Under his guidance, Brooklyn Tech was repeatedly selected by the College Board as an exemplary AP® program, and its practices and students outcomes were featured in several publications. In addition to his writing role, John regularly evaluates course materials and programs for alignment and quality.

Contributing authors

Connie Rye, East Mississippi Community College
Robert Wise, The University of Wisconsin Oshkosh
Vladimir Jurukovski, Suffolk County Community College
Jean DeSaix, The University of North Carolina at Chapel Hill
Jung Choi, Georgia Institute of Technology
Yael Avissar, Rhode Island College

Curriculum Framework for AP® Biology

Big Idea 1: The process of evolution drives the diversity and unity of life.

Enduring understanding 1.A. Change in the genetic makeup of a population over time is evolution.	**Chapter/Key Concepts**
1.A.1. Natural selection is a major mechanism of evolution.	5.3, 18.1, 18.2, 19.1, 19.2, 19.3, 21.2, 23.5
1.A.2. Natural selection acts on phenotypic variations in populations.	7.3, 7.6, 18.2, 19.2, 19.3, 36.5
1.A.3. Evolutionary change is also driven by random processes.	19.1, 19.2
1.A.4. Biological evolution is supported by scientific evidence from many disciplines, including mathematics.	2.1, 5.2, 8.2, 11.1, 14.1, 17.1 18.1, 19.3
Enduring understanding 1.B. Organisms are linked by lines of descent from common ancestry.	**Chapter/Key Concepts**
1.B.1. Organisms share many conserved core processes and features that evolved and are widely distributed among organisms today.	3.4, 4.3, 4.6, 8.2, 15.3, 13.2, 14.1, 15.5, 18.1, 20.1, 20.2
1.B.2. Phylogenetic trees and cladograms are graphical representations (models) of evolutionary history that can be tested.	14.4, 20.1, 20.2, 20.3
Enduring understanding 1.C. Life continues to evolve within a changing environment.	**Chapter/Key Concepts**
1.C.1. Speciation and extinction have occurred throughout the Earth's history.	14.4, 18.2, 20.1, 38.1
1.C.2. Speciation may occur when two populations become reproductively isolated from each other.	18.2, 19.2, 23.5
1.C.3. Populations of organisms continue to evolve.	7.3, 7.6, 18.1, 18.3, 19.1, 19.2, 20.1, 20.2, 23.5
Enduring understanding 1.D. The origin of living systems is explained by natural processes.	**Chapter/Key Concepts**
1.D.1. There are several hypotheses about the natural origin of life on Earth, each with supporting scientific evidence.	8.2, 18.1, 20.1, 21.1, 20.3
1.D.2. Scientific evidence from many different disciplines supports models of the origin of life.	8.2, 18.1, 20.2, 28.1

Big Idea 2: Biological systems utilize free energy and molecular building blocks to grow, to reproduce and to maintain dynamic homeostasis.

Enduring understanding 2.A. Growth, reproduction and maintenance of the organization of living systems require free energy and matter.	**Chapter/Key Concepts**
2.A.1. All living systems require constant input of free energy	6.1, 6.2, 6.3, 6.4, 6.7, 7.1, 7.2, 7.3, 7.4, 7.5, 7.6, 8.2, 23.1, 23.5, 36.3, 37.2
2.A.2. Organisms capture and store free energy for use in biological processes.	3.2, 4.3, 6.1, 6.4, 6.5, 7.1, 7.2, 7.3, 7.4, 7.4, 7.5, 7.6, 8.1, 8.2, 8.3, 9.2, 22.1, 22.2, 23.1, 23.5, 37.2
2.A.3. Organisms must exchange matter with the environment to grow, reproduce and maintain organization.	2.1, 2.2, 3.3, 4.2, 4.6, 6.1, 6.8, 22.4, 22.5, 23.5, 25.8, 37.3
Enduring understanding 2.B. Growth, reproduction and dynamic homeostasis require that cells create and maintain internal environments that are different from their external environments.	**Chapter/Key Concepts**
2.B.1. Cell membranes are selectively permeable due to their structure.	3.2, 3.3, 5.1, 5.2, 5.3, 5.4, 8.3
2.B.2. Growth and dynamic homeostasis are maintained by the constant movement of molecules across membranes.	2.3, 3.3, 5.2, 5.3, 5.4
2.B.3. Eukaryotic cells maintain internal membranes that partition the cell into specialized regions.	3.3, 4.2, 4.3, 4.4
Enduring understanding 2.C. Organisms use feedback mechanisms to regulate growth and reproduction, and to maintain dynamic homeostasis.	**Chapter/Key Concepts**
2.C.1. Organisms use feedback mechanisms to maintain their internal environments and respond to external environmental changes.	5.2, 5.3, 7.1, 7.2, 7.3, 7.4, 7.5, 7.6, 8.2, 10.1, 11.1, 21.1, 23.5, 24.3, 28.3
2.C.2. Organisms respond to changes in their external environments.	2.1, 6.4, 7.5, 7.6, 22.5, 23.5, 26.3, 26.5
Enduring understanding 2.D. Growth and dynamic homeostasis of a biological system are influenced by changes in the system's environment.	**Chapter/Key Concepts**
2.D.1. All biological systems from cells and organisms to populations, communities and ecosystems are affected by complex biotic and abiotic interactions involving exchange of matter and free energy.	2.1, 2.2, 7.1, 7.4, 7.5, 7.6, 8.2, 15.2, 15.3, 17.3, 21.1, 22.4, 35.1, 37.1
2.D.2. Homeostatic mechanisms reflect both common ancestry and divergence due to adaptation in different environments.	4.3, 5.2, 6.1, 18.2, 21.1, 25.1, 32.1, 32.3, 34.1
2.D.3. Biological systems are affected by disruptions to their dynamic homeostasis.	3.2, 22.3, 22.5, 23.1, 28.3, 38.2
2.D.4. Plants and animals have a variety of chemical defenses against infections that affect dynamic homeostasis.	23.6, 33.1, 33.2
Enduring understanding 2.E. Many biological processes involved in growth, reproduction and dynamic homeostasis include temporal regulation and coordination.	**Chapter/Key Concepts**
2.E.1. Timing and coordination of specific events are necessary for the normal development of an organism, and these events are regulated by a variety of mechanisms.	10.2, 10.3, 14.3, 23.5, 30.1, 32.3, 34.1, 34.6
2.E.2. Timing and coordination of physiological events are regulated by multiple mechanisms.	6.8, 10.1, 10.2, 15.3, 22.3, 23.2, 24.1, 30.6, 36.1, 36.2, 36.3, 36.4, 36.5, 43.6, 43.7

Big Idea 2: Biological systems utilize free energy and molecular building blocks to grow, to reproduce and to maintain dynamic homeostasis.

2.E.3. Timing and coordination of behavior are regulated by various mechanisms and are important in natural selection.	11.1, 21.2, 23.5, 30.6, 35.2, 45.7

Big Idea 3: Living systems store, retrieve, transmit and respond to information essential to life processes.

Enduring understanding 3.A. Heritable information provides for continuity of life.	**Chapter/Key Concepts**
3.A.1. DNA, and in some cases RNA, is the primary source of heritable information.	3.5, 10.3, 13.1, 13.2, 14.1, 14.2, 14.3, 14.5, 15.1, 15.2, 15.3, 15.4, 15.5, 16.1, 16.2, 16.3, 17.1, 17.3, 21.1, 21.2, 22.4
3.A.2. In eukaryotes, heritable information is passed to the next generation via processes that include the cell cycle and mitosis or meiosis plus fertilization.	10.1, 10.2, 10.3, 11.1, 11.2, 13.1
3.A.3. The chromosomal basis of inheritance provides an understanding of the pattern of passage (transmission) of genes from parent to offspring.	11.2, 12.1, 12.2, 13.1, 14.2, 17.1, 17.4
3.A.4. The inheritance pattern of many traits cannot be explained by simple Mendelian genetics.	4.3, 12.2, 13.1
Enduring understanding 3.B. Expression of genetic information involves cellular and molecular mechanisms.	**Chapter/Key Concepts**
3.B.1. Gene regulation results in differential gene expression, leading to cell specialization.	7.3, 7.6, 16.1, 16.2, 16.3, 16.4, 16.5, 17.3
3.B.2. A variety of intercellular and intracellular signal transmissions mediate gene expression.	9.1, 9.2, 9.3, 15.3, 17.1
Enduring understanding 3.C. The processing of genetic information is imperfect and is a source of genetic variation.	**Chapter/Key Concepts**
3.C.1. Changes in genotype can result in changes in phenotype.	5.3, 11.2, 13.1, 13.2, 14.6, 15.1, 17.1, 18.1, 19.1, 19.3
3.C.2. Biological systems have multiple processes that increase genetic variation.	11.2, 13.1, 14.1, 14.6, 15.2, 17.1, 20.3, 21.2, 22.4
3.C.3. Viral replication results in genetic variation, and viral infection can introduce genetic variation into the hosts.	21.1, 21.2
Enduring understanding 3.D. Cells communicate by generating, transmitting and receiving chemical signals	**Chapter/Key Concepts**
3.D.1. Cell communication processes share common features that reflect a shared evolutionary history.	4.6, 9.1, 9.2, 9.3, 9.4, 10.4, 37.2, 37.3
3.D.2. Cells communicate with each other through direct contact with other cells or from a distance via chemical signaling.	9.1, 9.3
3.D.3. Signal transduction pathways link signal reception with cellular response.	9.1, 9.2
3.D.4. Changes in signal transduction pathways can alter cellular response.	9.2, 9.3, 9.4

Big Idea 3: Living systems store, retrieve, transmit and respond to information essential to life processes.

Enduring understanding 3.E. Transmission of information results in changes within and between biological systems.	**Chapter/Key Concepts**
3.E.1. Individuals can act on information and communicate it to others.	9.2, 9.4, 21.2, 36.1, 36.2, 36.3, 36.4, 36.5
3.E.2. Animals have nervous systems that detect external and internal signals, transmit and integrate information, and produce responses.	6.1, 35.1, 35.2, 35.3, 35.4

Big Idea 4: Biological systems interact, and these systems and their interactions possess complex properties.

Enduring understanding 4.A Interactions within biological systems lead to complex properties.	**Chapter/Key Concepts**
4.A.1. The subcomponents of biological molecules and their sequence determine the properties of that molecule.	3.1, 3.2, 3.3, 3.4, 3.5, 5.2, 6.2, 14.1, 14.3, 14.4, 17.1
4.A.2. The structure and function of subcellular components, and their interactions, provide essential cellular processes.	3.4, 4.3, 4.4, 4.6, 10.3, 15.3
4.A.3. Interactions between external stimuli and regulated gene expression result in specialization of cells, tissues and organs.	16.1, 22.3, 43.6, 43.7
4.A.4. Organisms exhibit complex properties due to interactions between their constituent parts.	15.2, 17.1, 18.1, 22.3, 22.5, 30.5, 33.3, 34.3
4.A.5. Communities are composed of populations of organisms that interact in complex ways.	22.5, 23.5, 45.5, 45.6
4.A.6. Interactions among living systems and with their environment result in the movement of matter and energy.	3.2, 3.3, 6.2, 6.3, 6.6, 7.5, 7.6, 8.2, 10.3, 18.1, 23.1, 22.4, 45.2, 45.6, 46.2, 47.3
Enduring understanding 4.B Competition and cooperation are important aspects of biological systems.	**Chapter/Key Concepts**
4.B.1. Interactions between molecules affect their structure and function.	3.5, 5.2, 6.2, 6.5, 8.3
4.B.2. Cooperative interactions within organisms promote efficiency in the use of energy and matter.	4.3, 7.3, 7.6, 45.6
4.B.3. Interactions between and within populations influence patterns of species distribution and abundance.	45.4, 45.6
4.B.4. Distribution of local and global ecosystems changes over time.	22.4, 23.1, 46.1, 47.1, 47.3
Enduring understanding 4.C. Naturally occurring diversity among and between components within biological systems affects interactions with the environment.	**Chapter/Key Concepts**
4.C.1. Variation in molecular units provides cells with a wider range of functions.	3.4, 9.2, 10.3, 13.1, 15.5, 42.2, 49.1
4.C.2. Environmental factors influence the expression of the genotype in an organism.	14.2, 19.3, 22.3, 30.4, 43.1
4.C.3. The level of variation in a population affects population dynamics.	7.5, 7.6, 19.1, 45.6, 47.1

Big Idea 4: Biological systems interact, and these systems and their interactions possess complex properties.

4.C.4. The diversity of species within an ecosystem may influence the stability of the ecosystem.	45.6, 46.1

1 | THE STUDY OF LIFE

Figure 1.1 This NASA image is a composite of several satellite-based views of Earth. To make the whole-Earth image, NASA scientists combine observations of different parts of the planet. (credit: NASA/GSFC/NOAA/USGS)

Chapter Outline

Introduction

Viewed from space, Earth offers no clues about the diversity of life it harbors. The first forms of life on Earth are thought be microorganisms that existed for billions of years in the ocean before plants and animals appeared. The mammals, birds, and flowers that we see in modern times are mostly "recent" species, originating 130 to 200 million years ago. In fact, only in the last 200,000 years have humans started looking like we do today.

Organisms evolve in response to each other. One of the best examples is disease causing organisms, which have to adapt to overcome the defenses of the organisms they infect. One such organism that has evolved to specialize in infection in humans is *Plasmodium*, the organism that causes malaria. Biologists use the process of science to learn about the world and the organisms living in it. For example, people have suspected for quite some time that people with blood type O are less likely to die from severe malaria. Now, a team of scientists have been able to explain why. By examining data from several experiments, and by using both inductive and deductive reasoning, the scientists concluded that A and B type blood reacts with a protein excreted by *Plasmodium*. This reaction causes severe illness. However, type O blood does not react with the protein. You can **read more (http://openstaxcollege.org/l/32plasmodium)** about the response of type A and B blood groups to infection by *Plasmodium*.

1.1 | The Science of Biology

In this section, you will explore the following questions:

- What are the characteristics shared by the natural sciences?
- What are the steps of the scientific method?

Connection for AP® courses

Biology is the science that studies living organisms and their interactions with one another and with their environment. The process of science attempts to describe and understand the nature of the universe by rational means. Science has many fields; those fields related to the physical world, including biology, are considered natural sciences. All of the natural sciences follow the laws of chemistry and physics. For example, when studying biology, you must remember living organisms obey the laws of thermodynamics while using free energy and matter from the environment to carry out life processes that are explored in later chapters, such as metabolism and reproduction.

Two types of logical reasoning are used in science: inductive reasoning and deductive reasoning. **Inductive reasoning** uses particular results to produce general scientific principles. **Deductive reasoning** uses logical thinking to predict results by applying scientific principles or practices. The scientific method is a step-by-step process that consists of: making observations, defining a problem, posing hypotheses, testing these hypotheses by designing and conducting investigations, and drawing conclusions from data and results. Scientists then communicate their results to the scientific community. Scientific theories are subject to revision as new information is collected.

The content presented in this section supports the Learning Objectives outlined in Big Idea 2 of the AP® Biology Curriculum Framework. The Learning Objectives merge Essential Knowledge content with one or more of the seven Science Practices. These objectives provide a transparent foundation for the AP® Biology course, along with inquiry-based laboratory experiences, instructional activities, and AP® Exam questions.

Big Idea 2	Biological systems utilize free energy and molecular building blocks to grow, to reproduce, and to maintain dynamic homeostasis.
Enduring Understanding 2.A	Growth, reproduction and maintenance of living systems require free energy and matter.
Essential Knowledge	**2.A.1** All living systems require constant input of free energy.
Science Practice	**6.4** The student can make claims and predictions about natural phenomena based on scientific theories and models
Learning Objectives	**2.3** The student is able to predict how changes in free energy availability affect organisms, populations and ecosystems.

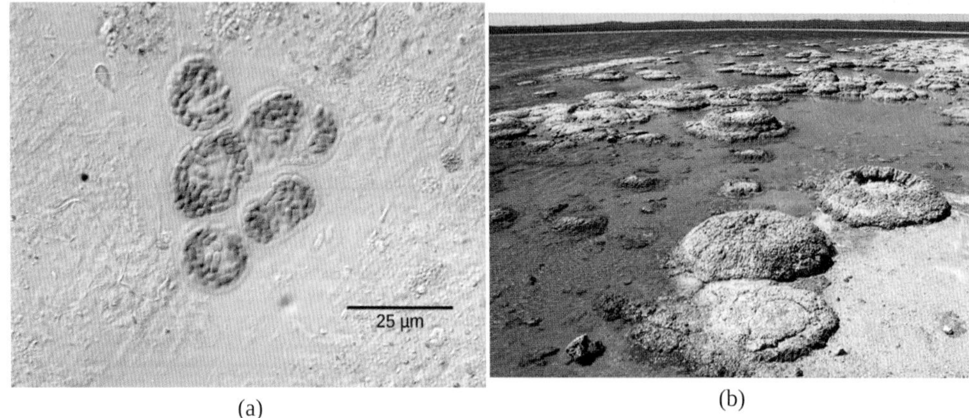

Figure 1.2 Formerly called blue-green algae, these (a) cyanobacteria, shown here at 300x magnification under a light microscope, are some of Earth's oldest life forms. These (b) stromatolites along the shores of Lake Thetis in Western Australia are ancient structures formed by the layering of cyanobacteria in shallow waters. (credit a: modification of work by NASA; credit b: modification of work by Ruth Ellison; scale-bar data from Matt Russell)

What is biology? In simple terms, **biology** is the study of living organisms and their interactions with one another and their environments. This is a very broad definition because the scope of biology is vast. Biologists may study anything from the microscopic or submicroscopic view of a cell to ecosystems and the whole living planet (Figure 1.2). Listening to the daily news, you will quickly realize how many aspects of biology are discussed every day. For example, recent news topics include *Escherichia coli* (Figure 1.3) outbreaks in spinach and *Salmonella* contamination in peanut butter. On a global scale, many researchers are committed to finding ways to protect the planet, solve environmental issues, and reduce the effects of climate change. All of these diverse endeavors are related to different facets of the discipline of biology.

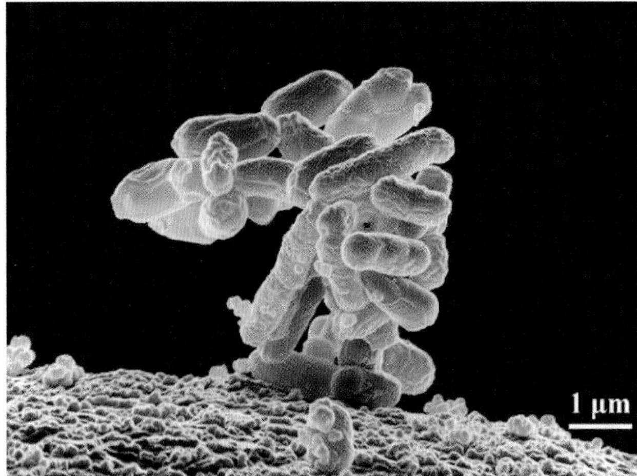

Figure 1.3 *Escherichia coli* (*E. coli*) bacteria, seen in this scanning electron micrograph, are normal residents of our digestive tracts that aid in the absorption of vitamin K and other nutrients. However, virulent strains are sometimes responsible for disease outbreaks. (credit: Eric Erbe, digital colorization by Christopher Pooley, both of USDA, ARS, EMU)

The Process of Science

Biology is a science, but what exactly is science? What does the study of biology share with other scientific disciplines? **Science** (from the Latin *scientia*, meaning “knowledge”) can be defined as knowledge that covers general truths or the operation of general laws, especially when acquired and tested by the scientific method. It becomes clear from this definition that the application of the scientific method plays a major role in science. The **scientific method** is a method of research with defined steps that include experiments and careful observation.

The steps of the scientific method will be examined in detail later, but one of the most important aspects of this method is the testing of hypotheses by means of repeatable experiments. A **hypothesis** is a suggested explanation for an event, which can be tested. Although using the scientific method is inherent to science, it is inadequate in determining what science is. This is because it is relatively easy to apply the scientific method to disciplines such as physics and chemistry, but when it comes to disciplines like archaeology, psychology, and geology, the scientific method becomes less applicable as it becomes more difficult to repeat experiments.

These areas of study are still sciences, however. Consider archaeology—even though one cannot perform repeatable experiments, hypotheses may still be supported. For instance, an archaeologist can hypothesize that an ancient culture existed based on finding a piece of pottery. Further hypotheses could be made about various characteristics of this culture, and these hypotheses may be found to be correct or false through continued support or contradictions from other findings. A hypothesis may become a verified theory. A **theory** is a tested and confirmed explanation for observations or phenomena. Science may be better defined as fields of study that attempt to comprehend the nature of the universe.

Natural Sciences

What would you expect to see in a museum of natural sciences? Frogs? Plants? Dinosaur skeletons? Exhibits about how the brain functions? A planetarium? Gems and minerals? Or, maybe all of the above? Science includes such diverse fields as astronomy, biology, computer sciences, geology, logic, physics, chemistry, and mathematics (Figure 1.4). However, those fields of science related to the physical world and its phenomena and processes are considered **natural sciences**. Thus, a museum of natural sciences might contain any of the items listed above.

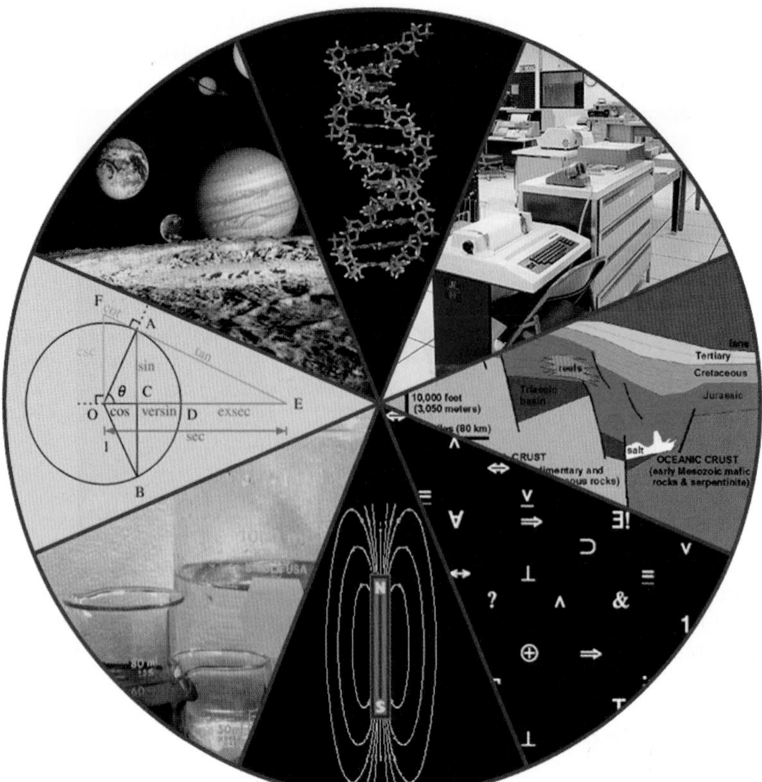

Figure 1.4 The diversity of scientific fields includes astronomy, biology, computer science, geology, logic, physics, chemistry, mathematics, and many other fields. (credit: "Image Editor"/Flickr)

There is no complete agreement when it comes to defining what the natural sciences include, however. For some experts, the natural sciences are astronomy, biology, chemistry, earth science, and physics. Other scholars choose to divide natural sciences into **life sciences**, which study living things and include biology, and **physical sciences**, which study nonliving matter and include astronomy, geology, physics, and chemistry. Some disciplines such as biophysics and biochemistry build on both life and physical sciences and are interdisciplinary. Natural sciences are sometimes referred to as "hard science" because they rely on the use of quantitative data; social sciences that study society and human behavior are more likely to use qualitative assessments to drive investigations and findings.

Not surprisingly, the natural science of biology has many branches or subdisciplines. Cell biologists study cell structure and function, while biologists who study anatomy investigate the structure of an entire organism. Those biologists studying physiology, however, focus on the internal functioning of an organism. Some areas of biology focus on only particular types of living things. For example, botanists explore plants, while zoologists specialize in animals.

Scientific Reasoning

One thing is common to all forms of science: an ultimate goal "to know." Curiosity and inquiry are the driving forces for the development of science. Scientists seek to understand the world and the way it operates. To do this, they use two methods of logical thinking: inductive reasoning and deductive reasoning.

Inductive reasoning is a form of logical thinking that uses related observations to arrive at a general conclusion. This type of reasoning is common in descriptive science. A life scientist such as a biologist makes observations and records them. These data can be qualitative or quantitative, and the raw data can be supplemented with drawings, pictures, photos, or videos. From many observations, the scientist can infer conclusions (inductions) based on evidence. Inductive reasoning involves formulating generalizations inferred from careful observation and the analysis of a large amount of data. Brain studies provide an example. In this type of research, many live brains are observed while people are doing a specific activity, such as viewing images of food. The part of the brain that "lights up" during this activity is then predicted to be the part controlling the response to the selected stimulus, in this case, images of food. The "lighting up" of the various areas of the brain is caused by excess absorption of radioactive sugar derivatives by active areas of the brain. The resultant increase in radioactivity is observed by a scanner. Then, researchers can stimulate that part of the brain to see if similar responses result.

Deductive reasoning or deduction is the type of logic used in hypothesis-based science. In deductive reason, the pattern of thinking moves in the opposite direction as compared to inductive reasoning. Deductive reasoning is a form of logical thinking that uses a general principle or law to forecast specific results. From those general principles, a scientist can extrapolate and predict the specific results that would be valid as long as the general principles are valid. Studies in climate change can illustrate this type of reasoning. For example, scientists may predict that if the climate becomes warmer in a particular region, then the distribution of plants and animals should change. These predictions have been made and tested, and many such changes have been found, such as the modification of arable areas for agriculture, with change based on temperature averages.

Both types of logical thinking are related to the two main pathways of scientific study: descriptive science and hypothesis-based science. **Descriptive (or discovery) science**, which is usually inductive, aims to observe, explore, and discover, while **hypothesis-based science**, which is usually deductive, begins with a specific question or problem and a potential answer or solution that can be tested. The boundary between these two forms of study is often blurred, and most scientific endeavors combine both approaches. The fuzzy boundary becomes apparent when thinking about how easily observation can lead to specific questions. For example, a gentleman in the 1940s observed that the burr seeds that stuck to his clothes and his dog's fur had a tiny hook structure. On closer inspection, he discovered that the burrs' gripping device was more reliable than a zipper. He eventually developed a company and produced the hook-and-loop fastener often used on lace-less sneakers and athletic braces. Descriptive science and hypothesis-based science are in continuous dialogue.

The Scientific Method

Biologists study the living world by posing questions about it and seeking science-based responses. This approach is common to other sciences as well and is often referred to as the scientific method. The scientific method was used even in ancient times, but it was first documented by England's Sir Francis Bacon (1561–1626) (Figure 1.5), who set up inductive methods for scientific inquiry. The scientific method is not exclusively used by biologists but can be applied to almost all fields of study as a logical, rational problem-solving method.

Figure 1.5 Sir Francis Bacon (1561–1626) is credited with being the first to define the scientific method. (credit: Paul van Somer)

The scientific process typically starts with an observation (often a problem to be solved) that leads to a question. Let's think about a simple problem that starts with an observation and apply the scientific method to solve the problem. One Monday morning, a student arrives at class and quickly discovers that the classroom is too warm. That is an observation that also describes a problem: the classroom is too warm. The student then asks a question: "Why is the classroom so warm?"

Proposing a Hypothesis

Recall that a hypothesis is a suggested explanation that can be tested. To solve a problem, several hypotheses may be proposed. For example, one hypothesis might be, "The classroom is warm because no one turned on the air conditioning." But there could be other responses to the question, and therefore other hypotheses may be proposed. A second hypothesis might be, "The classroom is warm because there is a power failure, and so the air conditioning doesn't work."

Once a hypothesis has been selected, the student can make a prediction. A prediction is similar to a hypothesis but it typically has the format "If . . . then . . . ." For example, the prediction for the first hypothesis might be, "*If* the student turns on the air conditioning, *then* the classroom will no longer be too warm."

Testing a Hypothesis

A valid hypothesis must be testable. It should also be **falsifiable**, meaning that it can be disproven by experimental results. Importantly, science does not claim to "prove" anything because scientific understandings are always subject to modification with further information. This step—openness to disproving ideas—is what distinguishes sciences from non-sciences. The presence of the supernatural, for instance, is neither testable nor falsifiable. To test a hypothesis, a researcher will conduct one or more experiments designed to eliminate one or more of the hypotheses. Each experiment will have one or more variables and one or more controls. A **variable** is any part of the experiment that can vary or change during the experiment. The **control group** contains every feature of the experimental group except it is not given the manipulation that is hypothesized about. Therefore, if the results of the experimental group differ from the control group, the difference must be due to the hypothesized manipulation, rather than some outside factor. Look for the variables and controls in the examples that follow. To test the first hypothesis, the student would find out if the air conditioning is on. If the air conditioning is turned on but does not work, there should be another reason, and this hypothesis should be rejected. To test the second hypothesis, the student could check if the lights in the classroom are functional. If so, there is no power failure and this hypothesis should be rejected. Each hypothesis should be tested by carrying out appropriate experiments. Be aware that rejecting one hypothesis does not determine whether or not the other hypotheses can be accepted; it simply eliminates one hypothesis that is not valid (see this figure). Using the scientific method, the hypotheses that are inconsistent with experimental data are rejected.

While this "warm classroom" example is based on observational results, other hypotheses and experiments might have clearer controls. For instance, a student might attend class on Monday and realize she had difficulty concentrating on the lecture. One observation to explain this occurrence might be, "When I eat breakfast before class, I am better able to pay attention." The student could then design an experiment with a control to test this hypothesis.

In hypothesis-based science, specific results are predicted from a general premise. This type of reasoning is called deductive reasoning: deduction proceeds from the general to the particular. But the reverse of the process is also possible: sometimes, scientists reach a general conclusion from a number of specific observations. This type of reasoning is called inductive reasoning, and it proceeds from the particular to the general. Inductive and deductive reasoning are often used in tandem to advance scientific knowledge (see this figure)

science practices CONNECTION for AP® Courses

Think About It

Almost all plants use water, carbon dioxide, and energy from the sun to make sugars. Think about what would happen to plants that don't have sunlight as an energy source or sufficient water. What would happen to organisms that depend on those plants for their own survival?

Make a prediction about what would happen to the organisms living in a rain forest if 50% of its trees were destroyed. How would you test your prediction?

visual CONNECTION

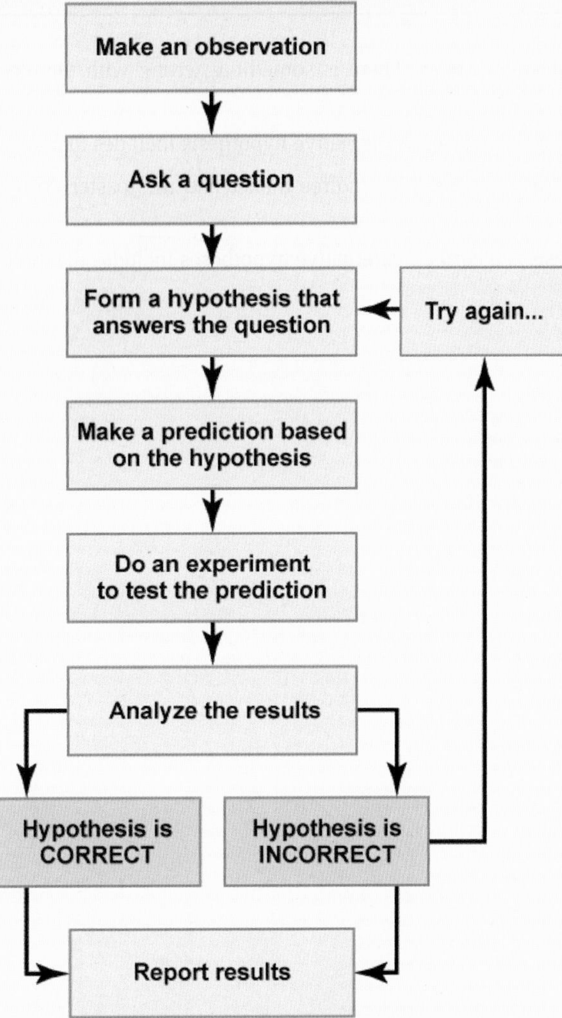

Figure 1.6 The scientific method consists of a series of well-defined steps. If a hypothesis is not supported by experimental data, a new hypothesis can be proposed.

In the example below, the scientific method is used to solve an everyday problem. Order the scientific method steps (numbered items) with the process of solving the everyday problem (lettered items). Based on the results of the experiment, is the hypothesis correct? If it is incorrect, propose some alternative hypotheses.

	Scientific Method		Everyday process
1	Observation	A	There is something wrong with the electrical outlet.
2	Question	B	If something is wrong with the outlet, my coffeemaker also won't work when plugged into it.
3	Hypothesis (answer)	C	My toaster doesn't toast my bread.
4	Prediction	D	I plug my coffee maker into the outlet.
5	Experiment	E	My coffeemaker works.

	Scientific Method		Everyday process
6	Result	F	What is preventing my toaster from working?

a. The original hypothesis is correct. There is something wrong with the electrical outlet and therefore the toaster doesn’t work.

b. The original hypothesis is incorrect. Alternative hypothesis includes that toaster wasn’t turned on.

c. The original hypothesis is correct. The coffee maker and the toaster do not work when plugged into the outlet.

d. The original hypothesis is incorrect. Alternative hypotheses includes that both coffee maker and toaster were broken.

visual CONNECTION

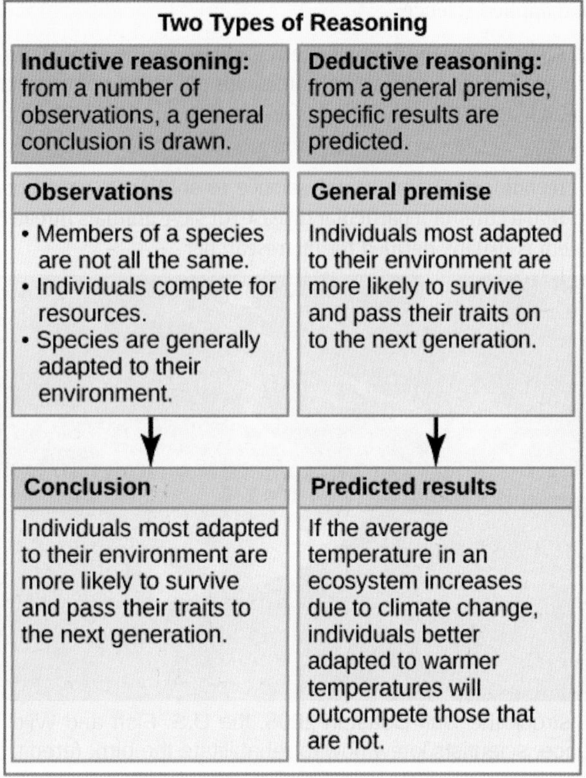

Figure 1.7 Scientists use two types of reasoning, inductive and deductive reasoning, to advance scientific knowledge. As is the case in this example, the conclusion from inductive reasoning can often become the premise for deductive reasoning.

Decide if each of the following is an example of inductive or deductive reasoning.

1. All flying birds and insects have wings. Birds and insects flap their wings as they move through the air. Therefore, wings enable flight.
2. Insects generally survive mild winters better than harsh ones. Therefore, insect pests will become more problematic if global temperatures increase.
3. Chromosomes, the carriers of DNA, separate into daughter cells during cell division. Therefore, DNA is the genetic material.
4. Animals as diverse as insects and wolves all exhibit social behavior. Therefore, social behavior must have an evolutionary advantage for humans.
   a. 1- Inductive, 2- Deductive, 3- Deductive, 4- Inductive
   b. 1- Deductive, 2- Inductive, 3- Deductive, 4- Inductive
   c. 1- Inductive, 2- Deductive, 3- Inductive, 4- Deductive
   d. 1- Inductive, 2-Inductive, 3- Inductive, 4- Deductive

The scientific method may seem too rigid and structured. It is important to keep in mind that, although scientists often follow this sequence, there is flexibility. Sometimes an experiment leads to conclusions that favor a change in approach; often, an experiment brings entirely new scientific questions to the puzzle. Many times, science does not operate in a linear fashion; instead, scientists continually draw inferences and make generalizations, finding patterns as their research proceeds. Scientific reasoning is more complex than the scientific method alone suggests. Notice, too, that the scientific method can be applied to solving problems that aren’t necessarily scientific in nature.

Two Types of Science: Basic Science and Applied Science

The scientific community has been debating for the last few decades about the value of different types of science. Is it valuable to pursue science for the sake of simply gaining knowledge, or does scientific knowledge only have worth if we can apply it to solving a specific problem or to bettering our lives? This question focuses on the differences between two types of science: basic science and applied science.

Basic science or "pure" science seeks to expand knowledge regardless of the short-term application of that knowledge. It is not focused on developing a product or a service of immediate public or commercial value. The immediate goal of basic science is knowledge for knowledge's sake, though this does not mean that, in the end, it may not result in a practical application.

In contrast, **applied science** or "technology," aims to use science to solve real-world problems, making it possible, for example, to improve a crop yield, find a cure for a particular disease, or save animals threatened by a natural disaster (Figure 1.8). In applied science, the problem is usually defined for the researcher.

Figure 1.8 After Hurricane Ike struck the Gulf Coast in 2008, the U.S. Fish and Wildlife Service rescued this brown pelican. Thanks to applied science, scientists knew how to rehabilitate the bird. (credit: FEMA)

Some individuals may perceive applied science as "useful" and basic science as "useless." A question these people might pose to a scientist advocating knowledge acquisition would be, "What for?" A careful look at the history of science, however, reveals that basic knowledge has resulted in many remarkable applications of great value. Many scientists think that a basic understanding of science is necessary before an application is developed; therefore, applied science relies on the results generated through basic science. Other scientists think that it is time to move on from basic science and instead to find solutions to actual problems. Both approaches are valid. It is true that there are problems that demand immediate attention; however, few solutions would be found without the help of the wide knowledge foundation generated through basic science.

One example of how basic and applied science can work together to solve practical problems occurred after the discovery of DNA structure led to an understanding of the molecular mechanisms governing DNA replication. Strands of DNA, unique in every human, are found in our cells, where they provide the instructions necessary for life. During DNA replication, DNA makes new copies of itself, shortly before a cell divides. Understanding the mechanisms of DNA replication enabled scientists to develop laboratory techniques that are now used to identify genetic diseases. Without basic science, it is unlikely that applied science would exist.

Another example of the link between basic and applied research is the Human Genome Project, a study in which each human chromosome was analyzed and mapped to determine the precise sequence of DNA subunits and the exact location of each gene. (The gene is the basic unit of heredity; an individual's complete collection of genes is his or her genome.) Other less complex organisms have also been studied as part of this project in order to gain a better understanding of human chromosomes. The Human Genome Project (Figure 1.9) relied on basic research carried out with simple organisms and, later, with the human genome. An important end goal eventually became using the data for applied research, seeking cures and early diagnoses for genetically related diseases.

Figure 1.9 The Human Genome Project was a 13-year collaborative effort among researchers working in several different fields of science. The project, which sequenced the entire human genome, was completed in 2003. (credit: the U.S. Department of Energy Genome Programs (http://genomics.energy.gov))

While research efforts in both basic science and applied science are usually carefully planned, it is important to note that some discoveries are made by **serendipity**, that is, by means of a fortunate accident or a lucky surprise. Penicillin was discovered when biologist Alexander Fleming accidentally left a petri dish of *Staphylococcus* bacteria open. An unwanted mold grew on the dish, killing the bacteria. The mold turned out to be *Penicillium*, and a new antibiotic was discovered. Even in the highly organized world of science, luck—when combined with an observant, curious mind—can lead to unexpected breakthroughs.

Reporting Scientific Work

Whether scientific research is basic science or applied science, scientists must share their findings in order for other researchers to expand and build upon their discoveries. Collaboration with other scientists—when planning, conducting, and analyzing results—are all important for scientific research. For this reason, important aspects of a scientist's work are communicating with peers and disseminating results to peers. Scientists can share results by presenting them at a scientific meeting or conference, but this approach can reach only the select few who are present. Instead, most scientists present their results in peer-reviewed manuscripts that are published in scientific journals. **Peer-reviewed manuscripts** are scientific papers that are reviewed by a scientist's colleagues, or peers. These colleagues are qualified individuals, often experts in the same research area, who judge whether or not the scientist's work is suitable for publication. The process of peer review helps to ensure that the research described in a scientific paper or grant proposal is original, significant, logical, and thorough. Grant proposals, which are requests for research funding, are also subject to peer review. Scientists publish their work so other scientists can reproduce their experiments under similar or different conditions to expand on the findings. The experimental results must be consistent with the findings of other scientists.

A scientific paper is very different from creative writing. Although creativity is required to design experiments, there are fixed guidelines when it comes to presenting scientific results. First, scientific writing must be brief, concise, and accurate. A scientific paper needs to be succinct but detailed enough to allow peers to reproduce the experiments.

The scientific paper consists of several specific sections—introduction, materials and methods, results, and discussion. This structure is sometimes called the "IMRaD" format. There are usually acknowledgment and reference sections as well as an **abstract** (a concise summary) at the beginning of the paper. There might be additional sections depending on the type of paper and the journal where it will be published; for example, some review papers require an outline.

The **introduction** starts with brief, but broad, background information about what is known in the field. A good introduction also gives the rationale of the work; it justifies the work carried out and also briefly mentions the end of the paper, where the hypothesis or research question driving the research will be presented. The introduction refers to the published scientific work of others and therefore requires citations following the style of the journal. Using the work or ideas of others without proper citation is considered **plagiarism**.

The **materials and methods** section includes a complete and accurate description of the substances used, and the method and techniques used by the researchers to gather data. The description should be thorough enough to allow another researcher to repeat the experiment and obtain similar results, but it does not have to be verbose. This section will also include information on how measurements were made and what types of calculations and statistical analyses were used to examine raw data. Although the materials and methods section gives an accurate description of the experiments, it does not discuss them.

Some journals require a results section followed by a discussion section, but it is more common to combine both. If the journal does not allow the combination of both sections, the **results** section simply narrates the findings without any further interpretation. The results are presented by means of tables or graphs, but no duplicate information should be presented. In the **discussion** section, the researcher will interpret the results, describe how variables may be related, and attempt to explain the observations. It is indispensable to conduct an extensive literature search to put the results in the context of previously published scientific research. Therefore, proper citations are included in this section as well.

Finally, the **conclusion** section summarizes the importance of the experimental findings. While the scientific paper almost certainly answered one or more scientific questions that were stated, any good research should lead to more questions. Therefore, a well-done scientific paper leaves doors open for the researcher and others to continue and expand on the findings.

Review articles do not follow the IMRAD format because they do not present original scientific findings, or primary literature; instead, they summarize and comment on findings that were published as primary literature and typically include extensive reference sections.

1.2 | Themes and Concepts of Biology

By the end of this section, you will be able to:

- Identify and describe the properties of life
- Describe the levels of organization among living things
- Recognize and interpret a phylogenetic tree

Connection for AP® Courses

The AP® Biology curriculum is organized around four major themes called the Big Ideas that apply to all levels of biological organization—from molecules and cells to populations and ecosystems. Each Big Idea identifies key concepts called Enduring Understandings, and Essential Knowledges, along with supporting examples. Simple descriptions define the focus of each Big Idea: Big Idea 1, Evolution; Big Idea 2, Energy and Homeostasis; Big Idea 3, Information and Communication; and Big Idea 4, Systems and Interactions. Evolution explains both the unity and diversity of life, Big Idea 1, and all organisms require energy and molecules to carry out life functions, such as growth and reproduction, Big Idea 2. Living systems also store, transmit, and respond to information, from DNA sequences to nerve impulses and behaviors, Big Idea 3. All biological systems interact, and these interactions result in emergent properties and characteristics unique to life, Big Idea 4.

The redesigned AP® Biology course also emphasizes the investigative practices that students should master. Scientific inquiry usually uses a series of steps to gain new knowledge. The scientific method begins with an observation and follows with a hypothesis to explain the observation; then experiments are conducted to test the hypothesis, gather results, and draw conclusions from data. The AP® program has identified seven major categories of Science Practices, which can be described by short phrases: using representations and models to communicate information and solve problems; using mathematics appropriately; engaging in questioning; planning and implementing data collection strategies; analyzing and evaluating data; justifying scientific explanations; and connecting concepts. A Learning Objective merges content with one or more of the seven Science Practices.

The information presented and the examples highlighted in this section support concepts and Learning Objectives outlined in Big Idea 1 of the AP® Biology Curriculum. The Learning Objectives listed in the Curriculum Framework provide a transparent foundation for the AP® Biology course, an inquiry-based laboratory experience, instructional activities, and AP® Exam questions. A Learning Objective merges required content with one or more of the seven Science Practices.

Big Idea 1	The process of evolution drives the diversity and unity of life.
Enduring Understanding 1.B	Organisms are linked by lines of descent from common ancestry.
Essential Knowledge	**1.B.1** Organisms share many conserved core processes and features that evolved and are widely distributed among organisms today.
Science Practice	**3.1** The student can pose scientific questions.
Learning Objective	**1.14** The student is able to pose scientific questions that correctly identify essential properties of share, core life processes that provide insights into the history of life on Earth.
Essential Knowledge	**1.B.1** Organisms share many conserved core processes and features that evolved and are widely distributed among organisms today.
Science Practice	**5.3** The student can evaluate the evidence provided by data sets in relation to a particular scientific question.
Learning Objective	**1.18** The student is able to evaluate evidence provided by a data set in conjunction with a phylogenetic tree or simply cladogram to determine evolutionary history and speciation.

Biology is the science that studies life, but what exactly is life? This may sound like a silly question with an obvious response, but it is not always easy to define life. For example, a branch of biology called virology studies viruses, which exhibit some of the characteristics of living entities but lack others. It turns out that although viruses can attack living organisms, cause diseases, and even reproduce, they do not meet the criteria that biologists use to define life. Consequently, virologists are not biologists, strictly speaking. Similarly, some biologists study the early molecular evolution that gave rise to life; since the events that preceded life are not biological events, these scientists are also excluded from biology in the strict sense of the term.

From its earliest beginnings, biology has wrestled with three questions: What are the shared properties that make something "alive"? And once we know something is alive, how do we find meaningful levels of organization in its structure? And, finally, when faced with the remarkable diversity of life, how do we organize the different kinds of organisms so that we can better understand them? As new organisms are discovered every day, biologists continue to seek answers to these and other questions.

Properties of Life

All living organisms share several key characteristics or functions: order, sensitivity or response to the environment, reproduction, adaptation, growth and development, regulation, homeostasis, energy processing, and evolution. When viewed together, these nine characteristics serve to define life.

Order

Figure 1.10 A toad represents a highly organized structure consisting of cells, tissues, organs, and organ systems. (credit: "Ivengo"/Wikimedia Commons)

Organisms are highly organized, coordinated structures that consist of one or more cells. Even very simple, single-celled organisms are remarkably complex: inside each cell, atoms make up molecules; these in turn make up cell organelles and other cellular inclusions. In multicellular organisms (Figure 1.10), similar cells form tissues. Tissues, in turn, collaborate to create organs (body structures with a distinct function). Organs work together to form organ systems.

Sensitivity or Response to Stimuli

Figure 1.11 The leaves of this sensitive plant (*Mimosa pudica*) will instantly droop and fold when touched. After a few minutes, the plant returns to normal. (credit: Alex Lomas)

Organisms respond to diverse stimuli. For example, plants can bend toward a source of light, climb on fences and walls, or respond to touch (Figure 1.11). Even tiny bacteria can move toward or away from chemicals (a process called *chemotaxis*) or light (*phototaxis*). Movement toward a stimulus is considered a positive response, while movement away from a stimulus is considered a negative response.

Watch this video (http://openstaxcollege.org/l/movement_plants) to see how plants respond to a stimulus—from opening to light, to wrapping a tendril around a branch, to capturing prey.

Which example most clearly shows a way that humans can respond directly to a change in the environment?

a. We shiver when we are cold and sweat when we are hot.

b. We walk by putting our front leg forward and pushing off with our back leg.

c. We are able to breath in and out unconsciously.

d. Our hair and fingernails grow at a constant rate over time.

Reproduction

Single-celled organisms reproduce by first duplicating their DNA, and then dividing it equally as the cell prepares to divide to form two new cells. Multicellular organisms often produce specialized reproductive germline cells that will form new individuals. When reproduction occurs, genes containing DNA are passed along to an organism's offspring. These genes ensure that the offspring will belong to the same species and will have similar characteristics, such as size and shape.

Growth and Development

Organisms grow and develop following specific instructions coded for by their genes. These genes provide instructions that will direct cellular growth and development, ensuring that a species' young (Figure 1.12) will grow up to exhibit many of the same characteristics as its parents.

Figure 1.12 Although no two look alike, these kittens have inherited genes from both parents and share many of the same characteristics. (credit: Rocky Mountain Feline Rescue)

Regulation

Even the smallest organisms are complex and require multiple regulatory mechanisms to coordinate internal functions, respond to stimuli, and cope with environmental stresses. Two examples of internal functions regulated in an organism are nutrient transport and blood flow. Organs (groups of tissues working together) perform specific functions, such as carrying oxygen throughout the body, removing wastes, delivering nutrients to every cell, and cooling the body.

Homeostasis

Figure 1.13 Polar bears (*Ursus maritimus*) and other mammals living in ice-covered regions maintain their body temperature by generating heat and reducing heat loss through thick fur and a dense layer of fat under their skin. (credit: "longhorndave"/Flickr)

In order to function properly, cells need to have appropriate conditions such as proper temperature, pH, and appropriate concentration of diverse chemicals. These conditions may, however, change from one moment to the next. Organisms are able to maintain internal conditions within a narrow range almost constantly, despite environmental changes, through **homeostasis** (literally, "steady state"). For example, an organism needs to regulate body temperature through a process known as thermoregulation. Organisms that live in cold climates, such as the polar bear (Figure 1.13), have body structures that help them withstand low temperatures and conserve body heat. Structures that aid in this type of insulation include fur, feathers, blubber, and fat. In hot climates, organisms have methods (such as perspiration in humans or panting in dogs) that help them to shed excess body heat.

Energy Processing

Figure 1.14 The California condor (*Gymnogyps californianus*) uses chemical energy derived from food to power flight. California condors are an endangered species; this bird has a wing tag that helps biologists identify the individual. (credit: Pacific Southwest Region U.S. Fish and Wildlife Service)

All organisms use a source of energy for their metabolic activities. Some organisms capture energy from the sun and convert it into chemical energy in food; others use chemical energy in molecules they take in as food (Figure 1.14).

science practices CONNECTION for AP® Courses

Activity

Select an ecosystem of your choice, such as a tropical rainforest, desert, or coral reef, and create a representation to show how several organisms found in the ecosystem interact with each other and the environment. Then, using similarities and differences among the organisms make a hypothesis about their relatedness.

Consider the levels of organization of the biological world and create a diagram to place these items in order from the smallest level of organization to the most encompassing: skin cell, planet Earth, elephant, tropical rainforest, water molecule, liver, wolf pack, and oxygen atom. Justify the reason why you placed the items in the hierarchy that you did.

Think About It

Homeostasis—the ability to "stay the same"—is a feature shared by all living organisms. You go for a long walk on a hot day. Describe how homeostasis keeps your body healthy even though you are sweating profusely. Then describe an example of an adaptation that evolved in a desert plant or animal that allows them to survive in extreme temperatures.

Levels of Organization of Living Things

Living things are highly organized and structured, following a hierarchy that can be examined on a scale from small to large. The **atom** is the smallest and most fundamental unit of matter. It consists of a nucleus surrounded by electrons. Atoms form molecules. A **molecule** is a chemical structure consisting of at least two atoms held together by one or more chemical bonds. Many molecules that are biologically important are **macromolecules**, large molecules that are typically formed by polymerization (a polymer is a large molecule that is made by combining smaller units called monomers, which are simpler than macromolecules). An example of a macromolecule is deoxyribonucleic acid (DNA) (Figure 1.15), which contains the instructions for the structure and functioning of all living organisms.

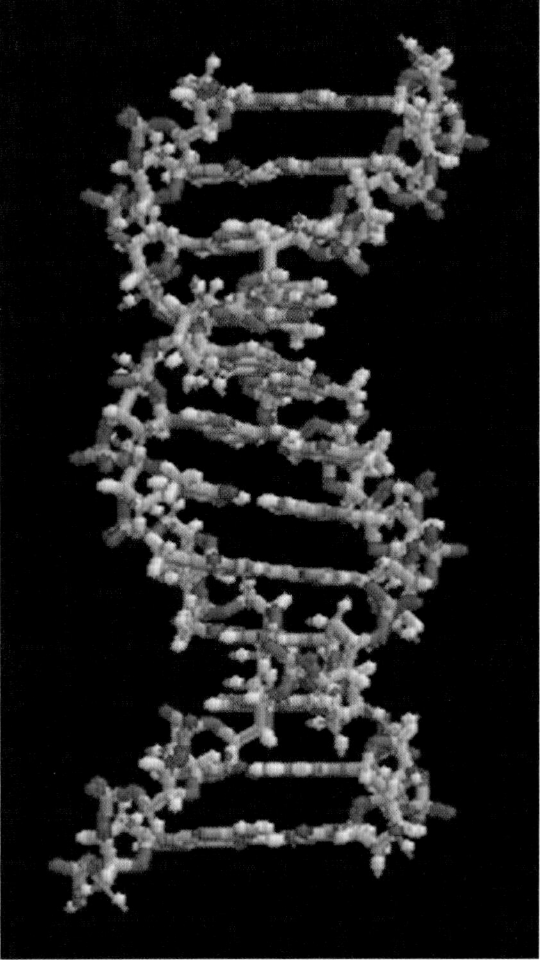

Figure 1.15 All molecules, including this DNA molecule, are composed of atoms. (credit: "brian0918"/Wikimedia Commons)

Watch this video (http://openstaxcollege.org/l/rotating_DNA) that animates the three-dimensional structure of the DNA molecule shown in this figure.

The word helix means spiral. What does this tell you about the structure of DNA, which is a double helix macromolecule?

a. The nucleotides of the two strands bond together with spiral bonds.

b. A double-stranded DNA molecule has two spiral stands bound together.

c. DNA is a double helix because it has two spiral strands held together like a spiral staircase.

d. Nucleotides are spiral-shaped molecules that bond together to form DNA.

Some cells contain aggregates of macromolecules surrounded by membranes; these are called **organelles**. Organelles are small structures that exist within cells. Examples of organelles include mitochondria and chloroplasts, which carry out indispensable functions: mitochondria produce energy to power the cell, while chloroplasts enable green plants to utilize the energy in sunlight to make sugars. All living things are made of cells; the **cell** itself is the smallest fundamental unit of structure and function in living organisms. (This requirement is why viruses are not considered living: they are not made of cells. To make new viruses, they have to invade and hijack the reproductive mechanism of a living cell; only then can they obtain the materials they need to reproduce.) Some organisms consist of a single cell and others are multicellular. Cells are classified as prokaryotic or eukaryotic. **Prokaryotes** are single-celled or colonial organisms that do not have membrane-bound nuclei; in contrast, the cells of **eukaryotes** do have membrane-bound organelles and a membrane-bound nucleus.

In larger organisms, cells combine to make **tissues**, which are groups of similar cells carrying out similar or related functions. **Organs** are collections of tissues grouped together performing a common function. Organs are present not only in animals but also in plants. An **organ system** is a higher level of organization that consists of functionally related organs. Mammals have many organ systems. For instance, the circulatory system transports blood through the body and to and from the lungs; it includes organs such as the heart and blood vessels. **Organisms** are individual living entities. For example, each tree in a forest is an organism. Single-celled prokaryotes and single-celled eukaryotes are also considered organisms and are typically referred to as microorganisms.

All the individuals of a species living within a specific area are collectively called a **population**. For example, a forest may include many pine trees. All of these pine trees represent the population of pine trees in this forest. Different populations may live in the same specific area. For example, the forest with the pine trees includes populations of flowering plants and also insects and microbial populations. A **community** is the sum of populations inhabiting a particular area. For instance, all of the trees, flowers, insects, and other populations in a forest form the forest's community. The forest itself is an ecosystem. An **ecosystem** consists of all the living things in a particular area together with the abiotic, non-living parts of that environment such as nitrogen in the soil or rain water. At the highest level of organization (**see this figure**), the **biosphere** is the collection of all ecosystems, and it represents the zones of life on earth. It includes land, water, and even the atmosphere to a certain extent.

visual CONNECTION

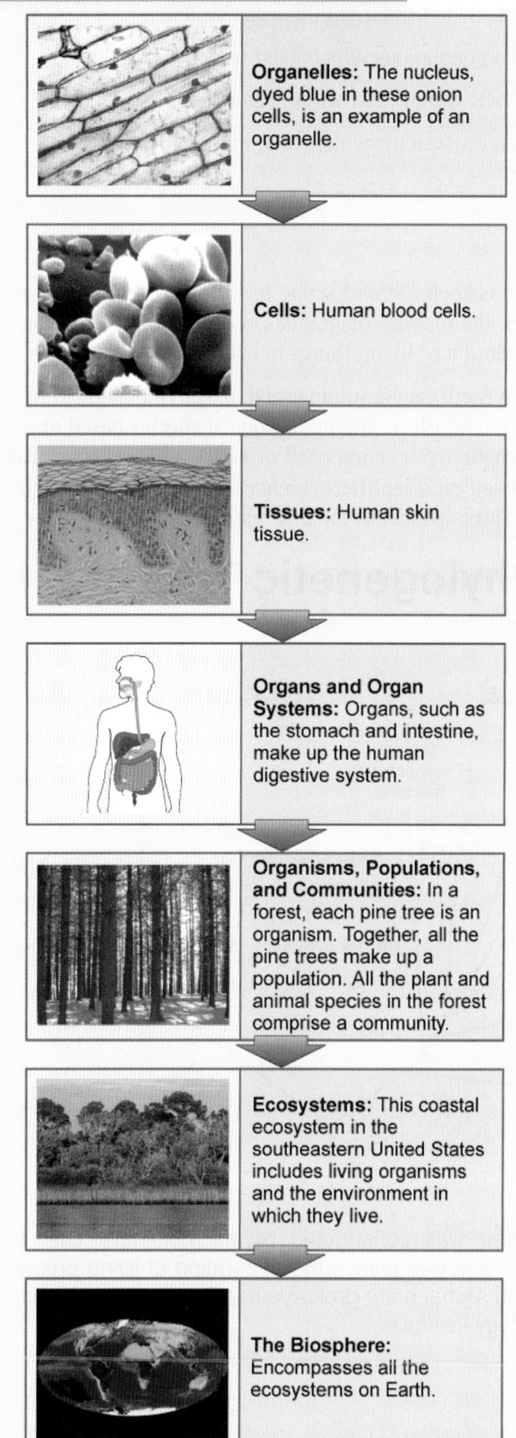

Organelles: The nucleus, dyed blue in these onion cells, is an example of an organelle.
Cells: Human blood cells.
Tissues: Human skin tissue.
Organs and Organ Systems: Organs, such as the stomach and intestine, make up the human digestive system.
Organisms, Populations, and Communities: In a forest, each pine tree is an organism. Together, all the pine trees make up a population. All the plant and animal species in the forest comprise a community.
Ecosystems: This coastal ecosystem in the southeastern United States includes living organisms and the environment in which they live.
The Biosphere: Encompasses all the ecosystems on Earth.

Figure 1.16 The biological levels of organization of living things are shown. From a single organelle to the entire biosphere, living organisms are parts of a highly structured hierarchy. (credit "organelles": modification of work by Umberto Salvagnin; credit "cells": modification of work by Bruce Wetzel, Harry Schaefer/ National Cancer Institute; credit "tissues": modification of work by Kilbad; Fama Clamosa; Mikael Häggström; credit "organs": modification of work by Mariana Ruiz Villareal; credit "organisms": modification of work by "Crystal"/Flickr; credit "ecosystems":

modification of work by US Fish and Wildlife Service Headquarters; credit "biosphere": modification of work by NASA)

Which of the following statements is false?

a. Tissues exist within organs which exist within organ systems.
b. Communities exist within populations which exist within ecosystems.
c. Organelles exist within cells which exist within tissues.
d. Communities exist within ecosystems which exist in the biosphere.

The Diversity of Life

The fact that biology, as a science, has such a broad scope has to do with the tremendous diversity of life on earth. The source of this diversity is **evolution**, the process of gradual change during which new species arise from older species. Evolutionary biologists study the evolution of living things in everything from the microscopic world to ecosystems.

The evolution of various life forms on Earth can be summarized in a phylogenetic tree (Figure 1.17). A **phylogenetic tree** is a diagram showing the evolutionary relationships among biological species based on similarities and differences in genetic or physical traits or both. A phylogenetic tree is composed of nodes and branches. The internal nodes represent ancestors and are points in evolution when, based on scientific evidence, an ancestor is thought to have diverged to form two new species. The length of each branch is proportional to the time elapsed since the split.

Phylogenetic Tree of Life

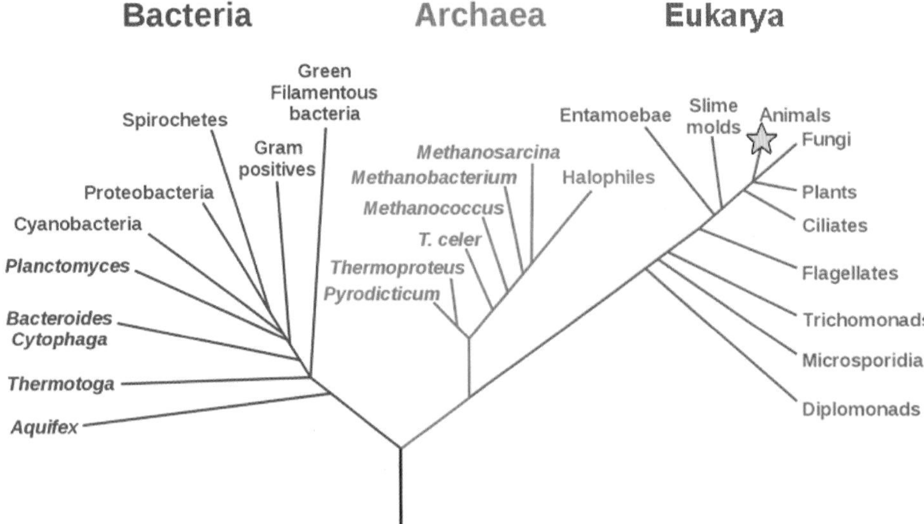

Figure 1.17 This phylogenetic tree was constructed by microbiologist Carl Woese using data obtained from sequencing ribosomal RNA genes. The tree shows the separation of living organisms into three domains: Bacteria, Archaea, and Eukarya. Bacteria and Archaea are prokaryotes, single-celled organisms lacking intracellular organelles. (credit: Eric Gaba; NASA Astrobiology Institute)

evolution CONNECTION

Carl Woese and the Phylogenetic Tree

In the past, biologists grouped living organisms into five kingdoms: animals, plants, fungi, protists, and bacteria. The organizational scheme was based mainly on physical features, as opposed to physiology, biochemistry, or molecular biology, all of which are used by modern systematics. The pioneering work of American microbiologist Carl Woese in the early 1970s has shown, however, that life on Earth has evolved along three lineages, now called domains—Bacteria, Archaea, and Eukarya. The first two are prokaryotic cells with microbes that lack membrane-enclosed nuclei and organelles. The third domain contains the eukaryotes and includes unicellular microorganisms together with the four original kingdoms (excluding bacteria). Woese defined Archaea as a new domain, and this resulted in a new taxonomic tree (see this figure). Many organisms belonging to the Archaea domain live under extreme conditions and are called extremophiles. To construct his tree, Woese used genetic relationships rather than similarities based on morphology (shape).

Woese's tree was constructed from comparative sequencing of the genes that are universally distributed, present in every organism, and conserved (meaning that these genes have remained essentially unchanged throughout evolution). Woese's approach was revolutionary because comparisons of physical features are insufficient to differentiate between the prokaryotes that appear fairly similar in spite of their tremendous biochemical diversity and genetic variability (Figure 1.18). The comparison of homologous DNA and RNA sequences provided Woese with a sensitive device that revealed the extensive variability of prokaryotes, and which justified the separation of the prokaryotes into two domains: bacteria and archaea.

Figure 1.18 These images represent different domains. The (a) bacteria in this micrograph belong to Domain Bacteria, while the (b) extremophiles (not visible) living in this hot vent belong to Domain Archaea. Both the (c) sunflower and (d) lion are part of Domain Eukarya. (credit a: modification of work by Drew March; credit b: modification of work by Steve Jurvetson; credit c: modification of work by Michael Arrighi; credit d: modification of work by Leszek Leszczynski)

In which domain would a fish be classified? Why?

a. Archaea, because fish are multicellular.
b. Eukarya, because fish are multicellular.
c. Archaea, because fish are single-celled.
d. Eukarya because fish are single-celled.

everyday CONNECTION for AP® Courses

Phylogenetic trees can represent traits that are derived or lost due to evolution. One example is the absence of legs in some sea mammals. For example, Cetaceans are marine mammals that include toothed whales, such as dolphins and killer whales, and baleen whales, such as humpback whales. Cetaceans are descended from even-toed ungulates and share a common ancestry with the hippopotamus, cow, sheep, camel, and pig.

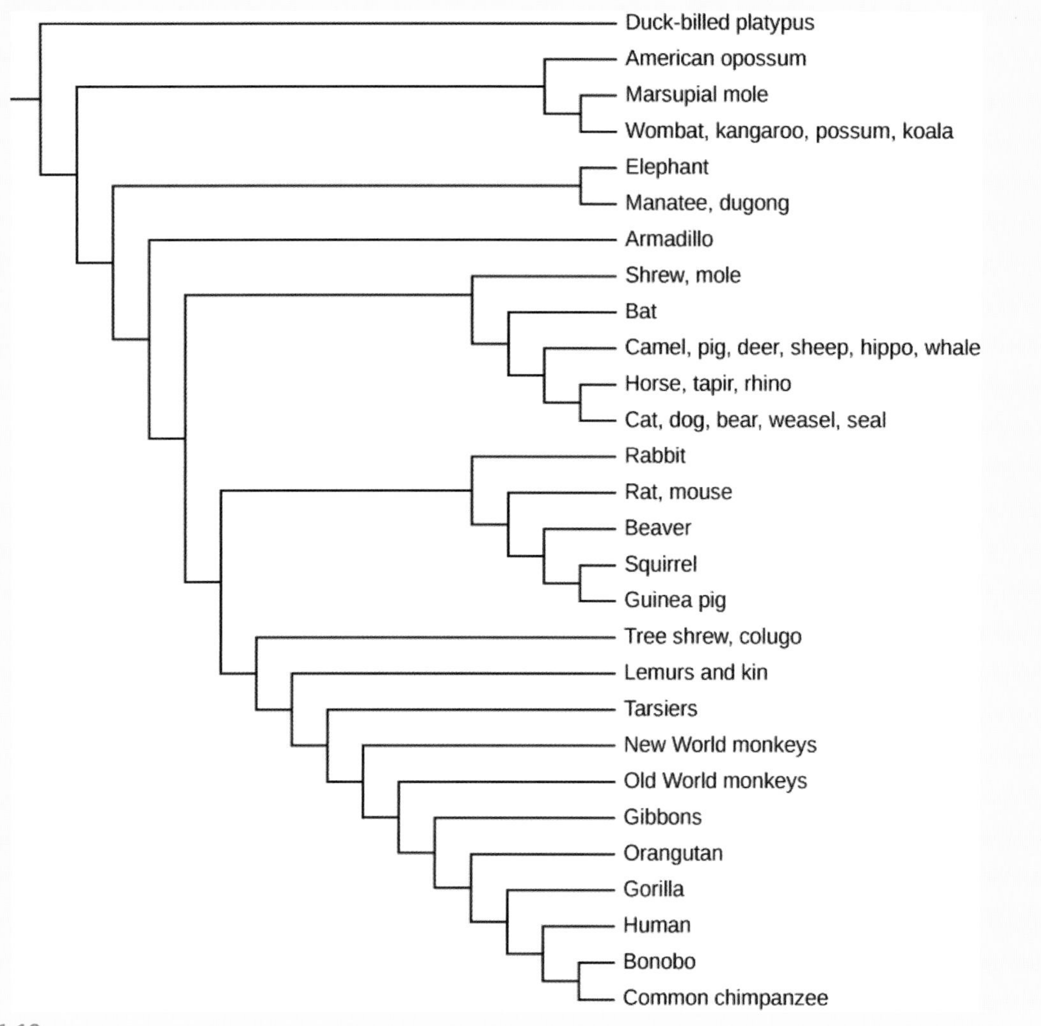

Figure 1.19

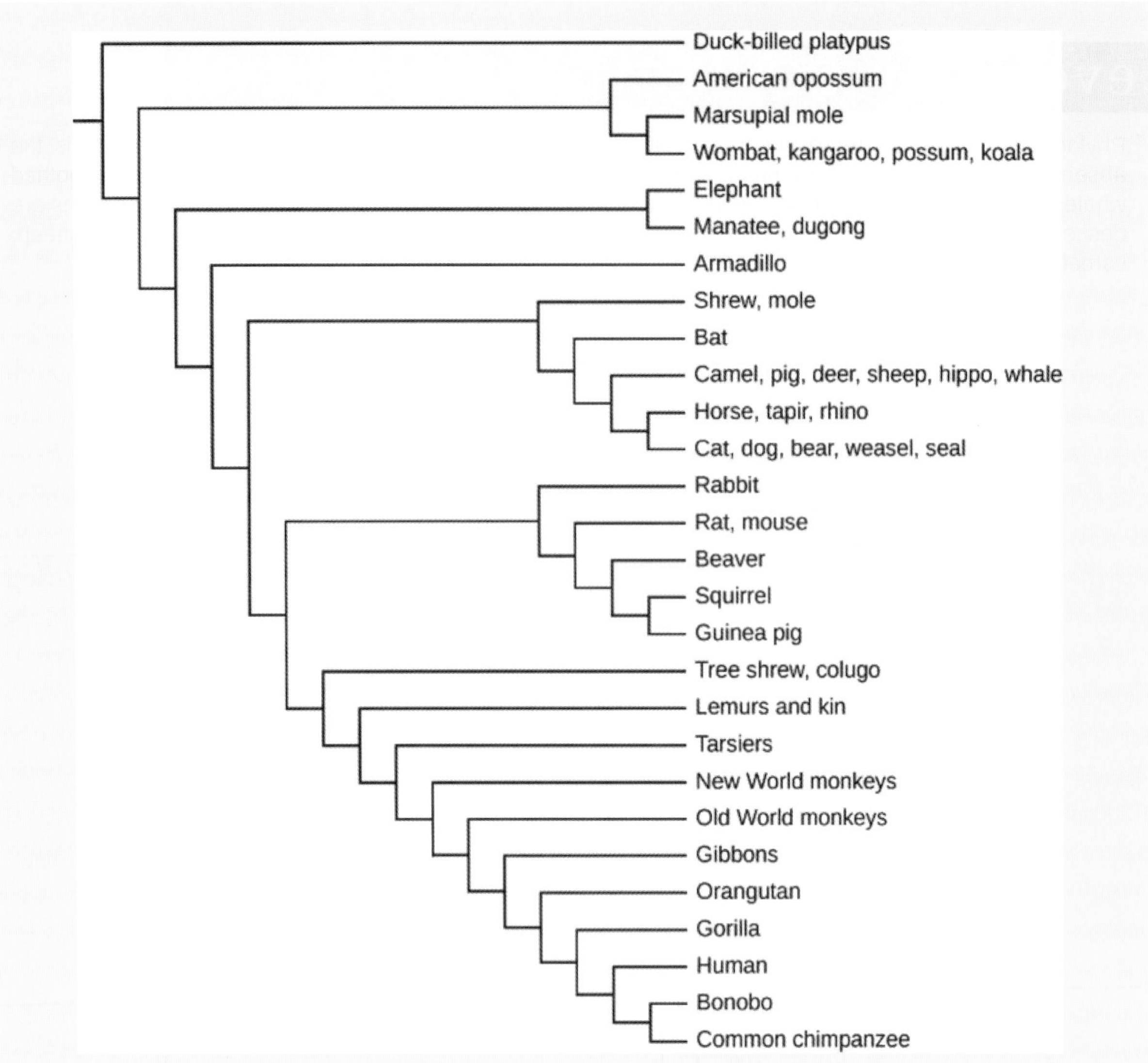

Phylogenetic trees can represent traits that are derived or lost due to evolution. One example is the absence of legs in some marine mammals. One such group is the Cetaceans, which includes toothed whales, such as dolphins and killer whales, and baleen whales, such as humpback whales. Cetaceans are descended from even-toed ungulates and share a common ancestry with the hippopotamus, cows, sheep, camel, and pig. Based on this phylogenetic tree, which of the following animal is the most closely related to a horse?

a. an armadillo
b. a camel
c. a bat
d. a cat

Branches of Biological Study

The scope of biology is broad and therefore contains many branches and subdisciplines. Biologists may pursue one of those subdisciplines and work in a more focused field. For instance, **molecular biology** and **biochemistry** study biological processes at the molecular and chemical level, including interactions among molecules such as DNA, RNA, and proteins, as well as the way they are regulated. **Microbiology**, the study of microorganisms, is the study of the structure and function of organisms that cannot be seen with the naked eye. It is quite a broad branch itself, and depending on the subject of study, there are also microbial physiologists, ecologists, and geneticists, among others.

career CONNECTION

Forensic science is the application of science to answer questions related to the law. Biologists as well as chemists and biochemists can be forensic scientists. Forensic scientists provide scientific evidence for use in courts, and their job involves examining trace materials associated with crimes. Interest in forensic science has increased in the last few years, possibly because of popular television shows that feature forensic scientists on the job. Also, the development of molecular techniques and the establishment of DNA databases have expanded the types of work that forensic scientists can do. Their work involves analyzing samples such as hair, blood, and other body fluids and also processing DNA (Figure 1.20) found in many different environments and materials. Forensic scientists also analyze other biological evidence left at crime scenes, such as insect larvae or pollen grains. Students who want to pursue careers in forensic science will most likely be required to take chemistry and biology courses as well as some intensive math courses.

Figure 1.20 This forensic scientist works in a DNA extraction room at the U.S. Army Criminal Investigation Laboratory at Fort Gillem, GA. (credit: United States Army CID Command Public Affairs)

Another field of biological study, **neurobiology**, studies the biology of the nervous system, and although it is considered a branch of biology, it is also recognized as an interdisciplinary field of study known as neuroscience. Because of its interdisciplinary nature, this subdiscipline studies different functions of the nervous system using molecular, cellular, developmental, medical, and computational approaches.

Figure 1.21 Researchers work on excavating dinosaur fossils at a site in Castellón, Spain. (credit: Mario Modesto)

Paleontology, another branch of biology, uses fossils to study life’s history (Figure 1.21). **Zoology** and **botany** are the study of animals and plants, respectively. Biologists can also specialize as biotechnologists, ecologists, or physiologists, to name just a few areas. This is just a small sample of the many fields that biologists can pursue.

Biology is the culmination of the achievements of the natural sciences from their inception to today. Excitingly, it is the cradle of emerging sciences, such as the biology of brain activity, genetic engineering of custom organisms, and the biology of evolution that uses the laboratory tools of molecular biology to retrace the earliest stages of life on earth. A scan of news headlines—whether reporting on immunizations, a newly discovered species, sports doping, or a genetically-modified food—demonstrates the way biology is active in and important to our everyday world.

KEY TERMS

abstract opening section of a scientific paper that summarizes the research and conclusions

applied science form of science that aims to solve real-world problems

atom smallest and most fundamental unit of matter

basic science science that seeks to expand knowledge and understanding regardless of the short-term application of that knowledge

biochemistry study of the chemistry of biological organisms

biology the study of living organisms and their interactions with one another and their environments

biosphere collection of all the ecosystems on Earth

botany study of plants

cell smallest fundamental unit of structure and function in living things

community set of populations inhabiting a particular area

conclusion section of a scientific paper that summarizes the importance of the experimental findings

control part of an experiment that does not change during the experiment

deductive reasoning form of logical thinking that uses a general inclusive statement to forecast specific results

descriptive science (also, discovery science) form of science that aims to observe, explore, and investigate

discussion section of a scientific paper in which the author interprets experimental results, describes how variables may be related, and attempts to explain the phenomenon in question

ecosystem all the living things in a particular area together with the abiotic, nonliving parts of that environment

eukaryote organism with cells that have nuclei and membrane-bound organelles

evolution process of gradual change during which new species arise from older species and some species become extinct

falsifiable able to be disproven by experimental results

homeostasis ability of an organism to maintain constant internal conditions

hypothesis suggested explanation for an observation, which can be tested

hypothesis-based science form of science that begins with a specific question and potential testable answers

inductive reasoning form of logical thinking that uses related observations to arrive at a general conclusion

introduction opening section of a scientific paper, which provides background information about what was known in the field prior to the research reported in the paper

life science field of science, such as biology, that studies living things

macromolecule large molecule, typically formed by the joining of smaller molecules

materials and methods section of a scientific paper that includes a complete description of the substances, methods, and techniques used by the researchers to gather data

microbiology study of the structure and function of microorganisms

molecular biology study of biological processes and their regulation at the molecular level, including interactions among molecules such as DNA, RNA, and proteins

molecule chemical structure consisting of at least two atoms held together by one or more chemical bonds

natural science field of science that is related to the physical world and its phenomena and processes

neurobiology study of the biology of the nervous system

organ collection of related tissues grouped together performing a common function

organ system level of organization that consists of functionally related interacting organs

organelle small structures that exist within cells and carry out cellular functions

organism individual living entity

paleontology study of life's history by means of fossils

peer-reviewed manuscript scientific paper that is reviewed by a scientist's colleagues who are experts in the field of study

phylogenetic tree diagram showing the evolutionary relationships among various biological species based on similarities and differences in genetic or physical traits or both; in essence, a hypothesis concerning evolutionary connections

physical science field of science, such as geology, astronomy, physics, and chemistry, that studies nonliving matter

plagiarism using other people's work or ideas without proper citation, creating the false impression that those are the author's original ideas

population all of the individuals of a species living within a specific area

prokaryote single-celled organism that lacks organelles and does not have nuclei surrounded by a nuclear membrane

results section of a scientific paper in which the author narrates the experimental findings and presents relevant figures, pictures, diagrams, graphs, and tables, without any further interpretation

review article paper that summarizes and comments on findings that were published as primary literature

science knowledge that covers general truths or the operation of general laws, especially when acquired and tested by the scientific method

scientific method method of research with defined steps that include observation, formulation of a hypothesis, testing, and confirming or falsifying the hypothesis

serendipity fortunate accident or a lucky surprise

theory tested and confirmed explanation for observations or phenomena

tissue group of similar cells carrying out related functions

variable part of an experiment that the experimenter can vary or change

zoology study of animals

CHAPTER SUMMARY

1.1 The Science of Biology

Biology is the science that studies living organisms and their interactions with one another and their environments. Science attempts to describe and understand the nature of the universe in whole or in part by rational means. Science has many fields; those fields related to the physical world and its phenomena are considered natural sciences.

Science can be basic or applied. The main goal of basic science is to expand knowledge without any expectation of short-term practical application of that knowledge. The primary goal of applied research, however, is to solve practical problems.

Two types of logical reasoning are used in science. Inductive reasoning uses particular results to produce general scientific principles. Deductive reasoning is a form of logical thinking that predicts results by applying general principles. The common thread throughout scientific research is the use of the scientific method, a step-based process that consists of making observations, defining a problem, posing hypotheses, testing these hypotheses, and drawing one or more conclusions. The testing uses proper controls. Scientists present their results in peer-reviewed scientific papers published in scientific journals. A scientific research paper consists of several well-defined sections: introduction, materials and methods, results, and, finally, a concluding discussion. Review papers summarize the research done in a particular field over a period of time.

1.2 Themes and Concepts of Biology

Biology is the science of life. All living organisms share several key properties such as order, sensitivity or response to stimuli, reproduction, growth and development, regulation, homeostasis, and energy processing. Living things are highly organized parts of a hierarchy that includes atoms, molecules, organelles, cells, tissues, organs, and organ systems. Organisms, in turn, are grouped as populations, communities, ecosystems, and the biosphere. The great diversity of life today evolved from less-diverse ancestral organisms over billions of years. A diagram called a phylogenetic tree can be used to show evolutionary relationships among organisms.

Biology is very broad and includes many branches and subdisciplines. Examples include molecular biology, microbiology, neurobiology, zoology, and botany, among others.

REVIEW QUESTIONS

1. What is a suggested and testable explanation for an event called?

a. discovery
b. hypothesis
c. scientific method
d. theory

2. Which of the following sciences is not considered a natural science?

a. Astronomy
b. Biology
c. Computer science
d. Physics

3. What is the name for the formal process through which scientific research is checked for originality, significance, and quality before being accepted into scientific literature?

a. publication
b. public speaking
c. peer review
d. the scientific method

4. What are two topics that are likely to be studied by biologists and two areas of scientific study that would fall outside the realm of biology?

a. diseases affecting humans, pollution affecting species habitat,
calculating surface area of rectangular ground, functioning of planetary orbitals
b. calculating surface area of rectangular ground, functioning of planetary orbitals,
formation of metamorphic rocks, galaxy formation and evolution
c. plant responses to external stimuli, functioning of planetary orbitals,
formation of metamorphic rocks, galaxy formation and evolution
d. plant responses to external stimuli, study of the shape and motion of physical objects,
formation of metamorphic rocks, galaxy formation and evolution

5. Which of the following is an example of deductive reasoning?

a. Most swimming animals use fins; therefore, fins are an adaptation to swimming.
b. Mitochondria are inherited from the mother; therefore, maternally inherited traits are encoded by mitochondrial DNA
c. Small animals lose more heat than larger animals. One would not expect to find wild mice in the poles.
d. Water conservation is a major requirement to survive in the desert. Long leaves increase loss of water by evaporation. Therefore, desert plants should have smaller leaves.

6. Why are viruses not considered living?

a. They are not made of cells.

b. Viruses do not have genetic material.

c. Viruses have DNA and RNA.

d. Viruses are obligate parasites and require a host.

7. The presence of a membrane-enclosed nucleus is a characteristic of what?

a. bacteria

b. eukaryotic cells

c. all living organisms

d. prokaryotic cells

8. What is a group of individuals of the same species living in the same area called?

a. a community

b. an ecosystem

c. a family

d. a population

9. Which of the following sequences represents the hierarchy of biological organization from the most inclusive to the least complex level?

a. biosphere, ecosystem, community, population, organism

b. organelle, tissue, biosphere, ecosystem, population

c. organism, organ, tissue, organelle, molecule

d. organism, community, biosphere, molecule, tissue, organ

10. Where in a phylogenetic tree would you expect to find the organism that had evolved most recently?

a. at the base

b. at the nodes

c. at the branch tips

d. within the branches

11. What is a characteristic that is not present in all living things?

a. homeostasis and regulation

b. metabolism

c. nucleus containing DNA

d. reproduction

CRITICAL THINKING QUESTIONS

12. Is mathematics a natural science? Explain your reasoning.

a. No, it is not a natural science because it is not used in the study of the natural world.

b. No, it is not a natural science. Mathematics focuses on understanding mathematical relations and calculations, which is useful in natural sciences but which is distinct.

c. Yes, it is a natural science. Mathematics deals with verifying the experimental data.

d. Yes, it is a natural science. It uses chemical and physical measurements.

13. Although the scientific method is used by most of the sciences, it can also be applied to everyday situations. A situation is given below. Using the scientific method try to arrange the given steps in the correct order. Situation:

1. If the car doesn't start the problem might be in the battery.
2. Car doesn't start.
3. After changing the battery. Car starts working.
4. The car should start after charging the battery or changing the battery.
5. The car doesn't start because the battery is dead.
6. The car doesn't start even after charging the battery, the battery must have stopped working.

a. 1, 2, 3, 4, 5, 6

b. 2, 1, 3, 4, 5, 6

c. 2, 1, 5, 4, 6, 3

d. 2, 1, 5, 6, 3, 4

14. Read the following questions. Does the statement lend itself to investigation using the scientific method? In other words, is the hypothesis falsifiable (can be proven false)?

1. Is macaroni and cheese tastier than broccoli soup?
2. Are hummingbirds attracted to the color red?
3. Is the moon made out of green cheese?
4. Is plagiarism dishonest?

a. Questions 1 and 2 are subjective and cannot be disproven using scientific method. Questions 3 and 4 can be tested using scientific method.

b. Questions 3 and 4 are subjective and cannot be disproven using scientific method. Questions 1 and 2 can be tested using scientific method.

c. Questions 1 and 3 are subjective and cannot be disproven using scientific method. Questions 2 and 4 can be tested using scientific method.

d. Questions 1 and 4 are subjective and cannot be disproven using scientific method. Questions 2 and 3 can be tested using scientific method.

15. Consider the levels of organization of the biological world and place each of these items in order from smallest level of organization to most encompassing: skin cell, elephant, water molecule, planet Earth, tropical rainforest, hydrogen atom, wolf pack, liver.

a. hydrogen atom, water molecule, skin cell, liver, elephant, wolf pack, tropical rainforest, planet Earth
b. hydrogen atom, skin cell, water molecule, liver, elephant, wolf pack, tropical rainforest, planet Earth
c. hydrogen atom, skin cell, water molecule, liver, wolf pack, elephant, tropical rainforest, planet Earth
d. water molecule, hydrogen atom, skin cell, liver, elephant, wolf pack, tropical rainforest, planet Earth

16. What scientific evidence was used by Carl Woese to determine there should be a separate domain for Archaea?

a. a sequence of DNA
b. a sequence of rRNA
c. a sequence of mRNA.
d. a sequence of tRNA.

17. Both astronomy and astrology study the stars. Which one is considered a natural science? Explain your reasoning.

a. Astrology is a natural science as it indirectly influences human affairs and the natural world.
b. Astronomy is a natural science as it deals with observations and prediction of events in the sky, which is based on the laws of physics.
c. Astrology is a natural science as it deals with observations and prediction of events in the sky, influences human affairs and the natural world.
d. Astrology is a natural science as it deals with the study of asteroids and comets, which is based on the laws of natural sciences.

TEST PREP FOR AP® COURSES

18. Which of the following structures is conserved in all living organisms and points to a common origin?

a. All living organisms have mitochondria that produce energy.
b. All living organisms store genetic material in DNA/RNA.
c. All living organisms use the energy from sunlight
d. All living organisms have a nucleus.

19. Which of the following statements is the strongest argument in favor of two organisms, A and B, being closely related evolutionarily?

a. A and B look alike.
b. A and B live in the same ecosystem.
c. A and B use the same metabolic pathways.
d. The DNA sequences of A and B are highly homologous.

20.

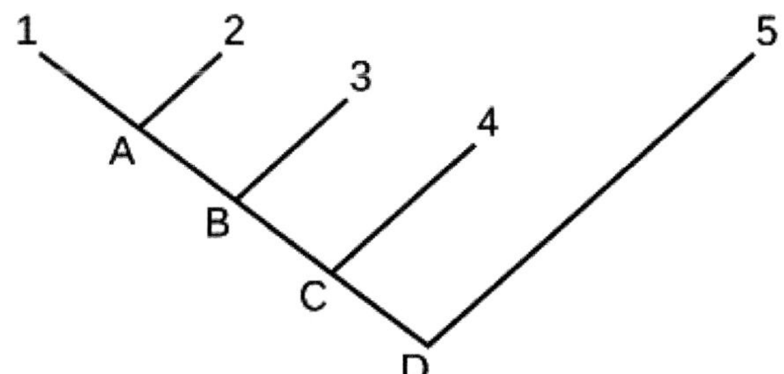

In the phylogenetic tree shown, which organism is most distantly related to 2?

a. 1
b. 3
c. 4
d. 5

21.

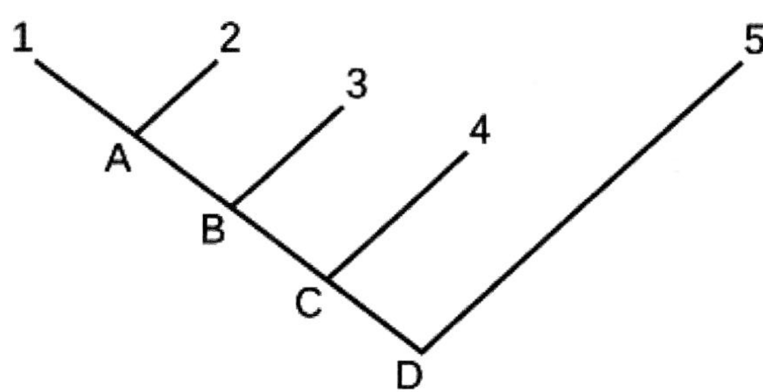

In the diagram shown which is the most recent common ancestor of 1 and 3?

a. A
b. B
c. C
d. D

22. The French scientist Jacques Monod famously said, “Anything found to be true of *E. coli* must also be true of elephants.” How is this statement based on the notion that living organisms share a common ancestor?

a. *E. coli* is a eukaryote and share similarities with most of the living organisms.
b. *E. coli* is a prokaryote. The various metabolic processes and core functions in *E. coli* share homology with higher organisms.
c. *E. coli* contains a nucleus and membrane bound cell organelles that are shared by all the living organisms.
d. *E. coli* is a prokaryote and reproduces through binary fission which is common to most of the living organisms.

23. Birds have been reclassified as reptiles. What is one line of evidence that has led to this reclassification?

a. *Archeopteryx* is the connecting link between birds and reptiles which shows that birds and reptiles are related.
b. Birds have scales, having the same origin as that of reptiles.
c. Birds and reptiles have the same circulatory and excretory systems and both are egg laying animals.
d. Birds and reptiles have similar anatomical and morphological features.

2 | THE CHEMICAL FOUNDATION OF LIFE

Figure 2.1 Atoms are the building blocks of molecules found in the universe—air, soil, water, rocks . . . and also the cells of all living organisms. In this model of an organic molecule, the atoms of carbon (black), hydrogen (white), nitrogen (blue), oxygen (red), and sulfur (yellow) are shown in proportional atomic size. The silver rods indicate chemical bonds. (credit: modification of work by Christian Guthier)

Chapter Outline

Introduction

All matter, including living things, is made up of various combinations of elements. Some of the most abundant elements in living organisms include carbon, hydrogen, nitrogen, oxygen, sulfur, and phosphorus. These elements form the major biological molecules—nucleic acids, proteins, carbohydrates, and lipids—that are the fundamental components of living matter. Biologists study these important molecules to understand their unique structures which determine their specialized functions.

All biological processes follow the laws of physics and chemistry. Therefore, in order to understand how biological systems work, it is important to understand the underlying physics and chemistry. For example, the flow of blood within the circulatory system follows the laws of physics regulating the modes of fluid flow. Chemical laws dictate the breakdown of large, complex food molecules into smaller molecules as well as their conversion to energy stored in adenosine triphosphate (ATP). Polar molecules, the formation of hydrogen bonds, and the resulting properties of water are key to understanding living processes. Recognizing the properties of acids and bases is important to understand various biological processes such as digestion. Therefore, the fundamentals of physics and chemistry are the foundation for gaining insight into biological processes.

An example of how understanding of chemical processes can give insight to a biological process is recent research on seasonal affective disorder (SAD). This form of depression affects up to 10% of the population in the fall and winter. Symptoms include a tendency to overeat, oversleep, lack of energy, and difficulty concentrating on tasks. Now scientists have found out that not only may SAD be caused by a deficiency in vitamin D, but that it is more common in individuals with darker skin pigmentation. You can read more about it here (http://openstaxcollege.org/l/32vitdsad) .

2.1 | Atoms, Isotopes, Ions, and Molecules: The Building Blocks

In this section, you will explore the following questions:

- How does atomic structure determine the properties of elements, molecules, and matter?
- What are the differences among ionic bonds, covalent bonds, polar covalent bonds, and hydrogen bonds?

Connection for AP® Courses

Living systems obey the laws of chemistry and physics. Matter is anything that occupies space and mass. The 92 naturally occurring elements have unique properties, and various combinations of them create molecules, which combine to form organelles, cells, tissues, organ system, and organisms. **Atoms**, which consist of protons, neutrons, and electrons, are the smallest units of matter that retain all their characteristics and are most stable when their outermost or valence electron shells contain the maximum number of electrons. Electrons can be transferred, shared, or cause charge disparities between atoms to create bonds, including ionic, covalent, and hydrogen bonds, as well as van del Waals interactions. **Isotopes** are different forms of an element that have different numbers of neutrons while retaining the same number of protons; many isotopes, such as carbon-14, are radioactive.

The information presented and examples highlighted in this section support concepts and Learning Objectives outlined in Big Idea 2 of the AP® Biology Curriculum Framework. The Learning Objectives listed in the Curriculum Framework provide a transparent foundation for the AP® Biology course, an inquiry-based laboratory experience, instructional activities, and AP® Exam questions. A Learning Objective merges required content with one or more of the seven Science Practices.

Big Idea 2	Biological systems utilize free energy and molecular building blocks to grow, to reproduce, and to maintain dynamic homeostasis.
Enduring Understanding 2.A	Growth, reproduction and maintenance of living systems require free energy and matter.
Essential Knowledge	**2.A.1** All living systems require constant input of free energy.
Science Practice	**4.1** The student can justify the selection of the kind of data needed to answer a particular scientific question.
Science Practice	**6.2** The student can construct explanations of phenomena based on evidence produced through scientific practices.
Science Practice	**6.4** The student can make claims and predictions about natural phenomena based on scientific theories and models.
Learning Objective	**2.8** The student is able to justify the selection of data regarding the types of molecules that an animal, plant, or bacterium will take up as necessary building blocks and excrete as waste products.

The Science Practice Challenge Questions contain additional test questions for this section that will help you prepare for the AP exam. These questions address the following standards:
[APLO 1.12] [APLO 2.9] [APLO 2.42] [APLO 2.22]

At its most fundamental level, life is made up of matter. Matter is any substance that occupies space and has mass. **Elements** are unique forms of matter with specific chemical and physical properties that cannot be broken down into smaller substances by ordinary chemical reactions. There are 118 elements, but only 98 occur naturally. The remaining elements are synthesized in laboratories and are unstable.

Each element is designated by its chemical symbol, which is a single capital letter or, when the first letter is already "taken" by another element, a combination of two letters. Some elements follow the English term for the element, such as C for carbon and Ca for calcium. Other elements' chemical symbols derive from their Latin names; for example, the symbol for sodium is Na, referring to *natrium*, the Latin word for sodium.

The four elements common to all living organisms are oxygen (O), carbon (C), hydrogen (H), and nitrogen (N). In the non-living world, elements are found in different proportions, and some elements common to living organisms are relatively rare on the earth as a whole, as shown in Table 2.1. For example, the atmosphere is rich in nitrogen and oxygen but contains little carbon and hydrogen, while the earth's crust, although it contains oxygen and a small amount of hydrogen, has little nitrogen and carbon. In spite of their differences in abundance, all elements and the chemical reactions between them obey the same chemical and physical laws regardless of whether they are a part of the living or non-living world.

Approximate Percentage of Elements in Living Organisms (Humans) Compared to the Non-living World

Element	Life (Humans)	Atmosphere	Earth's Crust
Oxygen (O)	65%	21%	46%
Carbon (C)	18%	trace	trace
Hydrogen (H)	10%	trace	0.1%
Nitrogen (N)	3%	78%	trace

Table 2.1

The Structure of the Atom

To understand how elements come together, we must first discuss the smallest component or building block of an element, the atom. An atom is the smallest unit of matter that retains all of the chemical properties of an element. For example, one gold atom has all of the properties of gold in that it is a solid metal at room temperature. A gold coin is simply a very large number of gold atoms molded into the shape of a coin and containing small amounts of other elements known as impurities. Gold atoms cannot be broken down into anything smaller while still retaining the properties of gold.

An atom is composed of two regions: the **nucleus**, which is in the center of the atom and contains protons and neutrons, and the outermost region of the atom which holds its electrons in orbit around the nucleus, as illustrated in Figure 2.2. Atoms contain protons, electrons, and neutrons, among other subatomic particles. The only exception is hydrogen (H), which is made of one proton and one electron with no neutrons.

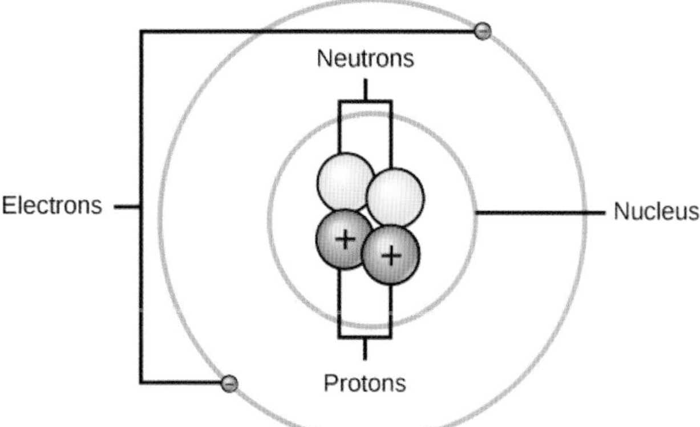

Figure 2.2 Elements, such as helium, depicted here, are made up of atoms. Atoms are made up of protons and neutrons located within the nucleus, with electrons in orbitals surrounding the nucleus.

Protons and neutrons have approximately the same mass, about 1.67×10^{-24} grams. Scientists arbitrarily define this amount of mass as one atomic mass unit (amu) or one Dalton, as shown in Table 2.2. Although similar in mass, protons and neutrons differ in their electric charge. A **proton** is positively charged whereas a **neutron** is uncharged. Therefore, the number of neutrons in an atom contributes significantly to its mass, but not to its charge. **Electrons** are much smaller in mass than protons, weighing only 9.11×10^{-28} grams, or about 1/1800 of an atomic mass unit. Hence, they do not contribute much to an element's overall atomic mass. Therefore, when considering atomic mass, it is customary to ignore the mass of any electrons and calculate the atom's mass based on the number of protons and neutrons alone. Although not significant contributors to mass, electrons do contribute greatly to the atom's charge, as each electron has a negative charge equal to the positive charge of a proton. In uncharged, neutral atoms, the number of electrons orbiting the nucleus is equal to the number of protons inside the nucleus. In these atoms, the positive and negative charges cancel each other out, leading to an atom with no net charge.

Accounting for the sizes of protons, neutrons, and electrons, most of the volume of an atom—greater than 99 percent—is, in fact, empty space. With all this empty space, one might ask why so-called solid objects do not just pass through one another. The reason they do not is that the electrons that surround all atoms are negatively charged and negative charges repel each other.

Protons, Neutrons, and Electrons

	Charge	Mass (amu)	Location
Proton	+1	1	nucleus
Neutron	0	1	nucleus
Electron	–1	0	orbitals

Table 2.2

Atomic Number and Mass

Atoms of each element contain a characteristic number of protons and electrons. The number of protons determines an element's **atomic number** and is used to distinguish one element from another. The number of neutrons is variable, resulting in isotopes, which are different forms of the same atom that vary only in the number of neutrons they possess. Together, the number of protons and the number of neutrons determine an element's **mass number**, as illustrated in this figure. Note that the small contribution of mass from electrons is disregarded in calculating the mass number. This approximation of mass can be used to easily calculate how many neutrons an element has by simply subtracting the number of protons from the mass number. Since an element's isotopes will have slightly different mass numbers, scientists also determine the **atomic mass**, which is the calculated mean of the mass number for its naturally occurring isotopes. Often, the resulting number contains a fraction. For example, the atomic mass of chlorine (Cl) is 35.45 because chlorine is composed of several isotopes, some (the majority) with atomic mass 35 (17 protons and 18 neutrons) and some with atomic mass 37 (17 protons and 20 neutrons).

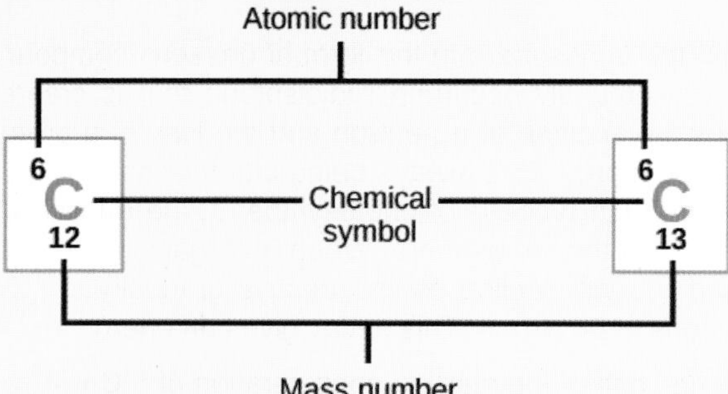

Figure 2.3 Carbon has an atomic number of six, and two stable isotopes with mass numbers of twelve and thirteen, respectively. Its relative atomic mass is 12.011.

How many neutrons do carbon-12 and carbon-13 have, respectively?

a. Carbon-12 contains 6 neutrons while carbon-13 contains 7 neutrons.
b. Carbon-12 contains 7 neutrons while carbon-13 contains 6 neutrons.
c. Carbon-12 contains 12 neutrons while carbon-13 contains 13 neutrons.
d. Carbon-12 contains 13 neutrons while carbon-13 contains 12 neutrons.

Isotopes

Isotopes are different forms of an element that have the same number of protons but a different number of neutrons. Some elements—such as carbon, potassium, and uranium—have naturally occurring isotopes. Carbon-12 contains six protons, six neutrons, and six electrons; therefore, it has a mass number of 12 (six protons and six neutrons). Carbon-14 contains six protons, eight neutrons, and six electrons; its atomic mass is 14 (six protons and eight neutrons). These two alternate forms of carbon are isotopes. Some isotopes may emit neutrons, protons, and electrons, and attain a more stable atomic configuration (lower level of potential energy); these are radioactive isotopes, or radioisotopes. Radioactive decay (carbon-14 losing neutrons to eventually become nitrogen-14) describes the energy loss that occurs when an unstable atom's nucleus releases radiation.

evolution CONNECTION

Carbon Dating

Carbon is normally present in the atmosphere in the form of gaseous compounds like carbon dioxide and methane. Carbon-14 (^{14}C) is a naturally occurring radioisotope that is created in the atmosphere from atmospheric ^{14}N (nitrogen) by the addition of a neutron and the loss of a proton because of cosmic rays. This is a continuous process, so more ^{14}C is always being created. As a living organism incorporates ^{14}C initially as carbon dioxide fixed in the process of photosynthesis, the relative amount of ^{14}C in its body is equal to the concentration of ^{14}C in the atmosphere. When an organism dies, it is no longer ingesting ^{14}C, so the ratio between ^{14}C and ^{12}C will decline as ^{14}C decays gradually to ^{14}N by a process called beta decay—the emission of electrons or positrons. This decay gives off energy in a slow process.

After approximately 5,730 years, half of the starting concentration of ^{14}C will have been converted back to ^{14}N. The time it takes for half of the original concentration of an isotope to decay back to its more stable form is called its half-life. Because the half-life of ^{14}C is long, it is used to date formerly living objects such as old bones or wood. Comparing the ratio of the ^{14}C concentration found in an object to the amount of ^{14}C detected in the atmosphere, the amount of the isotope that has not yet decayed can be determined. On the basis of this amount, the age of the material, such as the pygmy mammoth shown in Figure 2.4, can be calculated with accuracy if it is not much older than about 50,000 years. Other elements have isotopes with different half lives. For example, ^{40}K (potassium-40) has a half-life of 1.25 billion years, and ^{235}U (Uranium 235) has a half-life of about 700 million years. Through the use of radiometric dating, scientists can study the age of fossils or other remains of extinct organisms to understand how organisms have evolved from earlier species.

Figure 2.4 The age of carbon-containing remains less than about 50,000 years old, such as this pygmy mammoth, can be determined using carbon dating. (credit: Bill Faulkner, NPS)

Based on carbon dating, scientists estimate this pygmy mammoth died 11,000 years ago. How would the ratio of ^{14}C to ^{12}C in a living elephant compare to the ^{14}C to ^{12}C ratio found in the mammoth?

a. The ratio would be the same in the elephant and the mammoth.

b. The ratio would be lower in the elephant than the mammoth.

c. The ratio would be higher in the elephant than the mammoth.

d. The ratio would depend on the diet of each animal.

To learn more about atoms, isotopes, and how to tell one isotope from another, visit this site (http://openstaxcollege.org/l/atoms_isotopes) and run the simulation.

K-41 is one of the naturally occurring isotopes of potassium. Use the periodic table to explain how the structure of K-41 differs from the normal K atom.

a. K-41 has a total of 24 neutrons and normal K atom has 22 neutrons

b. K-41 has a total of 22 neutrons and normal K atom has 20 neutrons

c. K-41 has one more neutron than the normal K atom

d. K-41 has one less neutron than normal K atom

The Periodic Table

The different elements are organized and displayed in the **periodic table**. Devised by Russian chemist Dmitri Mendeleev (1834–1907) in 1869, the table groups elements that, although unique, share certain chemical properties with other elements. The properties of elements are responsible for their physical state at room temperature: they may be gases, solids, or liquids. Elements also have specific **chemical reactivity**, the ability to combine and to chemically bond with each other.

In the periodic table, shown in Figure 2.5, the elements are organized and displayed according to their atomic number and are arranged in a series of rows and columns based on shared chemical and physical properties. In addition to providing the atomic number for each element, the periodic table also displays the element's atomic mass. Looking at carbon, for example, its symbol (C) and name appear, as well as its atomic number of six (in the upper left-hand corner) and its atomic mass of 12.11.

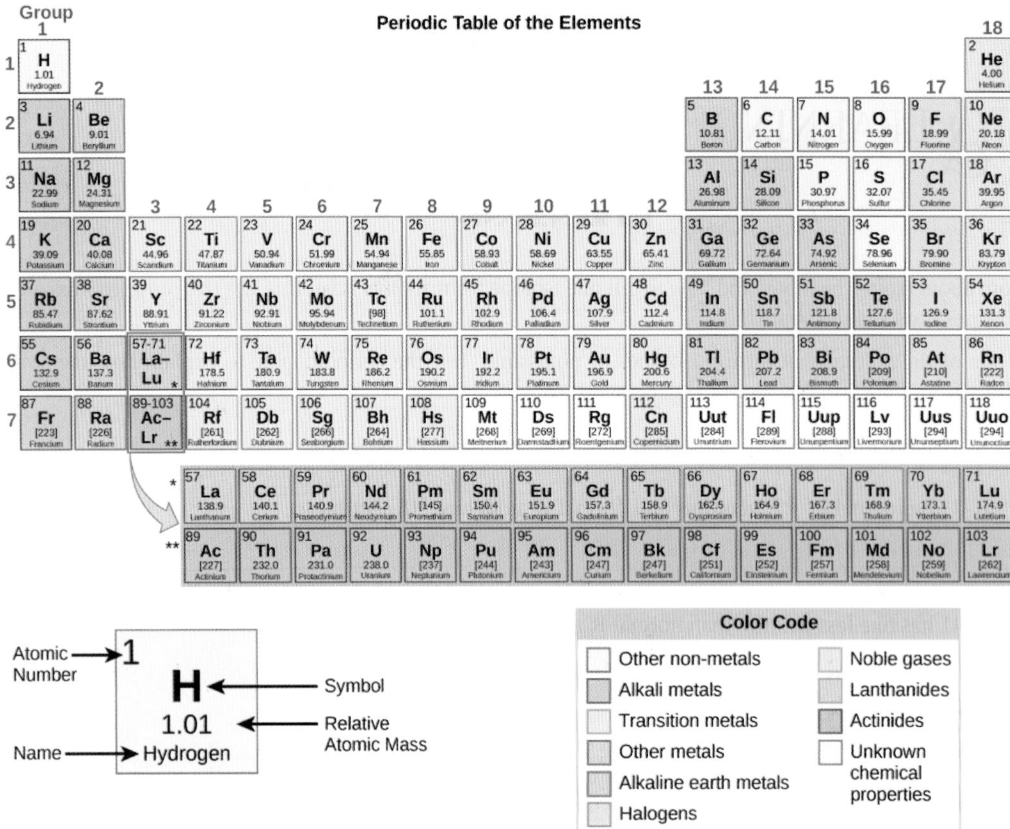

Figure 2.5 The periodic table shows the atomic mass and atomic number of each element. The atomic number appears above the symbol for the element and the approximate atomic mass appears below it.

The periodic table groups elements according to chemical properties. The differences in chemical reactivity between the elements are based on the number and spatial distribution of an atom's electrons. Atoms that chemically react and bond to each other form molecules. **Molecules** are simply two or more atoms chemically bonded together. Logically, when two atoms chemically bond to form a molecule, their electrons, which form the outermost region of each atom, come together first as the atoms form a chemical bond.

Electron Shells and the Bohr Model

It should be stressed that there is a connection between the number of protons in an element, the atomic number that distinguishes one element from another, and the number of electrons it has. In all electrically neutral atoms, the number of electrons is the same as the number of protons. Thus, each element, at least when electrically neutral, has a characteristic number of electrons equal to its atomic number.

An early model of the atom was developed in 1913 by Danish scientist Niels Bohr (1885–1962). The Bohr model shows the atom as a central nucleus containing protons and neutrons, with the electrons in circular **orbitals** at specific distances from the nucleus, as illustrated in Figure 2.6. These orbits form electron shells or energy levels, which are a way of visualizing the number of electrons in the outermost shells. These energy levels are designated by a number and the symbol "n." For example, 1n represents the first energy level located closest to the nucleus.

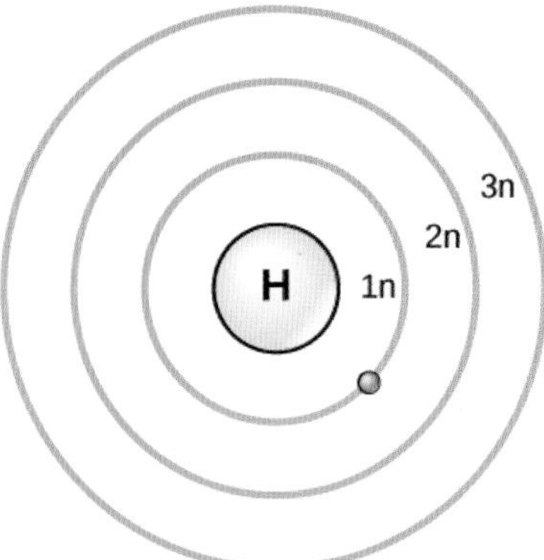

Figure 2.6 The Bohr model was developed by Niels Bohr in 1913. In this model, electrons exist within principal shells. An electron normally exists in the lowest energy shell available, which is the one closest to the nucleus. Energy from a photon of light can bump it up to a higher energy shell, but this situation is unstable, and the electron quickly decays back to the ground state. In the process, a photon of light is released.

Electrons fill orbitals in a consistent order: they first fill the orbitals closest to the nucleus, then they continue to fill orbitals of increasing energy further from the nucleus. If there are multiple orbitals of equal energy, they will be filled with one electron in each energy level before a second electron is added. The electrons of the outermost energy level determine the energetic stability of the atom and its tendency to form chemical bonds with other atoms to form molecules.

Under standard conditions, atoms fill the inner shells first, often resulting in a variable number of electrons in the outermost shell. The innermost shell has a maximum of two electrons but the next two electron shells can each have a maximum of eight electrons. This is known as the **octet rule**, which states, with the exception of the innermost shell, that atoms are more stable energetically when they have eight electrons in their **valence shell**, the outermost electron shell. Examples of some neutral atoms and their electron configurations are shown in this figure. Notice that in this Figure 2.7, helium has a complete outer electron shell, with two electrons filling its first and only shell. Similarly, neon has a complete outer 2n shell containing eight electrons. In contrast, chlorine and sodium have seven and one in their outer shells, respectively, but theoretically they would be more energetically stable if they followed the octet rule and had eight.

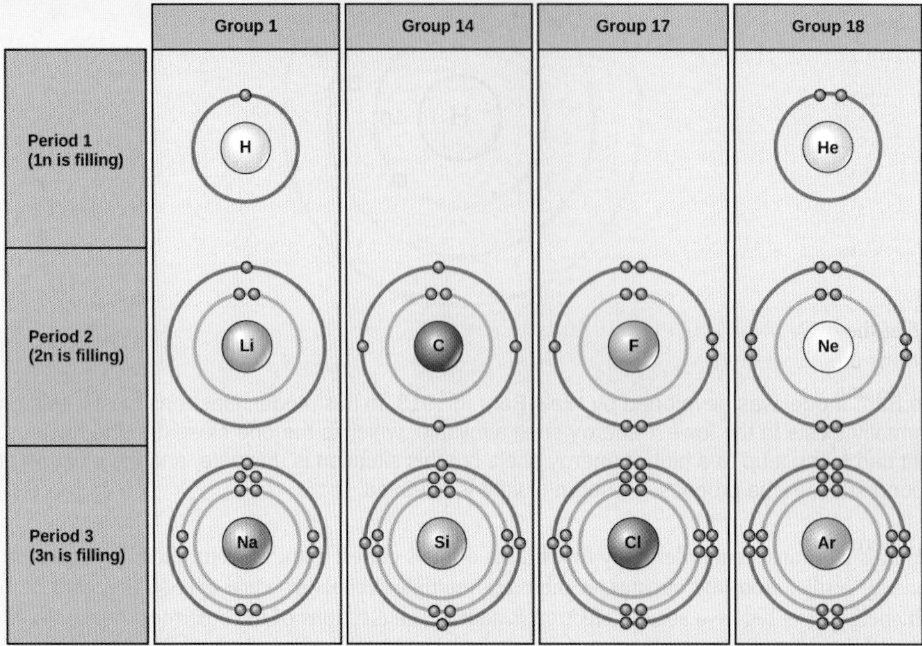

Figure 2.7 Bohr diagrams indicate how many electrons fill each principal shell. Group 18 elements (helium, neon, and argon are shown) have a full outer, or valence, shell. A full valence shell is the most stable electron configuration. Elements in other groups have partially filled valence shells and gain or lose electrons to achieve a stable electron configuration.

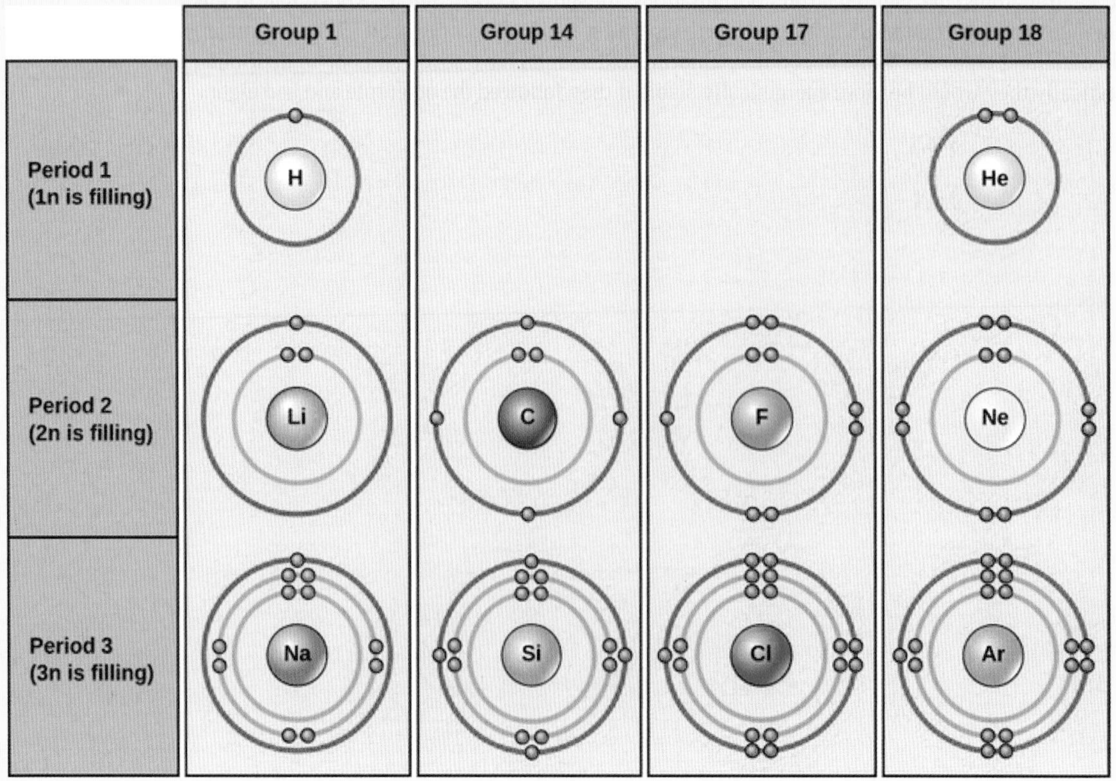

An atom may give, take, or share electrons with another atom to achieve a full valence shell, the most stable electron configuration. Looking at this figure, how many electrons do elements in group 1 need to lose in order to achieve a stable electron configuration? How many electrons do elements in groups 14 and 17 need to gain to achieve a stable configuration?

a. Elements of group 1 need to lose one electron, elements of group 14 need to gain 4 electrons, and elements of group 17 need to gain 1 electron

b. Elements of group 1 need to lose 4 electrons while elements of group 14 and 17 need to gain 1 electron each.

c. Elements of group 1 need to lose 2 electrons, elements of group 14 need to gain 4 electrons and elements of group 17 need to gain 1 electron.

d. Elements of group 1 need to gain 1 electron while, elements of group 14 need to lose 4 electrons and elements of group 17 need to lose 1 electron.

Understanding that the organization of the periodic table is based on the total number of protons (and electrons) helps us know how electrons are distributed among the shells. The periodic table is arranged in columns and rows based on the number of electrons and where these electrons are located. Take a closer look at the some of the elements in the table's far right column in the periodic table. The group 18 atoms helium (He), neon (Ne), and argon (Ar) all have filled outer electron shells, making it unnecessary for them to share electrons with other atoms to attain stability; they are highly stable as single atoms. Their non-reactivity has resulted in their being named the **inert gases** (or **noble gases**). Compare this to the group 1 elements in the left-hand column. These elements, including hydrogen (H), lithium (Li), and sodium (Na), all have one electron in their outermost shells. That means that they can achieve a stable configuration and a filled outer shell by donating or sharing one electron with another atom or a molecule such as water. Hydrogen will donate or share its electron to achieve this configuration, while lithium and sodium will donate their electron to become stable. As a result of losing a negatively charged electron, they become positively charged **ions**. Group 17 elements, including fluorine and chlorine, have seven electrons in their outmost shells, so they tend to fill this shell with an electron from other atoms or molecules, making them negatively charged ions. Group 14 elements, of which carbon is the most important to living systems, have four electrons in their outer shell allowing them to make several covalent bonds (discussed below) with other atoms. Thus, the columns of the periodic table represent the potential shared state of these elements' outer electron shells that is responsible for their similar chemical characteristics.

Electron Orbitals

Although useful to explain the reactivity and chemical bonding of certain elements, the Bohr model of the atom does not accurately reflect how electrons are spatially distributed surrounding the nucleus. They do not circle the nucleus like the earth orbits the sun, but are found in **electron orbitals**. These relatively complex shapes result from the fact that electrons behave not just like particles, but also like waves. Mathematical equations from quantum mechanics known as wave functions can predict within a certain level of probability where an electron might be at any given time. The area where an electron is most likely to be found is called its orbital.

Recall that the Bohr model depicts an atom's electron shell configuration. Within each electron shell are subshells, and each subshell has a specified number of orbitals containing electrons. While it is impossible to calculate exactly where an electron is located, scientists know that it is most probably located within its orbital path. Subshells are designated by the letter s, *p*, *d*, and *f*. The *s* subshell is spherical in shape and has one orbital. Principal shell 1n has only a single *s* orbital, which can hold two electrons. Principal shell 2n has one *s* and one *p* subshell, and can hold a total of eight electrons. The *p* subshell has three dumbbell-shaped orbitals, as illustrated in Figure 2.8. Subshells *d* and *f* have more complex shapes and contain five and seven orbitals, respectively. These are not shown in the illustration. Principal shell 3n has *s*, *p*, and *d* subshells and can hold 18 electrons. Principal shell 4n has *s*, *p*, *d* and *f* orbitals and can hold 32 electrons. Moving away from the nucleus, the number of electrons and orbitals found in the energy levels increases. Progressing from one atom to the next in the periodic table, the electron structure can be worked out by fitting an extra electron into the next available orbital.

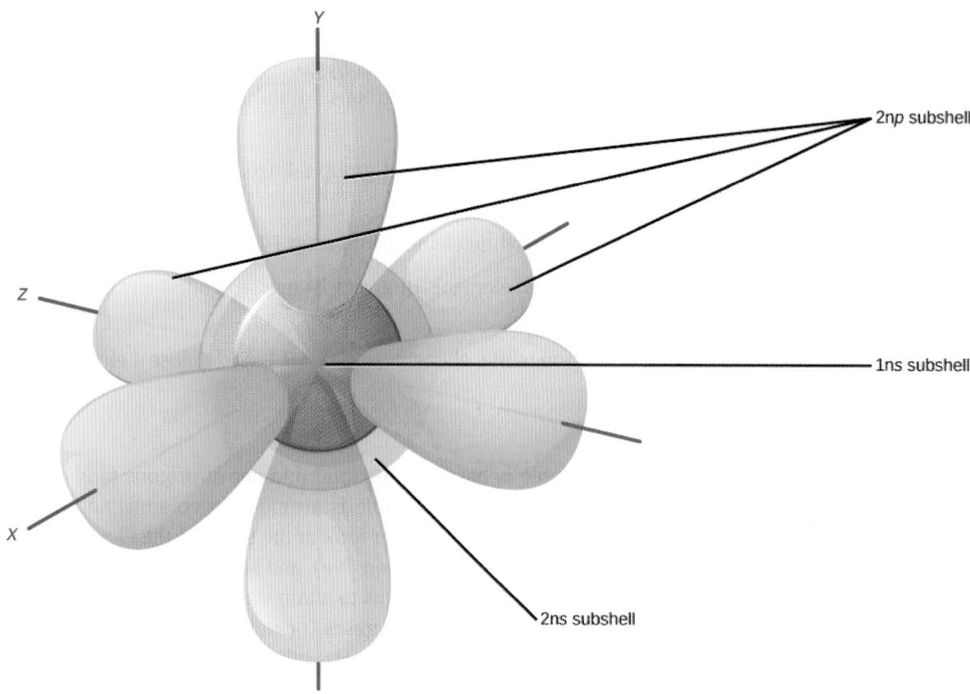

Figure 2.8 The *s* subshells are shaped like spheres. Both the 1n and 2n principal shells have an *s* orbital, but the size of the sphere is larger in the 2n orbital. Each sphere is a single orbital. *p* subshells are made up of three dumbbell-shaped orbitals. Principal shell 2n has a *p* subshell, but shell 1 does not.

The closest orbital to the nucleus, called the 1s orbital, can hold up to two electrons. This orbital is equivalent to the innermost electron shell of the Bohr model of the atom. It is called the 1*s* orbital because it is spherical around the nucleus. The 1*s* orbital is the closest orbital to the nucleus, and it is always filled first, before any other orbital can be filled. Hydrogen has one electron; therefore, it has only one spot within the 1*s* orbital occupied. This is designated as $1s^1$, where the superscripted 1 refers to the one electron within the 1*s* orbital. Helium has two electrons; therefore, it can completely fill the 1*s* orbital with its two electrons. This is designated as $1s^2$, referring to the two electrons of helium in the 1*s* orbital. On the periodic table Figure 2.5, hydrogen and helium are the only two elements in the first row (period); this is because they only have electrons in their first shell, the 1*s* orbital. Hydrogen and helium are the only two elements that have the 1*s* and no other electron orbitals in the electrically neutral state.

The second electron shell may contain eight electrons. This shell contains another spherical *s* orbital and three "dumbbell" shaped *p* orbitals, each of which can hold two electrons, as shown in Figure 2.8. After the 1*s* orbital is filled, the second electron shell is filled, first filling its 2*s* orbital and then its three *p* orbitals. When filling the *p* orbitals, each takes a single electron; once each *p* orbital has an electron, a second may be added. Lithium (Li) contains three electrons that occupy the first and second shells. Two electrons fill the 1*s* orbital, and the third electron then fills the 2*s* orbital. Its **electron configuration** is $1s^2 2s^1$. Neon (Ne), on the other hand, has a total of ten electrons: two are in its innermost 1*s* orbital and eight fill its second shell (two each in the 2*s* and three *p* orbitals); thus, it is an inert gas and energetically stable as a single atom that will rarely form a chemical bond with other atoms. Larger elements have additional orbitals, making up the third electron shell. While the concepts of electron shells and orbitals are closely related, orbitals provide a more accurate depiction of the electron configuration of an atom because the orbital model specifies the different shapes and special orientations of all the places that electrons may occupy.

Watch **this visual animation (http://openstaxcollege.org/l/orbitals)** to see the spatial arrangement of the *p* and *s* orbitals.

Use the periodic table to describe what a Bohr model of Fluorine (F) would look like and explain why the Bohr model is not an accurate representation of the electron orbitals in fluorine.

a. A Bohr model would have 2 electron rings, and a Bohr model would not give information about atomic mass

b. A Bohr model would have one electron ring, and a Bohr model would not show the sub-shells of first ring

c. A Bohr model would have 2 electron rings, and a Bohr model would not show the sub-shell of second ring

d. A Bohr model would have one electron ring, and a Bohr model would not give information about number of electron in each ring

science practices CONNECTION for AP® Courses

Activity

Create diagrams to show the placement of protons, neutrons, and electrons in an atom of carbon-12 and carbon-14, respectably. Based on their subatomic difference(s), determine which element is an organism more likely to use to synthesize glucose ($C_6H_{12}O_6$) and give a reason for your choice.

Chemical Reactions and Molecules

All elements are most stable when their outermost shell is filled with electrons according to the octet rule. This is because it is energetically favorable for atoms to be in that configuration and it makes them stable. However, since not all elements have enough electrons to fill their outermost shells, atoms form **chemical bonds** with other atoms thereby obtaining the electrons they need to attain a stable electron configuration. When two or more atoms chemically bond with each other, the resultant chemical structure is a molecule. The familiar water molecule, H_2O, consists of two hydrogen atoms and one oxygen atom; these bond together to form water, as illustrated in **Figure 2.9**. Atoms can form molecules by donating, accepting, or sharing electrons to fill their outer shells.

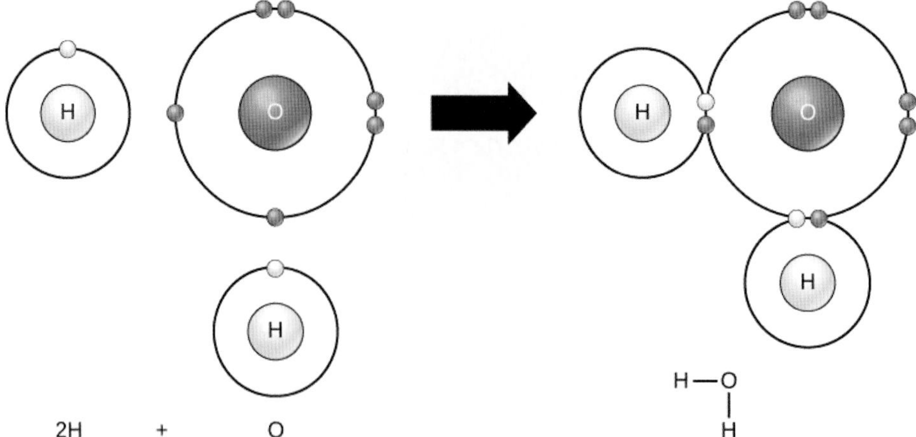

Figure 2.9 Two or more atoms may bond with each other to form a molecule. When two hydrogens and an oxygen share electrons via covalent bonds, a water molecule is formed.

Chemical reactions occur when two or more atoms bond together to form molecules or when bonded atoms are broken apart. The substances used in the beginning of a chemical reaction are called the **reactants** (usually found on the left side of a chemical equation), and the substances found at the end of the reaction are known as the **products** (usually found on the right side of a chemical equation). An arrow is typically drawn between the reactants and products to indicate the direction of the chemical reaction; this direction is not always a "one-way street." For the creation of the water molecule shown above, the chemical equation would be:

$$2H + O \rightarrow H_2O$$

An example of a simple chemical reaction is the breaking down of hydrogen peroxide molecules, each of which consists of two hydrogen atoms bonded to two oxygen atoms (H_2O_2). The reactant hydrogen peroxide is broken down into water, containing one oxygen atom bound to two hydrogen atoms (H_2O), and oxygen, which consists of two bonded oxygen atoms (O_2). In the equation below, the reaction includes two hydrogen peroxide molecules and two water molecules. This is an example of a **balanced chemical equation**, wherein the number of atoms of each element is the same on each side of the equation. According to the law of conservation of matter, the number of atoms before and after a chemical reaction should be equal, such that no atoms are, under normal circumstances, created or destroyed.

$$2H_2O_2 \text{ (hydrogen peroxide)} \rightarrow 2H_2O \text{ (water)} + O_2 \text{ (oxygen)}$$

Even though all of the reactants and products of this reaction are molecules (each atom remains bonded to at least one other atom), in this reaction only hydrogen peroxide and water are representatives of **compounds**: they contain atoms of more than one type of element. Molecular oxygen, on the other hand, as shown in Figure 2.10, consists of two doubly bonded oxygen atoms and is not classified as a compound but as a homonuclear molecule.

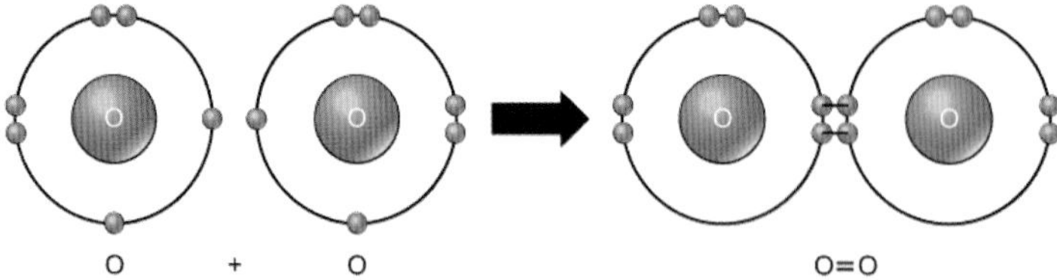

Figure 2.10 The oxygen atoms in an O_2 molecule are joined by a double bond.

Some chemical reactions, such as the one shown above, can proceed in one direction until the reactants are all used up. The equations that describe these reactions contain a unidirectional arrow and are **irreversible**. **Reversible reactions** are those that can go in either direction. In reversible reactions, reactants are turned into products, but when the concentration of product goes beyond a certain threshold (characteristic of the particular reaction), some of these products will be converted back into reactants; at this point, the designations of products and reactants are reversed. This back and forth continues until a certain relative balance between reactants and products occurs—a state called **equilibrium**. These situations of reversible reactions are often denoted by a chemical equation with a double headed arrow pointing towards both the reactants and products.

For example, in human blood, excess hydrogen ions (H^+) bind to bicarbonate ions (HCO_3^-) forming an equilibrium state with carbonic acid (H_2CO_3). If carbonic acid were added to this system, some of it would be converted to bicarbonate and hydrogen ions.

$$HCO^- + H^+ \text{ — } H_2CO_3$$

In biological reactions, however, equilibrium is rarely obtained because the concentrations of the reactants or products or both are constantly changing, often with a product of one reaction being a reactant for another. To return to the example of excess hydrogen ions in the blood, the formation of carbonic acid will be the major direction of the reaction. However, the carbonic acid can also leave the body as carbon dioxide gas (via exhalation) instead of being converted back to bicarbonate ion, thus driving the reaction to the right by the chemical law known as **law of mass action**. These reactions are important for maintaining the homeostasis of our blood.

$$HCO^- + H^+ \text{ — } H_2CO_3 \leftrightarrow CO_2 + H_2O$$

Ions and Ionic Bonds

Some atoms are more stable when they gain or lose an electron (or possibly two) and form ions. This fills their outermost electron shell and makes them energetically more stable. Because the number of electrons does not equal the number of protons, each ion has a net charge. **Cations** are positive ions that are formed by losing electrons. Negative ions are formed by gaining electrons and are called anions. **Anions** are designated by their elemental name being altered to end in "-ide": the anion of chlorine is called chloride, and the anion of sulfur is called sulfide, for example.

This movement of electrons from one element to another is referred to as **electron transfer**. As Figure 2.11 illustrates, sodium (Na) only has one electron in its outer electron shell. It takes less energy for sodium to donate that one electron than it does to accept seven more electrons to fill the outer shell. If sodium loses an electron, it now has 11 protons, 11 neutrons, and only 10 electrons, leaving it with an overall charge of +1. It is now referred to as a sodium ion. Chlorine (Cl) in its lowest energy state (called the ground state) has seven electrons in its outer shell. Again, it is more energy-efficient for chlorine to gain one electron than to lose seven. Therefore, it tends to gain an electron to create an ion with 17 protons, 17 neutrons, and 18 electrons, giving it a net negative (–1) charge. It is now referred to as a chloride ion. In this example, sodium will donate its one electron to empty its shell, and chlorine will accept that electron to fill its shell. Both ions now satisfy the octet rule and have complete outermost shells. Because the number of electrons is no longer equal to the number of protons, each is now an ion and has a +1 (sodium cation) or –1 (chloride anion) charge. Note that these transactions can normally only take place simultaneously: in order for a sodium atom to lose an electron, it must be in the presence of a suitable recipient like a chlorine atom.

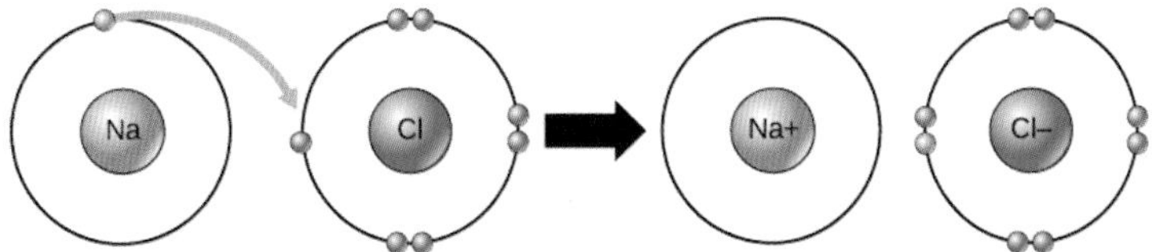

Figure 2.11 In the formation of an ionic compound, metals lose electrons and nonmetals gain electrons to achieve an octet.

Ionic bonds are formed between ions with opposite charges. For instance, positively charged sodium ions and negatively charged chloride ions bond together to make crystals of sodium chloride, or table salt, creating a crystalline molecule with zero net charge.

Certain salts are referred to in physiology as **electrolytes** (including sodium, potassium, and calcium), ions necessary for nerve impulse conduction, muscle contractions and water balance. Many sports drinks and dietary supplements provide these ions to replace those lost from the body via sweating during exercise.

Covalent Bonds and Other Bonds and Interactions

Another way the octet rule can be satisfied is by the sharing of electrons between atoms to form **covalent bonds**. These bonds are stronger and much more common than ionic bonds in the molecules of living organisms. Covalent bonds are commonly found in carbon-based organic molecules, such as our DNA and proteins. Covalent bonds are also found in inorganic molecules like H_2O, CO_2, and O_2. One, two, or three pairs of electrons may be shared, making single, double, and triple bonds, respectively. The more covalent bonds between two atoms, the stronger their connection. Thus, triple bonds are the strongest.

The strength of different levels of covalent bonding is one of the main reasons living organisms have a difficult time in acquiring nitrogen for use in constructing their molecules, even though molecular nitrogen, N_2, is the most abundant gas in the atmosphere. Molecular nitrogen consists of two nitrogen atoms triple bonded to each other and, as with all molecules, the sharing of these three pairs of electrons between the two nitrogen atoms allows for the filling of their outer electron shells, making the molecule more stable than the individual nitrogen atoms. This strong triple bond makes it difficult for living systems to break apart this nitrogen in order to use it as constituents of proteins and DNA.

The formation of water molecules provides an example of covalent bonding. The hydrogen and oxygen atoms that combine to form water molecules are bound together by covalent bonds, as shown in Figure 2.9. The electron from the hydrogen splits its time between the incomplete outer shell of the hydrogen atoms and the incomplete outer shell of the oxygen atoms. To completely fill the outer shell of oxygen, which has six electrons in its outer shell but which would be more stable with eight, two electrons (one from each hydrogen atom) are needed: hence the well-known formula H_2O. The electrons are shared between the two elements to fill the outer shell of each, making both elements more stable.

View this short video (http://openstaxcollege.org/l/ionic_covalent) to see an animation of ionic and covalent bonding.

What makes ionic bonds different from covalent bonds?

a. Ionic bond involves the transfer of electrons whereas covalent bond involves the sharing of electrons.

b. Ionic bond involves the van der Waals force of interaction whereas covalent bond involves the sharing of electrons.

c. Ionic bond involves the sharing of electrons whereas a covalent bond involves the transfer of electrons.

d. An ionic bond involves the transfer of electrons whereas a covalent bond involves the van der Waals force of interaction.

Polar Covalent Bonds

There are two types of covalent bonds: polar and nonpolar. In a **polar covalent bond**, shown in this figure, the electrons are unequally shared by the atoms and are attracted more to one nucleus than the other. Because of the unequal distribution of electrons between the atoms of different elements, a slightly positive (δ+) or slightly negative (δ–) charge develops. This partial charge is an important property of water and accounts for many of its characteristics.

Water is a polar molecule, with the hydrogen atoms acquiring a partial positive charge and the oxygen a partial negative charge. This occurs because the nucleus of the oxygen atom is more attractive to the electrons of the hydrogen atoms than the hydrogen nucleus is to the oxygen's electrons. Thus oxygen has a higher **electronegativity** than hydrogen and the shared electrons spend more time in the vicinity of the oxygen nucleus than they do near the nucleus of the hydrogen atoms, giving the atoms of oxygen and hydrogen slightly negative and positive charges, respectively. Another way of stating this is that the probability of finding a shared electron near an oxygen nucleus is more likely than finding it near a hydrogen nucleus. Either way, the atom's relative electronegativity contributes to the development of partial charges whenever one element is significantly more electronegative than the other, and the charges generated by these polar bonds may then be used for the formation of hydrogen bonds based on the attraction of opposite partial charges. (Hydrogen bonds, which are discussed in detail below, are weak bonds between slightly positively charged hydrogen atoms to slightly negatively charged atoms in other molecules.) Since macromolecules often have atoms within them that differ in electronegativity, polar bonds are often present in organic molecules.

Nonpolar Covalent Bonds

Nonpolar covalent bonds form between two atoms of the same element or between different elements that share electrons equally. For example, molecular oxygen (O_2) is nonpolar because the electrons will be equally distributed between the two oxygen atoms.

Another example of a nonpolar covalent bond is methane (CH_4), also shown in this figure. Carbon has four electrons in its outermost shell and needs four more to fill it. It gets these four from four hydrogen atoms, each atom providing one, making a stable outer shell of eight electrons. Carbon and hydrogen do not have the same electronegativity but are similar; thus, nonpolar bonds form. The hydrogen atoms each need one electron for their outermost shell, which is filled when it contains two electrons. These elements share the electrons equally among the carbons and the hydrogen atoms, creating a nonpolar covalent molecule.

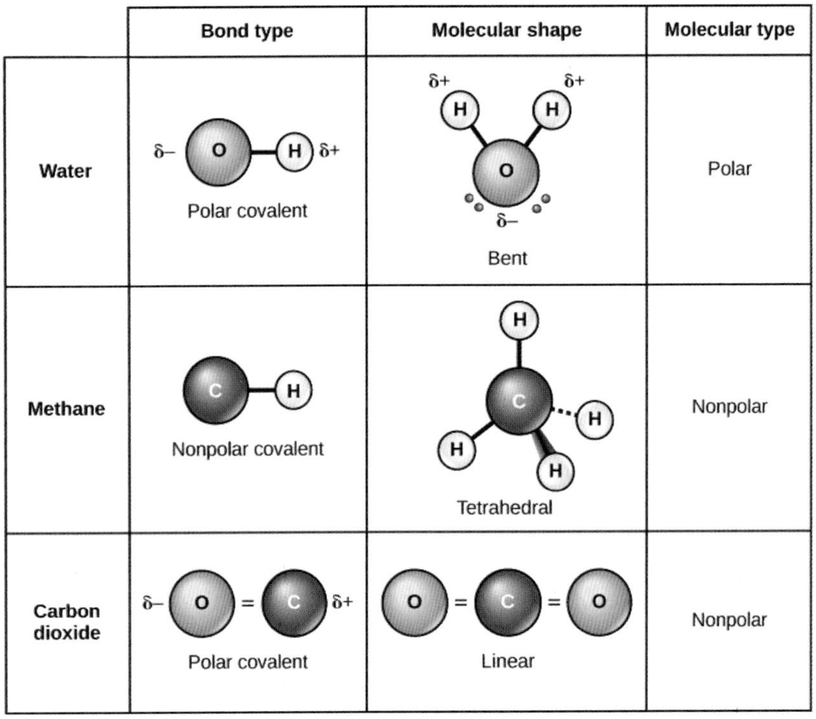

	Bond type	Molecular shape	Molecular type
Water	δ– O–H δ+ Polar covalent	δ+ H, δ+ H, O, δ– Bent	Polar
Methane	C–H Nonpolar covalent	H, C, H, H, H Tetrahedral	Nonpolar
Carbon dioxide	δ– O = C δ+ Polar covalent	O = C = O Linear	Nonpolar

Figure 2.12 Whether a molecule is polar or nonpolar depends both on bond type and molecular shape. Both water and carbon dioxide have polar covalent bonds, but carbon dioxide is linear, so the partial charges on the molecule cancel each other out.

Hydrogen Bonds and Van Der Waals Interactions

Ionic and covalent bonds between elements require energy to break. Ionic bonds are not as strong as covalent, which determines their behavior in biological systems. However, not all bonds are ionic or covalent bonds. Weaker bonds can also form between molecules. Two weak bonds that occur frequently are hydrogen bonds and van der Waals interactions. Without these two types of bonds, life as we know it would not exist. Hydrogen bonds provide many of the critical, life-sustaining properties of water and also stabilize the structures of proteins and DNA, the building block of cells.

When polar covalent bonds containing hydrogen form, the hydrogen in that bond has a slightly positive charge because hydrogen's electron is pulled more strongly toward the other element and away from the hydrogen. Because the hydrogen is slightly positive, it will be attracted to neighboring negative charges. When this happens, a weak interaction occurs between the $\delta^+$of the hydrogen from one molecule and the δ– charge on the more electronegative atoms of another molecule, usually oxygen or nitrogen, or within the same molecule. This interaction is called a **hydrogen bond**. This type of bond is common and occurs regularly between water molecules. Individual hydrogen bonds are weak and easily broken; however, they occur in very large numbers in water and in organic polymers, creating a major force in combination. Hydrogen bonds are also responsible for zipping together the DNA double helix.

Like hydrogen bonds, **van der Waals interactions** are weak attractions or interactions between molecules. Van der Waals attractions can occur between any two or more molecules and are dependent on slight fluctuations of the electron densities, which are not always symmetrical around an atom. For these attractions to happen, the molecules need to be very close to one another. These bonds—along with ionic, covalent, and hydrogen bonds—contribute to the three-dimensional structure of the proteins in our cells that is necessary for their proper function.

career CONNECTION

Pharmaceutical chemists are responsible for the development of new drugs and trying to determine the mode of action of both old and new drugs. They are involved in every step of the drug development process. Drugs can be found in the natural environment or can be synthesized in the laboratory. In many cases, potential drugs found in nature are changed chemically in the laboratory to make them safer and more effective, and sometimes synthetic versions of drugs substitute for the version found in nature.

After the initial discovery or synthesis of a drug, the chemist then develops the drug, perhaps chemically altering it, testing it to see if the drug is toxic, and then designing methods for efficient large-scale production. Then, the process of getting the drug approved for human use begins. In the United States, drug approval is handled by the Food and Drug Administration (FDA) and involves a series of large-scale experiments using human subjects to make sure the drug is not harmful and effectively treats the condition it aims to treat. This process often takes several years and requires the participation of physicians and scientists, in addition to chemists, to complete testing and gain approval.

An example of a drug that was originally discovered in a living organism is Paclitaxel, an anti-cancer drug. This drug was discovered in the bark of the pacific yew tree. Another example is aspirin, originally isolated from willow tree bark. Finding drugs often means testing hundreds of samples of plants, fungi, and other forms of life to see if any biologically active compounds are found within them. Sometimes, traditional medicine can give modern medicine clues to where an active compound can be found. For example, the use of willow bark to make medicine has been known for thousands of years, dating back to ancient Egypt. It was not until the late 1800s, however, that the aspirin molecule, known as acetylsalicylic acid, was purified and marketed for human use.

Occasionally, drugs developed for one use are found to have unforeseen effects that allow these drugs to be used in other, unrelated ways. For example, the drug minoxidil was originally developed to treat high blood pressure. When tested on humans, it was noticed that individuals taking the drug would grow new hair. Eventually the drug was marketed to men and women with baldness to restore lost hair.

The career of the pharmaceutical chemist may involve detective work, experimentation, and drug development, all with the goal of making human beings healthier.

everyday CONNECTION for AP® Courses

Bonds Can Be Flexible

Proteins are mostly made up of carbon, hydrogen, oxygen, nitrogen, phosphorus, and sulfur. The proteins that make up hair contain sulfur bonded to another sulfur, which is called a disulfide bond. These covalent bonds give hair its shape and texture. Heat from a hair straightener breaks the disulfide bonds, which causes the hair to lose its curl. Why do you think this method of hair straightening isn't permanent?

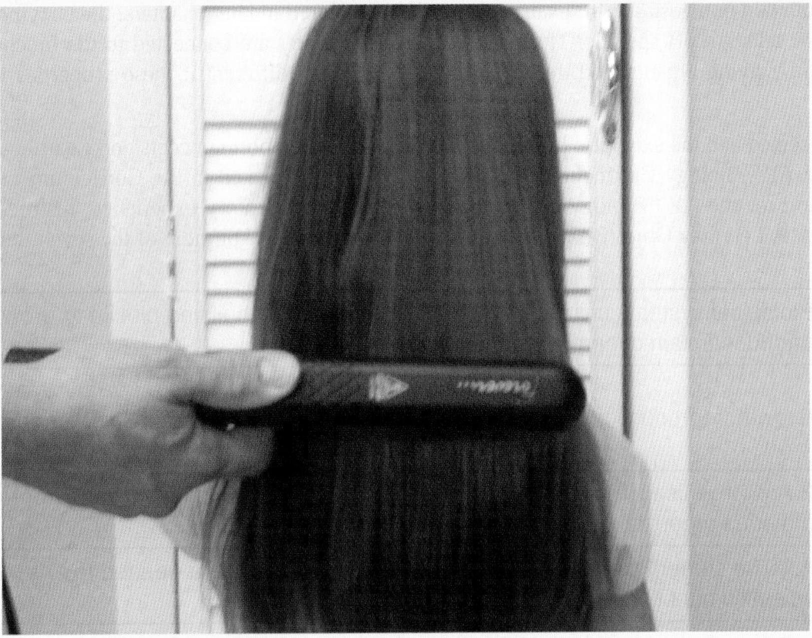

Figure 2.13

The shape of hair proteins is maintained by a combination of hydrogen bonds and covalent, disulfide bonds. Heat is sufficient to break the hydrogen bonds, but harsh chemicals are required to break the disulfide bonds. Why is it harder to break the disulfide bonds than the hydrogen bonds?

a. Covalent bonds are stronger than hydrogen bonds.
b. There are many more disulfide bonds than hydrogen bonds.
c. Covalent bonds are stronger than disulfide bonds.
d. Covalent bonds are less elastic than hydrogen bonds.

2.2 | Water

In this section, you will investigate the following questions:

- How does the molecular structure of water result in unique properties of water that are critical to maintaining life?
- What are the role of acids, bases, and buffers in dynamic homeostasis?

Connection for AP® Courses

Covalent bonds form between atoms when they share electrons to fill their valence electron shells. When the sharing of electrons between atoms is equal, such as O_2 (oxygen) or CH_4 (methane), the covalent bond is said to be **nonpolar**. However, when electrons are shared, but not equally due to differences in **electronegativity** (the tendency to attract electrons), the covalent bond is said to be **polar**. H_2O (water) is an example of a polar molecule. Because oxygen is more electronegative than hydrogen, the electrons are drawn toward oxygen and away from the hydrogen atoms; consequently, the oxygen atom acquires a slight negative charge and each hydrogen atoms acquires a slightly positive charge. It is important to remember that the electrons are still shared, just not equally.

Water's polarity allows for the formation of hydrogen bonds between adjacent water molecules, resulting in many unique properties that are critical to maintaining life. For example, water is an excellent solvent because hydrogen bonds allow ions and other polar molecules to dissolve in water. Water's hydrogen bonds also contribute to its high heat capacity and high heat of vaporization, resulting in greater temperature stability. Hydrogen bond formation makes ice less dense as a solid than as a liquid, insulating aquatic environments. Water's cohesive and adhesive properties are seen as it rises inside capillary tubes or travels up a large tree from roots to leaves. The pH or hydrogen ion concentration of a solution is highly regulated to help organisms maintain homeostasis; for example, as will be explored in later chapters, the enzymes that catalyze most chemical reactions in cells are pH specific. Thus, the properties of water are connected to the biochemical and physical processes performed by living organisms. Life on Earth would be very different if these properties were altered—if life could exist at all.

The information presented and the examples highlighted in this section support concepts and Learning Objectives outlined in Big Idea 2 of the AP® Biology Curriculum. The Learning Objectives listed in the Curriculum Framework provide a transparent foundation for the AP® Biology course, an inquiry-based laboratory experience, instructional activities, and AP® Exam questions. A Learning Objective merges required content with one or more of the seven Science Practices.

Big Idea 2	Biological systems utilize free energy and molecular building blocks to grow, to reproduce, and to maintain dynamic homeostasis.
Enduring Understanding 2.A	Growth, reproduction and maintenance of living systems require free energy and matter.
Essential Knowledge	**2.A.3** Organisms must exchange matter with the environment to grow, reproduce and maintain organization.
Science Practice	**4.1** The student can justify the selection of the kind of data needed to answer a particular scientific question.
Learning Objective	**2.8** The student is able to justify the selection of data regarding the types of molecules that an animal, plant, or bacterium will take up as necessary building blocks and excrete as waste products.

The Science Practice Challenge Questions contain additional test questions for this section that will help you prepare for the AP exam. These questions address the following standards:
[APLO 2.8] [APLO 2.23]

Why do scientists spend time looking for water on other planets? Why is water so important? It is because water is essential to life as we know it. Water is one of the more abundant molecules and the one most critical to life on Earth. Approximately 60–70 percent of the human body is made up of water. Without it, life as we know it simply would not exist.

The polarity of the water molecule and its resulting hydrogen bonding make water a unique substance with special properties that are intimately tied to the processes of life. Life originally evolved in a watery environment, and most of an organism's cellular chemistry and metabolism occur inside the watery contents of the cell's cytoplasm. Special properties of water are its high heat capacity and heat of vaporization, its ability to dissolve polar molecules, its cohesive and adhesive properties, and its dissociation into ions that leads to the generation of pH. Understanding these characteristics of water helps to elucidate its importance in maintaining life.

Water's Polarity

One of water's important properties is that it is composed of polar molecules: the hydrogen and oxygen within water molecules (H_2O) form polar covalent bonds. While there is no net charge to a water molecule, the polarity of water creates a slightly positive charge on hydrogen and a slightly negative charge on oxygen, contributing to water's properties of attraction. Water's charges are generated because oxygen is more electronegative than hydrogen, making it more likely that a shared electron would be found near the oxygen nucleus than the hydrogen nucleus, thus generating the partial negative charge near the oxygen.

As a result of water's polarity, each water molecule attracts other water molecules because of the opposite charges between water molecules, forming hydrogen bonds. Water also attracts or is attracted to other polar molecules and ions. A polar substance that interacts readily with or dissolves in water is referred to as **hydrophilic** (hydro- = "water"; -philic = "loving"). In contrast, non-polar molecules such as oils and fats do not interact well with water, as shown in Figure 2.14 and separate from it rather than dissolve in it, as we see in salad dressings containing oil and vinegar (an acidic water solution). These nonpolar compounds are called **hydrophobic** (hydro- = "water"; -phobic = "fearing").

Figure 2.14 Oil and water do not mix. As this macro image of oil and water shows, oil does not dissolve in water but forms droplets instead. This is due to it being a nonpolar compound. (credit: Gautam Dogra).

Water's States: Gas, Liquid, and Solid

The formation of hydrogen bonds is an important quality of the liquid water that is crucial to life as we know it. As water molecules make hydrogen bonds with each other, water takes on some unique chemical characteristics compared to other liquids and, since living things have a high water content, understanding these chemical features is key to understanding life. In liquid water, hydrogen bonds are constantly formed and broken as the water molecules slide past each other. The breaking of these bonds is caused by the motion (kinetic energy) of the water molecules due to the heat contained in the system. When the heat is raised as water is boiled, the higher kinetic energy of the water molecules causes the hydrogen bonds to break completely and allows water molecules to escape into the air as gas (steam or water vapor). On the other hand, when the temperature of water is reduced and water freezes, the water molecules form a crystalline structure maintained by hydrogen bonding (there is not enough energy to break the hydrogen bonds) that makes ice less dense than liquid water, a phenomenon not seen in the solidification of other liquids.

Water's lower density in its solid form is due to the way hydrogen bonds are oriented as it freezes: the water molecules are pushed farther apart compared to liquid water. With most other liquids, solidification when the temperature drops includes the lowering of kinetic energy between molecules, allowing them to pack even more tightly than in liquid form and giving the solid a greater density than the liquid.

The lower density of ice, illustrated and pictured in Figure 2.15, an anomaly, causes it to float at the surface of liquid water, such as in an iceberg or in the ice cubes in a glass of ice water. In lakes and ponds, ice will form on the surface of the water creating an insulating barrier that protects the animals and plant life in the pond from freezing. Without this layer of insulating ice, plants and animals living in the pond would freeze in the solid block of ice and could not survive. The detrimental effect of freezing on living organisms is caused by the expansion of ice relative to liquid water. The ice crystals that form upon freezing rupture the delicate membranes essential for the function of living cells, irreversibly damaging them. Cells can only survive freezing if the water in them is temporarily replaced by another liquid like glycerol.

Figure 2.15 Hydrogen bonding makes ice less dense than liquid water. The (a) lattice structure of ice makes it less dense than the freely flowing molecules of liquid water, enabling it to (b) float on water. (credit a: modification of work by Jane Whitney, image created using Visual Molecular Dynamics (VMD) software[1]; credit b: modification of work by Carlos Ponte)

Click **here (http://openstaxcollege.org/l/ice_lattice2)** to see a 3-D animation of the structure of an ice lattice. (Image credit: Jane Whitney. Image created using Visual Molecular Dynamics VMD software.[2])

Identify the red and white balls in the model and explain how arrangement of the molecules supports the fact that ice floats on water.

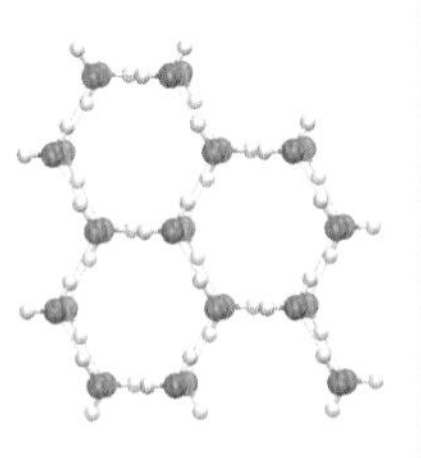

a. Red and white balls represent oxygen and hydrogen, respectively, loose arrangement of molecules results in low density of ice

b. Red and white balls represent oxygen and hydrogen respectively, tightly packed arrangement of molecules results in a low density of ice

c. Red and white balls represent hydrogen and oxygen, respectively, loose arrangement of molecules results in low density of ice

d. Red and white balls represent oxygen and hydrogen, respectively, tightly packed arrangement of molecules results in high density of ice

Water's High Heat Capacity

Water's high heat capacity is a property caused by hydrogen bonding among water molecules. Water has the highest **specific**

1. W. Humphrey W., A. Dalke, and K. Schulten, "VMD—Visual Molecular Dynamics," *Journal of Molecular Graphics* 14 (1996): 33-38.
2. W. Humphrey W., A. Dalke, and K. Schulten, "VMD—Visual Molecular Dynamics," *Journal of Molecular Graphics* 14 (1996): 33-38.

heat capacity of any liquids. Specific heat is defined as the amount of heat one gram of a substance must absorb or lose to change its temperature by one degree Celsius. For water, this amount is one **calorie**. It therefore takes water a long time to heat and long time to cool. In fact, the specific heat capacity of water is about five times more than that of sand. This explains why the land cools faster than the sea. Due to its high heat capacity, water is used by warm blooded animals to more evenly disperse heat in their bodies: it acts in a similar manner to a car's cooling system, transporting heat from warm places to cool places, causing the body to maintain a more even temperature.

Water's Heat of Vaporization

Water also has a high **heat of vaporization**, the amount of energy required to change one gram of a liquid substance to a gas. A considerable amount of heat energy (586 cal) is required to accomplish this change in water. This process occurs on the surface of water. As liquid water heats up, hydrogen bonding makes it difficult to separate the liquid water molecules from each other, which is required for it to enter its gaseous phase (steam). As a result, water acts as a heat sink or heat reservoir and requires much more heat to boil than does a liquid such as ethanol, whose hydrogen bonding with other ethanol molecules is weaker than water's hydrogen bonding. Eventually, as water reaches its boiling point of 100° Celsius (212° Fahrenheit), the heat is able to break the hydrogen bonds between the water molecules, and the kinetic energy (motion) between the water molecules allows them to escape from the liquid as a gas. Even when below its boiling point, water's individual molecules acquire enough energy from other water molecules such that some surface water molecules can escape and vaporize: this process is known as **evaporation**.

The fact that hydrogen bonds need to be broken for water to evaporate means that a substantial amount of energy is used in the process. As the water evaporates, energy is taken up by the process, cooling the environment where the evaporation is taking place. In many living organisms, including in humans, the evaporation of sweat, which is 90 percent water, allows the organism to cool so that homeostasis of body temperature can be maintained.

Water's Solvent Properties

Since water is a polar molecule with slightly positive and slightly negative charges, ions and polar molecules can readily dissolve in it. Therefore, water is referred to as a **solvent**, a substance capable of dissolving other polar molecules and ionic compounds. The charges associated with these molecules will form hydrogen bonds with water, surrounding the particle with water molecules. This is referred to as a **sphere of hydration**, or a hydration shell, as illustrated in Figure 2.16 and serves to keep the particles separated or dispersed in the water.

When ionic compounds are added to water, the individual ions react with the polar regions of the water molecules and their ionic bonds are disrupted in the process of **dissociation**. Dissociation occurs when atoms or groups of atoms break off from molecules and form ions. Consider table salt (NaCl, or sodium chloride): when NaCl crystals are added to water, the molecules of NaCl dissociate into Na^+ and Cl^- ions, and spheres of hydration form around the ions, illustrated in Figure 2.16. The positively charged sodium ion is surrounded by the partially negative charge of the water molecule's oxygen. The negatively charged chloride ion is surrounded by the partially positive charge of the hydrogen on the water molecule.

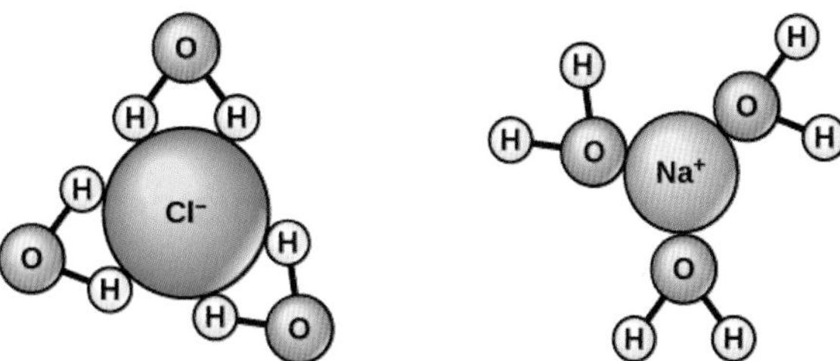

Figure 2.16 When table salt (NaCl) is mixed in water, spheres of hydration are formed around the ions.

Water's Cohesive and Adhesive Properties

Have you ever filled a glass of water to the very top and then slowly added a few more drops? Before it overflows, the water forms a dome-like shape above the rim of the glass. This water can stay above the glass because of the property of **cohesion**. In cohesion, water molecules are attracted to each other (because of hydrogen bonding), keeping the molecules together at the liquid-gas (water-air) interface, although there is no more room in the glass.

Cohesion allows for the development of **surface tension**, the capacity of a substance to withstand being ruptured when placed under tension or stress. This is also why water forms droplets when placed on a dry surface rather than being flattened out by gravity. When a small scrap of paper is placed onto the droplet of water, the paper floats on top of the water droplet even though paper is denser (heavier) than the water. Cohesion and surface tension keep the hydrogen bonds of water molecules intact and support the item floating on the top. It's even possible to "float" a needle on top of a glass of water if it is placed gently without breaking the surface tension, as shown in Figure 2.17.

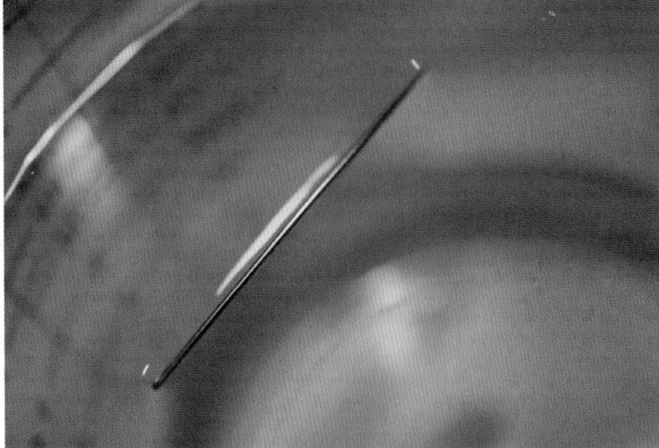

Figure 2.17 The weight of the needle is pulling the surface downward; at the same time, the surface tension is pulling it up, suspending it on the surface of the water and keeping it from sinking. Notice the indentation in the water around the needle. (credit: Cory Zanker)

These cohesive forces are related to water's property of **adhesion**, or the attraction between water molecules and other molecules. This attraction is sometimes stronger than water's cohesive forces, especially when the water is exposed to charged surfaces such as those found on the inside of thin glass tubes known as capillary tubes. Adhesion is observed when water "climbs" up the tube placed in a glass of water: notice that the water appears to be higher on the sides of the tube than in the middle. This is because the water molecules are attracted to the charged glass walls of the capillary more than they are to each other and therefore adhere to it. This type of adhesion is called **capillary action**, and is illustrated in Figure 2.18.

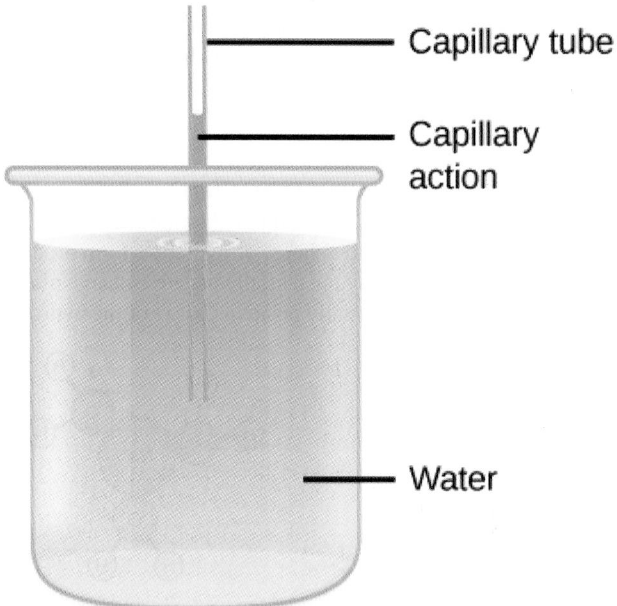

Figure 2.18 Capillary action in a glass tube is caused by the adhesive forces exerted by the internal surface of the glass exceeding the cohesive forces between the water molecules themselves. (credit: modification of work by Pearson-Scott Foresman, donated to the Wikimedia Foundation)

Why are cohesive and adhesive forces important for life? Cohesive and adhesive forces are important for the transport of water from the roots to the leaves in plants. These forces create a "pull" on the water column. This pull results from the tendency of water molecules being evaporated on the surface of the plant to stay connected to water molecules below them, and so they are pulled along. Plants use this natural phenomenon to help transport water from their roots to their leaves. Without these properties of water, plants would be unable to receive the water and the dissolved minerals they require. In another example, insects such as the water strider, shown in Figure 2.19, use the surface tension of water to stay afloat on the surface layer of water and even mate there.

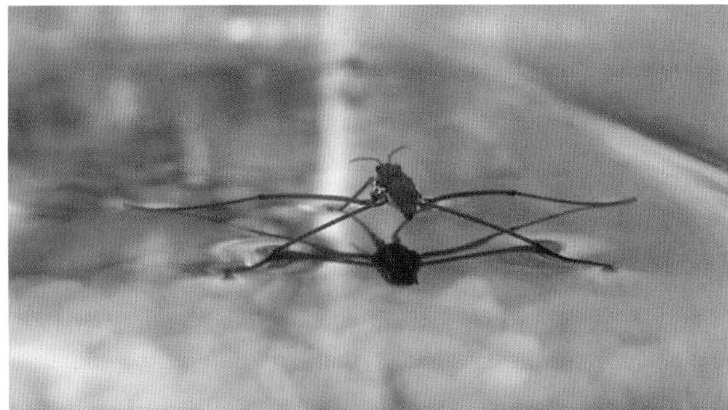

Figure 2.19 Water's cohesive and adhesive properties allow this water strider (*Gerris* sp.) to stay afloat. (credit: Tim Vickers)

science practices CONNECTION for AP® Courses

Activity

During a process called transpiration, water evaporates through a plant's leaves. Water in the ground travels up from the roots to the leaves. Based on water's molecular properties, create a visual representation (e.g., diagrams or models) with annotations to explain how water travels up a 300-ft. California redwood tree. What other unique properties of water are attributed to its molecular structure, and how are these properties important to life?

pH, Buffers, Acids, and Bases

The pH of a solution indicates its acidity or alkalinity.

$$H_2O(l) \leftrightarrow H^+(aq) + OH^-(aq)$$

litmus or pH paper, filter paper that has been treated with a natural water-soluble dye so it can be used as a pH indicator, to test how much acid (acidity) or base (alkalinity) exists in a solution. You might have even used some to test whether the water in a swimming pool is properly treated. In both cases, the pH test measures the concentration of hydrogen ions in a given solution.

Hydrogen ions are spontaneously generated in pure water by the dissociation (ionization) of a small percentage of water molecules into equal numbers of hydrogen (H^+) ions and hydroxide (OH^-) ions. While the hydroxide ions are kept in solution by their hydrogen bonding with other water molecules, the hydrogen ions, consisting of naked protons, are immediately attracted to un-ionized water molecules, forming hydronium ions (H_30^+). Still, by convention, scientists refer to hydrogen ions and their concentration as if they were free in this state in liquid water.

The concentration of hydrogen ions dissociating from pure water is 1×10^{-7} moles H^+ ions per liter of water. Moles (mol) are a way to express the amount of a substance (which can be atoms, molecules, ions, etc), with one mole being equal to 6.02×10^{23} particles of the substance. Therefore, 1 mole of water is equal to 6.02×10^{23} water molecules. The pH is calculated as the negative of the base 10 logarithm of this concentration. The log10 of 1×10^{-7} is -7.0, and the negative of this number (indicated by the "p" of "pH") yields a pH of 7.0, which is also known as neutral pH. The pH inside of human cells and blood are examples of two areas of the body where near-neutral pH is maintained.

Non-neutral pH readings result from dissolving acids or bases in water. Using the negative logarithm to generate positive integers, high concentrations of hydrogen ions yield a low pH number, whereas low levels of hydrogen ions result in a high pH. An **acid** is a substance that increases the concentration of hydrogen ions (H^+) in a solution, usually by having one of its hydrogen atoms dissociate. A **base** provides either hydroxide ions ($OH^–$) or other negatively charged ions that combine with hydrogen ions, reducing their concentration in the solution and thereby raising the pH. In cases where the base releases hydroxide ions, these ions bind to free hydrogen ions, generating new water molecules.

The stronger the acid, the more readily it donates H^+. For example, hydrochloric acid (HCl) completely dissociates into hydrogen and chloride ions and is highly acidic, whereas the acids in tomato juice or vinegar do not completely dissociate and are considered weak acids. Conversely, strong bases are those substances that readily donate $OH^–$ or take up hydrogen ions. Sodium hydroxide (NaOH) and many household cleaners are highly alkaline and give up OH^- rapidly when placed in water, thereby raising the pH. An example of a weak basic solution is seawater, which has a pH near 8.0, close enough to neutral pH that marine organisms adapted to this saline environment are able to thrive in it.

The **pH scale** is, as previously mentioned, an inverse logarithm and ranges from 0 to 14 (Figure 2.20). Anything below 7.0 (ranging from 0.0 to 6.9) is acidic, and anything above 7.0 (from 7.1 to 14.0) is alkaline. Extremes in pH in either direction from 7.0 are usually considered inhospitable to life. The pH inside cells (6.8) and the pH in the blood (7.4) are both very close to neutral. However, the environment in the stomach is highly acidic, with a pH of 1 to 2. So how do the cells of the stomach survive in such an acidic environment? How do they homeostatically maintain the near neutral pH inside them? The answer is that they cannot do it and are constantly dying. New stomach cells are constantly produced to replace dead ones, which are digested by the stomach acids. It is estimated that the lining of the human stomach is completely replaced every seven to ten days.

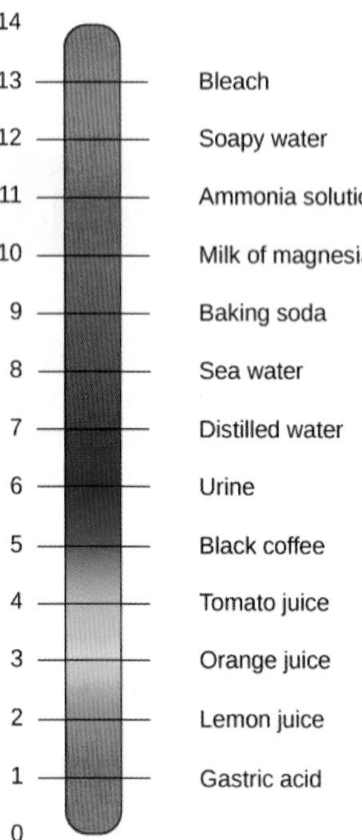

Figure 2.20 The pH scale measures the concentration of hydrogen ions (H^+) in a solution. (credit: modification of work by Edward Stevens)

Watch this video (http://openstaxcollege.org/l/pH_scale) for a straightforward explanation of pH and its logarithmic scale.

One of the risks for people with diabetes is diabetic ketoacidosis, a build-up of acid in the blood stream. Explain why this is dangerous to humans.

a. Diabetic ketoacidosis decreases the normal pH (8.35-8.45) to a lower value.

b. Diabetic ketoacidosis increases normal pH level of blood disrupting biological processes.

c. Diabetic ketoacidosis keeps pH level of blood constant which disrupts biological processes.

d. Diabetic ketoacidosis decreases normal pH (7.35-7.45) to a lower value.

So how can organisms whose bodies require a near-neutral pH ingest acidic and basic substances (a human drinking orange juice, for example) and survive? Buffers are the key. **Buffers** readily absorb excess H^+ or $OH^–$, keeping the pH of the body carefully maintained in the narrow range required for survival. Maintaining a constant blood pH is critical to a person's well-being. The buffer maintaining the pH of human blood involves carbonic acid (H_2CO_3), bicarbonate ion ($HCO_3^–$), and carbon dioxide (CO_2). When bicarbonate ions combine with free hydrogen ions and become carbonic acid, hydrogen ions are removed, moderating pH changes. Similarly, as shown in Figure 2.21, excess carbonic acid can be converted to carbon dioxide gas and exhaled through the lungs. This prevents too many free hydrogen ions from building up in the blood and dangerously reducing the blood's pH. Likewise, if too much $OH^–$ is introduced into the system, carbonic acid will combine with it to create bicarbonate, lowering the pH. Without this buffer system, the body's pH would fluctuate enough to put survival in jeopardy.

Figure 2.21 This diagram shows the body's buffering of blood pH levels. The blue arrows show the process of raising pH as more CO_2 is made. The purple arrows indicate the reverse process: the lowering of pH as more bicarbonate is created.

Other examples of buffers are antacids used to combat excess stomach acid. Many of these over-the-counter medications work in the same way as blood buffers, usually with at least one ion capable of absorbing hydrogen and moderating pH, bringing relief to those that suffer "heartburn" after eating. The unique properties of water that contribute to this capacity to balance pH—as well as water's other characteristics—are essential to sustaining life on Earth.

To learn more about water. Visit the U.S. Geological Survey Water Science for Schools (http://openstaxcollege.org/l/all_about_water) All About Water! website.

Water takes up 333 million cubic miles on Earth, yet access to drinking water is a critical issue for many communities around the world. Explain why this is so.

a. Drinking water is only obtained by rain water harvesting.

b. Only 4 percent of the total water on earth is freshwater which is found only in glaciers.

c. Only 4 percent of the total water on earth is freshwater, out of which 68 percent is found in glaciers.

d. Drinking water is only obtained by desalination treatments of salt water found on earth.

everyday CONNECTION for AP® Courses

Acid Rain

Figure 2.22 When rain water is too acidic, it can greatly damage living organisms, such as this forest in the Czech Republic.

Limestone is a naturally occurring mineral rich in calcium carbonate ($CaCO_3$). In water, calcium carbonate dissolves to form carbonate (CO_3^{2-}), a weak base that acts as a buffer. Which would you expect to be more affected by acid rain, an environment rich in limestone or an environment poor in limestone?

a. The presence of limestone would not make a difference.
b. An environment rich in limestone would be more affected by acid rain.
c. An environment poor in limestone would be more affected by acid rain.
d. The impact would depend on the type of vegetation present.

2.3 | Carbon

In this section, you will investigate the following questions:

- Why is carbon important for life?
- How do functional groups determine the properties of biological molecules?

Connection for AP® Courses

The unique properties of **carbon** make it a central part of biological molecules. With four valence electrons, carbon can covalently bond to oxygen, hydrogen, and nitrogen to form the many molecules important for cellular function. Carbon and hydrogen can form either hydrocarbon chains or rings. **Functional groups**, such as $–CH_3$ (methyl) and –COOH (carboxyl), are groups of atoms that give specific properties to hydrocarbon chains or rings that define their overall chemical characteristics and function. For example, the attachment of a carboxyl group (-COOH) makes a molecule more acidic, whereas the presence of an amine group (NH_2) makes a molecule more basic. (As we will explore in the next chapter, amino acids have both a carboxyl group and an amine group.) **Isomers** are molecules with the same molecular formula (i.e., same kinds and numbers of atoms), but different molecular structures resulting in different properties or functions. (Don't confuse "isomer" with "isotope"!)

The information presented and examples highlighted in this section support concepts and Learning Objectives outlined in Big Idea 2 of the AP® Biology Curriculum Framework. The Learning Objectives listed in the Curriculum Framework provide a transparent foundation for the AP® Biology course, an inquiry-based laboratory experience, instructional activities, and AP® Exam questions. A Learning Objective merges required content with one or more of the seven Science Practices.

Big Idea 2	Biological systems utilize free energy and molecular building blocks to grow, to reproduce, and to maintain dynamic homeostasis.
Enduring Understanding 2.A	Growth, reproduction and maintenance of living systems require free energy and matter.
Essential Knowledge	**2.A.3** Organisms must exchange matter with the environment to grow, reproduce and maintain organization.
Science Practice	**4.1** The student can justify the selection of the kind of data needed to answer a particular scientific question.
Learning Objective	**2.8** The student is able to justify the selection of data regarding the types of molecules that an animal, plant, or bacterium will take up as necessary building blocks and excrete as waste products.

Cells are made of many complex molecules called macromolecules, such as proteins, nucleic acids (RNA and DNA), carbohydrates, and lipids. The macromolecules are a subset of **organic molecules** (any carbon-containing liquid, solid, or gas) that are especially important for life. The fundamental component for all of these macromolecules is carbon. The carbon atom has unique properties that allow it to form covalent bonds to as many as four different atoms, making this versatile element ideal to serve as the basic structural component, or "backbone," of the macromolecules.

Individual carbon atoms have an incomplete outermost electron shell. With an atomic number of 6 (six electrons and six protons), the first two electrons fill the inner shell, leaving four in the second shell. Therefore, carbon atoms can form up to four covalent bonds with other atoms to satisfy the octet rule. The methane molecule provides an example: it has the chemical formula CH_4. Each of its four hydrogen atoms forms a single covalent bond with the carbon atom by sharing a pair of electrons. This results in a filled outermost shell.

Hydrocarbons

Hydrocarbons are organic molecules consisting entirely of carbon and hydrogen, such as methane (CH_4) described above. We often use hydrocarbons in our daily lives as fuels—like the propane in a gas grill or the butane in a lighter. The many covalent bonds between the atoms in hydrocarbons store a great amount of energy, which is released when these molecules are burned (oxidized). Methane, an excellent fuel, is the simplest hydrocarbon molecule, with a central carbon atom bonded to four different hydrogen atoms, as illustrated in Figure 2.23. The geometry of the methane molecule, where the atoms reside in three dimensions, is determined by the shape of its electron orbitals. The carbons and the four hydrogen atoms form a shape known as a tetrahedron, with four triangular faces; for this reason, methane is described as having tetrahedral geometry.

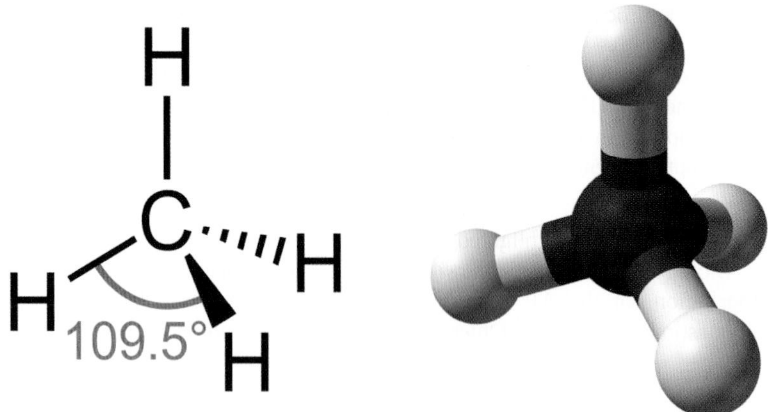

Figure 2.23 Methane has a tetrahedral geometry, with each of the four hydrogen atoms spaced 109.5° apart.

As the backbone of the large molecules of living things, hydrocarbons may exist as linear carbon chains, carbon rings, or combinations of both. Furthermore, individual carbon-to-carbon bonds may be single, double, or triple covalent bonds, and each type of bond affects the geometry of the molecule in a specific way. This three-dimensional shape or conformation of the large molecules of life (macromolecules) is critical to how they function.

Hydrocarbon Chains

Hydrocarbon chains are formed by successive bonds between carbon atoms and may be branched or unbranched. Furthermore, the overall geometry of the molecule is altered by the different geometries of single, double, and triple covalent bonds, illustrated in Figure 2.24. The hydrocarbons ethane, ethene, and ethyne serve as examples of how different carbon-to-carbon bonds affect the geometry of the molecule. The names of all three molecules start with the prefix "eth-," which is the prefix for two carbon hydrocarbons. The suffixes "-ane," "-ene," and "-yne" refer to the presence of single, double, or triple carbon-carbon bonds, respectively. Thus, propane, propene, and propyne follow the same pattern with three carbon molecules, butane, butene, and butyne for four carbon molecules, and so on. Double and triple bonds change the geometry of the molecule: single bonds allow rotation along the axis of the bond, whereas double bonds lead to a planar configuration and triple bonds to a linear one. These geometries have a significant impact on the shape a particular molecule can assume.

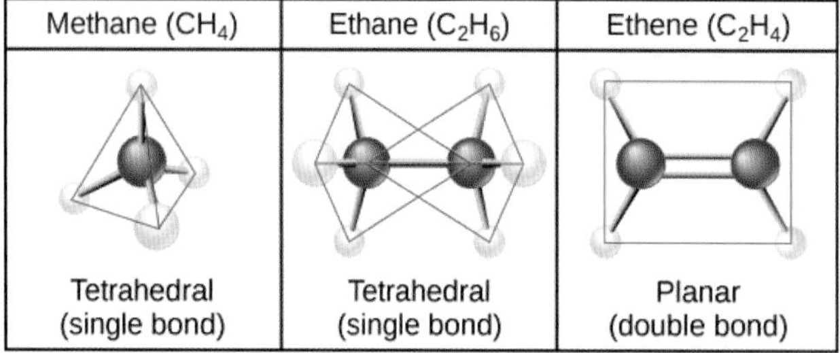

Methane (CH_4)
Ethane (C_2H_6)
Ethene (C_2H_4)
Tetrahedral (single bond)
Tetrahedral (single bond)
Planar (double bond)

Figure 2.24 When carbon forms single bonds with other atoms, the shape is tetrahedral. When two carbon atoms form a double bond, the shape is planar, or flat. Single bonds, like those found in ethane, are able to rotate. Double bonds, like those found in ethene cannot rotate, so the atoms on either side are locked in place.

Hydrocarbon Rings

So far, the hydrocarbons we have discussed have been **aliphatic hydrocarbons**, which consist of linear chains of carbon atoms. Another type of hydrocarbon, **aromatic hydrocarbons**, consists of closed rings of carbon atoms. Ring structures are found in hydrocarbons, sometimes with the presence of double bonds, which can be seen by comparing the structure of cyclohexane to benzene in Figure 2.25. Examples of biological molecules that incorporate the benzene ring include some amino acids and cholesterol and its derivatives, including the hormones estrogen and testosterone. The benzene ring is also found in the herbicide 2,4-D. Benzene is a natural component of crude oil and has been classified as a carcinogen. Some hydrocarbons have both aliphatic and aromatic portions; beta-carotene is an example of such a hydrocarbon.

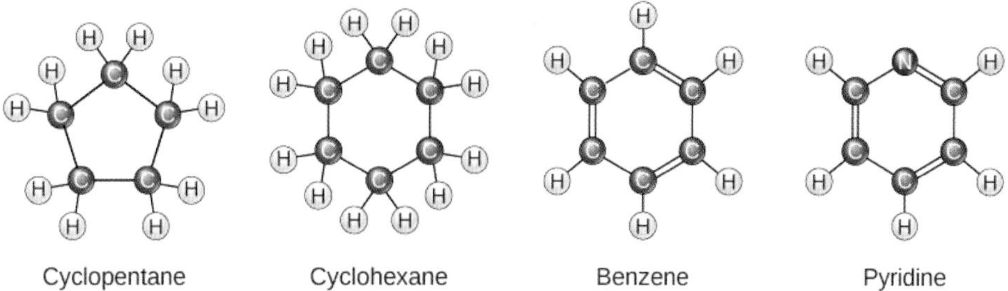

Figure 2.25 Carbon can form five-and six membered rings. Single or double bonds may connect the carbons in the ring, and nitrogen may be substituted for carbon.

Isomers

The three-dimensional placement of atoms and chemical bonds within organic molecules is central to understanding their chemistry. Molecules that share the same chemical formula but differ in the placement (structure) of their atoms and/ or chemical bonds are known as isomers. **Structural isomers** (like butane and isobutene shown in figure**a**) differ in the placement of their covalent bonds: both molecules have four carbons and ten hydrogens (C_4H_{10}), but the different arrangement of the atoms within the molecules leads to differences in their chemical properties. For example, due to their different chemical properties, butane is suited for use as a fuel for torches, whereas isobutene is suited for use as a refrigerant and a propellant in spray cans.

Geometric isomers, on the other hand, have similar placements of their covalent bonds but differ in how these bonds are made to the surrounding atoms, especially in carbon-to-carbon double bonds. In the simple molecule butene (C_4H_8), the two methyl groups (CH_3) can be on either side of the double covalent bond central to the molecule, as illustrated in figure**b**. When the carbons are bound on the same side of the double bond, this is the *cis* configuration; if they are on opposite sides of the double bond, it is a *trans* configuration. In the *trans* configuration, the carbons form a more or less linear structure, whereas the carbons in the *cis* configuration make a bend (change in direction) of the carbon backbone.

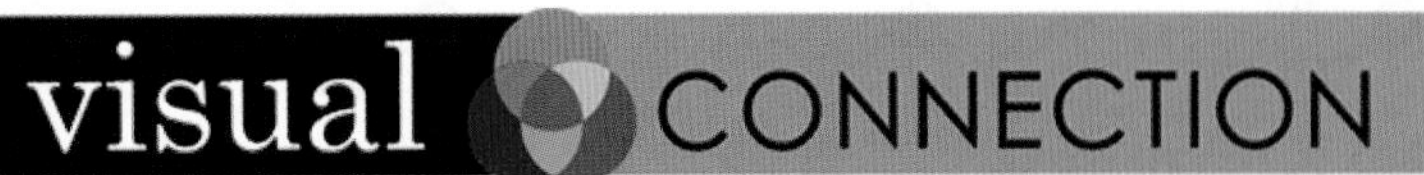

(a) Structural isomers

Butane

Isobutane

(b) Geometric isomers

cis-2-butene

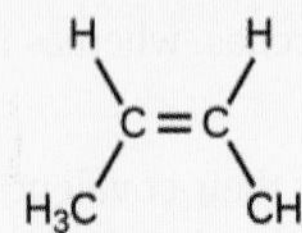

methyl groups on same side of double bond

trans-2-butene

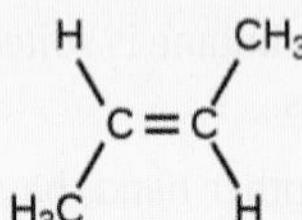

methyl groups on opposite sides of double bond

(c) Enantiomers

L-isomer

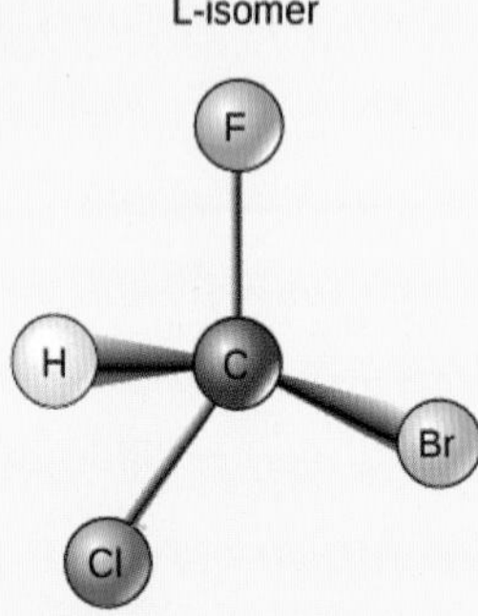

D-isomer

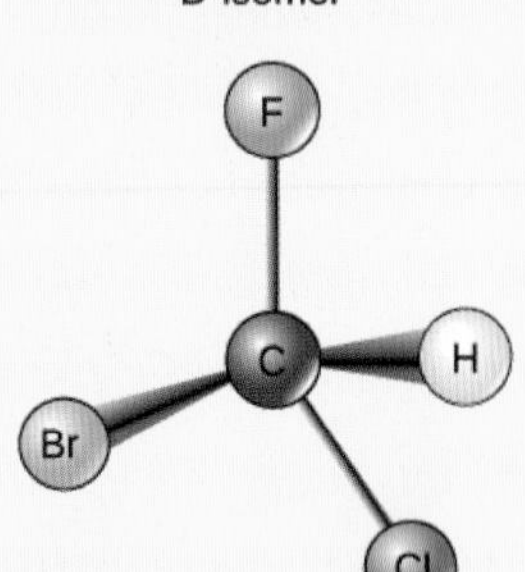

Figure 2.26 Molecules that have the same number and type of atoms arranged differently are called isomers. (a) Structural isomers have a different covalent arrangement of atoms. (b) Geometric isomers have a different arrangement of atoms around a double bond. (c) Enantiomers are mirror images of each other.

Which of the following statements is false?

a. Molecules with the formulas CH_3CH_2COOH and $C_3H_6O_2$ could be structural isomers.

b. Molecules must have a double bond to be cis-trans isomers.

c. To be enantiomers, a molecule must have at least three different atoms or groups connected to a central carbon.

d. To be enantiomers, a molecule must have at least four different atoms or groups connected to a central carbon.

In triglycerides (fats and oils), long carbon chains known as fatty acids may contain double bonds, which can be in either the *cis* or *trans* configuration, illustrated in Figure 2.27. Fats with at least one double bond between carbon atoms are unsaturated fats. When some of these bonds are in the *cis* configuration, the resulting bend in the carbon backbone of the chain means that triglyceride molecules cannot pack tightly, so they remain liquid (oil) at room temperature. On the other hand, triglycerides with *trans* double bonds (popularly called trans fats), have relatively linear fatty acids that are able to pack tightly together at room temperature and form solid fats. In the human diet, trans fats are linked to an increased risk of cardiovascular disease, so many food manufacturers have reduced or eliminated their use in recent years. In contrast to unsaturated fats, triglycerides without double bonds between carbon atoms are called saturated fats, meaning that they contain all the hydrogen atoms available. Saturated fats are a solid at room temperature and usually of animal origin.

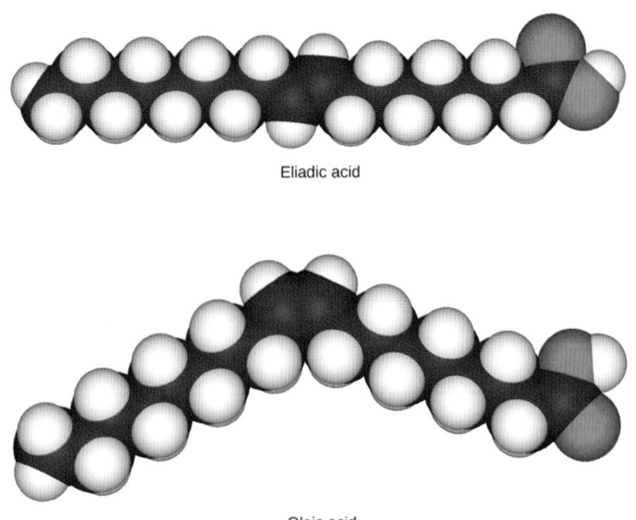

Figure 2.27 These space-filling models show a *cis* (oleic acid) and a *trans* (eliadic acid) fatty acid. Notice the bend in the molecule caused by the *cis* configuration.

Enantiomers

Enantiomers are molecules that share the same chemical structure and chemical bonds but differ in the three-dimensional placement of atoms so that they are mirror images. As shown in Figure 2.28, an amino acid alanine example, the two structures are non-superimposable. In nature, only the L-forms of amino acids are used to make proteins. Some D forms of amino acids are seen in the cell walls of bacteria, but never in their proteins. Similarly, the D-form of glucose is the main product of photosynthesis and the L-form of the molecule is rarely seen in nature.

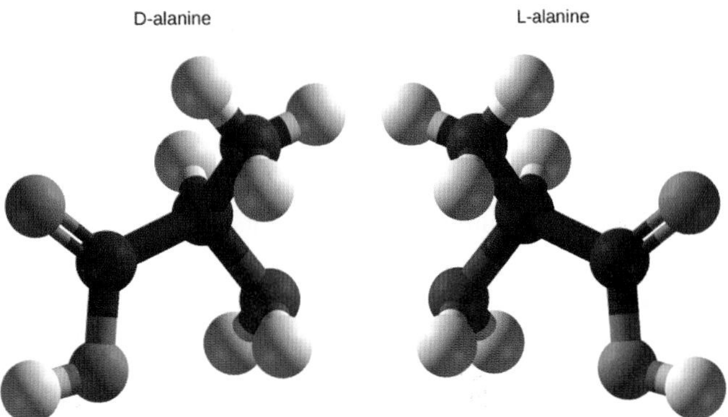

Figure 2.28 D-alanine and L-alanine are examples of enantiomers or mirror images. Only the L-forms of amino acids are used to make proteins.

Functional Groups

Functional groups are groups of atoms that occur within molecules and confer specific chemical properties to those molecules. They are found along the "carbon backbone" of macromolecules. This carbon backbone is formed by chains and/or rings of carbon atoms with the occasional substitution of an element such as nitrogen or oxygen. Molecules with other elements in their carbon backbone are **substituted hydrocarbons**.

The functional groups in a macromolecule are usually attached to the carbon backbone at one or more different places along its chain and/or ring structure. Each of the four types of macromolecules—proteins, lipids, carbohydrates, and nucleic acids—has its own characteristic set of functional groups that contributes greatly to its differing chemical properties and its function in living organisms.

A functional group can participate in specific chemical reactions. Some of the important functional groups in biological molecules are shown in Figure 2.29; they include: hydroxyl, methyl, carbonyl, carboxyl, amino, phosphate, and sulfhydryl. These groups play an important role in the formation of molecules like DNA, proteins, carbohydrates, and lipids. Functional groups are usually classified as hydrophobic or hydrophilic depending on their charge or polarity characteristics. An example of a hydrophobic group is the non-polar methyl molecule. Among the hydrophilic functional groups is the carboxyl group found in amino acids, some amino acid side chains, and the fatty acids that form triglycerides and phospholipids. This carboxyl group ionizes to release hydrogen ions (H^+) from the COOH group resulting in the negatively charged COO^- group; this contributes to the hydrophilic nature of whatever molecule it is found on. Other functional groups, such as the carbonyl group, have a partially negatively charged oxygen atom that may form hydrogen bonds with water molecules, again making the molecule more hydrophilic.

Functional Group	Structure	Properties
Hydroxyl	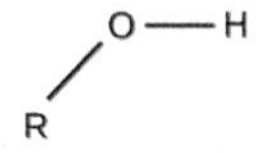 R—O—H	Polar
Methyl	R—CH_3	Nonpolar
Carbonyl	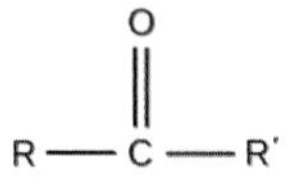 R—C(=O)—R′	Polar
Carboxyl	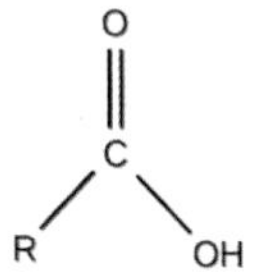 R—C(=O)—OH	Charged, ionizes to release H^+. Since carboxyl groups can release H^+ ions into solution, they are considered acidic.
Amino	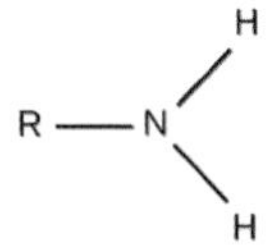 R—N(—H)—H	Charged, accepts H^+ to form NH_3^+. Since amino groups can remove H^+ from solution, they are considered basic.
Phosphate	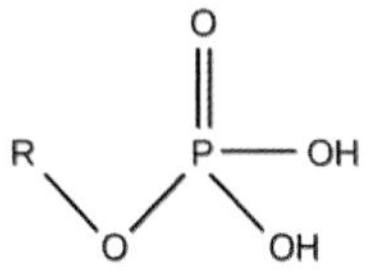 R—O—P(=O)(—OH)—OH	Charged, ionizes to release H^+. Since phosphate groups can release H^+ ions into solution, they are considered acidic.
Sulfhydryl	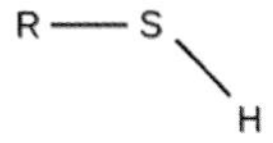 R—S—H	Polar

Figure 2.29 The functional groups shown here are found in many different biological molecules.

Hydrogen bonds between functional groups (within the same molecule or between different molecules) are important to the function of many macromolecules and help them to fold properly into and maintain the appropriate shape for functioning. Hydrogen bonds are also involved in various recognition processes, such as DNA complementary base pairing and the binding of an enzyme to its substrate, as illustrated in Figure 2.30.

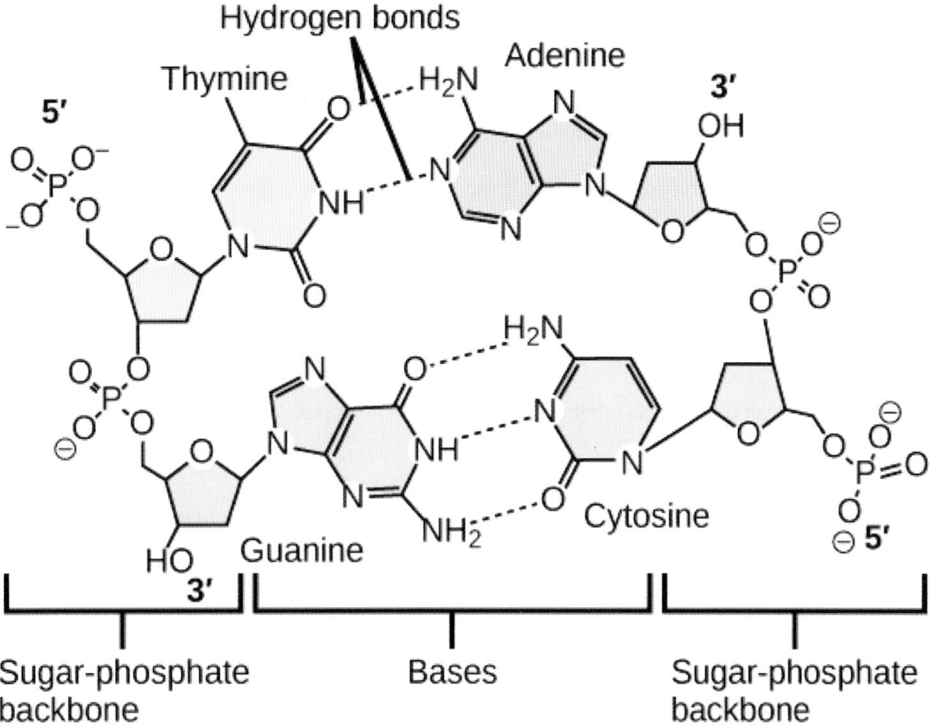

Figure 2.30 Hydrogen bonds connect two strands of DNA together to create the double-helix structure.

science practices CONNECTION for AP® Courses

Activity

Carbon forms the backbone of important biological molecules. Create a mini-poster of a simple food chain that shows how carbon enters and exits each organism on the chain. Based on the food chain you created, make a prediction regarding the impact of human activity on the supply of carbon in the food chain.

KEY TERMS

acid molecule that donates hydrogen ions and increases the concentration of hydrogen ions in a solution

adhesion attraction between water molecules and other molecules

aliphatic hydrocarbon hydrocarbon consisting of a linear chain of carbon atoms

anion negative ion that is formed by an atom gaining one or more electrons

aromatic hydrocarbon hydrocarbon consisting of closed rings of carbon atoms

atom the smallest unit of matter that retains all of the chemical properties of an element

atomic mass calculated mean of the mass number for an element's isotopes

atomic number total number of protons in an atom

balanced chemical equation statement of a chemical reaction with the number of each type of atom equalized for both the products and reactants

base molecule that donates hydroxide ions or otherwise binds excess hydrogen ions and decreases the concentration of hydrogen ions in a solution

buffer substance that prevents a change in pH by absorbing or releasing hydrogen or hydroxide ions

calorie amount of heat required to change the temperature of one gram of water by one degree Celsius

capillary action occurs because water molecules are attracted to charges on the inner surfaces of narrow tubular structures such as glass tubes, drawing the water molecules to the sides of the tubes

cation positive ion that is formed by an atom losing one or more electrons

chemical bond interaction between two or more of the same or different atoms that results in the formation of molecules

chemical reaction process leading to the rearrangement of atoms in molecules

chemical reactivity the ability to combine and to chemically bond with each other

cohesion intermolecular forces between water molecules caused by the polar nature of water; responsible for surface tension

compound substance composed of molecules consisting of atoms of at least two different elements

covalent bond type of strong bond formed between two atoms of the same or different elements; forms when electrons are shared between atoms

dissociation release of an ion from a molecule such that the original molecule now consists of an ion and the charged remains of the original, such as when water dissociates into H^+ and OH^-

electrolyte ion necessary for nerve impulse conduction, muscle contractions and water balance

electron negatively charged subatomic particle that resides outside of the nucleus in the electron orbital; lacks functional mass and has a negative charge of –1 unit

electron configuration arrangement of electrons in an atom's electron shell (for example, $1s^2 2s^2 2p^6$)

electron orbital how electrons are spatially distributed surrounding the nucleus; the area where an electron is most likely to be found

electron transfer movement of electrons from one element to another; important in creation of ionic bonds

electronegativity ability of some elements to attract electrons (often of hydrogen atoms), acquiring partial negative charges in molecules and creating partial positive charges on the hydrogen atoms

element one of 118 unique substances that cannot be broken down into smaller substances; each element has unique properties and a specified number of protons

enantiomers molecules that share overall structure and bonding patterns, but differ in how the atoms are three dimensionally placed such that they are mirror images of each other

equilibrium steady state of relative reactant and product concentration in reversible chemical reactions in a closed system

evaporation separation of individual molecules from the surface of a body of water, leaves of a plant, or the skin of an organism

functional group group of atoms that provides or imparts a specific function to a carbon skeleton

geometric isomer isomer with similar bonding patterns differing in the placement of atoms alongside a double covalent bond

heat of vaporization of water high amount of energy required for liquid water to turn into water vapor

hydrocarbon molecule that consists only of carbon and hydrogen

hydrogen bond weak bond between slightly positively charged hydrogen atoms and slightly negatively charged atoms in other molecules

hydrophilic describes ions or polar molecules that interact well with other polar molecules such as water

hydrophobic describes uncharged non-polar molecules that do not interact well with polar molecules such as water

inert gas (also, noble gas) element with filled outer electron shell that is unreactive with other atoms

ion atom or chemical group that does not contain equal numbers of protons and electrons

ionic bond chemical bond that forms between ions with opposite charges (cations and anions)

irreversible chemical reaction chemical reaction where reactants proceed uni-directionally to form products

isomers molecules that differ from one another even though they share the same chemical formula

isotope one or more forms of an element that have different numbers of neutrons

law of mass action chemical law stating that the rate of a reaction is proportional to the concentration of the reacting substances

litmus paper (also, pH paper) filter paper that has been treated with a natural water-soluble dye that changes its color as the pH of the environment changes so it can be used as a pH indicator

mass number total number of protons and neutrons in an atom

matter anything that has mass and occupies space

molecule two or more atoms chemically bonded together

neutron uncharged particle that resides in the nucleus of an atom; has a mass of one amu

noble gas see inert gas

nonpolar covalent bond type of covalent bond that forms between atoms when electrons are shared equally between them

nucleus core of an atom; contains protons and neutrons

octet rule rule that atoms are most stable when they hold eight electrons in their outermost shells

orbital region surrounding the nucleus; contains electrons

organic molecule any molecule containing carbon (except carbon dioxide)

periodic table organizational chart of elements indicating the atomic number and atomic mass of each element; provides key information about the properties of the elements

pH paper see litmus paper

pH scale scale ranging from zero to 14 that is inversely proportional to the concentration of hydrogen ions in a solution

polar covalent bond type of covalent bond that forms as a result of unequal sharing of electrons, resulting in the creation of slightly positive and slightly negative charged regions of the molecule

product molecule found on the right side of a chemical equation

proton positively charged particle that resides in the nucleus of an atom; has a mass of one amu and a charge of +1

radioisotope isotope that emits radiation composed of subatomic particles to form more stable elements

reactant molecule found on the left side of a chemical equation

reversible chemical reaction chemical reaction that functions bi-directionally, where products may turn into reactants if their concentration is great enough

solvent substance capable of dissolving another substance

specific heat capacity the amount of heat one gram of a substance must absorb or lose to change its temperature by one degree Celsius

sphere of hydration when polar water molecules surround charged or polar molecules thus keeping them dissolved and in solution

structural isomers molecules that share a chemical formula but differ in the placement of their chemical bonds

substituted hydrocarbon hydrocarbon chain or ring containing an atom of another element in place of one of the backbone carbons

surface tension tension at the surface of a body of liquid that prevents the molecules from separating; created by the attractive cohesive forces between the molecules of the liquid

valence shell outermost shell of an atom

van der Waals interaction very weak interaction between molecules due to temporary charges attracting atoms that are very close together

CHAPTER SUMMARY

2.1 Atoms, Isotopes, Ions, and Molecules: The Building Blocks

Matter is anything that occupies space and has mass. It is made up of elements. All of the 98 elements that occur naturally have unique qualities that allow them to combine in various ways to create molecules, which in turn combine to form cells, tissues, organ systems, and organisms. Atoms, which consist of protons, neutrons, and electrons, are the smallest units of an element that retain all of the properties of that element. Electrons can be transferred, shared, or cause charge disparities between atoms to create bonds, including ionic, covalent, and hydrogen bonds, as well as van der Waals interactions.

2.2 Water

Water has many properties that are critical to maintaining life. It is a polar molecule, allowing for the formation of hydrogen bonds. Hydrogen bonds allow ions and other polar molecules to dissolve in water. Therefore, water is an excellent solvent. The hydrogen bonds between water molecules cause the water to have a high heat capacity, meaning it takes a lot of added heat to raise its temperature. As the temperature rises, the hydrogen bonds between water continually break and form anew. This allows for the overall temperature to remain stable, although energy is added to the system. Water also exhibits a high heat of vaporization, which is key to how organisms cool themselves by the evaporation of sweat. Water's cohesive forces allow for the property of surface tension, whereas its adhesive properties are seen as water rises inside capillary tubes. The pH value is a measure of hydrogen ion concentration in a solution and is one of many chemical characteristics that is highly regulated in living organisms through homeostasis. Acids and bases can change pH values, but buffers tend to moderate the changes they cause. These properties of water are intimately connected to the biochemical and physical processes performed by living organisms, and life would be very different if these properties were altered, if it could exist at all.

2.3 Carbon

The unique properties of carbon make it a central part of biological molecules. Carbon binds to oxygen, hydrogen, and nitrogen covalently to form the many molecules important for cellular function. Carbon has four electrons in its outermost shell and can form four bonds. Carbon and hydrogen can form hydrocarbon chains or rings. Functional groups are groups of atoms that confer specific properties to hydrocarbon (or substituted hydrocarbon) chains or rings that define their overall chemical characteristics and function.

REVIEW QUESTIONS

1. What are atoms that vary in the number of neutrons found in their nuclei called?

a. Ions
b. Isotopes
c. Isobars
d. Neutral atoms

2. Potassium has an atomic number of 19. What is its electron configuration?

a. Shells 1 and 2 are full, and shell 3 has nine electrons.
b. Shells 1, 2, and 3 are full, and shell 4 has three electrons.
c. Shells 1, 2, and 3 are full, and shell 4 has one electron.
d. Shells 1, 2, and 3 are full, and no other electrons are present.

3. Which type of bond exemplifies a weak chemical bond?

a. Covalent bond
b. Hydrogen bond
c. Ionic bond
d. Nonpolar covalent bond

4. Which of the following statements is false?

a. Electrons are unequally shared in polar covalent bonds.
b. Electrons are equally shared in nonpolar covalent bonds.
c. Hydrogen bonds are weak bonds based on electrostatic forces.
d. Ionic bonds are generally stronger than covalent bonds.

5. If xenon has an atomic number of 54 and a mass number of 108, how many neutrons does it have?

a. 27
b. 54
c. 100
d. 108

6. What forms ionic bonds?

a. atoms that share electrons equally
b. atoms that share electrons unequally
c. ions with similar charges
d. ions with opposite charges

7.

Element	Electronegativity
N	3.04
H	2.20
Cl	3.16
O	3.44
Li	0.98
F	3.98

Based on the information provided, which of the following statements is false?

a. In NH_2, the nitrogen atom acquires a partial positive charge and the hydrogen atoms acquire a partial negative charge.

b. In H_2O, the hydrogen atoms acquire a partial negative charge, and the oxygen atom acquires a partial positive charge.

c. In HCl, the hydrogen atom acquires a partial positive charge, and the chlorine atom acquires a partial negative charge.

d. In LiF, the lithium atom acquires a negative charge, and the fluorine atom acquires a positive charge.

8. Which of the following statements is not true?

a. Water is polar.

b. Water can stabilize the temperature of nearby air.

c. Water is essential for life.

d. Water is the most abundant molecule in the Earth's atmosphere.

9. Why do hydrogen and oxygen form polar covalent bonds within water molecules?

a. Hydrogen is more electronegative than oxygen, generating a partial negative charge near the hydrogen atom.

b. Hydrogen is more electronegative than oxygen, generating a partial positive charge near the hydrogen atom.

c. Oxygen is more electronegative than hydrogen, generating a partial negative charge near the oxygen atoms.

d. Oxygen is more electronegative than hydrogen, generating a partial positive charge near the oxygen atoms.

10. What happens to the pH of a solution when acids are added?

a. The pH of the solution decreases.

b. The pH of the solution increases.

c. The pH of the solution increases and then decreases.

d. The pH of the solution stays the same.

11. Which of the following statements is true?

a. Acids and bases cannot mix together.

b. Acids and bases can neutralize each other.

c. Acids, not bases, can change the pH of a solution.

d. Acids donate hydroxide ions (OH^-); bases donate hydrogen ions (H^+).

12. Define water's property of adhesion.

a. a force that allows surface water molecules to escape and vaporize

b. the attraction between water molecules and other molecules

c. the intermolecular force between water molecules

d. the force that keeps particles dispersed in water

13. In a solution, what kind of molecule binds up excess hydrogen ions?

a. acid

b. base

c. donator

d. isotope

14. What is the maximum number of atoms or molecules a single carbon atom can bond with?

a. 4

b. 1

c. 6

d. 2

15. Which of the following statements is true?

a. Molecules with the formulas CH_3CH_2OH and $C_3H_6O_2$ could be structural isomers.

b. Molecules must have a single bond to be cis-trans isomers.

c. To be enantiomers, a molecule must have at least three different atoms or groups connected to a central carbon

d. To be enantiomers, a molecule must have at least four different atoms or groups connected to a central carbon

16. Which of the following is not a functional group that can bond with carbon?

a. carbonyl

b. hydroxyl

c. phosphate

d. sodium

17. Which of the following functional groups is not polar?

a. carbonyl

b. hydroxyl

c. methyl

d. sulfhydryl

18. What are enantiomers?

a. Hydrocarbon consisting of closed rings of carbon atoms
b. Isomers with similar bonding patterns differing in the placement of atoms along a double covalent bond.
c. Molecules that share the same chemical bonds but are mirror images of each other.
d. Molecules with the same chemical formula but differ in the placement of their chemical bonds

CRITICAL THINKING QUESTIONS

19. List the mass number and atomic number of carbon-12 and carbon-13, respectively.

a. The mass number and atomic number of carbon-13 is 13 and 6, while that of carbon-12 is 12 and 6, respectively.
b. The mass number and atomic number of carbon-13 is 13 and 12, while that of carbon-12 is 12 and 6, respectively.
c. The mass number and atomic number of carbon-13 is 13 and 13, while that of carbon-12 is 12 and 6, respectively.
d. The mass number and atomic number of carbon-13 is 13 and 12, while that of carbon-12 is 12 and 12, respectively.

20. Why are hydrogen bonds and van der Waals interactions necessary for cells?

a. Hydrogen bonds and van der Waals interactions form weak associations between molecules, providing the necessary shape and structure of DNA and proteins to function in the body.
b. Hydrogen bonds and van der Waals interactions form strong associations between molecules, providing the necessary shape and structure of DNA and proteins to function in the body.
c. Hydrogen bonds and van der Waals interactions form weak associations between different molecules, providing the necessary shape and structure for acids to function in the body.
d. Hydrogen bonds and van der Waals interactions form strong associations between same molecules, providing the necessary shape and structure for acids to function in the body.

21. Looking at Figure 2.7, can you infer which two groups together will form a strong ionic bond?

a. Group 1 and Group 17
b. Group 1 and Group 14
c. Group 14 and Group 18
d. Group 1 and Group 18

22. Why can some insects walk on water?

a. Insects can walk on water because of its high surface tension.
b. Insects can walk on water because it is a polar solvent.
c. Insects can walk on water because they are less dense than water.
d. Insects can walk on water because they are denser than water.

23. Discuss how buffers help prevent drastic swings in pH.

a. Buffers absorb excess hydrogen and hydroxide ions to prevent increases or decrease in pH. An example is the bicarbonate system in human body.
b. Buffers absorb extra hydrogen ions to prevent increases or decreases in pH. An example is the bicarbonate system in the human body.
c. Buffers absorb excess hydroxide ions to prevent increases or decreases in pH. An example of that is the bicarbonate system in the human body.
d. Buffers absorb excess hydrogen and hydroxide ions to prevent increases or decreases in pH. An example of that is carbonate system in human body.

24. What are three examples of how the characteristics of water are important in maintaining life?

a. First, the lower density of water as a solid versus a liquid allows ice to float, forming an insulating surface layer for aquatic life. Second, the high specific heat capacity of water insulates aquatic life or bodily fluids from temperature changes. Third, the high heat of vaporization of water allows animals to cool themselves by sweating.

b. First, the higher density of water as a solid versus a liquid allows ice to float, forming an insulating surface layer for aquatic life. Second, the high specific heat capacity of water insulates aquatic life or bodily fluids from temperature changes. Third, the low heat of vaporization of water allows animals to cool themselves by sweating.

c. First, the lower density of water as a solid versus a liquid allows ice to float, forming an insulating surface layer for aquatic life. Second, the low specific heat capacity of water insulates aquatic life or bodily fluids from temperature changes. Third, the high heat of vaporization of water allows animals to cool themselves by sweating.

d. First, the lower density of water as a solid versus a liquid allows ice to float, forming an insulating surface layer for aquatic life. Second, the low specific heat capacity of water insulates aquatic life or bodily fluids from temperature changes. Third, the low heat of vaporization of water allows animals to cool themselves by sweating.

25. Describe the pH scale and how it relates to living systems. Give an example of how drastic pH changes are prevented in living systems.

a. The pH scale ranges from 0 to 14, where anything below 7 is acidic and above 7 is alkaline. The bicarbonate system in the human body buffers the blood.

b. The pH scale ranges from 0 to 14, where anything below 7 is alkaline and above 7 is acidic. The bicarbonate system in human body buffers the blood.

c. The pH scale ranges from 0 to 7, where anything below 7 is acidic and above 7 is alkaline. Water in the human body buffers the blood.

d. pH scale ranges from 0 to 7, where anything below 4 is acidic and above 4 is alkaline. Water in the human body buffers the blood.

26. What property of carbon makes it essential for organic life?

a. Carbon can form up to four covalent bonds, allowing it to form long chains.

b. Carbon can form more than four covalent bonds, allowing it to form long chains.

c. Carbon can form more than four covalent bonds, but can only form short chains.

d. Carbon can form up to four covalent bonds, but can only form short chains.

27. What property of carboxyl makes carboxyl containing molecules hydrophilic? Which macromolecules contain carboxyl?

a. Carboxyl groups release H^+ , making its parent molecule hydrophilic. It is found amino acids and fatty acids.

b. Carboxyl groups absorb H^+ ion, making its parent molecule hydrophilic. It is found in phospholipids and triglycerides.

c. Carboxyl groups release OH^- , making its parent molecule hydrophilic. It is found in phospholipids phosphates and triglycerides

d. Carboxyl groups release OH^- , making its parent molecule hydrophilic. It is found in phospholipids and DNA.

28. Compare and contrast saturated and unsaturated triglycerides.

a. Saturated triglycerides contain single bonds and are solids at room temperature, while unsaturated triglycerides contain double bonds and are liquids at room temperature.

b. Saturated triglycerides contain double bonds and are solids at room temperature, while unsaturated triglycerides contain single bonds and are liquids at room temperature.

c. Saturated triglycerides contain single bonds and are liquids at room temperature, while unsaturated triglycerides contain double bonds and are solids at room temperature.

d. Saturated triglycerides contain double bonds and are liquids at room temperature, while unsaturated triglycerides contain single bond and are solids at room temperature.

TEST PREP FOR AP® COURSES

29. Why can water be a good insulator within the body of endothermic (warm-blooded) animals?

a. adhesive properties

b. surface tension

c. heat of vaporization

d. specific heat capacity

30. The unique properties of water are important in biological processes. For the following three properties of water, define the property and give one example of how the property affects living organisms:

1. cohesion
2. adhesion
3. high heat of vaporization

a. Cohesion is the attraction between the water molecules, which helps create surface tension. Insects can walk on water because of cohesion. Adhesion is the attraction between water molecules and other molecules. Water moving up from the roots of plants to the leaves as a result of capillary action is because of adhesion. Heat of vaporization is the amount of energy required to convert liquid into gas. This property helps humans maintain homeostasis of body temperature by evaporation.

b. Cohesion is the attraction between water and other molecules, which help create surface tension. Insects can walk on water because of cohesion. Adhesion is the attraction between water molecules. Water moving up from the roots of plants to the leaves as a result of capillary action is because of adhesion. Heat of vaporization is the amount of energy required to convert liquid into gas. This property helps humans maintain homeostasis of body temperature by evaporation.

c. Cohesion is the attraction between the water molecules, which helps create surface tension. Insects can walk on water because of cohesion. Adhesion is the attraction between water molecules and other molecules. Water moving up from the roots of plants to the leaves as a result of capillary action is because of adhesion. Heat of vaporization is the amount of energy required to convert solid into gas. This property helps humans maintain homeostasis of body temperature by evaporation.

d. Cohesion is the attraction between the water molecules, which helps create surface tension. Water moving up from the roots of plants to the leaves as a result of capillary action is because of cohesion. Adhesion is the attraction between water molecules and other molecules. Some insects can walk on water because of adhesion. Heat of vaporization is the amount of energy required to convert solid into gas. This property helps humans maintain homeostasis of body temperature by evaporation.

SCIENCE PRACTICE CHALLENGE QUESTIONS

31. At a time when the theory of evolution was controversial (the year following the Scopes Monkey Trial), Macallum (*Physiological Reviews*, 2, 1926) made an observation that is still contested by some who do not see the pattern in the data below showing percentages (g solute /100 g solution) of major biologically important inorganic elements in a variety of sources.

	Na^+	K^+	Ca^{+2}	Mg^{+2}	Cl^-
Ocean water	0.306	0.011	0.012	0.0037	0.55
Lobster	0.903	0.0337	0.0438	0.0156	1.547
Dog fish	0.5918	0.02739	0.01609	0.0146	0.9819

Table 2.3

	Na^+	K^+	Ca^{+2}	Mg^{+2}	Cl^-
Sand shark	0.6173	0.0355	0.0184	0.0172	1.042
Cod	0.416	0.0395	0.0163	0.00589	0.6221
Pollock	0.4145	0.017497	0.01286	0.00608	0.5613
Frog	0.195	0.0233	0.00627	0.00155	0.2679
Dog lymph	0.3033	0.0201	0.0085	0.0023	0.4231
Human					
Blood	0.302	0.0204	0.0094	0.0021	0.389
Lung	0.2956	0.02095	0.00839	0.0021	0.3425
Testes	0.3023	0.01497	0.00842	0.001914	0.3737
Ab-dominal cavity	0.2935	0.0164	0.0091	0.00184	0.3888

Table 2.3

A. Using a spreadsheet, or by sharing calculations with your classmates, **construct a quantitative model** of these data from these percentages as ratios of mass fractions relative to that of sodium, %X/%Na. Of course, you will not be asked to use a spreadsheet on the AP Biology Exam. However, the ability to develop a quantitative model through the transformation of numerical data can be assessed. The question that led Macallum to investigate the elemental composition of different species and compare these with the composition of seawater follows from the central organizing principle of biology: the theory of evolution.

B. The elements in the table above all occur in aqueous solution as ions. The net charges on the inside and outside of a cell are both zero. A very large difference in the concentrations of ions, though, results in stresses that the cell must expend energy to relieve. Based on this constraint on the total number of ions, **connect** this refined model based on ratios of ion concentration rather than absolute ionic concentrations to the modern concept of shared ancestry.

Frequently, a follow-up question regarding scientific data on the AP Biology Exam will ask you to pose questions that are raised by the data. Credit will be awarded for scientific questions. These questions usually look for a cause-and-effect relationship, and are testable.

C. Examine relative concentrations of potassium and magnesium ions in terrestrial and marine organisms. **Pose** a **question** that could be investigated to connect concentrations of these ions to adaptations to a change in the environment.

Macallum noted the high potassium to sodium ratio relative to seawater, and made this claim about what the ratio implied about the oceans of early Earth:

"At once it is suggested that as the cell is older than its media is [presently] the relative proportions of the inorganic elements in it are of more ancient origin than the relative proportions of the same amount of elements which prevail in the media, blood plasma and lymph or in the ocean and river water of today."

D. In your own words, summarize the argument that Macallum is using to **justify this claim**.

32. Approximately half the energy that flows through the Earth's biosphere is captured by phytoplankton, photosynthetic microscopic organisms in the surface waters of the oceans. Scientists think the growth of phytoplankton in the Atlantic Ocean is limited by the availability of nitrogen, whereas growth in the Pacific Ocean is limited by the availability of iron.

The concentration of oxygen (O_2) in the atmosphere of early Earth was low and, therefore, so was the concentration of dissolved oxygen in the early ocean. Because insoluble iron oxides (rust) do not form in the absence of oxygen, soluble iron ions (Fe^{2+}) were more available in the early ocean than at present since the concentration of oxygen is high. Nitrogen (N_2), while always abundant in the atmosphere, was not available until the evolution of molybdenum-based nitrogen-fixing proteins.

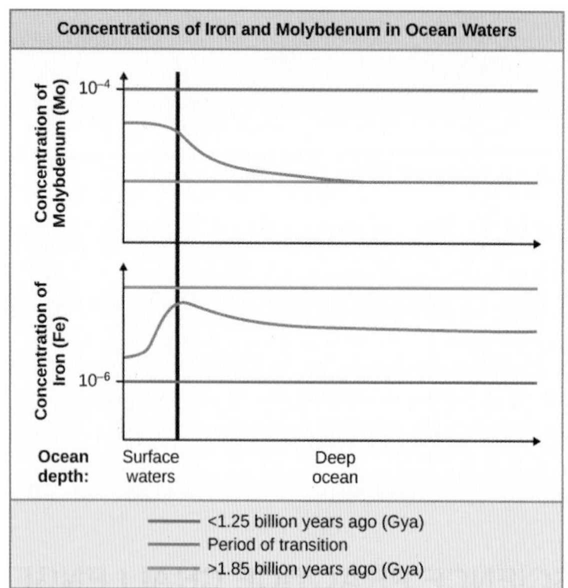

Figure 2.31

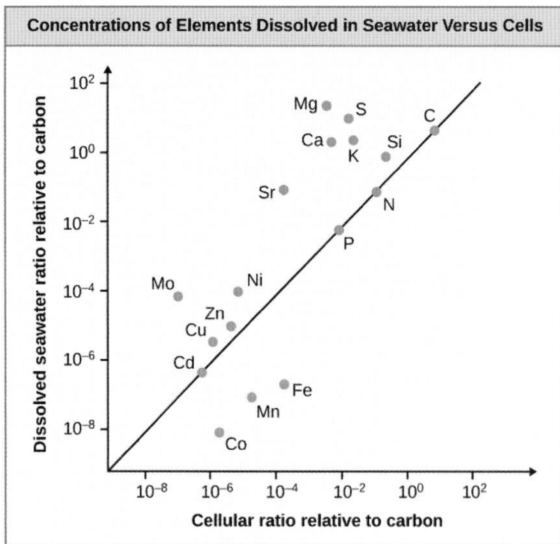

Figure 2.32

The graphs (Anbar and Knoll, *Science*, 297, 2002) show models of concentrations of two trace elements, iron (Fe) and molybdenum (Mo), in ocean waters. The model describes the change over time of these elements from early Earth (>1.85 billion years ago, Gya) to a modern era (<1.25 Gya) and a period of transition between these. Surface waters of the oceans lie to the left of the vertical double line. Modern concentrations of dissolved iron and molybdenum (relative to dissolved carbon) are shown.

A. The principle chemical processes of life today have been conserved through evolution from early Earth conditions. Using this fact, **justify the selection of these data** shown in the graphs in the construction of a model of ocean photosynthetic productivity.

Iron and molybdenum are two of 30 elements that are required by the chemical processes supporting life on Earth. Concentrations of these two and 15 others are shown in the graph at the right. Of these elements, the three most abundant in cells are also found in seawater in approximately the same concentrations. By increasing the mass of phytoplankton in the ocean, we may be able to compensate for the increasing concentration of carbon produced by the combustion of gas, oil, and coal.

B. **Select, with justification**, the element or elements that, if added in large amounts to the ocean, could boost the growth of phytoplankton.

C. Before implementing a large-scale geo-engineering effort to avert the effects of climate change due to carbon pollution, we must test the legitimacy of this solution. **Describe a plan** for collecting data that could be used to evaluate the effect of enrichment on phytoplankton productivity.

3 | BIOLOGICAL MACROMOLECULES

Figure 3.1 Foods such as bread, fruit, and cheese are rich sources of biological macromolecules. (credit: modification of work by Bengt Nyman)

Chapter Outline

Introduction

Food provides the body with the nutrients it needs to survive. Many of these critical nutrients are biological macromolecules, or large molecules, necessary for and built by living things. For example, the amino acids found in protein are needed to build healthy bone and muscle. The body uses fat molecules to build new cells, store energy, and for proper digestion. Carbohydrates are the primary source of the body's energy. Nucleic acids contain genetic information.

While all living things, including humans, need macromolecules in their daily diet, an imbalance of any one of them can lead to health problems. For example, eating too much fat can lead to cardiovascular problems, and too much protein can lead to problems with the kidneys. Some people think that removing whole grains, such as wheat, from one's diet can be beneficial. However, scientists have found that to not be true for the majority of people. In fact, just the opposite may be true, because whole wheat contains more dietary fiber than other types of grains. The full research review can be found **here (http://openstaxcollege.org/l/32wholegrain)** .

3.1 | Synthesis of Biological Macromolecules

In this section, you will explore the following questions:

- How are complex macromolecule polymers synthesized from monomers?
- What is the difference between dehydration (or condensation) and hydrolysis reactions?

Connection for AP® Courses

Living organisms need food to survive as it contains critical nutrients in the form of biological macromolecules. These large molecules are composed mainly of six elements—sulfur, phosphorus, oxygen, nitrogen, carbon, and hydrogen (SPONCH)—in different quantities and arrangements. Complex polymers are built from combinations of smaller monomers by dehydration synthesis, a chemical reaction in which a molecule of water is removed between two linking monomers. (Think of a train: each boxcar, including the caboose, represents a monomer, and the entire train is a polymer.) During digestion, polymers can be broken down by hydrolysis, or the addition of water. Both dehydration and hydrolysis reactions in cells are catalyzed by specific enzymes. Dehydration reactions typically require an investment of energy for new bond formation, whereas hydrolysis reactions typically release energy that can be used to power cellular processes. The four categories of macromolecules are carbohydrates, lipids, proteins, and nucleic acids. Evidence supports scientists' claim that the organic precursors of these biological molecules were present on primitive Earth.

Information presented and the examples highlighted in the section support concepts and Learning Objectives outlined in Big Idea 1 of the AP® Biology Curriculum Framework. The Learning Objectives listed in the Curriculum Framework provide a transparent foundation for the AP® Biology course, an inquiry-based laboratory experience, instructional activities, and AP® Exam questions. A learning objective merges required content with one or more of the seven Science Practices.

Big Idea 1	The process of evolution drives the diversity and unity of life.
Enduring Understanding 1.D	The origin of living systems is explained by natural processes.
Essential Knowledge	**1.D.1** There are several hypotheses about the natural origin of life on Earth, each with supporting scientific evidence.
Science Practice	**1.2** The student can make claims and predictions about natural phenomena based on scientific theories and models.
Learning Objective	**1.27** The student is able to describe a scientific hypothesis about the origin of life on Earth.
Essential Knowledge	**1.D.1** There are several hypotheses about the natural origin of life on Earth, each with supporting scientific evidence.
Science Practice	**3.3** The student can evaluate scientific questions.
Learning Objective	**1.28** The student is able to evaluate scientific questions based on hypotheses about the origin of life on Earth.

Dehydration Synthesis

As you've learned, **biological macromolecules** are large molecules, necessary for life, that are built from smaller organic molecules. There are four major classes of biological macromolecules (carbohydrates, lipids, proteins, and nucleic acids); each is an important cell component and performs a wide array of functions. Combined, these molecules make up the majority of a cell's dry mass (recall that water makes up the majority of its complete mass). Biological macromolecules are organic, meaning they contain carbon. In addition, they may contain hydrogen, oxygen, nitrogen, and additional minor elements.

Most macromolecules are made from single subunits, or building blocks, called **monomers**. The monomers combine with each other using covalent bonds to form larger molecules known as **polymers**. In doing so, monomers release water molecules as byproducts. This type of reaction is known as **dehydration synthesis**, which means "to put together while losing water."

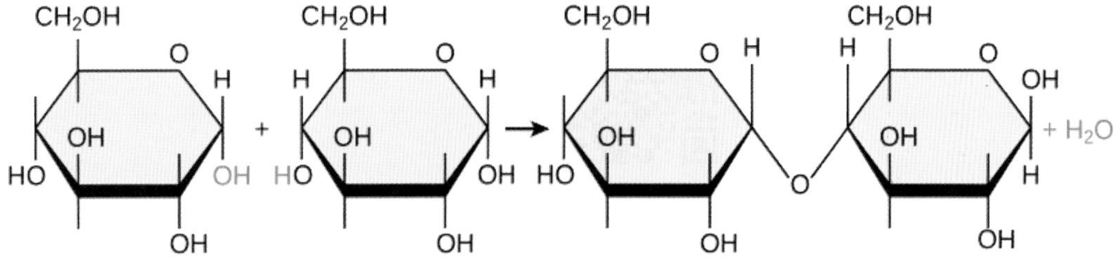

Figure 3.2 In the dehydration synthesis reaction depicted above, two molecules of glucose are linked together to form the disaccharide maltose. In the process, a water molecule is formed.

In a dehydration synthesis reaction (Figure 3.2), the hydrogen of one monomer combines with the hydroxyl group of another monomer, releasing a molecule of water. At the same time, the monomers share electrons and form covalent bonds. As additional monomers join, this chain of repeating monomers forms a polymer. Different types of monomers can combine in many configurations, giving rise to a diverse group of macromolecules. Even one kind of monomer can combine in a variety of ways to form several different polymers: for example, glucose monomers are the constituents of starch, glycogen, and cellulose.

Hydrolysis

Polymers are broken down into monomers in a process known as hydrolysis, which means "to split with water." Hydrolysis is a reaction in which a water molecule is used during the breakdown of another compound (Figure 3.3). During these reactions, the polymer is broken into two components: one part gains a hydrogen atom (H+) and the other gains a hydroxyl molecule (OH–) from a split water molecule.

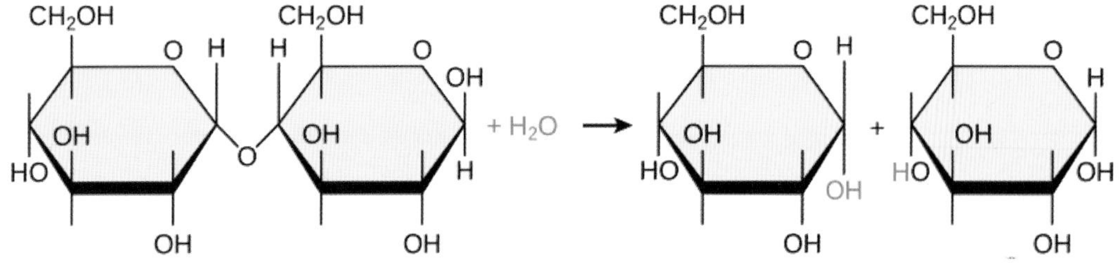

Figure 3.3 In the hydrolysis reaction shown here, the disaccharide maltose is broken down to form two glucose monomers with the addition of a water molecule. Note that this reaction is the reverse of the synthesis reaction shown in Figure 3.2.

Dehydration and **hydrolysis reactions** are catalyzed, or "sped up," by specific enzymes; dehydration reactions involve the formation of new bonds, requiring energy, while hydrolysis reactions break bonds and release energy. These reactions are similar for most macromolecules, but each monomer and polymer reaction is specific for its class. For example, in our bodies, food is hydrolyzed, or broken down, into smaller molecules by catalytic enzymes in the digestive system. This allows for easy absorption of nutrients by cells in the intestine. Each macromolecule is broken down by a specific enzyme. For instance, carbohydrates are broken down by amylase, sucrase, lactase, or maltase. Proteins are broken down by the enzymes pepsin and peptidase, and by hydrochloric acid. Lipids are broken down by lipases. Breakdown of these macromolecules provides energy for cellular activities.

Visit this site (http://openstaxcollege.org/l/hydrolysis) to see visual representations of dehydration synthesis and hydrolysis.

What role do electrons play in dehydration synthesis and hydrolysis?

a. Sharing of electrons between monomers occurs in both dehydration synthesis and hydrolysis.

b. The sharing of electrons between monomers occurs in hydrolysis only.

c. H^+ and OH^- ions share electrons with the respective monomers in dehydration synthesis.

d. H^+ and OH^- ions share electrons with the respective monomers in hydrolysis.

everyday CONNECTION for AP® Courses

Recreating Primordial Earth

Many people wonder how life formed on Earth. In 1953, Stanley Miller and Harold Urey developed an apparatus like the one shown in Figure 3.4 to model early conditions on earth. They wanted to test if organic molecules could form from inorganic precursors believed to exist very early in Earth's history. They used boiling water to mimic early Earth's oceans. Steam from the "ocean" combined with methane, ammonia, and hydrogen gases from the early Earth's atmosphere and was exposed to electrical sparks to act as lightning. As the gas mixture cooled and condensed, it was found to contain organic compounds, such as amino acids and nucleotides. According to the abiogenesis theory, these organic molecules came together to form the earliest form of life about 3.5 billion years ago. (credit: Yassine Mrabet)

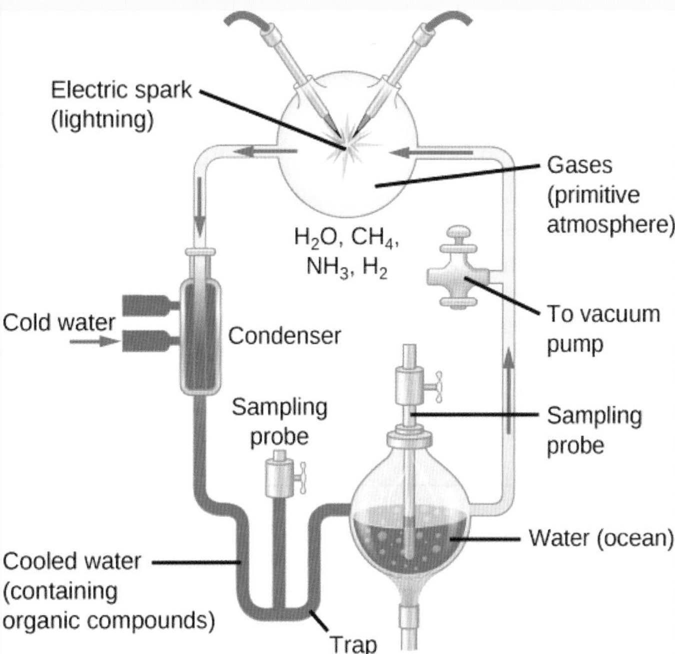

Figure 3.4

science practices CONNECTION for AP® Courses

Think About It

How does Stanley Miller's and Harold Urey's model support the claim that organic precursors present on early Earth could have assembled into large, complex molecules necessary for life? What chemical "ingredients" were present on early Earth?

3.2 | Carbohydrates

By the end of this section, you will be able to:

- What is the role of carbohydrates in cells and in the extracellular materials of animals and plants?
- What are the different classifications of carbohydrates?
- How are monosaccharide building blocks assembled into disaccharides and complex polysaccharides?

Connection for AP® Courses

Carbohydrates provide energy for the cell and structural support to plants, fungi, and arthropods such as insects, spiders, and crustaceans. Consisting of carbon, hydrogen, and oxygen in the ratio CH_2O or carbon hydrated with water, carbohydrates are classified as monosaccharides, disaccharides, and polysaccharides depending on the number of monomers in the macromolecule. Monosaccharides are linked by glycosidic bonds that form as a result of dehydration synthesis. Glucose, galactose, and fructose are common isomeric monosaccharides, whereas sucrose or table sugar is a disaccharide. Examples of polysaccharides include cellulose and starch in plants and glycogen in animals. Although storing glucose in the form of polymers like starch or glycogen makes it less accessible for metabolism, this prevents it from leaking out of cells or creating a high osmotic pressure that could cause excessive water uptake by the cell. Insects have a hard outer skeleton made of chitin, a unique nitrogen-containing polysaccharide.

Information presented and the examples highlighted in the section support concepts and Learning Objectives outlined in Big Idea 4 of the AP® Biology Curriculum Framework. The Learning Objectives listed in the Curriculum Framework provide a transparent foundation for the AP® Biology course, an inquiry-based laboratory experience, instructional activities, and AP® Exam questions. A Learning Objective merges required content with one or more of the seven Science Practices.

Big Idea 4	Biological systems interact, and these systems and their interactions possess complex properties.
Enduring Understanding 4.A	Interactions within biological systems lead to complex properties.
Essential Knowledge	**4.A.1** The subcomponents of biological molecules and their sequence determine the properties of that molecule.
Science Practice	**7.1** The student can connect phenomena and models across spatial and temporal scales.
Learning Objective	**4.1** The student is able to refine representations and models to explain how the subcomponents of a biological polymer and their sequence determine the properties of that polymer.
Essential Knowledge	**4.A.1** The subcomponents of biological molecules and their sequence determine the properties of that molecule.
Science Practice	**1.3** The student can refine representations and models of natural or man-made phenomena and systems in the domain.
Learning Objective	**4.2** The student is able to refine representations and models to explain how the subcomponents of a biological polymer and their sequence determine the properties of that polymer.
Essential Knowledge	**4.A.1** The subcomponents of biological molecules and their sequence determine the properties of that molecule.
Science Practice	**6.1** The student can justify claims with evidence.

Science Practice	**6.4** The student can make claims and predictions about natural phenomena based on scientific theories and models.
Learning Objective	**4.3** The student is able to use models to predict and justify that changes in the subcomponents of a biological polymer affect the functionality of the molecules.

The Science Practice Challenge Questions contain additional test questions for this section that will help you prepare for the AP exam. These questions address the following standards:
[APLO 4.15] [APLO 2.5]

Molecular Structures

Most people are familiar with carbohydrates, one type of macromolecule, especially when it comes to what we eat. To lose weight, some individuals adhere to “low-carb” diets. Athletes, in contrast, often “carb-load” before important competitions to ensure that they have enough energy to compete at a high level. Carbohydrates are, in fact, an essential part of our diet; grains, fruits, and vegetables are all natural sources of carbohydrates. Carbohydrates provide energy to the body, particularly through glucose, a simple sugar that is a component of **starch** and an ingredient in many staple foods. Carbohydrates also have other important functions in humans, animals, and plants.

Carbohydrates can be represented by the stoichiometric formula $(CH_2O)_n$, where n is the number of carbons in the molecule. In other words, the ratio of carbon to hydrogen to oxygen is 1:2:1 in carbohydrate molecules. This formula also explains the origin of the term “carbohydrate”: the components are carbon (“carbo”) and the components of water (hence, “hydrate”). Carbohydrates are classified into three subtypes: monosaccharides, disaccharides, and polysaccharides.

Monosaccharides

Monosaccharides (mono- = “one”; sacchar- = “sweet”) are simple sugars, the most common of which is glucose. In monosaccharides, the number of carbons usually ranges from three to seven. Most monosaccharide names end with the suffix -ose. If the sugar has an aldehyde group (the functional group with the structure R-CHO), it is known as an aldose, and if it has a ketone group (the functional group with the structure RC(=O)R'), it is known as a ketose. Depending on the number of carbons in the sugar, they also may be known as trioses (three carbons), pentoses (five carbons), and or hexoses (six carbons). See **Figure 3.5** for an illustration of the monosaccharides.

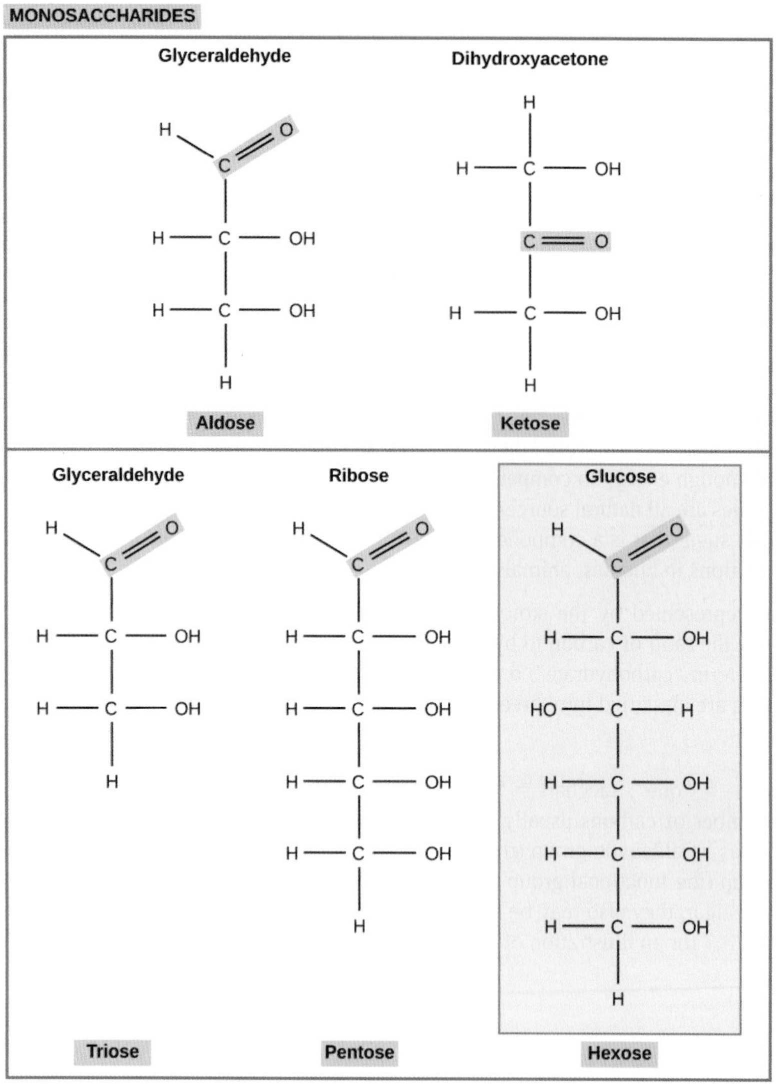

Figure 3.5 Monosaccharides are classified based on the position of their carbonyl group and the number of carbons in the backbone. Aldoses have a carbonyl group (indicated in green) at the end of the carbon chain, and ketoses have a carbonyl group in the middle of the carbon chain. Trioses, pentoses, and hexoses have three-, five-, and six-carbon backbones, respectively.

The chemical formula for glucose is $C_6H_{12}O_6$. In humans, glucose is an important source of energy. During cellular respiration, energy is released from glucose, and that energy is used to help make adenosine triphosphate (ATP). Plants synthesize glucose using carbon dioxide and water, and glucose in turn is used for energy requirements for the plant. Excess glucose is often stored as starch that is catabolized (the breakdown of larger molecules by cells) by humans and other animals that feed on plants.

Galactose (part of lactose, or milk sugar) and fructose (found in sucrose, in fruit) are other common monosaccharides. Although glucose, galactose, and fructose all have the same chemical formula ($C_6H_{12}O_6$), they differ structurally and chemically (and are known as isomers) because of the different arrangement of functional groups around the asymmetric carbon; all of these monosaccharides have more than one asymmetric carbon (Figure 3.6).

visual CONNECTION

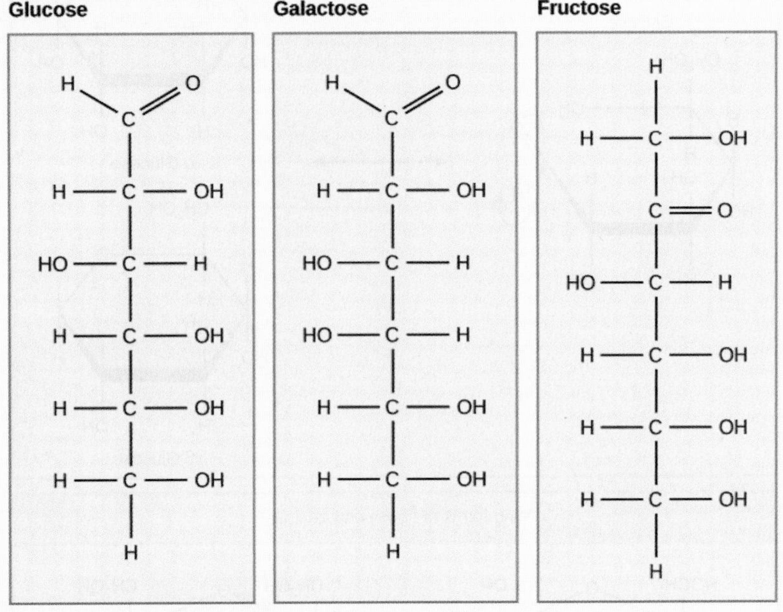

Figure 3.6 Glucose, galactose, and fructose are all hexoses. They are structural isomers, meaning they have the same chemical formula ($C_6H_{12}O_6$) but a different arrangement of atoms.

Identify each sugar as an aldose or ketose.

1. fructose
2. galactose
3. glucose

   a. Glucose and galactose are aldoses. Fructose is a ketose
   b. Glucose and fructose are aldoses. Galactose is a ketose.
   c. Galactose and fructose are ketoses. Glucose is an aldose.
   d. Glucose and fructose are ketoses. Galactose is an aldose.

Glucose, galactose, and fructose are isomeric monosaccharides (hexoses), meaning they have the same chemical formula but have slightly different structures. Glucose and galactose are aldoses, and fructose is a ketose.

Monosaccharides can exist as a linear chain or as ring-shaped molecules; in aqueous solutions they are usually found in ring forms (Figure 3.7). Glucose in a ring form can have two different arrangements of the hydroxyl group (OH) around the anomeric carbon (carbon 1 that becomes asymmetric in the process of ring formation). If the hydroxyl group is below carbon number 1 in the sugar, it is said to be in the alpha (α) position, and if it is above the plane, it is said to be in the beta (β) position.

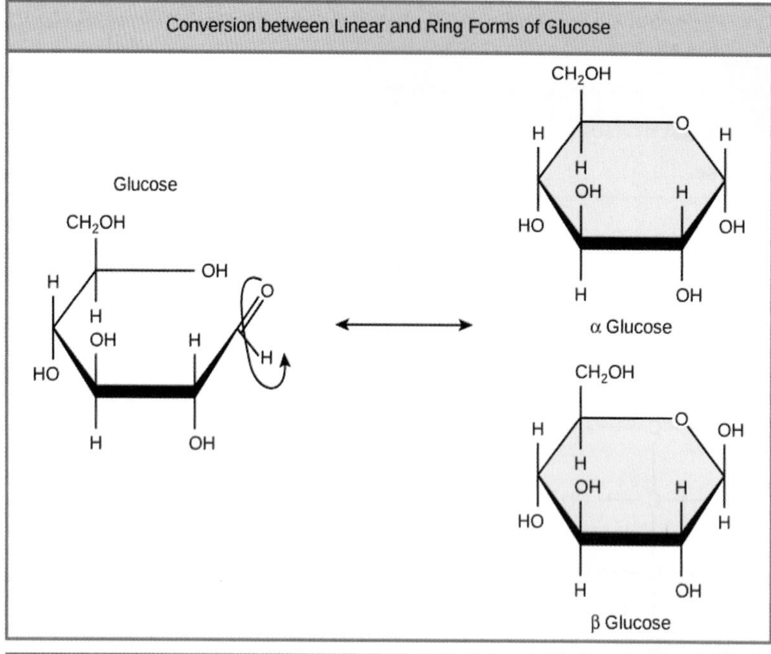

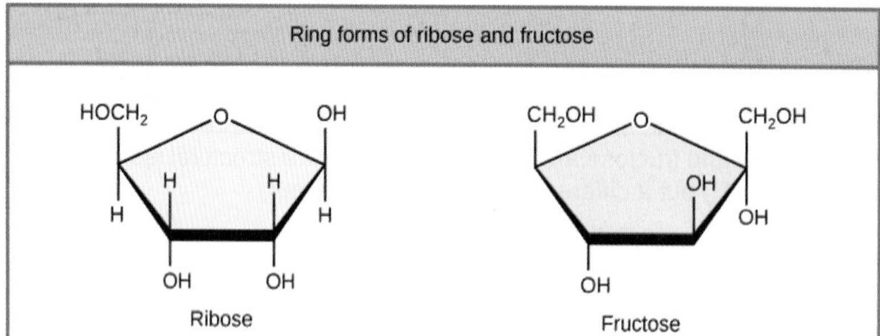

Figure 3.7 Five and six carbon monosaccharides exist in equilibrium between linear and ring forms. When the ring forms, the side chain it closes on is locked into an *α* or *β* position. Fructose and ribose also form rings, although they form five-membered rings as opposed to the six-membered ring of glucose.

Disaccharides

Disaccharides (di- = "two") form when two monosaccharides undergo a dehydration reaction (also known as a condensation reaction or dehydration synthesis). During this process, the hydroxyl group of one monosaccharide combines with the hydrogen of another monosaccharide, releasing a molecule of water and forming a covalent bond. A covalent bond formed between a carbohydrate molecule and another molecule (in this case, between two monosaccharides) is known as a **glycosidic bond** (Figure 3.8). Glycosidic bonds (also called glycosidic linkages) can be of the alpha or the beta type.

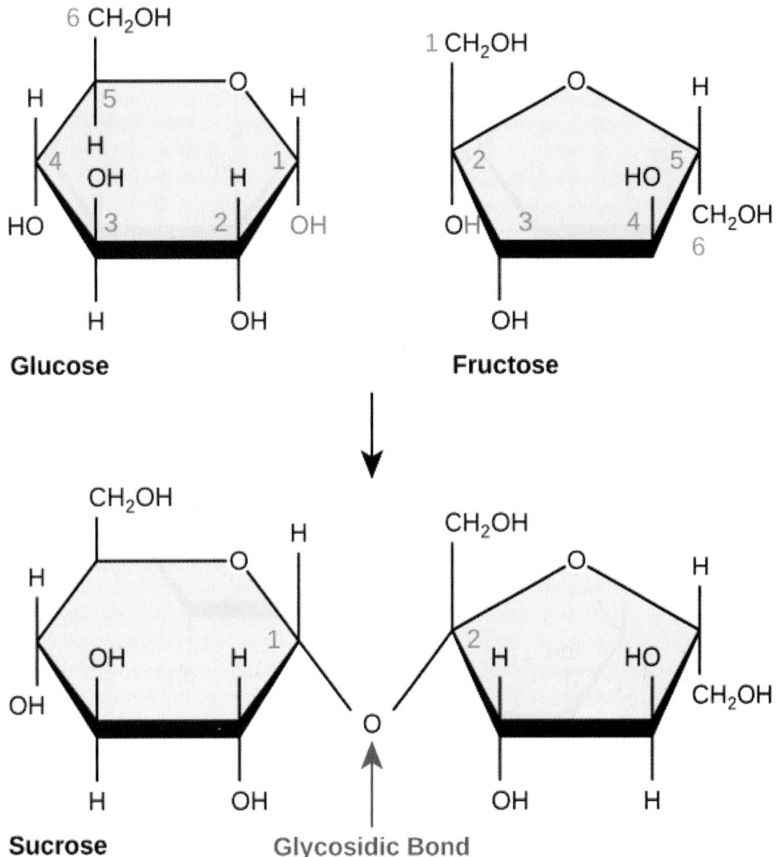

Figure 3.8 Sucrose is formed when a monomer of glucose and a monomer of fructose are joined in a dehydration reaction to form a glycosidic bond. In the process, a water molecule is lost. By convention, the carbon atoms in a monosaccharide are numbered from the terminal carbon closest to the carbonyl group. In sucrose, a glycosidic linkage is formed between carbon 1 in glucose and carbon 2 in fructose.

Common disaccharides include lactose, maltose, and sucrose (Figure 3.9). Lactose is a disaccharide consisting of the monomers glucose and galactose. It is found naturally in milk. Maltose, or malt sugar, is a disaccharide formed by a dehydration reaction between two glucose molecules. The most common disaccharide is sucrose, or table sugar, which is composed of the monomers glucose and fructose.

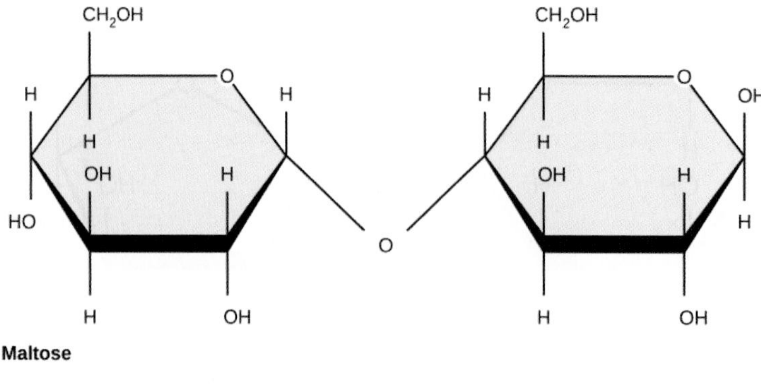

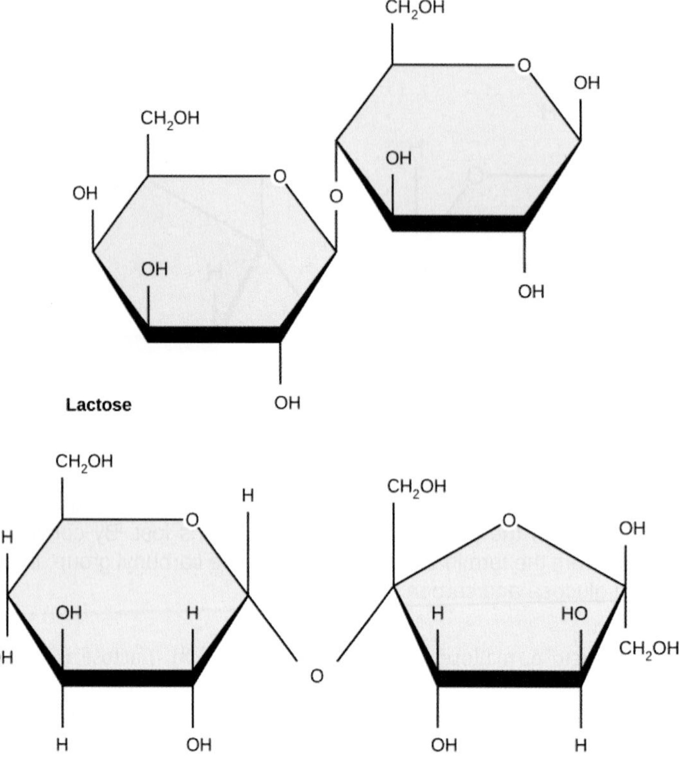

Figure 3.9 Common disaccharides include maltose (grain sugar), lactose (milk sugar), and sucrose (table sugar).

Polysaccharides

A long chain of monosaccharides linked by glycosidic bonds is known as a **polysaccharide** (poly- = "many"). The chain may be branched or unbranched, and it may contain different types of monosaccharides. The molecular weight may be 100,000 daltons or more depending on the number of monomers joined. Starch, glycogen, cellulose, and chitin are primary examples of polysaccharides.

Starch is the stored form of sugars in plants and is made up of a mixture of amylose and amylopectin (both polymers of glucose). Plants are able to synthesize glucose, and the excess glucose, beyond the plant's immediate energy needs, is stored as starch in different plant parts, including roots and seeds. The starch in the seeds provides food for the embryo as it germinates and can also act as a source of food for humans and animals. The starch that is consumed by humans is broken down by enzymes, such as salivary amylases, into smaller molecules, such as maltose and glucose. The cells can then absorb the glucose.

Starch is made up of glucose monomers that are joined by α 1-4 or α 1-6 glycosidic bonds. The numbers 1-4 and 1-6 refer to the carbon number of the two residues that have joined to form the bond. As illustrated in Figure 3.10, amylose is starch formed by unbranched chains of glucose monomers (only α 1-4 linkages), whereas amylopectin is a branched polysaccharide (α 1-6 linkages at the branch points).

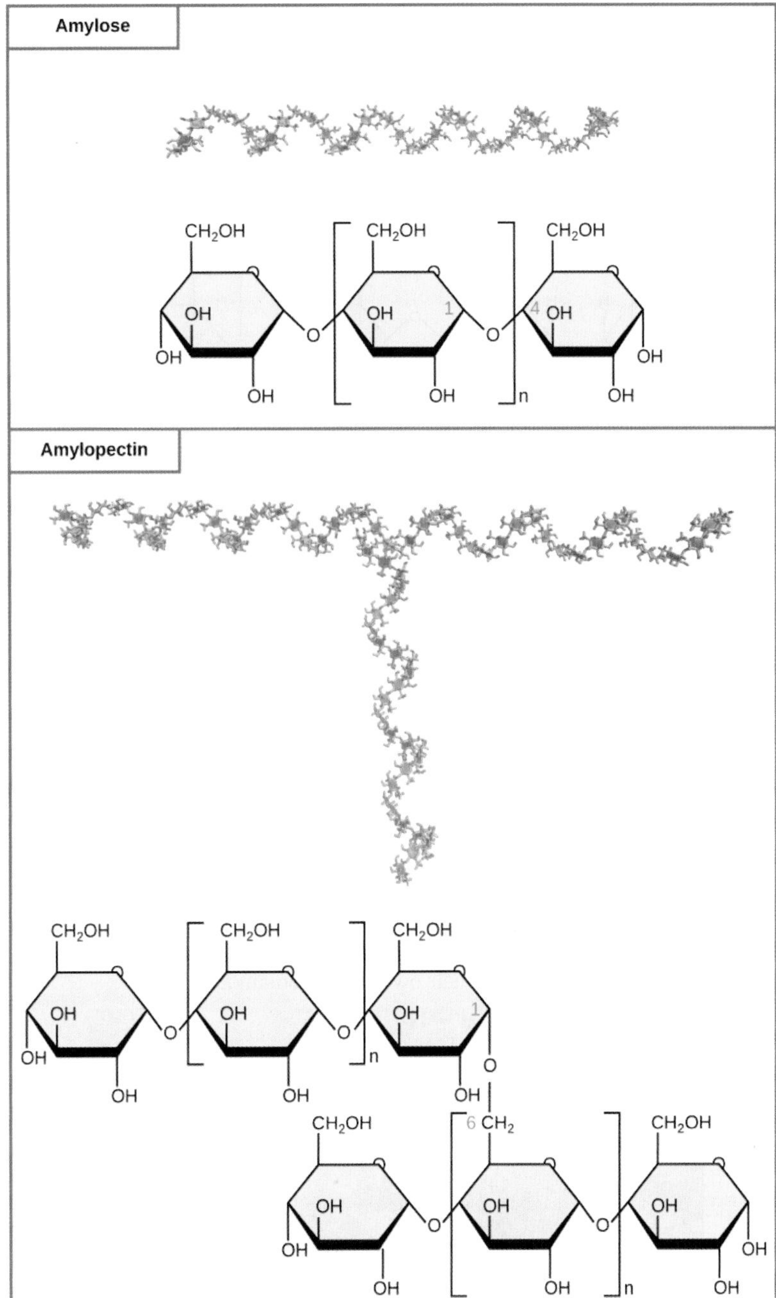

Figure 3.10 Amylose and amylopectin are two different forms of starch. Amylose is composed of unbranched chains of glucose monomers connected by α 1,4 glycosidic linkages. Amylopectin is composed of branched chains of glucose monomers connected by α 1,4 and α 1,6 glycosidic linkages. Because of the way the subunits are joined, the glucose chains have a helical structure. Glycogen (not shown) is similar in structure to amylopectin but more highly branched.

Glycogen is the storage form of glucose in humans and other vertebrates and is made up of monomers of glucose. Glycogen is the animal equivalent of starch and is a highly branched molecule usually stored in liver and muscle cells. Whenever blood glucose levels decrease, glycogen is broken down to release glucose in a process known as glycogenolysis.

Cellulose is the most abundant natural biopolymer. The cell wall of plants is mostly made of cellulose; this provides structural support to the cell. Wood and paper are mostly cellulosic in nature. Cellulose is made up of glucose monomers that are linked by β 1-4 glycosidic bonds (Figure 3.11).

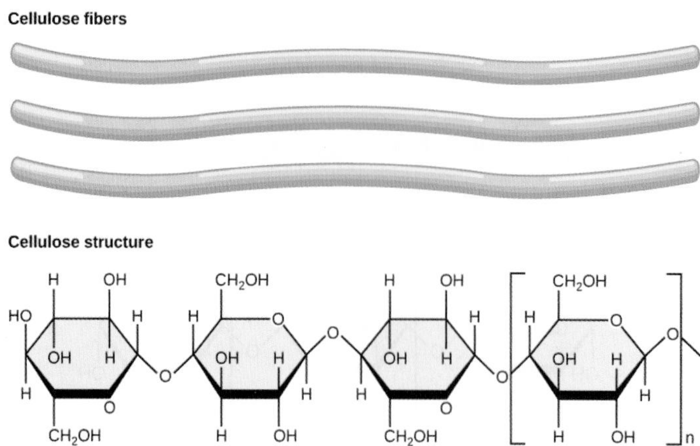

Figure 3.11 In cellulose, glucose monomers are linked in unbranched chains by β 1-4 glycosidic linkages. Because of the way the glucose subunits are joined, every glucose monomer is flipped relative to the next one resulting in a linear, fibrous structure.

As shown in Figure 3.11, every other glucose monomer in cellulose is flipped over, and the monomers are packed tightly as extended long chains. This gives cellulose its rigidity and high tensile strength—which is so important to plant cells. While the β 1-4 linkage cannot be broken down by human digestive enzymes, herbivores such as cows, koalas, and buffalos are able, with the help of the specialized flora in their stomach, to digest plant material that is rich in cellulose and use it as a food source. In these animals, certain species of bacteria and protists reside in the rumen (part of the digestive system of herbivores) and secrete the enzyme cellulase. The appendix of grazing animals also contains bacteria that digest cellulose, giving it an important role in the digestive systems of ruminants. Cellulases can break down cellulose into glucose monomers that can be used as an energy source by the animal. Termites are also able to break down cellulose because of the presence of other organisms in their bodies that secrete cellulases.

Carbohydrates serve various functions in different animals. Arthropods (insects, crustaceans, and others) have an outer skeleton, called the exoskeleton, which protects their internal body parts (as seen in the bee in Figure 3.12). This exoskeleton is made of the biological macromolecule **chitin**, which is a polysaccharide-containing nitrogen. It is made of repeating units of N-acetyl-β-d-glucosamine, a modified sugar. Chitin is also a major component of fungal cell walls; fungi are neither animals nor plants and form a kingdom of their own in the domain Eukarya.

Figure 3.12 Insects have a hard outer exoskeleton made of chitin, a type of polysaccharide. (credit: Louise Docker)

career CONNECTION

Registered dietitians help plan nutrition programs for individuals in various settings. They often work with patients in health care facilities, designing nutrition plans to treat and prevent diseases. For example, dietitians may teach a patient with diabetes how to manage blood sugar levels by eating the correct types and amounts of carbohydrates. Dietitians may also work in nursing homes, schools, and private practices.

To become a registered dietitian, one needs to earn at least a bachelor's degree in dietetics, nutrition, food technology, or a related field. In addition, registered dietitians must complete a supervised internship program and pass a national exam. Those who pursue careers in dietetics take courses in nutrition, chemistry, biochemistry, biology, microbiology, and human physiology. Dietitians must become experts in the chemistry and physiology (biological functions) of food (proteins, carbohydrates, and fats).

Benefits of Carbohydrates

Are carbohydrates good for you? People who wish to lose weight are often told that carbohydrates are bad for them and should be avoided. Some diets completely forbid carbohydrate consumption, claiming that a low-carbohydrate diet helps people to lose weight faster. However, carbohydrates have been an important part of the human diet for thousands of years; artifacts from ancient civilizations show the presence of wheat, rice, and corn in our ancestors' storage areas.

Carbohydrates should be supplemented with proteins, vitamins, and fats to be parts of a well-balanced diet. Calorie-wise, a gram of carbohydrate provides 4.3 Kcal. For comparison, fats provide 9 Kcal/g, a less desirable ratio. Carbohydrates contain soluble and insoluble elements; the insoluble part is known as fiber, which is mostly cellulose. Fiber has many uses; it promotes regular bowel movement by adding bulk, and it regulates the rate of consumption of blood glucose. Fiber also helps to remove excess cholesterol from the body: fiber binds to the cholesterol in the small intestine, then attaches to the cholesterol and prevents the cholesterol particles from entering the bloodstream, and then cholesterol exits the body via the feces. In addition, a meal containing whole grains and vegetables gives a feeling of fullness. As an immediate source of energy, glucose is broken down during the process of cellular respiration, which produces ATP, the energy currency of the cell. Without the consumption of carbohydrates, the availability of "instant energy" would be reduced. Eliminating carbohydrates from the diet is not the best way to lose weight. A low-calorie diet that is rich in whole grains, fruits, vegetables, and lean meat, together with plenty of exercise and plenty of water, is the more sensible way to lose weight.

For an additional perspective on carbohydrates, explore "Biomolecules: the Carbohydrates" through this **interactive animation (http://openstaxcollege.org/l/carbohydrates)** .

Fiber is not really a nutrient, because it passes through our body undigested. Why can't fiber be digested and why is it important to our diet?

a. The enzymes required to digest cellulose are not produced in human body; undigested fiber adds bulk to the food easing bowel movements.

b. The enzymes that digests cellulose cannot bind to the cellulose due to altered active sites; undigested fiber adds bulk to the food easing bowel movements.

c. The enzymes required to digest cellulose are not produced in human body; fiber produces energy for the metabolism.

d. Competitive inhibitors are not the reason that fiber is indigestible.

science practices CONNECTION for AP® Courses

Activity

Use a molecular model kit to construct a polysaccharide from several different monosaccharide monomers. Explain how the structure of the polysaccharide determines its primary function as an energy storage molecule. Then use your model to describe how changes in structure result in changes in function.

Think About It

- Explain why athletes often "carb-load" before a big game or tournament.
- Explain why it is difficult for some animals, including humans, to digest cellulose. Describe a structural difference between cellulose and starch, which is easily digested by humans. How are cows and other ruminants able to digest cellulose?

3.3 | Lipids

In this section, you will explore the following questions:

- What are the four major types of lipids?
- What are functions of fats in living organisms?
- What is the difference between saturated and unsaturated fatty acids?
- What is the molecular structure of phospholipids, and what is the role of phospholipids in cells?
- What is the basic structure of a steroid, and what are examples of their functions?
- How does cholesterol help maintain the fluid nature of the plasma membrane of cells?

Connection for AP® Courses

Lipids also are sources of energy that power cellular processes. Like carbohydrates, lipids are composed of carbon, hydrogen, and oxygen, but these atoms are arranged differently. Most lipids are nonpolar and hydrophobic. Major types include fats and oils, waxes, phospholipids, and steroids. A typical fat consists of three fatty acids bonded to one molecule of glycerol, forming triglycerides or triacylglycerols. The fatty acids may be saturated or unsaturated, depending on the presence or absence of double bonds in the hydrocarbon chain; a saturated fatty acid has the maximum number of hydrogen atoms bonded to carbon and, thus, only single bonds. In general, fats that are liquid at room temperature (e.g., canola oil) tend to be more unsaturated than fats that are solid at room temperature. In the food industry, oils are artificially hydrogenated to make them chemically more appropriate for use in processed foods. During this hydrogenation process, double bonds in the cis- conformation in the hydrocarbon chain may be converted to double bonds in the trans-conformation; unfortunately, trans fats have been shown to contribute to heart disease. Phospholipids are a special type of lipid associated with cell membranes and typically have a glycerol (or sphingosine) backbone to which two fatty acid chains and a phosphate-containing group are attached. As a result, phospholipids are considered amphipathic because they have both hydrophobic and hydrophilic components. (In Chapters 4 and 5 we will explore in more detail how the amphipathic nature of phospholipids in plasma cell membranes helps regulate the passage of substances into and out of the cell.) Although the molecular structures of steroids differ from that of triglycerides and phospholipids, steroids are classified as lipids based on their hydrophobic properties. Cholesterol is a type of steroid in animal cells' plasma membrane. Cholesterol is also the precursor of steroid hormones such as testosterone.

Information presented and the examples highlighted in the section, support concepts outlined in Big Idea 4 of the AP® Biology Curriculum Framework. The learning objectives listed in the Curriculum Framework provide a transparent foundation for the AP® Biology course, an inquiry-based laboratory experience, instructional activities, and AP® exam questions. A Learning Objective merges required content with one or more of the seven Science Practices.

Big Idea 4	Biological systems interact, and these systems and their interactions possess complex properties.
Enduring Understanding 4.A	Interactions within biological systems lead to complex properties.
Essential Knowledge	**4.A.1** The subcomponents of biological molecules and their sequence determine the properties of that molecule.
Science Practice	**7.1** The student can connect phenomena and models across spatial and temporal scales.
Learning Objective	**4.1** The student is able to explain the connection between the sequence and the subcomponents of a biological polymer and its properties.
Essential Knowledge	**4.A.1** The subcomponents of biological molecules and their sequence determine the properties of that molecule.
Science Practice	**1.3** The student can refine representations and models of natural or man-made phenomena and systems in the domain.
Learning Objective	**4.2** The student is able to refine representations and models to explain how the subcomponents of a biological polymer and their sequence determine the properties of that polymer.
Essential Knowledge	**4.A.1** The subcomponents of biological molecules and their sequence determine the properties of that molecule.
Science Practice	**6.1** The student can justify claims with evidence.
Science Practice	**6.4** The student can make claims and predictions about natural phenomena based on scientific theories and models.
Learning Objective	**4.3** The student is able to use models to predict and justify that changes in the subcomponents of a biological polymer affect the functionality of the molecules.

The Science Practice Challenge Questions contain additional test questions for this section that will help you prepare for the AP exam. These questions address the following standards:
[APLO 2.9] [APLO 2.10] [APLO 2.12] [APLO 2.13][APLO 2.14][APLO 4.14]

Fats and Oils

Lipids include a diverse group of compounds that are largely nonpolar in nature. This is because they are hydrocarbons that include mostly nonpolar carbon–carbon or carbon–hydrogen bonds. Non-polar molecules are hydrophobic ("water fearing"), or insoluble in water. Lipids perform many different functions in a cell. Cells store energy for long-term use in the form of fats. Lipids also provide insulation from the environment for plants and animals (Figure 3.13). For example, their water-repellant hydrophobic nature can help keep aquatic birds and mammals dry by forming a protective layer over fur or feathers. Lipids are also the building blocks of many hormones and an important constituent of all cellular membranes. Lipids include fats, waxes, phospholipids, and steroids.

Figure 3.13 Hydrophobic lipids in the fur of aquatic mammals, such as this river otter, protect them from the elements. (credit: Ken Bosma)

A fat molecule consists of two main components—glycerol and fatty acids. Glycerol is an organic compound (alcohol) with three carbons, five hydrogens, and three hydroxyl (OH) groups. Fatty acids have a long chain of hydrocarbons to which a carboxyl group is attached, hence the name "fatty acid." The number of carbons in the fatty acid may range from 4 to 36; most common are those containing 12–18 carbons. In a fat molecule, the fatty acids are attached to each of the three carbons of the glycerol molecule with an ester bond through an oxygen atom (Figure 3.14).

Glycerol

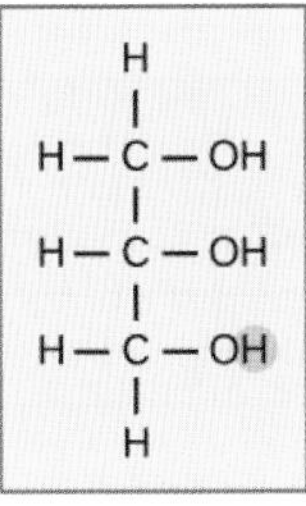

\+

Fatty Acid

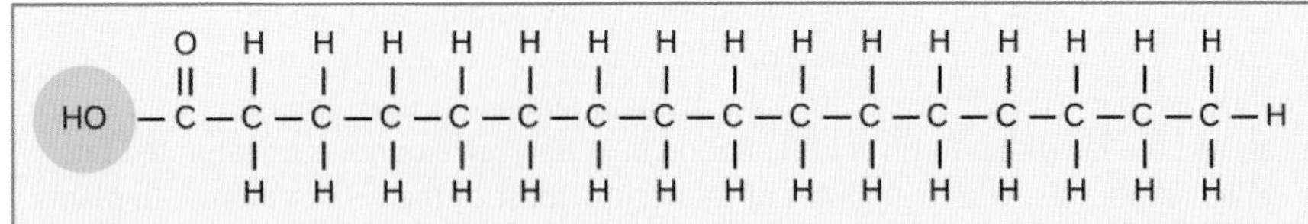

Triacylglycerol

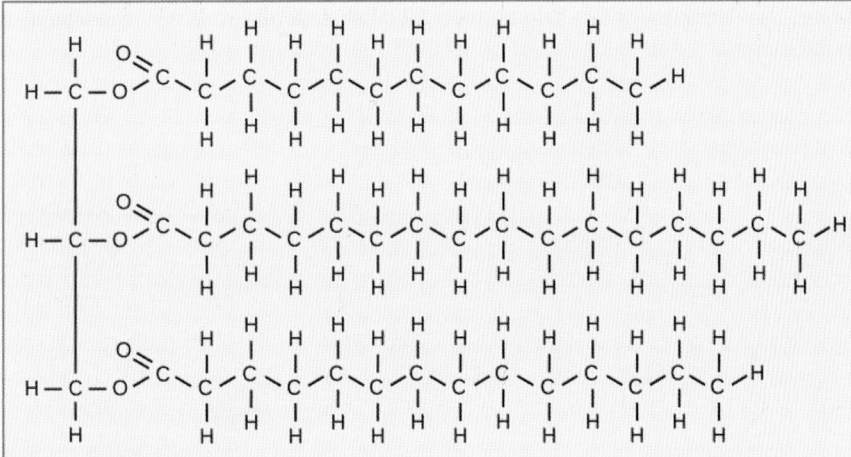

Figure 3.14 Triacylglycerol is formed by the joining of three fatty acids to a glycerol backbone in a dehydration reaction. Three molecules of water are released in the process.

During this ester bond formation, three water molecules are released. The three fatty acids in the triacylglycerol may be similar or dissimilar. Fats are also called **triacylglycerols** or **triglycerides** because of their chemical structure. Some fatty acids have common names that specify their origin. For example, palmitic acid, a **saturated fatty acid**, is derived from the palm tree. Arachidic acid is derived from *Arachis hypogea*, the scientific name for groundnuts or peanuts.

Fatty acids may be saturated or unsaturated. In a fatty acid chain, if there are only single bonds between neighboring carbons in the hydrocarbon chain, the fatty acid is said to be saturated. Saturated fatty acids are saturated with hydrogen; in other words, the number of hydrogen atoms attached to the carbon skeleton is maximized. Stearic acid is an example of a saturated fatty acid (Figure 3.15)

Figure 3.15 Stearic acid is a common saturated fatty acid.

When the hydrocarbon chain contains a double bond, the fatty acid is said to be **unsaturated**. Oleic acid is an example of an unsaturated fatty acid (Figure 3.16).

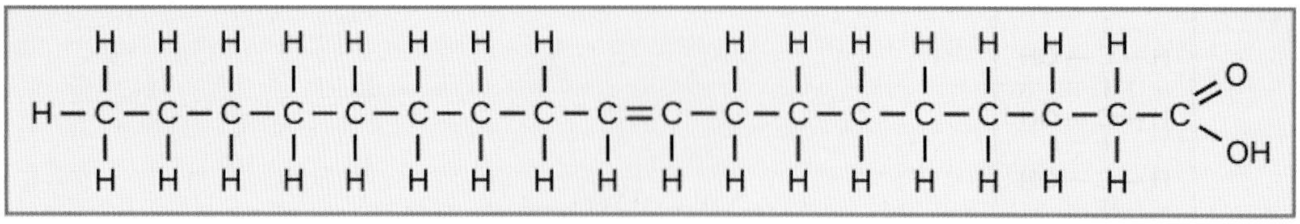

```
    H   H   H   H   H   H   H   H           H   H   H   H   H   H   H
    |   |   |   |   |   |   |   |           |   |   |   |   |   |   |     //O
H — C — C — C — C — C — C — C — C — C = C — C — C — C — C — C — C — C — C
    |   |   |   |   |   |   |   |   |   |   |   |   |   |   |   |   |     \
    H   H   H   H   H   H   H   H   H   H   H   H   H   H   H   H   H      OH
```

Figure 3.16 Oleic acid is a common unsaturated fatty acid.

Most unsaturated fats are liquid at room temperature and are called oils. If there is one double bond in the molecule, then it is known as a monounsaturated fat (e.g., olive oil), and if there is more than one double bond, then it is known as a polyunsaturated fat (e.g., canola oil).

When a fatty acid has no double bonds, it is known as a saturated fatty acid because no more hydrogen may be added to the carbon atoms of the chain. A fat may contain similar or different fatty acids attached to glycerol. Long straight fatty acids with single bonds tend to get packed tightly and are solid at room temperature. Animal fats with stearic acid and palmitic acid (common in meat) and the fat with butyric acid (common in butter) are examples of saturated fats. Mammals store fats in specialized cells called adipocytes, where globules of fat occupy most of the cell's volume. In plants, fat or oil is stored in many seeds and is used as a source of energy during seedling development. Unsaturated fats or oils are usually of plant origin and contain *cis* unsaturated fatty acids. *Cis* and *trans* indicate the configuration of the molecule around the double bond. If hydrogens are present in the same plane, it is referred to as a cis fat; if the hydrogen atoms are on two different planes, it is referred to as a **trans fat**. The *cis* double bond causes a bend or a "kink" that prevents the fatty acids from packing tightly, keeping them liquid at room temperature (Figure 3.17). Olive oil, corn oil, canola oil, and cod liver oil are examples of unsaturated fats. Unsaturated fats help to lower blood cholesterol levels whereas saturated fats contribute to plaque formation in the arteries.

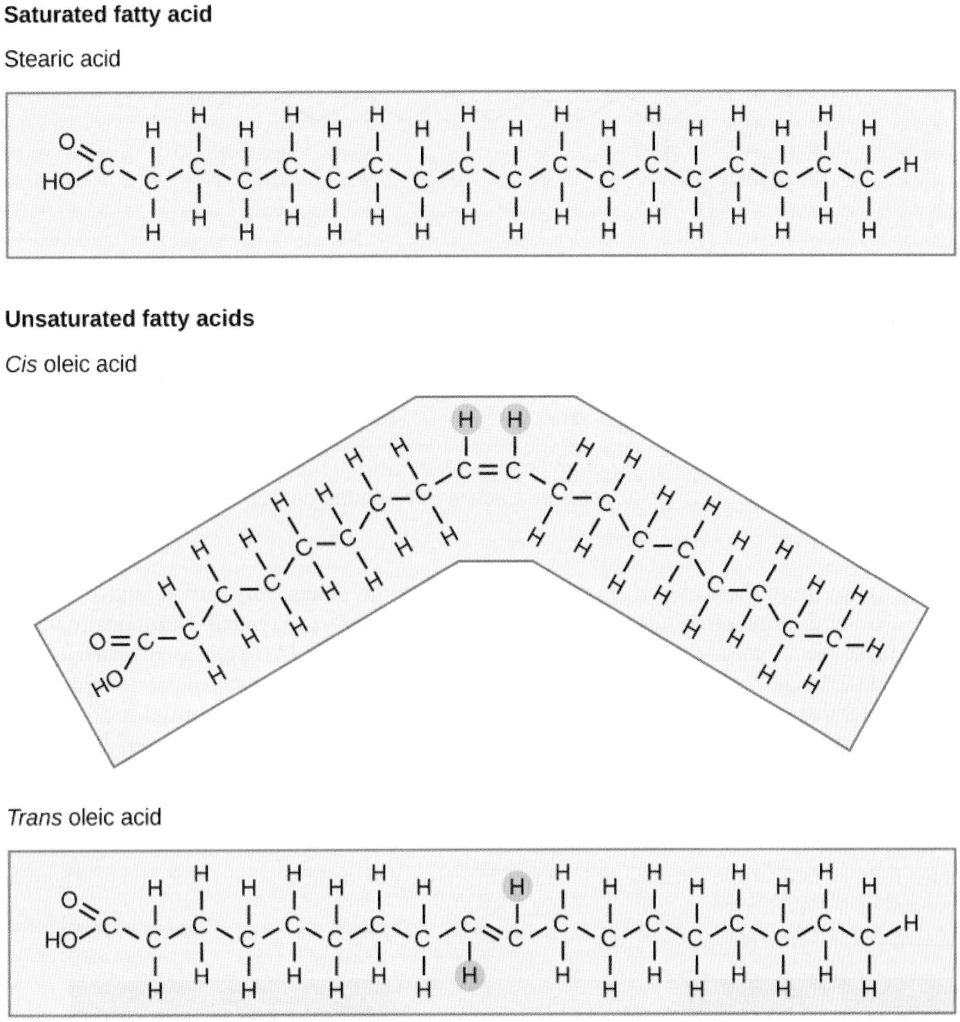

Saturated fatty acid

Stearic acid

Unsaturated fatty acids

Cis oleic acid

Trans oleic acid

Figure 3.17 Saturated fatty acids have hydrocarbon chains connected by single bonds only. Unsaturated fatty acids have one or more double bonds. Each double bond may be in a *cis* or *trans* configuration. In the *cis* configuration, both hydrogens are on the same side of the hydrocarbon chain. In the *trans* configuration, the hydrogens are on opposite sides. A *cis* double bond causes a kink in the chain.

Trans Fats

In the food industry, oils are artificially hydrogenated to make them semi-solid and of a consistency desirable for many processed food products. Simply speaking, hydrogen gas is bubbled through oils to solidify them. During this hydrogenation process, double bonds of the *cis*- conformation in the hydrocarbon chain may be converted to double bonds in the trans-conformation.

Margarine, some types of peanut butter, and shortening are examples of artificially hydrogenated trans fats. Recent studies have shown that an increase in trans fats in the human diet may lead to an increase in levels of low-density lipoproteins (LDL), or "bad" cholesterol, which in turn may lead to plaque deposition in the arteries, resulting in heart disease. Many fast food restaurants have recently banned the use of trans fats, and food labels are required to display the trans fat content.

Omega Fatty Acids

Essential fatty acids are fatty acids required but not synthesized by the human body. Consequently, they have to be supplemented through ingestion via the diet. **Omega**-3 fatty acids (like that shown in Figure 3.18) fall into this category and are one of only two known for humans (the other being omega-6 fatty acid). These are polyunsaturated fatty acids and are called omega-3 because the third carbon from the end of the hydrocarbon chain is connected to its neighboring carbon by a double bond.

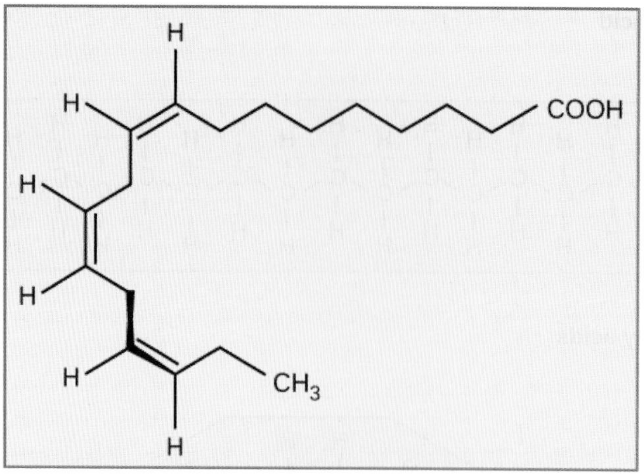

Figure 3.18 Alpha-linolenic acid is an example of an omega-3 fatty acid. It has three *cis* double bonds and, as a result, a curved shape. For clarity, the carbons are not shown. Each singly bonded carbon has two hydrogens associated with it, also not shown.

The farthest carbon away from the carboxyl group is numbered as the omega (ω) carbon, and if the double bond is between the third and fourth carbon from that end, it is known as an omega-3 fatty acid. Nutritionally important because the body does not make them, omega-3 fatty acids include alpha-linoleic acid (ALA), eicosapentaenoic acid (EPA), and docosahexaenoic acid (DHA), all of which are polyunsaturated. Salmon, trout, and tuna are good sources of omega-3 fatty acids. Research indicates that omega-3 fatty acids reduce the risk of sudden death from heart attacks, reduce triglycerides in the blood, lower blood pressure, and prevent thrombosis by inhibiting blood clotting. They also reduce inflammation, and may help reduce the risk of some cancers in animals.

Like carbohydrates, fats have received a lot of bad publicity. It is true that eating an excess of fried foods and other “fatty” foods leads to weight gain. However, fats do have important functions. Many vitamins are fat soluble, and fats serve as a long-term storage form of fatty acids: a source of energy. They also provide insulation for the body. Therefore, “healthy” fats in moderate amounts should be consumed on a regular basis.

science practices CONNECTION for AP® Courses

Think About It

Explain why trans fats have been banned from some restaurants. How are trans fats made, and what effect does a simple chemical change have on the properties of the lipid?

Waxes

Wax covers the feathers of some aquatic birds and the leaf surfaces of some plants. Because of the hydrophobic nature of waxes, they prevent water from sticking on the surface (Figure 3.19). Waxes are made up of long fatty acid chains esterified to long-chain alcohols.

Figure 3.19 Waxy coverings on some leaves are made of lipids. (credit: Roger Griffith)

Phospholipids

Phospholipids are major constituents of the plasma membrane, the outermost layer of all living cells. Like fats, they are composed of fatty acid chains attached to a glycerol or sphingosine backbone. Instead of three fatty acids attached as in triglycerides, however, there are two fatty acids forming diacylglycerol, and the third carbon of the glycerol backbone is occupied by a modified phosphate group (Figure 3.20). A phosphate group alone attached to a diaglycerol does not qualify as a phospholipid; it is phosphatidate (diacylglycerol 3-phosphate), the precursor of phospholipids. The phosphate group is modified by an alcohol. Phosphatidylcholine and phosphatidylserine are two important phospholipids that are found in plasma membranes.

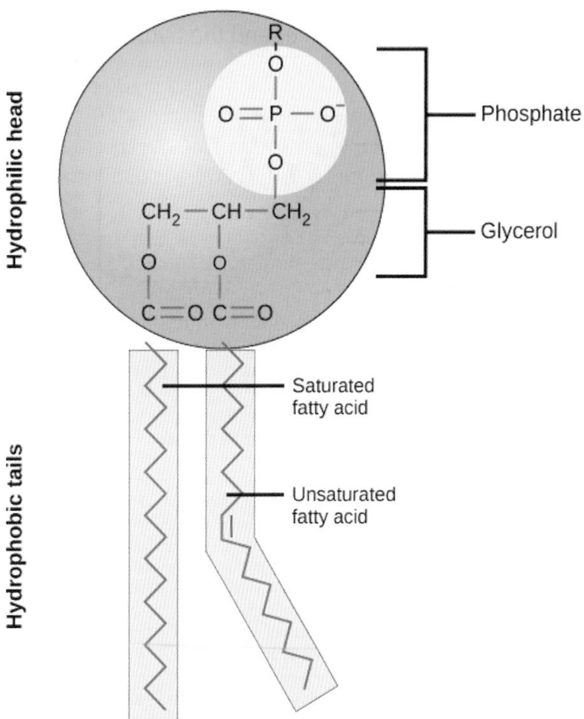

Figure 3.20 A phospholipid is a molecule with two fatty acids and a modified phosphate group attached to a glycerol backbone. The phosphate may be modified by the addition of charged or polar chemical groups.

A phospholipid is an amphipathic molecule, meaning it has a hydrophobic and a hydrophilic part. The fatty acid chains are hydrophobic and cannot interact with water, whereas the phosphate-containing group is hydrophilic and interacts with water (Figure 3.21).

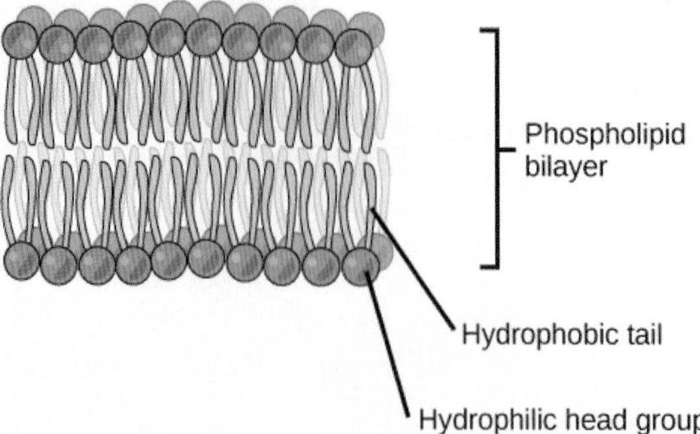

Figure 3.21 The phospholipid bilayer is the major component of all cellular membranes. The hydrophilic head groups of the phospholipids face the aqueous solution. The hydrophobic tails are sequestered in the middle of the bilayer.

The head is the hydrophilic part, and the tail contains the hydrophobic fatty acids. In a membrane, a bilayer of phospholipids forms the matrix of the structure, the fatty acid tails of phospholipids face inside, away from water, whereas the phosphate group faces the outside, aqueous side (Figure 3.21).

Phospholipids are responsible for the dynamic nature of the plasma membrane. If a drop of phospholipids is placed in water, it spontaneously forms a structure known as a micelle, where the hydrophilic phosphate heads face the outside and the fatty acids face the interior of this structure.

Fats are amphiphilic molecules. In other words, the long hydrocarbon tail is hydrophobic, and the glycerol part of the molecule is hydrophilic. When in water, fats will arrange themselves into a ball called a **micelle** so that the hydrophilic "heads" are on the outer surface, and the hydrophobic "tails" are on the inside where they are protected from the surrounding water.

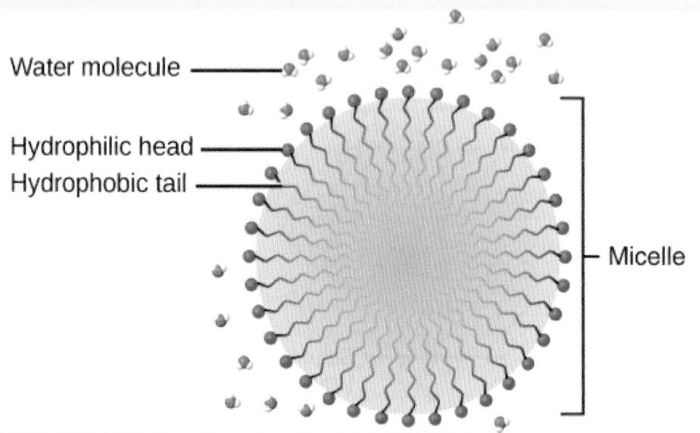

Figure 3.22

Steroids

Unlike the phospholipids and fats discussed earlier, **steroids** have a fused ring structure. Although they do not resemble the other lipids, they are grouped with them because they are also hydrophobic and insoluble in water. All steroids have four linked carbon rings and several of them, like cholesterol, have a short tail (Figure 3.23). Many steroids also have the –OH functional group, which puts them in the alcohol classification (sterols).

Cholesterol

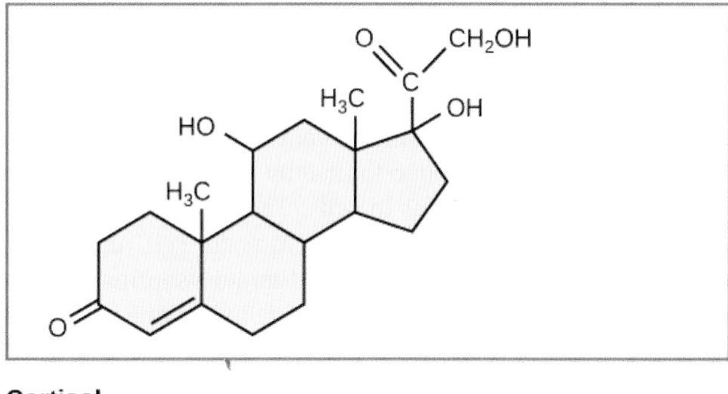

Cortisol

Figure 3.23 Steroids such as cholesterol and cortisol are composed of four fused hydrocarbon rings.

Cholesterol is the most common steroid. Cholesterol is mainly synthesized in the liver and is the precursor to many steroid hormones such as testosterone and estradiol, which are secreted by the gonads and endocrine glands. It is also the precursor to Vitamin D. Cholesterol is also the precursor of bile salts, which help in the emulsification of fats and their subsequent absorption by cells. Although cholesterol is often spoken of in negative terms by lay people, it is necessary for proper functioning of the body. It is a component of the plasma membrane of animal cells and is found within the phospholipid bilayer. Being the outermost structure in animal cells, the plasma membrane is responsible for the transport of materials and cellular recognition and it is involved in cell-to-cell communication.

For an additional perspective on lipids, explore the interactive animation "Biomolecules: The Lipids" (http://openstaxcollege.org/l/lipids) .

What is cholesterol specifically classified as?

a. a lipid

b. a phospholipid

c. a steroid

d. a wax

3.4 | Proteins

In this section, you will investigate the following questions:

- What are functions of proteins in cells and tissues?
- What is the relationship between amino acids and proteins?
- What are the four levels of protein organization?
- What is the relationship between protein shape and function?

Connection for AP® Courses

Proteins are long chains of different sequences of the 20 amino acids that each contain an amino group (-NH_2), a carboxyl group (-COOH), and a variable group. (Think of how many protein "words" can be made with 20 amino acid "letters"). Each amino acid is linked to its neighbor by a peptide bond formed by a dehydration reaction. A long chain of amino acids is known as a polypeptide. Proteins serve many functions in cells. They act as enzymes that catalyze chemical reactions, provide structural support, regulate the passage of substances across the cell membrane, protect against disease, and coordinate cell signaling pathways. Protein structure is organized at four levels: primary, secondary, tertiary, and quaternary. The primary structure is the unique sequence of amino acids. A change in just one amino acid can change protein structure and function. For example, sickle cell anemia results from just one amino acid substitution in a hemoglobin molecule consisting of 574 amino acids. The secondary structure consists of the local folding of the polypeptide by hydrogen bond formation; leading to the α helix and β pleated sheet conformations. In the tertiary structure, various interactions, e.g., hydrogen bonds, ionic bonds, disulfide linkages, and hydrophobic interactions between R groups, contribute to the folding of the polypeptide into different three-dimensional configurations. Most enzymes are of tertiary configuration. If a protein is denatured, loses its three-dimensional shape, it may no longer be functional. Environmental conditions such as temperature and pH can denature proteins. Some proteins, such as hemoglobin, are formed from several polypeptides, and the interactions of these subunits form the quaternary structure of proteins.

Information presented and the examples highlighted in the section, support concepts and Learning Objectives outlined in Big Idea 4 of the AP® Biology Curriculum Framework. The Learning Objectives listed in the Curriculum Framework provide a transparent foundation for the AP® Biology course, an inquiry-based laboratory experience, instructional activities, and AP® exam questions. A Learning Objective merges required content with one or more of the seven science practices.

Big Idea 4	Biological systems interact, and these systems and their interactions possess complex properties.
Enduring Understanding 4.A	Interactions within biological systems lead to complex properties.
Essential Knowledge	**4.A.1** The subcomponents of biological molecules and their sequence determine the properties of that molecule.
Science Practice	**7.1** The student can connect phenomena and models across spatial and temporal scales.
Learning Objective	**4.1** The student is able to explain the connection between the sequence and the subcomponents of a biological polymer and its properties.
Essential Knowledge	**4.A.1** The subcomponents of biological molecules and their sequence determine the properties of that molecule.
Science Practice	**1.3** The student can refine representations and models of natural or man-made phenomena and systems in the domain.

Learning Objective	**4.2** The student is able to refine representations and models to explain how the subcomponents of a biological polymer and their sequence determine the properties of that polymer.
Essential Knowledge	**4.A.1** The subcomponents of biological molecules and their sequence determine the properties of that molecule.
Science Practice	**6.1** The student can justify claims with evidence.
Science Practice	**6.4** The student can make claims and predictions about natural phenomena based on scientific theories and models.
Learning Objective	**4.3** The student is able to use models to predict and justify that changes in the subcomponents of a biological polymer affect the functionality of the molecules.

The Science Practice Challenge Questions contain additional test questions for this section that will help you prepare for the AP exam. These questions address the following standards:
[APLO 1.14] [APLO 2.12] [APLO 4.1] [APLO 4.3][APLO 4.15][APLO 4.22]

Types and Functions of Proteins

Proteins are one of the most abundant organic molecules in living systems and have the most diverse range of functions of all macromolecules. Proteins may be structural, regulatory, contractile, or protective; they may serve in transport, storage, or membranes; or they may be toxins or enzymes. Each cell in a living system may contain thousands of proteins, each with a unique function. Their structures, like their functions, vary greatly. They are all, however, polymers of amino acids, arranged in a linear sequence.

Enzymes, which are produced by living cells, are catalysts in biochemical reactions (like digestion) and are usually complex or conjugated proteins. Each enzyme is specific for the substrate (a reactant that binds to an enzyme) it acts on. The enzyme may help in breakdown, rearrangement, or synthesis reactions. Enzymes that break down their substrates are called catabolic enzymes, enzymes that build more complex molecules from their substrates are called anabolic enzymes, and enzymes that affect the rate of reaction are called catalytic enzymes. It should be noted that all enzymes increase the rate of reaction and, therefore, are considered to be organic catalysts. An example of an enzyme is salivary amylase, which hydrolyzes its substrate amylose, a component of starch.

Hormones are chemical-signaling molecules, usually small proteins or steroids, secreted by endocrine cells that act to control or regulate specific physiological processes, including growth, development, metabolism, and reproduction. For example, insulin is a protein hormone that helps to regulate the blood glucose level. The primary types and functions of proteins are listed in Table 3.1.

Protein Types and Functions

Type	Examples	Functions
Digestive Enzymes	Amylase, lipase, pepsin, trypsin	Help in digestion of food by catabolizing nutrients into monomeric units
Transport	Hemoglobin, albumin	Carry substances in the blood or lymph throughout the body
Structural	Actin, tubulin, keratin	Construct different structures, like the cytoskeleton
Hormones	Insulin, thyroxine	Coordinate the activity of different body systems
Defense	Immunoglobulins	Protect the body from foreign pathogens
Contractile	Actin, myosin	Effect muscle contraction
Storage	Legume storage proteins, egg white (albumin)	Provide nourishment in early development of the embryo and the seedling

Table 3.1

Proteins have different shapes and molecular weights; some proteins are globular in shape whereas others are fibrous in nature. For example, hemoglobin is a globular protein, but collagen, found in our skin, is a fibrous protein. Protein shape is critical to its function, and this shape is maintained by many different types of chemical bonds. Changes in temperature, pH, and exposure to chemicals may lead to permanent changes in the shape of the protein, leading to loss of function, known as **denaturation**. All proteins are made up of different arrangements of the most common 20 types of amino acids.

Amino Acids

Amino acids are the monomers that make up proteins. Each amino acid has the same fundamental structure, which consists of a central carbon atom, also known as the alpha (α) carbon, bonded to an amino group (NH_2), a carboxyl group (COOH), and to a hydrogen atom. Every amino acid also has another atom or group of atoms bonded to the central atom known as the R group (Figure 3.24).

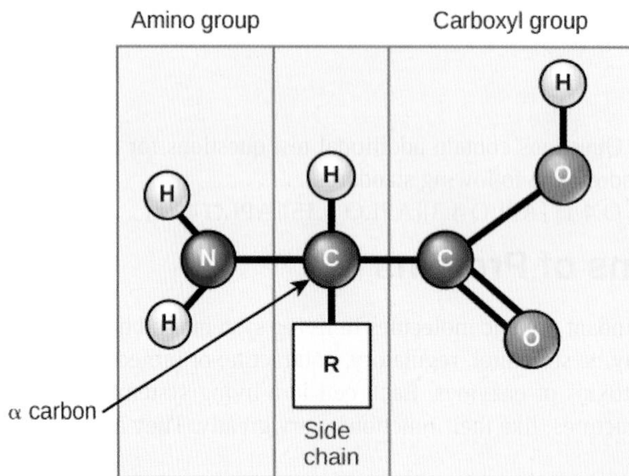

Figure 3.24 Amino acids have a central asymmetric carbon to which an amino group, a carboxyl group, a hydrogen atom, and a side chain (R group) are attached.

The name "amino acid" is derived from the fact that they contain both amino group and carboxyl-acid-group in their basic structure. As mentioned, there are 20 common amino acids present in proteins. Nine of these are considered essential amino acids in humans because the human body cannot produce them and they are obtained from the diet. For each amino acid, the R group (or side chain) is different (Figure 3.25).

visual CONNECTION

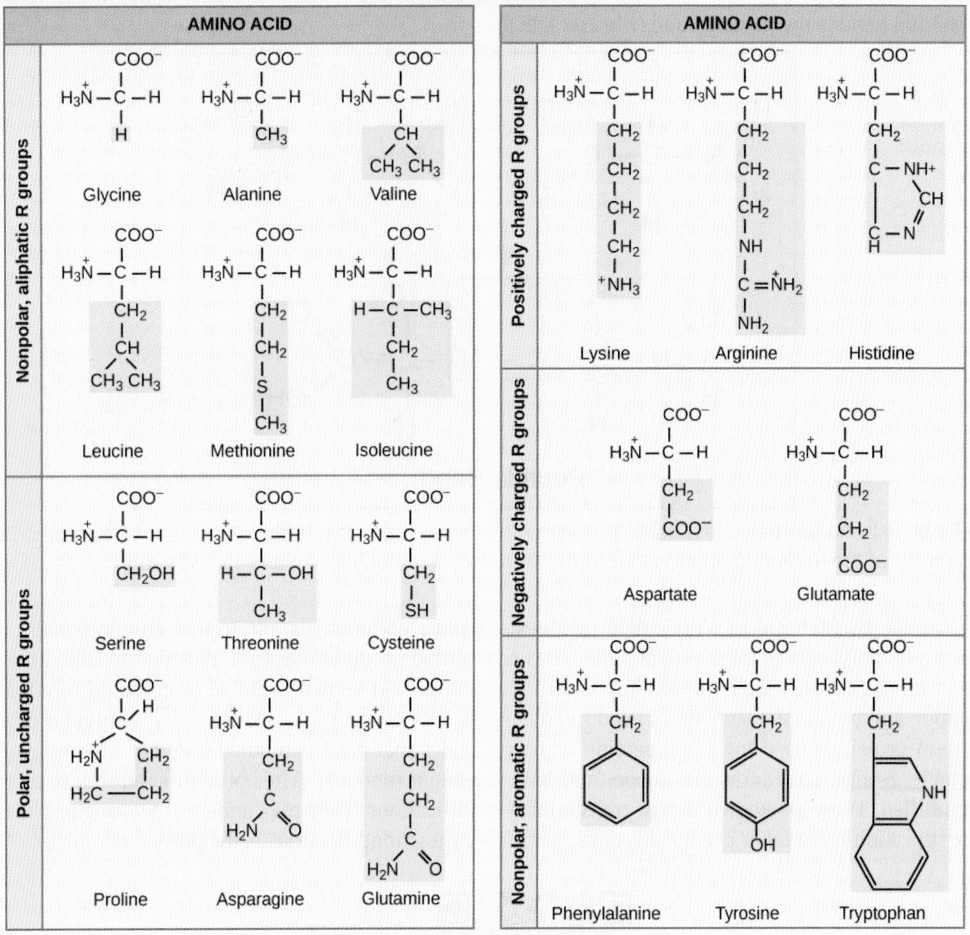

Figure 3.25 There are typically 20 common amino acids commonly found in proteins, each with a different R group (variant group) that determines its chemical nature.

Which categories of amino acid would you expect to find on the surface of a soluble protein, and which would you expect to find in the interior?

a. Polar and charged amino acids will be found on the surface. Non-polar amino acids will be found in the interior.

b. Polar and charged amino acids will be found in the interior. Non-polar amino acids will be found on the surface.

c. Non-polar and uncharged proteins will be found on the surface as well as in the interior.

The chemical nature of the side chain determines the nature of the amino acid (that is, whether it is acidic, basic, polar, or nonpolar). For example, the amino acid glycine has a hydrogen atom as the R group. Amino acids such as valine, methionine, and alanine are nonpolar or hydrophobic in nature, while amino acids such as serine, threonine, and cysteine are polar and have hydrophilic side chains. The side chains of lysine and arginine are positively charged, and therefore these amino acids are also known as basic amino acids. Proline has an R group that is linked to the amino group, forming a ring-like structure. Proline is an exception to the standard structure of an animo acid since its amino group is not separate from the side chain (Figure 3.25).

Amino acids are represented by a single upper case letter or a three-letter abbreviation. For example, valine is known by the letter V or the three-letter symbol val. Just as some fatty acids are essential to a diet, some amino acids are necessary as well. They are known as essential amino acids, and in humans they include isoleucine, leucine, and cysteine. Essential amino acids refer to those necessary for construction of proteins in the body, although not produced by the body; which amino acids are essential varies from organism to organism.

The sequence and the number of amino acids ultimately determine the protein's shape, size, and function. Each amino acid is attached to another amino acid by a covalent bond, known as a **peptide bond**, which is formed by a dehydration reaction. The carboxyl group of one amino acid and the amino group of the incoming amino acid combine, releasing a molecule of water. The resulting bond is the peptide bond (Figure 3.26).

Figure 3.26 Peptide bond formation is a dehydration synthesis reaction. The carboxyl group of one amino acid is linked to the amino group of the incoming amino acid. In the process, a molecule of water is released.

The products formed by such linkages are called peptides. As more amino acids join to this growing chain, the resulting chain is known as a polypeptide. Each polypeptide has a free amino group at one end. This end is called the N terminal, or the amino terminal, and the other end has a free carboxyl group, also known as the C or carboxyl terminal. While the terms polypeptide and protein are sometimes used interchangeably, a polypeptide is technically a polymer of amino acids, whereas the term protein is used for a polypeptide or polypeptides that have combined together, often have bound non-peptide prosthetic groups, have a distinct shape, and have a unique function. After protein synthesis (translation), most proteins are modified. These are known as post-translational modifications. They may undergo cleavage or phosphorylation, or may require the addition of other chemical groups. Only after these modifications is the protein completely functional.

Click through the steps of protein synthesis in this interactive tutorial (http://openstaxcollege.org/l/protein_synth) .

Why is the process of protein synthesis critical to life?

a. Protein is the body's preferred source for energy for rapid energy production.

b. Protein is stored in the liver and muscles to supply energy for future use.

c. Protein is required for tissue formation and constitutes hormones and enzymes.

d. Proteins are required for the absorption of all fat soluble vitamins.

evolution CONNECTION

Cytochrome c is an important component of the electron transport chain, a part of cellular respiration, and it is normally found in the cellular organelle, the mitochondrion. This protein has a heme prosthetic group, and the central ion of the heme gets alternately reduced and oxidized during electron transfer. Because this essential protein's role in producing cellular energy is crucial, it has changed very little over millions of years. Protein sequencing has shown that there is a considerable amount of cytochrome c amino acid sequence homology among different species; in other words, evolutionary kinship can be assessed by measuring the similarities or differences among various species' DNA or protein sequences.

Scientists have determined that human cytochrome c contains 104 amino acids. For each cytochrome c molecule from different organisms that has been sequenced to date, 37 of these amino acids appear in the same position in all samples of cytochrome c. This indicates that there may have been a common ancestor. On comparing the human and chimpanzee protein sequences, no sequence difference was found. When human and rhesus monkey sequences were compared, the single difference found was in one amino acid. In another comparison, human to yeast sequencing shows a difference in the 44th position.

The protein sequence of cytochrome c from chimpanzees and humans is identical. The protein sequence of cytochrome c from rhesus monkeys differs from the human sequence by one amino acid. What do these comparisons suggest?

a. Rhesus monkeys are more closely related to humans than chimpanzees.
b. Chimpanzees are more closely related to rhesus monkeys than to humans.
c. Humans are related to chimpanzees, but are not related to rhesus monkeys.
d. Chimpanzees are more closely related to humans than rhesus monkeys.

Protein Structure

As discussed earlier, the shape of a protein is critical to its function. For example, an enzyme can bind to a specific substrate at a site known as the active site. If this active site is altered because of local changes or changes in overall protein structure, the enzyme may be unable to bind to the substrate. To understand how the protein gets its final shape or conformation, we need to understand the four levels of protein structure: primary, secondary, tertiary, and quaternary.

Primary Structure

The unique sequence of amino acids in a polypeptide chain is its **primary structure**. For example, the pancreatic hormone insulin has two polypeptide chains, A and B, and they are linked together by disulfide bonds. The N terminal amino acid of the A chain is glycine, whereas the C terminal amino acid is asparagine (Figure 3.27). The sequences of amino acids in the A and B chains are unique to insulin.

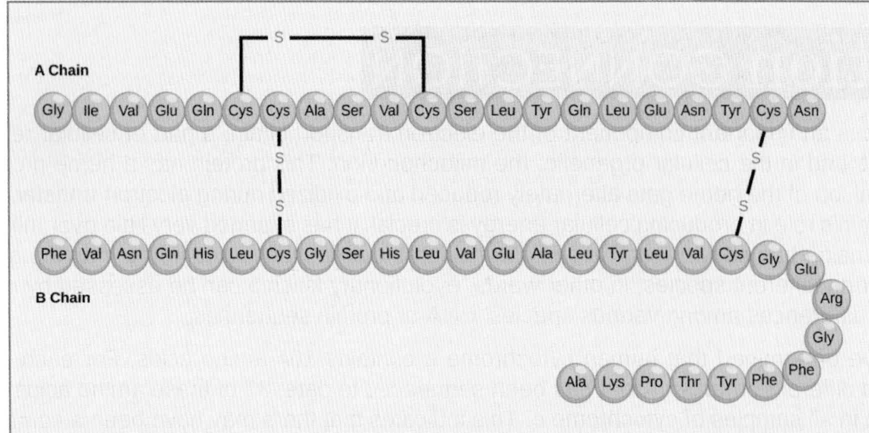

Figure 3.27 Bovine serum insulin is a protein hormone made of two peptide chains, A (21 amino acids long) and B (30 amino acids long). In each chain, primary structure is indicated by three-letter abbreviations that represent the names of the amino acids in the order they are present. The amino acid cysteine (cys) has a sulfhydryl (SH) group as a side chain. Two sulfhydryl groups can react in the presence of oxygen to form a disulfide (S-S) bond. Two disulfide bonds connect the A and B chains together, and a third helps the A chain fold into the correct shape. Note that all disulfide bonds are the same length, but are drawn different sizes for clarity.

The unique sequence for every protein is ultimately determined by the gene encoding the protein. A change in nucleotide sequence of the gene's coding region may lead to a different amino acid being added to the growing polypeptide chain, causing a change in protein structure and function. In sickle cell anemia, the hemoglobin β chain (a small portion of which is shown in Figure 3.28) has a single amino acid substitution, causing a change in protein structure and function. Specifically, the amino acid glutamic acid is substituted by valine in the β chain. What is most remarkable to consider is that a hemoglobin molecule is made up of two alpha chains and two beta chains that each consist of about 150 amino acids. The molecule, therefore, has about 600 amino acids. The structural difference between a normal hemoglobin molecule and a sickle cell molecule—which dramatically decreases life expectancy—is a single amino acid of the 600. What is even more remarkable is that those 600 amino acids are encoded by three nucleotides each, and the mutation is caused by a single base change (point mutation), 1 in 1800 bases.

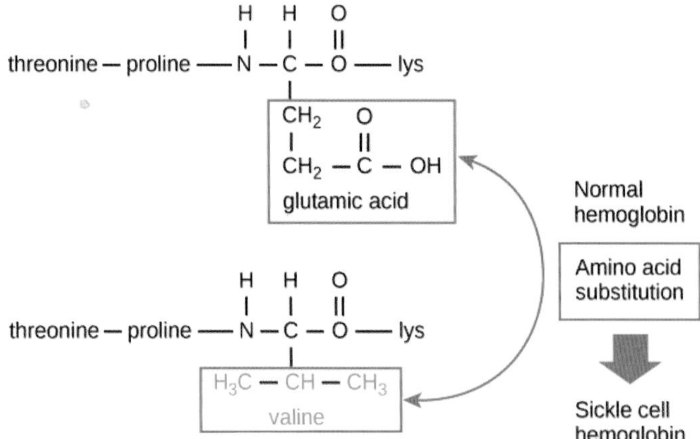

Figure 3.28 The beta chain of hemoglobin is 147 residues in length, yet a single amino acid substitution leads to sickle cell anemia. In normal hemoglobin, the amino acid at position seven is glutamate. In sickle cell hemoglobin, this glutamate is replaced by a valine.

Because of this change of one amino acid in the chain, hemoglobin molecules form long fibers that distort the biconcave, or disc-shaped, red blood cells and cause them to assume a crescent or "sickle" shape, which clogs blood vessels (Figure 3.29). This can lead to myriad serious health problems such as breathlessness, dizziness, headaches, and abdominal pain for those affected by this disease.

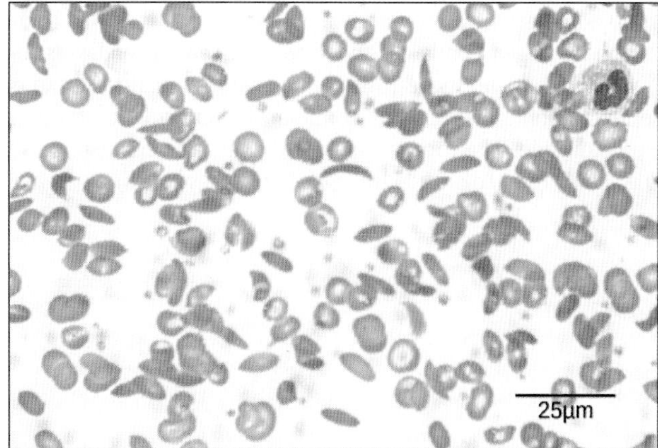

Figure 3.29 In this blood smear, visualized at 535x magnification using bright field microscopy, sickle cells are crescent shaped, while normal cells are disc-shaped. (credit: modification of work by Ed Uthman; scale-bar data from Matt Russell)

Secondary Structure

The local folding of the polypeptide in some regions gives rise to the **secondary structure** of the protein. The most common are the ***α*-helix** and ***β*-pleated sheet** structures (Figure 3.30). Both structures are held together by hydrogen bonds. In the *α*-helix structure, the hydrogen bonds form between the oxygen atom in the carbonyl group in one amino acid and another amino acid that is four amino acids farther along the chain.

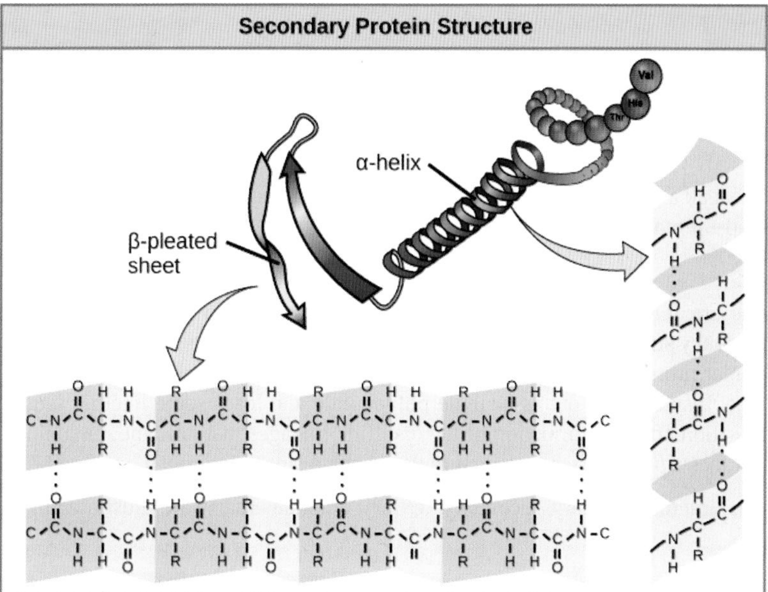

Figure 3.30 The *α*-helix and *β*-pleated sheet are secondary structures of proteins that form because of hydrogen bonding between carbonyl and amino groups in the peptide backbone. Certain amino acids have a propensity to form an *α*-helix, while others have a propensity to form a *β*-pleated sheet.

Every helical turn in an alpha helix has 3.6 amino acid residues. The R groups (the variant groups) of the polypeptide protrude out from the *α*-helix chain. In the *β*-pleated sheet, the "pleats" are formed by hydrogen bonding between atoms on the backbone of the polypeptide chain. The R groups are attached to the carbons and extend above and below the folds of the pleat. The pleated segments align parallel or antiparallel to each other, and hydrogen bonds form between the partially positive nitrogen atom in the amino group and the partially negative oxygen atom in the carbonyl group of the peptide backbone. The *α*-helix and *β*-pleated sheet structures are found in most globular and fibrous proteins and they play an important structural role.

Tertiary Structure

The unique three-dimensional structure of a polypeptide is its **tertiary structure** (Figure 3.31). This structure is in part due to chemical interactions at work on the polypeptide chain. Primarily, the interactions among R groups creates the complex three-dimensional tertiary structure of a protein. The nature of the R groups found in the amino acids involved can counteract the formation of the hydrogen bonds described for standard secondary structures. For example, R groups with like charges are repelled by each other and those with unlike charges are attracted to each other (ionic bonds). When protein folding takes place, the hydrophobic R groups of nonpolar amino acids lie in the interior of the protein, whereas the hydrophilic R groups lie on the outside. The former types of interactions are also known as hydrophobic interactions. Interaction between cysteine side chains forms disulfide linkages in the presence of oxygen, the only covalent bond forming during protein folding.

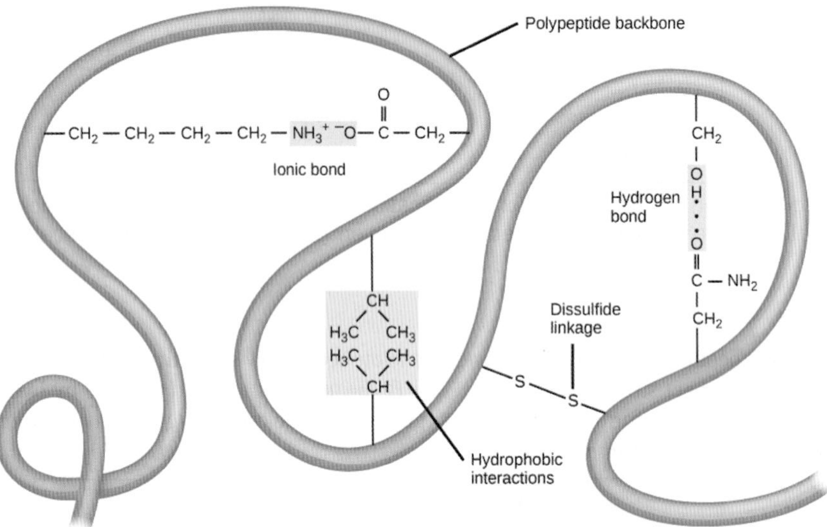

Figure 3.31 The tertiary structure of proteins is determined by a variety of chemical interactions. These include hydrophobic interactions, ionic bonding, hydrogen bonding and disulfide linkages.

All of these interactions, weak and strong, determine the final three-dimensional shape of the protein. When a protein loses its three-dimensional shape, it may no longer be functional.

Quaternary Structure

In nature, some proteins are formed from several polypeptides, also known as subunits, and the interaction of these subunits forms the **quaternary structure**. Weak interactions between the subunits help to stabilize the overall structure. For example, insulin (a globular protein) has a combination of hydrogen bonds and disulfide bonds that cause it to be mostly clumped into a ball shape. Insulin starts out as a single polypeptide and loses some internal sequences in the presence of post-translational modification after the formation of the disulfide linkages that hold the remaining chains together. Silk (a fibrous protein), however, has a β-pleated sheet structure that is the result of hydrogen bonding between different chains.

The four levels of protein structure (primary, secondary, tertiary, and quaternary) are illustrated in Figure 3.32.

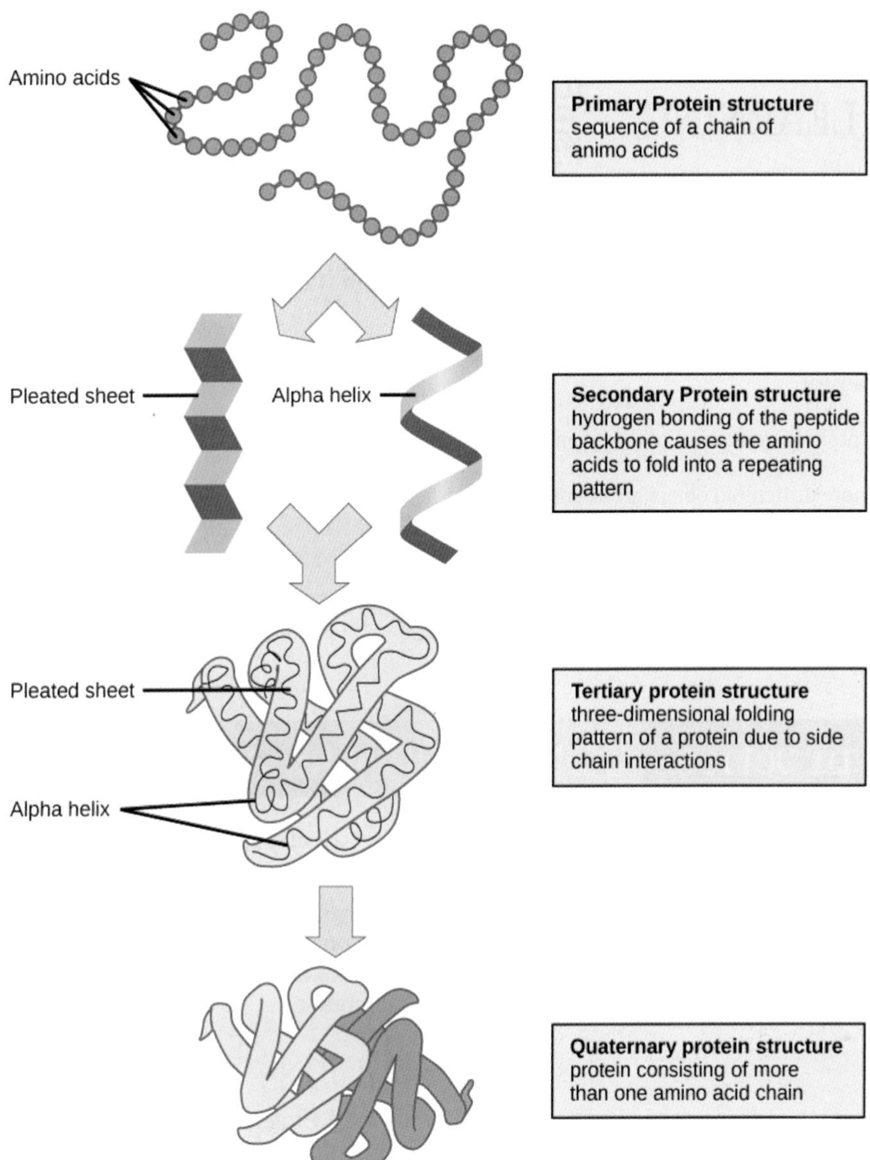
Amino acids
Primary Protein structure
sequence of a chain of animo acids
Pleated sheet
Alpha helix
Secondary Protein structure
hydrogen bonding of the peptide backbone causes the amino acids to fold into a repeating pattern
Pleated sheet
Alpha helix
Tertiary protein structure
three-dimensional folding pattern of a protein due to side chain interactions
Quaternary protein structure
protein consisting of more than one amino acid chain

Figure 3.32 The four levels of protein structure can be observed in these illustrations. (credit: modification of work by National Human Genome Research Institute)

Denaturation and Protein Folding

Each protein has its own unique sequence and shape that are held together by chemical interactions. If the protein is subject to changes in temperature, changes in pH, or exposure to chemicals, the protein structure may change, losing its shape without losing its primary sequence in what is known as denaturation. Denaturation is often reversible because the primary structure of the polypeptide is conserved in the process if the denaturing agent is removed, allowing the protein to resume its function. Sometimes denaturation is irreversible, leading to loss of function. One example of irreversible protein denaturation is when an egg is fried. The albumin protein in the liquid egg white is denatured when placed in a hot pan. Not all proteins are denatured at high temperatures; for instance, bacteria that survive in hot springs have proteins that function at temperatures close to boiling. The stomach is also very acidic, has a low pH, and denatures proteins as part of the digestion process; however, the digestive enzymes of the stomach retain their activity under these conditions.

Protein folding is critical to its function. It was originally thought that the proteins themselves were responsible for the folding process. Only recently was it found that often they receive assistance in the folding process from protein helpers known as **chaperones** (or chaperonins) that associate with the target protein during the folding process. They act by preventing aggregation of polypeptides that make up the complete protein structure, and they disassociate from the protein once the target protein is folded.

For an additional perspective on proteins, view this animation (http://openstaxcollege.org/l/proteins) called "Biomolecules: The Proteins."

Vegans are people who do not consume any animal products in their diet. Why do vegans need to pay special attention to the protein they eat?

a. Plant proteins contain all of the essential as well as non-essential amino acids.

b. It is more difficult to obtain all essential amino acids from single plant sources.

c. Plant proteins contain only non-essential amino acids.

d. Plants proteins do not have all of the non-essential amino acids, but do contain the essential amino acids.

science practices CONNECTION for AP® Courses

Think About It

- Predict what happens if even one amino acid is substituted for another in a polypeptide and provide a specific example.
- What categories of amino acids would you expect to find on the surface of a soluble protein, and which would you expect to find in the interior? What distribution of amino acids would you expect to find in a protein embedded in a lipid bilayer of a plasma cell membrane?

Activity

Folding is an important property of proteins, especially enzymes. Proteins have a narrow range of conditions in which they fold properly; outside that range, proteins can unfold (denature) and often cannot refold and become functional again. Investigate one disease that results from improper folding of a protein. Describe causes of the unfolding and consequences to the molecular structure of the polypeptide that result in the disease.

3.5 | Nucleic Acids

In this section, you will investigate the following questions:

- What are the two types of nucleic acid?
- What is the structure and role of DNA?
- What is the structure and roles of RNA?

Connection for AP® Courses

Nucleic acids (DNA and RNA) comprise the fourth group of biological macromolecules and contain phosphorus (P) in addition to carbon, hydrogen, oxygen, and nitrogen. Conserved through evolution in all organisms, nucleic acids store and transmit hereditary information. As will be explored in more detail in Chapters 14-17, DNA contains the instructions for the synthesis of proteins by dictating the sequences of amino acids in polypeptides through processes known as transcription and translation. Nucleic acids are made up of nucleotides; in turn, each nucleotide consists of a pentose sugar (deoxyribose in DNA and ribose in RNA), a nitrogenous base (adenine, cytosine, guanine, and thymine or uracil), and a phosphate group. DNA carries the genetic blueprint of the cell that is passed from parent to offspring via cell division. DNA has a double-helical structure with the two strands running in opposite directions (antiparallel), connected by hydrogen bonds and complementary to each other. In DNA, purines pair with pyrimidines: adenine pairs with thymine (A-T), and cytosine pairs with guanine (C-G). In RNA, uracil replaces thymine to pair with adenine (U-A). RNA also differs from DNA in that it is single-stranded and has many forms, such as messenger RNA (mRNA), ribosomal RNA (rRNA), and transfer RNA (tRNA) that all participate in the synthesis of proteins. MicroRNAs (miRNAs) regulate the use of mRNA. The flow of genetic information is usually DNA → RNA → protein, also known as the Central Dogma of Life.

Information presented and the examples highlighted in the section support concepts and Learning Objectives outlined in Big Idea 3 and Big Idea 4 of the AP® Biology Curriculum Framework. The Learning Objectives listed in the Curriculum Framework provide a transparent foundation for the AP® Biology course, an inquiry-based laboratory experience, instructional activities, and AP® Exam questions. A Learning Objective merges required content with one or more of the seven Science Practices.

Big Idea 3	Living systems store, retrieve, transmit and respond to information essential to life processes.
Enduring Understanding 3.A	Heritable information provides for continuity of life.
Essential Knowledge	**3.A.1** DNA, and in some cases RNA, is the primary source of heritable information.
Science Practice	**6.5** The student can evaluate alternative scientific explanations.
Learning Objective	**3.1** The student is able to construct scientific explanations that use the structures and mechanisms of DNA and RNA to support the claim that DNA and, in some cases, that RNA are the primary sources of heritable information.
Essential Knowledge	**3.A.1** DNA, and in some cases RNA, is the primary source of heritable information.
Science Practice	**6.4** The student can make claims and predictions about natural phenomena based on scientific theories and models.
Learning Objective	**3.6** The student can predict how a change in a specific DNA or RNA sequence can result in changes in gene expression.
Big Idea 4	Biological systems interact, and these systems and their interactions possess complex properties.
Enduring Understanding 4.A	Interactions within biological systems lead to complex properties.
Essential Knowledge	**4.A.1** The subcomponents of biological molecules and their sequence determine the properties of that molecule.
Science Practice	**7.1** The student can connect phenomena and models across spatial and temporal scales.
Learning Objective	**4.1** The student is able to explain the connection between the sequence and the subcomponents of a biological polymer and its properties.
Essential Knowledge	**4.A.1** The subcomponents of biological molecules and their sequence determine the properties of that molecule.

Science Practice	**1.3** The student can refine representations and models of natural or man-made phenomena and systems in the domain.
Learning Objective	**4.2** The student is able to refine representations and models to explain how the subcomponents of a biological polymer and their sequence determine the properties of that polymer.
Essential Knowledge	**4.A.1** The subcomponents of biological molecules and their sequence determine the properties of that molecule.
Science Practice	**6.1** The student can justify claims with evidence.
	6.4 The student can make claims and predictions about natural phenomena based on scientific theories and models.
Learning Objective	**4.3** The student is able to use models to predict and justify that changes in the subcomponents of a biological polymer affect the functionality of the molecules.

The Science Practice Challenge Questions contain additional test questions for this section that will help you prepare for the AP exam. These questions address the following standards:
[APLO 3.1] [APLO 4.17]

DNA and RNA

Nucleic acids are the most important macromolecules for the continuity of life. They carry the genetic blueprint of a cell and carry instructions for the functioning of the cell.

The two main types of nucleic acids are **deoxyribonucleic acid (DNA)** and **ribonucleic acid (RNA)**. DNA is the genetic material found in all living organisms, ranging from single-celled bacteria to multicellular mammals. It is found in the nucleus of eukaryotes and in the organelles, chloroplasts, and mitochondria. In prokaryotes, the DNA is not enclosed in a membranous envelope.

The entire genetic content of a cell is known as its genome, and the study of genomes is genomics. In eukaryotic cells but not in prokaryotes, DNA forms a complex with histone proteins to form chromatin, the substance of eukaryotic chromosomes. A chromosome may contain tens of thousands of genes. Many genes contain the information to make protein products; other genes code for RNA products. DNA controls all of the cellular activities by turning the genes "on" or "off."

The other type of nucleic acid, RNA, is mostly involved in protein synthesis. The DNA molecules never leave the nucleus but instead use an intermediary to communicate with the rest of the cell. This intermediary is the **messenger RNA (mRNA)**. Other types of RNA—like rRNA, tRNA, and microRNA—are involved in protein synthesis and its regulation.

DNA and RNA are made up of monomers known as **nucleotides**. The nucleotides combine with each other to form a **polynucleotide**, DNA or RNA. Each nucleotide is made up of three components: a nitrogenous base, a pentose (five-carbon) sugar, and a phosphate group (Figure 3.33). Each nitrogenous base in a nucleotide is attached to a sugar molecule, which is attached to one or more phosphate groups.

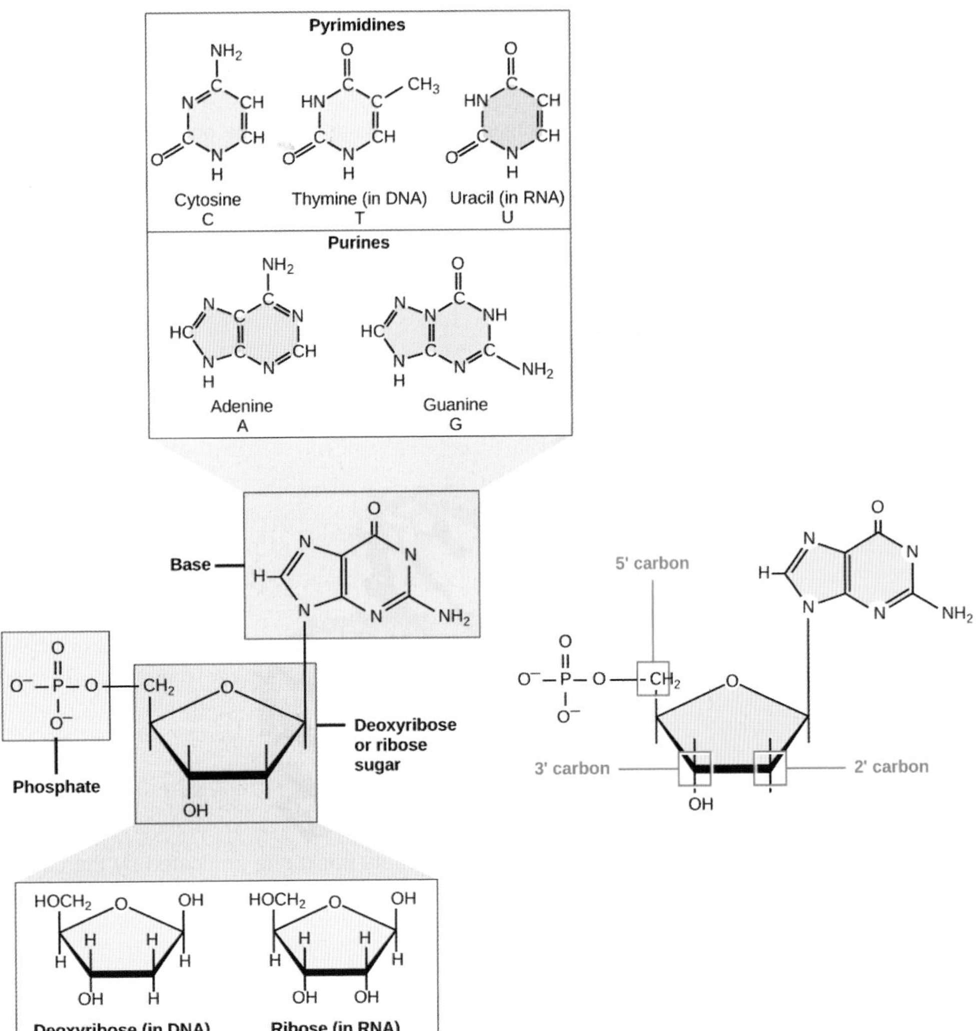

Figure 3.33 A nucleotide is made up of three components: a nitrogenous base, a pentose sugar, and one or more phosphate groups. Carbon residues in the pentose are numbered 1′ through 5′ (the prime distinguishes these residues from those in the base, which are numbered without using a prime notation). The base is attached to the 1′ position of the ribose, and the phosphate is attached to the 5′ position. When a polynucleotide is formed, the 5′ phosphate of the incoming nucleotide attaches to the 3′ hydroxyl group at the end of the growing chain. Two types of pentose are found in nucleotides, deoxyribose (found in DNA) and ribose (found in RNA). Deoxyribose is similar in structure to ribose, but it has an H instead of an OH at the 2′ position. Bases can be divided into two categories: purines and pyrimidines. Purines have a double ring structure, and pyrimidines have a single ring.

The nitrogenous bases, important components of nucleotides, are organic molecules and are so named because they contain carbon and nitrogen. They are bases because they contain an amino group that has the potential of binding an extra hydrogen, thus decreasing the hydrogen ion concentration in its environment, making it more basic. Each nucleotide in DNA contains one of four possible nitrogenous bases: adenine (A), guanine (G) cytosine (C), and thymine (T).

Adenine and guanine are classified as **purines**. The primary structure of a purine is two carbon-nitrogen rings. Cytosine, thymine, and uracil are classified as **pyrimidines** which have a single carbon-nitrogen ring as their primary structure (Figure 3.33). Each of these basic carbon-nitrogen rings has different functional groups attached to it. In molecular biology shorthand, the nitrogenous bases are simply known by their symbols A, T, G, C, and U. DNA contains A, T, G, and C whereas RNA contains A, U, G, and C.

The pentose sugar in DNA is deoxyribose, and in RNA, the sugar is ribose (Figure 3.33). The difference between the sugars is the presence of the hydroxyl group on the second carbon of the ribose and hydrogen on the second carbon of the deoxyribose. The carbon atoms of the sugar molecule are numbered as 1′, 2′, 3′, 4′, and 5′ (1′ is read as “one prime”). The phosphate residue is attached to the hydroxyl group of the 5′ carbon of one sugar and the hydroxyl group of the 3′ carbon of the sugar of the next nucleotide, which forms a 5′–3′ **phosphodiester** linkage. The phosphodiester linkage is not formed by simple dehydration reaction like the other linkages connecting monomers in macromolecules: its formation involves the removal of two phosphate groups. A polynucleotide may have thousands of such phosphodiester linkages.

DNA Double-Helix Structure

DNA has a double-helix structure (Figure 3.34). The sugar and phosphate lie on the outside of the helix, forming the backbone of the DNA. The nitrogenous bases are stacked in the interior, like the steps of a staircase, in pairs; the pairs are bound to each other by hydrogen bonds. Every base pair in the double helix is separated from the next base pair by 0.34 nm. The two strands of the helix run in opposite directions, meaning that the 5′ carbon end of one strand will face the 3′ carbon end of its matching strand. (This is referred to as antiparallel orientation and is important to DNA replication and in many nucleic acid interactions.)

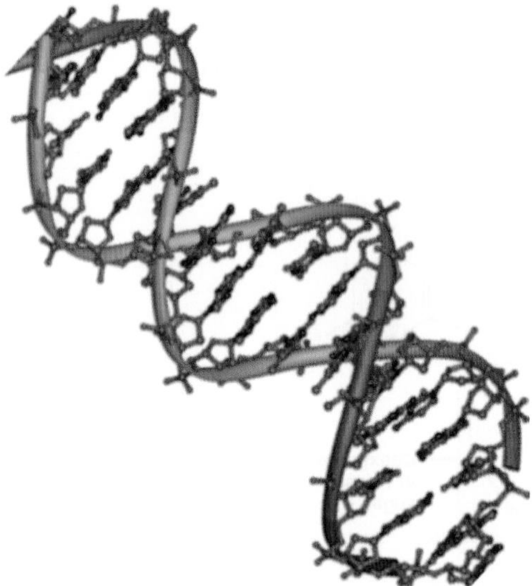

Figure 3.34 Native DNA is an antiparallel double helix. The phosphate backbone (indicated by the curvy lines) is on the outside, and the bases are on the inside. Each base from one strand interacts via hydrogen bonding with a base from the opposing strand. (credit: Jerome Walker/Dennis Myts)

Only certain types of base pairing are allowed. For example, a certain purine can only pair with a certain pyrimidine. This means A can pair with T, and G can pair with C, as shown in Figure 3.35. This is known as the base complementary rule. In other words, the DNA strands are complementary to each other. If the sequence of one strand is AATTGGCC, the complementary strand would have the sequence TTAACCGG. During DNA replication, each strand is copied, resulting in a daughter DNA double helix containing one parental DNA strand and a newly synthesized strand.

visual CONNECTION

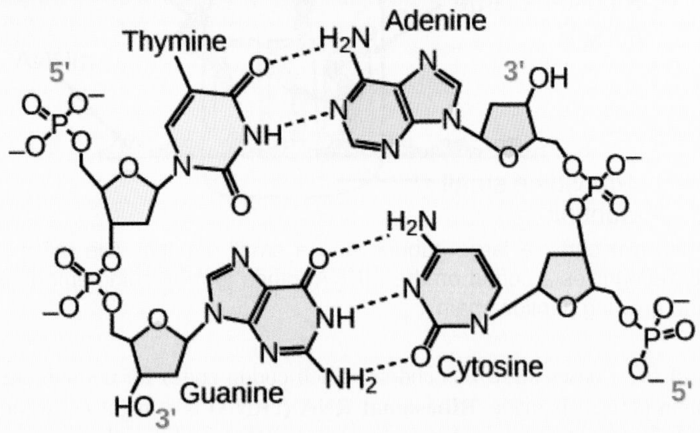

Figure 3.35 In a double stranded DNA molecule, the two strands run antiparallel to one another so that one strand runs 5′ to 3′ and the other 3′ to 5′. The phosphate backbone is located on the outside, and the bases are in the middle. Adenine forms hydrogen bonds (or base pairs) with thymine, and guanine base pairs with cytosine.

A mutation occurs, and cytosine is replaced with adenine. What impact do you think this will have on the DNA structure?

a. The DNA will normally pair its adenine with thymine, causing no change in the DNA structure.
b. The DNA will bulge in the places where cytosine is replaced by adenine.
c. The adenine substituted in the place of cytosine will get methylated and will not be transcribed further.
d. The DNA will cause another mutation to replace this incorrect DNA base.

RNA

Ribonucleic acid, or RNA, is mainly involved in the process of protein synthesis under the direction of DNA. RNA is usually single-stranded and is made of ribonucleotides that are linked by phosphodiester bonds. A ribonucleotide in the RNA chain contains ribose (the pentose sugar), one of the four nitrogenous bases (A, U, G, and C), and the phosphate group.

There are four major types of RNA: messenger RNA (mRNA), ribosomal RNA (rRNA), transfer RNA (tRNA), and microRNA (miRNA). The first, mRNA, carries the message from DNA, which controls all of the cellular activities in a cell. If a cell requires a certain protein to be synthesized, the gene for this product is turned "on" and the messenger RNA is synthesized in the nucleus. The RNA base sequence is complementary to the coding sequence of the DNA from which it has been copied. However, in RNA, the base T is absent and U is present instead. If the DNA strand has a sequence AATTGCGC, the sequence of the complementary RNA is UUAACGCG. In the cytoplasm, the mRNA interacts with ribosomes and other cellular machinery (Figure 3.36).

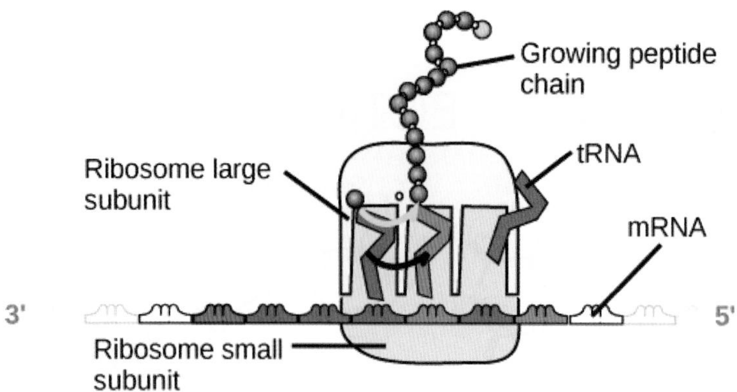

Figure 3.36 A ribosome has two parts: a large subunit and a small subunit. The mRNA sits in between the two subunits. A tRNA molecule recognizes a codon on the mRNA, binds to it by complementary base pairing, and adds the correct amino acid to the growing peptide chain.

The mRNA is read in sets of three bases known as codons. Each codon codes for a single amino acid. In this way, the mRNA is read and the protein product is made. **Ribosomal RNA (rRNA)** is a major constituent of ribosomes on which the mRNA binds. The rRNA ensures the proper alignment of the mRNA and the ribosomes; the rRNA of the ribosome also has an enzymatic activity (peptidyl transferase) and catalyzes the formation of the peptide bonds between two aligned amino acids. **Transfer RNA (tRNA)** is one of the smallest of the four types of RNA, usually 70–90 nucleotides long. It carries the correct amino acid to the site of protein synthesis. It is the base pairing between the tRNA and mRNA that allows for the correct amino acid to be inserted in the polypeptide chain. microRNAs are the smallest RNA molecules and their role involves the regulation of gene expression by interfering with the expression of certain mRNA messages. Table 3.2 summarizes features of DNA and RNA.

Features of DNA and RNA

	DNA	RNA
Function	Carries genetic information	Involved in protein synthesis
Location	Remains in the nucleus	Leaves the nucleus
Structure	Double helix	Usually single-stranded
Sugar	Deoxyribose	Ribose
Pyrimidines	Cytosine, thymine	Cytosine, uracil
Purines	Adenine, guanine	Adenine, guanine

Table 3.2

Even though the RNA is single stranded, most RNA types show extensive intramolecular base pairing between complementary sequences, creating a predictable three-dimensional structure essential for their function.

As you have learned, information flow in an organism takes place from DNA to RNA to protein. DNA dictates the structure of mRNA in a process known as **transcription**, and RNA dictates the structure of protein in a process known as **translation**. This is known as the Central Dogma of Life, which holds true for all organisms; however, exceptions to the rule occur in connection with viral infections.

To learn more about DNA, explore the **Howard Hughes Medical Institute BioInteractive animations (http://openstaxcollege.org/l/DNA)** on the topic of DNA.

Why is DNA replication like an assembly line?

a. It consists of many biochemical machines that functions specifically in order to drive a specific action like an assembly line.

b. It consists of many biochemical machines that have the same function in order to drive a specific action like an assembly line.

c. It consists of many biochemical machines where each functions randomly in order to drive a specific action like an assembly line.

d. It consists of many biochemical machines that functions in order to drive a non-specific action like an assembly line.

science practices CONNECTION for AP® Courses

Activity

Using construction paper, markers, and scissors, construct a model of DNA with at least 8 nucleotides. Then, use the model to distinguish between DNA and RNA and hypothesize how the DNA molecule is replicated during cell division. (Keep your molecule to model the processes of transcription and translation that you will explore in Chapter 15.)

Think About It

A mutation occurs, and cytosine is replaced with adenine. Explain how this affects how the changed strand will base pair with its complimentary strand of DNA.

KEY TERMS

alpha-helix structure (α-helix) type of secondary structure of proteins formed by folding of the polypeptide into a helix shape with hydrogen bonds stabilizing the structure

amino acid monomer of a protein; has a central carbon or alpha carbon to which an amino group, a carboxyl group, a hydrogen, and an R group or side chain is attached; the R group is different for the most common 20 amino acids

beta-pleated sheet (β-pleated) secondary structure found in proteins in which “pleats” are formed by hydrogen bonding between atoms on the backbone of the polypeptide chain

biological macromolecule large molecule necessary for life that is built from smaller organic molecules

carbohydrate biological macromolecule in which the ratio of carbon to hydrogen and to oxygen is 1:2:1; carbohydrates serve as energy sources and structural support in cells and form the a cellular exoskeleton of arthropods

cellulose polysaccharide that makes up the cell wall of plants; provides structural support to the cell

chaperone (also, chaperonin) protein that helps nascent protein in the folding process

chitin type of carbohydrate that forms the outer skeleton of all arthropods that include crustaceans and insects; it also forms the cell walls of fungi

dehydration synthesis (also, condensation) reaction that links monomer molecules together, releasing a molecule of water for each bond formed

denaturation loss of shape in a protein as a result of changes in temperature, pH, or exposure to chemicals

deoxyribonucleic acid (DNA) double-helical molecule that carries the hereditary information of the cell

disaccharide two sugar monomers that are linked together by a glycosidic bond

enzyme catalyst in a biochemical reaction that is usually a complex or conjugated protein

glycogen storage carbohydrate in animals

glycosidic bond bond formed by a dehydration reaction between two monosaccharides with the elimination of a water molecule

hormone chemical signaling molecule, usually protein or steroid, secreted by endocrine cells that act to control or regulate specific physiological processes

hydrolysis reaction that causes breakdown of larger molecules into smaller molecules with the utilization of water

lipid macromolecule that is nonpolar and insoluble in water

messenger RNA (mRNA) RNA that carries information from DNA to ribosomes during protein synthesis

monomer smallest unit of larger molecules called polymers

monosaccharide single unit or monomer of carbohydrates

nucleic acid biological macromolecule that carries the genetic blueprint of a cell and carries instructions for the functioning of the cell

nucleotide monomer of nucleic acids; contains a pentose sugar, one or more phosphate groups, and a nitrogenous base

omega fat type of polyunsaturated fat that is required by the body; the numbering of the carbon omega starts from the methyl end or the end that is farthest from the carboxylic end

peptide bond bond formed between two amino acids by a dehydration reaction

phosphodiester linkage covalent chemical bond that holds together the polynucleotide chains, with a phosphate group linking two pentose sugars of neighboring nucleotides

phospholipid major constituent of the membranes; composed of two fatty acids and a phosphate-containing group attached to a glycerol backbone

polymer chain of monomer residues that is linked by covalent bonds; polymerization is the process of polymer formation from monomers by condensation

polynucleotide long chain of nucleotides

polypeptide long chain of amino acids linked by peptide bonds

polysaccharide long chain of monosaccharides; may be branched or unbranched

primary structure linear sequence of amino acids in a protein

protein biological macromolecule composed of one or more chains of amino acids

purine type of nitrogenous base in DNA and RNA; adenine and guanine are purines

pyrimidine type of nitrogenous base in DNA and RNA; cytosine, thymine, and uracil are pyrimidines

quaternary structure association of discrete polypeptide subunits in a protein

ribonucleic acid (RNA) single-stranded, often internally base paired, molecule that is involved in protein synthesis

ribosomal RNA (rRNA) RNA that ensures the proper alignment of the mRNA and the ribosomes during protein synthesis and catalyzes the formation of the peptide linkage

saturated fatty acid long-chain of hydrocarbon with single covalent bonds in the carbon chain; the number of hydrogen atoms attached to the carbon skeleton is maximized

secondary structure regular structure formed by proteins by intramolecular hydrogen bonding between the oxygen atom of one amino acid residue and the hydrogen attached to the nitrogen atom of another amino acid residue

starch storage carbohydrate in plants

steroid type of lipid composed of four fused hydrocarbon rings forming a planar structure

tertiary structure three-dimensional conformation of a protein, including interactions between secondary structural elements; formed from interactions between amino acid side chains

trans fat fat formed artificially by hydrogenating oils, leading to a different arrangement of double bond(s) than those found in naturally occurring lipids

transcription process through which messenger RNA forms on a template of DNA

transfer RNA (tRNA) RNA that carries activated amino acids to the site of protein synthesis on the ribosome

translation process through which RNA directs the formation of protein

triacylglycerol (also, triglyceride) fat molecule; consists of three fatty acids linked to a glycerol molecule

unsaturated fatty acid long-chain hydrocarbon that has one or more double bonds in the hydrocarbon chain

wax lipid made of a long-chain fatty acid that is esterified to a long-chain alcohol; serves as a protective coating on some feathers, aquatic mammal fur, and leaves

CHAPTER SUMMARY

3.1 Synthesis of Biological Macromolecules

Proteins, carbohydrates, nucleic acids, and lipids are the four major classes of biological macromolecules—large molecules necessary for life that are built from smaller organic molecules. Macromolecules are made up of single units known as monomers that are joined by covalent bonds to form larger polymers. The polymer is more than the sum of its parts: it acquires new characteristics, and leads to an osmotic pressure that is much lower than that formed by its ingredients; this is an important advantage in the maintenance of cellular osmotic conditions. A monomer joins with another monomer with the release of a water molecule, leading to the formation of a covalent bond. These types of reactions are known as dehydration or condensation reactions. When polymers are broken down into smaller units (monomers), a molecule of water is used for each bond broken by these reactions; such reactions are known as hydrolysis reactions. Dehydration and hydrolysis reactions are similar for all macromolecules, but each monomer and polymer reaction is specific to its class. Dehydration reactions typically require an investment of energy for new bond formation, while hydrolysis reactions typically release energy by breaking bonds.

3.2 Carbohydrates

Carbohydrates are a group of macromolecules that are a vital energy source for the cell and provide structural support to plant cells, fungi, and all of the arthropods that include lobsters, crabs, shrimp, insects, and spiders. Carbohydrates are classified as monosaccharides, disaccharides, and polysaccharides depending on the number of monomers in the molecule. Monosaccharides are linked by glycosidic bonds that are formed as a result of dehydration reactions, forming disaccharides and polysaccharides with the elimination of a water molecule for each bond formed. Glucose, galactose, and fructose are common monosaccharides, whereas common disaccharides include lactose, maltose, and sucrose. Starch and glycogen, examples of polysaccharides, are the storage forms of glucose in plants and animals, respectively. The long polysaccharide chains may be branched or unbranched. Cellulose is an example of an unbranched polysaccharide, whereas amylopectin, a constituent of starch, is a highly branched molecule. Storage of glucose, in the form of polymers like starch of glycogen, makes it slightly less accessible for metabolism; however, this prevents it from leaking out of the cell or creating a high osmotic pressure that could cause excessive water uptake by the cell.

3.3 Lipids

Lipids are a class of macromolecules that are nonpolar and hydrophobic in nature. Major types include fats and oils, waxes, phospholipids, and steroids. Fats are a stored form of energy and are also known as triacylglycerols or triglycerides. Fats are made up of fatty acids and either glycerol or sphingosine. Fatty acids may be unsaturated or saturated, depending on the presence or absence of double bonds in the hydrocarbon chain. If only single bonds are present, they are known as saturated fatty acids. Unsaturated fatty acids may have one or more double bonds in the hydrocarbon chain. Phospholipids make up the matrix of membranes. They have a glycerol or sphingosine backbone to which two fatty acid chains and a phosphate-containing group are attached. Steroids are another class of lipids. Their basic structure has four fused carbon rings. Cholesterol is a type of steroid and is an important constituent of the plasma membrane, where it helps to maintain the fluid nature of the membrane. It is also the precursor of steroid hormones such as testosterone.

3.4 Proteins

Proteins are a class of macromolecules that perform a diverse range of functions for the cell. They help in metabolism by providing structural support and by acting as enzymes, carriers, or hormones. The building blocks of proteins (monomers) are amino acids. Each amino acid has a central carbon that is linked to an amino group, a carboxyl group, a hydrogen atom, and an R group or side chain. There are 20 commonly occurring amino acids, each of which differs in the R group. Each amino acid is linked to its neighbors by a peptide bond. A long chain of amino acids is known as a polypeptide.

Proteins are organized at four levels: primary, secondary, tertiary, and (optional) quaternary. The primary structure is the unique sequence of amino acids. The local folding of the polypeptide to form structures such as the α helix and β-pleated sheet constitutes the secondary structure. The overall three-dimensional structure is the tertiary structure. When two or more polypeptides combine to form the complete protein structure, the configuration is known as the quaternary structure of a protein. Protein shape and function are intricately linked; any change in shape caused by changes in temperature or pH may lead to protein denaturation and a loss in function.

3.5 Nucleic Acids

Nucleic acids are molecules made up of nucleotides that direct cellular activities such as cell division and protein synthesis. Each nucleotide is made up of a pentose sugar, a nitrogenous base, and a phosphate group. There are two types of nucleic acids: DNA and RNA. DNA carries the genetic blueprint of the cell and is passed on from parents to offspring (in the form of chromosomes). It has a double-helical structure with the two strands running in opposite directions, connected by hydrogen bonds, and complementary to each other. RNA is single-stranded and is made of a pentose sugar (ribose), a nitrogenous base, and a phosphate group. RNA is involved in protein synthesis and its regulation. Messenger

RNA (mRNA) is copied from the DNA, is exported from the nucleus to the cytoplasm, and contains information for the construction of proteins. Ribosomal RNA (rRNA) is a part of the ribosomes at the site of protein synthesis, whereas transfer RNA (tRNA) carries the amino acid to the site of protein synthesis. MicroRNA regulates the use of mRNA for protein synthesis.

REVIEW QUESTIONS

1. Dehydration synthesis leads to the formation of what?

a. monomers
b. polymers
c. carbohydrates only
d. water only

2. What is removed during the formation of nucleic acid polymers?

a. carbon
b. hydroxyl groups
c. phosphates
d. amino acids

3. During the breakdown of polymers, which of the following reactions takes place?

a. condensation
b. covalent bond
c. dehydration
d. hydrolysis

4. Energy is released as a result of which of the following chemical reactions?

a. condensation
b. dehydration synthesis
c. hydrolysis
d. dissolution

5. In the metabolism of cell, why is hydrolysis used?

a. Hydrolysis breaks down polymers.
b. Hydrolysis is used to form linkages in DNA.
c. Hydrolysis is used to produce proteins.
d. Hydrolysis synthesizes new macromolecules.

6. Plant cell walls contain which of the following in abundance?

a. cellulose
b. glycogen
c. lactose
d. starch

7. What makes up the outer layer of some insects?

a. carbohydrate
b. protein
c. RNA
d. triglyceride

8. What is an example of a monosaccharide?

a. cellulose
b. fructose
c. lactose
d. sucrose

9. Cellulose and starch are examples of ________.

a. disaccharides
b. lipids
c. monosaccharides
d. polysaccharides

10. What type of bond joins the molecules in the disaccharide lactose? What molecule is joined with glucose to form lactose?

a. a glycosidic bond between glucose and lactose
b. a glycosidic bond between glucose and galactose
c. a hydrogen bond between glucose and sucrose
d. a hydrogen bond between glucose and fructose

11. What is structurally different about cellulose when compared to starch?

a. an extra hydrogen atom is left on the monomer
b. β-1,4 glycosidic linkages are used
c. α-1,6 glycosidic linkages are used
d. an extra hydroxyl group is removed during synthesis

12. Which of the following are classified as lipids?

a. disaccharides and cellulose
b. essential amino acids
c. mRNA and DNA
d. oils and waxes

13. What is cholesterol specifically classified as?

a. a lipid
b. a phospholipid
c. a steroid
d. a wax

14. Which fat serves as an animal's major form of energy storage?

a. cholesterol
b. glycerol
c. phospholipid
d. triglycerides

15. Which hormones are made from cholesterol?

a. estradiol and testosterone
b. insulin and growth hormone
c. progesterone and glucagon
d. prolactin and thyroid hormone

16. Which of the following characteristics is not true for saturated fats?

a. They are solid at room temperature.
b. They have single bonds within the carbon chain.
c. They tend to dissolve in water easily.

17. Which fat has the least number of hydrogen atoms?

a. trans fat
b. saturated fat
c. unsaturated fat
d. wax

18. Of what are phospholipids important components?

a. the double bond in hydrocarbon chains
b. the plasma membrane of animal cells
c. the ring structure of steroids
d. the waxy covering on leaves

19. What is a diacylglycerol 3-phosphate?

a. phospholipid
b. phosphatidylcholine
c. phosphatidylserine
d. phosphatidate

20. What is the basic structure of a steroid?

a. four fused hydrocarbon rings
b. glycerol with three fatty acid chains
c. two fatty acid chains and a phosphate group
d. two six carbon rings

21. Besides its use in hormone production, for what does the body use cholesterol?

a. mRNA transport
b. production of bile salts
c. water reabsorption in the kidney
d. wax production

22. Where is cholesterol found in cell membranes?

a. attached to the inner side of the membrane
b. attached to the outer side of the membrane
c. floating in the phospholipid tail layer
d. penetrating both lipid layers

23. Which type of body cell would have a higher amount of cholesterol in its membrane?

a. a cartilage cell
b. a liver cell
c. a red blood cell
d. a spleen cell

24. Which of the following is a function of proteins in cells?

a. energy storage
b. gene storage and access
c. membrane fluidity
d. structure

25. What type of protein facilitates or accelerates chemical reactions?

a. an enzyme
b. a hormone
c. a membrane transport protein
d. a tRNA molecule

26. What type of amino acids would you expect to find on the surface of proteins that must interact closely with water?

27. What are the monomers that make up proteins called?

a. amino acids
b. chaperones
c. disaccharides
d. nucleotides

28. Where is the linkage made that combines two amino acids?

a. between the R group of one amino acid and the R group of the second
b. between the carboxyl group of one amino acid and the amino group of the other
c. between the 6 carbon of both amino acids
d. between the nitrogen atoms of the amino groups in the amino acids

29. The α-helix and the β-pleated sheet are part of which protein structure?

a. the primary structure
b. the secondary structure
c. the tertiary structure
d. the quaternary structure

30. Which structural level of proteins is most often associated with their biological function?

a. the primary structure
b. the secondary structure
c. the tertiary structure
d. the quaternary structure

31. Which of the following may cause a protein to denature?

a. changes in pH
b. high temperatures
c. the addition of some chemicals
d. all of the above

32. What is a protein's chaperone?

a. a chemical that assists the protein in its enzymatic functions
b. a second protein that completes the quaternary structure
c. a chemical that helps the protein fold properly
d. a chemical that functions as a cofactor for the protein

33. What are the building blocks of nucleic acids?

a. nitrogenous bases
b. nucleotides
c. peptides
d. sugars

34. What may a nucleotide of DNA contain?

a. ribose, uracil, and a phosphate group
b. deoxyribose, uracil, and a phosphate group
c. deoxyribose, thymine, and a phosphate group
d. ribose, thymine, and a phosphate group

35. What is DNA's structure described as?

a. a step ladder
b. a double helix
c. a tertiary protein-like structure
d. barber pole

36. What is found in RNA that is not in DNA?

a. deoxyribose and adenine
b. fructose and thymine
c. glucose and quinine
d. ribose and uracil

37. What is the smallest type of RNA?

a. mRNA
b. microRNA
c. rRNA
d. tRNA

38. Where is the largest amount of DNA found in a eukaryotic cell?

a. attached to the inner layer of the cell membrane
b. in the nucleus
c. in the cytoplasm
d. on ribosomes

CRITICAL THINKING QUESTIONS

39. The word hydrolysis is defined as the lysis of water. How does this apply to polymers?

a. Polymers break by separating water into hydrogen and hydroxyl group that are added to the monomers.
b. Polymers are synthesized by using the energy released by the breaking of water molecules into hydrogen and hydroxyl group.
c. Polymers are separated into monomers producing energy and water molecules.
d. Polymers are hydrolyzed into monomers using water in the process and are called as dehydration synthesis.

40. What role do electrons play in dehydration synthesis and hydrolysis?

a. Electrons are added to OH and H ion in the dehydration synthesis. They are removed from OH and H in hydrolysis.

b. Electrons are transferred from OH and H ions to the monomers in dehydration synthesis. They are taken up by the H and OH ions from the monomers in hydrolysis.

c. Electrons are removed from OH and H in the dehydration synthesis. They are added to OH and H in hydrolysis.

d. Electrons are transferred from monomers to H and OH ions in hydrolysis and from OH and H to monomers in dehydration synthesis.

41. Which of the following bodily process would most likely be hindered by a lack of water in the body?

a. digestion

b. protein synthesis

c. copying DNA

d. breathing

42. Why is it impossible for humans to digest food that contains cellulose?

a. There is no energy available in fiber.

b. An inactive form of cellulase in human digestive tract renders it undigested and removes it as waste.

c. The acidic environment in the human stomach makes it impossible to break the bonds in cellulose.

d. Human digestive enzymes cannot break down the β-1,4 glycosidic linkage in cellulose, which requires a special enzyme that is absent in humans.

43. Which of these describe some of the similarities and differences between glycogen and starch?

a. Glycogen is less branched than starch and is found in animals.

b. Glycogen is more highly branched than starch and is found in plants.

c. Starch is less branched than glycogen and is found in plants.

d. Starch is more branched than glycogen and is found in animals.

44. Which of these best describes the production of sucrose, maltose, and lactose?

a. Glucose and fructose combine to form sucrose. Glucose and galactose combine to form lactose. Two glucose monomers combine to form maltose.

b. Glucose and fructose combine to form sucrose. Glucose and galactose combine to form maltose. Two glucose combine to form lactose.

c. Two glucose combine to form lactose. Glucose and galactose combine to form sucrose. Glucose and fructose combine to form maltose.

d. Two galactose combine to form sucrose. Fructose and glucose combine to form lactose. Two glucose combine to form maltose.

45. What are the four classes of lipids and what is an example of each?

a. 1. lipids like margarine
   2. wax like the coating on feathers
   3. phospholipids like cell membrane constituents
   4. steroid like cholesterol

b. 1. lipids like phosphatidylserine
   2. wax like phosphatidic acid
   3. phospholipids like oleic acid
   4. steroid like epinephrine

c. 1. lipids like phosphatidic acid
   2. waxes like margarine
   3. phospholipids like phosphatidylcholine
   4. steroids like testosterone

d. 1. lipids like cholesterol
   2. waxes like the coating on feathers
   3. phospholipids like phosphatidylserine
   4. steroids like margarine

46. What are three functions that lipids serve in plants and/or animals?

a. Lipids serve in the storage of energy, as a structural component of hormones, and also as signaling molecules.

b. Lipids serve in the storage of energy, as carriers for the transport of proteins across the membrane, and as signaling molecules.

c. Lipids serve in the breakdown of stored energy molecules, as signaling molecules, and as structural components of hormones.

d. Lipids serve in the breakdown of stored energy molecules, as signaling molecules, and as channels for protein transport.

47. Why have trans fats been banned from some restaurants? How are they created?

a. Trans fat is produced by the hydrogenation of oil that makes it more saturated and isomerized. It increases LDL amounts.

b. The dehydrogenation of oil forms the trans fat, which contains single bonds in its structure. This increases HDL in the body and has been banned.

c. Trans fat is produced by dehydrogenation of oils, which makes it unsaturated. It increases LDL in body.

d. The hydrogenation of oil makes the trans fat, which contains double bonds in its structure. It decreases HDL in the body.

48. How do phospholipids contribute to cell membrane structure?

a. Phospholipids orient their heads towards the polar molecules and tails in the interior of the membrane, thus forming a bilayer.

b. Phospholipids orient their tails towards the polar molecules of water solutions, and heads in the interior of the membrane, thus forming a bilayer.

c. Phospholipids orient their heads towards the non-polar molecules and tails in the interior of the membrane, forming a bilayer.

d. Phospholipids orient their tails towards the polar molecules and heads in the non-polar side of the membrane, forming a bilayer.

49. What type of compound functions in hormone production, contributes to membrane flexibility, and is the starting molecule for bile salts?

a. All steroid molecules help in the mentioned functions.

b. Cholesterol, which is a lipid and also a steroid, functions here.

c. Glycogen, which is a multi-branched polysaccharide of glucose, is the compound.

d. Phosphatidylcholine that is a phospholipid with a choline head group, which serves the functions.

50. What part of cell membranes gives flexibility to the structure?

a. carbohydrates

b. cytoskeleton filaments

c. lipids

d. proteins

51. How do the differences in amino acid sequences lead to different protein functions?

a. Different amino acids produce different proteins based on the bonds formed between them.

b. Differences in amino acids lead to the recycling of proteins, which produces other functional proteins.

c. Different amino acids cause rearrangements of amino acids to produce a functional protein.

d. Differences in the amino acids cause post-translational modification of the protein, which reassembles to produce a functional protein.

52. What causes the changes in protein structure through the three or four levels of structure?

a. The primary chain forms secondary α-helix and β-pleated sheets which fold onto each other forming the tertiary structure.

b. The primary structure undergoes alternative splicing to form secondary structures, which fold on other protein chains to form tertiary structures.

c. The primary structure forms secondary α-helix and β-pleated sheets. This further undergoes phosphorylation and acetylation to form the tertiary structure.

d. The primary structure undergoes alternative splicing to form a secondary structure, and then disulfide bonds give way to tertiary structures.

53. What structural level of proteins is functional? Why?

a. The secondary structure is functional as it attains its 2-dimensional shape which has the necessary bonds.

b. The tertiary structure is functional as it possesses the geometric shape showing the necessary loops and bends.

c. The tertiary structure is functional as it has the non-covalent and covalent bonds along with the subunits attached at the right places, which help it function properly.

d. Quaternary structure is functional as it has the essential set of subunits.

54. How does a chaperone work with proteins?

a. Chaperones assist proteins in folding.

b. Chaperones cause the aggregation of polypeptides.

c. Chaperones associate with proteins once the target protein is folded.

d. Chaperones escort proteins during translation.

55. What are some differences between DNA and RNA?

a. DNA is made from nucleotides; RNA is not.
b. DNA contains deoxyribose and thymine, while RNA contains ribose and uracil.
c. DNA contains adenine, while RNA contains guanine.
d. DNA is double stranded, while RNA may be double stranded in animals.

56. Which molecule carries information in a form that is inherited from one generation to another?

a. Hereditary information is stored in DNA.
b. Hereditary information is stored in mRNA.
c. Hereditary information is stored in proteins.
d. Hereditary information is stored in tRNA.

57. What are the four types and functions of RNA?

a. mRNA is a single stranded transcript of DNA. rRNA is found in ribosomes. tRNA transfers specific amino acids to a developing protein strand. miRNA regulates the expression of mRNA strands.
b. mRNA is a single stranded transcript of rRNA. rRNA is translated in ribosomes to make proteins. tRNA transfers specific amino acids to a developing protein strand. microRNA (miRNA) regulates the expression of the mRNA strand.
c. mRNA regulates the expression of the miRNA strand. rRNA are found in ribosomes. tRNA transfers specific amino acids to a developing protein strand. miRNA is a single stranded transcript of DNA.
d. mRNA is a single stranded transcript of DNA. rRNA transfers specific amino acids to a developing protein strand. tRNA is found in ribosomes. miRNA regulates the expression of the mRNA strand.

TEST PREP FOR AP® COURSES

58. Urey and Miller constructed an experiment to illustrate the early atmosphere of the Earth and possible development of organic molecules in the absence of living cells. Which assumption did Urey and Miller make regarding conditions on Earth?

a. electric sparks occurred to catalyze the reaction
b. the composition of the gases in the atmosphere
c. there was sufficient oxygen for creating life
d. it produced water-soluble organic molecules

59. Urey and Miller proposed that a series of reactions occurred, which ultimately resulted in amino acid formation. Which of the following is true based upon their theory?

a. Hydrogen and nitrogen combined to create amino acids.
b. Hydrogen and oxygen combined to create macromolecules.
c. Nitrogenous bases combined to form monomers then RNA.
d. Periodic elements combined to create molecules then DNA.

60. How does Stanley Miller and Harold Urey's model support the claim that simple precursors present on early Earth could have assembled into complex molecules necessary for life?

a. The simple molecules assembled to form amino acids and nucleic acids.
b. The organic molecules assembled to form the large complexes such as water and methane.
c. The inorganic molecules assembled to form the amino acids and nucleic acids.
d. The inorganic molecules assembled to form the large complexes such as water and methane.

61. Which statement most accurately describes the importance of the condensation stage during Urey and Miller's experiment?

a. Condensed water enabled the formation of monomers.
b. Condensation and evaporation simulated lightning storms.
c. Condensation and evaporation simulated the water cycle.
d. Condensed water enabled the formation of polymers.

62. According to the findings of the Urey and Miller experiment, the primitive atmosphere consisted of water in the form of steam, methane, ammonia, and hydrogen gases. If there was so much hydrogen gas in the early atmosphere, why is there so little now?

a. Hydrogen gas is so light with a molecular weight of 1 that the excess diffused into space over time and is now absent from the atmosphere.
b. Hydrogen combined with ammonia to make ammonium.
c. It was all used up in the production of organic molecules.
d. The excess hydrogen gas was dissolved in the early oceans.

63. Could the primitive atmosphere illustrated by the Urey and Miller experiment be reproduced on today's Earth? Why or why not?

a. The primitive atmosphere cannot be created due to the oxidizing atmosphere and lack of hydrogen.
b. The primitive atmosphere can be created as the atmosphere is reducing and the Earth has sufficient hydrogen to reproduce the conditions.
c. The primitive atmosphere cannot be created due to the presence of abundant water and hydrogen in the atmosphere.
d. The primitive atmosphere can be created as the atmosphere is oxidizing and has less of hydrogen.

64. What is structurally different between starch and cellulose that gives them different physical properties?

a. Cellulose is formed by β-1,4 glycosidic linkages and crosslinks, making it rigid. Starch has α-1.4 and α-1.6 glycosidic linkages without the tight crosslinks of cellulose.
b. Cellulose has rigid α-1,4 glycosidic linkages while starch has less rigid β-1,4 glycosidic linkages
c. Cellulose has amylose and amylopectin, making it more rigid than starch.
d. Starch has amylose and amylopectin that make it more rigid than cellulose.

65.

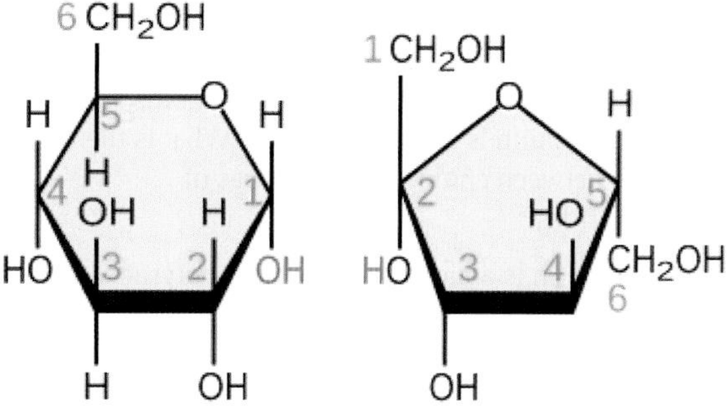

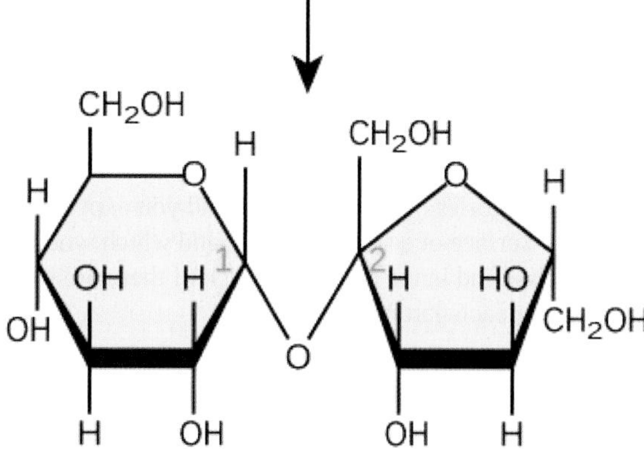

Complex polymers are built from combinations of smaller monomers. What type of reaction is shown, and what is a product of the following reaction? Assume water is also produced.

a. a synthesis reaction producing glucose and water
b. a hydrolysis reaction producing fructose and water
c. a condensation reaction producing lactose and water
d. a dehydration reaction producing sucrose and water

66. The fatty acids of triglycerides are classified as saturated, unsaturated, or trans fats. What is it about the structure of these compounds that gives them their physical characteristics?

a. Saturated fats and trans fats contain the greatest possible number of hydrogen atoms, while unsaturated fats do not.
b. Saturated and unsaturated fats have stable configurations, while trans fats are transient.
c. Unsaturated fats and trans fats have some double bonded carbon atoms, while saturated fats do not.
d. Unsaturated and trans fats are the same; the fatty acids are just found on opposite sides of a trans fat.

67. Carbohydrates serve various functions in different animals. Arthropods like insects, crustaceans, and others, have an outer layer, called the exoskeleton, which protects their internal body parts. This exoskeleton is made mostly of chitin. Chitin is also a major component of the cell walls of fungi, the kingdom that includes molds and mushrooms. Chitin is a polysaccharide. What is the major difference between chitin and other types of polysaccharides?

a. Chitin is a nitrogen-containing polysaccharide, with repeating units of N-acetyl- β -D-glucosamine, a modified sugar.
b. Chitin is similar to amylase, but with sulfur linkages between the monomers.
c. Chitin is similar to inulin, a polysaccharide with fructose, but with additional glucose monomers.
d. Chitin contains phosphate groups that give it a stiffness not found in other polysaccharides.

68. What categories of amino acids would you expect to find on the surface of a soluble protein and which would you expect to find in the interior? Which of these are some examples for each part of the answer?

a. Non-polar and charged amino acids will be present on the surface and polar in the interior of the membrane whereas non-polar will be found in the membrane embedded proteins.
b. Non-polar and uncharged proteins will be found on the surface with non-polar in the interior, while only non-polar will be found in the embedded proteins.
c. Polar and charged amino acids will be found on the surface whereas non-polar in the interior.
d. Polar and charged amino acids will be found on the surface of a membrane protein whereas non-polar in the interior. The membrane protein will be polar and hydrophobic.

69. You have been identifying the sequence of a segment of a protein. The sequence to date is: leucine-methionine-tyrosine-alanine-glutamine-lysine-glutamate. You insert arginine between the leucine and methionine. What effect would this have on the segment?

a. Arginine is a negatively charged amino acid and could attach to the glutamate at the end of the segment
b. Inserting arginine places a positively charged amino acid in a portion that is non-polar, creating the possibility of a hydrogen bond in this area.
c. There would be no effect other than an additional amino acid.
d. The arginine could attach to the lysine and bend the protein chain at this point.

70. What would happen if even one amino acid is substituted for another in a polypeptide? What would be an example?

a. The change will definitely not be sufficient to have any effect on the function and structure of the protein.
b. The amino acid may not show any significant effect the protein structure and function or it may have a significant effect, as in the case of hemoglobin in individuals with sickle cell trait.
c. These changes would increase the possibility of having extra bends and loops in the proteins as in Leber congenital disease.
d. These changes would modify the structures of proteins making them nonfunctional.

71. HIV is an RNA virus that affects CD4 cells, also known as T cells, in the human body. Which mechanism is most likely responsible for the fast rate at which HIV can spread?

a. recombination
b. mutation
c. reassortment
d. formation errors

72. For many years, scientist believed that proteins were the source of heritable information. There are many thousands of different proteins in a cell, and they mediate the cell's metabolism, producing the traits and characteristics of a species. Researchers working with DNA viruses proved that it is DNA that stores and passes on genes. They worked with viruses with an outer coat of protein and a DNA strand inside. How did they prove that it was DNA, not protein, which is the primary source of heritable information?

a. The DNA and protein of the virus were tagged with different isotopes and exposed to host cell where only the DNA was transferred to the host.
b. The DNA was tagged with an isotope, which was retained in the virus, proving it to be the genetic material.
c. The viral protein was tagged with an isotope, and the host cell was infected by it. This protein was transferred to the host.
d. The viral DNA, when sequenced, was found to be present in the host cell proving it to be the hereditary material instead of protein.

73. The genetic code is based on each amino acid being coded for by a distinctive series of three nucleic acid bases called a codon. The following is a short segment of DNA using the slash symbol (/) to separate the codons for easy viewing: ATC/GTT/GAA/CTG/TAG/GAT/AAA

A change has occurred in the segment resulting in the following:

ATC/GTT/GTA/CTG/TAG/GAT/AAA

What kind of change has occurred?

a. A substitution of T for A, changing the coding for the third codon
b. An addition of C for G, lengthening the strand and changing every codon past the addition
c. A deletion of an A, resulting in a shortening and changing every codon past the deletion
d. No change has occurred; the same one base was replaced with the same one

74. A change in DNA on a chromosome affects all proteins made from that gene for the life of the cell. A change in the RNA involved in protein production is short lived. What is the difference between the effects of the changes in the two types of nucleic acids?

a. DNA is the genetic material that is passed from parent cells to daughter cells and to future generations.
b. DNA would not affect the individuals as the proteins made are finally altered and modified. RNA would cause harm to the person as the RNA is encoded by the DNA and is not altered.
c. DNA is the genetic material and is transferred from one generation to another making use of repair mechanisms for every mutation. The RNA does not use a repair mechanism.
d. DNA, when mutated, makes use of the repair mechanisms and can be repaired whereas RNA is not repaired and is transferred in generations.

SCIENCE PRACTICE CHALLENGE QUESTIONS

75. The capture of radiant energy through the conversion of carbon dioxide and water into carbohydrates is the engine that drives life on Earth. Ribose, $C_5H_{10}O_5$, and hexose, $C_6H_{12}O_6$, form stable five- and six-carbon rings.

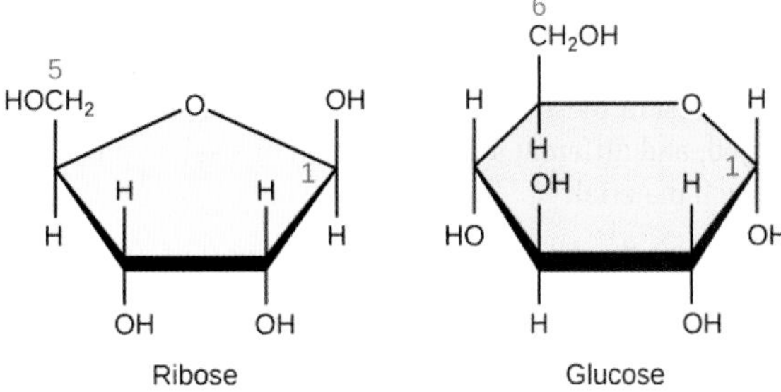

Figure 3.37

The numbering of the carbons on these rings is important in organizing our description of the role these molecules play in biological energy transfer and information storage and retrieval. Glycolysis is a sequence of chemical reactions that convert glucose to two three-carbon compounds called pyruvic acid.

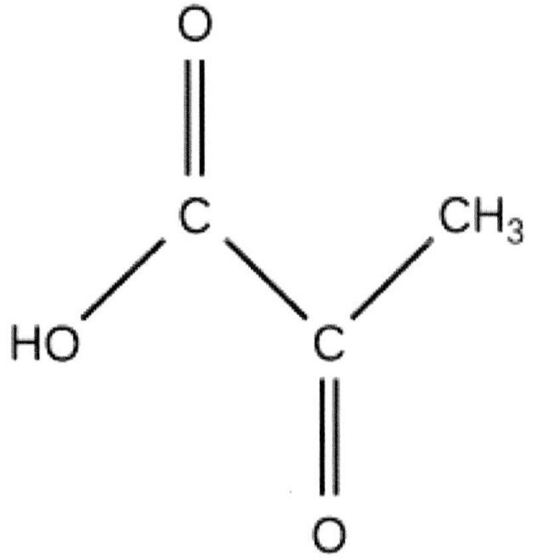

Figure 3.38

A. **Create visual representations** to show how when bonds in the glucose molecules are broken between carbon number 1 and the oxygen atom and between carbons 3 and 4, two molecules of pyruvic acid are produced.

Several enzymes in the cell are involved in converting glucose to pyruvic acid. These enzymes are proteins whose amino acid sequences provide these functions. This protein structure is information that was inherited from the cell's parent, and is stored in deoxyribonucleic acid (DNA). The "deoxyribo" component of that name is a shorthand for 2-deoxyribose.

B. **Create a visual representation** of 2-deoxyribose, 5-phosphate by replacing the OH at carbon 2 with a hydrogen atom and replacing the OH at carbon 5 with a hydrogen phosphate ion, HPO_3^{-2}, whose structure is shown in problem AP3.2. Use your representation to show that both phosphorylation (the addition of a phosphate ion) at carbon 5 and removal of the hydroxide at carbon 2 produce water molecules in an aqueous solution where hydrogen ions are abundant.

DNA is a polymer formed from a chain with repeated 2-deoxyribose, 5-phosphate molecules.

C. **Create a visual representation** of three 2-deoxyribose, 5-phosphate molecules forming a chain in which an oxygen atom in the phosphate that is attached to the 5-carbon replaces the OH on the 3-carbon of the next ribose sugar.

76. Cells are bounded by membranes composed of phospholipids. A phospholipid consists of a pair of fatty acids that may or may not have carbon-carbon double bonds, fused at the carboxylic acid with a three-carbon glycerol that is terminated by a phosphate, as shown in the figure below. Most cell membranes comprise two phospholipid layers with the hydrophilic phosphate ends of each molecule in the outer and inner surfaces. The hydrophobic chains of carbon atoms extend into the space between these two surfaces.

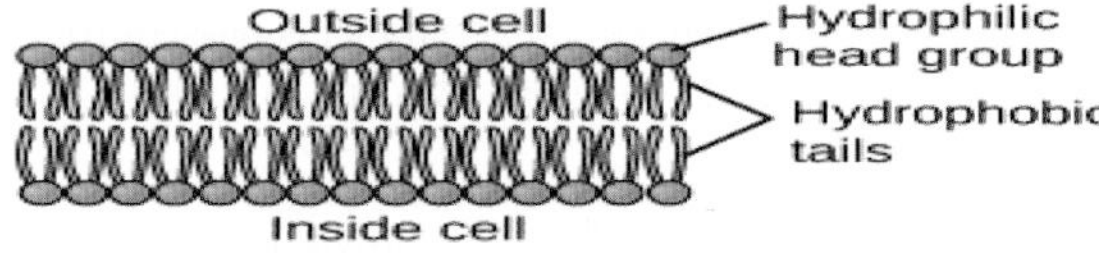

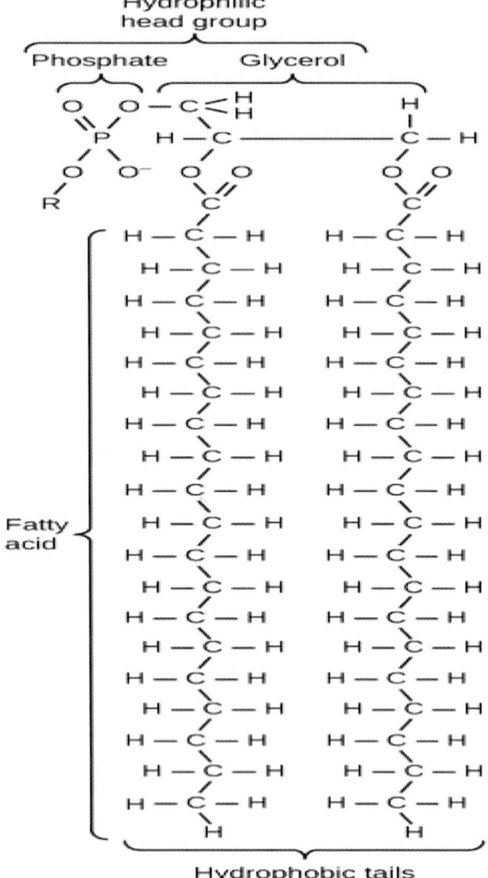

Figure 3.39

The exchange of matter between the interior of the cell and the environment is mediated by this membrane with selective permeability.

A. **Pose questions** that identify

- the important characteristics of this lipid bilayer structure
- the molecules that must be acquired from the environment and eliminated from the cell
- relationships between the structures of these molecules and the structure of the bilayer

Because the plasma cell membrane has both hydrophilic and hydrophobic properties, few types of molecules possess structures that allow them to pass between the interior of the cell and the environment through passive diffusion. The fluidity of the membrane affects passive transport, and the incorporation of other molecules in the membrane, in particular cholesterols, has a strong effect on its fluidity. Fluidity is also affected by temperature.

Measurements of the speed of movement of oxygen molecules, O_2, through three types of membranes were made (Widomska et al., *Biochimica et Biophysica Acta*, 1,768, 2007) and compared with the speed of movement of O_2 through water. These measurements were carried out at four different temperatures. One type of membrane was obtained from the cells in the eyeball of a calf (lens lipid). Synthetic membranes composed of palmitic acid with cholesterol (POPC/CHOL) and without cholesterol (POPC) were also used. The results from these experiments are shown in the table below.

	Temperature (°C)			
	15	25	35	45
Material	Speed (cm/s)			
Lens lipids	15	30	65	110
POPC/CHOL	15	30	60	95
POPC	55	100	155	280
Water	45	55	65	75

Table 3.3

B. **Represent** these **data graphically**. The axes should be labeled, and different symbols should be used to plot data for each material.

C. **Analyze** the data by comparing transport of oxygen through the biological membrane, water, and the synthetic membranes. Consider both membrane composition and temperature in your analysis.

The plasma membrane separates the interior and the exterior of the cell. A potential to do work is established by defining regions inside and outside the cell with different concentrations of key molecules and net charge. In addition to the membrane defining the cell boundary, eukaryotic cells have internal membranes.

D. **Explain** how internal membranes significantly increase the functional capacity of the cells of eukaryotes relative to those of prokaryotes.

77. Proteins are polymers whose sub-components are amino acids connected by peptide bonds. The carboxylic acid carbon, O = C – OH, of one amino acid can form a bond with the amine, NH_2, of another amino acid. In the formation of this peptide bond, the amine replaces the OH to form O = C – NH_2. The other product of this reaction is water, H_2O.

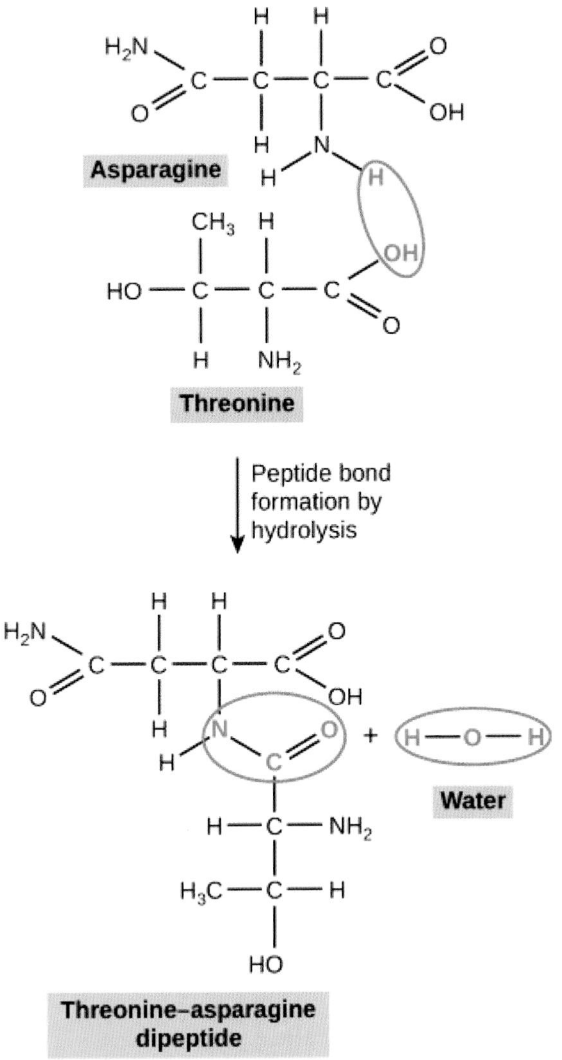

Figure 3.40

Amino acids can be synthesized in the laboratory from simpler molecules of ammonia (NH_3), water (H_2O), methane (CH_4), and hydrogen (H_2) if energy is provided by processes that simulate lightning strikes or volcanic eruptions (Miller, *Science*, 117, 1953; Johnson et al., *Science*, 322, 2008).

A. The synthesis of amino acids in solutions under laboratory conditions consistent with early Earth was a step toward an explanation of how life began. **Pose a question** that should have been asked but was not until 2014 (Parker et al., *Angewandte Chemie*, 53, 2014), when these solutions that had been stored in a refrigerator were analyzed.

The diversity and complexity of life begins in the variety of sequences of the 20 common amino acids.

B. Apply mathematical reasoning to **explain** the source of biocomplexity by calculating the possible variations in a polymer composed of just three amino acids.

Polarity in a bond between atoms occurs when electrons are distributed unequally. Polarity in a molecule also is caused by charge asymmetry. Life on Earth has evolved within a framework of water, H_2O, one of the most polar molecules. The polarities of the amino acids that compose a protein determine the properties of the polymer.

The electric polarity of an amino acid in an aqueous solution depends on the pH of the solution. Here are three forms of the general structure of an amino acid.

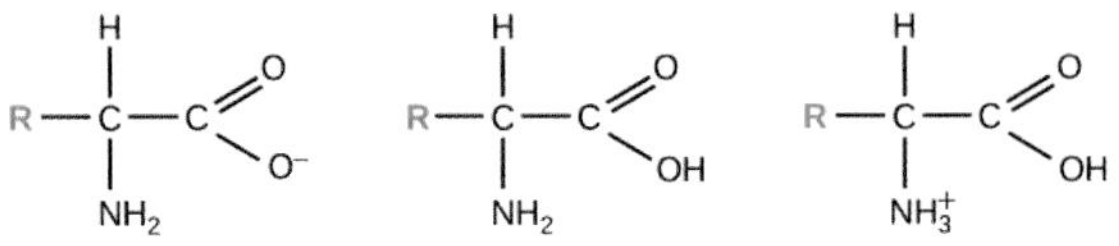

Figure 3.41

C. Qualitatively **predict** the relationship between solution pH and the form of the amino acid for three solutions of pH: pH < 7, pH $= 7$, and pH > 7.

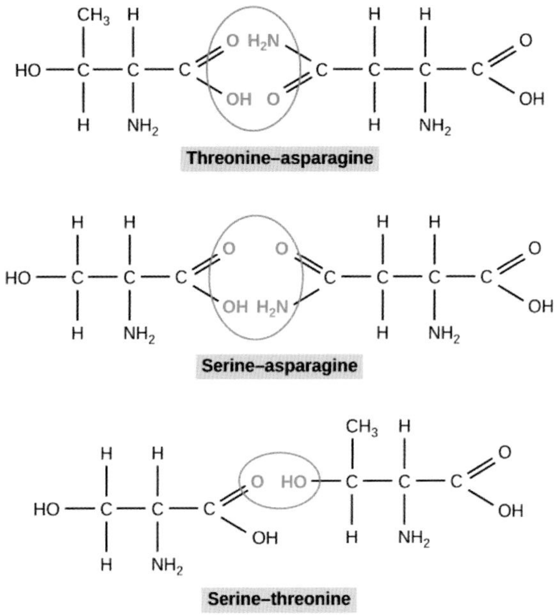

Figure 3.42

The properties of proteins are determined by interactions among the amino acids in the peptide-bonded chain. The protein subcomponents, especially amino R (variable) groups, can interact with very strong charge-charge forces, with attractive forces between groups of atoms with opposite polarities and with repulsive forces between groups of atoms with the same or no polarity. Attractive polar forces often arise between molecules through interactions between oxygen and hydrogen atoms or between nitrogen and hydrogen atoms.

D. Consider particular orientations of pairs of three different amino acids. **Predict** the relative strength of attractive interaction of all pairs; rank them and provide your reasoning.

In an amino acid, the atoms attached to the α carbon are

called the R group.

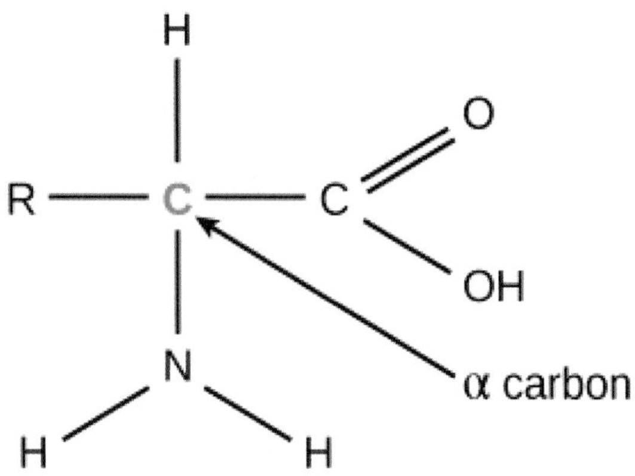

Figure 3.43

Interactions between R groups of a polypeptide give three-dimensional structure to the one-dimensional, linear sequence of amino acids in a polypeptide.

E. **Construct an explanation** for the effect of R-group interactions on the properties of a polymer with drawings showing molecular orientations with stronger and weaker polar forces between R groups on asparagine and threonine and between asparagine and alanine.

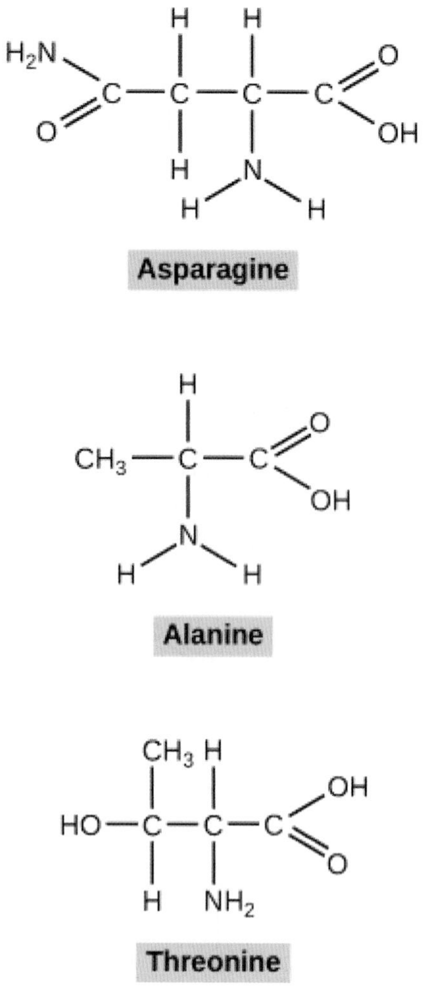

Figure 3.44

78. The nucleobase part of deoxyribonucleic acid encodes information in each component in the sequence making up the polymer. There are five nucleobases that are commonly represented by only a single letter: A (adenine), C (cytosine), G (guanine), T (thymine), and U (uracil). These molecules form a bond with the 1-carbon of deoxyribose. In this problem, we need to look at the molecules in slightly more detail so that you can development the ability to explain why DNA, and sometimes RNA, is the primary source of heritable information.

Edwin Chargaff and his team isolated nucleobases from salmon sperm and determined the fraction of each (Chargaff et al., *Journal of Biological Chemistry*, 192, 1951). Experiments in which the fraction of all four nucleobases was determined are shown. Also shown are averages as two standard deviations and the sum of total fractions for each experiment. Precision is calculated with each average.

Shown below are the chemical structures of these four nucleobases. In these structures, the nitrogen that attaches to the 2-deoxyribose, 5-phosphate polymer is indicated as N*. The partial charges of particular atoms are indicated with δ^+ and δ^-.

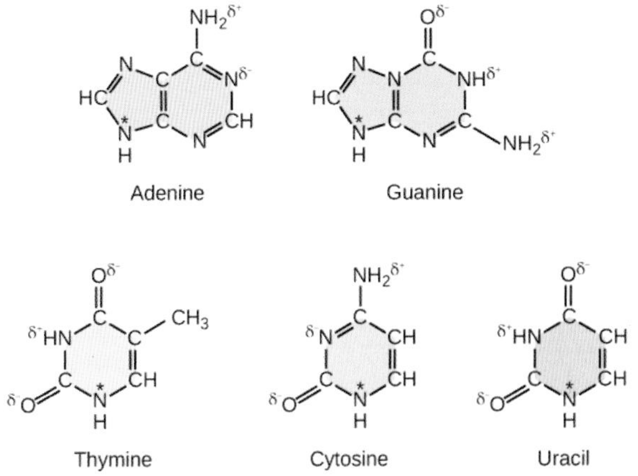

Figure 3.45

A. **Analyze** Chargaff's data in terms of the partial charges on these molecules to show how molecular interactions affect the function of these molecules in the storage and retrieval of biological information.

Experiment	Adenine	Guanine	Cytosine	Thymine	Total
5	0.28	0.20	0.21	0.27	0.96
6	0.30	0.22	0.20	0.29	1.01
7	0.27	0.18	0.19	0.25	0.89
8	0.28	0.21	0.20	0.27	0.96
11	0.29	0.18	0.20	0.27	0.94
12	0.28	0.21	0.19	0.26	0.94
13	0.30	0.21	0.20	0.30	1.01
	0.29±0.02	0.20±0.03	0.20±0.01	0.27±0.02	0.96±0.08

Figure 3.46

The interactions between nucleobase molecules are strong enough to produce the association of pairs observed in Chargaff's data. However, these pairs are bonded by much weaker hydrogen bonds, chemical bonds within the molecules.

Demonstrating an understanding of the replication of DNA requires the ability to explain how the two polymer strands of the double helix interact and grow. To retrieve information from DNA, the strands must be separated. The proteins that perform that task interact with the polymer without forming new chemical bonds. In their paper (Watson and Crick, *Nature*, 3, 1953) announcing the structure of the polymer that we consider in this problem, Watson and Crick stated, "It has not escaped our notice that the specific pairing we have postulated immediately suggests a possible copying mechanism for the genetic material."

Eschenmoser and Lowenthal (*Chemical Society Reviews*, 21, 1992) asked why the 5-carbon sugar ribose is used in DNA when the 6-carbon sugar glucose is so common in biological systems. To answer the question, they synthesized polymeric chains with this alternative form of sugar. They discovered that the strength of the interaction between pairs of nucleobases increased in the new material. Paired strands of hexose-based polymers were more stable.

The AP Biology Curriculum Framework (College Board, 2012) states, "The double-stranded structure of DNA provides a simple and elegant solution for the transmission of heritable information to the next generation; by using each strand as a template, existing information can be preserved and duplicated with high fidelity within the replication process. However, the process of replication is imperfect…."

B. **Explain** why the weaker interaction observed by Eschenmoser and Lowenthal, and the acknowledgement in the Framework that "replication is imperfect," support the claim implied by Watson and Crick that DNA is the source of heritable information.

4 | CELL STRUCTURE

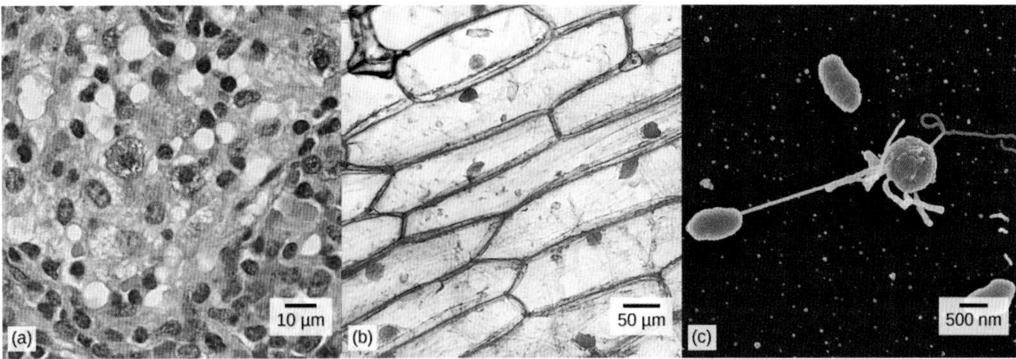

Figure 4.1 (a) Nasal sinus cells (viewed with a light microscope), (b) onion cells (viewed with a light microscope), and (c) *Vibrio tasmaniensis* bacterial cells (seen through a scanning electron microscope) are from very different organisms, yet all share certain characteristics of basic cell structure. (credit a: modification of work by Ed Uthman, MD; credit b: modification of work by Umberto Salvagnin; credit c: modification of work by Anthony D'Onofrio, William H. Fowle, Eric J. Stewart, and Kim Lewis of the Lewis Lab at Northeastern University; scale-bar data from Matt Russell)

Chapter Outline

Introduction

Close your eyes and picture a brick wall. What is the basic building block of that wall? A single brick, of course. Like a brick wall, your body is composed of basic building blocks called “cells.”

Your body has many kinds of cells, each specialized for a specific purpose. Just as a home is made from a variety of building materials, the human body is constructed from many cell types. For example, epithelial cells protect the surface of the body and cover the organs and body cavities within. Bone cells help to support and protect the body. Immune system cells fight invading pathogens. Additionally, blood cells carry nutrients and oxygen throughout the body while removing carbon dioxide and other waste. Each of these cell types plays a vital role during the growth, development, and ongoing maintenance of the body. In spite of their enormous variety, however, cells from all organisms—even organisms as diverse as bacteria, onion, and human—share certain fundamental characteristics.

In humans, before a cell develops into its specialized type, it is called a stem cell. A stem cell is a cell that has not undergone the changes involved in specialization. In this state, it may differentiate to become one of many different specialized cells, and it may divide to produce more stem cells. Under normal circumstances, once a cell becomes specialized, it remains that way. However, scientists have been working on coaxing stem cells in the laboratory to become a particular specialization. For example, scientists at the Cincinnati Children’s Hospital Medical Center have learned how to use stem cells to grow stomach tissue in plastic cell and tissue culture dishes. This accomplishment will enable researchers to study gastric human diseases, such as stomach cancer. You can read more about it **here (http://openstaxcollege.org/l/32cellsize)** .

4.1 | Studying Cells

In this section, you will explore the following questions:

- What is the role of cells in organisms?
- What is the difference between light microscopy and electron microscopy?
- What is the cell theory?

Connection for AP® Courses

A cell is the smallest unit of a living thing. A living thing, whether made of one cell (like bacteria) or many cells (like a human), is called an organism. Thus, cells are the basic building blocks of all organisms.

Several cells of one kind that interconnect with each other and perform a shared function form a tissue; several tissues combine to form an organ (your stomach, heart, or brain), and several organs make up an organ system (such as the digestive system, circulatory system, or nervous system). Several systems that function together form an organism (like a human being). Here, we will examine the structure and function of cells.

There are many types of cells, all grouped into one of two broad categories: prokaryotic and eukaryotic. For example, both animal and plant cells are classified as eukaryotic cells, whereas bacterial cells are classified as prokaryotic. Before discussing the criteria for determining whether a cell is prokaryotic or eukaryotic, let's first examine how biologists study cells.

Microscopy

Cells vary in size. With few exceptions, individual cells cannot be seen with the naked eye, so scientists use microscopes (micro- = "small"; -scope = "to look at") to study them. A **microscope** is an instrument that magnifies an object. Most photographs of cells are taken with a microscope, and these images can also be called micrographs.

The optics of a compound microscope's lenses change the orientation of the image that the user sees. A specimen that is right-side up and facing right on the microscope slide will appear upside-down and facing left when viewed through a microscope, and vice versa. Similarly, if the slide is moved left while looking through the microscope, it will appear to move right, and if moved down, it will seem to move up. This occurs because microscopes use two sets of lenses to magnify the image. Because of the manner by which light travels through the lenses, this system of two lenses produces an inverted image (binocular, or dissecting microscopes, work in a similar manner, but include an additional magnification system that makes the final image appear to be upright).

Light Microscopes

To give you a sense of cell size, a typical human red blood cell is about eight millionths of a meter or eight micrometers (abbreviated as eight μm) in diameter; the head of a pin of is about two thousandths of a meter (two mm) in diameter. That means about 250 red blood cells could fit on the head of a pin.

Most student microscopes are classified as **light microscopes** (Figure 4.2**a**). Visible light passes and is bent through the lens system to enable the user to see the specimen. Light microscopes are advantageous for viewing living organisms, but since individual cells are generally transparent, their components are not distinguishable unless they are colored with special stains. Staining, however, usually kills the cells.

Light microscopes commonly used in the undergraduate college laboratory magnify up to approximately 400 times. Two parameters that are important in microscopy are magnification and resolving power. Magnification is the process of enlarging an object in appearance. Resolving power is the ability of a microscope to distinguish two adjacent structures as separate: the higher the resolution, the better the clarity and detail of the image. When oil immersion lenses are used for the study of small objects, magnification is usually increased to 1,000 times. In order to gain a better understanding of cellular structure and function, scientists typically use electron microscopes.

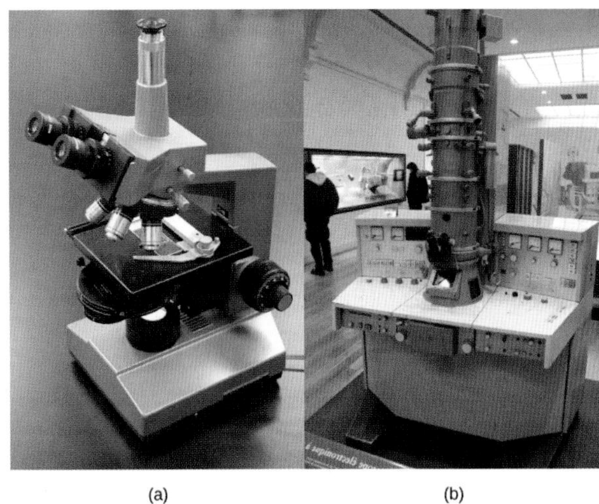

(a) (b)

Figure 4.2 (a) Most light microscopes used in a college biology lab can magnify cells up to approximately 400 times and have a resolution of about 200 nanometers. (b) Electron microscopes provide a much higher magnification, 100,000x, and a have a resolution of 50 picometers. (credit a: modification of work by "GcG"/Wikimedia Commons; credit b: modification of work by Evan Bench)

Electron Microscopes

In contrast to light microscopes, **electron microscopes** (Figure 4.2**b**) use a beam of electrons instead of a beam of light. Not only does this allow for higher magnification and, thus, more detail (Figure 4.3), it also provides higher resolving power. The method used to prepare the specimen for viewing with an electron microscope kills the specimen. Electrons have short wavelengths (shorter than photons) that move best in a vacuum, so living cells cannot be viewed with an electron microscope.

In a scanning electron microscope, a beam of electrons moves back and forth across a cell's surface, creating details of cell surface characteristics. In a transmission electron microscope, the electron beam penetrates the cell and provides details of a cell's internal structures. As you might imagine, electron microscopes are significantly more bulky and expensive than light microscopes.

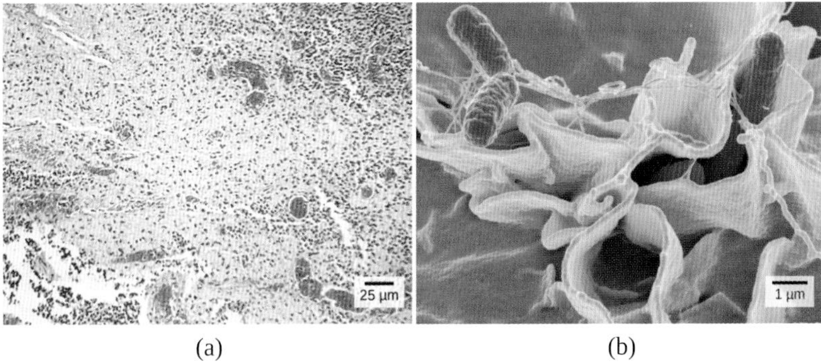

(a) (b)

Figure 4.3 (a) These *Salmonella* bacteria appear as tiny purple dots when viewed with a light microscope. (b) This scanning electron microscope micrograph shows *Salmonella* bacteria (in red) invading human cells (yellow). Even though subfigure (b) shows a different *Salmonella* specimen than subfigure (a), you can still observe the comparative increase in magnification and detail. (credit a: modification of work by CDC/Armed Forces Institute of Pathology, Charles N. Farmer, Rocky Mountain Laboratories; credit b: modification of work by NIAID, NIH; scale-bar data from Matt Russell)

For another perspective on cell size, try the HowBig interactive at **this site (http://openstaxcollege.org/l/cell_sizes)** .

Why are electron microscopes crucial for the study of cell biology?

a. Only electron microscopes can be used to view internal structures.

b. Some electron microscopes allow visualization of three dimensional external shapes at very high magnification in a way that is not possible with standard light microscopes.

c. Scanning electron microscopes can show internal structures clearly at very high magnifications.

d. Electron microscopes are easier to use and less expensive than light microscopes.

Cell Theory

The microscopes we use today are far more complex than those used in the 1600s by Antony van Leeuwenhoek, a Dutch shopkeeper who had great skill in crafting lenses. Despite the limitations of his now-ancient lenses, van Leeuwenhoek observed the movements of single-celled organisms, which he collectively termed "animalcules."

In a 1665 publication called *Micrographia*, experimental scientist Robert Hooke coined the term "cell" for the box-like structures he observed when viewing cork tissue through a lens. In the 1670s, van Leeuwenhoek discovered bacteria and protozoa. Later advances in lenses, microscope construction, and staining techniques enabled other scientists to see some components inside cells.

By the late 1830s, botanist Matthias Schleiden and zoologist Theodor Schwann were studying tissues and proposed the **unified cell theory**, which states that all living things are composed of one or more cells, the cell is the basic unit of life, and new cells arise from existing cells. Rudolf Virchow later made important contributions to this theory.

career CONNECTION

Have you ever heard of a medical test called a Pap smear (Figure 4.4)? In this test, a doctor takes a small sample of cells from the uterine cervix of a patient and sends it to a medical lab where a cytotechnologist stains the cells and examines them for any changes that could indicate abnormal cell growth or a microbial infection.

Cytotechnologists (cyto- = "cell") are professionals who study cells via microscopic examinations and other laboratory tests. They are trained to determine which cellular changes are within normal limits and which are abnormal. Their focus is not limited to cervical cells; they study cellular specimens that come from all organs. When they notice abnormalities, they consult a pathologist, who is a medical doctor who can make a clinical diagnosis.

Cytotechnologists play a vital role in saving people's lives. When abnormalities are discovered early, a patient's treatment can begin sooner, which usually increases the chances of a successful outcome.

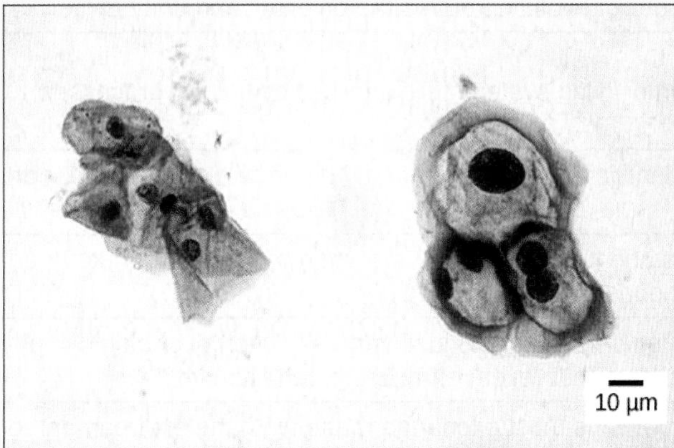

Figure 4.4 These uterine cervix cells, viewed through a light microscope, were obtained from a Pap smear. Normal cells are on the left. The cells on the right are infected with human papillomavirus (HPV). Notice that the infected cells are larger; also, two of these cells each have two nuclei instead of one, the normal number. (credit: modification of work by Ed Uthman, MD; scale-bar data from Matt Russell)

Section Summary

A cell is the smallest unit of life. Most cells are so tiny that they cannot be seen with the naked eye. Therefore, scientists use microscopes to study cells. Electron microscopes provide higher magnification, higher resolution, and more detail than light microscopes. The unified cell theory states that all organisms are composed of one or more cells, the cell is the basic unit of life, and new cells arise from existing cells.

4.2 | Prokaryotic Cells

In this section, you will explore the following questions:

- What are the major structures of prokaryotic cells?
- What limits the size of a cell?

Connection for AP® Courses

According to the cell theory, all living organisms, from bacteria to humans, are composed of cells, the smallest units of living matter. Often too small to be seen without a microscope, cells come in all sizes and shapes, and their small size allows for a large surface area-to-volume ratio that enables a more efficient exchange of nutrients and wastes with the environment.

There are three basic types of cells: archaea, bacteria, and eukaryotes. Both archaea and bacteria are classified as prokaryotes, whereas cells of animals, plants, fungi, and protists are eukaryotes. Archaea are a unique group of organisms and likely evolved in the harsh conditions of early Earth and are still prevalent today in extreme environments, such as hot springs and polar regions. All cells share features that reflect their evolution from a common ancestor; these features are 1) a plasma membrane that separates the cell from its environment; 2) cytoplasm comprising the jelly-like cytosol inside the cell; 3) ribosomes that are important for the synthesis of proteins, and 4) DNA to store and transmit hereditary information.

Prokaryotes may also have a cell wall that acts as an extra layer of protection against the external environment. The term "prokaryote" means "before nucleus," and prokaryotes do not have nuclei. Rather, their DNA exists as a single circular chromosome in the central part of the cell called the nucleoid. Some bacterial cells also have circular DNA plasmids that often carry genes for resistance to antibiotics (Chapter 17). Other common prokaryotic cell features include flagella and pili.

The content presented in this section supports the learning objectives outlined in Big Idea 1 and Big Idea 2 of the AP® Biology Curriculum Framework. The AP® Learning Objectives merge essential knowledge content with one or more of the seven Science Practices. These objectives provide a transparent foundation for the AP® Biology course, along with inquiry-based laboratory experiences, instructional activities, and AP® exam questions.

Big Idea 1	The process of evolution drives the diversity and unity of life.
Enduring Understanding 1.D	The origin of living systems is explained by natural processes.
Essential Knowledge	**1.D.2** Scientific evidence from many different disciplines supports models of the origin of life.
Science Practice	**4.1** The student can justify the selection of the kind of data needed to answer a particular scientific question.
Learning Objective	**1.32** The student is able to justify the selection of geological, physical, chemical, and biological data that reveal early Earth conditions.
Essential Knowledge	**2.A.3** Organisms must exchange matter with the environment to grow, reproduce and maintain organization.
Science Practice	**2.2** The student can apply mathematical routines to quantities that describe natural phenomena.
Learning Objective	**2.6** The student is able to use calculated surface area-to-volume ratios to predict which cell(s) might eliminate wastes or procure nutrients faster by diffusion.
Essential Knowledge	**2.A.3** Organisms must exchange matter with the environment to grow, reproduce and maintain organization.
Science Practice	**6.2** The student can construct explanations of phenomena based on evidence produced through scientific practices.
Learning Objective	**2.7** The student will be able to explain how cell sizes and shapes affect the overall rate of nutrient intake and the rate of waste elimination.

Cells fall into one of two broad categories: prokaryotic and eukaryotic. Only the predominantly single-celled organisms of the domains Bacteria and Archaea are classified as prokaryotes (pro- = "before"; -kary- = "nucleus"). Cells of animals, plants, fungi, and protists are all eukaryotes (eu- = "true") and have a nucleus.

Components of Prokaryotic Cells

All cells share four common components: 1) a plasma membrane, an outer covering that separates the cell's interior from its surrounding environment; 2) cytoplasm, consisting of a jelly-like cytosol within the cell in which other cellular components are found; 3) DNA, the genetic material of the cell; and 4) ribosomes, which synthesize proteins. However, prokaryotes differ from eukaryotic cells in several ways.

A **prokaryote** is a simple, single-celled (unicellular) organism that lacks a nucleus, or any other membrane-bound organelle. We will shortly come to see that this is significantly different in eukaryotes. Prokaryotic DNA is found in a central part of the cell: the **nucleoid** (Figure 4.5).

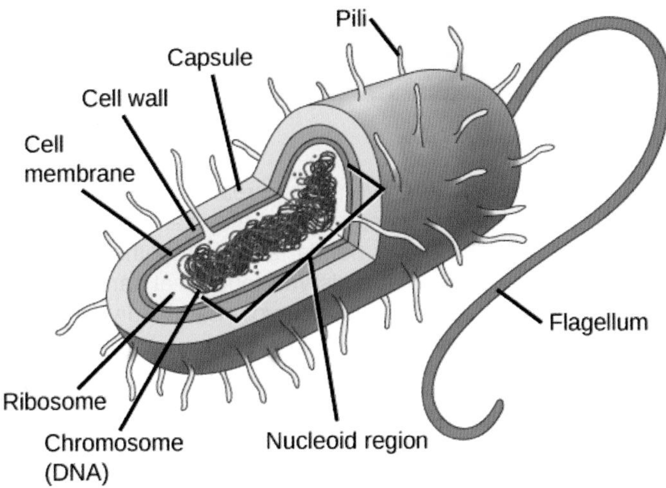

Figure 4.5 This figure shows the generalized structure of a prokaryotic cell. All prokaryotes have chromosomal DNA localized in a nucleoid, ribosomes, a cell membrane, and a cell wall. The other structures shown are present in some, but not all, bacteria.

everyday CONNECTION for AP® Courses

While the Earth is approximately 4.6 billion years old, the earliest fossil evidence for life are of microbial mats that date back to 3.5 billion years.

What type of evidence for life was most likely found in a 3.5 billion year old rock?

a. Scientists found bones buried in the rock that resemble bones of living animals.
b. Dead cells buried in the rock superficially resemble living prokaryotic cells.
c. The fossil superficially resembles living microbial mats that exist today.
d. Scientists found fossilized prokaryotic cells in the rock that are able to grow and divide.

Most prokaryotes have a peptidoglycan cell wall and many have a polysaccharide capsule (Figure 4.5). The cell wall acts as an extra layer of protection, helps the cell maintain its shape, and prevents dehydration. The capsule enables the cell to attach to surfaces in its environment. Some prokaryotes have flagella, pili, or fimbriae. Flagella are used for locomotion. Pili are used to exchange genetic material during a type of reproduction called conjugation. Fimbriae are used by bacteria to attach to a host cell.

Microbiologist

The most effective action anyone can take to prevent the spread of contagious illnesses is to wash his or her hands. Why? Because microbes (organisms so tiny that they can only be seen with microscopes) are ubiquitous. They live on doorknobs, money, your hands, and many other surfaces. If someone sneezes into his hand and touches a doorknob, and afterwards you touch that same doorknob, the microbes from the sneezer's mucus are now on your hands. If you touch your hands to your mouth, nose, or eyes, those microbes can enter your body and could make you sick.

However, not all microbes (also called microorganisms) cause disease; most are actually beneficial. You have microbes in your gut that make vitamin K.

Microbiologists are scientists who study microbes. Microbiologists can pursue a number of careers. Not only do they work in the food industry, they are also employed in the veterinary and medical fields. They can work in the pharmaceutical sector, serving key roles in research and development by identifying new sources of antibiotics that could be used to treat bacterial infections.

Environmental microbiologists may look for new ways to use specially selected or genetically engineered microbes for the removal of pollutants from soil or groundwater, as well as hazardous elements from contaminated sites. These uses of microbes are called bioremediation technologies. Microbiologists can also work in the field of bioinformatics, providing specialized knowledge and insight for the design, development, and specificity of computer models of, for example, bacterial epidemics.

Cell Size

At 0.1 to 5.0 μm in diameter, prokaryotic cells are significantly smaller than eukaryotic cells, which have diameters ranging from 10 to 100 μm (**Figure 4.6**). The small size of prokaryotes allows ions and organic molecules that enter them to quickly diffuse to other parts of the cell. Similarly, any wastes produced within a prokaryotic cell can quickly diffuse out. This is not the case in eukaryotic cells, which have developed different structural adaptations to enhance intracellular transport.

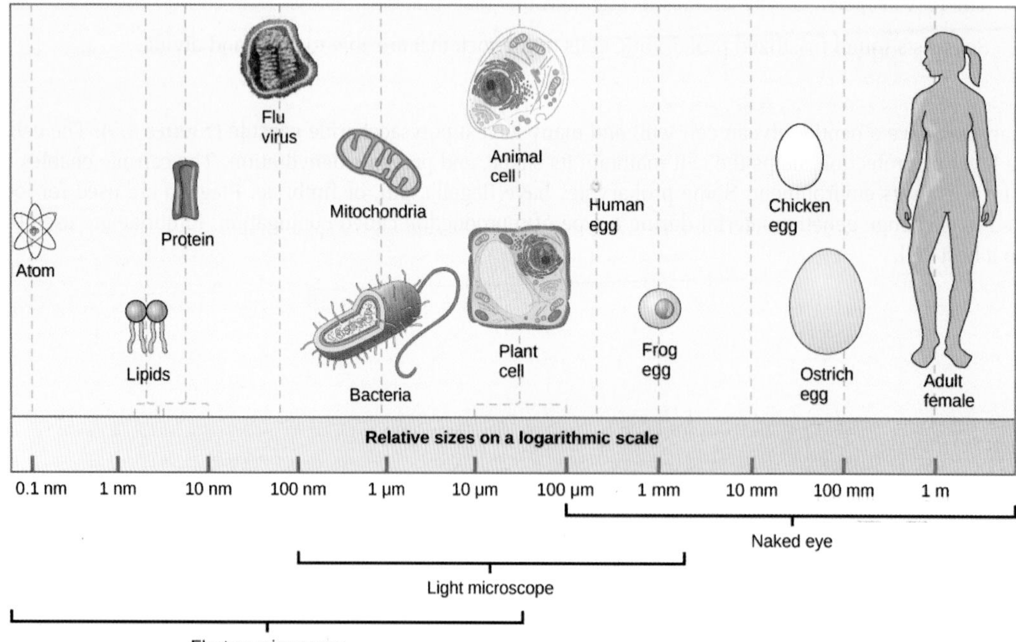

Figure 4.6 This figure shows relative sizes of microbes on a logarithmic scale (recall that each unit of increase in a logarithmic scale represents a 10-fold increase in the quantity being measured).

Small size, in general, is necessary for all cells, whether prokaryotic or eukaryotic. Let's examine why that is so. First, we'll consider the area and volume of a typical cell. Not all cells are spherical in shape, but most tend to approximate a sphere. You may remember from your high school geometry course that the formula for the surface area of a sphere is $4\pi r^2$, while the formula for its volume is $4\pi r^3/3$. Thus, as the radius of a cell increases, its surface area increases as the square of its radius, but its volume increases as the cube of its radius (much more rapidly). Therefore, as a cell increases in size, its surface area-to-volume ratio decreases. This same principle would apply if the cell had the shape of a cube (see this figure). If the cell grows too large, the plasma membrane will not have sufficient surface area to support the rate of diffusion required for the increased volume. In other words, as a cell grows, it becomes less efficient. One way to become more efficient is to divide; another way is to develop organelles that perform specific tasks. These adaptations lead to the development of more sophisticated cells called eukaryotic cells.

Besides the volume of the cell, the size of the cell is also important for survival. As mentioned before, most cells are approximately spherical in shape. This is because a sphere is the shape with the largest surface area-to-volume ratio. As nutrients diffuse into the cell, a sphere is the shape where nutrients would have to travel the least distance to reach the center. This is important because nutrients and wastes are always exchanged at the periphery of the cell. The shorter the distance these nutrients and wastes have to travel, the faster the exchange of these molecules are.

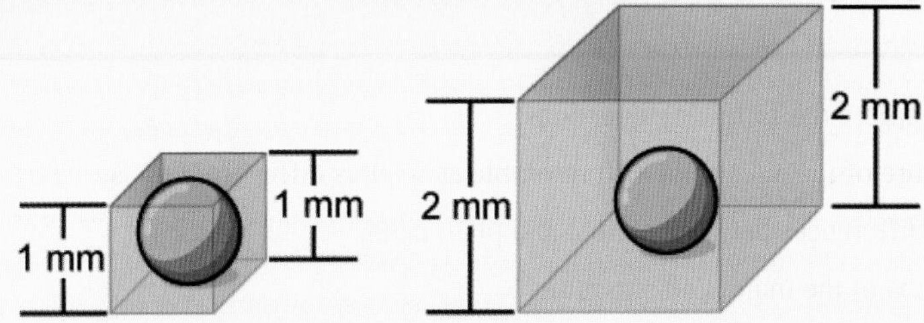

Figure 4.7 Notice that as a cell increases in size, its surface area-to-volume ratio decreases. When there is insufficient surface area to support a cell's increasing volume, a cell will either divide or die. The cell on the left has a volume of 1 mm^3 and a surface area of 6 mm^2, with a surface area-to-volume ratio of 6 to 1, whereas the cell on the right has a volume of 8 mm^3 and a surface area of 24 mm^2, with a surface area-to-volume ratio of 3 to 1.

On average, prokaryotic cells are smaller than eukaryotic cells. What are some advantages to small cell size? What are some advantages to large cell size?

a. Small, prokaryotic cells do not expend energy in intracellular transport of substances. Larger eukaryotic cells have organelles, which enable them to produce complex substances.

b. Small, prokaryotic cells easily escape the spontaneous changes in environmental conditions. Large, eukaryotic cells have complex mechanisms to cope with such changes.

c. Small, prokaryotic cells divide at a higher rate. Large, eukaryotic cells show division with genetic variations.

d. Small, prokaryotic cells have fewer phospholipids in their membrane. Large, eukaryotic cells have more transport proteins in their phospholipid bilayer, supporting efficient transport of molecules.

science practices CONNECTION for AP® Courses

Activity

Create an annotated diagram to explain how approximately 300 million alveoli in a human lung increases surface area for gas exchange to the size of a tennis court. Use the diagram to explain how the cellular structures of alveoli, capillaries, and red blood cells allow for rapid diffusion of O_2 and CO_2 among them.

Think About It

Which of the following cells would likely exchange nutrients and wastes with its environment more efficiently: a spherical cell with a diameter of 5 μm or a cubed-shaped cell with a side length of 7μm? Provide a quantitative justification for your answer based on surface area-to-volume ratios.

4.3 | Eukaryotic Cells

In this section, you will explore the following questions:

- How does the structure of the eukaryotic cell resemble as well as differ from the structure of the prokaryotic cell?
- What are structural differences between animal and plant cells?
- What are the functions of the major cell structures?

Connection for AP® Courses

Eukaryotic cells possess many features that prokaryotic cells lack, including a nucleus with a double membrane that encloses DNA. In addition, eukaryotic cells tend to be larger and have a variety of membrane-bound organelles that perform specific, compartmentalized functions. Evidence supports the hypothesis that eukaryotic cells likely evolved from prokaryotic ancestors; for example, mitochondria and chloroplasts feature characteristics of independently-living prokaryotes. Eukaryotic cells come in all shapes, sizes, and types (e.g. animal cells, plant cells, and different types of cells in the body). (Hint: This a rare instance where you should create a list of organelles and their respective functions because later you will focus on how various organelles work together, similar to how your body's organs work together to keep you healthy.) Like prokaryotes, all eukaryotic cells have a plasma membrane, cytoplasm, ribosomes, and DNA. Many organelles are bound by membranes composed of phospholipid bilayers embedded with proteins to compartmentalize functions such as the storage of hydrolytic enzymes and the synthesis of proteins. The nucleus houses DNA, and the nucleolus within the nucleus is the site of ribosome assembly. Functional ribosomes are found either free in the cytoplasm or attached to the rough endoplasmic reticulum where they perform protein synthesis. The Golgi apparatus receives, modifies, and packages small molecules like lipids and proteins for distribution. Mitochondria and chloroplasts participate in free energy capture and transfer through the processes of cellular respiration and photosynthesis, respectively. Peroxisomes oxidize fatty acids and amino acids, and they are equipped to break down hydrogen peroxide formed from these reactions without letting it into the cytoplasm where it can cause damage. Vesicles and vacuoles store substances, and in plant cells, the central vacuole stores pigments, salts, minerals, nutrients, proteins, and degradation enzymes and helps maintain rigidity. In contrast, animal cells have centrosomes and lysosomes but lack cell walls.

Information presented and the examples highlighted in the section support concepts and Learning Objectives outlined in Big Idea 1, Big Idea 2, and Big Idea 4 of the AP® Biology Curriculum Framework. The Learning Objectives listed in the Curriculum Framework provide a transparent foundation for the AP® Biology course, an inquiry-based laboratory experience, instructional activities, and AP® exam questions. A Learning Objective merges required content with one or more of the seven Science Practices.

Big Idea 1	The process of evolution drives the diversity and unity of life.

Enduring Understanding 1.B	Organisms are linked by lines of descent from common ancestry
Essential Knowledge	**1.B.1** Organisms share many conserved core processes and features that evolved and are widely distributed among organisms today.
Science Practice	**7.2** The student can connect concepts in and across domains to generalize or extrapolate in and/or across enduring understandings
Learning Objective	**1.15** The student is able to describe specific examples of conserved core biological processes and features shared by all domains or within one domain of life and how these shared, conserved core processes and features support the concept of common ancestry for all organisms.
Big Idea 2	Biological systems utilize free energy and molecular building blocks to grow, to reproduce and to maintain dynamic homeostasis.
Enduring Understanding 2.B	Growth, reproduction and dynamic homeostasis require that cells create and maintain internal environments that are different from their external environments.
Essential Knowledge	**2.B.3** Eukaryotic cells maintain internal membranes that partition the cell into specialized regions.
Science Practice	**6.2** The student can construct explanations of phenomena based on evidence produced through scientific practices.
Learning Objective	**2.13** The student is able to explain how internal membranes and organelles contribute to cell functions.
Essential Knowledge	**2.B.3** Eukaryotic cells maintain internal membranes that partition the cell into specialized regions.
Science Practice	**1.4** The student can use representations and models to analyze situations or solve problems qualitatively and quantitatively.
Learning Objective	**2.14** The student is able to use representations and models to describe differences in prokaryotic and eukaryotic cells.
Big Idea 4	Biological systems interact, and these systems and their interactions possess complex properties.
Enduring Understanding 4.A	Interactions within biological systems lead to complex properties.
Essential Knowledge	**4.A.2** The structure and function of subcellular components, and their interactions, provide essential cellular processes.
Science Practice	**6.2** The student can construct explanations of phenomena based on evidence produced through scientific practices.
Learning Objective	**4.5** The student is able to construct explanations based on scientific evidence as to how interactions of subcellular structures provide essential functions.

The Science Practice Challenge Questions contain additional test questions for this section that will help you prepare for the AP exam. These questions address the following standards:
[APLO 1.15] [APLO 2.5][APLO 2.25][APLO 1.16]

Have you ever heard the phrase "form follows function?" It's a philosophy practiced in many industries. In architecture, this means that buildings should be constructed to support the activities that will be carried out inside them. For example, a skyscraper should be built with several elevator banks; a hospital should be built so that its emergency room is easily accessible.

Our natural world also utilizes the principle of form following function, especially in cell biology, and this will become clear as we explore eukaryotic cells (Figure 4.8). Unlike prokaryotic cells, **eukaryotic cells** have: 1) a membrane-bound nucleus; 2) numerous membrane-bound **organelles** such as the endoplasmic reticulum, Golgi apparatus, chloroplasts, mitochondria, and others; and 3) several, rod-shaped chromosomes. Because a eukaryotic cell's nucleus is surrounded by a membrane, it is often said to have a "true nucleus." The word "organelle" means "little organ," and, as already mentioned, organelles have specialized cellular functions, just as the organs of your body have specialized functions.

At this point, it should be clear to you that eukaryotic cells have a more complex structure than prokaryotic cells. Organelles allow different functions to be compartmentalized in different areas of the cell. Before turning to organelles, let's first examine two important components of the cell: the plasma membrane and the cytoplasm.

visual CONNECTION

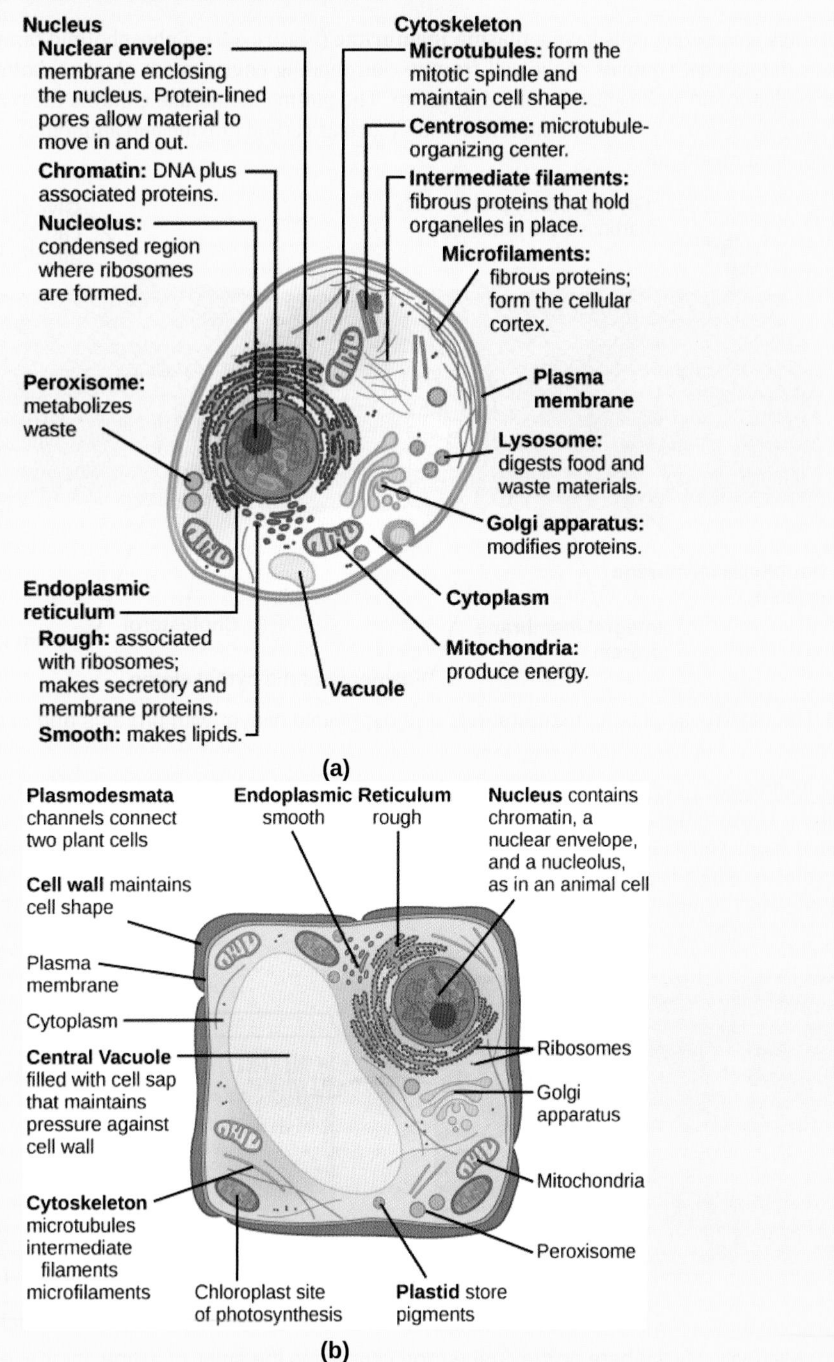

Figure 4.8 These figures show the major organelles and other cell components of (a) a typical animal cell and (b) a typical eukaryotic plant cell. The plant cell has a cell wall, chloroplasts, plastids, and a central vacuole—structures not found in animal cells. Most plant cells do not have lysosomes or centrosomes.

If the nucleolus were not able to carry out its function, what other cellular organelles would be affected?

a. The structure of endoplasmic reticulum would not form.
b. The function of lysosomes would be hindered, as hydrolases are formed by nucleolus.
c. The free ribosomes and the rough endoplasmic reticulum, which contains ribosomes, would not form.

d. The Golgi apparatus will not be able to sort proteins properly.

The Plasma Membrane

Like prokaryotes, eukaryotic cells have a **plasma membrane** (Figure 4.9), a phospholipid bilayer with embedded proteins that separates the internal contents of the cell from its surrounding environment. A phospholipid is a lipid molecule with two fatty acid chains and a phosphate-containing group. The plasma membrane controls the passage of organic molecules, ions, water, and oxygen into and out of the cell. Wastes (such as carbon dioxide and ammonia) also leave the cell by passing through the plasma membrane.

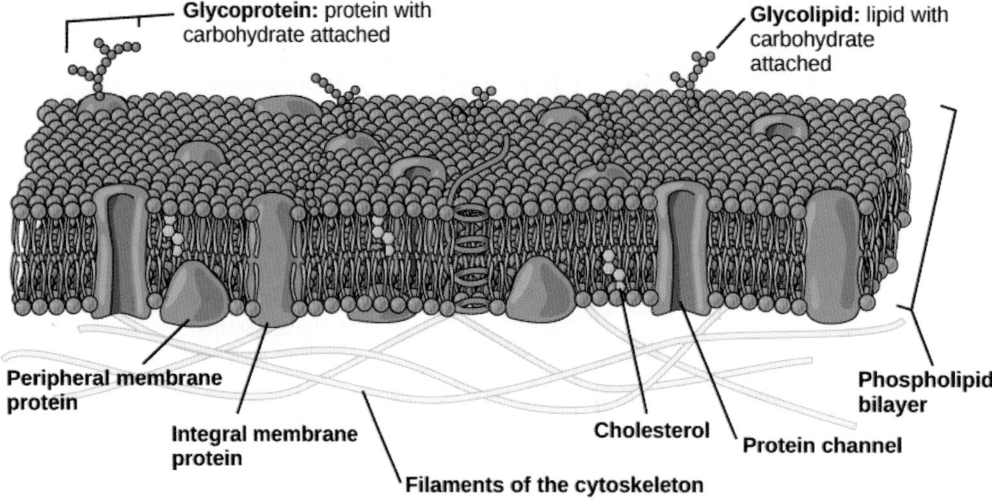

Figure 4.9 The eukaryotic plasma membrane is a phospholipid bilayer with proteins and cholesterol embedded in it.

The plasma membranes of cells that specialize in absorption are folded into fingerlike projections called microvilli (singular = microvillus); (Figure 4.10). Such cells are typically found lining the small intestine, the organ that absorbs nutrients from digested food. This is an excellent example of form following function. People with celiac disease have an immune response to gluten, which is a protein found in wheat, barley, and rye. The immune response damages microvilli, and thus, afflicted individuals cannot absorb nutrients. This leads to malnutrition, cramping, and diarrhea. Patients suffering from celiac disease must follow a gluten-free diet.

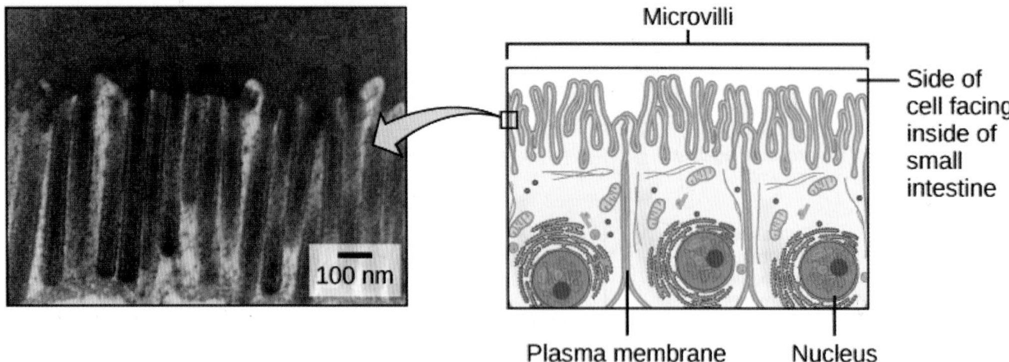

Figure 4.10 Microvilli, shown here as they appear on cells lining the small intestine, increase the surface area available for absorption. These microvilli are only found on the area of the plasma membrane that faces the cavity from which substances will be absorbed. (credit "micrograph": modification of work by Louisa Howard)

The Cytoplasm

The **cytoplasm** is the entire region of a cell between the plasma membrane and the nuclear envelope (a structure to be discussed shortly). It is made up of organelles suspended in the gel-like **cytosol**, the cytoskeleton, and various chemicals (Figure 4.8). Even though the cytoplasm consists of 70 to 80 percent water, it has a semi-solid consistency, which comes from the proteins within it. However, proteins are not the only organic molecules found in the cytoplasm. Glucose and other simple sugars, polysaccharides, amino acids, nucleic acids, fatty acids, and derivatives of glycerol are found there, too. Ions of sodium, potassium, calcium, and many other elements are also dissolved in the cytoplasm. Many metabolic reactions, including protein synthesis, take place in the cytoplasm.

The Nucleus

Typically, the nucleus is the most prominent organelle in a cell (Figure 4.8). The **nucleus** (plural = nuclei) houses the cell's DNA and directs the synthesis of ribosomes and proteins. Let's look at it in more detail (Figure 4.11).

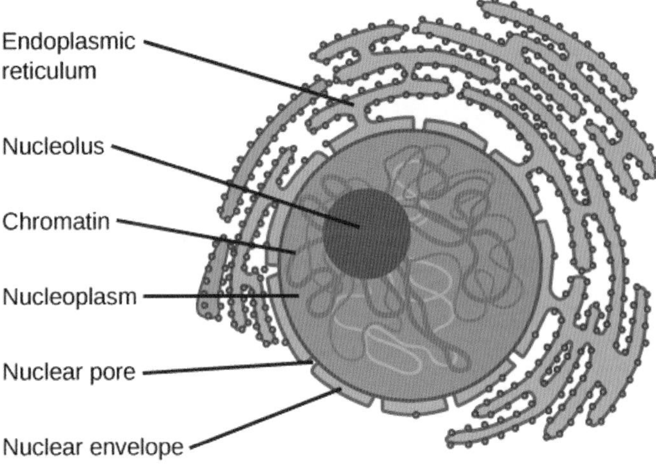

Figure 4.11 The nucleus stores chromatin (DNA plus proteins) in a gel-like substance called the nucleoplasm. The nucleolus is a condensed region of chromatin where ribosome synthesis occurs. The boundary of the nucleus is called the nuclear envelope. It consists of two phospholipid bilayers: an outer membrane and an inner membrane. The nuclear membrane is continuous with the endoplasmic reticulum. Nuclear pores allow substances to enter and exit the nucleus.

The Nuclear Envelope

The **nuclear envelope** is a double-membrane structure that constitutes the outermost portion of the nucleus (Figure 4.11). Both the inner and outer membranes of the nuclear envelope are phospholipid bilayers.

The nuclear envelope is punctuated with pores that control the passage of ions, molecules, and RNA between the nucleoplasm and cytoplasm. The **nucleoplasm** is the semi-solid fluid inside the nucleus, where we find the chromatin and the nucleolus.

Chromatin and Chromosomes

To understand chromatin, it is helpful to first consider chromosomes. **Chromosomes** are structures within the nucleus that are made up of DNA, the hereditary material. You may remember that in prokaryotes, DNA is organized into a single circular chromosome. In eukaryotes, chromosomes are linear structures. Every eukaryotic species has a specific number of chromosomes in the nucleus of each cell. For example, in humans, the chromosome number is 46, while in fruit flies, it is eight. Chromosomes are only visible and distinguishable from one another when the cell is getting ready to divide. When the cell is in the growth and maintenance phases of its life cycle, proteins are attached to chromosomes, and they resemble an unwound, jumbled bunch of threads. These unwound protein-chromosome complexes are called **chromatin** (Figure 4.12); chromatin describes the material that makes up the chromosomes both when condensed and decondensed.

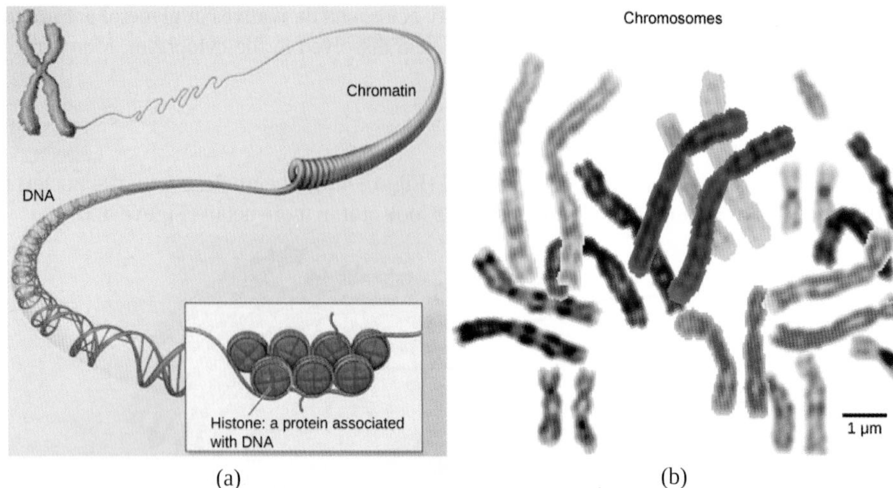

Figure 4.12 (a) This image shows various levels of the organization of chromatin (DNA and protein). (b) This image shows paired chromosomes. (credit b: modification of work by NIH; scale-bar data from Matt Russell)

The Nucleolus

We already know that the nucleus directs the synthesis of ribosomes, but how does it do this? Some chromosomes have sections of DNA that encode ribosomal RNA. A darkly staining area within the nucleus called the **nucleolus** (plural = nucleoli) aggregates the ribosomal RNA with associated proteins to assemble the ribosomal subunits that are then transported out through the pores in the nuclear envelope to the cytoplasm.

Ribosomes

Ribosomes are the cellular structures responsible for protein synthesis. When viewed through an electron microscope, ribosomes appear either as clusters (polyribosomes) or single, tiny dots that float freely in the cytoplasm. They may be attached to the cytoplasmic side of the plasma membrane or the cytoplasmic side of the endoplasmic reticulum and the outer membrane of the nuclear envelope (Figure 4.8). Electron microscopy has shown us that ribosomes, which are large complexes of protein and RNA, consist of two subunits, aptly called large and small (Figure 4.13). Ribosomes receive their "orders" for protein synthesis from the nucleus where the DNA is transcribed into messenger RNA (mRNA). The mRNA travels to the ribosomes, which translate the code provided by the sequence of the nitrogenous bases in the mRNA into a specific order of amino acids in a protein. Amino acids are the building blocks of proteins.

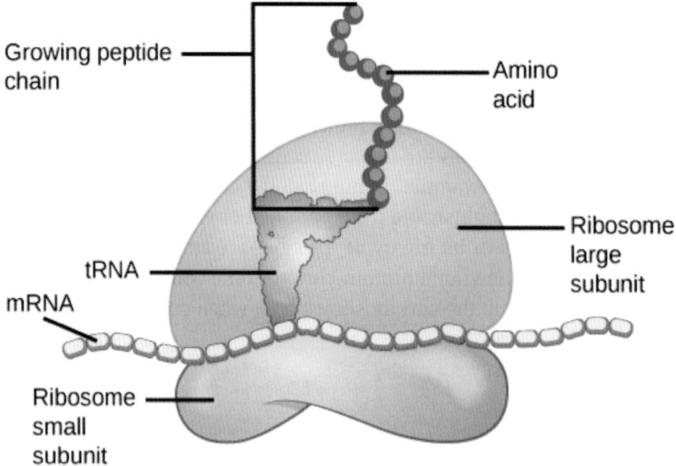

Figure 4.13 Ribosomes are made up of a large subunit (top) and a small subunit (bottom). During protein synthesis, ribosomes assemble amino acids into proteins.

Because protein synthesis is an essential function of all cells (including enzymes, hormones, antibodies, pigments, structural components, and surface receptors), ribosomes are found in practically every cell. Ribosomes are particularly abundant in cells that synthesize large amounts of protein. For example, the pancreas is responsible for creating several digestive enzymes and the cells that produce these enzymes contain many ribosomes. Thus, we see another example of form following function.

Mitochondria

Mitochondria (singular = mitochondrion) are often called the “powerhouses” or “energy factories” of a cell because they are responsible for making adenosine triphosphate (ATP), the cell’s main energy-carrying molecule. ATP represents the short-term stored energy of the cell. Cellular respiration is the process of making ATP using the chemical energy found in glucose and other nutrients. In mitochondria, this process uses oxygen and produces carbon dioxide as a waste product. In fact, the carbon dioxide that you exhale with every breath comes from the cellular reactions that produce carbon dioxide as a byproduct.

In keeping with our theme of form following function, it is important to point out that muscle cells have a very high concentration of mitochondria that produce ATP. Your muscle cells need a lot of energy to keep your body moving. When your cells don’t get enough oxygen, they do not make a lot of ATP. Instead, the small amount of ATP they make in the absence of oxygen is accompanied by the production of lactic acid.

Mitochondria are oval-shaped, double membrane organelles (Figure 4.14) that have their own ribosomes and DNA. Each membrane is a phospholipid bilayer embedded with proteins. The inner layer has folds called cristae. The area surrounded by the folds is called the mitochondrial matrix. The cristae and the matrix have different roles in cellular respiration.

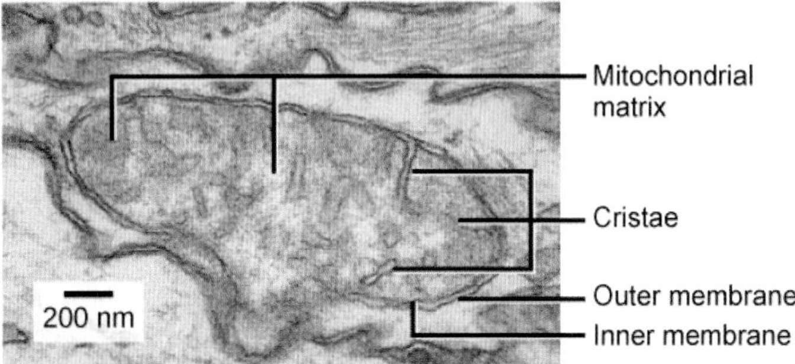

Figure 4.14 This electron micrograph shows a mitochondrion as viewed with a transmission electron microscope. This organelle has an outer membrane and an inner membrane. The inner membrane contains folds, called cristae, which increase its surface area. The space between the two membranes is called the intermembrane space, and the space inside the inner membrane is called the mitochondrial matrix. ATP synthesis takes place on the inner membrane. (credit: modification of work by Matthew Britton; scale-bar data from Matt Russell)

Peroxisomes

Peroxisomes are small, round organelles enclosed by single membranes. They carry out oxidation reactions that break down fatty acids and amino acids. They also detoxify many poisons that may enter the body. (Many of these oxidation reactions release hydrogen peroxide, H_2O_2, which would be damaging to cells; however, when these reactions are confined to peroxisomes, enzymes safely break down the H_2O_2 into oxygen and water.) Glyoxysomes, which are specialized peroxisomes in plants, are responsible for converting stored fats into sugars.

Vesicles and Vacuoles

Vesicles and **vacuoles** are membrane-bound sacs that function in storage and transport. Other than the fact that vacuoles are somewhat larger than vesicles, there is a very subtle distinction between them: The membranes of vesicles can fuse with either the plasma membrane or other membrane systems within the cell. Additionally, some agents such as enzymes within plant vacuoles break down macromolecules. The membrane of a vacuole does not fuse with the membranes of other cellular components.

Animal Cells versus Plant Cells

At this point, you know that each eukaryotic cell has a plasma membrane, cytoplasm, a nucleus, ribosomes, mitochondria, peroxisomes, and in some, vacuoles, but there are some striking differences between animal and plant cells. While both animal and plant cells have microtubule organizing centers (MTOCs), animal cells also have centrioles associated with the MTOC: a complex called the centrosome. Animal cells each have a centrosome and lysosomes, whereas most plant cells do not. Plant cells have a cell wall, chloroplasts and other specialized plastids, and a large central vacuole, whereas animal cells do not.

The Centrosome

The **centrosome** is a microtubule-organizing center found near the nuclei of animal cells. It contains a pair of centrioles, two structures that lie perpendicular to each other (Figure 4.15). Each centriole is a cylinder of nine triplets of microtubules.

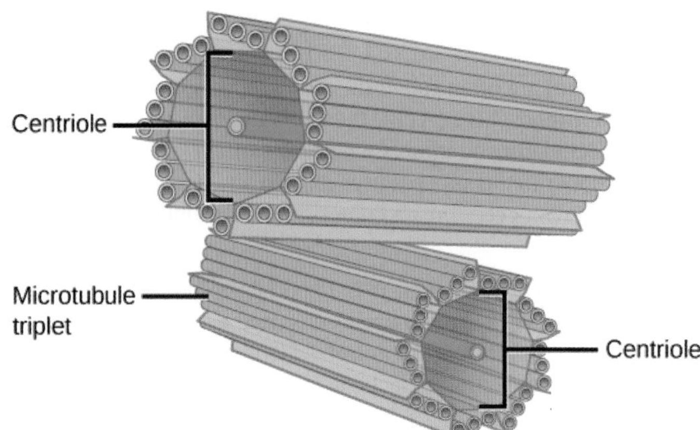

Figure 4.15 The centrosome consists of two centrioles that lie at right angles to each other. Each centriole is a cylinder made up of nine triplets of microtubules. Nontubulin proteins (indicated by the green lines) hold the microtubule triplets together.

The centrosome (the organelle where all microtubules originate) replicates itself before a cell divides, and the centrioles appear to have some role in pulling the duplicated chromosomes to opposite ends of the dividing cell. However, the exact function of the centrioles in cell division isn't clear, because cells that have had the centrosome removed can still divide, and plant cells, which lack centrosomes, are capable of cell division.

Lysosomes

Animal cells have another set of organelles not found in most plant cells: lysosomes. The **lysosomes** are the cell's "garbage disposal." In plant cells, the digestive processes take place in vacuoles. Enzymes within the lysosomes aid the breakdown of proteins, polysaccharides, lipids, nucleic acids, and even worn-out organelles. These enzymes are active at a much lower pH than that of the cytoplasm. Therefore, the pH within lysosomes is more acidic than the pH of the cytoplasm. Many reactions that take place in the cytoplasm could not occur at a low pH, so again, the advantage of compartmentalizing the eukaryotic cell into organelles is apparent.

The Cell Wall

If you examine Figure 4.8**b**, the diagram of a plant cell, you will see a structure external to the plasma membrane called the cell wall. The **cell wall** is a rigid covering that protects the cell, provides structural support, and gives shape to the cell. Fungal and protistan cells also have cell walls. While the chief component of prokaryotic cell walls is peptidoglycan, the major organic molecule in the plant cell wall is cellulose (Figure 4.16), a polysaccharide made up of glucose units. Have you ever noticed that when you bite into a raw vegetable, like celery, it crunches? That's because you are tearing the rigid cell walls of the celery cells with your teeth.

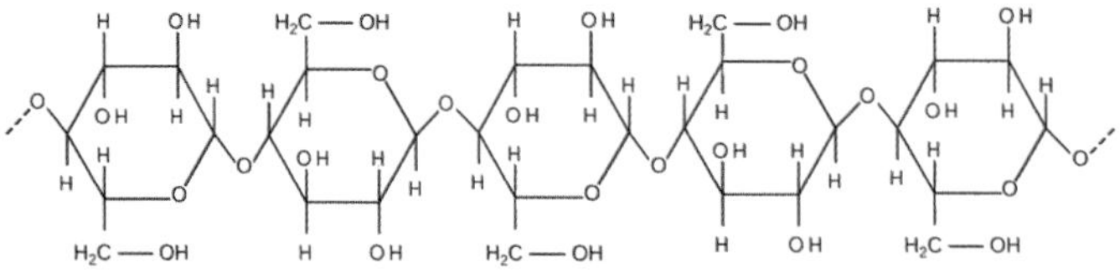

Figure 4.16 Cellulose is a long chain of β-glucose molecules connected by a 1-4 linkage. The dashed lines at each end of the figure indicate a series of many more glucose units. The size of the page makes it impossible to portray an entire cellulose molecule.

Chloroplasts

Like the mitochondria, chloroplasts have their own DNA and ribosomes, but chloroplasts have an entirely different function. **Chloroplasts** are plant cell organelles that carry out photosynthesis. Photosynthesis is the series of reactions that use carbon dioxide, water, and light energy to make glucose and oxygen. This is a major difference between plants and animals; plants (autotrophs) are able to make their own food, like sugars, while animals (heterotrophs) must ingest their food.

Like mitochondria, chloroplasts have outer and inner membranes, but within the space enclosed by a chloroplast's inner membrane is a set of interconnected and stacked fluid-filled membrane sacs called thylakoids (Figure 4.17). Each stack of thylakoids is called a granum (plural = grana). The fluid enclosed by the inner membrane that surrounds the grana is called the stroma.

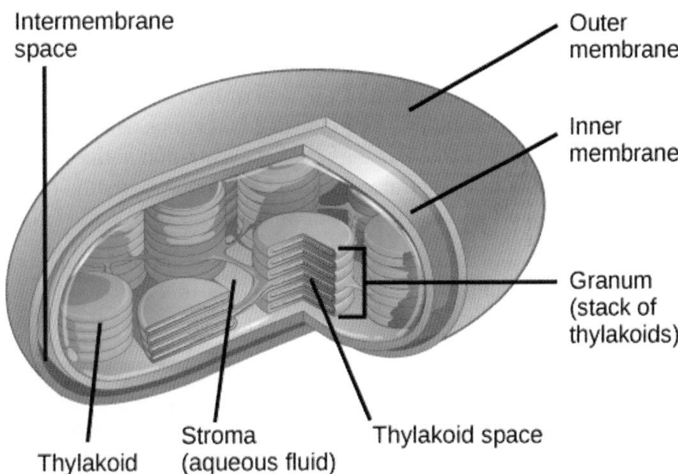

Figure 4.17 The chloroplast has an outer membrane, an inner membrane, and membrane structures called thylakoids that are stacked into grana. The space inside the thylakoid membranes is called the thylakoid space. The light harvesting reactions take place in the thylakoid membranes, and the synthesis of sugar takes place in the fluid inside the inner membrane, which is called the stroma. Chloroplasts also have their own genome, which is contained on a single circular chromosome.

The chloroplasts contain a green pigment called **chlorophyll**, which captures the light energy that drives the reactions of photosynthesis. Like plant cells, photosynthetic protists also have chloroplasts. Some bacteria perform photosynthesis, but their chlorophyll is not relegated to an organelle.

evolution CONNECTION

Endosymbiosis

We have mentioned that both mitochondria and chloroplasts contain DNA and ribosomes. Have you wondered why? Strong evidence points to endosymbiosis as the explanation.

Symbiosis is a relationship in which organisms from two separate species depend on each other for their survival. Endosymbiosis (endo- = "within") is a mutually beneficial relationship in which one organism lives inside the other. Endosymbiotic relationships abound in nature. We have already mentioned that microbes that produce vitamin K live inside the human gut. This relationship is beneficial for us because we are unable to synthesize vitamin K. It is also beneficial for the microbes because they are protected from other organisms and from drying out, and they receive abundant food from the environment of the large intestine.

Scientists have long noticed that bacteria, mitochondria, and chloroplasts are similar in size. We also know that bacteria have DNA and ribosomes, just as mitochondria and chloroplasts do. Scientists believe that host cells and bacteria formed an endosymbiotic relationship when the host cells ingested both aerobic and autotrophic bacteria (cyanobacteria) but did not destroy them. Through many millions of years of evolution, these ingested bacteria became more specialized in their functions, with the aerobic bacteria becoming mitochondria and the autotrophic bacteria becoming chloroplasts.

Based on what you know about plant and animals cells, which of the following events are most likely to have occurred?

a. A host cell that ingested aerobic bacteria gave rise to modern animals, while ancestor of that cell that also ingested photoautotrophic bacteria that gave rise to modern plants.

b. A host cell that gave rise to modern plants ingested photoautotrophic bacteria only, while a host cell that gave rise to modern animals ingested aerobic bacteria only.

c. A host cell that gave rise to modern plants ingested both aerobic and photoautotrophic bacteria, while a host cell that gave rise to modern animals ingested photoautotrophic bacteria only.

d. A host cell that gave rise to modern plants and animals ingested both aerobic and photoautotrophic bacteria.

The Central Vacuole

Previously, we mentioned vacuoles as essential components of plant cells. If you look at Figure 4.8**b**, you will see that plant cells each have a large central vacuole that occupies most of the area of the cell. The **central vacuole** plays a key role in regulating the cell's concentration of water in changing environmental conditions. Have you ever noticed that if you forget to water a plant for a few days, it wilts? That's because as the water concentration in the soil becomes lower than the water concentration in the plant, water moves out of the central vacuoles and cytoplasm. As the central vacuole shrinks, it leaves the cell wall unsupported. This loss of support to the cell walls of plant cells results in the wilted appearance of the plant.

The central vacuole also supports the expansion of the cell. When the central vacuole holds more water, the cell gets larger without having to invest a lot of energy in synthesizing new cytoplasm.

science practices CONNECTION for AP® Courses

Activity

- Construct a concept map or Venn diagram to describe the relationships that exist among the three domains of life (Archaea, Bacteria, and Eukarya) based on cellular features. Share your diagram with other students in the class for review and revision.
- Mystery Cell ID. Using a microscope, identify several types of cells, e.g., prokaryote/eukaryote, plant/animal, based on general features and justify your identification.
- Ten-Minute Debate. Working in small teams, create a visual representation to support the claim that eukaryotes evolved from symbiotic relationships among groups of prokaryotes.

Think About It

- If the nucleolus were not able to carry out its function, what other cellular organelles would be affected? Would a human liver cell that lacked endoplasmic reticulum be able to metabolize toxins?
- Antibiotics are medicines that are used to fight bacterial infections. These medicines kill prokaryotic cells without harming human cells. What part(s) of the bacterial cell do antibiotics target and provide reasoning for your answer.

Section Summary

Like a prokaryotic cell, a eukaryotic cell has a plasma membrane, cytoplasm, and ribosomes, but a eukaryotic cell is typically larger than a prokaryotic cell, has a true nucleus (meaning its DNA is surrounded by a membrane), and has other membrane-bound organelles that allow for compartmentalization of functions. The plasma membrane is a phospholipid bilayer embedded with proteins. The nucleus's nucleolus is the site of ribosome assembly. Ribosomes are either found in the cytoplasm or attached to the cytoplasmic side of the plasma membrane or endoplasmic reticulum. They perform protein synthesis. Mitochondria participate in cellular respiration; they are responsible for the majority of ATP produced in the cell. Peroxisomes hydrolyze fatty acids, amino acids, and some toxins. Vesicles and vacuoles are storage and transport compartments. In plant cells, vacuoles also help break down macromolecules.

Animal cells also have a centrosome and lysosomes. The centrosome has two bodies perpendicular to each other, the centrioles, and has an unknown purpose in cell division. Lysosomes are the digestive organelles of animal cells.

Plant cells and plant-like cells each have a cell wall, chloroplasts, and a central vacuole. The plant cell wall, whose primary component is cellulose, protects the cell, provides structural support, and gives shape to the cell. Photosynthesis takes place in chloroplasts. The central vacuole can expand without having to produce more cytoplasm.

4.4 | The Endomembrane System and Proteins

In this section, you will explore the following questions:

- What is the relationship between the structure and function of the components of the endomembrane system, especially with regard to the synthesis of proteins?

Connection for AP® Courses

In addition to the presence of nuclei, eukaryotic cells are distinguished by an endomembrane system that includes the plasma membrane, nuclear envelope, lysosomes, vesicles, endoplasmic reticulum, and Golgi apparatus. These subcellular components work together to modify, tag, package, and transport proteins and lipids. The rough endoplasmic reticulum (RER) with its attached ribosomes is the site of protein synthesis and modification. The smooth endoplasmic reticulum (SER) synthesizes carbohydrates, lipids including phospholipids and cholesterol, and steroid hormones; engages in the detoxification of medications and poisons; and stores calcium ions. Lysosomes digest macromolecules, recycle worn-out organelles, and destroy pathogens. Just like your body uses different organs that work together, cells use these organelles interact to perform specific functions. For example, proteins that are synthesized in the RER then travel to the Golgi apparatus for modification and packaging for either storage or transport. If these proteins are hydrolytic enzymes, they can be stored in lysosomes. Mitochondria produce the energy needed for these processes. This functional flow through several organelles, a process which is dependent on energy produced by yet another organelle, serves as a hallmark illustration of the cell's complex, interconnected dependence on its organelles.

Information presented and the examples highlighted in the section support concepts and Learning Objectives outlined in Big Idea 2 and Big Idea 4 of the AP® Biology Curriculum Framework. The Learning Objectives listed in the Curriculum Framework provide a transparent foundation for the AP® Biology course, an inquiry-based laboratory experience, instructional activities, and AP® exam questions. A Learning Objective merges required content with one or more of the seven Science Practices.

Big Idea 2	Biological systems utilize free energy and molecular building blocks to grow, to reproduce, and to maintain dynamic homeostasis.
Enduring Understanding 2.B	Growth, reproduction and dynamic homeostasis require that cells create and maintain internal environments that are different from their external environments.
Essential Knowledge	**2.B.3** Eukaryotic cells maintain internal membranes that partition the cell into specialized regions.
Science Practice	**6.2** The student can construct explanations of phenomena based on evidence produced through scientific practices.
Learning Objective	**2.13** The student is able to explain how internal membranes and organelles contribute to cell functions.
Big Idea 4	Biological systems interact, and these systems and their interactions possess complex properties.
Enduring Understanding 4.A	Interactions within biological systems lead to complex properties.
Essential Knowledge	**4.A.2** The structure and function of subcellular components, and their interactions, provide essential cellular processes.
Science Practice	**6.2** The student can construct explanations of phenomena based on evidence produced through scientific practices.
Learning Objective	**4.5** The student is able to construct explanations based on scientific evidence as to how interactions of subcellular structures provide essential functions.

The Science Practice Challenge Questions contain additional test questions for this section that will help you prepare for the AP exam. These questions address the following standards:
[APLO 4.6]

The Endoplasmic Reticulum

The endomembrane system (endo = "within") is a group of membranes and organelles (Figure 4.18) in eukaryotic cells that works together to modify, package, and transport lipids and proteins. It includes the nuclear envelope, lysosomes, and vesicles, which we've already mentioned, and the endoplasmic reticulum and Golgi apparatus, which we will cover shortly.

Although not technically *within* the cell, the plasma membrane is included in the endomembrane system because, as you will see, it interacts with the other endomembranous organelles. The endomembrane system does not include the membranes of either mitochondria or chloroplasts.

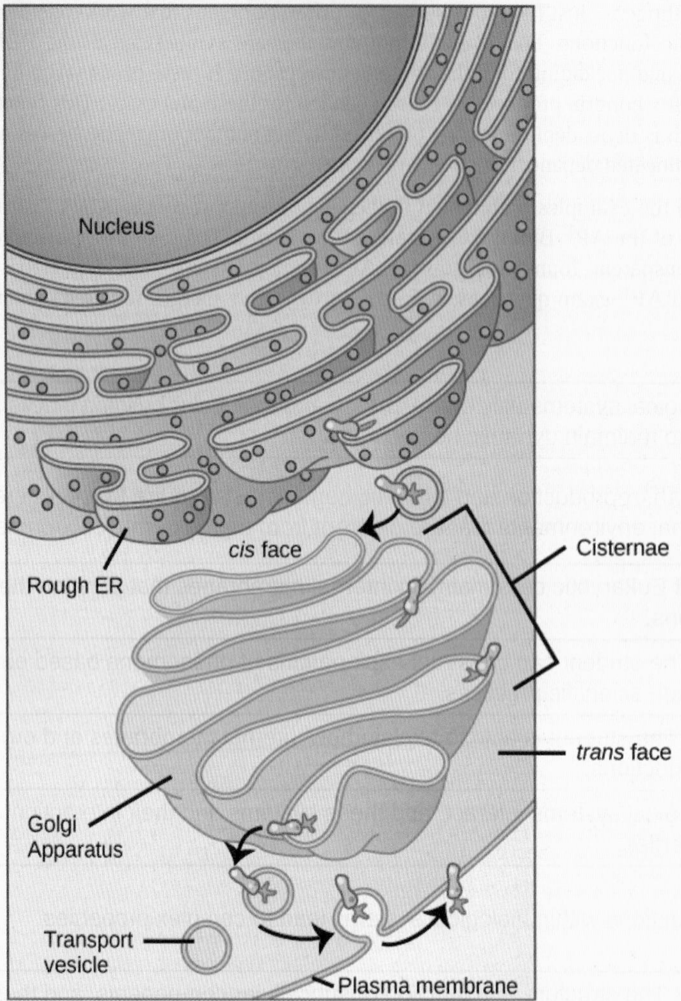

Figure 4.18 Membrane and secretory proteins are synthesized in the rough endoplasmic reticulum (RER). The RER also sometimes modifies proteins. In this illustration, a (green) integral membrane protein in the ER is modified by attachment of a (purple) carbohydrate. Vesicles with the integral protein bud from the ER and fuse with the cis face of the Golgi apparatus. As the protein passes along the Golgi's cisternae, it is further modified by the addition of more carbohydrates. After its synthesis is complete, it exits as an integral membrane protein of the vesicles that bud from the Golgi's **trans** face. When the vesicle fuses with the cell membrane, the protein becomes an integral portion of that cell membrane. (credit: modification of work by Magnus Manske)

If a peripheral membrane protein were synthesized inside the lumen of the ER, would it end up on the inside or outside of the plasma membrane?

a. The vesicle travels from the endoplasmic reticulum to get embedded in plasma membrane.

b. The vesicle travels from the Golgi to the plasma membrane to release the protein outside.

c. The vesicle travels from the endoplasmic reticulum to the plasma membrane, and returns to the Golgi apparatus to get modified.

d. The vesicle moves from the endoplasmic reticulum into the cytoplasmic area, remaining there.

The **endoplasmic reticulum (ER)** (Figure 4.18) is a series of interconnected membranous sacs and tubules that collectively modifies proteins and synthesizes lipids. However, these two functions are performed in separate areas of the ER: the rough ER and the smooth ER, respectively.

The hollow portion of the ER tubules is called the lumen or cisternal space. The membrane of the ER, which is a phospholipid bilayer embedded with proteins, is continuous with the nuclear envelope.

Rough ER

The **rough endoplasmic reticulum (RER)** is so named because the ribosomes attached to its cytoplasmic surface give it a studded appearance when viewed through an electron microscope (Figure 4.19).

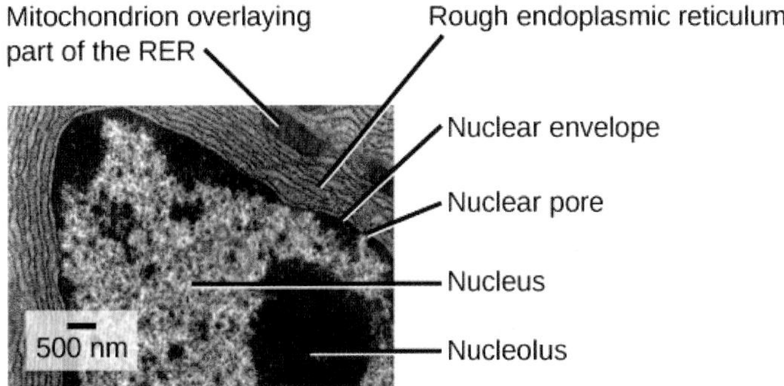

Figure 4.19 This transmission electron micrograph shows the rough endoplasmic reticulum and other organelles in a pancreatic cell. (credit: modification of work by Louisa Howard)

Ribosomes transfer their newly synthesized proteins into the lumen of the RER where they undergo structural modifications, such as folding or the acquisition of side chains. These modified proteins will be incorporated into cellular membranes—the membrane of the ER or those of other organelles—or secreted from the cell (such as protein hormones, enzymes). The RER also makes phospholipids for cellular membranes.

If the phospholipids or modified proteins are not destined to stay in the RER, they will reach their destinations via transport vesicles that bud from the RER's membrane (Figure 4.18).

Since the RER is engaged in modifying proteins (such as enzymes, for example) that will be secreted from the cell, you would be correct in assuming that the RER is abundant in cells that secrete proteins. This is the case with cells of the liver, for example.

Smooth ER

The **smooth endoplasmic reticulum (SER)** is continuous with the RER but has few or no ribosomes on its cytoplasmic surface (Figure 4.18). Functions of the SER include synthesis of carbohydrates, lipids, and steroid hormones; detoxification of medications and poisons; and storage of calcium ions.

In muscle cells, a specialized SER called the sarcoplasmic reticulum is responsible for storage of the calcium ions that are needed to trigger the coordinated contractions of the muscle cells.

You can watch an excellent animation of the endomembrane system here (http://openstaxcollege.org/l/endomembrane)
.

How do the nucleus and the endomembrane system work together for protein synthesis?

a. The endomembrane system processes and ships proteins specified by the nucleus. In the nucleus, DNA is used to make RNA which exits the nucleus and enters the cytoplasm of the cell. The ribosomes on the rough ER use the RNA to create the different types of protein needed by the body.

b. The endomembrane system processes and ships proteins specified by the nucleus. From the nucleus, RNA exits and enters the cytoplasm of the cell. The ribosomes on the rough ER use the RNA to create the different types of protein needed by the body.

c. The endomembrane system processes and ships proteins specified by the nucleus. In the nucleus, DNA is used to make RNA which exits the nucleus and enters the cytoplasm of the cell. The smooth ER uses the RNA to create the different types of protein needed by the body.

d. The endomembrane system processes and ships proteins specified by the nucleus. In the nucleus, DNA is used to make RNA which exits the nucleus and enters the cytoplasm of the cell. The ribosomes on the smooth ER use the RNA to create the different types of protein needed by the body.

Cardiologist

Heart disease is the leading cause of death in the United States. This is primarily due to our sedentary lifestyle and our high trans-fat diets.

Heart failure is just one of many disabling heart conditions. Heart failure does not mean that the heart has stopped working. Rather, it means that the heart can't pump with sufficient force to transport oxygenated blood to all the vital organs. Left untreated, heart failure can lead to kidney failure and failure of other organs.

The wall of the heart is composed of cardiac muscle tissue. Heart failure occurs when the endoplasmic reticula of cardiac muscle cells do not function properly. As a result, an insufficient number of calcium ions are available to trigger a sufficient contractile force.

Cardiologists (cardi- = "heart"; -ologist = "one who studies") are doctors who specialize in treating heart diseases, including heart failure. Cardiologists can make a diagnosis of heart failure via physical examination, results from an electrocardiogram (ECG, a test that measures the electrical activity of the heart), a chest X-ray to see whether the heart is enlarged, and other tests. If heart failure is diagnosed, the cardiologist will typically prescribe appropriate medications and recommend a reduction in table salt intake and a supervised exercise program.

The Golgi Apparatus

We have already mentioned that vesicles can bud from the ER and transport their contents elsewhere, but where do the vesicles go? Before reaching their final destination, the lipids or proteins within the transport vesicles still need to be sorted, packaged, and tagged so that they wind up in the right place. Sorting, tagging, packaging, and distribution of lipids and proteins takes place in the **Golgi apparatus** (also called the Golgi body), a series of flattened membranes (Figure 4.20).

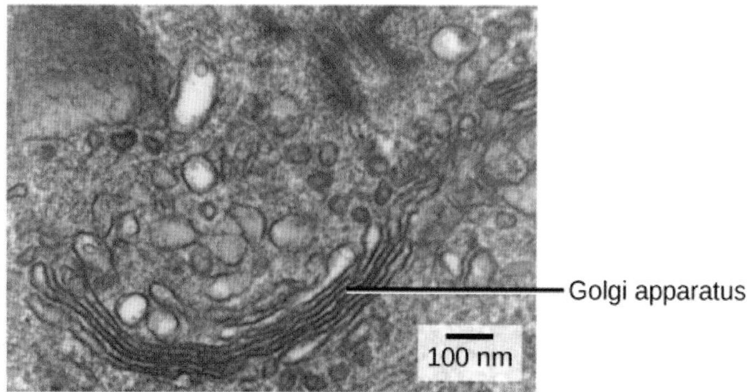

Figure 4.20 The Golgi apparatus in this white blood cell is visible as a stack of semicircular, flattened rings in the lower portion of the image. Several vesicles can be seen near the Golgi apparatus. (credit: modification of work by Louisa Howard)

The receiving side of the Golgi apparatus is called the *cis* face. The opposite side is called the *trans* face. The transport vesicles that formed from the ER travel to the *cis* face, fuse with it, and empty their contents into the lumen of the Golgi apparatus. As the proteins and lipids travel through the Golgi, they undergo further modifications that allow them to be sorted. The most frequent modification is the addition of short chains of sugar molecules. These newly modified proteins and lipids are then tagged with phosphate groups or other small molecules so that they can be routed to their proper destinations.

Finally, the modified and tagged proteins are packaged into secretory vesicles that bud from the *trans* face of the Golgi. While some of these vesicles deposit their contents into other parts of the cell where they will be used, other secretory vesicles fuse with the plasma membrane and release their contents outside the cell.

In another example of form following function, cells that engage in a great deal of secretory activity (such as cells of the salivary glands that secrete digestive enzymes or cells of the immune system that secrete antibodies) have an abundance of Golgi.

In plant cells, the Golgi apparatus has the additional role of synthesizing polysaccharides, some of which are incorporated into the cell wall and some of which are used in other parts of the cell.

career CONNECTION

Geneticist

Many diseases arise from genetic mutations that prevent the synthesis of critical proteins. One such disease is Lowe disease (also called oculocerebrorenal syndrome, because it affects the eyes, brain, and kidneys). In Lowe disease, there is a deficiency in an enzyme localized to the Golgi apparatus. Children with Lowe disease are born with cataracts, typically develop kidney disease after the first year of life, and may have impaired mental abilities.

Lowe disease is a genetic disease caused by a mutation on the X chromosome. The X chromosome is one of the two human sex chromosomes, as these chromosomes determine a person's sex. Females possess two X chromosomes while males possess one X and one Y chromosome. In females, the genes on only one of the two X chromosomes are expressed. Females who carry the Lowe disease gene on one of their X chromosomes are carriers and do not show symptoms of the disease. However, males only have one X chromosome and the genes on this chromosome are always expressed. Therefore, males will always have Lowe disease if their X chromosome carries the Lowe disease gene. The location of the mutated gene, as well as the locations of many other mutations that cause genetic diseases, has now been identified. Through prenatal testing, a woman can find out if the fetus she is carrying may be afflicted with one of several genetic diseases.

Geneticists analyze the results of prenatal genetic tests and may counsel pregnant women on available options. They may also conduct genetic research that leads to new drugs or foods, or perform DNA analyses that are used in forensic investigations.

Lysosomes

In addition to their role as the digestive component and organelle-recycling facility of animal cells, lysosomes are considered to be parts of the endomembrane system. Lysosomes also use their hydrolytic enzymes to destroy pathogens (disease-causing organisms) that might enter the cell. A good example of this occurs in a group of white blood cells called macrophages, which are part of your body's immune system. In a process known as phagocytosis or endocytosis, a section of the plasma membrane of the macrophage invaginates (folds in) and engulfs a pathogen. The invaginated section, with the pathogen inside, then pinches itself off from the plasma membrane and becomes a vesicle. The vesicle fuses with a lysosome. The lysosome's hydrolytic enzymes then destroy the pathogen (Figure 4.21).

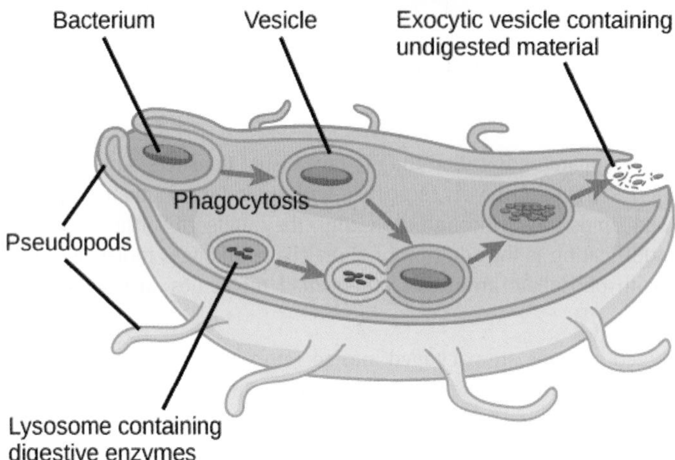

Figure 4.21 A macrophage has engulfed (phagocytized) a potentially pathogenic bacterium which then fuses with a lysosome within the cell to destroy the pathogen. Other organelles are present in the cell but for simplicity are not shown.

science practices CONNECTION for AP® Courses

Activity

Homemade Cell Project. Using inexpensive and common household items, create a model of a specific eukaryotic cell (e.g., neuron, white blood cell, plant root cell, or *Paramecium*) that demonstrates how at least three organelles work together to perform a specific function.

Think About It

A certain cell type functions primarily to synthesize proteins for export. What is the most likely route the newly made protein takes through the cell? Justify your prediction.

Section Summary

The endomembrane system includes the nuclear envelope, lysosomes, vesicles, the ER, and Golgi apparatus, as well as the plasma membrane. These cellular components work together to modify, package, tag, and transport proteins and lipids that form the membranes.

The RER modifies proteins and synthesizes phospholipids used in cell membranes. The SER synthesizes carbohydrates, lipids, and steroid hormones; engages in the detoxification of medications and poisons; and stores calcium ions. Sorting, tagging, packaging, and distribution of lipids and proteins take place in the Golgi apparatus. Lysosomes are created by the budding of the membranes of the RER and Golgi. Lysosomes digest macromolecules, recycle worn-out organelles, and destroy pathogens.

4.5 | Cytoskeleton

In this section, you will explore the following questions:

- How do the various components of the cytoskeleton perform their functions?

Connection for AP® Courses

All cells, from simple bacteria to complex eukaryotes, possess a cytoskeleton composed of different types of protein elements, including microfilaments, intermediate filaments, and microtubules. The cytoskeleton serves a variety of purposes: provides rigidity and shape to the cell, facilitates cellular movement, anchors the nucleus and other organelles in place, moves vesicles through the cell, and pulls replicated chromosomes to the poles of a dividing cell. These protein elements are also integral to the movement of centrioles, flagella, and cilia.

The information presented and the examples highlighted in the section support concepts and Learning Objectives outlined in Big Idea 1 of the AP Biology Curriculum Framework, as shown in the table below.

The Learning Objectives listed in the Curriculum Framework provide a transparent foundation for the AP® Biology course, an inquiry-based laboratory experience, instructional activities, and AP® exam questions. A Learning Objective merges required content with one or more of the seven Science Practices.

Big Idea 1	The process of evolution drives the diversity and unity of life.
Enduring Understanding 1.B	Organisms are linked by lines of descent from common ancestry
Essential Knowledge	**1.B.1** Organisms share many conserved core processes and features that evolved and are widely distributed among organisms today.
Science Practice	**7.2** The student can connect concepts in and across domain(s) to generalize or extrapolate in and/or across enduring understandings and/or big ideas.
Learning Objective	**1.15** The student is able to describe specific examples of conserved core biological processes and features shared by all domains or within one domain of life and how these shared, conserved core processes and features support the concept of common ancestry for all organisms.

Microfilaments

If you were to remove all the organelles from a cell, would the plasma membrane and the cytoplasm be the only components left? No. Within the cytoplasm, there would still be ions and organic molecules, plus a network of protein fibers that help maintain the shape of the cell, secure some organelles in specific positions, allow cytoplasm and vesicles to move within the cell, and enable cells within multicellular organisms to move. Collectively, this network of protein fibers is known as the **cytoskeleton**. There are three types of fibers within the cytoskeleton: microfilaments, intermediate filaments, and microtubules (Figure 4.22). Here, we will examine each.

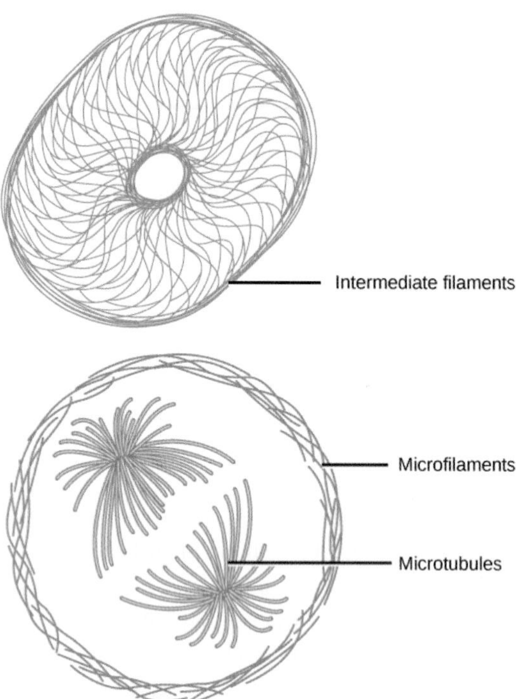

Figure 4.22 Microfilaments thicken the cortex around the inner edge of a cell; like rubber bands, they resist tension. Microtubules are found in the interior of the cell where they maintain cell shape by resisting compressive forces. Intermediate filaments are found throughout the cell and hold organelles in place.

Of the three types of protein fibers in the cytoskeleton, **microfilaments** are the narrowest. They function in cellular movement, have a diameter of about 7 nm, and are made of two intertwined strands of a globular protein called actin (Figure 4.23). For this reason, microfilaments are also known as actin filaments.

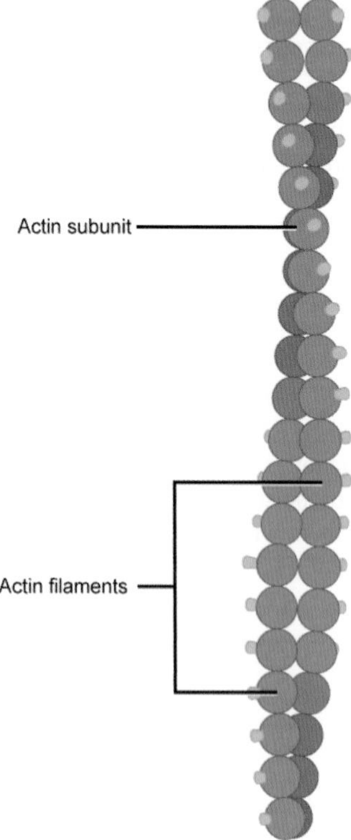

Figure 4.23 Microfilaments are made of two intertwined strands of actin.

Actin is powered by ATP to assemble its filamentous form, which serves as a track for the movement of a motor protein called myosin. This enables actin to engage in cellular events requiring motion, such as cell division in eukaryotic cells and cytoplasmic streaming, which is the circular movement of the cell cytoplasm in plant cells. Actin and myosin are plentiful in muscle cells. When your actin and myosin filaments slide past each other, your muscles contract.

Microfilaments also provide some rigidity and shape to the cell. They can depolymerize (disassemble) and reform quickly, thus enabling a cell to change its shape and move. White blood cells (your body's infection-fighting cells) make good use of this ability. They can move to the site of an infection and phagocytize the pathogen.

To see an example of a white blood cell in action, click here (http://openstaxcollege.org/l/chasing_bcteria) and watch a short time-lapse video of the cell capturing two bacteria. It engulfs one and then moves on to the other.

The Human Immunodeficiency Virus (HIV) infects and kills white blood cells. Over time, what affect does this have on the body's immune system?

a. The body's immune system would not be affected by this.

b. The body's immune system would not be able to fight off pathogens like bacteria with fewer white blood cells. This can increase the risk of illness in HIV patients.

c. The body's immune system, in order to recoup this loss, will produce more WBC's.

d. The body's immune system will fight the pathogens more vigorously in order to compensate for the fewer white blood cells.

Intermediate Filaments

Intermediate filaments are made of several strands of fibrous proteins that are wound together (Figure 4.24). These elements of the cytoskeleton get their name from the fact that their diameter, 8 to 10 nm, is between those of microfilaments and microtubules.

Figure 4.24 Intermediate filaments consist of several intertwined strands of fibrous proteins.

Intermediate filaments have no role in cell movement. Their function is purely structural. They bear tension, thus maintaining the shape of the cell, and anchor the nucleus and other organelles in place. Figure 4.22 shows how intermediate filaments create a supportive scaffolding inside the cell.

The intermediate filaments are the most diverse group of cytoskeletal elements. Several types of fibrous proteins are found in the intermediate filaments. You are probably most familiar with keratin, the fibrous protein that strengthens your hair, nails, and the epidermis of the skin.

Microtubules

As their name implies, microtubules are small hollow tubes. The walls of the microtubule are made of polymerized dimers of α-tubulin and β-tubulin, two globular proteins (Figure 4.25). With a diameter of about 25 nm, **microtubules** are the widest components of the cytoskeleton. They help the cell resist compression, provide a track along which vesicles move through the cell, and pull replicated chromosomes to opposite ends of a dividing cell. Like microfilaments, microtubules can disassemble and reform quickly.

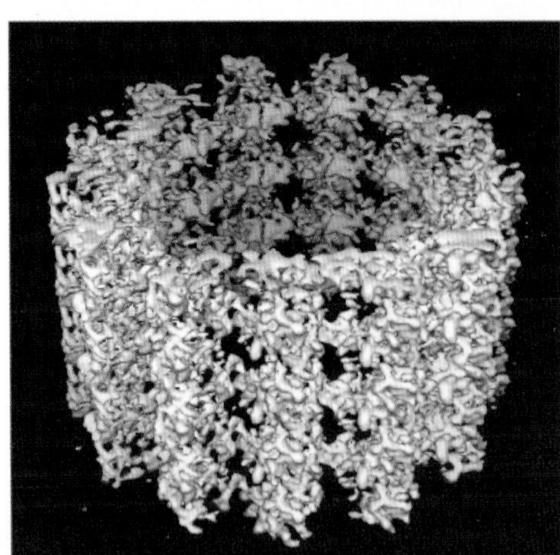

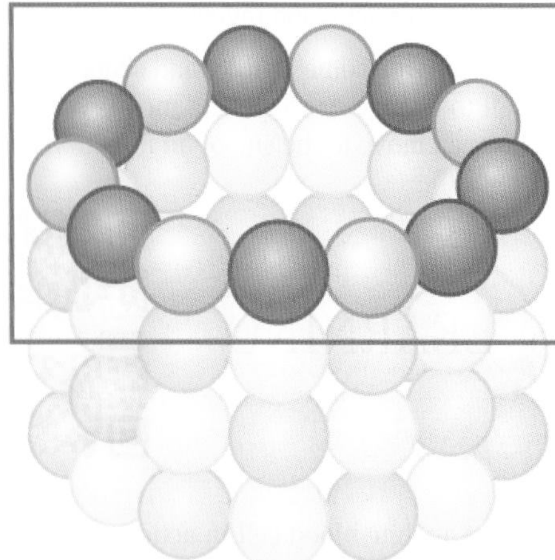

Figure 4.25 Microtubules are hollow. Their walls consist of 13 polymerized dimers of α-tubulin and β-tubulin (right image). The left image shows the molecular structure of the tube.

Microtubules are also the structural elements of flagella, cilia, and centrioles (the latter are the two perpendicular bodies of the centrosome). In fact, in animal cells, the centrosome is the microtubule-organizing center. In eukaryotic cells, flagella and cilia are quite different structurally from their counterparts in prokaryotes, as discussed below.

Flagella and Cilia

To refresh your memory, **flagella** (singular = flagellum) are long, hair-like structures that extend from the plasma membrane and are used to move an entire cell (for example, sperm, *Euglena*). When present, the cell has just one flagellum or a few flagella. When **cilia** (singular = cilium) are present, however, many of them extend along the entire surface of the plasma membrane. They are short, hair-like structures that are used to move entire cells (such as paramecia) or substances along the outer surface of the cell (for example, the cilia of cells lining the Fallopian tubes that move the ovum toward the uterus, or cilia lining the cells of the respiratory tract that trap particulate matter and move it toward your nostrils.)

Despite their differences in length and number, flagella and cilia share a common structural arrangement of microtubules called a "9 + 2 array." This is an appropriate name because a single flagellum or cilium is made of a ring of nine microtubule doublets, surrounding a single microtubule doublet in the center (Figure 4.26).

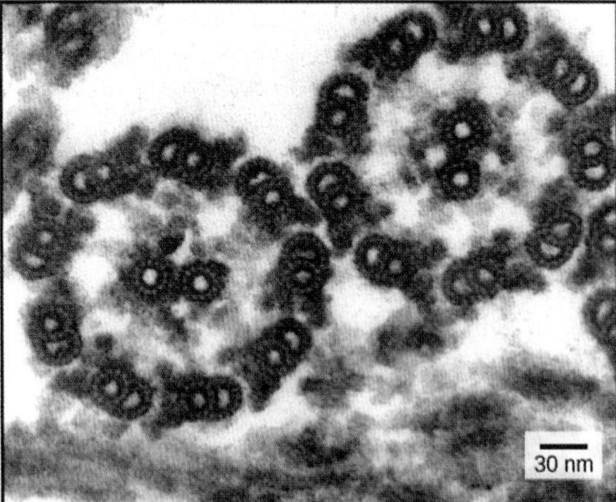

Figure 4.26 This transmission electron micrograph of two flagella shows the 9 + 2 array of microtubules: nine microtubule doublets surround a single microtubule doublet. (credit: modification of work by Dartmouth Electron Microscope Facility, Dartmouth College; scale-bar data from Matt Russell)

science practices CONNECTION for AP® Courses

Think About It

The ribosomes in bacterial cells and in human cells are made up of proteins and ribosomal RNA, suggesting that both kinds of cells share a common ancestor cell type. What are examples of other features of cells that provide evidence for common ancestry?

You have now completed a broad survey of the components of prokaryotic and eukaryotic cells. For a summary of cellular components in prokaryotic and eukaryotic cells, see Table 4.1.

Components of Prokaryotic and Eukaryotic Cells

Cell Component	Function	Present in Prokaryotes?	Present in Animal Cells?	Present in Plant Cells?
Plasma membrane	Separates cell from external environment; controls passage of organic molecules, ions, water, oxygen, and wastes into and out of cell	Yes	Yes	Yes
Cytoplasm	Provides turgor pressure to plant cells as fluid inside the central vacuole; site of many metabolic reactions; medium in which organelles are found	Yes	Yes	Yes
Nucleolus	Darkened area within the nucleus where ribosomal subunits are synthesized.	No	Yes	Yes
Nucleus	Cell organelle that houses DNA and directs synthesis of ribosomes and proteins	No	Yes	Yes
Ribosomes	Protein synthesis	Yes	Yes	Yes
Mitochondria	ATP production/cellular respiration	No	Yes	Yes
Peroxisomes	Oxidizes and thus breaks down fatty acids and amino acids, and detoxifies poisons	No	Yes	Yes
Vesicles and vacuoles	Storage and transport; digestive function in plant cells	No	Yes	Yes
Centrosome	Unspecified role in cell division in animal cells; source of microtubules in animal cells	No	Yes	No
Lysosomes	Digestion of macromolecules; recycling of worn-out organelles	No	Yes	No
Cell wall	Protection, structural support and maintenance of cell shape	Yes, primarily peptidoglycan	No	Yes, primarily cellulose
Chloroplasts	Photosynthesis	No	No	Yes
Endoplasmic reticulum	Modifies proteins and synthesizes lipids	No	Yes	Yes

Table 4.1

Components of Prokaryotic and Eukaryotic Cells

Cell Component	Function	Present in Prokaryotes?	Present in Animal Cells?	Present in Plant Cells?
Golgi apparatus	Modifies, sorts, tags, packages, and distributes lipids and proteins	No	Yes	Yes
Cytoskeleton	Maintains cell's shape, secures organelles in specific positions, allows cytoplasm and vesicles to move within cell, and enables unicellular organisms to move independently	Yes	Yes	Yes
Flagella	Cellular locomotion	Some	Some	No, except for some plant sperm cells.
Cilia	Cellular locomotion, movement of particles along extracellular surface of plasma membrane, and filtration	Some	Some	No

Table 4.1

Section Summary

The cytoskeleton has three different types of protein elements. From narrowest to widest, they are the microfilaments (actin filaments), intermediate filaments, and microtubules. Microfilaments are often associated with myosin. They provide rigidity and shape to the cell and facilitate cellular movements. Intermediate filaments bear tension and anchor the nucleus and other organelles in place. Microtubules help the cell resist compression, serve as tracks for motor proteins that move vesicles through the cell, and pull replicated chromosomes to opposite ends of a dividing cell. They are also the structural element of centrioles, flagella, and cilia.

4.6 | Connections between Cells and Cellular Activities

In this section, you will explore the following questions:

- What are the components of the extracellular matrix?
- What are the roles of tight junctions, gap junctions, and plasmodesmata in allowing cells to exchange materials with the environment and communicate with other cells?

Connection for AP® Courses

With the exception of gap junctions between animal cells and plasmodesmata between plant cells that facilitate the exchange of substances, the information presented in Section 4.6| Connections between Cells and Cellular Activities is not required for AP®. Concepts about cell communication and signaling processes that are required for AP®, including the features of cells that make communication possible, are covered in Chapter 9.

You already know that a group of similar cells working together is called a tissue. As you might expect that, if cells are to work together, they must communicate with one another, just as you need to communicate with others when you work on a group project. Let's take a look at how cells communicate with one another.

You already know that a group of similar cells working together is called a tissue. As you might expect, if cells are to work together, they must communicate with each other, just as you need to communicate with others if you work on a group project. Let's take a look at how cells communicate with each other.

The Science Practice Challenge Questions contain additional test questions for this section that will help you prepare for

the AP exam. These questions address the following standards:
[APLO 4.5][APLO 3.32][APLO 1.16][APLO 3.33][APLO 1.14][APLO 2.7][APLO 4.4]

Extracellular Matrix of Animal Cells

Most animal cells release materials into the extracellular space. The primary components of these materials are proteins, and the most abundant protein is collagen. Collagen fibers are interwoven with carbohydrate-containing protein molecules called proteoglycans. Collectively, these materials are called the **extracellular matrix** (Figure 4.27). Not only does the extracellular matrix hold the cells together to form a tissue, but it also allows the cells within the tissue to communicate with each other. How can this happen?

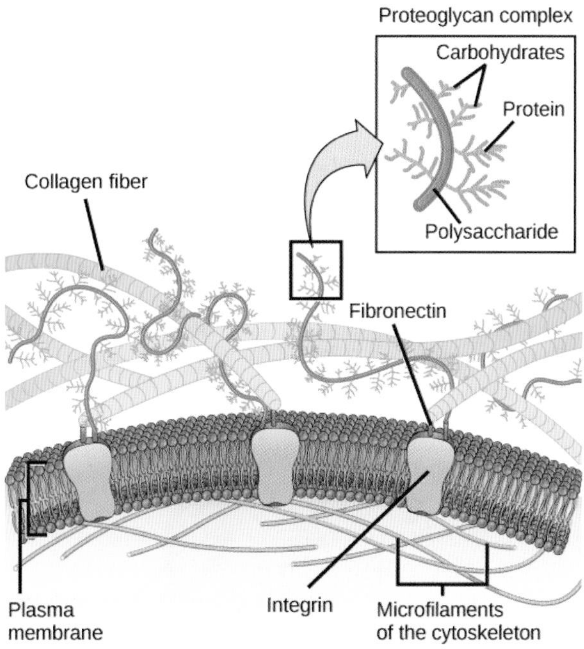

Figure 4.27 The extracellular matrix consists of a network of proteins and carbohydrates.

Cells have protein receptors on the extracellular surfaces of their plasma membranes. When a molecule within the matrix binds to the receptor, it changes the molecular structure of the receptor. The receptor, in turn, changes the conformation of the microfilaments positioned just inside the plasma membrane. These conformational changes induce chemical signals inside the cell that reach the nucleus and turn "on" or "off" the transcription of specific sections of DNA, which affects the production of associated proteins, thus changing the activities within the cell.

Blood clotting provides an example of the role of the extracellular matrix in cell communication. When the cells lining a blood vessel are damaged, they display a protein receptor called tissue factor. When tissue factor binds with another factor in the extracellular matrix, it causes platelets to adhere to the wall of the damaged blood vessel, stimulates the adjacent smooth muscle cells in the blood vessel to contract (thus constricting the blood vessel), and initiates a series of steps that stimulate the platelets to produce clotting factors.

Intercellular Junctions

Cells can also communicate with each other via direct contact, referred to as intercellular junctions. There are some differences in the ways that plant and animal cells do this. Plasmodesmata are junctions between plant cells, whereas animal cell contacts include tight junctions, gap junctions, and desmosomes.

Plasmodesmata

In general, long stretches of the plasma membranes of neighboring plant cells cannot touch one another because they are separated by the cell wall that surrounds each cell (Figure 4.8**b**). How then, can a plant transfer water and other soil nutrients from its roots, through its stems, and to its leaves? Such transport uses the vascular tissues (xylem and phloem) primarily. There also exist structural modifications called **plasmodesmata** (singular = plasmodesma), numerous channels that pass between cell walls of adjacent plant cells, connect their cytoplasm, and enable materials to be transported from cell to cell, and thus throughout the plant (Figure 4.28).

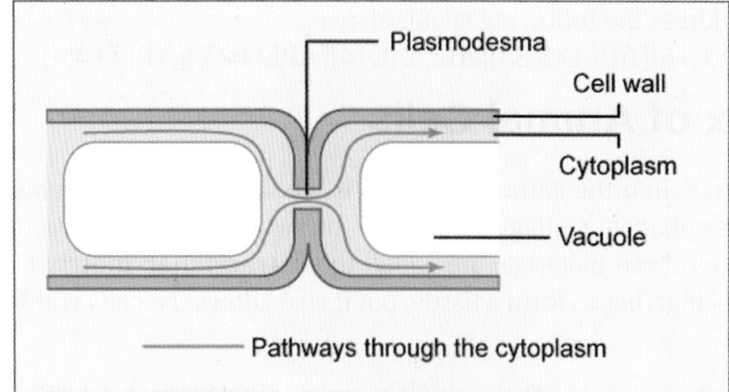

Figure 4.28 A plasmodesma is a channel between the cell walls of two adjacent plant cells. Plasmodesmata allow materials to pass from the cytoplasm of one plant cell to the cytoplasm of an adjacent cell.

Tight Junctions

A **tight junction** is a watertight seal between two adjacent animal cells (Figure 4.29). The cells are held tightly against each other by proteins (predominantly two proteins called claudins and occludins).

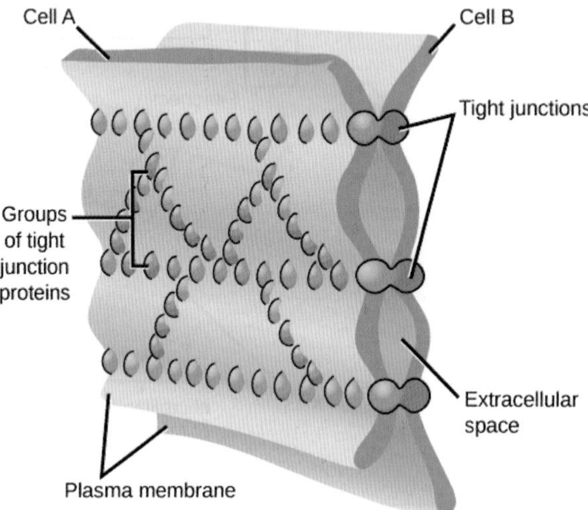

Figure 4.29 Tight junctions form watertight connections between adjacent animal cells. Proteins create tight junction adherence. (credit: modification of work by Mariana Ruiz Villareal)

This tight adherence prevents materials from leaking between the cells; tight junctions are typically found in epithelial tissues that line internal organs and cavities, and comprise most of the skin. For example, the tight junctions of the epithelial cells lining your urinary bladder prevent urine from leaking out into the extracellular space.

Desmosomes

Also found only in animal cells are **desmosomes**, which act like spot welds between adjacent epithelial cells (Figure 4.30). Short proteins called cadherins in the plasma membrane connect to intermediate filaments to create desmosomes. The cadherins join two adjacent cells together and maintain the cells in a sheet-like formation in organs and tissues that stretch, like the skin, heart, and muscles.

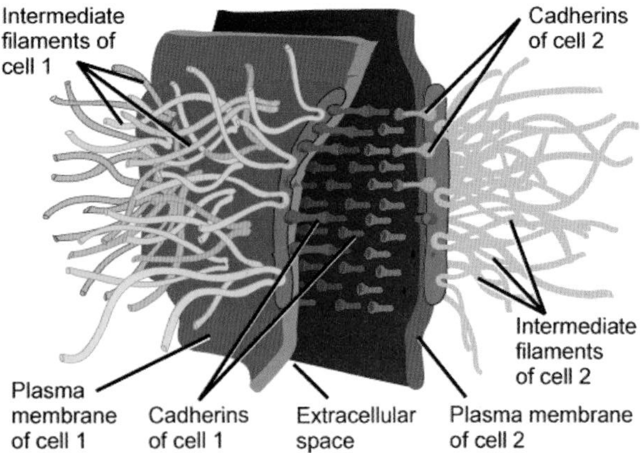

Figure 4.30 A desmosome forms a very strong spot weld between cells. It is created by the linkage of cadherins and intermediate filaments. (credit: modification of work by Mariana Ruiz Villareal)

Gap Junctions

Gap junctions in animal cells are like plasmodesmata in plant cells in that they are channels between adjacent cells that allow for the transport of ions, nutrients, and other substances that enable cells to communicate (Figure 4.31). Structurally, however, gap junctions and plasmodesmata differ.

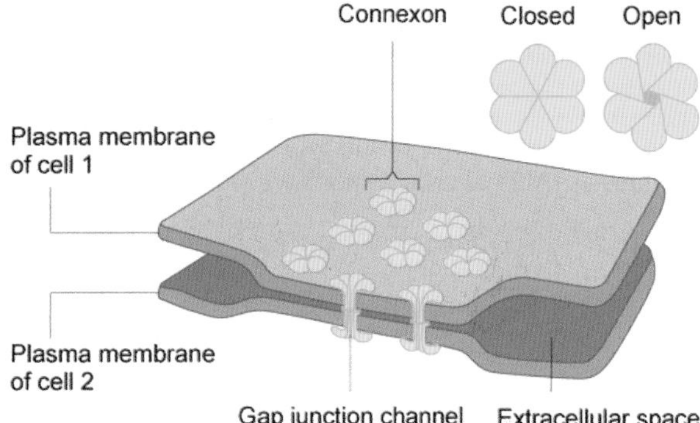

Figure 4.31 A gap junction is a protein-lined pore that allows water and small molecules to pass between adjacent animal cells. (credit: modification of work by Mariana Ruiz Villareal)

Gap junctions develop when a set of six proteins (called connexins) in the plasma membrane arrange themselves in an elongated donut-like configuration called a connexon. When the pores ("doughnut holes") of connexons in adjacent animal cells align, a channel between the two cells forms. Gap junctions are particularly important in cardiac muscle: The electrical signal for the muscle to contract is passed efficiently through gap junctions, allowing the heart muscle cells to contract in tandem.

To conduct a virtual microscopy lab and review the parts of a cell, work through the steps of this **interactive assignment (http://openstaxcollege.org/l/microscopy_lab)** .

What are two similarities and two differences between plant and animal cells that can be seen under a microscope?

a. Plant cells have cell walls which provide structure to the plant and also chloroplasts which allow for photosynthesis. Animal cells do not have either of these structures. Both cells have nuclei, the command center of the cell, and cytoplasm, the gel-like solution that fills the cell.

b. Plant cells and animal cells have cell walls as well as nuclei. Plant cells have chloroplasts as well as plasmodesmata which are lacking in animal cells.

c. Plant cells have cell walls which provide structure to the plant and also chloroplasts which allow for photosynthesis. Animal cells do not have either of these structures. Animal cells and plant cells both have glyoxysomes as well cytoplasm.

d. Plant cells and animal cells both have a rigid plasma membrane as well as cytoplasm which is the gel-like solution that fills the cell. Plant cells have cell walls which provide structure to the plant and also chloroplasts which allow for photosynthesis. Animal cells do not have either of these structures.

KEY TERMS

cell theory see unified cell theory

cell wall rigid cell covering made of various molecules that protects the cell, provides structural support, and gives shape to the cell

central vacuole large plant cell organelle that regulates the cell's storage compartment, holds water, and plays a significant role in cell growth as the site of macromolecule degradation

centrosome region in animal cells made of two centrioles

chlorophyll green pigment that captures the light energy that drives the light reactions of photosynthesis

chloroplast plant cell organelle that carries out photosynthesis

chromatin protein-DNA complex that serves as the building material of chromosomes

chromosome structure within the nucleus that is made up of chromatin that contains DNA, the hereditary material

cilium (plural = cilia) short, hair-like structure that extends from the plasma membrane in large numbers and is used to move an entire cell or move substances along the outer surface of the cell

cytoplasm entire region between the plasma membrane and the nuclear envelope, consisting of organelles suspended in the gel-like cytosol, the cytoskeleton, and various chemicals

cytoskeleton network of protein fibers that collectively maintain the shape of the cell, secure some organelles in specific positions, allow cytoplasm and vesicles to move within the cell, and enable unicellular organisms to move independently

cytosol gel-like material of the cytoplasm in which cell structures are suspended

desmosome linkage between adjacent epithelial cells that forms when cadherins in the plasma membrane attach to intermediate filaments

electron microscope an instrument that magnifies an object using a beam of electrons passed and bent through a lens system to visualize a specimen

endomembrane system group of organelles and membranes in eukaryotic cells that work together modifying, packaging, and transporting lipids and proteins

endoplasmic reticulum (ER) series of interconnected membranous structures within eukaryotic cells that collectively modify proteins and synthesize lipids

eukaryotic cell cell that has a membrane-bound nucleus and several other membrane-bound compartments or sacs

extracellular matrix material (primarily collagen, glycoproteins, and proteoglycans) secreted from animal cells that provides mechanical protection and anchoring for the cells in the tissue

flagellum (plural = flagella) long, hair-like structure that extends from the plasma membrane and is used to move the cell

gap junction channel between two adjacent animal cells that allows ions, nutrients, and low molecular weight substances to pass between cells, enabling the cells to communicate

Golgi apparatus eukaryotic organelle made up of a series of stacked membranes that sorts, tags, and packages lipids and proteins for distribution

intermediate filament cytoskeletal component, composed of several intertwined strands of fibrous protein, that bears tension, supports cell-cell junctions, and anchors cells to extracellular structures

light microscope an instrument that magnifies an object using a beam visible light passed and bent through a lens system to visualize a specimen

lysosome organelle in an animal cell that functions as the cell's digestive component; it breaks down proteins, polysaccharides, lipids, nucleic acids, and even worn-out organelles

microfilament narrowest element of the cytoskeleton system; it provides rigidity and shape to the cell and enables cellular movements

microscope an instrument that magnifies an object

microtubule widest element of the cytoskeleton system; it helps the cell resist compression, provides a track along which vesicles move through the cell, pulls replicated chromosomes to opposite ends of a dividing cell, and is the structural element of centrioles, flagella, and cilia

mitochondria (singular = mitochondrion) cellular organelles responsible for carrying out cellular respiration, resulting in the production of ATP, the cell's main energy-carrying molecule

nuclear envelope double-membrane structure that constitutes the outermost portion of the nucleus

nucleoid central part of a prokaryotic cell in which the chromosome is found

nucleolus darkly staining body within the nucleus that is responsible for assembling the subunits of the ribosomes

nucleoplasm semi-solid fluid inside the nucleus that contains the chromatin and nucleolus

nucleus cell organelle that houses the cell's DNA and directs the synthesis of ribosomes and proteins

organelle compartment or sac within a cell

peroxisome small, round organelle that contains hydrogen peroxide, oxidizes fatty acids and amino acids, and detoxifies many poisons

plasma membrane phospholipid bilayer with embedded (integral) or attached (peripheral) proteins, that separates the internal content of the cell from its surrounding environment

plasmodesma (plural = plasmodesmata) channel that passes between the cell walls of adjacent plant cells, connects their cytoplasm, and allows materials to be transported from cell to cell

prokaryote unicellular organism that lacks a nucleus or any other membrane-bound organelle

ribosome cellular structure that carries out protein synthesis

rough endoplasmic reticulum (RER) region of the endoplasmic reticulum that is studded with ribosomes and engages in protein modification and phospholipid synthesis

smooth endoplasmic reticulum (SER) region of the endoplasmic reticulum that has few or no ribosomes on its cytoplasmic surface and synthesizes carbohydrates, lipids, and steroid hormones; detoxifies certain chemicals (like pesticides, preservatives, medications, and environmental pollutants), and stores calcium ions

tight junction firm seal between two adjacent animal cells created by protein adherence

unified cell theory a biological concept that states that all organisms are composed of one or more cells; the cell is the basic unit of life; and new cells arise from existing cells

vacuole membrane-bound sac, somewhat larger than a vesicle, which functions in cellular storage and transport

vesicle small, membrane-bound sac that functions in cellular storage and transport; its membrane is capable of fusing with the plasma membrane and the membranes of the endoplasmic reticulum and Golgi apparatus

CHAPTER SUMMARY

4.1 Studying Cells

A cell is the smallest unit of life. Most cells are so tiny that they cannot be seen with the naked eye. Therefore, scientists use microscopes to study cells. Electron microscopes provide higher magnification, higher resolution, and more detail than light microscopes. The unified cell theory states that all organisms are composed of one or more cells, the cell is the basic unit of life, and new cells arise from existing cells.

4.2 Prokaryotic Cells

Prokaryotes are single-celled organisms of the domains Bacteria and Archaea. All prokaryotes have plasma membranes, cytoplasm, ribosomes, and DNA that is not membrane-bound. Most have peptidoglycan cell walls and many have polysaccharide capsules. Prokaryotic cells range in diameter from 0.1 to 5.0 μm.

As a cell increases in size, its surface area-to-volume ratio decreases. If the cell grows too large, the plasma membrane will not have sufficient surface area to support the rate of diffusion required for the increased volume.

4.3 Eukaryotic Cells

Like a prokaryotic cell, a eukaryotic cell has a plasma membrane, cytoplasm, and ribosomes, but a eukaryotic cell is typically larger than a prokaryotic cell, has a true nucleus (meaning its DNA is surrounded by a membrane), and has other membrane-bound organelles that allow for compartmentalization of functions. The plasma membrane is a phospholipid bilayer embedded with proteins. The nucleus's nucleolus is the site of ribosome assembly. Ribosomes are either found in the cytoplasm or attached to the cytoplasmic side of the plasma membrane or endoplasmic reticulum. They perform protein synthesis. Mitochondria participate in cellular respiration; they are responsible for the majority of ATP produced in the cell. Peroxisomes hydrolyze fatty acids, amino acids, and some toxins. Vesicles and vacuoles are storage and transport compartments. In plant cells, vacuoles also help break down macromolecules.

Animal cells also have a centrosome and lysosomes. The centrosome has two bodies perpendicular to each other, the centrioles, and has an unknown purpose in cell division. Lysosomes are the digestive organelles of animal cells.

Plant cells and plant-like cells each have a cell wall, chloroplasts, and a central vacuole. The plant cell wall, whose primary component is cellulose, protects the cell, provides structural support, and gives shape to the cell. Photosynthesis takes place in chloroplasts. The central vacuole can expand without having to produce more cytoplasm.

4.4 The Endomembrane System and Proteins

The endomembrane system includes the nuclear envelope, lysosomes, vesicles, the ER, and Golgi apparatus, as well as the plasma membrane. These cellular components work together to modify, package, tag, and transport proteins and lipids that form the membranes.

The RER modifies proteins and synthesizes phospholipids used in cell membranes. The SER synthesizes carbohydrates, lipids, and steroid hormones; engages in the detoxification of medications and poisons; and stores calcium ions. Sorting, tagging, packaging, and distribution of lipids and proteins take place in the Golgi apparatus. Lysosomes are created by the budding of the membranes of the RER and Golgi. Lysosomes digest macromolecules, recycle worn-out organelles, and destroy pathogens.

4.5 Cytoskeleton

The cytoskeleton has three different types of protein elements. From narrowest to widest, they are the microfilaments (actin filaments), intermediate filaments, and microtubules. Microfilaments are often associated with myosin. They provide rigidity and shape to the cell and facilitate cellular movements. Intermediate filaments bear tension and anchor the nucleus and other organelles in place. Microtubules help the cell resist compression, serve as tracks for motor proteins that move vesicles through the cell, and pull replicated chromosomes to opposite ends of a dividing cell. They are also the structural element of centrioles, flagella, and cilia.

4.6 Connections between Cells and Cellular Activities

Animal cells communicate via their extracellular matrices and are connected to each other via tight junctions, desmosomes, and gap junctions. Plant cells are connected and communicate with each other via plasmodesmata.

When protein receptors on the surface of the plasma membrane of an animal cell bind to a substance in the extracellular matrix, a chain of reactions begins that changes activities taking place within the cell. Plasmodesmata are channels between adjacent plant cells, while gap junctions are channels between adjacent animal cells. However, their structures are quite different. A tight junction is a watertight seal between two adjacent cells, while a desmosome acts like a spot weld.

REVIEW QUESTIONS

1. When viewing a specimen through a light microscope, what is a method that scientists use to make it easier to see individual components of cells?

a. a beam of electrons
b. high temperatures
c. radioactive isotopes
d. special stains

2. What is the basic unit of life?

a. cell
b. organism
c. organ
d. tissue

3. Which of the following statements is part of the cell theory?

a. All living organisms are made of cells.
b. All cells contain DNA that they pass on to daughter cells.
c. All cells depend on their surroundings to provide energy.
d. All cells have a nucleus.

4. Which of the following could most effectively be visualized with a scanning electron microscope?

a. cells swimming in a drop of pond water.
b. details of structures inside cells
c. a three-dimensional view of the surface of a membrane
d. the movement of molecules inside the cell

5. Who was the first to clearly identify and name individual cells?

a. Anton van Leeuwenhoek.
b. Matthias Schleiden
c. Robert Hooke
d. Theodore Schwann

6. Which of the following observations contributed to the cell theory?

a. Animal and plant cells have nuclei and organelles.
b. Non-living material cannot give rise to living organisms.
c. Prokaryotic and eukaryotic cells are surrounded by a plasma membrane.
d. Viruses replicate.

7. In order to obtain some materials and remove waste, what process is used by prokaryotes?

a. cell division
b. diffusion
c. flagellar motion
d. ribosomes

8. When bacteria lack fimbriae, what are they less likely to do?

a. Adhere to cell surfaces
b. retain the ability to divide
c. swim through bodily fluids
d. synthesize proteins

9. What is a difference between prokaryotic and eukaryotic cells?

a. Both cells have a nucleus but prokaryotic cells lack cytoplasm.
b. Both cells have cytoplasm but prokaryotic cells lack a nucleus.
c. Both cells have DNA but prokaryotic cells lack a cell membrane.
d. Both cells have a cell membrane but prokaryotic cells lack DNA.

10. Eukaryotic cells contain complex organelles that carry out their chemical reactions. Prokaryotes lack many of these complex organelles, although they have a variety of unique structures of their own. However, most prokaryotic cells can exchange nutrients with the outside environment faster than most eukaryotic cells. Why is this so?

a. Most prokaryotic cells are smaller, and have a higher surface-to-volume ratio, than eukaryotic cells.
b. Most prokaryotic cells are larger, and have a higher surface-to-volume ratio than eukaryotic cells.
c. Most prokaryotic cells are smaller, and have a lower surface-to-volume ratio than eukaryotic cells.
d. Prokaryotic cells are larger and have a lower surface-to-volume ratio than eukaryotic cells.

11. Which of the following is surrounded by two phospholipid bilayers?

a. lysosomes
b. ribosomes
c. nucleolus
d. nucleus

12. Peroxisomes got their name because hydrogen peroxide is ______.

a. a cofactor for the organelles' enzymes
b. incorporated into their membranes
c. produced during their oxidation reactions
d. used in their detoxification reactions

13. In plant cells, the function of the lysosomes is carried out by what?

a. nuclei
b. peroxisomes
c. ribosomes
d. vacuole

14. Which of the following is found both in eukaryotic and prokaryotic cells?

a. mitochondrion
b. nucleus
c. ribosomes
d. centrosomes

15. Which of the following structures is not found in prokaryotic cells?

a. plasma membrane
b. chloroplast
c. nucleoid
d. ribosome

16. Where would you find DNA, the genetic material, in an animal cell?

a. in the centriole
b. only in the mitochondria
c. in the mitochondria and the nucleus

17. Which of the following is most likely to have the greatest concentration of smooth endoplasmic reticulum (SER)?

a. a cell that secretes enzymes
b. a cell that destroys pathogens
c. a cell that makes steroid hormones
d. a cell that engages in photosynthesis

18. Which of the following sequences correctly lists in order the steps involved in the incorporation of a protein within a cell membrane?

a. synthesis of the protein on the ribosome; modification in the Golgi apparatus; packaging in the endoplasmic reticulum; modification in the vesicle
b. synthesis of the protein on the lysosome; modification in the Golgi; packaging in the vesicle; distribution in the endoplasmic reticulum
c. synthesis of the protein on the ribosome; modification in the endoplasmic reticulum; tagging in the Golgi; distribution via the vesicle
d. synthesis of the protein on the lysosome; packaging in the vesicle; distribution via the Golgi; modification in the endoplasmic reticulum

19. Which of the following is not a component of the endomembrane system?

a. endoplasmic reticulum
b. Golgi apparatus
c. lysosome
d. mitochondrion

20. Which of the following have the ability to disassemble and reform quickly?

a. intermediate filaments and microtubules
b. microfilaments and intermediate filaments
c. microfilaments and microtubules
d. only intermediate filaments

21. Which of the following do not play a role in intracellular movement?

a. intermediate filaments and microtubules
b. microfilaments and intermediate filaments
c. microfilaments and microtubules
d. only intermediate filaments

22. Which components of the cytoskeleton are responsible for the contraction of muscles?

a. intermediate filaments
b. microfilaments
c. microtubules

23. What type of junctions prevent the movement of chemicals between two adjacent animal cells?

a. desmosomes
b. gap junctions
c. plasmodesmata
d. tight junctions

24. Gap junctions are formed by ________.

a. gaps in the cell wall of plants

b. protein complexes that form channels between cells

c. tight, rivet-like regions in the membranes of adjacent cells

d. a tight knitting of membranes

25. Some animal cells produce extensive extracellular matrix. You would expect their ribosomes to synthesize large amounts of which of the following proteins?

a. actin

b. collagen

c. myosin

d. tubulin

26. Which of the following molecules are typically found in the extracellular matrix?

a. nucleic acids such as DNA

b. peptidoglycans

c. cellulose

d. proteoglycans

CRITICAL THINKING QUESTIONS

27. Which element of the cell theory has practical applications in health care because it promotes the use of sterilization and disinfection?

a. All cells come from pre-existing cells.

b. All living organisms are composed of one or more cells.

c. A cell is the basic unit of life.

d. A nucleus and organelles are found in prokaryotic cells.

28. What are the advantages and disadvantages of light microscopes? What are the advantages and disadvantages of electron microscopes?

a. Advantage: In light microscopes, the light beam does not kill the cell. Electron microscopes are helpful in viewing intricate details of a specimen and have high resolution. Disadvantage: Light microscopes have low resolving power. Electron microscopes are costly and require killing the specimen.

b. Advantage: Light microscopes have high resolution. Electron microscopes are helpful in viewing surface details of a specimen. Disadvantage: Light microscopes kill the cell. Electron microscopes are costly and low resolution.

c. Advantage: Light microscopes have high resolution. Electron microscopes are helpful in viewing surface details of a specimen. Disadvantage: Light microscopes can be used only in the presence of light and are costly. Electron microscopes uses short wavelength of electrons and hence have lower magnification.

d. Advantage: Light microscopes have high magnification. Electron microscopes are helpful in viewing surface details of a specimen. Disadvantage: Light microscopes can be used only in the presence of light and have lower resolution. Electron microscopes can be used only for viewing ultra-thin specimens.

29. Mitochondria are observed in plant cells that contain chloroplasts. Why do you find mitochondria in photosynthetic tissue?

a. Mitochondria are not needed but are an evolutionary relic.

b. Mitochondria and chloroplasts work together to use light energy to make sugars.

c. Mitochondria participate in the Calvin cycle/ light independent reactions of photosynthesis.

d. Mitochondria are required to break down sugars and other materials for energy.

30. In what situation, or situations, would the use of a light microscope be ideal? Why?

a. A light microscope is used to view the details of the surface of a cell as it cannot be viewed in detail by the transmission microscope.

b. A light microscope allows visualization of small living cells, which have been stained and cannot be viewed by scanning electron microscope.

c. A standard light microscope is used to view living organisms with little contrast to distinguish them from the background, which would be harder to see with the electron microscope.

d. A light microscope reveals the internal structures of a cell, which cannot be viewed by transmission electron microscopy.

31. The major role of the cell wall in bacteria is protecting the cell against changes in osmotic pressure, pressure caused by different solute concentrations in the environment. Bacterial cells swell, but do not burst, in low solute concentrations. What happens to bacterial cells if a compound that interferes with the synthesis of the cell wall is added to an environment with low solute concentrations?

a. Bacterial cells will shrink due to the lack of cell wall material.

b. Bacterial cells will shrink in size.

c. Bacterial cells may burst due to the influx of water.

d. Bacterial cells remain normal; they have alternative pathways to synthesize cell walls.

32. We have discussed the upper limits of cell size; yet, there is a lower limit to cell size. What determines how small a cell can be?

a. The cell should be large enough to escape detection.

b. The cell should be able to accommodate all the structures and metabolic activities necessary to survival.

c. The size of the cell should be large enough to reproduce itself.

d. The cell should be large enough to adapt to the changing environmental conditions.

33. Which of these is a possible explanation for the presence of a rigid cell wall in plants?

a. Plants remain exposed to changes in temperature and thus require rigid cell walls to protect themselves.

b. Plants are subjected to osmotic pressure and a cell wall helps them against bursting or shrinking.

c. Plant cells have a rigid cell wall to protect themselves from grazing animals.

d. Plant cells have a rigid cell wall to prevent the influx of waste material.

34. Bacteria do not have organelles; yet, the same reactions that take place on the mitochondria inner membrane, the phosphorylation of ADP to ATP, and chloroplasts, photosynthesis, take place in bacteria. Where do these reactions take place?

a. These reactions take place in the nucleoid of the bacteria.

b. These reactions occur in the cytoplasm present in the bacteria.

c. These reactions occur on the plasma membrane of bacteria.

d. These reactions take place in the mesosomes.

35. What are the structural and functional similarities and differences between mitochondria and chloroplasts?

a. Similarities: double membrane, inter-membrane space, ATP production, contain DNA. Differences: mitochondria have inner folds called cristae, chloroplast contains accessory pigments in thylakoids, which form grana and a stroma.

b. Similarities: DNA, inter-membrane space, ATP production, and chlorophyll. Differences: mitochondria have a matrix and inner folds called cristae; chloroplast contains accessory pigments in thylakoids, which form grana and a stroma.

c. Similarities: double membrane and ATP production. Differences: mitochondria have inter-membrane space and inner folds called cristae; chloroplast contains accessory pigments in thylakoids, which form grana and a stroma.

d. Similarities: double membrane and ATP production. Differences: mitochondria have inter-membrane space, inner folds called cristae, ATP synthase for ATP synthesis, and DNA; chloroplast contains accessory pigments in thylakoids, which, form grana and a stroma.

36. Is the nuclear membrane part of the endomembrane system? Why or why not?

a. The nuclear membrane is not a part of the endomembrane system as the endoplasmic reticulum is a separate organelle of the cell.
b. The nuclear membrane is considered a part of the endomembrane system as it is continuous with the Golgi body.
c. The nuclear membrane is part of the endomembrane system as it is continuous with the rough endoplasmic reticulum.
d. The nuclear membrane is not considered a part of the endomembrane system as the nucleus is a separate organelle.

37. What happens to the proteins that are synthesized on free ribosomes in the cytoplasm? Do they go through the Golgi apparatus?

a. These proteins move through the Golgi apparatus and enter in the nucleus.
b. These proteins go through the Golgi apparatus and remain in the cytosol.
c. The proteins do not go through the Golgi apparatus and move into the nucleus for processing.
d. The proteins do not go through the Golgi apparatus and remain free in the cytosol.

38. What are the similarities and differences between the structures of centrioles and flagella?

a. Centrioles and flagella are made of microtubules but show different arrangements.
b. Centrioles are made of microtubules but flagella are made of microfilaments and both show the same arrangement.
c. Centrioles and flagella are made of microfilaments. Centrioles have a 9 + 2 arrangement.
d. Centrioles are made of microtubules and flagella are made of microfilaments and both have different structures.

39. Inhibitors of microtubule assembly, vinblastine for example, are used for cancer chemotherapy. How does an inhibitor of microtubule assembly affect cancerous cells?

a. The inhibitors restrict the separation of chromosomes, thereby stopping cell division.
b. The inhibition of microtubules interferes with the synthesis of proteins.
c. The inhibitors bind the microtubule to the nuclear membrane, stopping cell division.
d. The inhibitor interferes with energy production.

40. How do cilia and flagella differ?

a. Cilia are made of microfilaments and flagella of microtubules.
b. Cilia are helpful in the process of engulfing food. Flagella are involved in the movement of the organism.
c. Cilia are short and found in large numbers on the cell surface whereas flagella are long and fewer in number.
d. Cilia are found in prokaryotic cells and flagella in eukaryotic cells.

41. In which human tissues would you find desmosomes? Think of tissues that undergo strong mechanical stress and must be held together with some flexibility.

a. bone cells and cartilage cells
b. muscle cells and skin cells
c. nerve cells and muscle cells
d. secretory cells and muscle cells

42. If there is a mutation in the gene for collagen, such as the one involved in Ehlers-Danlos syndrome, and the individual produces defective collagen, how would it affect coagulation?

a. The syndrome affects the clotting factors and platelet aggregation.
b. The disease leads to hyper-coagulation of blood.
c. Coagulation is not affected because collagen is not required for coagulation.
d. The disease occurs due to the breakdown of platelets.

43. How does the structure of a plasmodesma differ from that of a gap junction?

a. Gap junctions are essential for transportation in animal cells and plasmodesmata are essential for the movement of substances in plant cells.
b. Gap junctions are found to provide attachment in animal cells and plasmodesmata are essential for attachment of plant cells.
c. Plasmodesmata are essential for communication between animal cells and gap junctions are necessary for attachment of cells in plant cells.
d. Plasmodesmata help in transportation and gap junctions help in attachment, in plant cells.

TEST PREP FOR AP® COURSES

44. Which of the following organisms appear first in the fossil record?

a. archaea

b. fish

c. protists

d. plants

45. Why is it challenging to study bacterial fossils and determine if the fossils are members of the domain archaea, rather than bacteria?

a. Bacteria lack rigid structures, thus do not form fossils.

b. Bacteria have rigid structures, but their fossil impression is scarce.

c. Fossils of bacteria are rarely found because bacteria were not abundant in the past.

d. A fossil of bacteria changes overtime due to the presence of new bacteria living on them.

46.

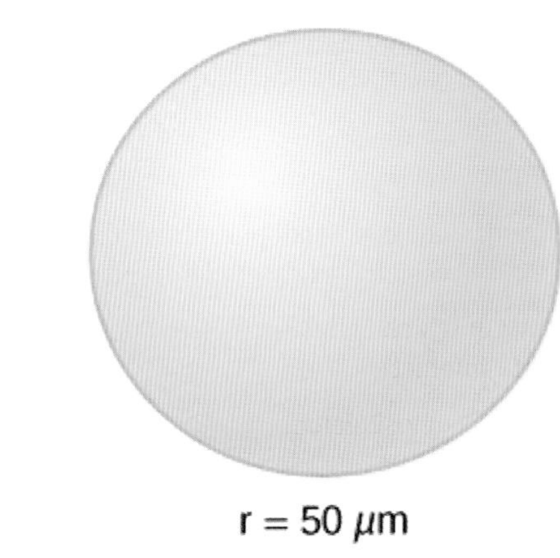

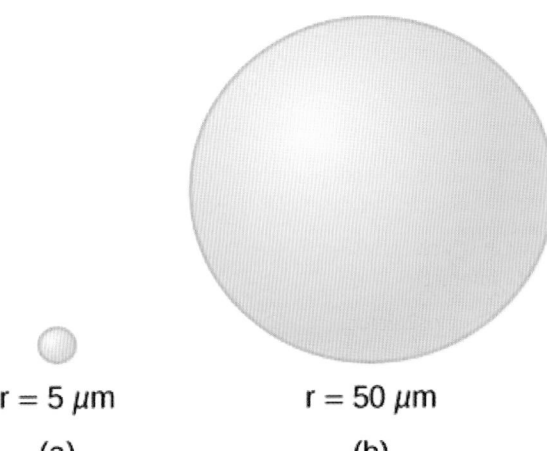

Pictured are two cells along with their radius. What does cell B likely have when compared to cell A?

a. smaller surface area and larger volume

b. larger surface area and smaller volume

c. smaller surface area-to-volume ratio

d. larger surface area-to-volume ratio

47.

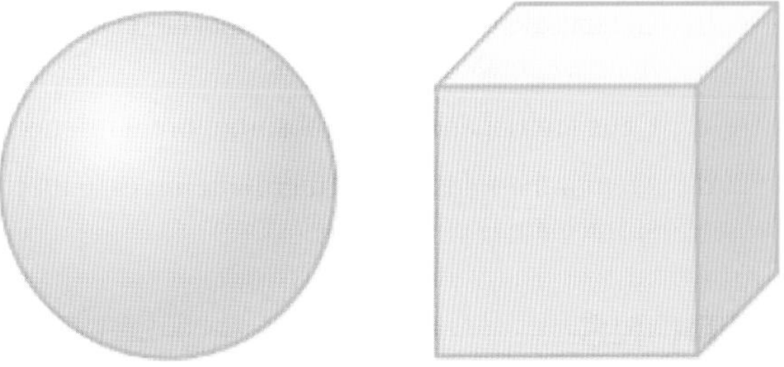

Consider the shapes. The diameter of the sphere is equal to 1 mm and the side of the cube is also equal to 1 mm. What is the ratio of the surface to volume ratios for the sphere and the cube?

a. $3 : 1$

b. $4 : 1$

c. $1 : 1$

d. $2 : 1$

48.

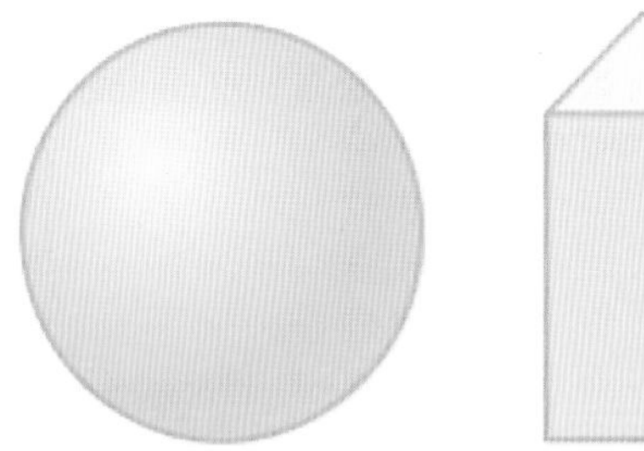

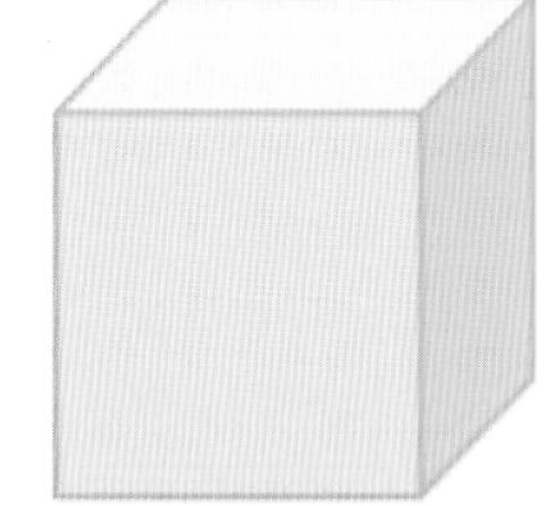

Which of the following is true regarding the surface-to-volume ratios of the cube and the sphere?

a. The sphere will have a higher surface area than the cube.

b. The sphere will have a higher volume than the cube.

c. The sphere will have a higher surface area-to-volume ratio than the cube.

d. Their surface area-to-volume ratios will be equal.

e. The sphere will have a lower surface area-to-volume ratio than the cube.

49. What is the major consideration in setting the lower limit of cell size?

a. The cell must be large enough to fight the pathogens

b. The cell must be large enough to attach to a substrate.

c. The lower limit should be small enough, for the cell to move in the fluid efficiently.

d. The cell size must be small as to fit all the processes and structures to support life.

50. Which of the following structures has the same general structure in Archaea, Bacteria, and Eukarya, pointing to a common origin?

a. centriole

b. cytoplasmic membrane

c. Golgi apparatus

d. nucleus

51. Why does the structure of the cytoplasmic membrane point to a common ancestor?

a. The presence of a cytoplasmic membrane in every organism does not point to a common ancestry.
b. The similar arrangement of phospholipids and proteins points to common ancestry.
c. The lipid nature of the membrane makes it the most primitive trait.
d. The similar effect of temperature on the membrane makes it the ancestral trait.

52. Which organelles would be present in high numbers in the leg muscles of a marathon runner?

a. centrioles
b. chloroplasts
c. mitochondria
d. peroxisome

53. Macrophages ingest and digest many pathogens. Which organelle plays a major role in the activity of macrophages?

a. chloroplast
b. lysosome
c. nucleus
d. peroxisome

54. You are looking at a sample under a light microscope and observe a new type of cell. You come to the conclusion that it is a bacterium and not a eukaryotic cell. What would you observe to come to this conclusion?

a. the cell has a cell wall
b. the cell has a flagellum
c. the cell does not have a nucleus

55. Thiomargarita namibiensis is a large single cell organism, which can reach lengths of $700\,\mu\text{m}$. The cell is classified as a bacterium. What is the main argument to justify the classification?

a. This organism shows simple diffusion for the uptake of nutrients and is thus classified as a bacterium.
b. This organism does not show presence of any cell organelles, and thus is classified as a bacterium.
c. the existence of these organisms in long chains and pearl appearance
d. The organism demonstrates characteristics of gram-negative bacteria, and thus is classified as a bacterium.

56. Radioactive amino acids are fed to a cell in culture for a short amount of time. This is called a pulse. You follow the appearance of radioactive proteins in the cell compartments. In which organelles and in what order does radioactivity appear?

a. endoplasmic reticulum - lysosomes - Golgi body - vesicle - extracellular region
b. endoplasmic reticulum - vesicles - Golgi body - vesicles - extracellular region
c. Golgi Body - vesicles - endoplasmic reticulum - vesicles - extracellular region
d. nucleus - endoplasmic reticulum - Golgi body - vesicle - extracellular region

57. With which cellular structure does the extracellular matrix interact?

a. cytoskeleton
b. nucleus
c. smooth endoplasmic reticulum

58. Which structure or structures allow bacteria to move about?

a. fimbriae only
b. flagella only
c. flagella and fimbriae
d. plasmid and capsule

59. Cells lining the intestine absorb a lot of nutrients. How did those cells adapt to their function?

a. Cells use cilia to move nutrients to their surface.
b. Cells grow much larger than adjacent cells to increase intake
c. Cells are flat and thin to absorb more nutrients.
d. Membrane folds called microvilli increase the surface area.

SCIENCE PRACTICE CHALLENGE QUESTIONS

60. Describe structural and functional similarities between mitochondria and chloroplasts that provide evidence of common ancestry.

61. Explain how the structural and functional differences between mitochondria and chloroplasts provide evidence of adaptations among common ancestral organisms.

62. Examine the differences and similarities in the structural features of animal and plant cells. **Justify the claim** that both animals and plants have common ancestors based on your observations.

63. What conserved core processes are common to both animals and plants? **Construct an explanation** of the differences based on the selective advantages provided in different environments.

64. Louis Sullivan described architectural design as "form follows function." For example, a window is designed to add light to a space without heat transport. A door is designed to allow access to a space. Windows and doors have different functions and so take different forms. Biological systems are not designed, but selected from random trials by interaction with the environment. Apply Sullivan's principle to **explain** the relationship of function and form for each pair of cellular structures below.

a. Plasma membrane and endoplasmic reticulum
b. Mitochondrion and chloroplast
c. Rough endoplasmic reticulum and smooth endoplasmic reticulum
d. Flagella and cilia
e. Muscle cells and secretory cells

65. Complex multicellular organisms share nutrients and resources, and their cells communicate with each other. A society may encourage cooperation among individuals while discouraging selfish behavior to increase the overall success of the social system, sometimes at the expense of the individual. Scientific questions are testable and often attempt to reveal a mechanism responsible for a phenomenon. **Pose** three **questions** that can be used to examine the ways in which a social system regulates itself. Be prepared to share these in small group discussions with your classmates about the similarities between these regulatory strategies and the analogous roles of plasmodesmata and gap junctions in cell communication.

66. Plasmodesmata in vascular plants and gap junctions in animals are examples of specialized features of cells. Mechanisms by which transport occurs between cells evolved independently within several eukaryotic clades. **Explain**, in terms of cellular cooperation, the selective advantages provided by such structures.

67. Mammalian red blood cells have no nuclei, must originate in other tissue systems, are relatively long-lived, are small with shapes that actively respond to their environment, and are metabolic anaerobes. Other vertebrates have red blood cells that are usually nucleated and are often relatively large, aerobic, self-replicating, and short-lived.

To connect these facts to biology, questions need to be asked. The questions that you pose will depend on the path your class is taking through the curriculum. Begin by summarizing what you know:

- What are the functions of a eukaryotic cell nucleus?
- What is the approximate average size of a human red blood cell?
- What is the range of blood vessel diameters in adult humans?
- What is the range of red blood cell size in vertebrates?
- What is the average lifetime of a human red blood cell?
- How can you show how cell production is stimulated using examples from particular systems?
- How is cell death controlled?
- What biochemical cycles are associated with anaerobic and aerobic respiration, and what are the important differences between these?
- What process is involved in the transport of oxygen and carbon dioxide into and out of red blood cells?
- What behaviors and dynamic homeostatic processes might be associated with the properties of red blood cells in mammalian and nonmammalian organisms?
- What do you know about the evolutionary divergences among vertebrates?

Your summary has revealed some similarities and differences among vertebrate erythrocyte and circulatory system structures. Scientific questions are testable. They can be addressed by making observations and measurements and analyzing the resulting data.

A. **Pose** three scientific **questions** that arise from your summaries of what you know about erythrocytes and capillary size.
B. For each question you pose, **predict** what you believe would be the answer and **provide reasoning** for your prediction.
C. **Describe** an approach you think can be used to obtain data to test your prediction.
D. In the production of mammalian red blood cells, erythrocytes that have not yet matured and are still synthesizing heme proteins are surrounded by a macrophage. Predict the role of the macrophage in the maturation of a red blood cell.

68. Mitochondria have DNA that encode proteins related to the structures and functions of the organelles. The replication appears to occur continuously, however, many questions about control of replication rate and segregation during mitosis are yet unanswered. Many diseases are caused by mitochondrial dysfunction. Mitophagy, as the name suggests, leads to the destruction of mitochondria. **Predict** whether or not cellular control mechanisms involving the regulation of mitochondrial DNA by the nucleus exist. Make use of what you know about selection and homeostasis as they apply to both the organism and to the organelle.

5 | STRUCTURE AND FUNCTION OF PLASMA MEMBRANES

Figure 5.1 Despite its seeming hustle and bustle, Grand Central Station functions with a high level of organization: People and objects move from one location to another, they cross or are contained within certain boundaries, and they provide a constant flow as part of larger activity. Analogously, a plasma membrane's functions involve movement within the cell and across boundaries in the process of intracellular and intercellular activities. (credit: modification of work by Randy Le'Moine)

Chapter Outline

Introduction

The plasma membrane, which is also called the cell membrane, has many functions; but, the most basic one is to define the borders and act as gatekeeper for the cell. The plasma membrane is selectively permeable, meaning some molecules can freely enter or leave the cell. Others require help from specialized structures, other molecules, or require energy in order to cross. One example of a molecule that assists other molecules across the plasma membrane is a protein called NPC1. This protein is involved in moving cholesterol and other types of fats across the plasma membrane. Some people have a genetic condition resulting in improperly functioning NPC1. As a result, excessive cholesterol accumulates within cells causing a condition called NPC Disease.

Scientists from the Albert Einstein College of Medicine, Harvard Medical School, and the Whitehead Institute for Biomedical Research discovered that the Ebola virus also uses NPC1 to hitch a ride into cells and replicate. The scientists used mice that lacked the NPC1 protein to test this hypothesis. When the scientists tried to infect these mice with Ebola, none of the mice got sick. Then they tried to infect mice with partially functioning NPC1 and found that they got sick, but did not die. In other words, without properly functioning NPC1, the Ebola virus cannot infect a mouse. If this pattern also exists in humans, it means that anyone with NPC Disease and its subsequent problem with high cholesterol may also be protected from Ebola.

The complete research report can be found here (http://openstaxcollege.org/l/32ebolaentry) .

5.1 | Components and Structure

In this section, you will explore the following questions:

- How does the fluid mosaic model describe the structure and components of the plasma cell membrane?
- How do the molecular components of the membrane provide fluidity?

Connection for AP® Courses

Like an art mosaic, the plasma membrane consists of several different components. Phospholipids (which we studied in previously) form a bilayer; the hydrophobic, fatty acid tails are in contact with each other and hydrophilic portions of the phospholipids are oriented toward the aqueous internal and external environments. Several types of proteins with different functions stud the membrane. Integral proteins often span the membrane and can transport materials into or out of the cells; these embedded proteins can be hydrophilic or hydrophobic, depending on their placement within the membrane. Peripheral proteins found on the exterior and interior surfaces of membranes can serve as enzymes, structural attachments for fibers of the cytoskeleton, and part of a cell's recognition sites. These "cell-specific" proteins play a vital role in immune function; enable cells of a certain type (e.g., liver cells) to identify each other when forming a tissue; and allow hormones and other molecules to recognize target cells. These proteins "float" throughout the membrane, constantly in flux.

Information presented and the examples highlighted in the section support concepts and learning objectives outlined in Big Idea 2 of the AP® Biology Curriculum Framework. The learning objectives provide a transparent foundation for the AP® Biology course, an inquiry-based laboratory experience, instructional activities, and AP® exam questions. A learning objective merges required content with one or more of the seven science practices.

Big Idea 2	Biological systems utilize free energy and molecular building blocks to grow, to reproduce, and to maintain dynamic homeostasis.
Enduring Understanding 2.B	Growth, reproduction and dynamic homeostasis require that cells create and maintain internal environments that are different from their external environments.
Essential Knowledge	**2.B.1** Cell membranes are selectively permeable due to their structure.
Science Practice	**1.4** The student can use representations and models to analyze situations or solve problems qualitatively and quantitatively.
Science Practice	**3.1** The student can pose scientific questions.
Learning Objective	**2.10** The student is able to use representations and models to pose scientific questions about the properties of cell membranes and selective permeability based on molecular structure.
Essential Knowledge	**2.B.1** Cell membranes are selectively permeable due to their structure.
Science Practice	**1.1** The student can create representations and models of natural or man-made phenomena and systems in the domain.
Science Practice	**7.1** The student can connect phenomena and models across spatial and temporal scales.
Science Practice	**7.2** The student can connect concepts in and across domain(s) to generalize and extrapolate in and/or across enduring understandings and/or big ideas.

Learning Objective	**2.11** The student is able to construct models that connect the movement of molecules across membrane with membrane structure and function.

A cell's plasma membrane defines the cell, outlines its borders, and determines the nature of its interaction with its environment (see Figure 5.2 for a summary). Cells exclude some substances, take in others, and excrete still others, all in controlled quantities. The plasma membrane must be very flexible to allow certain cells, such as red blood cells and white blood cells, to change shape as they pass through narrow capillaries. These are the more obvious functions of a plasma membrane. In addition, the surface of the plasma membrane carries markers that allow cells to recognize one another, which is vital for tissue and organ formation during early development, and which later plays a role in the "self" versus "non-self" distinction of the immune response.

Among the most sophisticated functions of the plasma membrane is the ability to transmit signals by means of complex, integral proteins known as receptors. These proteins act both as receivers of extracellular inputs and as activators of intracellular processes. These membrane receptors provide extracellular attachment sites for effectors like hormones and growth factors, and they activate intracellular response cascades when their effectors are bound. Occasionally, receptors are hijacked by viruses that use them to gain entry into cells, and at times, the genes encoding receptors become mutated, causing the process of signal transduction to malfunction with disastrous consequences.

Fluid Mosaic Model

The existence of the plasma membrane was identified in the 1890s, and its chemical components were identified in 1915. The principal components identified at that time were lipids and proteins. The first widely accepted model of the plasma membrane's structure was proposed in 1935 by Hugh Davson and James Danielli; it was based on the "railroad track" appearance of the plasma membrane in early electron micrographs. They theorized that the structure of the plasma membrane resembles a sandwich, with protein being analogous to the bread, and lipids being analogous to the filling. In the 1950s, advances in microscopy, notably transmission electron microscopy (TEM), allowed researchers to see that the core of the plasma membrane consisted of a double, rather than a single, layer. A new model that better explains both the microscopic observations and the function of that plasma membrane was proposed by S.J. Singer and Garth L. Nicolson in 1972.

The explanation proposed by Singer and Nicolson is called the **fluid mosaic model**. The model has evolved somewhat over time, but it still best accounts for the structure and functions of the plasma membrane as we now understand them. The fluid mosaic model describes the structure of the plasma membrane as a mosaic of components—including phospholipids, cholesterol, proteins, and carbohydrates—that gives the membrane a fluid character. Plasma membranes range from 5 to 10 nm in thickness. For comparison, human red blood cells, visible via light microscopy, are approximately 8 µm wide, or approximately 1,000 times wider than a plasma membrane. The membrane does look a bit like a sandwich (Figure 5.2).

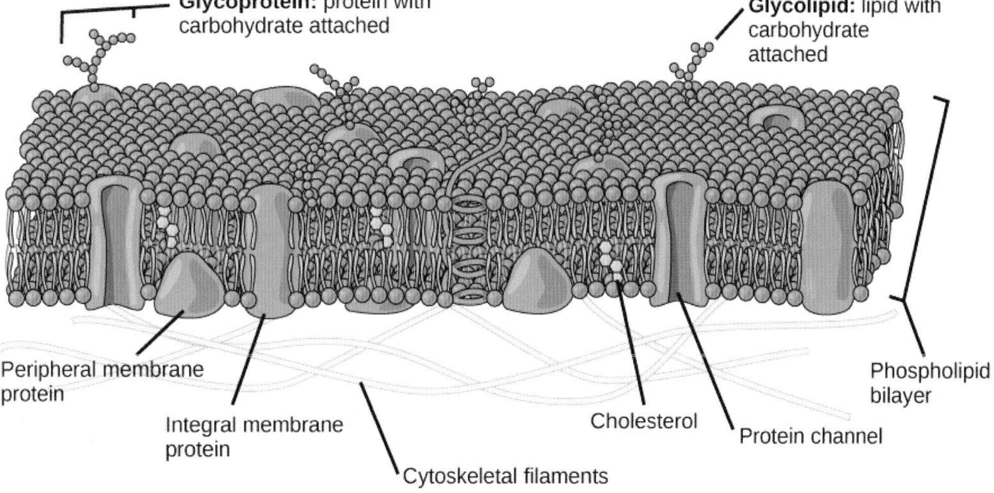

Figure 5.2 The fluid mosaic model of the plasma membrane describes the plasma membrane as a fluid combination of phospholipids, cholesterol, and proteins. Carbohydrates attached to lipids (glycolipids) and to proteins (glycoproteins) extend from the outward-facing surface of the membrane.

The principal components of a plasma membrane are lipids (phospholipids and cholesterol), proteins, and carbohydrates attached to some of the lipids and some of the proteins. A phospholipid is a molecule consisting of glycerol, two fatty acids, and a phosphate-linked head group. Cholesterol, another lipid composed of four fused carbon rings, is found alongside the phospholipids in the core of the membrane. The proportions of proteins, lipids, and carbohydrates in the plasma membrane vary with cell type, but for a typical human cell, protein accounts for about 50 percent of the composition by mass, lipids (of all types) account for about 40 percent of the composition by mass, with the remaining 10 percent of the composition by mass being carbohydrates. However, the concentration of proteins and lipids varies with different cell membranes. For example, myelin, an outgrowth of the membrane of specialized cells that insulates the axons of the peripheral nerves, contains only 18 percent protein and 76 percent lipid. The mitochondrial inner membrane contains 76 percent protein and only 24 percent lipid. The plasma membrane of human red blood cells is 30 percent lipid. Carbohydrates are present only on the exterior surface of the plasma membrane and are attached to proteins, forming **glycoproteins**, or attached to lipids, forming **glycolipids**.

Phospholipids

The main fabric of the membrane is composed of amphiphilic, phospholipid molecules. The **hydrophilic** or "water-loving" areas of these molecules (which look like a collection of balls in an artist's rendition of the model) (Figure 5.2) are in contact with the aqueous fluid both inside and outside the cell. **Hydrophobic**, or water-hating molecules, tend to be non-polar. They interact with other non-polar molecules in chemical reactions, but generally do not interact with polar molecules. When placed in water, hydrophobic molecules tend to form a ball or cluster. The hydrophilic regions of the phospholipids tend to form hydrogen bonds with water and other polar molecules on both the exterior and interior of the cell. Thus, the membrane surfaces that face the interior and exterior of the cell are hydrophilic. In contrast, the interior of the cell membrane is hydrophobic and will not interact with water. Therefore, phospholipids form an excellent two-layer cell membrane that separates fluid within the cell from the fluid outside of the cell.

A phospholipid molecule (Figure 5.3) consists of a three-carbon glycerol backbone with two fatty acid molecules attached to carbons 1 and 2, and a phosphate-containing group attached to the third carbon. This arrangement gives the overall molecule an area described as its head (the phosphate-containing group), which has a polar character or negative charge, and an area called the tail (the fatty acids), which has no charge. The head can form hydrogen bonds, but the tail cannot. A molecule with this arrangement of a positively or negatively charged area and an uncharged, or non-polar, area is referred to as **amphiphilic** or "dual-loving."

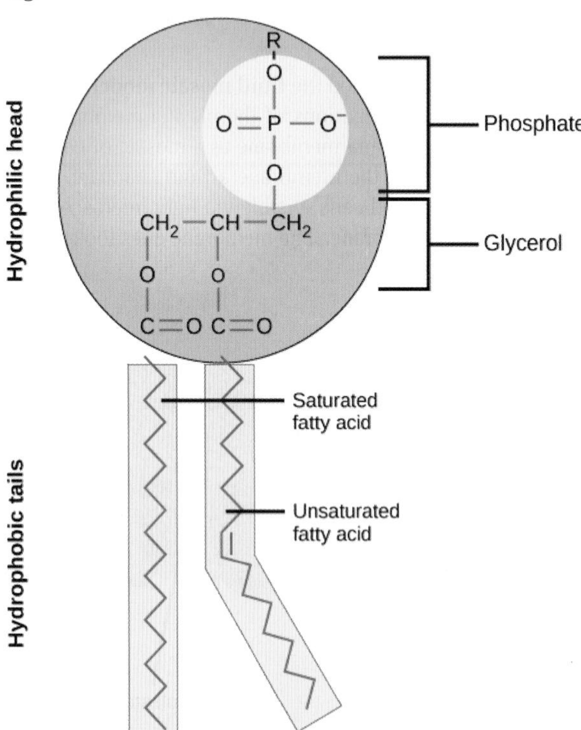

Figure 5.3 This phospholipid molecule is composed of a hydrophilic head and two hydrophobic tails. The hydrophilic head group consists of a phosphate-containing group attached to a glycerol molecule. The hydrophobic tails, each containing either a saturated or an unsaturated fatty acid, are long hydrocarbon chains.

This characteristic is vital to the structure of a plasma membrane because, in water, phospholipids tend to become arranged with their hydrophobic tails facing each other and their hydrophilic heads facing out. In this way, they form a lipid bilayer—a barrier composed of a double layer of phospholipids that separates the water and other materials on one side of the barrier from the water and other materials on the other side. In fact, phospholipids heated in an aqueous solution tend to spontaneously form small spheres or droplets (called micelles or liposomes), with their hydrophilic heads forming the exterior and their hydrophobic tails on the inside (Figure 5.4).

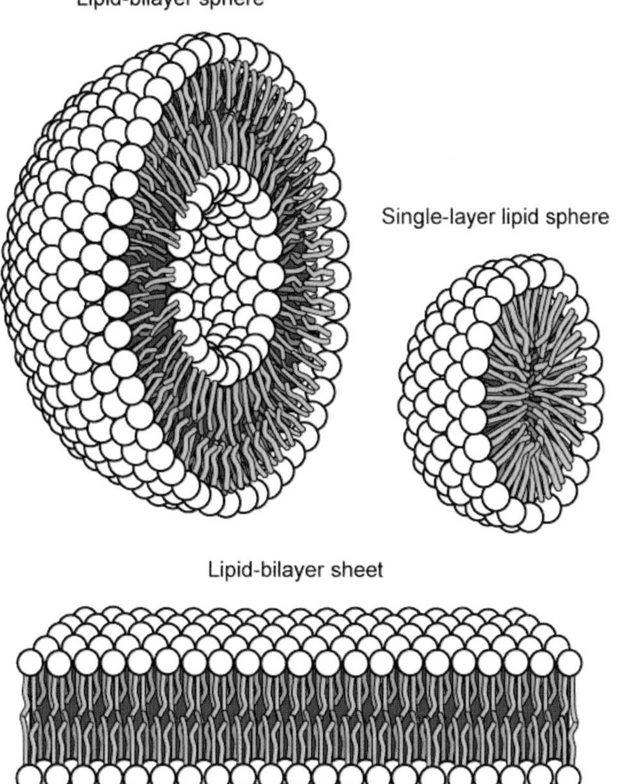

Figure 5.4 In an aqueous solution, phospholipids tend to arrange themselves with their polar heads facing outward and their hydrophobic tails facing inward. (credit: modification of work by Mariana Ruiz Villareal)

Proteins

Proteins make up the second major component of plasma membranes. **Integral proteins** (some specialized types are called integrins) are, as their name suggests, integrated completely into the membrane structure, and their hydrophobic membrane-spanning regions interact with the hydrophobic region of the the phospholipid bilayer (Figure 5.2). Single-pass integral membrane proteins usually have a hydrophobic transmembrane segment that consists of 20–25 amino acids. Some span only part of the membrane—associating with a single layer—while others stretch from one side of the membrane to the other, and are exposed on either side. Some complex proteins are composed of up to 12 segments of a single protein, which are extensively folded and embedded in the membrane (Figure 5.5). This type of protein has a hydrophilic region or regions, and one or several mildly hydrophobic regions. This arrangement of regions of the protein tends to orient the protein alongside the phospholipids, with the hydrophobic region of the protein adjacent to the tails of the phospholipids and the hydrophilic region or regions of the protein protruding from the membrane and in contact with the cytosol or extracellular fluid.

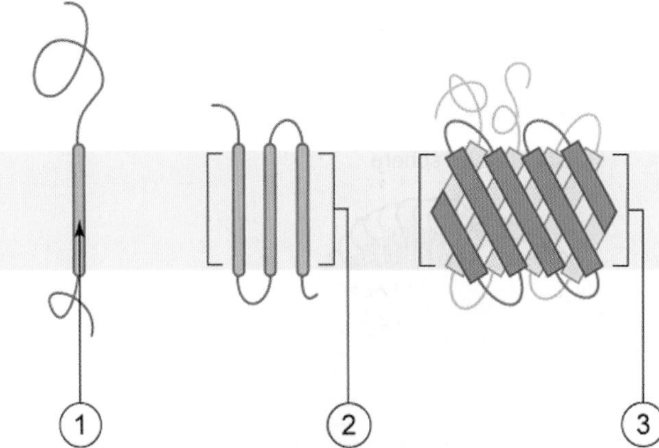

Figure 5.5 Integral membranes proteins may have one or more alpha-helices that span the membrane (examples 1 and 2), or they may have beta-sheets that span the membrane (example 3). (credit: "Foobar"/Wikimedia Commons)

Peripheral proteins are found on the exterior and interior surfaces of membranes, attached either to integral proteins or to phospholipids. Peripheral proteins, along with integral proteins, may serve as enzymes, as structural attachments for the fibers of the cytoskeleton, or as part of the cell's recognition sites. These are sometimes referred to as "cell-specific" proteins. The body recognizes its own proteins and attacks foreign proteins associated with invasive pathogens.

Carbohydrates

Carbohydrates are the third major component of plasma membranes. They are always found on the exterior surface of cells and are bound either to proteins (forming glycoproteins) or to lipids (forming glycolipids) (Figure 5.2). These carbohydrate chains may consist of 2–60 monosaccharide units and can be either straight or branched. Along with peripheral proteins, carbohydrates form specialized sites on the cell surface that allow cells to recognize each other. These sites have unique patterns that allow the cell to be recognized, much the way that the facial features unique to each person allow him or her to be recognized. This recognition function is very important to cells, as it allows the immune system to differentiate between body cells (called "self") and foreign cells or tissues (called "non-self"). Similar types of glycoproteins and glycolipids are found on the surfaces of viruses and may change frequently, preventing immune cells from recognizing and attacking them.

These carbohydrates on the exterior surface of the cell—the carbohydrate components of both glycoproteins and glycolipids—are collectively referred to as the glycocalyx (meaning "sugar coating"). The glycocalyx is highly hydrophilic and attracts large amounts of water to the surface of the cell. This aids in the interaction of the cell with its watery environment and in the cell's ability to obtain substances dissolved in the water. As discussed above, the glycocalyx is also important for cell identification, self/non-self determination, and embryonic development, and is used in cell-cell attachments to form tissues.

evolution CONNECTION

How Viruses Infect Specific Organs

Glycoprotein and glycolipid patterns on the surfaces of cells give many viruses an opportunity for infection. HIV and hepatitis viruses infect only specific organs or cells in the human body. HIV is able to penetrate the plasma membranes of a subtype of lymphocytes called T-helper cells, as well as some monocytes and central nervous system cells. The hepatitis virus attacks liver cells.

These viruses are able to invade these cells, because the cells have binding sites on their surfaces that are specific to and compatible with certain viruses (Figure 5.6). Other recognition sites on the virus's surface interact with the human immune system, prompting the body to produce antibodies. Antibodies are made in response to the antigens or proteins associated with invasive pathogens, or in response to foreign cells, such as might occur with an organ transplant. These same sites serve as places for antibodies to attach and either destroy or inhibit the activity of the virus. Unfortunately, these recognition sites on HIV change at a rapid rate because of mutations, making the production of an effective vaccine against the virus very difficult, as the virus evolves and adapts. A person infected with HIV will quickly develop different populations, or variants, of the virus that are distinguished by differences in these recognition sites. This rapid change of surface markers decreases the effectiveness of the person's immune system in attacking the virus, because the antibodies will not recognize the new variations of the surface patterns. In the case of HIV, the problem is compounded by the fact that the virus specifically infects and destroys cells involved in the immune response, further incapacitating the host.

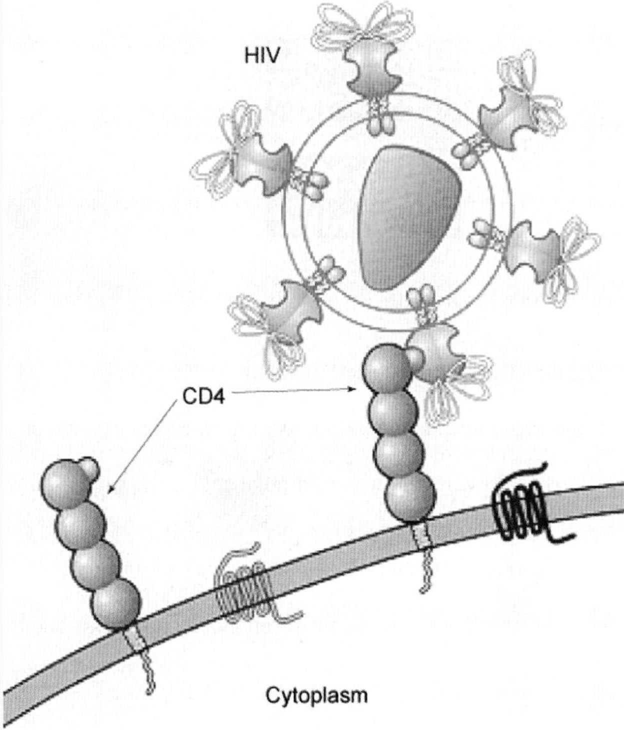

Figure 5.6 HIV binds to the CD4 receptor, a glycoprotein on the surfaces of T cells. (credit: modification of work by NIH, NIAID)

Why does the immune system attack a transplanted organ?

a. Glycoproteins and glycolipids on the surface of the organ are similar to those found on pathogens.
b. Glycoproteins and glycolipids on the surface of the organ are not recognized by the immune system.
c. Glycoproteins and glycolipids on the surface of the organ are toxic to the body.
d. Glycoproteins and glycolipids on the surface of the organ are similar to those found on immune cells.

Membrane Fluidity

The mosaic characteristic of the membrane, described in the fluid mosaic model, helps to illustrate its nature. The integral proteins and lipids exist in the membrane as separate but loosely attached molecules. These resemble the separate, multicolored tiles of a mosaic picture, and they float, moving somewhat with respect to one another. The membrane is not like a balloon, however, that can expand and contract; rather, it is fairly rigid and can burst if penetrated or if a cell takes in too much water. However, because of its mosaic nature, a very fine needle can easily penetrate a plasma membrane without causing it to burst, and the membrane will flow and self-seal when the needle is extracted.

The mosaic characteristics of the membrane explain some but not all of its fluidity. There are two other factors that help maintain this fluid characteristic. One factor is the nature of the phospholipids themselves. In their saturated form, the fatty acids in phospholipid tails are saturated with bound hydrogen atoms. There are no double bonds between adjacent carbon atoms. This results in tails that are relatively straight. In contrast, unsaturated fatty acids do not contain a maximal number of hydrogen atoms, but they do contain some double bonds between adjacent carbon atoms; a double bond results in a bend in the string of carbons of approximately 30 degrees (**Figure 5.3**).

Thus, if saturated fatty acids, with their straight tails, are compressed by decreasing temperatures, they press in on each other, making a dense and fairly rigid membrane. If unsaturated fatty acids are compressed, the "kinks" in their tails elbow adjacent phospholipid molecules away, maintaining some space between the phospholipid molecules. This "elbow room" helps to maintain fluidity in the membrane at temperatures at which membranes with saturated fatty acid tails in their phospholipids would "freeze" or solidify. The relative fluidity of the membrane is particularly important in a cold environment. A cold environment tends to compress membranes composed largely of saturated fatty acids, making them less fluid and more susceptible to rupturing. Many organisms (fish are one example) are capable of adapting to cold environments by changing the proportion of unsaturated fatty acids in their membranes in response to the lowering of the temperature.

Visit this **site (http://openstaxcollege.org/l/biological_memb)** to see animations of the fluidity and mosaic quality of membranes.

Explain why glucose cannot pass directly through the cell membrane.

a. The plasma membrane is impermeable to polar molecules, so transport proteins are required.

b. The plasma membrane is selectively permeable to polar molecules, and a transport protein is required for larger molecules.

c. The plasma membrane is permeable to all polar molecules, but a transport protein is required.

d. The plasma membrane is selectively permeable to all polar molecules and a transport protein is never required for them.

Animals have an additional membrane constituent that assists in maintaining fluidity. Cholesterol, which lies alongside the phospholipids in the membrane, tends to dampen the effects of temperature on the membrane. Thus, this lipid functions as a buffer, preventing lower temperatures from inhibiting fluidity and preventing increased temperatures from increasing fluidity too much. Thus, cholesterol extends, in both directions, the range of temperature in which the membrane is appropriately fluid and consequently functional. Cholesterol also serves other functions, such as organizing clusters of transmembrane proteins into lipid rafts.

The Components and Functions of the Plasma Membrane

Component	Location
Phospholipid	Main fabric of the membrane
Cholesterol	Attached between phospholipids and between the two phospholipid layers
Integral proteins (for example, integrins)	Embedded within the phospholipid layer(s). May or may not penetrate through both layers
Peripheral proteins	On the inner or outer surface of the phospholipid bilayer; not embedded within the phospholipids
Carbohydrates (components of glycoproteins and glycolipids)	Generally attached to proteins on the outside membrane layer

Table 5.1

Immunologist

The variations in peripheral proteins and carbohydrates that affect a cell's recognition sites are of prime interest in immunology. These changes are taken into consideration in vaccine development. Many infectious diseases, such as smallpox, polio, diphtheria, and tetanus, were conquered by the use of vaccines.

Immunologists are the physicians and scientists who research and develop vaccines, as well as treat and study allergies or other immune problems. Some immunologists study and treat autoimmune problems (diseases in which a person's immune system attacks his or her own cells or tissues, such as lupus) and immunodeficiencies, whether acquired (by a virus, for example) or hereditary (such as severe combined immunodeficiency, or SCID). Immunologists are called in to help treat organ transplantation patients, who must have their immune systems suppressed so that their bodies will not reject a transplanted organ. Some immunologists work to understand natural immunity and the effects of a person's environment on it. Others work on questions about how the immune system affects the development of certain chronic diseases.

To work as an immunologist, a PhD or MD is required. In addition, immunologists undertake at least 2–3 years of training in an accredited program and must pass an examination given by the American Board of Allergy and Immunology. Immunologists must possess knowledge of the functions of the human body as they relate to issues beyond immunization, and knowledge of pharmacology and medical technology, such as medications, therapies, test materials, and surgical procedures.

science practices CONNECTION for AP® Courses

Activity

Using appropriate media, construct a model of the plasma membrane and its molecular components. In the next section, you will use the model to demonstrate the movement of different substances across the membrane.

Think About It

What research questions can be asked about plasma membranes? State three questions relating to plasma membranes along with possible solutions to the questions.

5.2 | Passive Transport

By the end of this section, you will be able to:

- Identify and describe the properties of life. Why and how does passive transport occur across membranes?
- What is tonicity, and how is it relevant to passive transport?

Connection for AP® Courses

Preventing dehydration is important for both plants and animals. Water moves across plasma membranes by a specific type of diffusion called osmosis. The concentration gradient of water across a membrane is inversely proportional to the concentration of solutes; that is, water moves through channel proteins called aquaporins from higher water concentration to lower water concentration. Solute concentration outside and inside the cell influences the rate of osmosis. Tonicity describes how the extracellular concentration of solutes can change the volume of a cell by affecting osmosis, often correlating with the osmolarity of the solution, i.e., the total solute concentration of the solution. In a hypotonic situation, because the extracellular fluid has a lower concentration of solutes (lower osmolarity) than the fluid inside the cell, water enters the cell, causing it to swell and possibly burst. The cell walls of plants prevent them from bursting, but animal cells, such as red blood cells, can lyse. When a cell is placed in a hypertonic solution, water leaves the cell because the cell has a higher water potential than the extracellular solution. When the concentrations of solute are equal on both sides of the membrane (isotonic), no net movement of water into or out of the cell occurs. Living organisms have evolved a variety of ways to maintain osmotic balance; for example, marine fish secrete excess salt through the gills to maintain dynamic homeostasis.

Information presented and the examples highlighted in the section support concepts and learning objectives outlined in Big Idea 2 of the AP® Biology Curriculum Framework. The learning objectives listed in the Curriculum Framework provide a transparent foundation for the AP® Biology course, an inquiry-based laboratory experience, instructional activities, and AP® exam questions. A learning objective merges required content with one or more of the seven science practices.

Essential Knowledge	**2.B.2** Growth and dynamic homeostasis are maintained by the constant movement of molecules across membranes.
Science Practice	**1.4** The student can use representations and models to analyze situations or solve problems qualitatively and quantitatively.
Science Practice	**3.1** The student can pose scientific questions.
Learning Objective	**2.11** The student is able to construct models that connect the movement of molecules across membranes with membrane structure and function.
Essential Knowledge	**2.B.2** Growth and dynamic homeostasis are maintained by the constant movement of molecules across membranes.
Science Practice	**1.4** The student can use representations and models to analyze situations or solve problems qualitatively and quantitatively.
Science Practice	**3.1** The student can pose scientific questions.
Learning Objective	**2.12** The student is able to use representations and models to analyze situation or solve problems qualitatively and quantitatively to investigate whether dynamic homeostasis is maintained by the active movement of molecules across membranes.

The Science Practice Challenge Questions contain additional test questions for this section that will help you prepare for the AP exam. These questions address the following standards:
[APLO 2.25][APLO 2.27][APLO 4.3][APLO 4.17][APLO1.9] [APLO 2.16][APLO 2.17][APLO 2.18]

Plasma membranes must allow certain substances to enter and leave a cell, and prevent some harmful materials from entering and some essential materials from leaving. In other words, plasma membranes are **selectively permeable**—they allow some substances to pass through, but not others. If they were to lose this selectivity, the cell would no longer be able to sustain itself, and it would be destroyed. Some cells require larger amounts of specific substances than do other cells; they must have a way of obtaining these materials from extracellular fluids. This may happen passively, as certain materials move back and forth, or the cell may have special mechanisms that facilitate transport. Some materials are so important to a cell that it spends some of its energy, hydrolyzing adenosine triphosphate (ATP), to obtain these materials. Red blood cells use some of their energy doing just that. Most cells spend the majority of their energy to maintain an imbalance of sodium and potassium ions between the interior and exterior of the cell.

The most direct forms of membrane transport are passive. **Passive transport** is a naturally occurring phenomenon and does not require the cell to exert any of its energy to accomplish the movement. In passive transport, substances move from an area of higher concentration to an area of lower concentration. A physical space in which there is a range of concentrations of a single substance is said to have a **concentration gradient**.

Selective Permeability

Plasma membranes are asymmetric: the interior of the membrane is not identical to the exterior of the membrane. In fact, there is a considerable difference between the array of phospholipids and proteins between the two leaflets that form a membrane. On the interior of the membrane, some proteins serve to anchor the membrane to fibers of the cytoskeleton. There are peripheral proteins on the exterior of the membrane that bind elements of the extracellular matrix. Carbohydrates, attached to lipids or proteins, are also found on the exterior surface of the plasma membrane. These carbohydrate complexes help the cell bind substances that the cell needs in the extracellular fluid. This adds considerably to the selective nature of plasma membranes (Figure 5.7).

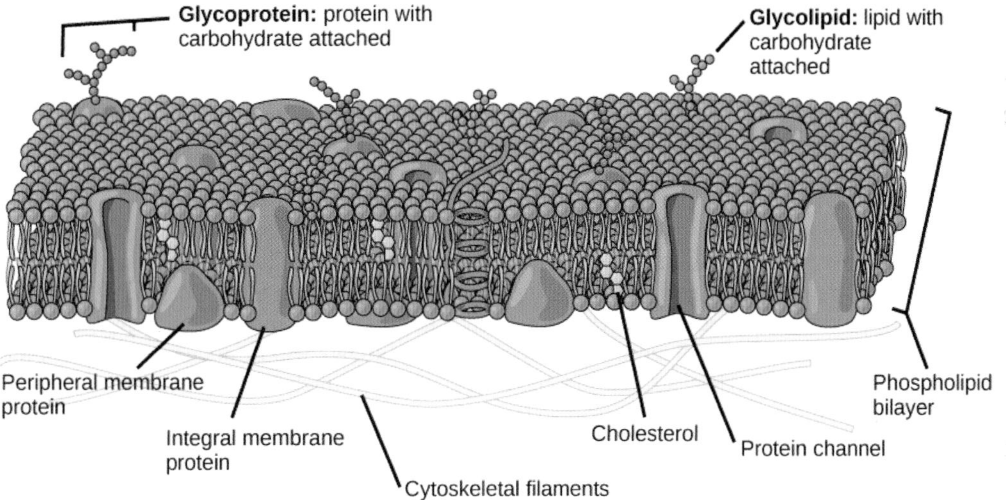

Figure 5.7 The exterior surface of the plasma membrane is not identical to the interior surface of the same membrane.

Recall that plasma membranes are amphiphilic: They have hydrophilic and hydrophobic regions. This characteristic helps the movement of some materials through the membrane and hinders the movement of others. Lipid-soluble material with a low molecular weight can easily slip through the hydrophobic lipid core of the membrane. Substances such as the fat-soluble vitamins A, D, E, and K readily pass through the plasma membranes in the digestive tract and other tissues. Fat-soluble drugs and hormones also gain easy entry into cells and are readily transported into the body's tissues and organs. Similarly, molecules of oxygen and carbon dioxide have no charge and so pass through membranes by simple diffusion.

Polar substances present problems for the membrane. While some polar molecules connect easily with the outside of a cell, they cannot readily pass through the lipid core of the plasma membrane. Additionally, while small ions could easily slip through the spaces in the mosaic of the membrane, their charge prevents them from doing so. Ions such as sodium, potassium, calcium, and chloride must have special means of penetrating plasma membranes. Simple sugars and amino acids also need help with transport across plasma membranes, achieved by various transmembrane proteins (channels).

Diffusion

Diffusion is a passive process of transport. A single substance tends to move from an area of high concentration to an area of low concentration until the concentration is equal across a space. You are familiar with diffusion of substances through the air. For example, think about someone opening a bottle of ammonia in a room filled with people. The ammonia gas is at its highest concentration in the bottle; its lowest concentration is at the edges of the room. The ammonia vapor will diffuse, or spread away, from the bottle, and gradually, more and more people will smell the ammonia as it spreads. Materials move within the cell's cytosol by diffusion, and certain materials move through the plasma membrane by diffusion (Figure 5.8). Diffusion expends no energy. On the contrary, concentration gradients are a form of potential energy, dissipated as the gradient is eliminated.

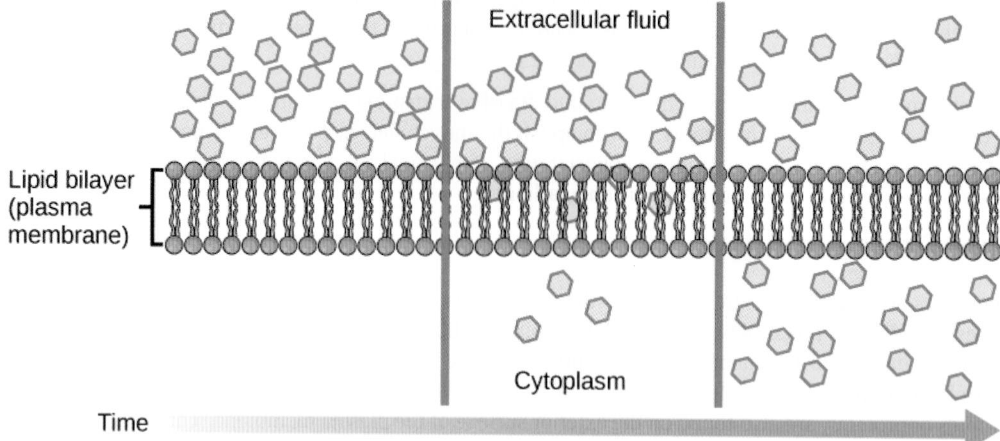

Figure 5.8 Diffusion through a permeable membrane moves a substance from an area of high concentration (extracellular fluid, in this case) down its concentration gradient (into the cytoplasm). (credit: modification of work by Mariana Ruiz Villareal)

Each separate substance in a medium, such as the extracellular fluid, has its own concentration gradient, independent of the concentration gradients of other materials. In addition, each substance will diffuse according to that gradient. Within a system, there will be different rates of diffusion of the different substances in the medium.

Factors That Affect Diffusion

Molecules move constantly in a random manner, at a rate that depends on their mass, their environment, and the amount of thermal energy they possess, which in turn is a function of temperature. This movement accounts for the diffusion of molecules through whatever medium in which they are localized. A substance will tend to move into any space available to it until it is evenly distributed throughout it. After a substance has diffused completely through a space, removing its concentration gradient, molecules will still move around in the space, but there will be no *net* movement of the number of molecules from one area to another. This lack of a concentration gradient in which there is no net movement of a substance is known as dynamic equilibrium. While diffusion will go forward in the presence of a concentration gradient of a substance, several factors affect the rate of diffusion.

- Extent of the concentration gradient: The greater the difference in concentration, the more rapid the diffusion. The closer the distribution of the material gets to equilibrium, the slower the rate of diffusion becomes.
- Mass of the molecules diffusing: Heavier molecules move more slowly; therefore, they diffuse more slowly. The reverse is true for lighter molecules.
- Temperature: Higher temperatures increase the energy and therefore the movement of the molecules, increasing the rate of diffusion. Lower temperatures decrease the energy of the molecules, thus decreasing the rate of diffusion.
- Solvent density: As the density of a solvent increases, the rate of diffusion decreases. The molecules slow down because they have a more difficult time getting through the denser medium. If the medium is less dense, diffusion increases. Because cells primarily use diffusion to move materials within the cytoplasm, any increase in the cytoplasm's density will inhibit the movement of the materials. An example of this is a person experiencing dehydration. As the body's cells lose water, the rate of diffusion decreases in the cytoplasm, and the cells' functions deteriorate. Neurons tend to be very sensitive to this effect. Dehydration frequently leads to unconsciousness and possibly coma because of the decrease in diffusion rate within the cells.
- Solubility: As discussed earlier, nonpolar or lipid-soluble materials pass through plasma membranes more easily than polar materials, allowing a faster rate of diffusion.
- Surface area and thickness of the plasma membrane: Increased surface area increases the rate of diffusion, whereas a thicker membrane reduces it.
- Distance travelled: The greater the distance that a substance must travel, the slower the rate of diffusion. This places an upper limitation on cell size. A large, spherical cell will die because nutrients or waste cannot reach or leave the

center of the cell, respectively. Therefore, cells must either be small in size, as in the case of many prokaryotes, or be flattened, as with many single-celled eukaryotes.

A variation of diffusion is the process of filtration. In filtration, material moves according to its concentration gradient through a membrane; sometimes the rate of diffusion is enhanced by pressure, causing the substances to filter more rapidly. This occurs in the kidney, where blood pressure forces large amounts of water and accompanying dissolved substances, or **solutes**, out of the blood and into the renal tubules. The rate of diffusion in this instance is almost totally dependent on pressure. One of the effects of high blood pressure is the appearance of protein in the urine, which is "squeezed through" by the abnormally high pressure.

Facilitated transport

In **facilitated transport**, also called facilitated diffusion, materials diffuse across the plasma membrane with the help of membrane proteins. A concentration gradient exists that would allow these materials to diffuse into the cell without expending cellular energy. However, these materials are polar molecules that are repelled by the hydrophobic parts of the cell membrane. Facilitated transport proteins shield these materials from the repulsive force of the membrane, allowing them to diffuse into the cell.

The material being transported is first attached to protein or glycoprotein receptors on the exterior surface of the plasma membrane. This allows the material that is needed by the cell to be removed from the extracellular fluid. The substances are then passed to specific integral proteins that facilitate their passage. Some of these integral proteins are collections of beta pleated sheets that form a pore or channel through the phospholipid bilayer. Others are carrier proteins which bind with the substance and aid its diffusion through the membrane.

Channels

The integral proteins involved in facilitated transport are collectively referred to as **transport proteins**, and they function as either channels for the material or carriers. In both cases, they are transmembrane proteins. Channels are specific for the substance that is being transported. **Channel proteins** have hydrophilic domains exposed to the intracellular and extracellular fluids; they additionally have a hydrophilic channel through their core that provides a hydrated opening through the membrane layers (Figure 5.9). Passage through the channel allows polar compounds to avoid the nonpolar central layer of the plasma membrane that would otherwise slow or prevent their entry into the cell. **Aquaporins** are channel proteins that allow water to pass through the membrane at a very high rate.

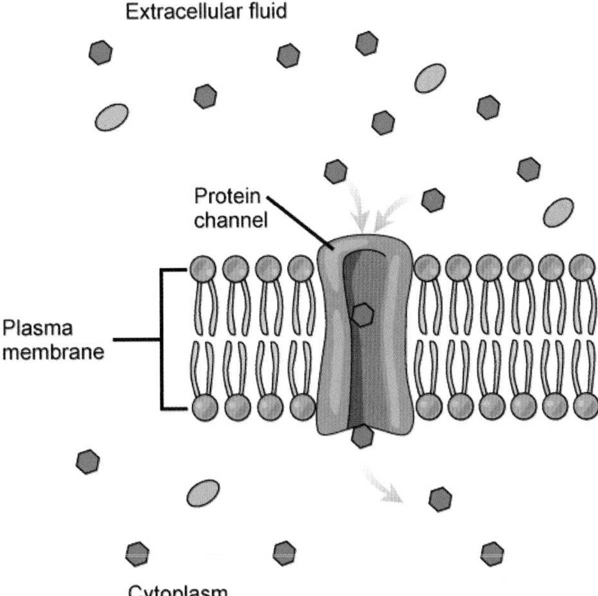

Figure 5.9 Facilitated transport moves substances down their concentration gradients. They may cross the plasma membrane with the aid of channel proteins. (credit: modification of work by Mariana Ruiz Villareal)

Channel proteins are either open at all times or they are "gated," which controls the opening of the channel. The attachment of a particular ion to the channel protein may control the opening, or other mechanisms or substances may be involved. In some tissues, sodium and chloride ions pass freely through open channels, whereas in other tissues a gate must be opened to allow passage. An example of this occurs in the kidney, where both forms of channels are found in different parts of the renal tubules. Cells involved in the transmission of electrical impulses, such as nerve and muscle cells, have gated channels for sodium, potassium, and calcium in their membranes. Opening and closing of these channels changes the relative concentrations on opposing sides of the membrane of these ions, resulting in the facilitation of electrical transmission along membranes (in the case of nerve cells) or in muscle contraction (in the case of muscle cells).

Carrier Proteins

Another type of protein embedded in the plasma membrane is a **carrier protein**. This aptly named protein binds a substance and, in doing so, triggers a change of its own shape, moving the bound molecule from the outside of the cell to its interior (Figure 5.10); depending on the gradient, the material may move in the opposite direction. Carrier proteins are typically specific for a single substance. This selectivity adds to the overall selectivity of the plasma membrane. The exact mechanism for the change of shape is poorly understood. Proteins can change shape when their hydrogen bonds are affected, but this may not fully explain this mechanism. Each carrier protein is specific to one substance, and there are a finite number of these proteins in any membrane. This can cause problems in transporting enough of the material for the cell to function properly. When all of the proteins are bound to their ligands, they are saturated and the rate of transport is at its maximum. Increasing the concentration gradient at this point will not result in an increased rate of transport.

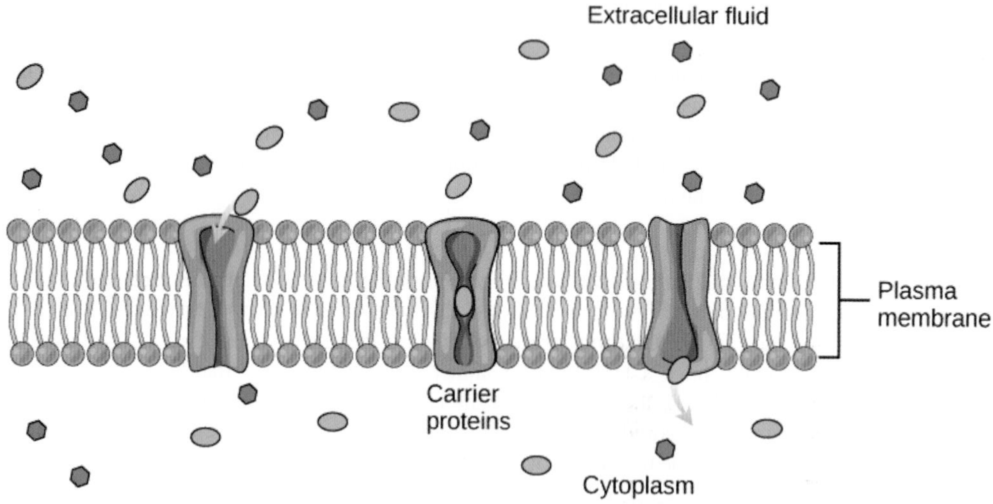

Figure 5.10 Some substances are able to move down their concentration gradient across the plasma membrane with the aid of carrier proteins. Carrier proteins change shape as they move molecules across the membrane. (credit: modification of work by Mariana Ruiz Villareal)

An example of this process occurs in the kidney. Glucose, water, salts, ions, and amino acids needed by the body are filtered in one part of the kidney. This filtrate, which includes glucose, is then reabsorbed in another part of the kidney. Because there are only a finite number of carrier proteins for glucose, if more glucose is present than the proteins can handle, the excess is not transported and it is excreted from the body in the urine. In a diabetic individual, this is described as "spilling glucose into the urine." A different group of carrier proteins called glucose transport proteins, or GLUTs, are involved in transporting glucose and other hexose sugars through plasma membranes within the body.

Channel and carrier proteins transport material at different rates. Channel proteins transport much more quickly than do carrier proteins. Channel proteins facilitate diffusion at a rate of tens of millions of molecules per second, whereas carrier proteins work at a rate of a thousand to a million molecules per second.

Osmosis

Osmosis is the movement of water through a semipermeable membrane according to the concentration gradient of water across the membrane, which is inversely proportional to the concentration of solutes. While diffusion transports material across membranes and within cells, osmosis transports *only water* across a membrane and the membrane limits the diffusion of solutes in the water. Not surprisingly, the aquaporins that facilitate water movement play a large role in osmosis, most prominently in red blood cells and the membranes of kidney tubules.

Mechanism

Osmosis is a special case of diffusion. Water, like other substances, moves from an area of high concentration to one of low concentration. An obvious question is what makes water move at all? Imagine a beaker with a semipermeable membrane separating the two sides or halves (Figure 5.11). On both sides of the membrane the water level is the same, but there are different concentrations of a dissolved substance, or **solute**, that cannot cross the membrane (otherwise the concentrations on each side would be balanced by the solute crossing the membrane). If the volume of the solution on both sides of the membrane is the same, but the concentrations of solute are different, then there are different amounts of water, the solvent, on either side of the membrane.

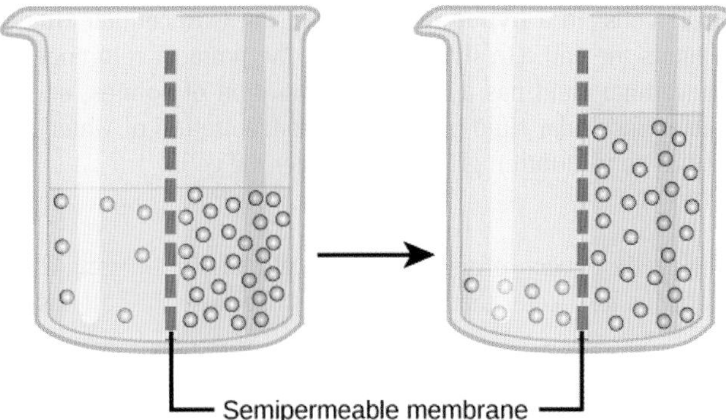

Figure 5.11 In osmosis, water always moves from an area of higher water concentration to one of lower concentration. In the diagram shown, the solute cannot pass through the selectively permeable membrane, but the water can.

To illustrate this, imagine two full glasses of water. One has a single teaspoon of sugar in it, whereas the second one contains one-quarter cup of sugar. If the total volume of the solutions in both cups is the same, which cup contains more water? Because the large amount of sugar in the second cup takes up much more space than the teaspoon of sugar in the first cup, the first cup has more water in it.

Returning to the beaker example, recall that it has a mixture of solutes on either side of the membrane. A principle of diffusion is that the molecules move around and will spread evenly throughout the medium if they can. However, only the material capable of getting through the membrane will diffuse through it. In this example, the solute cannot diffuse through the membrane, but the water can. Water has a concentration gradient in this system. Thus, water will diffuse down its concentration gradient, crossing the membrane to the side where it is less concentrated. This diffusion of water through the membrane—osmosis—will continue until the concentration gradient of water goes to zero or until the hydrostatic pressure of the water balances the osmotic pressure. Osmosis proceeds constantly in living systems.

The beaker example here occurs in an open system where the volume of fluid can increase and decrease freely. Cells, on the other hand, are composed of proteins and other substances embedded in the aqueous cytoplasm. These substances could be considered solutes for the purposes of predicting osmosis. The cell membrane keeps most of the proteins and other substances within the cell, causing the cell to have a higher osmolarity than pure water.

Suppose you perform an experiment where you placed red blood cells in an environment of pure water. What do you suppose would happen to the cells? Because the concentration of solute is higher in the red blood cell than it is in the beaker, water would rush into the red blood cell. What do you think would happen to the red blood cell, given that its cell membrane is made up of a fixed surface area? It is likely that the red blood cell will undergo hemolysis, where they swell up with water and burst. It should be noted, however, that most cells have mechanisms to prevent them from taking on too much water. However, red blood cells lack these controls, making them ideal for osmolarity studies.

This is an important consideration for clinicians delivering drugs intravenously. How would the drug have to be formulated, in terms of osmolarity, to prevent red blood cells from undergoing hemolysis? In order to prevent hemolysis of red blood cells in the blood, drugs are typically formulated in an isotonic solution with the blood to maintain osmolarity.

Tonicity

Tonicity describes how an extracellular solution can change the volume of a cell by affecting osmosis. A solution's tonicity often directly correlates with the osmolarity of the solution. **Osmolarity** describes the total solute concentration of the solution. A solution with low osmolarity has a greater number of water molecules relative to the number of solute particles; a solution with high osmolarity has fewer water molecules with respect to solute particles. In a situation in which solutions of two different osmolarities are separated by a membrane permeable to water, though not to the solute, water will move from the side of the membrane with lower osmolarity (and more water) to the side with higher osmolarity (and less water). This effect makes sense if you remember that the solute cannot move across the membrane, and thus the only component in the system that can move—the water—moves along its own concentration gradient. An important distinction that concerns living systems is that osmolarity measures the number of particles (which may be molecules) in a solution. Therefore, a solution that is cloudy with cells may have a lower osmolarity than a solution that is clear, if the second solution contains more dissolved molecules than there are cells.

Hypotonic Solutions

Three terms—hypotonic, isotonic, and hypertonic—are used to relate the osmolarity of a cell to the osmolarity of the extracellular fluid that contains the cells. In a **hypotonic** situation, the extracellular fluid has lower osmolarity than the fluid inside the cell, and water enters the cell. (In living systems, the point of reference is always the cytoplasm, so the prefix *hypo-* means that the extracellular fluid has a lower concentration of solutes, or a lower osmolarity, than the cell cytoplasm.) It also means that the extracellular fluid has a higher concentration of water in the solution than does the cell. In this situation, water will follow its concentration gradient and enter the cell.

Hypertonic Solutions

As for a **hypertonic** solution, the prefix *hyper-* refers to the extracellular fluid having a higher osmolarity than the cell's cytoplasm; therefore, the fluid contains less water than the cell does. Because the cell has a relatively higher concentration of water, water will leave the cell.

Isotonic Solutions

In an **isotonic** solution, the extracellular fluid has the same osmolarity as the cell. If the osmolarity of the cell matches that of the extracellular fluid, there will be no net movement of water into or out of the cell, although water will still move in and out. Blood cells and plant cells in hypertonic, isotonic, and hypotonic solutions take on characteristic appearances (Figure 5.12).

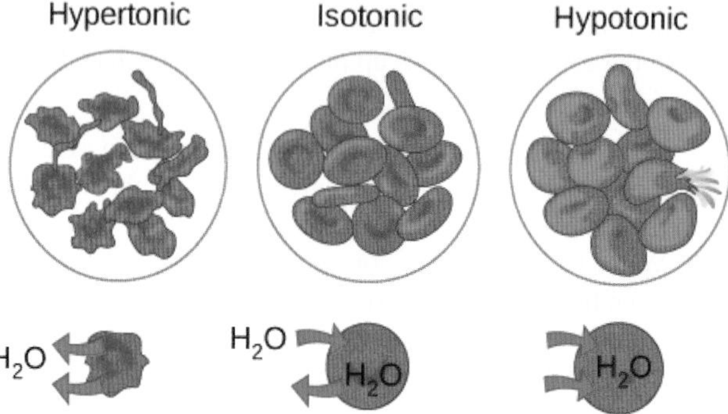

Figure 5.12 Osmotic pressure changes the shape of red blood cells in hypertonic, isotonic, and hypotonic solutions (credit: Mariana Ruiz Villareal)

For a video illustrating the process of diffusion in solutions, visit this site (http://openstaxcollege.org/l/dispersion) .

Explain the difference between the two beakers (http://openstaxcollege.org/l/dispersion) .

a. The lower temperature of left beaker causes yellow dye to diffuse faster than the right beaker.

b. The lower temperature in left beaker causes yellow dye to diffuse slower in it than in the right beaker.

c. The higher temperature of left beaker causes faster diffusion of yellow dye in the left beaker.

d. The higher temperature of right beaker causes slower diffusion of yellow dye in the right beaker.

Tonicity in Living Systems

In a hypotonic environment, water enters a cell, and the cell swells. In an isotonic condition, the relative concentrations of solute and solvent are equal on both sides of the membrane. There is no net water movement; therefore, there is no change in the size of the cell. In a hypertonic solution, water leaves a cell and the cell shrinks. If either the hypo- or hyper- condition goes to excess, the cell's functions become compromised, and the cell may be destroyed.

A red blood cell will burst, or lyse, when it swells beyond the plasma membrane's capability to expand. Remember, the membrane resembles a mosaic, with discrete spaces between the molecules composing it. If the cell swells, and the spaces between the lipids and proteins become too large, the cell will break apart.

In contrast, when excessive amounts of water leave a red blood cell, the cell shrinks, or crenates. This has the effect of concentrating the solutes left in the cell, making the cytosol denser and interfering with diffusion within the cell. The cell's ability to function will be compromised and may also result in the death of the cell.

Various living things have ways of controlling the effects of osmosis—a mechanism called osmoregulation. Some organisms, such as plants, fungi, bacteria, and some protists, have cell walls that surround the plasma membrane and prevent cell lysis in a hypotonic solution. The plasma membrane can only expand to the limit of the cell wall, so the cell will not lyse. In fact, the cytoplasm in plants is always slightly hypertonic to the cellular environment, and water will always enter a cell if water is available. This inflow of water produces turgor pressure, which stiffens the cell walls of the plant (Figure 5.13). In nonwoody plants, turgor pressure supports the plant. Conversly, if the plant is not watered, the extracellular fluid will become hypertonic, causing water to leave the cell. In this condition, the cell does not shrink because the cell wall is not flexible. However, the cell membrane detaches from the wall and constricts the cytoplasm. This is called **plasmolysis**. Plants lose turgor pressure in this condition and wilt (Figure 5.14).

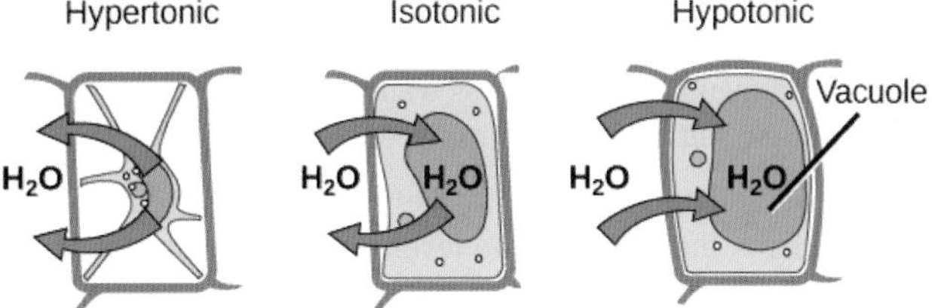

Figure 5.13 The turgor pressure within a plant cell depends on the tonicity of the solution that it is bathed in. (credit: modification of work by Mariana Ruiz Villareal)

Figure 5.14 Without adequate water, the plant on the left has lost turgor pressure, visible in its wilting; the turgor pressure is restored by watering it (right). (credit: Victor M. Vicente Selvas)

Tonicity is a concern for all living things. For example, paramecia and amoebas, which are protists that lack cell walls, have contractile vacuoles. This vesicle collects excess water from the cell and pumps it out, keeping the cell from lysing as it takes on water from its environment (Figure 5.15).

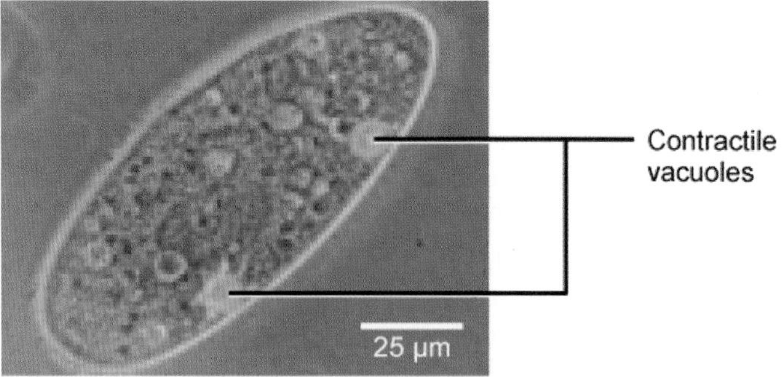

Figure 5.15 A paramecium's contractile vacuole, here visualized using bright field light microscopy at 480x magnification, continuously pumps water out of the organism's body to keep it from bursting in a hypotonic medium. (credit: modification of work by NIH; scale-bar data from Matt Russell)

Many marine invertebrates have internal salt levels matched to their environments, making them isotonic with the water in which they live. Fish, however, must spend approximately five percent of their metabolic energy maintaining osmotic homeostasis. Freshwater fish live in an environment that is hypotonic to their cells. These fish actively take in salt through their gills and excrete diluted urine to rid themselves of excess water. Saltwater fish live in the reverse environment, which is hypertonic to their cells, and they secrete salt through their gills and excrete highly concentrated urine.

In vertebrates, the kidneys regulate the amount of water in the body. Osmoreceptors are specialized cells in the brain that monitor the concentration of solutes in the blood. If the levels of solutes increase beyond a certain range, a hormone is released that retards water loss through the kidney and dilutes the blood to safer levels. Animals also have high concentrations of albumin, which is produced by the liver, in their blood. This protein is too large to pass easily through plasma membranes and is a major factor in controlling the osmotic pressures applied to tissues.

science practices CONNECTION for AP® Courses

Activity

Use the model of the plasma cell membrane you constructed to demonstrate how O_2 and CO_2, H_2O, Na^+ and K^+, and glucose are transported across the membrane.

Think About It

Why should farmers consider the salinity of the soil in which they grow crops?

Answer: Farmers need to consider the salinity of soil, because the movement of water into and out of plant cells depends on the solute concentration of their environment. In soil high in saline, water will be drawn out of root cells causing the cells to shrivel, and the plant to die.

5.3 | Active Transport

By the end of this section, you will be able to:

- How do electrochemical gradients affect the active transport of ions and molecules across membranes?

Connection for AP® Courses

If a substance must move into the cell against its concentration gradient, the cell must use free energy, often provided by ATP, and carrier proteins acting as pumps to move the substance. Substances that move across membranes by this mechanism, a process called active transport, include ions, such as Na^+ and K^+. The combined gradients that affect movement of an ion are its concentration gradient and its electrical gradient (the difference in charge across the membrane); together these gradients are called the electrochemical gradient. To move substances against an electrochemical gradient requires free energy. The sodium-potassium pump, which maintains electrochemical gradients across the membranes of nerve cells in animals, is an example of primary active transport. The formation of H^+ gradients by secondary active transport (co-transport) is important in cellular respiration and photosynthesis and moving glucose into cells.

Information presented and the examples highlighted in the section support concepts and learning objectives outlined in Big Idea 2 of the AP® Biology Curriculum Framework. The learning objectives listed in the Curriculum Framework provide a transparent foundation for the AP® Biology course, an inquiry-based laboratory experience, instructional activities, and AP® exam questions. A learning objective merges required content with one or more of the seven science practices (SP).

Big Idea 2	Biological systems utilize free energy and molecular building blocks to grow, to reproduce, and to maintain dynamic homeostasis.
Enduring Understanding 2.B	Growth, reproduction and dynamic homeostasis require that cells create and maintain internal environments that are different from their external environments.
Essential Knowledge	**2.B.2** Growth and dynamic homeostasis are maintained by the constant movement of molecules across membranes.
Science Practice	**1.4** The student can use representations and models to analyze situations or solve problems qualitatively and quantitatively.
Learning Objective	**2.12** The student is able to use representations and models to analyze situations or solve problems qualitatively and quantitatively to investigate whether dynamic homeostasis is maintained by the active movement of molecules across membranes.

The Science Practice Challenge Questions contain additional test questions for this section that will help you prepare for the AP exam. These questions address the following standards:
[APLO 2.10][APLO 2.17][APLO 1.2][APLO 3.24]

Active transport mechanisms require the use of the cell's energy, usually in the form of adenosine triphosphate (ATP). If a substance must move into the cell against its concentration gradient—that is, if the concentration of the substance inside the cell is greater than its concentration in the extracellular fluid (and vice versa)—the cell must use energy to move the substance. Some active transport mechanisms move small-molecular weight materials, such as ions, through the membrane. Other mechanisms transport much larger molecules.

Electrochemical Gradient

We have discussed simple concentration gradients—differential concentrations of a substance across a space or a membrane—but in living systems, gradients are more complex. Because ions move into and out of cells and because cells contain proteins that do not move across the membrane and are mostly negatively charged, there is also an electrical gradient, a difference of charge, across the plasma membrane. The interior of living cells is electrically negative with respect to the extracellular fluid in which they are bathed, and at the same time, cells have higher concentrations of potassium (K^+) and lower concentrations of sodium (Na^+) than does the extracellular fluid. So in a living cell, the concentration gradient of Na^+ tends to drive it into the cell, and the electrical gradient of Na^+ (a positive ion) also tends to drive it inward to the negatively charged interior. The situation is more complex, however, for other elements such as potassium. The electrical gradient of K^+, a positive ion, also tends to drive it into the cell, but the concentration gradient of K^+ tends to drive K^+ *out* of the cell (Figure 5.16). The combined gradient of concentration and electrical charge that affects an ion is called its **electrochemical gradient**.

visual CONNECTION

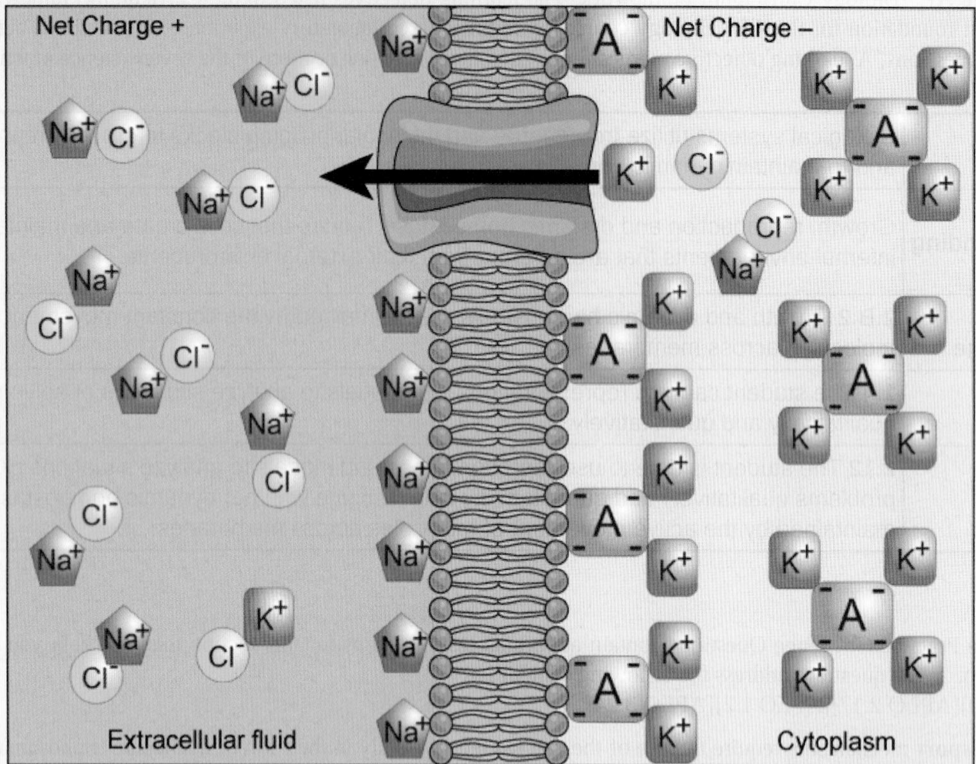

Figure 5.16 Electrochemical gradients arise from the combined effects of concentration gradients and electrical gradients. Structures labeled A represent proteins. (credit: "Synaptitude"/Wikimedia Commons)

If the pH outside the cell decreases, would you expect the amount of amino acids transported into the cell to increase or decrease?

a. Transport of amino acids into the cell increases
b. Transport of amino acids into the cell stops.
c. Transport of amino acids into the cell is not affected by pH.
d. Transport of amino acid into the cell decreases.

Moving Against a Gradient

To move substances against a concentration or electrochemical gradient, the cell must use energy. This energy is harvested from ATP generated through the cell's metabolism. Active transport mechanisms, collectively called **pumps**, work against electrochemical gradients. Small substances constantly pass through plasma membranes. Active transport maintains concentrations of ions and other substances needed by living cells in the face of these passive movements. Much of a cell's supply of metabolic energy may be spent maintaining these processes. (Most of a red blood cell's metabolic energy is used to maintain the imbalance between exterior and interior sodium and potassium levels required by the cell.) Because active transport mechanisms depend on a cell's metabolism for energy, they are sensitive to many metabolic poisons that interfere with the supply of ATP.

Two mechanisms exist for the transport of small-molecular weight material and small molecules. **Primary active transport** moves ions across a membrane and creates a difference in charge across that membrane, which is directly dependent on ATP. **Secondary active transport** describes the movement of material that is due to the electrochemical gradient established by primary active transport that does not directly require ATP.

Carrier Proteins for Active Transport

An important membrane adaption for active transport is the presence of specific carrier proteins or pumps to facilitate movement: there are three types of these proteins or **transporters** (Figure 5.17). A **uniporter** carries one specific ion or molecule. A **symporter** carries two different ions or molecules, both in the same direction. An **antiporter** also carries two different ions or molecules, but in different directions. All of these transporters can also transport small, uncharged organic molecules like glucose. These three types of carrier proteins are also found in facilitated diffusion, but they do not require ATP to work in that process. Some examples of pumps for active transport are Na^+-K^+ ATPase, which carries sodium and potassium ions, and H^+-K^+ ATPase, which carries hydrogen and potassium ions. Both of these are antiporter carrier proteins. Two other carrier proteins are Ca^{2+} ATPase and H^+ ATPase, which carry only calcium and only hydrogen ions, respectively. Both are pumps.

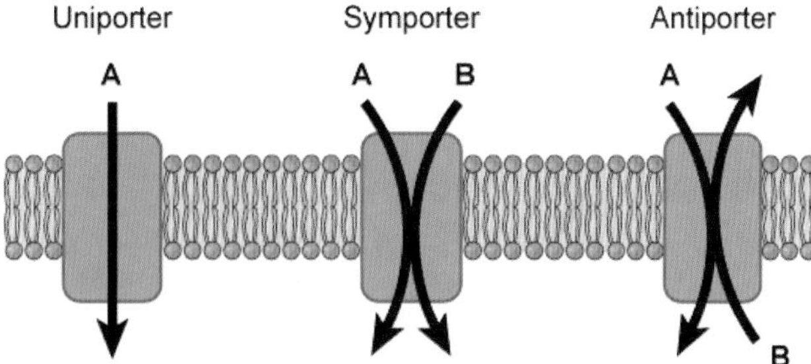

Figure 5.17 A uniporter carries one molecule or ion. A symporter carries two different molecules or ions, both in the same direction. An antiporter also carries two different molecules or ions, but in different directions. (credit: modification of work by "Lupask"/Wikimedia Commons)

everyday CONNECTION for AP® Courses

The primary active transport that functions with the active transport of sodium and potassium allows secondary active transport to occur. The second transport method is still considered active because it depends on the use of energy as does primary transport (illustrative example).

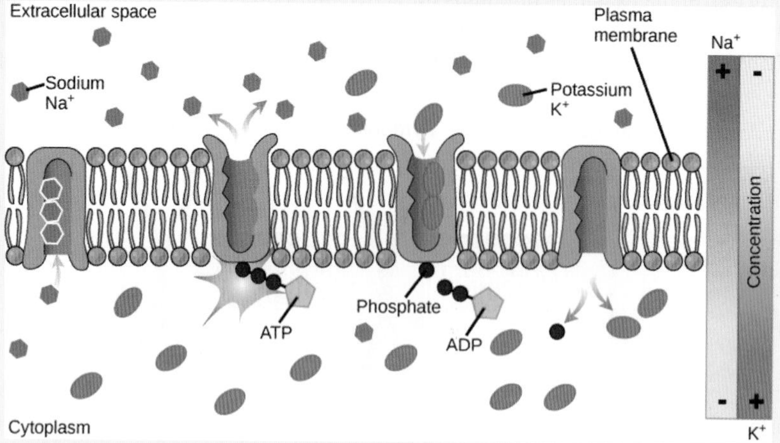

Figure 5.18 Primary active transport moves ions across a membrane, creating an electrochemical gradient (electrogenic transport). (credit: modification of work by Mariana Ruiz Villareal)

One of the most important pumps in animal cells is the sodium-potassium pump (Na^+-K^+ ATPase), which maintains the electrochemical gradient (and the correct concentrations of Na^+ and K^+) in living cells. The sodium-potassium pump moves K^+ into the cell while moving Na^+ out at the same time, at a ratio of three Na^+ for every two K^+ ions moved in. The Na^+-K^+ ATPase exists in two forms, depending on its orientation to the interior or exterior of the cell and its affinity for either sodium or potassium ions. The process consists of the following six steps:

1. With the enzyme oriented towards the interior of the cell, the carrier has a high affinity for sodium ions. Three ions bind to the protein.
2. The protein carrier hydrolyzes ATP and a low-energy phosphate group attaches to it.
3. As a result, the carrier changes shape and re-orients itself towards the exterior of the membrane. The protein's affinity for sodium decreases and the three sodium ions leave the carrier.
4. The shape change increases the carrier's affinity for potassium ions, and two such ions attach to the protein. Subsequently, the low-energy phosphate group detaches from the carrier.
5. With the phosphate group removed and potassium ions attached, the carrier protein repositions itself towards the interior of the cell.
6. The carrier protein, in its new configuration, has a decreased affinity for potassium, and the two ions are released into the cytoplasm. The protein now has a higher affinity for sodium ions, and the process starts again.

Several things have happened as a result of this process. At this point, there are more sodium ions outside of the cell than inside and more potassium ions inside than out. For every three ions of sodium that move out, two ions of potassium move in. This results in the interior being slightly more negative relative to the exterior. This difference in charge is important to creating the conditions necessary for the secondary process. Therefore, the sodium-potassium pump is an **electrogenic pump** (a pump that creates a charge imbalance) contributing to the membrane potential.

What will happen to the opening of the sodium-potassium pump if no ATP is present in a cell?

a. It will remain facing the extracellular space, with sodium ions bound.

b. It will remain facing the extracellular space, with potassium ions bound.

c. It will remain facing the cytoplasm, but no sodium ions would bind.

d. It will remain facing the cytoplasm, with sodium ions bound.

Visit the site (http://openstaxcollege.org/l/Na_K_ATPase) to see a simulation of active transport in a sodium-potassium ATPase.

Sodium and potassium are necessary electrolytes. As a result, the human body uses a great deal of energy keeping these electrolytes in balance. Explain why the body needs to use energy for this process.

a. ATP is required to move sodium ions against their concentration gradient outside the cell.

b. ATP is required to allow entry of potassium ions inside the cell.

c. ATP is required to allow entry of sodium ions inside the cell.

d. ATP is required to release potassium ions outside the cell.

science practices CONNECTION for AP® Courses

Activity

Create a representation/diagram (or use the model you constructed of the plasma cell membrane) to explain how the sodium-potassium pump contributes to the net negative change of the interior of an animal nerve cell.

Think About It

If the pH outside the cell decreases, would you expect the amount of amino acids and glucose transported into the cell to increase or decrease? Justify your reasoning.

Secondary Active Transport (Co-transport)

Secondary active transport brings sodium ions, and possibly other compounds, into the cell. As sodium ion concentrations build outside of the plasma membrane because of the action of the primary active transport process, an electrochemical gradient is created. If a channel protein exists and is open, the sodium ions will be pulled through the membrane. This movement is used to transport other substances that can attach themselves to the transport protein through the membrane (Figure 5.19). Many amino acids, as well as glucose, enter a cell this way. This secondary process is also used to store high-energy hydrogen ions in the mitochondria of plant and animal cells for the production of ATP. The potential energy that accumulates in the stored hydrogen ions is translated into kinetic energy as the ions surge through the channel protein ATP synthase, and that energy is used to convert ADP into ATP.

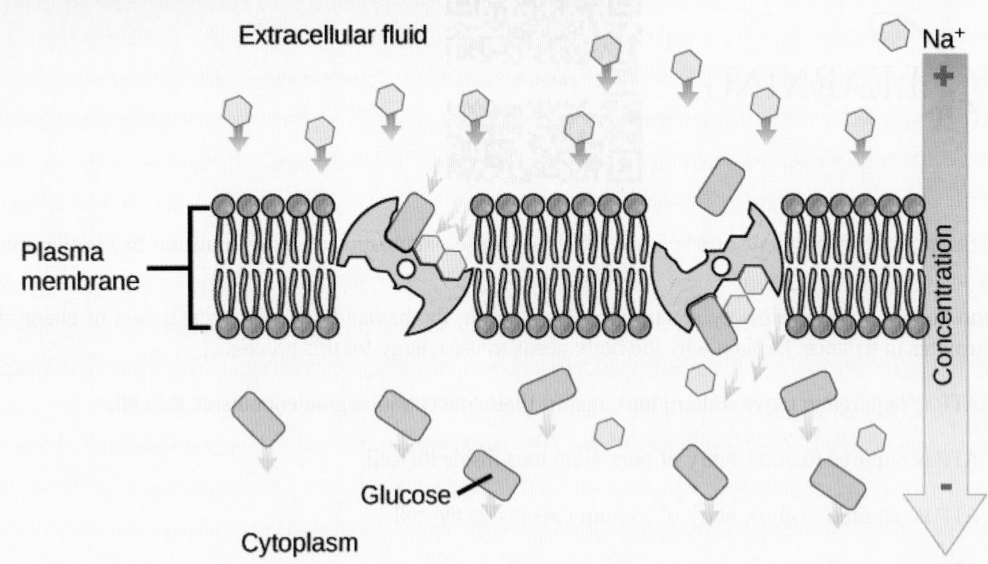

Figure 5.19 An electrochemical gradient, created by primary active transport, can move other substances against their concentration gradients, a process called co-transport or secondary active transport. (credit: modification of work by Mariana Ruiz Villareal)

Injection of a potassium solution into a person's blood is lethal. Potassium is used in capital punishment and euthanasia. Why do you think a potassium solution injection is lethal?

a. Excess potassium disrupts the membrane components
b. Excess potassium increases action potential generation, leading to uncoordinated organ activity.
c. Potassium dissipates the electrochemical gradient in cardiac muscle cells, preventing them from contracting.
d. Potassium creates a new concentration gradient across the cell membrane, preventing sodium from leaving the cell.

5.4 | Bulk Transport

By the end of this section, you will be able to:

- What are the differences among the different types of endocytosis: (phagocytosis, pinocytosis, and receptor-mediated endocytosis) and exocytosis?

Connection for AP® Courses

Diffusion, osmosis, and active transport are used to transport fairly small molecules across plasma cell membranes. However, sometimes large particles, such as macromolecules, parts of cells, or even unicellular microorganisms, can be engulfed by other cells in a process called phagocytosis or "cell eating." In this form of endocytosis, the cell membrane surrounds the particle, pinches off, and brings the particle into the cell. For example, when bacteria invade the human body, a type of white blood cell called a neutrophil will remove the invaders by this process. Similarly, in pinocytosis or "cell drinking," the cell takes in droplets of liquid. In receptor-mediated endocytosis, uptake of substances by the cell is targeted to a single type of substance that binds to a specific receptor protein on the external surface of the cell membrane (e.g., hormones and their target cells) before under going endocytosis. Some human diseases, such as familial hypercholesterolemia, are caused by the failure of receptor-mediated endocytosis. Exocytosis is the process of exporting material out of the cell; vesicles containing substances fuse with the plasma membrane and the contents are released to the exterior of the cell. The secretion of neurotransmitters at synapses between neurons is an example of exocytosis.

Information presented and the examples highlighted in the section support concepts and learning objectives outlined in Big Idea 2 of the AP® Biology Curriculum Framework. The learning objectives listed in the Curriculum Framework provide a transparent foundation for the AP® Biology course, an inquiry-based laboratory experience, instructional activities, and AP® exam questions. A learning objective merges required content with one or more of the seven science practices.

Big Idea 2	Biological systems utilize free energy and molecular building blocks to grow, to reproduce, and to maintain dynamic homeostasis.
Enduring Understanding 2.B	Growth, reproduction and dynamic homeostasis require that cells create and maintain internal environments that are different from their external environments.
Essential Knowledge	**2.B.2** Growth and dynamic homeostasis are maintained by the constant movement of molecules across membranes.
Science Practice	**1.4** The student can use representations and models to analyze situations or solve problems qualitatively and quantitatively.
Learning Objective	**2.12** The student is able to use representations and models to analyze situations or solve problems qualitatively and quantitatively to investigate whether dynamic homeostasis is maintained by the active movement of molecules across membranes.
Big Idea 2	Biological systems utilize free energy and molecular building blocks to grow, to reproduce, and to maintain dynamic homeostasis.
Enduring Understanding 2.D	Growth and dynamic homeostasis of a biological system are influenced by changes in the system's environment.
Essential Knowledge	**2.D.4** Plants and animals have a variety of chemical defenses against infections that affect dynamic homeostasis.
Science Practice	**1.1** The student can create representations and models of natural or man-made phenomena and systems in the domain.
Science Practice	**1.2** The student can describe representations and models of natural or man-made phenomena and systems in the domain.
Learning Objective	**2.30** The student can create representations or models to describe nonspecific immune defenses in plants and animals.

In addition to moving small ions and molecules through the membrane, cells also need to remove and take in larger molecules and particles (see Table 5.2 for examples). Some cells are even capable of engulfing entire unicellular microorganisms. You might have correctly hypothesized that the uptake and release of large particles by the cell requires energy. A large particle, however, cannot pass through the membrane, even with energy supplied by the cell.

Endocytosis

Endocytosis is a type of active transport that moves particles, such as large molecules, parts of cells, and even whole cells, into a cell. There are different variations of endocytosis, but all share a common characteristic: The plasma membrane of the cell invaginates, forming a pocket around the target particle. The pocket pinches off, resulting in the particle being contained in a newly created intracellular vesicle formed from the plasma membrane.

Phagocytosis

Phagocytosis (the condition of "cell eating") is the process by which large particles, such as cells or relatively large particles, are taken in by a cell. For example, when microorganisms invade the human body, a type of white blood cell called a neutrophil will remove the invaders through this process, surrounding and engulfing the microorganism, which is then destroyed by the neutrophil (Figure 5.20).

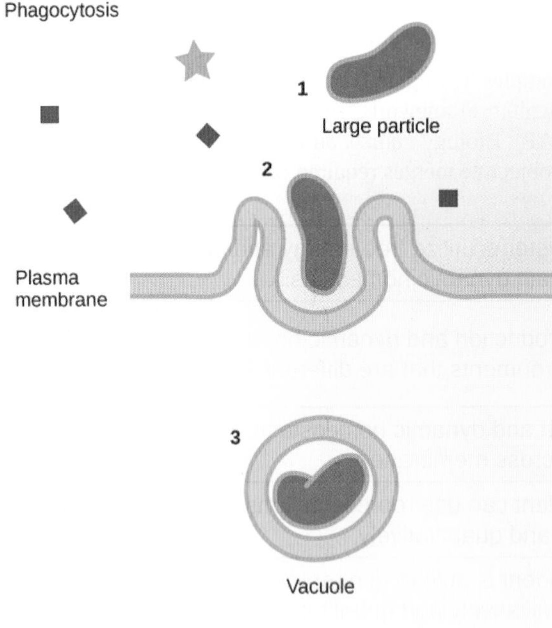

Figure 5.20 In phagocytosis, the cell membrane surrounds the particle and engulfs it. (credit: Mariana Ruiz Villareal)

In preparation for phagocytosis, a portion of the inward-facing surface of the plasma membrane becomes coated with a protein called **clathrin**, which stabilizes this section of the membrane. The coated portion of the membrane then extends from the body of the cell and surrounds the particle, eventually enclosing it. Once the vesicle containing the particle is enclosed within the cell, the clathrin disengages from the membrane and the vesicle merges with a lysosome for the breakdown of the material in the newly formed compartment (endosome). When accessible nutrients from the degradation of the vesicular contents have been extracted, the newly formed endosome merges with the plasma membrane and releases its contents into the extracellular fluid. The endosomal membrane again becomes part of the plasma membrane.

science practices CONNECTION for AP® Courses

Activity

Create a representation/diagram to describe how a neutrophil, a type of human white blood cell, attacks and destroys an invading bacterium. What cellular organelles are involved in this process?

Pinocytosis

A variation of endocytosis is called **pinocytosis**. This literally means "cell drinking" and was named at a time when the assumption was that the cell was purposefully taking in extracellular fluid. In reality, this is a process that takes in molecules, including water, which the cell needs from the extracellular fluid. Pinocytosis results in a much smaller vesicle than does phagocytosis, and the vesicle does not need to merge with a lysosome (Figure 5.21).

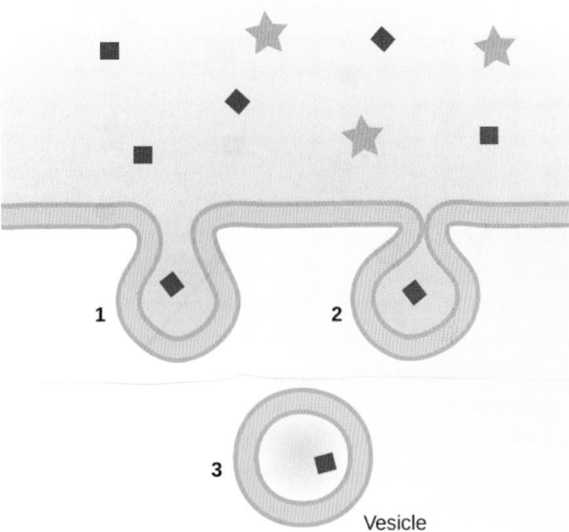

Figure 5.21 In pinocytosis, the cell membrane invaginates, surrounds a small volume of fluid, and pinches off. (credit: Mariana Ruiz Villareal)

A variation of pinocytosis is called **potocytosis**. This process uses a coating protein, called **caveolin**, on the cytoplasmic side of the plasma membrane, which performs a similar function to clathrin. The cavities in the plasma membrane that form the vacuoles have membrane receptors and lipid rafts in addition to caveolin. The vacuoles or vesicles formed in caveolae (singular caveola) are smaller than those in pinocytosis. Potocytosis is used to bring small molecules into the cell and to transport these molecules through the cell for their release on the other side of the cell, a process called transcytosis.

Receptor-mediated Endocytosis

A targeted variation of endocytosis employs receptor proteins in the plasma membrane that have a specific binding affinity for certain substances (Figure 5.22).

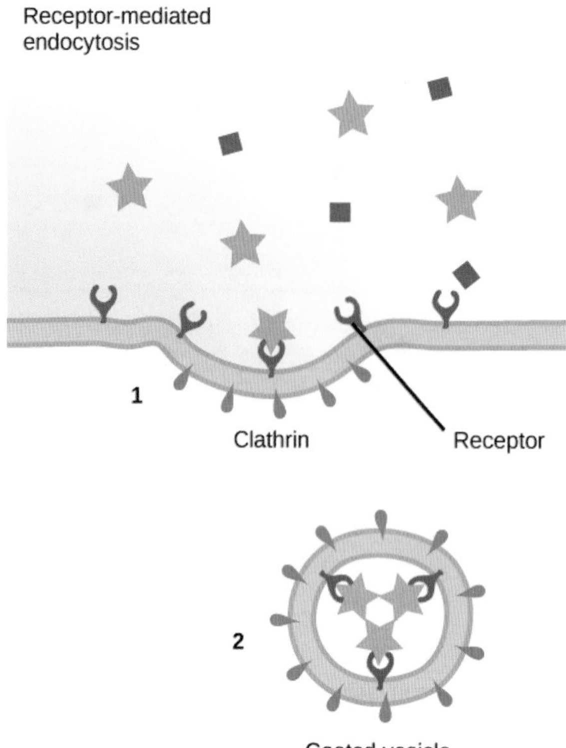

Figure 5.22 In receptor-mediated endocytosis, uptake of substances by the cell is targeted to a single type of substance that binds to the receptor on the external surface of the cell membrane. (credit: modification of work by Mariana Ruiz Villareal)

In **receptor-mediated endocytosis**, as in phagocytosis, clathrin is attached to the cytoplasmic side of the plasma membrane. If uptake of a compound is dependent on receptor-mediated endocytosis and the process is ineffective, the material will not be removed from the tissue fluids or blood. Instead, it will stay in those fluids and increase in concentration. Some human diseases are caused by the failure of receptor-mediated endocytosis. For example, the form of cholesterol termed low-density lipoprotein or LDL (also referred to as "bad" cholesterol) is removed from the blood by receptor-mediated endocytosis. In the human genetic disease familial hypercholesterolemia, the LDL receptors are defective or missing entirely. People with this condition have life-threatening levels of cholesterol in their blood, because their cells cannot clear LDL particles from their blood.

Although receptor-mediated endocytosis is designed to bring specific substances that are normally found in the extracellular fluid into the cell, other substances may gain entry into the cell at the same site. Flu viruses, diphtheria, and cholera toxin all have sites that cross-react with normal receptor-binding sites and gain entry into cells.

See receptor-mediated endocytosis in action, and click on different parts (http://openstaxcollege.org/l/endocytosis) for a focused animation.

Salmonella is one of the most common food borne illnesses. When salmonella bacteria are engulfed by a white blood cell during phagocytosis, it secretes a protein that prevents the fusion of the encased bacteria with the lysosome of the cell. What effect would this have?

a. The bacteria will be destroyed and will not cause any illness.

b. The bacteria will survive and will definitely result in illness.

c. The bacteria will be destroyed, but will still cause illness.

d. The bacteria will survive and possibly will cause illness.

Exocytosis

The reverse process of moving material into a cell is the process of exocytosis. **Exocytosis** is the opposite of the processes discussed above in that its purpose is to expel material from the cell into the extracellular fluid. Waste material is enveloped in a membrane and fuses with the interior of the plasma membrane. This fusion opens the membranous envelope on the exterior of the cell, and the waste material is expelled into the extracellular space (Figure 5.23). Other examples of cells releasing molecules via exocytosis include the secretion of proteins of the extracellular matrix and secretion of neurotransmitters into the synaptic cleft by synaptic vesicles.

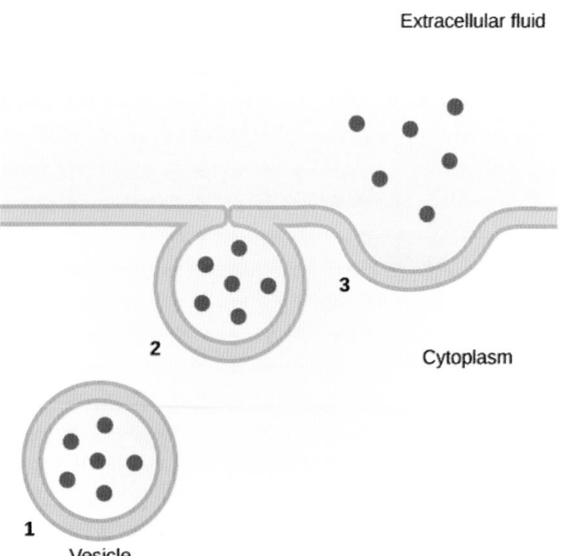

Figure 5.23 In exocytosis, vesicles containing substances fuse with the plasma membrane. The contents are then released to the exterior of the cell. (credit: modification of work by Mariana Ruiz Villareal)

Methods of Transport, Energy Requirements, and Types of Material Transported

Transport Method	Active/ Passive	Material Transported
Diffusion	Passive	Small-molecular weight material
Osmosis	Passive	Water
Facilitated transport/diffusion	Passive	Sodium, potassium, calcium, glucose
Primary active transport	Active	Sodium, potassium, calcium
Secondary active transport	Active	Amino acids, lactose
Phagocytosis	Active	Large macromolecules, whole cells, or cellular structures
Pinocytosis and potocytosis	Active	Small molecules (liquids/water)
Receptor-mediated endocytosis	Active	Large quantities of macromolecules

Table 5.2

KEY TERMS

active transport method of transporting material that requires energy

amphiphilic molecule possessing a polar or charged area and a nonpolar or uncharged area capable of interacting with both hydrophilic and hydrophobic environments

antiporter transporter that carries two ions or small molecules in different directions

aquaporin channel protein that allows water through the membrane at a very high rate

carrier protein membrane protein that moves a substance across the plasma membrane by changing its own shape

caveolin protein that coats the cytoplasmic side of the plasma membrane and participates in the process of liquid uptake by potocytosis

channel protein membrane protein that allows a substance to pass through its hollow core across the plasma membrane

clathrin protein that coats the inward-facing surface of the plasma membrane and assists in the formation of specialized structures, like coated pits, for phagocytosis

concentration gradient area of high concentration adjacent to an area of low concentration

diffusion passive process of transport of low-molecular weight material according to its concentration gradient

electrochemical gradient gradient produced by the combined forces of an electrical gradient and a chemical gradient

electrogenic pump pump that creates a charge imbalance

endocytosis type of active transport that moves substances, including fluids and particles, into a cell

exocytosis process of passing bulk material out of a cell

facilitated transport process by which material moves down a concentration gradient (from high to low concentration) using integral membrane proteins

fluid mosaic model describes the structure of the plasma membrane as a mosaic of components including phospholipids, cholesterol, proteins, glycoproteins, and glycolipids (sugar chains attached to proteins or lipids, respectively), resulting in a fluid character (fluidity)

glycolipid combination of carbohydrates and lipids

glycoprotein combination of carbohydrates and proteins

hydrophilic molecule with the ability to bond with water; “water-loving”

hydrophobic molecule that does not have the ability to bond with water; “water-hating”

hypertonic situation in which extracellular fluid has a higher osmolarity than the fluid inside the cell, resulting in water moving out of the cell

hypotonic situation in which extracellular fluid has a lower osmolarity than the fluid inside the cell, resulting in water moving into the cell

integral protein protein integrated into the membrane structure that interacts extensively with the hydrocarbon chains of membrane lipids and often spans the membrane; these proteins can be removed only by the disruption of the membrane by detergents

isotonic situation in which the extracellular fluid has the same osmolarity as the fluid inside the cell, resulting in no net movement of water into or out of the cell

osmolarity total amount of substances dissolved in a specific amount of solution

osmosis transport of water through a semipermeable membrane according to the concentration gradient of water across the membrane that results from the presence of solute that cannot pass through the membrane

passive transport method of transporting material through a membrane that does not require energy

peripheral protein protein found at the surface of a plasma membrane either on its exterior or interior side

pinocytosis a variation of endocytosis that imports macromolecules that the cell needs from the extracellular fluid

plasmolysis detaching of the cell membrane from the cell wall and constriction of the cell membrane when a plant cell is in a hypertonic solution

potocytosis variation of pinocytosis that uses a different coating protein (caveolin) on the cytoplasmic side of the plasma membrane

primary active transport active transport that moves ions or small molecules across a membrane and may create a difference in charge across that membrane

pump active transport mechanism that works against electrochemical gradients

receptor-mediated endocytosis variation of endocytosis that involves the use of specific binding proteins in the plasma membrane for specific molecules or particles, and clathrin-coated pits that become clathrin-coated vesicles

secondary active transport movement of material that is due to the electrochemical gradient established by primary active transport

selectively permeable characteristic of a membrane that allows some substances through but not others

solute substance dissolved in a liquid to form a solution

symporter transporter that carries two different ions or small molecules, both in the same direction

tonicity amount of solute in a solution

transport protein membrane protein that facilitates passage of a substance across a membrane by binding it

transporter specific carrier proteins or pumps that facilitate movement

uniporter transporter that carries one specific ion or molecule

CHAPTER SUMMARY

5.1 Components and Structure

The modern understanding of the plasma membrane is referred to as the fluid mosaic model. The plasma membrane is composed of a bilayer of phospholipids, with their hydrophobic, fatty acid tails in contact with each other. The landscape of the membrane is studded with proteins, some of which span the membrane. Some of these proteins serve to transport materials into or out of the cell. Carbohydrates are attached to some of the proteins and lipids on the outward-facing surface of the membrane, forming complexes that function to identify the cell to other cells. The fluid nature of the membrane is due to temperature, the configuration of the fatty acid tails (some kinked by double bonds), the presence of cholesterol embedded in the membrane, and the mosaic nature of the proteins and protein-carbohydrate combinations, which are not firmly fixed in place. Plasma membranes enclose and define the borders of cells, but rather than being a static bag, they are dynamic and constantly in flux.

5.2 Passive Transport

The passive forms of transport, diffusion and osmosis, move materials of small molecular weight across membranes. Substances diffuse from areas of high concentration to areas of lower concentration, and this process continues until the substance is evenly distributed in a system. In solutions containing more than one substance, each type of molecule diffuses according to its own concentration gradient, independent of the diffusion of other substances. Many factors can affect the rate of diffusion, including concentration gradient, size of the particles that are diffusing, temperature of the system, and so on.

In living systems, diffusion of substances into and out of cells is mediated by the plasma membrane. Some materials diffuse readily through the membrane, but others are hindered, and their passage is made possible by specialized proteins, such as channels and transporters. The chemistry of living things occurs in aqueous solutions, and balancing the concentrations of those solutions is an ongoing problem. In living systems, diffusion of some substances would be slow or difficult without membrane proteins that facilitate transport.

5.3 Active Transport

The combined gradient that affects an ion includes its concentration gradient and its electrical gradient. A positive ion, for example, might tend to diffuse into a new area, down its concentration gradient, but if it is diffusing into an area of net positive charge, its diffusion will be hampered by its electrical gradient. When dealing with ions in aqueous solutions, a combination of the electrochemical and concentration gradients, rather than just the concentration gradient alone, must be considered. Living cells need certain substances that exist inside the cell in concentrations greater than they exist in the extracellular space. Moving substances up their electrochemical gradients requires energy from the cell. Active transport uses energy stored in ATP to fuel this transport. Active transport of small molecular-sized materials uses integral proteins in the cell membrane to move the materials: These proteins are analogous to pumps. Some pumps, which carry out primary active transport, couple directly with ATP to drive their action. In co-transport (or secondary active transport), energy from primary transport can be used to move another substance into the cell and up its concentration gradient.

5.4 Bulk Transport

Active transport methods require the direct use of ATP to fuel the transport. Large particles, such as macromolecules, parts of cells, or whole cells, can be engulfed by other cells in a process called phagocytosis. In phagocytosis, a portion of the membrane invaginates and flows around the particle, eventually pinching off and leaving the particle entirely enclosed by an envelope of plasma membrane. Vesicle contents are broken down by the cell, with the particles either used as food or dispatched. Pinocytosis is a similar process on a smaller scale. The plasma membrane invaginates and pinches off, producing a small envelope of fluid from outside the cell. Pinocytosis imports substances that the cell needs from the extracellular fluid. The cell expels waste in a similar but reverse manner: it pushes a membranous vacuole to the plasma membrane, allowing the vacuole to fuse with the membrane and incorporate itself into the membrane structure, releasing its contents to the exterior.

REVIEW QUESTIONS

1. Which plasma membrane component can be either found on its surface or embedded in the membrane structure?

a. carbohydrates
b. cholesterol
c. glycolipid
d. protein

2. In addition to a plasma membrane, eukaryotic cell organelles, such as mitochondria, also have membranes. In which way would these membranes differ?

a. The proportion of phosphate within the phospholipids will vary.
b. Only certain membranes contain phospholipids.
c. Only certain membranes are selectively permeable.
d. The proportions of proteins, lipids, and carbohydrates will vary.

3. Which characteristic of a phospholipid increases the fluidity of the membrane?

a. cholesterol
b. its head
c. saturated fatty acid tail
d. unsaturated fatty acid tail

4. How would an organism maintain membrane fluidity in an environment where temperatures fluctuated from very high to very low?

a. Greater proportion of unsaturated phospholipids in membranes.
b. Greater proportion of saturated phospholipids in membranes.
c. Greater proportion of carbohydrates in membranes.
d. Greater proportion of proteins in membranes.

5. According to the fluid mosaic model of the plasma cell membrane, what is the primary function of carbohydrates attached to the exterior of cell membranes?

a. Carbohydrates are in contact with the aqueous fluid both inside and outside the cell.
b. Carbohydrates are present only on the interior surface of a membrane.
c. Carbohydrates are present only on the exterior surface of a membrane.
d. Carbohydates span only the interior of a membrane.

6. What do double bonds in phospholipid fatty acid tails contribute to?

a. the fluidity of membranes
b. the hydrophobic nature of membranes
c. the hydrophilic nature of membranes
d. preventing high temperatures from increasing fluidity of membranes

7. Identify the principal force driving movement in diffusion.

a. concentration gradient
b. membrane surface area
c. particle size
d. temperature

8. Which of the following is an example of passive transport across a membrane?

a. the movement of H^+ into a thylakoid disc during photosynthesis
b. the uptake of glucose in the intestine
c. the uptake of mineral ions into root hair cells of plants
d. the movement of water from a nephron into the collecting duct of the kidney

9. Water moves via osmosis across plasma cell membranes in which direction?

a. from an area with a high concentration of other solutes to a lower one
b. from an area with a high concentration of water to one of lower concentration
c. from an area with a low concentration of water to one of higher concentration.
d. throughout the cytoplasm

10. What problem is faced by organisms that live in fresh water?

a. They will have higher concentrations of body solutes.
b. Without compensating mechanisms, their bodies tend to take in too much water.
c. They have no way of controlling their tonicity.
d. Their bodies tend to lose too much water to their environment.

11. Which of the following questions can be asked about organisms that live in fresh water?

a. Will their bodies take in too much water?
b. Can they control their tonicity?
c. Can they survive in salt water?
d. Will their bodies lose too much water to their environment?

12. Which of the following explains why active movement of molecules across membranes must function continuously?

13. Why must active transport of molecules across plasma membranes function continuously?

a. Diffusion cannot occur in certain cells.
b. Diffusion is constantly moving solutes in opposite directions.
c. Facilitated diffusion works in the same direction as active transport.
d. Not all membranes are amphiphilic.

14. How does the sodium-potassium pump make the interior of the cell negatively charged?

a. by expelling anions
b. by pulling in anions
c. by expelling more cations than it takes in
d. By taking in and expelling an equal number of cations.

15. What is the difference between primary and secondary active transport?

a. Primary active transport is indirectly dependent on ATP, while secondary active transport is directly dependent on ATP.
b. Primary active transport is directly dependent on ATP, while secondary active transport is indirectly dependent on ATP.
c. Primary active transport does not require ATP, while secondary active transport is indirectly dependent on ATP.
d. Primary active transport is indirectly dependent on ATP, while secondary active transport does not require ATP

16. What happens to the membrane of a vesicle after exocytosis?

a. It leaves the cell.
b. It is disassembled by the cell.
c. It fuses with and becomes part of the plasma membrane.
d. It is used again in another exocytosis event.

17. In what important way does receptor-mediated endocytosis differ from phagocytosis?

a. It transports only small amounts of fluid.
b. It does not involve the pinching off of membrane.
c. It brings in only a specifically targeted substance.
d. It brings substances into the cell, while phagocytosis removes substances.

CRITICAL THINKING QUESTIONS

18. Why do phospholipids tend to spontaneously orient themselves into something resembling a membrane?

a. Phospholipids are amphipathic molecules. The polar head faces towards water and the nonpolar fatty acid tails face towards other fatty acid tails.
b. Phospholipids are lipophilic molecules. The polar head faces towards water and the nonpolar fatty acid tails face towards other fatty acid tails
c. Phospholipids are amphipathic molecules. The nonpolar head faces towards other fatty acid tails and the polar fatty acid tails face towards water.
d. Phospholipids are hydrophilic molecules. The polar head faces towards water and the nonpolar fatty acid tails face towards other fatty acid tails.

19. Why is it advantageous for the plasma membrane to be fluid in nature?

a. Fluidity allows greater flexibility to the cell and motion of membrane components required for transport.
b. Fluidity helps only in transport of some materials, and does not contribute to the flexibility.
c. Fluidity helps in maintaining the pH of intracellular fluid, and helps in maintaining the physiological pH of the cell.
d. Fluidity helps in providing mechanical strength to the plasma membrane.

20. List four components of a plasma membrane and explain their function.

a. Phospholipids: form the bilayer; Carbohydrates: help in adhesion; Cholesterol: provide flexibility; Integral proteins: form transporters; Peripheral proteins: part of the cell's recognition sites.
b. Phospholipids: form the bilayer; Carbohydrates: help in adhesion; Cholesterol: form transporters; Integral proteins: provide flexibility; Peripheral proteins: part of the cell's recognition sites.
c. Phospholipids: form the bilayer; Carbohydrates: part of the cell's recognition sites; Cholesterol: provide flexibility to the membrane; Integral proteins: form transporters; Intermediate filaments: help in adhesion.
d. Phospholipids: form the bilayer; Carbohydrates: function as adhesion; Cholesterol: provide flexibility to the membrane, Integral proteins: form transporters; Intermediate filaments: part of the cell's recognition sites.

21. Discuss why the following affect the rate of diffusion: molecular size, temperature, solution density, and the distance that must be traveled.

a. Larger molecules move faster than lighter molecules. Temperature affects the molecular movement. Density is directly proportional to the molecular movement. Greater distance slows the diffusion.

b. Larger molecules move slower than lighter molecules. Increasing or decreasing temperature increases or decreases the energy in the medium, affecting molecular movement. Density is inversely proportional to molecular movement. Greater distance slows the diffusion.

c. Larger molecules move slower than lighter molecules. Temperature does not affect the rate of diffusion. Density is inversely proportional to molecular movement. Greater distance speeds up the diffusion.

d. Larger molecules move slower than lighter molecules. Increasing or decreasing temperature increases or decreases the energy in the medium, affecting molecular movement. Density is inversely proportional to the molecular movement. Greater distance speeds up the diffusion.

22. Both of the regular intravenous solutions administered in medicine, normal saline and lactated Ringer's solution, are isotonic. Why is this important?

a. Isotonic solutions maintain equilibrium and avoid the exchange of materials to or from the blood.

b. Isotonic solutions disrupt equilibrium and allow better exchange of materials in the blood.

c. Isotonic solutions increase the pH of blood and allow better absorption of saline in blood.

d. Isotonic solutions decrease the pH of the blood and avoid the exchange of materials to or from the blood.

23. If a doctor injected a patient with what was labeled as an isotonic saline solution, but then the patient died, and an autopsy revealed that several of the patient's red blood cells had burst, would it be true that the injected solution was really isotonic? Why or why not?

a. False, the solution was hypertonic.

b. False, the solution was osmotic.

c. False, the solution was hypotonic.

d. True, the solution was isotonic.

24. How does the sodium-potassium pump contribute to the net negative charge of the interior of the cell?

a. The sodium-potassium pump forces out three (positive) Na^+ ions for every two (positive) K^+ ions it pumps in, thus the cell loses a net positive charge of one at every cycle of the pump.

b. The sodium-potassium pump expels three ions K^+ for every two Na^+ inside the cells, creating a net positive charge outside the cell and a net negative charge inside the cell.

c. The sodium-potassium pump helps the development of negative charge inside the cell by making the membrane more permeable to negatively charged proteins.

d. The sodium-potassium pump helps in the development of negative charge inside the cell by making the membrane impermeable to positively charged ions.

25. Potassium is a necessary nutrient in order to maintain the function of our cells. What would occur to a person that is deficient in potassium?

a. The excess sodium disrupts the membrane components.

b. The excess sodium increases action potential generation.

c. The cell would not be able to get rid of extra sodium.

d. The cell would not be able to bring sodium into the cell.

26. Choose the statement that describes processes of receptor-mediated endocytosis, exocytosis, and the changes in the membrane organization.

a. Endocytosis involves the opsonization of a receptor and its ligand in clathrin-coated vesicles, along with the inward budding of the plasma membrane. In exocytosis, waste material is enveloped in a membrane that fuses with the interior of the plasma membrane via attachment proteins.

b. In endocytosis, waste material is enveloped in a membrane that fuses with the interior of the plasma membrane via attachment proteins. Exocytosis involves the opsonization of the receptor and its ligand in a clathrin-coated vesicles.

c. In endocytosis, waste material is enveloped in a membrane that fuses with the interior of the plasma membrane via attachment proteins. Exocytosis involves the opsonization of the receptor and its ligand in caveolae-coated vesicles.

d. Endocytosis involves the opsonization of the receptor and its ligand in clathrin-coated vesicles. In exocytosis, waste material is enveloped in a membrane that fuses with the exterior of the plasma membrane via attachment proteins.

27. Describe the process of potocytosis and explain how it differs from pinocytosis.

a. Potocytosis is a form of receptor-mediated endocytosis where molecules are transported via caveolae-coated vesicles. Pinocytosis is a form of exocytosis used for excreting excess water.

b. Potocytosis is a form of exocytosis where molecules are transported via clathrin-coated vesicles. Pinocytosis is a form of receptor-mediated endocytosis used for excreting excess water.

c. Potocytosis is a form of receptor-mediated endocytosis where molecules are transported via caveolae-coated vesicles. Pinocytosis is a mode of endocytosis used for absorption of extracellular water.

d. Potocytosis is a form of receptor-mediated endocytosis used for absorption of water. Pinocytosis is a mode of endocytosis used for excretion of extracellular water.

TEST PREP FOR AP® COURSES

28. One type of mutation in the CFTR protein prevents the transport of chloride ions through the channel. Which of the following is most likely to be observed in the lungs of patients with this mutation?

a. dehydrated epithelial cells

b. dehydrated mucus

c. mucus with excess water

d. mucus with high electrolyte concentration

29. Arsenic poisoning disrupts ATP production by inhibiting several of the enzymes in the oxidative phosphorylation pathway. Some of the symptoms of arsenic poisoning are similar to cystic fibrosis (difficulty breathing and frequent lung infections). Explain what impact arsenic poisoning may have on components of the plasma membrane and transport that result in CF like symptoms.

a. Arsenic poisoning disrupts ATP production, leading to decreased transport of Cl^- ions by epithelial cells. This leads to decreased electrolyte concentration in the mucus and retention of water into the cells. The mucus becomes dehydrated, as in CF.

b. Arsenic poisoning disrupts the Na^+ / Cl^- pump, leading to decreased transport of Cl^- ions outside the epithelial cells. This increases the electrolyte concentration in the mucus and movement of water out of the cells. The mucus becomes hydrated as in CF.

c. Arsenic poisoning affects the oxidative phosphorylation pathway, leading to decreased transport of Na^+ ions outside the epithelial cells. This leads to increased electrolyte concentration in the mucus and movement of water into the cells. The mucus becomes dehydrated as in CF.

d. Arsenic poisoning disrupts the binding sites for Cl^- ions, leading to decreased transport of Cl^- ions outside the epithelial cells. This leads to decreased electrolyte concentration in the mucus and movement of water outside the cells. The mucus becomes hydrated as in CF.

30. In individuals with normally functioning CFTR

protein, which substances are transported via active transport?

a. Cl^-

b. mucus

c. Na^+

d. water

31.

Experiment	ATP present inside cells?	ATP present outside cells?	Ouabain present inside cells?	Ouabain present outside cells?	Was Na^+ trans-ported?	Was K^+ trans-ported?
1	Yes	Yes	No	No	Yes	Yes
2	Yes	No	No	No	Yes	Yes
3	No	Yes	No	No	No	No
4	No	No	No	No	No	No
5	Yes	No	Yes	Yes	No	No
6	Yes	No	Yes	No	No	Yes
7	Yes	No	No	Yes	Yes	No

The sodium-potassium (Na^+ / K^+) pump functions like an anti-porter transporting Na^+ and K^+ across membranes using ATP. This protein spans the membrane with intracellular and extracellular domains. It has a binding site for Na^+ , K^+ , and ATP. An experiment was conducted to determine the locations of these binding sites. Artificial cells were created and incubated in buffers containing ATP, ouabain (or oubain), Na^+ , and K^+ in varying combinations inside and outside of the cell as indicated in the chart. The transport of Na^+ and K^+ was measured to determine activity of the Na^+ / K^+ pump. Which of the following conclusions is supported by the data?

a. Ouabain can disrupt ATP binding to the Na^+ / K^+ pump.

b. ATP is required for transport of Na^+ and not for transport of K^+ .

c. The ATP binding site of the Na^+ / K^+ pump is located on the intracellular domain of the pump.

d. The ATP binding site of the Na^+ / K^+ pump is located on the extracellular domain of the pump.

32.

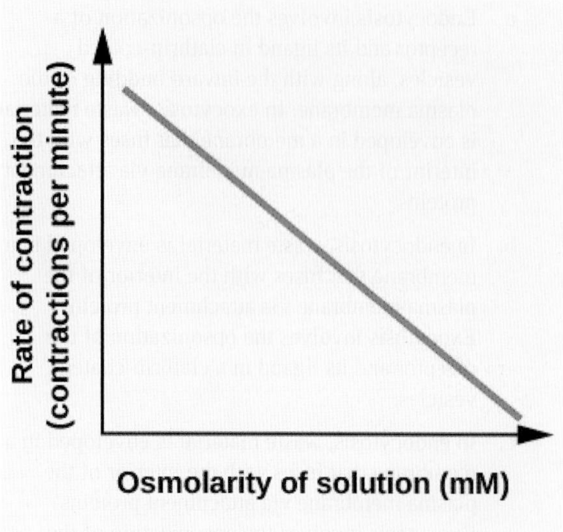

Paramecia are unicellular protists that have contractile vacuoles to remove excess intracellular water. In an experimental investigation, *Paramecia* were placed in salt solutions of increasing osmolarity. The rate at which a *Paramecium*'s contractile vacuole contracted to pump out excess water was determined and plotted against osmolarity of the solutions, as shown in the graph. Which of the following is the correct explanation for the data?

a. At higher osmolarity, lower rates of contraction are required because more salt diffuses into the *Paramecium*.

b. In an isosmotic salt solution, there is no diffusion of water into or out of the *Paramecium*, so the contraction rate is zero.

c. The contraction rate increases as the osmolarity decreases because the amount of water entering the *Paramecium* by osmosis increases.

d. The contractile vacuole is less efficient in solutions of high osmolarity because of the reduced amount of ATP produced from cellular respiration.

33. What is most likely to happen if *Paramecia* are moved from a hypertonic solution to solutions of decreasing osmolarity?

a. The rate of contraction would increase with decreasing osmolarity because more water diffuses into the *Paramecium*.

b. The rate of contraction would decrease with decreasing osmolarity because more water diffuses into the *Paramecium*.

c. The rate of contraction would increase with decreasing osmolarity because more salt diffuses into the *Paramecium*.

d. The rate of contraction would decrease with decreasing osmolarity because more salt diffuses into the *Paramecium*.

34.

Experiment	ATP present inside cells?	ATP present outside cells?	Ouabain present inside cells?	Ouabain present outside cells?	Was Na^+ trans-ported?	Was K^+ trans-ported?
1	Yes	Yes	No	No	Yes	Yes
2	Yes	No	No	No	Yes	Yes
3	No	Yes	No	No	No	No
4	No	No	No	No	No	No
5	Yes	No	Yes	Yes	No	No
6	Yes	No	Yes	No	No	Yes
7	Yes	No	No	Yes	Yes	No

Describe the Na^+ / K^+ pump, labeling the binding sites for Na^+ , K^+ , and ATP. Explain how the data indicates the location of the binding sites for Na^+ and K^+ on the pump. Based on the data, choose the correct statement describing the location of the binding sites for Na^+ and K^+ on the pump.

a. The binding of Na^+ occurs on the outer surface of the cell, as its transportation remains unaffected by the presence of ouabain. The binding of K^+ occurs on the inner surface of the cell, as its transportation is blocked when ouabain is present inside the cell

b. The binding of K^+ occurs on the outer surface of the cell, as its transportation is blocked when ouabain is present outside the cell. The binding of Na^+ occurs on the inner surface of the cell as its transportation remains unaffected by the presence of ouabain.

c. The binding of K^+ occurs on the outer surface of the cell and the binding of Na^+ occurs on the inner surface of the cell, as they are not transported when ATP is absent.

d. The binding of Na^+ occurs on the outer surface of the cell and the binding of K^+ occurs on the inner surface of the cell, as they are not transported when ATP is absent.

35.

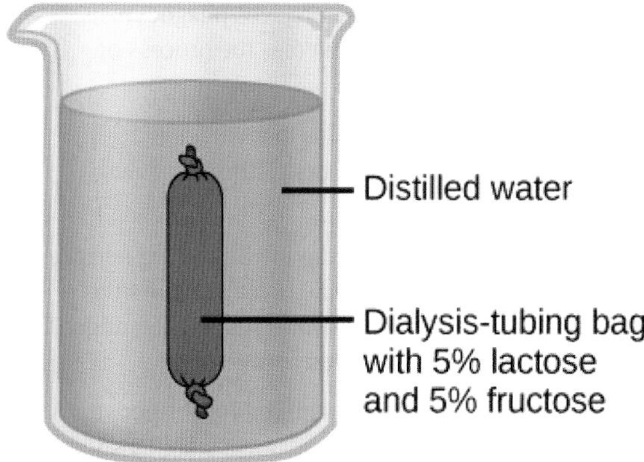

An experiment was set up to determine the movement of molecules through a dialysis-tubing bag into water. A dialysis-tubing bag containing 5% lactose and 5% fructose was placed in a beaker of distilled water, as illustrated. After four hours, fructose is detected in the distilled water outside of the dialysis-tubing bag, but lactose is not. What conclusions can be made about the movement of molecules in this experiment?

a. Fructose, being a monosaccharide, diffused through the dialysis bag into the distilled water. However, lactose, being a disaccharide, could not diffuse through the dialysis bag.

b. Fructose was homogenized by lactose, allowing the fructose to diffuse through the dialysis bag and into the distilled water. Lactose is not homogenized, so it could not pass through the dialysis bag.

c. Fructose and lactose are oppositely charged and separated out due to the force of repulsion.

d. Fructose diffused because of the pore specificity of the semipermeable membrane, not because of its concentration gradient.

36. Based on the information provided, which cell types are most likely to contain clathrin?

a. monocytes and mast cells

b. neutrophils, monocytes, and mast cells

c. neutrophils and mast cells

d. neutrophils and monocytes

37. Which of the following statements appropriately describe the role of opsonin and clathrin proteins in neutrophils based on your understanding of phagocytosis?

a. A clathrin coating enhances phagocytosis, whereas opsonin reverses the process of phagocytosis.

b. Opsonins are proteins that enhance phagocytosis, whereas clathrin opposes phagocytosis.

c. Opsonin stabilizes the inward facing surface of the plasma membrane, which engulfs the antigen, whereas clathrin marks the antigen for phagocytosis by neutrophils.

d. Opsonin marks the antigen for phagocytosis by neutrophils, whereas clathrin stabilizes the inward facing surface of the plasma membrane, which engulfs the antigen.

38. Based on the information provided, which cell types produce endosomes?

a. monocytes and mast cells

b. neutrophils, monocytes, and mast cells

c. neutrophils and mast cells

d. neutrophils and monocytes

SCIENCE PRACTICE CHALLENGE QUESTIONS

39. Membrane fluidity is influenced by the number of C-C double bonds (unsaturation) in the hydrocarbon tails of the lipids composing cell membranes. Fluidity is also dependent on temperature. The transit of materials through the cell membrane is controlled by fluidity. To maintain homeostasis, all organisms, including the simple bacterium *E. coli*, must sense the temperature of the environment and adapt to changes.

Samples of *E. coli* were grown at four different temperatures, and then researchers determined the fatty acid composition of their plasma membranes. The data are shown in the following table.

	Growth Temperature (°C)			
Fatty acid	10	20	30	40
Myristic	17%	14%	14%	16%
Palmitic	18%	25%	29%	48%
Palmitoleic	26%	24%	23%	9%
Oleic	38%	34%	30%	12%
Ratio (U/S)				

Table 5.3

Fatty acid compositions of the plasma membrane of *E. coli* were incubated at the temperatures shown. Myristic and palmitic acid are saturated, while palmitoleic and oleic acids each have one C-C double bond.

A. **Analyze** the data to calculate the ratio of the fraction of unsaturated (U) to the fraction of saturated (S) fatty acids in the plasma membrane, and complete the table.

B. **Graph** the ratio U/S versus growth temperature.

C. **Explain** the response of *E. coli* to the temperature of the environment.

D. We know that the temperature of the environment is sensed by *E. coli* through the temperature-dependent confirmation of enzymes that convert a single bond in the lipid tail to a double bond, and vice versa. **Explain** how the discovery of a mutant strain of *E. coli* could lead to this insight.

TeachingTip: This question connects concepts drawn from Big Ideas 2, 4, and 1.

40. Aquaporins that allow for the movement of water across a cell membrane are gated. Both low and high pH within a plant cell can cause alterations of the membrane-spanning protein. **Describe** the advantage of this feedback mechanism. **Predict** how conditions of flooding or drought could activate this mechanism.

41. Rice plants grown in high-salt environments can actively transport sodium ions into the vacuole by the antiporter movement of protons out of the vacuole. In a study aimed at the development of salt-tolerant rye, researchers produced several varieties of transgenic rye. Measurements of height and stem diameter for the transgenic varieties (TG1 – TG4) are compared with the wild type varieties WT1 and WT2. Shown in the table below are the mean and standard deviation from measurements of a very large sample size.

Variety	Height (cm)	Stem thickness (cm)
WT1	9.667±0.333	1.975±0.095
WT2	11.867±0.376	2.238±0.204
TG1	15.420±1.146	2.723±0.261
TG2	15.600±0.909	2.903±0.323
TG3	14.925±0.767	2.633±0.073
TG4	16.100±0.682	3.160±0.169

Table 5.4

A. **Analyze** the data. Are the heights and stem thicknesses in the transgenic plants significantly different than in the wild type plant? **Justify** your claim with evidence.

B. Are the heights and stem thicknesses among the transgenic plants significantly different? **Justify** your claim with evidence.

C. Plants from which these data were taken were grown in 10 mM NaCl solutions. **Pose one question** that researchers can investigate by growing the same varieties in a series of lower-salinity conditions.

D. The Na+/H+ antiporter is an active transport system. Briefly **explain** negative feedback regulation of the movement of sodium into the vacuole of rye cells.

6 | METABOLISM

Figure 6.1 A hummingbird needs energy to maintain prolonged periods of flight. The bird obtains its energy from taking in food and transforming the nutrients into energy through a series of biochemical reactions. The flight muscles in birds are extremely efficient in energy production. (credit: modification of work by Cory Zanker)

Chapter Outline

Introduction

Virtually every task performed by living organisms requires energy. Energy is needed to perform heavy labor and exercise. Humans also use a great deal of energy while thinking and even during sleep. In fact, the living cells of every organism constantly use energy. Nutrients and other molecules are imported, metabolized (broken down), synthesized into new molecules, modified if needed, transported around the cell, and, in some cases, distributed to the entire organism. For example, the large proteins that make up muscles are actively built from smaller molecules. Complex carbohydrates are broken down into simple sugars that the cell uses for energy. Just as energy is required to both build and demolish a building, energy is required for both the synthesis and breakdown of molecules. Additionally, signaling molecules such as hormones and neurotransmitters are actively transported between cells. Pathogenic bacteria and viruses are ingested and broken down by cells. Cells must also export waste and toxins to stay healthy. Many cells swim or move surrounding materials via the beating motion of cellular appendages such as cilia and flagella.

All of the cellular processes listed above require a steady supply of energy. From where, and in what form, does this energy come? How do living cells obtain energy and how do they use it? This chapter will discuss different forms of energy and the physical laws that govern energy transfer.

How enzymes lower the activation energy required to begin a chemical reaction in the body will also be discussed in this chapter. Enzymes are crucial for life; without them the chemical reactions required to survive would not happen fast enough for an organism to survive. For example, in an individual who lacks one of the enzymes needed to break down a type of carbohydrate known as a mucopolysaccharide, waste products accumulate in the cells and cause progressive brain damage. This deadly genetic disease is called Sanfilippo Syndrome type B or Mucopolysaccharidosis III. Previously incurable, scientists have now discovered a way to replace the missing enzyme in the brain of mice. Read more about the scientists' research here (http://openstaxcollege.org/l/32mpsiiib) .

6.1 | Energy and Metabolism

In this section, you will explore the following questions:

- What are metabolic pathways?
- What are the differences between anabolic and catabolic pathways?
- How do chemical reactions play a role in energy transfer?

Connection for AP® Courses

All living systems, from simple cells to complex ecosystems, require free energy to conduct cell processes such as growth and reproduction.

Organisms have evolved various strategies to capture, store, transform, and transfer free energy. A cell's metabolism refers to the chemical reactions that occur within it. Some metabolic reactions involve the breaking down of complex molecules into simpler ones with a release of energy (catabolism), whereas other metabolic reactions require energy to build complex molecules (anabolism). A central example of these pathways is the synthesis and breakdown of glucose.

The content presented in this section supports the Learning Objectives outlined in Big Idea 1 and Big Idea 2 of the AP® Biology Curriculum Framework listed below. The AP® Learning Objectives merge Essential Knowledge content with one or more of the seven Science Practices. These objectives provide a transparent foundation for the AP® Biology course, along with inquiry-based laboratory experiences, instructional activities, and AP® exam questions.

Big Idea 1	The process of evolution drives the diversity and unity of life.
Enduring Understanding 1.B	Organisms are linked by lines of descent from common ancestry.
Essential Knowledge	**1.B.1** Organisms share many conserved core processes and features that evolved and are widely distributed among organisms today.
Science Practice	**3.1** The student can pose scientific questions.
Learning Objective	**1.14** The student is able to pose scientific questions that correctly identify essential properties of shared, core life processes that provide insight into the history of life on Earth.
Essential Knowledge	**1.B.1** Organisms share many conserved core processes and features that evolved and are widely distributed among organisms today.
Science Practice	**7.2** The student can connect concepts in and across domain(s) to generalize or extrapolate in and/or across enduring understandings and/or big ideas.
Learning Objective	**1.15** The student is able to describe specific examples of conserved core biological processes and features shared by all domains or within one domain of life, and how these shared, conserved core processes and features support the concept of common ancestry for all organisms.
Essential Knowledge	**1.B.1** Organisms share many conserved core processes and features that evolved and are widely distributed among organisms today.
Science Practice	**6.1** The student can justify claims with evidence.
Learning Objective	**1.16** The student is able to justify the scientific claim that organisms share many conserved core processes and features that evolved and are widely distributed among organisms today.

Big Idea 2	Biological systems utilize free energy and molecular building blocks to grow, to reproduce, and to maintain dynamic homeostasis.
Enduring Understanding 2.A	Growth, reproduction and maintenance of living systems require free energy and matter.
Essential Knowledge	**2.A.1** All living systems require a constant input of free energy.
Science Practice	**6.2** The student can construct explanations of phenomena based on evidence produced through scientific practices.
Learning Objective	**2.1** The student is able to explain how biological systems use free energy based on empirical data that all organisms require constant energy input to maintain organization, to grow and to reproduce.

The Science Practice Challenge Questions contain additional test questions for this section that will help you prepare for the AP exam. These questions address the following standards:
[APLO 2.1][APLO 2.3][APLO 4.3][APLO 4.15][APLO 4.17][APLO 2.21]

Scientists use the term **bioenergetics** to discuss the concept of energy flow (Figure 6.2) through living systems, such as cells. Cellular processes such as the building and breaking down of complex molecules occur through stepwise chemical reactions. Some of these chemical reactions are spontaneous and release energy, whereas others require energy to proceed. Just as living things must continually consume food to replenish what has been used, cells must continually produce more energy to replenish that used by the many energy-requiring chemical reactions that constantly take place. All of the chemical reactions that take place inside cells, including those that use energy and those that release energy, are the cell's **metabolism**.

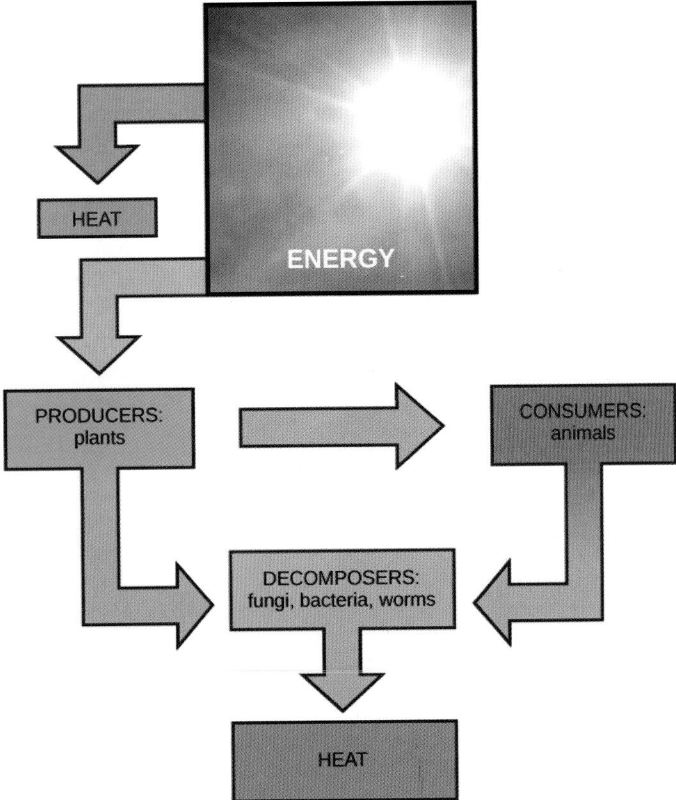

Figure 6.2 Most life forms on earth get their energy from the sun. Plants use photosynthesis to capture sunlight, and herbivores eat those plants to obtain energy. Carnivores eat the herbivores, and decomposers digest plant and animal matter.

Metabolism of Carbohydrates

The metabolism of sugar (a simple carbohydrate) is a classic example of the many cellular processes that use and produce energy. Living things consume sugar as a major energy source, because sugar molecules have a great deal of energy stored within their bonds. The breakdown of glucose, a simple sugar, is described by the equation:

$$C_6H_{12}O_6 + 6O_2 \rightarrow 6CO_2 + 6H_2O + \text{energy}$$

Carbohydrates that are consumed have their origins in photosynthesizing organisms like plants (**Figure 6.3**). During photosynthesis, plants use the energy of sunlight to convert carbon dioxide gas (CO_2) into sugar molecules, like glucose ($C_6H_{12}O_6$). Because this process involves synthesizing a larger, energy-storing molecule, it requires an input of energy to proceed. The synthesis of glucose is described by this equation (notice that it is the reverse of the previous equation):

$$6CO_2 + 6H_2O + \text{energy} \rightarrow C_6H_{12}O_6 + 6O_2$$

During the chemical reactions of photosynthesis, energy is provided in the form of a very high-energy molecule called ATP, or adenosine triphosphate, which is the primary energy currency of all cells. Just as the dollar is used as currency to buy goods, cells use molecules of ATP as energy currency to perform immediate work. The sugar (glucose) is stored as starch or glycogen. Energy-storing polymers like these are broken down into glucose to supply molecules of ATP.

Solar energy is required to synthesize a molecule of glucose during the reactions of photosynthesis. In photosynthesis, light energy from the sun is initially transformed into chemical energy that is temporally stored in the energy carrier molecules ATP and NADPH (nicotinamide adenine dinucleotide phosphate). The stored energy in ATP and NADPH is then used later in photosynthesis to build one molecule of glucose from six molecules of CO_2. This process is analogous to eating breakfast in the morning to acquire energy for your body that can be used later in the day. Under ideal conditions, energy from 18 molecules of ATP is required to synthesize one molecule of glucose during the reactions of photosynthesis. Glucose molecules can also be combined with and converted into other types of sugars. When sugars are consumed, molecules of glucose eventually make their way into each living cell of the organism. Inside the cell, each sugar molecule is broken down through a complex series of chemical reactions. The goal of these reactions is to harvest the energy stored inside the sugar molecules. The harvested energy is used to make high-energy ATP molecules, which can be used to perform work, powering many chemical reactions in the cell. The amount of energy needed to make one molecule of glucose from six molecules of carbon dioxide is 18 molecules of ATP and 12 molecules of NADPH (each one of which is energetically equivalent to three molecules of ATP), or a total of 54 ATP molecule equivalents required for the synthesis of one molecule of glucose. This process is a fundamental and efficient way for cells to generate the molecular energy that they require.

Figure 6.3 Plants, like this oak tree, use energy from sunlight to make sugar and other organic molecules. Both plants and animals, like this squirrel, use cellular respiration to derive energy from the organic molecules originally produced by plants.

Metabolic Pathways

The processes of making and breaking down sugar molecules illustrate two types of metabolic pathways. A metabolic pathway is a series of interconnected biochemical reactions that convert a substrate molecule or molecules, step-by-step, through a series of metabolic intermediates, eventually yielding a final product or products. In the case of sugar metabolism, the first metabolic pathway synthesized sugar from smaller molecules, and the other pathway broke sugar down into smaller molecules. These two opposite processes—the first requiring energy and the second producing energy—are referred to as anabolic (building) and catabolic (breaking down) pathways, respectively. Consequently, metabolism is composed of building (anabolism) and degradation (catabolism).

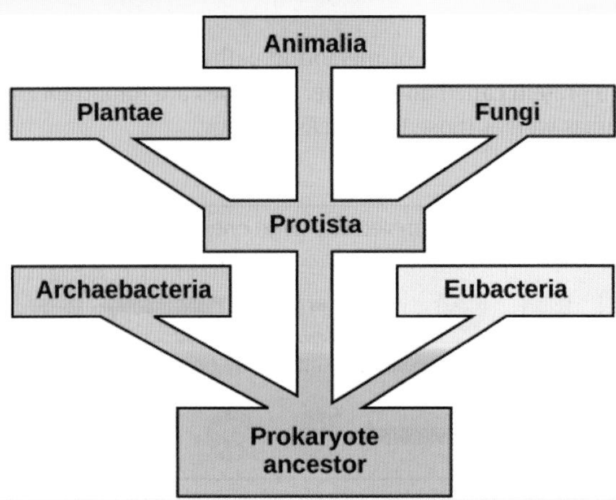

Figure 6.4 This tree shows the evolution of the various branches of life. The vertical dimension is time. Early life forms, in blue, used anaerobic metabolism to obtain energy from their surroundings.

Evolution of Metabolic Pathways

There is more to the complexity of metabolism than understanding the metabolic pathways alone. Metabolic complexity varies from organism to organism. Photosynthesis is the primary pathway in which photosynthetic organisms like plants (the majority of global synthesis is done by planktonic algae) harvest the sun's energy and convert it into carbohydrates. The by-product of photosynthesis is oxygen, required by some cells to carry out cellular respiration. During cellular respiration, oxygen aids in the catabolic breakdown of carbon compounds, like carbohydrates. Among the products of this catabolism are CO_2 and ATP. In addition, some eukaryotes perform catabolic processes without oxygen (fermentation); that is, they perform or use anaerobic metabolism.

Organisms probably evolved anaerobic metabolism to survive (living organisms came into existence about 3.8 billion years ago, when the atmosphere lacked oxygen). Despite the differences between organisms and the complexity of metabolism, researchers have found that all branches of life share some of the same metabolic pathways, suggesting that all organisms evolved from the same ancient common ancestor (Figure 6.4). Evidence indicates that over time, the pathways diverged, adding specialized enzymes to allow organisms to better adapt to their environment, thus increasing their chance to survive. However, the underlying principle remains that all organisms must harvest energy from their environment and convert it to ATP to carry out cellular functions.

The early atmosphere lacked oxygen. Why do you think this is the case?

a. Oxygen is a byproduct of photosynthesis, so there was very little oxygen in the atmosphere until photosynthetic organisms evolved.

b. Oxygen is a byproduct of anaerobic respiration, so there was very little oxygen in the atmosphere until anaerobic organisms evolved.

c. Oxygen is a byproduct of fermentation, so there was very little oxygen in the atmosphere until fermentative organisms evolved.

Anabolic and Catabolic Pathways

Anabolic pathways require an input of energy to synthesize complex molecules from simpler ones. Synthesizing sugar from CO_2 is one example. Other examples are the synthesis of large proteins from amino acid building blocks, and the synthesis of new DNA strands from nucleic acid building blocks. These biosynthetic processes are critical to the life of the cell, take place constantly, and demand energy provided by ATP and other high-energy molecules like NADH (nicotinamide adenine dinucleotide) and NADPH (Figure 6.5).

ATP is an important molecule for cells to have in sufficient supply at all times. The breakdown of sugars illustrates how a single molecule of glucose can store enough energy to make a great deal of ATP, 36 to 38 molecules. This is a **catabolic** pathway. Catabolic pathways involve the degradation (or breakdown) of complex molecules into simpler ones. Molecular energy stored in the bonds of complex molecules is released in catabolic pathways and harvested in such a way that it can be used to produce ATP. Other energy-storing molecules, such as fats, are also broken down through similar catabolic reactions to release energy and make ATP (Figure 6.5).

It is important to know that the chemical reactions of metabolic pathways don't take place spontaneously. Each reaction step is facilitated, or catalyzed, by a protein called an enzyme. Enzymes are important for catalyzing all types of biological reactions—those that require energy as well as those that release energy.

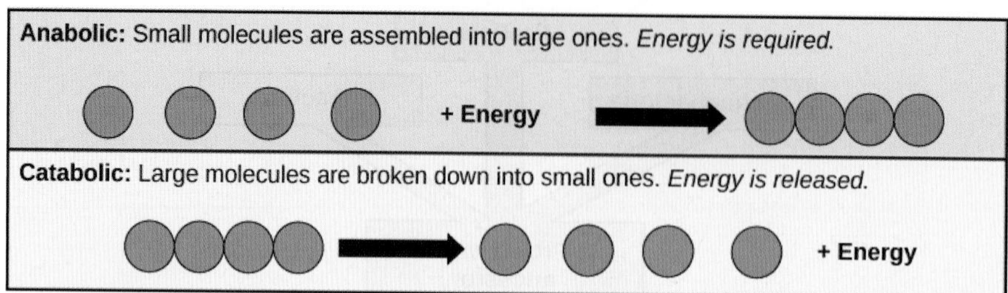

Figure 6.5 Anabolic pathways are those that require energy to synthesize larger molecules. Catabolic pathways are those that generate energy by breaking down larger molecules. Both types of pathways are required for maintaining the cell's energy balance.

Think About It

Describe two different cellular functions in different organisms that require energy that parallel human energy-requiring functions such as physical exercise.

Section Summary

Cells perform the functions of life through various chemical reactions. A cell's metabolism refers to the chemical reactions that take place within it. There are metabolic reactions that involve the breaking down of complex chemicals into simpler ones, such as the breakdown of large macromolecules. This process is referred to as catabolism, and such reactions are associated with a release of energy. On the other end of the spectrum, anabolism refers to metabolic processes that build complex molecules out of simpler ones, such as the synthesis of macromolecules. Anabolic processes require energy. Glucose synthesis and glucose breakdown are examples of anabolic and catabolic pathways, respectively.

6.2 | Potential, Kinetic, Free, and Activation Energy

In this section, you will explore the following questions:

- What is "energy"?
- What is the difference between kinetic and potential energy?
- What is free energy, and how does free energy related to activation energy?
- What is the difference between endergonic and exergonic reactions?

Connection for AP® Courses

Although cells and organisms require free energy to survive, they cannot spontaneously create energy, as stated in the Law of Conservation of Energy. Energy is available in different forms. For example, objects in motion possess kinetic energy, whereas objects that are not in motion possess potential energy. The chemical energy in molecules, such as glucose, is potential energy because when bonds break in chemical reactions, free energy is released. Free energy is a measure of energy that is available to do work. The free energy of a system changes during energy transfers such as chemical reactions, and this change is referred to as ΔG or Gibbs free energy. The ΔG of a reaction can be negative or positive, depending on whether the reaction releases energy (exergonic) or requires energy input (endergonic). All reactions require an input of energy called activation energy in order to reach the transition state at which they will proceed. (In another section, we will explore how enzymes speed up chemical reactions by lowering activation energy barriers.)

Information presented and the examples highlighted in the section support concepts and Learning Objectives outlined in Big Idea 2 of the AP® Biology Curriculum Framework. The Learning Objectives listed in the Curriculum Framework provide a transparent foundation for the AP® Biology course, an inquiry-based laboratory experience, instructional activities, and AP® Exam questions. A Learning Objective merges required content with one or more of the seven Science Practices.

Big Idea 2	Biological systems utilize free energy and molecular building blocks to grow, to reproduce, and to maintain dynamic homeostasis.
Enduring Understanding 2.A	Growth, reproduction and maintenance of living systems require free energy and matter.
Essential Knowledge	**2.A.1** All living systems require constant input of free energy.
Science Practice	**6.2** The student can construct explanations of phenomena based on evidence produced through scientific practices.
Learning Objective	**2.1** The student is able to explain how biological systems use free energy based on empirical data that all organisms require constant energy input to maintain organization, to grow, and to reproduce.
Essential Knowledge	**2.A.1** All living systems require constant input of free energy.
Science Practice	**6.2** The student can justify claims with evidence.
Learning Objective	**2.2** The student is able to justify a scientific claim that free energy is required for living systems to maintain organization, to grow or to reproduce, but that multiple strategies exist in different living systems.

The Science Practice Challenge Questions contain additional test questions for this section that will help you prepare for the AP exam. These questions address the following standards:
[APLO 2.5]

Energy is defined as the ability to do work. As you've learned, energy exists in different forms. For example, electrical energy, light energy, and heat energy are all different types of energy. While these are all familiar types of energy that one can see or feel, there is another type of energy that is much less tangible. This energy is associated with something as simple as an object held above the ground. In order to appreciate the way energy flows into and out of biological systems, it is important to understand more about the different types of energy that exist in the physical world.

Types of Energy

When an object is in motion, there is energy associated with that object. In the example of an airplane in flight, there is a great deal of energy associated with the motion of the airplane. This is because moving objects are capable of enacting a change, or doing work. Think of a wrecking ball. Even a slow-moving wrecking ball can do a great deal of damage to other objects. However, a wrecking ball that is not in motion is incapable of performing work. Energy associated with objects in motion is called **kinetic energy**. A speeding bullet, a walking person, the rapid movement of molecules in the air (which produces heat), and electromagnetic radiation like light all have kinetic energy.

Now what if that same motionless wrecking ball is lifted two stories above a car with a crane? If the suspended wrecking ball is unmoving, is there energy associated with it? The answer is yes. The suspended wrecking ball has energy associated with it that is fundamentally different from the kinetic energy of objects in motion. This form of energy results from the fact that there is the *potential* for the wrecking ball to do work. If it is released, indeed it would do work. Because this type of energy refers to the potential to do work, it is called **potential energy**. Objects transfer their energy between kinetic and potential in the following way: As the wrecking ball hangs motionless, it has 0 kinetic and 100 percent potential energy. Once it is released, its kinetic energy begins to increase because it builds speed due to gravity. At the same time, as it nears the ground, it loses potential energy. Somewhere mid-fall it has 50 percent kinetic and 50 percent potential energy. Just before it hits the ground, the ball has nearly lost its potential energy and has near-maximal kinetic energy. Other examples of potential energy include the energy of water held behind a dam (Figure 6.6), or a person about to skydive out of an airplane.

Figure 6.6 Water behind a dam has potential energy. Moving water, such as in a waterfall or a rapidly flowing river, has kinetic energy. (credit "dam": modification of work by "Pascal"/Flickr; credit "waterfall": modification of work by Frank Gualtieri)

Potential energy is not only associated with the location of matter (such as a child sitting on a tree branch), but also with the structure of matter. A spring on the ground has potential energy if it is compressed; so does a rubber band that is pulled taut. The very existence of living cells relies heavily on structural potential energy. On a chemical level, the bonds that hold the atoms of molecules together have potential energy. Remember that anabolic cellular pathways require energy to synthesize complex molecules from simpler ones, and catabolic pathways release energy when complex molecules are broken down. The fact that energy can be released by the breakdown of certain chemical bonds implies that those bonds have potential energy. In fact, there is potential energy stored within the bonds of all the food molecules we eat, which is eventually harnessed for use. This is because these bonds can release energy when broken. The type of potential energy that exists within chemical bonds, and is released when those bonds are broken, is called **chemical energy** (Figure 6.7). Chemical energy is responsible for providing living cells with energy from food. The release of energy is brought about by breaking the molecular bonds within fuel molecules.

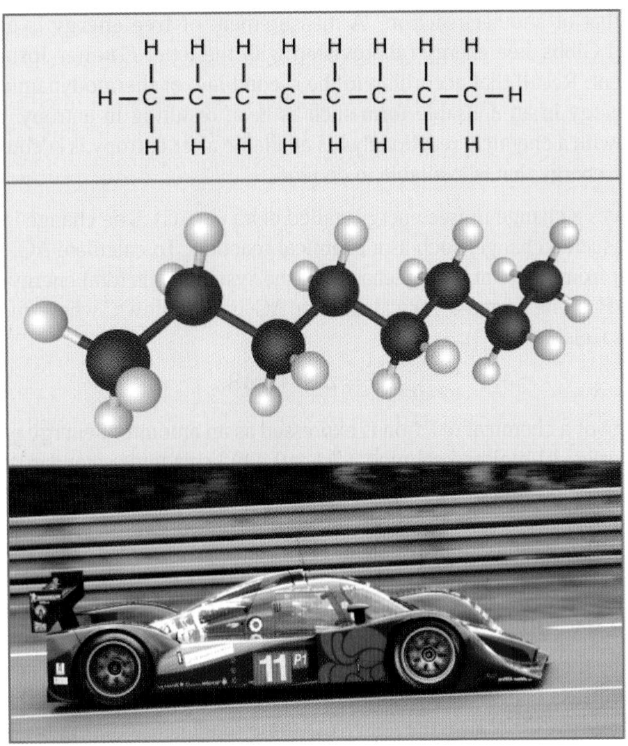

Figure 6.7 The molecules in gasoline (octane, the chemical formula shown) contain chemical energy within the chemical bonds. This energy is transformed into kinetic energy that allows a car to race on a racetrack. (credit "car": modification of work by Russell Trow)

Visit this site (http://openstaxcollege.org/l/simple_pendulum) and select "A simple pendulum" on the menu (under "Harmonic Motion") to see the shifting kinetic (K) and potential energy (U) of a pendulum in motion.

Explain how the potential and kinetic energy shown in the pendulum model (http://openstaxcollege.org/l/simple_pendulum) relates to a child swinging on a swing set.

a. Kinetic energy increases when the child swings downward, potential energy increases when the child swings upward.

b. Kinetic energy decreases when the child swings downward, potential energy decreases when the child swings upward.

c. Kinetic energy increases when the child swings upward, potential energy increases when the child swings downward.

d. Kinetic energy increases when child swings downward, potential energy increases when the child swings downward.

Free Energy

After learning that chemical reactions release energy when energy-storing bonds are broken, an important next question is how is the energy associated with chemical reactions quantified and expressed? How can the energy released from one reaction be compared to that of another reaction? A measurement of **free energy** is used to quantitate these energy transfers. Free energy is called Gibbs free energy (abbreviated with the letter G) after Josiah Willard Gibbs, the scientist who developed the measurement. Recall that according to the second law of thermodynamics, all energy transfers involve the loss of some amount of energy in an unusable form such as heat, resulting in entropy. Gibbs free energy specifically refers to the energy associated with a chemical reaction that is available after entropy is accounted for. In other words, Gibbs free energy is usable energy, or energy that is available to do work.

Every chemical reaction involves a change in free energy, called delta G (ΔG). The change in free energy can be calculated for any system that undergoes such a change, such as a chemical reaction. To calculate ΔG, subtract the amount of energy lost to entropy (denoted as ΔS) from the total energy change of the system. This total energy change in the system is called **enthalpy** and is denoted as ΔH . The formula for calculating ΔG is as follows, where the symbol T refers to absolute temperature in Kelvin (degrees Celsius + 273):

$$\Delta G = \Delta H - T\Delta S$$

The standard free energy change of a chemical reaction is expressed as an amount of energy per mole of the reaction product (either in kilojoules or kilocalories, kJ/mol or kcal/mol; 1 kJ = 0.239 kcal) under standard pH, temperature, and pressure conditions. Standard pH, temperature, and pressure conditions are generally calculated at pH 7.0 in biological systems, 25 degrees Celsius, and 100 kilopascals (1 atm pressure), respectively. It is important to note that cellular conditions vary considerably from these standard conditions, and so standard calculated ΔG values for biological reactions will be different inside the cell.

Endergonic Reactions and Exergonic Reactions

If energy is released during a chemical reaction, then the resulting value from the above equation will be a negative number. In other words, reactions that release energy have a $\Delta G < 0$. A negative ΔG also means that the products of the reaction have less free energy than the reactants, because they gave off some free energy during the reaction. Reactions that have a negative ΔG and consequently release free energy are called **exergonic reactions**. Think: *ex*ergonic means energy is *ex*iting the system. These reactions are also referred to as spontaneous reactions, because they can occur without the addition of energy into the system. Understanding which chemical reactions are spontaneous and release free energy is extremely useful for biologists, because these reactions can be harnessed to perform work inside the cell. An important distinction must be drawn between the term spontaneous and the idea of a chemical reaction that occurs immediately. Contrary to the everyday use of the term, a spontaneous reaction is not one that suddenly or quickly occurs. The rusting of iron is an example of a spontaneous reaction that occurs slowly, little by little, over time.

If a chemical reaction requires an input of energy rather than releasing energy, then the ΔG for that reaction will be a positive value. In this case, the products have more free energy than the reactants. Thus, the products of these reactions can be thought of as energy-storing molecules. These chemical reactions are called **endergonic reactions**, and they are non-spontaneous. An endergonic reaction will not take place on its own without the addition of free energy.

Let’s revisit the example of the synthesis and breakdown of the food molecule, glucose. Remember that the building of complex molecules, such as sugars, from simpler ones is an anabolic process and requires energy. Therefore, the chemical reactions involved in anabolic processes are endergonic reactions. On the other hand, the catabolic process of breaking sugar down into simpler molecules releases energy in a series of exergonic reactions. Like the example of rust above, the breakdown of sugar involves spontaneous reactions, but these reactions don’t occur instantaneously. Figure 6.8 shows some other examples of endergonic and exergonic reactions. Later sections will provide more information about what else is required to make even spontaneous reactions happen more efficiently.

visual CONNECTION

Figure 6.8 Shown are some examples of endergonic processes (ones that require energy) and exergonic processes (ones that release energy). These include (a) a compost pile decomposing, (b) a chick developing from a fertilized egg, (c) sand art being destroyed, and (d) a ball rolling down a hill. (credit a: modification of work by Natalie Maynor; credit b: modification of work by USDA; credit c: modification of work by "Athlex"/Flickr; credit d: modification of work by Harry Malsch)

(a) (b) (c) (d)

Look at each of the processes shown, and decide if it is endergonic or exergonic. In each case, does enthalpy increase or decrease, and does entropy increase or decrease?

a. Compost pile decomposition is endergonic, enthalpy increases and entropy increases. A baby developing from egg is an endergonic process, enthalpy decreases and entropy decreases. Sand art being destroyed is exergonic, no change in enthalpy and entropy increases. A ball rolling downhill is exergonic process, enthalpy decreases and no change in entropy.
b. Compost pile decomposition is exergonic, enthalpy increases and entropy increases. A baby developing from egg is an endergonic process, enthalpy decreases and entropy decreases. Sand art being destroyed is exergonic, no change in enthalpy and entropy decreases. A ball rolling downhill is exergonic process, enthalpy decreases and no change in entropy.
c. Compost pile decomposition is exergonic, enthalpy increases and entropy increases. A baby developing from egg is an endergonic process, enthalpy decreases and entropy decreases. Sand art being destroyed is exergonic, no change in enthalpy and entropy increases. A ball rolling downhill is exergonic process, enthalpy decreases and entropy increases.
d. A ball rolling down the hill doesn't affect the order of system; therefore, the entropy would remain unchanged.

An important concept in the study of metabolism and energy is that of chemical equilibrium. Most chemical reactions are reversible. They can proceed in both directions, releasing energy into their environment in one direction, and absorbing it from the environment in the other direction (**Figure 6.9**). The same is true for the chemical reactions involved in cell metabolism, such as the breaking down and building up of proteins into and from individual amino acids, respectively. Reactants within a closed system will undergo chemical reactions in both directions until a state of equilibrium is reached. This state of equilibrium is one of the lowest possible free energy and a state of maximal entropy. Energy must be put into the system to push the reactants and products away from a state of equilibrium. Either reactants or products must be added, removed, or changed. If a cell were a closed system, its chemical reactions would reach equilibrium, and it would die because there would be insufficient free energy left to perform the work needed to maintain life. In a living cell, chemical reactions are constantly moving towards equilibrium, but never reach it. This is because a living cell is an open system. Materials pass in and out, the cell recycles the products of certain chemical reactions into other reactions, and chemical equilibrium is never reached. In this way, living organisms are in a constant energy-requiring, uphill battle against equilibrium and entropy. This constant supply of energy ultimately comes from sunlight, which is used to produce nutrients in the process of photosynthesis.

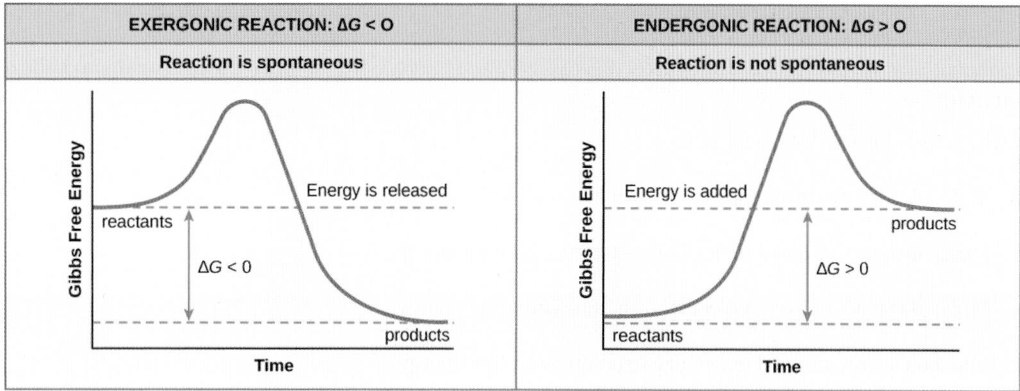

Figure 6.9 Exergonic and endergonic reactions result in changes in Gibbs free energy. Exergonic reactions release energy; endergonic reactions require energy to proceed.

Activation Energy

There is another important concept that must be considered regarding endergonic and exergonic reactions. Even exergonic reactions require a small amount of energy input to get going before they can proceed with their energy-releasing steps. These reactions have a net release of energy, but still require some energy in the beginning. This small amount of energy input necessary for all chemical reactions to occur is called the **activation energy** (or free energy of activation) and is abbreviated E_A (Figure 6.10).

Why would an energy-releasing, negative ΔG reaction actually require some energy to proceed? The reason lies in the steps that take place during a chemical reaction. During chemical reactions, certain chemical bonds are broken and new ones are formed. For example, when a glucose molecule is broken down, bonds between the carbon atoms of the molecule are broken. Since these are energy-storing bonds, they release energy when broken. However, to get them into a state that allows the bonds to break, the molecule must be somewhat contorted. A small energy input is required to achieve this contorted state. This contorted state is called the **transition state**, and it is a high-energy, unstable state. For this reason, reactant molecules don't last long in their transition state, but very quickly proceed to the next steps of the chemical reaction. Free energy diagrams illustrate the energy profiles for a given reaction. Whether the reaction is exergonic or endergonic determines whether the products in the diagram will exist at a lower or higher energy state than both the reactants and the products. However, regardless of this measure, the transition state of the reaction exists at a higher energy state than the reactants, and thus, E_A is always positive.

Watch an animation of the move from free energy to transition state at **this (http://openstaxcollege.org/l/energy_reaction)** site.

Explain why transitional states are unstable.

a. Molecules have relaxed molecular structure with low energy.

b. Molecules have strained molecular structure with high energy.

c. Molecules have relaxed molecular structure with high energy.

d. Molecules have strained molecular structure with low energy.

Where does the activation energy required by chemical reactants come from? The source of the activation energy needed to push reactions forward is typically heat energy from the surroundings. **Heat energy** (the total bond energy of reactants or products in a chemical reaction) speeds up the motion of molecules, increasing the frequency and force with which they collide; it also moves atoms and bonds within the molecule slightly, helping them reach their transition state. For this reason, heating up a system will cause chemical reactants within that system to react more frequently. Increasing the pressure on a system has the same effect. Once reactants have absorbed enough heat energy from their surroundings to reach the transition state, the reaction will proceed.

The activation energy of a particular reaction determines the rate at which it will proceed. The higher the activation energy, the slower the chemical reaction will be. The example of iron rusting illustrates an inherently slow reaction. This reaction occurs slowly over time because of its high E_A. Additionally, the burning of many fuels, which is strongly exergonic, will take place at a negligible rate unless their activation energy is overcome by sufficient heat from a spark. Once they begin to burn, however, the chemical reactions release enough heat to continue the burning process, supplying the activation energy for surrounding fuel molecules. Like these reactions outside of cells, the activation energy for most cellular reactions is too high for heat energy to overcome at efficient rates. In other words, in order for important cellular reactions to occur at appreciable rates (number of reactions per unit time), their activation energies must be lowered (**Figure 6.10**); this is referred to as catalysis. This is a very good thing as far as living cells are concerned. Important macromolecules, such as proteins, DNA, and RNA, store considerable energy, and their breakdown is exergonic. If cellular temperatures alone provided enough heat energy for these exergonic reactions to overcome their activation barriers, the essential components of a cell would disintegrate.

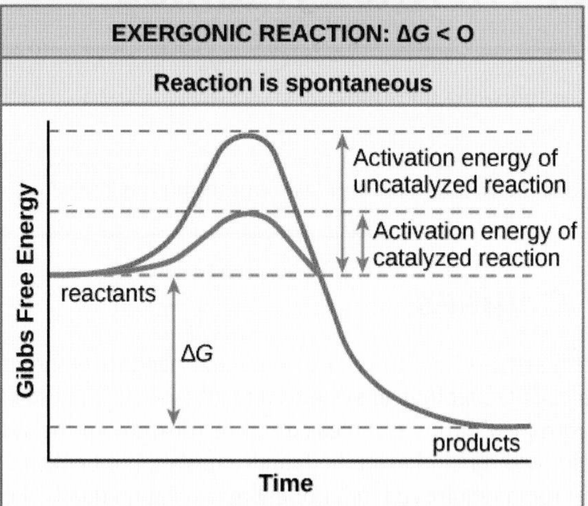

Figure 6.10 Activation energy is the energy required for a reaction to proceed, and it is lower if the reaction is catalyzed. The horizontal axis of this diagram describes the sequence of events in time.

How does the change in Gibbs free energy (ΔG) differ between the catalyzed versus uncatalyzed reaction?

a. ΔG is greater for the forward direction than for the reverse direction.

b. ΔG is greater for the uncatalyzed than the catalyzed reaction.

c. ΔG is greater for the catalyzed than the uncatalyzed reaction.

d. ΔG is the same for the catalyzed and uncatalyzed reactions.

science practices CONNECTION for AP® Courses

Think About It

All plants use water, carbon dioxide, and energy from the sun to make sugars. Think about what would happen to plants that do not have sunlight as an energy source or sufficient water. What would happen to organisms that depend on those plants for their own survival? How does depletion or destruction of forests by human activity affect free energy availability to organisms living in the rain forest? What measures can be taken to try and restore the free energy to an acceptable level?

Section Summary

Energy comes in many different forms. Objects in motion do physical work, and kinetic energy is the energy of objects in motion. Objects that are not in motion may have the potential to do work, and thus, have potential energy. Molecules also have potential energy because the breaking of molecular bonds has the potential to release energy. Living cells depend on the harvesting of potential energy from molecular bonds to perform work. Free energy is a measure of energy that is available to do work. The free energy of a system changes during energy transfers such as chemical reactions, and this change is referred to as ΔG.

The ΔG of a reaction can be negative or positive, meaning that the reaction releases energy or consumes energy, respectively. A reaction with a negative ΔG that gives off energy is called an exergonic reaction. One with a positive ΔG that requires energy input is called an endergonic reaction. Exergonic reactions are said to be spontaneous, because their products have less energy than their reactants. The products of endergonic reactions have a higher energy state than the reactants, and so these are nonspontaneous reactions. However, all reactions (including spontaneous –ΔG reactions) require an initial input of energy in order to reach the transition state, at which they'll proceed. This initial input of energy is called the activation energy.

6.3 | The Laws of Thermodynamics

In this section, you will explore the following questions:

- What is entropy?
- What is the difference between the first and second laws of thermodynamics?

Connection for AP® Courses

In studying energy, scientists use the term system to refer to the matter and its environment involved in energy transfers, such as an ecosystem. Even single cells are biological systems and all systems require energy to maintain order. The more ordered a system is, the lower its entropy. Entropy is a measure of the disorder of the system. (Think of your bedroom as a system. On Sunday evening, you throw dirty clothes in the laundry basket, put books back on the shelves, and return dirty dishes to the kitchen. Cleaning your room requires an input of energy. What gradually happens as the week progresses? You guessed it: entropy.) All biological systems obey the laws of chemistry and physics, including the laws of thermodynamics that describe the properties and processes of energy transfer in systems. The first law states that the total amount of energy in the universe is constant; energy cannot be created or destroyed, but it can be transformed and transferred. The second law states that every energy transfer involves some loss of energy in an unusable form, such as heat energy, resulting in a more disordered system (e.g., your bedroom over the course of a week). Thus, no energy transfer is completely efficient. (We will explore how free energy is stored, transferred, and used in more detail when we study photosynthesis and cellular respiration.)

Information presented and the examples highlighted in the section, support concepts and Learning Objectives outlined in Big Idea 2 of the AP® Biology Curriculum Framework. The Learning Objectives listed in the Curriculum Framework provide a transparent foundation for the AP® Biology course, an inquiry-based laboratory experience, instructional activities, and AP® Exam questions. A Learning Objective merges required content with one or more of the seven Science Practices.

Big Idea 2	Biological systems utilize free energy and molecular building blocks to grow, to reproduce, and to maintain dynamic homeostasis.
Enduring Understanding 2.A	Growth, reproduction and maintenance of living systems require free energy and matter.
Essential Knowledge	**2.A.1** All living systems require constant input of free energy.
Science Practice	**6.2** The student can construct explanations of phenomena based on evidence produced through scientific practices.
Learning Objective	**2.1** The student is able to explain how biological systems use free energy based on empirical data that all organisms require constant energy input to maintain organization, to grow, and to reproduce.

The Science Practice Challenge Questions contain additional test questions for this section that will help you prepare for the AP exam. These questions address the following standards:
[APLO 2.1][APLO 2.2][APLO 2.4][APLO 4.16][APLO 2.3]

Thermodynamics refers to the study of energy and energy transfer involving physical matter. The matter and its environment relevant to a particular case of energy transfer are classified as a system, and everything outside of that system is called the surroundings. For instance, when heating a pot of water on the stove, the system includes the stove, the pot, and the water. Energy is transferred within the system (between the stove, pot, and water). There are two types of systems: open and closed. An open system is one in which energy can be transferred between the system and its surroundings. The stovetop system is open because heat can be lost into the air. A closed system is one that cannot transfer energy to its surroundings.

Biological organisms are open systems. Energy is exchanged between them and their surroundings, as they consume energy-storing molecules and release energy to the environment by doing work. Like all things in the physical world, energy is subject to the laws of physics. The laws of thermodynamics govern the transfer of energy in and among all systems in the universe.

The First Law of Thermodynamics

The first law of thermodynamics deals with the total amount of energy in the universe. It states that this total amount of energy is constant. In other words, there has always been, and always will be, exactly the same amount of energy in the universe. Energy exists in many different forms. According to the first law of thermodynamics, energy may be transferred from place to place or transformed into different forms, but it cannot be created or destroyed. The transfers and transformations of energy take place around us all the time. Light bulbs transform electrical energy into light energy. Gas stoves transform chemical energy from natural gas into heat energy. Plants perform one of the most biologically useful energy transformations on earth: that of converting the energy of sunlight into the chemical energy stored within organic molecules, as shown in Figure 6.2. Some examples of energy transformations are shown in Figure 6.11.

The challenge for all living organisms is to obtain energy from their surroundings in forms that they can transfer or transform into usable energy to do work. Living cells have evolved to meet this challenge very well. Chemical energy stored within organic molecules such as sugars and fats is transformed through a series of cellular chemical reactions into energy within molecules of ATP. Energy in ATP molecules is easily accessible to do work. Examples of the types of work that cells need to do include building complex molecules, transporting materials, powering the beating motion of cilia or flagella, contracting muscle fibers to create movement, and reproduction.

Figure 6.11 Shown are two examples of energy being transferred from one system to another and transformed from one form to another. Humans can convert the chemical energy in food, like this ice cream cone, into kinetic energy (the energy of movement to ride a bicycle). Plants can convert electromagnetic radiation (light energy) from the sun into chemical energy. (credit "ice cream": modification of work by D. Sharon Pruitt; credit "kids on bikes": modification of work by Michelle Riggen-Ransom; credit "leaf": modification of work by Cory Zanker)

The Second Law of Thermodynamics

A living cell's primary tasks of obtaining, transforming, and using energy to do work may seem simple. However, the second law of thermodynamics explains why these tasks are harder than they appear. None of the energy transfers we've discussed, along with all energy transfers and transformations in the universe, is completely efficient. In every energy transfer, some amount of energy is lost in a form that is unusable. In most cases, this form is heat energy. Thermodynamically, **heat energy** is defined as the energy transferred from one system to another that is not doing work. For example, when an airplane flies through the air, some of the energy of the flying plane is lost as heat energy due to friction with the surrounding air. This friction actually heats the air by temporarily increasing the speed of air molecules. Likewise, some energy is lost as heat energy during cellular metabolic reactions. This is good for warm-blooded creatures like us, because heat energy helps to maintain our body temperature. Strictly speaking, no energy transfer is completely efficient, because some energy is lost in an unusable form.

An important concept in physical systems is that of order and disorder (also known as randomness). The more energy that is lost by a system to its surroundings, the less ordered and more random the system is. Scientists refer to the measure of randomness or disorder within a system as **entropy**. High entropy means high disorder and low energy (Figure 6.12). To better understand entropy, think of a student's bedroom. If no energy or work were put into it, the room would quickly become messy. It would exist in a very disordered state, one of high entropy. Energy must be put into the system, in the form of the student doing work and putting everything away, in order to bring the room back to a state of cleanliness and order. This state is one of low entropy. Similarly, a car or house must be constantly maintained with work in order to keep it in an ordered state. Left alone, the entropy of the house or car gradually increases through rust and degradation. Molecules and chemical reactions have varying amounts of entropy as well. For example, as chemical reactions reach a state of equilibrium, entropy increases, and as molecules at a high concentration in one place diffuse and spread out, entropy also increases.

scientific method CONNECTION

Transfer of Energy and the Resulting Entropy

Set up a simple experiment to understand how energy is transferred and how a change in entropy results.

1. Take a block of ice. This is water in solid form, so it has a high structural order. This means that the molecules cannot move very much and are in a fixed position. The temperature of the ice is 0°C. As a result, the entropy of the system is low.
2. Allow the ice to melt at room temperature. What is the state of molecules in the liquid water now? How did the energy transfer take place? Is the entropy of the system higher or lower? Why?
3. Heat the water to its boiling point. What happens to the entropy of the system when the water is heated?

All physical systems can be thought of in this way: Living things are highly ordered, requiring constant energy input to be maintained in a state of low entropy. As living systems take in energy-storing molecules and transform them through chemical reactions, they lose some amount of usable energy in the process, because no reaction is completely efficient. They also produce waste and by-products that aren't useful energy sources. This process increases the entropy of the system's surroundings. Since all energy transfers result in the loss of some usable energy, the second law of thermodynamics states that every energy transfer or transformation increases the entropy of the universe. Even though living things are highly ordered and maintain a state of low entropy, the entropy of the universe in total is constantly increasing due to the loss of usable energy with each energy transfer that occurs. Essentially, living things are in a continuous uphill battle against this constant increase in universal entropy.

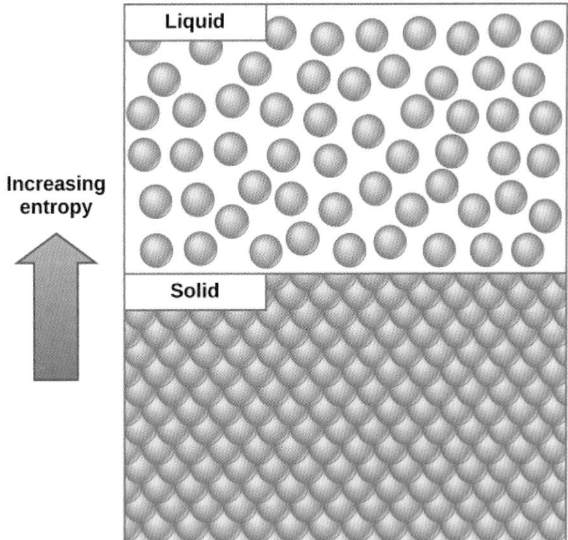

Figure 6.12 Entropy is a measure of randomness or disorder in a system. Gases have higher entropy than liquids, and liquids have higher entropy than solids.

science practices CONNECTION for AP® Courses

Think About It

- Imagine a large ant colony with an elaborate nest, containing many tunnels and passageways. Now imagine that an earthquake shakes the ground and demolishes the nest. Did the ant nest have higher entropy before or after the earthquake? What can the ants do to restore their nest to close to its original amount of entropy? Explain your answers.
- Energy transfers take place constantly in everyday activities. Think of two scenarios: cooking on a stove and driving a car. Explain how the second law of thermodynamics applies to these two scenarios.

Section Summary

In studying energy, scientists use the term “system” to refer to the matter and its environment involved in energy transfers. Everything outside of the system is called the surroundings. Single cells are biological systems. Systems can be thought of as having a certain amount of order. It takes energy to make a system more ordered. The more ordered a system is, the lower its entropy. Entropy is a measure of the disorder of a system. As a system becomes more disordered, the lower its energy and the higher its entropy become.

A series of laws, called the laws of thermodynamics, describe the properties and processes of energy transfer. The first law states that the total amount of energy in the universe is constant. This means that energy can’t be created or destroyed, only transferred or transformed. The second law of thermodynamics states that every energy transfer involves some loss of energy in an unusable form, such as heat energy, resulting in a more disordered system. In other words, no energy transfer is completely efficient and tends toward disorder.

6.4 | ATP: Adenosine Triphosphate

In this section, you will explore the following questions:

- Why is ATP considered the energy currency of the cell?
- How is energy released through the hydrolysis of ATP?

Connection for AP® Courses

Adenosine triphosphate or ATP is the energy "currency" or carrier of the cell. When cells require an input of energy, they use ATP. An ATP nucleotide molecule consists of a five-carbon sugar, the nitrogenous base adenine, and three phosphate groups. (Do not confuse ATP with the nucleotides of DNA and RNA, although they have structural similarities.) The bonds that connect the phosphate have high-energy content, and the energy released from the hydrolysis of ATP to ADP + P_i (Adenosine Diphosphate + Pyrophosphate) is used to perform cellular work, such as contracting a muscle or pumping a solute across a cell membrane in active transport. Cells use ATP by coupling the exergonic reaction of ATP hydrolysis with endergonic reactions, with ATP donating its phosphate group to another molecule via a process called phosphorylation. The phosphorylated molecule is at a higher energy state and is less stable than its unphosphorylated form and free energy is released to substrates to perform work during this process. Phosphorylation is an example of energy transfer between molecules.

Information presented and the examples highlighted in the section support concepts and Learning Objectives outlined in Big Idea 2 of the AP® Biology Curriculum Framework. The Learning Objectives listed in the Curriculum Framework provide a transparent foundation for the AP® Biology course, an inquiry-based laboratory experience, instructional activities, and AP® Exam questions. A Learning Objective merges required content with one or more of the seven Science Practices.

Big Idea 2	Biological systems utilize free energy and molecular building blocks to grow, to reproduce, and to maintain dynamic homeostasis.
Enduring Understanding 2.A	Growth, reproduction and maintenance of living systems require free energy and matter.
Essential Knowledge	**2.A.1** All living systems require constant input of free energy.
Science Practice	**6.2** The student can construct explanations of phenomena based on evidence produced through scientific practices.
Learning Objective	**2.1** The student is able to explain how biological systems use free energy based on empirical data that all organisms require constant energy input to maintain organization, to grow, and to reproduce.

The Science Practices Assessment Ancillary contains additional test questions for this section that will help you prepare for the AP exam. These questions address the following standards:
[APLO 2.2][APLO 4.14][APLO 2.7][APLO 2.35]

Even exergonic, energy-releasing reactions require a small amount of activation energy in order to proceed. However, consider endergonic reactions, which require much more energy input, because their products have more free energy than their reactants. Within the cell, where does energy to power such reactions come from? The answer lies with an energy-supplying molecule called **adenosine triphosphate**, or **ATP**. ATP is a small, relatively simple molecule (Figure 6.13), but within some of its bonds, it contains the potential for a quick burst of energy that can be harnessed to perform cellular work. This molecule can be thought of as the primary energy currency of cells in much the same way that money is the currency that people exchange for things they need. ATP is used to power the majority of energy-requiring cellular reactions.

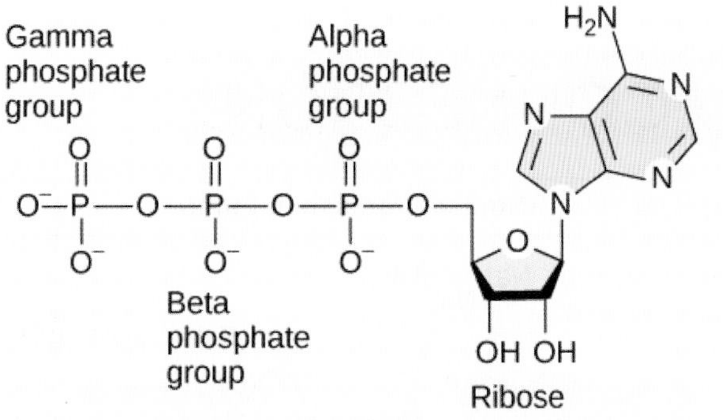

Gamma phosphate group — Alpha phosphate group — Beta phosphate group — Ribose — H_2N, N, O, OH OH, O^-, P

Figure 6.13 ATP is the primary energy currency of the cell. It has an adenosine backbone with three phosphate groups attached.

As its name suggests, adenosine triphosphate is comprised of adenosine bound to three phosphate groups (Figure 6.13). Adenosine is a nucleoside consisting of the nitrogenous base adenine and a five-carbon sugar, ribose. The three phosphate groups, in order of closest to furthest from the ribose sugar, are labeled alpha, beta, and gamma. Together, these chemical groups constitute an energy powerhouse. However, not all bonds within this molecule exist in a particularly high-energy state. Both bonds that link the phosphates are equally high-energy bonds (**phosphoanhydride bonds**) that, when broken, release sufficient energy to power a variety of cellular reactions and processes. These high-energy bonds are the bonds between the second and third (or beta and gamma) phosphate groups and between the first and second phosphate groups. The reason that these bonds are considered "high-energy" is because the products of such bond breaking—adenosine diphosphate (ADP) and one inorganic phosphate group (P_i)—have considerably lower free energy than the reactants: ATP and a water molecule. Because this reaction takes place with the use of a water molecule, it is considered a hydrolysis reaction. In other words, ATP is hydrolyzed into ADP in the following reaction:

$$\text{ATP} + \text{H}_2\text{O} \rightarrow \text{ADP} + \text{P}_\text{i} + \text{free energy}$$

Like most chemical reactions, the hydrolysis of ATP to ADP is reversible. The reverse reaction regenerates ATP from ADP + P_i. Indeed, cells rely on the regeneration of ATP just as people rely on the regeneration of spent money through some sort of income. Since ATP hydrolysis releases energy, ATP regeneration must require an input of free energy. The formation of ATP is expressed in this equation:

$$\text{ADP} + \text{P}_\text{i} + \text{free energy} \rightarrow \text{ATP} + \text{H}_2\text{O}$$

Two prominent questions remain with regard to the use of ATP as an energy source. Exactly how much free energy is released with the hydrolysis of ATP, and how is that free energy used to do cellular work? The calculated ΔG for the hydrolysis of one mole of ATP into ADP and P_i is −7.3 kcal/mole (−30.5 kJ/mol). Since this calculation is true under standard conditions, it would be expected that a different value exists under cellular conditions. In fact, the ΔG for the hydrolysis of one mole of ATP in a living cell is almost double the value at standard conditions: -14 kcal/mol (−57 kJ/mol).

ATP is a highly unstable molecule. Unless quickly used to perform work, ATP spontaneously dissociates into ADP + P_i, and the free energy released during this process is lost as heat. The second question posed above, that is, how the energy released by ATP hydrolysis is used to perform work inside the cell, depends on a strategy called energy coupling. Cells couple the exergonic reaction of ATP hydrolysis with endergonic reactions, allowing them to proceed. One example of energy coupling using ATP involves a transmembrane ion pump that is extremely important for cellular function. This sodium-potassium pump (Na^+/K^+ pump) drives sodium out of the cell and potassium into the cell (Figure 6.14). A large percentage of a cell's ATP is spent powering this pump, because cellular processes bring a great deal of sodium into the cell and potassium out of the cell. The pump works constantly to stabilize cellular concentrations of sodium and potassium. In order for the pump to turn one cycle (exporting three Na+ ions and importing two K^+ ions), one molecule of ATP must be hydrolyzed. When ATP is hydrolyzed, its gamma phosphate doesn't simply float away, but is actually transferred onto the pump protein. This process of a phosphate group binding to a molecule is called phosphorylation. As with most cases of ATP hydrolysis, a phosphate from ATP is transferred onto another molecule. In a phosphorylated state, the Na^+/K^+ pump has more free energy and is triggered to undergo a conformational change. This change allows it to release Na^+ to the outside of the cell. It then binds extracellular K^+, which, through another conformational change, causes the phosphate to detach from the pump. This release of phosphate triggers the K^+ to be released to the inside of the cell. Essentially, the energy released from the hydrolysis of ATP is coupled with the energy required to power the pump and transport Na^+ and K^+ ions. ATP performs cellular work using this basic form of energy coupling through phosphorylation.

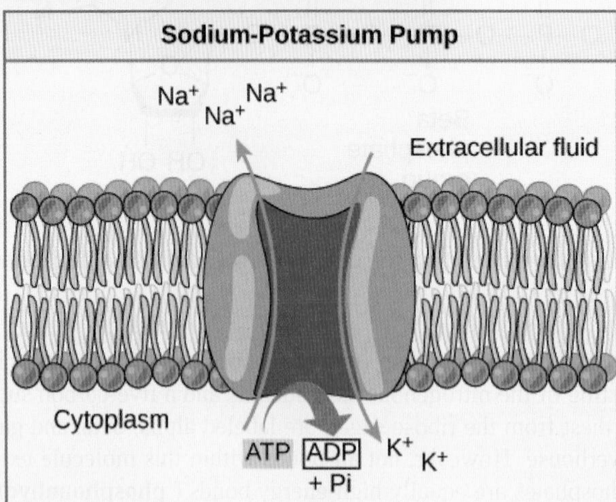

Figure 6.14 The sodium-potassium pump is an example of energy coupling. The energy derived from exergonic ATP hydrolysis is used to pump sodium and potassium ions across the cell membrane.

The hydrolysis of one ATP molecule releases 7.3 kcal/mol of energy ($\Delta G = -7.3$ kcal/mol of energy). If it takes 2.1 kcal/mol of energy to move one Na^+ across the membrane ($\Delta G = +2.1$ kcal/mol of energy), what is the maximum number of sodium ions that could be moved by the hydrolysis of one ATP molecule?

a. five
b. four
c. three
d. two

Often during cellular metabolic reactions, such as the synthesis and breakdown of nutrients, certain molecules must be altered slightly in their conformation to become substrates for the next step in the reaction series. One example is during the very first steps of cellular respiration, when a molecule of the sugar glucose is broken down in the process of glycolysis. In the first step of this process, ATP is required for the phosphorylation of glucose, creating a high-energy but unstable intermediate. This phosphorylation reaction powers a conformational change that allows the phosphorylated glucose molecule to be converted to the phosphorylated sugar fructose. Fructose is a necessary intermediate for glycolysis to move forward. Here, the exergonic reaction of ATP hydrolysis is coupled with the endergonic reaction of converting glucose into a phosphorylated intermediate in the pathway. Once again, the energy released by breaking a phosphate bond within ATP was used for the phosphorylation of another molecule, creating an unstable intermediate and powering an important conformational change.

See an interactive animation of the ATP-producing glycolysis process at this site (http://openstaxcollege.org/l/glycolysis_stgs) .

Explain why the lock-and-key model does not adequately represent the relationship between hexokinase and glucose.

a. Hexokinase changes conformation in presence of glucose

b. Hexokinase induces change in the glucose structure

c. Hexokinase requires an effector molecule to bind at allosteric site

d. Hexokinase binds glucose without any conformational change

science practices CONNECTION for AP® Courses

Think About It

The hydrolysis of one ATP molecules releases 7.3 kcal/mol of energy ($\Delta G = -7.3$ kcal/mol energy). If it takes 2.1 kcal/mol of energy to move one Na^+ across the membrane ($\Delta G = +2.1$ kcal/mol of energy), how many sodium ions could be moved by the hydrolysis of one ATP molecule?

Section Summary

ATP is the primary energy-supplying molecule for living cells. ATP is made up of a nucleotide, a five-carbon sugar, and three phosphate groups. The bonds that connect the phosphates (phosphoanhydride bonds) have high-energy content. The energy released from the hydrolysis of ATP into ADP + P_i is used to perform cellular work. Cells use ATP to perform work by coupling the exergonic reaction of ATP hydrolysis with endergonic reactions. ATP donates its phosphate group to another molecule via a process known as phosphorylation. The phosphorylated molecule is at a higher-energy state and is less stable than its unphosphorylated form, and this added energy from the addition of the phosphate allows the molecule to undergo its endergonic reaction.

6.5 | Enzymes

In this section, you will explore the following questions:

- What is the role of enzymes in metabolic pathways?
- How do enzymes function as molecular catalysts?

Connection for AP® Courses

Many chemical reactions in cells occur spontaneously, but happen too slowly to meet the needs of a cell. For example, a teaspoon of sucrose (table sugar), a disaccharide, in a glass of iced tea will take time to break down into two monosaccharides, glucose and fructose; however, if you add a small amount of the enzyme sucrase to the tea, sucrose breaks down almost immediately. Sucrase is an example of an enzyme, a type of biological catalyst. Enzymes are macromolecules—most often proteins—that speed up chemical reactions by lowering activation energy barriers. Enzymes are very specific for the reactions they catalyze; because they are polypeptides, enzymes can have a variety of shapes attributed to interactions among amino acid R-groups. One part of the enzyme, the active site, interacts with the substrate via the induced fit model of interaction. Substrate binding alters the shape of the enzyme to facilitate the chemical reaction in several different ways, including bringing substrates together in an optimal orientation. After the reaction finishes, the product(s) are released, and the active site returns to its original shape.

Enzyme activity, and thus the rate of an enzyme-catalyzed reaction, is regulated by environmental conditions, including the amount of substrate, temperature, pH, and the presence of coenzymes, cofactors, activators, and inhibitors. Inhibitors, coenzymes, and cofactors can act competitively by binding to the enzyme's active site, or noncompetitively by binding to the enzyme's allosteric site. An allosteric site is an alternate part of the enzyme that can bind to non–substrate molecules. Enzymes work most efficiently under optimal conditions that are specific to the enzyme. For example, trypsin, an enzyme in the human small intestine, works most efficiently at pH 8, whereas pepsin in the stomach works best under acidic conditions. Sometimes environmental factors, especially low pH and high temperatures, alter the shape of the active site; if the shape cannot be restored, the enzyme denatures. The most common method of enzyme regulation in metabolic pathways is via feedback inhibition.

How can various factors, such as feedback inhibition, regulate enzyme activity?

Information presented and the examples highlighted in the section support concepts and Learning Objectives outlined in Big Idea 4 of the AP® Biology Curriculum Framework. The learning objectives listed in the Curriculum Framework provide a transparent foundation for the AP® Biology course, an inquiry-based laboratory experience, instructional activities, and AP® Exam questions. A Learning Objective merges required content with one or more of the seven science practices.

Big Idea 4	Biological systems interact, and these systems and their interactions possess complex properties.
Enduring Understanding 4.B	Competition and cooperation are important aspects of biological systems.
Essential Knowledge	**4.B.1** Interactions between molecules affect their structure and function.
Science Practice	**5.1** The student can analyze data to identify patterns or relationships.
Learning Objective	**4.17** The student is able to analyze data to identify how molecular interactions affect structure and function.

The Science Practice Challenge Questions contain additional test questions for this section that will help you prepare for the AP exam. These questions address the following standards:
[APLO 2.15][APLO 4.8][APLO 2.16]

A substance that helps a chemical reaction to occur is a catalyst, and the special molecules that catalyze biochemical reactions are called enzymes. Almost all enzymes are proteins, made up of chains of amino acids, and they perform the critical task of lowering the activation energies of chemical reactions inside the cell. Enzymes do this by binding to the reactant molecules, and holding them in such a way as to make the chemical bond-breaking and bond-forming processes take place more readily. It is important to remember that enzymes don't change the ΔG of a reaction. In other words, they don't change whether a reaction is exergonic (spontaneous) or endergonic. This is because they don't change the free energy of the reactants or products. They only reduce the activation energy required to reach the transition state (**Figure 6.15**).

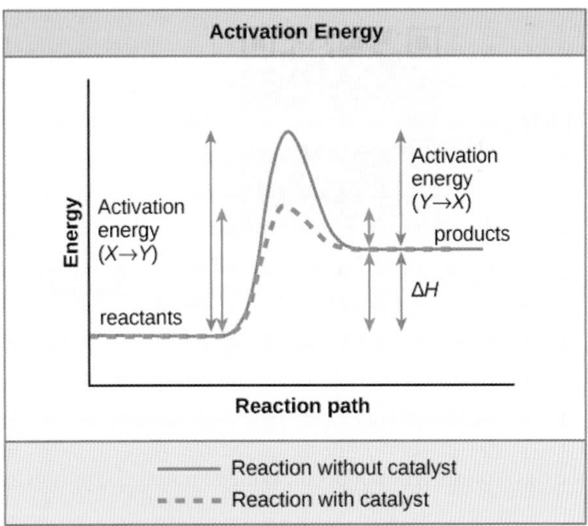

Figure 6.15 Enzymes lower the activation energy of the reaction but do not change the free energy of the reaction.

Enzyme Active Site and Substrate Specificity

The chemical reactants to which an enzyme binds are the enzyme's **substrates**. There may be one or more substrates, depending on the particular chemical reaction. In some reactions, a single-reactant substrate is broken down into multiple products. In others, two substrates may come together to create one larger molecule. Two reactants might also enter a reaction, both become modified, and leave the reaction as two products. The location within the enzyme where the substrate binds is called the enzyme's **active site**. The active site is where the "action" happens, so to speak. Since enzymes are proteins, there is a unique combination of amino acid residues (also called side chains, or R groups) within the active site. Each residue is characterized by different properties. Residues can be large or small, weakly acidic or basic, hydrophilic or hydrophobic, positively or negatively charged, or neutral. The unique combination of amino acid residues, their positions, sequences, structures, and properties, creates a very specific chemical environment within the active site. This specific environment is suited to bind, albeit briefly, to a specific chemical substrate (or substrates). Due to this jigsaw puzzle-like match between an enzyme and its substrates (which adapts to find the best fit between the transition state and the active site), enzymes are known for their specificity. The "best fit" results from the shape and the amino acid functional group's attraction to the substrate. There is a specifically matched enzyme for each substrate and, thus, for each chemical reaction; however, there is flexibility as well.

The fact that active sites are so perfectly suited to provide specific environmental conditions also means that they are subject to influences by the local environment. It is true that increasing the environmental temperature generally increases reaction rates, enzyme-catalyzed or otherwise. However, increasing or decreasing the temperature outside of an optimal range can affect chemical bonds within the active site in such a way that they are less well suited to bind substrates. High temperatures will eventually cause enzymes, like other biological molecules, to **denature**, a process that changes the natural properties of a substance. Likewise, the pH of the local environment can also affect enzyme function. Active site amino acid residues have their own acidic or basic properties that are optimal for catalysis. These residues are sensitive to changes in pH that can impair the way substrate molecules bind. Enzymes are suited to function best within a certain pH range, and, as with temperature, extreme pH values (acidic or basic) of the environment can cause enzymes to denature.

Induced Fit and Enzyme Function

For many years, scientists thought that enzyme-substrate binding took place in a simple "lock-and-key" fashion. This model asserted that the enzyme and substrate fit together perfectly in one instantaneous step. However, current research supports a more refined view called **induced fit** (Figure 6.16). The induced-fit model expands upon the lock-and-key model by describing a more dynamic interaction between enzyme and substrate. As the enzyme and substrate come together, their interaction causes a mild shift in the enzyme's structure that confirms an ideal binding arrangement between the enzyme and the transition state of the substrate. This ideal binding maximizes the enzyme's ability to catalyze its reaction.

View an animation of induced fit at **this website (http://openstaxcollege.org/l/hexokinase)** .

Phosphofructokinase deficiency occurs when a person lacks an enzyme needed to perform glycolysis in skeletal muscles. What effect could this have on the body?

a. Production of energy by glycolysis will occur, skeletal muscles will function properly

b. Production of energy by glycolysis will not occur, skeletal muscles will function properly

c. Production of energy by glycolysis will occur, skeletal muscles will not function properly

d. Production of energy will not occur, skeletal muscles will not function properly

When an enzyme binds its substrate, an enzyme-substrate complex is formed. This complex lowers the activation energy of the reaction and promotes its rapid progression in one of many ways. On a basic level, enzymes promote chemical reactions that involve more than one substrate by bringing the substrates together in an optimal orientation. The appropriate region (atoms and bonds) of one molecule is juxtaposed to the appropriate region of the other molecule with which it must react. Another way in which enzymes promote the reaction of their substrates is by creating an optimal environment within the active site for the reaction to occur. Certain chemical reactions might proceed best in a slightly acidic or non-polar environment. The chemical properties that emerge from the particular arrangement of amino acid residues within an active site create the perfect environment for an enzyme's specific substrates to react.

You've learned that the activation energy required for many reactions includes the energy involved in manipulating or slightly contorting chemical bonds so that they can easily break and allow others to reform. Enzymatic action can aid this process. The enzyme-substrate complex can lower the activation energy by contorting substrate molecules in such a way as to facilitate bond-breaking, helping to reach the transition state. Finally, enzymes can also lower activation energies by taking part in the chemical reaction itself. The amino acid residues can provide certain ions or chemical groups that actually form covalent bonds with substrate molecules as a necessary step of the reaction process. In these cases, it is important to remember that the enzyme will always return to its original state at the completion of the reaction. One of the hallmark properties of enzymes is that they remain ultimately unchanged by the reactions they catalyze. After an enzyme is done catalyzing a reaction, it releases its product(s).

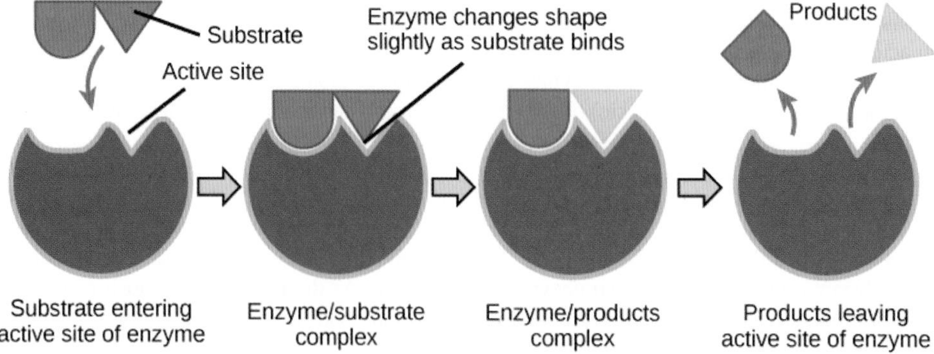

Figure 6.16 According to the induced-fit model, both enzyme and substrate undergo dynamic conformational changes upon binding. The enzyme contorts the substrate into its transition state, thereby increasing the rate of the reaction.

science practices CONNECTION for AP® Courses

Activity

AP Biology Investigation 13: Enzyme Activity. This investigation allows you to design and conduct experiments to explore the effects of environmental variables, such as temperature and pH, on the rates of enzymatic reactions.

Control of Metabolism Through Enzyme Regulation

It would seem ideal to have a scenario in which all of the enzymes encoded in an organism's genome existed in abundant supply and functioned optimally under all cellular conditions, in all cells, at all times. In reality, this is far from the case. A variety of mechanisms ensure that this does not happen. Cellular needs and conditions vary from cell to cell, and change within individual cells over time. The required enzymes and energetic demands of stomach cells are different from those of fat storage cells, skin cells, blood cells, and nerve cells. Furthermore, a digestive cell works much harder to process and break down nutrients during the time that closely follows a meal compared with many hours after a meal. As these cellular demands and conditions vary, so do the amounts and functionality of different enzymes.

Since the rates of biochemical reactions are controlled by activation energy, and enzymes lower and determine activation energies for chemical reactions, the relative amounts and functioning of the variety of enzymes within a cell ultimately determine which reactions will proceed and at which rates. This determination is tightly controlled. In certain cellular environments, enzyme activity is partly controlled by environmental factors, like pH and temperature. There are other mechanisms through which cells control the activity of enzymes and determine the rates at which various biochemical reactions will occur.

Regulation of Enzymes by Molecules

Enzymes can be regulated in ways that either promote or reduce their activity. There are many different kinds of molecules that inhibit or promote enzyme function, and various mechanisms exist for doing so. In some cases of enzyme inhibition, for example, an inhibitor molecule is similar enough to a substrate that it can bind to the active site and simply block the substrate from binding. When this happens, the enzyme is inhibited through **competitive inhibition**, because an inhibitor molecule competes with the substrate for active site binding (Figure 6.17). On the other hand, in noncompetitive inhibition, an inhibitor molecule binds to the enzyme in a location other than an allosteric site and still manages to block substrate binding to the active site.

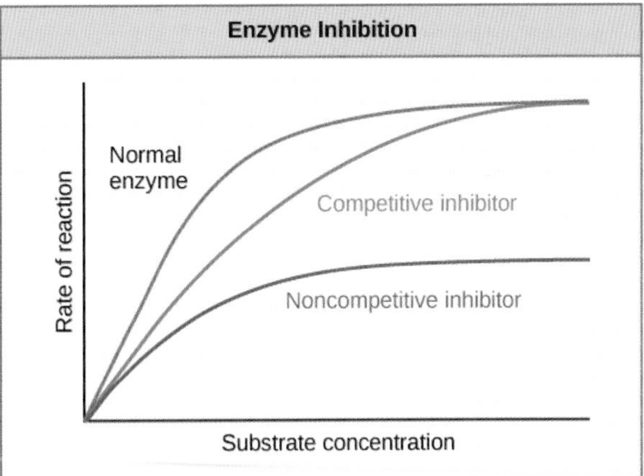

Figure 6.17 Competitive and noncompetitive inhibition affect the rate of reaction differently. Competitive inhibitors affect the initial rate but do not affect the maximal rate, whereas noncompetitive inhibitors affect the maximal rate.

Some inhibitor molecules bind to enzymes in a location where their binding induces a conformational change that reduces the affinity of the enzyme for its substrate. This type of inhibition is called **allosteric inhibition** (Figure 6.18). Most allosterically regulated enzymes are made up of more than one polypeptide, meaning that they have more than one protein subunit. When an allosteric inhibitor binds to an enzyme, all active sites on the protein subunits are changed slightly such that they bind their substrates with less efficiency. There are allosteric activators as well as inhibitors. Allosteric activators bind to locations on an enzyme away from the active site, inducing a conformational change that increases the affinity of the enzyme's active site(s) for its substrate(s).

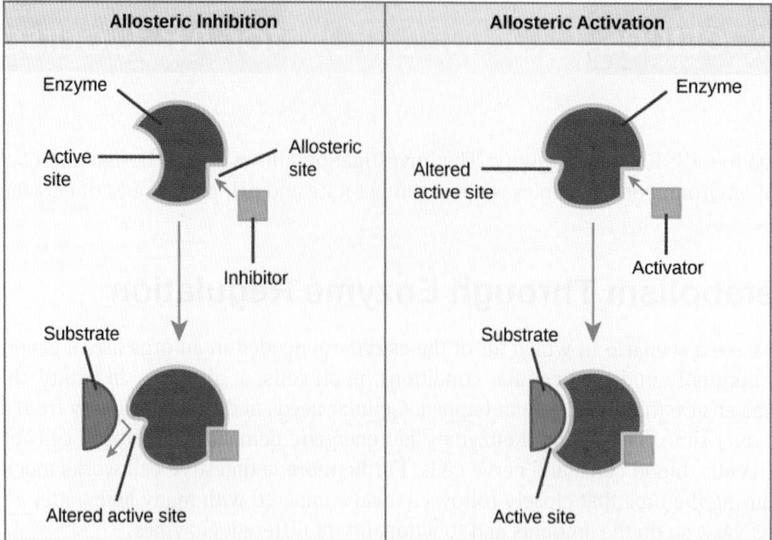

Figure 6.18 Allosteric inhibitors modify the active site of the enzyme so that substrate binding is reduced or prevented. In contrast, allosteric activators modify the active site of the enzyme so that the affinity for the substrate increases.

everyday CONNECTION

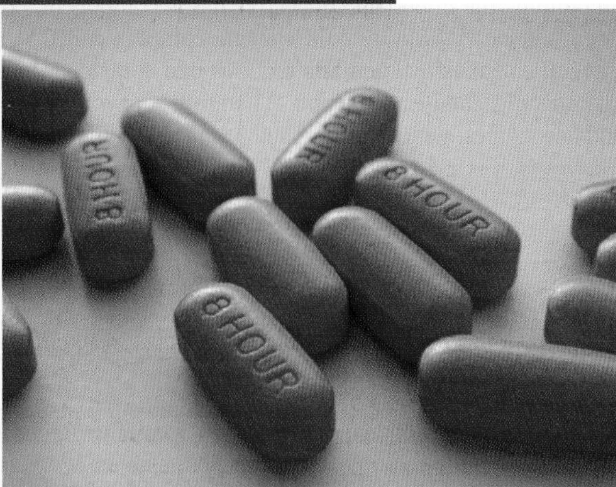

Figure 6.19 Have you ever wondered how pharmaceutical drugs are developed? (credit: Deborah Austin)

Drug Discovery by Looking for Inhibitors of Key Enzymes in Specific Pathways

Enzymes are key components of metabolic pathways. Understanding how enzymes work and how they can be regulated is a key principle behind the development of many of the pharmaceutical drugs (Figure 6.19) on the market today. Biologists working in this field collaborate with other scientists, usually chemists, to design drugs.

Consider statins for example—which is the name given to the class of drugs that reduces cholesterol levels. These compounds are essentially inhibitors of the enzyme HMG-CoA reductase. HMG-CoA reductase is the enzyme that synthesizes cholesterol from lipids in the body. By inhibiting this enzyme, the levels of cholesterol synthesized in the body can be reduced. Similarly, acetaminophen is an inhibitor of the enzyme cyclooxygenase. While it is effective in providing relief from fever and inflammation (pain), its mechanism of action is still not completely understood.

How are drugs developed? One of the first challenges in drug development is identifying the specific molecule that the drug is intended to target. In the case of statins, HMG-CoA reductase is the drug target. Drug targets are identified through painstaking research in the laboratory. Identifying the target alone is not sufficient; scientists also need to know how the target acts inside the cell and which reactions go awry in the case of disease. Once the target and the pathway are identified, then the actual process of drug design begins. During this stage, chemists and biologists work together to design and synthesize molecules that can either block or activate a particular reaction. However, this is only the beginning: both if and when a drug prototype is successful in performing its function, then it must undergo many tests from *in vitro* experiments to clinical trials before it can get FDA approval to be on the market.

Statins reduce the level of cholesterol in the blood. Based on the everyday connection, which of the following might also reduce cholesterol levels in the blood?

a. a drug that increases HMG-CoA reductase levels

b. a drug that reduces cyclooxygenase levels

c. a drug that reduces lipid levels in the body

d. a drug that blocks the action of acetaminophen

Many enzymes don't work optimally, or even at all, unless bound to other specific non-protein helper molecules, either temporarily through ionic or hydrogen bonds or permanently through stronger covalent bonds. Two types of helper molecules are **cofactors** and **coenzymes**. Binding to these molecules promotes optimal conformation and function for their respective enzymes. Cofactors are inorganic ions such as iron (Fe++) and magnesium (Mg++). One example of an enzyme that requires a metal ion as a cofactor is the enzyme that builds DNA molecules, DNA polymerase, which requires a bound zinc ion (Zn++) to function. Coenzymes are organic helper molecules, with a basic atomic structure made up of carbon and hydrogen, which are required for enzyme action. The most common sources of coenzymes are dietary vitamins (Figure 6.20). Some vitamins are precursors to coenzymes and others act directly as coenzymes. Vitamin C is a coenzyme for multiple enzymes that take part in building the important connective tissue component, collagen. An important step in the breakdown of glucose to yield energy is catalysis by a multi-enzyme complex called pyruvate dehydrogenase. Pyruvate dehydrogenase is a complex of several enzymes that actually requires one cofactor (a magnesium ion) and five different organic coenzymes to catalyze its specific chemical reaction. Therefore, enzyme function is, in part, regulated by an abundance of various cofactors and coenzymes, which are supplied primarily by the diets of most organisms.

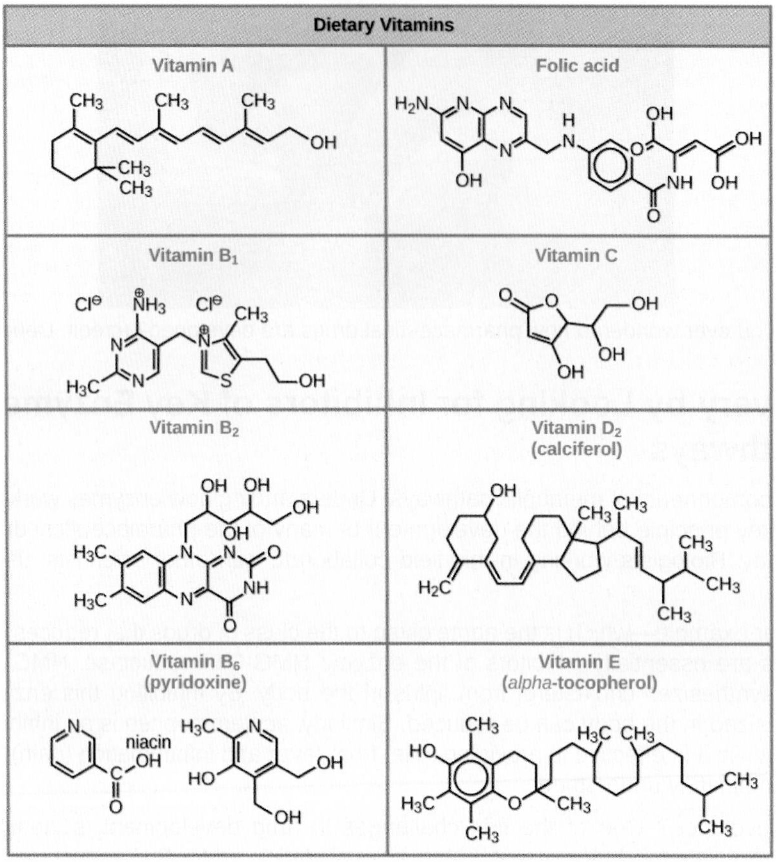

Figure 6.20 Vitamins are important coenzymes or precursors of coenzymes, and are required for enzymes to function properly. Multivitamin capsules usually contain mixtures of all the vitamins at different percentages.

Enzyme Compartmentalization

In eukaryotic cells, molecules such as enzymes are usually compartmentalized into different organelles. This allows for yet another level of regulation of enzyme activity. Enzymes required only for certain cellular processes can be housed separately along with their substrates, allowing for more efficient chemical reactions. Examples of this sort of enzyme regulation based on location and proximity include the enzymes involved in the latter stages of cellular respiration, which take place exclusively in the mitochondria, and the enzymes involved in the digestion of cellular debris and foreign materials, located within lysosomes.

Feedback Inhibition in Metabolic Pathways

Molecules can regulate enzyme function in many ways. A major question remains, however: What are these molecules and where do they come from? Some are cofactors and coenzymes, ions, and organic molecules, as you've learned. What other molecules in the cell provide enzymatic regulation, such as allosteric modulation, and competitive and noncompetitive inhibition? The answer is that a wide variety of molecules can perform these roles. Some of these molecules include pharmaceutical and non-pharmaceutical drugs, toxins, and poisons from the environment. Perhaps the most relevant sources of enzyme regulatory molecules, with respect to cellular metabolism, are the products of the cellular metabolic reactions themselves. In a most efficient and elegant way, cells have evolved to use the products of their own reactions for feedback inhibition of enzyme activity. **Feedback inhibition** involves the use of a reaction product to regulate its own further production (Figure 6.21). The cell responds to the abundance of specific products by slowing down production during anabolic or catabolic reactions. Such reaction products may inhibit the enzymes that catalyzed their production through the mechanisms described above.

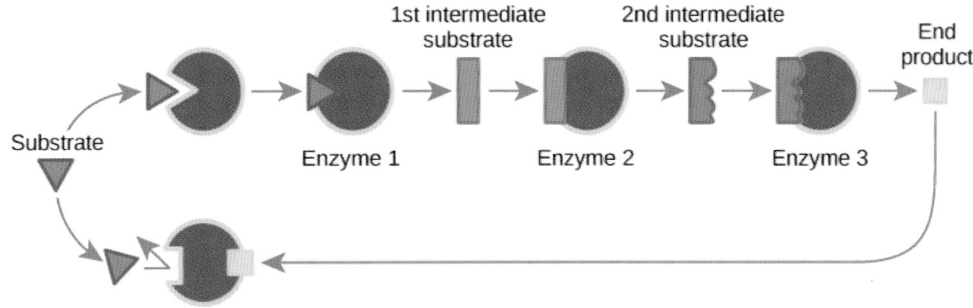

Figure 6.21 Metabolic pathways are a series of reactions catalyzed by multiple enzymes. Feedback inhibition, where the end product of the pathway inhibits an upstream step, is an important regulatory mechanism in cells.

The production of both amino acids and nucleotides is controlled through feedback inhibition. Additionally, ATP is an allosteric regulator of some of the enzymes involved in the catabolic breakdown of sugar, the process that produces ATP. In this way, when ATP is abundant, the cell can prevent its further production. Remember that ATP is an unstable molecule that can spontaneously dissociate into ADP. If too much ATP were present in a cell, much of it would go to waste. On the other hand, ADP serves as a positive allosteric regulator (an allosteric activator) for some of the same enzymes that are inhibited by ATP. Thus, when relative levels of ADP are high compared to ATP, the cell is triggered to produce more ATP through the catabolism of sugar.

Section Summary

Enzymes are chemical catalysts that accelerate chemical reactions at physiological temperatures by lowering their activation energy. Enzymes are usually proteins consisting of one or more polypeptide chains. Enzymes have an active site that provides a unique chemical environment, made up of certain amino acid R groups (residues). This unique environment is perfectly suited to convert particular chemical reactants for that enzyme, called substrates, into unstable intermediates called transition states. Enzymes and substrates are thought to bind with an induced fit, which means that enzymes undergo slight conformational adjustments upon substrate contact, leading to full, optimal binding. Enzymes bind to substrates and catalyze reactions in four different ways: bringing substrates together in an optimal orientation, compromising the bond structures of substrates so that bonds can be more easily broken, providing optimal environmental conditions for a reaction to occur, or participating directly in their chemical reaction by forming transient covalent bonds with the substrates.

Enzyme action must be regulated so that in a given cell at a given time, the desired reactions are being catalyzed and the undesired reactions are not. Enzymes are regulated by cellular conditions, such as temperature and pH. They are also regulated through their location within a cell, sometimes being compartmentalized so that they can only catalyze reactions under certain circumstances. Inhibition and activation of enzymes via other molecules are other important ways that enzymes are regulated. Inhibitors can act competitively, noncompetitively, or allosterically; noncompetitive inhibitors are usually allosteric. Activators can also enhance the function of enzymes allosterically. The most common method by which cells regulate the enzymes in metabolic pathways is through feedback inhibition. During feedback inhibition, the products of a metabolic pathway serve as inhibitors (usually allosteric) of one or more of the enzymes (usually the first committed enzyme of the pathway) involved in the pathway that produces them.

KEY TERMS

activation energy energy necessary for reactions to occur

active site specific region of the enzyme to which the substrate binds

allosteric inhibition inhibition by a binding event at a site different from the active site, which induces a conformational change and reduces the affinity of the enzyme for its substrate

anabolic (also, anabolism) pathways that require an input of energy to synthesize complex molecules from simpler ones

ATP adenosine triphosphate, the cell's energy currency

bioenergetics study of energy flowing through living systems

catabolic (also, catabolism) pathways in which complex molecules are broken down into simpler ones

chemical energy potential energy in chemical bonds that is released when those bonds are broken

coenzyme small organic molecule, such as a vitamin or its derivative, which is required to enhance the activity of an enzyme

cofactor inorganic ion, such as iron and magnesium ions, required for optimal regulation of enzyme activity

competitive inhibition type of inhibition in which the inhibitor competes with the substrate molecule by binding to the active site of the enzyme

denature process that changes the natural properties of a substance

endergonic describes chemical reactions that require energy input

enthalpy total energy of a system

entropy (S) measure of randomness or disorder within a system

exergonic describes chemical reactions that release free energy

feedback inhibition effect of a product of a reaction sequence to decrease its further production by inhibiting the activity of the first enzyme in the pathway that produces it

free energy Gibbs free energy is the usable energy, or energy that is available to do work.

heat energy energy transferred from one system to another that is not work (energy of the motion of molecules or particles)

heat energy total bond energy of reactants or products in a chemical reaction

induced fit dynamic fit between the enzyme and its substrate, in which both components modify their structures to allow for ideal binding

kinetic energy type of energy associated with objects or particles in motion

metabolism all the chemical reactions that take place inside cells, including anabolism and catabolism

phosphoanhydride bond bond that connects phosphates in an ATP molecule

potential energy type of energy that has the potential to do work; stored energy

substrate molecule on which the enzyme acts

thermodynamics study of energy and energy transfer involving physical matter

transition state high-energy, unstable state (an intermediate form between the substrate and the product) occurring during a chemical reaction

CHAPTER SUMMARY

6.1 Energy and Metabolism

Cells perform the functions of life through various chemical reactions. A cell's metabolism refers to the chemical reactions that take place within it. There are metabolic reactions that involve the breaking down of complex chemicals into simpler ones, such as the breakdown of large macromolecules. This process is referred to as catabolism, and such reactions are associated with a release of energy. On the other end of the spectrum, anabolism refers to metabolic processes that build complex molecules out of simpler ones, such as the synthesis of macromolecules. Anabolic processes require energy. Glucose synthesis and glucose breakdown are examples of anabolic and catabolic pathways, respectively.

6.2 Potential, Kinetic, Free, and Activation Energy

Energy comes in many different forms. Objects in motion do physical work, and kinetic energy is the energy of objects in motion. Objects that are not in motion may have the potential to do work, and thus, have potential energy. Molecules also have potential energy because the breaking of molecular bonds has the potential to release energy. Living cells depend on the harvesting of potential energy from molecular bonds to perform work. Free energy is a measure of energy that is available to do work. The free energy of a system changes during energy transfers such as chemical reactions, and this change is referred to as ΔG.

The ΔG of a reaction can be negative or positive, meaning that the reaction releases energy or consumes energy, respectively. A reaction with a negative ΔG that gives off energy is called an exergonic reaction. One with a positive ΔG that requires energy input is called an endergonic reaction. Exergonic reactions are said to be spontaneous, because their products have less energy than their reactants. The products of endergonic reactions have a higher energy state than the reactants, and so these are nonspontaneous reactions. However, all reactions (including spontaneous $-\Delta G$ reactions) require an initial input of energy in order to reach the transition state, at which they'll proceed. This initial input of energy is called the activation energy.

6.3 The Laws of Thermodynamics

In studying energy, scientists use the term "system" to refer to the matter and its environment involved in energy transfers. Everything outside of the system is called the surroundings. Single cells are biological systems. Systems can be thought of as having a certain amount of order. It takes energy to make a system more ordered. The more ordered a system is, the lower its entropy. Entropy is a measure of the disorder of a system. As a system becomes more disordered, the lower its energy and the higher its entropy become.

A series of laws, called the laws of thermodynamics, describe the properties and processes of energy transfer. The first law states that the total amount of energy in the universe is constant. This means that energy can't be created or destroyed, only transferred or transformed. The second law of thermodynamics states that every energy transfer involves some loss of energy in an unusable form, such as heat energy, resulting in a more disordered system. In other words, no energy transfer is completely efficient and tends toward disorder.

6.4 ATP: Adenosine Triphosphate

ATP is the primary energy-supplying molecule for living cells. ATP is made up of a nucleotide, a five-carbon sugar, and three phosphate groups. The bonds that connect the phosphates (phosphoanhydride bonds) have high-energy content. The energy released from the hydrolysis of ATP into ADP + P_i is used to perform cellular work. Cells use ATP to perform work by coupling the exergonic reaction of ATP hydrolysis with endergonic reactions. ATP donates its phosphate group to another molecule via a process known as phosphorylation. The phosphorylated molecule is at a higher-energy state and is less stable than its unphosphorylated form, and this added energy from the addition of the phosphate allows the molecule to undergo its endergonic reaction.

6.5 Enzymes

Enzymes are chemical catalysts that accelerate chemical reactions at physiological temperatures by lowering their activation energy. Enzymes are usually proteins consisting of one or more polypeptide chains. Enzymes have an active site that provides a unique chemical environment, made up of certain amino acid R groups (residues). This unique environment is perfectly suited to convert particular chemical reactants for that enzyme, called substrates, into unstable intermediates called transition states. Enzymes and substrates are thought to bind with an induced fit, which means that enzymes undergo slight conformational adjustments upon substrate contact, leading to full, optimal binding. Enzymes bind to substrates and catalyze reactions in four different ways: bringing substrates together in an optimal orientation, compromising the bond structures of substrates so that bonds can be more easily broken, providing optimal environmental conditions for a reaction to occur, or participating directly in their chemical reaction by forming transient covalent bonds with the substrates.

Enzyme action must be regulated so that in a given cell at a given time, the desired reactions are being catalyzed and the undesired reactions are not. Enzymes are regulated by cellular conditions, such as temperature and pH. They are also regulated through their location within a cell, sometimes being compartmentalized so that they can only catalyze reactions under certain circumstances. Inhibition and activation of enzymes via other molecules are other important ways that enzymes are regulated. Inhibitors can act competitively, noncompetitively, or allosterically; noncompetitive inhibitors are usually allosteric. Activators can also enhance the function of enzymes allosterically. The most common method by which cells regulate the enzymes in metabolic pathways is through feedback inhibition. During feedback inhibition, the products of a metabolic pathway serve as inhibitors (usually allosteric) of one or more of the enzymes (usually the first committed enzyme of the pathway) involved in the pathway that produces them.

REVIEW QUESTIONS

1. Energy can be taken in as glucose, then has to be converted to a form that can be easily used to perform work in cells. What is the name of the latter molecule?

a. anabolic molecules
b. cholesterol
c. electrolytes
d. adenosine triphosphate

2. When cellular respiration occurs, what is the primary molecule used to store the energy that is released?

a. AMP
b. ATP
c. mRNA
d. phosphate

3. DNA replication involves unwinding two strands of parent DNA, copying each strand to synthesize complementary strands and releasing the resulting two semi-conserved strands of DNA. Which of the following accurately describes this process?

a. This is an anabolic process.
b. This is a catabolic process.
c. This is both an anabolic and a catabolic process.
d. This is a metabolic process, but is neither anabolic nor catabolic.

4. Which of the following is a catabolic process?

a. digestion of sucrose
b. dissolving sugar in water
c. DNA replication
d. RNA translation

5. What food molecule used by animals for energy and obtained from plants is most directly related to the use of sun energy?

a. glucose
b. protein
c. triglycerides
d. tRNA

6. What reaction will release the largest amount of energy to help power another reaction?

a. AMP to ATP
b. ATP to ADP
c. DNA to proteins
d. glucose to starch

7. Consider a pendulum swinging. Which type(s) of energy is/are associated with the pendulum in the following instances:

1. the moment at which it completes one cycle, just before it begins to fall back towards the other end
2. the moment that it is in the middle between the two ends
3. just before it reaches the end of one cycle (before step 1)

a. 1. potential and kinetic
   2. potential and kinetic
   3. kinetic
b. 1. potential
   2. potential and kinetic
   3. potential and kinetic
c. 1. potential
   2. kinetic
   3. potential and kinetic
d. 1. potential and kinetic
   2. kinetic
   3. kinetic

8. Which of the following best describes energy?

a. the transfer of genetic information
b. the ability to assemble a large number of functional catalysts
c. the ability to store solar output
d. the ability to do work

9. What is the ultimate source of energy on this planet?

a. glucose
b. plants
c. metabolic pathways
d. the sun

10. Which of the following molecules is likely to have the most potential energy?

a. ATP
b. ADP
c. glucose
d. sucrose

11. Which of the following is the best way to judge the relative activation energies between two given chemical reactions?

a. Compare the ΔG values between the two reactions.
b. Compare their reaction rates.
c. Compare their ideal environmental conditions.
d. Compare the spontaneity between the two reactions.

12. Which of the terms in the Gibbs free energy equation denotes enthalpy?

a. ΔG
b. ΔH
c. ΔS
d. ΔT

13. Which chemical reaction is more likely to occur?

a. dehydration synthesis
b. endergonic
c. endothermic
d. exergonic

14. Which of the following comparisons or contrasts between endergonic and exergonic reactions is false?

a. Both endergonic and exergonic reactions require a small amount of energy to overcome an activation barrier.
b. Endergonic reactions have a positive ΔG and exergonic reactions have a negative ΔG.
c. Endergonic reactions consume energy and exergonic reactions release energy.
d. Endergonic reactions take place slowly and exergonic reactions take place quickly.

15. Label each of the following systems as high or low entropy:

1. perfume the instant after it is sprayed into the air
2. an unmaintained 1950s car compared with a brand new car
3. a living cell compared with a dead cell

a. 1. low
   2. high
   3. low
b. 1. low
   2. high
   3. high
c. 1. high
   2. low
   3. high
d. 1. high
   2. low
   3. low

16. What counteracts entropy?

a. energy release
b. endergonic reactions
c. input of energy
d. time

17. Which of the following is the best example of the first law of thermodynamics?

a. a body getting warmer after exercise
b. a piece of fruit spoiling in the fridge
c. a power plant burning coal and producing electricity
d. an exothermic chemical reaction

18. What is the difference between the first and second laws of thermodynamics?

a. The first law involves creating energy while the second law involves expending it.

b. The first law involves expending energy while the second involves creating it.

c. The first law involves conserving energy while the second law involves the inability to recapture energy.

d. The first law discusses creating energy while the second law discusses the energy requirement for reactions.

19. Which best describes the effect of inputting energy into a living system?

a. It decreases entropy within the system.

b. It fuels catabolic reactions.

c. It causes enthalpy.

d. The energy is used to produce carbohydrates.

20. Why is ATP considered the energy currency of the cell?

a. It accepts energy from chemical reactions.

b. It holds energy at the site of release from substrates.

c. It is a protein.

d. It can transport energy to locations within the cell.

21. What is ATP made from?

a. adenosine + high energy electrons

b. ADP + pyrophosphate

c. AMP + ADP

d. the conversion of guanine to adenosine

22. What is true about the energy released by the hydrolosis of ATP?

a. It is equal to $-57\,\text{kJ/mol}$.

b. The cell harnesses it as heat energy in order to perform work.

c. It is primarily stored between the alpha and beta phosphates.

d. It provides energy to coupled reactions.

23. What part of ATP is broken to release energy for use in chemical reactions?

a. the adenosine molecule

b. the bond between the first and second phosphates

c. the bond between the first phosphate and the adenosine molecule

d. the bond between the second and third phosphates

24. An allosteric inhibitor does which of the following?

a. binds to an enzyme away from the active site and changes the conformation of the active site, increasing its affinity for substrate binding

b. binds to an active site and blocks it from binding substrate

c. binds to an enzyme away from the active site and changes the conformation of the active site, decreasing its affinity for the substrate

d. binds directly to the active site and mimics the substrate

25. What happens if an enzyme is not functioning in a chemical reaction in a living organism that needs it?

a. The reaction stops.

b. The reaction proceeds, but much more slowly.

c. The reaction proceeds faster without the interference.

d. There is no change in the reaction rate.

26. Which of the following is not true about enzymes?

a. They increase the ΔG of reactions.

b. They are usually made of amino acids.

c. They lower the activation energy of chemical reactions.

d. Each one is specific to the particular substrate, or substrates, to which it binds.

27. Which of the following analogies best describe the induced-fit model of enzyme-substrate binding?

a. a hug between two people

b. a key fitting into a lock

c. a square peg fitting through the square hole and a round peg fitting through the round hole of a children's toy

d. the fitting together of two jigsaw puzzle pieces

28. What is the function of enzymes?

a. to increase the ΔG of reactions

b. to increase the ΔH of reactions

c. to lower the entropy of the chemicals in the reaction

d. to lower the activation energy of a reaction

CRITICAL THINKING QUESTIONS

29. Describe the connection between anabolic and catabolic chemical reactions in a metabolic pathway.

a. Catabolic reactions produce energy and simpler compounds, whereas anabolic reactions involve the use of energy to make more complex compounds.

b. Catabolic reactions produce energy and complex compounds are formed, whereas in anabolic reactions free energy is utilized by complex compounds to make simpler molecules.

c. Catabolic reactions utilize energy and gives simpler compounds, whereas in anabolic reactions reactions, energy is produced and simpler compounds are used to make complex molecules.

d. Catabolic reactions produce energy and water molecules, whereas in anabolic reactions this free energy is utilized by simpler compounds to make only proteins and nucleic acids.

30. Does physical exercise involve anabolic processes, catabolic processes, or both? Give evidence for your answer.

a. Physical exercise involves both catabolic and anabolic processes. Glucose is broken down into simpler compounds during physical activity. The simpler compounds are then used to provide energy to the muscles for contraction by the anabolic pathway.

b. Physical exercise is just a catabolic process. Glucose is broken down into simpler compounds during physical activity and the simpler compounds are then used to provide energy to the muscles for contraction.

c. Physical activity involves only anabolic processes. Glucose is broken down into simpler compounds during physical activity and the simpler compounds are then used to provide energy to the muscles for contraction by anabolic pathways.

d. Physical exercise involves both anabolic and catabolic processes. Cellulose is broken down into simpler compounds during physical activity. The simpler compounds are then used to provide energy to the muscles for contraction by anabolic pathways.

31. How do chemical reactions play a role in energy transfer?

a. Energy from the breakdown of glucose and other molecules in animals is released as ATP, which transfer energy to other reactions.

b. Energy from the breakdown of glucose and other molecules in animals is released in the form of NADP, which transfers energy to other reactions.

c. Energy is released in the form of glucose from the breakdown of ATP molecules. These ATP molecules transfer energy from one reaction to other.

d. Energy is released in the form of water from the breakdown of glucose. These molecules transfer energy from one reaction to other.

32. Name two different cellular functions that require energy.

a. Phagocytosis helps amoebae take up nutrients and pseudopodia help the amoebae move.

b. Phagocytosis allows amoebae to move and pseudopodia help in the uptake of nutrients.

c. Phagocytosis helps amoebae to take up nutrients and cilia help amoebae move.

d. Phagocytosis helps amoebae in cell division and pseudopodia help amoebae move.

33. Explain the conversion of energy that takes place when the sluice of a dam is opened.

a. Potential energy stored in the water held by the dam will convert to kinetic energy when it falls through the opening of the sluice.

b. Kinetic energy stored in the water held by the dam will convert to potential energy when it falls through the opening of the sluice.

c. Potential energy stored in the water held by the dam will convert to electrical energy, when it falls through the opening of the sluice.

d. Hydrothermal energy stored in the water held by the dam will convert to kinetic energy, when it falls through the opening of the sluice.

34. Explain in your own words the difference between a spontaneous reaction and one that occurs instantaneously.

a. A spontaneous reaction is one which releases free energy and moves to a more stable state. Instantaneous reactions occur rapidly with sudden release of energy.
b. A spontaneous reaction is one which utilizes free energy and moves to a more stable state. Instantaneous reactions occur rapidly with sudden release of energy.
c. A spontaneous reaction is one which releases free energy and moves to a more stable state. Instantaneous reactions occur rapidly within a system by uptake of energy.
d. A spontaneous reaction is one in which the reaction occurs rapidly with sudden release of energy. Instantaneous reaction releases free energy and moves to a more stable state.

35. Describe the position of the transition state on a vertical energy scale, from low to high, relative to the position of the reactants and products, for both endergonic and exergonic reactions.

a. The transition state of the reaction exists at a lower energy level than the reactants. Activation energy is always positive regardless of whether the reaction is exergonic or endergonic.
b. The transition state of the reaction exists at a higher energy level than the reactants. Activation energy is always positive regardless of whether the reaction is exergonic or endergonic.
c. The transition state of the reaction exists at a lower energy level than the reactants. Activation energy is always negative regardless of whether the reaction is exergonic or endergonic.
d. The transition state of the reaction exists at an intermediate energy level than that of the reactants. Activation energy is always positive regardless of whether the reaction is exergonic or endergonic.

36. Imagine an elaborate ant farm with tunnels and passageways through the sand where ants live in a large community. Now imagine that an earthquake shook the ground and demolished the ant farm. In which of these two scenarios, before or after the earthquake, was the ant farm system in a state of higher or lower entropy? Why?

a. The ant farm is in the state of high entropy after the earthquake and energy must be spent to bring the system to low entropy.
b. The ant farm is in the state of lower entropy after the earthquake and energy must be spent to bring the system to high entropy.
c. The ant farm is in the state of higher entropy before the earthquake and energy is given out of the system after the earthquake.
d. The ant farm is in the state of lower entropy before the earthquake and energy is given out of the system after the earthquake.

37. Energy transfers take place constantly in every day activities. Think of two scenarios: cooking on a stove and driving. Explain how the second law of thermodynamics applies to these scenarios.

a. Heat is lost into the room while cooking and into the metal of the engine during gasoline combustion.
b. Heat gained while cooking helps to make the food and heat released due to gasoline combustion helps the car accelerate.
c. The energy given to the system remains constant during cooking and more energy is added to the car engine when the gasoline combusts.
d. The energy given to the system for cooking helps to make food and energy in the car engine remains conserved when gasoline combustion takes place.

38. What does it mean for a system to be in a higher level of entropy? How can it be reduced?

a. Higher level of entropy refers to higher state of disorder in the system and it can be reduced by input of energy to lower the entropy.
b. Higher level of entropy refers to higher state of symmetry in the system and it can be reduced by release of energy to lower the entropy.
c. Higher level of entropy refers to low disorder in the system and it can be reduced by input of energy to increase the entropy.
d. Higher level of entropy refers to higher state of disorder in the system and it can be reduced by providing a catalyst to lower the entropy.

39. When the air temperature drops and rain turns to snow, which law of thermodynamics is exhibited?

a. first law of thermodynamics
b. second law of thermodynamics
c. third law of thermodynamics
d. zeroth law of thermodynamics

40. How does ATP supply energy to chemical reactions?

a. ATP dissociates and the energy released by breaking of a phosphate bond within ATP is used for phosphorylation of another molecule. ATP hydrolysis also provides energy to power coupling reactions.

b. ATP utilizes energy to power exergonic reactions by hydrolysis of ATP molecule. The free energy released as a result of ATP breakdown is used to carry out metabolism of products.

c. ATP utilizes energy to power endergonic reactions by dehydration of ATP molecule. The free energy released as a result of ATP breakdown is used to carry out metabolism of products.

d. ATP utilizes the energy released from the coupling reactions and that energy is used to power the endergonic and exergonic reactions.

41. Is the E_A for ATP hydrolysis relatively low or high? Explain your reasoning.

a. E_A for ATP hydrolysis is high because considerable energy is released.

b. E_A for ATP hydrolysis is low because considerable energy is released.

c. E_A for ATP hydrolysis is intermediate because considerable energy is released.

d. E_A for ATP hydrolysis is high because a low amount of energy is released.

42. What is phosphorylation as it occurs in chemical reactions?

a. Phosphorylation refers to the attachment of a phosphate to another molecule to facilitate a chemical reaction.

b. Phosphorylation is the uptake of a phosphorous molecule by an ATP molecule to power chemical reactions.

c. Phosphorylation is the release of a third phosphorous molecule of ATP during hydrolysis.

d. Phosphorylation is the breakdown of a pyrophosphate molecule which gives phosphate ions.

43. If a chemical reaction could occur without an enzyme, why is it important to have one?

a. Enzymes are important because they give the desired products only from the reaction.

b. Enzymes are important because the products are obtained consistently with time.

c. Enzymes are important because it does not disturb the concentration of the products.

d. Enzymes are important because energy remains conserved and no loss of energy occurs.

44. How does enzyme feedback inhibition benefit a cell?

a. Feedback inhibition benefits the cell by blocking the production of the products by changing the configuration of enzymes. This will prevent the cells from becoming toxic.

b. Feedback inhibition benefits the cell by blocking the production of the reactants by changing the configuration of enzymes. This will prevent the cells from becoming toxic.

c. Feedback inhibition benefits the cell by blocking the production of the products by changing the configuration of reactants. This will prevent the cells from becoming toxic.

d. Feedback inhibition benefits the cell by blocking the production of the products by reducing the reactants. This will prevent the cells from becoming toxic.

45. What type of reaction allows chemicals to be available for an organism's growth and maintenance in a timely manner?

a. enzymatically facilitated reactions

b. redox reactions

c. catabolic reactions

d. hydrolysis of ATP

TEST PREP FOR AP® COURSES

46. Cell metabolism is a complex process that uses many types of chemicals in a variety of processes. Which of the following statements is true?

a. A loss of free nucleotides would result in cancer.

b. A loss of assorted carbohydrates would result in mitosis.

c. A loss of triglycerides would result in cell death.

d. A loss of enzymes would result in cell death.

47. Which pair of descriptors of chemical reactions go

together?

a. anabolic and exergonic
b. exergonic and dehydration synthesis
c. endergonic and catabolic
d. hydrolysis and exergonic

48. What is the underlying principle that supports the idea that all living organisms share the same core processes and features?

a. All organisms must harvest energy from their environment and convert it to ATP to carry out cellular functions.
b. Plants produce their own energy and pass it on to animals.
c. Herbivores, carnivores, and omnivores coexist for the survival of all.
d. Glucose is the primary source of energy for all cellular functions.

49. It has been accepted that life on the Earth started out as single celled, simple organisms, which then evolved into complex organisms. How did evolution proceed to produce such a wide variety of living organisms from a simple ancestor?

a. Prokaryotes produced the fungi, then the protists which then branches to plants and animals.
b. Protists evolved first, then the prokaryotes, which branched into the fungi, plants, and animals
c. Prokaryotes produced the protists, which branched into the fungi, plants, and animals.
d. Prokaryotes produced the protists, then the fungi, which branched into the plants and animals.

50. Plants make glucose through a pathway called photosynthesis. The amount of energy captured from light can be expressed as the number of energy containing molecules used to make one molecule of glucose. Which of the following best states the number of each molecule needed?

a. 54 molecules of ATP and 18 molecules of nicotinamide adenine dinucleotide phosphate (NADPH)
b. 18 molecules of ATP and 12 molecules of NADPH
c. 24 molecules of ATP and 18 molecules of NADPH
d. 12 molecules of ATP and 18 molecules of NADPH

51. What is an anabolic pathway? Which of these is an example of an anabolic pathway used by cells in their metabolism?

a. Anabolic pathways involve the breakdown of nutrient molecules into usable forms. An example is the harvesting of amino acids from dietary proteins.
b. Anabolic pathways involve the breakdown of nutrient molecules into useable forms. An example is the use of glycogen by the liver to maintain blood glucose levels.
c. Anabolic pathways build new molecules out of the products of catabolic pathways. An example is the separation of fatty acids from triglycerides to satisfy energy needs.
d. Anabolic pathways build new molecules out of the products of catabolic pathways. An example is the linkage of nucleotides to form a molecule of mRNA.

52. If glucose is broken down through aerobic respiration, a number of ATP can be made from the energy extracted. How many ATP are possible?

a. 2 to 4
b. 36 to 38
c. 10 to 12
d. 24 to 30

53. Plants must have adequate resources to complete their functions. If they do not have what they need, there are changes in the organism's metabolism. What happens to the metabolism of a plant that does not have adequate sunlight?

a. Photosynthesis slows and less glucose is produced for energy use.
b. The plant switches to anaerobic metabolism.
c. The plant goes into a dormant state until the sunlight returns.
d. The plant flowers quickly to reproduce while it can.

54. Water deficiency is arguably the easiest deficiency to detect in plants. This is because plants that are lacking water will wilt, as water within the plant's cells helps to supports the plant's weight. Plant cells become water deficient because their cells use the water for metabolic processes. What happens to the metabolism of a plant that does not have adequate water?

a. Photosynthesis is inhibited, less glucose is produced, and water used by the cells is not replaced.
b. The plant increases its breakdown of glucose to create more water at the end of the process.
c. The plant will stop photosynthesizing for long periods of time until it has enough water to do so.
d. The cell will bring in more CO_2, to compensate for the lack of water, allowing glucose synthesis to continue.

55. Enzymes facilitate chemical reactions that result in changes to a substrate. How does the induced fit model of enzymes and substrates explain their function?

a. Both enzyme and substrate undergo dynamic changes, inducing the transitions state of the substrate.
b. The enzyme induces a change in the substrate, but is not changed itself during the reaction.
c. The substrates attach to the enzyme and the chemical reaction proceeds.
d. The enzyme changes shape to fit the substrate causing the transition state to occur.

56. Enzyme inhibitors play an important part in the control of enzyme functions, allowing them to continue, or inhibiting them for a period of time. Which inhibitor affects the initial rate but do not affect the maximal rate?

a. allosteric
b. competitive
c. non-competitive
d. uncompetitive

SCIENCE PRACTICE CHALLENGE QUESTIONS

57. Activation energy is required for a reaction to proceed, and it is lower if the reaction is catalyzed. Sucrose (table sugar) is a disaccharide. When we eat sucrose it is converted to carbon dioxide and water, as with other carbohydrates.

1. **Identify** if the breakdown of sucrose is endergonic or exergonic. **Explain** the reasoning for your identification.
2. Based on your identification, **explain** if cubes of sugar can be stored in a sugar bowl by creating a diagram similar to Figure 6.10.
3. If table sugar is placed in a spoon held over a high flame, the sugar is charred and becomes a blackened mixture composed primarily of carbon. **Create a visual representation** that includes a chemical equation to **explain** the role of the flame in this process.
4. In terms of your answers to questions 1-3, **predict** if sugar cubes in a bowl placed in a dish of water can be stored on a table, and **justify** your prediction.
5. **[Extension]** The energy of activation of a chemical reaction can be determined by measurement of the effect of temperature on reaction rate. The natural logarithm of the reaction rate constant is a linear function of the inverse of the temperature in Kelvin degrees. The negative of the slope of that graph is the energy of activation divided by the universal ideal gas constant, R = 8.314 J/Kmol. Using the following data (R. Wolfenden and Yang Yean, *Journal of the American Chemical Society*, 2008 Jun 18; 130(24): 7,548–7,549) evaluate the energy of activation of the following reaction.

$$\text{sucrose} \rightarrow \text{fructose} + \text{glucose}$$

Temperature (K)	ln(rate)
440	-3.8
423	-4.5
403	-5
388	-6

Table 6.1

(a) **Construct a graph** of ln(rate) versus 1/T(K) and determine the energy of activation for the uncatalyzed reaction.

(b) Based on the data, **explain** the importance of enzymes for time scales characteristic of living systems on Earth—that is to say, life as we know it.

The time scale required for half of the molecules of initial sucrose to remain can be estimated. The relationship between the half-life and the activation energy is:

$$t_{1/2} = 0.69 \times 10^{E_A / 2.3RT}$$

At a temperature of 300K, approximately room temperature, RT is equal to 2,494 J/mole.

58. Physical exercise involves both anabolic and catabolic processes. For each process, **explain** an expected outcome and **describe** an example of a specific exercise that can lead to the expected outcome.

59. Explanations in science are often constructed by analogy. Explanations of the behavior of a poorly understood phenomenon can often be constructed by analogy to a phenomenon that is well understood. For each of the following cellular functions that require free energy, **describe** a parallel human activity and **identify** a source of free energy for that activity. For example, the synthesis of proteins can be expected to proceed as an assembly of a small set of sub-components, just as the construction of a building is accomplished by gathering and joining materials. It is consistent with our analogy to expect that there must be a free-energy resource that is consumed in the synthesis of proteins, just as hydrocarbon fuels are a source of energy for the construction of a building.

60. Look at each of the processes shown in Figure 6.8 that show examples of endergonic and exergonic processes.

1. For each process, **identify** if it is endergonic or exergonic, and **provide reasoning** for your identification that includes your definition of the system.
2. For each process, does entropy increase or decrease? **Explain** your reasoning in terms of changes in the amount of order within the system.
3. For each process, is there an input of energy? **Explain** your reasoning in terms of (a) the source of the energy input into the system and (b) the interaction between the system and its environment that provides that input of energy.

61. Energy transfers occur constantly in daily activities. Think of two scenarios: cooking on a stove and driving a car. For each scenario, **describe** the system and **explain** how the second law of thermodynamics applies to the system in terms of energy input and change in entropy.

62. Consider a simple process that illustrates the change in entropy when energy is transferred.

1. Take a block of ice as a system with a temperature of 0°C. This is water as a solid, so it has a high structural order. This means that the molecules are in a fixed position. As a result, the entropy of the system is low.
2. Allow the ice to melt at room temperature. **Describe** changes in the motion and interactions of water molecules before and after melting. **Explain** where the energy came from whose transfer produced melting. **Predict** the effect of the energy transfer on the entropy on the system, and **justify** your prediction.
3. Heat the water until the temperature reaches boiling point. **Explain** what happens to the entropy of the system when the water is heated.
4. Continue to heat the water at the constant temperature of the boiling point. **Describe** changes in the motion and interactions of water molecules before and after boiling. **Predict** the effect of the energy transfer on the entropy of the system, and **justify** your prediction.
5. **[Extension/Connection]** Molecules of water have simple responses to heating: The molecules move faster and interact less strongly with other neighboring molecules. Consider the primary producers of an aquatic ecosystem in summer. **Describe** the source of energy transfer to the system of photosynthetic plants and algae. **Predict** changes in the system in response. **Explain** what happens to the entropy of this trophic level when energy transfer occurs. Now consider the primary producers and their aqueous environment as the system. **Explain** what happens to the entropy of this system composed of photosynthetic organisms and their abiotic environment.
6. **Predict** the change in entropy of the system when both autotrophs and their abiotic environment are considered. **Justify** your prediction. **Predict** the signs of the entropy changes in both biotic and abiotic components of this system. **Predict** the relative magnitudes of these entropy changes, and justify your prediction.

63. The sodium-potassium pump is an example of free-energy coupling. The free energy derived from exergonic ATP hydrolysis is used to pump sodium and potassium ions across the cell membrane. The hydrolysis of one ATP molecule releases 7.3 kcal/mol of free energy ($\Delta G = -7.3$ kcal/mol). If it takes 2.1 kcal/mol of free energy to move one Na^+ across the membrane ($\Delta G = +2.1$ kcal/mol), how many sodium ions could be moved by the hydrolysis of one ATP molecule? **Show your calculations to provide reasoning for your answer.**

64. Is the E_A for ATP hydrolysis in cells likely relatively low or high compared to the E_A for the combustion of gasoline in an internal combustion engine?

1. **Explain** your reasoning in terms of the relative stabilities of ATP and gasoline compared to air in which no catalysts are present.
2. **Describe** how the role of the enzyme ATPase in the hydrolysis of ATP in a cell differs from a spark in the cylinder of an internal combustion engine.
3. **Describe** a strategy for collecting data that can be used to measure the energies of activation (E_A) of each of these two processes with instruments that can measure concentrations of reactions produced in each system.

65. Vitamin B_{12} is a co-enzyme involved in a wide variety of cellular processes. Synthesis of vitamin B_{12} occurs only in bacteria; in animals, these bacteria populate anaerobic environments in the gut. Consequently, vegan diets in developing nations and diets common to developing nations provide no source of B_{12}. Researchers (Ghosh et al. http://dx.doi.org/10.3389/fnut.2016.00001]) found that rats whose diets contained limited (L) and no (N) B_{12} displayed symptoms that were not observed in the control group (C) whose diet included B_{12} and was otherwise identical. Chemical analysis of adipocytokines in the plasma after feeding periods of 4 and 12 weeks are shown in the following table.

Adi-pocytokines Tissue of origin	Feeding duration (weeks)	C	L	N
Leptin (pg/L)	4	5.7± 0.21	5.8± 0.25	6.1± 0.25
Adipose	12	5.8± 0.39	6.5± 0.36	9.9± 0.68
MCP-1 (mg/L)	4	43.0± 1.18	44.4± 1.95	46.9± 2.08
Mono-cytes	12	43.2± 2.47	45.3± 3.02	49.5± 1.27
IL-6 (mg/L)	4	150± 3.2	154± 4.5	184± 8.0
Mono-cytes	12	151± 6.7	176± 11.0	185± 8.2

Table 6.2

The sample size for these data are small: n = 6, within each group. Also shown in the table are cells in which these cytokine messages originate. Adipose cells store fats. Monocytes are white blood cells of the immune system. Over the 12 weeks of feeding, the weights of all three groups were equivalent, while the percent of body fat increased relative to the control for the rats fed a diet of limited and no B_{12}: 40% (N) and 20% (L), respectively.

a. **Identify** which adipocytokines show significant increases, relative to the control group, after only 4 weeks of treatment. **Justify** your identification.

b. **Identify** which adipocytokines show only significant increases, relative to the control group, after 12 weeks of treatment. **Justify** your identification.

c. **Identify** which adipocytokines show significant increases, relative to the control group, after 4 weeks of treatment but no further increase after 12 weeks. **Justify** your identification.

Adipocytokines are chemical messengers that regulate metabolism and blood vessel production and dilation. High concentrations of adipocytokines are commonly found among individuals with abnormal autoimmune response. Monocyte chemoattractant protein 1 (MCP-1) is involved in the trafficking or guiding of monocytes to damaged tissue, as in a wound. In mice, leptin receptors of cells in the hypothalamus suppress hunger. Interleukin (IL-6) is released to initiate and then regulate inflammation in response to an infection. The mice in this study were not infected or wounded.

d. **Construct an explanation**, with reasoning based on the evidence provided by these data, for the observed variations in adipocytokines.

Many noncommunicable diseases are associated with abnormal autoimmune responses, and the number of diseases that involve abnormal autoimmune response is increasing. Many autoimmune diseases, such as diabetes and heart disease, occur in developed nations at a much higher frequency than in developing nations.

e. **Evaluate**, based on these data concerning the effect of restrictions on the availability of B_{12}, the following question: Does the increased lack of exposure to pathogens in developed nations lead to reduced or abnormal immune response?

66. Using an example, **explain** how enzyme feedback inhibition regulation regulates a cellular process.

7 | CELLULAR RESPIRATION

Figure 7.1 This geothermal energy plant transforms thermal energy from deep in the ground into electrical energy, which can be easily used. (credit: modification of work by the U.S. Department of Defense)

Chapter Outline

Introduction

The electrical energy plant in Figure 7.1 converts energy from one form to another form that can be more easily used. This type of generating plant starts with underground thermal energy (heat) and transforms it into electrical energy that will be transported to homes and factories. Like a generating plant, plants and animals also must take in energy from the environment and convert it into a form that their cells can use. Energy enters an organism's body in one form and is converted into another form that can fuel the organism's life functions. In the process of photosynthesis, plants and other photosynthetic producers take in energy in the form of light (solar energy) and convert it into chemical energy, glucose, which stores this energy in its chemical bonds. Then, a series of metabolic pathways, collectively called cellular respiration, extract the energy from the carbon–carbon bonds of glucose and convert it into a form that all living things can use—both producers, such as plants, and consumers, such as animals.

Nearly all organisms perform glycolysis, the first part of both aerobic and anaerobic respiration. One of the key enzymes of glycolysis is pyruvate kinase. Without this enzyme, an organism will die because it is unable to convert nutrients into the energy it needs for survival. Scientists have taken advantage of that fact by blocking pyruvate kinase in some deadly parasites, such as the ones that cause African Sleeping Sickness and Chagas disease. Read more about this research **here (http://openstaxcollege.org/l/32africa)** .

7.1 | Energy in Living Systems

In this section, you will explore the following questions:

- What is the importance of electrons for the transfer of energy in living systems?
- How is ATP used by the cell as an energy source?

Connection for AP® Courses

As we learned in previous chapters, living organisms require free energy to power life processes such as growth, reproduction, movement, and active transport. ATP (adenosine triphosphate) functions as the energy currency for cells. It allows the cells to store energy and transfer it within the cells to provide energy for cellular processes such as growth, movement and active transport. The ATP molecule consists of a ribose sugar and an adenine base with three phosphates attached. In the hydrolysis of ATP, free energy is supplied when a phosphate group or two are detached, and either ADP (adenosine diphosphate) or AMP (adenosine monophosphate) is produced. Energy derived from the metabolism of glucose is used to convert ADP to ATP during cellular respiration. As we explore cellular respiration, we'll learn that the two ways ATP is regenerated by the cell are called substrate-level phosphorylation and oxidative phosphorylation.

Information presented and the examples highlighted in the section support concepts and Learning Objectives outlined in Big Idea 2 and Big Idea 4 of the AP® Biology Curriculum Framework, as shown in the table. The Learning Objectives listed in the Curriculum Framework provide a transparent foundation for the AP® Biology course, an inquiry-based laboratory experience, instructional activities, and AP® exam questions. A Learning Objective merges required content with one or more of the seven Science Practices.

Big Idea 2	Biological systems utilize free energy and molecular building blocks to grow, to reproduce, and to maintain dynamic homeostasis.
Enduring Understanding 2.A	Growth, reproduction and maintenance of living systems require free energy and matter.
Essential Knowledge	**2.A.2** Organisms capture and store free energy for use in biological processes.
Science Practice	**1.4** The student can use representations and models to analyze situations or solve problems qualitatively and quantitatively.
Science Practice	**3.1** The student can pose scientific questions.
Learning Objective	**2.4** The student is able to use representations to pose scientific questions about what mechanisms and structural features allow organisms to capture, store, and use free energy.
Essential Knowledge	**2.A.2** Organisms capture and store free energy for use in biological processes.
Science Practice	**6.2** The student can construct explanations of phenomena based on evidence produced through scientific practices.
Learning Objective	**2.5** The student is able to construct explanations of the mechanisms and structural features of cells that allow organisms to capture, store, or use free energy.

The Science Practice Challenge Questions contain additional test questions for this section that will help you prepare for the AP exam. These questions address the following standards:
[APLO 2.5][APLO 2.16]

Energy production within a cell involves many coordinated chemical pathways. Most of these pathways are combinations of oxidation and reduction reactions. Oxidation and reduction occur in tandem. An oxidation reaction strips an electron from an atom in a compound, and the addition of this electron to another compound is a reduction reaction. Because oxidation and reduction usually occur together, these pairs of reactions are called oxidation reduction reactions, or **redox reactions**.

Electrons and Energy

The removal of an electron from a molecule, oxidizing it, results in a decrease in potential energy in the oxidized compound. The electron (sometimes as part of a hydrogen atom), does not remain unbonded, however, in the cytoplasm of a cell. Rather, the electron is shifted to a second compound, reducing the second compound. The shift of an electron from one compound to another removes some potential energy from the first compound (the oxidized compound) and increases the potential energy of the second compound (the reduced compound). The transfer of electrons between molecules is important because most of the energy stored in atoms and used to fuel cell functions is in the form of high-energy electrons. The transfer of energy in the form of electrons allows the cell to transfer and use energy in an incremental fashion—in small packages rather than in a single, destructive burst. This chapter focuses on the extraction of energy from food; you will see that as you track the path of the transfers, you are tracking the path of electrons moving through metabolic pathways.

Electron Carriers

In living systems, a small class of compounds functions as electron shuttles: They bind and carry high-energy electrons between compounds in pathways. The principal electron carriers we will consider are derived from the B vitamin group and are derivatives of nucleotides. These compounds can be easily reduced (that is, they accept electrons) or oxidized (they lose electrons). Nicotinamide adenine dinucleotide (NAD) (Figure 7.2) is derived from vitamin B3, niacin. NAD^+ is the oxidized form of the molecule; NADH is the reduced form of the molecule after it has accepted two electrons and a proton (which together are the equivalent of a hydrogen atom with an extra electron).

NAD^+ can accept electrons from an organic molecule according to the general equation:

$$\underset{\substack{\text{Reducing}\\\text{agent}}}{\text{RH}} + \underset{\substack{\text{Oxidizing}\\\text{agent}}}{\text{NAD}^+} \rightarrow \underset{\text{Reduced}}{\text{NADH}} + \underset{\text{Oxidized}}{\text{R}}$$

When electrons are added to a compound, they are reduced. A compound that reduces another is called a reducing agent. In the above equation, RH is a reducing agent, and NAD^+ is reduced to NADH. When electrons are removed from compound, it is oxidized. A compound that oxidizes another is called an oxidizing agent. In the above equation, NAD^+ is an oxidizing agent, and RH is oxidized to R.

Similarly, flavin adenine dinucleotide (FAD^+) is derived from vitamin B_2, also called riboflavin. Its reduced form is $FADH_2$. A second variation of NAD, NADP, contains an extra phosphate group. Both NAD^+ and FAD^+ are extensively used in energy extraction from sugars, and NADP plays an important role in anabolic reactions and photosynthesis.

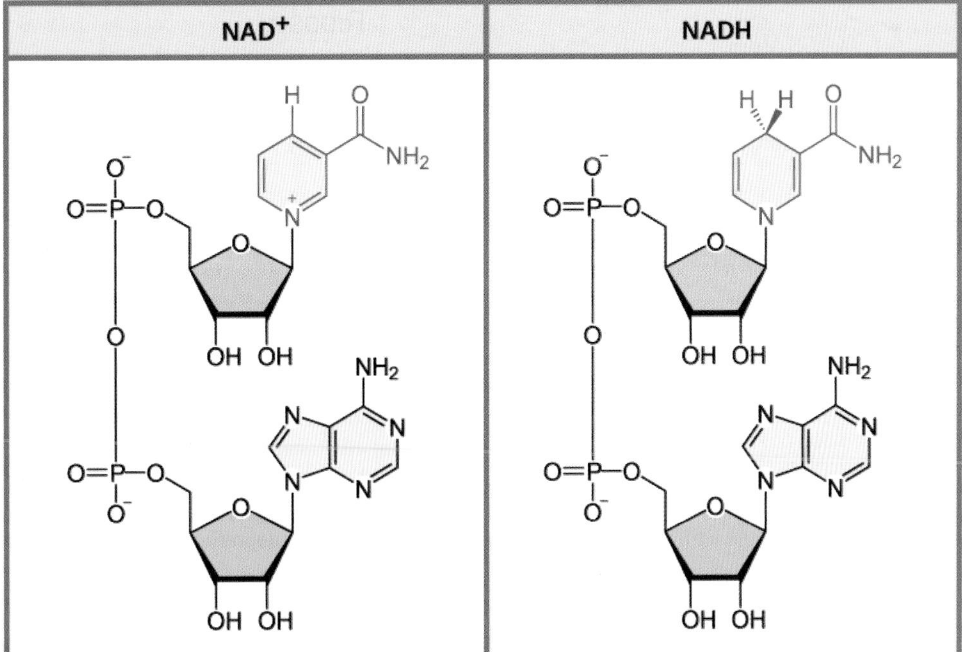

Figure 7.2 The oxidized form of the electron carrier (NAD^+) is shown on the left and the reduced form (NADH) is shown on the right. The nitrogenous base in NADH has one more hydrogen ion and two more electrons than in NAD^+.

ATP in Living Systems

A living cell cannot store significant amounts of free energy. Excess free energy would result in an increase of heat in the cell, which would result in excessive thermal motion that could damage and then destroy the cell. Rather, a cell must be able to handle that energy in a way that enables the cell to store energy safely and release it for use only as needed. Living cells accomplish this by using the compound adenosine triphosphate (ATP). ATP is often called the "energy currency" of the cell, and, like currency, this versatile compound can be used to fill any energy need of the cell. How? It functions similarly to a rechargeable battery.

When ATP is broken down, usually by the removal of its terminal phosphate group, energy is released. The energy is used to do work by the cell, usually by the released phosphate binding to another molecule, activating it. For example, in the mechanical work of muscle contraction, ATP supplies the energy to move the contractile muscle proteins. Recall the active transport work of the sodium-potassium pump in cell membranes. ATP alters the structure of the integral protein that functions as the pump, changing its affinity for sodium and potassium. In this way, the cell performs work, pumping ions against their electrochemical gradients.

ATP Structure and Function

At the heart of ATP is a molecule of adenosine monophosphate (AMP), which is composed of an adenine molecule bonded to a ribose molecule and to a single phosphate group (Figure 7.3). The addition of a second phosphate group to this core molecule results in the formation of adenosine diphosphate (ADP); the addition of a third phosphate group forms adenosine triphosphate (ATP).

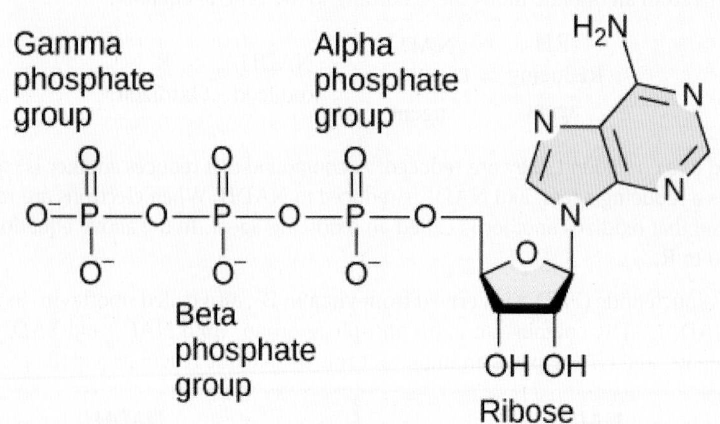

Figure 7.3 ATP (adenosine triphosphate) has three phosphate groups that can be removed by hydrolysis to form ADP (adenosine diphosphate) or AMP (adenosine monophosphate).The negative charges on the phosphate group naturally repel each other, requiring energy to bond them together and releasing energy when these bonds are broken.

The addition of a phosphate group to a molecule requires energy. Phosphate groups are negatively charged and thus repel one another when they are arranged in series, as they are in ADP and ATP. This repulsion makes the ADP and ATP molecules inherently unstable. The release of one or two phosphate groups from ATP, a process called **dephosphorylation**, releases energy.

Energy from ATP

Hydrolysis is the process of breaking complex macromolecules apart. During hydrolysis, water is split, or lysed, and the resulting hydrogen atom (H^+) and a hydroxyl group (OH^-) are added to the larger molecule. The hydrolysis of ATP produces ADP, together with an inorganic phosphate ion (P_i), and the release of free energy. To carry out life processes, ATP is continuously broken down into ADP, and like a rechargeable battery, ADP is continuously regenerated into ATP by the reattachment of a third phosphate group. Water, which was broken down into its hydrogen atom and hydroxyl group during ATP hydrolysis, is regenerated when a third phosphate is added to the ADP molecule, reforming ATP.

Obviously, energy must be infused into the system to regenerate ATP. Where does this energy come from? In nearly every living thing on earth, the energy comes from the metabolism of glucose. In this way, ATP is a direct link between the limited set of exergonic pathways of glucose catabolism and the multitude of endergonic pathways that power living cells.

Phosphorylation

Recall that, in some chemical reactions, enzymes may bind to several substrates that react with each other on the enzyme, forming an intermediate complex. An intermediate complex is a temporary structure, and it allows one of the substrates (such as ATP) and reactants to more readily react with each other; in reactions involving ATP, ATP is one of the substrates and ADP is a product. During an endergonic chemical reaction, ATP forms an intermediate complex with the substrate and enzyme in the reaction. This intermediate complex allows the ATP to transfer its third phosphate group, with its energy, to the substrate, a process called phosphorylation. **Phosphorylation** refers to the addition of the phosphate (~P). This is illustrated by the following generic reaction:

$$\text{A} + \text{enzyme} + \text{ATP} \rightarrow [\text{A} - \text{enzyme} - \sim\text{P}] \rightarrow \text{B} + \text{enzyme} + \text{ADP} + \text{phosphate ion}$$

When the intermediate complex breaks apart, the energy is used to modify the substrate and convert it into a product of the reaction. The ADP molecule and a free phosphate ion are released into the medium and are available for recycling through cell metabolism.

Substrate Phosphorylation

ATP is generated through two mechanisms during the breakdown of glucose. A few ATP molecules are generated (that is, regenerated from ADP) as a direct result of the chemical reactions that occur in the catabolic pathways. A phosphate group is removed from an intermediate reactant in the pathway, and the free energy of the reaction is used to add the third phosphate to an available ADP molecule, producing ATP (Figure 7.4). This very direct method of phosphorylation is called **substrate-level phosphorylation**.

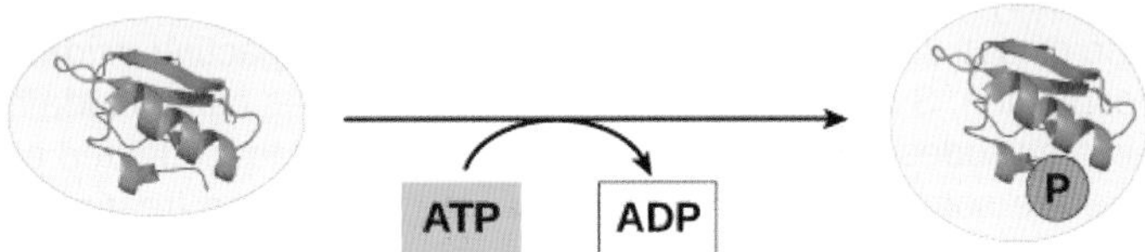

Figure 7.4 In phosphorylation reactions, the gamma phosphate of ATP is attached to a protein.

Oxidative Phosphorylation

Most of the ATP generated during glucose catabolism, however, is derived from a much more complex process, chemiosmosis, which takes place in mitochondria (Figure 7.5) within a eukaryotic cell or the plasma membrane of a prokaryotic cell. **Chemiosmosis**, a process of ATP production in cellular metabolism, is used to generate 90 percent of the ATP made during glucose catabolism and is also the method used in the light reactions of photosynthesis to harness the energy of sunlight. The production of ATP using the process of chemiosmosis is called **oxidative phosphorylation** because of the involvement of oxygen in the process.

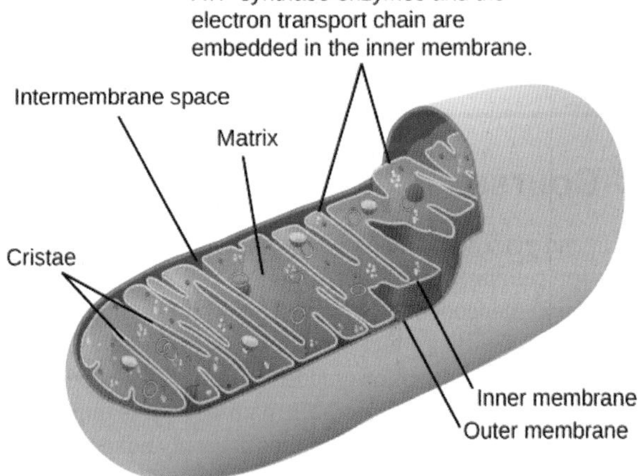

Figure 7.5 In eukaryotes, oxidative phosphorylation takes place in mitochondria. In prokaryotes, this process takes place in the plasma membrane. (Credit: modification of work by Mariana Ruiz Villareal)

science practices CONNECTION for AP® Courses

Think About It

Explain why it is more metabolically efficient for cells to extract energy from ATP rather than from the bonds of carbohydrates directly.

Mitochondrial Disease Physician

What happens when the critical reactions of cellular respiration do not proceed correctly? Mitochondrial diseases are genetic disorders of metabolism. Mitochondrial disorders can arise from mutations in nuclear or mitochondrial DNA, and they result in the production of less energy than is normal in body cells. In type 2 diabetes, for instance, the oxidation efficiency of NADH is reduced, impacting oxidative phosphorylation but not the other steps of respiration. Symptoms of mitochondrial diseases can include muscle weakness, lack of coordination, stroke-like episodes, and loss of vision and hearing. Most affected people are diagnosed in childhood, although there are some adult-onset diseases. Identifying and treating mitochondrial disorders is a specialized medical field. The educational preparation for this profession requires a college education, followed by medical school with a specialization in medical genetics. Medical geneticists can be board certified by the American Board of Medical Genetics and go on to become associated with professional organizations devoted to the study of mitochondrial diseases, such as the Mitochondrial Medicine Society and the Society for Inherited Metabolic Disease.

7.2 | Glycolysis

In this section, you will explore the following question:

- What is the overall result, in terms of molecules produced, in the breakdown of glucose by glycolysis?

Connection for AP® Courses

All organisms, from simple bacteria and yeast to complex plants and animals, carry out some form of cellular respiration to capture and supply free energy for cellular processes. Although cellular respiration and photosynthesis evolved as independent processes, today they are interdependent. The products of photosynthesis, carbohydrates and oxygen gas, are used during cellular respiration. Likewise, the byproduct of cellular respiration, CO_2 gas, is used during photosynthesis. Glycolysis is the first pathway used in the breakdown of glucose to extract free energy. Used by nearly all organisms on earth today, glycolysis likely evolved as one of the first metabolic pathways. It is important to note that glycolysis occurs in the cytoplasm of both prokaryotic and eukaryotic cells. (Remember that only eukaryotic cells have mitochondria.)

Like all metabolic pathways, glycolysis occurs in steps or stages. In the first stage, the six-carbon ring of glucose is prepared for cleavage ("splitting") into two three-carbon molecules by investing two molecules of ATP to energize the separation. (Don't worry; the cell will get the investment of ATP back. It's like the stock market: You have to invest money to, hopefully, make money!) As glucose is metabolized further, bonds are rearranged through a series of enzyme-catalyzed steps, and free energy is released to form ATP from ADP and free phosphate molecules. The availability of enzymes can affect the rate of glucose metabolism. Two molecules of pyruvate are ultimately produced. High-energy electrons and hydrogen atoms pass to NAD^+, reducing it to NADH. Although two molecules of ATP were invested to destabilize glucose at the beginning of the process, four molecules of ATP are formed by substrate-level phosphorylation, resulting in a net gain of two ATP and two NADH molecules for the cell.

Information presented and the examples highlighted in the section support concepts and Learning Objectives outlined in

Big Idea 1 and Big Idea 2 of the AP® Biology Curriculum Framework, as shown in the table. The Learning Objectives listed in the Curriculum Framework provide a transparent foundation for the AP® Biology course, an inquiry-based laboratory experience, instructional activities, and AP® exam questions. A Learning Objective merges required content with one or more of the seven Science Practices.

Big Idea 1	The process of evolution drives the diversity and unity of life.
Enduring Understanding 1.B	Organisms are linked by lines of descent from common ancestry.
Essential Knowledge	**1.B.1** Organisms share many conserved core processes and features that evolved and are widely distributed among organisms today.
Science Practice	**7.2** The student can connect concepts in and across domain(s) to generalize or extrapolate in and/or across enduring understandings and/or big ideas.
Learning Objective	**1.15** The student is able to describe specific examples of conserved core biological processes and features shared by all domains or within one domain of life, and how these shared, conserved core processes and features support the concept of common ancestry for all organisms.
Big Idea 2	Biological systems utilize free energy and molecular building blocks to grow, to reproduce, and to maintain dynamic homeostasis.
Enduring Understanding 2.A	Growth, reproduction and maintenance of living systems require free energy and matter.
Essential Knowledge	**2.A.2** Organisms capture and store free energy for use in biological processes.
Science Practice	**1.4** The student can use representations and models to analyze situations or solve problems qualitatively and quantitatively.
Science Practice	**3.1** The student can pose scientific questions.
Learning Objective	**2.4** The student is able to use representations to pose scientific questions about what mechanisms and structural features allow organisms to capture, store, and use free energy.
Essential Knowledge	**2.A.2** Organisms capture and store free energy for use in biological processes.
Science Practice	**6.2** The student can construct explanations of phenomena based on evidence produced through scientific practices.
Learning Objective	**2.5** The student is able to construct explanations of the mechanisms and structural features of cells that allow organisms to capture, store, or use free energy.

You have read that nearly all of the energy used by living cells comes to them in the bonds of the sugar, glucose. **Glycolysis** is the first step in the breakdown of glucose to extract energy for cellular metabolism. Nearly all living organisms carry out glycolysis as part of their metabolism. The process does not use oxygen and is therefore **anaerobic**. Glycolysis takes place in the cytoplasm of both prokaryotic and eukaryotic cells. Glucose enters heterotrophic cells in two ways. One method is through secondary active transport in which the transport takes place against the glucose concentration gradient. The other mechanism uses a group of integral proteins called GLUT proteins, also known as glucose transporter proteins. These transporters assist in the facilitated diffusion of glucose.

Glycolysis begins with the six carbon ring-shaped structure of a single glucose molecule and ends with two molecules of a three-carbon sugar called **pyruvate**. Glycolysis consists of two distinct phases. The first part of the glycolysis pathway traps the glucose molecule in the cell and uses energy to modify it so that the six-carbon sugar molecule can be split evenly into the two three-carbon molecules. The second part of glycolysis extracts energy from the molecules and stores it in the form of ATP and NADH, the reduced form of NAD^+.

First Half of Glycolysis (Energy-Requiring Steps)

Step 1. The first step in glycolysis (Figure 7.6) is catalyzed by hexokinase, an enzyme with broad specificity that catalyzes the phosphorylation of six-carbon sugars. Hexokinase phosphorylates glucose using ATP as the source of the phosphate, producing glucose-6-phosphate, a more reactive form of glucose. This reaction prevents the phosphorylated glucose molecule from continuing to interact with the GLUT proteins, and it can no longer leave the cell because the negatively charged phosphate will not allow it to cross the hydrophobic interior of the plasma membrane.

Step 2. In the second step of glycolysis, an isomerase converts glucose-6-phosphate into one of its isomers, fructose-6-phosphate. An **isomerase** is an enzyme that catalyzes the conversion of a molecule into one of its isomers. (This change from phosphoglucose to phosphofructose allows the eventual split of the sugar into two three-carbon molecules.).

Step 3. The third step is the phosphorylation of fructose-6-phosphate, catalyzed by the enzyme phosphofructokinase. A second ATP molecule donates a high-energy phosphate to fructose-6-phosphate, producing fructose-1,6-bisphosphate. In this pathway, phosphofructokinase is a rate-limiting enzyme. It is active when the concentration of ADP is high; it is less active when ADP levels are low and the concentration of ATP is high. Thus, if there is "sufficient" ATP in the system, the pathway slows down. This is a type of end product inhibition, since ATP is the end product of glucose catabolism.

Step 4. The newly added high-energy phosphates further destabilize fructose-1,6-bisphosphate. The fourth step in glycolysis employs an enzyme, aldolase, to cleave fructose-1,6-bisphosphate into two three-carbon isomers: dihydroxyacetone-phosphate and glyceraldehyde-3-phosphate.

Step 5. In the fifth step, an isomerase transforms the dihydroxyacetone-phosphate into its isomer, glyceraldehyde-3-phosphate. Thus, the pathway will continue with two molecules of glyceraldehyde-3-phosphate. At this point in the pathway, there is a net investment of energy from two ATP molecules in the breakdown of one glucose molecule.

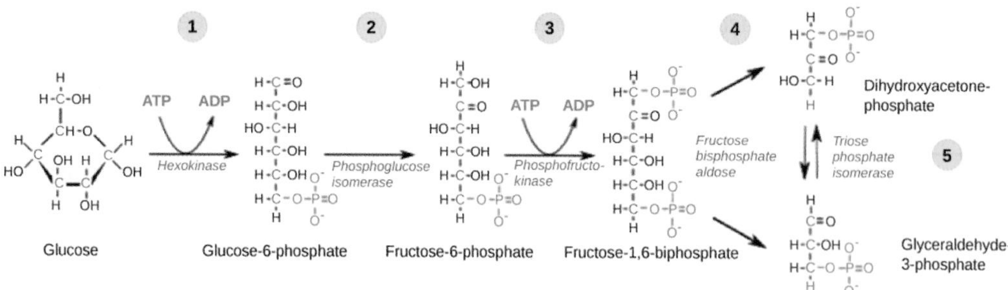

Figure 7.6 The first half of glycolysis uses two ATP molecules in the phosphorylation of glucose, which is then split into two three-carbon molecules.

Second Half of Glycolysis (Energy-Releasing Steps)

So far, glycolysis has cost the cell two ATP molecules and produced two small, three-carbon sugar molecules. Both of these molecules will proceed through the second half of the pathway, and sufficient energy will be extracted to pay back the two ATP molecules used as an initial investment and produce a profit for the cell of two additional ATP molecules and two even higher-energy NADH molecules.

Step 6. The sixth step in glycolysis (Figure 7.7) oxidizes the sugar (glyceraldehyde-3-phosphate), extracting high-energy electrons, which are picked up by the electron carrier NAD^+, producing NADH. The sugar is then phosphorylated by the addition of a second phosphate group, producing 1,3-bisphosphoglycerate. Note that the second phosphate group does not require another ATP molecule.

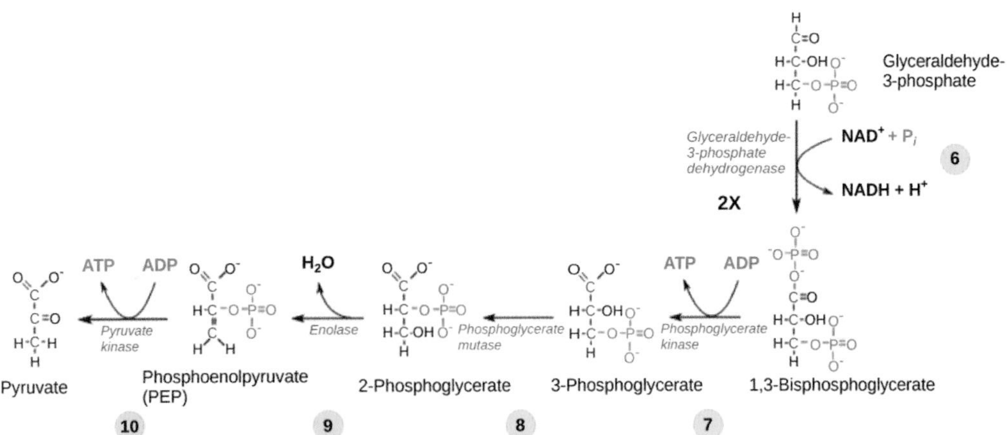

Figure 7.7 The second half of glycolysis involves phosphorylation without ATP investment (step 6) and produces two NADH and four ATP molecules per glucose.

Here again is a potential limiting factor for this pathway. The continuation of the reaction depends upon the availability of the oxidized form of the electron carrier, NAD^+. Thus, NADH must be continuously oxidized back into NAD^+ in order to keep this step going. If NAD^+ is not available, the second half of glycolysis slows down or stops. If oxygen is available in the system, the NADH will be oxidized readily, though indirectly, and the high-energy electrons from the hydrogen released in this process will be used to produce ATP. In an environment without oxygen, an alternate pathway (fermentation) can provide the oxidation of NADH to NAD^+.

Step 7. In the seventh step, catalyzed by phosphoglycerate kinase (an enzyme named for the reverse reaction), 1,3-bisphosphoglycerate donates a high-energy phosphate to ADP, forming one molecule of ATP. (This is an example of substrate-level phosphorylation.) A carbonyl group on the 1,3-bisphosphoglycerate is oxidized to a carboxyl group, and 3-phosphoglycerate is formed.

Step 8. In the eighth step, the remaining phosphate group in 3-phosphoglycerate moves from the third carbon to the second carbon, producing 2-phosphoglycerate (an isomer of 3-phosphoglycerate). The enzyme catalyzing this step is a mutase (isomerase).

Step 9. Enolase catalyzes the ninth step. This enzyme causes 2-phosphoglycerate to lose water from its structure; this is a dehydration reaction, resulting in the formation of a double bond that increases the potential energy in the remaining phosphate bond and produces phosphoenolpyruvate (PEP).

Step 10. The last step in glycolysis is catalyzed by the enzyme pyruvate kinase (the enzyme in this case is named for the reverse reaction of pyruvate's conversion into PEP) and results in the production of a second ATP molecule by substrate-level phosphorylation and the compound pyruvic acid (or its salt form, pyruvate). Many enzymes in enzymatic pathways are named for the reverse reactions, since the enzyme can catalyze both forward and reverse reactions (these may have been described initially by the reverse reaction that takes place in vitro, under non-physiological conditions).

Gain a better understanding of the breakdown of glucose by glycolysis by visiting this site (http://openstaxcollege.org/l/glycolysis) to see the process in action.

everyday CONNECTION for AP® Courses

Glycolysis occurs in the cytoplasm of nearly every cell. Organisms, from the small, circular colonies of bacteria pictured here to the human holding the petri dish, perform glycolysis using the same ten enzymes. Because of this, it is thought that glycolysis must have evolved in the very earliest forms of life.

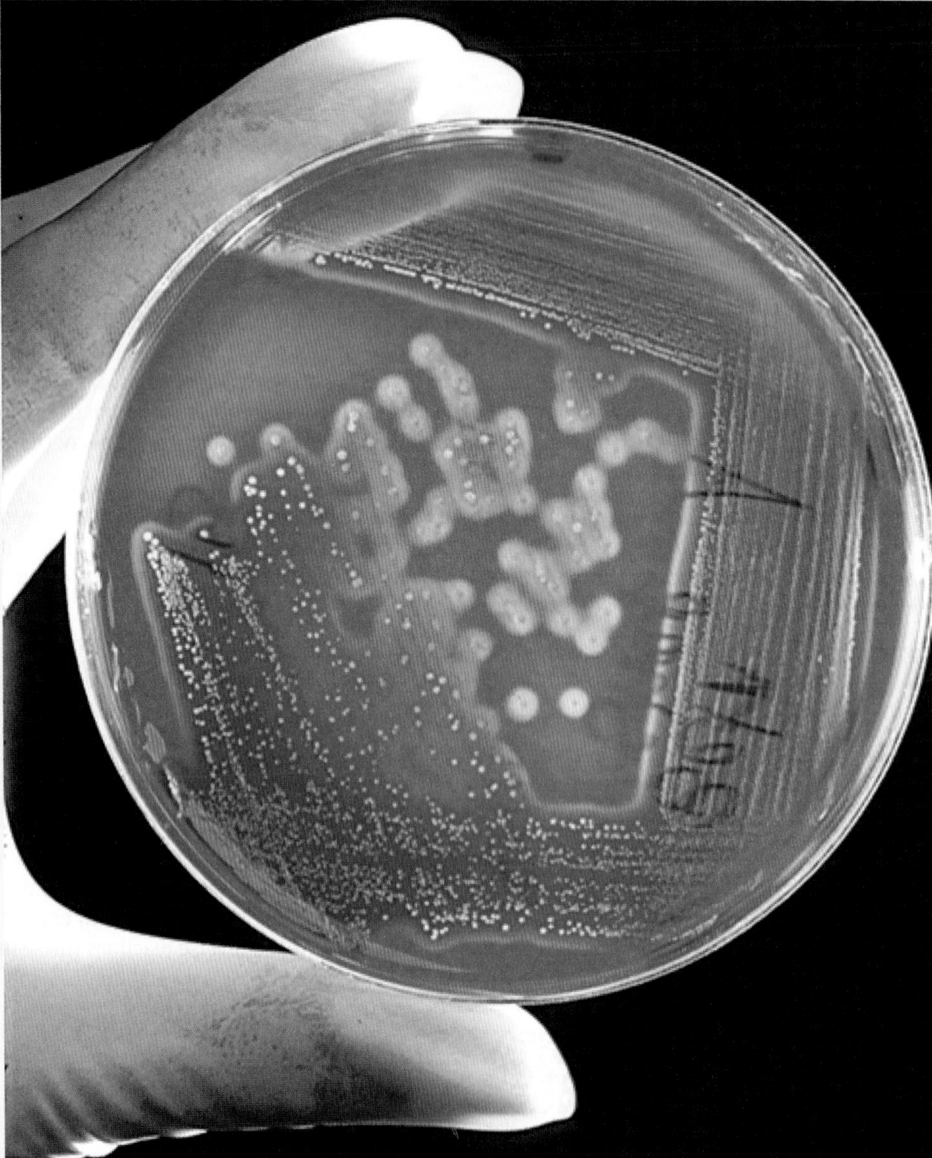

Figure 7.8

ATP energy is needed for glycolysis. Explain how this ATP debt is paid off during the reaction. How is this ATP debt paid off during the reaction?

a. by the phosphorylation of fructose-6-phosphate
b. by the oxidation of glyceraldehyde-3-phosphate
c. by the formation of 3-phosphoglycerate
d. by the formation of phosphoenolpyruvate

Outcomes of Glycolysis

Glycolysis starts with glucose and ends with two pyruvate molecules, a total of four ATP molecules and two molecules of NADH. Two ATP molecules were used in the first half of the pathway to prepare the six-carbon ring for cleavage, so the cell has a net gain of two ATP molecules and 2 NADH molecules for its use. If the cell cannot catabolize the pyruvate molecules further, it will harvest only two ATP molecules from one molecule of glucose. Mature mammalian red blood cells are not capable of **aerobic respiration**—the process in which organisms convert energy in the presence of oxygen—and glycolysis is their sole source of ATP. If glycolysis is interrupted, these cells lose their ability to maintain their sodium-potassium pumps, and eventually, they die.

The last step in glycolysis will not occur if pyruvate kinase, the enzyme that catalyzes the formation of pyruvate, is not available in sufficient quantities. In this situation, the entire glycolysis pathway will proceed, but only two ATP molecules will be made in the second half. Thus, pyruvate kinase is a rate-limiting enzyme for glycolysis.

science practices CONNECTION for AP® Courses

Think About It

- Nearly all organisms on Earth carry out some form of glycolysis. How does that fact support or not support the assertion that glycolysis is one of the oldest metabolic pathways? Justify your answer.
- Human red blood cells do not perform aerobic respiration, but they do perform glycolysis. What might happen if glycolysis were blocked in a red blood cell? Could red blood cells tap into other sources of free energy needed for their functions?

7.3 | Oxidation of Pyruvate and the Citric Acid Cycle

In this section, you will explore the following question:

- How is pyruvate, the product of glycolysis, prepared for entry into the citric acid cycle?
- What are the products of the citric acid cycle?

Connection for AP® Courses

In the next stage of cellular respiration—and in the presence of oxygen—pyruvate produced in glycolysis is transformed into an acetyl group attached to a carrier molecule of coenzyme A. The resulting acetyl CoA is usually delivered from the cytoplasm to the mitochondria, a process that uses some ATP. In the mitochondria, acetyl CoA continues on to the citric acid cycle. The citric acid cycle (CAC or TCA- tricarboxylic acid cycle) is also known as the Krebs cycle. During the conversion of pyruvate into the acetyl group, a molecule of CO_2 and two high-energy electrons are removed. (Remember that glycolysis produces two molecules of pyruvate, and each can attach to a molecule of CoA and then enter the citric acid cycle. (A simple rule is to "count the carbons." Because matter and energy cannot be created or destroyed, we must account for everything.) The electrons are picked up by NAD^+, and NADH carries the electrons to a later pathway (the electron transport chain described below) for ATP production. The glucose molecule that originally entered cellular respiration in glycolysis has been completely oxidized. Chemical potential energy stored within the glucose molecules has been transferred to NADH or has been used to synthesize ATP molecules.

The citric acid cycle occurs in the mitochondrial matrix and involves a series of redox and decarboxylation reactions that again remove high energy electrons and produce CO_2. These electrons are carried by NADH and $FADH_2$ to the electron transport chain located in the cristae of the mitochondrion. (You do not need to memorize the steps in the citric acid cycle, but if provided with a diagram of the cycle, you should be able to interpret the steps.) During the cycle, ATP is synthesized from ADP and inorganic phosphate by substrate-level phosphorylation.

Big Idea 2	Biological systems utilize free energy and molecular building blocks to grow, to reproduce, and to maintain dynamic homeostasis.
Enduring Understanding 2.A	Growth, reproduction and maintenance of living systems require free energy and matter.
Essential Knowledge	**2.A.2** Organisms capture and store free energy for use in biological processes.
Science Practice	**1.4** The student can use representations and models to analyze situations or solve problems qualitatively and quantitatively.
Science Practice	**3.1** The student can pose scientific questions.
Learning Objective	**2.4** The student is able to use representations to pose scientific questions about what mechanisms and structural features allow organisms to capture, store, and use free energy.
Essential Knowledge	**2.A.2** Organisms capture and store free energy for use in biological processes
Science Practice	**6.2** The student can construct explanations of phenomena based on evidence produced through scientific practices.
Learning Objective	**2.5** The student is able to construct explanations of the mechanisms and structural features of cells that allow organisms to capture, store, or use free energy.
Big Idea 4	Biological systems interact, and these systems and their interactions possess complex properties.
Enduring Understanding 4.A	Interactions within biological systems lead to complex properties.
Essential Knowledge	**4.A.2** The structure and function of subcellular components, and their interactions, provide essential cellular processes.
Science Practice	**1.4** The student can use representations and models to analyze situations or solve problems qualitatively and quantitatively.
Learning Objective	**4.6** The student is able to use representations and models to analyze situations qualitatively to describe how interactions of subcellular structures, which possess specialized functions, provide essential functions.

The Science Practice Challenge Questions contain additional test questions for this section that will help you prepare for the AP exam. These questions address the following standards:
[APLO 2.1][APLO 2.5][APLO 2.16][APLO 2.17][APLO 2.18]

If oxygen is available, aerobic respiration will go forward. In eukaryotic cells, the pyruvate molecules produced at the end of glycolysis are transported into mitochondria. There, pyruvate will be transformed into an acetyl group that will be picked up and activated by a carrier compound called coenzyme A (CoA). The resulting compound is called **acetyl CoA**. CoA is made from vitamin B5, pantothenic acid. Acetyl CoA can be used in a variety of ways by the cell, but its major function is to deliver the acetyl group derived from pyruvate to the next stage of the pathway in glucose catabolism.

Breakdown of Pyruvate

In order for pyruvate, the product of glycolysis, to enter the next pathway, it must undergo several changes. The conversion is a three-step process (**Figure 7.9**).

Step 1. A carboxyl group is removed from pyruvate, releasing a molecule of carbon dioxide into the surrounding medium. The result of this step is a two-carbon hydroxyethyl group bound to the enzyme (pyruvate dehydrogenase). This is the first of the six carbons from the original glucose molecule to be removed. This step proceeds twice (remember: there are *two* pyruvate molecules produced at the end of glycolsis) for every molecule of glucose metabolized; thus, two of the six carbons will have been removed at the end of both steps.

Step 2. The hydroxyethyl group is oxidized to an acetyl group, and the electrons are picked up by NAD^+, forming NADH. The high-energy electrons from NADH will be used later to generate ATP.

Step 3. The enzyme-bound acetyl group is transferred to CoA, producing a molecule of acetyl CoA.

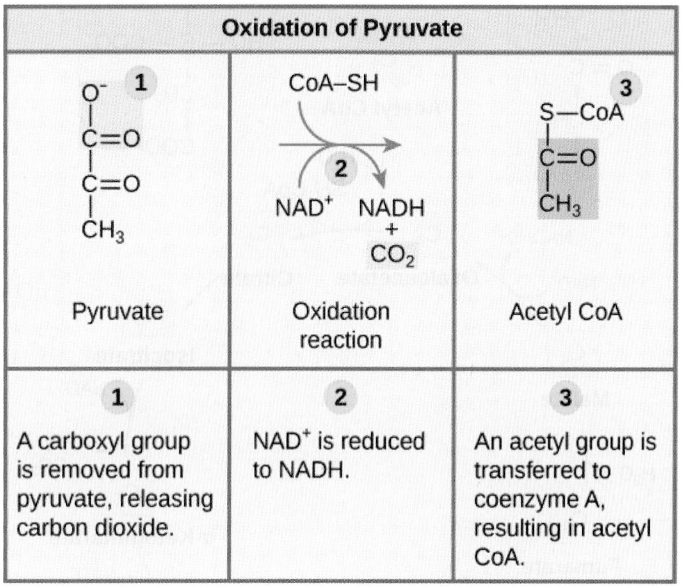

Oxidation of Pyruvate		
1 O^-–C=O–C=O–CH_3 Pyruvate	CoA–SH; 2 NAD^+ → NADH + CO_2 Oxidation reaction	3 S—CoA–C=O–CH_3 Acetyl CoA
1 A carboxyl group is removed from pyruvate, releasing carbon dioxide.	2 NAD^+ is reduced to NADH.	3 An acetyl group is transferred to coenzyme A, resulting in acetyl CoA.

Figure 7.9 Upon entering the mitochondrial matrix, a multi-enzyme complex converts pyruvate into acetyl CoA. In the process, carbon dioxide is released and one molecule of NADH is formed.

Note that during the second stage of glucose metabolism, whenever a carbon atom is removed, it is bound to two oxygen atoms, producing carbon dioxide, one of the major end products of cellular respiration.

Acetyl CoA to CO_2

In the presence of oxygen, acetyl CoA delivers its acetyl group to a four-carbon molecule, oxaloacetate, to form citrate, a six-carbon molecule with three carboxyl groups; this pathway will harvest the remainder of the extractable energy from what began as a glucose molecule. This single pathway is called by different names: the **citric acid cycle** (for the first intermediate formed—citric acid, or citrate—when acetate joins to the oxaloacetate), the **TCA cycle** (since citric acid or citrate and isocitrate are tricarboxylic acids), and the **Krebs cycle**, after Hans Krebs, who first identified the steps in the pathway in the 1930s in pigeon flight muscles.

Citric Acid Cycle

Like the conversion of pyruvate to acetyl CoA, the citric acid cycle takes place in the matrix of mitochondria. Almost all of the enzymes of the citric acid cycle are soluble, with the single exception of the enzyme succinate dehydrogenase, which is embedded in the inner membrane of the mitochondrion. Unlike glycolysis, the citric acid cycle is a closed loop: The last part of the pathway regenerates the compound used in the first step. The eight steps of the cycle are a series of redox, dehydration, hydration, and decarboxylation reactions that produce two carbon dioxide molecules, one GTP/ATP, and reduced forms of NADH and $FADH_2$ (Figure 7.10). This is considered an aerobic pathway because the NADH and $FADH_2$ produced must transfer their electrons to the next pathway in the system, which will use oxygen. If this transfer does not occur, the oxidation steps of the citric acid cycle also do not occur. Note that the citric acid cycle produces very little ATP directly and does not directly consume oxygen.

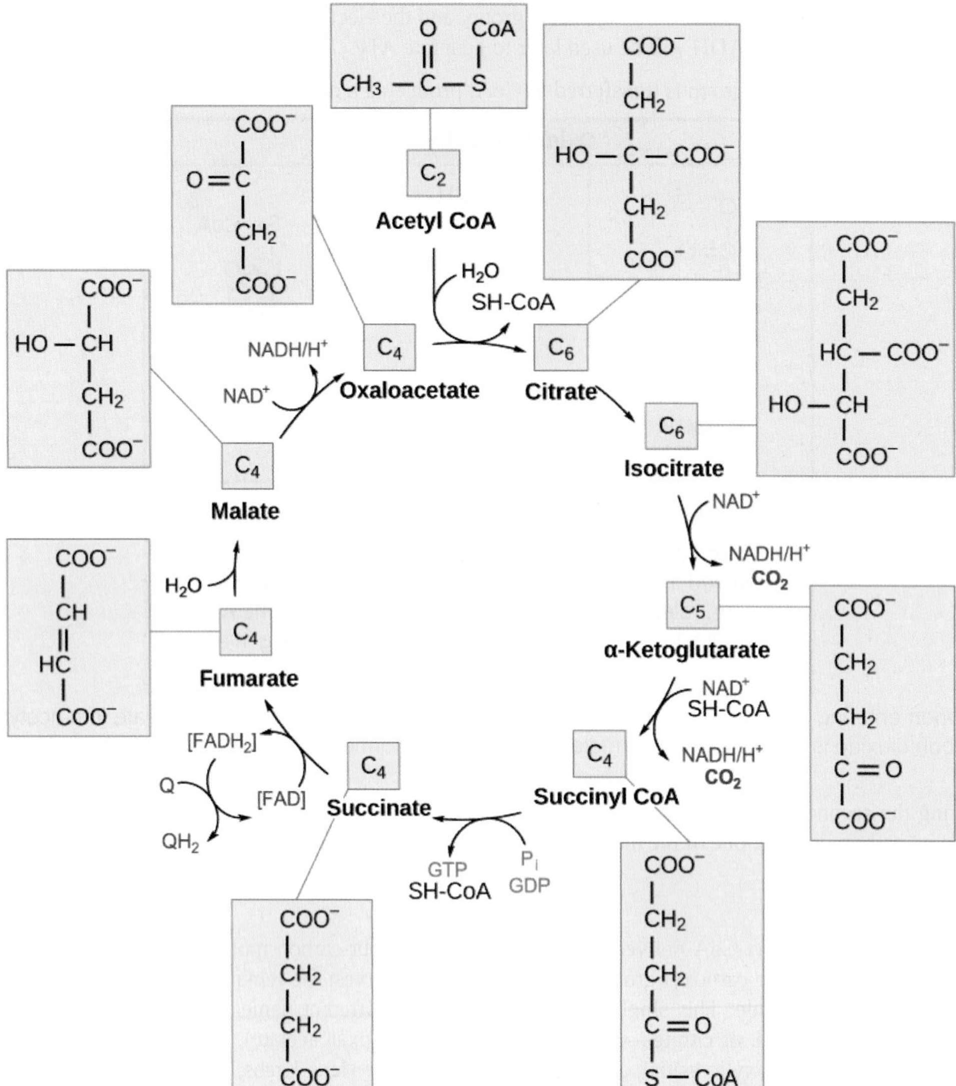

Figure 7.10 In the citric acid cycle, the acetyl group from acetyl CoA is attached to a four-carbon oxaloacetate molecule to form a six-carbon citrate molecule. Through a series of steps, citrate is oxidized, releasing two carbon dioxide molecules for each acetyl group fed into the cycle. In the process, three NAD^+ molecules are reduced to NADH, one FAD molecule is reduced to $FADH_2$, and one ATP or GTP (depending on the cell type) is produced (by substrate-level phosphorylation). Because the final product of the citric acid cycle is also the first reactant, the cycle runs continuously in the presence of sufficient reactants. (credit: modification of work by “Yikrazuul”/Wikimedia Commons)

Steps in the Citric Acid Cycle

Step 1. Prior to the start of the first step, a transitional phase occurs during which pyruvic acid is converted to acetyl CoA. Then, the first step of the cycle begins: This is a condensation step, combining the two-carbon acetyl group with a four-carbon oxaloacetate molecule to form a six-carbon molecule of citrate. CoA is bound to a sulfhydryl group (-SH) and diffuses away to eventually combine with another acetyl group. This step is irreversible because it is highly exergonic. The rate of this reaction is controlled by negative feedback and the amount of ATP available. If ATP levels increase, the rate of this reaction decreases. If ATP is in short supply, the rate increases.

Step 2. In step two, citrate loses one water molecule and gains another as citrate is converted into its isomer, isocitrate.

Step 3. In step three, isocitrate is oxidized, producing a five-carbon molecule, α-ketoglutarate, together with a molecule of CO_2 and two electrons, which reduce NAD^+ to NADH. This step is also regulated by negative feedback from ATP and NADH, and a positive effect of ADP.

Steps 3 and 4. Steps three and four are both oxidation and decarboxylation steps, which release electrons that reduce NAD^+ to NADH and release carboxyl groups that form CO_2 molecules. α-Ketoglutarate is the product of step three, and a succinyl group is the product of step four. CoA binds the succinyl group to form succinyl CoA. The enzyme that catalyzes step four is regulated by feedback inhibition of ATP, succinyl CoA, and NADH.

Step 5. In step five, a phosphate group is substituted for coenzyme A, and a high-energy bond is formed. This energy is used in substrate-level phosphorylation (during the conversion of the succinyl group to succinate) to form either guanine triphosphate (GTP) or ATP. There are two forms of the enzyme, called isoenzymes, for this step, depending upon the type of animal tissue in which they are found. One form is found in tissues that use large amounts of ATP, such as heart and skeletal muscle. This form produces ATP. The second form of the enzyme is found in tissues that have a high number of anabolic pathways, such as liver tissues. This form produces GTP. GTP is energetically equivalent to ATP; however, its use is more restricted. In particular, protein synthesis primarily uses GTP.

Step 6. Step six is a dehydration process that converts succinate into fumarate. Two hydrogen atoms are transferred to FAD, producing $FADH_2$. The energy contained in the electrons of these atoms is insufficient to reduce NAD^+ but adequate to reduce FAD. Unlike NADH, this carrier remains attached to the enzyme and transfers the electrons to the electron transport chain directly. This process is made possible by the localization of the enzyme catalyzing this step inside the inner membrane of the mitochondrion.

Step 7. Water is added to fumarate during step seven, and malate is produced. The last step in the citric acid cycle regenerates oxaloacetate by oxidizing malate. Another molecule of NADH is produced in the process.

Click through each step of the citric acid cycle here (http://openstaxcollege.org/l/krebs_cycle) .

Why is the mitochondria considered the powerhouse of the cell?

a. Glycolysis takes place in mitochondria which extract energy by glucose breakdown for cellular metabolism.

b. Most of the ATP is produced in mitochondria by oxidative phosphorylation.

c. All the pathways involved in ATP production take place in the mitochondria.

d. The outer membrane of mitochondria is loaded with proteins involved in electron transfer and ATP synthesis.

Products of the Citric Acid Cycle

Two carbon atoms come into the citric acid cycle from each acetyl group, representing four out of the six carbons of one glucose molecule. Two carbon dioxide molecules are released on each turn of the cycle; however, these do not necessarily contain the most recently added carbon atoms. The two acetyl carbon atoms will eventually be released on later turns of the cycle; thus, all six carbon atoms from the original glucose molecule are eventually incorporated into carbon dioxide. Each turn of the cycle forms three NADH molecules and one $FADH_2$ molecule. These carriers will connect with the last portion of aerobic respiration to produce ATP molecules. One GTP or ATP is also made in each cycle. Several of the intermediate compounds in the citric acid cycle can be used in synthesizing non-essential amino acids; therefore, the cycle is amphibolic (both catabolic and anabolic).

science practices CONNECTION for AP® Courses

Think About It

Explain how citrate from the citric acid cycle might affect glycolysis. What other factors might affect the efficiency of the citric acid cycle and its products?

7.4 | Oxidative Phosphorylation

In this section, you will explore the following questions:

- How do electrons move through the electron transport chain and what happens to their energy levels?
- How is a proton (H^+) gradient established and maintained by the electron transport chain and how many ATP molecules are produced by chemiosmosis?

Connection for AP® Courses

The electron transport chain (ETC) is the stage of aerobic respiration that uses free oxygen as the final electron acceptor of the electrons removed during glucose metabolism in glycolysis and the citric acid cycle. The ETC is located in membrane of the mitochondrial cristae, an area with many folds that increase the surface area available for chemical reactions. Electrons carried by NADH and $FADH_2$ are delivered to electron acceptor proteins embedded in the membrane as they move toward the final electron acceptor, O_2, forming water. The electrons pass through a series of redox reactions, using free energy at three points to transport hydrogen ions across the membrane. This process contributes to the formation of the H^+ gradient used in chemiosmosis. As the protons are driven down their concentration gradient through ATP synthase, ATP is generated from ADP and inorganic phosphate. Under aerobic conditions, the stages of cellular respiration can generate 36-38 ATP.

Information presented and the examples highlighted in the section support concepts outlined in Big Idea 2 of the AP® Biology Curriculum Framework, as shown in the table. As shown in the table, concepts covered in this section also align to the Learning Objectives listed in the Curriculum Framework that provide a transparent foundation for the AP® Biology course, an inquiry-based laboratory experience, instructional activities, and AP® exam questions. A Learning Objective merges required content with one or more of the seven Science Practices.

Big Idea 2	Biological systems utilize free energy and molecular building blocks to grow, to reproduce, and to maintain dynamic homeostasis.
Enduring Understanding 2.A	Growth, reproduction and maintenance of living systems require free energy and matter.
Essential Knowledge	**2.A.1** All living systems require constant input of free energy.
Science Practice	**1.4** The student can use representations and models to analyze situations or solve problems qualitatively and quantitatively.
Science Practice	**3.1** The student can pose scientific questions.
Learning Objective	**2.4** The student is able to use representations to pose scientific questions about what mechanisms and structural features allow organisms to capture, store, and use free energy.
Essential Knowledge	**2.A.1** All living systems require constant input of free energy.
Science Practice	**6.2** The student can construct explanations of phenomena based on evidence produced through scientific practices.
Learning Objective	**2.5** The student is able to construct explanations of the mechanisms and structural features of cells that allow organisms to capture, store, or use free energy.

The Science Practice Challenge Questions contain additional test questions for this section that will help you prepare for the AP exam. These questions address the following standards:
[APLO 2.5][APLO 2.15][APLO 2.18][APLO 2.22]

You have just read about two pathways Introduce glucose catabolism—glycolysis and the citric acid cycle—that generate ATP. Most of the ATP generated during the aerobic catabolism of glucose, however, is not generated directly from these pathways. Rather, it is derived from a process that begins with moving electrons through a series of electron transporters that undergo redox reactions. This causes hydrogen ions to accumulate within the matrix space. Therefore, a concentration gradient forms in which hydrogen ions diffuse out of the matrix space by passing through ATP synthase. The current of hydrogen ions powers the catalytic action of ATP synthase, which phosphorylates ADP, producing ATP.

Electron Transport Chain

The electron transport chain (Figure 7.11) is the last component of aerobic respiration and is the only part of glucose metabolism that uses atmospheric oxygen. Oxygen continuously diffuses into plants; in animals, it enters the body through the respiratory system. Electron transport is a series of redox reactions that resemble a relay race or bucket brigade in that electrons are passed rapidly from one component to the next, to the endpoint of the chain where the electrons reduce molecular oxygen, producing water. There are four complexes composed of proteins, labeled I through IV in Figure 7.11, and the aggregation of these four complexes, together with associated mobile, accessory electron carriers, is called the electron transport chain. The electron transport chain is present in multiple copies in the inner mitochondrial membrane of eukaryotes and the plasma membrane of prokaryotes.

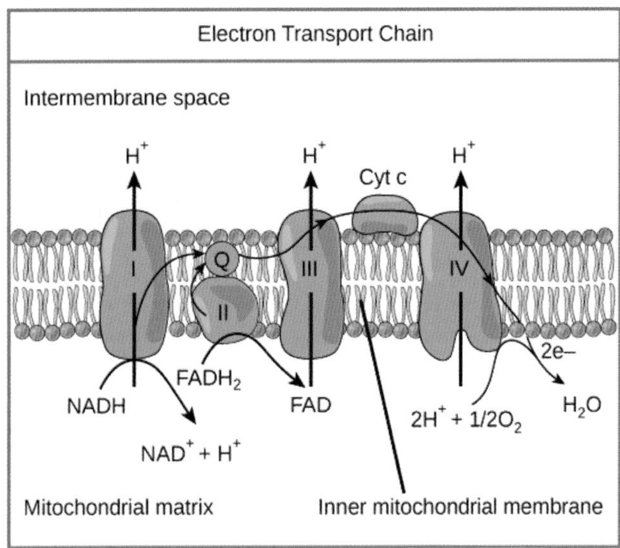

Figure 7.11 The electron transport chain is a series of electron transporters embedded in the inner mitochondrial membrane that shuttles electrons from NADH and $FADH_2$ to molecular oxygen. In the process, protons are pumped from the mitochondrial matrix to the intermembrane space, and oxygen is reduced to form water.

Complex I

To start, two electrons are carried to the first complex aboard NADH. This complex, labeled I, is composed of flavin mononucleotide (FMN) and an iron-sulfur (Fe-S)-containing protein. FMN, which is derived from vitamin B_2, also called riboflavin, is one of several prosthetic groups or co-factors in the electron transport chain. A **prosthetic group** is a non-protein molecule required for the activity of a protein. Prosthetic groups are organic or inorganic, non-peptide molecules bound to a protein that facilitate its function; prosthetic groups include co-enzymes, which are the prosthetic groups of enzymes. The enzyme in complex I is NADH dehydrogenase and is a very large protein, containing 45 amino acid chains. Complex I can pump four hydrogen ions across the membrane from the matrix into the intermembrane space, and it is in this way that the hydrogen ion gradient is established and maintained between the two compartments separated by the inner mitochondrial membrane.

Q and Complex II

Complex II directly receives $FADH_2$, which does not pass through complex I. The compound connecting the first and second complexes to the third is **ubiquinone** (Q). The Q molecule is lipid soluble and freely moves through the hydrophobic core of the membrane. Once it is reduced, (QH_2), ubiquinone delivers its electrons to the next complex in the electron transport chain. Q receives the electrons derived from NADH from complex I, and the electrons derived from $FADH_2$ from complex II. This enzyme and $FADH_2$ form a small complex that delivers electrons directly to the electron transport chain, bypassing the first complex. Since these electrons bypass and thus do not energize the proton pump in the first complex, fewer ATP molecules are made from the $FADH_2$ electrons. The number of ATP molecules ultimately obtained is directly proportional to the number of protons pumped across the inner mitochondrial membrane.

Complex III

The third complex is composed of cytochrome b, another Fe-S protein, Rieske center (2Fe-2S center), and cytochrome c proteins; this complex is also called cytochrome oxidoreductase. Cytochrome proteins have a prosthetic group of heme. The heme molecule is similar to the heme in hemoglobin, but it carries electrons, not oxygen. As a result, the iron ion at its core is reduced and oxidized as it passes the electrons, fluctuating between different oxidation states: Fe^{++} (reduced) and Fe^{+++} (oxidized). The heme molecules in the cytochromes have slightly different characteristics due to the effects of the different proteins binding them, giving slightly different characteristics to each complex. Complex III pumps protons through the membrane and passes its electrons to cytochrome c for transport to the fourth complex of proteins and enzymes (cytochrome c is the acceptor of electrons from Q; however, whereas Q carries pairs of electrons, cytochrome c can accept only one at a time).

Complex IV

The fourth complex is composed of cytochrome proteins c, a, and a_3. This complex contains two heme groups (one in each of the two cytochromes, a, and a_3) and three copper ions (a pair of Cu_A and one Cu_B in cytochrome a_3). The cytochromes hold an oxygen molecule very tightly between the iron and copper ions until the oxygen is completely reduced. The reduced oxygen then picks up two hydrogen ions from the surrounding medium to make water (H_2O). The removal of the hydrogen ions from the system contributes to the ion gradient used in the process of chemiosmosis.

Chemiosmosis

In chemiosmosis, the free energy from the series of redox reactions just described is used to pump hydrogen ions (protons) across the membrane. The uneven distribution of H^+ ions across the membrane establishes both concentration and electrical gradients (thus, an electrochemical gradient), owing to the hydrogen ions' positive charge and their aggregation on one side of the membrane.

If the membrane were open to diffusion by the hydrogen ions, the ions would tend to diffuse back across into the matrix, driven by their electrochemical gradient. Recall that many ions cannot diffuse through the nonpolar regions of phospholipid membranes without the aid of ion channels. Similarly, hydrogen ions in the matrix space can only pass through the inner mitochondrial membrane through an integral membrane protein called ATP synthase (Figure 7.12). This complex protein acts as a tiny generator, turned by the force of the hydrogen ions diffusing through it, down their electrochemical gradient. The turning of parts of this molecular machine facilitates the addition of a phosphate to ADP, forming ATP, using the potential energy of the hydrogen ion gradient.

visual CONNECTION

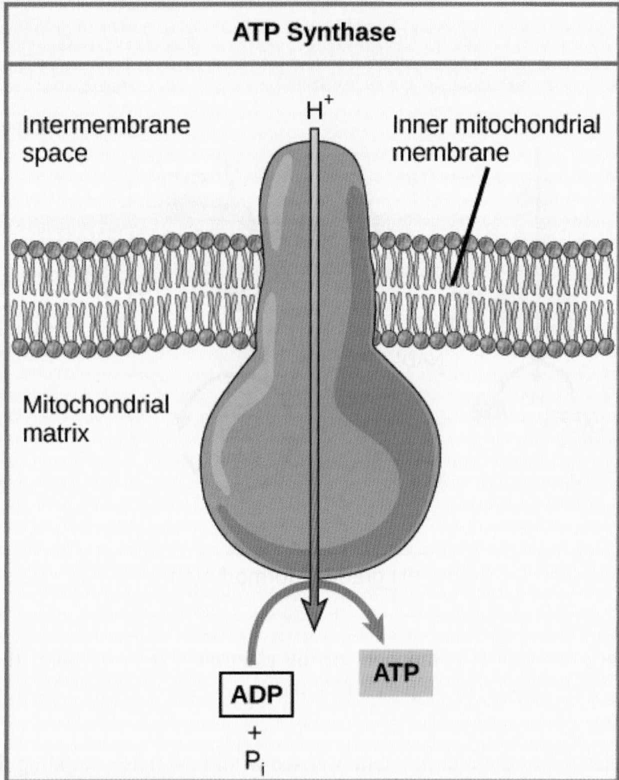

Figure 7.12 ATP synthase is a complex, molecular machine that uses a proton (H^+) gradient to form ATP from ADP and inorganic phosphate (Pi). (Credit: modification of work by Klaus Hoffmeier)

Dinitrophenol (DNP) is an uncoupler that makes the inner mitochondrial membrane leak protons (H^+). It was used until 1938 as a weight-loss drug. Why do you think this might be an effective weight-loss drug?

a. DNP dissipates the proton gradient in the matrix, preventing the production of ATP. The body then increases its metabolic rate, leading to weight loss.

b. DNP decreases the proton gradient in the inner mitochondrial space, leading to rapid consumption of acetyl-CoA, which causes weight loss.

c. DNP blocks the movement of protons through the ATP synthase, halting ATP production. The stored energy dissipates as heat, causing weight loss.

d. DNP uncouples the production of ATP by increasing the proton gradient in the matrix. The stored energy dissipates as heat, causing weight loss.

Chemiosmosis (Figure 7.13) is used to generate 90 percent of the ATP made during aerobic glucose catabolism; it is also the method used in the light reactions of photosynthesis to harness the energy of sunlight in the process of photophosphorylation. Recall that the production of ATP using the process of chemiosmosis in mitochondria is called oxidative phosphorylation. The overall result of these reactions is the production of ATP from the energy of the electrons removed from hydrogen atoms. These atoms were originally part of a glucose molecule. At the end of the pathway, the electrons are used to reduce an oxygen molecule to oxygen ions. The extra electrons on the oxygen attract hydrogen ions (protons) from the surrounding medium, and water is formed.

visual CONNECTION

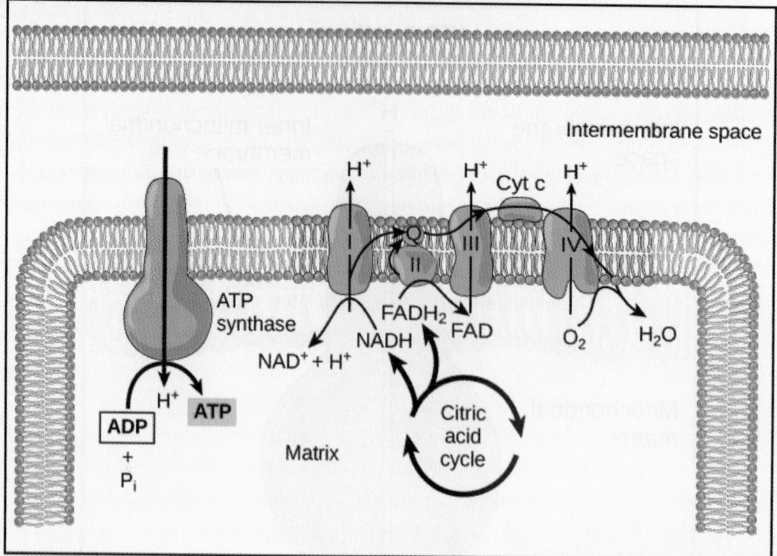

Figure 7.13 In oxidative phosphorylation, the pH gradient formed by the electron transport chain is used by ATP synthase to form ATP.

Cyanide inhibits cytochrome c oxidase, a component of the electron transport chain. If cyanide poisoning occurs, would you expect the pH of the intermembrane space to increase or decrease? What effect would cyanide have on ATP synthesis?

a. The proton concentration of the intermembrane space would decrease, stopping the production of ATP.
b. The proton concentration of the intermembrane space would increase, leading to ATP formation.
c. The hydrogen ion concentration of the intermembrane space would decrease, causing a high production of ATP.
d. The proton concentration of the intermembrane space would increase, causing production of ATP in large amounts.

ATP Yield

The number of ATP molecules generated from the catabolism of glucose varies. For example, the number of hydrogen ions that the electron transport chain complexes can pump through the membrane varies between species. Another source of variance stems from the shuttle of electrons across the membranes of the mitochondria. (The NADH generated from glycolysis cannot easily enter mitochondria.) Thus, electrons are picked up on the inside of mitochondria by either NAD^+ or FAD^+. As you have learned earlier, these FAD^+ molecules can transport fewer ions; consequently, fewer ATP molecules are generated when FAD^+ acts as a carrier. NAD^+ is used as the electron transporter in the liver and FAD^+ acts in the brain.

Another factor that affects the yield of ATP molecules generated from glucose is the fact that intermediate compounds in these pathways are used for other purposes. Glucose catabolism connects with the pathways that build or break down all other biochemical compounds in cells, and the result is somewhat messier than the ideal situations described thus far. For example, sugars other than glucose are fed into the glycolytic pathway for energy extraction. Moreover, the five-carbon sugars that form nucleic acids are made from intermediates in glycolysis. Certain nonessential amino acids can be made from intermediates of both glycolysis and the citric acid cycle. Lipids, such as cholesterol and triglycerides, are also made from intermediates in these pathways, and both amino acids and triglycerides are broken down for energy through these pathways. Overall, in living systems, these pathways of glucose catabolism extract about 34 percent of the energy contained in glucose.

science practices CONNECTION for AP® Courses

Activity

Use construction paper and other art materials to create your own diagram of the electron transport chain (ETC). Be sure to include all parts of the electron transport chain, as well as the electrons themselves, NAD+ and NADH, and oxygen. On your diagram, label all parts of the ETC that transfers the free energy from electrons to another form. Then, use your model to make predictions about each of the following. Then, share your answers with the class.

a. What would happen to free energy release if a cytochrome failed to undergo one of the redox reactions involved in the electron transport chain?
b. What ultimately happens to the free energy in the electrons that travel down the ETC?
c. Did you remember to have a pair of electrons travel down the ETC? What would happen if only one electron reached oxygen?

Think About It

- Dinitrophenol (DNP) is an uncoupler that makes the inner mitochondrial membrane leaky to protons. It was used until 1938 as a weight loss drug. What effect would DNP have on the change in pH across the inner mitochondrial membrane and the overall process of cellular respiration? Why do you think DNP might be an effective weight-loss drug? Why is DNP no longer used?
- Cyanide inhibits cytochrome c oxidase, a component of the electron transport chain. If cyanide poisoning occurs, would you expect the pH of the intermembrane space to increase or decrease? Explain the effect of cyanide on ATP synthesis.

7.5 | Metabolism without Oxygen

In this section, you will explore the following question:

- What is the fundamental difference between anaerobic cellular respiration and the different types of fermentation?

Connection for AP® Courses

As was previously stated, under aerobic conditions cellular respiration can yield 36-38 ATP molecules. If oxygen is not present, ATP is only produced by substrate-level phosphorylation. Without oxygen, organisms must use another electron acceptor. Most organisms will use some form of fermentation to accomplish the regeneration of NAD^+ to ensure the continuation of glycolysis. In alcohol fermentation, pyruvate from glycolysis is converted to ethyl alcohol; during lactic acid fermentation, pyruvate is reduced to form lactate as an end-product. Without fermentation and anaerobic respiration, we wouldn't have yogurt or soy sauce. Nor would our muscle cells cramp from the buildup of lactate when we exercise vigorously and oxygen is scarce.

Information presented and the examples highlighted in the section support concepts and Learning Objectives outlined in Big Idea 2 of the AP® Biology Curriculum Framework, as shown in the table. The Learning Objectives listed in the Curriculum Framework provide a transparent foundation for the AP® Biology course, an inquiry-based laboratory experience, instructional activities, and AP® exam questions. A Learning Objective merges required content with one or more of the seven Science Practices.

Big Idea 2	Biological systems utilize free energy and molecular building blocks to grow, to reproduce, and to maintain dynamic homeostasis.

Enduring Understanding 2.A	Growth, reproduction and maintenance of living systems require free energy and matter.
Essential Knowledge	**2.A.2** Organisms capture and store free energy for use in biological processes.
Science Practice	**1.4** The student can use representations and models to analyze situations or solve problems qualitatively and quantitatively.
Science Practice	**3.1** The student can pose scientific questions.
Learning Objective	**2.4** The student is able to use representations to pose scientific questions about what mechanisms and structural features allow organisms to capture, store, and use free energy.
Essential Knowledge	**2.A.2** Organisms capture and store free energy for use in biological processes.
Science Practice	**6.2** The student can construct explanations of phenomena based on evidence produced through scientific practices.
Learning Objective	**2.5** The student is able to construct explanations of the mechanisms and structural features of cells that allow organisms to capture, store, or use free energy.

The Science Practice Challenge Questions contain additional test questions for this section that will help you prepare for the AP exam. These questions address the following standards:
[APLO 2.21][APLO 2.24][APLO 4.14][APLO 4.26]

In aerobic respiration, the final electron acceptor is an oxygen molecule, O_2. If aerobic respiration occurs, then ATP will be produced using the energy of high-energy electrons carried by NADH or $FADH_2$ to the electron transport chain. If aerobic respiration does not occur, NADH must be reoxidized to NAD^+ for reuse as an electron carrier for the glycolytic pathway to continue. How is this done? Some living systems use an organic molecule as the final electron acceptor. Processes that use an organic molecule to regenerate NAD^+ from NADH are collectively referred to as **fermentation**. In contrast, some living systems use an inorganic molecule as a final electron acceptor. Both methods are called **anaerobic cellular respiration** in which organisms convert energy for their use in the absence of oxygen.

Anaerobic Cellular Respiration

Certain prokaryotes, including some species of bacteria and Archaea, use anaerobic respiration. For example, the group of Archaea called methanogens reduces carbon dioxide to methane to oxidize NADH. These microorganisms are found in soil and in the digestive tracts of ruminants, such as cows and sheep. Similarly, sulfate-reducing bacteria and Archaea, most of which are anaerobic (Figure 7.14), reduce sulfate to hydrogen sulfide to regenerate NAD^+ from NADH.

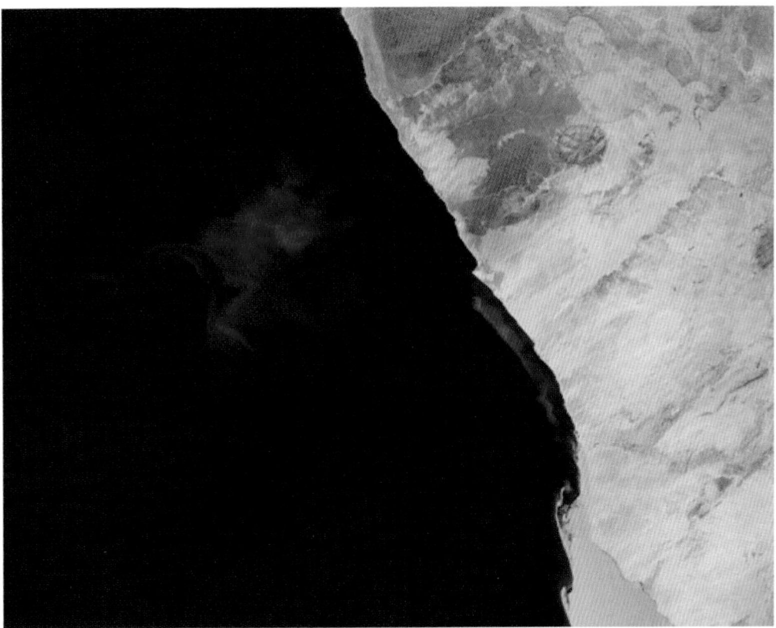

Figure 7.14 The green color seen in these coastal waters is from an eruption of hydrogen sulfide-producing bacteria. These anaerobic, sulfate-reducing bacteria release hydrogen sulfide gas as they decompose algae in the water. (credit: modification of work by NASA/Jeff Schmaltz, MODIS Land Rapid Response Team at NASA GSFC, Visible Earth Catalog of NASA images)

Visit this site (http://openstaxcollege.org/l/fermentation) to see anaerobic cellular respiration in action.

How does the formation of NAD^+ differ between aerobic and anaerobic respiration?

a. NAD^+ is formed in aerobic respiration by a fermentation process and formed in anaerobic respiration by oxidation of $NADH$.

b. NAD^+ is formed by a fermentation process in anaerobic conditions by the conversion of pyruvate into lactate and by simple oxidation of $NADH$ in aerobic respiration.

c. Under aerobic conditions, the electron acceptor is a molecule other than oxygen for NAD^+ production, whereas under anaerobic conditions the electron acceptor is oxygen.

d. NAD^+ is formed by a fermentation process in anaerobic conditions whereas in aerobic respiration it is formed by the breakdown of pyruvate into lactic acid or alcohol.

Lactic Acid Fermentation

The fermentation method used by animals and certain bacteria, like those in yogurt, is lactic acid fermentation (Figure 7.15). This type of fermentation is used routinely in mammalian red blood cells and in skeletal muscle that has an insufficient oxygen supply to allow aerobic respiration to continue (that is, in muscles used to the point of fatigue). In muscles, lactic acid accumulation must be removed by the blood circulation and the lactate brought to the liver for further metabolism. The chemical reactions of lactic acid fermentation are the following:

$$\text{Pyruvic acid} + \text{NADH} \leftrightarrow \text{lactic acid} + \text{NAD}^+$$

The enzyme used in this reaction is lactate dehydrogenase (LDH). The reaction can proceed in either direction, but the reaction from left to right is inhibited by acidic conditions. Such lactic acid accumulation was once believed to cause muscle stiffness, fatigue, and soreness, although more recent research disputes this hypothesis. Once the lactic acid has been removed from the muscle and circulated to the liver, it can be reconverted into pyruvic acid and further catabolized for energy.

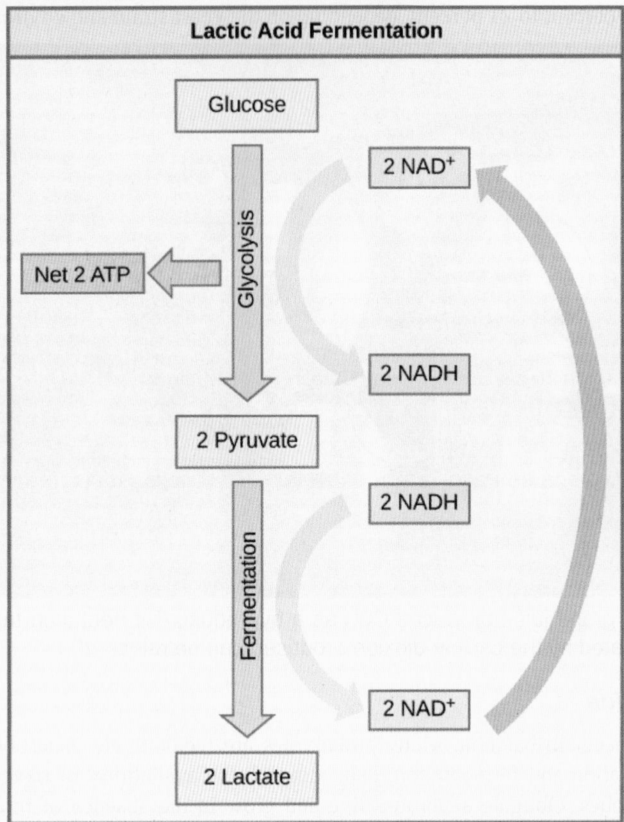

Figure 7.15 Lactic acid fermentation is common in muscle cells that have run out of oxygen.

Tremetol, a metabolic poison found in the white snake root plant, prevents the metabolism of lactate. When cows eat this plant, it is concentrated in the milk they produce. Humans who consume the milk become ill. Symptoms of this disease, which include vomiting, abdominal pain, and tremors, become worse after exercise. Why do you think this is the case?

Tremetol, a metabolic poison found in the white snake root plant, prevents the metabolism of lactate. When cows eat this plant, it is concentrated in the milk they produce. Humans who consume the milk become ill. Symptoms of this disease, which include vomiting, abdominal pain, and tremors, become worse after exercise. Why do you think this is the case?

a. Tremetol inhibits enzymes that convert lactate into less harmful compounds. Exercise worsens this by producing more lactate.

b. Tremetol increases the production of lactate dehydrogenase, causing lactic acid to accumulate in the body.

c. Tremetol inhibits the production of NAD^+ after exercise. The lack of oxygen causes lactic acid to accumulate in the body.

d. Tremetol binds to lactic acid, inhibiting its breakdown into other compounds and causing it to accumulate after exercising.

Alcohol Fermentation

Another familiar fermentation process is alcohol fermentation (**Figure 7.16**) that produces ethanol, an alcohol. The first chemical reaction of alcohol fermentation is the following (CO_2 does not participate in the second reaction):

$$\text{pyruvic acid} + H^+ \rightarrow CO_2 + \text{acetaldehyde} + \text{NADH} + H^+ \rightarrow \text{ethanol} + NAD^+$$

The first reaction is catalyzed by pyruvate decarboxylase, a cytoplasmic enzyme, with a coenzyme of thiamine pyrophosphate (TPP, derived from vitamin B_1 and also called thiamine). A carboxyl group is removed from pyruvic acid, releasing carbon dioxide as a gas. The loss of carbon dioxide reduces the size of the molecule by one carbon, making acetaldehyde. The second reaction is catalyzed by alcohol dehydrogenase to oxidize NADH to NAD^+ and reduce acetaldehyde to ethanol. The fermentation of pyruvic acid by yeast produces the ethanol. Ethanol tolerance of yeast is variable, ranging from about 5 percent to 21 percent, depending on the yeast strain and environmental conditions.

Figure 7.16 Fermentation of grape juice produces CO_2 as a byproduct. Fermentation tanks have valves so that the pressure inside the tanks created by the carbon dioxide produced can be released.

Other Types of Fermentation

Other fermentation methods occur in bacteria. Many prokaryotes are facultatively anaerobic. This means that they can switch between aerobic respiration and fermentation, depending on the availability of oxygen. Certain prokaryotes, like *Clostridia*, are obligate anaerobes. Obligate anaerobes live and grow in the absence of molecular oxygen. Oxygen is a poison to these microorganisms and kills them on exposure. It should be noted that all forms of fermentation, except lactic acid fermentation, produce gas. The production of particular types of gas is used as an indicator of the fermentation of specific carbohydrates, which plays a role in the laboratory identification of the bacteria. Various methods of fermentation are used by assorted organisms to ensure an adequate supply of NAD^+ for the sixth step in glycolysis. Without these pathways, that step would not occur and no ATP would be harvested from the breakdown of glucose.

science practices CONNECTION for AP® Courses

Lab Investigation

Lab Investigation: Respiration of Sugars by Yeast. You are given the opportunity to design and conduct experiments to investigate whether yeasts are able to metabolize a variety of sugars, using gas pressure sensors or other means to measure CO_2 production.

Think About It

Tremetol, a metabolic poison found in the white snake plant root, prevents the metabolism of lactate. When female cows eat this plant, tremetol becomes concentrated in their milk. Humans who consume the milk become ill. Explain why the symptoms of this disease, which include vomiting, abdominal pain, and tremors, becomes worse after exercise.

7.6 | Connections of Carbohydrate, Protein, and Lipid Metabolic Pathways

In this section, you will explore the following question:

- How do carbohydrate metabolic pathways, glycolysis, and the citric acid cycle interrelate with protein and lipid metabolism pathways?

Connection for AP® Courses

The breakdown and synthesis of carbohydrates, proteins, lipids, and nucleic acids connect with the metabolic pathways of glycolysis and the citric acid cycle but enter the pathways at different points. Thus, these macromolecules can be used as sources of free energy.

Information presented and the examples highlighted in the section support concepts and Learning Objectives outlined in Big Idea 2 of the AP® Biology Curriculum Framework, as shown in the table. The Learning Objectives listed in the Curriculum Framework provide a transparent foundation for the AP® Biology course, an inquiry-based laboratory experience, instructional activities, and AP® exam questions. A Learning Objective merges required content with one or more of the seven Science Practices.

Essential Knowledge	**2.A.2** Organisms capture and store free energy for use in biological processes.
Science Practice	**6.2** The student can construct explanations of phenomena based on evidence produced through scientific practices.
Learning Objective	**2.5** The student is able to construct explanations of the mechanisms and structural features of cells that allow organisms to capture, store, or use free energy.
Essential Knowledge	**2.A.1** All living systems require constant input of free energy.
Science Practice	**6.1** The student can justify claims with evidence.
Learning Objective	**2.2** The student is able to justify a scientific claim that free energy is required for living systems to maintain organization, to grow or to reproduce, but that multiple strategies exist in different living systems.

The Science Practice Challenge Questions contain additional test questions for this section that will help you prepare for the AP exam. These questions address the following standards:
[APLO 2.5][APLO 2.15][APLO 3.20][APLO 1.5][APLO 1.26][APLO 4.18]

You have learned about the catabolism of glucose, which provides energy to living cells. But living things consume more than glucose for food. How does a turkey sandwich end up as ATP in your cells? This happens because all of the catabolic pathways for carbohydrates, proteins, and lipids eventually connect into glycolysis and the citric acid cycle pathways (see Figure 7.18). Metabolic pathways should be thought of as porous—that is, substances enter from other pathways, and intermediates leave for other pathways. These pathways are not closed systems. Many of the substrates, intermediates, and products in a particular pathway are reactants in other pathways.

Connections of Other Sugars to Glucose Metabolism

Glycogen, a polymer of glucose, is an energy storage molecule in animals. When there is adequate ATP present, excess glucose is shunted into glycogen for storage. Glycogen is made and stored in both liver and muscle. The glycogen will be hydrolyzed into glucose 1-phosphate monomers (G-1-P) if blood sugar levels drop. The presence of glycogen as a source of glucose allows ATP to be produced for a longer period of time during exercise. Glycogen is broken down into G-1-P and converted into G-6-P in both muscle and liver cells, and this product enters the glycolytic pathway.

Sucrose is a disaccharide with a molecule of glucose and a molecule of fructose bonded together with a glycosidic linkage. Fructose is one of the three dietary monosaccharides, along with glucose and galactose (which is part of the milk sugar, the disaccharide lactose), which are absorbed directly into the bloodstream during digestion. The catabolism of both fructose and galactose produces the same number of ATP molecules as glucose.

Connections of Proteins to Glucose Metabolism

Proteins are hydrolyzed by a variety of enzymes in cells. Most of the time, the amino acids are recycled into the synthesis of new proteins. If there are excess amino acids, however, or if the body is in a state of starvation, some amino acids will be shunted into the pathways of glucose catabolism (Figure 7.17). Each amino acid must have its amino group removed prior to entry into these pathways. The amino group is converted into ammonia. In mammals, the liver synthesizes urea from two ammonia molecules and a carbon dioxide molecule. Thus, urea is the principal waste product in mammals, produced from the nitrogen originating in amino acids, and it leaves the body in urine.

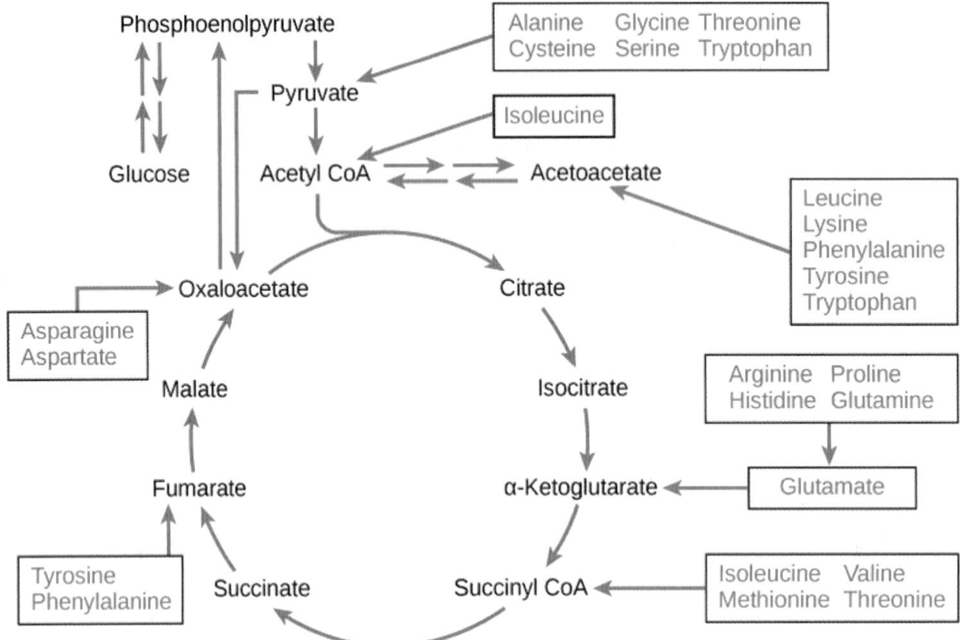

Figure 7.17 The carbon skeletons of certain amino acids (indicated in boxes) derived from proteins can feed into the citric acid cycle. (credit: modification of work by Mikael Häggström)

Connections of Lipid and Glucose Metabolisms

The lipids that are connected to the glucose pathways are cholesterol and triglycerides. Cholesterol is a lipid that contributes to cell membrane flexibility and is a precursor of steroid hormones. The synthesis of cholesterol starts with acetyl groups and proceeds in only one direction. The process cannot be reversed.

Triglycerides are a form of long-term energy storage in animals. Triglycerides are made of glycerol and three fatty acids. Animals can make most of the fatty acids they need. Triglycerides can be both made and broken down through parts of the glucose catabolism pathways. Glycerol can be phosphorylated to glycerol-3-phosphate, which continues through glycolysis. Fatty acids are catabolized in a process called beta-oxidation that takes place in the matrix of the mitochondria and converts their fatty acid chains into two carbon units of acetyl groups. The acetyl groups are picked up by CoA to form acetyl CoA that proceeds into the citric acid cycle.

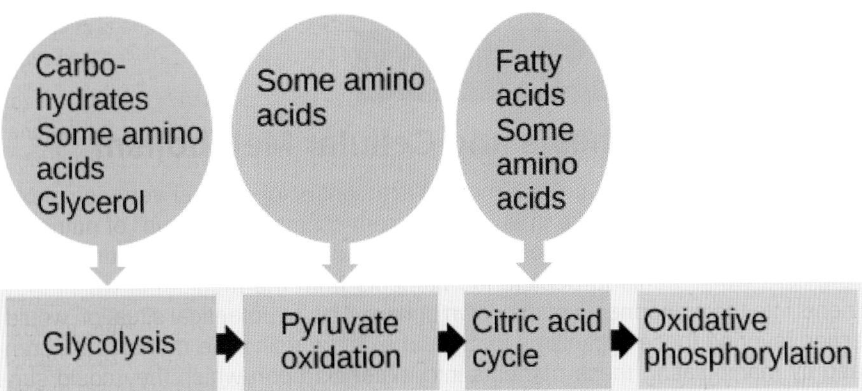

Figure 7.18 Glycogen from the liver and muscles, hydrolyzed into glucose-1-phosphate, together with fats and proteins, can feed into the catabolic pathways for carbohydrates.

Pathways of Photosynthesis and Cellular Metabolism

The processes of photosynthesis and cellular metabolism consist of several very complex pathways. It is generally thought that the first cells arose in an aqueous environment—a "soup" of nutrients—probably on the surface of some porous clays. If these cells reproduced successfully and their numbers climbed steadily, it follows that the cells would begin to deplete the nutrients from the medium in which they lived as they shifted the nutrients into the components of their own bodies. This hypothetical situation would have resulted in natural selection favoring those organisms that could exist by using the nutrients that remained in their environment and by manipulating these nutrients into materials upon which they could survive. Selection would favor those organisms that could extract maximal value from the nutrients to which they had access.

An early form of photosynthesis developed that harnessed the sun's energy using water as a source of hydrogen atoms, but this pathway did not produce free oxygen (anoxygenic photosynthesis). (Early photosynthesis did not produce free oxygen because it did not use water as the source of hydrogen ions; instead, it used materials like hydrogen sulfide and consequently produced sulfur). It is thought that glycolysis developed at this time and could take advantage of the simple sugars being produced, but these reactions were unable to fully extract the energy stored in the carbohydrates. The development of glycolysis probably predated the evolution of photosynthesis, as it was well suited to extract energy from materials spontaneously accumulating in the "primeval soup." A later form of photosynthesis used water as a source of electrons and hydrogen, and generated free oxygen. Over time, the atmosphere became oxygenated, but not before the oxygen released oxidized metals in the ocean and created a "rust" layer in the sediment, permitting the dating of the rise of the first oxygenic photosynthesizers. Living things adapted to exploit this new atmosphere that allowed aerobic respiration as we know it to evolve. When the full process of oxygenic photosynthesis developed and the atmosphere became oxygenated, cells were finally able to use the oxygen expelled by photosynthesis to extract considerably more energy from the sugar molecules using the citric acid cycle and oxidative phosphorylation.

According to the Evolution Connection passage, in what order did the metabolic pathways evolve?

a. 1. anoxygenic photosynthesis
   2. glycolysis
   3. oxygenic photosynthesis
   4. citric acid cycle and oxidative phosphorylation

b. 1. glycolysis
   2. citric acid cycle and oxidative phosphorylation
   3. anoxygenic photosynthesis
   4. oxygenic photosynthesis

c. 1. anoxygenic photosynthesis
   2. oxygenic photosynthesis
   3. glycolysis
   4. citric acid cycle and oxidative phosphorylation

d. 1. glycolysis
   2. anoxygenic photosynthesis
   3. oxygenic photosynthesis
   4. citric acid cycle and oxidative phosphorylation

science practices CONNECTION for AP® Courses

Think About It

Explain how free energy can be obtained from the metabolism of carbohydrates, proteins, lipids, and even nucleic acids. Which of these molecules provides the largest amount of free energy? Justify your answer.

7.7 | Regulation of Cellular Respiration

In this section, you will explore the following question:

- What mechanisms control cellular respiration?

Connection for AP® Courses

Cellular respiration is controlled by a variety of means. For example, the entry of glucose into a cell is controlled by the transport proteins that aid glucose passage through the cell membrane. However, most of the control of the respiration processes is accomplished through negative feedback inhibition of specific enzymes that respond to the intracellular concentrations of ATP, ADP, NAD^+, and FAD, etc.

Information presented and the examples highlighted in the section support concepts and learning objectives outlined in Big Idea 2 of the AP® Biology Curriculum Framework, as shown in the table. The Learning Objectives listed in the Curriculum Framework provide a transparent foundation for the AP® Biology course, an inquiry-based laboratory experience, instructional activities, and AP® exam questions. A Learning Objective merges required content with one or more of the seven Science Practices.

Big Idea 2	Biological systems utilize free energy and molecular building blocks to grow, to reproduce, and to maintain dynamic homeostasis.
Enduring Understanding 2.C	Organisms use feedback mechanisms to regulate growth and reproduction, and to maintain dynamic homeostasis.
Essential Knowledge	**2.C.1** Organisms use feedback mechanisms to maintain their internal environments and respond to external environmental changes.
Science Practice	**7.2** The student can connect concepts in and across domain(s) to generalize or extrapolate in and/or across enduring understandings and/or big ideas.
Learning Objective	**2.16** The student is able to connect how organisms use negative feedback to maintain their internal environments.
Essential Knowledge	**2.C.1** Organisms use feedback mechanisms to maintain their internal environments and respond to external environmental changes.
Science Practice	**5.3** The student can evaluate the evidence provided by data sets in relation to a particular scientific question.
Learning Objective	**2.17** The student is able to evaluate data that show the effect(s) of changes in concentration of key molecules on negative feedback mechanisms.

Cellular respiration must be regulated in order to provide balanced amounts of energy in the form of ATP. The cell also must generate a number of intermediate compounds that are used in the anabolism and catabolism of macromolecules. Without controls, metabolic reactions would quickly come to a stand-still as the forward and backward reactions reached a state of equilibrium. Resources would be used inappropriately. A cell does not need the maximum amount of ATP that it can make all the time: At times, the cell needs to shunt some of the intermediates to pathways for amino acid, protein, glycogen, lipid, and nucleic acid production. In short, the cell needs to control its metabolism.

Regulatory Mechanisms

A variety of mechanisms is used to control cellular respiration. Some type of control exists at each stage of glucose metabolism. Access of glucose to the cell can be regulated using the **GLUT proteins** that transport glucose (Figure 7.19). Different forms of the GLUT protein control passage of glucose into the cells of specific tissues.

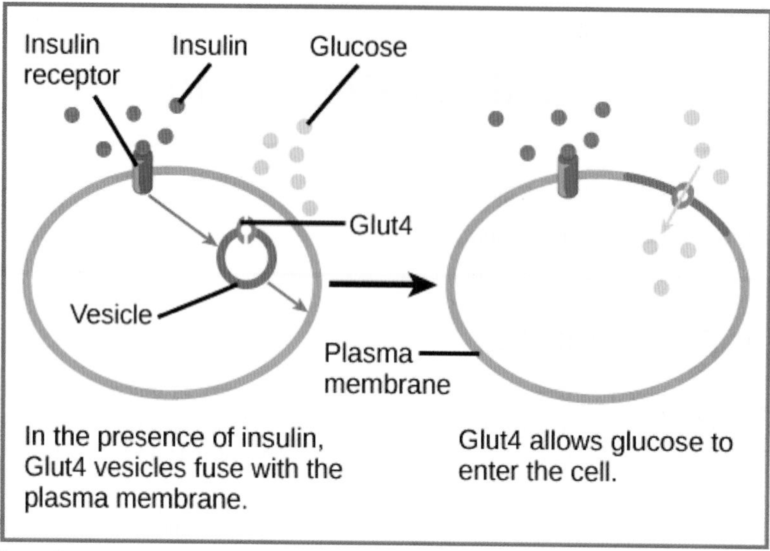

Figure 7.19 GLUT4 is a glucose transporter that is stored in vesicles. A cascade of events that occurs upon insulin binding to a receptor in the plasma membrane causes GLUT4-containing vesicles to fuse with the plasma membrane so that glucose may be transported into the cell.

Some reactions are controlled by having two different enzymes—one each for the two directions of a reversible reaction. Reactions that are catalyzed by only one enzyme can go to equilibrium, stalling the reaction. In contrast, if two different enzymes (each specific for a given direction) are necessary for a reversible reaction, the opportunity to control the rate of the reaction increases, and equilibrium is not reached.

A number of enzymes involved in each of the pathways—in particular, the enzyme catalyzing the first committed reaction of the pathway—are controlled by attachment of a molecule to an allosteric site on the protein. The molecules most commonly used in this capacity are the nucleotides ATP, ADP, AMP, NAD^+, and NADH. These regulators, allosteric effectors, may increase or decrease enzyme activity, depending on the prevailing conditions. The allosteric effector alters the steric structure of the enzyme, usually affecting the configuration of the active site. This alteration of the protein's (the enzyme's) structure either increases or decreases its affinity for its substrate, with the effect of increasing or decreasing the rate of the reaction. The attachment signals to the enzyme. This binding can increase or decrease the enzyme's activity, providing feedback. This feedback type of control is effective as long as the chemical affecting it is attached to the enzyme. Once the overall concentration of the chemical decreases, it will diffuse away from the protein, and the control is relaxed.

Control of Catabolic Pathways

Enzymes, proteins, electron carriers, and pumps that play roles in glycolysis, the citric acid cycle, and the electron transport chain tend to catalyze non-reversible reactions. In other words, if the initial reaction takes place, the pathway is committed to proceeding with the remaining reactions. Whether a particular enzyme activity is released depends upon the energy needs of the cell (as reflected by the levels of ATP, ADP, and AMP).

Glycolysis

The control of glycolysis begins with the first enzyme in the pathway, hexokinase (Figure 7.20). This enzyme catalyzes the phosphorylation of glucose, which helps to prepare the compound for cleavage in a later step. The presence of the negatively charged phosphate in the molecule also prevents the sugar from leaving the cell. When hexokinase is inhibited, glucose diffuses out of the cell and does not become a substrate for the respiration pathways in that tissue. The product of the hexokinase reaction is glucose-6-phosphate, which accumulates when a later enzyme, phosphofructokinase, is inhibited.

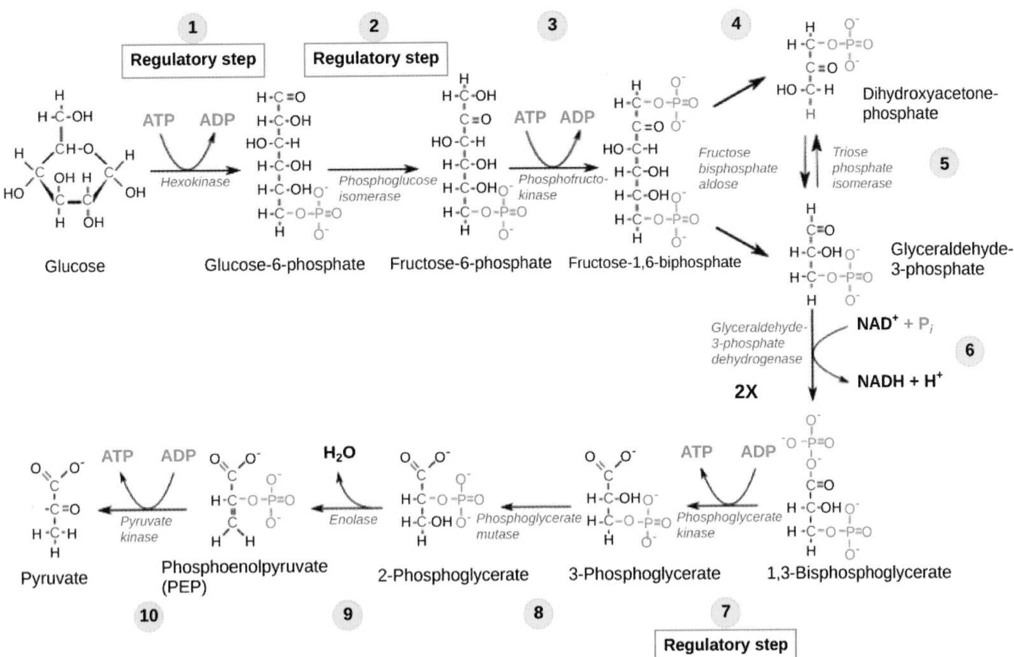

Figure 7.20 The glycolysis pathway is primarily regulated at the three key enzymatic steps (1, 2, and 7) as indicated. Note that the first two steps that are regulated occur early in the pathway and involve hydrolysis of ATP.

Phosphofructokinase is the main enzyme controlled in glycolysis. High levels of ATP, citrate, or a lower, more acidic pH decrease the enzyme's activity. An increase in citrate concentration can occur because of a blockage in the citric acid cycle. Fermentation, with its production of organic acids like lactic acid, frequently accounts for the increased acidity in a cell; however, the products of fermentation do not typically accumulate in cells.

The last step in glycolysis is catalyzed by pyruvate kinase. The pyruvate produced can proceed to be catabolized or converted into the amino acid alanine. If no more energy is needed and alanine is in adequate supply, the enzyme is inhibited. The enzyme's activity is increased when fructose-1,6-bisphosphate levels increase. (Recall that fructose-1,6-bisphosphate is an intermediate in the first half of glycolysis.) The regulation of pyruvate kinase involves phosphorylation by a kinase (pyruvate kinase kinase), resulting in a less-active enzyme. Dephosphorylation by a phosphatase reactivates it. Pyruvate kinase is also regulated by ATP (a negative allosteric effect).

If more energy is needed, more pyruvate will be converted into acetyl CoA through the action of pyruvate dehydrogenase. If either acetyl groups or NADH accumulate, there is less need for the reaction and the rate decreases. Pyruvate dehydrogenase is also regulated by phosphorylation: A kinase phosphorylates it to form an inactive enzyme, and a phosphatase reactivates it. The kinase and the phosphatase are also regulated.

Citric Acid Cycle

The citric acid cycle is controlled through the enzymes that catalyze the reactions that make the first two molecules of NADH (Figure 7.10). These enzymes are isocitrate dehydrogenase and α-ketoglutarate dehydrogenase. When adequate ATP and NADH levels are available, the rates of these reactions decrease. When more ATP is needed, as reflected in rising ADP levels, the rate increases. α-ketoglutarate dehydrogenase will also be affected by the levels of succinyl CoA—a subsequent intermediate in the cycle—causing a decrease in activity. A decrease in the rate of operation of the pathway at this point is not necessarily negative, as the increased levels of the α-ketoglutarate not used by the citric acid cycle can be used by the cell for amino acid (glutamate) synthesis.

Electron Transport Chain

Specific enzymes of the electron transport chain are unaffected by feedback inhibition, but the rate of electron transport through the pathway is affected by the levels of ADP and ATP. Greater ATP consumption by a cell is indicated by a buildup of ADP. As ATP usage decreases, the concentration of ADP decreases, and now, ATP begins to build up in the cell. This change in the relative concentration of ADP to ATP triggers the cell to slow down the electron transport chain.

Visit this site (http://openstaxcollege.org/l/electron_transp) to see an animation of the electron transport chain and ATP synthesis.

Which statement best describes the formation and importance of the hydrogen ion gradient during the electron transport chain?

a. A hydrogen ion gradient across the membrane establishes a concentration gradient and not an electrical gradient, thus assisting during the electron transport chain.

b. A hydrogen ion gradient is established by pumping two hydrogen ions across the membrane from the matrix in the intermembrane space. Its uneven distribution across the membrane establishes both concentration and electrical gradients.

c. A hydrogen ion gradient is established by pumping four hydrogen ions across the membrane from the matrix into the intermembrane space and its uneven distribution across the membrane establishes concentration and electrical gradients.

d. Hydrogen ions are present in the intermembrane space from the beginning and results in the formation of gradients necessary for the function of ATP synthase.

For a summary of feedback controls in cellular respiration, see Table 7.1.

Summary of Feedback Controls in Cellular Respiration

Pathway	Enzyme affected	Elevated levels of effector	Effect on pathway activity
glycolysis	hexokinase	glucose-6-phosphate	decrease
	phosphofructokinase	low-energy charge (ATP, AMP), fructose-6-phosphate via fructose-2,6-bisphosphate	increase
		high-energy charge (ATP, AMP), citrate, acidic pH	decrease
	pyruvate kinase	fructose-1,6-bisphosphate	increase
		high-energy charge (ATP, AMP), alanine	decrease
pyruvate to acetyl CoA conversion	pyruvate dehydrogenase	ADP, pyruvate	increase
		acetyl CoA, ATP, NADH	decrease
citric acid cycle	isocitrate dehydrogenase	ADP	increase
		ATP, NADH	decrease

Table 7.1

Summary of Feedback Controls in Cellular Respiration

Pathway	Enzyme affected	Elevated levels of effector	Effect on pathway activity
	α-ketoglutarate dehydrogenase	Calcium ions, ADP	increase
		ATP, NADH, succinyl CoA	decrease
electron transport chain		ADP	increase
		ATP	decrease

Table 7.1

Think About It

Phosphofructokinase is a key enzyme in glycolysis. High levels of ATP or citrate or low pH can decrease the enzyme's activity. Explain why this is beneficial to the cell.

KEY TERMS

acetyl CoA combination of an acetyl group derived from pyruvic acid and coenzyme A, which is made from pantothenic acid (a B-group vitamin)

aerobic respiration process in which organisms convert energy in the presence of oxygen

anaerobic process that does not use oxygen

anaerobic cellular respiration process in which organisms convert energy for their use in the absence of oxygen

ATP synthase (also, F1F0 ATP synthase) membrane-embedded protein complex that adds a phosphate to ADP with energy from protons diffusing through it

chemiosmosis process in which there is a production of adenosine triphosphate (ATP) in cellular metabolism by the involvement of a proton gradient across a membrane

citric acid cycle (also, Krebs cycle) series of enzyme-catalyzed chemical reactions of central importance in all living cells

dephosphorylation removal of a phosphate group from a molecule

fermentation process of regenerating NAD^+ with either an inorganic or organic compound serving as the final electron acceptor; occurs in the absence of oxygen

GLUT protein integral membrane protein that transports glucose

glycolysis process of breaking glucose into two three-carbon molecules with the production of ATP and NADH

isomerase enzyme that converts a molecule into its isomer

Krebs cycle (also, citric acid cycle) alternate name for the citric acid cycle, named after Hans Krebs who first identified the steps in the pathway in the 1930s in pigeon flight muscles; see citric acid cycle

oxidative phosphorylation production of ATP using the process of chemiosmosis and oxygen

phosphorylation addition of a high-energy phosphate to a compound, usually a metabolic intermediate, a protein, or ADP

prosthetic group (also, prosthetic cofactor) molecule bound to a protein that facilitates the function of the protein

pyruvate three-carbon sugar that can be decarboxylated and oxidized to make acetyl CoA, which enters the citric acid cycle under aerobic conditions; the end product of glycolysis

redox reaction chemical reaction that consists of the coupling of an oxidation reaction and a reduction reaction

substrate-level phosphorylation production of ATP from ADP using the excess energy from a chemical reaction and a phosphate group from a reactant

TCA cycle (also, citric acid cycle) alternate name for the citric acid cycle, named after the group name for citric acid, tricarboxylic acid (TCA); see citric acid cycle

ubiquinone soluble electron transporter in the electron transport chain that connects the first or second complex to the third

CHAPTER SUMMARY

7.1 Energy in Living Systems

ATP functions as the energy currency for cells. It allows the cell to store energy briefly and transport it within the cell to support endergonic chemical reactions. The structure of ATP is that of an RNA nucleotide with three phosphates attached. As ATP is used for energy, a phosphate group or two are detached, and either ADP or AMP is produced. Energy derived from glucose catabolism is used to convert ADP into ATP. When ATP is used in a reaction, the third phosphate is temporarily attached to a substrate in a process called phosphorylation. The two processes of ATP regeneration that are used in conjunction with glucose catabolism are substrate-level phosphorylation and oxidative phosphorylation through the process of chemiosmosis.

7.2 Glycolysis

Glycolysis is the first pathway used in the breakdown of glucose to extract energy. It was probably one of the earliest metabolic pathways to evolve and is used by nearly all of the organisms on earth. Glycolysis consists of two parts: The first part prepares the six-carbon ring of glucose for cleavage into two three-carbon sugars. ATP is invested in the process during this half to energize the separation. The second half of glycolysis extracts ATP and high-energy electrons from hydrogen atoms and attaches them to NAD^+. Two ATP molecules are invested in the first half and four ATP molecules are formed by substrate phosphorylation during the second half. This produces a net gain of two ATP and two NADH molecules for the cell.

7.3 Oxidation of Pyruvate and the Citric Acid Cycle

In the presence of oxygen, pyruvate is transformed into an acetyl group attached to a carrier molecule of coenzyme A. The resulting acetyl CoA can enter several pathways, but most often, the acetyl group is delivered to the citric acid cycle for further catabolism. During the conversion of pyruvate into the acetyl group, a molecule of carbon dioxide and two high-energy electrons are removed. The carbon dioxide accounts for two (conversion of two pyruvate molecules) of the six carbons of the original glucose molecule. The electrons are picked up by NAD^+, and the NADH carries the electrons to a later pathway for ATP production. At this point, the glucose molecule that originally entered cellular respiration has been completely oxidized. Chemical potential energy stored within the glucose molecule has been transferred to electron carriers or has been used to synthesize a few ATPs.

The citric acid cycle is a series of redox and decarboxylation reactions that remove high-energy electrons and carbon dioxide. The electrons temporarily stored in molecules of NADH and $FADH_2$ are used to generate ATP in a subsequent pathway. One molecule of either GTP or ATP is produced by substrate-level phosphorylation on each turn of the cycle. There is no comparison of the cyclic pathway with a linear one.

7.4 Oxidative Phosphorylation

The electron transport chain is the portion of aerobic respiration that uses free oxygen as the final electron acceptor of the electrons removed from the intermediate compounds in glucose catabolism. The electron transport chain is composed of four large, multiprotein complexes embedded in the inner mitochondrial membrane and two small diffusible electron carriers shuttling electrons between them. The electrons are passed through a series of redox reactions, with a small amount of free energy used at three points to transport hydrogen ions across a membrane. This process contributes to the gradient used in chemiosmosis. The electrons passing through the electron transport chain gradually lose energy, High-energy electrons donated to the chain by either NADH or $FADH_2$ complete the chain, as low-energy electrons reduce oxygen molecules and form water. The level of free energy of the electrons drops from about 60 kcal/mol in NADH or 45 kcal/mol in $FADH_2$ to about 0 kcal/mol in water. The end products of the electron transport chain are water and ATP. A number of intermediate compounds of the citric acid cycle can be diverted into the anabolism of other biochemical molecules, such as nonessential amino acids, sugars, and lipids. These same molecules can serve as energy sources for the glucose pathways.

7.5 Metabolism without Oxygen

If NADH cannot be oxidized through aerobic respiration, another electron acceptor is used. Most organisms will use some form of fermentation to accomplish the regeneration of NAD^+, ensuring the continuation of glycolysis. The regeneration of NAD^+ in fermentation is not accompanied by ATP production; therefore, the potential of NADH to produce ATP using an electron transport chain is not utilized.

7.6 Connections of Carbohydrate, Protein, and Lipid Metabolic Pathways

The breakdown and synthesis of carbohydrates, proteins, and lipids connect with the pathways of glucose catabolism. The simple sugars are galactose, fructose, glycogen, and pentose. These are catabolized during glycolysis. The amino acids from proteins connect with glucose catabolism through pyruvate, acetyl CoA, and components of the citric acid cycle. Cholesterol synthesis starts with acetyl groups, and the components of triglycerides come from glycerol-3-phosphate from glycolysis and acetyl groups produced in the mitochondria from pyruvate.

7.7 Regulation of Cellular Respiration

Cellular respiration is controlled by a variety of means. The entry of glucose into a cell is controlled by the transport proteins that aid glucose passage through the cell membrane. Most of the control of the respiration processes is accomplished through the control of specific enzymes in the pathways. This is a type of negative feedback, turning the enzymes off. The enzymes respond most often to the levels of the available nucleosides ATP, ADP, AMP, NAD^+, and FAD. Other intermediates of the pathway also affect certain enzymes in the systems.

REVIEW QUESTIONS

1. What is the most important energy currency used by cells?

a. ATP
b. ADP
c. AMP
d. adenosine

2. What happens when a chemical is reduced during a reaction?

a. The compound is reduced to a simpler form.
b. An electron is added to the chemical.
c. A hydrogen atom is removed from the substrate.
d. acts as a catabolic reaction

3. Which of the following molecules are oxidizing agents?

a. FAD^+ and NAD^+
b. $FADH_2$ and NADH
c. FAD and $FADH_2$
d. NAD^+ and NADH

4. Which of the following reactions releases energy?

a. $\text{AMP} + \text{phosphate} \rightarrow \text{ADP} + H_2O$
b. $\text{ADP} + \text{phosphate} \rightarrow \text{ATP} + H_2O$
c. $\text{ATP} + H_2O \rightarrow \text{ADP} + \text{Phosphate}$
d. $\text{AMP} + H_2O \rightarrow \text{ATP} + \text{Phosphate}$

5. During the second half of glycolysis, what occurs?

a. ATP is used up.
b. Fructose is split in two.
c. ATP is produced.
d. Glucose becomes fructose.

6. GLUTs are integral membrane proteins that assist in the facilitated diffusion of glucose into and out of cells. What reaction in glycolysis prevents glucose from being transported back out of the cell?

a. Hexokinase dephosphorylates glucose using ATP, creating a glucose molecules that can't cross the hydrophilic portion of the plasma membrane.
b. Hexokinase phosphorylates glucose using ADP, creating a glucose molecules that can't cross the hydrophobic interior of the plasma membrane.
c. Hexokinase dephosphorylates glucose using ADP, creating a glucose molecule that can't cross the hydrophilic portion of the plasma membrane.
d. Hexokinase phosphorylates glucose using ATP, creating a glucose molecule that can't cross the hydrophobic interior of the plasma membrane.

7. How many ATP molecules are used and produced per molecule of glucose during glycolysis?

a. The first half of glycolysis uses 2 ATPs, and the second half of glycolysis produces 4 ATPs.
b. The first half of glycolysis produces 2 ATPs, and the second half of glycolysis uses 4 ATPs.
c. The first half of glycolysis uses 4 ATPs, and the second half of glycolysis produces 2 ATPs.
d. The first half of glycolysis produces 4 ATPS, and the second half of glycolysis uses 2 ATPs.

8. What is removed from pyruvate during its conversion into an acetyl group?

a. oxygen
b. ATP
c. B vitamin
d. carbon dioxide

9. What do the electrons added to NAD^+ do in aerobic respiration?

a. They become part of a fermentation pathway.
b. They go to another pathway for ATP production.
c. They energize the acetyl group in the citric acid cycle.
d. They are converted to NADP.

10. GTP, which can be converted to ATP, is produced during which reaction of the citric acid cycle?

a. isocitrate into α-ketoglutarate
b. succinyl-CoA into succinate
c. fumarate into malate
d. malate into oxaloacetate

11. How many NADH molecules are produced on each turn of the citric acid cycle?

a. one
b. two
c. three
d. four

12. What compound receives electrons from NADH?

a. FMN
b. ubiquinone
c. cytochrome c1
d. oxygen

13. Chemiosmosis involves the movement of what? Where does it occur?

a. electrons across the cell membrane
b. hydrogen atoms across a mitochondrial membrane
c. hydrogen ions across a mitochondrial membrane
d. glucose through the cell membrane

14. What is the function of an electron in the electron transport chain?

a. to dephosphorylate ATP, producing ADP
b. to power active transport pumps
c. to reduce heme in complex III
d. to oxidize oxygen

15. What would be the outcome if hydrogen ions were able to diffuse through the mitochondrial membrane into the mitochondria without the need for integral membrane proteins?

a. ATP would not be produced.
b. Pyruvate would not be produced.
c. Citric acid would not be produced.
d. Carbon dioxide would not be produced.

16. Which of the following fermentation methods can occur in animal skeletal muscles?

a. lactic acid fermentation
b. alcohol fermentation
c. mixed acid fermentation
d. propionic fermentation

17. Which molecules are produced in glycolysis and used in fermentation?

a. acetyl-CoA and NADH
b. lactate, ATP, and CO_2
c. glucose, ATP, and NAD^+
d. pyruvate and NADH

18. What are the products of alcohol fermentation?

a. methane and NADH
b. lactic acid and FAD^+
c. ethanol and NAD^+
d. pyruvic acid and NADH

19. In the first step of glycolysis, what is glucose transformed into?

a. glucose-6-phosphate
b. fructose-1,6-bisphosphate
c. dihydroxyacetone phosphate
d. phosphoenolpyruvate

20. What is beta-oxidation?

a. the main process used to break down glucose
b. the main process used to assemble glucose
c. the main process used to break down fatty acids
d. the main process used to remove amino groups from amino acids

21. Which of the following statements about catabolic pathways is false?

a. Carbohydrates can feed into oxidative phosphorylation.
b. Glycerol can be broken down into glucose and feed into glycolysis.
c. Amino acids can feed into pyruvate oxidation.
d. Fatty acids can feed into the citric acid cycle.

22. What impact, if any, do high levels of ADP have on glycolysis?

a. They increase the activity of enzymes involved with glycolysis.
b. The high levels decrease the activity of enzymes involved with glycolysis.
c. They have no effect on the activity of any enzymes involved with glycolysis.
d. The high levels slow down all pathways involved with glycolysis.

23. The control of which enzyme exerts the greatest control of glycolysis?

a. hexokinase
b. phosphofructokinase
c. glucose-6-phosphatase
d. aldolase

24. Which of the following does not occur as ATP concentration increases relative to ADP?

a. decreased activity of phosphofructokinase
b. increased activity of pyruvate kinase
c. decreased activity of isocitrate dehydrogenase
d. slowdown of the electron transport chain

CRITICAL THINKING QUESTIONS

25. Why is it beneficial for cells to use ATP rather than directly using the energy stored in the bonds of carbohydrates to power cellular reactions? What are the greatest drawbacks to harnessing energy from the bonds of several different compounds?

a. ATP is readily available in the form of a single unit that provides a consistent, appropriate amount of energy. The cell would need to tailor each reaction to each energy source if it harvested energy from different compounds.
b. ATP energy cannot activate the ROS dependent stress response whereas food molecules are responsible for activating ROS.
c. ATP is low in energy, but food molecules possess higher levels of energy that cells can use.
d. ATP is readily available to cells, unlike compounds that have to first be phosphorylated in order to release their energy.

26. What role does NAD^+ play in redox reactions?

a. NAD^+, an oxidizing agent, can accept electrons and protons from organic molecules and get reduced to $NADH$.
b. NAD^+, a reducing agent, can donate its electrons and protons to organic molecules.
c. NAD^+, an oxidizing agent, can accept electrons from organic molecules and get reduced to $NADH_2$.
d. NAD^+, a reducing agent, can donate its electrons and protons to inorganic molecules.

27. Which statement best explains how electrons are transferred and the role of each species. Remember that R represents a hydrocarbon molecule and RH represents the same molecule with a particular hydrogen identified.
$RH + NAD^+ \rightarrow NADH + R$

a. RH acts as a reducing agent and donates its electrons to the oxidizing agent NAD^+, forming $NADH$ and R.
b. NAD^+, the oxidizing agent, donates its electrons to the reducing agent RH, forming R and $NADH$.
c. RH acts as an oxidizing agent and donates electrons to the reducing agent NAD^+, producing $NADH$ and R.
d. NAD^+, the reducing agent, accepts electrons from the oxidizing agent RH, producing $NADH$ and R.

28. Nearly all organisms on earth carry out some form of glycolysis. How does this fact support or not support the assertion that glycolysis is one of the oldest metabolic pathways?

a. To be present in so many different organisms, glycolysis was probably present in a common ancestor rather than evolving many separate times.
b. Glycolysis is present in nearly all organisms because it is an advanced and recently evolved pathway that has been widely used as it is so beneficial.
c. Glycolysis is absent in a few higher organisms. This contradicts the fact that it is one of the oldest metabolic pathways.
d. Glycolysis is present in some organisms and absent in others. The mentioned fact may or may not support this assertion.

29. Red blood cells (RBCs) do not perform aerobic respiration, but they do perform glycolysis. Why do all cells need an energy source and what would happen if glycolysis were blocked in a red blood cell?

a. Cells require energy to perform certain basic functions. Blocking glycolysis in RBCs causes imbalance in the membrane potential, leading to cell death.
b. Cells need energy to perform cell division. Blocking glycolysis in RBCs interrupts the process of mitosis leading to nondisjunction.
c. Cells maintain the influx and efflux of organic substances using energy. Blocking glycolysis stops the binding of CO_2 to the RBCs, causing cell death.
d. Cells require energy to recognize attacking pathogens. Blocked glycolysis inhibits the process of recognition, causing invasion of the RBCs by a pathogen.

30. What is the primary difference between a circular pathway and a linear pathway?

a. The reactant and the product are the same in a circular pathway but different in a linear pathway.
b. The circular pathway components get exhausted whereas those of the linear pathway do not and are continually regenerated.
c. Circular pathways are not suited for amphibolic pathways whereas linear pathways are.
d. Circular pathways contain a single chemical reaction that is repeated while linear pathways have multiple events.

31. Cellular respiration breaks down glucose and releases carbon dioxide and water. Which steps in the oxidation of pyruvate produces carbon dioxide?

a. Removal of a carboxyl group from pyruvate releases carbon dioxide. The pyruvate dehydrogenase complex comes into play.
b. Removal of an acetyl group from pyruvate releases carbon dioxide. The pyruvate decarboxylase complex comes into play.
c. Removal of a carbonyl group from pyruvate releases carbon dioxide. The pyruvate dehydrogenase complex comes into play.
d. Removal of an acetyl group from pyruvate releases carbon dioxide. The pyruvate dehydrogenase complex comes into play.

32. What three steps are included in the breakdown of pyruvate?

a. Pyruvate dehydrogenase removes a carboxyl group from pyruvate producing carbon dioxide. Dihydrolipoyl transacetylase oxidizes a hydroxyethyl group to an acetyl group, producing NADH. Lastly, an enzyme-bound acetyl group is transferred to CoA, producing a molecule of acetyl-CoA.
b. Pyruvate dehydrogenase oxidizes hydroxyethyl group to an acetyl group, producing NADH. It further removes a carboxyl group from pyruvate producing carbon dioxide. Lastly, dihydrolipoyl transacetylase transfers enzyme-bound acetyl group to CoA forming an acetyl-CoA molecule.
c. Pyruvate dehydrogenase transfers enzyme-bound acetyl group to CoA forming an acetyl CoA molecule. It then oxidizes a hydroxyethyl group to an acetyl group, producing NADH. Dihydrolipoyl transacetylase removes a carboxyl group from pyruvate producing carbon dioxide.
d. Pyruvate dehydrogenase removes carboxyl group from pyruvate producing carbon dioxide. Dihydrolipoyl dehydrogenase transfers enzyme-bound acetyl groups to CoA forming an acetyl-CoA molecule. Lastly, a hydroxyethyl group is oxidized to an acetyl group, producing NADH.

33. How do the roles of ubiquinone and cytochrome c differ from the other components of the electron transport chain?

a. CoQ and cytochrome c are mobile electron carriers while NADH dehydrogenase and succinate dehydrogenase are bound to the inner mitochondrial membrane.
b. CoQ and cytochrome covalently bind electrons while NADH dehydrogenase and succinate dehydrogenase are bound to the inner mitochondrial membrane.
c. CoQ and cytochrome c are bound to the inner mitochondrial membrane while NADH dehydrogenase and succinate dehydrogenase are mobile electron carriers.
d. CoQ and cytochrome c covalently bind electrons while NADH dehydrogenase and succinate dehydrogenase are mobile electron carriers.

34. What accounts for the different number of ATP molecules that are formed through cellular respiration?

a. Transport of NADH from cytosol to mitochondria is an active process that decreases the number of ATP produced.

b. The ATPs produced are utilized in the anaplerotic reactions that are used for the replenishment of the intermediates.

c. Most of the ATP's produced are rapidly used for the phosphorylation of certain compounds found in plants.

d. A large number of ATP molecules are used in the detoxification of xenobiotic compounds produced during cellular respiration.

35. Which of the following best describes complex IV in the electron transport chain?

a. Complex IV consists of an oxygen molecule held between the cytochrome and copper ions. The electrons flowing finally reach the oxygen, producing water.

b. Complex IV contains a molecule of flavin mononucleotide and iron-sulfur clusters. The electrons from NADH are transported here to coenzyme Q.

c. Complex IV contains cytochrome b, c, and Fe-S. Here, the proton motive Q cycle takes place.

d. Complex IV contains a membrane-bound enzyme that accepts electrons from $FADH_2$ to make FAD. This electron is then transferred to ubiquinone.

36. What is the primary difference between fermentation and anaerobic respiration?

a. Fermentation uses only glycolysis and its final electron acceptor is an organic molecule, whereas anaerobic respiration uses glycolysis, TCA and the ETC but finally give electrons to an inorganic molecule.

b. Fermentation uses glycolysis, TCA and ETC but finally gives electrons to an inorganic molecule, whereas anaerobic respiration uses only glycolysis and its final electron acceptor is an organic molecule.

c. Fermentation uses glycolysis and its final electron acceptor is an inorganic molecule, whereas anaerobic respiration uses glycolysis, TCA and ETC but finally give electrons to an organic molecule.

d. Fermentation uses glycolysis, TCA and ETC but finally gives electrons to an organic molecule, whereas anaerobic respiration uses only glycolysis and its final electron acceptor is an inorganic molecule.

37. What type of cellular respiration is represented in the following equation, and why?

$$CO_2 + H_2 + NADH \rightarrow CH_4 + H_2O + NAD^+$$

a. Anaerobic respiration, because the final electron acceptor is inorganic.

b. Aerobic respiration, because oxygen is the final electron acceptor.

c. Anaerobic respiration, because NADH donates its electrons to a methane molecule.

d. Aerobic respiration, because water is being produced as a product.

38. Would you describe metabolic pathways as inherently wasteful or inherently economical, and why?

a. Metabolic pathways are economical due to feedback inhibition. Also, intermediates from one pathway can be utilized by other pathways.

b. Metabolic pathways are wasteful as they perform uncoordinated catabolic and anabolic reactions that wastes some of the energy that is stored.

c. Metabolic pathways are economical due to the presence of anaplerotic reactions that replenish the intermediates.

d. Metabolic pathways are wasteful as most of the energy produced is utilized in maintaining the reduced environment of the cytosol.

39. What lipids are connected to glucose catabolism pathways and how are they connected?

a. Cholesterol and triglycerides can be converted to glycerol-3-phosphate that continues through glycolysis.

b. Glucagon and glycogen can be converted to 3-phosphoglyceraldehyde that is an intermediate of glycolysis.

c. Chylomicrons and fatty acids get converted to 1,3-bisphosphoglycerate that continues in glycolysis, forming pyruvate.

d. Sphingolipids and triglycerides form glucagon that can be fed into glycolysis.

40. How does citrate from the citric acid cycle affect glycolysis?

a. Citrate and ATP are negative regulators of phosphofructokinase-1.

b. Citrate and ATP are negative regulators of hexokinase.

c. Citrate and ATP are positive regulators of phosphofructokinase-1.

d. Citrate and ATP are positive regulators of hexokinase.

41. Why might negative feedback mechanisms be more common than positive feedback mechanisms in living cells?

a. Negative feedback mechanisms maintain homeostasis whereas positive feedback drives the system away from equilibrium.

b. Positive feedback mechanisms maintain a balanced amount of substances whereas negative feedback restricts them.

c. Negative feedback turns the system off, making it deficient of certain substances. Positive feedback balances out these deficits.

d. Positive feedback brings substance amounts back to equilibrium while negative feedback produces excess amounts of the substance.

TEST PREP FOR AP® COURSES

42.

Organism	Temperature (°C)	Average respiration (mL O2/g/min)
Mouse	10	0.0518
Mouse	25	0.0321
Cricket	10	0.0013
Cricket	25	0.0038

The table shows the amount of oxygen consumed (third column) by different animals (first column) at different temperatures. This type of apparatus measures the change in volume of air to detect the removal of oxygen. However, organisms produce carbon dioxide as they take in oxygen. To provide accurate measurements, what would you need to add to the setup?

a. a substance that removes carbon dioxide gas

b. a plant that will add oxygen to allow an animal to breathe

c. a glucose reserve

d. a substance that adds carbon dioxide gas

43.

Organism	Temperature (°C)	Average respiration (mL O2/g/min)
Mouse	10	0.0518
Mouse	25	0.0321
Cricket	10	0.0013
Cricket	25	0.0038

According to the data, the crickets at 25° C have greater oxygen consumption per gram of tissue than do the crickets at 10° C. This trend in oxygen consumption is the opposite of that in mice. The difference in trends in oxygen consumption among crickets and mice is due to what?

a. their difference in size

b. their mode of nutrition

c. their difference in metabolic heat production

d. their mode of ATP production

44. Where in a cell does glycolysis take place in both prokaryotes and eukaryotes?

a. the cytosol

b. the mitochondria

c. the plasma membrane

d. the nucleus

45. A new species of obligate anaerobe, a bacterium, has been found that lives in hot, acidic conditions. While other pathways may also be present, which metabolic pathway is the most likely to be present in this species?

a. aerobic respiration

b. the citric acid cycle

c. oxidative phosphorylation

d. glycolysis

46. What evidence provides the strongest support that glycolysis is an older and more conserved pathway than the citric acid cycle?

a. Glycolysis is the primitive pathway as it is found in all three domains. It also occurs in anaerobic conditions and in the cytosol.

b. This pathway occurs in the cytosol, is found in all animals and plants, and does not require oxygen.

c. Glycolysis takes place in anaerobic conditions, can metabolize cholesterol and fatty acids, and occurs even in methanogens.

d. This pathway only occurs in the mitochondria. It is highly flexible because it is found in almost all organisms.

47.

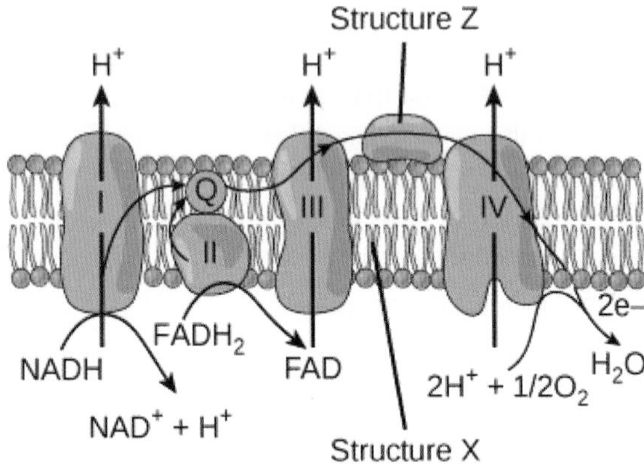

What is Structure X in the graphic?

a. the inner mitochondrial membrane

b. the mitochondrial matrix

c. a eukaryotic plasma membrane

d. the cytosol

48.

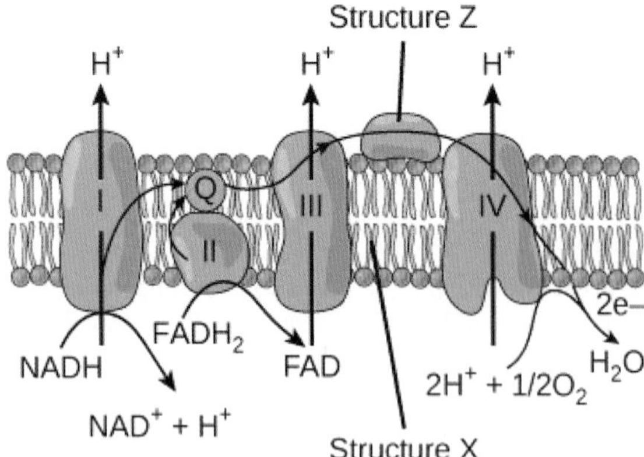

What would be the most direct result of blocking structure Z in the graphic?

a. Cytochrome c would not pass electrons from complex III to complex IV.

b. Ubiquinone would not pass electrons from complex III to complex IV.

c. $NADH$ would not be converted to NAD_{+} and the electron transport chain would stop.

d. No protons would be pumped across the membrane.

49.

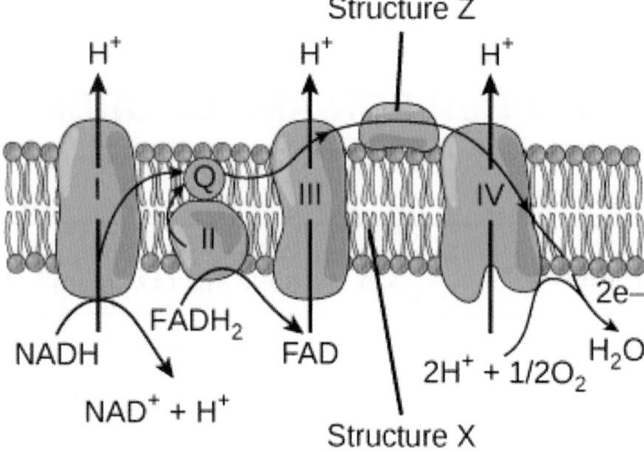

Where do the electrons moving along the membrane in the figure come from, and where do the electrons end up?

a. The electrons are released by $NADH$ and $FADH_2$ and finally accepted by oxygen to form water.

b. The electrons are given off by water and finally accepted by NAD^+ and FAD^+ to produce the energy currencies $NADH$ and $FADH_2$.

c. The electrons are emitted by ubiquinone that are, in turn, transferred from complex I to complex II. Water finally accepts the electrons.

d. The electrons are given out by $NADH$ and $FADH_2$ and are, in turn, finally accepted by H_2O.

50. Glucose catabolism pathways are sequential and lead to the production of ATP. What is the correct order of the pathways for the breakdown of a molecule of glucose as shown in the formula?

$C_6H_{12}O_6 + O_2 \rightarrow CO_2 + H_2O + \text{energy}$

a. oxidative phosphorylation → citric acid cycle → oxidation of pyruvate → glycolysis

b. the oxidation of pyruvate → citric acid cycle → glycolysis → oxidative phosphorylation

c. glycolysis → oxidation of pyruvate → citric acid cycle → oxidative phosphorylation

d. citric acid cycle → glycolysis → oxidative phosphorylation → oxidation of pyruvate

51. Which of the following statements most directly supports the claim that different species of organisms use different metabolic strategies to meet their energy requirements for growth, reproduction, and homeostasis?

a. During cold periods, pond-dwelling animals can increase the number of unsaturated fatty acids in their cell membranes while some plants make antifreeze proteins to prevent ice crystal formation in their tissues.

b. Bacteria lack introns while many eukaryotic genes contain many of these intervening sequences.

c. Carnivores have more teeth that are specialized for ripping food while herbivores have more teeth specialized for grinding food.

d. Plants generally use starch molecules for storage while animals use glycogen and fats for storage.

52. Which of the following best describes how the citric acid cycle relates to glycolysis, oxidative phosphorylation, and chemiosmosis?

a. Glycolysis produces pyruvate, which is converted to acetyl-CoA and enters the citric acid cycle. This cycle produces $NADH$ and $FADH_2$, which donate electrons to the electron transport chain to pump protons and produce ATP through chemiosmosis. Production of ATP using an electron transport chain and chemiosmosis is called oxidative phosphorylation.

b. The citric acid produces pyruvate, which converts to glucose to enter glycolysis. This pathway produces $NADH$ and $FADH_2$, which enter oxidative phosphorylation to produce ATP through chemiosmosis.

c. Citric acid produces $NADH$ and $FADH_2$, which undergo oxidative phosphorylation. This produces ATP by pumping protons through chemiosmosis. The ATP produced is utilized in large amount in the process of glycolysis.

d. Glycolysis produces pyruvate, which directly enters the citric acid cycle. This cycle produces the energy currency that undergoes the electron transport chain to produce water and ATP.

SCIENCE PRACTICE CHALLENGE QUESTIONS

53. Combustion of carbohydrates, like in a fireplace, is a reduction-oxidation reaction in which the carbon atom is oxidized and the oxygen atom is reduced, producing water and carbon dioxide. Oxidative phosphorylation and glycolysis are also reduction-oxidation reactions that produce the same products. Explain the differences and similarities among these abiotic and biotic processes in terms of the changes in entropy and heat that contribute to the free energy extracted from chemical bonds, the spontaneity of each, and the role of catalysis.

54. A. **[Extension]** Living systems require free energy to carry out cellular functions, and employ various strategies to capture, use, and store free energy. **Explain** the advantage that the higher energy efficiency per kg of the Krebs cycle provides to *you* compared to a metabolism based on glycolysis alone. Your explanation should make use of all the following facts:

- ΔG for glycolysis is -135kJ per mole of glucose
- ΔG for aerobic respiration is -2880kJ per mole glucose
- the basal metabolic rate of mammals is often represented as -300kJ/day • $m^{0.75}$
- the molar mass of glucose is 180 g/mole

B. **Explain** the bioenergetic difference between aerobic and anaerobic respiration in terms of the difference between free-energy production and power. Your explanation should make use of all the following facts:

- power is the rate of free-energy production
- cancer cells derive most of their free energy from glycolysis
- enzymes of the citric acid (Kreb's) cycle form coordinate complexes on the cytoskeleton within the mitochondria

C. The life cycle of the human parasite *Trypanosoma brucei* is divided between the body of the tsetse fly and the human blood stream. The parasite causes "sleeping sickness" in Sub-Saharan Africa. Within the human bloodstream, the parasite depends on glycolysis, with enzymes compartmentalized in a membrane-bound organelle called the glycosome. In the insect host, the parasite utilizes glycolysis as well as substrate-level and oxidative phosphorylation. **Explain** the advantage of a life cycle in the human host that employs anaerobic respiration with a rate of free-energy production that is enhanced by compartmentalization in the glycosome and a life cycle in the insect host that is aerobic.

D. **Predict** the advantages of a biological system that uses both glycolysis and oxidative phosphorylation. Your prediction should make use of all the following facts:

- signaling can be used to detect low-oxygen environments and to regulate response
- some cells, such as muscle and blood cells, must function in both low- and high-oxygen environments
- glycolysis is reversible
- the citric acid cycle is not reversible
- thermoregulation is needed for homeostasis

55. Dinitrophenol (DNP) was used in the manufacture of munitions in World War I. In the 1930s, it was used as a weight loss drug. Use in the U.S. cannot be regulated by the FDA because DNP is considered a dietary supplement. Attempts to ban the drug in the U.K. following the death of four users in 2015 failed in Parliament. DNP is a small molecule that is soluble in the mitochondrial inner membrane. The hydroxyl group reversibly dissociates a proton.

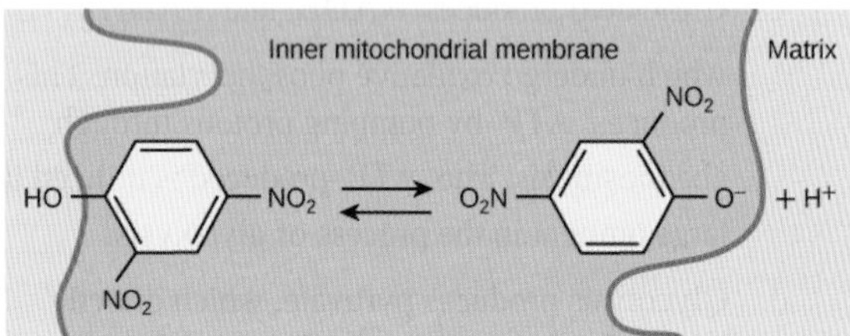

Figure 7.21

A. **Predict** the effect of DNP on the electrochemical gradient across the inner mitochondrial membrane.

B. **Explain** how DNP can be used to reduce weight.

C. The effects of DNP can be reversed by administering glucose. However, treatment with a combination of glucose and 2-deoxyglucose, which is an inhibitor of glycolysis, does not reverse the effects of DNP. **Explain**, in terms of the products of glycolysis, why this reversal of the effects of DNP was unexpected. (Hint: It might be useful to review the reactants and products of glycolysis.)

D. Obesity correlates with an epidemic of other health issues, such as elevated blood pressure, heart disease, and diabetes II. A slow-release form of DNP (CRMP) is patented. With slow-release technology, a drug can be delivered in small doses over time from a pill whose matrix limits solubility. A simple but nonscientific question that can be raised is: Will a slow-release drug retard progress toward behavioral changes that can reduce the magnitude of this epidemic? Scientific questions can be pursued by testing the outcomes predicted by possible answers. **Refine this question** for discussion in small groups. Be prepared to **justify** the merits of your question.

56. As shown in Figure 7.11, cyanide inhibits the electron transport chain by competing with O_2 molecules for the cytochrome c oxidase heme group. Carbon monoxide (CO) has a similar effect. Both cyanide and carbon monoxide cause poisoning in victims of smoke inhalation.

A. **Predict** the effects of these poisons on the following properties of mitochondria just after exposure: the pH of the intermembrane space, the concentration of NADH, and the rate of production of ATP in the matrix. **Justify** your predictions.

B. Rotenone is a poison that blocks the transfer of electrons from Complex I of the electron transport chain to ubiquinone. Methylene blue is a molecule with many uses involving its reduction-oxidation properties. Recent studies show the effectiveness of methylene blue in increasing the body's metabolic rate and as a treatment for Alzheimer's patients. The oxidized form of methylene blue is reduced by NADH, and its reduced form is oxidized by O_2. **Explain** the use of methylene blue as an antidote for rotenone poisoning.

57. *E. coli* are enteric (gut-dwelling) facultative anaerobic bacteria. (Facultative anaerobes can grow either with or without free oxygen. Obligatory anaerobes grow only in the absence of free oxygen.) Researchers planned to grow cultures of *E. coli* under a range of conditions to model the transition from strictly anaerobic to aerobic respiration.

The oxygen content of atmospheres at constant total pressure will be controlled by volumes of nitrogen and oxygen gases. Ratios of volume, $r = V_{O_2}/V_{N_2}$ between 0 and 0.25 of shaken growth flasks can be measured in terms of optical density, which is the percent of transmission of light through a sample of the growing *E. coli* culture. A rule of thumb is that the range of strict anaerobes is when $r < 0.01$, and the boundary for aerobic respiration is when $r = 0.05$. A large number of flasks that can be constantly shaken at fixed temperature, and from which samples can be taken without atmospheric contamination, are available for this study.

These results of the experiment will be used to infer growth rates of *E. coli* along the entire 7.5 m length of the average human intestine (small intestine and large intestine), where the oxygen content varies from atmospheric to anaerobic conditions. The retention time of food in the small intestine, whose average length is 2.5 m, is approximately four hours. The retention time of food over the entire length of the intestine is between 24 and 72 hours.

A. **Describe and apply a mathematical model** that can be used to represent the variation of oxygen environments of a bacterium that is being transported with the food along the length of the intestine.

B. **Design** the experimental sampling times in terms of growth intervals of interest in this study: i) the time when the bacteria is passing the small-large intestine boundary; ii) the time when the bacteria reaches the end of the large intestine; and iii) the time when the bacterium reaches facultative anaerobic conditions, $r < 0.05$.

C. Sketch a graph that **predicts** the distribution of aerobic, facultative anaerobic and obligatory anaerobic bacteria along the length of the entire intestine based on these parameters. Keep in mind that anaerobes have a lower respiration rate.

58. White snakeroot is a plant that contains chemicals that deactivate the enzyme lactate dehydrogenase. Humans who consume milk from cows or goats that eat white snakeroot can become ill. Symptoms of milk poisoning include vomiting, abdominal pain, and tremors, which become worse after exercise. Beyond childhood, most people do not express the enzyme lactase that catalyzes the breakdown of lactose into glucose and galactose. Consumption of milk can produce symptoms similar to those of milk poisoning. After a period of consumption of dairy foods, though, prebiotic adaptation (changes in the microbes in the intestine) imparts lactose tolerance. Since dairy foods are a valuable source of calcium, proteins, and vitamin D, considerable research has been conducted to characterize adaptation.

Explain the similarities and differences between the effect of milk poisoning by white snakeroot and lactose intolerance, and the possibility of prebiotic adaptation for each.

8 | PHOTOSYNTHESIS

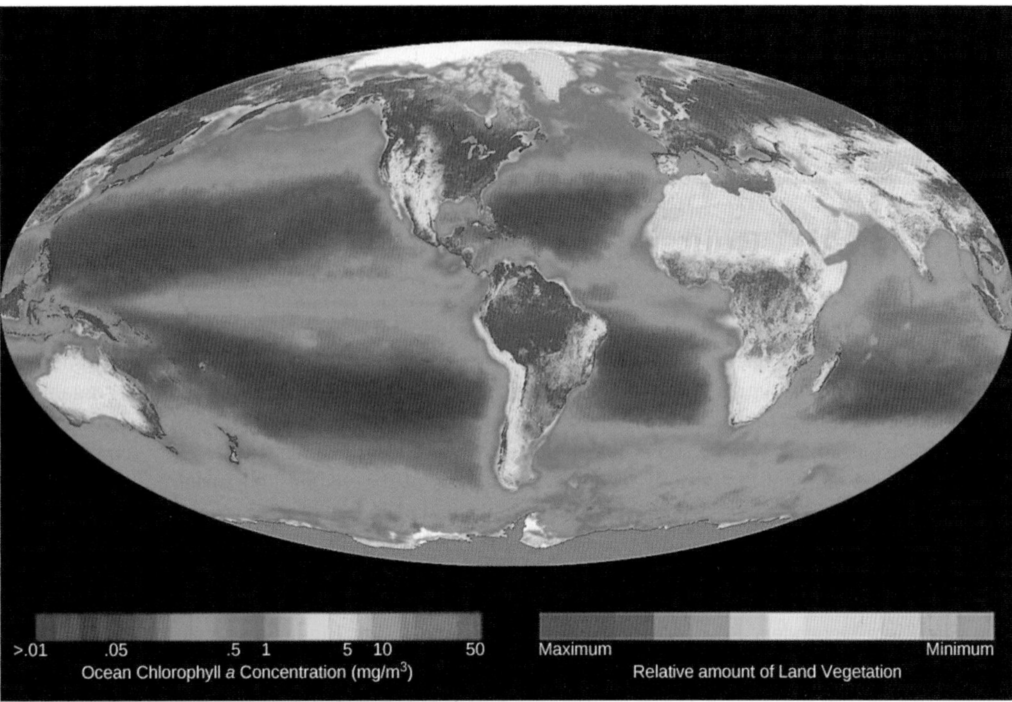

Figure 8.1 This world map shows Earth's distribution of photosynthesis as seen via chlorophyll *a* concentrations. On land, this is evident via terrestrial plants, and in oceanic zones, via phytoplankton. (credit: modification of work by SeaWiFS Project, NASA/Goddard Space Flight Center and ORBIMAGE)

Chapter Outline

Introduction

All biological processes require energy. To get this energy, many organisms access stored energy by eating, that is, by ingesting other organisms. But where does the stored energy in food originate? Almost all of this energy can be traced back to photosynthesis.

Photosynthetic organisms are the basis for almost all of the food webs on the planet. For example, the Indian River Lagoon, a 156 mile mixture of fresh and salt water along the eastern coast of Florida, depends on its sea grass for the survival of its marine life. Unfortunately, when certain algal phytoplankton species grow in overabundance, it destroys the sea grass. Scientists conducted a 16 year study of algal blooms and found that extreme climate conditions, such as cold weather and low rainfall, change which particular species of phytoplankton is more likely to bloom, resulting in a die-off of sea grass, decrease in other marine life, and changes in salinity. The research study can be found **here (http://openstaxcollege.org/l/32algae)** .

8.1 | Overview of Photosynthesis

In this section, you will explore the following questions:

- What is the relevance of photosynthesis to living organisms?
- What are the main cellular structures involved in photosynthesis?
- What are the substrates and products of photosynthesis?

Connection for AP® Courses

As we learned in Chapter 7, all living organisms, from simple bacteria to complex plants and animals, require free energy to carry out cellular processes, such as growth and reproduction. Organisms use various strategies to capture, store, transform, and transfer free energy, including photosynthesis. Photosynthesis allows organisms to access enormous amounts of free energy from the sun and transform it to the chemical energy of sugars. Although all organisms carry out some form of cellular respiration, only certain organisms, called photoautotrophs, can perform photosynthesis. Examples of photoautotrophs include plants, algae, some unicellular eukaryotes, and cyanobacteria. They require the presence of chlorophyll, a specialized pigment that absorbs certain wavelengths of the visible light spectrum to harness free energy from the sun. Photosynthesis is a process where components of water and carbon dioxide are used to assemble carbohydrate molecules and where oxygen waste products are released into the atmosphere. In eukaryotes, the reactions of photosynthesis occur in chloroplasts; in prokaryotes, such as cyanobacteria, the reactions are less localized and occur within membranes and in the cytoplasm. (The structural features of the chloroplast that participate in photosynthesis will be explored in more detail later in The Light-Dependent Reactions of Photosynthesis and Using Light Energy to Make Organic Molecules.) Although photosynthesis and cellular respiration evolved as independent processes—with photosynthesis creating an oxidizing atmosphere early in Earth's history—today they are interdependent. As we studied in Cellular Respiration, aerobic cellular respiration taps into the oxidizing ability of oxygen to synthesize the organic compounds that are used to power cellular processes.

Information presented and the examples highlighted in the section support concepts and learning objectives outlined in Big Idea 1 and Big Idea 2 of the AP® Biology Curriculum Framework, as shown in the table. The learning objectives listed in the Curriculum Framework provide a transparent foundation for the AP® Biology course, an inquiry-based laboratory experience, instructional activities, and AP® exam questions. A learning objective merges required content with one or more of the seven science practices.

Big Idea 1	The process of evolution drives the diversity and unity of life.
Enduring Understanding 1.B	Organisms are linked by lines of descent from common ancestry.
Essential Knowledge	**1.B.1** Structural and functional evidence supports the relatedness of all domains, with organisms shared many conserved core processes.
Science Practice	**6.1** The student can justify claims with evidence.
Learning Objective	**1.15** The student is able to describe specific examples of conserved core biological processes and features shared by all domains s or within one domain of life, and how these shared, conserved core processes and features support the concept of common ancestry for all organisms.
Big Idea 2	Biological systems utilize free energy and molecular building blocks to grow, to reproduce, and to maintain dynamic homeostasis.
Enduring Understanding 2.A	Growth, reproduction and maintenance of living systems require free energy and matter.

Essential Knowledge	**2.A.2** Organisms use various strategies to capture and store free energy for use in biological processes.
Science Practice	**1.4** The student can use representations and models to analyze situations or solve problems qualitatively and quantitatively.
Science Practice	**3.1** The student can pose scientific questions.
Learning Objective	**2.4** The student is able to use representations to pose scientific questions about what mechanisms and structural features allow organisms to capture, store, and use free energy.
Essential Knowledge	**2.A.2** Organisms use various strategies to capture and store free energy for use in biological processes.
Science Practice	**6.2** The student can construct explanations of phenomena based on evidence produced through scientific practices.
Learning Objective	**2.5** The student is able to construct explanations of the mechanisms and structural features of cells that allow organisms to capture, store, or use free energy.

Importance of Photosynthesis

Photosynthesis is essential to all life on earth; both plants and animals depend on it. It is the only biological process that can capture energy that originates in outer space (sunlight) and convert it into chemical compounds (carbohydrates) that every organism uses to power its metabolism. In brief, the energy of sunlight is captured and used to energize electrons, whose energy is then stored in the covalent bonds of sugar molecules. How long lasting and stable are those covalent bonds? The energy extracted today by the burning of coal and petroleum products represents sunlight energy captured and stored by photosynthesis almost 200 million years ago.

Plants, algae, and a group of bacteria called cyanobacteria are the only organisms capable of performing photosynthesis (Figure 8.2). Because they use light to manufacture their own food, they are called **photoautotrophs** (literally, “self-feeders using light”). Other organisms, such as animals, fungi, and most other bacteria, are termed **heterotrophs** (“other feeders”), because they must rely on the sugars produced by photosynthetic organisms for their energy needs. A third very interesting group of bacteria synthesize sugars, not by using sunlight’s energy, but by extracting energy from inorganic chemical compounds; hence, they are referred to as **chemoautotrophs**.

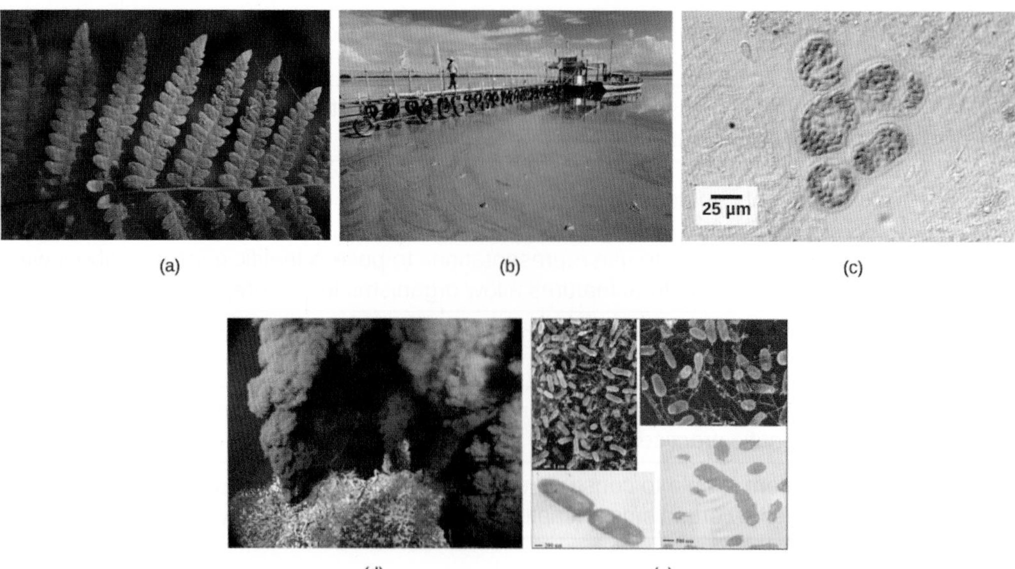

Figure 8.2 Photoautotrophs including (a) plants, (b) algae, and (c) cyanobacteria synthesize their organic compounds via photosynthesis using sunlight as an energy source. Cyanobacteria and planktonic algae can grow over enormous areas in water, at times completely covering the surface. In a (d) deep sea vent, chemoautotrophs, such as these (e) thermophilic bacteria, capture energy from inorganic compounds to produce organic compounds. The ecosystem surrounding the vents has a diverse array of animals, such as tubeworms, crustaceans, and octopi that derive energy from the bacteria. (credit a: modification of work by Steve Hillebrand, U.S. Fish and Wildlife Service; credit b: modification of work by "eutrophication&hypoxia"/Flickr; credit c: modification of work by NASA; credit d: University of Washington, NOAA; credit e: modification of work by Mark Amend, West Coast and Polar Regions Undersea Research Center, UAF, NOAA)

The importance of photosynthesis is not just that it can capture sunlight's energy. A lizard sunning itself on a cold day can use the sun's energy to warm up. Photosynthesis is vital because it evolved as a way to store the energy in solar radiation (the "photo-" part) as energy in the carbon-carbon bonds of carbohydrate molecules (the "-synthesis" part). Those carbohydrates are the energy source that heterotrophs use to power the synthesis of ATP via respiration. Therefore, photosynthesis powers 99 percent of Earth's ecosystems. When a top predator, such as a wolf, preys on a deer (Figure 8.3), the wolf is at the end of an energy path that went from nuclear reactions on the surface of the sun, to light, to photosynthesis, to vegetation, to deer, and finally to wolf.

Figure 8.3 The energy stored in carbohydrate molecules from photosynthesis passes through the food chain. The predator that eats these deer receives a portion of the energy that originated in the photosynthetic vegetation that the deer consumed. (credit: modification of work by Steve VanRiper, U.S. Fish and Wildlife Service)

science practices CONNECTION for AP® Courses

Think About It

- Why do scientists think that photosynthesis evolved before aerobic cellular respiration?
- Why do carnivores, such as lions, depend on photosynthesis to survive? What evidence supports the claim that photosynthesis and cellular respiration are interdependent processes?

Main Structures and Summary of Photosynthesis

Photosynthesis is a multi-step process that requires sunlight, carbon dioxide (which is low in energy), and water as substrates (Figure 8.4). After the process is complete, it releases oxygen and produces glyceraldehyde-3-phosphate (GA3P), simple carbohydrate molecules (which are high in energy) that can subsequently be converted into glucose, sucrose, or any of dozens of other sugar molecules. These sugar molecules contain energy and the energized carbon that all living things need to survive.

Figure 8.4 Photosynthesis uses solar energy, carbon dioxide, and water to produce energy-storing carbohydrates. Oxygen is generated as a waste product of photosynthesis.

The following is the chemical equation for photosynthesis (Figure 8.5):

Photosynthesis Equation						
Carbon dioxide	+	Water	SUNLIGHT →	Sugar	+	Oxygen
$6CO_2$		$6H_2O$		$C_6H_{12}O_6$		$6O_2$

Figure 8.5 The basic equation for photosynthesis is deceptively simple. In reality, the process takes place in many steps involving intermediate reactants and products. Glucose, the primary energy source in cells, is made from two three-carbon GA3Ps.

Although the equation looks simple, the many steps that take place during photosynthesis are actually quite complex. Before learning the details of how photoautotrophs turn sunlight into food, it is important to become familiar with the structures involved.

In plants, photosynthesis generally takes place in leaves, which consist of several layers of cells. The process of photosynthesis occurs in a middle layer called the **mesophyll**. The gas exchange of carbon dioxide and oxygen occurs through small, regulated openings called **stomata** (singular: stoma), which also play roles in the regulation of gas exchange and water balance. The stomata are typically located on the underside of the leaf, which helps to minimize water loss. Each stoma is flanked by guard cells that regulate the opening and closing of the stomata by swelling or shrinking in response to osmotic changes.

In all autotrophic eukaryotes, photosynthesis takes place inside an organelle called a **chloroplast**. For plants, chloroplast-containing cells exist in the mesophyll. Chloroplasts have a double membrane envelope (composed of an outer membrane and an inner membrane). Within the chloroplast are stacked, disc-shaped structures called **thylakoids**. Embedded in the thylakoid membrane is chlorophyll, a **pigment** (molecule that absorbs light) responsible for the initial interaction between light and plant material, and numerous proteins that make up the electron transport chain. The thylakoid membrane encloses an internal space called the **thylakoid lumen**. As shown in Figure 8.6, a stack of thylakoids is called a **granum**, and the liquid-filled space surrounding the granum is called **stroma** or "bed" (not to be confused with stoma or "mouth," an opening on the leaf epidermis).

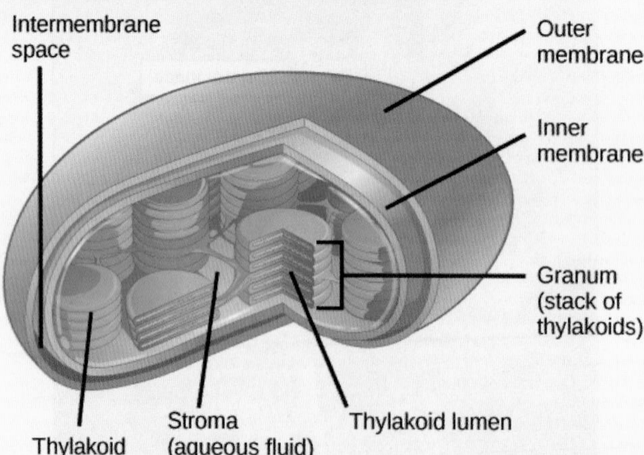

Figure 8.6 Photosynthesis takes place in chloroplasts, which have an outer membrane and an inner membrane. Stacks of thylakoids called grana form a third membrane layer.

On a hot, dry day, plants close their stomata to conserve water. What impact will this have on photosynthesis?

a. Rate of photosynthesis will be inhibited as the level of carbon dioxide decreases.
b. Rate of photosynthesis will be inhibited as the level of oxygen decreases.
c. The rate of photosynthesis will increase as the level of carbon dioxide increases.
d. Rate of photosynthesis will increase as the level of oxygen increases.

The Two Parts of Photosynthesis

Photosynthesis takes place in two sequential stages: the light-dependent reactions and the light independent-reactions. In the **light-dependent reactions**, energy from sunlight is absorbed by chlorophyll and that energy is converted into stored chemical energy. In the **light-independent reactions**, the chemical energy harvested during the light-dependent reactions drives the assembly of sugar molecules from carbon dioxide. Therefore, although the light-independent reactions do not use light as a reactant, they require the products of the light-dependent reactions to function. In addition, several enzymes of the light-independent reactions are activated by light. The light-dependent reactions utilize certain molecules to temporarily store the energy: These are referred to as energy carriers. The energy carriers that move energy from light-dependent reactions to light-independent reactions can be thought of as "full" because they are rich in energy. After the energy is released, the "empty" energy carriers return to the light-dependent reaction to obtain more energy. Figure 8.7 illustrates the components inside the chloroplast where the light-dependent and light-independent reactions take place.

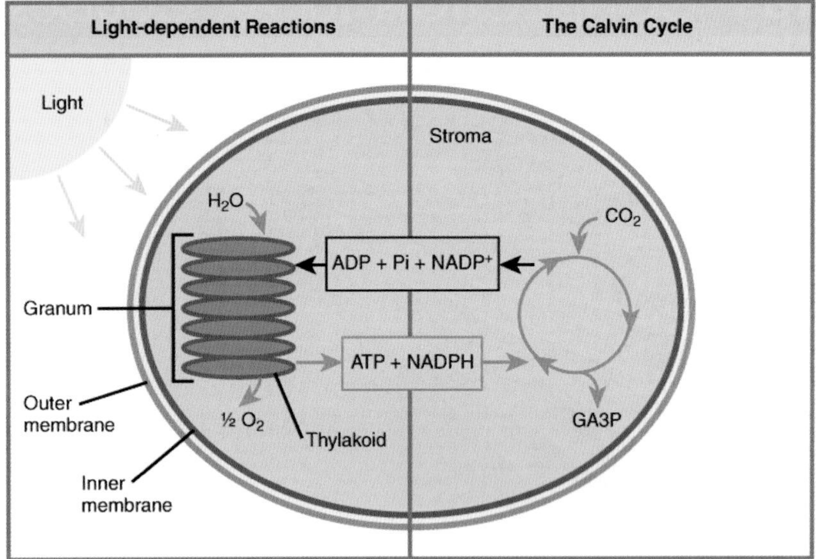

Figure 8.7 Photosynthesis takes place in two stages: light dependent reactions and the Calvin cycle. Light-dependent reactions, which take place in the thylakoid membrane, use light energy to make ATP and NADPH. The Calvin cycle, which takes place in the stroma, uses energy derived from these compounds to make GA3P from CO_2.

Click the link (http://openstaxcollege.org/l/photosynthesis) to learn more about photosynthesis.

Explain how the light reactions and light independent reactions (Calvin cycle) of photosynthesis are interdependent on each other.

a. The light reactions produces ATP and NADPH, which are then used in the Calvin cycle.

b. The light reactions produces $NADP^+$ and ADP, which are then used in the Calvin cycle.

c. The light reactions uses NADPH and ATP, which are produced by the Calvin cycle.

d. The light reactions produce only NADPH, which is produced by the Calvin cycle.

everyday CONNECTION for AP® Courses

Photosynthesis at the Grocery Store

Figure 8.8 Foods that humans consume originate from photosynthesis. (credit: Associação Brasileira de Supermercados)

Major grocery stores in the United States are organized into departments, such as dairy, meats, produce, bread, cereals, and so forth. Each aisle (Figure 8.8) contains hundreds, if not thousands, of different products for customers to buy and consume.

Although there is a large variety, each item links back to photosynthesis. Meats and dairy link, because the animals were fed plant-based foods. The breads, cereals, and pastas come largely from starchy grains, which are the seeds of photosynthesis-dependent plants. What about desserts and drinks? All of these products contain sugar—sucrose is a plant product, a disaccharide, a carbohydrate molecule, which is built directly from photosynthesis. Moreover, many items are less obviously derived from plants: For instance, paper goods are generally plant products, and many plastics (abundant as products and packaging) are derived from algae. Virtually every spice and flavoring in the spice aisle was produced by a plant as a leaf, root, bark, flower, fruit, or stem. Ultimately, photosynthesis connects to every meal and every food a person consumes.

Where would photosynthetic organisms likely be placed on a food web within most ecosystems?

a. at the base
b. near the top
c. in the middle, but generally closer to the top
d. in the middle, but generally closer to the base

8.2 | The Light-Dependent Reaction of Photosynthesis

In this section, you will explore the following questions:

- How do plants absorb energy from sunlight?
- What are the differences between short and long wavelengths of light? What wavelengths are used in photosynthesis?
- How and where does photosynthesis occur within a plant?

Connection for AP® Courses

Photosynthesis consists of two stages: the light-dependent reactions and the light-independent reactions or Calvin cycle. The light-dependent reactions occur when light is available. The overall equation for photosynthesis shows that is it a redox reaction; carbon dioxide is reduced and water is oxidized to produce oxygen:

$$\text{Energy} + 6CO_2 + H_2O \rightarrow C_6H_{12}O_6 + 6O_2$$

The light-dependent reactions occur in the thylakoid membranes of chloroplasts, whereas the Calvin cycle occurs in the stroma of chloroplasts. Embedded in the thylakoid membranes are two photosystems (PS I and PS II), which are complexes of pigments that capture solar energy. Chlorophylls *a* and *b* absorb violet, blue, and red wavelengths from the visible light spectrum and reflect green. The carotenoid pigments absorb violet-blue-green light and reflect yellow-to-orange light. Environmental factors such as day length and temperature influence which pigments predominant at certain times of the year. Although the two photosystems run simultaneously, it is easier to explore them separately. Let's begin with photosystem II.

A photon of light strikes the antenna pigments of PS II to initiate photosynthesis. In the noncyclic pathway, PS II captures photons at a slightly higher energy level than PS I. (Remember that shorter wavelengths of light carry more energy.) The absorbed energy travels to the reaction center of the antenna pigment that contains chlorophyll *a* and boosts chlorophyll *a* electrons to a higher energy level. The electrons are accepted by a primary electron acceptor protein and then pass to the electron transport chain also embedded in the thylakoid membrane. The energy absorbed in PS II is enough to oxidize (split) water, releasing oxygen into the atmosphere; the electrons released from the oxidation of water replace the electrons that were boosted from the reaction center chlorophyll. As the electrons from the reaction center chlorophyll pass through the series of electron carrier proteins, hydrogen ions (H^+) are pumped across the membrane via chemiosmosis into the interior of the thylakoid. (If this sounds familiar, it should. We studied chemiosmosis in our exploration of cellular respiration in Cellular Respiration.) This action builds up a high concentration of H+ ions, and as they flow through ATP synthase, molecules of ATP are formed. These molecules of ATP will be used to provide free energy for the synthesis of carbohydrate in the Calvin cycle, the second stage of photosynthesis. The electron transport chain connects PS II and PS I. Similar to the events occurring in PS II, this second photosystem absorbs a second photon of light, resulting in the formation of a molecule of NADPH from $NADP_+$. The energy carried in NADPH also is used to power the chemical reactions of the Calvin cycle.

Information presented and the examples highlighted in the section support concepts and learning objectives outlined in Big Idea 2 of the AP® Biology Curriculum Framework, as shown in the table. The learning objectives listed in the Curriculum Framework provide a transparent foundation for the AP® Biology course, an inquiry-based laboratory experience, instructional activities, and AP® exam questions. A learning objective merges required content with one or more of the seven science practices.

Big Idea 2	Biological systems utilize free energy and molecular building blocks to grow, to reproduce, and to maintain dynamic homeostasis.
Enduring Understanding 2.A	Growth, reproduction and maintenance of living systems require free energy and matter.
Essential Knowledge	**2.A.2** The light-independent reactions of photosynthesis in eukaryotes involve a series of reactions that capture free energy present in light.
Science Practice	**1.4** The student can use representations and models to analyze situations or solve problems qualitatively and quantitatively.
Science Practice	**3.1** The student can pose scientific questions.
Learning Objective	**2.4** The student is able to use representations to pose scientific questions about what mechanisms and structural features allow organisms to capture, store, and use free energy.
Essential Knowledge	**2.A.2** The light-independent reactions of photosynthesis in eukaryotes involve a series of reactions that capture free energy present in light.
Science Practice	**6.2** The student can construct explanations of phenomena based on evidence produced through scientific practices.

Learning Objective	**2.5** The student is able to construct explanations of the mechanisms and structural features of cells that allow organisms to capture, store, or use free energy.
Big Idea 4	Biological systems interact, and these systems and their interactions possess complex properties.
Enduring Understanding 4.A	Interactions within biological systems lead to complex properties.
Essential Knowledge	**4.A.2** Chloroplasts are specialized organelles that capture energy through photosynthesis.
Science Practice	**6.4** The student can make claims and predictions about natural phenomena based on scientific theories and models.
Learning Objective	**4.4** The student is able to make a prediction about the interactions of subcellular organelles.
Essential Knowledge	**4.A.2** Chloroplasts are specialized organelles that capture energy through photosynthesis.
Science Practice	**6.2** The student can construct explanations of phenomena based on evidence produced through scientific practices.
Learning Objective	**4.5** The student is able to construct explanations based on scientific evidence as to how interactions of subcellular structures provide essential functions.
Essential Knowledge	**4.A.2** Chloroplasts are specialized organelles that capture energy through photosynthesis.
Science Practice	**1.4** The student can use representations and models to analyze situations or solve problems qualitatively and quantitatively.
Learning Objective	**4.6** The student is able to use representations and models to analyze situations qualitatively to describe how interactions of subcellular structures, which possess specialized functions, provide essential functions.

The Science Practice Challenge Questions contain additional test questions for this section that will help you prepare for the AP exam. These questions address the following standards:
[APLO 2.5][APLO 2.16][APLO 2.18][APLO 1.9][APLO 1.32][APLO 4.14][APLO 2.2][APLO 2.3][APLO 2.23][APLO 1.15][APLO 1.29]

How can light be used to make food? When a person turns on a lamp, electrical energy becomes light energy. Like all other forms of kinetic energy, light can travel, change form, and be harnessed to do work. In the case of photosynthesis, light energy is converted into chemical energy, which photoautotrophs use to build carbohydrate molecules (Figure 8.9). However, autotrophs only use a few specific components of sunlight.

Figure 8.9 Photoautotrophs can capture light energy from the sun, converting it into the chemical energy used to build food molecules. (credit: Gerry Atwell)

What Is Light Energy?

The sun emits an enormous amount of electromagnetic radiation (solar energy). Humans can see only a fraction of this energy, which portion is therefore referred to as "visible light." The manner in which solar energy travels is described as waves. Scientists can determine the amount of energy of a wave by measuring its **wavelength**, the distance between consecutive points of a wave. A single wave is measured from two consecutive points, such as from crest to crest or from trough to trough (Figure 8.10).

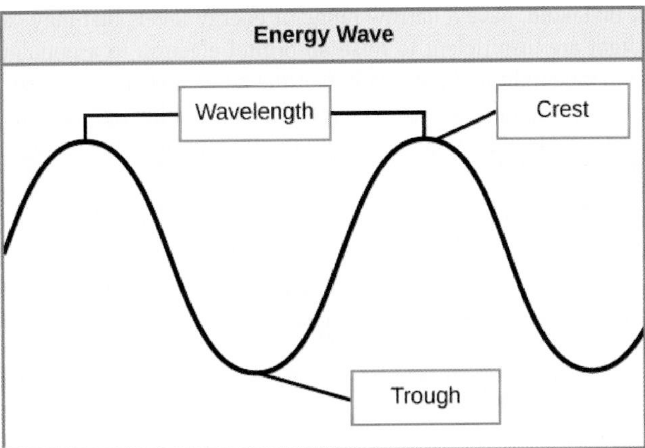

Figure 8.10 The wavelength of a single wave is the distance between two consecutive points of similar position (two crests or two troughs) along the wave.

Visible light constitutes only one of many types of electromagnetic radiation emitted from the sun and other stars. Scientists differentiate the various types of radiant energy from the sun within the electromagnetic spectrum. The **electromagnetic spectrum** is the range of all possible frequencies of radiation (Figure 8.11). The difference between wavelengths relates to the amount of energy carried by them.

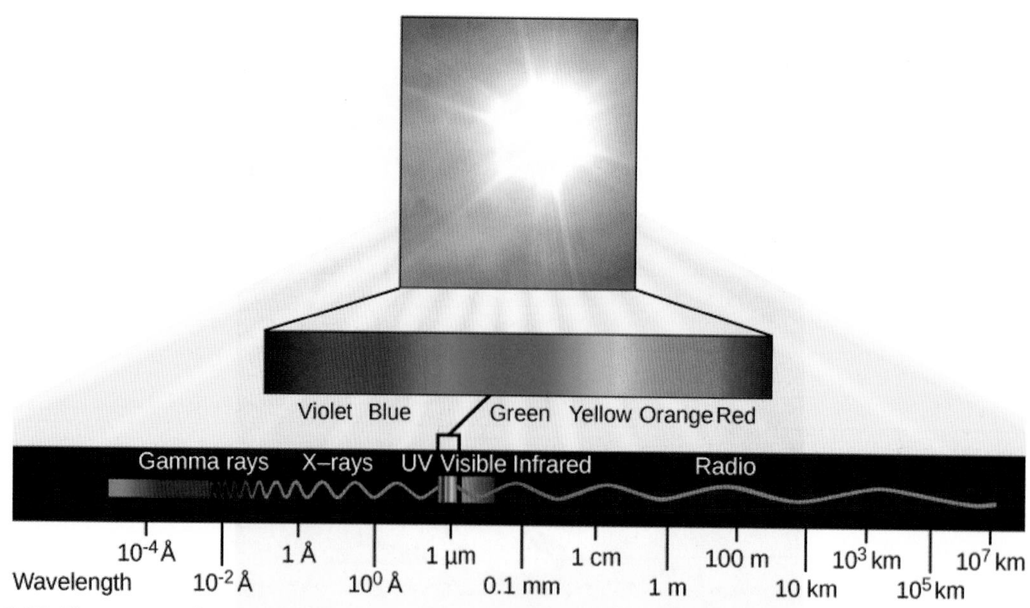

Figure 8.11 The sun emits energy in the form of electromagnetic radiation. This radiation exists at different wavelengths, each of which has its own characteristic energy. All electromagnetic radiation, including visible light, is characterized by its wavelength.

Each type of electromagnetic radiation travels at a particular wavelength. The longer the wavelength (or the more stretched out it appears in the diagram), the less energy is carried. Short, tight waves carry the most energy. This may seem illogical, but think of it in terms of a piece of moving a heavy rope. It takes little effort by a person to move a rope in long, wide waves. To make a rope move in short, tight waves, a person would need to apply significantly more energy.

The electromagnetic spectrum (Figure 8.11) shows several types of electromagnetic radiation originating from the sun, including X-rays and ultraviolet (UV) rays. The higher-energy waves can penetrate tissues and damage cells and DNA, explaining why both X-rays and UV rays can be harmful to living organisms.

Absorption of Light

Light energy initiates the process of photosynthesis when pigments absorb the light. Organic pigments, whether in the human retina or the chloroplast thylakoid, have a narrow range of energy levels that they can absorb. Energy levels lower than those represented by red light are insufficient to raise an orbital electron to a populatable, excited (quantum) state. Energy levels higher than those in blue light will physically tear the molecules apart, called bleaching. So retinal pigments can only “see” (absorb) 700 nm to 400 nm light, which is therefore called visible light. For the same reasons, plants pigment molecules absorb only light in the wavelength range of 700 nm to 400 nm; plant physiologists refer to this range for plants as photosynthetically active radiation.

The visible light seen by humans as white light actually exists in a rainbow of colors. Certain objects, such as a prism or a drop of water, disperse white light to reveal the colors to the human eye. The visible light portion of the electromagnetic spectrum shows the rainbow of colors, with violet and blue having shorter wavelengths, and therefore higher energy. At the other end of the spectrum toward red, the wavelengths are longer and have lower energy (Figure 8.12).

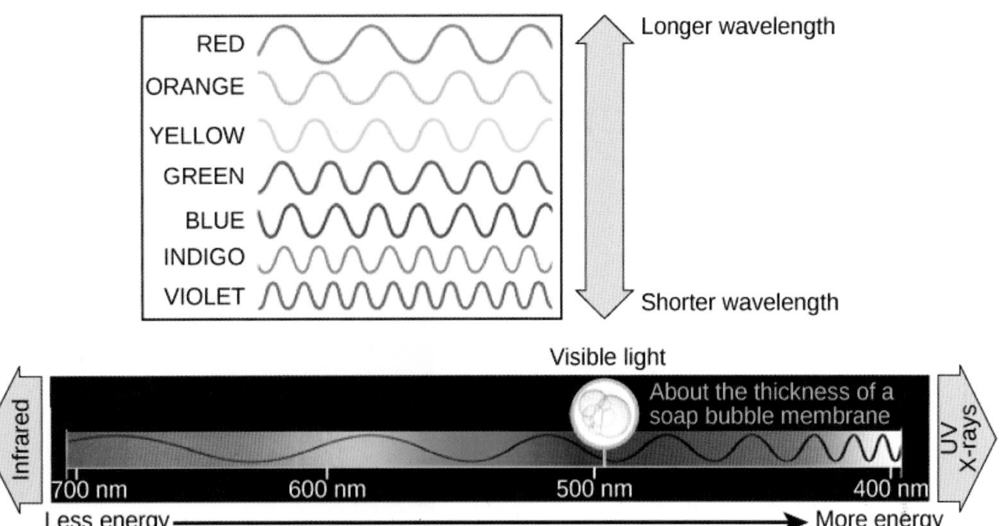

Figure 8.12 The colors of visible light do not carry the same amount of energy. Violet has the shortest wavelength and therefore carries the most energy, whereas red has the longest wavelength and carries the least amount of energy. (credit: modification of work by NASA)

Understanding Pigments

Different kinds of pigments exist, and each absorbs only certain wavelengths (colors) of visible light. Pigments reflect or transmit the wavelengths they cannot absorb, making them appear in the corresponding color.

Chlorophylls and carotenoids are the two major classes of photosynthetic pigments found in plants and algae; each class has multiple types of pigment molecules. There are five major chlorophylls: *a*, *b*, *c* and *d* and a related molecule found in prokaryotes called bacteriochlorophyll. **Chlorophyll *a*** and **chlorophyll *b*** are found in higher plant chloroplasts and will be the focus of the following discussion.

With dozens of different forms, carotenoids are a much larger group of pigments. The carotenoids found in fruit—such as the red of tomato (lycopene), the yellow of corn seeds (zeaxanthin), or the orange of an orange peel (β-carotene)—are used as advertisements to attract seed dispersers. In photosynthesis, **carotenoids** function as photosynthetic pigments that are very efficient molecules for the disposal of excess energy. When a leaf is exposed to full sun, the light-dependent reactions are required to process an enormous amount of energy; if that energy is not handled properly, it can do significant damage. Therefore, many carotenoids reside in the thylakoid membrane, absorb excess energy, and safely dissipate that energy as heat.

Each type of pigment can be identified by the specific pattern of wavelengths it absorbs from visible light, which is the **absorption spectrum**. The graph in Figure 8.13 shows the absorption spectra for chlorophyll *a*, chlorophyll *b*, and a type of carotenoid pigment called β-carotene (which absorbs blue and green light). Notice how each pigment has a distinct set of peaks and troughs, revealing a highly specific pattern of absorption. Chlorophyll *a* absorbs wavelengths from either end of the visible spectrum (blue and red), but not green. Because green is reflected or transmitted, chlorophyll appears green. Carotenoids absorb in the short-wavelength blue region, and reflect the longer yellow, red, and orange wavelengths.

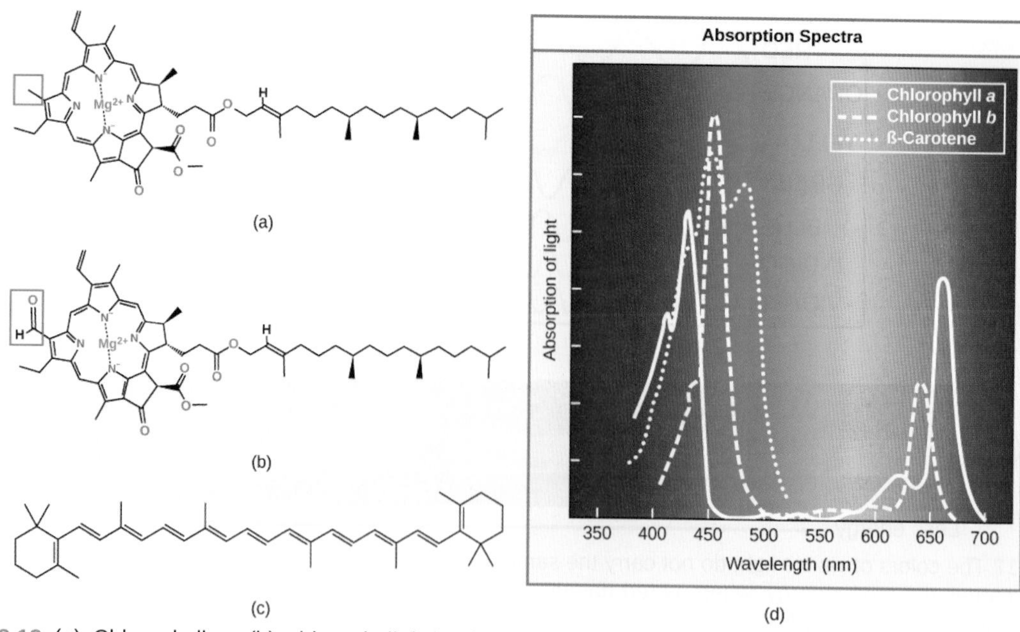

Figure 8.13 (a) Chlorophyll *a*, (b) chlorophyll *b*, and (c) β-carotene are hydrophobic organic pigments found in the thylakoid membrane. Chlorophyll *a* and *b*, which are identical except for the part indicated in the red box, are responsible for the green color of leaves. β-carotene is responsible for the orange color in carrots. Each pigment has (d) a unique absorbance spectrum.

Many photosynthetic organisms have a mixture of pigments; using them, the organism can absorb energy from a wider range of wavelengths. Not all photosynthetic organisms have full access to sunlight. Some organisms grow underwater where light intensity and quality decrease and change with depth. Other organisms grow in competition for light. Plants on the rainforest floor must be able to absorb any bit of light that comes through, because the taller trees absorb most of the sunlight and scatter the remaining solar radiation (Figure 8.14).

Figure 8.14 Plants that commonly grow in the shade have adapted to low levels of light by changing the relative concentrations of their chlorophyll pigments. (credit: Jason Hollinger)

When studying a photosynthetic organism, scientists can determine the types of pigments present by generating absorption spectra. An instrument called a **spectrophotometer** can differentiate which wavelengths of light a substance can absorb. Spectrophotometers measure transmitted light and compute from it the absorption. By extracting pigments from leaves and placing these samples into a spectrophotometer, scientists can identify which wavelengths of light an organism can absorb. Additional methods for the identification of plant pigments include various types of chromatography that separate the pigments by their relative affinities to solid and mobile phases.

How Light-Dependent Reactions Work

The overall function of light-dependent reactions is to convert solar energy into chemical energy in the form of NADPH and ATP. This chemical energy supports the light-independent reactions and fuels the assembly of sugar molecules. The light-dependent reactions are depicted in Figure 8.15. Protein complexes and pigment molecules work together to produce NADPH and ATP.

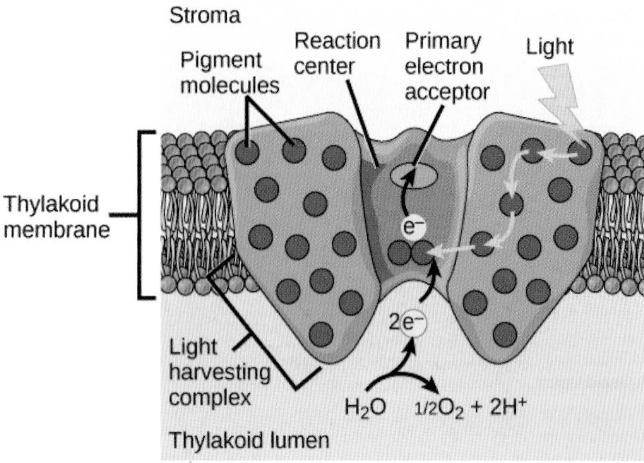

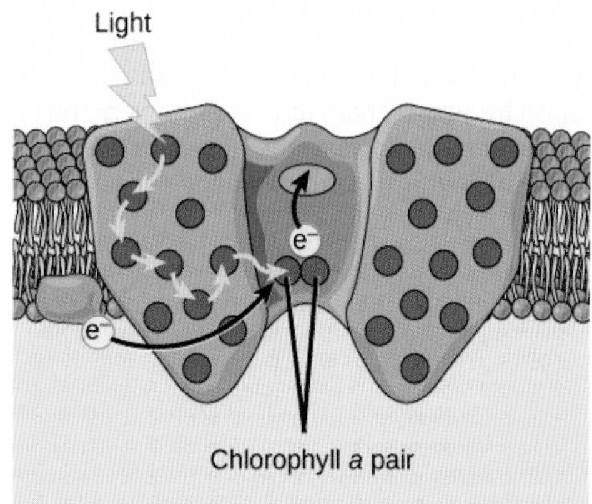

Figure 8.15 A photosystem consists of a light-harvesting complex and a reaction center. Pigments in the light-harvesting complex pass light energy to two special chlorophyll *a* molecules in the reaction center. The light excites an electron from the chlorophyll *a* pair, which passes to the primary electron acceptor. The excited electron must then be replaced. In (a) photosystem II, the electron comes from the splitting of water, which releases oxygen as a waste product. In (b) photosystem I, the electron comes from the chloroplast electron transport chain discussed below.

The actual step that converts light energy into chemical energy takes place in a multiprotein complex called a **photosystem**, two types of which are found embedded in the thylakoid membrane, **photosystem II** (PSII) and **photosystem I** (PSI) (Figure 8.16). The two complexes differ on the basis of what they oxidize (that is, the source of the low-energy electron supply) and what they reduce (the place to which they deliver their energized electrons).

Both photosystems have the same basic structure; a number of **antenna proteins** to which the chlorophyll molecules are bound surround the **reaction center** where the photochemistry takes place. Each photosystem is serviced by the **light-harvesting complex**, which passes energy from sunlight to the reaction center; it consists of multiple antenna proteins that contain a mixture of 300–400 chlorophyll *a* and *b* molecules as well as other pigments like carotenoids. The absorption of a single **photon** or distinct quantity or "packet" of light by any of the chlorophylls pushes that molecule into an excited state. In short, the light energy has now been captured by biological molecules but is not stored in any useful form yet. The energy is transferred from chlorophyll to chlorophyll until eventually (after about a millionth of a second), it is delivered to the reaction center. Up to this point, only energy has been transferred between molecules, not electrons.

visual CONNECTION

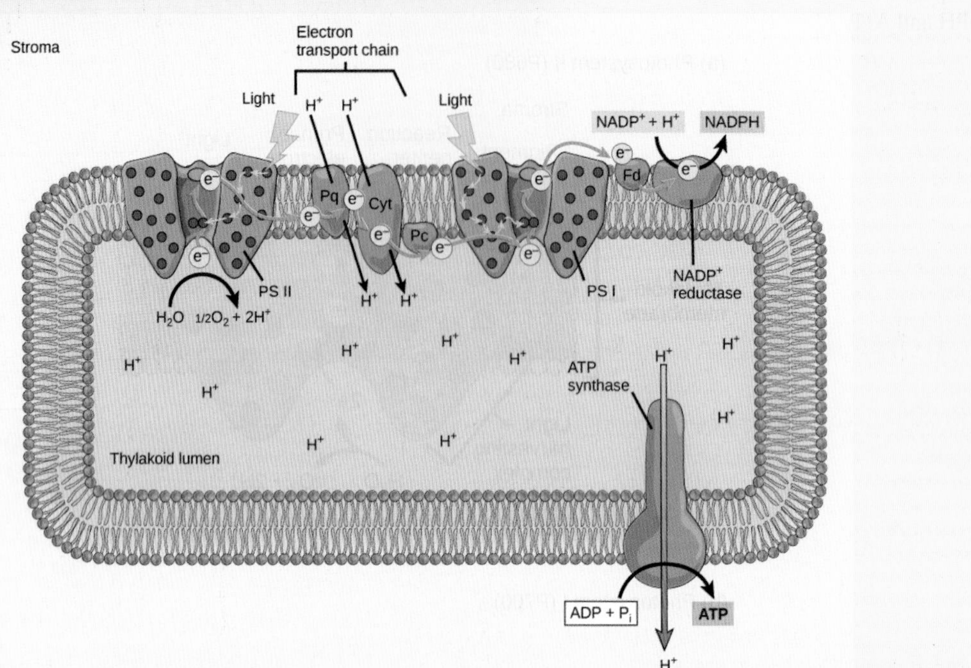

Figure 8.16 In the photosystem II (PSII) reaction center, energy from sunlight is used to extract electrons from water. The electrons travel through the chloroplast electron transport chain to photosystem I (PSI), which reduces $NADP^+$ to NADPH. The electron transport chain moves protons across the thylakoid membrane into the lumen. At the same time, splitting of water adds protons to the lumen, and reduction of NADPH removes protons from the stroma. The net result is a low pH in the thylakoid lumen, and a high pH in the stroma. ATP synthase uses this electrochemical gradient to make ATP.

What is the external source of the electrons that ultimately pass through photosynthetic electron transport chains?

a. carbon dioxide
b. NADPH
c. oxygen
d. water

The reaction center contains a pair of chlorophyll *a* molecules with a special property. Those two chlorophylls can undergo oxidation upon excitation; they can actually give up an electron in a process called a **photoact**. It is at this step in the reaction center, this step in photosynthesis, that light energy is converted into an excited electron. All of the subsequent steps involve getting that electron onto the energy carrier NADPH for delivery to the Calvin cycle where the electron is deposited onto carbon for long-term storage in the form of a carbohydrate.PSII and PSI are two major components of the photosynthetic **electron transport chain**, which also includes the **cytochrome complex**. The cytochrome complex, an enzyme composed of two protein complexes, transfers the electrons from the carrier molecule plastoquinone (Pq) to the protein plastocyanin (Pc), thus enabling both the transfer of protons across the thylakoid membrane and the transfer of electrons from PSII to PSI.

The reaction center of PSII (called **P680**) delivers its high-energy electrons, one at the time, to the **primary electron acceptor**, and through the electron transport chain (Pq to cytochrome complex to plastocyanine) to PSI. P680's missing electron is replaced by extracting a low-energy electron from water; thus, water is split and PSII is re-reduced after every photoact. Splitting one H_2O molecule releases two electrons, two hydrogen atoms, and one atom of oxygen. Splitting two molecules is required to form one molecule of diatomic O_2 gas. About 10 percent of the oxygen is used by mitochondria in the leaf to support oxidative phosphorylation. The remainder escapes to the atmosphere where it is used by aerobic organisms to support respiration.

As electrons move through the proteins that reside between PSII and PSI, they lose energy. That energy is used to move hydrogen atoms from the stromal side of the membrane to the thylakoid lumen. Those hydrogen atoms, plus the ones produced by splitting water, accumulate in the thylakoid lumen and will be used to synthesize ATP in a later step. Because the electrons have lost energy prior to their arrival at PSI, they must be re-energized by PSI, hence, another photon is absorbed by the PSI antenna. That energy is relayed to the PSI reaction center (called **P700**). P700 is oxidized and sends a high-energy electron to $NADP^+$ to form NADPH. Thus, PSII captures the energy to create proton gradients to make ATP, and PSI captures the energy to reduce $NADP^+$ into NADPH. The two photosystems work in concert, in part, to guarantee that the production of NADPH will roughly equal the production of ATP. Other mechanisms exist to fine tune that ratio to exactly match the chloroplast's constantly changing energy needs.

Generating an Energy Carrier: ATP

As in the intermembrane space of the mitochondria during cellular respiration, the buildup of hydrogen ions inside the thylakoid lumen creates a concentration gradient. The passive diffusion of hydrogen ions from high concentration (in the thylakoid lumen) to low concentration (in the stroma) is harnessed to create ATP, just as in the electron transport chain of cellular respiration. The ions build up energy because of diffusion and because they all have the same electrical charge, repelling each other.

To release this energy, hydrogen ions will rush through any opening, similar to water jetting through a hole in a dam. In the thylakoid, that opening is a passage through a specialized protein channel called the ATP synthase. The energy released by the hydrogen ion stream allows ATP synthase to attach a third phosphate group to ADP, which forms a molecule of ATP (Figure 8.16). The flow of hydrogen ions through ATP synthase is called chemiosmosis because the ions move from an area of high to an area of low concentration through a semi-permeable structure.

Visit this site (http://openstaxcollege.org/l/light_reactions) and click through the animation to view the process of photosynthesis within a leaf.

What role do electrons play in the formation of NADPH?

a. Electrons from PS I cause the reduction of NADPH to $NADP^+$.

b. Electrons from PSII cause the reduction of $NADP^+$ to NADPH.

c. Electrons from PS I cause the reduction of $NADP^+$ to NADPH.

d. Electrons are gained which causes the oxidation of $NADP^+$.

everyday CONNECTION for AP® Courses

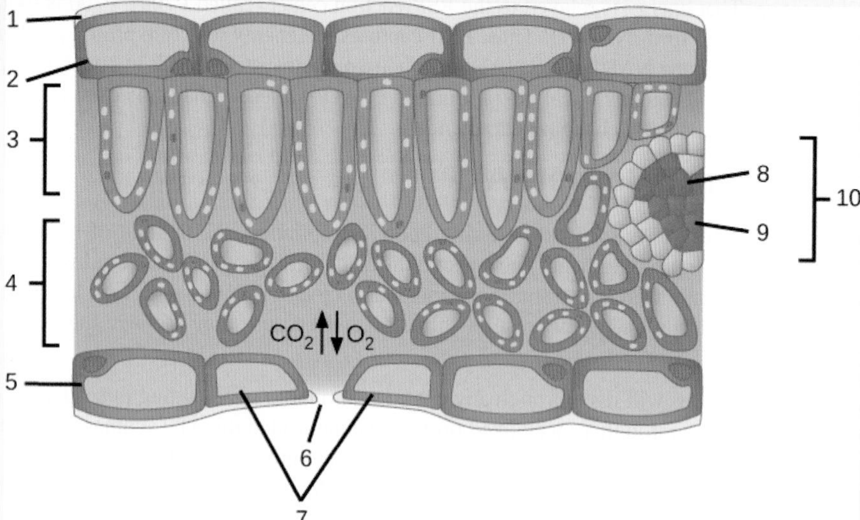

Figure 8.17 The anatomy of a leaf. The cuticle and epidermis are the outer layers of the leaf and protect it from drying out. Chloroplasts are found in the mesophyll cells and are where photosynthesis occurs. Gas is exchanged through pores called stomata, which are opened and closed by the guard cells. Legend: 1) cuticle 2) upper epidermis 3) palisade mesophyll 4) spongy mesophyll 5) lower epidermis 6) stoma 7) guard cells 8) xylem 9) phloem 10) vascular bundle.

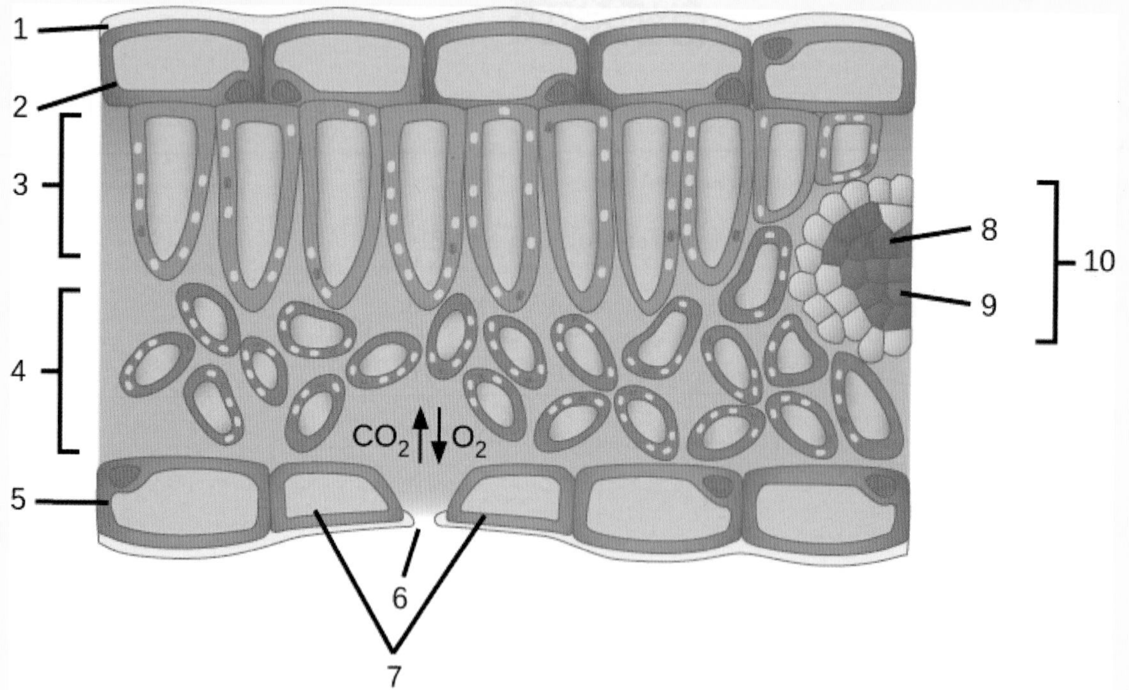

If the stomata were sealed, what would happen to oxygen (O_2) and carbon dioxide (CO_2) levels in a photosynthesizing leaf?

a. O_2 levels would increase and CO_2 levels would decrease.

b. CO_2 levels would increase and O_2 levels would decrease.

c. O_2 and CO_2 levels would both decrease.

d. O_2 and CO_2 levels would both increase.

science practices CONNECTION for AP® Courses

Think About It

On a hot, dry day, plants close their stomata to conserve water. Predict the impact of this on photosynthesis and justify your prediction.

8.3 | Using Light to Make Organic Molecules

In this section, you will explore the following questions:

- What are the reactions in the Calvin cycle described as the light-independent reactions?
- Why does the term "carbon fixation" describe the products of the Calvin cycle?
- What is the role of photosynthesis in the energy cycle of all living organisms?

Connection for AP® Courses

The free energy stored in ATP and NADPH produced in the light-dependent reactions is used to power the chemical reactions of the light-independent reactions or Calvin cycle, which can occur during both the day and night. In the Calvin cycle, an enzyme called ribulose biphosphate carboxylase (RuBisCO), catalyzes a reaction with CO_2 and another molecule called ribulose biphosphate (RuBP) that is regenerated from a previous Calvin cycle. After a series of chemical reactions, the carbon from carbon dioxide in the atmosphere is "fixed" into carbohydrates, specifically a three-carbon molecule called glyceraldehydes-3-phosphate (G3P). (Again, count the carbons as we explore the Calvin cycle.) After three turns of the cycle, a three-carbon molecule of G3P leaves the cycle to become part of a carbohydrate molecule. The remaining G3P molecules stay in the cycle to be regenerated into RuBP, which is then ready to react with more incoming CO_2. In other words, the cell generates a stockpile of G3P to be assembled into organic molecules, including carbohydrates. Each step of the Calvin cycle is catalyzed by specific enzymes. (You do not have to memorize the reactions of the Calvin cycle; however, if provided with a diagram of the cycle, you should be able to interpret it.) Some plants evolved chemical modifications to more efficiently trap CO_2 if environmental conditions limit its availability. For example, when it's hot outside, plants tend to keep their stomata closed to prevent excessive water loss; when the outside temperature cools, stomata open and plants take in CO_2 and use a more efficient system to feed it into the Calvin cycle.

As we explored in Overview of Photosynthesis, photosynthesis forms an energy link with cellular respiration. Plants need both photosynthesis and respiration in order to conduct metabolic processes during both light and dark times. Therefore, plant cells contain both chloroplasts and mitochondria.

Information presented and the examples highlighted in the section, support concepts and learning objectives outlined in Big Idea 2 of the AP® Biology Curriculum Framework, as shown in the table. The learning objectives listed in the Curriculum Framework provide a transparent foundation for the AP® Biology course, an inquiry-based laboratory experience, instructional activities, and AP® exam questions. A learning objective merges required content with one or more of the seven science practices.

Big Idea 2	Biological systems utilize free energy and molecular building blocks to grow, to reproduce, and to maintain dynamic homeostasis.

Enduring Understanding 2.A	Growth, reproduction and maintenance of living systems require free energy and matter.
Essential Knowledge	**2.A.2** Light energy captured in photosynthesis is stored in carbohydrates produced during the Calvin cycle.
Science Practice	**1.4** The student can use representations and models to analyze situations or solve problems qualitatively and quantitatively.
Learning Objective	**2.4** The student is able to use representations to pose scientific questions about what mechanisms and structural features allow organisms to capture, store, and use free energy.
Essential Knowledge	**2.A.2** Light energy captured in photosynthesis is stored in carbohydrates produced during the Calvin cycle
Science Practice	**6.2** The student can construct explanations of phenomena based on evidence produced through scientific practices.
Learning Objective	**2.5** The student is able to construct explanations of the mechanisms and structural features of cells that allow organisms to capture, store, or use free energy.

The Science Practice Challenge Questions contain additional test questions for this section that will help you prepare for the AP exam. These questions address the following standards:
[APLO 2.5][APLO 2.11][APLO 4.17]

The Calvin Cycle

After the energy from the sun is converted into chemical energy and temporarily stored in ATP and NADPH molecules, the cell has the fuel needed to build carbohydrate molecules for long-term energy storage. The products of the light-dependent reactions, ATP and NADPH, have lifespans in the range of millionths of seconds, whereas the products of the light-independent reactions (carbohydrates and other forms of reduced carbon) can survive for hundreds of millions of years. The carbohydrate molecules made will have a backbone of carbon atoms. Where does the carbon come from? It comes from carbon dioxide, the gas that is a waste product of respiration in microbes, fungi, plants, and animals.

In plants, carbon dioxide (CO_2) enters the leaves through stomata, where it diffuses over short distances through intercellular spaces until it reaches the mesophyll cells. Once in the mesophyll cells, CO_2 diffuses into the stroma of the chloroplast—the site of light-independent reactions of photosynthesis. These reactions actually have several names associated with them. Another term, the **Calvin cycle**, is named for the man who discovered it, and because these reactions function as a cycle. Others call it the Calvin-Benson cycle to include the name of another scientist involved in its discovery. The most outdated name is dark reactions, because light is not directly required (Figure 8.18). However, the term dark reaction can be misleading because it implies incorrectly that the reaction only occurs at night or is independent of light, which is why most scientists and instructors no longer use it.

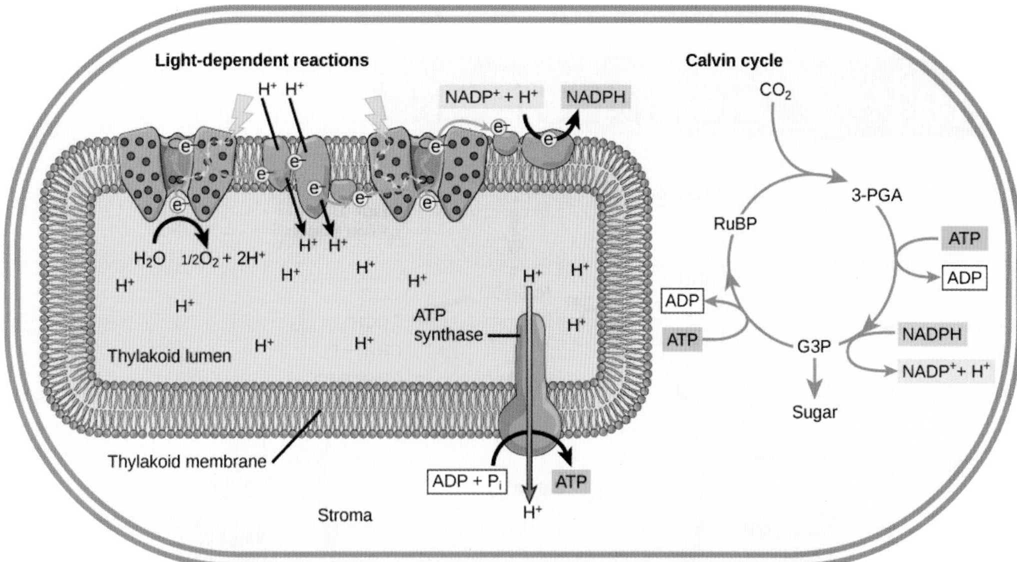

Figure 8.18 Light reactions harness energy from the sun to produce chemical bonds, ATP, and NADPH. These energy-carrying molecules are made in the stroma where carbon fixation takes place.

The light-independent reactions of the Calvin cycle can be organized into three basic stages: fixation, reduction, and regeneration.

Stage 1: Fixation

In the stroma, in addition to CO_2, two other components are present to initiate the light-independent reactions: an enzyme called ribulose-1,5-bisphosphate carboxylase/oxygenase (RuBisCO), and three molecules of ribulose bisphosphate (RuBP), as shown in Figure 8.19. RuBP has five atoms of carbon, flanked by two phosphates.

visual CONNECTION

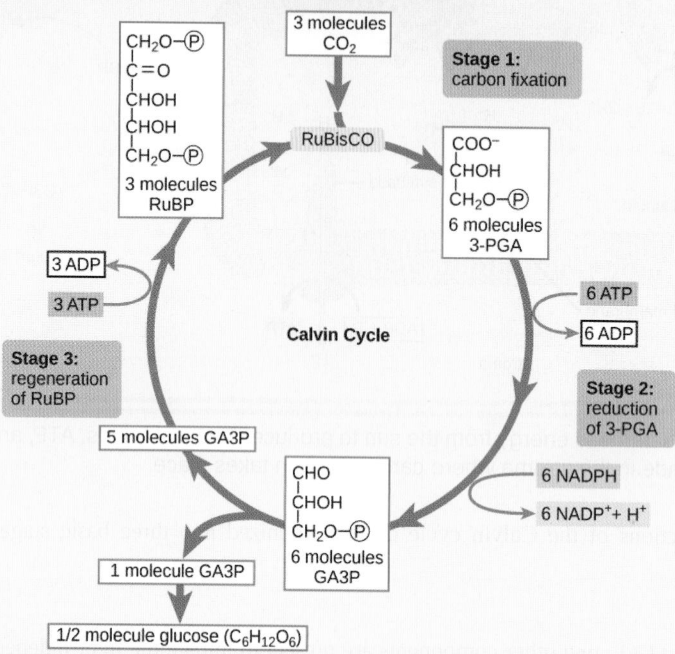

Figure 8.19 The Calvin cycle has three stages. In stage 1, the enzyme RuBisCO incorporates carbon dioxide into an organic molecule, 3-PGA. In stage 2, the organic molecule is reduced using electrons supplied by NADPH. In stage 3, RuBP, the molecule that starts the cycle, is regenerated so that the cycle can continue. Only one carbon dioxide molecule is incorporated at a time, so the cycle must be completed three times to produce a single three-carbon GA3P molecule, and six times to produce a six-carbon glucose molecule.

Which of the following statements is true?

a. In photosynthesis, oxygen, carbon dioxide, ATP and NADPH are reactants. GA3P and water are products.
b. In photosynthesis, chlorophyll, water and carbon dioxide are reactants. GA3P and oxygen are products.
c. In photosynthesis, water, carbon dioxide, ATP and NADPH are reactants. RuBP and oxygen are products.
d. In photosynthesis, water and carbon dioxide are reactants. GA3P and oxygen are products.

RuBisCO catalyzes a reaction between CO_2 and RuBP. For each CO_2 molecule that reacts with one RuBP, two molecules of another compound (3-PGA) form. PGA has three carbons and one phosphate. Each turn of the cycle involves only one RuBP and one carbon dioxide and forms two molecules of 3-PGA. The number of carbon atoms remains the same, as the atoms move to form new bonds during the reactions (3 atoms from $3CO_2$ + 15 atoms from 3RuBP = 18 atoms in 3 atoms of 3-PGA). This process is called **carbon fixation**, because CO_2 is "fixed" from an inorganic form into organic molecules.

Stage 2: Reduction

ATP and NADPH are used to convert the six molecules of 3-PGA into six molecules of a chemical called glyceraldehyde 3-phosphate (G3P). That is a reduction reaction because it involves the gain of electrons by 3-PGA. Recall that a **reduction** is the gain of an electron by an atom or molecule. Six molecules of both ATP and NADPH are used. For ATP, energy is released with the loss of the terminal phosphate atom, converting it into ADP; for NADPH, both energy and a hydrogen atom are lost, converting it into $NADP^+$. Both of these molecules return to the nearby light-dependent reactions to be reused and reenergized.

Stage 3: Regeneration

Interestingly, at this point, only one of the G3P molecules leaves the Calvin cycle and is sent to the cytoplasm to contribute to the formation of other compounds needed by the plant. Because the G3P exported from the chloroplast has three carbon atoms, it takes three "turns" of the Calvin cycle to fix enough net carbon to export one G3P. But each turn makes two G3Ps, thus three turns make six G3Ps. One is exported while the remaining five G3P molecules remain in the cycle and are used to regenerate RuBP, which enables the system to prepare for more CO_2 to be fixed. Three more molecules of ATP are used in these regeneration reactions.

This link (http://openstaxcollege.org/l/calvin_cycle) leads to an animation of the Calvin cycle. Click stage 1, stage 2, and then stage 3 to see G3P and ATP regenerate to form RuBP.

Explain why the process of producing glucose in plants is a cycle.

a. Three RuBP molecules get converted to three G3P, and two G3P molecules with the help of three ATPs are converted back to three molecules of RuBP.

b. Three RuBP molecules get converted to six G3P, and five G3P molecules with the help of three ATPs are converted back to three molecules of RuBP.

c. Three RuBP molecules get converted to five G3P, and three G3P molecules with the help of three ATPs are converted back to three molecules of RuBP.

d. Three RuBP molecules get converted to six G3P, and five G3P molecules with the help of five ATPs are converted back to three molecules of RuBP.

evolution CONNECTION

Figure 8.20 The harsh conditions of the desert have led plants like these cacti to evolve variations of the light-independent reactions of photosynthesis. These variations increase the efficiency of water usage, helping to conserve water and energy. (credit: Piotr Wojtkowski)

Which of the following events is associated with the development of oxygenic photosynthesis?

a. Photosynthetic organisms began to use NADPH and ATP as an energy source.
b. Photosynthetic organisms evolved from single-celled bacteria into multicellular plants.
c. Photosynthetic organisms began to use two photosystems instead of one.
d. Photosynthetic organisms began to use light reactions as well as dark reactions.

The Energy Cycle

Whether the organism is a bacterium, plant, or animal, all living things access energy by breaking down carbohydrate molecules. But if plants make carbohydrate molecules, why would they need to break them down, especially when it has been shown that the gas organisms release as a “waste product” (CO_2) acts as a substrate for the formation of more food in photosynthesis? Remember, living things need energy to perform life functions. In addition, an organism can either make its own food or eat another organism—either way, the food still needs to be broken down. Finally, in the process of breaking down food, called cellular respiration, heterotrophs release needed energy and produce “waste” in the form of CO_2 gas.

In nature, there is no such thing as waste. Every single atom of matter and energy is conserved, recycling over and over infinitely. Substances change form or move from one type of molecule to another, but their constituent atoms never disappear. (Figure 1.21 is an illustrative example of this process.)

CO_2 is no more a form of waste than oxygen is wasteful to photosynthesis. Both are byproducts of reactions that move on to other reactions. Photosynthesis absorbs light energy to build carbohydrates in chloroplasts, and aerobic cellular respiration releases energy by using oxygen to metabolize carbohydrates in the cytoplasm and mitochondria. Both processes use electron transport chains to capture the energy necessary to drive other reactions. These two powerhouse processes, photosynthesis and cellular respiration, function in biological, cyclical harmony to allow organisms to access life-sustaining energy that originates millions of miles away in a burning star humans call the sun.

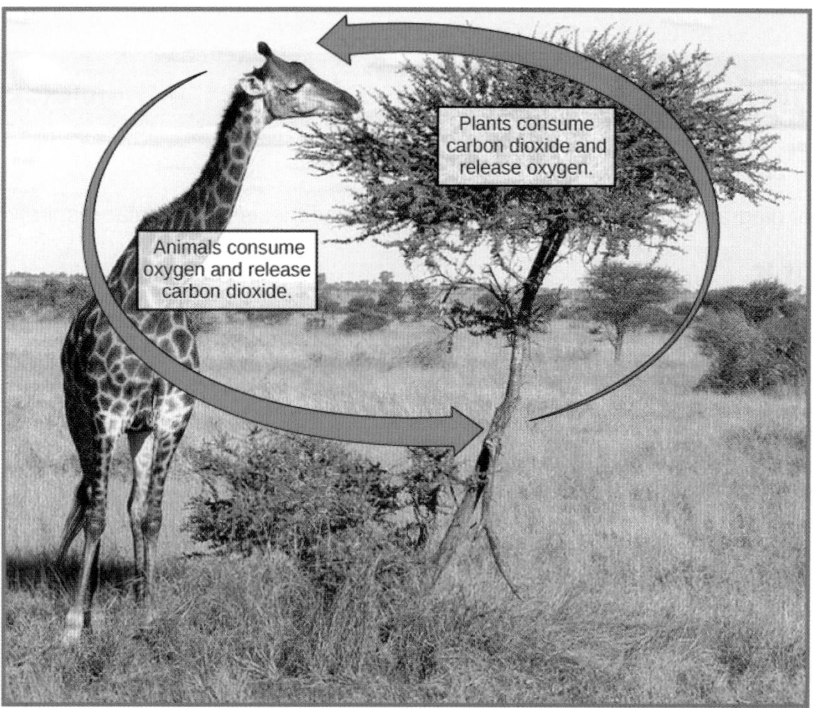

Figure 8.21 Photosynthesis consumes carbon dioxide and produces oxygen. Aerobic respiration consumes oxygen and produces carbon dioxide. These two processes play an important role in the carbon cycle. (credit: modification of work by Stuart Bassil)

everyday CONNECTION for AP® Courses

Photosynthesis and aerobic respiration are interrelated in important ways. During photosynthesis, plants take in carbon dioxide and water. The water molecule is split, the oxygen is released into the atmosphere, and the carbon dioxide is used to build carbohydrates. During aerobic respiration, organisms take in water and oxygen for respiration and produce carbon dioxide.

The Earth did not contain oxygen in its atmosphere throughout much of its history, even after life on Earth had already began. It did, however, contain carbon dioxide. What does this suggest about when photosynthetic organisms evolved, relative to non-photosynthetic organisms, and why?

a. Photosynthetic organisms evolved before non-photosynthetic organisms because no oxygen was present in the atmosphere when life began.
b. Photosynthetic organisms evolved after non-photosynthetic organisms because no oxygen was present in the atmosphere when life began.
c. Non-photosynthetic organisms evolved before photosynthetic organisms because no oxygen was present in the atmosphere when life began.
d. Photosynthetic organisms evolved before non-photosynthetic organisms because no oxygen was present in the atmosphere when life began.

Activity

Create a model or diagram to show the links between photosynthesis and cellular respiration.

Think About It

What cellular features and processes are similar in both respiration and photosynthesis?

KEY TERMS

absorption spectrum range of wavelengths of electromagnetic radiation absorbed by a given substance

antenna protein pigment molecule that directly absorbs light and transfers the energy absorbed to other pigment molecules

Calvin cycle light-independent reactions of photosynthesis that convert carbon dioxide from the atmosphere into carbohydrates using the energy and reducing power of ATP and NADPH

carbon fixation process of converting inorganic CO_2 gas into organic compounds

carotenoid photosynthetic pigment that functions to dispose of excess energy

chemoautotroph organism that can build organic molecules using energy derived from inorganic chemicals instead of sunlight

chlorophyll *a* form of chlorophyll that absorbs violet-blue and red light and consequently has a bluish-green color; the only pigment molecule that performs the photochemistry by getting excited and losing an electron to the electron transport chain

chlorophyll *b* accessory pigment that absorbs blue and red-orange light and consequently has a yellowish-green tint

chloroplast organelle in which photosynthesis takes place

cytochrome complex group of reversibly oxidizable and reducible proteins that forms part of the electron transport chain between photosystem II and photosystem I

electromagnetic spectrum range of all possible frequencies of radiation

electron transport chain group of proteins between PSII and PSI that pass energized electrons and use the energy released by the electrons to move hydrogen ions against their concentration gradient into the thylakoid lumen

granum stack of thylakoids located inside a chloroplast

heterotroph organism that consumes organic substances or other organisms for food

light harvesting complex complex that passes energy from sunlight to the reaction center in each photosystem; it consists of multiple antenna proteins that contain a mixture of 300–400 chlorophyll *a* and *b* molecules as well as other pigments like carotenoids

light-dependent reaction first stage of photosynthesis where certain wavelengths of the visible light are absorbed to form two energy-carrying molecules (ATP and NADPH)

light-independent reaction second stage of photosynthesis, though which carbon dioxide is used to build carbohydrate molecules using energy from ATP and NADPH

mesophyll middle layer of chlorophyll-rich cells in a leaf

P680 reaction center of photosystem II

P700 reaction center of photosystem I

photoact ejection of an electron from a reaction center using the energy of an absorbed photon

photoautotroph organism capable of producing its own organic compounds from sunlight

photon distinct quantity or “packet” of light energy

photosystem group of proteins, chlorophyll, and other pigments that are used in the light-dependent reactions of photosynthesis to absorb light energy and convert it into chemical energy

photosystem I integral pigment and protein complex in thylakoid membranes that uses light energy to transport electrons from plastocyanin to $NADP^+$ (which becomes reduced to NADPH in the process)

photosystem II integral protein and pigment complex in thylakoid membranes that transports electrons from water to the electron transport chain; oxygen is a product of PSII

pigment molecule that is capable of absorbing certain wavelengths of light and reflecting others (which accounts for its color)

primary electron acceptor pigment or other organic molecule in the reaction center that accepts an energized electron from the reaction center

reaction center complex of chlorophyll molecules and other organic molecules that is assembled around a special pair of chlorophyll molecules and a primary electron acceptor; capable of undergoing oxidation and reduction

reduction gain of electron(s) by an atom or molecule

spectrophotometer instrument that can measure transmitted light and compute the absorption

stoma opening that regulates gas exchange and water evaporation between leaves and the environment, typically situated on the underside of leaves

stroma fluid-filled space surrounding the grana inside a chloroplast where the light-independent reactions of photosynthesis take place

thylakoid disc-shaped, membrane-bound structure inside a chloroplast where the light-dependent reactions of photosynthesis take place; stacks of thylakoids are called grana

thylakoid lumen aqueous space bound by a thylakoid membrane where protons accumulate during light-driven electron transport

wavelength distance between consecutive points of equal position (two crests or two troughs) of a wave in a graphic representation; inversely proportional to the energy of the radiation

CHAPTER SUMMARY

8.1 Overview of Photosynthesis

The process of photosynthesis transformed life on Earth. By harnessing energy from the sun, the evolution of photosynthesis allowed living things access to enormous amounts of energy. Because of photosynthesis, living things gained access to sufficient energy that allowed them to build new structures and achieve the biodiversity evident today.

Only certain organisms, called photoautotrophs, can perform photosynthesis; they require the presence of chlorophyll, a specialized pigment that absorbs certain portions of the visible spectrum and can capture energy from sunlight. Photosynthesis uses carbon dioxide and water to assemble carbohydrate molecules and release oxygen as a waste product into the atmosphere. Eukaryotic autotrophs, such as plants and algae, have organelles called chloroplasts in which photosynthesis takes place, and starch accumulates. In prokaryotes, such as cyanobacteria, the process is less localized and occurs within folded membranes, extensions of the plasma membrane, and in the cytoplasm.

8.2 The Light-Dependent Reaction of Photosynthesis

The pigments of the first part of photosynthesis, the light-dependent reactions, absorb energy from sunlight. A photon strikes the antenna pigments of photosystem II to initiate photosynthesis. The energy travels to the reaction center that contains chlorophyll *a* and then to the electron transport chain, which pumps hydrogen ions into the thylakoid interior. This action builds up a high concentration of ions. The ions flow through ATP synthase via chemiosmosis to form molecules of ATP, which are used for the formation of sugar molecules in the second stage of photosynthesis. Photosystem I absorbs a second photon, which results in the formation of an NADPH molecule, another energy and reducing power carrier for the light-independent reactions.

8.3 Using Light to Make Organic Molecules

Using the energy carriers formed in the first steps of photosynthesis, the light-independent reactions, or the Calvin cycle, take in CO_2 from the environment. An enzyme, RuBisCO, catalyzes a reaction with CO_2 and another molecule, RuBP.

After three cycles, a three-carbon molecule of G3P leaves the cycle to become part of a carbohydrate molecule. The remaining G3P molecules stay in the cycle to be regenerated into RuBP, which is then ready to react with more CO_2. Photosynthesis forms an energy cycle with the process of cellular respiration. Plants need both photosynthesis and respiration for their ability to function in both the light and dark, and to be able to interconvert essential metabolites. Therefore, plants contain both chloroplasts and mitochondria.

REVIEW QUESTIONS

1. Which of the following components is not used by both plants and cyanobacteria to carry out photosynthesis?

a. carbon dioxide
b. chlorophyll
c. chloroplasts
d. water

2. Why are chemoautotrophs not considered the same as photoautotrophs if they both extract energy and make sugars?

a. Chemoautotrophs use wavelengths of light not available to photoautotrophs.
b. Chemoautotrophs extract energy from inorganic chemical compounds.
c. Photoautotrophs prefer the blue side of the visible light spectrum.
d. Photoautotrophs make glucose, while chemoautotrophs make galactose.

3. In which compartment of the plant cell do the light-independent reactions of photosynthesis take place?

a. mesophyll
b. outer membrane
c. stroma
d. thylakoid

4. What is a part of grana?

a. the Calvin cycle
b. the inner membrane
c. stroma
d. thylakoids

5. What are two major products of photosynthesis?

a. chlorophyll and oxygen
b. oxygen and carbon dioxide
c. sugars/carbohydrates and oxygen
d. sugars/carbohydrates and carbon dioxide

6. What is the primary energy source for cells?

a. glucose
b. starch
c. sucrose
d. triglycerides

7. Which portion of the electromagnetic radiation originating from the sun is harmful to living tissues?

a. blue
b. green
c. infrared
d. ultraviolet

8. The amount of energy in a wave can be measured using what trait?

a. color intensity
b. distance from trough to crest
c. the amount of sugar produced
d. wavelength

9. What portion of the electromagnetic radiation emitted by the sun has the least energy?

a. gamma
b. infrared
c. radio
d. X-rays

10. What is the function of carotenoids in photosynthesis?

a. They supplement chlorophyll absorption.
b. They are visible in the fall during leaf color changes.
c. They absorb excess energy and dissipate it as heat.
d. They limit chlorophyll absorption.

11. Which of the following structures is not a component of a photosystem?

a. antenna molecule
b. ATP synthase
c. primary electron acceptor
d. reaction center

12. Which complex is not involved in producing the electromotive force of ATP synthesis?

a. ATP synthase
b. cytochrome complex
c. Photosystem I
d. Photosystem II

13. What can be calculated from a wavelength

measurement of light?

a. a specific portion of the visible spectrum
b. color intensity
c. the amount of energy of a wave of light
d. the distance from trough to crest of the wave

14. Which molecule must enter the Calvin cycle continually for the light-independent reactions to take place?

a. CO_2
b. RuBisCO
c. RuBP
d. 3-PGA

15. Which order of molecular conversions is correct for the Calvin cycle?

a. RuBP + G3P → 3-PGA → sugar
b. RuBisCO → CO_2 → RuBP → G3P
c. RuBP + CO_2 → [RuBisCO]3-PGA → G3P
d. CO_2 → 3-PGA → RuBP → G3P

16. Which statement correctly describes carbon fixation?

a. the conversion of CO_2 into an organic compound
b. the use of RuBisCO to form 3-PGA
c. the production of carbohydrate molecules from G3P
d. the use of ATP and NADPH to reduce CO_2

17. Which substance catalyzes carbon fixation?

a. 3-PGA
b. NADPH
c. RuBisCO
d. RuBP

18. Which pathway is used by both plants and animals?

a. carbon fixation
b. cellular respiration
c. photosystem II
d. photosynthesis

19. Which of the following organisms is a heterotroph?

a. Cyanobacterium
b. intestinal bacteria
c. kelp
d. pond algae

20. What is the role of ribulose-1,5-bisphosphate, abreviated RuBisCO, in photosynthesis?

a. It catalyzes the reaction between CO_2 and ribulose bisphosphate (RuBP).
b. It catalyzes the reaction that produces glyceraldehyde3-phosphate (G3P).
c. It catalyzes the reaction that regenerates RuBP.
d. It catalyzes the reaction utilizing ATP and NADPH.

21. What is the product of the Calvin cycle?

a. Glucose
b. Glyceraldehyde-3-Phosphate
c. Phosphoglycerate (PGA)
d. sucrose

CRITICAL THINKING QUESTIONS

22. What are the roles of ATP and NADPH in photosynthesis?

a. ATP and NADPH are forms of chemical energy produced from the light dependent reactions to be used in the light independent reactions that produce sugars.
b. ATP and NADPH are forms of chemical energy produced from the light independent reactions, to be used in the light dependent reactions that produce sugars.
c. ATP and NADPH are forms of chemical energy produced from the light dependent reactions to be used in the light independent reactions that produce proteins.
d. ATP and NADPH are forms of chemical energy produced from the light dependent reactions to be used in the light independent reactions that use sugars as reactants.

23. What is the overall outcome of the light reactions in photosynthesis?

a. NADPH and ATP molecules are produced during the light reactions and are used to power the light independent reactions.

b. NADPH and ATP molecules are produced during the light reactions, which are used to power the light dependent reactions.

c. Sugar and ATP are produced during the light reactions, which are used to power the light independent reactions.

d. Carbon dioxide and NADPH are produced during the light reactions, which are used to power the light dependent reactions.

24.

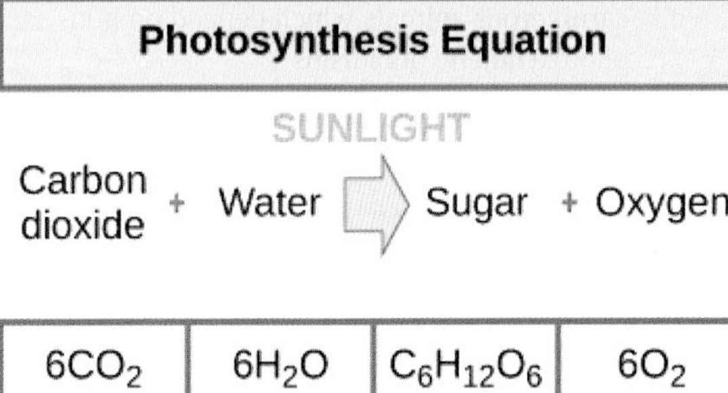

How does the equation relate to both photosynthesis and cellular respiration?

a. Photosynthesis utilizes energy to build carbohydrates while cellular respiration metabolizes carbohydrates.

b. Photosynthesis utilizes energy to metabolize carbohydrates while cellular respiration builds carbohydrates.

c. Photosynthesis and cellular respiration both utilize carbon dioxide and water to produce carbohydrates.

d. Photosynthesis and cellular respiration both metabolize carbohydrates to produce carbon dioxide and water.

25. How is the energy from the sun transported within chloroplasts?

a. When photons strike photosystem (PS) II, pigments pass the light energy to chlorophyll a molecules that excite an electron, which is then passed to the electron transport chain. The cytochrome complex transfers protons across the thylakoid membrane and transfers electrons from PS-II to PS-I. The products of the light dependent reaction are used to power the Calvin cycle to produce glucose.

b. When photons strike photosystem (PS) I, pigments pass the light energy to chlorophyll, molecules that excite electrons, which is then passed to the electron transport chain. The cytochrome complex then transfers protons across the thylakoid membrane and transfers electrons from PS-II to PS-I. The products of the light dependent reaction are used to power the Calvin cycle to produce glucose.

c. When photons strike photosystem (PS) II, pigments pass the light energy to chlorophyll molecules that in turn excite electrons, which are then passed to the electron transport chain. The cytochrome complex transfers protons across the thylakoid membrane and transfers electrons from PS-I to PS-II. The products of the light dependent reaction are used to power the Calvin cycle to produce glucose.

d. When photons strike photosystem (PS) II, pigments pass the light energy to chlorophyll molecules that excite electrons, which is then passed to the electron transport chain. The cytochrome complex transfers protons across the thylakoid membrane and transfers electrons from PS II to PS I. The products of the light independent reaction are used to power the Calvin cycle to produce glucose.

26. Explain why X-rays and ultraviolet light wavelengths are dangerous to living tissues.

a. UV and X-rays are high energy waves that penetrate the tissues and damage cells.

b. UV and X-rays are low energy waves that penetrate the tissues and damage cells.

c. UV and X-rays cannot penetrate tissues and thus damage the cells.

d. UV and X-rays can penetrate tissues and thus do not damage the cells.

27. If a plant were to be exposed to only red light, would photosynthesis be possible?

a. Photosynthesis does not take place.

b. The rate of photosynthesis increases sharply.

c. The rate of photosynthesis decreases drastically.

d. The rate of photosynthesis decreases and then increases.

28. Describe the electron transfer pathway from photosystem II to photosystem I in the light-dependent reactions.

a. After splitting water in PS-II, high energy electrons are delivered through the chloroplast electron transport chain to PS-I.

b. After splitting water in PS-I, high energy electrons are delivered through the chloroplast electron transport chain to PS-II.

c. After the photosynthesis reaction, the released products like glucose help in the transfer of electrons from PS-II to PS-I.

d. After the completion of the light dependent reactions, the electrons are transferred from PS-II to PS-I.

29. What will happen to a plant leaf that loses CO_2 too quickly?

a. no effect on the rate of photosynthesis

b. Photosynthesis will slow down or stop possibly.

c. Photosynthesis will increase exponentially.

d. Photosynthesis will decrease and then increase.

30. Carbon, in the form of CO_2, must be taken from the atmosphere and attached to an existing organic molecule in the Calvin cycle. Therefore, the carbon is bound to the molecule. The products of the cycle only occur because of the added carbon. What are the products of the Calvin cycle and what is regenerated?

a. The product of the Calvin cycle is glyceraldehyde-3 phosphate and RuBP is regenerated.

b. The product of the Calvin cycle is glyceraldehyde-3 phosphate and RuBisCO is regenerated.

c. The product of the Calvin cycle is a 3-PGA molecule and glyceraldehyde-3 phosphate is regenerated.

d. The product of the Calvin cycle is glyceraldehyde-3 phosphate and oxygen is regenerated.

31. How do desert plants prevent water loss from the heat, which would compromise photosynthesis?

a. by using CAM photosynthesis and by closing stomatal pores during the night

b. by using CAM photosynthesis and by opening of stomatal pores during the night

c. by using CAM photosynthesis and by keeping stomatal pores closed at all times

d. by bypassing CAM photosynthesis and by keeping stomatal pores closed at night

32. Why are carnivores, such as lions, dependent on photosynthesis to survive?

a. because the prey of lions are generally herbivores which depend on heterotrophs

b. because the prey of lions are generally smaller carnivorous animals which depend on non-photosynthetic organisms

c. because the prey of lions are generally herbivores which depend on autotrophs

d. because the prey of lions are generally omnivores that depend only on autotrophs.

33. Why does it take three turns of the Calvin cycle to produce G3P, the initial product of photosynthesis?

a. To fix enough carbon to export one G3P molecule.

b. To fix enough oxygen to export one G3P molecule.

c. To produce RuBisCO as an end product.

d. To produce ATP and NADPH for fixation of G3P.

TEST PREP FOR AP® COURSES

34. Photosynthesis and cellular respiration are found throughout the eukaryotic world. They are complementary to each other because they each use products of the other process. What do the two pathways share?

a. chloroplasts and mitochondria

b. Photosystems I and II

c. the cytochrome complex

d. thylakoids

35. What evidence exists that the evolution of photosynthesis and cellular respiration support the concept that there is a common ancestry for all organisms?

a. All organisms perform cellular respiration, using oxygen and glucose, which are produced by photosynthesis.

b. All organisms perform cellular respiration using carbon dioxide and glucose, which are produced by photosynthesis.

c. All organisms perform cellular respiration using oxygen and lipids, which are produced by photosynthesis.

d. All organisms perform cellular respiration using carbon dioxide and lipids, which are produced by photosynthesis.

36.

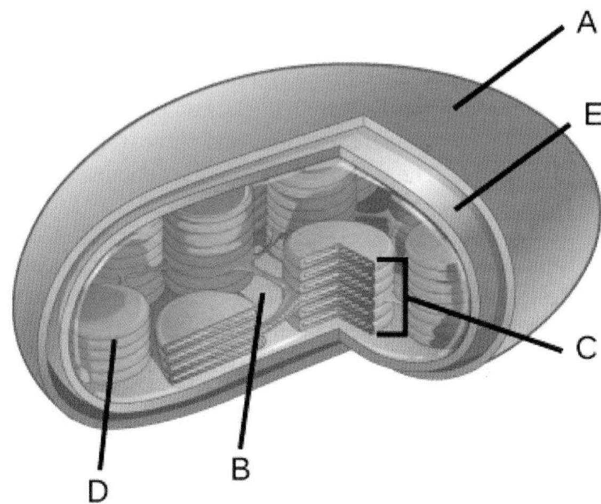

Correctly label the indicated parts of a chloroplast.

a. A. stroma, B. outer membrane, C. granum, D. thylakoid, E. inner membrane

b. A. outer membrane, B. stroma,C. granum, D. thylakoid, E. inner membrane

c. A. outer membrane, B. stroma, C. granum, D. inner membrane, E. thylakoid

d. A. stroma, B. outer membrane, C. inner membrane, D. granum, E. thylakoid

37. What cellular features and processes are similar in both photosynthesis and cellular respiration?

a. Both processes are contained in organelles with single membranes, and both use a version of the cytochrome complex.

b. Both processes are contained in organelles with double membranes, and neither use a version of the cytochrome complex.

c. Both processes are contained in organelles with double membranes, and use a version of the cytochrome complex.

d. Both processes are contained in organelles with single membranes, and neither use a version of the cytochrome complex.

38. Why do the light-dependent reactions of photosynthesis take place in the thylakoid?

a. Photosystem I is anchored to the membrane, but not photosystem II.

b. The cytochrome complex requires a membrane for chemiosmosis to occur.

c. The light-dependent reactions depend on the presence of carbon dioxide.

d. Light energy is absorbed by the thylakoid membrane.

39. Metabolic pathways both produce and use energy to perform their reactions. How does the Calvin cycle help to harness, store, and use energy in its pathway?

a. The Calvin cycle harnesses energy in the form of 6 ATP and 6 NADPH that are used to produce Fructose-3- phosphate (F3P) molecules. These store the energy captured from photosynthesis. The cycle uses this energy to regenerate RuBP.

b. The Calvin cycle harnesses energy in the form of 6 ATP and 6 NADPH that are used to produce Glyceraldehyde-3- phosphate (GA3P) molecules. These store the energy captured from photosynthesis. The cycle uses this energy to regenerate RuBP.

c. The Calvin cycle harnesses energy in the form of 3 ATP and 3 NADPH that are used to produce Glyceraldehyde-3- phosphate (GA3P) molecules. These store the energy captured from photosynthesis. The cycle uses this energy to regenerate the RuBP.

d. The Calvin cycle harnesses energy in the form of 6 ATP and 3 NADPH that are used to produce Glyceraldehyde-3- phosphate (GA3P) molecules. These store energy captured from photosynthesis. The cycle uses this energy to regenerate RuBP.

40. Based on Figure 8.18, which would most likely cause a plant to run out of NADP?

a. missing the ATP synthase enzyme

b. exposure to light

c. A lack of water would prevent H^+ and $NADP^+$ from forming NADPH

d. not enough CO_2

41. As temperatures increase, gases such as CO_2 diffuse faster. As a result, plant leaves will lose CO_2 at a faster rate than normal. If the amount of light impacting on the leaf and the amount of water available is adequate, predict how this loss of gas will affect photosynthesis in the leaf.

a. Loss of gases, mainly CO_2, will not affect photosynthesis in the leaf, as adequate amounts of water and light are still present which will let the Calvin cycle run smoothly.

b. Loss of gases, mainly CO_2, will affect photosynthesis in the leaf, as the Calvin cycle will become faster to compensate for the loss.

c. Loss of gases, mainly CO_2, will not affect photosynthesis in the leaf, as stored reservoirs of CO_2 in the leaf can be utilized in such times.

d. Loss of gases, mainly CO_2, will affect photosynthesis in the leaf, as the Calvin cycle will slow down and possibly stop because of inadequate carbon to fix in the system.

42. How do the cytochrome complex components involved in photosynthesis contribute to the electron transport chain?

a. Photosystem I excites the electron as it moves down the electron transport chain into Photosystem II.

b. Plastoquinone and plastocyanine perform redox reactions that allow the electron to move down the electron transport chain into Photosystem I.

c. ATP synthase "de-excites" the electron as it moves down the electron transport chain into Photosystem I.

d. RuBisCO excites the electron as it moves down the electron transport chain into Photosystem II.

43. Discuss how membranes in chloroplasts contribute to the organelles' essential functions.

a. The inner membrane contains the chemicals needed for the Calvin cycle and also components of the light dependent reactions. The thylakoid membrane contains photosystems I and II, as well as the enzyme NAD^+ reductase.

b. The inner membrane contains only the chemicals needed for the Calvin cycle. The thylakoid membrane contains components of the light dependent reactions, photosystems I and II, and the enzyme NAD^+ reductase.

c. The inner membrane contains components of the light dependent reactions as well as photosystems I and II. The thylakoid membrane contains the chemicals needed for the Calvin cycle and also the enzyme NAD^+ reductase.

d. The inner membrane contains the chemicals needed for the Calvin cycle, components of the light dependent reactions and photosystems I and II. The thylakoid membrane contains the enzyme NAD^+ reductase.

44. If the absorption spectrum of photosynthetic pigments was restricted to the green portion of the spectrum, which pigment or pigments would be affected the least?

a. carotenoids

b. chlorophyll a

c. chlorophyll b

d. chlorophyll c

45. Describe the passage of energy from light until it is captured in the primary electron acceptor.

a. Chlorophyll molecules in the photosystems are excited and pass the energy to the primary electron acceptor where the energy is used to excite electrons from the splitting of water.

b. Chlorophyll a molecules in the photosystems are excited and pass the energy to the primary electron acceptor where the energy is used to excite electrons from the splitting of water.

c. Chlorophyll b molecules in the photosystems are excited and pass the energy to the primary electron acceptor where the energy is used to excite electrons from the splitting of water.

d. Chlorophyll molecules in the photosystems absorb light and get excited in the primary electron acceptor from where the energy is used to excite electrons from the splitting of water.

SCIENCE PRACTICE CHALLENGE QUESTIONS

46. On a hot, dry day, plants close their stomata to conserve water. **Explain** the connection between the oxidation of water in photosystem II of the light-dependent reactions and the synthesis of glyceraldehyde-3-phosphate (G3PA) in the light-independent reactions. **Predict** the effect of closed stomata on the synthesis of G3PA and **justify** the prediction.

47. The emergence of photosynthetic organisms is recorded in layers of sedimentary rock known as a banded iron formation. Dark-colored and iron-rich bands composed of hematite (Fe_2O_3) and magnetite (Fe_3O_4) only a few millimeters thick alternate with light-colored and iron-poor shale or chert. Hematite and magnetite can form precipitates from water that has a high concentration of dissolved oxygen. Shale and chert can form under conditions that have high concentrations of carbonates (CO_3^{-2}). These banded iron formations appeared 3.7 billion years ago (and became less common 1.8 billion years ago). **Justify the claim** that these sedimentary rock formations reveal early Earth conditions.

48. The following diagram summarizes the light reactions of photosynthesis.

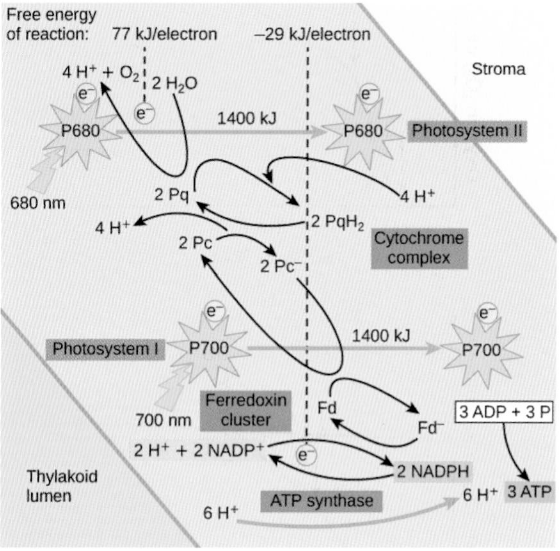

Figure 8.22

The diagram shows light-dependent reactions of photosynthesis, including the reaction centers, electron transport chains, and the overall reactions within each of these. The free energy per electron is shown for the oxidation-reduction reactions. The free change of the captured radiant energy is shown.

$$2NADP^+ + 2H^+ + 2H_2O + 3ADP + 3P_i \rightarrow$$

$$O_2 + 4H^+ + 2NADPH + 3ATP$$

A. In the *overall* mass balance equation for the light reactions shown above, **identify** the source of electrons for the synthesis of NADPH.

B. **Calculate** the number of electrons transferred in this reaction.

C. Using the free energies per electron displayed, **calculate** the free energy change of the light-dependent reactions.

D. Given that the free energy change for the hydrolysis of ATP is -31.5 kJ/mole and the free energy change for the formation of NADPH from $NADP^+$ is 18 kJ/mole, **calculate** the total production of free energy for the light reactions.

E. Using this definition of energy efficiency, **calculate** the efficiency of the light reaction of photosynthesis: energy efficiency = free energy produced/energy input.

49. Algae can be used for food and fuel. To maximize profit from algae production under artificial light, researchers proposed an experiment to determine the dependence of the efficiency of the process used to grow the algae on light intensity ("brightness") that will be purchased from the electric company.

The algae will be grown on a flat sheet that will be continuously washed with dissolved carbon dioxide and nutrients. Light-emitting diodes (LEDs) will be used to illuminate the growth sheet. Photodiodes placed above and below the sheet will be used to detect light transmitted through and reflected from the algal mat. The intensity of light can be varied, and the algae can be removed, filtered, and dried. The amount of stored energy in the algal mats can be determined by calorimetry.

A. **Identify** a useful definition of efficiency for this study and **justify** your choice.

B. Frequencies of light emitted by the LEDs will not be variables but must be specified for the construction of the apparatus. **Identify** the frequencies of light that should be used in the experiment and justify your choice.

C. **Evaluate the claim** that the experiment is based on the assumption that there is an upper limit on the intensity of light used to support growth of algae. **Predict** a possible effect on algal growth if light with too great an intensity is used and **justify** the prediction.

D. **Design an experiment** by describing a procedure that can be used to determine the relationship between light intensity and efficiency.

50. The classical theory of evolution is based on a gradual transformation, the accumulation of many random mutations that are selected. The biological evidence for evolution is overwhelming, particularly when one considers what has not changed: core conserved characteristics.

A. **Describe** three conserved characteristics common to both chloroplasts and mitochondria.

Some hypotheses that have been proposed to account for biological diversity are saltatory, involving sudden changes, rather than gradualist. In defense of the classical gradualist theory of evolution, nearly all biologists in the late 1960s rejected the theory of endosymbiosis as presented by Lynn Margulis in 1967.

B. Suppose that you want to disprove the theory of endosymbiosis.

Explain how the following evidence could disprove the theory:

i. a "transitional species" with cellular features that are intermediate cells with and without mitochondria

ii. a "transitional organelle" with some features, such as compartmentalized metabolic processes, but not other features, such as DNA

Explain how the following evidence supports the theory of endosymbiosis:

iii. bacteria live within your intestines, but you still have a separate identity

iv. no one has directly observed the fusion of two organisms in which a single organism results

51. Discovering the carbon-fixation reactions (or light-independent reactions) of photosynthesis earned Melvin Calvin a Nobel Prize in 1961. The isolation and identification of the products of algae exposed to ^{14}C revealed the path of carbon in photosynthesis. ^{14}C was fed to the algal culture in the form of bicarbonate ion (HCO_3^-). To agitate the culture, air, which contains CO_2, was bubbled through the system, so there were two sources of carbon.

Since Calvin's experiment, research has focused on the way carbon from a solution containing bicarbonate ions is absorbed by algae. In aqueous solution, the bicarbonate anion (HCO_3^-) is in equilibrium with dissolved CO_2 as shown in the equation below:

$$H^+ + HCO_3^- \rightleftarrows H_2O + CO_2$$

In a later experiment, Larsson and Axelsson (1999) used acetazolamide (AZ), a carbonate anhydrase inhibitor, to inhibit enzymes that convert bicarbonate into carbon dioxide. They also used disulfonate (DIDS), an inhibitor of the transport of anions, such as the bicarbonate ion, through the plasma membrane.

A. **Pose a scientific** question that can be pursued with AZ and DIDS in terms of the path of carbon in photosynthesis.

B. The plasma membrane is permeable to the nonpolar, uncharged carbon dioxide molecule. However, the concentration of carbon dioxide in solution can be very small. **Explain** how the enzyme carbonate anhydrase can increase the availability of carbon dioxide to the cell.

C. Larsson and Axelsson conducted experiments in which the growth medium was fixed at two different pH levels and determined the effects of AZ and DIDS on the rate of photosynthesis by measuring oxygen concentrations at various times. The results are shown in the two graphs below. The arrows indicate the time points during which HCO_3^-, AZ, and DIDS were added to each system.

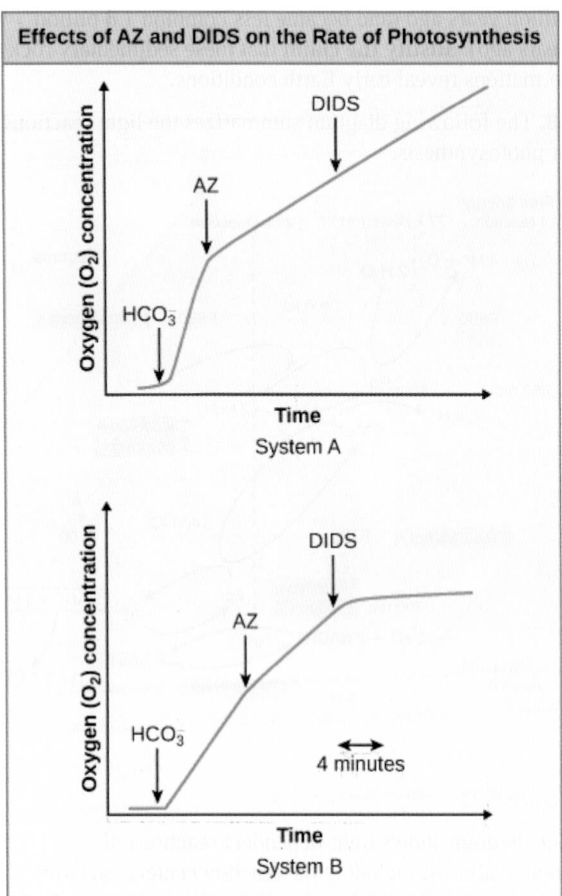

Figure 8.23 This figure displays the effects of AZ and DIDS on the rate of photosynthesis of two systems, system A and system B, in a line graph. The line graph plots the oxygen concentration over time.

In which system, A or B, is there a strong reliance on the bicarbonate ion as the mechanism of carbon uptake by the cell? **Justify** your answer using the data.

D. If both systems are dosed with the same concentrations of bicarbonate ion, in which system, A or B, is the pH higher? **Justify** your answer using the data and the bicarbonate-carbon dioxide equilibrium equation.

9 | CELL COMMUNICATION

Figure 9.1 Have you ever become separated from a friend while in a crowd? If so, you know the challenge of searching for someone when surrounded by thousands of other people. If you and your friend have cell phones, your chances of finding each other are good. A cell phone's ability to send and receive messages makes it an ideal communication device. (credit: modification of work by Vincent and Bella Productions)

Chapter Outline

Introduction

Imagine what life would be like if you and the people around you could not communicate. You would not be able to express your wishes, nor could you ask questions to find out more about your environment. Social organization is dependent on communication between the individuals; without communication, society would fall apart.

As with people, it is vital for a cell to interact with its environment. This is true whether it is a unicellular organism or one of many cells forming a larger organism. In order to respond to external stimuli, cells have developed complex mechanisms of communication that can receive a message, transfer the information across the plasma membrane, and produce changes within the cell in response to the message. In multicellular organisms, cells send and receive chemical messages constantly to coordinate the actions of distant organs, tissues, and cells.

While the necessity for cellular communication in larger organisms seems obvious, even single-celled organisms communicate with each other. Yeast cells signal each other to aid in mating. Some forms of bacteria coordinate their actions in order to form large complexes called biofilms (Figure 9.18) or to organize the production of toxins to remove competing organisms. The ability of cells to communicate through chemical signals originated in single cells and was essential for the evolution of multicellular organisms.

Cell signaling is vital to the survival of organisms. For example, chemical signals tell cells when to make hormones such as insulin. Cell division also depends on chemical signals. When the chemical signals do not function properly, cells can divide uncontrollably, forming cancerous tumors. Scientists recently discovered a cell signaling pathway that protects cancer cells from being killed by the body's immune system. The hope is to use this knowledge to create treatments that target this cell signaling pathway so that the cancer cells self destruct. More about that can be found here (http://openstaxcollege.org/l/32cancerdefense) : "Scientists pinpoint a new line of defense used by cancer cells."

9.1 | Signaling Molecules and Cellular Receptors

In this section, you will explore the following questions:

- What are the four types of signaling that are found in multicellular organisms?
- What are the differences between internal receptors and cell-surface receptors?
- What is the relationship between a ligand's structure and its mechanism of action?

Connection for AP® Courses

Just like you communicate with your classmates face-to-face, using your phone, or via e-mail, cells communicate with each other by both inter'and intracellular signaling. Cells detect and respond to changes in the environment using signaling pathways. Signaling pathways enable organisms to coordinate cellular activities and metabolic processes. Errors in these pathways can cause disease. Signaling cells secrete molecules called ligands that bind to target cells and initiate a chain of events within the target cell. For example, when epinephrine is released, binding to target cells, those cells respond by converting glycogen to glucose. Cell communication can happen over short distances. For example, neurotransmitters are released across a synapse to transfer messages between neurons Figure 1.3. Gap junctions and plasmodesmata allow small molecules, including signaling molecules, to flow between neighboring cells. Cell communication can also happen over long distances using. For example, hormones released from endocrine cells travel to target cells in multiple body systems. How does a ligand such as a hormone traveling through the bloodstream "know" when it has reached its target organ to initiate a cellular response? Nearly all cell signaling pathways involve three stages: reception, signal transduction, and cellular response.

Cell signaling pathways begin when the ligand binds to a receptor, a protein that is embedded in the plasma membrane of the target cell or found in the cell cytoplasm. The receptors are very specific, and each ligand is recognized by a different one. This stage of the pathway is called reception. Molecules that are nonpolar, such as steroids, diffuse across the cell membrane and bind to internal receptors. In turn, the receptor-ligand complex moves to the nucleus and interacts with cellular DNA. This changes how a gene is expressed. Polar ligands, on the other hand, interact with membrane receptor protein. Some membrane receptors work by changing conformation so that certain ions, such as Na^+ and K^+, can pass through the plasma membrane. Other membrane receptors interact with a G-protein on the cytoplasmic side of the plasma membrane, which causes a series of reactions inside the cell. Disruptions to this process are linked to several diseases, including cholera.

It is important to keep in mind that each cell has a variety of receptors, allowing it to respond to a variety of stimuli. Some receptors can bind several different ligands; for example, odorant molecules/receptors associated with the sense of smell in animals. Once the signaling molecule and receptor interact, a cascade of events called signal transduction usually amplifies the signal inside the cell.

The content presented in this section supports the Learning Objectives outlined in Big Idea 3 of the AP® Biology Curriculum Framework listed. The AP® Learning Objectives merge Essential knowledge content with one or more of the seven Science Practices. These objectives provide a transparent foundation for the AP® Biology course, along with inquiry-based laboratory experiences, instructional activities, and AP® Exam questions.

Big Idea 3	Living systems store, retrieve, transmit and respond to information essential to life processes.
Enduring Understanding 3.D	Cells communicate by generating, transmitting and receiving chemical signals.

Essential Knowledge	**3.D.3** Signal transduction pathways link signal reception with cellular response.
Science Practice	**6.2** The student can construct explanations of phenomena based on evidence produced through scientific practices.
Learning Objective	**3.34** The student is able to construct explanations of cell communication through cell-to-cell direct contact or through chemical signaling.
Essential Knowledge	**3.D.3** Signal transduction pathways link signal reception with cellular response.
Science Practice	**1.1** The student can create representations and models of natural or man-made phenomena and systems in the domain.
Learning Objective	**3.35** The student is able to create representations that depict how cell-to-cell communication occurs by direct contact or from a distance through chemical signaling.

The Science Practice Challenge Questions contain contains additional test questions for this section that will help you prepare for the AP exam. These questions address the following standards:
[APLO 3.33][APLO 3.36]

There are two kinds of communication in the world of living cells. Communication between cells is called **intercellular signaling**, and communication within a cell is called **intracellular signaling**. An easy way to remember the distinction is by understanding the Latin origin of the prefixes: inter- means "between" (for example, intersecting lines are those that cross each other) and intra- means "inside" (like intravenous).

Chemical signals are released by **signaling cells** in the form of small, usually volatile or soluble molecules called ligands. A **ligand** is a molecule that binds another specific molecule, in some cases, delivering a signal in the process. Ligands can thus be thought of as signaling molecules. Ligands interact with proteins in **target cells**, which are cells that are affected by chemical signals; these proteins are also called **receptors**. Ligands and receptors exist in several varieties; however, a specific ligand will have a specific receptor that typically binds only that ligand.

Forms of Signaling

There are four categories of chemical signaling found in multicellular organisms: paracrine signaling, endocrine signaling, autocrine signaling, and direct signaling across gap junctions (Figure 9.2). The main difference between the different categories of signaling is the distance that the signal travels through the organism to reach the target cell. Not all cells are affected by the same signals.

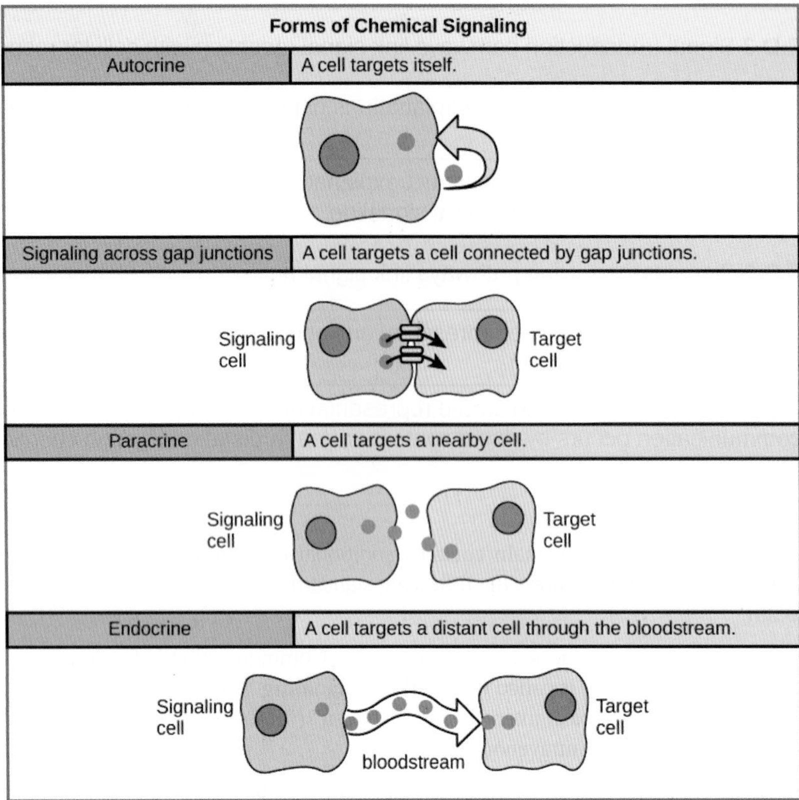

Figure 9.2 In chemical signaling, a cell may target itself (autocrine signaling), a cell connected by gap junctions, a nearby cell (paracrine signaling), or a distant cell (endocrine signaling). Paracrine signaling acts on nearby cells, endocrine signaling uses the circulatory system to transport ligands, and autocrine signaling acts on the signaling cell. Signaling via gap junctions involves signaling molecules moving directly between adjacent cells.

Paracrine Signaling

Signals that act locally between cells that are close together are called **paracrine signals**. Paracrine signals move by diffusion through the extracellular matrix. These types of signals usually elicit quick responses that last only a short amount of time. In order to keep the response localized, paracrine ligand molecules are normally quickly degraded by enzymes or removed by neighboring cells. Removing the signals will reestablish the concentration gradient for the signal, allowing them to quickly diffuse through the intracellular space if released again.

One example of paracrine signaling is the transfer of signals across synapses between nerve cells. A nerve cell consists of a cell body, several short, branched extensions called dendrites that receive stimuli, and a long extension called an axon, which transmits signals to other nerve cells or muscle cells. The junction between nerve cells where signal transmission occurs is called a synapse. A **synaptic signal** is a chemical signal that travels between nerve cells. Signals within the nerve cells are propagated by fast-moving electrical impulses. When these impulses reach the end of the axon, the signal continues on to a dendrite of the next cell by the release of chemical ligands called **neurotransmitters** by the presynaptic cell (the cell emitting the signal). The neurotransmitters are transported across the very small distances between nerve cells, which are called **chemical synapses** (Figure 9.3). The small distance between nerve cells allows the signal to travel quickly; this enables an immediate response, such as, Take your hand off the stove!

When the neurotransmitter binds the receptor on the surface of the postsynaptic cell, the electrochemical potential of the target cell changes, and the next electrical impulse is launched. The neurotransmitters that are released into the chemical synapse are degraded quickly or get reabsorbed by the presynaptic cell so that the recipient nerve cell can recover quickly and be prepared to respond rapidly to the next synaptic signal.

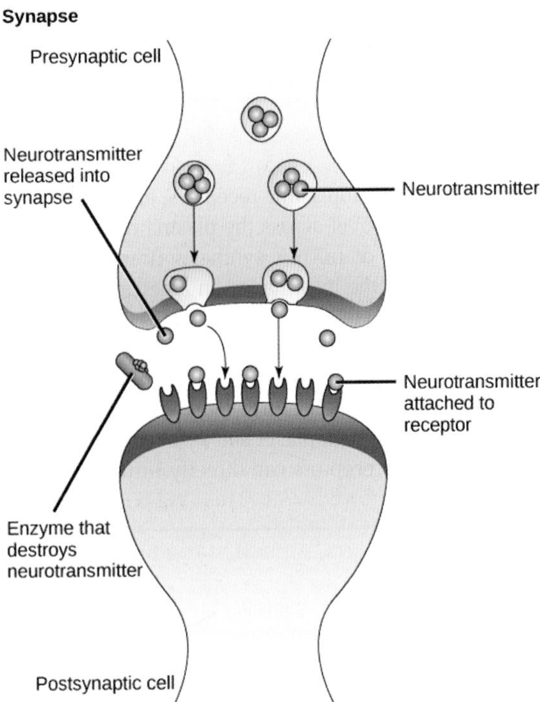

Figure 9.3 The distance between the presynaptic cell and the postsynaptic cell—called the synaptic gap—is very small and allows for rapid diffusion of the neurotransmitter. Enzymes in the synapatic cleft degrade some types of neurotransmitters to terminate the signal.

Endocrine Signaling

Signals from distant cells are called **endocrine signals**, and they originate from **endocrine cells**. (In the body, many endocrine cells are located in endocrine glands, such as the thyroid gland, the hypothalamus, and the pituitary gland.) These types of signals usually produce a slower response but have a longer-lasting effect. The ligands released in endocrine signaling are called hormones, signaling molecules that are produced in one part of the body but affect other body regions some distance away.

Hormones travel the large distances between endocrine cells and their target cells via the bloodstream, which is a relatively slow way to move throughout the body. Because of their form of transport, hormones get diluted and are present in low concentrations when they act on their target cells. This is different from paracrine signaling, in which local concentrations of ligands can be very high.

Autocrine Signaling

Autocrine signals are produced by signaling cells that can also bind to the ligand that is released. This means the signaling cell and the target cell can be the same or a similar cell (the prefix *auto-* means self, a reminder that the signaling cell sends a signal to itself). This type of signaling often occurs during the early development of an organism to ensure that cells develop into the correct tissues and take on the proper function. Autocrine signaling also regulates pain sensation and inflammatory responses. Further, if a cell is infected with a virus, the cell can signal itself to undergo programmed cell death, killing the virus in the process. In some cases, neighboring cells of the same type are also influenced by the released ligand. In embryological development, this process of stimulating a group of neighboring cells may help to direct the differentiation of identical cells into the same cell type, thus ensuring the proper developmental outcome.

Direct Signaling Across Gap Junctions

Gap junctions in animals and plasmodesmata in plants are connections between the plasma membranes of neighboring cells. These fluid-filled channels allow small signaling molecules, called **intracellular mediators**, to diffuse between the two cells. Small molecules, such as calcium ions (Ca^{2+}), are able to move between cells, but large molecules like proteins and DNA cannot fit through the channels. The specificity of the channels ensures that the cells remain independent but can quickly and easily transmit signals. The transfer of signaling molecules communicates the current state of the cell that is directly next to the target cell; this allows a group of cells to coordinate their response to a signal that only one of them may have received. In plants, plasmodesmata are ubiquitous, making the entire plant into a giant communication network.

Types of Receptors

Receptors are protein molecules in the target cell or on its surface that bind ligand. There are two types of receptors, internal receptors and cell-surface receptors.

Internal receptors

Internal receptors, also known as intracellular or cytoplasmic receptors, are found in the cytoplasm of the cell and respond to hydrophobic ligand molecules that are able to travel across the plasma membrane. Once inside the cell, many of these molecules bind to proteins that act as regulators of mRNA synthesis (transcription) to mediate gene expression. Gene expression is the cellular process of transforming the information in a cell's DNA into a sequence of amino acids, which ultimately forms a protein. When the ligand binds to the internal receptor, a conformational change is triggered that exposes a DNA-binding site on the protein. The ligand-receptor complex moves into the nucleus, then binds to specific regulatory regions of the chromosomal DNA and promotes the initiation of transcription (Figure 9.4). Transcription is the process of copying the information in a cells DNA into a special form of RNA called messenger RNA (mRNA); the cell uses information in the mRNA (which moves out into the cytoplasm and associates with ribosomes) to link specific amino acids in the correct order, producing a protein. Internal receptors can directly influence gene expression without having to pass the signal on to other receptors or messengers.

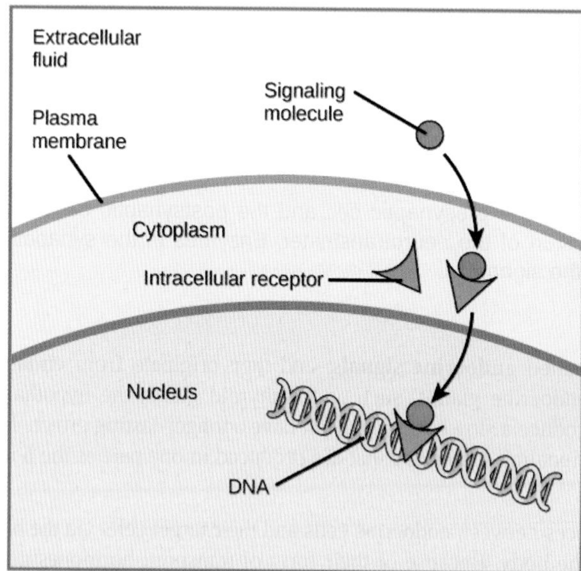

Figure 9.4 Hydrophobic signaling molecules typically diffuse across the plasma membrane and interact with intracellular receptors in the cytoplasm. Many intracellular receptors are transcription factors that interact with DNA in the nucleus and regulate gene expression.

Cell-Surface Receptors

Cell-surface receptors, also known as transmembrane receptors, are cell surface, membrane-anchored (integral) proteins that bind to external ligand molecules. This type of receptor spans the plasma membrane and performs signal transduction, in which an extracellular signal is converted into an intracellular signal. Ligands that interact with cell-surface receptors do not have to enter the cell that they affect. Cell-surface receptors are also called cell-specific proteins or markers because they are specific to individual cell types.

Because cell-surface receptor proteins are fundamental to normal cell functioning, it should come as no surprise that a malfunction in any one of these proteins could have severe consequences. Errors in the protein structures of certain receptor molecules have been shown to play a role in hypertension (high blood pressure), asthma, heart disease, and cancer.

Each cell-surface receptor has three main components: an external ligand-binding domain, a hydrophobic membrane-spanning region, and an intracellular domain inside the cell. The ligand-binding domain is also called the **extracellular domain**. The size and extent of each of these domains vary widely, depending on the type of receptor.

How Viruses Recognize a Host

Unlike living cells, many viruses do not have a plasma membrane or any of the structures necessary to sustain life. Some viruses are simply composed of an inert protein shell containing DNA or RNA. To reproduce, viruses must invade a living cell, which serves as a host, and then take over the hosts cellular apparatus. But how does a virus recognize its host?

Viruses often bind to cell-surface receptors on the host cell. For example, the virus that causes human influenza (flu) binds specifically to receptors on membranes of cells of the respiratory system. Chemical differences in the cell-surface receptors among hosts mean that a virus that infects a specific species (for example, humans) cannot infect another species (for example, chickens).

However, viruses have very small amounts of DNA or RNA compared to humans, and, as a result, viral reproduction can occur rapidly. Viral reproduction invariably produces errors that can lead to changes in newly produced viruses; these changes mean that the viral proteins that interact with cell-surface receptors may evolve in such a way that they can bind to receptors in a new host. Such changes happen randomly and quite often in the reproductive cycle of a virus, but the changes only matter if a virus with new binding properties comes into contact with a suitable host. In the case of influenza, this situation can occur in settings where animals and people are in close contact, such as poultry and swine farms. [1] Once a virus jumps to a new host, it can spread quickly. Scientists watch newly appearing viruses (called emerging viruses) closely in the hope that such monitoring can reduce the likelihood of global viral epidemics.

What requirements must be met for a new virus to emerge and spread?

a. The virus must infect at least two different animals before infecting humans.
b. The virus must come into contact with a new host so mutations will occur which allow the virus to bind to that host.
c. A mutation must occur in the host allowing the virus to bind to the host.
d. A mutation must occur in the virus allowing the virus to infect a new host, and the virus must come into contact with this host.

Cell-surface receptors are involved in most of the signaling in multicellular organisms. There are three general categories of cell-surface receptors: ion channel-linked receptors, G-protein-linked receptors, and enzyme-linked receptors.

Ion channel-linked receptors bind a ligand and open a channel through the membrane that allows specific ions to pass through. To form a channel, this type of cell-surface receptor has an extensive membrane-spanning region. In order to interact with the phospholipid fatty acid tails that form the center of the plasma membrane, many of the amino acids in the membrane-spanning region are hydrophobic in nature. Conversely, the amino acids that line the inside of the channel are hydrophilic to allow for the passage of water or ions. When a ligand binds to the extracellular region of the channel, there is a conformational change in the proteins structure that allows ions such as sodium, calcium, magnesium, and hydrogen to pass through (Figure 9.5).

1. A. B. Sigalov, The School of Nature. IV. Learning from Viruses, *Self/Nonself* 1, no. 4 (2010): 282-298. Y. Cao, X. Koh, L. Dong, X. Du, A. Wu, X. Ding, H. Deng, Y. Shu, J. Chen, T. Jiang, Rapid Estimation of Binding Activity of Influenza Virus Hemagglutinin to Human and Avian Receptors, *PLoS One* 6, no. 4 (2011): e18664.

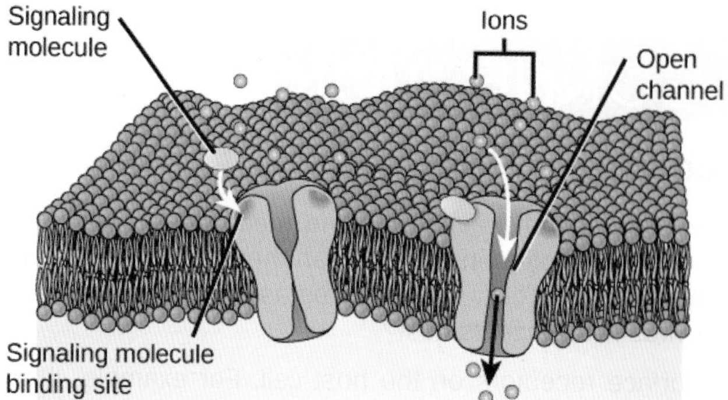

Figure 9.5 Gated ion channels form a pore through the plasma membrane that opens when the signaling molecule binds. The open pore then allows ions to flow into or out of the cell.

G-protein-linked receptors bind a ligand and activate a membrane protein called a G-protein. The activated G-protein then interacts with either an ion channel or an enzyme in the membrane (Figure 9.6). All G-protein-linked receptors have seven transmembrane domains, but each receptor has its own specific extracellular domain and G-protein-binding site.

Cell signaling using G-protein-linked receptors occurs as a cyclic series of events. Before the ligand binds, the inactive G-protein can bind to a newly revealed site on the receptor specific for its binding. Once the G-protein binds to the receptor, the resultant shape change activates the G-protein, which releases GDP and picks up GTP. The subunits of the G-protein then split into the α subunit and the $\beta\gamma$ subunit. One or both of these G-protein fragments may be able to activate other proteins as a result. After awhile, the GTP on the active α subunit of the G-protein is hydrolyzed to GDP and the $\beta\gamma$ subunit is deactivated. The subunits reassociate to form the inactive G-protein and the cycle begins anew.

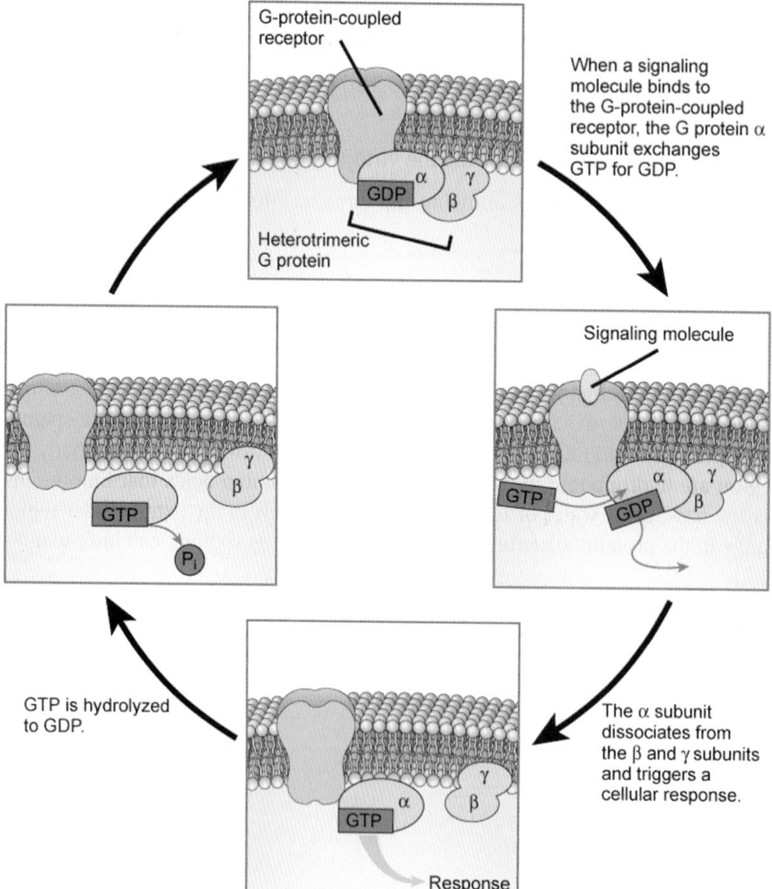

Figure 9.6 Heterotrimeric G proteins have three subunits: α, β, and γ. When a signaling molecule binds to a G-protein-coupled receptor in the plasma membrane, a GDP molecule associated with the α subunit is exchanged for GTP. The β and γ subunits dissociate from the α subunit, and a cellular response is triggered either by the α subunit or the dissociated $\beta\gamma$ pair. Hydrolysis of GTP to GDP terminates the signal.

G-protein-linked receptors have been extensively studied and much has been learned about their roles in maintaining health. Bacteria that are pathogenic to humans can release poisons that interrupt specific G-protein-linked receptor function, leading to illnesses such as pertussis, botulism, and cholera. In cholera (Figure 9.7), for example, the water-borne bacterium *Vibrio cholerae* produces a toxin, choleragen, that binds to cells lining the small intestine. The toxin then enters these intestinal cells, where it modifies a G-protein that controls the opening of a chloride channel and causes it to remain continuously active, resulting in large losses of fluids from the body and potentially fatal dehydration as a result.

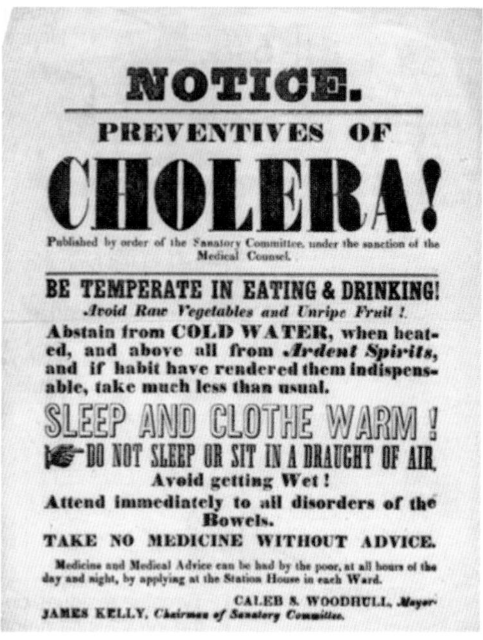

Figure 9.7 Transmitted primarily through contaminated drinking water, cholera is a major cause of death in the developing world and in areas where natural disasters interrupt the availability of clean water. The cholera bacterium, *Vibrio cholerae*, creates a toxin that modifies G-protein-mediated cell signaling pathways in the intestines. Modern sanitation eliminates the threat of cholera outbreaks, such as the one that swept through New York City in 1866. This poster from that era shows how, at that time, the way that the disease was transmitted was not understood. (credit: New York City Sanitary Commission)

Enzyme-linked receptors are cell-surface receptors with intracellular domains that are associated with an enzyme. In some cases, the intracellular domain of the receptor itself is an enzyme. Other enzyme-linked receptors have a small intracellular domain that interacts directly with an enzyme. The enzyme-linked receptors normally have large extracellular and intracellular domains, but the membrane-spanning region consists of a single alpha-helical region of the peptide strand. When a ligand binds to the extracellular domain, a signal is transferred through the membrane, activating the enzyme. Activation of the enzyme sets off a chain of events within the cell that eventually leads to a response. One example of this type of enzyme-linked receptor is the tyrosine kinase receptor (Figure 9.8). A kinase is an enzyme that transfers phosphate groups from ATP to another protein. The tyrosine kinase receptor transfers phosphate groups to tyrosine molecules (tyrosine residues). First, signaling molecules bind to the extracellular domain of two nearby tyrosine kinase receptors. The two neighboring receptors then bond together, or dimerize. Phosphates are then added to tyrosine residues on the intracellular domain of the receptors (phosphorylation). The phosphorylated residues can then transmit the signal to the next messenger within the cytoplasm.

visual CONNECTION

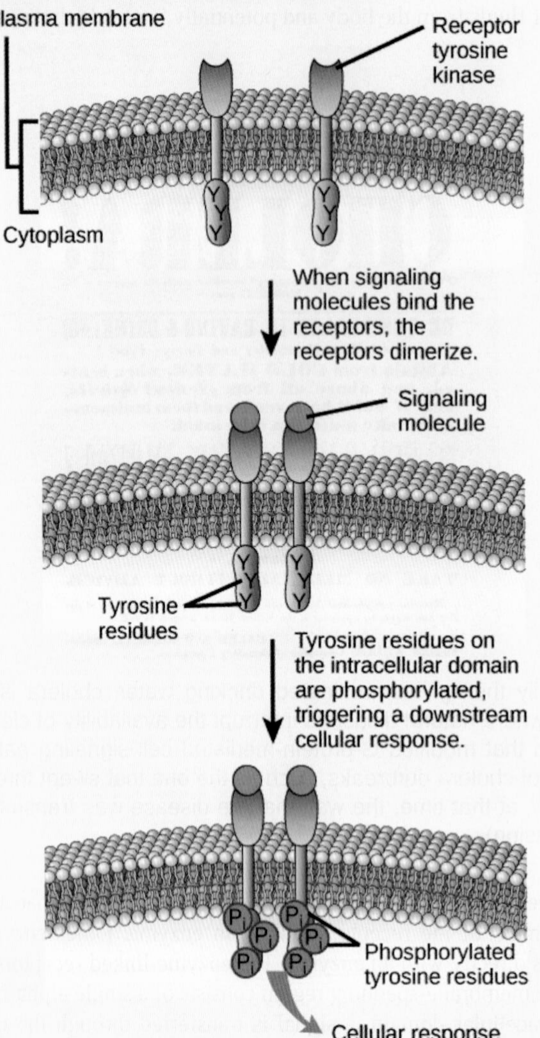

Figure 9.8 A receptor tyrosine kinase is an enzyme-linked receptor with a single transmembrane region, and extracellular and intracellular domains. Binding of a signaling molecule to the extracellular domain causes the receptor to dimerize. Tyrosine residues on the intracellular domain are then autophosphorylated, triggering a downstream cellular response. The signal is terminated by a phosphatase that removes the phosphates from the phosphotyrosine residues.

HER2 is a receptor tyrosine kinase. In 20 percent of human breast cancer cases, HER2 is permanently activated, resulting in unregulated cell division. Lapatinib, a drug used to treat breast cancer, inhibits HER2 receptor tyrosine kinase autophosphorylation, the process by which the receptor adds phosphates onto itself. This reduces tumor growth by 50 percent. Besides autophosphorylation, which of the following steps would be inhibited by Lapatinib?

a. dimerization and the downstream cellular response

b. phosphatase activity, dimerization, and the downstream cellular response

c. signaling molecule binding, dimerization, and the downstream cellular response

d. the downstream cellular response

Signaling Molecules

Produced by signaling cells and the subsequent binding to receptors in target cells, ligands act as chemical signals that travel to the target cells to coordinate responses. The types of molecules that serve as ligands are incredibly varied and range from small proteins to small ions like calcium (Ca^{2+}).

Small Hydrophobic Ligands

Small hydrophobic ligands can directly diffuse through the plasma membrane and interact with internal receptors. Important members of this class of ligands are the steroid hormones. Steroids are lipids that have a hydrocarbon skeleton with four fused rings; different steroids have different functional groups attached to the carbon skeleton. Steroid hormones include the female sex hormone, estradiol, which is a type of estrogen; the male sex hormone, testosterone; and cholesterol, which is an important structural component of biological membranes and a precursor of steriod hormones (Figure 9.9). Other hydrophobic hormones include thyroid hormones and vitamin D. In order to be soluble in blood, hydrophobic ligands must bind to carrier proteins while they are being transported through the bloodstream.

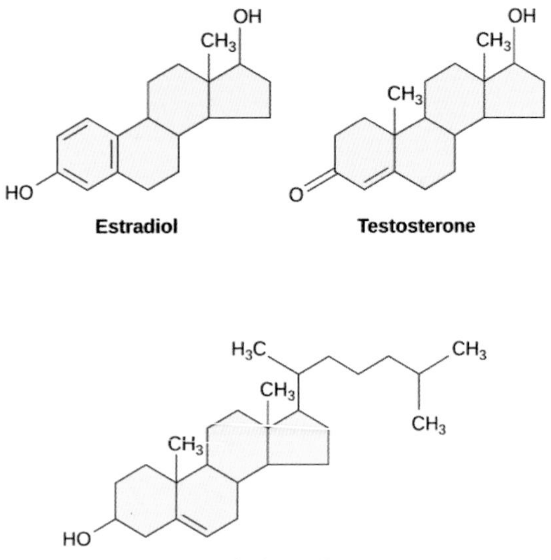

Figure 9.9 Steroid hormones have similar chemical structures to their precursor, cholesterol. Because these molecules are small and hydrophobic, they can diffuse directly across the plasma membrane into the cell, where they interact with internal receptors.

Water-Soluble Ligands

Water-soluble ligands are polar and therefore cannot pass through the plasma membrane unaided; sometimes, they are too large to pass through the membrane at all. Instead, most water-soluble ligands bind to the extracellular domain of cell-surface receptors. This group of ligands is quite diverse and includes small molecules, peptides, and proteins.

Other Ligands

Nitric oxide (NO) is a gas that also acts as a ligand. It is able to diffuse directly across the plasma membrane, and one of its roles is to interact with receptors in smooth muscle and induce relaxation of the tissue. NO has a very short half-life and therefore only functions over short distances. Nitroglycerin, a treatment for heart disease, acts by triggering the release of NO, which causes blood vessels to dilate (expand), thus restoring blood flow to the heart.

science practices CONNECTION for AP® Courses

Think About It

- Cells grown in the laboratory are placed in a solution containing a dye that is unable to pass through the plasma membrane. If a ligand is then added to the solution, observations show that the dye enters the cell. Describe the type of receptor the ligand most likely binds to and explain your reasoning.
- HER2 is a receptor tyrosine kinase. In 30 percent of human breast cancers, HER2 is permanently activated, resulting in unregulated cell division. Lapatinib, a drug used to treat breast cancer, inhibits HER2 receptor tyrosine kinase autophosphorylation (the process by which the receptor adds phosphate onto itself), thus reducing tumor growth. Besides autophosphorylation, explain another feature of the cell signaling pathway that can be affected by Lapatinib.
- In certain cancers, the GTPase activity of RAS G-protein in inhibited. This means that the RAS G-protein can no longer hydrolyze GTP into GDP. Explain what effect this would have on downstream cellular events.

9.2 | Propagation of the Signal

In this section, you will explore the following questions:

- How does the binding of a ligand initiate signal transduction throughout a cell?
- What is the role of second messengers in signal transduction?

Connection for AP® Courses

During signal transduction, a series of relay proteins inside the cytoplasm of the target cell activate target proteins, resulting in a cellular response. These cascades are complex because of the interplay between proteins. A significant contributor to cell signaling cascades is the phosphorylation of molecules by enzymes known as kinases. (Substrate–level phosphorylation was studied when you learned about glycolysis.) By adding a phosphate group, phosphorylation changes the shapes of proteins. This change in shape activates or inactivates them. Second messengers, e.g., cAMP and Ca^{2+}, are often used to transmit signals within a cell.

Information presented and the examples highlighted in the section support concepts and Learning Objectives outlined in Big Idea 3 of the AP® Biology Curriculum Framework. The Learning Objectives listed in the Curriculum Framework provide a transparent foundation for the AP® Biology course, an inquiry-based laboratory experience, instructional activities, and AP® Exam questions. A Learning Objective merges required content with one or more of the seven Science Practices.

Big Idea 3	Living systems store, retrieve, transmit and respond to information essential to life processes.
Enduring Understanding 3.D	Cells communicate by generating, transmitting and receiving chemical signals.
Essential Knowledge	**3.D.3** Signal transduction pathways link signal reception with cellular response.
Science Practice	**1.5** The student can re-express key elements of natural phenomena across multiple representations in the domain.
Learning Objective	**3.36** The student is able to describe a model that expresses the key elements of signal transduction pathways by which a signal is converted to a cellular response.

The Science Practice Challenge Questions contain additional test questions for this section that will help you prepare for the AP exam. These questions address the following standards:
[APLO 3.33][APLO 3.4][APLO 4.22][APLO 2.5][APLO 3.32][APLO 3.38]

Once a ligand binds to a receptor, the signal is transmitted through the membrane and into the cytoplasm. Continuation of a signal in this manner is called **signal transduction**. Signal transduction only occurs with cell-surface receptors because internal receptors are able to interact directly with DNA in the nucleus to initiate protein synthesis.

When a ligand binds to its receptor, conformational changes occur that affect the receptor's intracellular domain. Conformational changes of the extracellular domain upon ligand binding can propagate through the membrane region of the receptor and lead to activation of the intracellular domain or its associated proteins. In some cases, binding of the ligand causes **dimerization** of the receptor, which means that two receptors bind to each other to form a stable complex called a dimer. A **dimer** is a chemical compound formed when two molecules (often identical) join together. The binding of the receptors in this manner enables their intracellular domains to come into close contact and activate each other.

Binding Initiates a Signaling Pathway

After the ligand binds to the cell-surface receptor, the activation of the receptor's intracellular components sets off a chain of events that is called a **signaling pathway** or a signaling cascade. In a signaling pathway, second messengers, enzymes, and activated proteins interact with specific proteins, which are in turn activated in a chain reaction that eventually leads to a change in the cell's environment (Figure 9.10). The events in the cascade occur in a series, much like a current flows in a river. Interactions that occur before a certain point are defined as upstream events, and events after that point are called downstream events.

visual CONNECTION

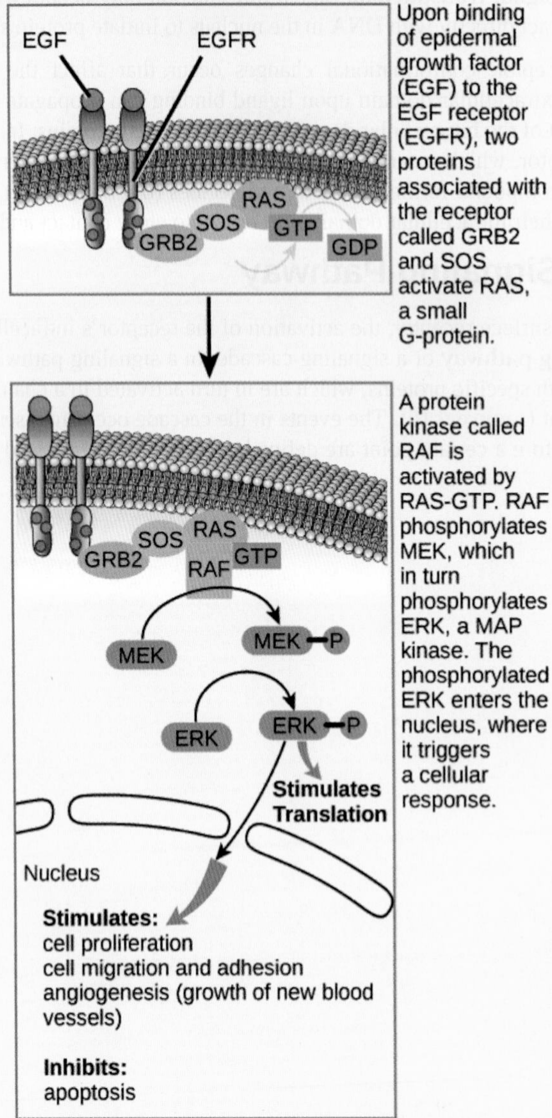
EGF
EGFR
RAS
SOS
GTP
GRB2
GDP
Upon binding of epidermal growth factor (EGF) to the EGF receptor (EGFR), two proteins associated with the receptor called GRB2 and SOS activate RAS, a small G-protein.
SOS
RAS
GRB2
GTP
RAF
MEK
MEK—P
ERK
ERK—P
A protein kinase called RAF is activated by RAS-GTP. RAF phosphorylates MEK, which in turn phosphorylates ERK, a MAP kinase. The phosphorylated ERK enters the nucleus, where it triggers a cellular response.
Stimulates Translation
Nucleus
Stimulates:
cell proliferation
cell migration and adhesion
angiogenesis (growth of new blood vessels)
Inhibits:
apoptosis

Figure 9.10 The epidermal growth factor (EGF) receptor (EGFR) is a receptor tyrosine kinase involved in the regulation of cell growth, wound healing, and tissue repair. When EGF binds to the EGFR, a cascade of downstream events causes the cell to grow and divide. If EGFR is activated at inappropriate times, uncontrolled cell growth may occur.

In certain cancers, the GTPase activity of the RAS G-protein is inhibited. This means that the RAS protein can no longer hydrolyze GTP into GDP. What effect would this have on downstream cellular events?

a. Cells will not proliferate.

b. ERK is permanently inactivated.

c. Regulated cell division.

d. Uncontrolled cell proliferation.

Signaling pathways can get very complicated very quickly because most cellular proteins can affect different downstream events, depending on the conditions within the cell. A single pathway can branch off toward different endpoints based on the interplay between two or more signaling pathways, and the same ligands are often used to initiate different signals in different cell types. This variation in response is due to differences in protein expression in different cell types. Another complicating element is **signal integration** of the pathways, in which signals from two or more different cell-surface receptors merge to activate the same response in the cell. This process can ensure that multiple external requirements are met before a cell commits to a specific response.

The effects of extracellular signals can also be amplified by enzymatic cascades. At the initiation of the signal, a single ligand binds to a single receptor. However, activation of a receptor-linked enzyme can activate many copies of a component of the signaling cascade, which amplifies the signal.

Methods of Intracellular Signaling

The induction of a signaling pathway depends on the modification of a cellular component by an enzyme. There are numerous enzymatic modifications that can occur, and they are recognized in turn by the next component downstream. The following are some of the more common events in intracellular signaling.

Observe an animation of cell signaling at this site (http://openstaxcollege.org/l/cell_signals) .

Hemophilia is a rare condition in which the blood lacks sufficient clotting factors. These factors are required for the platelets to bind together and form clots. How does this interfere with the cell signals during wound healing?

a. delay and prevention of the cell signal required for wound healing

b. activate the cell signal required for wound healing

c. activate and enhance the cell signals for wound healing

d. cell signal will remain unaffected

Phosphorylation

One of the most common chemical modifications that occurs in signaling pathways is the addition of a phosphate group (PO_4^{-3}) to a molecule such as a protein in a process called phosphorylation. The phosphate can be added to a nucleotide such as GMP to form GDP or GTP. Phosphates are also often added to serine, threonine, and tyrosine residues of proteins, where they replace the hydroxyl group of the amino acid (Figure 9.11). The transfer of the phosphate is catalyzed by an enzyme called a **kinase**. Various kinases are named for the substrate they phosphorylate. Phosphorylation of serine and threonine residues often activates enzymes. Phosphorylation of tyrosine residues can either affect the activity of an enzyme or create a binding site that interacts with downstream components in the signaling cascade. Phosphorylation may activate or inactivate enzymes, and the reversal of phosphorylation, dephosphorylation by a phosphatase, will reverse the effect.

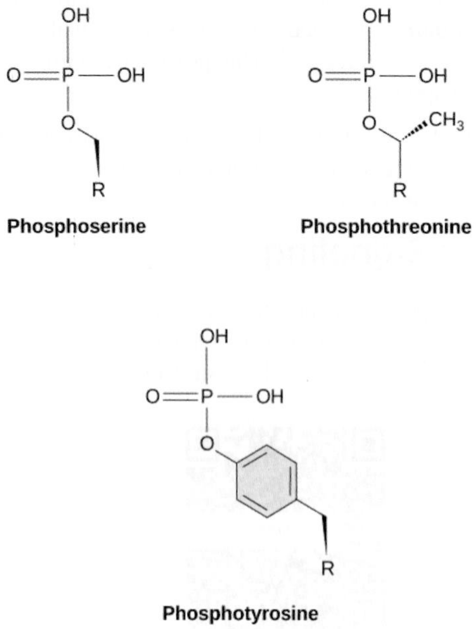

Figure 9.11 In protein phosphorylation, a phosphate group (PO_4^{-3}) is added to residues of the amino acids serine, threonine, and tyrosine.

Second Messengers

Second messengers are small molecules that propagate a signal after it has been initiated by the binding of the signaling molecule to the receptor. These molecules help to spread a signal through the cytoplasm by altering the behavior of certain cellular proteins.

Calcium ion is a widely used second messenger. The free concentration of calcium ions (Ca^{2+}) within a cell is very low because ion pumps in the plasma membrane continuously use adenosine-5'-triphosphate (ATP) to remove it. For signaling purposes, Ca^{2+} is stored in cytoplasmic vesicles, such as the endoplasmic reticulum, or accessed from outside the cell. When signaling occurs, ligand-gated calcium ion channels allow the higher levels of Ca^{2+} that are present outside the cell (or in intracellular storage compartments) to flow into the cytoplasm, which raises the concentration of cytoplasmic Ca^{2+}. The response to the increase in Ca^{2+} varies, depending on the cell type involved. For example, in the β-cells of the pancreas, Ca^{2+} signaling leads to the release of insulin, and in muscle cells, an increase in Ca^{2+} leads to muscle contractions.

Another second messenger utilized in many different cell types is **cyclic AMP (cAMP)**. Cyclic AMP is synthesized by the enzyme adenylyl cyclase from ATP (Figure 9.12). The main role of cAMP in cells is to bind to and activate an enzyme called **cAMP-dependent kinase (A-kinase)**. A-kinase regulates many vital metabolic pathways: It phosphorylates serine and threonine residues of its target proteins, activating them in the process. A-kinase is found in many different types of cells, and the target proteins in each kind of cell are different. Differences give rise to the variation of the responses to cAMP in different cells.

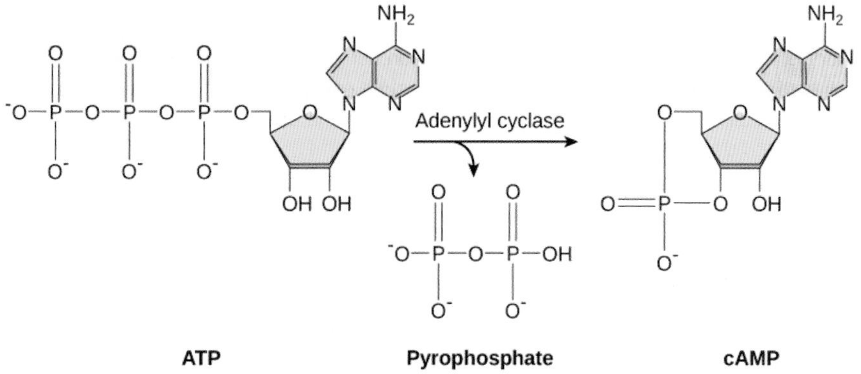

Figure 9.12 This diagram shows the mechanism for the formation of cyclic AMP (cAMP). cAMP serves as a second messenger to activate or inactivate proteins within the cell. Termination of the signal occurs when an enzyme called phosphodiesterase converts cAMP into AMP.

Present in small concentrations in the plasma membrane, **inositol phospholipids** are lipids that can also be converted into second messengers. Because these molecules are membrane components, they are located near membrane-bound receptors and can easily interact with them. Phosphatidylinositol (PI) is the main phospholipid that plays a role in cellular signaling. Enzymes known as kinases phosphorylate PI to form PI-phosphate (PIP) and PI-bisphosphate (PIP_2).

The enzyme phospholipase C cleaves PIP_2 to form **diacylglycerol (DAG)** and **inositol triphosphate (IP_3)** (Figure 9.13). These products of the cleavage of PIP_2 serve as second messengers. Diacylglycerol (DAG) remains in the plasma membrane and activates protein kinase C (PKC), which then phosphorylates serine and threonine residues in its target proteins. IP_3 diffuses into the cytoplasm and binds to ligand-gated calcium channels in the endoplasmic reticulum to release Ca^{2+} that continues the signal cascade.

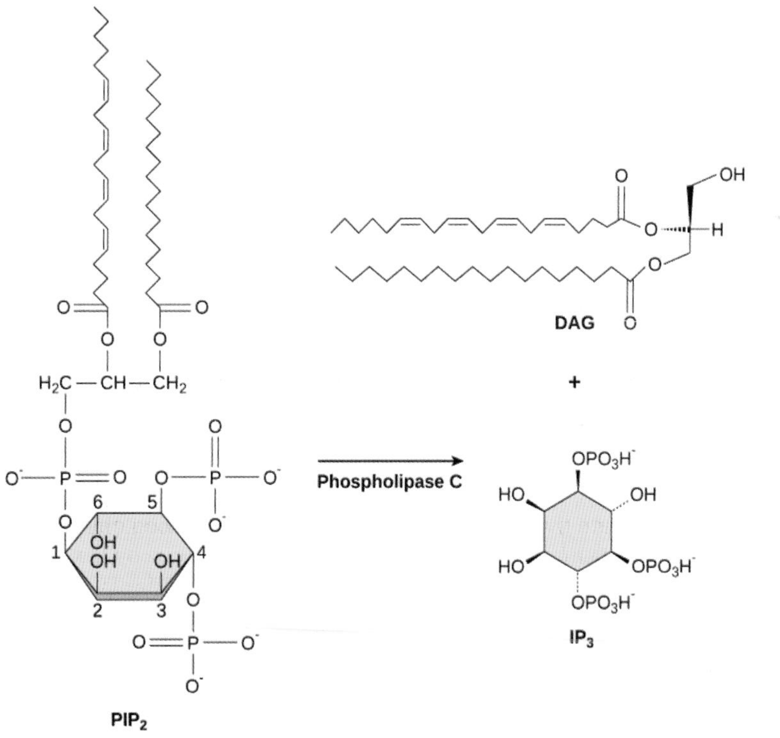

Figure 9.13 The enzyme phospholipase C breaks down PIP_2 into IP_3 and DAG, both of which serve as second messengers.

science practices CONNECTION for AP® Courses

Think About It

The same second messengers are used in many different cells, but the response to second messengers is different in each cell. How is this possible?

9.3 | Response to the Signal

In this section you will explore the following questions:

- How do signaling pathways direct protein expression, cellular metabolism, and cell growth?
- What is the role of apoptosis in the development and maintenance of a healthy organism?

Connection for AP® Courses

The initiation of a signaling pathway results in a cellular response to changes in the external environment. This response can take many different forms, including protein synthesis, a change in cell metabolism, cell division and growth, or even cell death. As we will explore in more detail in later chapters, some pathways activate enzymes that interact within DNA transcription factors to promote gene expression, others can cause cells to store energy as glycogen as fat, or result in free energy availability in the form of glucose. Cell division and growth are almost always stimulated by external signals called growth factors; left unregulated, cell growth leads to cancer. Programmed cell death, or apoptosis, removes damaged or unnecessary cells and plays a vital role in development, including morphogenesis of fingers and toes. Termination of the cell signaling cascade is important to ensure that the response to a signal is appropriate in timing and intensity. Degradation of signaling molecules and dephosphorylation of intermediates of the pathway are two ways signals are terminated within cells. Conditions where signaling pathways are blocked or defective can be deleterious, preventative, or prophylactic; examples include diabetes, heart disease, autoimmune disease, toxins, anesthetics, and birth control pills.

Information presented and the examples highlighted in the section support concepts and learning objectives outlined in Big Idea 3 and Big Idea 2 of the AP® Biology Curriculum Framework. The Learning Objectives listed in the Curriculum Framework provide a transparent foundation for the AP® Biology course, an inquiry-based laboratory experience, instructional activities, and AP® exam questions. A learning objective merges required content with one or more of the seven science practices.

Big Idea 3	Living systems store, retrieve, transmit and respond to information essential to life processes.
Enduring Understanding 3.D	Cells communicate by generating, transmitting and receiving chemical signals.
Essential Knowledge	**3.D.4** Changes in signal transduction pathways can alter cellular response.
Science Practice	**1.5** The student can re-express key elements of natural phenomena across multiple representations in the domain.
Learning Objective	**3.36** The student is able to describe a model that expresses the key elements of signal transduction pathways by which a signal is converted to a cellular response.
Essential Knowledge	**3.D.4** Changes in signal transduction pathways can alter cellular response.

Science Practice	**6.1** The student can justify claims with evidence.
Learning Objective	**3.37** The student is able to justify claims based on scientific evidence that changes in signal transduction pathways can alter cellular response.
Essential Knowledge	**3.D.4** Changes in signal transduction pathways can alter cellular response.
Science Practice	**6.2** The student can construct explanations of phenomena based on evidence produced through scientific practices.
Learning Objective	**3.39** The student is able to construct an explanation of how certain drugs affect signal reception and, consequently, signal transduction pathways.
Big Idea 2	Biological systems utilize free energy and molecular building blocks to grow, to reproduce, and to maintain dynamic homeostasis.
Enduring Understanding 2.E	Many biological processes involved in growth, reproduction and dynamic homeostasis include temporal regulation and coordination.
Essential Knowledge	**2.E.1** Timing and coordination of specific events are necessary for the normal development of an organism, and these events are regulated by a variety of mechanisms.
Science Practice	**7.1** The student can connect phenomena and models across spatial and temporal scales.
Learning Objective	**2.34** The student is able to describe the role of programmed cell death in development and differentiation, the reuse of molecules, and the maintenance of dynamic homeostasis.

The Science Practice Challenge Questions contain additional test questions for this section that will help you prepare for the AP exam. These questions address the following standards:
[APLO 3.33][APLO 3.35]

Inside the cell, ligands bind to their internal receptors, allowing them to directly affect the cell's DNA and protein-producing machinery. Using signal transduction pathways, receptors in the plasma membrane produce a variety of effects on the cell. The results of signaling pathways are extremely varied and depend on the type of cell involved as well as the external and internal conditions. A small sampling of responses is described below.

Gene Expression

Some signal transduction pathways regulate the transcription of RNA. Others regulate the translation of proteins from mRNA. An example of a protein that regulates translation in the nucleus is the MAP kinase ERK. ERK is activated in a phosphorylation cascade when epidermal growth factor (EGF) binds the EGF receptor (see **Figure 9.10**). Upon phosphorylation, ERK enters the nucleus and activates a protein kinase that, in turn, regulates protein translation (**Figure 9.14**).

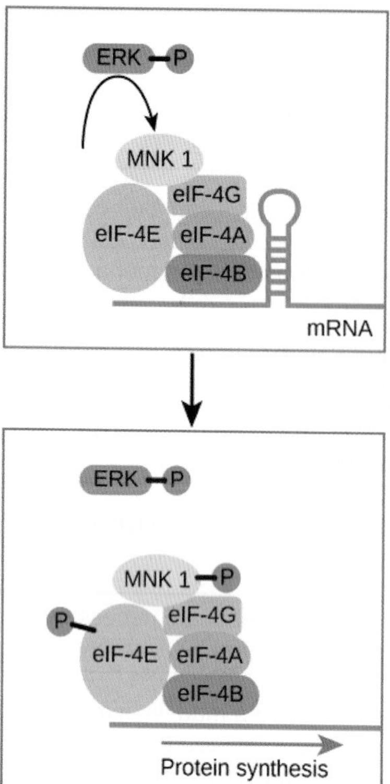
ERK
P
MNK 1
eIF-4G
eIF-4E
eIF-4A
eIF-4B
mRNA
The MAP kinase ERK phosphorylates MNK1. MNK1 in turn phosphorylates eIF-4E, which is associated with mRNA. The mRNA unfolds and protein sythesis begins.
ERK
P
MNK 1
P
P
eIF-4G
eIF-4E
eIF-4A
eIF-4B
Protein synthesis

Figure 9.14 ERK is a MAP kinase that activates translation when it is phosphorylated. ERK phosphorylates MNK1, which in turn phosphorylates eIF-4E, an elongation initiation factor that, with other initiation factors, is associated with mRNA. When eIF-4E becomes phosphorylated, the mRNA unfolds, allowing protein synthesis in the nucleus to begin. (See Figure 9.10 for the phosphorylation pathway that activates ERK.)

The second kind of protein with which PKC can interact is a protein that acts as an inhibitor. An **inhibitor** is a molecule that binds to a protein and prevents it from functioning or reduces its function. In this case, the inhibitor is a protein called Iκ-B, which binds to the regulatory protein NF-κB. (The symbol κ represents the Greek letter kappa.) When Iκ-B is bound to NF-κB, the complex cannot enter the nucleus of the cell, but when Iκ-B is phosphorylated by PKC, it can no longer bind NF-κB, and NF-κB (a transcription factor) can enter the nucleus and initiate RNA transcription. In this case, the effect of phosphorylation is to inactivate an inhibitor and thereby activate the process of transcription.

Increase in Cellular Metabolism

The result of another signaling pathway affects muscle cells. The activation of β-adrenergic receptors in muscle cells by adrenaline leads to an increase in cyclic AMP (cAMP) inside the cell. Also known as epinephrine, adrenaline is a hormone (produced by the adrenal gland attached to the kidney) that readies the body for short-term emergencies. Cyclic AMP activates PKA (protein kinase A), which in turn phosphorylates two enzymes. The first enzyme promotes the degradation of glycogen by activating intermediate glycogen phosphorylase kinase (GPK) that in turn activates glycogen phosphorylase (GP) that catabolizes glycogen into glucose. (Recall that your body converts excess glucose to glycogen for short-term storage. When energy is needed, glycogen is quickly reconverted to glucose.) Phosphorylation of the second enzyme, glycogen synthase (GS), inhibits its ability to form glycogen from glucose. In this manner, a muscle cell obtains a ready pool of glucose by activating its formation via glycogen degradation and by inhibiting the use of glucose to form glycogen, thus preventing a futile cycle of glycogen degradation and synthesis. The glucose is then available for use by the muscle cell in response to a sudden surge of adrenaline—the “fight or flight” reflex.

Cell Growth

Cell signaling pathways also play a major role in cell division. Cells do not normally divide unless they are stimulated by signals from other cells. The ligands that promote cell growth are called **growth factors**. Most growth factors bind to cell-surface receptors that are linked to tyrosine kinases. These cell-surface receptors are called receptor tyrosine kinases (RTKs). Activation of RTKs initiates a signaling pathway that includes a G-protein called RAS, which activates the MAP kinase pathway described earlier. The enzyme MAP kinase then stimulates the expression of proteins that interact with other cellular components to initiate cell division.

career CONNECTION

Cancer biologists study the molecular origins of cancer with the goal of developing new prevention methods and treatment strategies that will inhibit the growth of tumors without harming the normal cells of the body. As mentioned earlier, signaling pathways control cell growth. These signaling pathways are controlled by signaling proteins, which are, in turn, expressed by genes. Mutations in these genes can result in malfunctioning signaling proteins. This prevents the cell from regulating its cell cycle, triggering unrestricted cell division and cancer. The genes that regulate the signaling proteins are one type of oncogene, which is a gene that has the potential to cause cancer. The gene encoding RAS is an oncogene that was originally discovered when mutations in the RAS protein were linked to cancer. Further studies have indicated that 30 percent of cancer cells have a mutation in the RAS gene that leads to uncontrolled growth. If left unchecked, uncontrolled cell division can lead to tumor formation and metastasis, the growth of cancer cells in new locations in the body.

Cancer biologists have been able to identify many other oncogenes that contribute to the development of cancer. For example, HER2 is a cell-surface receptor that is present in excessive amounts in 20 percent of human breast cancers. Cancer biologists realized that gene duplication led to HER2 overexpression in 25 percent of breast cancer patients and developed a drug called Herceptin (trastuzumab). Herceptin is a monoclonal antibody that targets HER2 for removal by the immune system. Herceptin therapy helps to control signaling through HER2. The use of Herceptin in combination with chemotherapy has helped to increase the overall survival rate of patients with metastatic breast cancer.

More information on cancer biology research can be found at the National Cancer Institute website (http://openstaxcollege.org/l/32NCI) .

Cell Death

When a cell is damaged, superfluous, or potentially dangerous to an organism, a cell can initiate a mechanism to trigger programmed cell death, or **apoptosis**. Apoptosis allows a cell to die in a controlled manner that prevents the release of potentially damaging molecules from inside the cell. There are many internal checkpoints that monitor a cell's health; if abnormalities are observed, a cell can spontaneously initiate the process of apoptosis. However, in some cases, such as a viral infection or uncontrolled cell division, the cell's normal checks and balances fail. External signaling can also initiate apoptosis. For example, most normal animal cells have receptors that interact with the extracellular matrix, a network of glycoproteins that provides structural support for cells in an organism. The binding of cellular receptors to the extracellular matrix initiates a signaling cascade within the cell. However, if the cell moves away from the extracellular matrix, the signaling ceases, and the cell undergoes apoptosis. This system keeps cells from traveling through the body and proliferating out of control.

Another example of external signaling that leads to apoptosis occurs in T-cell development. T-cells are immune cells that bind to foreign macromolecules and particles, and target them for destruction by the immune system. Normally, T-cells do not target "self" proteins (those of their own organism), a process that can lead to autoimmune diseases. In order to develop the ability to discriminate between self and non-self, immature T-cells undergo screening to determine whether they bind to so-called self proteins. If the T-cell receptor binds to self proteins, the cell initiates apoptosis to remove the potentially dangerous cell.

Apoptosis is also essential for normal embryological development. In vertebrates, for example, early stages of development include the formation of web-like tissue between individual fingers and toes (Figure 9.15). During the course of normal development, these unneeded cells must be eliminated, enabling fully separated fingers and toes to form. A cell signaling mechanism triggers apoptosis, which destroys the cells between the developing digits.

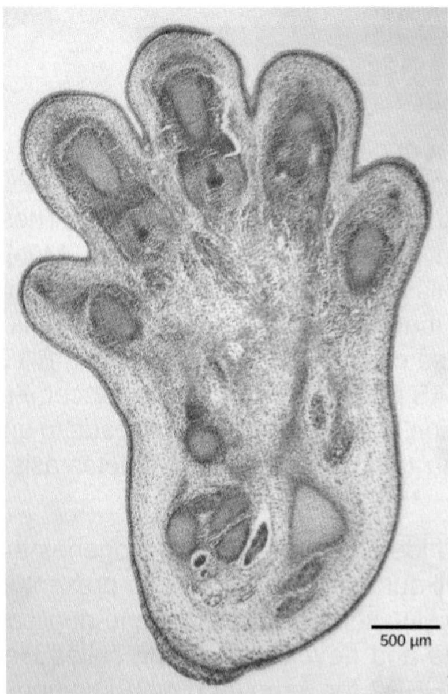

Figure 9.15 The histological section of a foot of a 15-day-old mouse embryo, visualized using light microscopy, reveals areas of tissue between the toes, which apoptosis will eliminate before the mouse reaches its full gestational age at 27 days. (credit: modification of work by Michal Mañas)

Termination of the Signal Cascade

The aberrant signaling often seen in tumor cells is proof that the termination of a signal at the appropriate time can be just as important as the initiation of a signal. One method of stopping a specific signal is to degrade the ligand or remove it so that it can no longer access its receptor. One reason that hydrophobic hormones like estrogen and testosterone trigger long-lasting events is because they bind carrier proteins. These proteins allow the insoluble molecules to be soluble in blood, but they also protect the hormones from degradation by circulating enzymes.

Inside the cell, many different enzymes reverse the cellular modifications that result from signaling cascades. For example, **phosphatases** are enzymes that remove the phosphate group attached to proteins by kinases in a process called dephosphorylation. Cyclic AMP (cAMP) is degraded into AMP by **phosphodiesterase**, and the release of calcium stores is reversed by the Ca^{2+} pumps that are located in the external and internal membranes of the cell.

science practices CONNECTION for AP® Courses

Activity

Explain the mechanism by which a specific disease is caused by a defective signaling pathway. Then, investigate online how a specific drug works by blocking a signaling pathway.

9.4 | Signaling in Single-Celled Organisms

In this section, you will explore the following questions:

- How do single-celled yeasts use cell signaling to communicate with each other?
- How does quorum sensing allow some bacteria to form biofilms?

Connection for AP® Courses

Cell signaling allows bacteria to respond to environmental cues, such as nutrient levels and quorum sensing (cell density).

Yeasts are eukaryotes (fungi), and the components and processes found in yeast signals are similar to those of cell-surface receptor signals in multicellular organisms. For example, budding yeasts often release mating factors that enable them to participate in a process that is similar to sexual reproduction.

Information presented and the examples highlighted in the section support concepts and Learning Objectives outlined in Big Idea 3 of the AP® Biology Curriculum Framework. The Learning Objectives listed in the Curriculum Framework provide a transparent foundation for the AP® Biology course, an inquiry-based laboratory experience, instructional activities, and AP® Exam questions. A Learning Objective merges required content with one or more of the seven Science Practices.

Big Idea 3	Living systems store, retrieve, transmit and respond to information essential to life processes.
Enduring Understanding 3.D	Cells communicate by generating, transmitting and receiving chemical signals.
Essential Knowledge	**3.D.1** Cell communication processes share common features that reflect a shared evolutionary history.
Science Practice	**1.5** The student can re-express key elements of natural phenomena across multiple representations in the domain.
Learning Objective	**3.36** The student is able to describe a model that expresses the key elements of signal transduction pathways by which a signal is converted to a cellular response.
Essential Knowledge	**3.D.1** Cell communication processes share common features that reflect a shared evolutionary history.
Science Practice	**6.1** The student can justify claims with evidence.
Learning Objective	**3.37** The student is able to justify claims based on scientific evidence that changes in signal transduction pathways can alter cellular response.

The Science Practice Challenge Questions contain additional test questions for this section that will help you prepare for the AP exam. These questions address the following standards:
[APLO 3.31][APLO 3.37]

Within-cell signaling allows bacteria to respond to environmental cues, such as nutrient levels. Some single-celled organisms also release molecules to signal to each other.

Signaling in Yeast

Yeasts are eukaryotes (fungi), and the components and processes found in yeast signals are similar to those of cell-surface receptor signals in multicellular organisms. Budding yeasts (Figure 9.16) are able to participate in a process that is similar to sexual reproduction that entails two haploid cells (cells with one-half the normal number of chromosomes) combining to form a diploid cell (a cell with two sets of each chromosome, which is what normal body cells contain). In order to find another haploid yeast cell that is prepared to mate, budding yeasts secrete a signaling molecule called **mating factor**. When mating factor binds to cell-surface receptors in other yeast cells that are nearby, they stop their normal growth cycles and initiate a cell signaling cascade that includes protein kinases and GTP-binding proteins that are similar to G-proteins.

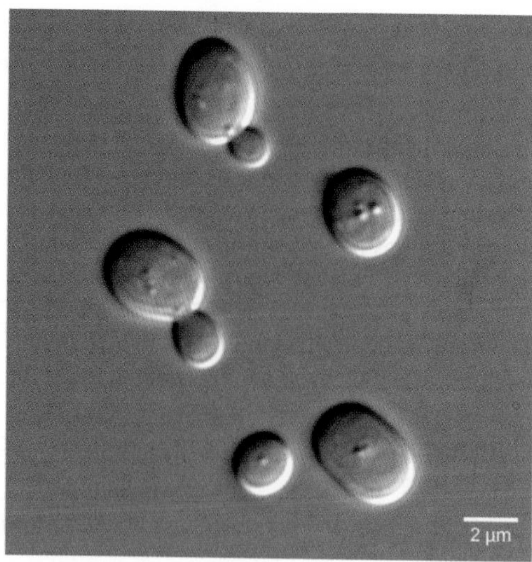

Figure 9.16 Budding *Saccharomyces cerevisiae* yeast cells can communicate by releasing a signaling molecule called mating factor. In this micrograph, they are visualized using differential interference contrast microscopy, a light microscopy technique that enhances the contrast of the sample.

Signaling in Bacteria

Signaling in bacteria enables bacteria to monitor extracellular conditions, ensure that there are sufficient amounts of nutrients, and ensure that hazardous situations are avoided. There are circumstances, however, when bacteria communicate with each other.

The first evidence of bacterial communication was observed in a bacterium that has a symbiotic relationship with Hawaiian bobtail squid. When the population density of the bacteria reaches a certain level, specific gene expression is initiated, and the bacteria produce bioluminescent proteins that emit light. Because the number of cells present in the environment (cell density) is the determining factor for signaling, bacterial signaling was named **quorum sensing**. In politics and business, a quorum is the minimum number of members required to be present to vote on an issue.

Quorum sensing uses autoinducers as signaling molecules. **Autoinducers** are signaling molecules secreted by bacteria to communicate with other bacteria of the same kind. The secreted autoinducers can be small, hydrophobic molecules such as acyl-homoserine lactone (AHL) or larger peptide-based molecules; each type of molecule has a different mode of action. When AHL enters target bacteria, it binds to transcription factors, which then switch gene expression on or off (Figure 9.17). The peptide autoinducers stimulate more complicated signaling pathways that include bacterial kinases. The changes in bacteria following exposure to autoinducers can be quite extensive. The pathogenic bacterium *Pseudomonas aeruginosa* has 616 different genes that respond to autoinducers.

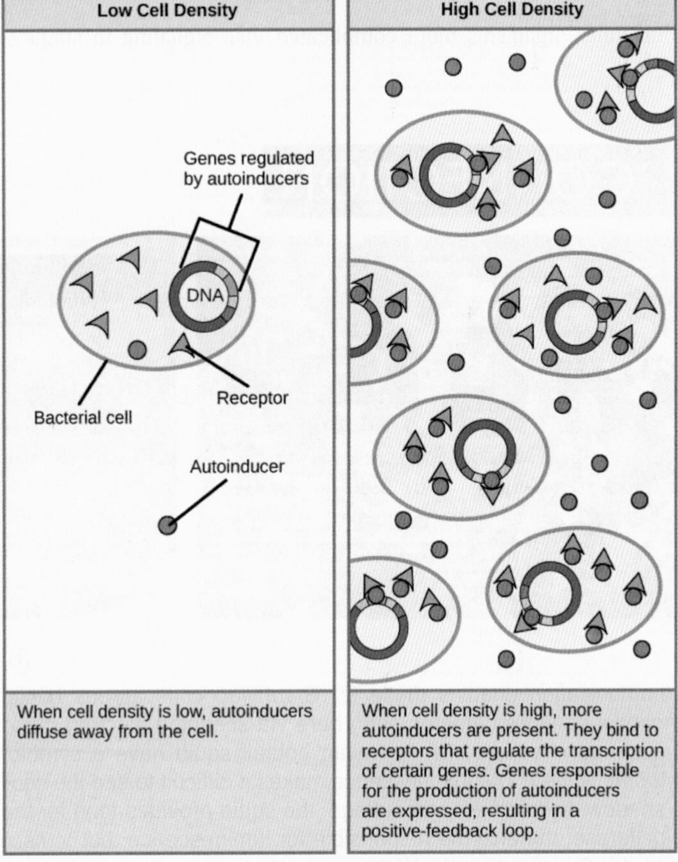

Figure 9.17 Autoinducers are small molecules or proteins produced by bacteria that regulate gene expression.

Which of the following statements about quorum sensing is false?

a. Autoinducers must bind to receptors to turn on transcription of genes responsible for the production of more autoinducers.

b. Autoinducers can only act on a different cell. It cannot act on the cell in which it is made.

c. Autoinducers turn on genes that enable the bacteria to form a biofilm.

d. The receptor stays in the bacterial cell, but the autoinducers diffuse out.

Some species of bacteria that use quorum sensing form biofilms, complex colonies of bacteria (often containing several species) that exchange chemical signals to coordinate the release of toxins that will attack the host. Bacterial biofilms (Figure 9.18) can sometimes be found on medical equipment; when biofilms invade implants such as hip or knee replacements or heart pacemakers, they can cause life-threatening infections.

The ability of certain bacteria to form biofilms has evolved because of a selection of genes that enable cell-cell communication confers an evolutionary advantage. When bacterial colonies form biofilms, they create barriers that prevent toxins and antibacterial drugs from affecting the population living in the biofilm. As a result, these populations are more likely to survive, even in the presence of antibacterial agents. This often means that bacteria living in biofilms have higher fitness than bacteria living on their own.

science practices CONNECTION for AP® Courses

Think About It

Why is signaling in multicellular organisms more complicated than signaling in single-celled organisms such as microbes?

everyday CONNECTION

Figure 9.18 Cell-cell communication enables these (a) *Staphylococcus aureus* bacteria to work together to form a biofilm inside a hospital patient's catheter, seen here via scanning electron microscopy. *S. aureus* is the main cause of hospital-acquired infections. (b) Hawaiian bobtail squid have a symbiotic relationship with the bioluminescent bacteria *Vibrio fischeri*. The luminescence makes it difficult to see the squid from below because it effectively eliminates its shadow. In return for camouflage, the squid provides food for the bacteria. Free-living *V. fischeri* do not produce luciferase, the enzyme responsible for luminescence, but *V. fischeri* living in a symbiotic relationship with the squid do. Quorum sensing determines whether the bacteria should produce the luciferase enzyme. (credit a: modifications of work by CDC/Janice Carr; credit b: modifications of work by Cliff1066/Flickr)

Free-living *V. fischeri* do not luminesce. Why?

a. The squid provides certain nutrients that allow the bacteria to luminesce.
b. The squid produces the luminescent luciferase enzyme, so bacteria living outside the squid do not luminesce.
c. The ability to luminesce does not benefit free-living bacteria, so free-living bacteria do not produce luciferase.
d. Luciferase is toxic to free-living bacteria, so free-living bacteria do not produce this enzyme.

Research on the details of quorum sensing has led to advances in growing bacteria for industrial purposes. Recent discoveries suggest that it may be possible to exploit bacterial signaling pathways to control bacterial growth; this process could replace or supplement antibiotics that are no longer effective in certain situations.

Watch geneticist Bonnie Bassler discuss her discovery (http://openstaxcollege.org/l/bacteria_talk) of quorum sensing in biofilm bacteria in squid.

What does bioluminescence show about communication in bacteria?

a. Bacteria interact by physical signals among a colony.

b. Bacterium interact by chemical signals when it is alone.

c. Bacterium interact by physical signals when it is alone.

d. Bacteria interact by chemical signals among a colony.

evolution CONNECTION

The first life on our planet consisted of single-celled prokaryotic organisms that had limited interaction with each other. While some external signaling occurs between different species of single-celled organisms, the majority of signaling within bacteria and yeasts concerns only other members of the same species. The evolution of cellular communication is an absolute necessity for the development of multicellular organisms, and this innovation is thought to have required approximately 2.5 billion years to appear in early life forms.

Yeasts are single-celled eukaryotes, and therefore have a nucleus and organelles characteristic of more complex life forms. Comparisons of the genomes of yeasts, nematode worms, fruit flies, and humans illustrate the evolution of increasingly complex signaling systems that allow for the efficient inner workings that keep humans and other complex life forms functioning correctly.

Kinases are a major component of cellular communication, and studies of these enzymes illustrate the evolutionary connectivity of different species. Yeasts have 130 types of kinases. More complex organisms such as nematode worms and fruit flies have 454 and 239 kinases, respectively. Of the 130 kinase types in yeast, 97 belong to the 55 subfamilies of kinases that are found in other eukaryotic organisms. The only obvious deficiency seen in yeasts is the complete absence of tyrosine kinases. It is hypothesized that phosphorylation of tyrosine residues is needed to control the more sophisticated functions of development, differentiation, and cellular communication used in multicellular organisms.

Because yeasts contain many of the same classes of signaling proteins as humans, these organisms are ideal for studying signaling cascades. Yeasts multiply quickly and are much simpler organisms than humans or other multicellular animals. Therefore, the signaling cascades are also simpler and easier to study, although they contain similar counterparts to human signaling. [2]

Based on the Evolution Connection, which of the following best describes the evolution of kinases?

a. The tyrosine kinases evolved before yeast diverged from other eukaryotes, but the other fifty-five subfamilies of kinases evolved after yeast diverged.

b. Fifty-five subfamilies of kinases evolved before yeast diverged from other eukaryotes, but the tyrosine kinases evolved after yeast diverged.

c. All kinases evolved in yeast, but yeast later lost the tyrosine kinases because they do not need them.

d. The evolution of tyrosine kinases involved in cellular communication occurred about 2.5 billion years ago.

2. G. Manning, G.D. Plowman, T. Hunter, S. Sudarsanam, "Evolution of Protein Kinase Signaling from Yeast to Man," *Trends in Biochemical Sciences* 27, no. 10 (2002): 514–520.

Watch this **collection (http://openstaxcollege.org/l/bacteria_biofilm)** of interview clips with biofilm researchers in "What Are Bacterial Biofilms?"

Recurrent urinary tract infections occur when the urinary tract becomes reinfected by the same bacteria. Why are recurrent urinary infections difficult to treat?

a. Bacteria often form biofilms in recurrent infections and these may be more antibiotic resistant.

b. Bacteria rarely form biofilms in recurrent infections, making them more resistant to antibiotics than if they were not in a biofilm.

c. Bacteria produce biofilms which behave like a unicellular organism.

d. Bacteria don't produce biofilms in recurrent infections but become resistant due to repeated exposure to antibiotics.

KEY TERMS

apoptosis programmed cell death

autocrine signal signal that is sent and received by the same or similar nearby cells

autoinducer signaling molecule secreted by bacteria to communicate with other bacteria of its kind and others

cell-surface receptor cell-surface protein that transmits a signal from the exterior of the cell to the interior, even though the ligand does not enter the cell

chemical synapse small space between axon terminals and dendrites of nerve cells where neurotransmitters function

cyclic AMP (cAMP) second messenger that is derived from ATP

cyclic AMP-dependent kinase (also, protein kinase A, or PKA) kinase that is activated by binding to cAMP

diacylglycerol (DAG) cleavage product of PIP_2 that is used for signaling within the plasma membrane

dimer chemical compound formed when two molecules join together

dimerization (of receptor proteins) interaction of two receptor proteins to form a functional complex called a dimer

endocrine cell cell that releases ligands involved in endocrine signaling (hormones)

endocrine signal long-distance signal that is delivered by ligands (hormones) traveling through an organism's circulatory system from the signaling cell to the target cell

enzyme-linked receptor cell-surface receptor with intracellular domains that are associated with membrane-bound enzymes

extracellular domain region of a cell-surface receptor that is located on the cell surface

G-protein-linked receptor cell-surface receptor that activates membrane-bound G-proteins to transmit a signal from the receptor to nearby membrane components

growth factor ligand that binds to cell-surface receptors and stimulates cell growth

inhibitor molecule that binds to a protein (usually an enzyme) and keeps it from functioning

inositol phospholipid lipid present at small concentrations in the plasma membrane that is converted into a second messenger; it has inositol (a carbohydrate) as its hydrophilic head group

inositol triphosphate (IP_3) cleavage product of PIP_2 that is used for signaling within the cell

intercellular signaling communication between cells

internal receptor (also, intracellular receptor) receptor protein that is located in the cytosol of a cell and binds to ligands that pass through the plasma membrane

intracellular mediator (also, second messenger) small molecule that transmits signals within a cell

intracellular signaling communication within cells

ion channel-linked receptor cell-surface receptor that forms a plasma membrane channel, which opens when a ligand binds to the extracellular domain (ligand-gated channels)

kinase enzyme that catalyzes the transfer of a phosphate group from ATP to another molecule

ligand molecule produced by a signaling cell that binds with a specific receptor, delivering a signal in the process

mating factor signaling molecule secreted by yeast cells to communicate to nearby yeast cells that they are available to mate and communicating their mating orientation

neurotransmitter chemical ligand that carries a signal from one nerve cell to the next

paracrine signal signal between nearby cells that is delivered by ligands traveling in the liquid medium in the space between the cells

phosphatase enzyme that removes the phosphate group from a molecule that has been previously phosphorylated

phosphodiesterase enzyme that degrades cAMP, producing AMP, to terminate signaling

quorum sensing method of cellular communication used by bacteria that informs them of the abundance of similar (or different) bacteria in the environment

receptor protein in or on a target cell that bind to ligands

second messenger small, non-protein molecule that propagates a signal within the cell after activation of a receptor causes its release

signal integration interaction of signals from two or more different cell-surface receptors that merge to activate the same response in the cell

signal transduction propagation of the signal through the cytoplasm (and sometimes also the nucleus) of the cell

signaling cell cell that releases signal molecules that allow communication with another cell

signaling pathway (also signaling cascade) chain of events that occurs in the cytoplasm of the cell to propagate the signal from the plasma membrane to produce a response

synaptic signal chemical signal (neurotransmitter) that travels between nerve cells

target cell cell that has a receptor for a signal or ligand from a signaling cell

CHAPTER SUMMARY

9.1 Signaling Molecules and Cellular Receptors

Cells communicate by both inter- and intracellular signaling. Signaling cells secrete ligands that bind to target cells and initiate a chain of events within the target cell. The four categories of signaling in multicellular organisms are paracrine signaling, endocrine signaling, autocrine signaling, and direct signaling across gap junctions. Paracrine signaling takes place over short distances. Endocrine signals are carried long distances through the bloodstream by hormones, and autocrine signals are received by the same cell that sent the signal or other nearby cells of the same kind. Gap junctions allow small molecules, including signaling molecules, to flow between neighboring cells.

Internal receptors are found in the cell cytoplasm. Here, they bind ligand molecules that cross the plasma membrane; these receptor-ligand complexes move to the nucleus and interact directly with cellular DNA. Cell-surface receptors transmit a signal from outside the cell to the cytoplasm. Ion channel-linked receptors, when bound to their ligands, form a pore through the plasma membrane through which certain ions can pass. G-protein-linked receptors interact with a G-protein on the cytoplasmic side of the plasma membrane, promoting the exchange of bound GDP for GTP and interacting with other enzymes or ion channels to transmit a signal. Enzyme-linked receptors transmit a signal from outside the cell to an intracellular domain of a membrane-bound enzyme. Ligand binding causes activation of the enzyme. Small hydrophobic ligands (like steroids) are able to penetrate the plasma membrane and bind to internal receptors. Water-soluble hydrophilic ligands are unable to pass through the membrane; instead, they bind to cell-surface receptors, which transmit the signal to the inside of the cell.

9.2 Propagation of the Signal

Ligand binding to the receptor allows for signal transduction through the cell. The chain of events that conveys the signal through the cell is called a signaling pathway or cascade. Signaling pathways are often very complex because of the interplay between different proteins. A major component of cell signaling cascades is the phosphorylation of molecules by enzymes known as kinases. Phosphorylation adds a phosphate group to serine, threonine, and tyrosine residues in a protein, changing their shapes, and activating or inactivating the protein. Small molecules like nucleotides can also be phosphorylated. Second messengers are small, non-protein molecules that are used to transmit a signal within a cell. Some examples of second messengers are calcium ions (Ca^{2+}), cyclic AMP (cAMP), diacylglycerol (DAG), and inositol triphosphate (IP_3).

9.3 Response to the Signal

The initiation of a signaling pathway is a response to external stimuli. This response can take many different forms, including protein synthesis, a change in the cell's metabolism, cell growth, or even cell death. Many pathways influence the cell by initiating gene expression, and the methods utilized are quite numerous. Some pathways activate enzymes that interact with DNA transcription factors. Others modify proteins and induce them to change their location in the cell. Depending on the status of the organism, cells can respond by storing energy as glycogen or fat, or making it available in the form of glucose. A signal transduction pathway allows muscle cells to respond to immediate requirements for energy in the form of glucose. Cell growth is almost always stimulated by external signals called growth factors. Uncontrolled cell growth leads to cancer, and mutations in the genes encoding protein components of signaling pathways are often found in tumor cells. Programmed cell death, or apoptosis, is important for removing damaged or unnecessary cells. The use of cellular signaling to organize the dismantling of a cell ensures that harmful molecules from the cytoplasm are not released into the spaces between cells, as they are in uncontrolled death, necrosis. Apoptosis also ensures the efficient recycling of the components of the dead cell. Termination of the cellular signaling cascade is very important so that the response to a signal is appropriate in both timing and intensity. Degradation of signaling molecules and dephosphorylation of phosphorylated intermediates of the pathway by phosphatases are two ways to terminate signals within the cell.

9.4 Signaling in Single-Celled Organisms

Yeasts and multicellular organisms have similar signaling mechanisms. Yeasts use cell-surface receptors and signaling cascades to communicate information on mating with other yeast cells. The signaling molecule secreted by yeasts is called mating factor.

Bacterial signaling is called quorum sensing. Bacteria secrete signaling molecules called autoinducers that are either small, hydrophobic molecules or peptide-based signals. The hydrophobic autoinducers, such as AHL, bind transcription factors and directly affect gene expression. The peptide-based molecules bind kinases and initiate signaling cascades in the cells.

REVIEW QUESTIONS

1. Which of the following properties prevents the ligands of cell-surface receptors from entering the cell?

a. The molecules bind to the extracellular domain.
b. The molecules are hydrophilic and cannot penetrate the hydrophobic interior of the plasma membrane.
c. The molecules are attached to transport proteins that deliver them through the bloodstream to target cells.
d. The ligands are able to penetrate the membrane, directly influencing gene expression upon receptor binding.

2. The secretion of hormones by the pituitary gland is an example of which type of signaling?

a. autocrine signaling
b. direct signaling across gap junctions
c. endocrine signaling
d. paracrine signaling

3. Why are ion channels necessary to transport ions into or out of a cell?

a. Ions are too large to diffuse through the membrane.
b. Ions are charged particles and cannot diffuse through the hydrophobic interior of the membrane.
c. Ions bind to hydrophobic molecules within the ion channels.
d. Ions bind to carrier proteins in the bloodstream, which must be removed before transport into the cell.

4. Why are endocrine signals transmitted more slowly than paracrine signals?

a. The ligands are transported through the bloodstream and travel greater distances.
b. The target and signaling cells are close together.
c. The ligands are degraded rapidly.
d. The ligands do not bind to carrier proteins during transport.

5. Aldosterone is a steroid hormone that regulates reabsorption of sodium ions in the kidney tubular cells. What is the probable mechanism of action of aldosterone?

a. It binds gated ion channels and causes a flow of ions in the cell.

b. It binds cell surface receptors and activates synthesis of cAMP.

c. It binds to cell surface receptors and activates a phosphorylation cascade.

d. It binds to an intracellular receptor and activates gene transcription.

6. The gas nitric oxide has been identified as a signaling molecule. Which of the following mechanisms of action would you expect from a gaseous molecule?

a. It binds to a G-protein-linked receptor.

b. It binds to a receptor tyrosine kinase.

c. It binds to a gated ion channel.

d. It binds to an intracellular receptor.

7. Where do DAG and IP3 originate?

a. They are formed by phosphorylation of cAMP.

b. They are ligands expressed by signaling cells.

c. They are hormones that diffuse through the plasma membrane to stimulate protein production.

d. They are the cleavage products of the inositol phospholipid, PIP2.

8. What property enables the residues of the amino acids serine, threonine, and tyrosine to be phosphorylated?

a. They are polar.

b. They are nonpolar.

c. They contain a hydroxyl group.

d. They occur more frequently in the amino acid sequence of signaling proteins.

9. Dopamine is a neurotransmitter in the brain that causes long-term responses in neurons and binds to a G-protein-linked receptor. Which of the following chemicals would you expect to increase in concentration after dopamine binds its receptor?

a. ATP

b. cAMP

c. calcium ions

d. sodium ions

10. The hormone insulin binds to a receptor tyrosine kinase on the surface of target cells. Which of the following steps takes place before phosphorylation of tyrosine residues?

a. A tyrosine kinase enzyme must be activated.

b. GDP is exchanged for GTP.

c. The receptor forms a dimer.

d. The insulin molecule is internalized in the cytoplasm.

11. What is the function of a phosphatase?

a. A phosphatase removes phosphorylated amino acids from proteins.

b. A phosphatase removes the phosphate group from phosphorylated amino acid residues in a protein.

c. A phosphatase phosphorylates serine, threonine, and tyrosine residues.

d. A phosphatase degrades second messengers in the cell.

12. How does NF-κB induce gene expression?

a. A small, hydrophobic ligand binds to NF-κB, activating it.

b. NF-κB is phosphorylated and is then free to enter the nucleus to bind DNA.

c. NF-κB is a kinase that phosphorylates a transcription factor that binds DNA and promotes protein production.

d. Phosphorylation of the inhibitor IκB dissociates the complex between it and NF-κB, allowing NF-κB to enter the nucleus and stimulate transcription.

13. Apoptosis can occur in a cell under what conditions?

a. when a cell is infected by a virus

b. when a cell is damaged

c. when a cell is no longer needed

d. all of the above

14. Cancer cells that continue to divide when defective often show changes in what cellular function?

a. apoptosis

b. their mechanism of glycolysis

c. the mechanism of protein biosynthesis

d. replication of DNA

15. Epinephrine mediates the fight-or-fight response of the body. One of the effects is to increase the amount of glucose available to muscles. What does the signaling pathway triggered by epinephrine cause to occur in liver cells?

a. activation of metabolism

b. cell division

c. inhibition of glucose metabolism by liver cells

d. synthesis of enzymes

16. Which type of molecule acts as a signaling molecule in yeasts?

a. autoinducer
b. mating factor
c. second messenger
d. steroid

17. When is quorum sensing triggered to begin?

a. a sufficient number of bacteria are present
b. bacteria release growth hormones
c. bacterial protein expression is switched on
d. treatment with antibiotics occurs

18. Yeast releasing mating factor can be classified as which type of signal?

a. autocrine
b. endocrine
c. paracrine
d. gap junction

19. The bioluminescent bacteria *Vibrio fischeri* produces luminescence only if the population reaches a certain density. What is the advantage of an autoinducer?

a. An autoinducer allows the producer to act independently of the presence of other cells.
b. An autoinducer does not diffuse away from the cell.
c. An autoinducer allows a positive feedback loop, which increases the response in proportion to the population size.
d. An autoinducer presents no advantage for the cell.

CRITICAL THINKING QUESTIONS

20. What is the difference between intracellular signaling and intercellular signaling?

a. Intracellular signaling occurs between cells of two different species. Intercellular signaling occurs between two cells of the same species.
b. Intracellular signaling occurs between two cells of same species. Intercellular signaling occurs between cells of two different species.
c. Intracellular signaling occurs within a cell. Intercellular signaling occurs between cells.
d. Intracellular signaling occurs between cells. Intercellular signaling occurs within cell.

21. What are the differences between internal receptors and cell-surface receptors?

a. Internal receptors bind to ligands that are hydrophobic and the ligand-receptor complex directly enters the nucleus, initiating transcription and translation. Cell surface receptors bind to hydrophilic ligands and initiate a signaling cascade that indirectly influences the making of a functional protein.
b. Internal receptors bind to ligands that are hydrophilic and ligand-receptor complex directly enters the nucleus, initiating transcription and translation. Cell-surface receptors bind to hydrophobic ligands and initiate a signaling cascade that indirectly influences the making of a functional protein.
c. Internal receptors bind to ligands that are hydrophobic and initiate the signaling cascade that indirectly influences the making of a functional protein. Cell-surface receptors bind to hydrophilic ligands and a ligand-receptor complex directly enters the nucleus, initiating transcription and translation.
d. Internal receptors are integral membrane proteins that bind to hydrophobic ligands, initiating a signaling cascade, which indirectly influences the making of a functional protein. Cell-surface receptors bind to hydrophilic ligands and the ligand-receptor complex directly enters the nucleus, initiating transcription and translation.

22. Cells grown in the laboratory are mixed with a dye molecule that is unable to pass through the plasma membrane. If a ligand is added to the cells, the dye is observed entering the cells. What type of receptor did the ligand bind to on the cell surface?

a. G-protein-linked R receptor
b. ligand-gated ion channel
c. voltage-gated ion channel
d. receptor tyrosine kinase

23. The same second messengers are used in many different cells, but the response to second messengers is different in each cell. How is this possible?

a. Different cells produce the same receptor, which bind to the same ligands, but have a different response in each cell type.
b. Cells produce variants of a particular receptor for a particular ligand through alternative splicing, resulting in different response in each cell
c. Cells contain different genes, which produce different receptors that bind to same ligand, activating different responses in each cell.
d. Cells produce different receptors that bind to the same ligand or the same receptor that binds to the same ligand with different signaling components, activating different responses in each cell.

24. What would happen if the intracellular domain of a cell-surface receptor was switched with the domain from another receptor?

a. It would activate the pathway normally triggered by the receptor that contributed the intracellular domain.
b. It would activate the same pathway even after the intracellular domain is changed with the domain from another receptor.
c. The receptor will be mutated and become non-functional, not activating any pathway.
d. The receptor will become mutated and lead to continuous cell signaling, even in the absence of a ligand.

25. Explain how a chemical that blocks the binding of EGF to the EGFR would interfere with the replication of cancerous cells that overexpress EGFR.

a. It will activate the EGFR pathway.
b. It will block the EGFR pathway.
c. It will have no effect and the EGFR pathway will continue normally
d. It will lead to overexpression of the EGFR pathway

26. How does the extracellular matrix control the growth of cells?

a. Contact of receptors with the extracellular matrix maintains equilibrium of the cell and provides optimal pH for the growth of the cells.
b. Contact of the receptor with the extracellular matrix helps maintain concentration gradients across membrane, resulting in the flow of ions.
c. The extracellular matrix provides nutrients for the cell.
d. The extracellular matrix connects the cell to the external environment and ensures correct positioning of the cell to prevent metastasis.

27. Give an example for each one of the following effects of a cell signal: on protein expression, cellular metabolism, and cell division.

a. protein expression: binding of epinephrine (adrenaline) to a G-protein-linked receptor; cellular metabolism: the MAP-kinase cascade; cell division: promoted by the binding of the EGF to its receptor tyrosine kinase
b. protein expression: the MAP-kinase cascade; cellular metabolism- binding of epinephrine (adrenaline) to a G-protein-linked receptor; cell division promoted by the binding of the EGF to its receptor tyrosine kinase
c. protein expression: binding of the EGF to its receptor tyrosine kinase; cellular metabolism: the MAP-kinase cascade; cell division: FAS-RAS signaling.
d. protein expression: RAS signaling; cellular metabolism: binding of the EGF to its receptor tyrosine kinase promotes an increase; cell division: binding of epinephrine (adrenaline) to a G-protein-linked receptor.

28. The mitogen-activated protein (MAP) kinase cascade triggered by RTKs results in cell division. Create a few possible scenarios of abnormalities in the MAPK pathway leading to uncontrolled cell proliferation.

a. gain of function mutation in RAS protein, mutation in I κ -B, loss of function mutation in genes for MAPK kinase pathway, regulated phosphorylation cascade
b. loss of function mutation in RAS protein and gain of function mutation in RAF protein, I κ -B permanently bound to NF- κ B, regulated phosphorylation cascade
c. RAS protein unable to hydrolyze its bound GTP, loss of function mutation in I κ -B, gain of function mutation in genes for MAPK kinase pathway, unregulated phosphorylation cascade
d. unregulated phosphorylation cascade, loss of function mutation in RAS and RAF protein, mutation in genes for MAPK kinase pathway, regulated phosphorylation cascade

29. What characteristics make yeast a good model for learning about signaling in humans?

a. Yeasts are prokaryotes. They have a short life cycle, easy to grow, and share similarities with humans in certain regulating mechanisms.
b. Yeasts are eukaryotes. They have a short life cycle, easy to grow, and share similarities with humans in certain regulating mechanisms.
c. Yeasts are multicellular organisms. They have a short life cycle, easy to grow, and share similarities with humans in certain regulating mechanisms.
d. Yeasts are single celled organisms. They have a complex life cycle like that of humans and share similarities in regulating mechanisms.

30. Why is signaling in multicellular organisms more complicated than signaling in single-celled organisms?

a. Multicellular organisms coordinate between distantly located cells; single-celled organisms communicate only with nearby cells.
b. Multicellular organisms involve receptors for signaling; single-celled organisms communicate by fusion of plasma membrane with the nearby cells.
c. Multicellular organisms require more time for signal transduction than single-celled organisms, as they show compartmentalization.
d. Multicellular organisms require more time for signal transduction than single-celled organisms, as they lack compartmentalization.

31. Biofilms are a prominent danger in infectious disease treatment today because it is difficult to find drugs that can penetrate the biofilm. What characteristics would a drug have if it aimed to prevent bacteria from forming biofilms in the first place? Explain your answer.

32. Support the hypothesis that signaling pathways appeared early in evolution and are well-conserved using the yeast mating factor as an example.

a. Signaling in yeast uses the RTK pathway and is evolutionarily conserved, like insulin signaling in humans.
b. Signaling in yeast uses G-protein coupled receptors for signaling and is evolutionarily conserved, like insulin signaling in humans.
c. Signaling in yeast uses an endocrine pathway and is evolutionarily conserved, like insulin signaling in humans.
d. Mating factor in yeast uses an autocrine signaling pathway and is evolutionarily conserved.

TEST PREP FOR AP® COURSES

33. Upon ingestion of bacteria, white blood cells release a chemical messenger into the blood stream that causes the synthesis of inflammation response proteins by liver cells. What is this is an example of?

a. autocrine signaling
b. endocrine signaling
c. paracrine signaling
d. synaptic signaling

34. Molecules do not flow between the endothelial cells in the brain capillaries. The membranes of the cells must be joined by what?

a. gap junctions
b. ligand-gated channels
c. synapses
d. tight junctions

35. Analyze the possible benefits of having autocrine signaling.

a. Autocrine signaling helps to communicate with distantly located cells.
b. Autocrine signaling connects nearby located cells.
c. Autocrine signaling helps to amplify the signal by inducing more signaling production from the cell itself.
d. Autocrine signaling is specific only for the cell that produced it.

36. If a chemical is an inhibitor of the enzyme adenylyl cyclase, which of the following steps in the G-protein signaling pathway would be blocked?

a. activation of gene transcription
b. exchange of GTP for GDP
c. ligand bound receptor activation of G-protein
d. synthesis of cAMP

37. Thyroid hormone is a lipid-soluble signal molecule that crosses the membrane of all cells. Why would a cell fail to respond to the thyroid hormone?

a. The MAPK cascade leading to cell activation is defective in the target cells.
b. The DNA sequence it binds to underwent a mutation.
c. There is no intracellular receptor for thyroid hormone in the cell.
d. The second messenger does not recognize the signal from the receptor.

38. The poison form the krait snake's bungarotoxin binds irreversibly to acetylcholine receptors interfering with acetylcholine binding at the synapse. What is the effect of bungarotoxin binding on the post synaptic cell?

a. cAMP production is inhibited.
b. Bungarotoxin G-proteins are not activated.
c. Ion movement in the cell is inhibited.
d. Phosphorylation cascade is inhibited.

39. In autoimmune lymphoproliferative syndrome (ALPS), lymphocytes which multiplied during an infection persist in the body and damage tissue. The syndrome is caused by a mutation in the FAS gene which encodes a cell surface receptor. Which signaling pathway does the receptor initiate?

a. activated metabolism
b. apoptosis
c. cell division
d. cell differentiation

40. Place the following events in their sequential order:

1. protein kinase A is activated
2. glycogen breakdown
3. epinephrine binds to G-protein-linked receptor
4. G-protein activates adenylyl cyclase
5. GTP is exchanged for GDP on the G-protein
6. ATP is converted to cAMP

a. 1, 3, 5, 4, 6, 2
b. 3, 5, 4, 1, 6, 2
c. 3, 4, 5, 1, 6, 2
d. 3, 5, 4, 6, 1, 2

41. The RAS protein is a G-protein connected with the response to RTKs that initiates the MAPK kinase cascade when GDP is released and GTP uploaded. Mutations in the RAS protein which interfere with its GTPase activity are common in cancer. Evaluate the connection between the inability of RAS to hydrolyze GTP and uncontrolled cell proliferation.

a. RAS, when bound to GTP, becomes permanently inactive even in the presence of the ligand, and no longer regulates cell division.
b. RAS, when bound to GTP, becomes permanently active even in the absence of the ligand, and no longer regulates cell division.
c. RAS, when bound to GTP, forms a dimer after binding to the ligand, and causes uncontrolled division, but it remains inactive when the ligand is absent.
d. RAS, when bound to GTP, does not form a dimer after binding to the ligand but stimulates downstream signaling to occur and causes uncontrolled cell division.

42. Common medications called β-blockers bind to G-protein-linked receptors in heart muscles, blocking adrenaline. They are prescribed to patients with high blood pressure. Can you formulate a hypothesis on their mechanism of action?

a. Adrenaline has a stimulatory effect on heart rate and blood pressure. β-blockers are antagonistic to adrenaline and produces inhibitory effect.
b. Adrenaline has both a stimulatory and an inhibitory effect on heart rate and blood pressure. β-blockers bind to G-protein and stimulate the inhibitory effect of adrenaline.
c. Adrenaline has an inhibitory effect on heart rate and blood pressure. β-blockers have a synergistic effect along with adrenaline producing an inhibitory effect.
d. Adrenaline has both a stimulatory and an inhibitory effect on heart rate and blood pressure. β-blockers bind to G-protein and intervene with the inhibitory effect of adrenaline.

SCIENCE PRACTICE CHALLENGE QUESTIONS

43. The figure below shows a series of states for typical G protein signal transduction.

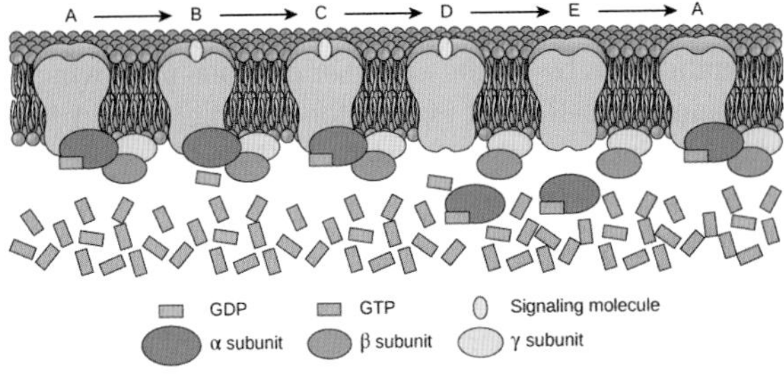

Figure 9.19

Use this representation to describe the following stages in this signaling process:

A. between A and B

B. between B and C

C. between C and D

D. between D and E

E. between E and A

44.

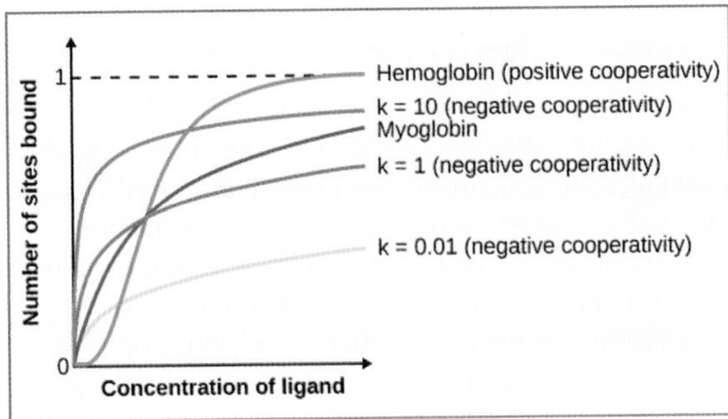

Tyrosine kinase receptors are pairs of proteins that span the plasma membrane. On the extracellular side of the membrane, one or more sites are present that bind to signaling ligands such as insulin or growth factors. On the intracellular side, the ends of peptide chains on each protein phosphorylate the other member of the pair, providing active docking sites that initiate cellular responses. The signal is switched off by dissociation of the ligand. For each ligand-receptor system, the equilibrium constant, k, controls the distribution of receptor-bound and unbound ligands. In systems with large values of k, a site is likely to be occupied, even at low concentrations of ligand. When k is small, the likelihood of binding is low, even when the concentration of ligand is high. To initiate a new stimulus response cycle for the receptor, the ligand must dissociate. Larger values of k mean that the receptor is more likely to be occupied and thus unavailable to bind another ligand.

Some ligand-binding systems have multiple binding sites. For example, hemoglobin binds four oxygen molecules, whereas myoglobin has only a single binding site. When multiple binding sites are present, the presence of an already-bound ligand can cooperatively affect the binding of other ligands on the same protein. For hemoglobin, the binding is positively cooperative. The affinity of oxygen for heme increases as the number of bound oxygen molecules increases.

A. **Describe** the features in the graph above for hemoglobin that demonstrate positive cooperativity.

B. The insulin receptor (IR) is a tyrosine kinase receptor that has two sites to which insulin can attach. IR is negatively cooperative. In the diagram above, the dependence of the bound fraction on available insulin is similar to the curve for k = 1 with negative cooperativity. **Describe** the features of this curve in the graph above that demonstrate negative cooperativity.

C. When viewed from above the cell-surface, the representation shows receptors with one and two bound insulin molecules. **Explain** the negative cooperation for this receptor based on the free energy of conformational changes in the receptor-peptide chains.

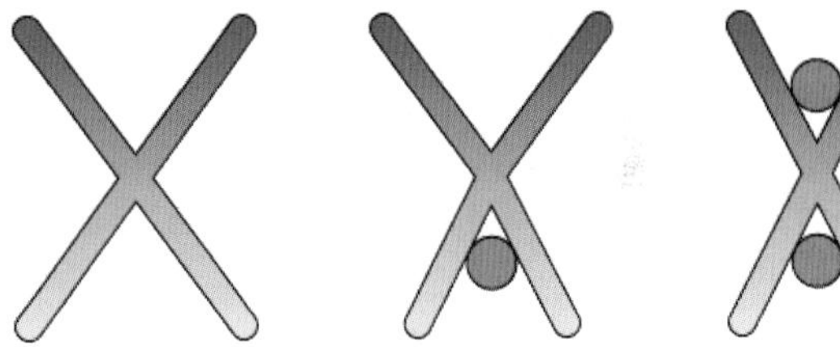

D.

E. **Explain** the advantages in terms of selection of two-site binding with negative cooperation relative to one-site binding.

F. Three binding curves with negative cooperativity and different values of k are shown on the graph. **Describe** conditions in which there is an advantage in having a low value of k with negative cooperativity.

45. Organisms, including plants, have evolved chemical signaling pathways to direct physiological responses to environmental changes. Stomata are pores, typically on the underside of leaves that regulate CO_2, O_2, and H_2O exchange between plants and the external environment. This interaction controls photosynthetic rate and transpiration rate. The opening and closing of stomata are controlled by specialized guard cells that surround the stomatal pore. The osmotic state within the guard cells determines their turgor; when the guard cells are flaccid, stomata close. Turgor in the guard cells is regulated by the active transport of several ions, including K^+ and H^+, across the plasma membrane. Several environmental factors can cause stomatal closing: water deficit, darkness, microbes, ozone, and sulfur dioxide and other pollutants. Intracellular carbon dioxide concentration and light can trigger stomata to open.

The system is regulated by a phytohormone (plant hormone) called abscisic acid (ABA) and the amino acid precursor of the synthesis of a second phytohormone called ethylene (ACC). The second messengers NO and Ca^{2+} in the signal response to changes in the concentrations of these hormones activate transcription factors that affect ion transport across guard cell membranes. High CO_2 levels and light also alter phytohormone concentrations.

A. **Explain** why plants must regulate the opening and closing of stomata. **Explain** how this response relates to the capture of free energy for cellular processes.

B. **Construct an explanation** in terms of the water potential, Y, for the efflux (outward flow) of H^+ during water stress (drought).

C. Consider a scenario involving environmental factors, such as water stress and daylight, which have opposing effects on the opening and closing of stomata; stomata would be signaled to close under drought conditions and to open during photosynthesis. **Pose** two scientific **questions** regarding the response of the system, one involving the phytohormones ABA and ACC, and the second involving the concentration of second messengers.

D. The data shown in the table below were obtained by treating rockcress (*Arabidopsis*) with doses of ABA, ACC, and ABA plus ACC. Using the terms *and* and *or*, **describe** the expected and unexpected responses of the system just after 10 minutes and around 45 minutes, as displayed by these data.

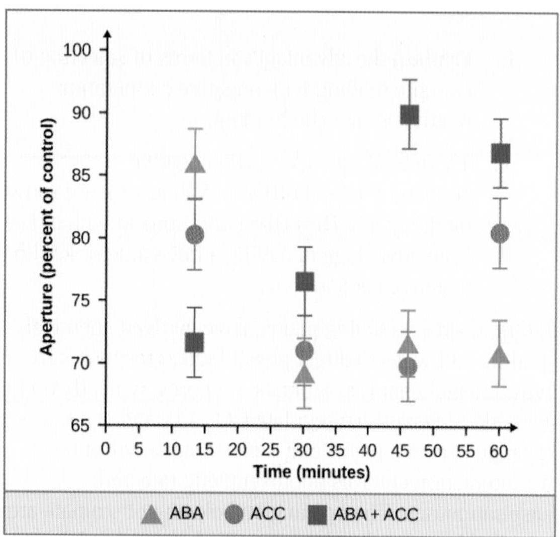

Figure 9.20

E. Researchers are investigating the interactions among multiple signaling pathways, a phenomenon referred to as "crosstalk." The same second messengers, NO and Ca^{2+}, are used in many different signaling pathways. **Construct an explanation** by analogy to other phenomena in which combining a small set of events (for example, 0 and 1 in a computer, the musical scale, or the R, G, and B components of a color) can lead to a vast assortment of outcomes.

46. Construct a graphical representation of information as a function of time during the transduction of a signal along a signaling pathway.

A. Use your graph to **describe** trends in the amount of information rather than the actual magnitude. In sketching your graph, consider how the shape of the curve would change during these events:

i. extracellular first messenger
ii. receptor binding and conformational changes
iii. release of second messengers
iv. cellular responses
v. halt signal and degrade intermediates

B. **Annotate** your representation for a specific signaling system, such as the effect of epinephrine on the free energy released from glucose.

47. Bacteria and fungi produce several extracellular chemicals, including antibiotics that affect other organisms in the environment. Antibiotics also are produced industrially in large bacteria-containing fermentation tanks. However, antibiotics that have been used by humans to control microbes are now found at subinhibitory concentrations in the environment. Low levels of antibiotics in the environment are mutagenic for bacteria and promote the development of antibiotic resistance.

Bacteria produce chemical signals that detect population density and regulate gene expression, a phenomenon called quorum sensing. Density is signaled by the extracellular concentration of small amino acid derivatives. To combat antibiotic resistance, an emerging strategy for the control of bacterial disease is quorum quenching.

A. **Describe** the advantage of antibiotics to the organisms that produce them.

B. Based on the name of the emerging strategy for controlling bacterial infections, **describe** a possible mechanism by which bacteria determine their population density. **Justify the claim** that quorum quenching may provide a more sustainable approach to disease control than the use of antibiotics.

10 | CELL REPRODUCTION

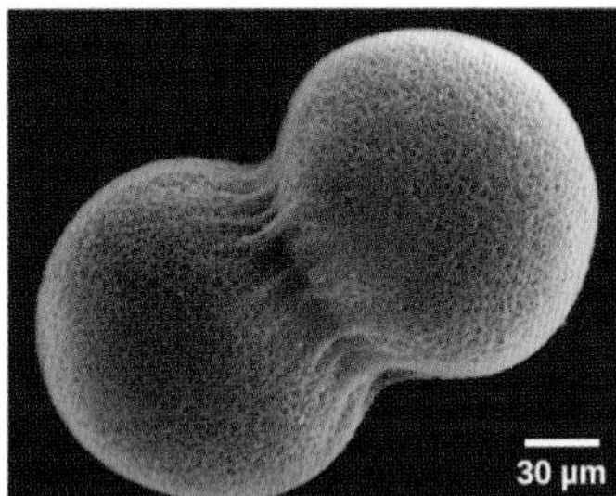

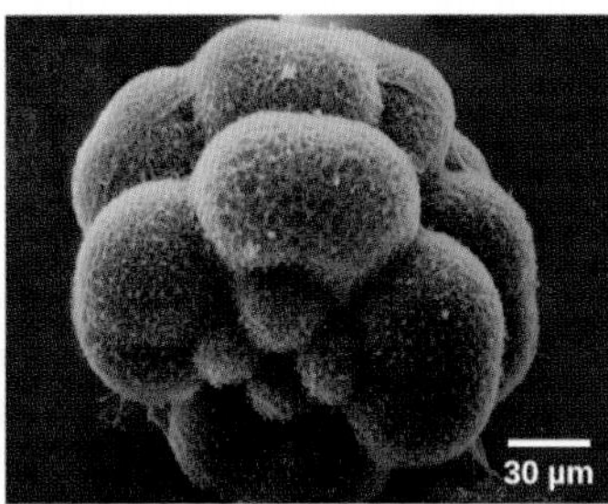

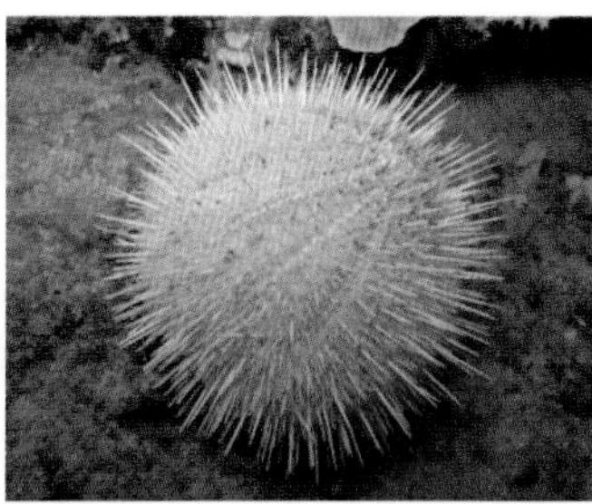

Figure 10.1 A sea urchin begins life as a single cell that (a) divides to form two cells, visible by scanning electron microscopy. After four rounds of cell division, (b) there are 16 cells, as seen in this SEM image. After many rounds of cell division, the individual develops into a complex, multicellular organism, as seen in this (c) mature sea urchin. (credit a: modification of work by Evelyn Spiegel, Louisa Howard; credit b: modification of work by Evelyn Spiegel, Louisa Howard; credit c: modification of work by Marco Busdraghi; scale-bar data from Matt Russell)

Chapter Outline

Introduction

A human, as well as every sexually reproducing organism, begins life as a fertilized egg (embryo) or zygote. Trillions of cell divisions subsequently occur in a controlled manner to produce a complex, multicellular human. In other words, that original single cell is the ancestor of every other cell in the body. Once a being is fully grown, cell reproduction is still necessary to repair or regenerate tissues. For example, new blood and skin cells are constantly being produced. All multicellular organisms use cell division for growth, maintenance, and repair of tissues. Cell division is tightly regulated, and the occasional failure of regulation can have life-threatening consequences. Single-celled organisms use cell division as their method of reproduction.

Not all cells in the body reproduce to repair tissues. Most nerve tissues, for example, are not capable of regeneration. This means people who have damaged their nerves or nervous system are often left paralyzed.

However, this may change in the future; scientists have discovered a new drug called intracellular signal peptide (ISP), which helps nerve cells regenerate in rats. It works by blocking an enzyme that causes scar tissue in damaged nerve cells allowing the nervous system a chance to repair itself. The full research study is located here (http://openstaxcollege.org/l/32scar) .

10.1 | Cell Division

In this section, you will explore the following question:

- What is the relationship between chromosomes, genes, and traits in prokaryotes and eukaryotes?

Connection for AP® Courses

All organisms, from bacteria to complex animals, must be able to store, retrieve, and transmit genetic information to continue life. In later chapters, we will explore how a cell's genetic information encoded in DNA, its genome, is replicated and passed to the next generation to direct the production of proteins, determining an organism's traits. Prokaryotes have single circular chromosome of DNA, whereas eukaryotes have multiple, linear chromosomes composed of chromatin (DNA wrapped around a histone protein) surrounded by a nuclear membrane. Cell division involves both mitosis, the division of the chromosomes, and cytokinesis, the division of the cytoplasm. Human somatic cells consist of 46 chromosomes—22 pairs of autosomal chromosomes and a pair of sex chromosomes. Prior to mitosis, each chromosome is duplicated to ensure that daughter cells receive the full amount of hereditary material contributed by both parents. The total number of autosomal chromosomes is referred to as the diploid ($2n$) number. (In the next chapter, we will study meiosis, the second type of cell division in sexually reproducing organisms.)

Information presented and the examples highlighted in the section support concepts and Learning Objectives outlined in Big Idea 3 of the AP® Biology Curriculum Framework, as shown in the table. The Learning Objectives listed in the Curriculum Framework provide a transparent foundation for the AP® Biology course, an inquiry-based laboratory experience, instructional activities, and AP® exam questions. A Learning Objective merges required content with one or more of the seven Science Practices.

Big Idea 3	Living systems store, retrieve, transmit and respond to information essential to life processes.
Enduring Understanding 3.A	Heritable information provides for continuity of life.
Essential Knowledge	**3.A.2** In eukaryotes, heritable information is passed to the next generation via processes that include the cell cycle and mitosis or meiosis plus fertilization.
Science Practice	**6.5** The student can evaluate alternative scientific explanations.
Learning Objective	**3.1** The student is able to construct scientific explanations that use the structures and mechanisms of DNA and RNA to support the claim that DNA, and in some cases, RNA are the primary sources of heritable information.

The continuity of life from one cell to another has its foundation in the reproduction of cells by way of the cell cycle. The cell cycle is an orderly sequence of events that describes the stages of a cell's life from the division of a single parent cell to the production of two new daughter cells. The mechanisms involved in the cell cycle are highly regulated.

Genomic DNA

Before discussing the steps a cell must undertake to replicate, a deeper understanding of the structure and function of a cell's genetic information is necessary. A cell's DNA, packaged as a double-stranded DNA molecule, is called its **genome**. In prokaryotes, the genome is composed of a single, double-stranded DNA molecule in the form of a loop or circle (Figure 10.2). The region in the cell containing this genetic material is called a nucleoid. Some prokaryotes also have smaller loops of DNA called plasmids that are not essential for normal growth. Bacteria can exchange these plasmids with other bacteria, sometimes receiving beneficial new genes that the recipient can add to their chromosomal DNA. Antibiotic resistance is one trait that often spreads through a bacterial colony through plasmid exchange.

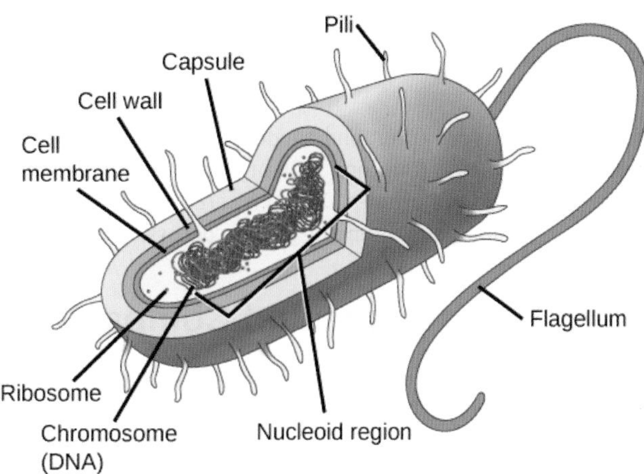

Figure 10.2 Prokaryotes, including bacteria and archaea, have a single, circular chromosome located in a central region called the nucleoid.

In eukaryotes, the genome consists of several double-stranded linear DNA molecules (Figure 10.3). Each species of eukaryotes has a characteristic number of chromosomes in the nuclei of its cells. Human body cells have 46 chromosomes, while human **gametes** (sperm or eggs) have 23 chromosomes each. A typical body cell, or somatic cell, contains two matched sets of chromosomes, a configuration known as **diploid**. The letter *n* is used to represent a single set of chromosomes; therefore, a diploid organism is designated 2*n*. Human cells that contain one set of chromosomes are called gametes, or sex cells; these are eggs and sperm, and are designated *1n*, or **haploid**.

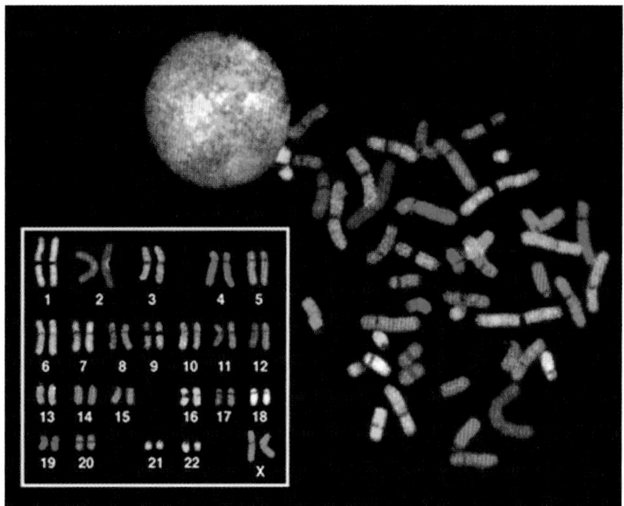

Figure 10.3 There are 23 pairs of homologous chromosomes in a female human somatic cell. The condensed chromosomes are viewed within the nucleus (top), removed from a cell in mitosis and spread out on a slide (right), and artificially arranged according to length (left); an arrangement like this is called a karyotype. In this image, the chromosomes were exposed to fluorescent stains for differentiation of the different chromosomes. A method of staining called "chromosome painting" employs fluorescent dyes that highlight chromosomes in different colors. (credit: National Human Genome Project/NIH)

Matched pairs of chromosomes in a diploid organism are called **homologous** ("same knowledge") **chromosomes**. Homologous chromosomes are the same length and have specific nucleotide segments called **genes** in exactly the same location, or **locus**. Genes, the functional units of chromosomes, determine specific characteristics by coding for specific proteins. Traits are the variations of those characteristics. For example, hair color is a characteristic with traits that are blonde, brown, or black.

Each copy of a homologous pair of chromosomes originates from a different parent; therefore, the genes themselves are not identical. The variation of individuals within a species is due to the specific combination of the genes inherited from both parents. Even a slightly altered sequence of nucleotides within a gene can result in an alternative trait. For example, there are three possible gene sequences on the human chromosome that code for blood type: sequence A, sequence B, and sequence O. Because all diploid human cells have two copies of the chromosome that determines blood type, the blood type (the trait) is determined by which two versions of the marker gene are inherited. It is possible to have two copies of the same gene sequence on both homologous chromosomes, with one on each (for example, AA, BB, or OO), or two different sequences, such as AB.

Minor variations of traits, such as blood type, eye color, and handedness, contribute to the natural variation found within a species. However, if the entire DNA sequence from any pair of human homologous chromosomes is compared, the difference is less than one percent. The sex chromosomes, X and Y, are the single exception to the rule of homologous chromosome uniformity: Other than a small amount of homology that is necessary to accurately produce gametes, the genes found on the X and Y chromosomes are different.

Eukaryotic Chromosomal Structure and Compaction

If the DNA from all 46 chromosomes in a human cell nucleus was laid out end to end, it would measure approximately two meters; however, its diameter would be only 2 nm. Considering that the size of a typical human cell is about 10 μm (100,000 cells lined up to equal one meter), DNA must be tightly packaged to fit in the cell's nucleus. At the same time, it must also be readily accessible for the genes to be expressed. During some stages of the cell cycle, the long strands of DNA are condensed into compact chromosomes. There are a number of ways that chromosomes are compacted.

In the first level of compaction, short stretches of the DNA double helix wrap around a core of eight **histone proteins** at regular intervals along the entire length of the chromosome (Figure 10.4). The DNA-histone complex is part of the chromatin. Each beadlike histone-DNA complex is called a **nucleosome**, and DNA connecting the nucleosomes is called linker DNA. A DNA molecule in this form is about seven times shorter than the double helix without the histones, and the beads are about 10 nm in diameter, in contrast with the 2-nm diameter of a DNA double helix. The next level of compaction occurs as the nucleosomes and the linker DNA between them are coiled into a 30-nm chromatin fiber. This coiling further shortens the chromosome so that it is now about 50 times shorter than the extended form. In the third level of packing, a variety of fibrous proteins is used to pack the chromatin. These fibrous proteins also ensure that each chromosome in a non-dividing cell occupies a particular area of the nucleus that does not overlap with that of any other chromosome (see the top image in Figure 10.3).

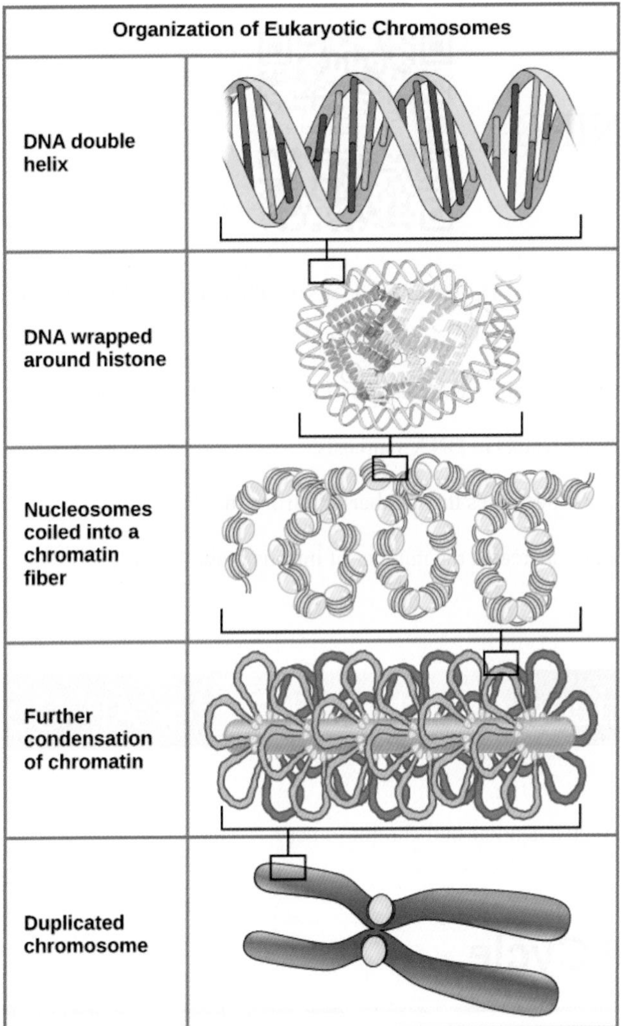

Figure 10.4 Double-stranded DNA wraps around histone proteins to form nucleosomes that have the appearance of “beads on a string.” The nucleosomes are coiled into a 30-nm chromatin fiber. When a cell undergoes mitosis, the chromosomes condense even further.

DNA replicates in the S phase of interphase. After replication, the chromosomes are composed of two linked sister **chromatids**. When fully compact, the pairs of identically packed chromosomes are bound to each other by cohesin proteins. The connection between the sister chromatids is closest in a region called the **centromere**. The conjoined sister chromatids, with a diameter of about 1 µm, are visible under a light microscope. The centromeric region is highly condensed and thus will appear as a constricted area.

This animation (http://openstaxcollege.org/l/Packaged_DNA) illustrates the different levels of chromosome packing.

Why is nucleosome formation required for the packaging of DNA?

a. Nucleosome formation results in compaction of the DNA to form chromatin.

b. Nucleosome formation results in DNA synthesis.

c. Nucleosome formation decreases the number of introns in DNA.

d. Nucleosome formation increases the number of introns in the DNA.

science practices CONNECTION for AP® Courses

Think About It

What is the relationship between a genome and chromosomes?

10.2 | The Cell Cycle

In this section, you will explore the following questions:

- What processes occur during the three stages of interphase?
- How do the chromosomes behave during the mitotic phase?

Connection for AP® Courses

The cell cycle describes an orderly sequence of events that are highly regulated. In eukaryotes, the cell cycle consists of a long preparatory period (interphase) followed by mitosis and cytokinesis. Interphase is divided into three phases: Gap 1 (G_1), DNA synthesis (S), and Gap 2 (G_2). Interphase represents the portion of the cell cycle between nuclear divisions. During this phase, preparations are made for division that include growth, duplication of most cellular contents, and replication of DNA. The cell's DNA is replicated during the S stage. (We will study the details of DNA replication in the chapter on DNA structure and function.) Following the G_2 stage of interphase, the cell begins mitosis, the process of active division by which duplicated chromosomes (chromatids) attach to spindle fibers, align themselves along the equator of the cell, and then separate from each other.

Following mitosis, the cell undergoes cytokinesis, the splitting of the parent cell into two daughter cells, complete with a full complement of genetic material. In animal cells, daughter cells are separated by an actin ring, whereas plant cells are separated by the cell plate, which will grow into a new cell wall. Sometimes cells enter a Gap zero (G_0) phase, during which they do not actively prepare to divide; the G_0 phase can be temporary until triggered by an external signal to enter G_1, or permanent, such as mature cardiac muscle cells and nerve cells.

Information presented and the examples highlighted in the section support concepts and Learning Objectives outlined in Big Idea 3 of the AP® Biology Curriculum Framework, as shown in the tables. The Learning Objectives listed in the Curriculum Framework provide a transparent foundation for the AP® Biology course, an inquiry-based laboratory experience, instructional activities, and AP® exam questions. A Learning Objective merges required content with one or more of the seven Science Practices.

Big Idea 3	Living systems store, retrieve, transmit and respond to information essential to life processes.
Enduring Understanding 3.A	Heritable information provides for continuity of life.
Essential Knowledge	**3.A.2** In eukaryotes, heritable information is passed to the next generation via processes that include the cell cycle and mitosis or meiosis plus fertilization.
Science Practice	**6.4** The student can make claims and predictions about natural phenomena based on scientific theories and models.
Learning Objective	**3.7** The student can make predictions about natural phenomena occurring during the cell cycle.
Essential Knowledge	**3.A.2** In eukaryotes, heritable information is passed to the next generation via processes that include the cell cycle and mitosis or meiosis plus fertilization.
Science Practice	**1.2** The student can describe representations and models of natural or man-made phenomena and systems in the domain.
Learning Objective	**3.8** The student can describe the events that occur in the cell cycle.
Essential Knowledge	**3.A.2** In eukaryotes, heritable information is passed to the next generation via processes that include the cell cycle and mitosis or meiosis plus fertilization.
Science Practice	**5.3** The student can evaluate the evidence provided by data sets in relation to a particular scientific question.
Learning Objective	**3.11** The student is able to evaluate evidence provided by data sets to support the claim that heritable information is passed from one generation to another generation through mitosis.

The Science Practice Challenge Questions contain additional test questions for this section that will help you prepare for the AP exam. These questions address the following standards:
[APLO 2.35][APLO 2.15][APLO 2.19][APLO 3.11][APLO 2.33][APLO 2.36][APLO 2.37][APLO 2.31]

The **cell cycle** is an ordered series of events involving cell growth and cell division that produces two new daughter cells. Cells on the path to cell division proceed through a series of precisely timed and carefully regulated stages of growth, DNA replication, and division that produces two identical (clone) cells. The cell cycle has two major phases: interphase and the mitotic phase (**Figure 10.5**). During **interphase**, the cell grows and DNA is replicated. During the **mitotic phase**, the replicated DNA and cytoplasmic contents are separated, and the cell divides.

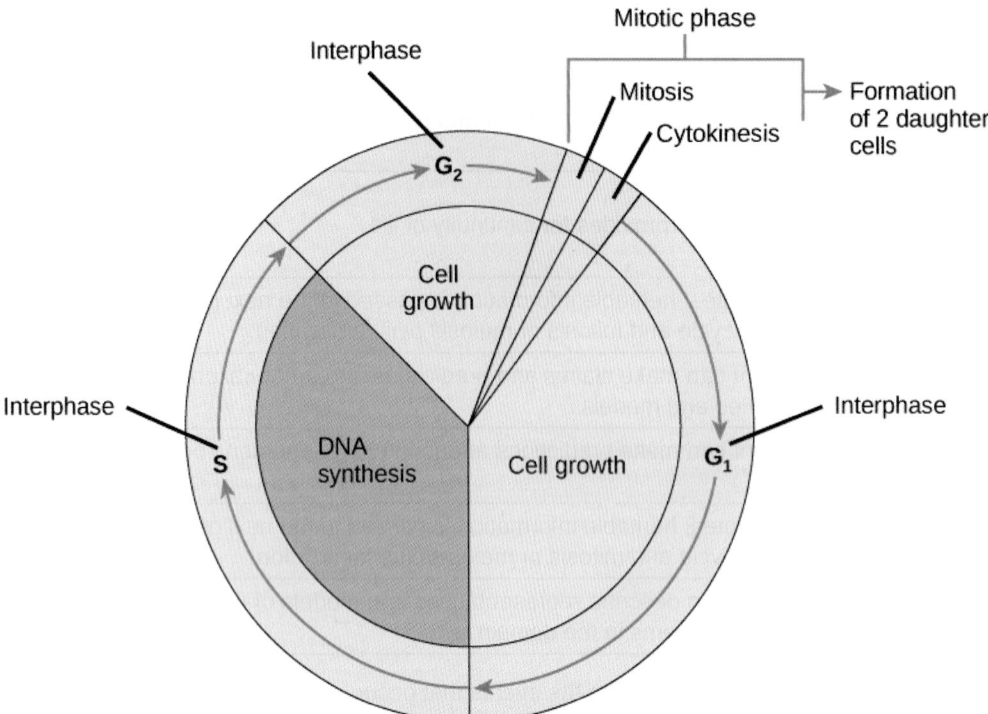

Figure 10.5 The cell cycle consists of interphase and the mitotic phase. During interphase, the cell grows and the nuclear DNA is duplicated. Interphase is followed by the mitotic phase. During the mitotic phase, the duplicated chromosomes are segregated and distributed into daughter nuclei. The cytoplasm is usually divided as well, resulting in two daughter cells.

Interphase

During interphase, the cell undergoes normal growth processes while also preparing for cell division. In order for a cell to move from interphase into the mitotic phase, many internal and external conditions must be met. The three stages of interphase are called G_1, S, and G_2.

G_1 Phase (First Gap)

The first stage of interphase is called the **G_1 phase** (first gap) because, from a microscopic aspect, little change is visible. However, during the G_1 stage, the cell is quite active at the biochemical level. The cell is accumulating the building blocks of chromosomal DNA and the associated proteins as well as accumulating sufficient energy reserves to complete the task of replicating each chromosome in the nucleus.

S Phase (Synthesis of DNA)

Throughout interphase, nuclear DNA remains in a semi-condensed chromatin configuration. In the **S phase**, DNA replication can proceed through the mechanisms that result in the formation of identical pairs of DNA molecules—sister chromatids—that are firmly attached to the centromeric region. The centrosome is duplicated during the S phase. The two centrosomes will give rise to the **mitotic spindle**, the apparatus that orchestrates the movement of chromosomes during mitosis. At the center of each animal cell, the centrosomes of animal cells are associated with a pair of rod-like objects, the **centrioles**, which are at right angles to each other. Centrioles help organize cell division. Centrioles are not present in the centrosomes of other eukaryotic species, such as plants and most fungi.

G_2 Phase (Second Gap)

In the **G_2 phase**, the cell replenishes its energy stores and synthesizes proteins necessary for chromosome manipulation. Some cell organelles are duplicated, and the cytoskeleton is dismantled to provide resources for the mitotic phase. There may be additional cell growth during G_2. The final preparations for the mitotic phase must be completed before the cell is able to enter the first stage of mitosis.

The Mitotic Phase

The mitotic phase is a multistep process during which the duplicated chromosomes are aligned, separated, and move into two new, identical daughter cells. The first portion of the mitotic phase is called **karyokinesis**, or nuclear division. The second portion of the mitotic phase, called cytokinesis, is the physical separation of the cytoplasmic components into the two daughter cells.

Revisit the stages of mitosis at this site (http://openstaxcollege.org/l/Cell_cycle_mito) .

Gout is a form of arthritis that causes a painful inflammation of joints. One treatment for gout is colchicine, a medication that inhibits mitosis. Explain why this medication is beneficial for people with gout and why it can cause undesirable side effects, such as low white blood cell counts.

a. Colchicine increases inflammation by inhibiting mitosis. Inhibition of mitosis results in decreased white blood count.

b. Colchicine decreases inflammation by inhibiting mitosis. Inhibition of mitosis results in decreased white blood count.

c. Colchicine increases inflammation by inhibiting mitosis. Inhibition of mitosis results in increased white blood count.

d. Colchicine decreases inflammation by inhibiting mitosis. Inhibition of mitosis results in increased white blood count.

Karyokinesis (Mitosis)

Karyokinesis, also known as **mitosis**, is divided into a series of phases—prophase, prometaphase, metaphase, anaphase, and telophase—that result in the division of the cell nucleus (Figure 10.7).

everyday CONNECTION for AP® Courses

These budding plants demonstrate asexual reproduction, one of the main purposes of mitosis. The other two purposes are growth and repair.

Figure 10.6

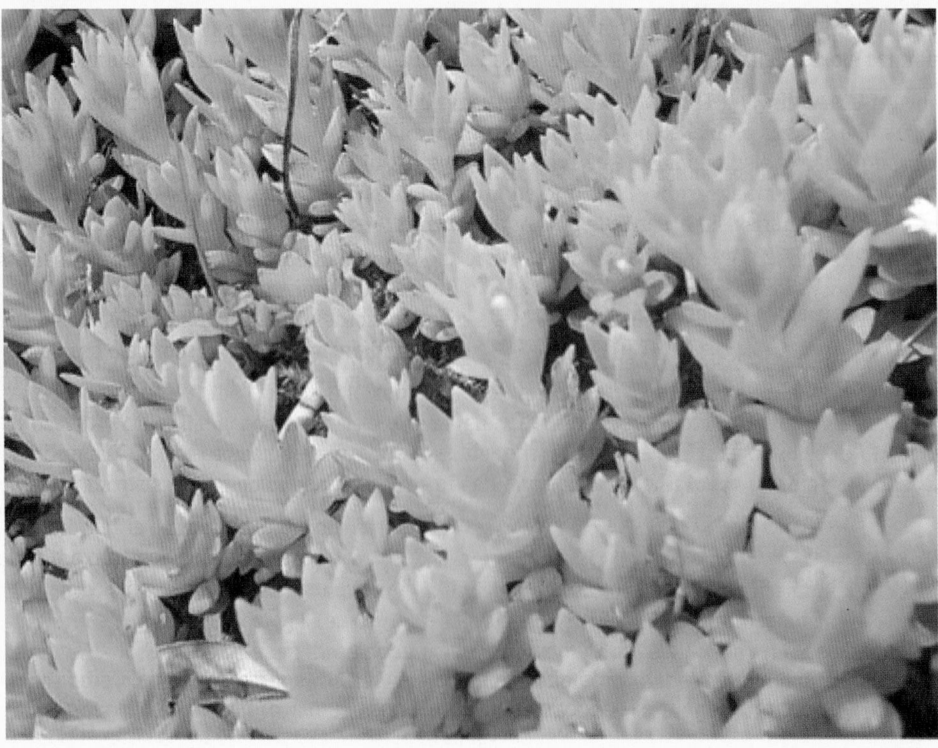

Which of the following statements best describes the relationship between mitosis and asexual reproduction?

a. Mitosis is a process that can result in asexual reproduction.

b. Mitosis is a process that always results in asexual reproduction.

c. Asexual reproduction is a process that always results in mitosis.

d. Asexual reproduction is a process that can result in mitosis.

visual CONNECTION

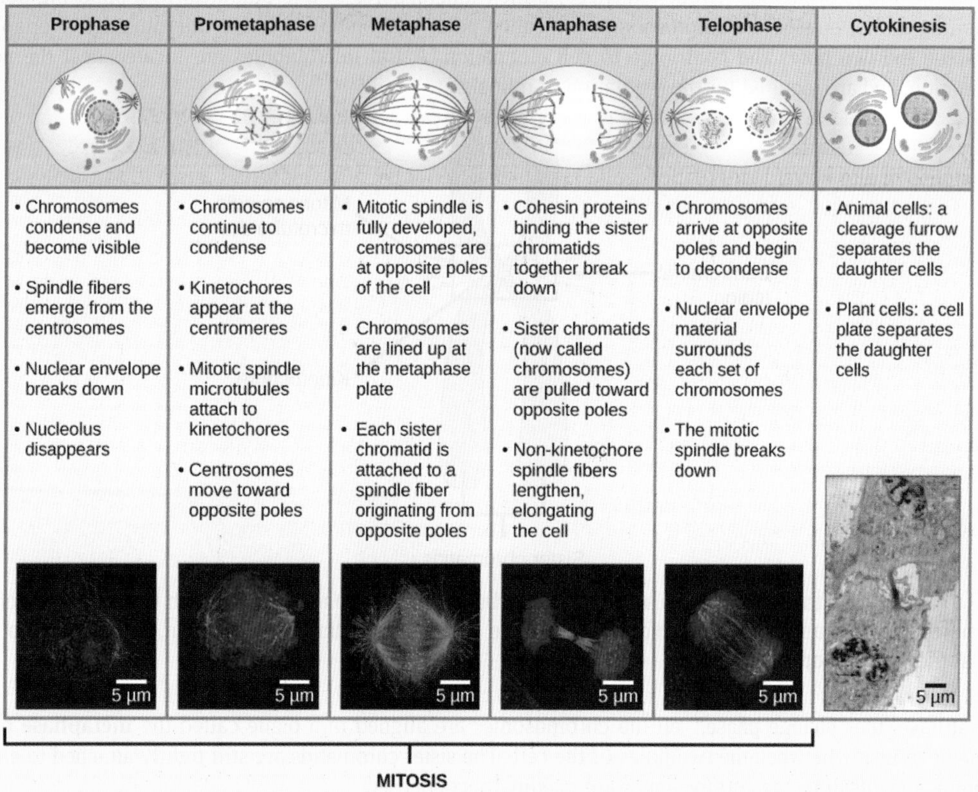

Prophase	Prometaphase	Metaphase	Anaphase	Telophase	Cytokinesis
• Chromosomes condense and become visible • Spindle fibers emerge from the centrosomes • Nuclear envelope breaks down • Nucleolus disappears	• Chromosomes continue to condense • Kinetochores appear at the centromeres • Mitotic spindle microtubules attach to kinetochores • Centrosomes move toward opposite poles	• Mitotic spindle is fully developed, centrosomes are at opposite poles of the cell • Chromosomes are lined up at the metaphase plate • Each sister chromatid is attached to a spindle fiber originating from opposite poles	• Cohesin proteins binding the sister chromatids together break down • Sister chromatids (now called chromosomes) are pulled toward opposite poles • Non-kinetochore spindle fibers lengthen, elongating the cell	• Chromosomes arrive at opposite poles and begin to decondense • Nuclear envelope material surrounds each set of chromosomes • The mitotic spindle breaks down	• Animal cells: a cleavage furrow separates the daughter cells • Plant cells: a cell plate separates the daughter cells
5 µm	5 µm	5 µm	5 µm	5 µm	5 µm

MITOSIS

Figure 10.7 Karyokinesis (or mitosis) is divided into five stages—prophase, prometaphase, metaphase, anaphase, and telophase. The pictures at the bottom were taken by fluorescence microscopy (hence, the black background) of cells artificially stained by fluorescent dyes: blue fluorescence indicates DNA (chromosomes) and green fluorescence indicates microtubules (spindle apparatus). (credit "mitosis drawings": modification of work by Mariana Ruiz Villareal; credit "micrographs": modification of work by Roy van Heesbeen; credit "cytokinesis micrograph": Wadsworth Center/New York State Department of Health; scale-bar data from Matt Russell)

Which of the following is the correct order of events in mitosis?

a. Sister chromatids line up at the metaphase plate. The kinetochore becomes attached to the mitotic spindle. The nucleus reforms and the cell divide. Cohesin proteins break down and the sister chromatids separate.

b. The kinetochore becomes attached to the mitotic spindle. Cohesin proteins break down and the sister chromatids separate. Sister chromatids line up at the metaphase plate. The nucleus reforms and the cell divides.

c. The kinetochore becomes attached to the cohesin proteins. Sister chromatids line up at the metaphase plate. The kinetochore breaks down and the sister chromatids separate. The nucleus reforms and the cell divides.

d. The kinetochore becomes attached to the mitotic spindle. Sister chromatids line up at the metaphase plate. Cohesin proteins break down and the sister chromatids separate. The nucleus reforms and the cell divide.

During **prophase**, the “first phase,” the nuclear envelope starts to dissociate into small vesicles, and the membranous organelles (such as the Golgi complex or Golgi apparatus, and endoplasmic reticulum), fragment and disperse toward the periphery of the cell. The nucleolus disappears (disperses). The centrosomes begin to move to opposite poles of the cell. Microtubules that will form the mitotic spindle extend between the centrosomes, pushing them farther apart as the microtubule fibers lengthen. The sister chromatids begin to coil more tightly with the aid of **condensin** proteins and become visible under a light microscope.

During **prometaphase**, the “first change phase,” many processes that were begun in prophase continue to advance. The remnants of the nuclear envelope fragment. The mitotic spindle continues to develop as more microtubules assemble and stretch across the length of the former nuclear area. Chromosomes become more condensed and discrete. Each sister chromatid develops a protein structure called a **kinetochore** in the centromeric region (Figure 10.8). The proteins of the kinetochore attract and bind mitotic spindle microtubules. As the spindle microtubules extend from the centrosomes, some of these microtubules come into contact with and firmly bind to the kinetochores. Once a mitotic fiber attaches to a chromosome, the chromosome will be oriented until the kinetochores of sister chromatids face the opposite poles. Eventually, all the sister chromatids will be attached via their kinetochores to microtubules from opposing poles. Spindle microtubules that do not engage the chromosomes are called polar microtubules. These microtubules overlap each other midway between the two poles and contribute to cell elongation. Astral microtubules are located near the poles, aid in spindle orientation, and are required for the regulation of mitosis.

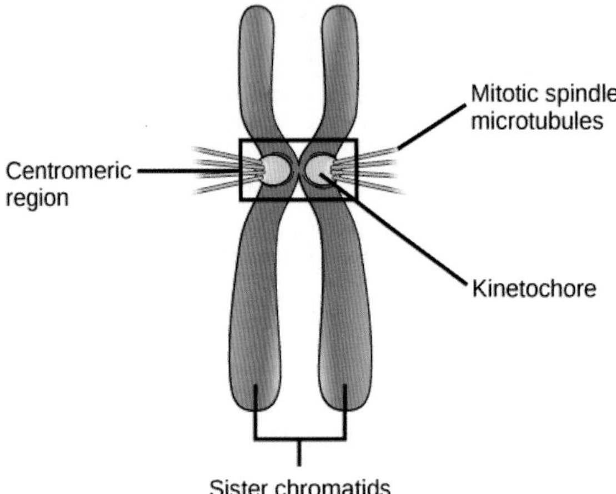

Figure 10.8 During prometaphase, mitotic spindle microtubules from opposite poles attach to each sister chromatid at the kinetochore. In anaphase, the connection between the sister chromatids breaks down, and the microtubules pull the chromosomes toward opposite poles.

During **metaphase**, the “change phase,” all the chromosomes are aligned in a plane called the **metaphase plate**, or the equatorial plane, midway between the two poles of the cell. The sister chromatids are still tightly attached to each other by cohesin proteins. At this time, the chromosomes are maximally condensed.

During **anaphase**, the “upward phase,” the cohesin proteins degrade, and the sister chromatids separate at the centromere. Each chromatid, now called a chromosome, is pulled rapidly toward the centrosome to which its microtubule is attached. The cell becomes visibly elongated (oval shaped) as the polar microtubules slide against each other at the metaphase plate where they overlap.

During **telophase**, the “distance phase,” the chromosomes reach the opposite poles and begin to decondense (unravel), relaxing into a chromatin configuration. The mitotic spindles are depolymerized into tubulin monomers that will be used to assemble cytoskeletal components for each daughter cell. Nuclear envelopes form around the chromosomes, and nucleosomes appear within the nuclear area.

Cytokinesis

Cytokinesis, or “cell motion,” is the second main stage of the mitotic phase, during which cell division is completed via the physical separation of the cytoplasmic components into two daughter cells. Division is not complete until the cell components have been apportioned and completely separated into the two daughter cells. Although the stages of mitosis are similar for most eukaryotes, the process of cytokinesis is quite different for eukaryotes that have cell walls, such as plant cells.

In cells such as animal cells that lack cell walls, cytokinesis starts during late anaphase. A contractile ring composed of actin filaments forms just inside the plasma membrane at the former metaphase plate. The actin filaments pull the equator of the cell inward, forming a fissure. This fissure, or "crack," is called the **cleavage furrow**. The furrow deepens as the actin ring contracts, and eventually the membrane is cleaved in two (Figure 10.9).

In plant cells, a new cell wall must form between the daughter cells. During interphase, the Golgi apparatus accumulates enzymes, structural proteins, and glucose molecules prior to breaking into vesicles and dispersing throughout the dividing cell. During telophase, these Golgi vesicles are transported on microtubules to form a phragmoplast (a vesicular structure) at the metaphase plate. There, the vesicles fuse and coalesce from the center toward the cell walls; this structure is called a **cell plate**. As more vesicles fuse, the cell plate enlarges until it merges with the cell walls at the periphery of the cell. Enzymes use the glucose that has accumulated between the membrane layers to build a new cell wall. The Golgi membranes become parts of the plasma membrane on either side of the new cell wall (Figure 10.9).

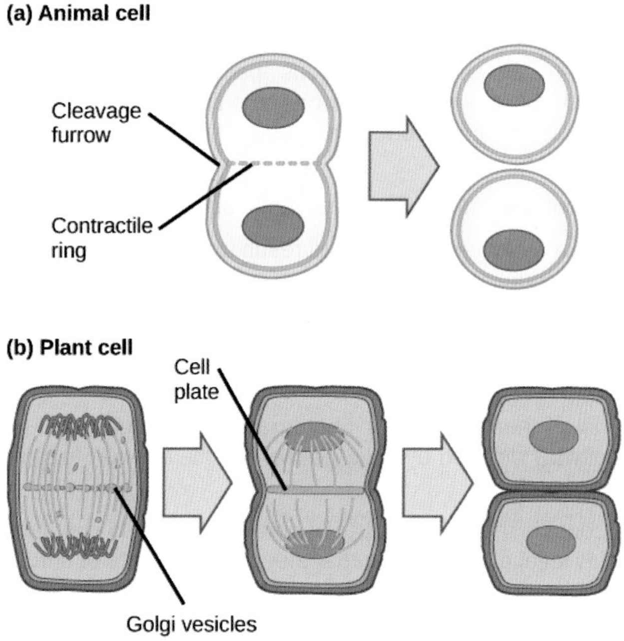

Figure 10.9 During cytokinesis in animal cells, a ring of actin filaments forms at the metaphase plate. The ring contracts, forming a cleavage furrow, which divides the cell in two. In plant cells, Golgi vesicles coalesce at the former metaphase plate, forming a phragmoplast. A cell plate formed by the fusion of the vesicles of the phragmoplast grows from the center toward the cell walls, and the membranes of the vesicles fuse to form a plasma membrane that divides the cell in two.

science practices CONNECTION for AP® Courses

Activity

- Use a set of pipe cleaners (or other materials as directed by your teacher) that you can use to model chromosomes during mitosis and meiosis:
  1. Each of the pipe cleaners represents a single, unreplicated chromosome. Each chromosome should differ in size, as they do in most organisms. Assume that your dividing cell contains 3 chromosomes: numbered chromosome 1, 2, and 3.
  2. Using both members of each homologous pair for chromosomes 1–3, model how the chromosomes would appear in a cell that had just finished the S phase of the cell cycle. Once your teacher has approved your model, have one member of your group document the model by photographing or drawing it.
  3. Now, repeat step 2 but show the cell at metaphase during mitosis.
  4. Finally, model the two daughter cells that will result from mitosis. Again, have one member of your group document the model.
  5. Repeat steps 2–5 for both meiosis I and meiosis II. Remember that you should have four daughter cells at the end of meiosis II. Also remember to ask your teacher for approval and document your model before moving on to the next phase of meiosis.
  6. Exchange/ copy all of the drawings or photographs that your group took of your models. As a group or individually (as directed by your teacher) create a report to turn in that labels and explain each picture of your model.
- An organism's ploidy count is the total number of chromosome sets contained in each body cell. Most organisms have a ploidy level of 2, meaning that they have two sets of chromosomes due to presence of homologous pairs. However, some plants are multiploid, meaning they can have ploidy levels greater than 2. The table shows possible multiploid levels of some common crop plants.

Common name	Multiploid chromosome count	Normal chromosome count
Bananas	33	11
Potatoes	48	12
Wheat	42	7
Sugar cane	80	10

Analyze the data with a partner of in a group as directed by your teacher. On a separate sheet of paper, answer the following questions.

a. How does the multiploid count of the crop plants relate to their normal chromosome count?

b. Explain the basis for the relationship you described in part a, in terms of what occurs to chromosomes during replication and meiosis.

c. Give one additional example of a possible multiploid chromosome count for each species in the table above.

Exercise 10.1

A. A comparison of the relative time intervals of mitotic stages can be made by completing the task described. In evaluating each time interval, the problem suggests that you assume that the length of time to complete one cell cycle is 24 hours. How can that assumption be tested?

Suppose that you have a growth chamber in which roots of a newly germinated plant can be examined visually with a lens that provides a magnification from which lengths can be determined with a precision of ± 0.05 mm. The field of view can be rotated so that measurements can be made of both the length and diameter of the growing tip. A large number of growing roots can be studied. Tips can be sampled, sectioned, and examined microscopically with a 25× magnification so that estimates of the diameter and length of cells can be made.

Cells in the growing tip of the root rapidly undergo mitosis, just as the whitefish blastula described in Figure 10.10. With increasing distance from the growing tip, the rate at which mitosis occurs slows until tissue is reached in which the initiation of the cell cycle is delayed.

A. **Describe** a sequence of measurements that could be used to test the assumption that the cell cycle, once started, has a total time interval of 24 hours. Hint: Rather than counting cells, it might be useful to measure the length of the root tip and the average length of a cell.

B. Using the data obtained from your measurements described in part A, how can the rate of cell division be calculated?

An experiment that is perhaps similar to one you have proposed was conducted previously (Beemster and Baxter, 1998), and the results are shown in the table.

Distance (mm)	Per hour
0	0.035 ± 0.01
0.1	0.047 ± 0.005
0.2	0.044 ± 0.01
0.3	0.039 ± 0.01
0.4	0.042 ± 0.01
0.5	0.031 ± 0.005

Table 10.1

C. Using these data, **estimate** the length of time of the cell cycle, including an estimate of precision by calculating the standard deviation.

Growth factors are signals that initiate cell division in eukaryotes. (The data in the table above show that cells in the plant root less than a mm from the root tip are showing a reduction of growth rate.) The interaction of two plant hormones, auxin and brassinosteroids, have been shown [Chaiwanon and Wang, *Cell*, 164(6), 1257, 2016] to regulate cell division in root tips. Auxin concentrations are higher near the root tip and decrease with distance from the tip. Brassinosteroids decrease in concentration near the root tip. Auxin is actively transported between cells, whereas brassinosteroids have limited transport between cells.

D. Based on these data and the observed distribution of brassinosteroids and auxin in the growing root, **predict** a mechanism for their interaction and **justify the claim** that brassinosteroid synthesis is negatively regulated by auxin transported to the cell, and that auxin is positively regulated and amplified.

Think About It

Chemotherapy drugs such as vincristine and colchicines disrupt mitosis by binding to tubulin (the subunit of microtubules) and interfering with microtubule assembly and disassembly. What mitotic structure is targeted by these drugs, and what effect would this have on cell division?

G_0 Phase

Not all cells adhere to the classic cell cycle pattern in which a newly formed daughter cell immediately enters the preparatory phases of interphase, closely followed by the mitotic phase. Cells in **G_0 phase** are not actively preparing to divide. The cell is in a **quiescent** (inactive) stage that occurs when cells exit the cell cycle. Some cells enter G_0 temporarily until an external signal triggers the onset of G_1. Other cells that never or rarely divide, such as mature cardiac muscle and nerve cells, remain in G_0 permanently.

Determine the Time Spent in Cell Cycle Stages

Problem: How long does a cell spend in interphase compared to each stage of mitosis?

Background: A prepared microscope slide of blastula cross-sections will show cells arrested in various stages of the cell cycle. It is not visually possible to separate the stages of interphase from each other, but the mitotic stages are readily identifiable. If 100 cells are examined, the number of cells in each identifiable cell cycle stage will give an estimate of the time it takes for the cell to complete that stage.

Problem Statement: Given the events included in all of interphase and those that take place in each stage of mitosis, estimate the length of each stage based on a 24-hour cell cycle. Before proceeding, state your hypothesis.

Test your hypothesis: Test your hypothesis by doing the following:

1. Place a fixed and stained microscope slide of whitefish blastula cross-sections under the scanning objective of a light microscope.
2. Locate and focus on one of the sections using the scanning objective of your microscope. Notice that the section is a circle composed of dozens of closely packed individual cells.
3. Switch to the low-power objective and refocus. With this objective, individual cells are visible.
4. Switch to the high-power objective and slowly move the slide left to right, and up and down to view all the cells in the section (Figure 10.10). As you scan, you will notice that most of the cells are not undergoing mitosis but are in the interphase period of the cell cycle.

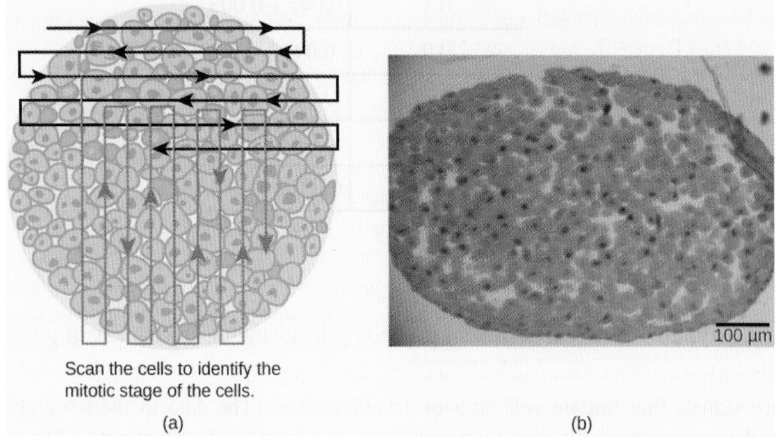

Figure 10.10 Slowly scan whitefish blastula cells with the high-power objective as illustrated in image (a) to identify their mitotic stage. (b) A microscopic image of the scanned cells is shown. (credit "micrograph": modification of work by Linda Flora; scale-bar data from Matt Russell)

5. Practice identifying the various stages of the cell cycle, using the drawings of the stages as a guide (Figure 10.7).
6. Once you are confident about your identification, begin to record the stage of each cell you encounter as you scan left to right, and top to bottom across the blastula section.
7. Keep a tally of your observations and stop when you reach 100 cells identified.
8. The larger the sample size (total number of cells counted), the more accurate the results. If possible, gather and record group data prior to calculating percentages and making estimates.

Record your observations: Make a table similar to Table 10.2 in which you record your observations.

Results of Cell Stage Identification

Phase or Stage	Individual Totals	Group Totals	Percent
Interphase			
Prophase			

Results of Cell Stage Identification

Phase or Stage	Individual Totals	Group Totals	Percent
Metaphase			
Anaphase			
Telophase			
Cytokinesis			
Totals	100	100	100 percent

Table 10.2

Analyze your data/report your results: To find the length of time whitefish blastula cells spend in each stage, multiply the percent (recorded as a decimal) by 24 hours. Make a table similar to Table 10.3 to illustrate your data.

Estimate of Cell Stage Length

Phase or Stage	Percent (as Decimal)	Time in Hours
Interphase		
Prophase		
Metaphase		
Anaphase		
Telophase		
Cytokinesis		

Table 10.3

10.3 | Control of the Cell Cycle

In this section, you will explore the following questions:

- What are examples of internal and external mechanisms that control the cell cycle?
- What molecules are involved in controlling the cell cycle through positive and negative regulation?

Connection for AP® Courses

Each step of the cell cycle is closely monitored by external signals and internal controls called checkpoints. There are three major checkpoints in the cell cycle: one near the end of G_1, a second at the G_2/M transition, and the third during metaphase. Growth factor proteins arriving at the dividing cell's plasma membrane can trigger the cell to begin dividing. Cyclins and cyclin-dependent kinases (Cdks) are internal molecular signals that regulate cell transitions through the various checkpoints. Passage through the G_1 checkpoint makes sure that the cell is ready for DNA replication in the S stage of interphase; passage through the G_2 checkpoint triggers the separation of chromatids during mitosis. Positive regulator molecules like the cyclins and Cdks allow the cell cycle to advance to the next stage; negative regulator molecules, such as tumor suppressor proteins, monitor cellular conditions and can halt the cycle until specific requirements are met. Errors in the regulation of the cell cycle can cause cancer, which is characterized by uncontrolled cell division.

Information presented and the examples highlighted in the section support concepts and Learning Objectives outlined in Big Idea 3 of the AP® Biology Curriculum Framework, as shown in the tables. The Learning Objectives listed in the Curriculum Framework provide a transparent foundation for the AP® Biology course, an inquiry-based laboratory experience, instructional activities, and AP® exam questions. A Learning Objective merges required content with one or more of the seven Science Practices.

Big Idea 3	Living systems store, retrieve, transmit and respond to information essential to life processes.
Enduring Understanding 3.A	Heritable information provides for continuity of life.
Essential Knowledge	**3.A.2** In eukaryotes, heritable information is passed to the next generation via processes that include the cell cycle and mitosis or meiosis plus fertilization.
Science Practice	**6.4** The student can make claims and predictions about natural phenomena based on scientific theories and models.
Learning Objective	**3.7** The student can make predictions about natural phenomena occurring during the cell cycle.
Essential Knowledge	**3.A.2** In eukaryotes, heritable information is passed to the next generation via processes that include the cell cycle and mitosis or meiosis plus fertilization.
Science Practice	**1.2** The student can describe representations and models of natural or man-made phenomena and systems in the domain.
Learning Objective	**3.8** The student can describe the events that occur in the cell cycle.

The length of the cell cycle is highly variable, even within the cells of a single organism. In humans, the frequency of cell turnover ranges from a few hours in early embryonic development, to an average of two to five days for epithelial cells, and to an entire human lifetime spent in G_0 by specialized cells, such as cortical neurons or cardiac muscle cells. There is also variation in the time that a cell spends in each phase of the cell cycle. When fast-dividing mammalian cells are grown in culture (outside the body under optimal growing conditions), the length of the cycle is about 24 hours. In rapidly dividing human cells with a 24-hour cell cycle, the G_1 phase lasts approximately nine hours, the S phase lasts 10 hours, the G_2 phase lasts about four and one-half hours, and the M phase lasts approximately one-half hour. In early embryos of fruit flies, the cell cycle is completed in about eight minutes. The timing of events in the cell cycle is controlled by mechanisms that are both internal and external to the cell.

Regulation of the Cell Cycle by External Events

Both the initiation and inhibition of cell division are triggered by events external to the cell when it is about to begin the replication process. An event may be as simple as the death of a nearby cell or as sweeping as the release of growth-promoting hormones, such as human growth hormone (HGH). A lack of HGH can inhibit cell division, resulting in dwarfism, whereas too much HGH can result in gigantism. Crowding of cells can also inhibit cell division. Another factor that can initiate cell division is the size of the cell; as a cell grows, it becomes inefficient due to its decreasing surface-to-volume ratio. The solution to this problem is to divide.

Whatever the source of the message, the cell receives the signal, and a series of events within the cell allows it to proceed into interphase. Moving forward from this initiation point, every parameter required during each cell cycle phase must be met or the cycle cannot progress.

Regulation at Internal Checkpoints

It is essential that the daughter cells produced be exact duplicates of the parent cell. Mistakes in the duplication or distribution of the chromosomes lead to mutations that may be passed forward to every new cell produced from an abnormal cell. To prevent a compromised cell from continuing to divide, there are internal control mechanisms that operate at three main **cell cycle checkpoints**. A checkpoint is one of several points in the eukaryotic cell cycle at which the progression of a cell to the next stage in the cycle can be halted until conditions are favorable. These checkpoints occur near the end of G_1, at the G_2/M transition, and during metaphase (**Figure 10.11**).

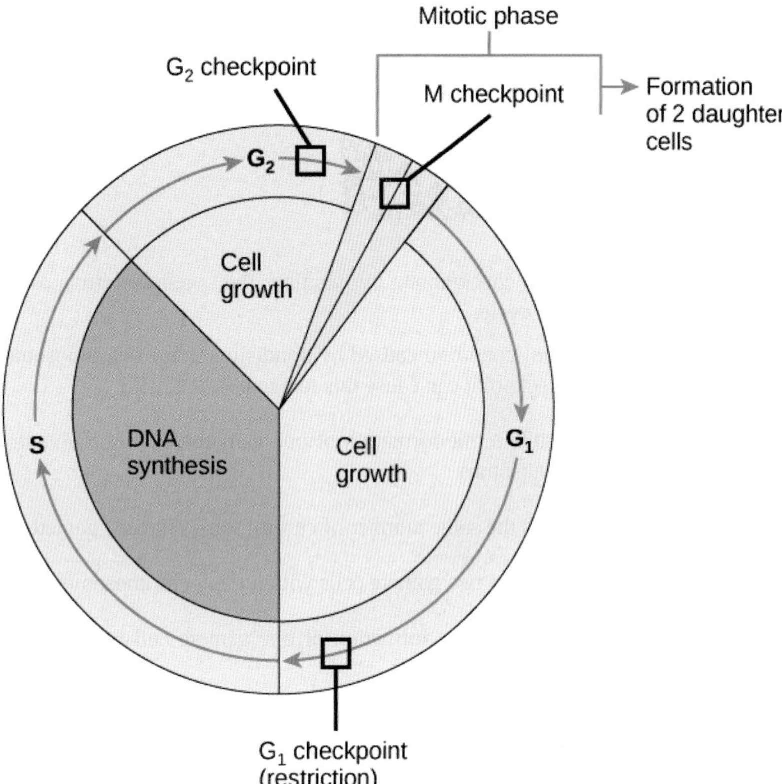

Figure 10.11 The cell cycle is controlled at three checkpoints. The integrity of the DNA is assessed at the G_1 checkpoint. Proper chromosome duplication is assessed at the G_2 checkpoint. Attachment of each kinetochore to a spindle fiber is assessed at the M checkpoint.

The G_1 Checkpoint

The G_1 checkpoint determines whether all conditions are favorable for cell division to proceed. The G_1 checkpoint, also called the restriction point (in yeast), is a point at which the cell commits to the cell division process. External influences, such as growth factors, play a large role in carrying the cell past the G_1 checkpoint. In addition to adequate reserves and cell size, there is a check for genomic DNA damage at the G_1 checkpoint. A cell that does not meet all the requirements will not be allowed to progress into the S phase. The cell can halt the cycle and attempt to remedy the problematic condition, or the cell can advance into G_0 and await further signals when conditions improve.

The G_2 Checkpoint

The G_2 checkpoint bars entry into the mitotic phase if certain conditions are not met. As at the G_1 checkpoint, cell size and protein reserves are assessed. However, the most important role of the G_2 checkpoint is to ensure that all of the chromosomes have been replicated and that the replicated DNA is not damaged. If the checkpoint mechanisms detect problems with the DNA, the cell cycle is halted, and the cell attempts to either complete DNA replication or repair the damaged DNA.

The M Checkpoint

The M checkpoint occurs near the end of the metaphase stage of karyokinesis. The M checkpoint is also known as the spindle checkpoint, because it determines whether all the sister chromatids are correctly attached to the spindle microtubules. Because the separation of the sister chromatids during anaphase is an irreversible step, the cycle will not proceed until the kinetochores of each pair of sister chromatids are firmly anchored to at least two spindle fibers arising from opposite poles of the cell.

Watch what occurs at the G_1, G_2, and M checkpoints by visiting this website (http://openstaxcollege.org/l/cell_checkpnts) to see an animation of the cell cycle.

Down Syndrome is a genetic, developmental condition caused by nondisjunction of chromosome 21 during meiosis. Explain how a problem with the spindle checkpoint can cause this to occur in the cell.

a. Failure in spindle checkpoint results in the formation of one gamete cell with two extra chromosomes and another gamete cell lacking chromosomes.

b. Failure in spindle checkpoint yields the same number of chromosomes in each gamete cell.

c. Failure in spindle checkpoint will form two gamete cells without any chromosomes.

d. Failure in spindle checkpoint results in the formation of one gamete cell with an extra chromosome and another gamete cell lacking a chromosome.

Regulator Molecules of the Cell Cycle

In addition to the internally controlled checkpoints, there are two groups of intracellular molecules that regulate the cell cycle. These regulatory molecules either promote progress of the cell to the next phase (positive regulation) or halt the cycle (negative regulation). Regulator molecules may act individually, or they can influence the activity or production of other regulatory proteins. Therefore, the failure of a single regulator may have almost no effect on the cell cycle, especially if more than one mechanism controls the same event. Conversely, the effect of a deficient or non-functioning regulator can be wide-ranging and possibly fatal to the cell if multiple processes are affected.

Positive Regulation of the Cell Cycle

Two groups of proteins, called **cyclins** and **cyclin-dependent kinases** (Cdks), are responsible for the progress of the cell through the various checkpoints. The levels of the four cyclin proteins fluctuate throughout the cell cycle in a predictable pattern (Figure 10.12). Increases in the concentration of cyclin proteins are triggered by both external and internal signals. After the cell moves to the next stage of the cell cycle, the cyclins that were active in the previous stage are degraded.

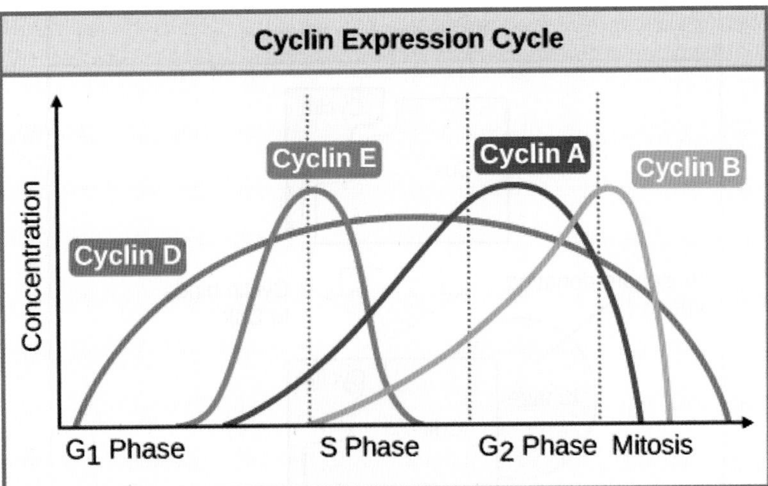

Figure 10.12 The concentrations of cyclin proteins change throughout the cell cycle. There is a direct correlation between cyclin accumulation and the three major cell cycle checkpoints. Also note the sharp decline of cyclin levels following each checkpoint (the transition between phases of the cell cycle), as cyclin is degraded by cytoplasmic enzymes. (credit: modification of work by "WikiMiMa"/Wikimedia Commons)

Cyclins regulate the cell cycle only when they are tightly bound to Cdks. To be fully active, the Cdk/cyclin complex must also be phosphorylated in specific locations. Like all kinases, Cdks are enzymes (kinases) that phosphorylate other proteins. Phosphorylation activates the protein by changing its shape. The proteins phosphorylated by Cdks are involved in advancing the cell to the next phase. (**Figure 10.13**). The levels of Cdk proteins are relatively stable throughout the cell cycle; however, the concentrations of cyclin fluctuate and determine when Cdk/cyclin complexes form. The different cyclins and Cdks bind at specific points in the cell cycle and thus regulate different checkpoints.

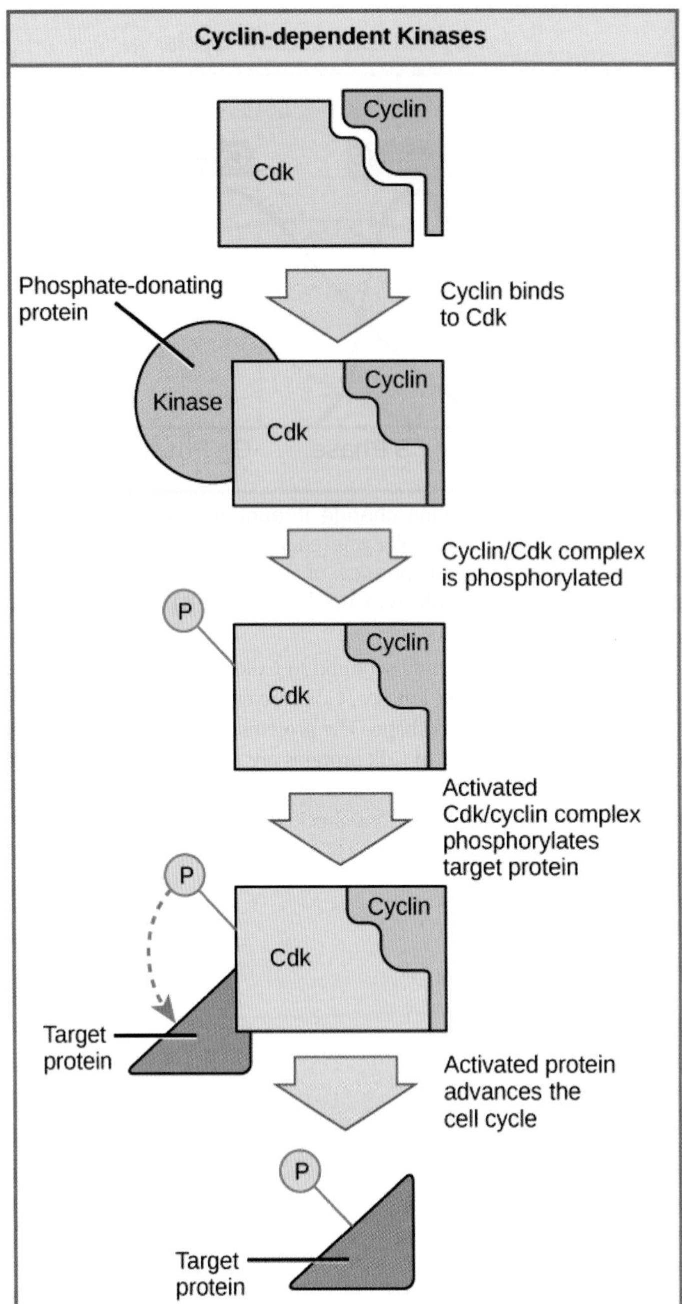

Figure 10.13 Cyclin-dependent kinases (Cdks) are protein kinases that, when fully activated, can phosphorylate and thus activate other proteins that advance the cell cycle past a checkpoint. To become fully activated, a Cdk must bind to a cyclin protein and then be phosphorylated by another kinase.

Since the cyclic fluctuations of cyclin levels are based on the timing of the cell cycle and not on specific events, regulation of the cell cycle usually occurs by either the Cdk molecules alone or the Cdk/cyclin complexes. Without a specific concentration of fully activated cyclin/Cdk complexes, the cell cycle cannot proceed through the checkpoints.

Although the cyclins are the main regulatory molecules that determine the forward momentum of the cell cycle, there are several other mechanisms that fine-tune the progress of the cycle with negative, rather than positive, effects. These mechanisms essentially block the progression of the cell cycle until problematic conditions are resolved. Molecules that prevent the full activation of Cdks are called Cdk inhibitors. Many of these inhibitor molecules directly or indirectly monitor a particular cell cycle event. The block placed on Cdks by inhibitor molecules will not be removed until the specific event that the inhibitor monitors is completed.

Negative Regulation of the Cell Cycle

The second group of cell cycle regulatory molecules are negative regulators. Negative regulators halt the cell cycle. Remember that in positive regulation, active molecules cause the cycle to progress.

The best understood negative regulatory molecules are **retinoblastoma protein (Rb)**, **p53**, and **p21**. Retinoblastoma proteins are a group of tumor-suppressor proteins common in many cells. The 53 and 21 designations refer to the functional molecular masses of the proteins (p) in kilodaltons. Much of what is known about cell cycle regulation comes from research conducted with cells that have lost regulatory control. All three of these regulatory proteins were discovered to be damaged or non-functional in cells that had begun to replicate uncontrollably (became cancerous). In each case, the main cause of the unchecked progress through the cell cycle was a faulty copy of the regulatory protein.

Rb, p53, and p21 act primarily at the G_1 checkpoint. p53 is a multi-functional protein that has a major impact on the commitment of a cell to division because it acts when there is damaged DNA in cells that are undergoing the preparatory processes during G_1. If damaged DNA is detected, p53 halts the cell cycle and recruits enzymes to repair the DNA. If the DNA cannot be repaired, p53 can trigger apoptosis, or cell death, to prevent the duplication of damaged chromosomes. As p53 levels rise, the production of p21 is triggered. p21 enforces the halt in the cycle dictated by p53 by binding to and inhibiting the activity of the Cdk/cyclin complexes. As a cell is exposed to more stress, higher levels of p53 and p21 accumulate, making it less likely that the cell will move into the S phase.

Rb exerts its regulatory influence on other positive regulator proteins. Chiefly, Rb monitors cell size. In the active, dephosphorylated state, Rb binds to proteins called transcription factors, most commonly, E2F (Figure 10.14). Transcription factors "turn on" specific genes, allowing the production of proteins encoded by that gene. When Rb is bound to E2F, production of proteins necessary for the G_1/S transition is blocked. As the cell increases in size, Rb is slowly phosphorylated until it becomes inactivated. Rb releases E2F, which can now turn on the gene that produces the transition protein, and this particular block is removed. For the cell to move past each of the checkpoints, all positive regulators must be "turned on," and all negative regulators must be "turned off."

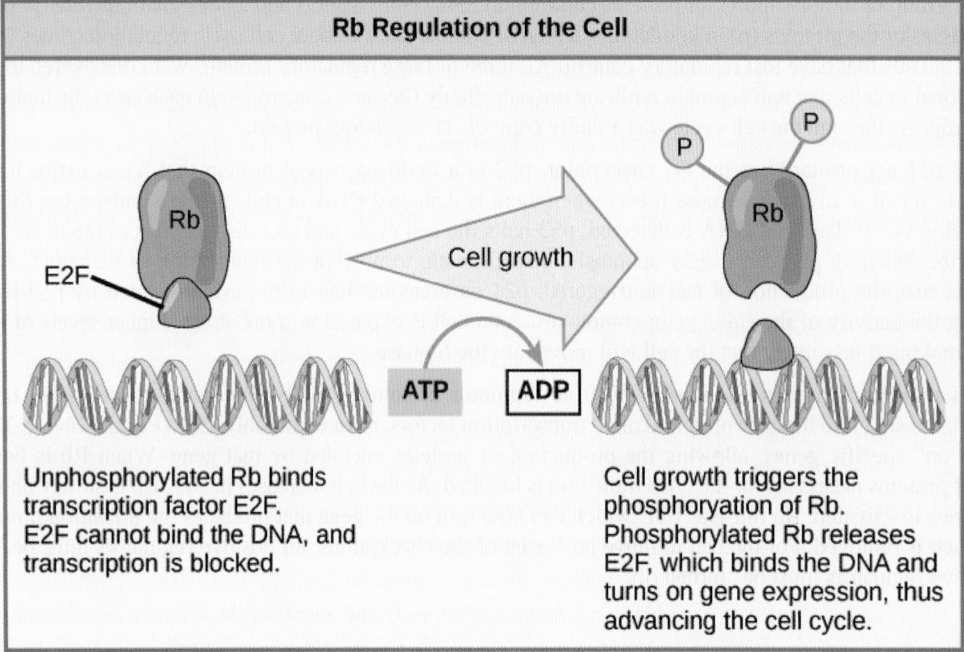

Figure 10.14 Rb halts the cell cycle and releases its hold in response to cell growth.

Rb and other proteins that negatively regulate the cell cycle are sometimes called tumor supressors. Why do you think the name tumor suppressor might be appropriate for these proteins?

a. They inhibit cell division.

b. They enhance the rate of cell division.

c. They start the cell cycle, thereby suppressing tumor formation.

d. These proteins, when phosphorylated, allow the cell cycle to proceed.

science practices CONNECTION for AP® Courses

- Rb is a negative regulator that blocks the cell cycle at the G_1 checkpoint until the cell achieves a requisite size. What is the most likely mechanism that Rb employs to halt the cell cycle?
- A cell has a mutation that results in the production of an abnormal cyclin-dependent kinase at the G_2/M checkpoint. What is a likely consequence of the mutation on the cell cycle?

10.4 | Cancer and the Cell Cycle

In this section, you will explore the following question:

- What causes uncontrolled cell growth, and why does it often cause cancer?

Connection for AP® Courses

Cancer results from unchecked cell division caused by a breakdown of the mechanisms that regulate the cell cycle. The loss of control begins with a change in the DNA sequence of a gene that codes for one of the regulatory molecules. Faulty instructions lead to a protein that does not function as it should. One culprit that has been identified is the p53 protein (coded for by the *p53* gene), a major regulator at the G_1 checkpoint. Normally, p53 proteins monitor DNA. If they find cells with damaged DNA, p53 will trigger repair mechanisms or destroy the cells, thus suppressing the formation of a tumor. However, mutations in *p53* can result in abnormal p53 proteins that fail to stop cell division if the cell's DNA is damaged. This results in an increased number of mutations, leading to abnormal daughter cells. Eventually, all checkpoints in the cell become nonfunctional, and the abnormal cells can crowd out normal cells.

Information presented and the examples highlighted in the section support concepts and Learning Objectives outlined in Big Idea 3 of the AP® Biology Curriculum Framework, as shown in the table. The Learning Objectives listed in the Curriculum Framework provide a transparent foundation for the AP® Biology course, an inquiry-based laboratory experience, instructional activities, and AP® exam questions. A Learning Objective merges required content with one or more of the seven Science Practices.

Big Idea 3	Living systems store, retrieve, transmit and respond to information essential to life processes.
Enduring Understanding 3.A	Heritable information provides for continuity of life.
Essential Knowledge	**3.A.2** In eukaryotes, heritable information is passed to the next generation via processes that include the cell cycle and mitosis or meiosis plus fertilization.
Science Practice	**6.4** The student can make claims and predictions about natural phenomena based on scientific theories and models.
Learning Objective	**3.7** The student can make predictions about natural phenomena occurring during the cell cycle.

The Science Practice Challenge Questions contain additional test questions for this section that will help you prepare for the AP exam. These questions address the following standards:
[APLO 2.32][APLO 2.34][APLO 3.6][APLO 3.7][APLO 3.8][APLO 4.6][APLO 4.14][APLO 4.22]

Cancer comprises many different diseases caused by a common mechanism: uncontrolled cell growth. Despite the redundancy and overlapping levels of cell cycle control, errors do occur. One of the critical processes monitored by the cell cycle checkpoint surveillance mechanism is the proper replication of DNA during the S phase. Even when all of the cell cycle controls are fully functional, a small percentage of replication errors (mutations) will be passed on to the daughter cells. If changes to the DNA nucleotide sequence occur within a coding portion of a gene and are not corrected, a gene mutation results. All cancers start when a gene mutation gives rise to a faulty protein that plays a key role in cell reproduction. The change in the cell that results from the malformed protein may be minor: perhaps a slight delay in the binding of Cdk to cyclin or an Rb protein that detaches from its target DNA while still phosphorylated. Even minor mistakes, however, may allow subsequent mistakes to occur more readily. Over and over, small uncorrected errors are passed from the parent cell to the daughter cells and amplified as each generation produces more non-functional proteins from uncorrected DNA damage. Eventually, the pace of the cell cycle speeds up as the effectiveness of the control and repair mechanisms decreases. Uncontrolled growth of the mutated cells outpaces the growth of normal cells in the area, and a tumor ("-oma") can result.

Proto-oncogenes

The genes that code for the positive cell cycle regulators are called **proto-oncogenes**. Proto-oncogenes are normal genes that, when mutated in certain ways, become **oncogenes**, genes that cause a cell to become cancerous. Consider what might happen to the cell cycle in a cell with a recently acquired oncogene. In most instances, the alteration of the DNA sequence will result in a less functional (or non-functional) protein. The result is detrimental to the cell and will likely prevent the cell from completing the cell cycle; however, the organism is not harmed because the mutation will not be carried forward. If a cell cannot reproduce, the mutation is not propagated and the damage is minimal. Occasionally, however, a gene mutation causes a change that increases the activity of a positive regulator. For example, a mutation that allows Cdk to be activated without being partnered with cyclin could push the cell cycle past a checkpoint before all of the required conditions are met. If the resulting daughter cells are too damaged to undergo further cell divisions, the mutation would not be propagated and no harm would come to the organism. However, if the atypical daughter cells are able to undergo further cell divisions, subsequent generations of cells will probably accumulate even more mutations, some possibly in additional genes that regulate the cell cycle.

The Cdk gene in the above example is only one of many genes that are considered proto-oncogenes. In addition to the cell cycle regulatory proteins, any protein that influences the cycle can be altered in such a way as to override cell cycle checkpoints. An oncogene is any gene that, when altered, leads to an increase in the rate of cell cycle progression.

Tumor Suppressor Genes

Like proto-oncogenes, many of the negative cell cycle regulatory proteins were discovered in cells that had become cancerous. **Tumor suppressor genes** are segments of DNA that code for negative regulator proteins, the type of regulators that, when activated, can prevent the cell from undergoing uncontrolled division. The collective function of the best-understood tumor suppressor gene proteins, Rb, p53, and p21, is to put up a roadblock to cell cycle progression until certain events are completed. A cell that carries a mutated form of a negative regulator might not be able to halt the cell cycle if there is a problem. Tumor suppressors are similar to brakes in a vehicle: Malfunctioning brakes can contribute to a car crash.

Mutated p53 genes have been identified in more than one-half of all human tumor cells. This discovery is not surprising in light of the multiple roles that the p53 protein plays at the G_1 checkpoint. A cell with a faulty p53 may fail to detect errors present in the genomic DNA (Figure 10.15). Even if a partially functional p53 does identify the mutations, it may no longer be able to signal the necessary DNA repair enzymes. Either way, damaged DNA will remain uncorrected. At this point, a functional p53 will deem the cell unsalvageable and trigger programmed cell death (apoptosis). The damaged version of p53 found in cancer cells, however, cannot trigger apoptosis.

visual CONNECTION

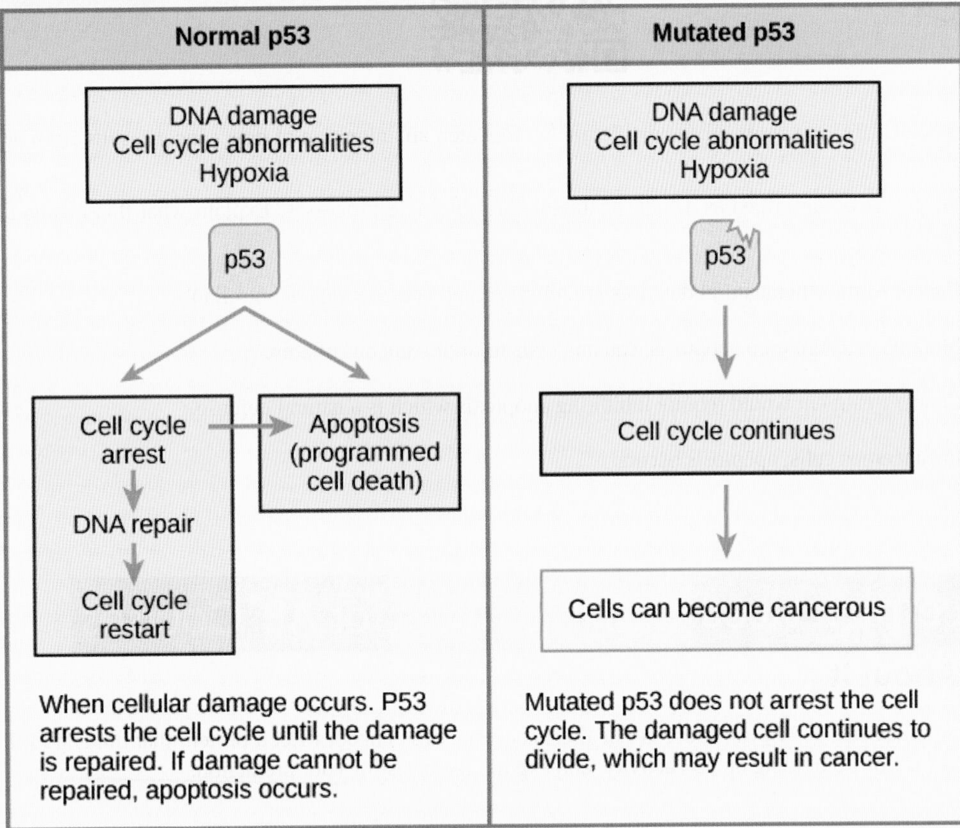

Figure 10.15 The role of normal p53 is to monitor DNA and the supply of oxygen (hypoxia is a condition of reduced oxygen supply). If damage is detected, p53 triggers repair mechanisms. If repairs are unsuccessful, p53 signals apoptosis. A cell with an abnormal p53 protein cannot repair damaged DNA and thus cannot signal apoptosis. Cells with abnormal p53 can become cancerous. (credit: modification of work by Thierry Soussi)

Human papillomavirus can cause cervical cancer. The virus encodes E6, a protein that binds p53. Based on this fact and what you know about p53, what effect do you think E6 binding has on p53 activity?

a. E6 activates p53
b. E6 inactivates p53
c. E6 mutates p53
d. E6 binding marks p53 for degradation

The loss of p53 function has other repercussions for the cell cycle. Mutated p53 might lose its ability to trigger p21 production. Without adequate levels of p21, there is no effective block on Cdk activation. Essentially, without a fully functional p53, the G_1 checkpoint is severely compromised and the cell proceeds directly from G_1 to S regardless of internal and external conditions. At the completion of this shortened cell cycle, two daughter cells are produced that have inherited the mutated p53 gene. Given the non-optimal conditions under which the parent cell reproduced, it is likely that the daughter cells will have acquired other mutations in addition to the faulty tumor suppressor gene. Cells such as these daughter cells quickly accumulate both oncogenes and non-functional tumor suppressor genes. Again, the result is tumor growth.

Go to this website (http://openstaxcollege.org/l/cancer) to watch an animation of how cancer results from errors in the cell cycle.

Treating cancer can be described as a fight against natural biologic processes. Explain what this means in terms of tumor formation.

a. Cancer forms when natural defenses are inhibited and cells divide uncontrollably.

b. Mutated cells undergo apoptosis, causing cells to divide uncontrollably.

c. Cancer treatment would require inhibiting apoptosis which is a natural defense.

d. In cancerous cells, apoptosis occurs.

Think About It

Human papillomavirus (HPV) can cause cervical cancer. The virus encodes E6, a protein that binds p53. Predict the most likely effect of E6 binding on p53 activity, and explain the basis for your prediction.

10.5 | Prokaryotic Cell Division

In this section, you will explore the following question:

- How does the process of binary fission in prokaryotes differ from cell division in eukaryotes?

Prokaryotes, such as bacteria, propagate by binary fission. For unicellular organisms, cell division is the only method to produce new individuals. In both prokaryotic and eukaryotic cells, the outcome of cell reproduction is a pair of daughter cells that are genetically identical to the parent cell. In unicellular organisms, daughter cells are individuals.

To achieve the outcome of cloned offspring, certain steps are essential. The genomic DNA must be replicated and then allocated into the daughter cells; the cytoplasmic contents must also be divided to give both new cells the machinery to sustain life. In bacterial cells, the genome consists of a single, circular DNA chromosome; therefore, the process of cell division is simplified. Karyokinesis is unnecessary because there is no nucleus and thus no need to direct one copy of the multiple chromosomes into each daughter cell. This type of cell division is called **binary (prokaryotic) fission**.

Binary Fission

Due to the relative simplicity of the prokaryotes, the cell division process, called binary fission, is a less complicated and much more rapid process than cell division in eukaryotes. The single, circular DNA chromosome of bacteria is not enclosed in a nucleus, but instead occupies a specific location, the nucleoid, within the cell (Figure 10.2). Although the DNA of the nucleoid is associated with proteins that aid in packaging the molecule into a compact size, there are no histone proteins and thus no nucleosomes in prokaryotes. The packing proteins of bacteria are, however, related to the cohesin and condensin proteins involved in the chromosome compaction of eukaryotes.

The bacterial chromosome is attached to the plasma membrane at about the midpoint of the cell. The starting point of replication, the **origin**, is close to the binding site of the chromosome to the plasma membrane (Figure 10.16). Replication of the DNA is bidirectional, moving away from the origin on both strands of the loop simultaneously. As the new double strands are formed, each origin point moves away from the cell wall attachment toward the opposite ends of the cell. As the cell elongates, the growing membrane aids in the transport of the chromosomes. After the chromosomes have cleared the midpoint of the elongated cell, cytoplasmic separation begins. The formation of a ring composed of repeating units of a protein called **FtsZ** directs the partition between the nucleoids. Formation of the FtsZ ring triggers the accumulation of other proteins that work together to recruit new membrane and cell wall materials to the site. A **septum** is formed between the nucleoids, extending gradually from the periphery toward the center of the cell. When the new cell walls are in place, the daughter cells separate.

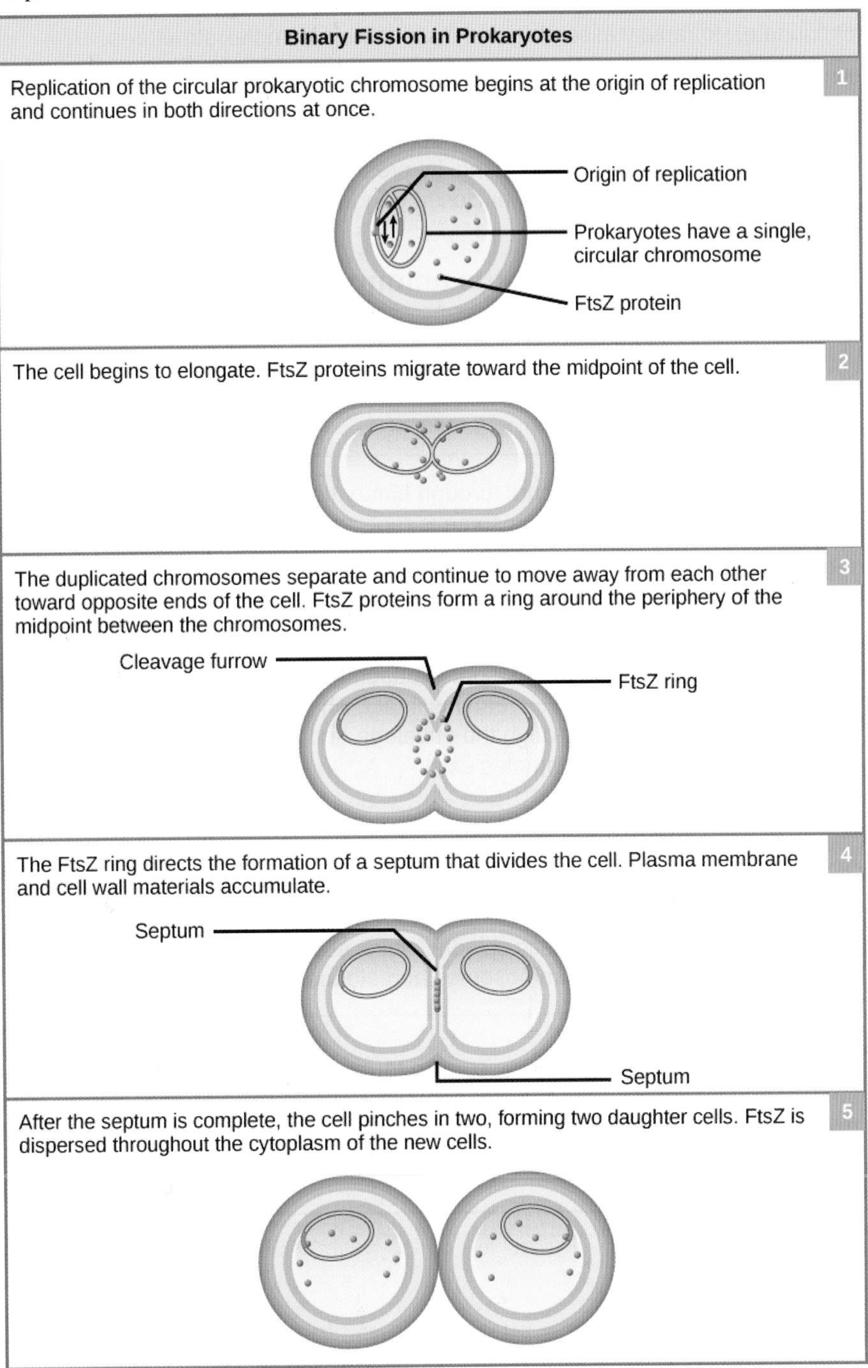

Figure 10.16 These images show the steps of binary fission in prokaryotes. (credit: modification of work by “Mcstrother”/Wikimedia Commons)

evolution CONNECTION

The precise timing and formation of the mitotic spindle is critical to the success of eukaryotic cell division. Prokaryotic cells, on the other hand, do not undergo karyokinesis and therefore have no need for a mitotic spindle. However, the FtsZ protein that plays such a vital role in prokaryotic cytokinesis is structurally and functionally very similar to tubulin, the building block of the microtubules that make up the mitotic spindle fibers that are necessary for eukaryotes. FtsZ proteins can form filaments, rings, and other three-dimensional structures that resemble the way tubulin forms microtubules, centrioles, and various cytoskeletal components. In addition, both FtsZ and tubulin employ the same energy source, GTP (guanosine triphosphate), to rapidly assemble and disassemble complex structures.

FtsZ and tubulin are homologous structures derived from common evolutionary origins. In this example, FtsZ is the ancestor protein to tubulin (a modern protein). While both proteins are found in extant organisms, tubulin function has evolved and diversified tremendously since evolving from its FtsZ prokaryotic origin. A survey of mitotic assembly components found in present-day unicellular eukaryotes reveals crucial intermediary steps to the complex membrane-enclosed genomes of multicellular eukaryotes (Table 10.4).

Cell Division Apparatus among Various Organisms

	Structure of genetic material	Division of nuclear material	Separation of daughter cells
Prokaryotes	There is no nucleus. The single, circular chromosome exists in a region of cytoplasm called the nucleoid.	Occurs through binary fission. As the chromosome is replicated, the two copies move to opposite ends of the cell by an unknown mechanism.	FtsZ proteins assemble into a ring that pinches the cell in two.
Some protists	Linear chromosomes exist in the nucleus.	Chromosomes attach to the nuclear envelope, which remains intact. The mitotic spindle passes through the envelope and elongates the cell. No centrioles exist.	Microfilaments form a cleavage furrow that pinches the cell in two.
Other protists	Linear chromosomes exist in the nucleus.	A mitotic spindle forms from the centrioles and passes through the nuclear membrane, which remains intact. Chromosomes attach to the mitotic spindle, which separates the chromosomes and elongates the cell.	Microfilaments form a cleavage furrow that pinches the cell in two.
Animal cells	Linear chromosomes exist in the nucleus.	A mitotic spindle forms from the centrosomes. The nuclear envelope dissolves. Chromosomes attach to the mitotic spindle, which separates the chromosomes and elongates the cell.	Microfilaments form a cleavage furrow that pinches the cell in two.

Table 10.4

FtsZ is a prokaryotic protein and tubulin is a eukaryotic protein. These two proteins share many structural and functional similarities and are believed to have evolved from the same ancestral protein. However, there are also some important differences between these proteins. In what way are these proteins different?

a. Tubulin proteins can rapidly disassemble, but FtsZ proteins cannot.

b. Tubulin proteins can form long filaments, but FtsZ proteins cannot.
c. Tubulin uses GTP as an energy source, but FtsZ does not.
d. Tubulin pulls chromosomes apart, but FtsZ does not.

KEY TERMS

anaphase stage of mitosis during which sister chromatids are separated from each other

binary fission prokaryotic cell division process

cell cycle ordered series of events involving cell growth and cell division that produces two new daughter cells

cell cycle checkpoint mechanism that monitors the preparedness of a eukaryotic cell to advance through the various cell cycle stages

cell plate structure formed during plant cell cytokinesis by Golgi vesicles, forming a temporary structure (phragmoplast) and fusing at the metaphase plate; ultimately leads to the formation of cell walls that separate the two daughter cells

centriole rod-like structure constructed of microtubules at the center of each animal cell centrosome

centromere region at which sister chromatids are bound together; a constricted area in condensed chromosomes

chromatid single DNA molecule of two strands of duplicated DNA and associated proteins held together at the centromere

cleavage furrow constriction formed by an actin ring during cytokinesis in animal cells that leads to cytoplasmic division

condensin proteins that help sister chromatids coil during prophase

cyclin one of a group of proteins that act in conjunction with cyclin-dependent kinases to help regulate the cell cycle by phosphorylating key proteins; the concentrations of cyclins fluctuate throughout the cell cycle

cyclin-dependent kinase one of a group of protein kinases that helps to regulate the cell cycle when bound to cyclin; it functions to phosphorylate other proteins that are either activated or inactivated by phosphorylation

cytokinesis division of the cytoplasm following mitosis that forms two daughter cells.

diploid cell, nucleus, or organism containing two sets of chromosomes ($2n$)

FtsZ tubulin-like protein component of the prokaryotic cytoskeleton that is important in prokaryotic cytokinesis (name origin: **F**ilamenting **t**emperature-**s**ensitive mutant **Z**)

G_0 phase distinct from the G_1 phase of interphase; a cell in G_0 is not preparing to divide

G_1 phase (also, first gap) first phase of interphase centered on cell growth during mitosis

G_2 phase (also, second gap) third phase of interphase during which the cell undergoes final preparations for mitosis

gamete haploid reproductive cell or sex cell (sperm, pollen grain, or egg)

gene physical and functional unit of heredity, a sequence of DNA that codes for a protein.

genome total genetic information of a cell or organism

haploid cell, nucleus, or organism containing one set of chromosomes (n)

histone one of several similar, highly conserved, low molecular weight, basic proteins found in the chromatin of all eukaryotic cells; associates with DNA to form nucleosomes

homologous chromosomes chromosomes of the same morphology with genes in the same location; diploid organisms have pairs of homologous chromosomes (homologs), with each homolog derived from a different parent

interphase period of the cell cycle leading up to mitosis; includes G_1, S, and G_2 phases (the interim period between two consecutive cell divisions

karyokinesis mitotic nuclear division

kinetochore protein structure associated with the centromere of each sister chromatid that attracts and binds spindle microtubules during prometaphase

locus position of a gene on a chromosome

metaphase stage of mitosis during which chromosomes are aligned at the metaphase plate

metaphase plate equatorial plane midway between the two poles of a cell where the chromosomes align during metaphase

mitosis (also, karyokinesis) period of the cell cycle during which the duplicated chromosomes are separated into identical nuclei; includes prophase, prometaphase, metaphase, anaphase, and telophase

mitotic phase period of the cell cycle during which duplicated chromosomes are distributed into two nuclei and cytoplasmic contents are divided; includes karyokinesis (mitosis) and cytokinesis

mitotic spindle apparatus composed of microtubules that orchestrates the movement of chromosomes during mitosis

nucleosome subunit of chromatin composed of a short length of DNA wrapped around a core of histone proteins

oncogene mutated version of a normal gene involved in the positive regulation of the cell cycle

origin (also, ORI) region of the prokaryotic chromosome where replication begins (origin of replication)

p21 cell cycle regulatory protein that inhibits the cell cycle; its levels are controlled by p53

p53 cell cycle regulatory protein that regulates cell growth and monitors DNA damage; it halts the progression of the cell cycle in cases of DNA damage and may induce apoptosis

prometaphase stage of mitosis during which the nuclear membrane breaks down and mitotic spindle fibers attach to kinetochores

prophase stage of mitosis during which chromosomes condense and the mitotic spindle begins to form

proto-oncogene normal gene that when mutated becomes an oncogene

quiescent refers to a cell that is performing normal cell functions and has not initiated preparations for cell division

retinoblastoma protein (Rb) regulatory molecule that exhibits negative effects on the cell cycle by interacting with a transcription factor (E2F)

S phase second, or synthesis, stage of interphase during which DNA replication occurs

septum structure formed in a bacterial cell as a precursor to the separation of the cell into two daughter cells

telophase stage of mitosis during which chromosomes arrive at opposite poles, decondense, and are surrounded by a new nuclear envelope

tumor suppressor gene segment of DNA that codes for regulator proteins that prevent the cell from undergoing uncontrolled division

CHAPTER SUMMARY

10.1 Cell Division

Prokaryotes have a single circular chromosome composed of double-stranded DNA, whereas eukaryotes have multiple, linear chromosomes composed of chromatin, all surrounded by a nuclear membrane. The 46 chromosomes of human somatic cells are composed of 22 pairs of autosomes (matched pairs) and a pair of sex chromosomes, which may or may not be matched. This is the $2n$ or diploid state. Human gametes have 23 chromosomes representing one complete set of chromosomes; a set of chromosomes is complete with either one of the sex chromosomes. This is the n or haploid state. Genes are segments of DNA that code for a specific protein. An organism's traits are determined by the genes inherited from each parent. Duplicated chromosomes are composed of two sister chromatids. Chromosomes are compacted using a variety of mechanisms during certain stages of the cell cycle. Several classes of protein are involved in the organization and packing of the chromosomal DNA into a highly condensed structure. The condensing complex compacts chromosomes, and the resulting condensed structure is necessary for chromosomal segregation during mitosis.

10.2 The Cell Cycle

The cell cycle is an orderly sequence of events. Cells on the path to cell division proceed through a series of precisely timed and carefully regulated stages. In eukaryotes, the cell cycle consists of a long preparatory period, called interphase. Interphase is divided into G_1, S, and G_2 phases. The mitotic phase begins with karyokinesis (mitosis), which consists of five stages: prophase, prometaphase, metaphase, anaphase, and telophase. The final stage of the mitotic phase is cytokinesis, during which the cytoplasmic components of the daughter cells are separated either by an actin ring (animal cells) or by cell plate formation (plant cells).

10.3 Control of the Cell Cycle

Each step of the cell cycle is monitored by internal controls called checkpoints. There are three major checkpoints in the cell cycle: one near the end of G_1, a second at the G_2/M transition, and the third during metaphase. Positive regulator molecules allow the cell cycle to advance to the next stage. Negative regulator molecules monitor cellular conditions and can halt the cycle until specific requirements are met.

10.4 Cancer and the Cell Cycle

Cancer is the result of unchecked cell division caused by a breakdown of the mechanisms that regulate the cell cycle. The loss of control begins with a change in the DNA sequence of a gene that codes for one of the regulatory molecules. Faulty instructions lead to a protein that does not function as it should. Any disruption of the monitoring system can allow other mistakes to be passed on to the daughter cells. Each successive cell division will give rise to daughter cells with even more accumulated damage. Eventually, all checkpoints become nonfunctional, and rapidly reproducing cells crowd out normal cells, resulting in a tumor or leukemia (blood cancer).

10.5 Prokaryotic Cell Division

In both prokaryotic and eukaryotic cell division, the genomic DNA is replicated and then each copy is allocated into a daughter cell. In addition, the cytoplasmic contents are divided evenly and distributed to the new cells. However, there are many differences between prokaryotic and eukaryotic cell division. Bacteria have a single, circular DNA chromosome but no nucleus. Therefore, mitosis is not necessary in bacterial cell division. Bacterial cytokinesis is directed by a ring composed of a protein called FtsZ. Ingrowth of membrane and cell wall material from the periphery of the cells results in the formation of a septum that eventually constructs the separate cell walls of the daughter cells.

REVIEW QUESTIONS

1. A diploid cell has how many times the number of chromosomes as a haploid cell?

a. four times
b. half
c. one-fourth
d. twice

2. The first level of DNA organization in a eukaryotic cell is maintained by which molecule?

a. cohesion
b. condensin
c. chromatin
d. histone

3. What inherited feature, in specific combinations, determines an organism's traits?

a. cell membranes
b. genes
c. proteins
d. RNA

4. What are identical copies of chromatin held together by cohesin at the centromere called?

a. histones
b. nucleosomes
c. chromatin
d. sister chromatids

5. Chromosomes are duplicated during what stage of the cell cycle?

a. G_1 phase
b. prophase
c. pro-metaphase
d. S-phase

6. Which of the following events does not occur during some stages of interphase?

a. DNA duplication
b. increase in cell size
c. organelle duplication
d. separation of sister chromatids

7. Attachment of the mitotic spindle fibers to the kinetochores is a characteristic of which stage of mitosis?

a. anaphase
b. prophase
c. prometaphase
d. metaphase

8. The fusing of Golgi vesicles at the metaphase plate of dividing plant cells forms what structure?

a. actin ring
b. cell plate
c. cleavage furrow
d. mitotic spindle

9. What would be the outcome of blocking S-phase of interphase?

a. The cell would enter karyokinesis.
b. DNA replication would not occur.
c. Centrosomes would be duplicated.
d. The cytoskeleton would be dismantled.

10. At which of the cell cycle checkpoints do external forces have the greatest influence?

a. G_1 checkpoint
b. G_2 checkpoint
c. M checkpoint
d. G_0 checkpoint

11. If the M checkpoint is not cleared, what stage of mitosis will be blocked?

a. prophase
b. prometaphase
c. metaphase
d. anaphase

12. Which protein is a positive regulator that phosphorylates other proteins when activated?

a. p53
b. Retinoblastoma protein (Rb)
c. cyclin
d. Cyclin-dependent kinase (Cdk)

13. Which negative regulatory molecule can trigger apoptosis if vital cell cycle events do not occur?

a. p53
b. p21
c. Retinoblastoma protein (Rb)
d. Cyclin-dependent kinase (Cdk)

14. What is the main prerequisite for clearance at the G_2 checkpoint?

a. The cell has a reached a sufficient size.
b. The cell has an adequate stockpile of nucleotides.
c. An accurate and complete DNA replication has occurred.
d. Proper attachment of mitotic spindle fibers to kinetochores has occurred.

15. What do you call changes to the order of nucleotides in a segment of DNA that codes for a protein?

a. proto-oncogenes
b. tumor suppressor genes
c. gene mutations
d. negative regulators

16. Human papillomavirus can cause cervical cancer. The virus encodes E6, a protein that binds p53. Based on this fact and what you know about p53, what effect do you think E6 binding has on p53 activity?

a. E6 activates p53.
b. E6 protects p53 from degradation.
c. E6 mutates p53.
d. E6 binding marks p53 for degradation.

17. What is a gene that codes for a positive cell cycle regulator called?

a. kinase inhibitor
b. oncogenes
c. proto-oncogenes
d. tumor suppressor genes

18. Which molecule is a Cdk inhibitor or is controlled by p53?

a. anti-kinase
b. cyclin
c. p21
d. Rb

19. Which eukaryotic cell cycle events are missing in binary fission?

a. cell growth

b. DNA duplication

c. karyokinesis

d. cytokinesis

20. Which of the following statements about binary fission is false?

a. In both prokaryotic and eukaryotic cells, the outcome of cell reproduction is a pair of daughter cells, which are genetically identical to the parent cell.

b. Karyokinesis is unnecessary in prokaryotes because there is no nucleus.

c. Replication of the prokaryotic chromosome begins at the origin of replication and continues in both directions at once.

d. The mitotic spindle draws the duplicated chromosomes to the opposite ends of the cell followed by formation of a septum and two daughter cells.

21. The formation of what structure, that will eventually form the new cell walls of the daughter cells, is directed by FtsZ?

a. contractile ring

b. cell plate

c. cytoskeleton

d. septum

CRITICAL THINKING QUESTIONS

22. Compare and contrast a human somatic cell to a human gamete.

a. Somatic cells have 46 chromosomes and are diploid, whereas gametes have half as many chromosomes as found in somatic cells.

b. Somatic cells have 23 chromosomes and are diploid, whereas gametes have half as many chromosomes are are present in somatic cells.

c. Somatic cells have 46 chromosomes and are haploid, whereas gametes have 23 chromosomes and are diploid.

d. Somatic cells have 46 chromosomes with one sex chromosome. In gametes, 23 chromosomes are present with two sex chromosomes.

23. Eukaryotic chromosomes are thousands of times longer than a typical cell. Explain how chromosomes can fit inside a eukaryotic nucleus.

a. The genetic material remains distributed in the nucleus, mitochondria, and chloroplast.

b. The genome is present in a looped structure, thus it fits the size of the nucleus.

c. The DNA remains coiled around proteins to form nucleosomes.

d. The genetic material remains bound to the nuclear envelope, forming invaginations.

24. Briefly describe the events that occur in each phase of interphase.

a. G_1 - assessment for DNA damage, S - duplication of genetic material, G_2 - duplication and dismantling organelles

b. G_1 - duplication of organelles, S - duplication of DNA, G_2 - assessment of DNA damage

c. G_1 - synthesis of DNA, S - synthesis of organelle genetic material, G_2 - assessment of DNA damage

d. G_1 - preparation for DNA synthesis, S - assessment of DNA damage, M - Division of cell

25. Chemotherapy drugs such as vincristine and colchicines disrupt mitosis by binding to tubulin (the subunit of microtubules) and interfering with microtubule assembly and disassembly. Exactly what mitotic structure do these drugs target, and what effect would that have on cell division?

a. The drugs bind tubulin and inhibit the binding of spindle to the chromosome. This can arrest the cell cycle.
b. The drugs bind the tubulin, which leads to an error in the chromosome separation. This could lead to apoptosis.
c. The drugs bind the tubulin, thereby inhibiting their division in S-phase. This inhibits cell division.
d. The drugs bind the spindle fiber and hinder the separation of chromatins. This promotes the division spontaneously.

26. List some reasons why a cell that has just completed cytokinesis might enter the G_0 phase instead of the G_1 phase.

a. Some cells are physiologically inhibited from undergoing any division and remain in the G_0 phase to provide assistance to their neighboring cells.
b. Some cells reproduce only under certain conditions and, until then, they remain in the G_0 phase.
c. Suspected DNA damage can lead the cell to undergo the G_0 phase.
d. The lack of important components of cell division makes cells stay in the G_0 phase.

27. Describe the general conditions that must be met at each of the three main cell cycle checkpoints.

a. G_1 checkpoint - assessment of DNA damage, G_2 - assessment of new DNA, M checkpoint - segregation of sister chromatids in anaphase.
b. G_1 checkpoint - Energy reserves for s phase, G_2 checkpoint - assessment of new DNA, M checkpoint- attachment of spindle to kinetochore.
c. G_1 checkpoint - assessment of DNA damage, G_2 checkpoint - energy reserves for duplication, M checkpoint - attachment of spindle to kinetochore
d. G_1 checkpoint - Energy reserves for S-phase, S checkpoint - synthesis of DNA, G_2 checkpoint - assessment of new DNA

28. Explain the roles of the positive cell cycle regulators compared to the negative regulators.

a. Positive regulators promote the cell cycle but negative regulators block the cell cycle.
b. Positive regulators block the cell division in cancerous cells but negative regulators promote in such cells.
c. Positive regulators promote the cell cycle but negative regulators arrest the cell cycle until certain events have occurred.
d. Positive regulators show positive feedback mechanisms but negative regulators show negative feedback in the cell cycle.

29. Describe what occurs at the M checkpoint and predict what would happen if the M checkpoint failed.

a. The M checkpoint checks for proper separation of sister chromatids and if it fails, then cells may undergo nondisjunction of chromosomes.
b. The M checkpoint checks if the DNA is damaged and promotes its repair. If it fails, then the daughters end up with damaged DNA.
c. The M checkpoint ensures the proper duplication of DNA and if it fails, the cells may undergo nondisjunction of chromosomes.
d. The M checkpoint ensures that all the components required for cell division are available and if it fails, the cell cycle will be inhibited.

30. List the regulatory mechanisms that might be lost in a cell producing faulty p53.

a. assessment of damaged DNA, recruiting repair enzymes, and binding of spindle to kinetochore
b. quality of DNA, triggering apoptosis, and recruiting repair enzymes
c. quality of DNA, binding of spindle to kinetochore, and assessment of DNA repair
d. triggering apoptosis, recruiting repair enzymes, and proper binding of spindle to kinetochore

31. p53 can trigger apoptosis if certain cell cycle events fail. How does this regulatory outcome benefit a multicellular organism?

a. The apoptosis helps in controlling the consumption of energy by the extra cells.
b. The apoptosis inhibits the production of faulty proteins, which could be produced due to the DNA damage.
c. The process of apoptosis stops the invasion of viruses in the other cells.
d. The cells are killed due to the production of reactive oxygen species produced, which could harm the organism.

32. Name the processes that eukaryotic cell division and binary fission have in common.

a. DNA duplication, division of cell organelles, division of the cytoplasmic contents

b. DNA duplication, segregation of duplicated chromosomes, and division of the cytoplasmic contents

c. formation of a septum, DNA duplication, division of the cytoplasmic contents

d. segregation of duplicated chromosomes, formation of a septum, division of cell organelles

TEST PREP FOR AP® COURSES

34.

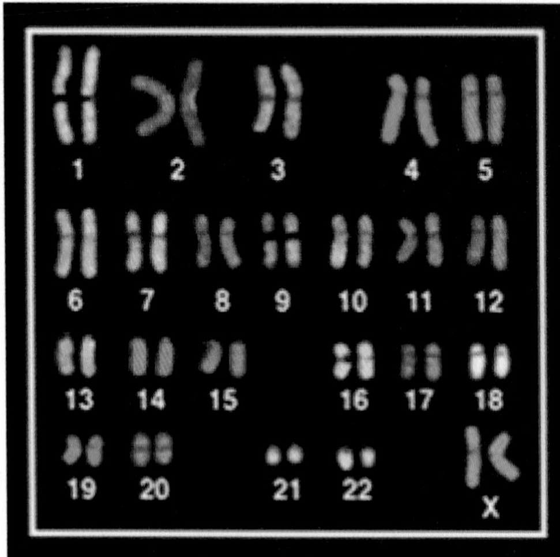

Which of the following statements cannot be inferred from the karyotype shown?

a. The cell contains DNA.

b. The cell contains 46 chromosomes.

c. The cell is diploid.

d. The cell is prokaryotic.

35. Explain how DNA, which in humans measures approximately two meters, can fit inside a human cell that is about $10\,\mu m$. Discuss how the organization of the genetic material in eukaryotes differs from prokaryotes.

33. The formation of what structure, that will eventually form the new cell walls of the daughter cells, is directed by FtsZ?

a. contractile ring

b. cell plate

c. cytoskeleton

d. septum

a. The DNA is found wrapped around histones to form nucleosomes, which further compact and ultimately form linear chromosomes. The prokaryotic genome is found as a loop and in eukaryotes as a double-stranded linear structure.

b. The DNA is wrapped around the nucleosomes to show a compact structure. The eukaryotes show a loop structure and prokaryotes show a double-stranded linear genome.

c. The genetic material shows ringed heterochromatin structure. The prokaryotes show multiple loops, and eukaryotes show a condensed chromatin.

d. The genetic material is wrapped around histones. The prokaryotes have a condensed structure in nucleoids, but eukaryotes have double-stranded linear structure.

36.

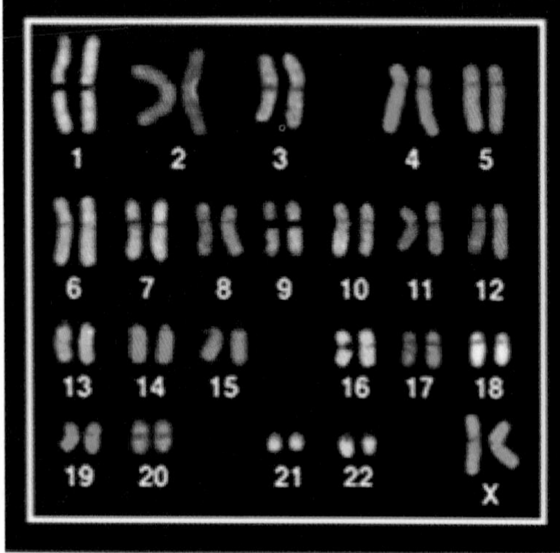

Which of the following statements about structure 1 on the karyotype is not true?

a. Structure 1 consists of homologous chromosomes.

b. The two parts of structure 1 will have genes in different loci.

c. The two parts of structure 1 originate from different parents.

d. The two parts of structure 1 will have slightly different sequences of nucleotides.

37.

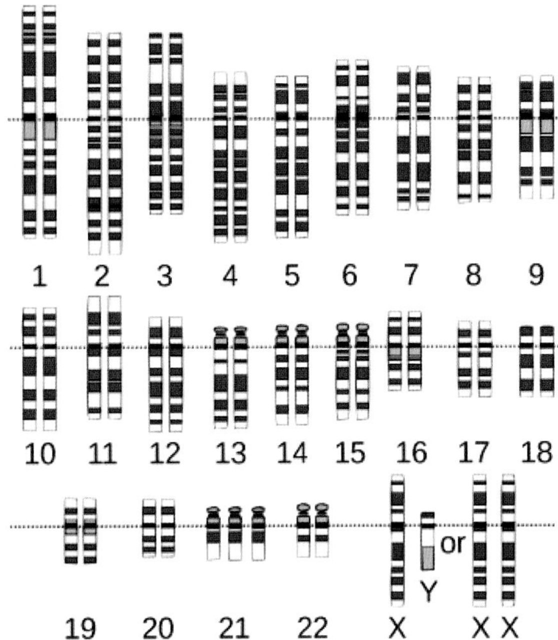

Based on the karyotype provided, the nondisjuction of which chromosome causes Down Syndrome?

a. chromosome 21

b. chromosome 22

c. X chromosome

d. Y chromosome

38. Describe the sequence of mitotic cell cycle for one pair of chromosome that is undergoing normal mitotic division.

a. anaphase - metaphase - prophase - cytokinesis

b. anaphase - prophase - metaphase - cytokinesis

c. prophase - anaphase - metaphase - cytokinesis

d. prophase - metaphase - anaphase - cytokinesis

39.

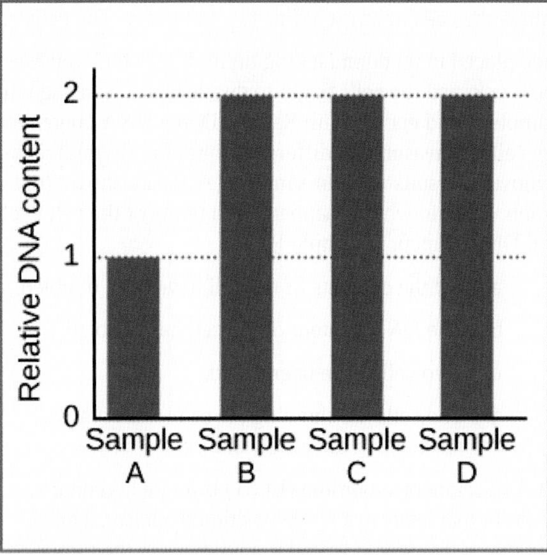

In a study on cell division, researchers culture synchronously dividing human cells with thymidine. This causes the cells to arrest at the G_1 boundary. The cells are then placed in medium lacking thymidine, which releases the block, and the cells begin to divide again. Starting with Sample A and ending with Sample D, the DNA content of the cells is measured at different times after thymidine is removed. Results for four samples (A-D) are shown in the graph. Which sample presents the expected results for cells in S-phase?

a. sample A

b. sample B

c. sample C

d. sample D

40.

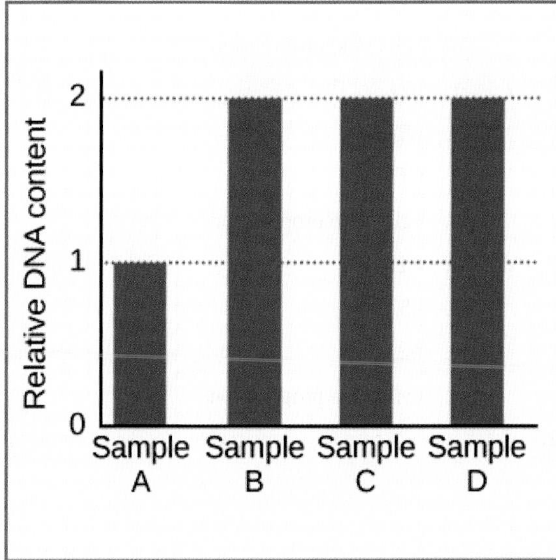

In a study on cell division, researchers culture synchronously dividing human cells with thymidine. This causes the cells to arrest at the G_1 boundary. The cells are then placed in medium lacking thymidine, which releases the block, and the cells begin to divide again. Starting with Sample A and ending with Sample D, the DNA content of the cells is measured at different times after thymidine is removed. Results for four samples (A-D) are shown in the graph. Explain what is happening in terms of the cell cycle and DNA content in sample B.

a. All the contents of the cell have been doubled.
b. The DNA content of the cell has doubled.
c. Two cells have been fused.
d. The cells are showing the semiconservative mechanism of cell division.

41. Li-Fraumeni syndrome (LFS1) is a rare hereditary disorder that leads to a predisposition to cancer. This hereditary disorder is linked to mutations in the tumor suppressor gene encoding the transcription factor p53. p53 acts at the G_1 checkpoint. If damaged DNA is detected, p53 halts the cell cycle. As p53 levels rise, the production of p21 is triggered. p21 enforces the halt in the cell cycle. A variant of Li-Fraumeni, called LFS2, is thought to occur due to a mutation of the CHK2 gene, which is also a tumor suppressor gene. CHK2 regulates the action of p53. Which of the following cascades is most likely to occur in a normal cell that does not contain the LFS mutation?

a.
1. cell cycle progression
2. p53
3. p21
4. CHK2

b.
1. p53
2. p21
3. CHK2
4. cell cycle progression

c.
1. p21
2. p53
3. CHK2
4. cell cycle progression

d.
1. CHK2
2. p53
3. p21
4. cell cycle progression

42.

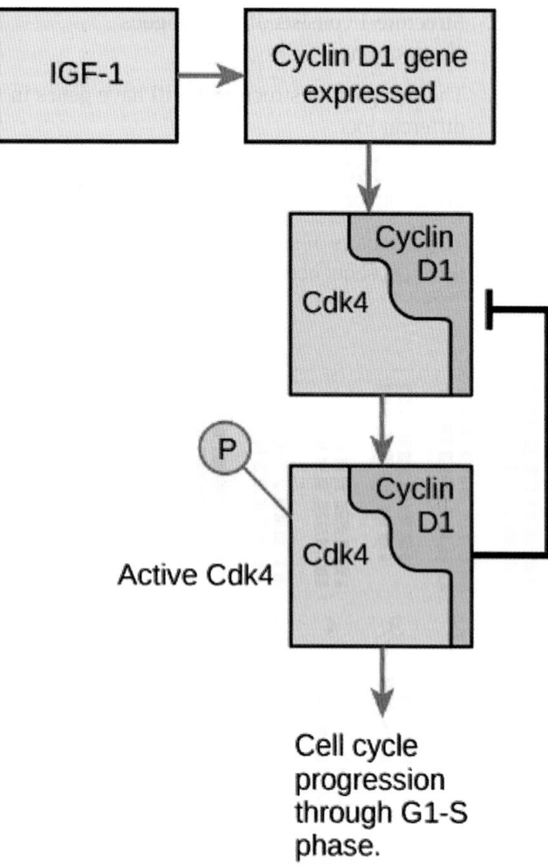

The insulin growth factor (IGF-1) promotes cell proliferation as shown in the diagram. The expression of which protein in the diagram is controlled through negative feedback?

a. active Cdk4
b. Cyclin D1
c. Cyclin D1/Cdk4 complex
d. IGF-1

43. Explain why p53, p21, and CHK2 are considered tumor suppressor genes, not proto-oncogenes. Give an example of a proto-oncogene.

a. p53, p21, and CHK2 suppress the proteins that regulate the cell cycle, whereas proto-oncogenes, like phosphorylated Rb, help in cell cycle progression.
b. p53, p21, and CHK2 are negative cell cycle regulators, whereas Cdks are proto-oncogenes, which could cause cancer when mutated.
c. p53, p21, and CHK2 suppress the proteins that regulate the cell cycle, whereas Rb is considered a proto-oncogene, as it is the most primitive
d. The three proteins help stop the formation of tumors, whereas Cdk’s are called proto-oncogenes because they are the most primitive of all.

SCIENCE PRACTICE CHALLENGE QUESTIONS

44. Many biological processes are synchronized with the 24-hour rotational period of Earth. Circadian (24-hour) periodicity is common across phyla. One of these processes is the cell cycle. The currently accepted explanation is that the low-oxygen atmosphere of early Earth had no ozone layer to filter out the solar ultraviolet radiation that damages DNA. Completing the S phase of the cell cycle at night provided a selective advantage. The internal clock controlling the cell cycle and the circadian clock became synchronized. Research has demonstrated that changes in one clock, either the circadian clock or the cell cycle clock, disrupt timing in the other. The question was, which clock controls the other?

Researchers have found that the circadian clock, which can be observed by fluorescent markers on proteins that carry the circadian signal, can be disrupted by changes in light, nutrition, or exposure to the steroid dexamethasone. Nutrition can also disrupt the cell cycle clock. Rat fibroblasts (cells constantly undergoing mitosis) were cultured on medium containing different levels of fetal bovine serum (FBS) with and without the addition of dexamethasone. Confluence is a phenomenon that occurs in tissue culture when the surface of the growth medium becomes covered with cells, and the cells stop dividing. The circadian and cell cycle periods were measured.

	FBS	Dexa-meth-asone	Con-flu-ence	Circa-dian Period (hr)	Cell Cycle Period (hr)
a	0%	no	no	24± 0.5	24± 0.5
b	10%	no	no	21.9± 1.1	21.3± 1.3
c	15%	no	no	19.4± 0.5	18.6± 0.6
d	10%	yes	no	24.2± 0.5	20.1± 0.94
e	*20%	yes	no	21.25± 0.36	19.5± 0.42
f	20%	yes	no	29± 1.05	16.05± 0.48
g	10%	yes	yes	24± 0.5	na

Table 10.5 * Subsets of samples with 20% FBS and dexamethasone were clustered around two means for each measured period.

A. Based on these data, **describe** the connections between the circadian period and the cell cycle period for each of the experimental conditions.

B. Based on these data, **justify the claim** that in cells that are actively dividing, the circadian period is set by the cell cycle period rather than the reverse.

45. Cells in different tissues of a fully developed human show significant variations in the length of time that they remain in the G0 phase of the cell cycle: muscle (lifetime), nerve (lifetime), adipose (years), liver (year), erythrocyte (months), bone osteoclasts (weeks), leukocyte (days), and epidermal (hours). For each of these types of tissues, **propose a reason** based on internal and external factors and function that might account for the differences among their longevities.

46. Describe the essential components and results of mitosis and the activities that occur during interphase to prepare the cell for mitosis.

47. Cancer comprises many different diseases with a common cause: uncontrolled cell growth. Cancer is a complex response to a host of environmental mutagens as well as the accumulation of random mutations. Since the "war on cancer" began in 1971, the death rate due to cancer has changed very little despite the discovery of several tumor suppressor genes, including p53.

A. Briefly **describe** the multiple functions of p53, including the role of p53 in apoptosis.

B. A principle of biology is that "form follows function." The protein p53, which has multiple functions, is named for its molecular mass—approximately 53 kDa. This is not a large polymer by comparison with other proteins; for example, ATP synthase, which has only one function, has a molecular mass of approximately 550 kDa. Based on analogies to processes involved in cellular signaling, **create a model(s) to explain** how so many functions can be supported by a single, relatively simple structure.

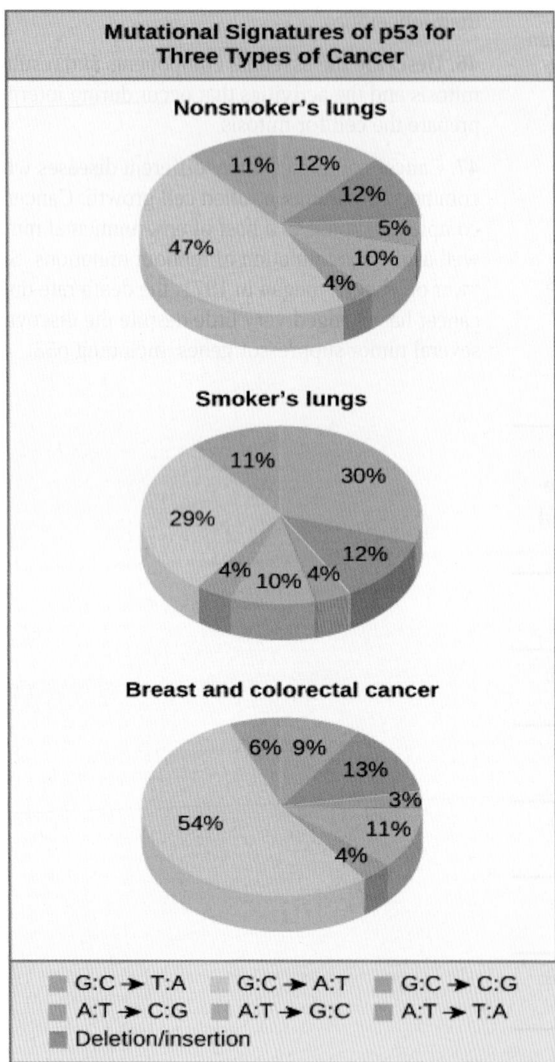

Figure 10.17

C. Mutational signatures of p53 are shown in the figure above [G.P. Pfeifer et al., Nature, 21(48), 2002] for the three types of cancer with the highest death rates in the U.S.: lung (~225,000 deaths in 2016), breast (246,000), and colorectal (381,000). These data can be obtained by sequencing the gene that encodes p53. Approximately 85% of lung cancers occur in smokers. Based on these data, **calculate** how many deaths due to lung cancer among nonsmokers were reported in 2016. How much does smoking increase the likelihood of death due to lung cancer?

D. As shown under each graph, particular transversions (replacement of a pyrimidine by a purine of vice versa) or transitions (replacement of a purine or pyrimidine by the alternative purine or pyrimidine) are features of specific mutational signatures. Based on these data, **identify** the transversion or transition that seems to be induced by cigarette smoke.

E. Using your answer to B above, **predict** possible mechanisms, that is, transversion or transition, for the different mutational signatures among lung cancers of smokers and those of other cancers, and for the very similar mutational signatures of lung cancers of nonsmokers and of breast and colorectal cancers. The partitioning of function along the length of the protein can lead to functional and nonfunctional segments. It is believed that the transversions due to smoking are caused by polyaromatic hydrocarbons. The hotspots for these mutations lie in the segment that binds to DNA. The transition hotspots are in segments that regulate apoptosis.

11 | MEIOSIS AND SEXUAL REPRODUCTION

(a) (b) (c)

Figure 11.1 Each of us, like these other large multicellular organisms, begins life as a fertilized egg. After trillions of cell divisions, each of us develops into a complex, multicellular organism. (credit a: modification of work by Frank Wouters; credit b: modification of work by Ken Cole, USGS; credit c: modification of work by Martin Pettitt)

Chapter Outline

Introduction

The ability to reproduce "in kind" is a basic characteristic of all living things. "In kind" means that the offspring of an organism closely resembles its parent or parents. Hippopotamuses give birth to hippopotamus calves, Joshua trees produce Joshua tree seedlings, and flamingos lay eggs that hatch into flamingo chicks. In kind can mean exactly the same. Many unicellular organisms, such as yeast, and a few multicellular organisms, such as sponges, can produce genetically identical clones of themselves through cell division. However, many single-celled organisms and most multicellular organisms reproduce regularly using a method requiring two parents. Sexual reproduction occurs through the production by each parent of a haploid cell (containing one half of an offspring's required genetic material) and the fusion of these two haploid cells to form a single, unique diploid cell with a complete set of genetic information. In most plants and animals, through multiple rounds of mitotic cell division, this diploid cell will develop into an adult organism. Haploid cells that are necessary for sexual reproduction are produced by a type of cell division called meiosis. Sexual reproduction, specifically meiosis and fertilization, introduces variation into offspring. Variation is an important component of a species evolutionary success. The vast majority of eukaryotic organisms employs some form of meiosis and fertilization to reproduce.

Not all sexually reproducing eukaryotes reproduce solely by sexual reproduction. For example, an Asian termite species, *Reticulitermes speratus*, can reproduce sexually or asexually. In a young colony, a single termite pair—the king and queen—produce worker offspring sexually by the union of haploid cells. However, after several years, as the queen begins to age, she produces some offspring asexually in a process called parthenogenesis. These offspring, which are destined to become new queens, are not fertilized by the king. They are genetic clones of the queen. More information about parthenogenesis in these termites can be found at **this article (http://openstaxcollege.org/l/32termitequeen)** .

11.1 | The Process of Meiosis

In this section, you will explore the following questions:

- How do chromosomes behave during meiosis?
- What cellular events occur during meiosis?
- What are the similarities and differences between meiosis and mitosis?
- How can the process of meiosis generate genetic variation?

Connection for AP® Courses

As we explored the cell cycle and mitosis in a previous chapter, we learned that cells divide to grow, replace other cells, and reproduce asexually. Without mutation, or changes in the DNA, the daughter cells produced by mitosis receive a set of genetic instructions that is identical to that of the parent cell. Because changes in genes drive both the unity and diversity of life, organisms without genetic variation cannot evolve through natural selection. Evolution occurs only because organisms have developed ways to vary their genetic material. This occurs through mutations in DNA, recombination of genes during meiosis, and meiosis followed by fertilization in sexually reproducing organisms.

Sexual reproduction requires that diploid ($2n$) organisms produce haploid ($1n$) cells through meiosis and that these haploid cells fuse to form new, diploid offspring. The union of these two haploid cells, one from each parent, is fertilization. Although the processes of meiosis and mitosis share similarities, their end products are different. Recall that eukaryotic DNA is contained in chromosomes, and that chromosomes occur in homologous pairs (homologues). At fertilization, the male parent contributes one member of each homologous pair to the offspring, and the female parent contributes the other. With the exception of the sex chromosomes, homologous chromosomes contain the same genes, but these genes can have different variations, called alleles. (For example, you might have inherited an allele for brown eyes from your father and an allele for blue eyes from your mother.) As in mitosis, homologous chromosomes are duplicated during the S-stage (synthesis) of interphase. However, unlike mitosis, in which there is just one nuclear division, meiosis has two complete rounds of nuclear division—meiosis I and meiosis II. These result in four nuclei and (usually) four daughter cells, each with half the number of chromosomes as the parent cell ($1n$). The first division, meiosis I, separates homologous chromosomes, and the second division, meiosis II, separates chromatids. (Remember: during meiosis, DNA replicates ONCE but divides TWICE, whereas in mitosis, DNA replicates ONCE but divides only ONCE.).

Although mitosis and meiosis are similar in many ways, they have different outcomes. The main difference is in the type of cell produced: mitosis produces identical cells, allowing growth or repair of tissues; meiosis generates reproductive cells, or gametes. Gametes, often called sex cells, unite with other sex cells to produce new, unique organisms.

Genetic variation occurs during meiosis I, in which homologous chromosomes pair and exchange non-sister chromatid segments (crossover). Here the homologous chromosomes separate into different nuclei, causing a reduction in "ploidy." During meiosis II—which is more similar to a mitotic division—the chromatids separate and segregate into four haploid sex cells. However, because of crossover, the resultant daughter cells do not contain identical genomes. As in mitosis, external factors and internal signals regulate the meiotic cell cycle. As we will explore in more detail in a later chapter, errors in meiosis can cause genetic disorders, such as Down syndrome.

Information presented and the examples highlighted in the section support concepts and learning objectives outlined in Big Idea 3 of the AP® Biology Curriculum Framework. The learning objectives listed in the Curriculum Framework provide a transparent foundation for the AP® Biology course, an inquiry-based laboratory experience, instructional activities, and AP® exam questions. A learning objective merges required content with one or more of the seven science practices.

Big Idea 3	Living systems store, retrieve, transmit and respond to information essential to life processes.
Enduring Understanding 3.A	Heritable information provides for continuity of life.

Essential Knowledge	**3.A.2** In eukaryotes, heritable information is passed to the next generation via processes that include the cell cycle and mitosis or meiosis plus fertilization.
Science Practice	**6.2** The student can construct explanations of phenomena based on evidence produced through scientific practices.
Learning Objective	**3.9** The student is able to construct an explanation, using visual representations or narratives, as to how DNA in chromosomes is transmitted to the next generation via mitosis, or meiosis followed by fertilization.
Essential Knowledge	**3.A.2** In eukaryotes, heritable information is passed to the next generation via processes that include the cell cycle and mitosis or meiosis plus fertilization.
Science Practice	**7.1** The student can connect phenomena and models across spatial and temporal scales.
Learning Objective	**3.10** The student is able to represent the connection between meiosis and increased genetic diversity necessary for evolution.

The Science Practice Challenge Questions contain additional test questions for this section that will help you prepare for the AP exam. These questions address the following standards:
[APLO 1.9][APLO 2.15][APLO 2.39][APLO 3.11][APLO 3.9]

You read that **fertilization** is the union of two sex cells from two individual organisms. If these two cells each contain one set of chromosomes, the resulting fertilized cell contains two sets of chromosomes. Haploid cells contain one set of chromosomes. Cells containing two sets of chromosomes are called diploid. The number of sets of chromosomes in a cell is called its ploidy level. If the reproductive cycle is to continue, a diploid cell must reduce the number of its chromosome sets before fertilization can occur again. Otherwise, the number of chromosome sets would double, and continue to double in every generation. So, in addition to fertilization, sexual reproduction includes a nuclear division that reduces the number of chromosome sets.

Most animals and plants are diploid, containing two sets of chromosomes. In an organism's **somatic cells**, sometimes referred to as "body" cells (all cells of a multicellular organism except the reproductive cells), the nucleus contains two copies of each chromosome, called homologous chromosomes. Homologous chromosomes are matched pairs containing the same genes in identical locations along their length. Diploid organisms inherit one copy of each homologous chromosome from each parent; all together, they are considered a full set of chromosomes. Haploid cells, containing a single copy of each homologous chromosome, are found only within an organism''s reproductive structures, such as the ovaries and testes. Haploid cells can be either gametes or spores. Male gametes are sperm and female gametes are eggs. All animals and most plants produce gametes. Spores are haploid cells that can produce a haploid organism or can fuse with another spore to form a diploid cell. Some plants and all fungi produce spores.

As you have learned, the nuclear division that forms haploid cells— **meiosis**—is closely related to mitosis. Mitosis is the part of a cell reproduction cycle that results in identical daughter nuclei that are also genetically identical to the original parent nucleus. In mitosis, both the parent and the daughter nuclei are at the same ploidy level—diploid for most plants and animals. Meiosis employs many of the same mechanisms as mitosis. However, the starting nucleus is always diploid and the nuclei that result at the end of a meiotic cell division are haploid. To achieve this reduction in chromosome number, meiosis consists of one round of chromosome duplication and two rounds of nuclear division. Because the events that occur during each of the division stages are analogous to the events of mitosis, the same stage names are assigned. However, because there are two rounds of division, the major process and the stages are designated with a "I" or a "II." Thus, **meiosis** I is the first round of meiotic division and consists of prophase I, prometaphase I, and so on. **Meiosis II**, in which the second round of meiotic division takes place, includes prophase II, prometaphase II, and so on.

Meiosis I

Meiosis is preceded by an interphase consisting of the G_1, S, and G_2 phases, which are nearly identical to the phases preceding mitosis. The G_1 phase, which is also called the first gap phase, is the first phase of the interphase and is focused on cell growth. The S phase is the second phase of interphase, during which the DNA of the chromosomes is replicated. Finally, the G_2 phase, also called the second gap phase, is the third and final phase of interphase; in this phase, the cell undergoes the final preparations for meiosis.

During DNA duplication in the S phase, each chromosome is replicated to produce two identical copies, called sister chromatids, that are held together at the centromere by **cohesin** proteins. Cohesin holds the chromatids together until anaphase II. The centrosomes, which are the structures that organize the microtubules of the meiotic spindle, also replicate. This prepares the cell to enter prophase I, the first meiotic phase.

Prophase I

Early in prophase I, before the chromosomes can be seen clearly microscopically, the homologous chromosomes are attached at their tips to the nuclear envelope by proteins. As the nuclear envelope begins to break down, the proteins associated with homologous chromosomes bring the pair close to each other. Recall that, in mitosis, homologous chromosomes do not pair together. In mitosis, homologous chromosomes line up end-to-end so that when they divide, each daughter cell receives a sister chromatid from both members of the homologous pair. The **synaptonemal complex**, a lattice of proteins between the homologous chromosomes, first forms at specific locations and then spreads to cover the entire length of the chromosomes. The tight pairing of the homologous chromosomes is called **synapsis**. In synapsis, the genes on the chromatids of the homologous chromosomes are aligned precisely with each other. The synaptonemal complex supports the exchange of chromosomal segments between non-sister homologous chromatids, a process called crossing over. Crossing over can be observed visually after the exchange as **chiasmata** (singular = chiasma) (Figure 11.2).

In species such as humans, even though the X and Y sex chromosomes are not homologous (most of their genes differ), they have a small region of homology that allows the X and Y chromosomes to pair up during prophase I. A partial synaptonemal complex develops only between the regions of homology.

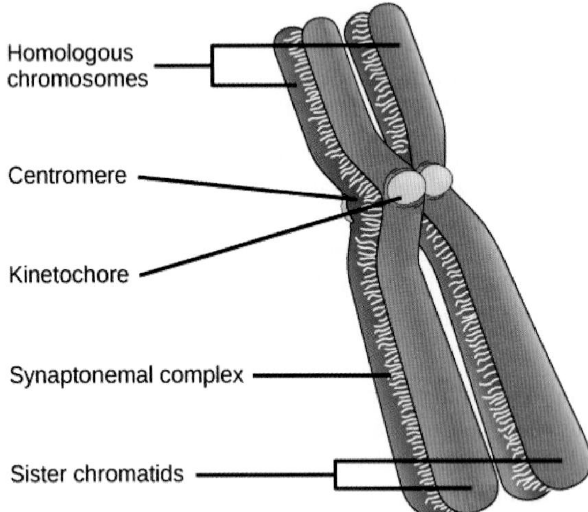

Figure 11.2 Early in prophase I, homologous chromosomes come together to form a synapse. The chromosomes are bound tightly together and in perfect alignment by a protein lattice called a synaptonemal complex and by cohesin proteins at the centromere.

Located at intervals along the synaptonemal complex are large protein assemblies called **recombination nodules**. These assemblies mark the points of later chiasmata and mediate the multistep process of **crossover**—or genetic recombination—between the non-sister chromatids. Near the recombination nodule on each chromatid, the double-stranded DNA is cleaved, the cut ends are modified, and a new connection is made between the non-sister chromatids. As prophase I progresses, the synaptonemal complex begins to break down and the chromosomes begin to condense. When the synaptonemal complex is gone, the homologous chromosomes remain attached to each other at the centromere and at chiasmata. The chiasmata remain until anaphase I. The number of chiasmata varies according to the species and the length of the chromosome. There must be at least one chiasma per chromosome for proper separation of homologous chromosomes during meiosis I, but there may be as many as 25. Following crossover, the synaptonemal complex breaks down and the cohesin connection between homologous pairs is also removed. At the end of prophase I, the pairs are held together only at the chiasmata (Figure 11.3) and are called **tetrads** because the four sister chromatids of each pair of homologous chromosomes are now visible.

The crossover events are the first source of genetic variation in the nuclei produced by meiosis. A single crossover event between homologous non-sister chromatids leads to a reciprocal exchange of equivalent DNA between a maternal chromosome and a paternal chromosome. Now, when that sister chromatid is moved into a gamete cell it will carry some DNA from one parent of the individual and some DNA from the other parent. The sister recombinant chromatid has a combination of maternal and paternal genes that did not exist before the crossover. Multiple crossovers in an arm of the chromosome have the same effect, exchanging segments of DNA to create recombinant chromosomes.

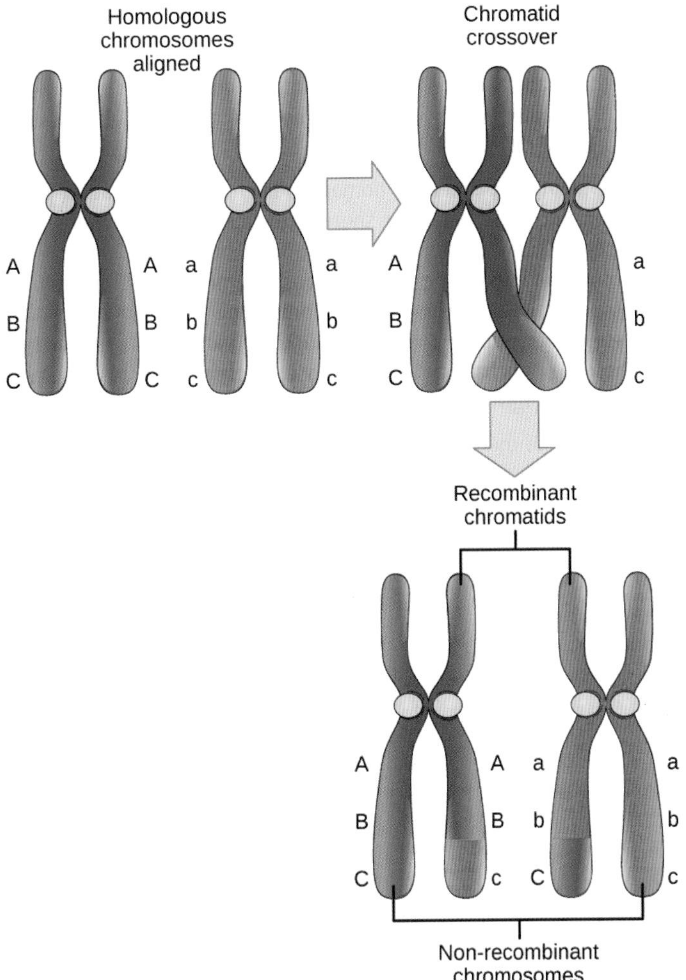

Figure 11.3 Crossover occurs between non-sister chromatids of homologous chromosomes. The result is an exchange of genetic material between homologous chromosomes.

Prometaphase I

The key event in prometaphase I is the attachment of the spindle fiber microtubules to the kinetochore proteins at the centromeres. Kinetochore proteins are multiprotein complexes that bind the centromeres of a chromosome to the microtubules of the mitotic spindle. Microtubules grow from centrosomes placed at opposite poles of the cell. The microtubules move toward the middle of the cell and attach to one of the two fused homologous chromosomes. The microtubules attach at each chromosomes' kinetochores. With each member of the homologous pair attached to opposite poles of the cell, in the next phase, the microtubules can pull the homologous pair apart. A spindle fiber that has attached to a kinetochore is called a kinetochore microtubule. At the end of prometaphase I, each tetrad is attached to microtubules from both poles, with one homologous chromosome facing each pole. The homologous chromosomes are still held together at chiasmata. In addition, the nuclear membrane has broken down entirely.

Metaphase I

During metaphase I, the homologous chromosomes are arranged in the center of the cell with the kinetochores facing opposite poles. The homologous pairs orient themselves randomly at the equator. For example, if the two homologous members of chromosome 1 are labeled a and b, then the chromosomes could line up a-b, or b-a. This is important in determining the genes carried by a gamete, as each will only receive one of the two homologous chromosomes. Recall that homologous chromosomes are not identical. They contain slight differences in their genetic information, causing each gamete to have a unique genetic makeup.

This randomness is the physical basis for the creation of the second form of genetic variation in offspring. Consider that the homologous chromosomes of a sexually reproducing organism are originally inherited as two separate sets, one from each parent. Using humans as an example, one set of 23 chromosomes is present in the egg donated by the mother. The father provides the other set of 23 chromosomes in the sperm that fertilizes the egg. Every cell of the multicellular offspring has copies of the original two sets of homologous chromosomes. In prophase I of meiosis, the homologous chromosomes form the tetrads. In metaphase I, these pairs line up at the midway point between the two poles of the cell to form the metaphase plate. Because there is an equal chance that a microtubule fiber will encounter a maternally or paternally inherited chromosome, the arrangement of the tetrads at the metaphase plate is random. Any maternally inherited chromosome may face either pole. Any paternally inherited chromosome may also face either pole. The orientation of each tetrad is independent of the orientation of the other 22 tetrads.

This event—the random (or independent) assortment of homologous chromosomes at the metaphase plate—is the second mechanism that introduces variation into the gametes or spores. In each cell that undergoes meiosis, the arrangement of the tetrads is different. The number of variations is dependent on the number of chromosomes making up a set. There are two possibilities for orientation at the metaphase plate; the possible number of alignments therefore equals $2n$, where n is the number of chromosomes per set. Humans have 23 chromosome pairs, which results in over eight million (2^{23}) possible genetically-distinct gametes. This number does not include the variability that was previously created in the sister chromatids by crossover. Given these two mechanisms, it is highly unlikely that any two haploid cells resulting from meiosis will have the same genetic composition (Figure 11.4).

To summarize the genetic consequences of meiosis I, the maternal and paternal genes are recombined by crossover events that occur between each homologous pair during prophase I. In addition, the random assortment of tetrads on the metaphase plate produces a unique combination of maternal and paternal chromosomes that will make their way into the gametes.

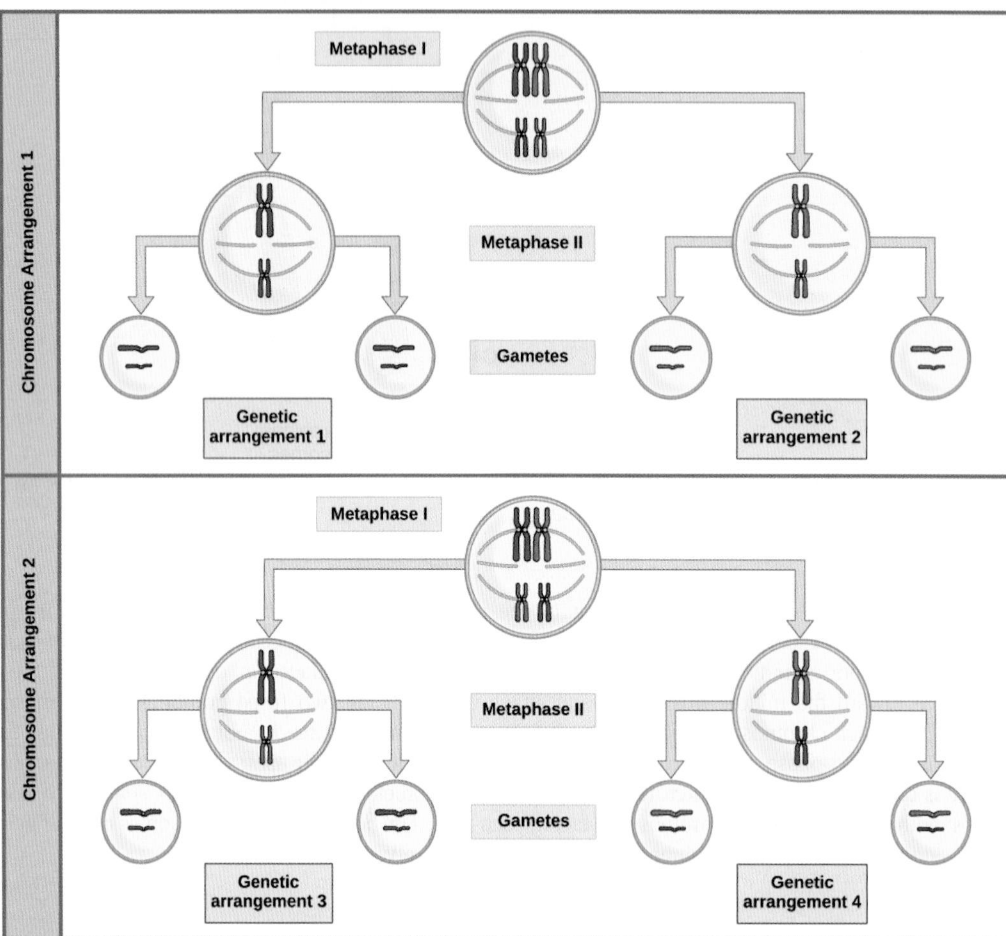

Figure 11.4 Random, independent assortment during metaphase I can be demonstrated by considering a cell with a set of two chromosomes ($n = 2$). In this case, there are two possible arrangements at the equatorial plane in metaphase I. The total possible number of different gametes is $2n$, where n equals the number of chromosomes in a set. In this example, there are four possible genetic combinations for the gametes. With $n = 23$ in human cells, there are over 8 million possible combinations of paternal and maternal chromosomes.

Anaphase I

In anaphase I, the microtubules pull the linked chromosomes apart. The sister chromatids remain tightly bound together at the centromere. The chiasmata are broken in anaphase I as the microtubules attached to the fused kinetochores pull the homologous chromosomes apart (Figure 11.5).

Telophase I and Cytokinesis

In telophase, the separated chromosomes arrive at opposite poles. The remainder of the typical telophase events may or may not occur, depending on the species. In some organisms, the chromosomes decondense and nuclear envelopes form around the chromatids in telophase I. In other organisms, cytokinesis—the physical separation of the cytoplasmic components into two daughter cells—occurs without reformation of the nuclei. In nearly all species of animals and some fungi, cytokinesis separates the cell contents via a cleavage furrow (constriction of the actin ring that leads to cytoplasmic division). In plants, a cell plate is formed during cell cytokinesis by Golgi vesicles fusing at the metaphase plate. This cell plate will ultimately lead to the formation of cell walls that separate the two daughter cells.

Two haploid cells are the end result of the first meiotic division. The cells are haploid because at each pole, there is just one of each pair of the homologous chromosomes. Therefore, only one full set of the chromosomes is present. This is why the cells are considered haploid—there is only one chromosome set, even though each homolog still consists of two sister chromatids. Recall that sister chromatids are merely duplicates of one of the two homologous chromosomes (except for changes that occurred during crossing over). In meiosis II, these two sister chromatids will separate, creating four haploid daughter cells.

Review the process of meiosis, observing how chromosomes align and migrate, at Meiosis: An Interactive Animation (http://openstaxcollege.org/l/animal_meiosis) .

Human males typically have XY chromosomes and females have XX chromosomes, but there are rare instances in which a male can inherit an XXY or an XYY, or a female can have three X chromosomes. Explain how an error in meiosis can cause these aberrations.

a. Errors can arise only during the recombination process which may result in deletions, duplications or translocations causing such abnormalities.

b. Aberrations caused when a pair of homologous chromosomes fails to separate during anaphase I or when sister chromatids fail to separate during anaphase II, the daughter cells will inherit unequal numbers of chromosomes.

c. Errors during anaphase I of meiosis only cause such aberrations resulting in unequal numbers of chromosomes.

d. Errors during meiosis introduce variations in the DNA sequence, which depends specifically on the size of the variant only.

Meiosis II

In some species, cells enter a brief interphase, or **interkinesis**, before entering meiosis II. Interkinesis lacks an S phase, so chromosomes are not duplicated. The two cells produced in meiosis I go through the events of meiosis II in synchrony. During meiosis II, the sister chromatids within the two daughter cells separate, forming four new haploid gametes. The mechanics of meiosis II is similar to mitosis, except that each dividing cell has only one set of homologous chromosomes. Therefore, each cell has half the number of sister chromatids to separate out as a diploid cell undergoing mitosis.

Prophase II

If the chromosomes decondensed in telophase I, they condense again. If nuclear envelopes were formed, they fragment into vesicles. The centrosomes that were duplicated during interkinesis move away from each other toward opposite poles, and new spindles are formed.

Prometaphase II

The nuclear envelopes are completely broken down, and the spindle is fully formed. Each sister chromatid forms an individual kinetochore that attaches to microtubules from opposite poles.

Metaphase II

The sister chromatids are maximally condensed and aligned at the equator of the cell.

Anaphase II

The sister chromatids are pulled apart by the kinetochore microtubules and move toward opposite poles. Non-kinetochore microtubules elongate the cell.

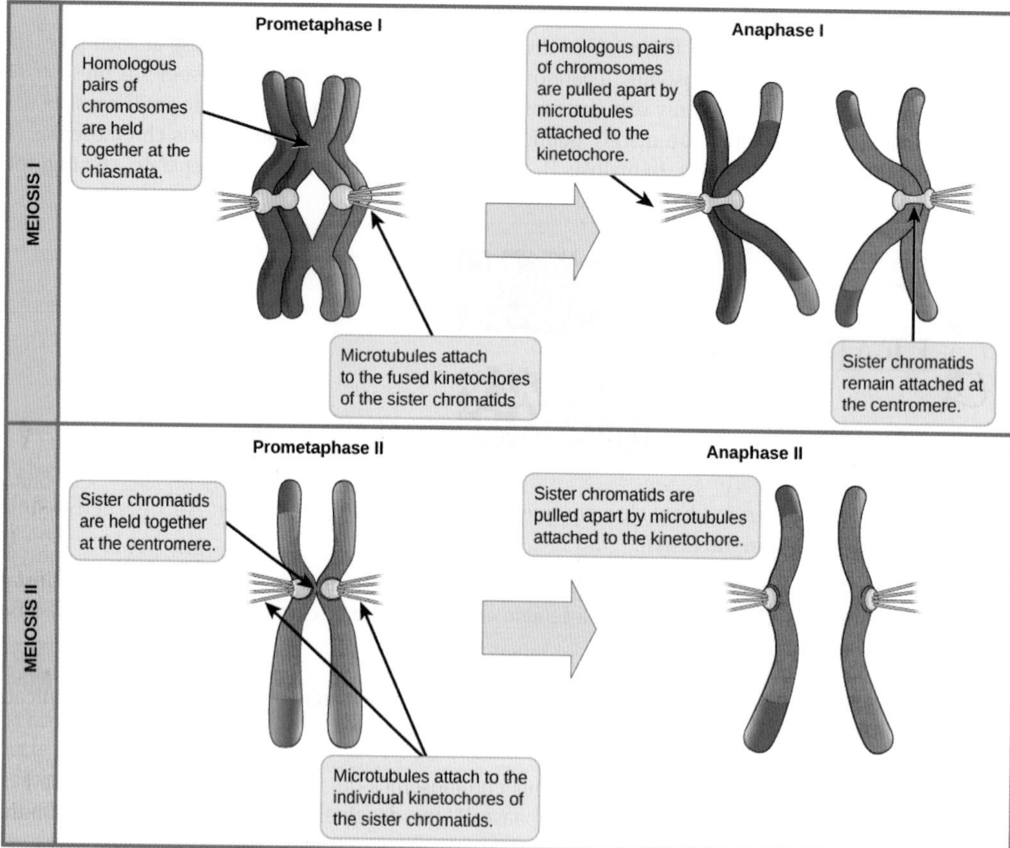

Figure 11.5 The process of chromosome alignment differs between meiosis I and meiosis II. In prometaphase I, microtubules attach to the fused kinetochores of homologous chromosomes, and the homologous chromosomes are arranged at the midpoint of the cell in metaphase I. In anaphase I, the homologous chromosomes are separated. In prometaphase II, microtubules attach to the kinetochores of sister chromatids, and the sister chromatids are arranged at the midpoint of the cells in metaphase II. In anaphase II, the sister chromatids are separated.

Telophase II and Cytokinesis

The chromosomes arrive at opposite poles and begin to decondense. Nuclear envelopes form around the chromosomes. Cytokinesis separates the two cells into four unique haploid cells. At this point, the newly formed nuclei are both haploid. The cells produced are genetically unique because of the random assortment of paternal and maternal homologs and because of the recombining of maternal and paternal segments of chromosomes (with their sets of genes) that occurs during crossover. The entire process of meiosis is outlined in Figure 11.6.

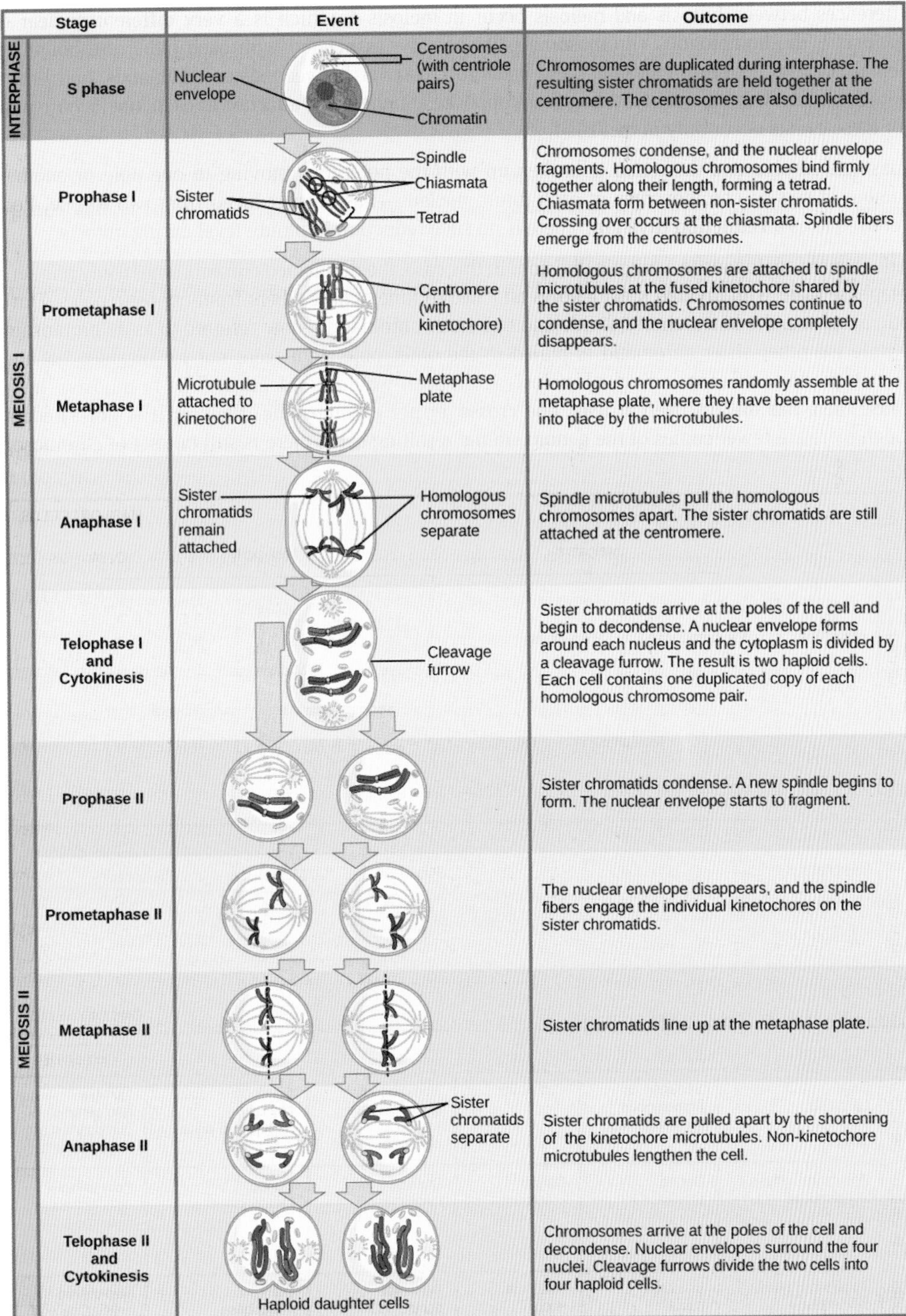

	Stage	Event	Outcome
INTERPHASE	S phase	Nuclear envelope; Centrosomes (with centriole pairs); Chromatin	Chromosomes are duplicated during interphase. The resulting sister chromatids are held together at the centromere. The centrosomes are also duplicated.
MEIOSIS I	Prophase I	Sister chromatids; Spindle; Chiasmata; Tetrad	Chromosomes condense, and the nuclear envelope fragments. Homologous chromosomes bind firmly together along their length, forming a tetrad. Chiasmata form between non-sister chromatids. Crossing over occurs at the chiasmata. Spindle fibers emerge from the centrosomes.
MEIOSIS I	Prometaphase I	Centromere (with kinetochore)	Homologous chromosomes are attached to spindle microtubules at the fused kinetochore shared by the sister chromatids. Chromosomes continue to condense, and the nuclear envelope completely disappears.
MEIOSIS I	Metaphase I	Microtubule attached to kinetochore; Metaphase plate	Homologous chromosomes randomly assemble at the metaphase plate, where they have been maneuvered into place by the microtubules.
MEIOSIS I	Anaphase I	Sister chromatids remain attached; Homologous chromosomes separate	Spindle microtubules pull the homologous chromosomes apart. The sister chromatids are still attached at the centromere.
MEIOSIS I	Telophase I and Cytokinesis	Cleavage furrow	Sister chromatids arrive at the poles of the cell and begin to decondense. A nuclear envelope forms around each nucleus and the cytoplasm is divided by a cleavage furrow. The result is two haploid cells. Each cell contains one duplicated copy of each homologous chromosome pair.
MEIOSIS II	Prophase II		Sister chromatids condense. A new spindle begins to form. The nuclear envelope starts to fragment.
MEIOSIS II	Prometaphase II		The nuclear envelope disappears, and the spindle fibers engage the individual kinetochores on the sister chromatids.
MEIOSIS II	Metaphase II		Sister chromatids line up at the metaphase plate.
MEIOSIS II	Anaphase II	Sister chromatids separate	Sister chromatids are pulled apart by the shortening of the kinetochore microtubules. Non-kinetochore microtubules lengthen the cell.
MEIOSIS II	Telophase II and Cytokinesis	Haploid daughter cells	Chromosomes arrive at the poles of the cell and decondense. Nuclear envelopes surround the four nuclei. Cleavage furrows divide the two cells into four haploid cells.

Figure 11.6 An animal cell with a diploid number of four ($2n = 4$) proceeds through the stages of meiosis to form four haploid daughter cells.

Comparing Meiosis and Mitosis

Mitosis and meiosis are both forms of division of the nucleus in eukaryotic cells. They share some similarities, but also exhibit distinct differences that lead to very different outcomes (**Figure 11.7**). Mitosis is a single nuclear division that results in two nuclei that are usually partitioned into two new cells. The nuclei resulting from a mitotic division are genetically identical to the original nucleus. They have the same number of sets of chromosomes, one set in the case of haploid cells and two sets in the case of diploid cells. In most plants and all animal species, it is typically diploid cells that undergo mitosis to form new diploid cells. In contrast, meiosis consists of two nuclear divisions resulting in four nuclei that are usually partitioned into four new cells. The nuclei resulting from meiosis are not genetically identical and they contain one chromosome set only. This is half the number of chromosome sets in the original cell, which is diploid.

The main differences between mitosis and meiosis occur in meiosis I, which is a very different nuclear division than mitosis. In meiosis I, the homologous chromosome pairs become associated with each other, are bound together with the synaptonemal complex, develop chiasmata and undergo crossover between sister chromatids, and line up along the metaphase plate in tetrads with kinetochore fibers from opposite spindle poles attached to each kinetochore of a homolog in a tetrad. All of these events occur only in meiosis I.

When the chiasmata resolve and the tetrad is broken up with the homologs moving to one pole or another, the ploidy level—the number of sets of chromosomes in each future nucleus—has been reduced from two to one. For this reason, meiosis I is referred to as a **reduction division**. There is no such reduction in ploidy level during mitosis.

Meiosis II is much more analogous to a mitotic division. In this case, the duplicated chromosomes (only one set of them) line up on the metaphase plate with divided kinetochores attached to kinetochore fibers from opposite poles. During anaphase II, as in mitotic anaphase, the kinetochores divide and one sister chromatid—now referred to as a chromosome—is pulled to one pole while the other sister chromatid is pulled to the other pole. If it were not for the fact that there had been crossover, the two products of each individual meiosis II division would be identical (like in mitosis). Instead, they are different because there has always been at least one crossover per chromosome. Meiosis II is not a reduction division because although there are fewer copies of the genome in the resulting cells, there is still one set of chromosomes, as there was at the end of meiosis I.

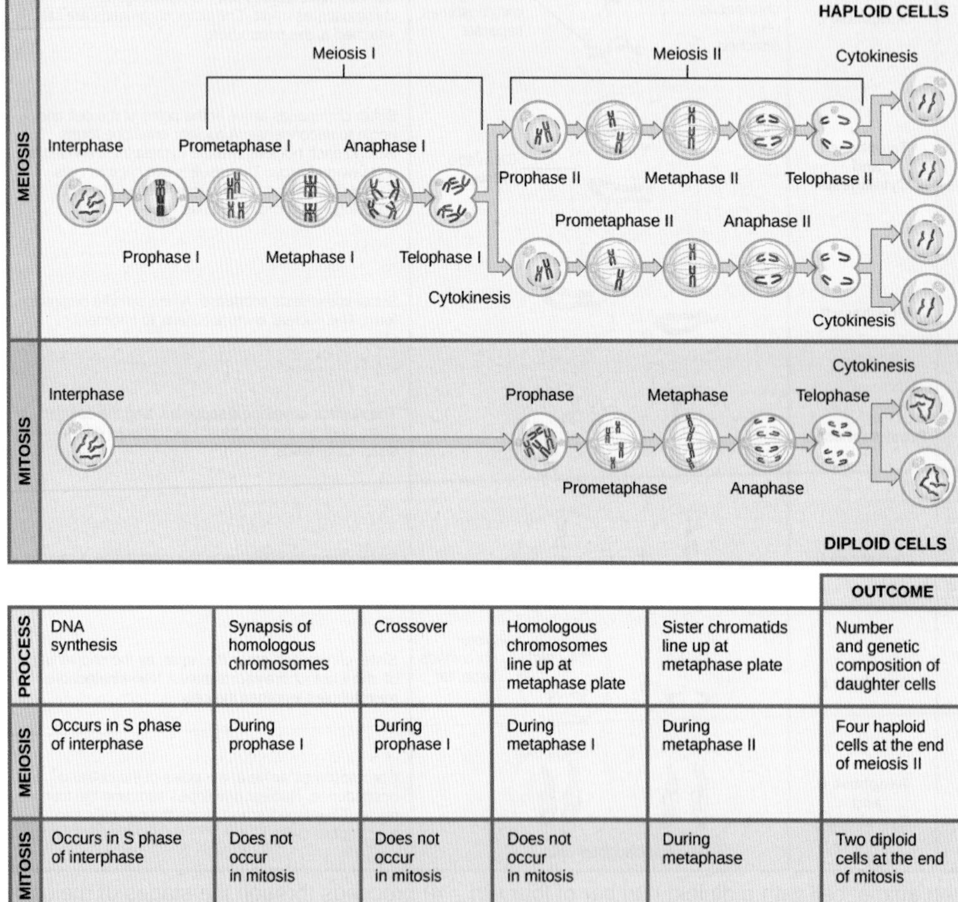

						OUTCOME
PROCESS	DNA synthesis	Synapsis of homologous chromosomes	Crossover	Homologous chromosomes line up at metaphase plate	Sister chromatids line up at metaphase plate	Number and genetic composition of daughter cells
MEIOSIS	Occurs in S phase of interphase	During prophase I	During prophase I	During metaphase I	During metaphase II	Four haploid cells at the end of meiosis II
MITOSIS	Occurs in S phase of interphase	Does not occur in mitosis	Does not occur in mitosis	Does not occur in mitosis	During metaphase	Two diploid cells at the end of mitosis

Figure 11.7 Meiosis and mitosis are both preceded by one round of DNA replication; however, meiosis includes two nuclear divisions. The four daughter cells resulting from meiosis are haploid and genetically distinct. The daughter cells resulting from mitosis are diploid and identical to the parent cell.

The Mystery of the Evolution of Meiosis

Some characteristics of organisms are so widespread and fundamental that it is sometimes difficult to remember that they evolved like other simpler traits. Meiosis is such an extraordinarily complex series of cellular events that biologists have had trouble hypothesizing and testing how it may have evolved. Although meiosis is inextricably entwined with sexual reproduction and its advantages and disadvantages, it is important to separate the questions of the evolution of meiosis and the evolution of sex, because early meiosis may have been advantageous for different reasons than it is now. Thinking outside the box and imagining what the early benefits from meiosis might have been is one approach to uncovering how it may have evolved.

Meiosis and mitosis share obvious cellular processes and it makes sense that meiosis evolved from mitosis. The difficulty lies in the clear differences between meiosis I and mitosis. Adam Wilkins and Robin Holliday[1] summarized the unique events that needed to occur for the evolution of meiosis from mitosis. These steps are homologous chromosome pairing, crossover exchanges, sister chromatids remaining attached during anaphase, and suppression of DNA replication in interphase. They argue that the first step is the hardest and most important, and that understanding how it evolved would make the evolutionary process clearer. They suggest genetic experiments that might shed light on the evolution of synapsis.

There are other approaches to understanding the evolution of meiosis in progress. Different forms of meiosis exist in single-celled protists. Some appear to be simpler or more "primitive" forms of meiosis. Comparing the meiotic divisions of different protists may shed light on the evolution of meiosis. Marilee Ramesh and colleagues[2] compared the genes involved in meiosis in protists to understand when and where meiosis might have evolved. Although research is still ongoing, recent scholarship into meiosis in protists suggests that some aspects of meiosis may have evolved later than others. This kind of genetic comparison can tell us what aspects of meiosis are the oldest and what cellular processes they may have borrowed from in earlier cells.

Which of the following events occurs in both mitosis and meiosis I?

a. Homologous chromosomes pair together.

b. Crossover occurs between chromosomes.

c. Chromosomes line up at the metaphase plate.

d. Sister chromatids remain attached during anaphase.

---

1. Adam S. Wilkins and Robin Holliday, "The Evolution of Meiosis from Mitosis," *Genetics* 181 (2009): 3–12.
2. Marilee A. Ramesh, Shehre-Banoo Malik and John M. Logsdon, Jr, "A Phylogenetic Inventory of Meiotic Genes: Evidence for Sex in *Giardia* and an Early Eukaryotic Origin of Meiosis," *Current Biology* 15 (2005):185–91.

Click through the steps of this interactive animation to compare the meiotic process of cell division to that of mitosis: **How Cells Divide (http://openstaxcollege.org/l/how_cells_dvide)** .

Single-celled organisms, like amoebas, reproduce by mitosis. Explain how the genetic makeup of these organisms differs from organisms that undergo meiosis.

a. Organisms reproducing through mitosis produce genetically different daughter cells whereas those producing through meiosis have genetically identical daughter cells.

b. Crossing over or mixing of chromosomes does not occur in meiosis whereas it is prevalent in mitosis.

c. Mitosis is a process of asexual reproduction in which the number of chromosomes are reduced by half producing two haploid cells whereas in meiosis two diploid cells are produced by cell division.

d. Organisms producing through mitosis create genetically identical offspring as only a single parent copies its entire genetic material to the offspring. In meiosis, two parents produces gametes and the offspring have only half the number of chromosomes of each parent and hence genetic variation is introduced.

science practices CONNECTION for AP® Courses

Activity

Create a series of diagrams with annotations to compare and contrast the processes of mitosis and meiosis in an organism with a haploid number of six. Then, using specific examples, explain how meiosis followed by fertilization increases genetic variation in a family of organisms.

11.2 | Sexual Reproduction

In this section, you will explore the following questions:

- Why are meiosis and sexual reproduction considered evolved traits?
- Why is variation among offspring a potential evolutionary advantage to sexual reproduction?
- What are the three different life-cycles among sexual multicellular organisms and their commonalities?

Connection for AP® Courses

Nearly all eukaryotes undergo sexual reproduction. The variation introduced into the reproductive cells (gametes or spores) by meiosis is advantageous for evolution via natural selection. Meiosis and fertilization alternate as the organisms pass through the haploid and diploid stages of their life cycles. In most animals, the diploid stage dominates, whereas in fungi, the haploid stage dominates. Identifying the haploid and diploid stages within the life cycles of different organisms is vital in understanding how organisms reproduce and in determining when mitosis and meiosis occur.

Information presented and the examples highlighted in the section support concepts and learning objectives outlined in Big Idea 3 of the AP® Biology Curriculum Framework. The learning objectives listed in the Curriculum Framework provide a transparent foundation for the AP® Biology course, an inquiry-based laboratory experience, instructional activities, and AP® exam questions. A Learning Objective merges required content with one or more of the seven science practices.

Big Idea 3	Living systems store, retrieve, transmit and respond to information essential to life processes.
Enduring Understanding 3.C	The processing of genetic information is imperfect and is a source of genetic variation.
Essential Knowledge	**3.C.2** Biological systems have multiple processes that increase genetic variation.
Science Practice	**7.2** The student can connect concepts in and across domain(s) to generalize or extrapolate in and/or across enduring understandings and/or big ideas.
Learning Objective	**3.27** The student is able to compare and contrast processes by which genetic variation is produced and maintained in organisms from multiple domains.

The Science Practice Challenge Questions contain additional test questions for this section that will help you prepare for the AP exam. These questions address the following standards:
[APLO 3.7][APLO 3.9][APLO 3.24][APLO 3.28]

Sexual reproduction was an early evolutionary innovation after the appearance of eukaryotic cells. It appears to have been very successful because most eukaryotes are able to reproduce sexually, and in many animals, it is the only mode of reproduction. And yet, scientists recognize some real disadvantages to sexual reproduction. On the surface, creating offspring that are genetic clones of the parent appears to be a better system. If the parent organism is successfully occupying a habitat, offspring with the same traits would be similarly successful. There is also the obvious benefit to an organism that can produce offspring whenever circumstances are favorable by asexual budding, fragmentation, or asexual eggs. These methods of reproduction do not require another organism of the opposite sex. Indeed, some organisms that lead a solitary lifestyle have retained the ability to reproduce asexually. In addition, in asexual populations, every individual is capable of reproduction. In sexual populations, the males are not producing the offspring themselves, so in theory an asexual population could grow twice as fast.

However, multicellular organisms that exclusively depend on asexual reproduction are exceedingly rare. Why is sexuality (and meiosis) so common? This is one of the important unanswered questions in biology and has been the focus of much research beginning in the latter half of the twentieth century. There are several possible explanations, one of which is that the variation that sexual reproduction creates among offspring is very important to the survival and reproduction of the population. Thus, on average, a sexually reproducing population will leave more descendants than an otherwise similar asexually reproducing population. The only source of variation in asexual organisms is mutation. This is the ultimate source of variation in sexual organisms, but in addition, those different mutations are continually reshuffled from one generation to the next when different parents combine their unique genomes and the genes are mixed into different combinations by crossovers during prophase I and random assortment at metaphase I.

The Red Queen Hypothesis

It is not in dispute that sexual reproduction provides evolutionary advantages to organisms that employ this mechanism to produce offspring. But why, even in the face of fairly stable conditions, does sexual reproduction persist when it is more difficult and costly for individual organisms? Variation is the outcome of sexual reproduction, but why are ongoing variations necessary? Enter the Red Queen hypothesis, first proposed by Leigh Van Valen in 1973.[3] The concept was named in reference to the Red Queen's race in Lewis Carroll's book, *Through the Looking-Glass*.

All species co-evolve with other organisms; for example predators evolve with their prey, and parasites evolve with their hosts. Each tiny advantage gained by favorable variation gives a species an edge over close competitors, predators, parasites, or even prey. The only method that will allow a co-evolving species to maintain its own share of the resources is to also continually improve its fitness. As one species gains an advantage, this increases selection pressure on the other species; they must also develop an advantage or they will be outcompeted. No single species progresses too far ahead because genetic variation among the progeny of sexual reproduction provides all species with a mechanism to improve rapidly. Species that cannot keep up become extinct. The Red Queen's catchphrase was, "It takes all the running you can do to stay in the same place." This is an apt description of co-evolution between competing species.

Which of the following scenarios provides the best support for the Red Queen Hypothesis?

a. An asexually reproducing plant rapidly populates a hillside left barren by a fire.
b. Individuals of a snail population that reproduce asexually die out after a parasite invades its territory.
c. A widely dispersed population of ruffed grouse disappears because individuals have difficulty finding mates.
d. A sexually-reproducing species of gophers goes extinct after a new predator is introduced.

Life Cycles of Sexually Reproducing Organisms

Fertilization and meiosis alternate in sexual **life cycles**. What happens between these two events depends on the organism. The process of meiosis reduces the chromosome number by half. Fertilization, the joining of two haploid gametes, restores the diploid condition. There are three main categories of life cycles in multicellular organisms: **diploid-dominant**, in which the multicellular diploid stage is the most obvious life stage, such as with most animals including humans; **haploid-dominant**, in which the multicellular haploid stage is the most obvious life stage, such as with all fungi and some algae; and **alternation of generations**, in which the two stages are apparent to different degrees depending on the group, as with plants and some algae.

Diploid-Dominant Life Cycle

Nearly all animals employ a diploid-dominant life-cycle strategy in which the only haploid cells produced by the organism are the gametes. Early in the development of the embryo, specialized diploid cells, called **germ cells**, are produced within the gonads, such as the testes and ovaries. Germ cells are capable of mitosis to perpetuate the cell line and meiosis to produce gametes. Once the haploid gametes are formed, they lose the ability to divide again. There is no multicellular haploid life stage. Fertilization occurs with the fusion of two gametes, usually from different individuals, restoring the diploid state (Figure 11.8).

3. Leigh Van Valen, "A New Evolutionary Law," *Evolutionary Theory* 1 (1973): 1–30

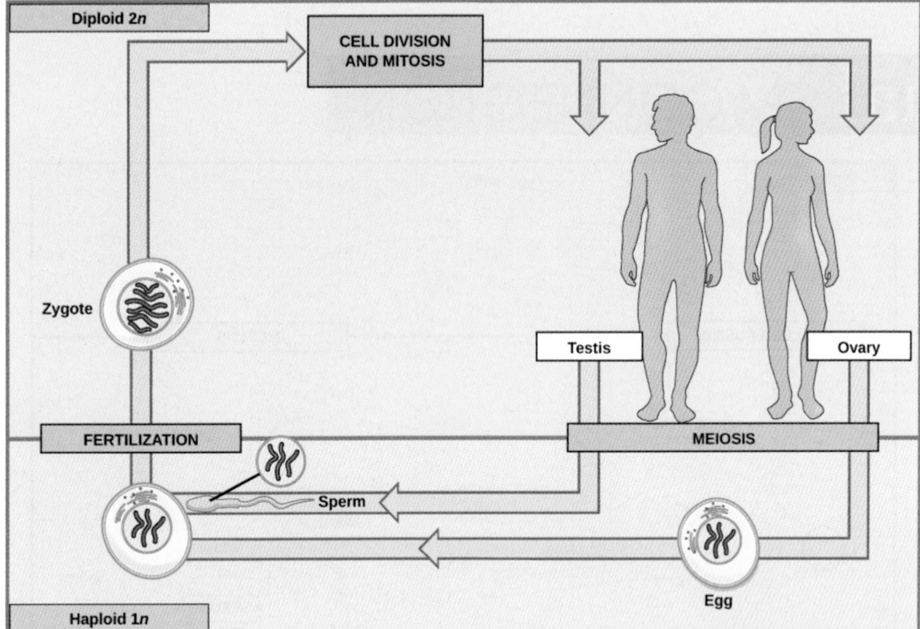

Figure 11.8 In animals, sexually reproducing adults form haploid gametes from diploid germ cells. Fusion of the gametes gives rise to a fertilized egg cell, or zygote. The zygote will undergo multiple rounds of mitosis to produce a multicellular offspring. The germ cells are generated early in the development of the zygote.

Haploid-Dominant Life Cycle

Most fungi and algae employ a life-cycle type in which the “body” of the organism—the ecologically important part of the life cycle—is haploid. The haploid cells that make up the tissues of the dominant multicellular stage are formed by mitosis. During sexual reproduction, specialized haploid cells from two individuals, designated the (+) and (−) mating types, join to form a diploid zygote. The zygote immediately undergoes meiosis to form four haploid cells called spores. Although haploid like the “parents,” these spores contain a new genetic combination from two parents. The spores can remain dormant for various time periods. Eventually, when conditions are conducive, the spores form multicellular haploid structures by many rounds of mitosis (Figure 11.9).

visual CONNECTION

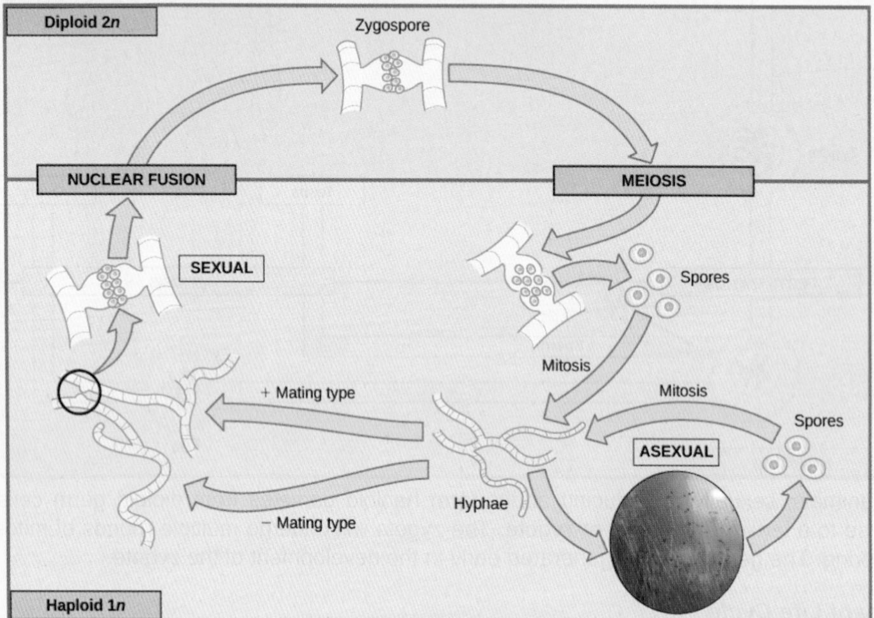

Figure 11.9 Fungi, such as black bread mold (*Rhizopus nigricans*), have haploid-dominant life cycles. The haploid multicellular stage produces specialized haploid cells by mitosis that fuse to form a diploid zygote. The zygote undergoes meiosis to produce haploid spores. Each spore gives rise to a multicellular haploid organism by mitosis. (credit "zygomycota" micrograph: modification of work by "Fanaberka"/Wikimedia Commons)

If a mutation occurs so that a fungus is no longer able to produce a minus mating type, will it still be able to reproduce?

a. No, sexual mode of reproduction is the only mode of reproduction in fungi.

b. No, absence of minus mating types will disrupt functions in fungi.

c. Yes, it will be able to reproduce asexually by the mitotic divisions of spores.

d. Yes, by action of some enzymes, it will be able to reproduce asexually.

Alternation of Generations

The third life-cycle type, employed by some algae and all plants, is a blend of the haploid-dominant and diploid-dominant extremes. Species with alternation of generations have both haploid and diploid multicellular organisms as part of their life cycle. The haploid multicellular plants are called **gametophytes**, because they produce gametes from specialized cells. Meiosis is not directly involved in the production of gametes in this case, because the organism that produces the gametes is already a haploid. Fertilization between the gametes forms a diploid zygote. The zygote will undergo many rounds of mitosis and give rise to a diploid multicellular plant called a **sporophyte**. Specialized cells of the sporophyte will undergo meiosis and produce haploid spores. The spores will subsequently develop into the gametophytes (Figure 11.10).

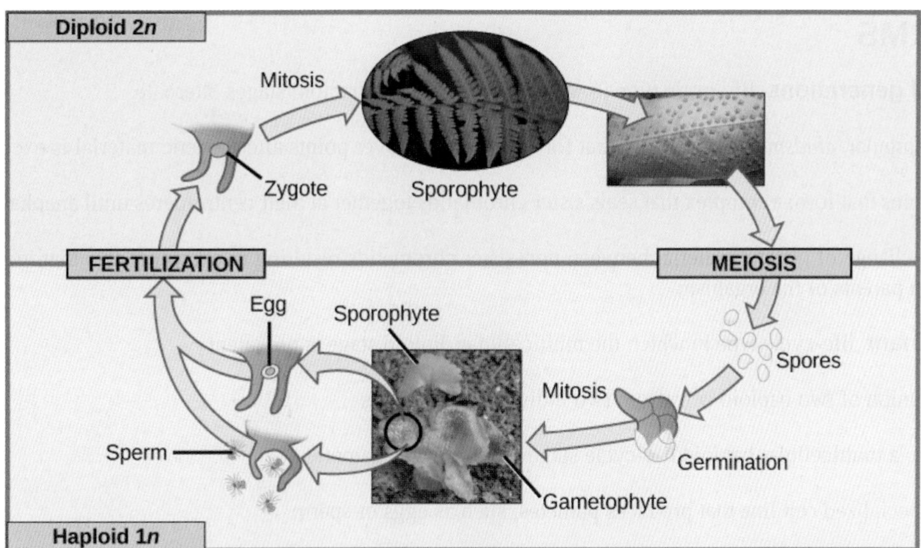

Figure 11.10 Plants have a life cycle that alternates between a multicellular haploid organism and a multicellular diploid organism. In some plants, such as ferns, both the haploid and diploid plant stages are free-living. The diploid plant is called a sporophyte because it produces haploid spores by meiosis. The spores develop into multicellular, haploid plants called gametophytes because they produce gametes. The gametes of two individuals will fuse to form a diploid zygote that becomes the sporophyte. (credit "fern": modification of work by Cory Zanker; credit "sporangia": modification of work by "Obsidian Soul"/Wikimedia Commons; credit "gametophyte and sporophyte": modification of work by "Vlmastra"/Wikimedia Commons)

Although all plants utilize some version of the alternation of generations, the relative size of the sporophyte and the gametophyte and the relationship between them vary greatly. In plants such as moss, the gametophyte organism is the free-living plant, and the sporophyte is physically dependent on the gametophyte. In other plants, such as ferns, both the gametophyte and sporophyte plants are free-living; however, the sporophyte is much larger. In seed plants, such as magnolia trees and daisies, the gametophyte is composed of only a few cells and, in the case of the female gametophyte, is completely retained within the sporophyte.

Sexual reproduction takes many forms in multicellular organisms. However, at some point in each type of life cycle, meiosis produces haploid cells that will fuse with the haploid cell of another organism. The mechanisms of variation—crossover, random assortment of homologous chromosomes, and random fertilization—are present in all versions of sexual reproduction. The fact that nearly every multicellular organism on Earth employs sexual reproduction is strong evidence for the benefits of producing offspring with unique gene combinations, though there are other possible benefits as well.

science practices CONNECTION for AP® Courses

Think About It

Compare and contrast the three main types of life cycles in multicellular organisms and give an example of an organism that employs each.

KEY TERMS

alternation of generations life-cycle type in which the diploid and haploid stages alternate

chiasmata (singular, *chiasma*) the structure that forms at the crossover points after genetic material is exchanged

cohesin proteins that form a complex that seals sister chromatids together at their centromeres until anaphase II of meiosis

crossover exchange of genetic material between non-sister chromatids resulting in chromosomes that incorporate genes from both parents of the organism

diploid-dominant life-cycle type in which the multicellular diploid stage is prevalent

fertilization union of two haploid cells from two individual organisms

gametophyte a multicellular haploid life-cycle stage that produces gametes

germ cells specialized cell line that produces gametes, such as eggs or sperm

haploid-dominant life-cycle type in which the multicellular haploid stage is prevalent

interkinesis (also, *interphase II*) brief period of rest between meiosis I and meiosis II

life cycle the sequence of events in the development of an organism and the production of cells that produce offspring

meiosis a nuclear division process that results in four haploid cells

meiosis I first round of meiotic cell division; referred to as reduction division because the ploidy level is reduced from diploid to haploid

meiosis II second round of meiotic cell division following meiosis I; sister chromatids are separated into individual chromosomes, and the result is four unique haploid cells

recombination nodules protein assemblies formed on the synaptonemal complex that mark the points of crossover events and mediate the multistep process of genetic recombination between non-sister chromatids

reduction division nuclear division that produces daughter nuclei each having one-half as many chromosome sets as the parental nucleus; meiosis I is a reduction division

somatic cell all the cells of a multicellular organism except the gametes or reproductive cells

spore haploid cell that can produce a haploid multicellular organism or can fuse with another spore to form a diploid cell

sporophyte a multicellular diploid life-cycle stage that produces haploid spores by meiosis

synapsis formation of a close association between homologous chromosomes during prophase I

synaptonemal complex protein lattice that forms between homologous chromosomes during prophase I, supporting crossover

tetrad two duplicated homologous chromosomes (four chromatids) bound together by chiasmata during prophase I

CHAPTER SUMMARY

11.1 The Process of Meiosis

Sexual reproduction requires that diploid organisms produce haploid cells that can fuse during fertilization to form diploid offspring. As with mitosis, DNA replication occurs prior to meiosis during the S-phase of the cell cycle. Meiosis is a series of events that arrange and separate chromosomes and chromatids into daughter cells. During the interphases of meiosis, each chromosome is duplicated. In meiosis, there are two rounds of nuclear division resulting in four nuclei and usually four daughter cells, each with half the number of chromosomes as the parent cell. The first separates homologs, and the second—like mitosis—separates chromatids into individual chromosomes. During meiosis, variation in the daughter nuclei is introduced because of crossover in prophase I and random alignment of tetrads at metaphase I. The cells that are produced by meiosis are genetically unique.

Meiosis and mitosis share similarities, but have distinct outcomes. Mitotic divisions are single nuclear divisions that produce daughter nuclei that are genetically identical and have the same number of chromosome sets as the original cell. Meiotic divisions include two nuclear divisions that produce four daughter nuclei that are genetically different and have one chromosome set instead of the two sets of chromosomes in the parent cell. The main differences between the processes occur in the first division of meiosis, in which homologous chromosomes are paired and exchange non-sister chromatid segments. The homologous chromosomes separate into different nuclei during meiosis I, causing a reduction of ploidy level in the first division. The second division of meiosis is more similar to a mitotic division, except that the daughter cells do not contain identical genomes because of crossover.

11.2 Sexual Reproduction

Nearly all eukaryotes undergo sexual reproduction. The variation introduced into the reproductive cells by meiosis appears to be one of the advantages of sexual reproduction that has made it so successful. Meiosis and fertilization alternate in sexual life cycles. The process of meiosis produces unique reproductive cells called gametes, which have half the number of chromosomes as the parent cell. Fertilization, the fusion of haploid gametes from two individuals, restores the diploid condition. Thus, sexually reproducing organisms alternate between haploid and diploid stages. However, the ways in which reproductive cells are produced and the timing between meiosis and fertilization vary greatly. There are three main categories of life cycles: diploid-dominant, demonstrated by most animals; haploid-dominant, demonstrated by all fungi and some algae; and the alternation of generations, demonstrated by plants and some algae.

REVIEW QUESTIONS

1. How many and what type of daughter cells does meiosis produce?

a. four haploid
b. four diploid
c. two haploid
d. two diploid

2. What structure is most important in forming the tetrads?

a. centromere
b. chiasmata
c. kinetochore
d. Synaptonemal complex

3. At which stage of meiosis are sister chromatids separated from each other?

a. anaphase I
b. anaphase II
c. prophase I
d. prophase II

4. At metaphase I, homologous chromosomes are connected only at what structures?

a. chiasmata
b. kinetochores
c. microtubules
d. recombination nodules

5. What phase(s) of mitotic interphase is missing from meiotic interkinesis?

a. G_0 phase
b. G_1 phase
c. G_2 phase
d. S-phase

6. What part of meiosis is most similar to mitosis?

a. reduction division
b. interkinesis
c. meiosis I
d. meiosis II

7. Which of the following is not true during crossing over?

a. Chiasmata are formed.
b. Non-sister chromatids exchange genetic material.
c. Recombination nodules mediate cross over events.
d. Spindle microtubules guide the movement of chromosomal material.

8. During which phase does the second round of genetic variation occur during meiosis?

a. anaphase I
b. metaphase I
c. prophase II
d. Genetic variation only occurs during prophase I.

9. Which type of life cycle has both a haploid and a

diploid multicellular stage?

a. alternation of generations
b. asexual
c. diploid-dominant
d. haploid-dominant

10. What is a source of variation in asexual reproduction?

a. crossing over of chromosomes
b. mutation of DNA
c. random assortment of chromosomes
d. There is no variation in asexual reproduction.

11. What is a likely evolutionary advantage of sexual reproduction over asexual reproduction?

a. Sexual reproduction involves fewer steps.
b. Sexual reproduction results in variation in the offspring.
c. Sexual reproduction is more metabolically efficient.
d. Sexual reproduction uses up fewer resources in a given environment.

12. What is a disadvantage of sexual reproduction over asexual forms of reproduction?

a. Half the population is capable of carrying offspring.
b. Identical offspring are not produced.
c. Adaptation to rapidly changing environments is more difficult.
d. Mutation rates are slower.

13. Fungi typically display which type of life cycle?

a. alternation of generations
b. asexual
c. diploid-dominant
d. haploid-dominant

14. What is a haploid cell produced in a diploid-dominant organism by meiosis called?

a. gamete
b. gametophyte
c. spore
d. sporophyte

CRITICAL THINKING QUESTIONS

15. Describe what happens to the tetrads after they form.

a. Prophase I of meiosis forms the tetrads. They line up at the midway point between the two poles of the cell to form the metaphase plate. There is equal chance of a microtubule fiber to encounter a maternally or a paternally inherited chromosome. Orientation of each tetrad is independent of the orientation of other tetrads.
b. Prophase II of meiosis forms the tetrads. They line up at the midway point between the two poles of the cell to form the metaphase plate. There is equal chance of microtubule fiber to encounter maternally or paternally inherited chromosome. Orientation of each tetrad is independent of the orientation of other tetrads.
c. Prophase I of mitosis forms the tetrads. They line up at the midway between the two poles of the cell to form the metaphase plate. There is equal chance of a microtubule fiber to encounter a maternally or a paternally inherited chromosome. Orientation of each tetrad is independent of the orientation of other tetrads.
d. Prophase I of meiosis forms the tetrads. They line up at the midway between the two poles of the cell to form the metaphase plate. There is a chance of microtubule fiber to encounter maternally inherited chromosome. Orientation of each tetrad is independent of the orientation of other tetrads.

16. Which of the following distinguishes metaphase I from metaphase II?

a. Metaphase I occurs when chromosomes appear in homologous pairs on the spindle. Metaphase II has a single line of chromosomes on the spindle. A Pair of chromosomes is pulled apart and migrate towards pole in anaphase I, while in anaphase II sister chromatids separate. Telophase I reconstitutes the nucleus and loosen the chromosomes, while telophase II mimics telophase I.

b. Prophase I condenses the chromosomes and eliminates the nuclear membrane. The microtubules arrange in a spindle. Prophase II mimics prophase I. Metaphase I occurs when chromosomes appear in homologous pairs on the spindle. Metaphase II has a single line of chromosomes on the spindle. Pairs of chromosomes are pulled apart and migrate towards the poles during anaphase I, while in anaphase II sister chromatids separate. Telophase I reconstitutes the nucleus and condenses the chromosomes, while telophase II mimics telophase I.

c. Prophase I condense the chromosomes and add nuclear membrane. The microtubules arrange in a spindle. Prophase II mimics prophase I. Metaphase I occurs when chromosomes appear in homologous pairs on the spindle. Metaphase II has a single line of chromosomes on the spindle. Pair of chromosomes are pulled apart and migrate towards the poles in anaphase I, while in anaphase II sister chromatids separate. Telophase I reconstitutes the nucleus and loosens the chromosomes, while telophase II mimics telophase I.

d. Prophase I condenses the chromosomes and eliminates the nuclear membrane. The microtubules arrange in a spindle. Prophase II mimics prophase I. Metaphase I occurs when chromosomes appear in homologous pairs on the spindle. During Metaphase II, the chromosomes line up in a double line across the spindle. Each pair of chromosomes is pulled apart and migrate towards the poles in anaphase I, while in anaphase II sister chromatids separate. Telophase I reconstitutes the nucleus and loosen the chromosomes, while telophase II mimics telophase I.

17. Though the stages of meiosis have the same names as the stages of mitosis, they exhibit fundamental differences. What are the main differences between the two processes?

a. Meiosis differs from mitosis in that the number of chromosomes is halved and genetic variation is introduced in meiosis, but not in mitosis.

b. Meiosis differs from mitosis in that the number of chromosomes is halved and genetic variation is reduced in meiosis, but not in mitosis.

c. Metaphase and telophase portions of meiosis and mitosis are the same. Meiosis and mitosis are also the same, except for the number of chromosomes. Anaphase I and anaphase are different.

d. Prophase and telophase portions of meiosis and mitosis are the same. Meiosis II and mitosis are also the same and have the same number of chromosomes. Anaphase I and anaphase are different.

18. Explain how the orientation of homologous chromosomes during metaphase I of meiosis contributes to greater variation in gametes.

a. The random alignment of homologous chromosomes at the metaphase plate ensures the random destination of the chromosomes in the daughter cells.

b. Because homologous chromosomes dissociate from the spindle fibers during metaphase I, they move randomly to the daughter cells.

c. The homologous chromosomes are paired tightly during metaphase I and undergo crossover as the synaptonemal complex forms a lattice around them.

d. Recombination of maternal and paternal chromosomes occurs in metaphase I because the homologous chromosomes are not connected at their centromeres.

19. Explain how the Red Queen's catchphrase, "It takes all the running you can do to stay in the same place," describes co-evolution between competing species.

a. When a sexually reproducing species and an asexually reproducing species compete for the same resources, they both "run [evolve] in the same place" because the increased genetic variation in the sexually reproducing species balances the loss in energy it uses to find and attract mates.

b. When one species gains an advantage with a favorable variation, selection increases on another species with which it competes. This species must also develop an advantage or it will be outcompeted. The two species "run [evolve] to stay in the same place."

c. When one species develops a mutation that decreases its ability to survive, a competing species will become better able to survive even though it has not changed in any way. In effect, this species "runs [evolves] to stay in the same place."

d. When two asexually reproducing species encounter rapid environmental change, the species that is also able to reproduce sexually will outcompete the other. This way it can "run [evolve] to stay in the same place."

20. Which three processes lead to variation among offspring that have the same two parents?

a. genetic recombination, fertilization, meiosis

b. crossing over, random chromosome assortment, genetic recombination

c. meiosis, crossing over, genetic recombination

d. fertilization, crossing over, random chromosome assortment

21. Compare the three main types of life cycles in multicellular organisms and give an example of an organism that employs each.

a. In a diploid dominant cycle, the multicellular diploid stage is present, as in humans. Haploid dominant life cycles have a multicellular haploid stage, as in fungi. In alternation of generations, both haploid dominant and diploid dominant stages alternate, as in plants.

b. In a diploid dominant cycle, the unicellular diploid stage is present, as in humans. In a haploid dominant life cycle, a unicellular haploid stage is present, as in fungi. In alternation of generations both haploid dominant and diploid dominant stages alternate, as in plants.

c. In a diploid dominant cycle, a multicellular haploid stage is present, as in humans. In a haploid dominant life cycle, a multicellular diploid stage is present, as in fungi. In alternation of generations, both haploid dominant and diploid dominant stages alternate, as in plants.

d. In a diploid dominant cycle, a multicellular diploid stage is present, as in algae. In a haploid dominant life cycle, a multicellular haploid stage is present, as in plants. In alternation of generations, both haploid dominant and diploid dominant stages alternate, as in fungi.

TEST PREP FOR AP® COURSES

22. Reproductive cells in most species are different from the cells that make up the rest of the organism. What are the "body" cells called and how are they different from the reproductive cells?

a. Body cells are called gametes and they have half the number of chromosomes found in reproductive cells.

b. Body cells are called somatic cells and have the same number of chromosomes as reproductive cells.

c. Body cells are called somatic cells and have double the number of chromosomes found in reproductive cells.

d. Body cells are called gametes and have double the number of chromosomes found in reproductive cells.

23. Spores are structures produced by some plants and all fungi. Which is true about them?

a. Spores are haploid reproductive cells that can produce haploid organisms through mitosis.

b. Spores are haploid precursors to gametes that give rise to gametes when environmental conditions are favorable.

c. Spores are haploid reproductive cells that can produce diploid cells without fertilization.

d. Spores are haploid cells formed only during asexual reproduction and so are not formed by meiosis.

24. In prophase I, the homologous chromosomes are paired up and linked together. What binds the chromosomes together and maintains their alignment?

a. cohesin proteins

b. tetrads

c. the centromere

d. synaptonemal complex

25. One of the ways that sexual reproduction enhances the diversity of offspring from the same parents is through a process called crossing over. What entities does this occur between during prophase I?

a. sister chromatids
b. tetrads
c. non-homologous chromosomes
d. non-sister chromatids of homologous chromosomes

26. There are three sources of genetic variation in sexual reproduction. Which is not considered random?

a. All are random.
b. Crossing over
c. Egg and sperm fertilization
d. Tetrad alignment on the meiotic spindle.

27. Which one of the three types of life cycles of sexually reproducing organisms does not have a multicellular haploid stage?

a. alternation of generations
b. diploid-dominant
c. haploid-dominant
d. They all have a multicellular haploid stage in their life cycles.

28. How are spores produced in haploid-dominant and alternation of generation life cycles?

a. by gametophytes
b. by germ cells
c. through mitosis
d. through meiosis

29. What is one thing that is true of haploid-dominant life cycles but not of alternation of generation life cycles?

a. meiosis
b. (+) and (−) mating types
c. spores
d. a free-living haploid stage

SCIENCE PRACTICE CHALLENGE QUESTIONS

30. Meiosis involves processes that are common to all eukaryotes, involving the same or similar genes. **Evaluate** the support for the theory of evolution provided by this evidence and, additionally, by the absence of any alternative process.

31. Meiotic phases of yeast cells were observed microscopically with fluorescent markers (Nachman et al., Cell, 131(3), 2007) to determine the time intervals of meiosis I and meiosis II. The data are displayed in the following figure:

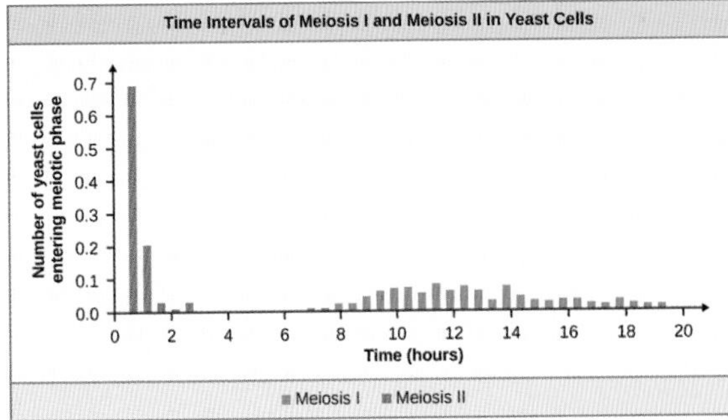

Figure 11.11

The duration of meiosis I is measured relative to the transfer of spores to the growth medium. The duration of meiosis II is measured relative to the emergence from meiosis I. On the *y-axis*, the fraction of cells observed to enter each phase are shown, where the sampling has been made in increments of 0.5 hours.

A. Qualitatively **compare** the mean and standard deviation for these two distributions.

B. The gene Ime1 is transcribed at the start of meiosis I in response to nitrogen starvation. This activates Ime2 that interacts with Ime1. If, during meiosis I, the cells are supplied with nitrogen, meiosis is halted. Based on these data, **justify the claim** that this interaction provides a negative feedback loop.

C. **Explain** the advantage provided to the population and the risk to individual cells of the timing of meiosis displayed in the graph above.

32. Construct an explanation as to how DNA is transmitted to the next generation via meiosis followed by fertilization.

33. In eukaryotes, sexual reproduction involves the recombination of heritable information from both parents via meiosis followed by fertilization. Meiosis reduces the number of chromosomes from diploid (2n) to haploid (1n) during the production of gametes. Meiosis begins with the duplication of DNA, producing four strands of DNA in two pairs of homologous chromosomes: 2(2n) becomes 4(n), that is, four haploid cells, where n is the number of strands of DNA in a chromosome.

A. **Construct** an explanation of the importance of random, independent assortment to genetic variation by **creating a diagram** that represents homologous chromosomes during prophase I without crossover and the possible arrangements of these chromosomes during metaphase I:

- without recombination during prophase I

- with recombination involving two chiasmata

B. An alternative would be to bypass the initial duplication of DNA: 2n becomes 2(n), that is, a diploid cell becomes two haploid cells. **Predict** the effect that this would have on genetic variation.

12 | MENDEL'S EXPERIMENTS AND HEREDITY

Figure 12.1 Experimenting with thousands of garden peas, Mendel uncovered the fundamentals of genetics. (credit: modification of work by Jerry Kirkhart)

Chapter Outline

Introduction

During the 19th century, long before chromosomes or genes had been identified, Johann Gregor Mendel set the framework for genetics by studying a simple biological system, the garden pea. He conducted methodical, quantitative analyses using large sample sizes. Mendel's work laid the foundation for the fundamental principles of heredity. We now know that genes, carried on chromosomes, are the basic functional units of heredity with the capacity to be replicated, expressed, repressed, modified and mutated. Today, the postulates put forth by Mendel form the basis of classical, or Mendelian, genetics. Genes do not all obey the tenets of Mendelian genetics, but Mendel's experiments serve as an excellent starting point for thinking about inheritance.

An understanding of genetic inheritance enables scientists to study and explain complex phenomena. For example, scientists studied the remains of 84 ancient dogs from North and South America. They found that some of the dogs had greater genetic diversity, indicating that these dogs might have interbred with American wolves. Other dogs in their sample had low diversity, indicating that ancient humans were purposely breeding dogs. The study also found that dogs migrated to the Americas with humans only about 10,000 years ago. You can read more about this fascinating story **here (http://openstaxcollege.org/l/32dogs)** .

12.1 | Mendel's Experiments and the Laws of Probability

In this section, you will explore the following questions:

- Why was Mendel's experimental work so successful?
- How do the sum and product rules of probability predict the outcomes of monohybrid crosses involving dominant and recessive alleles?

Connection for AP® Courses

Genetics is the science of heredity. Austrian monk Gregor Mendel set the framework for genetics long before chromosomes or genes had been identified, at a time when meiosis was not well understood. Working with garden peas, Mendel found that crosses between true-breading parents (P) that differed in one trait (e.g., color: green peas versus yellow peas) produced first generation (F1) offspring that all expressed the trait of one parent (e.g., all green or all yellow). Mendel used the term dominant to refer to the trait that was observed, and recessive to denote that non-expressed trait, or the trait that had "disappeared" in this first generation. When the F1 offspring were crossed with each other, the F2 offspring exhibited both traits in a 3:1 ratio. Other crosses (e.g., height: tall plants versus short plants) generated the same 3:1 ratio (in this example, tall to short) in the F2 offspring. By mathematically examining sample sizes, Mendel showed that genetic crosses behaved according to the laws of probability, and that the traits were inherited as independent events. In other words, Mendel used statistical methods to build his model of inheritance.

As you have likely noticed, the AP Biology course emphasizes the application of mathematics. Two rules of probability can be used to find the expected proportions of different traits in offspring from different crosses. To find the probability of two or more independent events (events where the outcome of one event has no influence on the outcome of the other event) occurring together, apply the product rule and *multiply* the probabilities of the individual events. To find the probability that one of two or more events occur, apply the sum rule and *add* their probabilities together.

The content presented in this section supports the learning objectives outlined in Big Idea 3 of the AP® Biology Curriculum Framework. The AP® learning objectives merge essential knowledge content with one or more of the seven science practices. These objectives provide a transparent foundation for the AP® Biology course, along with inquiry-based laboratory experiences, instructional activities, and AP® exam questions.

Big Idea 3	Living systems store, retrieve, transmit and respond to information essential to life processes.
Enduring Understanding 3.A	Heritable information provides for continuity of life.
Essential Knowledge	**3.A.3** The chromosomal basis of inheritance proposed by Mendel provides an understanding of the pattern of passage of genes from parent to offspring.
Science Practice	**3.1** The student can pose scientific questions.
Learning Objective	**3.13** The student is able to pose questions about ethical, social, or medical issues surrounding human genetic disorders.
Essential Knowledge	**3.A.3** The chromosomal basis of inheritance proposed by Mendel provides an understanding of the pattern of passage of genes from parent to offspring.
Science Practice	**2.2** The student can apply mathematical routines to quantities that describe natural phenomena.
Learning Objective	**3.14** The student is able to apply mathematical routines to determine Mendelian patterns of inheritance provided by data sets.

Figure 12.2 Johann Gregor Mendel is considered the father of genetics.

Johann Gregor Mendel (1822–1884) (Figure 12.2) was a lifelong learner, teacher, scientist, and man of faith. As a young adult, he joined the Augustinian Abbey of St. Thomas in Brno in what is now the Czech Republic. Supported by the monastery, he taught physics, botany, and natural science courses at the secondary and university levels. In 1856, he began a decade-long research pursuit involving inheritance patterns in honeybees and plants, ultimately settling on pea plants as his primary **model system** (a system with convenient characteristics used to study a specific biological phenomenon to be applied to other systems). In 1865, Mendel presented the results of his experiments with nearly 30,000 pea plants to the local Natural History Society. He demonstrated that traits are transmitted faithfully from parents to offspring independently of other traits and in dominant and recessive patterns. In 1866, he published his work, *Experiments in Plant Hybridization*,[1] in the proceedings of the Natural History Society of Brünn.

Mendel's work went virtually unnoticed by the scientific community that believed, incorrectly, that the process of inheritance involved a blending of parental traits that produced an intermediate physical appearance in offspring; this hypothetical process appeared to be correct because of what we know now as continuous variation. **Continuous variation** results from the action of many genes to determine a characteristic like human height. Offspring appear to be a "blend" of their parents' traits when we look at characteristics that exhibit continuous variation. The **blending theory of inheritance** asserted that the original parental traits were lost or absorbed by the blending in the offspring, but we now know that this is not the case. Mendel was the first researcher to see it. Instead of continuous characteristics, Mendel worked with traits that were inherited in distinct classes (specifically, violet versus white flowers); this is referred to as **discontinuous variation**. Mendel's choice of these kinds of traits allowed him to see experimentally that the traits were not blended in the offspring, nor were they absorbed, but rather that they kept their distinctness and could be passed on. In 1868, Mendel became abbot of the monastery and exchanged his scientific pursuits for his pastoral duties. He was not recognized for his extraordinary scientific contributions during his lifetime. In fact, it was not until 1900 that his work was rediscovered, reproduced, and revitalized by scientists on the brink of discovering the chromosomal basis of heredity.

Mendel's Model System

Mendel's seminal work was accomplished using the garden pea, *Pisum sativum*, to study inheritance. This species naturally self-fertilizes, such that pollen encounters ova within individual flowers. The flower petals remain sealed tightly until after pollination, preventing pollination from other plants. The result is highly inbred, or "true-breeding," pea plants. These are plants that always produce offspring that look like the parent. By experimenting with true-breeding pea plants, Mendel avoided the appearance of unexpected traits in offspring that might occur if the plants were not true breeding. The garden pea also grows to maturity within one season, meaning that several generations could be evaluated over a relatively short time. Finally, large quantities of garden peas could be cultivated simultaneously, allowing Mendel to conclude that his results did not come about simply by chance.

1.
Johann Gregor Mendel, *Versuche über Pflanzenhybriden Verhandlungen des naturforschenden Vereines in Brünn, Bd. IV für das Jahr*, 1865 Abhandlungen, 3–47. [go here for the English translation here (http://openstaxcollege.org/l/32mendelPlain)]

Mendelian Crosses

Mendel performed **hybridizations**, which involve mating two true-breeding individuals that have different traits. In the pea, which is naturally self-pollinating, this is done by manually transferring pollen from the anther of a mature pea plant of one variety to the stigma of a separate mature pea plant of the second variety. In plants, pollen carries the male gametes (sperm) to the stigma, a sticky organ that traps pollen and allows the sperm to move down the pistil to the female gametes (ova) below. To prevent the pea plant that was receiving pollen from self-fertilizing and confounding his results, Mendel painstakingly removed all of the anthers from the plant's flowers before they had a chance to mature.

Plants used in first-generation crosses were called $\mathbf{P_0}$, or parental generation one, plants (Figure 12.3). Mendel collected the seeds belonging to the P_0 plants that resulted from each cross and grew them the following season. These offspring were called the $\mathbf{F_1}$, or the first filial (*filial* = offspring, daughter or son), generation. Once Mendel examined the characteristics in the F_1 generation of plants, he allowed them to self-fertilize naturally. He then collected and grew the seeds from the F_1 plants to produce the $\mathbf{F_2}$, or second filial, generation. Mendel's experiments extended beyond the F_2 generation to the F_3 and F_4 generations, and so on, but it was the ratio of characteristics in the P_0−F_1−F_2 generations that were the most intriguing and became the basis for Mendel's postulates.

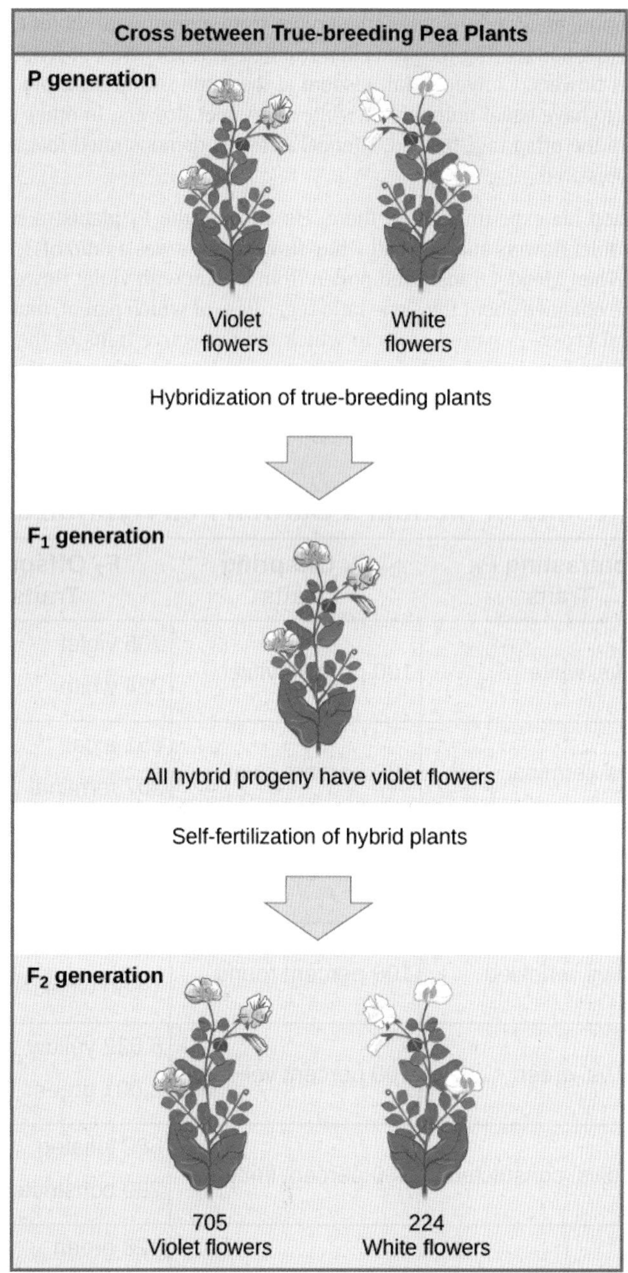

Figure 12.3 In one of his experiments on inheritance patterns, Mendel crossed plants that were true-breeding for violet flower color with plants true-breeding for white flower color (the P generation). The resulting hybrids in the F_1 generation all had violet flowers. In the F_2 generation, approximately three quarters of the plants had violet flowers, and one quarter had white flowers.

Garden Pea Characteristics Revealed the Basics of Heredity

In his 1865 publication, Mendel reported the results of his crosses involving seven different characteristics, each with two contrasting traits. A **trait** is defined as a variation in the physical appearance of a heritable characteristic. The characteristics included plant height, seed texture, seed color, flower color, pea pod size, pea pod color, and flower position. For the characteristic of flower color, for example, the two contrasting traits were white versus violet. To fully examine each characteristic, Mendel generated large numbers of F_1 and F_2 plants, reporting results from 19,959 F_2 plants alone. His findings were consistent.

What results did Mendel find in his crosses for flower color? First, Mendel confirmed that he had plants that bred true for white or violet flower color. Regardless of how many generations Mendel examined, all self-crossed offspring of parents with white flowers had white flowers, and all self-crossed offspring of parents with violet flowers had violet flowers. In addition, Mendel confirmed that, other than flower color, the pea plants were physically identical.

Once these validations were complete, Mendel applied the pollen from a plant with violet flowers to the stigma of a plant with white flowers. After gathering and sowing the seeds that resulted from this cross, Mendel found that 100 percent of the F_1 hybrid generation had violet flowers. Conventional wisdom at that time would have predicted the hybrid flowers to be pale violet or for hybrid plants to have equal numbers of white and violet flowers. In other words, the contrasting parental traits were expected to blend in the offspring. Instead, Mendel's results demonstrated that the white flower trait in the F_1 generation had completely disappeared.

Importantly, Mendel did not stop his experimentation there. He allowed the F_1 plants to self-fertilize and found that, of F_2-generation plants, 705 had violet flowers and 224 had white flowers. This was a ratio of 3.15 violet flowers per one white flower, or approximately 3:1. When Mendel transferred pollen from a plant with violet flowers to the stigma of a plant with white flowers and vice versa, he obtained about the same ratio regardless of which parent, male or female, contributed which trait. This is called a **reciprocal cross**—a paired cross in which the respective traits of the male and female in one cross become the respective traits of the female and male in the other cross. For the other six characteristics Mendel examined, the F_1 and F_2 generations behaved in the same way as they had for flower color. One of the two traits would disappear completely from the F_1 generation only to reappear in the F_2 generation at a ratio of approximately 3:1 (Table 12.1).

The Results of Mendel's Garden Pea Hybridizations

Characteristic	Contrasting P_0 Traits	F_1 Offspring Traits	F_2 Offspring Traits	F_2 Trait Ratios
Flower color	Violet vs. white	100 percent violet	705 violet 224 white	3.15:1
Flower position	Axial vs. terminal	100 percent axial	651 axial 207 terminal	3.14:1
Plant height	Tall vs. dwarf	100 percent tall	787 tall 277 dwarf	2.84:1
Seed texture	Round vs. wrinkled	100 percent round	5,474 round 1,850 wrinkled	2.96:1
Seed color	Yellow vs. green	100 percent yellow	6,022 yellow 2,001 green	3.01:1
Pea pod texture	Inflated vs. constricted	100 percent inflated	882 inflated 299 constricted	2.95:1
Pea pod color	Green vs. yellow	100 percent green	428 green 152 yellow	2.82:1

Table 12.1

Upon compiling his results for many thousands of plants, Mendel concluded that the characteristics could be divided into expressed and latent traits. He called these, respectively, dominant and recessive traits. **Dominant traits** are those that are inherited unchanged in a hybridization. **Recessive traits** become latent, or disappear, in the offspring of a hybridization. The recessive trait does, however, reappear in the progeny of the hybrid offspring. An example of a dominant trait is the violet-flower trait. For this same characteristic (flower color), white-colored flowers are a recessive trait. The fact that the recessive trait reappeared in the F_2 generation meant that the traits remained separate (not blended) in the plants of the F_1 generation. Mendel also proposed that plants possessed two copies of the trait for the flower-color characteristic, and that each parent transmitted one of its two copies to its offspring, where they came together. Moreover, the physical observation of a dominant trait could mean that the genetic composition of the organism included two dominant versions of the characteristic or that it included one dominant and one recessive version. Conversely, the observation of a recessive trait meant that the organism lacked any dominant versions of this characteristic.

So why did Mendel repeatedly obtain 3:1 ratios in his crosses? To understand how Mendel deduced the basic mechanisms of inheritance that lead to such ratios, we must first review the laws of probability.

science practices CONNECTION for AP® Courses

Think About It

Students are performing a cross involving seed color in garden pea plants. Yellow seed color is dominant to green seed color. What F1 offspring would be expected when cross true-breeding plants with green seeds with true-breading plants with yellow seeds? Express the answer(s) as percentage.

Probability Basics

Probabilities are mathematical measures of likelihood. The empirical probability of an event is calculated by dividing the number of times the event occurs by the total number of opportunities for the event to occur. It is also possible to calculate theoretical probabilities by dividing the number of times that an event is expected to occur by the number of times that it could occur. Empirical probabilities come from observations, like those of Mendel. Theoretical probabilities come from knowing how the events are produced and assuming that the probabilities of individual outcomes are equal. A probability of one for some event indicates that it is guaranteed to occur, whereas a probability of zero indicates that it is guaranteed not to occur. An example of a genetic event is a round seed produced by a pea plant. In his experiment, Mendel demonstrated that the probability of the event "round seed" occurring was one in the F_1 offspring of true-breeding parents, one of which has round seeds and one of which has wrinkled seeds. When the F_1 plants were subsequently self-crossed, the probability of any given F_2 offspring having round seeds was now three out of four. In other words, in a large population of F_2 offspring chosen at random, 75 percent were expected to have round seeds, whereas 25 percent were expected to have wrinkled seeds. Using large numbers of crosses, Mendel was able to calculate probabilities and use these to predict the outcomes of other crosses.

The Product Rule and Sum Rule

Mendel demonstrated that the pea-plant characteristics he studied were transmitted as discrete units from parent to offspring. As will be discussed, Mendel also determined that different characteristics, like seed color and seed texture, were transmitted independently of one another and could be considered in separate probability analyses. For instance, performing a cross between a plant with green, wrinkled seeds and a plant with yellow, round seeds still produced offspring that had a 3:1 ratio of green:yellow seeds (ignoring seed texture) and a 3:1 ratio of round:wrinkled seeds (ignoring seed color). The characteristics of color and texture did not influence each other.

The **product rule** of probability can be applied to this phenomenon of the independent transmission of characteristics. The product rule states that the probability of two independent events occurring together can be calculated by multiplying the individual probabilities of each event occurring alone. To demonstrate the product rule, imagine that you are rolling a six-sided die (D) and flipping a penny (P) at the same time. The die may roll any number from 1–6 ($D_\#$), whereas the penny may turn up heads (P_H) or tails (P_T). The outcome of rolling the die has no effect on the outcome of flipping the penny and vice versa. There are 12 possible outcomes of this action (Table 12.2), and each event is expected to occur with equal probability.

Twelve Equally Likely Outcomes of Rolling a Die and Flipping a Penny

Rolling Die	Flipping Penny
D_1	P_H
D_1	P_T
D_2	P_H
D_2	P_T
D_3	P_H

Table 12.2

Rolling Die	Flipping Penny
D_3	P_T
D_4	P_H
D_4	P_T
D_5	P_H
D_5	P_T
D_6	P_H
D_6	P_T

Table 12.2

Of the 12 possible outcomes, the die has a 2/12 (or 1/6) probability of rolling a two, and the penny has a 6/12 (or 1/2) probability of coming up heads. By the product rule, the probability that you will obtain the combined outcome 2 and heads is: (D_2) x (P_H) = (1/6) x (1/2) or 1/12 (Table 12.3). Notice the word "and" in the description of the probability. The "and" is a signal to apply the product rule. For example, consider how the product rule is applied to the dihybrid cross: the probability of having both dominant traits in the F_2 progeny is the product of the probabilities of having the dominant trait for each characteristic, as shown here:

$$\frac{3}{4} \times \frac{3}{4} = \frac{9}{16}$$

On the other hand, the **sum rule** of probability is applied when considering two mutually exclusive outcomes that can come about by more than one pathway. The sum rule states that the probability of the occurrence of one event or the other event, of two mutually exclusive events, is the sum of their individual probabilities. Notice the word "or" in the description of the probability. The "or" indicates that you should apply the sum rule. In this case, let's imagine you are flipping a penny (P) and a quarter (Q). What is the probability of one coin coming up heads and one coin coming up tails? This outcome can be achieved by two cases: the penny may be heads (P_H) and the quarter may be tails (Q_T), or the quarter may be heads (Q_H) and the penny may be tails (P_T). Either case fulfills the outcome. By the sum rule, we calculate the probability of obtaining one head and one tail as $[(P_H) \times (Q_T)] + [(Q_H) \times (P_T)] = [(1/2) \times (1/2)] + [(1/2) \times (1/2)] = 1/2$ (Table 12.3). You should also notice that we used the product rule to calculate the probability of P_H and Q_T, and also the probability of P_T and Q_H, before we summed them. Again, the sum rule can be applied to show the probability of having just one dominant trait in the F_2 generation of a dihybrid cross:

$$\frac{3}{16} + \frac{3}{4} = \frac{15}{16}$$

The Product Rule and Sum Rule

Product Rule	Sum Rule
For independent events A and B, the probability (P) of them both occurring (A *and* B) is $(P_A \times P_B)$	For mutually exclusive events A and B, the probability (P) that at least one occurs (A *or* B) is $(P_A + P_B)$

Table 12.3

To use probability laws in practice, it is necessary to work with large sample sizes because small sample sizes are prone to deviations caused by chance. The large quantities of pea plants that Mendel examined allowed him calculate the probabilities of the traits appearing in his F_2 generation. As you will learn, this discovery meant that when parental traits were known, the offspring's traits could be predicted accurately even before fertilization.

12.2 | Characteristics and Traits

In this section, you will explore the following questions:

- What is the relationship between genotypes and phenotypes in dominant and recessive gene systems?
- How can a Punnett square be used to calculate expected proportions of genotypes and phenotypes in a monohybrid cross?
- How do phenomena such as incomplete dominance, codominance, recessive lethals, multiple alleles, and sex linkage explain deviations from Mendel's model of inheritance?

Connection for AP® Courses

The characteristics that Mendel evaluated in his pea plants were each expressed as one of two versions, or traits (e.g., green peas versus yellow peas). As we will explore in more detail in later chapters, the physical expression of characteristics is accomplished through the expression of genes (sequences of DNA), carried on chromosomes. The genetic makeup of peas consists of two similar, or homologous (remember this term from Chapter 11), copies of each chromosome, one from each parent. Through meiosis, diploid organisms utilize meiosis to produce haploid (1*n*) gametes that participate in fertilization. For cases in which a single gene controls a single characteristic, such as pea color, a diploid organism has genetic copies that may or may not encode the same version of the characteristic. These gene variations (e.g., green peas versus yellow peas) are called alleles.

Different alleles for a given gene in a diploid organism interact to express physical characteristics such as pea color in plants or hairline appearance in humans. The observable traits of an organism are referred to as its phenotype. The organism's underlying genetic makeup, i.e., the combination of alleles, is called its genotype. When diploid organisms carry the same alleles for a given trait, they are said to be homozygous for the genotype; when they carry different alleles, they are said to be heterozygous. For a gene whose expression is Mendelian (Section 12.1), homozygous dominant and heterozygous organisms will look identical; that is, they will have different genotypes but the same phenotype. The recessive allele will only be observed in homozygous recessive individuals.

However, alleles do not always behave in dominant and recessive patterns. In other words, there are exceptions to Mendel's model of inheritance. For example, incomplete dominance describes situation in which the heterozygote exhibits a phenotype that is intermediate between the homozygous phenotypes (e.g., a pink-flowered offspring is produced from a cross between a red-flowered parent and a white-flowered parent). Codominance describes the simultaneous expression of both of the alleles in the heterozygote (e.g., human blood types). It is also common for more than two alleles of a gene to exist in a population (e.g., variations in sizes of pumpkins). In humans, as in many animals and some plants, females have two X chromosomes, and males have one X chromosome and one Y chromosome. Genes on the X chromosome are X-linked, and males inherit and express only one allele for the gene (e.g., hemophilia, color-blindness). Some alleles can also be lethal, so their phenotype will never be observed.

Many human genetic disorders, including albinism, cystic fibrosis, and Huntington's disease can be explained on the basis of simple Mendelian inheritance patterns created by pedigree analysis. (In later Chapters we will learn how DNA analysis can be used to diagnose genetic disorders). Punnett squares are useful tools that apply the rules of probability and meiosis to predict the possible outcomes of genetic crosses. Test crosses are done to determine whether or not an individual is homozygous or heterozygous by crossing the individual with a homozygous recessive.

Information presented and the examples highlighted in the section support concepts outlined in Big Idea 3 of the AP® Biology Curriculum Framework. The learning objectives (LO) listed in the Curriculum Framework provide a transparent foundation for the AP® Biology course, an inquiry-based laboratory experience, instructional activities, and AP® exam questions. A learning objective merges required content with one or more of the seven science practices (SP).

Big Idea 3	Living systems store, retrieve, transmit and respond to information essential to life processes.
Enduring Understanding 3.A	Heritable information provides for continuity of life.

Essential Knowledge	**3.A.3** The chromosomal basis of inheritance proposed by Mendel provides an understanding of the pattern of passage of genes from parent to offspring.
Science Practice	**1.1** The student can create representations and models of natural or man-made phenomena and systems in the domain.
Science Practice	**7.2** The student can connect concepts in and across domain(s) to generalize or extrapolate in and/or across enduring understandings and/or big ideas.
Learning Objective	**3.12** The student is able to construct a representation (e.g., Punnett square) that connects the process of meiosis to the passage of traits from parent to offspring.
Essential Knowledge	**3.A.3** The chromosomal basis of inheritance proposed by Mendel provides an understanding of the pattern of passage of genes from parent to offspring.
Science Practice	**3.1** The student can pose scientific questions.
Learning Objective	**3.13** The student is able to pose questions about ethical, social or medical issues surrounding human genetic disorders.
Essential Knowledge	**3.A.3** The chromosomal basis of inheritance proposed by Mendel provides an understanding of the pattern of passage of genes from parent to offspring.
Science Practice	**2.2** The student can apply mathematical routines to quantities that describe natural phenomena.
Learning Objective	**3.14** The student is able to apply mathematical routines to determine Mendelian patterns of inheritance provided by data sets.
Essential Knowledge	**3.A.4** The inheritance patterns of many traits cannot be explained by simple Mendelian genetics.
Science Practice	**6.5** The student can evaluate alternative scientific explanations.
Learning Objective	**3.15** The student is able to explain deviations from Mendel's model of the inheritance of traits.
Essential Knowledge	**3.A.4** The inheritance patterns of many traits cannot be explained by simple Mendelian genetics.
Science Practice	**6.3** The student can articulate the reasons that scientific explanations and theories are refined or replaced.
Learning Objective	**3.16** The student is able to explain how the inheritance pattern of many traits cannot be accounted for by Mendelian genetics.
Essential Knowledge	**3.A.4** The inheritance patterns of many traits cannot be explained by simple Mendelian genetics.
Science Practice	**1.2** The student can describe representations and models of natural or man-made phenomena and systems in the domain.
Learning Objective	**3.17** The student is able to describe representations of an appropriate example of inheritance patterns that cannot be explained by Mendel's model of the inheritance of traits.

The Science Practice Challenge Questions contain additional test questions for this section that will help you prepare for the AP exam. These questions address the following standards:
[APLO 3.12][APLO 3.14][APLO 3.16][APLO 3.11][APLO 3.13][APLO 3.17]

The seven characteristics that Mendel evaluated in his pea plants were each expressed as one of two versions, or traits. The physical expression of characteristics is accomplished through the expression of genes carried on chromosomes. The genetic makeup of peas consists of two similar or homologous copies of each chromosome, one from each parent. Each pair of homologous chromosomes has the same linear order of genes. In other words, peas are diploid organisms in that they have two copies of each chromosome. The same is true for many other plants and for virtually all animals. Diploid organisms utilize meiosis to produce haploid gametes, which contain one copy of each homologous chromosome that unite at fertilization to create a diploid zygote.

For cases in which a single gene controls a single characteristic, a diploid organism has two genetic copies that may or may not encode the same version of that characteristic. Gene variants that arise by mutation and exist at the same relative locations on homologous chromosomes are called **alleles**. Mendel examined the inheritance of genes with just two allele forms, but it is common to encounter more than two alleles for any given gene in a natural population.

Phenotypes and Genotypes

Two alleles for a given gene in a diploid organism are expressed and interact to produce physical characteristics. The observable traits expressed by an organism are referred to as its **phenotype**. An organism's underlying genetic makeup, consisting of both physically visible and non-expressed alleles, is called its **genotype**. Mendel's hybridization experiments demonstrate the difference between phenotype and genotype. When true-breeding plants in which one parent had yellow pods and one had green pods were cross-fertilized, all of the F_1 hybrid offspring had yellow pods. That is, the hybrid offspring were phenotypically identical to the true-breeding parent with yellow pods. However, we know that the allele donated by the parent with green pods was not simply lost because it reappeared in some of the F_2 offspring. Therefore, the F_1 plants must have been genotypically different from the parent with yellow pods.

The P_1 plants that Mendel used in his experiments were each homozygous for the trait he was studying. Diploid organisms that are **homozygous** at a given gene, or locus, have two identical alleles for that gene on their homologous chromosomes. Mendel's parental pea plants always bred true because both of the gametes produced carried the same trait. When P_1 plants with contrasting traits were cross-fertilized, all of the offspring were **heterozygous** for the contrasting trait, meaning that their genotype reflected that they had different alleles for the gene being examined.

Dominant and Recessive Alleles

Our discussion of homozygous and heterozygous organisms brings us to why the F_1 heterozygous offspring were identical to one of the parents, rather than expressing both alleles. In all seven pea-plant characteristics, one of the two contrasting alleles was dominant, and the other was recessive. Mendel called the dominant allele the expressed unit factor; the recessive allele was referred to as the latent unit factor. We now know that these so-called unit factors are actually genes on homologous chromosome pairs. For a gene that is expressed in a dominant and recessive pattern, homozygous dominant and heterozygous organisms will look identical (that is, they will have different genotypes but the same phenotype). The recessive allele will only be observed in homozygous recessive individuals (Table 12.4).

Human Inheritance in Dominant and Recessive Patterns

Dominant Traits	Recessive Traits
Achondroplasia	Albinism
Brachydactyly	Cystic fibrosis
Huntington's disease	Duchenne muscular dystrophy
Marfan syndrome	Galactosemia
Neurofibromatosis	Phenylketonuria
Widow's peak	Sickle-cell anemia
Wooly hair	Tay-Sachs disease

Table 12.4 This is a table of human inheritance traits and categorizes dominate versus recessive patterns.

Several conventions exist for referring to genes and alleles. For the purposes of this chapter, we will abbreviate genes using the first letter of the gene's corresponding dominant trait. For example, violet is the dominant trait for a pea plant's flower color, so the flower-color gene would be abbreviated as *V* (note that it is customary to italicize gene designations). Furthermore, we will use uppercase and lowercase letters to represent dominant and recessive alleles, respectively. Therefore, we would refer to the genotype of a homozygous dominant pea plant with violet flowers as *VV*, a homozygous recessive pea plant with white flowers as *vv*, and a heterozygous pea plant with violet flowers as *Vv*.

The Punnett Square Approach for a Monohybrid Cross

When fertilization occurs between two true-breeding parents that differ in only one characteristic, the process is called a

monohybrid cross, and the resulting offspring are monohybrids. Mendel performed seven monohybrid crosses involving contrasting traits for each characteristic. On the basis of his results in F_1 and F_2 generations, Mendel postulated that each parent in the monohybrid cross contributed one of two paired unit factors to each offspring, and every possible combination of unit factors was equally likely.

To demonstrate a monohybrid cross, consider the case of true-breeding pea plants with yellow versus green pea seeds. The dominant seed color is yellow; therefore, the parental genotypes were *YY* for the plants with yellow seeds and *yy* for the plants with green seeds, respectively. A **Punnett square**, devised by the British geneticist Reginald Punnett, can be drawn that applies the rules of probability to predict the possible outcomes of a genetic cross or mating and their expected frequencies. To prepare a Punnett square, all possible combinations of the parental alleles are listed along the top (for one parent) and side (for the other parent) of a grid, representing their meiotic segregation into haploid gametes. Then the combinations of egg and sperm are made in the boxes in the table to show which alleles are combining. Each box then represents the diploid genotype of a zygote, or fertilized egg, that could result from this mating. Because each possibility is equally likely, genotypic ratios can be determined from a Punnett square. If the pattern of inheritance (dominant or recessive) is known, the phenotypic ratios can be inferred as well. For a monohybrid cross of two true-breeding parents, each parent contributes one type of allele. In this case, only one genotype is possible. All offspring are *Yy* and have yellow seeds (Figure 12.4).

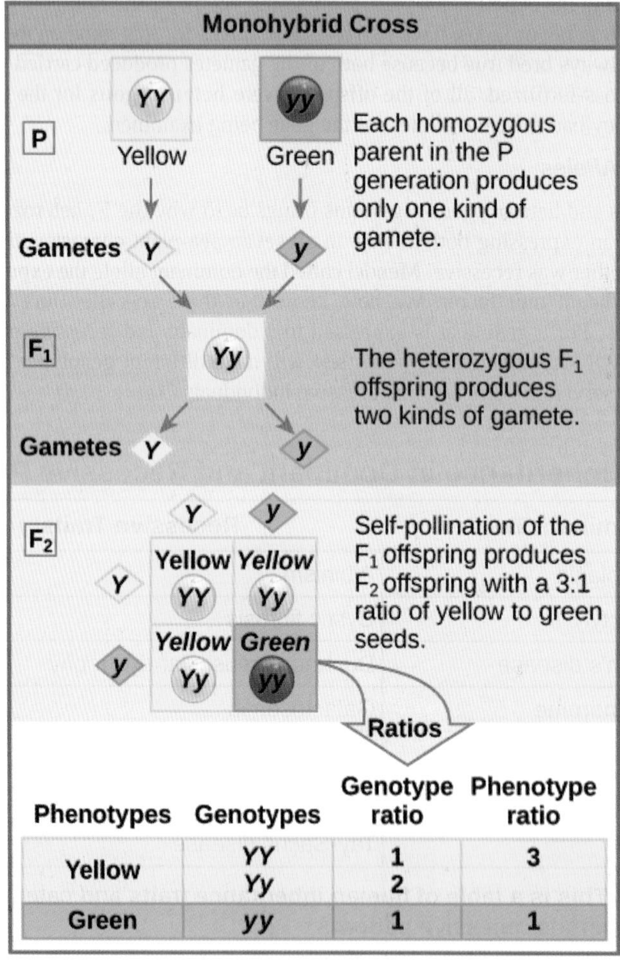

Figure 12.4 In the P generation, pea plants that are true-breeding for the dominant yellow phenotype are crossed with plants with the recessive green phenotype. This cross produces F_1 heterozygotes with a yellow phenotype. Punnett square analysis can be used to predict the genotypes of the F_2 generation.

A self-cross of one of the *Yy* heterozygous offspring can be represented in a 2 × 2 Punnett square because each parent can donate one of two different alleles. Therefore, the offspring can potentially have one of four allele combinations: *YY*, *Yy*, *yY*, or *yy* (Figure 12.4). Notice that there are two ways to obtain the *Yy* genotype: a *Y* from the egg and a *y* from the sperm, or a *y* from the egg and a *Y* from the sperm. Both of these possibilities must be counted. Recall that Mendel's pea-plant characteristics behaved in the same way in reciprocal crosses. Therefore, the two possible heterozygous combinations produce offspring that are genotypically and phenotypically identical despite their dominant and recessive alleles deriving from different parents. They are grouped together. Because fertilization is a random event, we expect each combination to be equally likely and for the offspring to exhibit a ratio of *YY*:*Yy*:*yy* genotypes of 1:2:1 (**Figure 12.4**). Furthermore, because the *YY* and *Yy* offspring have yellow seeds and are phenotypically identical, applying the sum rule of probability, we expect the offspring to exhibit a phenotypic ratio of 3 yellow:1 green. Indeed, working with large sample sizes, Mendel observed approximately this ratio in every F_2 generation resulting from crosses for individual traits.

Mendel validated these results by performing an F_3 cross in which he self-crossed the dominant- and recessive-expressing F_2 plants. When he self-crossed the plants expressing green seeds, all of the offspring had green seeds, confirming that all green seeds had homozygous genotypes of *yy*. When he self-crossed the F_2 plants expressing yellow seeds, he found that one-third of the plants bred true, and two-thirds of the plants segregated at a 3:1 ratio of yellow:green seeds. In this case, the true-breeding plants had homozygous (*YY*) genotypes, whereas the segregating plants corresponded to the heterozygous (*Yy*) genotype. When these plants self-fertilized, the outcome was just like the F_1 self-fertilizing cross.

The Test Cross Distinguishes the Dominant Phenotype

Beyond predicting the offspring of a cross between known homozygous or heterozygous parents, Mendel also developed a way to determine whether an organism that expressed a dominant trait was a heterozygote or a homozygote. Called the **test cross**, this technique is still used by plant and animal breeders. In a test cross, the dominant-expressing organism is crossed with an organism that is homozygous recessive for the same characteristic. If the dominant-expressing organism is a homozygote, then all F_1 offspring will be heterozygotes expressing the dominant trait (**Figure 12.5**). Alternatively, if the dominant expressing organism is a heterozygote, the F_1 offspring will exhibit a 1:1 ratio of heterozygotes and recessive homozygotes (**Figure 12.5**). The test cross further validates Mendel's postulate that pairs of unit factors segregate equally.

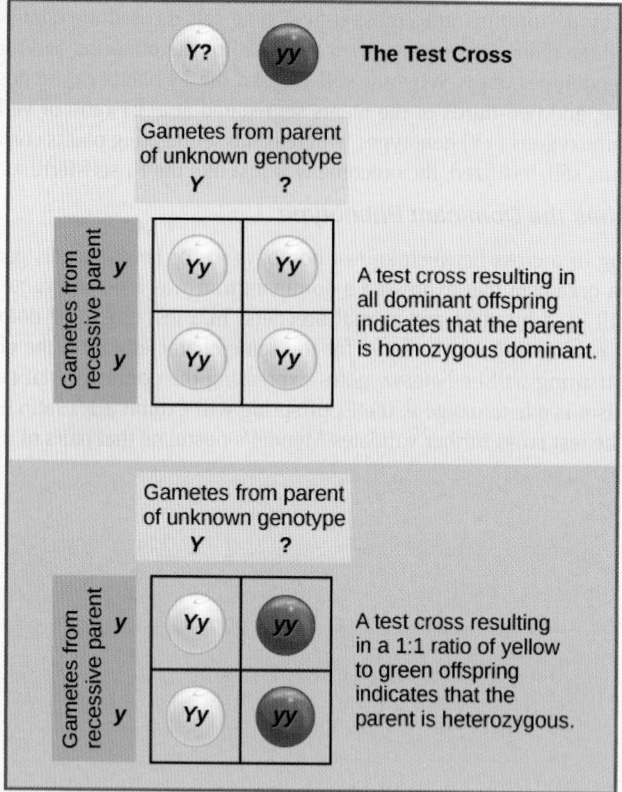

Figure 12.5 A test cross can be performed to determine whether an organism expressing a dominant trait is a homozygote or a heterozygote.

In pea plants, round peas (R) are dominant to wrinkled peas (r).You do a test cross between a pea plant with wrinkled peas (genotype rr) and a plant of unknown genotype that has round peas. You end up with three plants, all which have round peas. From this data, can you tell if the round pea parent plant is homozygous dominant or heterozygous? If the round pea parent plant is heterozygous, what is the probability that a random sample of 3 progeny peas will all be round?

a. The data set is too small to predict the genotype of the round pea plant. Assuming that the unknown parent is heterozygous, the probability of having only round pea plants from a random sample of 3 progeny will be $\frac{1}{8}$.

b. The genotype of the unknown round pea plant is Rr. Assuming that the unknown parent is heterozygous, then the probability of having only round pea plants from a random sample of 3 progeny will be $\frac{1}{4}$.

c. The genotype of the unknown round pea plant is Rr. Assuming that the unknown parent is heterozygous, the probability of having only round pea plants from a random sample of 3 progeny will be $\frac{1}{2}$.

d. The data set is too small to predict the genotype of the round pea plant. The probability of having only round pea plants from a random sample of 3 progeny will be $\frac{1}{6}$.

Many human diseases are genetically inherited. A healthy person in a family in which some members suffer from a recessive genetic disorder may want to know if he or she has the disease-causing gene and what risk exists of passing the disorder on to his or her offspring. Of course, doing a test cross in humans is unethical and impractical. Instead, geneticists use **pedigree**

analysis to study the inheritance pattern of human genetic diseases (**Figure 12.6**).

visual CONNECTION

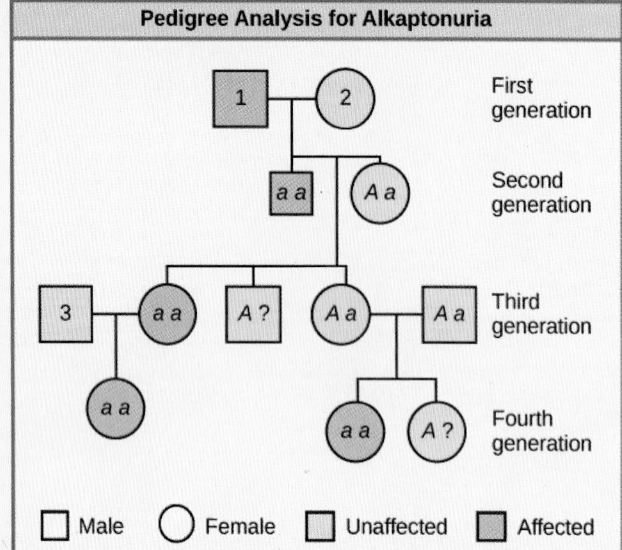

Figure 12.6 Alkaptonuria is a recessive genetic disorder in which two amino acids, phenylalanine and tyrosine, are not properly metabolized. Affected individuals may have darkened skin and brown urine, and may suffer joint damage and other complications. In this pedigree, individuals with the disorder are indicated in blue and have the genotype *aa*. Unaffected individuals are indicated in yellow and have the genotype *AA* or *Aa*. Note that it is often possible to determine a person's genotype from the genotype of their offspring. For example, if neither parent has the disorder but their child does, they must be heterozygous. Two individuals on the pedigree have an unaffected phenotype but unknown genotype. Because they do not have the disorder, they must have at least one normal allele, so their genotype gets the "*A?*" designation.

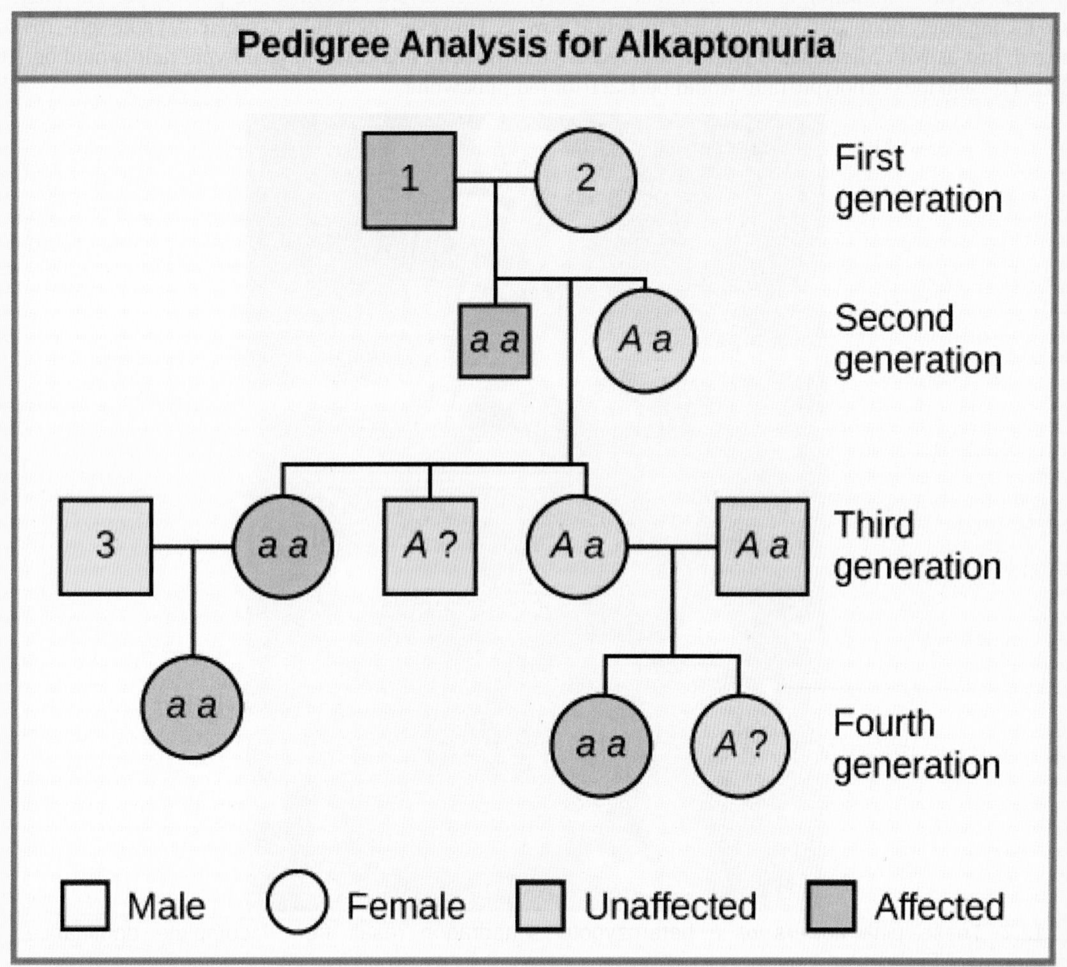

Using the pedigree above, what are the genotypes of the individuals labeled 1, 2 and 3?

a. 1- aa , 2-AA, 3- AA
b. 1-aa, 2-Aa, 3- Aa
c. 1-aa, 2-Aa, 3-AA
d. 1-Aa, 2-Aa, 3-Aa

Alternatives to Dominance and Recessiveness

Mendel's experiments with pea plants suggested that: (1) two "units" or alleles exist for every gene; (2) alleles maintain their integrity in each generation (no blending); and (3) in the presence of the dominant allele, the recessive allele is hidden and makes no contribution to the phenotype. Therefore, recessive alleles can be "carried" and not expressed by individuals. Such heterozygous individuals are sometimes referred to as "carriers." Further genetic studies in other plants and animals have shown that much more complexity exists, but that the fundamental principles of Mendelian genetics still hold true. In the sections to follow, we consider some of the extensions of Mendelism. If Mendel had chosen an experimental system that exhibited these genetic complexities, it's possible that he would not have understood what his results meant.

Incomplete Dominance

Mendel's results, that traits are inherited as dominant and recessive pairs, contradicted the view at that time that offspring exhibited a blend of their parents' traits. However, the heterozygote phenotype occasionally does appear to be intermediate between the two parents. For example, in the snapdragon, *Antirrhinum majus* (Figure 12.7), a cross between a homozygous parent with white flowers (C^WC^W) and a homozygous parent with red flowers (C^RC^R) will produce offspring with pink flowers (C^RC^W). (Note that different genotypic abbreviations are used for Mendelian extensions to distinguish these patterns from simple dominance and recessiveness.) This pattern of inheritance is described as **incomplete dominance**, denoting the expression of two contrasting alleles such that the individual displays an intermediate phenotype. The allele for red flowers is incompletely dominant over the allele for white flowers. However, the results of a heterozygote self-cross can still be predicted, just as with Mendelian dominant and recessive crosses. In this case, the genotypic ratio would be 1 C^RC^R:2 C^RC^W:1 C^WC^W, and the phenotypic ratio would be 1:2:1 for red:pink:white.

Figure 12.7 These pink flowers of a heterozygote snapdragon result from incomplete dominance. (credit: “storebukkebruse”/Flickr)

Codominance

A variation on incomplete dominance is **codominance**, in which both alleles for the same characteristic are simultaneously expressed in the heterozygote. An example of codominance is the MN blood groups of humans. The M and N alleles are expressed in the form of an M or N antigen present on the surface of red blood cells. Homozygotes (L^ML^M and L^NL^N) express either the M or the N allele, and heterozygotes (L^ML^N) express both alleles equally. In a self-cross between heterozygotes expressing a codominant trait, the three possible offspring genotypes are phenotypically distinct. However, the 1:2:1 genotypic ratio characteristic of a Mendelian monohybrid cross still applies.

Multiple Alleles

Mendel implied that only two alleles, one dominant and one recessive, could exist for a given gene. We now know that this is an oversimplification. Although individual humans (and all diploid organisms) can only have two alleles for a given gene, multiple alleles may exist at the population level such that many combinations of two alleles are observed. Note that when many alleles exist for the same gene, the convention is to denote the most common phenotype or genotype among wild animals as the **wild type** (often abbreviated “+”); this is considered the standard or norm. All other phenotypes or genotypes are considered **variants** of this standard, meaning that they deviate from the wild type. The variant may be recessive or dominant to the wild-type allele.

An example of multiple alleles is coat color in rabbits (Figure 12.8). Here, four alleles exist for the *c* gene. The wild-type version, C^+C^+, is expressed as brown fur. The chinchilla phenotype, $c^{ch}c^{ch}$, is expressed as black-tipped white fur. The Himalayan phenotype, c^hc^h, has black fur on the extremities and white fur elsewhere. Finally, the albino, or “colorless” phenotype, *cc*, is expressed as white fur. In cases of multiple alleles, dominance hierarchies can exist. In this case, the wild-type allele is dominant over all the others, chinchilla is incompletely dominant over Himalayan and albino, and Himalayan is dominant over albino. This hierarchy, or allelic series, was revealed by observing the phenotypes of each possible heterozygote offspring.

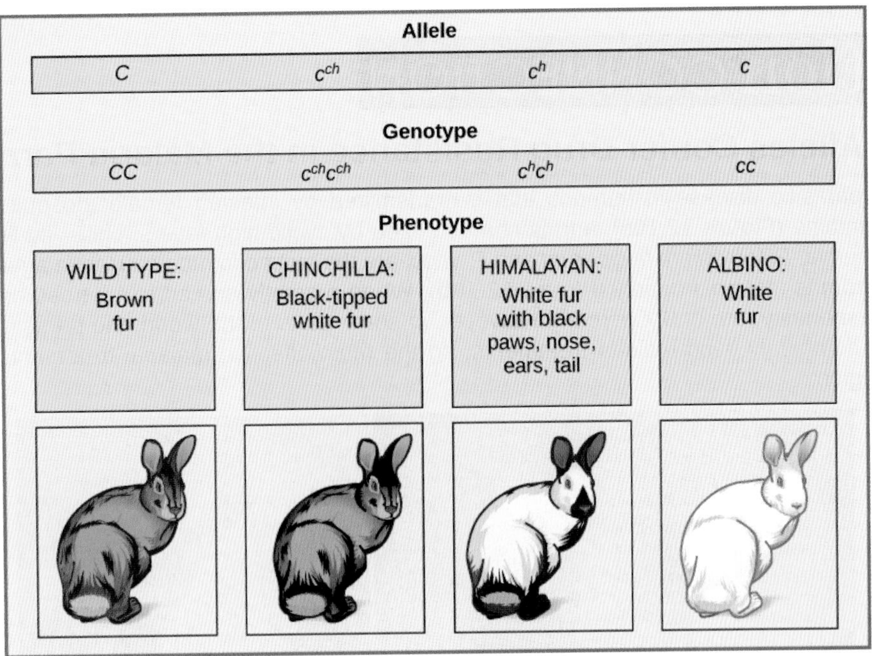

Figure 12.8 Four different alleles exist for the rabbit coat color (*C*) gene.

The complete dominance of a wild-type phenotype over all other mutants often occurs as an effect of "dosage" of a specific gene product, such that the wild-type allele supplies the correct amount of gene product whereas the mutant alleles cannot. For the allelic series in rabbits, the wild-type allele may supply a given dosage of fur pigment, whereas the mutants supply a lesser dosage or none at all. Interestingly, the Himalayan phenotype is the result of an allele that produces a temperature-sensitive gene product that only produces pigment in the cooler extremities of the rabbit's body.

Alternatively, one mutant allele can be dominant over all other phenotypes, including the wild type. This may occur when the mutant allele somehow interferes with the genetic message so that even a heterozygote with one wild-type allele copy expresses the mutant phenotype. One way in which the mutant allele can interfere is by enhancing the function of the wild-type gene product or changing its distribution in the body. One example of this is the *Antennapedia* mutation in *Drosophila* (Figure 12.9). In this case, the mutant allele expands the distribution of the gene product, and as a result, the *Antennapedia* heterozygote develops legs on its head where its antennae should be.

Figure 12.9 As seen in comparing the wild-type *Drosophila* (left) and the *Antennapedia* mutant (right), the *Antennapedia* mutant has legs on its head in place of antennae.

evolution CONNECTION

Multiple Alleles Confer Drug Resistance in the Malaria Parasite

Malaria is a parasitic disease in humans that is transmitted by infected female mosquitoes, including *Anopheles gambiae* (**Figure 12.10a**), and is characterized by cyclic high fevers, chills, flu-like symptoms, and severe anemia. *Plasmodium falciparum* and *P. vivax* are the most common causative agents of malaria, and *P. falciparum* is the most deadly (**Figure 12.10b**). When promptly and correctly treated, *P. falciparum* malaria has a mortality rate of 0.1 percent. However, in some parts of the world, the parasite has evolved resistance to commonly used malaria treatments, so the most effective malarial treatments can vary by geographic region.

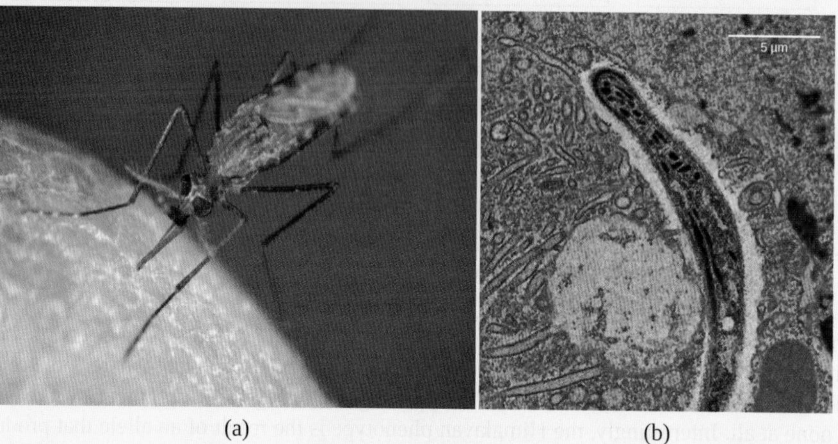

Figure 12.10 The (a) *Anopheles gambiae*, or African malaria mosquito, acts as a vector in the transmission to humans of the malaria-causing parasite (b) *Plasmodium falciparum*, here visualized using false-color transmission electron microscopy. (credit a: James D. Gathany; credit b: Ute Frevert; false color by Margaret Shear; scale-bar data from Matt Russell)

In Southeast Asia, Africa, and South America, *P. falciparum* has developed resistance to the anti-malarial drugs chloroquine, mefloquine, and sulfadoxine-pyrimethamine. *P. falciparum*, which is haploid during the life stage in which it is infectious to humans, has evolved multiple drug-resistant mutant alleles of the *dhps* gene. Varying degrees of sulfadoxine resistance are associated with each of these alleles. Being haploid, *P. falciparum* needs only one drug-resistant allele to express this trait.

In Southeast Asia, different sulfadoxine-resistant alleles of the *dhps* gene are localized to different geographic regions. This is a common evolutionary phenomenon that occurs because drug-resistant mutants arise in a population and interbreed with other *P. falciparum* isolates in close proximity. Sulfadoxine-resistant parasites cause considerable human hardship in regions where this drug is widely used as an over-the-counter malaria remedy. As is common with pathogens that multiply to large numbers within an infection cycle, *P. falciparum* evolves relatively rapidly (over a decade or so) in response to the selective pressure of commonly used anti-malarial drugs. For this reason, scientists must constantly work to develop new drugs or drug combinations to combat the worldwide malaria burden.[2]

According to this passage, why does *P. falciparum* only need one drug-resistant dhps allele to express the drug resistance trait?

a. The drug-resistant dhps allele is co-dominant with the wild type allele.

b. Only one dhps allele is present during all stages of the *P. falciparum* life cycle.

c. Only one dhps allele is present when *P. falciparum* is infectious.

d. The drug-resistant dhps allele prevents the wild type allele from being expressed.

---

2. Sumiti Vinayak, et al., "Origin and Evolution of Sulfadoxine Resistant *Plasmodium falciparum*," *Public Library of Science Pathogens* 6, no. 3 (2010): e1000830, doi:10.1371/journal.ppat.1000830.

X-Linked Traits

In humans, as well as in many other animals and some plants, the sex of the individual is determined by sex chromosomes. The sex chromosomes are one pair of non-homologous chromosomes. Until now, we have only considered inheritance patterns among non-sex chromosomes, or **autosomes**. In addition to 22 homologous pairs of autosomes, human females have a homologous pair of X chromosomes, whereas human males have an XY chromosome pair. Although the Y chromosome contains a small region of similarity to the X chromosome so that they can pair during meiosis, the Y chromosome is much shorter and contains many fewer genes. When a gene being examined is present on the X chromosome, but not on the Y chromosome, it is said to be **X-linked**.

Eye color in *Drosophila* was one of the first X-linked traits to be identified. Thomas Hunt Morgan mapped this trait to the X chromosome in 1910. Like humans, *Drosophila* males have an XY chromosome pair, and females are XX. In flies, the wild-type eye color is red (X^W) and it is dominant to white eye color (X^w) (Figure 12.11). Because of the location of the eye-color gene, reciprocal crosses do not produce the same offspring ratios. Males are said to be **hemizygous**, because they have only one allele for any X-linked characteristic. Hemizygosity makes the descriptions of dominance and recessiveness irrelevant for XY males. *Drosophila* males lack a second allele copy on the Y chromosome; that is, their genotype can only be X^WY or X^wY. In contrast, females have two allele copies of this gene and can be X^WX^W, X^WX^w, or X^wX^w.

Figure 12.11 In *Drosophila*, several genes determine eye color. The genes for white and vermilion eye colors are located on the X chromosome. Others are located on the autosomes. Clockwise from top left are brown, cinnabar, sepia, vermilion, white, and red. Red eye color is wild-type and is dominant to white eye color.

In an X-linked cross, the genotypes of F_1 and F_2 offspring depend on whether the recessive trait was expressed by the male or the female in the P_1 generation. With regard to *Drosophila* eye color, when the P_1 male expresses the white-eye phenotype and the female is homozygous red-eyed, all members of the F_1 generation exhibit red eyes (Figure 12.12). The F_1 females are heterozygous (X^WX^w), and the males are all X^WY, having received their X chromosome from the homozygous dominant P_1 female and their Y chromosome from the P_1 male. A subsequent cross between the X^WX^w female and the X^WY male would produce only red-eyed females (with X^WX^W or X^WX^w genotypes) and both red- and white-eyed males (with X^WY or X^wY genotypes). Now, consider a cross between a homozygous white-eyed female and a male with red eyes. The F_1 generation would exhibit only heterozygous red-eyed females (X^WX^w) and only white-eyed males (X^wY). Half of the F_2 females would be red-eyed (X^WX^w) and half would be white-eyed (X^wX^w). Similarly, half of the F_2 males would be red-eyed (X^WY) and half would be white-eyed (X^wY).

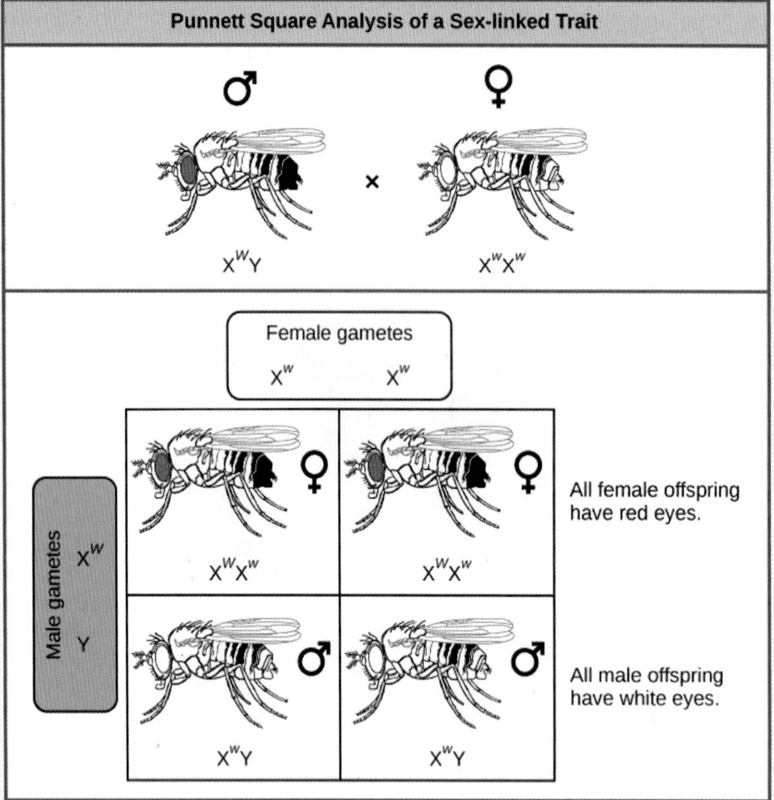

Figure 12.12 Punnett square analysis is used to determine the ratio of offspring from a cross between a red-eyed male fruit fly and a white-eyed female fruit fly.

What ratio of offspring would result from a cross between a white-eyed male fruit fly and a female fruit fly that is heterozygous for red eye color?

a. 25% of the offspring are males and hemizygous dominant with red eyes and 25% are male and hemizygous recessive with white eyes. 25% are female and heterozygous with red eyes and 25% are females and homozygous recessive with white eyes.

b. 50% of the offspring are male and hemizygous dominant with red eyes and 50% are male hemizygous recessive with white eyes. 50% are female and heterozygous with red eyes and 50% are female and homozygous recessive with white eyes.

c. 25% of the males are hemizygous dominant with red eyes and 50% of the male are hemizygous recessive with white eyes. 25% females are heterozygous with red eyes and 50% of the females are homozygous with white eyes.

d. 50% of the males are hemizygous dominant with red eyes and 25% of the male are hemizygous recessive with white eyes. 50% females are heterozygous with red eyes and 25% of the females are homozygous recessive with white eyes

Discoveries in fruit fly genetics can be applied to human genetics. When a female parent is homozygous for a recessive X-linked trait, she will pass the trait on to 100 percent of her offspring. Her male offspring are, therefore, destined to express the trait, as they will inherit their father's Y chromosome. In humans, the alleles for certain conditions (some forms of color blindness, hemophilia, and muscular dystrophy) are X-linked. Females who are heterozygous for these diseases are said to be carriers and may not exhibit any phenotypic effects. These females will pass the disease to half of their sons and will pass carrier status to half of their daughters; therefore, recessive X-linked traits appear more frequently in males than females.

In some groups of organisms with sex chromosomes, the sex with the non-homologous sex chromosomes is the female rather than the male. This is the case for all birds. In this case, sex-linked traits will be more likely to appear in the female, in which they are hemizygous.

Human Sex-linked Disorders

Sex-linkage studies in Morgan's laboratory provided the fundamentals for understanding X-linked recessive disorders in humans, which include red-green color blindness, and Types A and B hemophilia. Because human males need to inherit only one recessive mutant X allele to be affected, X-linked disorders are disproportionately observed in males. Females must inherit recessive X-linked alleles from both of their parents in order to express the trait. When they inherit one recessive X-linked mutant allele and one dominant X-linked wild-type allele, they are carriers of the trait and are typically unaffected. Carrier females can manifest mild forms of the trait due to the inactivation of the dominant allele located on one of the X chromosomes. However, female carriers can contribute the trait to their sons, resulting in the son exhibiting the trait, or they can contribute the recessive allele to their daughters, resulting in the daughters being carriers of the trait (Figure 12.13). Although some Y-linked recessive disorders exist, typically they are associated with infertility in males and are therefore not transmitted to subsequent generations.

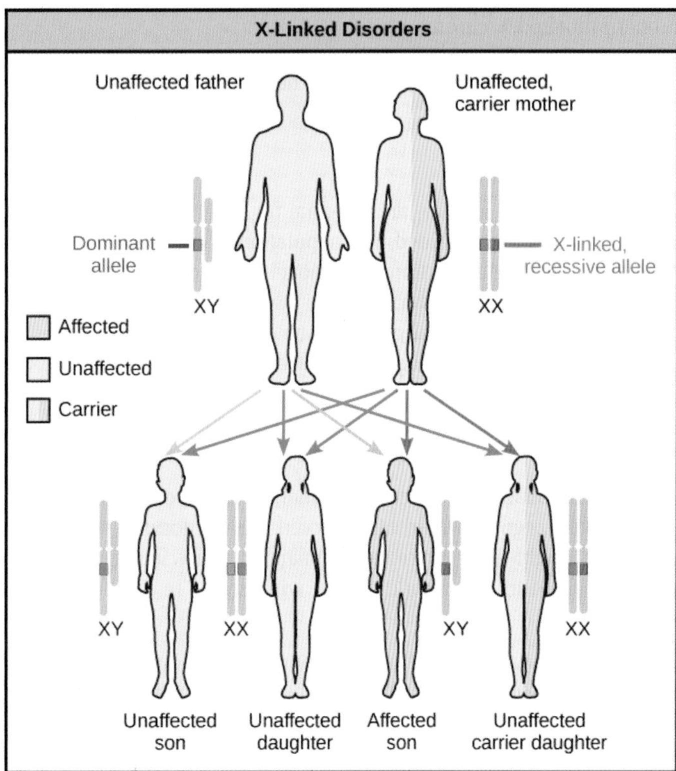

Figure 12.13 The son of a woman who is a carrier of a recessive X-linked disorder will have a 50 percent chance of being affected. A daughter will not be affected, but she will have a 50 percent chance of being a carrier like her mother.

Watch **this video (http://openstaxcollege.org/l/sex-linked_trts)** to learn more about sex-linked traits.

The most common form of hemophilia affects 1 out of every 5,000 male births worldwide, but the condition is much rarer in females. Explain why this is the case.

a. Females need two mutated X chromosomes to be hemophilic.

b. Females need one mutated X chromosome to be hemophilic.

c. Females do not inherit mutated X chromosomes.

d. Females need two mutated X chromosomes to not be hemophilic.

Lethality

A large proportion of genes in an individual's genome are essential for survival. Occasionally, a nonfunctional allele for an essential gene can arise by mutation and be transmitted in a population as long as individuals with this allele also have a wild-type, functional copy. The wild-type allele functions at a capacity sufficient to sustain life and is therefore considered to be dominant over the nonfunctional allele. However, consider two heterozygous parents that have a genotype of wild-type/nonfunctional mutant for a hypothetical essential gene. In one quarter of their offspring, we would expect to observe individuals that are homozygous recessive for the nonfunctional allele. Because the gene is essential, these individuals might fail to develop past fertilization, die *in utero*, or die later in life, depending on what life stage requires this gene. An inheritance pattern in which an allele is only lethal in the homozygous form and in which the heterozygote may be normal or have some altered non-lethal phenotype is referred to as **recessive lethal**.

For crosses between heterozygous individuals with a recessive lethal allele that causes death before birth when homozygous, only wild-type homozygotes and heterozygotes would be observed. The genotypic ratio would therefore be 2:1. In other instances, the recessive lethal allele might also exhibit a dominant (but not lethal) phenotype in the heterozygote. For instance, the recessive lethal *Curly* allele in *Drosophila* affects wing shape in the heterozygote form but is lethal in the homozygote.

A single copy of the wild-type allele is not always sufficient for normal functioning or even survival. The **dominant lethal** inheritance pattern is one in which an allele is lethal both in the homozygote and the heterozygote; this allele can only be transmitted if the lethality phenotype occurs after reproductive age. Individuals with mutations that result in dominant lethal alleles fail to survive even in the heterozygote form. Dominant lethal alleles are very rare because, as you might expect, the allele only lasts one generation and is not transmitted. However, just as the recessive lethal allele might not immediately manifest the phenotype of death, dominant lethal alleles also might not be expressed until adulthood. Once the individual reaches reproductive age, the allele may be unknowingly passed on, resulting in a delayed death in both generations. An example of this in humans is Huntington's disease, in which the nervous system gradually wastes away (**Figure 12.14**). People who are heterozygous for the dominant Huntington allele (*Hh*) will inevitably develop the fatal disease. However, the onset of Huntington's disease may not occur until age 40, at which point the afflicted persons may have already passed the allele to 50 percent of their offspring.

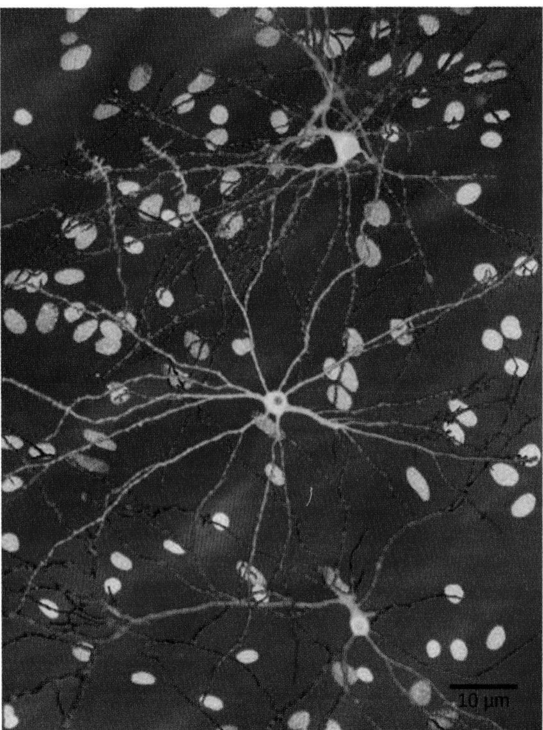

Figure 12.14 The neuron in the center of this micrograph (yellow) has nuclear inclusions characteristic of Huntington's disease (orange area in the center of the neuron). Huntington's disease occurs when an abnormal dominant allele for the Huntington gene is present. (credit: Dr. Steven Finkbeiner, Gladstone Institute of Neurological Disease, The Taube-Koret Center for Huntington's Disease Research, and the University of California San Francisco/Wikimedia)

science practices CONNECTION for AP® Courses

Activity

This section includes descriptions of genetically-inherited human diseases, such as sickle cell anemia, alkaptonuria, hemophilia, color blindness and Huntington's disease. One issue surrounding genetic disorders is the right to privacy. Can you think of other examples of ethical, social, or medical issue surrounding human genetic disorders?

Lab Investigation

Investigate inheritance patterns in an organism of choice, such as Wisconsin Fast Plants or *Drosophila melanogaster*, by performing several genetic crosses and comparing expected and observed phenotypic ratios. Virtual labs exploring Mendelian inheritance patterns are also available online.

Think About It

- In pea plants, round peas (*R*) are dominant to wrinkles peas (*r*) (Figure 12.5). You do a test cross between a pea plant with wrinkled peas (genotype *rr*) and a plant of unknown genotype that has round peas (genotype either *RR* or *Rr*). You end up with three offspring plants, all which have round peas. Based on the phenotype of the offspring plants, can you deduce the genotype of the round pea parent plant? If the round pea parent plant is heterozygous, calculate the probability that a random sample of 3 progeny peas will all be round.
- Can a human male be a carrier of red-green color blindness? Justify your answer.
- In pea plants, violet flowers (*V*) are dominant to white flowers (*v*). What are the possible genotypes and phenotypes for a cross between *Vv* and *vv* pea plants? Use a Punnett square to show all work.

12.3 | Laws of Inheritance

In this section, you will explore the following questions:

- What is the relationship between Mendel's law of segregation and independent assortment in terms of genetics and the events of meiosis?
- How can the forked-lined method and probability rules be used to calculate the probability of genotypes and phenotypes from multiple gene crosses?
- How do linkage, cross-over, epistasis, and recombination violate Mendel's laws of inheritance?

Connection for AP® Courses

As was described previously, Mendel proposed that genes are inherited as pairs of alleles that behave in a dominant and recessive pattern. During meiosis, alleles segregate, or separate, such that each gamete is equally likely to receive either one of the two alleles present in the diploid individual. Mendel called this phenomenon the law of segregation, which can be demonstrated in a monohybrid cross. In addition, genes carried on different chromosomes sort into gametes independently of one another. This is Mendel's law of independent assortment. This law can be demonstrated in a dihybrid cross involving two different traits located on different chromosomes. Punnett squares can be used to predict genotypes and phenotypes of offspring involving one or two genes.

Although chromosomes sort independently into gametes during meiosis, Mendel's law of independent assortment refers to genes, not chromosomes. In humans, single chromosomes may carry more than 1,000 genes. Genes located close together on the same chromosome are said to be linked genes. When genes are located in close proximity on the same chromosome, their alleles tend to be inherited together unless recombination occurs. This results in offspring ratios that violate Mendel's law of independent assortment. Genes that are located far apart on the same chromosome are likely to assort independently. The rules of probability can help to sort this out (pun intended). The law states that alleles of different genes assort independently of one another during gamete formation.

Information presented and the examples highlighted in the section support concepts outlined in Big Idea 3 of the AP® Biology Curriculum Framework. The Learning Objectives listed in the Curriculum Framework provide a transparent foundation for the AP® Biology course, an inquiry-based laboratory experience, instructional activities, and AP® exam questions. A learning objective merges required content with one or more of the seven Science Practices.

Big Idea 3	Living systems store, retrieve, transmit and respond to information essential to life processes.
Enduring Understanding 3.A	Heritable information provides for continuity of life.
Essential Knowledge	**3.A.3** The chromosomal basis of inheritance provides an understanding of the pattern of passage (transmission) of genes from parent to offspring.
Science Practice	**2.2** The student can apply mathematical routines to quantities that describe natural phenomena.
Learning Objective	**3.14** The student is able to apply mathematical routines to determine Mendelian patterns of inheritance provided by data.
Essential Knowledge	**3.A.4** The inheritance pattern of many traits cannot be explained by simple Mendelian genetics.
Science Practice	**6.5** The student can evaluate alternative scientific explanations.
Learning Objective	**3.15** The student is able to explain deviations from Mendel's model of the inheritance of traits.

Essential Knowledge	**3.A.4** The inheritance pattern of many traits cannot be explained by simple Mendelian genetics.
Science Practice	**6.3** The student can articulate the reasons that scientific explanations and theories are refined or replaced.
Learning Objective	**3.16** The student is able to explain how the inheritance patterns of many traits cannot be accounted for by Mendelian genetics.
Essential Knowledge	**3.A.4** The inheritance pattern of many traits cannot be explained by simple Mendelian genetics.
Science Practice	**1.2** The student can describe representations and models of natural or man-made phenomena and systems in the domain.
Learning Objective	**3.17** The student is able to describe representations of an appropriate example of inheritance patterns that cannot be explained by Mendel's model of the inheritance of traits.

The Science Practice Challenge Questions contain additional test questions for this section that will help you prepare for the AP exam. These questions address the following standards:
[APLO 3.11][APLO 3.15][APLO 3.14][APLO 3.17][APLO 3.12]

Mendel generalized the results of his pea-plant experiments into four postulates, some of which are sometimes called "laws," that describe the basis of dominant and recessive inheritance in diploid organisms. As you have learned, more complex extensions of Mendelism exist that do not exhibit the same F_2 phenotypic ratios (3:1). Nevertheless, these laws summarize the basics of classical genetics.

Pairs of Unit Factors, or Genes

Mendel proposed first that paired unit factors of heredity were transmitted faithfully from generation to generation by the dissociation and reassociation of paired factors during gametogenesis and fertilization, respectively. After he crossed peas with contrasting traits and found that the recessive trait resurfaced in the F_2 generation, Mendel deduced that hereditary factors must be inherited as discrete units. This finding contradicted the belief at that time that parental traits were blended in the offspring.

Alleles Can Be Dominant or Recessive

Mendel's **law of dominance** states that in a heterozygote, one trait will conceal the presence of another trait for the same characteristic. Rather than both alleles contributing to a phenotype, the dominant allele will be expressed exclusively. The recessive allele will remain "latent" but will be transmitted to offspring by the same manner in which the dominant allele is transmitted. The recessive trait will only be expressed by offspring that have two copies of this allele (**Figure 12.15**), and these offspring will breed true when self-crossed.

Since Mendel's experiments with pea plants, other researchers have found that the law of dominance does not always hold true. Instead, several different patterns of inheritance have been found to exist.

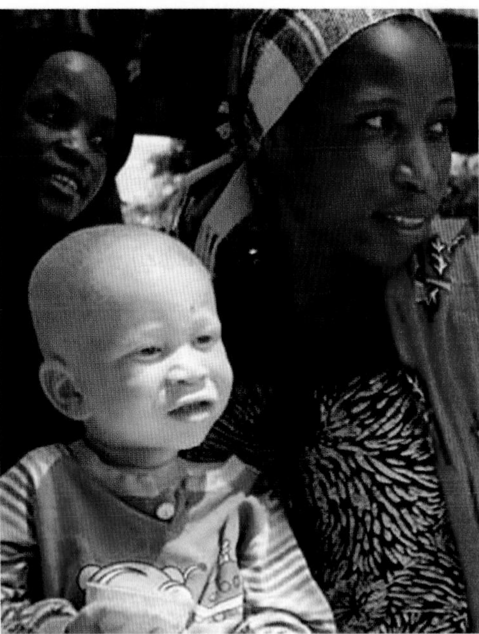

Figure 12.15 The child in the photo expresses albinism, a recessive trait.

Equal Segregation of Alleles

Observing that true-breeding pea plants with contrasting traits gave rise to F_1 generations that all expressed the dominant trait and F_2 generations that expressed the dominant and recessive traits in a 3:1 ratio, Mendel proposed the **law of segregation**. This law states that paired unit factors (genes) must segregate equally into gametes such that offspring have an equal likelihood of inheriting either factor. For the F_2 generation of a monohybrid cross, the following three possible combinations of genotypes could result: homozygous dominant, heterozygous, or homozygous recessive. Because heterozygotes could arise from two different pathways (receiving one dominant and one recessive allele from either parent), and because heterozygotes and homozygous dominant individuals are phenotypically identical, the law supports Mendel's observed 3:1 phenotypic ratio. The equal segregation of alleles is the reason we can apply the Punnett square to accurately predict the offspring of parents with known genotypes. The physical basis of Mendel's law of segregation is the first division of meiosis, in which the homologous chromosomes with their different versions of each gene are segregated into daughter nuclei. The role of the meiotic segregation of chromosomes in sexual reproduction was not understood by the scientific community during Mendel's lifetime.

Independent Assortment

Mendel's **law of independent assortment** states that genes do not influence each other with regard to the sorting of alleles into gametes, and every possible combination of alleles for every gene is equally likely to occur. The independent assortment of genes can be illustrated by the **dihybrid** cross, a cross between two true-breeding parents that express different traits for two characteristics. Consider the characteristics of seed color and seed texture for two pea plants, one that has green, wrinkled seeds (*yyrr*) and another that has yellow, round seeds (*YYRR*). Because each parent is homozygous, the law of segregation indicates that the gametes for the green/wrinkled plant all are *yr*, and the gametes for the yellow/round plant are all *YR*. Therefore, the F_1 generation of offspring all are *YyRr* (Figure 12.16).

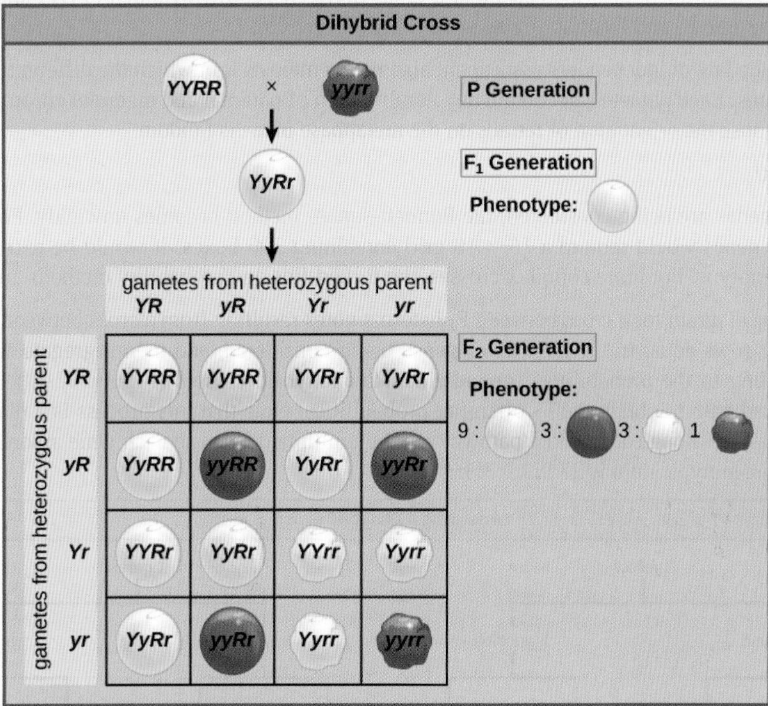

Figure 12.16 This dihybrid cross of pea plants involves the genes for seed color and texture.

In pea plants, purple flowers (P) are dominant to white flowers (p) and yellow peas (Y) are dominant to green peas (y). What are the possible genotypes and phenotypes for a cross between PpYY and ppYy pea plants? What is the minimum number of squares that you need to do a Punnett square analysis of this cross?

a. ppYY, Ppyy, ppYY, ppyy yielding white flowers with yellow peas, purple flowers with yellow peas, and white flowers with green peas. You can find this with a 3×3 Punnett square.

b. PPYY, PpYy, ppYY, ppyy yielding purple flowers with yellow peas, white flowers with yellow peas, and white flowers with green peas. You can find this with a 2×2 Punnett square.

c. Ppyy, PpYy, ppYY, ppyy yielding purple flowers with green peas, purple flowers with yellow peas, white flowers with yellow peas, and white flowers with green peas. You can find this with a 3×3 Punnett square.

d. PpYY, PpYy, ppYY, ppYy yielding purple flowers with yellow peas, and white flowers with yellow peas. You can find this with a 2×2 Punnett square.

For the F2 generation, the law of segregation requires that each gamete receive either an *R* allele or an *r* allele along with either a *Y* allele or a *y* allele. The law of independent assortment states that a gamete into which an *r* allele sorted would be equally likely to contain either a *Y* allele or a *y* allele. Thus, there are four equally likely gametes that can be formed when the *YyRr* heterozygote is self-crossed, as follows: *YR*, *Yr*, *yR*, and *yr*. Arranging these gametes along the top and left of a 4 × 4 Punnett square (Figure 12.16) gives us 16 equally likely genotypic combinations. From these genotypes, we infer a phenotypic ratio of 9 round/yellow:3 round/green:3 wrinkled/yellow:1 wrinkled/green (Figure 12.16). These are the offspring ratios we would expect, assuming we performed the crosses with a large enough sample size.

Because of independent assortment and dominance, the 9:3:3:1 dihybrid phenotypic ratio can be collapsed into two 3:1 ratios, characteristic of any monohybrid cross that follows a dominant and recessive pattern. Ignoring seed color and considering only seed texture in the above dihybrid cross, we would expect that three quarters of the F_2 generation offspring would be round, and one quarter would be wrinkled. Similarly, isolating only seed color, we would assume that three quarters of the F_2 offspring would be yellow and one quarter would be green. The sorting of alleles for texture and color are independent events, so we can apply the product rule. Therefore, the proportion of round and yellow F_2 offspring is expected to be (3/4) × (3/4) = 9/16, and the proportion of wrinkled and green offspring is expected to be (1/4) × (1/4) = 1/16. These proportions are identical to those obtained using a Punnett square. Round, green and wrinkled, yellow offspring can also be calculated using the product rule, as each of these genotypes includes one dominant and one recessive phenotype. Therefore, the proportion of each is calculated as (3/4) × (1/4) = 3/16.

The law of independent assortment also indicates that a cross between yellow, wrinkled (*YYrr*) and green, round (*yyRR*) parents would yield the same F_1 and F_2 offspring as in the *YYRR* x *yyrr* cross.

The physical basis for the law of independent assortment also lies in meiosis I, in which the different homologous pairs line up in random orientations. Each gamete can contain any combination of paternal and maternal chromosomes (and therefore the genes on them) because the orientation of tetrads on the metaphase plane is random.

Forked-Line Method

When more than two genes are being considered, the Punnett-square method becomes unwieldy. For instance, examining a cross involving four genes would require a 16 × 16 grid containing 256 boxes. It would be extremely cumbersome to manually enter each genotype. For more complex crosses, the forked-line and probability methods are preferred.

To prepare a forked-line diagram for a cross between F_1 heterozygotes resulting from a cross between *AABBCC* and *aabbcc* parents, we first create rows equal to the number of genes being considered, and then segregate the alleles in each row on forked lines according to the probabilities for individual monohybrid crosses (Figure 12.17). We then multiply the values along each forked path to obtain the F_2 offspring probabilities. Note that this process is a diagrammatic version of the product rule. The values along each forked pathway can be multiplied because each gene assorts independently. For a trihybrid cross, the F_2 phenotypic ratio is 27:9:9:9:3:3:3:1.

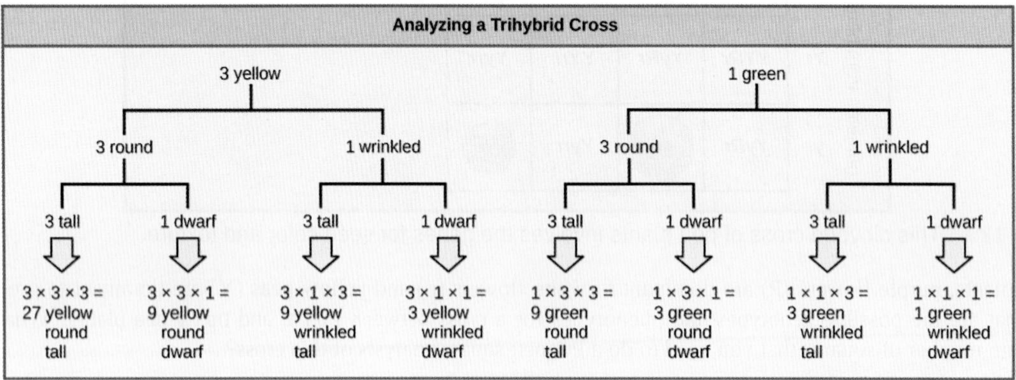

Figure 12.17 The forked-line method can be used to analyze a trihybrid cross. Here, the probability for color in the F_2 generation occupies the top row (3 yellow:1 green). The probability for shape occupies the second row (3 round:1 wrinked), and the probability for height occupies the third row (3 tall:1 dwarf). The probability for each possible combination of traits is calculated by multiplying the probability for each individual trait. Thus, the probability of F_2 offspring having yellow, round, and tall traits is 3 × 3 × 3, or 27.

Probability Method

While the forked-line method is a diagrammatic approach to keeping track of probabilities in a cross, the probability method gives the proportions of offspring expected to exhibit each phenotype (or genotype) without the added visual assistance. Both methods make use of the product rule and consider the alleles for each gene separately. Earlier, we examined the phenotypic proportions for a trihybrid cross using the forked-line method; now we will use the probability method to examine the genotypic proportions for a cross with even more genes.

For a trihybrid cross, writing out the forked-line method is tedious, albeit not as tedious as using the Punnett-square method. To fully demonstrate the power of the probability method, however, we can consider specific genetic calculations. For instance, for a tetrahybrid cross between individuals that are heterozygotes for all four genes, and in which all four genes are sorting independently and in a dominant and recessive pattern, what proportion of the offspring will be expected to be homozygous recessive for all four alleles? Rather than writing out every possible genotype, we can use the probability method. We know that for each gene, the fraction of homozygous recessive offspring will be 1/4. Therefore, multiplying this fraction for each of the four genes, (1/4) × (1/4) × (1/4) × (1/4), we determine that 1/256 of the offspring will be quadruply homozygous recessive.

For the same tetrahybrid cross, what is the expected proportion of offspring that have the dominant phenotype at all four loci? We can answer this question using phenotypic proportions, but let's do it the hard way—using genotypic proportions. The question asks for the proportion of offspring that are 1) homozygous dominant at *A* or heterozygous at *A*, and 2) homozygous at *B* or heterozygous at *B*, and so on. Noting the "or" and "and" in each circumstance makes clear where to apply the sum and product rules. The probability of a homozygous dominant at *A* is 1/4 and the probability of a heterozygote at *A* is 1/2. The probability of the homozygote or the heterozygote is 1/4 + 1/2 = 3/4 using the sum rule. The same probability can be obtained in the same way for each of the other genes, so that the probability of a dominant phenotype at *A* and *B* and *C* and *D* is, using the product rule, equal to 3/4 × 3/4 × 3/4 × 3/4, or 27/64. If you are ever unsure about how to combine probabilities, returning to the forked-line method should make it clear.

Rules for Multihybrid Fertilization

Predicting the genotypes and phenotypes of offspring from given crosses is the best way to test your knowledge of Mendelian genetics. Given a multihybrid cross that obeys independent assortment and follows a dominant and recessive pattern, several generalized rules exist; you can use these rules to check your results as you work through genetics calculations (Table 12.5). To apply these rules, first you must determine *n*, the number of heterozygous gene pairs (the number of genes segregating two alleles each). For example, a cross between *AaBb* and *AaBb* heterozygotes has an *n* of 2. In contrast, a cross between *AABb* and *AABb* has an *n* of 1 because *A* is not heterozygous.

General Rules for Multihybrid Crosses

General Rule	Number of Heterozygous Gene Pairs
Number of different F_1 gametes	2^n
Number of different F_2 genotypes	3^n
Given dominant and recessive inheritance, the number of different F_2 phenotypes	2^n

Table 12.5

Linked Genes Violate the Law of Independent Assortment

Although all of Mendel's pea characteristics behaved according to the law of independent assortment, we now know that some allele combinations are not inherited independently of each other. Genes that are located on separate non-homologous chromosomes will always sort independently. However, each chromosome contains hundreds or thousands of genes, organized linearly on chromosomes like beads on a string. The segregation of alleles into gametes can be influenced by **linkage**, in which genes that are located physically close to each other on the same chromosome are more likely to be inherited as a pair. However, because of the process of recombination, or "crossover," it is possible for two genes on the same chromosome to behave independently, or as if they are not linked. To understand this, let's consider the biological basis of gene linkage and recombination.

Homologous chromosomes possess the same genes in the same linear order. The alleles may differ on homologous chromosome pairs, but the genes to which they correspond do not. In preparation for the first division of meiosis, homologous chromosomes replicate and synapse. Like genes on the homologs align with each other. At this stage, segments of homologous chromosomes exchange linear segments of genetic material (Figure 12.18). This process is called recombination, or crossover, and it is a common genetic process. Because the genes are aligned during recombination, the gene order is not altered. Instead, the result of recombination is that maternal and paternal alleles are combined onto the same chromosome. Across a given chromosome, several recombination events may occur, causing extensive shuffling of alleles.

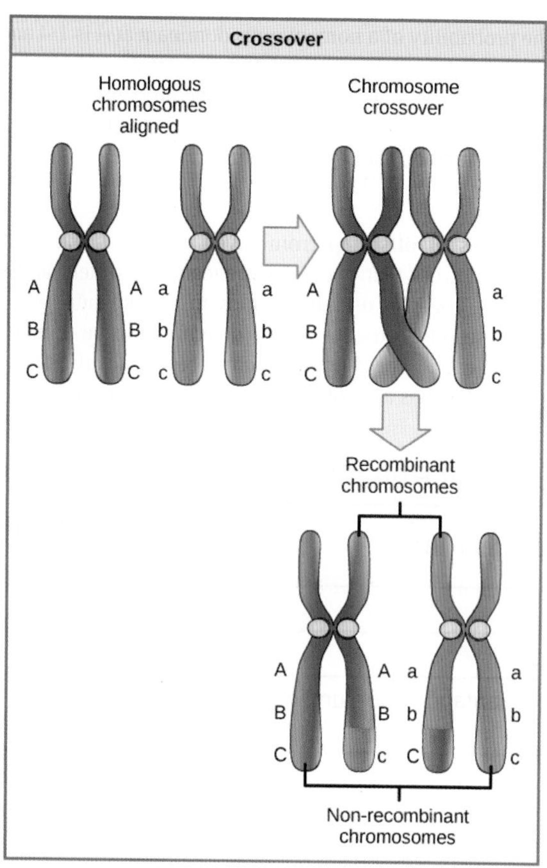

Figure 12.18 The process of crossover, or recombination, occurs when two homologous chromosomes align during meiosis and exchange a segment of genetic material. Here, the alleles for gene C were exchanged. The result is two recombinant and two non-recombinant chromosomes.

When two genes are located in close proximity on the same chromosome, they are considered linked, and their alleles tend to be transmitted through meiosis together. To exemplify this, imagine a dihybrid cross involving flower color and plant height in which the genes are next to each other on the chromosome. If one homologous chromosome has alleles for tall plants and red flowers, and the other chromosome has genes for short plants and yellow flowers, then when the gametes are formed, the tall and red alleles will go together into a gamete and the short and yellow alleles will go into other gametes. These are called the parental genotypes because they have been inherited intact from the parents of the individual producing gametes. But unlike if the genes were on different chromosomes, there will be no gametes with tall and yellow alleles and no gametes with short and red alleles. If you create the Punnett square with these gametes, you will see that the classical Mendelian prediction of a 9:3:3:1 outcome of a dihybrid cross would not apply. As the distance between two genes increases, the probability of one or more crossovers between them increases, and the genes behave more like they are on separate chromosomes. Geneticists have used the proportion of recombinant gametes (the ones not like the parents) as a measure of how far apart genes are on a chromosome. Using this information, they have constructed elaborate maps of genes on chromosomes for well-studied organisms, including humans.

Mendel's seminal publication makes no mention of linkage, and many researchers have questioned whether he encountered linkage but chose not to publish those crosses out of concern that they would invalidate his independent assortment postulate. The garden pea has seven chromosomes, and some have suggested that his choice of seven characteristics was not a coincidence. However, even if the genes he examined were not located on separate chromosomes, it is possible that he simply did not observe linkage because of the extensive shuffling effects of recombination.

Testing the Hypothesis of Independent Assortment

To better appreciate the amount of labor and ingenuity that went into Mendel's experiments, proceed through one of Mendel's dihybrid crosses.

Question: What will be the offspring of a dihybrid cross?

Background: Consider that pea plants mature in one growing season, and you have access to a large garden in which you can cultivate thousands of pea plants. There are several true-breeding plants with the following pairs of traits: tall plants with inflated pods, and dwarf plants with constricted pods. Before the plants have matured, you remove the pollen-producing organs from the tall/inflated plants in your crosses to prevent self-fertilization. Upon plant maturation, the plants are manually crossed by transferring pollen from the dwarf/constricted plants to the stigmata of the tall/inflated plants.

Hypothesis: Both trait pairs will sort independently according to Mendelian laws. When the true-breeding parents are crossed, all of the F_1 offspring are tall and have inflated pods, which indicates that the tall and inflated traits are dominant over the dwarf and constricted traits, respectively. A self-cross of the F_1 heterozygotes results in 2,000 F_2 progeny.

Test the hypothesis: Because each trait pair sorts independently, the ratios of tall:dwarf and inflated:constricted are each expected to be 3:1. The tall/dwarf trait pair is called *T/t*, and the inflated/constricted trait pair is designated *I/i*. Each member of the F_1 generation therefore has a genotype of *TtIi*. Construct a grid analogous to Figure 12.16, in which you cross two *TtIi* individuals. Each individual can donate four combinations of two traits: *TI*, *Ti*, *tI*, or *ti*, meaning that there are 16 possibilities of offspring genotypes. Because the *T* and *I* alleles are dominant, any individual having one or two of those alleles will express the tall or inflated phenotypes, respectively, regardless if they also have a *t* or *i* allele. Only individuals that are *tt* or *ii* will express the dwarf and constricted alleles, respectively. As shown in Figure 12.19, you predict that you will observe the following offspring proportions: tall/inflated:tall/constricted:dwarf/inflated:dwarf/constricted in a 9:3:3:1 ratio. Notice from the grid that when considering the tall/dwarf and inflated/constricted trait pairs in isolation, they are each inherited in 3:1 ratios.

		TtIi			
		TI	*Ti*	*tI*	*ti*
TtIi	*TI*	*TTII*	*TTIi*	*TtII*	*TtIi*
	Ti	*TTIi*	*TTii*	*TtIi*	*Ttii*
	tI	*TtII*	*TtIi*	*ttII*	*ttIi*
	ti	*TtIi*	*Ttii*	*ttIi*	*ttii*

Figure 12.19 This figure shows all possible combinations of offspring resulting from a dihybrid cross of pea plants that are heterozygous for the tall/dwarf and inflated/constricted alleles.

Test the hypothesis: You cross the dwarf and tall plants and then self-cross the offspring. For best results, this is repeated with hundreds or even thousands of pea plants. What special precautions should be taken in the crosses and in growing the plants?

Analyze your data: You observe the following plant phenotypes in the F_2 generation: 2706 tall/inflated, 930 tall/constricted, 888 dwarf/inflated, and 300 dwarf/constricted. Reduce these findings to a ratio and determine if they are consistent with Mendelian laws.

Form a conclusion: Were the results close to the expected 9:3:3:1 phenotypic ratio? Do the results support the prediction? What might be observed if far fewer plants were used, given that alleles segregate randomly into gametes? Try to imagine growing that many pea plants, and consider the potential for experimental error. For instance, what would happen if it was extremely windy one day?

science practices CONNECTION for AP® Courses

Think About It

In the shepherd's-purse plant (*Capsella bursa-pastoris*), seed shape is controlled by two genes, *A* and *B*. When both the *A* and *B* loci are homozygous recessive (*aabb*), the seeds are ovoid. However, if the dominant allele for either or both of these genes is present, the seeds are triangular. Based on this information, what are the expected phenotypic ratios for a cross between plants that are heterozygous for both traits?

What is the expected ratio of phenotypes from a dihybrid cross? How do you explain the difference between the expected dihybrid cross ratio and ratio observed in the shepherd's-purse plant?

Epistasis

Mendel's studies in pea plants implied that the sum of an individual's phenotype was controlled by genes (or as he called them, unit factors), such that every characteristic was distinctly and completely controlled by a single gene. In fact, single observable characteristics are almost always under the influence of multiple genes (each with two or more alleles) acting in unison. For example, at least eight genes contribute to eye color in humans.

Eye color in humans is determined by multiple genes. Use the **Eye Color Calculator (http://openstaxcollege.org/l/eye_color_calc)** to predict the eye color of children from parental eye color.

A couple produces a green-eyed child. Both of the parents have brown eyes. Explain how this is genetically possible.

a. Both parents are homozygous for the dominant trait of brown eyes.

b. Both parents are heterozygous, having the green trait on the green-blue eye gene.

c. Both parents are heterozygous with the recessive trait of brown eyes.

d. Both parents are homozygous having the green trait on the green-blue eye gene.

In some cases, several genes can contribute to aspects of a common phenotype without their gene products ever directly interacting. In the case of organ development, for instance, genes may be expressed sequentially, with each gene adding to the complexity and specificity of the organ. Genes may function in complementary or synergistic fashions, such that two or more genes need to be expressed simultaneously to affect a phenotype. Genes may also oppose each other, with one gene modifying the expression of another.

In **epistasis**, the interaction between genes is antagonistic, such that one gene masks or interferes with the expression of another. "Epistasis" is a word composed of Greek roots that mean "standing upon." The alleles that are being masked or silenced are said to be hypostatic to the epistatic alleles that are doing the masking. Often the biochemical basis of epistasis is a gene pathway in which the expression of one gene is dependent on the function of a gene that precedes or follows it in the pathway.

An example of epistasis is pigmentation in mice. The wild-type coat color, agouti (*AA*), is dominant to solid-colored fur (*aa*). However, a separate gene (*C*) is necessary for pigment production. A mouse with a recessive *c* allele at this locus is unable to produce pigment and is albino regardless of the allele present at locus *A* (**Figure 12.20**). Therefore, the genotypes *AAcc*, *Aacc*, and *aacc* all produce the same albino phenotype. A cross between heterozygotes for both genes (*AaCc* x *AaCc*) would generate offspring with a phenotypic ratio of 9 agouti:3 solid color:4 albino (Figure 12.20). In this case, the *C* gene is epistatic to the *A* gene.

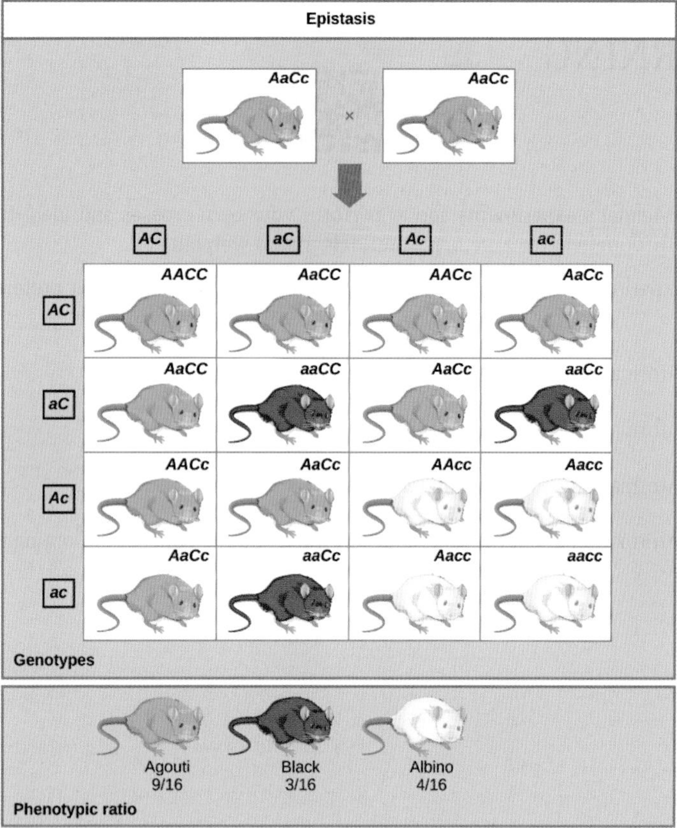

Figure 12.20 In mice, the mottled agouti coat color (*A*) is dominant to a solid coloration, such as black or gray. A gene at a separate locus (*C*) is responsible for pigment production. The recessive *c* allele does not produce pigment, and a mouse with the homozygous recessive *cc* genotype is albino regardless of the allele present at the *A* locus. Thus, the *C* gene is epistatic to the *A* gene.

Epistasis can also occur when a dominant allele masks expression at a separate gene. Fruit color in summer squash is expressed in this way. Homozygous recessive expression of the *W* gene (*ww*) coupled with homozygous dominant or heterozygous expression of the *Y* gene (*YY* or *Yy*) generates yellow fruit, and the *wwyy* genotype produces green fruit. However, if a dominant copy of the *W* gene is present in the homozygous or heterozygous form, the summer squash will produce white fruit regardless of the *Y* alleles. A cross between white heterozygotes for both genes (*WwYy* × *WwYy*) would produce offspring with a phenotypic ratio of 12 white:3 yellow:1 green.

Finally, epistasis can be reciprocal such that either gene, when present in the dominant (or recessive) form, expresses the same phenotype. In the shepherd's purse plant (*Capsella bursa-pastoris*), the characteristic of seed shape is controlled by two genes in a dominant epistatic relationship. When the genes *A* and *B* are both homozygous recessive (*aabb*), the seeds are ovoid. If the dominant allele for either of these genes is present, the result is triangular seeds. That is, every possible genotype other than *aabb* results in triangular seeds, and a cross between heterozygotes for both genes (*AaBb* x *AaBb*) would yield offspring with a phenotypic ratio of 15 triangular:1 ovoid.

As you work through genetics problems, keep in mind that any single characteristic that results in a phenotypic ratio that totals 16 is typical of a two-gene interaction. Recall the phenotypic inheritance pattern for Mendel's dihybrid cross, which considered two non-interacting genes—9:3:3:1. Similarly, we would expect interacting gene pairs to also exhibit ratios expressed as 16 parts. Note that we are assuming the interacting genes are not linked; they are still assorting independently into gametes.

For an excellent review of Mendel's experiments and to perform your own crosses and identify patterns of inheritance, visit the **Mendel's Peas (http://openstaxcollege.org/l/mendels_peas)** web lab.

Explain how Mendel's experiments help modern-day farmers breed crops that exhibit preferred traits, like tall height or large fruit size.

a. by providing information about the variety of pea plants

b. by providing information about soil condition

c. by providing information about organic feritilizers

d. by providing information about the inheritance of traits and the concept of dominance

KEY TERMS

allele gene variations that arise by mutation and exist at the same relative locations on homologous chromosomes

autosomes any of the non-sex chromosomes

blending theory of inheritance hypothetical inheritance pattern in which parental traits are blended together in the offspring to produce an intermediate physical appearance

codominance in a heterozygote, complete and simultaneous expression of both alleles for the same characteristic

continuous variation inheritance pattern in which a character shows a range of trait values with small gradations rather than large gaps between them

dihybrid result of a cross between two true-breeding parents that express different traits for two characteristics

discontinuous variation inheritance pattern in which traits are distinct and are transmitted independently of one another

dominant trait which confers the same physical appearance whether an individual has two copies of the trait or one copy of the dominant trait and one copy of the recessive trait

dominant lethal inheritance pattern in which an allele is lethal both in the homozygote and the heterozygote; this allele can only be transmitted if the lethality phenotype occurs after reproductive age

epistasis antagonistic interaction between genes such that one gene masks or interferes with the expression of another

F_1 first filial generation in a cross; the offspring of the parental generation

F_2 second filial generation produced when F_1 individuals are self-crossed or fertilized with each other

genotype underlying genetic makeup, consisting of both physically visible and non-expressed alleles, of an organism

hemizygous presence of only one allele for a characteristic, as in X-linkage; hemizygosity makes descriptions of dominance and recessiveness irrelevant

heterozygous having two different alleles for a given gene on the homologous chromosome

homozygous having two identical alleles for a given gene on the homologous chromosome

hybridization process of mating two individuals that differ with the goal of achieving a certain characteristic in their offspring

incomplete dominance in a heterozygote, expression of two contrasting alleles such that the individual displays an intermediate phenotype

law of dominance in a heterozygote, one trait will conceal the presence of another trait for the same characteristic

law of independent assortment genes do not influence each other with regard to sorting of alleles into gametes; every possible combination of alleles is equally likely to occur

law of segregation paired unit factors (i.e., genes) segregate equally into gametes such that offspring have an equal likelihood of inheriting any combination of factors

linkage phenomenon in which alleles that are located in close proximity to each other on the same chromosome are more likely to be inherited together

model system species or biological system used to study a specific biological phenomenon to be applied to other different species

monohybrid result of a cross between two true-breeding parents that express different traits for only one characteristic

P_0 parental generation in a cross

phenotype observable traits expressed by an organism

product rule probability of two independent events occurring simultaneously can be calculated by multiplying the individual probabilities of each event occurring alone

Punnett square visual representation of a cross between two individuals in which the gametes of each individual are denoted along the top and side of a grid, respectively, and the possible zygotic genotypes are recombined at each box in the grid

recessive trait that appears "latent" or non-expressed when the individual also carries a dominant trait for that same characteristic; when present as two identical copies, the recessive trait is expressed

recessive lethal inheritance pattern in which an allele is only lethal in the homozygous form; the heterozygote may be normal or have some altered, non-lethal phenotype

reciprocal cross paired cross in which the respective traits of the male and female in one cross become the respective traits of the female and male in the other cross

sex-linked any gene on a sex chromosome

sum rule probability of the occurrence of at least one of two mutually exclusive events is the sum of their individual probabilities

test cross cross between a dominant expressing individual with an unknown genotype and a homozygous recessive individual; the offspring phenotypes indicate whether the unknown parent is heterozygous or homozygous for the dominant trait

trait variation in the physical appearance of a heritable characteristic

X-linked gene present on the X, but not the Y chromosome

CHAPTER SUMMARY

12.1 Mendel's Experiments and the Laws of Probability

Working with garden pea plants, Mendel found that crosses between parents that differed by one trait produced F_1 offspring that all expressed the traits of one parent. Observable traits are referred to as dominant, and non-expressed traits are described as recessive. When the offspring in Mendel's experiment were self-crossed, the F_2 offspring exhibited the dominant trait or the recessive trait in a 3:1 ratio, confirming that the recessive trait had been transmitted faithfully from the original P_0 parent. Reciprocal crosses generated identical F_1 and F_2 offspring ratios. By examining sample sizes, Mendel showed that his crosses behaved reproducibly according to the laws of probability, and that the traits were inherited as independent events.

Two rules in probability can be used to find the expected proportions of offspring of different traits from different crosses. To find the probability of two or more independent events occurring together, apply the product rule and multiply the probabilities of the individual events. The use of the word "and" suggests the appropriate application of the product rule. To find the probability of two or more events occurring in combination, apply the sum rule and add their individual probabilities together. The use of the word "or" suggests the appropriate application of the sum rule.

12.2 Characteristics and Traits

When true-breeding or homozygous individuals that differ for a certain trait are crossed, all of the offspring will be heterozygotes for that trait. If the traits are inherited as dominant and recessive, the F_1 offspring will all exhibit the same phenotype as the parent homozygous for the dominant trait. If these heterozygous offspring are self-crossed, the resulting F_2 offspring will be equally likely to inherit gametes carrying the dominant or recessive trait, giving rise to offspring of which one quarter are homozygous dominant, half are heterozygous, and one quarter are homozygous recessive. Because homozygous dominant and heterozygous individuals are phenotypically identical, the observed traits in the F_2 offspring will exhibit a ratio of three dominant to one recessive.

Alleles do not always behave in dominant and recessive patterns. Incomplete dominance describes situations in which the heterozygote exhibits a phenotype that is intermediate between the homozygous phenotypes. Codominance describes the simultaneous expression of both of the alleles in the heterozygote. Although diploid organisms can only have two alleles for any given gene, it is common for more than two alleles of a gene to exist in a population. In humans, as in many animals and some plants, females have two X chromosomes and males have one X and one Y chromosome. Genes that are present on the X but not the Y chromosome are said to be X-linked, such that males only inherit one allele for the gene, and females inherit two. Finally, some alleles can be lethal. Recessive lethal alleles are only lethal in homozygotes, but dominant lethal alleles are fatal in heterozygotes as well.

12.3 Laws of Inheritance

Mendel postulated that genes (characteristics) are inherited as pairs of alleles (traits) that behave in a dominant and recessive pattern. Alleles segregate into gametes such that each gamete is equally likely to receive either one of the two alleles present in a diploid individual. In addition, genes are assorted into gametes independently of one another. That is, alleles are generally not more likely to segregate into a gamete with a particular allele of another gene. A dihybrid cross demonstrates independent assortment when the genes in question are on different chromosomes or distant from each other on the same chromosome. For crosses involving more than two genes, use the forked line or probability methods to predict offspring genotypes and phenotypes rather than a Punnett square.

Although chromosomes sort independently into gametes during meiosis, Mendel's law of independent assortment refers to genes, not chromosomes, and a single chromosome may carry more than 1,000 genes. When genes are located in close proximity on the same chromosome, their alleles tend to be inherited together. This results in offspring ratios that violate Mendel's law of independent assortment. However, recombination serves to exchange genetic material on homologous chromosomes such that maternal and paternal alleles may be recombined on the same chromosome. This is why alleles on a given chromosome are not always inherited together. Recombination is a random event occurring anywhere on a chromosome. Therefore, genes that are far apart on the same chromosome are likely to still assort independently because of recombination events that occurred in the intervening chromosomal space.

Whether or not they are sorting independently, genes may interact at the level of gene products such that the expression of an allele for one gene masks or modifies the expression of an allele for a different gene. This is called epistasis.

REVIEW QUESTIONS

1. Mendel performed hybridizations by transferring pollen to the female ova from what part of the male plant?

a. anther
b. pistil
c. stigma
d. seed

2. Which is one of the seven characteristics that Mendel observed in pea plants?

a. flower size
b. leaf shape
c. seed texture
d. stem color

3. Imagine you are performing a cross involving garden pea plants. What F_1 offspring would you expect if you cross true-breeding parents with green seeds and yellow seeds? Yellow seed color is dominant over green.

a. 100 percent yellow-green seeds
b. 100 percent yellow seeds
c. 50 percent yellow, 50 percent green seeds
d. 25 percent green, 75 percent yellow seeds

4. Consider a cross to investigate the pea pod texture trait, involving constricted or inflated pods. Mendel found that the traits behave according to a dominant/recessive pattern in which inflated pods were dominant. If you performed this cross and obtained 650 inflated-pod plants in the F_2 generation bred from true-breeding stock, approximately how many constricted-pod plants would you expect to have?

a. 600
b. 165
c. 217
d. 468

5. The observable traits expressed by an organism are described as its

a. alleles
b. genotype
c. phenotype
d. zygote

6. A recessive trait will be observed in individuals that are what for that trait?

a. diploid
b. heterozygous
c. homozygous or heterozygous
d. homozygous

7. If black and white true-breeding mice are mated and the result is all gray offspring, what inheritance pattern would this be indicative of?

a. codominance
b. dominance
c. incomplete dominance
d. multiple alleles

8. The ABO blood groups in humans are controlled by the IA, IB, and I alleles. The IA allele encodes the A blood group antigen, IB encodes B, and I encodes O. Both A and B are dominant to O. If a heterozygous blood type A parent (iAi) and a heterozygous blood type B parent (iBi) mate, one quarter of their offspring will have AB blood type (IAIB) in which both antigens are expressed equally. Therefore, the ABO blood groups are an example of _______.

a. codominance and incomplete dominance
b. incomplete dominance only
c. multiple alleles and incomplete dominance
d. multiple alleles and codominance

9. In a mating between two individuals that are heterozygous for a recessive lethal allele that is expressed in utero, what genotypic ratio (homozygous dominant : heterozygous : homozygous recessive) would you expect to observe in the off-spring?

a. 1 : 2 : 1
b. 3 : 1 : 1
c. 1 : 2 : 0
d. 0 : 2 : 1

10. The forked line and probability methods make use of what probability rule?

a. monohybrid rule
b. product rule
c. sum rule
d. test cross

11.

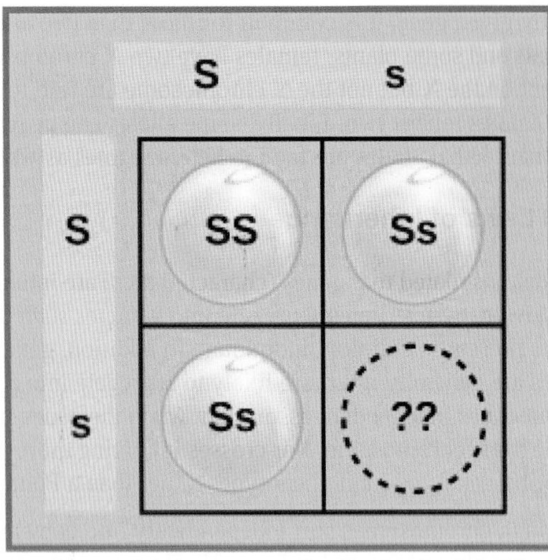

In pea plants, smooth seeds (S) are dominant to wrinkled seeds (s). In a genetic cross of two plants that are heterozygous for the seed shape trait, the Punnett square is shown. What is the missing genotype?

a. SS
b. Ss
c. sS
d. ss

12. If the inheritance of two traits fully obeys Mendelian laws of inheritance, where may you assume that the genes are located?

a. on any autosomal chromosome or chromosomes
b. on Y chromosomes
c. on the same chromosome
d. on separate chromosomes

13. How many different offspring genotypes are expected in a trihybrid cross between parents heterozygous for all three traits? How many phenotypes are expected if the traits behave in a dominant and recessive pattern?

a. 64 genotypes; 16 phenotypes
b. 16 genotypes; 64 phenotypes
c. 8 genotypes; 27 phenotypes
d. 27 genotypes; 8 phenotypes

14. Four-o' clock flowers may be red, pink or white. In the crossing of a true-breeding red and true-breeding white plants, all the offspring are pink. Use a Punnett square to determine the correct genotype of the offspring if the red parent has genotype RR and the white parent has genotype rr.

a. RR and Rr
b. Rr and rr
c. Rr only
d. RR only

15. Which cellular process underlies Mendel's law of independent assortment?

a. Chromosomes align randomly during meiosis.
b. Chromosomes can exchange genetic material during crossover.
c. Gametes contain half the number of chromosomes of somatic cells.
d. Daughter cells are genetically identical to parent cells after mitosis.

16. While studying meiosis, you observe that gametes receive one copy of each pair of homologous chromosomes and one copy of the sex chromosomes. This observation is the physical explanation of Mendel's law of ______.

a. dominance
b. independent assortment
c. random distribution of traits
d. segregation

17. In some primroses, the petal color blue is dominant. A cross between a true-breed blue primrose and a white primrose yields progeny with white petals. A second gene at another locus prevented the expression of the dominant coat color. This is an example of ______.

a. codominance
b. hemizygosity
c. incomplete dominance
d. epistasis

18.

Cross 1: Swollen pods X shriveled pods	
F1	314 swollen; 298 shriveled
Cross 2: swollen F1 X swollen F1	
F2	594 swollen 97 shriveled

Purple flowers (P) are dominant over red flowers (p) and long pollen grains are dominant over round pollen grains. When purple flowers and long pollen grain plants were crossed with plants with white flowers and round pollen grains, all the F_1 plants showed purple flowers and long pollen grains. The F_1 plants were crossed and the results are in the table. What conclusions about the physical relationship between the traits can be drawn from the experiment?

a. The traits are probably linked.
b. The traits follow the law of independent assortment
c. The traits are located on different chromosomes
d. There was epistasis.

19. When the expression of one gene pair masks or modifies the expression of another, the genes show ______.

a. codominance
b. epistasis
c. incomplete dominance
d. partial linkage

CRITICAL THINKING QUESTIONS

20. Describe one reason why the garden pea was an excellent model system for studying inheritance.

a. The garden pea has flowers that close tightly to promote cross-fertilization.
b. The garden pea has flowers that close tightly to prevent cross-fertilization.
c. The garden pea does not mature in one season and is a perennial plant.
d. Male and female reproductive parts attain maturity at different times, promoting self-fertilization.

21. How would you perform a reciprocal cross to test stem height in the garden pea?

a. First cross is performed by transferring the pollen of a heterozygous tall plant to the stigma of a true breeding dwarf plant. Second cross is performed by transferring the pollen of a heterozygous dwarf plant to the stigma of a true breeding tall plant.
b. First cross is performed by transferring the pollen of a true breeding tall plant to the stigma of a true breeding dwarf plant. Second cross is performed by transferring the pollen of a true breeding dwarf plant to the stigma of a true breeding tall plant.
c. First cross is performed by transferring the pollen of a true breeding tall plant to the stigma of a heterozygous dwarf plant. Second cross is performed by transferring the pollen of a heterozygous dwarf plant to the stigma of a true breeding tall plant.
d. First cross is performed by transferring the pollen of a heterozygous tall plant to the stigma of a heterozygous dwarf plant. Second cross is performed by transferring the pollen of a heterozygous tall plant to the stigma of a heterozygous dwarf plant.

22. Flower position in pea plants is determined by a gene with axial and terminal alleles. Given that axial is dominant to terminal, list all of the possible F_1 and F_2 genotypes and phenotypes from a cross involving parents that are homozygous for each trait. Express genotypes with conventional genetic abbreviations.

a. F_1: All AA-axial; F_2: AA-Axial and aa-terminal.
b. F_1: All aa-terminal; F_2: AA-Axial and Aa-terminal.
c. F_1: AA-axial and Aa-terminal; F_2: All AA-axial.
d. F_1: All Aa-axial; F_2: AA-Axial, Aa-Axial, and aa-terminal.

23. Use a Punnett square to predict the offspring in a cross between a dwarf pea plant (homozygous recessive) and a tall pea plant (heterozygous). What is the phenotypic ratio of the offspring?

a. 1 Tall : 1 dwarf
b. 1 tall : 2 dwarf
c. 3 tall : 1 dwarf
d. 1 dwarf : 4 tall

24. Can a human male be a carrier of red-green color blindness?

a. Yes, males can be the carriers of red-green color blindness, as color blindness is autosomal dominant.
b. No, males cannot be the carriers of red-green color blindness, as color blindness is X-linked.
c. No, males cannot be the carriers of red-green color blindness, as color blindness is Y-linked.
d. Yes, males can be the carriers of red-green color blindness, as color blindness is autosomal recessive.

25. Use the probability method to calculate the genotypes and genotypic proportions of a cross between AABBCc and Aabbcc parents.

a. Possible genotypes are AABBcc, AaBbCc, AaBbcc and the ratio $1:2:1$.
b. Possible genotypes are AABbcc, AaBbCc, AaBbcc and the ratio $1:3:1$.
c. Possible genotypes are AABbCc, AABbcc, AaBbCc, AaBbcc and the ratio $1:1:1:1$.
d. Possible genotypes are AABbcc, AaBbCC, AaBbcc and the ratio $1:1:1$.

26. How does the segregation of traits result in different combinations of gametes at the end of meiosis?

a. The chromosomes randomly align during metaphase I at the equator, and separation of homologous chromosomes occurs during anaphase I. Similarly separation of sister chromatids occurs at anaphase II of meiosis II. At the end of meiosis II, four different gametic combinations are produced, each containing a haploid set of chromosomes.
b. The chromosomes randomly align during anaphase I at the equator. Separation of bivalent chromosomes occur during metaphase I of meiosis I. Similarly, separation of sister chromatids occurs at metaphase II of meiosis II. At the end of meiosis II, four different gametic combinations are produced, each containing a haploid set of chromosomes.
c. The chromosomes randomly align during prophase I at the equator, and separation of sister chromatids occurs during metaphase I of meiosis I. Similarly separation of bivalent chromosomes occur at metaphase II of meiosis II. At the end of meiosis II, four different gametic combinations are produced, each containing a diploid set of chromosomes.
d. The chromosomes randomly align during prophase I at the equator, and separation of bivalent chromosomes occur during anaphase I of meiosis I. Similarly, separation of homologous chromosomes occurs at metaphase II of meiosis II. At the end of meiosis II, four different gametic combinations are produced, each containing a diploid set of chromosomes.

27. In Section 12.3, "Laws of Inheritance," an example of epistasis was given for summer squash. Cross white WwYy heterozygotes to demonstrate the phenotypic ratio of 12 white : 3 yellow : 1 green that was given in the text.

a. 12 offspring are white, as the W gene is epistatic to the Y gene. Three offspring are yellow, because w is not epistatic. Green offspring is obtained when the recessive form of both genes (wwyy) are present.
b. 12 offspring are white as W gene is hypostatic to Y gene. Three offspring are yellow because Y is epistatic to w. Green offspring is obtained when the dominant form of both the genes (WWYY) is present.
c. 12 offspring are white as W gene is dominant. Three offspring are yellow because Y is dominant and w is recessive. Green offspring is obtained when the recessive form of both the genes (wwyy) is present, showing codominance.
d. 12 offspring are white as W is epistatic to Y gene. Three offspring are yellow because Y is hypostatic to w. Green offspring is obtained when the recessive form of both the genes (wwyy) are present, showing codominance.

TEST PREP FOR AP® COURSES

28. The trait for widow's peak can be considered a monoallelic dominant trait in humans. If a man with a widow's peak and a woman with a straight hairline have a child together, what is the probability that the child will inherit the widow's peak if you know that the father's mother had a straight hairline?

a. 0.25
b. 0.5
c. 0.75
d. 1

29. Don't like Brussels sprouts? Blame your genes. The chemical PTC (phenylthiocarbamide), which is nearly identical to a compound found in the cabbage family, tastes very bitter for some people. Others cannot detect a taste. The ability to taste PTC is incompletely dominant and is controlled by a gene on chromosome 7. A woman who finds Brussel sprouts mildly distasteful (in other words, who can taste PTC weakly) has a child with a man who hates Brussel sprouts (in other words, who can taste PTC strongly). What is the probability that their son likes Brussel sprouts (in other words, cannot taste PTC)?

a. 0
b. 0.25
c. 0.5
d. 1

30. Tay-Sachs disease is an autosomal recessive disorder that causes severe problems in neurons. Children who receive two copies of the gene rarely live beyond the age of five. There is no cure for the disease. During a genetic screening, a couple is told that both partners carry the recessive gene. What kind of issue must the couple confront?

a. scientific
b. financial
c. ethical
d. educational

31. A couple has three daughters. What is the probability that the next child they have will be a daughter?

a. 0%

b. 25%

c. 50%

d. 100%

32. What is the probability that a couple will have three daughters?

a. $\frac{1}{2}$

b. $\frac{1}{3}$

c. $\frac{1}{6}$

d. $\frac{1}{8}$

33. Petunias can be blue, red, or violet. When a blue flower is crossed with a red flower, all the resulting flowers are violet. When a violet flower is crossed with a red flower, about half of the flowers are violet and half are red. How do you characterize the color trait?

a. complete dominance

b. codominance

c. incomplete dominance

d. sex-linked

34. Petunias can be blue, red, or violet. When a blue flower is crossed with a red flower, all the resulting flowers are violet. Two violet petunias are crossed. Which is the most probable result of the cross?

a. 75% of the flowers are blue and 25% of the flowers are red.

b. 50% of the flowers are blue and 50% of the flowers are red.

c. 75% of the flowers are red and 25% are blue.

d. 25% of the flowers are blue, 50% of the flowers are violet, and 25% of the flowers are red.

35. Fruit flies (*Drosophila melanogaster*) with a wild-type phenotype have gray bodies and red eyes. Certain mutations can cause changes to these traits. Mutant flies may have a black body and/or cinnabar eyes. To study the genetics of these traits, a researcher crossed a true-breeding wild-typed male fly with a true-breeding female fly with a black body and cinnabar eyes. All of the F1 progeny displayed a wild type phenotype. Which of the following is correct about the traits observed?

a. Gray body and cinnabar eyes are dominant.

b. Eye color is sex-linked.

c. Body color is sex-linked.

d. Gray body and red eyes are dominant.

36.

Body Color	Eye Color	Number Predicted
Gray	Red	244
Black	Cinnabar	244
Gray	Cinnabar	244
Black	Red	244

Female flies from the F_1 generation were crossed with true-breeding male flies with black bodies and cinnabar eyes. The table represents the predicted outcome and the data obtained from the cross. What was the assumption that lead to the predicted numbers?

a. The traits assort independently.

b. The traits are located on the X chromosome.

c. The traits are on the same chromosome.

d. The female flies were homozygous for wild type alleles.

37. Cats can be black, yellow, or calico (black and yellow patches). Coat color is carried on the X chromosome. What type of inheritance is color coat in cats?

1. Complete dominance
2. Codominance
3. Incomplete dominance
4. Sex-linked

a. 2

b. 3

c. 2,4

d. 3,4

38. Cats can be black, yellow or calico (black and yellow patches). Coat color is carried on the X chromosome. A yellow cat is crossed with a black cat. Assume that the offspring are both male and female. What are the phenotypes of the offspring and in what proportions?

a. All the cats are yellow.

b. All the cats are black.

c. All the cats are calico.

d. There is not enough information to answer the question.

SCIENCE PRACTICE CHALLENGE QUESTIONS

39. The gene *SLC24A5* encodes an antiporter membrane protein that exchanges sodium for calcium (R. Ginger et al., JBC, 2007). This process has a role in the synthesis of the melanosomes that cause skin pigmentation. A mutation in this gene affecting a single amino acid occurs in humans. The homozygous mutant gene is found in 99% of humans with European origins. Both the wild type and mutant display codominance.

A. Representing the wild-type form of the gene as +/+ and the mutant form of the gene as m/m for two homozygous parents, **construct** a Punnett square for this cross using the first grid below. **Annotate your representation** to **identify** the phenotypes with high (H), intermediate (I), and low (L) melanosome production. Use the second grid to represent an F_2 generation from the offspring of the first cross. Use annotation to show the phenotype.

F_1	m	m
+		
+		

Table 12.6

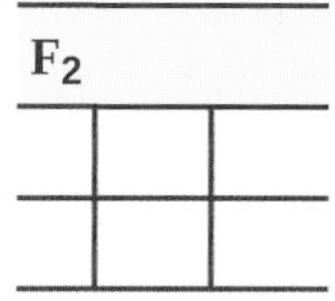

F_2		

Table 12.7

B. **Draw** sister chromatids at anaphase II for both parents in the F_1 generation and annotate your drawing to **identify** each genotype of the gametes using the cells of the Punnett square.

C. **Explain** which of Mendel's laws is violated by codominance.

D. Suppose that these data were available to evaluate the claim that the wild-type and mutant forms of *SLC24A5* are codominant:

F_2		
Phenotype	**Observed**	**Expected**
H	1206	
I	2238	
L	1124	

Table 12.8

Complete the table. **Explain** the values expected in terms of the genotype of the offspring.

E. Using a c^2 statistic at the 95% confidence level, **evaluate** the claim that the wild-type and mutant forms of *SCLO24A5* are codominant. The definition of the statistic $X_c^2 = \sum \frac{(O_i - E_i)^2}{E_i}$ where X is the chi-square test statistic, c is the significant level of the test (we will use 0.05), O is the observed value for variable *i*, and E is the expected value for variable *i*. The Chi-square statistic table is provided in the AP Biology Exam.

Degrees of Freedom								
p	1	2	3	4	5	6	7	8
0.05	3.84	5.99	7.82	9.49	11.07	12.59	14.07	15.51

Table 12.9

40. Adrenoleukodystrophy (ALD) is a genetic disorder in which lipids with very high molecular weights are not metabolized and accumulate within cells. Accumulation of these fats in the brain damages the myelin that surrounds nerves. This progressive disease has two causes: an autosomal recessive allele, which causes neonatal ALD, and a mutation in the ABCD1 gene located on the X chromosome. A controversial treatment is the use of Lorenzo's oil, which is expensive; despite this treatment, neurological degradation persists in many patients. Gene therapy as a potential treatment is currently in trials but is also very costly.

An infant patient exhibits symptoms of neonatal ALD, which are difficult to distinguish from the X-linked form of the disease. The infant's physician consults electronic health records to construct a pedigree showing family members who also presented symptoms similar to ALD. The pedigree is shown in this diagram. The infant patient is circled. Symbols for males (o) and females (m) are filled when symptoms are present.

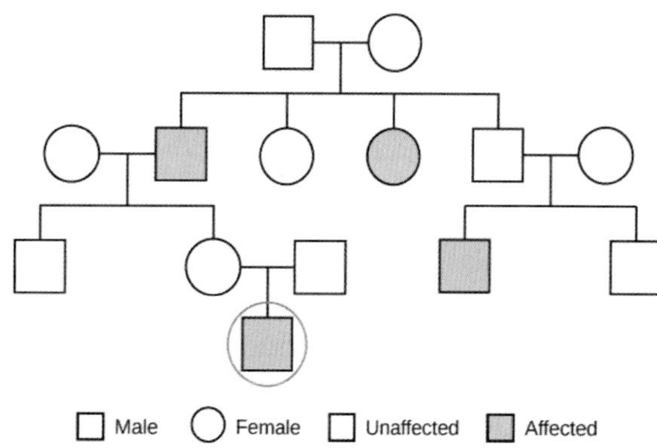

Figure 12.21

A. Using the pedigree, **explain** which form of ALD (neonatal or X-linked) is present in the infant.

B. Sharing of digital records among health providers is one method proposed to improve the quality and reduce the cost of health care in the U.S. The privacy of electronic health records is a concern. **Pose <u>three</u> questions** that must be addressed in developing policies that balance the costs of treatments and diagnoses, patient quality of life, and risks to individual privacy.

41. Two genes, A and B, are located adjacent to each other (linked) on the same chromosome. In the original cross (P_0), one parent is homozygous dominant for both traits (AB), whereas the other parent is recessive (ab).

Characteristic	Alleles	Chromosome
Seed color	yellow (I) / green (i)	1
Seed coat & flowers	colored (A) / white (a)	1
Mature pods	smooth (V) / wrinkled (v)	4
Flower stalk	from leaf axils (Fa) / umbellate at top of plant (fa)	4
Height	> 1 m (Le) / ~0.5 m (le)	4
Unripe pods	green (Gp) / yellow (gp)	5
Mature seeds	smooth (R) / wrinkled (r)	7

Table 12.10

A. **Describe** the distribution of genotypes and phenotypes in F_1.

B. **Describe** the distribution of genotypes and phenotypes when F_1 is crossed with the ab parent.

C. **Describe** the distribution of genotypes and phenotypes when F_1 is crossed with the AB parent.

D. **Explain** the observed non-Mendelian results in terms of the violation of the laws governing Mendelian genetics.

42. Gregor Mendel's 1865 paper described experiments on the inheritance of seven characteristics of *Pisum sativum* shown in the first column in the table below. Many years later, based on his reported outcomes and analysis of the inheritance of a single characteristic, Mendel developed the concepts of genes, their alleles, and dominance. These concepts are defined in the second column of the table using conventional symbols for the dominant allele for each characteristic. Even later, the location of each of these genes on one of the seven chromosomes in *P. sativum* were determined, as shown in the third column.

A. Before the acceptance of what Mendel called "factors" as the discrete units of inheritance, the accepted model was that the traits of progeny were "blended" traits of the parents. **Evaluate the evidence** provided by Mendel's experiments in disproving the blending theory of inheritance.

B. Mendel published experimental data and analysis for two experiments involving the inheritance of more than a single characteristic. He examined two-character inheritance of seed shape and seed color. He also reported three-character inheritance of seed shape, seed color, and flower color. **Evaluate the evidence** provided by the multiple-character experiments. **Identify** which of the following laws of inheritance depend upon these multiple-character experiments for support:

a. During gamete formation, the alleles for each gene segregate from each other so that each gamete carries only one allele for each gene.

b. Genes for different traits can segregate independently during the formation of gametes.

c. Some alleles are dominant, whereas others are recessive. An organism with at least one dominant allele will display the effect of the dominant allele.

d. All three laws can be inferred from the single-character experiments.

C. As shown in the table above, some chromosomes contain the gene for more than one of the seven characteristics Mendel studied, for example, seed color and flowers. The table below shows, with filled cells above the dashed diagonal line, the combinations of characteristics for which Mendel reported results. In the cells below the dotted diagonal line, **identify with an X** each cell where deviations from the law or laws identified in part B might be expected.

	I/i	*A/a*	*V/v*	*Fa/fa*	*Le/le*	*Gp/gp*	*R/r*
I/i							
A/a							
V/v							
Fa/fa							
Le/le							
Gp/gp							
R/r							

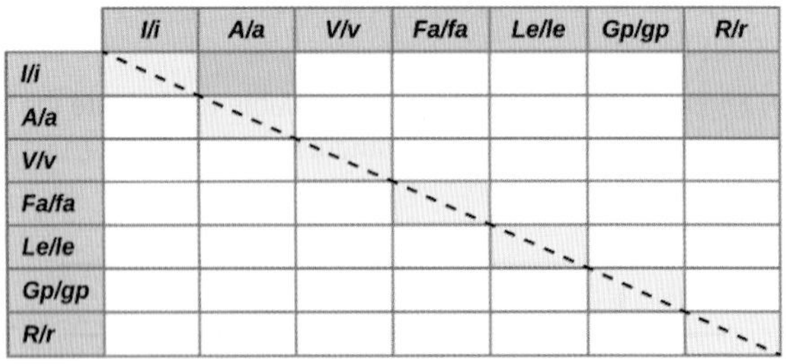

Figure 12.22

D. **Explain** the reasons for the expected deviations for those combinations of characteristics identified in part C.

E. In one of the experiments reported by Mendel, deviations from the law identified in part B might be expected. **Explain** how the outcomes of this experiment were consistent with Mendel's laws.

43. A dihybrid cross involves two traits. A cross of parental types AaBb and AaBb can be represented with a Punnett square:

	AB	Ab	aB	ab
AB	AABB	AABb	AaBB	AaBb
Ab	AAbB	AAbb	AabB	Aabb
aB	aABB	aABb	aaBB	aaBb
ab	aAbB	aAbb	aabB	aabb

Figure 12.23

This representation clearly organizes all of the possible genotypes and reveals the 9:3:3:1 distribution of phenotypes and a 4×4 grid of 16 cells. Expressed as a fraction of the 16 possible genotypes of the offspring, the phenotypic ratio describes the probability of each phenotype among the offspring: 3 (AA, Aa, aA) × 3 (BB, bB, Bb)/16 = 9/16; 3 (AA, Aa, aA) × 1 (bb) /16 = 3/16; 1 (aa) × 3 (BB, bB, Bb) = 3/16; and 1 (aa) × 1 (bb) = 1/16.

A. Using the probability method, calculate the likelihood of these phenotypes from each dihybrid cross:

- recessive in the gene with alleles A and a from the cross AaBb × aabb
- dominant in both genes from the cross AaBb × aabb
- recessive in both genes from the cross AaBb × aabb
- recessive in either gene from the cross AaBb × aabb

A Punnett square representation of a trihybrid cross, such as the self-cross of AaBbCc, is more cumbersome because there are eight columns and rows (2×2×2 ways to choose parental genotypes) and 64 cells. A less tedious representation is to calculate the number of each type of genotype in the offspring directly by counting the unique permutations of the letters representing the alleles. For example, the probability of the cross AaBbCc × AaBbCc is 3 (AA, Aa, aA) × 3 (BB, Bb, bB) × 3 (CC, Cc, cC)/64 = 27/64.

B. Using the probability method, **calculate** the likelihood of these phenotypes from each trihybrid cross:

- recessive in all traits from the cross AaBbCc × aabbcc
- recessive in the gene with alleles C and c and dominant in the other two traits from the cross AaBbCc × AaBbCc
- dominant in the gene with alleles A and a and recessive in the other two traits from the cross AaBbcc × AaBbCc

C. The probability method is an easy way to calculate the likelihood of each particular phenotype, but it doesn't simultaneously display the probability of all possible phenotypes. The forked line representation described in the text allows the entire phenotypic distribution to be displayed. Using the forked line method, calculate the probabilities in a cross between *AABBCc* and *Aabbcc* parents:

- all traits are recessive: aabbcc
- traits are dominant at each loci, A?B?C?
- traits are dominant at two genes and recessive at the third
- traits are dominant at one gene and recessive at the other two

44. Construct a representation showing the connection between the process of meiosis and the transmission of six possible phenotypes from parents to F2 offspring. The phenotypes are labeled A, a, B, b and C, c. Expression of each phenotype is controlled by a separate Mendelian gene. Your representation should show the proportion of every possible combination of phenotypes (e.g., ABC, AbC, etc.) that will be present in the F2 offspring.

13 | MODERN UNDERSTANDINGS OF INHERITANCE

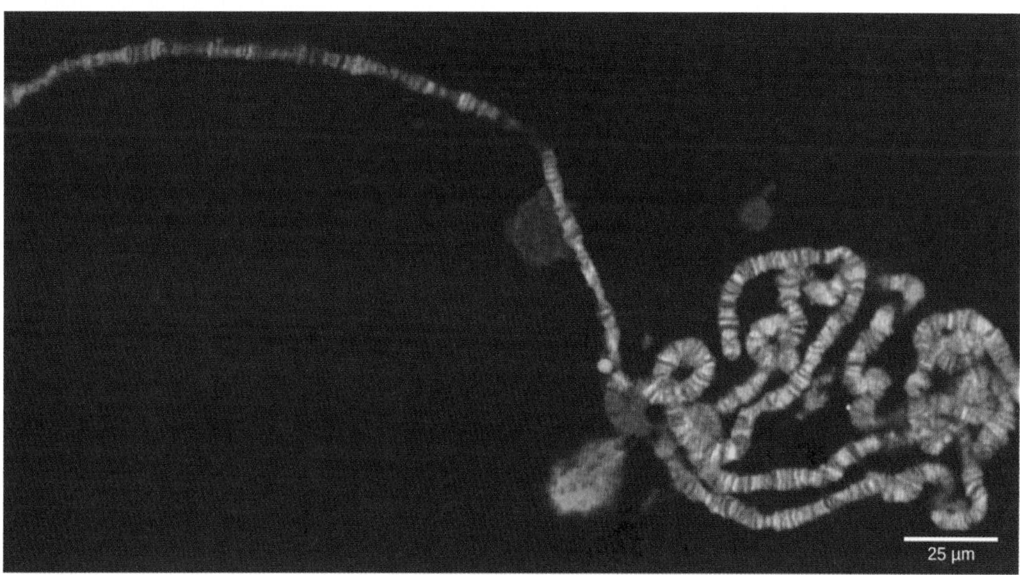

Figure 13.1 Chromosomes are threadlike nuclear structures consisting of DNA and proteins that serve as the repositories for genetic information. The chromosomes depicted here were isolated from a fruit fly's salivary gland, stained with dye, and visualized under a microscope. Akin to miniature bar codes, chromosomes absorb different dyes to produce characteristic banding patterns, which allows for their routine identification. (credit: modification of work by "LPLT"/Wikimedia Commons; scale-bar data from Matt Russell)

Chapter Outline

Introduction

According to the United Nations Office on Drugs and Crime, approximately 95% of those who commit homicide are men. While behavior is shaped by the environment one grows up and lives in, genetics also play a role. For example, scientists have discovered genes that appear to increase one's tendency to exhibit aggressive behavior. One of the genes, called MAOA, is located on the X chromosome. In one recent study involving a group of male prisoners in Finland, scientists found that the prisoners who inherited a variant of this gene were between 5% and 10% more likely to have committed a violent crime. Men only have one copy of the gene, since men only have one X chromosome. Women, however, have two copies of the X chromosome and therefore two copies of the gene. Therefore, women who inherit the variant allele will most likely also have a normal allele to counteract its effects. It is important to note that many men inherit the variant copy of MAOA and only some commit violent crimes. The environment seems to play a much more critical role. You can read more about nature/nurture roles in crime in this **article (http://openstaxcollege.org/l/32whysomany)** .

13.1 | Chromosomal Theory and Genetic Linkages

In this section, you will explore the following question:

- What is the relationship among genetic linkage, crossing over, and genetic variation?

Connection for AP® Courses

Proposed independently by Sutton and Boveri in the early 1900s, the Chromosomal Theory of Inheritance states that chromosomes are vehicles of genetic heredity. As we have discovered, patterns of inheritance are more complex than Mendel could have imagined. Mendel was investigating the behavior of genes. He was fortunate in choosing traits coded by genes that happened to be on different chromosomes or far apart on the same chromosome. When genes are linked or near each other on the same chromosome, patterns of segregation and independent assortment change. In 1913, Sturtevant devised a method to assess recombination frequency and infer the relative positions and distances of linked genes on a chromosome based on the average number of crossovers between them during meiosis.

The content presented in this section supports the Learning Objectives outlined in Big Idea 3 of the AP® Biology Curriculum Framework. The AP® Learning Objectives merge essential knowledge content with one or more of the seven Science Practices. These objectives provide a transparent foundation for the AP® Biology course, along with inquiry-based laboratory experiences, instructional activities, and AP® exam questions.

Big Idea 3	Living systems store, retrieve, transmit and respond to information essential to life processes.
Enduring Understanding 3.A	Heritable information provides for continuity of life.
Essential Knowledge	**3.A.2** In eukaryotes, heritable information is passed to the next generation via processes that include the cell cycle and mitosis or meiosis plus fertilization.
Science Practice	**7.1** The student can connect phenomena and models across spatial and temporal scales.
Learning Objective	**3.10** The student is able to represent the connection between meiosis and increased genetic diversity necessary for evolution.
Essential Knowledge	**3.A.3** The chromosomal basis of inheritance provides an understanding of the pattern of passage (transmission) of genes from parent to offspring.
Science Practice	**1.1** The student can create representations and models of natural or man-made phenomena and systems in the domain.
Science Practice	**7.2** The student can connect concepts in and across domain(s) to generalize or extrapolate in and/or across enduring understandings and/or big ideas.
Learning Objective	**3.12** The student is able to construct a representation that connects the process of meiosis to the passage of traits from parent to offspring.

The Science Practice Challenge Questions contain additional test questions for this section that will help you prepare for the AP exam. These questions address the following standards:
[APLO 3.2][APLO 3.11][APLO 3.14][APLO 3.15][APLO 3.28][APLO 3.26][APLO 3.17][APLO 4.22]

Long before chromosomes were visualized under a microscope, the father of modern genetics, Gregor Mendel, began studying heredity in 1843. With the improvement of microscopic techniques during the late 1800s, cell biologists could stain and visualize subcellular structures with dyes and observe their actions during cell division and meiosis. With each mitotic division, chromosomes replicated, condensed from an amorphous (no constant shape) nuclear mass into distinct X-shaped bodies (pairs of identical sister chromatids), and migrated to separate cellular poles.

Chromosomal Theory of Inheritance

The speculation that chromosomes might be the key to understanding heredity led several scientists to examine Mendel's publications and re-evaluate his model in terms of the behavior of chromosomes during mitosis and meiosis. In 1902, Theodor Boveri observed that proper embryonic development of sea urchins does not occur unless chromosomes are present. That same year, Walter Sutton observed the separation of chromosomes into daughter cells during meiosis (Figure 13.2). Together, these observations led to the development of the **Chromosomal Theory of Inheritance**, which identified chromosomes as the genetic material responsible for Mendelian inheritance.

(a) (b)

Figure 13.2 (a) Walter Sutton and (b) Theodor Boveri are credited with developing the Chromosomal Theory of Inheritance, which states that chromosomes carry the unit of heredity (genes).

The Chromosomal Theory of Inheritance was consistent with Mendel's laws and was supported by the following observations:

- During meiosis, homologous chromosome pairs migrate as discrete structures that are independent of other chromosome pairs.
- The sorting of chromosomes from each homologous pair into pre-gametes appears to be random.
- Each parent synthesizes gametes that contain only half of their chromosomal complement.
- Even though male and female gametes (sperm and egg) differ in size and morphology, they have the same number of chromosomes, suggesting equal genetic contributions from each parent.
- The gametic chromosomes combine during fertilization to produce offspring with the same chromosome number as their parents.

Despite compelling correlations between the behavior of chromosomes during meiosis and Mendel's abstract laws, the Chromosomal Theory of Inheritance was proposed long before there was any direct evidence that traits were carried on chromosomes. Critics pointed out that individuals had far more independently segregating traits than they had chromosomes. It was only after several years of carrying out crosses with the fruit fly, *Drosophila melanogaster*, that Thomas Hunt Morgan provided experimental evidence to support the Chromosomal Theory of Inheritance.

Genetic Linkage and Distances

Mendel's work suggested that traits are inherited independently of each other. Morgan identified a 1:1 correspondence between a segregating trait and the X chromosome, suggesting that the random segregation of chromosomes was the physical basis of Mendel's model. This also demonstrated that linked genes disrupt Mendel's predicted outcomes. The fact that each chromosome can carry many linked genes explains how individuals can have many more traits than they have chromosomes. However, observations by researchers in Morgan's laboratory suggested that alleles positioned on the same chromosome were not always inherited together. During meiosis, linked genes somehow became unlinked.

Homologous Recombination

In 1909, Frans Janssen observed chiasmata—the point at which chromatids are in contact with each other and may exchange segments—prior to the first division of meiosis. He suggested that alleles become unlinked and chromosomes physically exchange segments. As chromosomes condensed and paired with their homologs, they appeared to interact at distinct points. Janssen suggested that these points corresponded to regions in which chromosome segments were exchanged. It is now known that the pairing and interaction between homologous chromosomes, known as synapsis, does more than simply organize the homologs for migration to separate daughter cells. When synapsed, homologous chromosomes undergo reciprocal physical exchanges at their arms in a process called **homologous recombination**, or more simply, "crossing over."

To better understand the type of experimental results that researchers were obtaining at this time, consider a heterozygous individual that inherited dominant maternal alleles for two genes on the same chromosome (such as *AB*) and two recessive paternal alleles for those same genes (such as *ab*). If the genes are linked, one would expect this individual to produce gametes that are either *AB* or *ab* with a 1:1 ratio. If the genes are unlinked, the individual should produce *AB*, *Ab*, *aB*, and *ab* gametes with equal frequencies, according to the Mendelian concept of independent assortment. Because they correspond to new allele combinations, the genotypes Ab and aB are **nonparental types** that result from homologous recombination during meiosis. **Parental types** are progeny that exhibit the same allelic combination as their parents. Morgan and his colleagues, however, found that when such heterozygous individuals were test crossed to a homozygous recessive parent (*AaBb* × *aabb*), both parental and nonparental cases occurred. For example, 950 offspring might be recovered that were either *AaBb* or *aabb*, but 50 offspring would also be obtained that were either *Aabb* or *aaBb*. These results suggested that linkage occurred most often, but a significant minority of offspring were the products of recombination.

visual CONNECTION

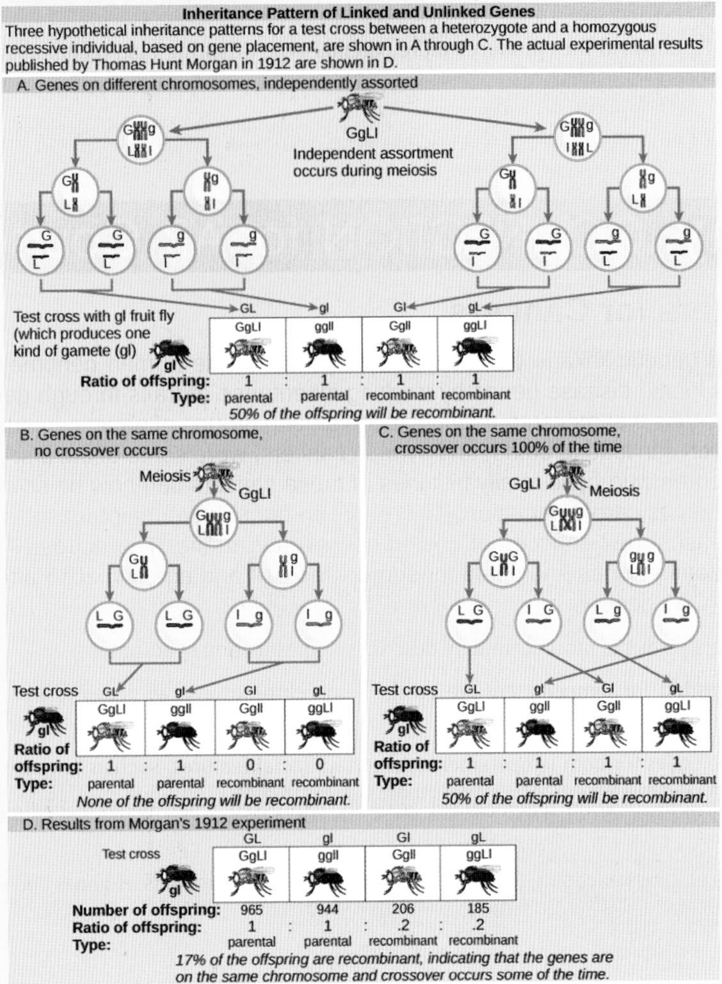

Figure 13.3 Inheritance patterns of unlinked and linked genes are shown. In (a), two genes are located on different chromosomes so independent assortment occurs during meiosis. The offspring have an equal chance of being the parental type (inheriting the same combination of traits as the parents) or a nonparental type (inheriting a different combination of traits than the parents). In (b), two genes are very close together on the same chromosome so that no crossing over occurs between them. The genes are therefore always inherited together and all of the offspring are the parental type. In (c), two genes are far apart on the chromosome such that crossing over occurs during every meiotic event. The recombination frequency will be the same as if the genes were on separate chromosomes. (d) The actual recombination frequency of fruit fly wing length and body color that Thomas Morgan observed in 1912 was 17 percent. A crossover frequency between 0 percent and 50 percent indicates that the genes are on the same chromosome and crossover occurs some of the time.

In a test cross for two characteristics such as the one shown here, can the predicted frequency of recombinant offspring be 60% ? Why or why not?

a. Yes, the predicted offspring frequencies range from 0% to 100%

b. No, the predicted offspring frequencies cannot be higher than 30% .

c. Yes, the predicted offspring frequencies range from 0% to 60% .

d. No, the predicted offspring frequencies range from 0% to 50% .

Think About It

A test cross involving F_1 dihybrid flies produces more parental-type offspring than recombinant-type offspring. How can you explain these observed results?

everyday CONNECTION for AP® Courses

Genetic Markers for Cancers

Scientists have used genetic linkage to discover the location in the human genome of many genes that cause disease. They locate disease genes by tracking inheritance of traits through generations of families and creating linkage maps that measure recombination among groups of genetic "markers." The two BRCA genes, mutations which can lead to breast and ovarian cancers, were some of the first genes discovered by genetic mapping. Women who have family histories of these cancers can now be screened to determine if one or both of these genes carry a mutation. If so, they can opt to have their breasts and ovaries surgically removed. This decreases their chances of getting cancer later in life. The actress Angelia Jolie brought this to the public's attention when she opted for surgery in 2014 and again in 2015 after doctors found she carried a mutated BRCA1 gene.

Which of the following statements most accurately describes domestication syndrome?

a. Genes responsible for temperament are on the same chromosome as genes responsible for certain facial features.

b. A single gene codes for both temperament and certain facial features, such as jaw size.

c. Genes responsible for mild temperament are only expressed when genes encoding a cute face are also present.

d. The products of genes encoding temperament interact with the products of genes encoding facial features.

Genetic Maps

Janssen did not have the technology to demonstrate crossing over so it remained an abstract idea that was not widely accepted. Scientists thought chiasmata were a variation on synapsis and could not understand how chromosomes could break and rejoin. Yet, the data were clear that linkage did not always occur. Ultimately, it took a young undergraduate student and an "all-nighter" to mathematically elucidate the problem of linkage and recombination.

In 1913, Alfred Sturtevant, a student in Morgan's laboratory, gathered results from researchers in the laboratory, and took them home one night to mull them over. By the next morning, he had created the first "chromosome map," a linear representation of gene order and relative distance on a chromosome (Figure 13.4).

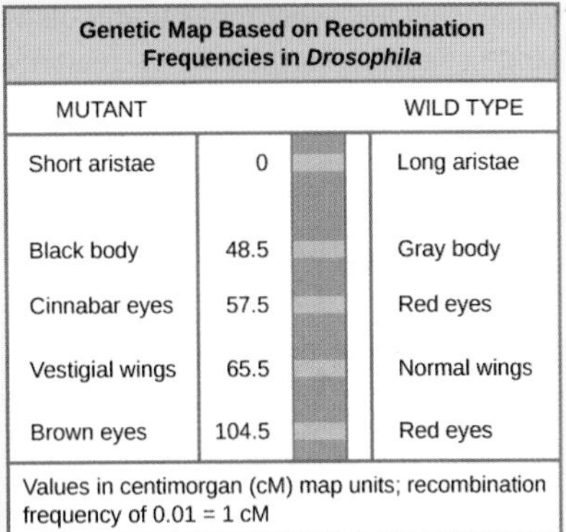

Genetic Map Based on Recombination Frequencies in Drosophila
MUTANT
WILD TYPE
Short aristae
0
Long aristae
Black body
48.5
Gray body
Cinnabar eyes
57.5
Red eyes
Vestigial wings
65.5
Normal wings
Brown eyes
104.5
Red eyes
Values in centimorgan (cM) map units; recombination frequency of 0.01 = 1 cM

Figure 13.4 This genetic map orders *Drosophila* genes on the basis of recombination frequency.

Which of the following statements is true?

a. Recombination of the red/brown eye and long/short aristae alleles will occur more frequently than recombination of the alleles for wing length and body color.

b. Recombination of the body color and red/cinnabar eye alleles will occur more frequently than recombination of the alleles for wing length and aristae length.

c. Recombination of the body color and aristae length alleles will occur more frequently than recombination of red/brown eye alleles and the aristae length alleles.

d. Recombination of the gray/black body color and long/short aristae alleles will not occur.

As shown in Figure 13.4, by using recombination frequency to predict genetic distance, the relative order of genes on chromosome 2 could be inferred. The values shown represent map distances in centimorgans (cM), which correspond to recombination frequencies (in percent). Therefore, the genes for body color and wing size were 65.5 − 48.5 = 17 cM apart, indicating that the maternal and paternal alleles for these genes recombine in 17 percent of offspring, on average.

To construct a chromosome map, Sturtevant assumed that genes were ordered serially on threadlike chromosomes. He also assumed that the incidence of recombination between two homologous chromosomes could occur with equal likelihood anywhere along the length of the chromosome. Operating under these assumptions, Sturtevant postulated that alleles that were far apart on a chromosome were more likely to dissociate during meiosis simply because there was a larger region over which recombination could occur. Conversely, alleles that were close to each other on the chromosome were likely to be inherited together. The average number of crossovers between two alleles—that is, their **recombination frequency**—correlated with their genetic distance from each other, relative to the locations of other genes on that chromosome. Considering the example cross between *AaBb* and *aabb* above, the frequency of recombination could be calculated as 50/1000 = 0.05. That is, the likelihood of a crossover between genes *A/a* and *B/b* was 0.05, or 5 percent. Such a result would indicate that the genes were definitively linked, but that they were far enough apart for crossovers to occasionally occur. Sturtevant divided his genetic map into map units, or **centimorgans (cM)**, in which a recombination frequency of 0.01 corresponds to 1 cM.

By representing alleles in a linear map, Sturtevant suggested that genes can range from being perfectly linked (recombination frequency = 0) to being perfectly unlinked (recombination frequency = 0.5) when genes are on different chromosomes or genes are separated very far apart on the same chromosome. Perfectly unlinked genes correspond to the frequencies predicted by Mendel to assort independently in a dihybrid cross. A recombination frequency of 0.5 indicates that 50 percent of offspring are recombinants and the other 50 percent are parental types. That is, every type of allele combination is represented with equal frequency. This representation allowed Sturtevant to additively calculate distances between several genes on the same chromosome. However, as the genetic distances approached 0.50, his predictions became less accurate because it was not clear whether the genes were very far apart on the same chromosome or on different chromosomes.

In 1931, Barbara McClintock and Harriet Creighton demonstrated the crossover of homologous chromosomes in corn plants. Weeks later, homologous recombination in *Drosophila* was demonstrated microscopically by Curt Stern. Stern observed several X-linked phenotypes that were associated with a structurally unusual and dissimilar X chromosome pair in which one X was missing a small terminal segment, and the other X was fused to a piece of the Y chromosome. By crossing flies, observing their offspring, and then visualizing the offspring's chromosomes, Stern demonstrated that every time the offspring allele combination deviated from either of the parental combinations, there was a corresponding exchange of an X chromosome segment. Using mutant flies with structurally distinct X chromosomes was the key to observing the products of recombination because DNA sequencing and other molecular tools were not yet available. It is now known that homologous chromosomes regularly exchange segments in meiosis by reciprocally breaking and rejoining their DNA at precise locations.

Review Sturtevant's process to create a genetic map on the basis of recombination frequencies here (http://openstaxcollege.org/l/gene_crossover) .

Genetic diversity is the total number of genetic characteristics in a species. Explain how chromosomal crossover contributes to genetic diversity.

a. Chromosomal crossover is a specific, non-random process during which chromosomes are linked together and exchange DNA, contributing to the genetic diversity.

b. Chromosomal crossover occurs during meiosis when chromosome pairs are linked and exchange DNA. Thus, crossover increases the variance of genetic combinations in the haploid gamete cell.

c. Chromosomal crossover results in the inheritance of genetic material by offspring and the recombination event is not variable in frequency or location.

d. Chromosomal crossover occurs during the mitotic process when chromosomes are linked together and recombination takes place, increasing the variance of genetic combinations in the haploid mitotic cells formed from mitosis.

Mendel's Mapped Traits

Homologous recombination is a common genetic process, yet Mendel never observed it. Had he investigated both linked and unlinked genes, it would have been much more difficult for him to create a unified model of his data on the basis of probabilistic calculations. Researchers who have since mapped the seven traits investigated by Mendel onto the seven chromosomes of the pea plant genome have confirmed that all of the genes he examined are either on separate chromosomes or are sufficiently far apart as to be statistically unlinked. Some have suggested that Mendel was enormously lucky to select only unlinked genes, whereas others question whether Mendel discarded any data suggesting linkage. In any case, Mendel consistently observed independent assortment because he examined genes that were effectively unlinked.

13.2 | Chromosomal Basis of Inherited Disorders

In this section, you will explore the following question:

- What are the genetic consequences that result from nondisjunction and errors in chromosome structure through inversions and translocations?

Connection for AP® Courses

The number, size, shape, and banding patterns of chromosomes make them easily identifiable in a karyogram and allows for the assessment of many chromosomal abnormalities. Although the cell cycle, mitosis, and meiosis are highly regulated to prevent errors, the processes are not perfect. One example is the failure of homologous chromosomes or sister chromatids to separate properly during meiosis I or meiosis II (a phenomenon referred to as nondisjunction). This results in gametes with too many or too few chromosomes. Disorders in chromosome number (aneuploidy) are typically lethal to the embryo, although a few trisomic genotypes are viable (e.g., Down syndrome). Because of X inactivation, aberrations in sex chromosomes typically have milder phenotypic effects (e.g., Turner syndrome) than aneuploidy. Sometimes segments of chromosome are duplicated, deleted, or rearranged by inversion or translocation. These aberrations can result in problematic phenotypic effects. Diagnostic testing can detect many of these chromosomal disorders in individuals well before birth, resulting in medical, ethical, and civic issues, such as the right to privacy.

A condition in which an organism has more than the normal number of chromosome sets (two for diploid species) is called polyploidy. Polyploidy resulting in odd numbers of chromosomes is rare because it results in sterile organisms. One set of chromosomes has no pair so meiosis cannot proceed normally. In contrast, polyploidy resulting in even chromosome numbers is very common in the plant kingdom. Polyploid plants tend to be larger and more robust than individuals with the normal number of chromosomes.

Information presented and the examples highlighted in the section support concepts outlined in Big Idea 3 of the AP® Biology Curriculum Framework. The Learning Objectives listed in the Curriculum Framework provide a transparent foundation for the AP® Biology course, an inquiry-based laboratory experience, instructional activities, and AP® exam questions. A Learning Objective merges required content with one or more of the seven Science Practices.

Big Idea 3	Living systems store, retrieve, transmit and respond to information essential to life processes.
Enduring Understanding 3.A	Heritable information provides for continuity of life.
Essential Knowledge	**3.A.2** In eukaryotes, heritable information is passed to the next generation via processes that include the cell cycle and mitosis or meiosis plus fertilization.
Science Practice	**6.2** The student can construct explanations of phenomena based on evidence produced through scientific practices.
Learning Objective	**3.9** The student is able to construct an explanation, using visual representations or narratives, as to how DNA in chromosomes is transmitted to the next generation via mitosis, or meiosis followed by fertilization.
Essential Knowledge	**3.A.3** The chromosomal basis of inheritance provides an understanding of the pattern of passage (transmission) of genes from parent to offspring.
Science Practice	**3.1** The student can pose scientific questions.
Learning Objective	**3.13** The student is able to pose questions about ethical, social or medical issues surrounding human genetic disorders.
Big Idea 3	Living systems store, retrieve, transmit and respond to information essential to life processes.
Enduring Understanding 3.C	The processing of genetic information is imperfect and is a source of genetic variation.
Essential Knowledge	**3.A.3** Changes in genotype can result in changes in phenotype.
Science Practice	**6.4** The student can make claims and predictions about natural phenomena based on scientific theories and models.
Science Practice	**7.2** The student can connect concepts in and across domain(s) to generalize or extrapolate in and/or across enduring understandings and/or big ideas.
Learning Objective	**3.24** The student is able to predict how a change in genotype, when expressed as a phenotype, provides a variation that can be subject to natural selection.

Inherited disorders can arise when chromosomes behave abnormally during meiosis. Chromosome disorders can be divided into two categories: abnormalities in chromosome number and chromosomal structural rearrangements. Because even small segments of chromosomes can span many genes, chromosomal disorders are characteristically dramatic and often fatal.

Identification of Chromosomes

The isolation and microscopic observation of chromosomes forms the basis of cytogenetics and is the primary method by which clinicians detect chromosomal abnormalities in humans. A **karyotype** is the number and appearance of chromosomes, and includes their length, banding pattern, and centromere position. To obtain a view of an individual's karyotype, cytologists photograph the chromosomes and then cut and paste each chromosome into a chart, or **karyogram**, also known as an ideogram (Figure 13.5).

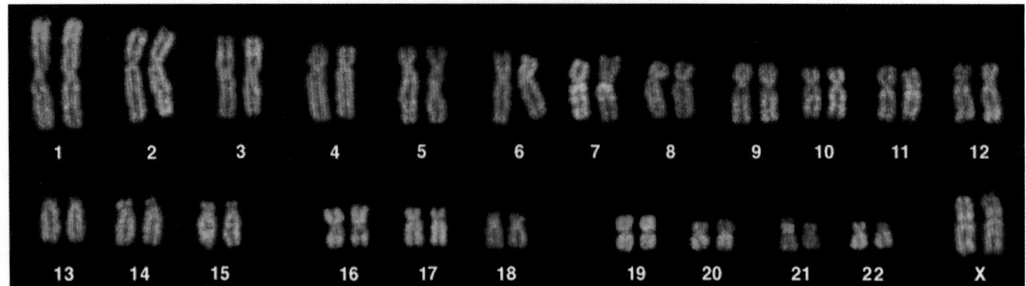

Figure 13.5 This karyotype is of a female human. Notice that homologous chromosomes are the same size, and have the same centromere positions and banding patterns. A human male would have an XY chromosome pair instead of the XX pair shown. (credit: Andreas Blozer et al)

In a given species, chromosomes can be identified by their number, size, centromere position, and banding pattern. In a human karyotype, **autosomes** or "body chromosomes" (all of the non–sex chromosomes) are generally organized in order of size from largest (chromosome 1) to smallest (chromosome 22). (The X and Y chromosomes, the 23rd pair, are not autosomes.) However, chromosome 21 is actually shorter than chromosome 22. This was discovered after the naming of Down syndrome as trisomy 21, reflecting how this disease results from possessing one extra chromosome 21 (three total). Not wanting to change the name of this disease, scientists retained the original numbering system. The chromosome "arms" projecting from either end of the centromere may be designated as short or long, depending on their relative lengths. The short arm is abbreviated *p* (for "petite"), whereas the long arm is abbreviated *q* (because it follows "p" alphabetically). Each arm is further subdivided and denoted by a number. For example, locus 3 on the short arm of chromosome 21 is denoted 21p3. Using this naming system, locations on chromosomes can be described consistently in the scientific literature.

Geneticists Use Karyograms to Identify Chromosomal Aberrations

Although Mendel is referred to as the "father of modern genetics," he performed his experiments with none of the tools that the geneticists of today routinely employ. One such powerful cytological technique is karyotyping, a method in which traits characterized by chromosomal abnormalities can be identified from a single cell. To observe an individual's karyotype, a person's cells (like white blood cells) are first collected from a blood sample or other tissue. In the laboratory, the isolated cells are stimulated to begin actively dividing. A chemical called colchicine is then applied to cells to arrest condensed chromosomes in metaphase. Cells are then made to swell using a hypotonic solution so the chromosomes spread apart. Finally, the sample is preserved in a fixative and applied to a slide.

The geneticist then stains chromosomes with one of several dyes to better visualize the distinct and reproducible banding patterns of each chromosome pair. Following staining, the chromosomes are viewed using bright-field microscopy. A common stain choice is the Giemsa stain. Giemsa staining results in approximately 400–800 bands (of tightly coiled DNA and condensed proteins) arranged along all of the 23 chromosome pairs; an experienced geneticist can identify each band. In addition to the banding patterns, chromosomes are further identified on the basis of size and centromere location. To obtain the classic depiction of the karyotype in which homologous pairs of chromosomes are aligned in numerical order from longest to shortest, the geneticist obtains a digital image, identifies each chromosome, and manually arranges the chromosomes into this pattern (Figure 13.5).

At its most basic, the karyogram may reveal genetic abnormalities in which an individual has too many or too few chromosomes per cell. Examples of this are Down Syndrome, which is identified by a third copy of chromosome 21, and Turner Syndrome, which is characterized by the presence of only one X chromosome in women instead of the normal two. Geneticists can also identify large deletions or insertions of DNA. For instance, Jacobsen Syndrome—which involves distinctive facial features as well as heart and bleeding defects—is identified by a deletion on chromosome 11. Finally, the karyotype can pinpoint **translocations**, which occur when a segment of genetic material breaks from one chromosome and reattaches to another chromosome or to a different part of the same chromosome.

During Mendel's lifetime, inheritance was an abstract concept that could only be inferred by performing crosses and observing the traits expressed by offspring. By observing a karyogram, today's geneticists can actually visualize the chromosomal composition of an individual to confirm or predict genetic abnormalities in offspring, even before birth.

Disorders in Chromosome Number

Of all of the chromosomal disorders, abnormalities in chromosome number are the most obviously identifiable from a karyogram. Disorders of chromosome number include the duplication or loss of entire chromosomes, as well as changes in the number of complete sets of chromosomes. They are caused by **nondisjunction**, which occurs when pairs of homologous chromosomes or sister chromatids fail to separate during meiosis. Misaligned or incomplete synapsis, or a dysfunction of the spindle apparatus that facilitates chromosome migration, can cause nondisjunction. The risk of nondisjunction occurring increases with the age of the parents.

Nondisjunction can occur during either meiosis I or II, with differing results (Figure 13.6). If homologous chromosomes fail to separate during meiosis I, the result is two gametes that lack that particular chromosome and two gametes with two copies of the chromosome. If sister chromatids fail to separate during meiosis II, the result is one gamete that lacks that chromosome, two normal gametes with one copy of the chromosome, and one gamete with two copies of the chromosome.

visual CONNECTION

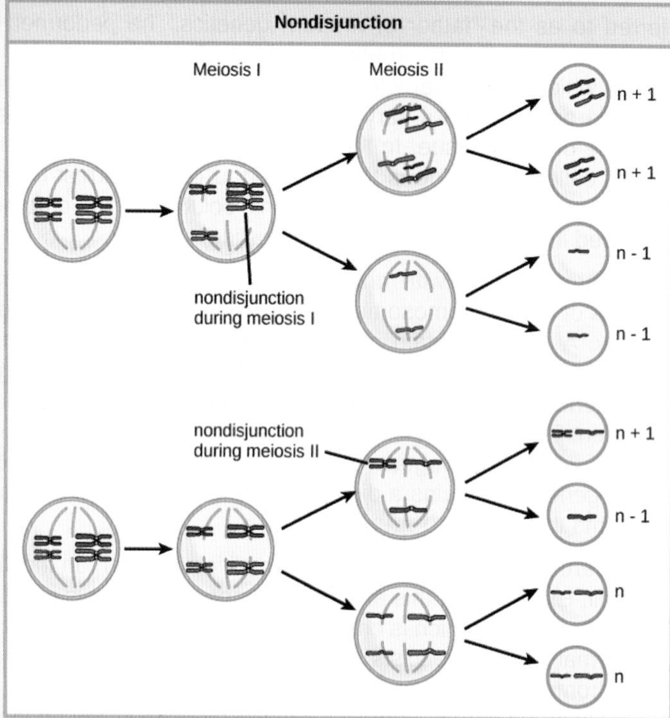

Figure 13.6 Nondisjunction occurs when homologous chromosomes or sister chromatids fail to separate during meiosis, resulting in an abnormal chromosome number. Nondisjunction may occur during meiosis I or meiosis II.

Which of the following statements about nondisjunction is true?

a. Nondisjunction only results in gametes with n+1 or n-1 chromosomes.

b. Nondisjunction occurring during meiosis II results in 50% normal gametes.

c. Nondisjunction during meiosis I results in 50% normal gametes.

d. Nondisjunction always results in four different kinds of gametes.

Aneuploidy

An individual with the appropriate number of chromosomes for their species is called **euploid**; in humans, euploidy corresponds to 22 pairs of autosomes and one pair of sex chromosomes. An individual with an error in chromosome number is described as **aneuploid**, a term that includes **monosomy** (loss of one chromosome) or **trisomy** (gain of an extraneous chromosome). Monosomic human zygotes missing any one copy of an autosome invariably fail to develop to birth because they lack essential genes. This underscores the importance of "gene dosage" in humans. Most autosomal trisomies also fail to develop to birth; however, duplications of some of the smaller chromosomes (13, 15, 18, 21, or 22) can result in offspring that survive for several weeks to many years. Trisomic individuals suffer from a different type of genetic imbalance: an excess in gene dose. Individuals with an extra chromosome may synthesize an abundance of the gene products encoded by that chromosome. This extra dose (150 percent) of specific genes can lead to a number of functional challenges and often precludes development. The most common trisomy among viable births is that of chromosome 21, which corresponds to Down Syndrome. Individuals with this inherited disorder are characterized by short stature and stunted digits, facial distinctions that include a broad skull and large tongue, and significant developmental delays. The incidence of Down syndrome is correlated with maternal age; older women are more likely to become pregnant with fetuses carrying the trisomy 21 genotype (**Figure 13.7**).

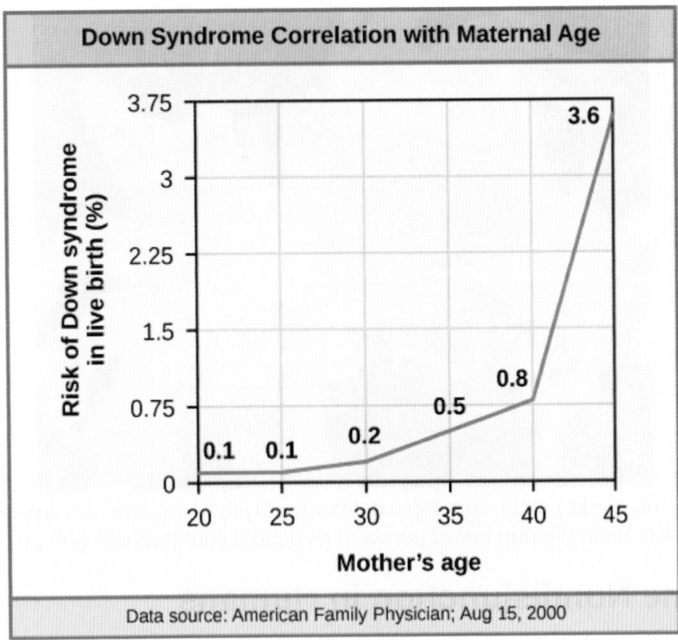

Figure 13.7 The incidence of having a fetus with trisomy 21 increases dramatically with maternal age.

Visualize the addition of a chromosome that leads to Down syndrome in this video simulation (http://openstaxcollege.org/l/down_syndrome) .

With increasing age, women are at increased risk of having a baby with a chromosomal abnormality such as Down syndrome. Why is age a risk factor?

a. Cells are more likely to make mistakes as we age due to an increase in the nondisjunction of cells during cell division, which is the reason for the occurrence of Down syndrome.

b. The chance of this disorder increases with age due to increased mistakes in the mitotic cells with age.

c. There are increased risks of translocation mutations with age, even though other mutation rates are constant, and this increases the risk.

d. The risk of having a child with Down syndrome is associated primarily with lifestyle factors that change with age.

Polyploidy

An individual with more than the correct number of chromosome sets (two for diploid species) is called **polyploid**. For instance, fertilization of an abnormal diploid egg with a normal haploid sperm would yield a triploid zygote. Polyploid animals are extremely rare, with only a few examples among the flatworms, crustaceans, amphibians, fish, and lizards. Polyploid animals are sterile because meiosis cannot proceed normally and instead produces mostly aneuploid daughter cells that cannot yield viable zygotes. Rarely, polyploid animals can reproduce asexually by haplodiploidy, in which an unfertilized egg divides mitotically to produce offspring. In contrast, polyploidy is very common in the plant kingdom, and polyploid plants tend to be larger and more robust than euploids of their species (Figure 13.8).

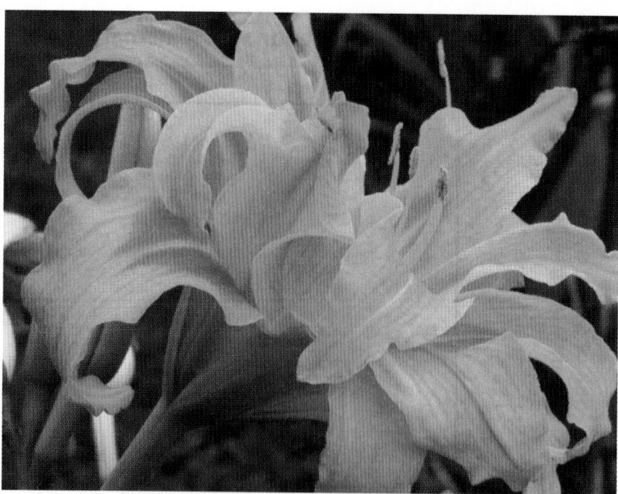

Figure 13.8 As with many polyploid plants, this triploid orange daylily (*Hemerocallis fulva*) is particularly large and robust, and grows flowers with triple the number of petals of its diploid counterparts. (credit: Steve Karg)

Sex Chromosome Nondisjunction in Humans

Humans display dramatic deleterious effects with autosomal trisomies and monosomies. Therefore, it may seem counterintuitive that human females and males can function normally, despite carrying different numbers of the X chromosome. Rather than a gain or loss of autosomes, variations in the number of sex chromosomes are associated with relatively mild effects. In part, this occurs because of a molecular process called **X inactivation**. Early in development, when female mammalian embryos consist of just a few thousand cells (relative to trillions in the newborn), one X chromosome in each cell inactivates by tightly condensing into a quiescent (dormant) structure called a Barr body. The chance that an X chromosome (maternally or paternally derived) is inactivated in each cell is random, but once the inactivation occurs, all cells derived from that one will have the same inactive X chromosome or Barr body. By this process, females compensate for their double genetic dose of X chromosome. In so-called "tortoiseshell" cats, embryonic X inactivation is observed as color variegation (Figure 13.9). Females that are heterozygous for an X-linked coat color gene will express one of two different coat colors over different regions of their body, corresponding to whichever X chromosome is inactivated in the embryonic cell progenitor of that region.

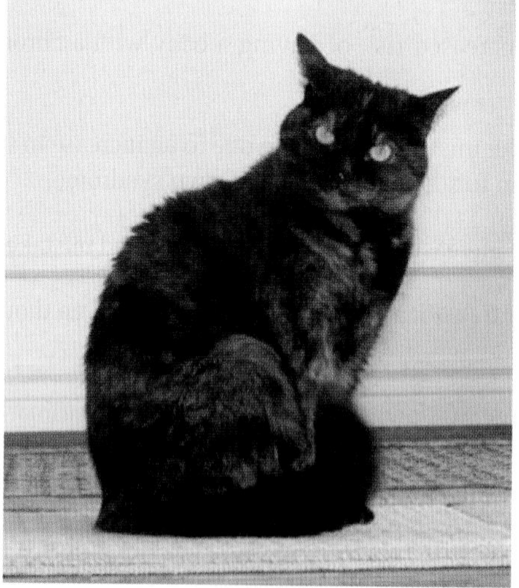

Figure 13.9 In cats, the gene for coat color is located on the X chromosome. In the embryonic development of female cats, one of the two X chromosomes is randomly inactivated in each cell, resulting in a tortoiseshell pattern if the cat has two different alleles for coat color. Male cats, having only one X chromosome, never exhibit a tortoiseshell coat color. (credit: Michael Bodega)

An individual carrying an abnormal number of X chromosomes will inactivate all but one X chromosome in each of her cells. However, even inactivated X chromosomes continue to express a few genes, and X chromosomes must reactivate for the proper maturation of female ovaries. As a result, X-chromosomal abnormalities are typically associated with mild mental and physical defects, as well as sterility. If the X chromosome is absent altogether, the individual will not develop in utero.

Several errors in sex chromosome number have been characterized. Individuals with three X chromosomes, called triplo-X, are phenotypically female but express developmental delays and reduced fertility. The XXY genotype, corresponding to one type of Klinefelter syndrome, corresponds to phenotypically male individuals with small testes, enlarged breasts, and reduced body hair. More complex types of Klinefelter syndrome exist in which the individual has as many as five X chromosomes. In all types, every X chromosome except one undergoes inactivation to compensate for the excess genetic dosage. This can be seen as several Barr bodies in each cell nucleus. Turner syndrome, characterized as an X0 genotype (i.e., only a single sex chromosome), corresponds to a phenotypically female individual with short stature, webbed skin in the neck region, hearing and cardiac impairments, and sterility.

Duplications and Deletions

In addition to the loss or gain of an entire chromosome, a chromosomal segment may be duplicated or lost. Duplications and deletions often produce offspring that survive but exhibit physical and mental abnormalities. Duplicated chromosomal segments may fuse to existing chromosomes or may be free in the nucleus. Cri-du-chat (from the French for "cry of the cat") is a syndrome associated with nervous system abnormalities and identifiable physical features that result from a deletion of most of 5p (the small arm of chromosome 5) (Figure 13.10). Infants with this genotype emit a characteristic high-pitched cry on which the disorder's name is based.

Figure 13.10 This individual with cri-du-chat syndrome is shown at two, four, nine, and 12 years of age. (credit: Paola Cerruti Mainardi)

Chromosomal Structural Rearrangements

Cytologists have characterized numerous structural rearrangements in chromosomes, but chromosome inversions and translocations are the most common. Both are identified during meiosis by the adaptive pairing of rearranged chromosomes with their former homologs to maintain appropriate gene alignment. If the genes carried on two homologs are not oriented correctly, a recombination event could result in the loss of genes from one chromosome and the gain of genes on the other. This would produce aneuploid gametes.

Chromosome Inversions

A **chromosome inversion** is the detachment, 180° rotation, and reinsertion of part of a chromosome. Inversions may occur in nature as a result of mechanical shear, or from the action of transposable elements (special DNA sequences capable of facilitating the rearrangement of chromosome segments with the help of enzymes that cut and paste DNA sequences). Unless they disrupt a gene sequence, inversions only change the orientation of genes and are likely to have more mild effects than aneuploid errors. However, altered gene orientation can result in functional changes because regulators of gene expression could be moved out of position with respect to their targets, causing aberrant levels of gene products.

An inversion can be **pericentric** and include the centromere, or **paracentric** and occur outside of the centromere (Figure 13.11). A pericentric inversion that is asymmetric about the centromere can change the relative lengths of the chromosome arms, making these inversions easily identifiable.

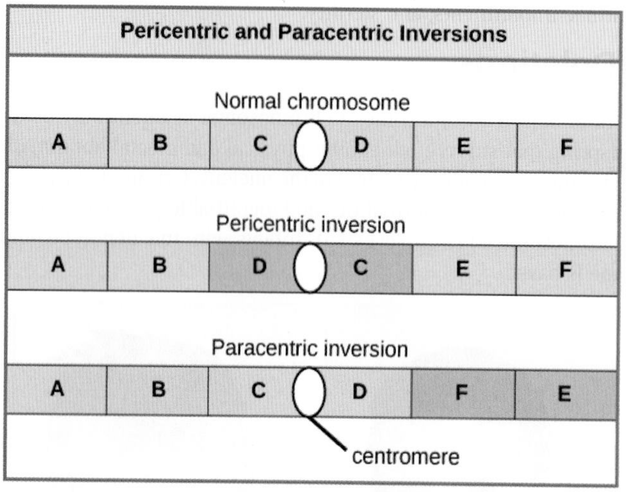

Figure 13.11 Pericentric inversions include the centromere, and paracentric inversions do not. A pericentric inversion can change the relative lengths of the chromosome arms; a paracentric inversion cannot.

When one homologous chromosome undergoes an inversion but the other does not, the individual is described as an inversion heterozygote. To maintain point-for-point synapsis during meiosis, one homolog must form a loop, and the other homolog must mold around it. Although this topology can ensure that the genes are correctly aligned, it also forces the homologs to stretch and can be associated with regions of imprecise synapsis (Figure 13.12).

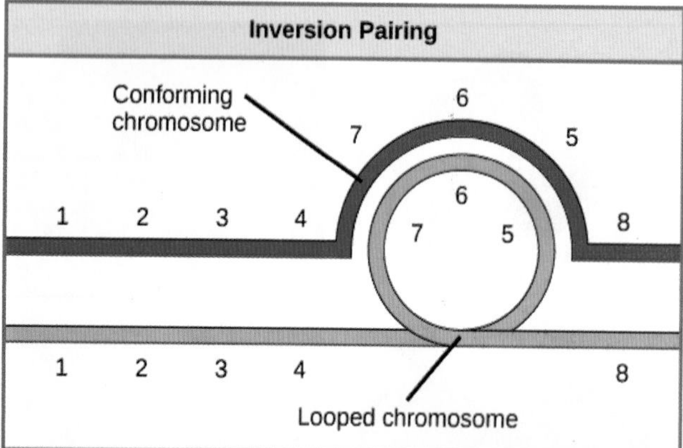

Figure 13.12 When one chromosome undergoes an inversion but the other does not, one chromosome must form an inverted loop to retain point-for-point interaction during synapsis. This inversion pairing is essential to maintaining gene alignment during meiosis and to allow for recombination.

The Chromosome 18 Inversion

Not all structural rearrangements of chromosomes produce nonviable, impaired, or infertile individuals. In rare instances, such a change can result in the evolution of a new species. In fact, a pericentric inversion in chromosome 18 appears to have contributed to the evolution of humans. This inversion is not present in our closest genetic relatives, the chimpanzees. Humans and chimpanzees differ cytogenetically by pericentric inversions on several chromosomes and by the fusion of two separate chromosomes in chimpanzees that correspond to chromosome two in humans.

The pericentric chromosome 18 inversion is believed to have occurred in early humans following their divergence from a common ancestor with chimpanzees approximately five million years ago. Researchers characterizing this inversion have suggested that approximately 19,000 nucleotide bases were duplicated on 18p, and the duplicated region inverted and reinserted on chromosome 18 of an ancestral human.

A comparison of human and chimpanzee genes in the region of this inversion indicates that two genes—*ROCK1* and *USP14*—that are adjacent on chimpanzee chromosome 17 (which corresponds to human chromosome 18) are more distantly positioned on human chromosome 18. This suggests that one of the inversion breakpoints occurred between these two genes. Interestingly, humans and chimpanzees express *USP14* at distinct levels in specific cell types, including cortical cells and fibroblasts. Perhaps the chromosome 18 inversion in an ancestral human repositioned specific genes and reset their expression levels in a useful way. Because both *ROCK1* and *USP14* encode cellular enzymes, a change in their expression could alter cellular function. It is not known how this inversion contributed to hominid evolution, but it appears to be a significant factor in the divergence of humans from other primates.[1]

According to the passage, which of the following events are believed to have occurred after humans diverged from their common ancestor with chimpanzees?

a. Paracentric inversions occurred at several chromosomes, including human chromosome 18.

b. Two separate chromosomes underwent a pericentric inversion, then fused to form chromosome 2 in humans.

c. $19,000$ nucleotide bases were duplicated, inverted, and reinserted at human chromosome 18.

d. The ROCK1 and USP14 genes were duplicated in early humans, which increased expression of these genes.

Translocations

A **translocation** occurs when a segment of a chromosome dissociates and reattaches to a different, nonhomologous chromosome. Translocations can be benign or have devastating effects depending on how the positions of genes are altered with respect to regulatory sequences. Reciprocal translocations result from the exchange of chromosome segments between two nonhomologous chromosomes such that there is no gain or loss of genetic information (Figure 13.13).

1. Violaine Goidts et al., "Segmental duplication associated with the human-specific inversion of chromosome 18: a further example of the impact of segmental duplications on karyotype and genome evolution in primates," *Human Genetics*. 115 (2004):116-122

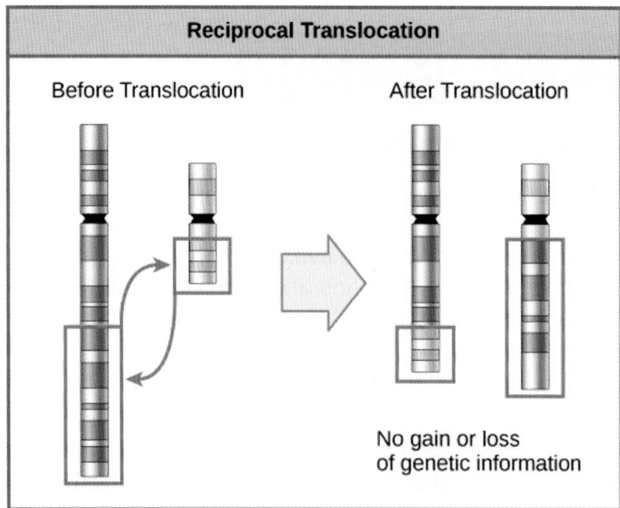

Figure 13.13 A reciprocal translocation occurs when a segment of DNA is transferred from one chromosome to another, nonhomologous chromosome. (credit: modification of work by National Human Genome Research/USA)

science practices CONNECTION for AP® Courses

Activity

A Day in the Life. Compose a short story, PowerPoint presentation, video, poem, or significant piece of art to describe a day in the life of a teenager afflicted with a single gene disorder or chromosomal abnormality. You need to include the causes and effects of the disorder and pose a question about a social, medical, or ethical issue(s) associated with human genetic disorders.

Think About It

Create a series of representations to show how nondisjunction can result in a trisomic zygote from a cell with 2n = 4.

KEY TERMS

aneuploid individual with an error in chromosome number; includes deletions and duplications of chromosome segments

autosome any of the non-sex chromosomes

centimorgan (cM) (also, map unit) relative distance that corresponds to a recombination frequency of 0.01

Chromosomal Theory of Inheritance theory proposing that chromosomes are the vehicles of genes and that their behavior during meiosis is the physical basis of the inheritance patterns that Mendel observed

chromosome inversion detachment, 180° rotation, and reinsertion of a chromosome arm

euploid individual with the appropriate number of chromosomes for their species

homologous recombination process by which homologous chromosomes undergo reciprocal physical exchanges at their arms, also known as crossing over

karyogram photographic image of a karyotype

karyotype number and appearance of an individuals chromosomes; includes the size, banding patterns, and centromere position

monosomy otherwise diploid genotype in which one chromosome is missing

nondisjunction failure of synapsed homologs to completely separate and migrate to separate poles during the first cell division of meiosis

nonparental (recombinant) type progeny resulting from homologous recombination that exhibits a different allele combination compared with its parents

paracentric inversion that occurs outside of the centromere

parental types progeny that exhibits the same allelic combination as its parents

pericentric inversion that involves the centromere

polyploid individual with an incorrect number of chromosome sets

recombination frequency average number of crossovers between two alleles; observed as the number of nonparental types in a population of progeny

translocation process by which one segment of a chromosome dissociates and reattaches to a different, nonhomologous chromosome

trisomy otherwise diploid genotype in which one entire chromosome is duplicated

X inactivation condensation of X chromosomes into Barr bodies during embryonic development in females to compensate for the double genetic dose

CHAPTER SUMMARY

13.1 Chromosomal Theory and Genetic Linkages

The Chromosomal Theory of inheritance, proposed by Sutton and Boveri, states that chromosomes are the vehicles of genetic heredity. Neither Mendelian genetics nor gene linkage is perfectly accurate; instead, chromosome behavior involves segregation, independent assortment, and occasionally, linkage. Sturtevant devised a method to assess recombination frequency and infer the relative positions and distances of linked genes on a chromosome on the basis of the average number of crossovers in the intervening region between the genes. Sturtevant correctly presumed that genes are arranged in serial order on chromosomes and that recombination between homologs can occur anywhere on a chromosome with equal likelihood. Whereas linkage causes alleles on the same chromosome to be inherited together, homologous recombination biases alleles toward an inheritance pattern of independent assortment.

13.2 Chromosomal Basis of Inherited Disorders

The number, size, shape, and banding pattern of chromosomes make them easily identifiable in a karyogram and allows for the assessment of many chromosomal abnormalities. Disorders in chromosome number, or aneuploidies, are typically lethal to the embryo, although a few trisomic genotypes are viable. Because of X inactivation, aberrations in sex chromosomes typically have milder phenotypic effects. Aneuploidies also include instances in which segments of a chromosome are duplicated or deleted. Chromosome structures may also be rearranged, for example by inversion or translocation. Both of these aberrations can result in problematic phenotypic effects. Because they force chromosomes to assume unnatural topologies during meiosis, inversions and translocations are often associated with reduced fertility because of the likelihood of nondisjunction.

REVIEW QUESTIONS

1. When comparing humans (or in *Drosophila*), are X-linked recessive traits observed more frequently in males, in similar numbers between males and females, more frequently in females, or is the frequency different depending on the trait? Why?

a. in more males than females
b. in more females than males
c. in males and females equally
d. in different distributions depending on the trait

2. Which recombination frequency corresponds to perfect linkage and violates the law of independent assortment?

a. 0
b. 0.25
c. 0.5
d. 0.75

3. Which recombination frequency corresponds to independent assortment and the absence of linkage?

a. 0
b. 0.25
c. 0.5
d. 0.75

4.

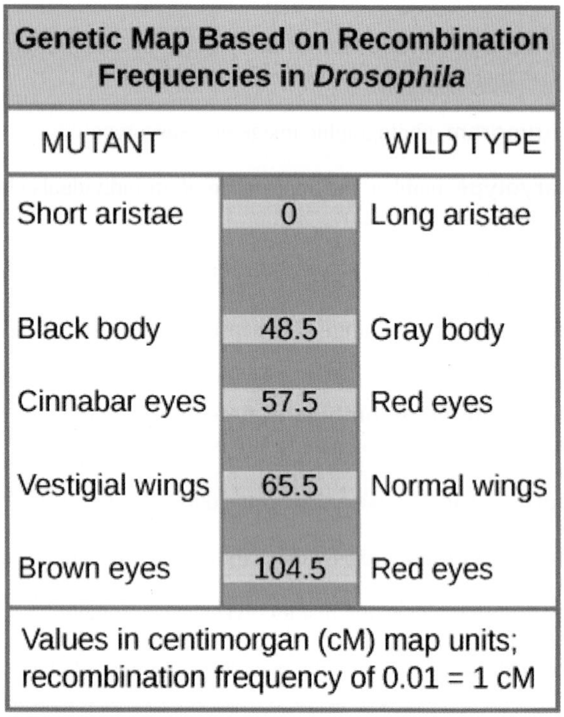

Genetic Map Based on Recombination Frequencies in *Drosophila*

MUTANT		WILD TYPE
Short aristae	0	Long aristae
Black body	48.5	Gray body
Cinnabar eyes	57.5	Red eyes
Vestigial wings	65.5	Normal wings
Brown eyes	104.5	Red eyes

Values in centimorgan (cM) map units; recombination frequency of 0.01 = 1 cM

Based on the diagram, which of the following statements is true?

a. Recombination of the body color and red/ cinnabar eye alleles will occur more frequently than recombination of the alleles for wing length and aristae length.
b. Recombination of the body color and aristae length alleles will occur more frequently than recombination of red/ brown eye alleles and the aristae length alleles.
c. Recombination of the gray/black body color and long/short aristae alleles will not occur.
d. Recombination of the red/brown eye and long/ short aristae alleles will occur more frequently than recombination of the alleles for wing length and body color.

5. Which of the following codes describes position 12 on the long arm of chromosome 13?

a. 13p12

b. 13q12

c. 12p13

d. 12q13

6. Assume a pericentric inversion occurred in one of two homologs prior to meiosis. The other homolog remains normal. During meiosis, what structure, if any, would these homologs assume in order to pair accurately along their lengths?

a. V formation

b. cruciform

c. a loop

d. pairing would not be possible

CRITICAL THINKING QUESTIONS

7. Which best describes the Chromosomal Theory of Inheritance?

a. The theory was proposed by Charles Darwin. It describes the units of inheritance between parents and offspring as well as the processes by which those units control offspring development.

b. The theory was proposed by Boveri-Sutton. It describes linkage, recombination, and crossing over and states that Mendelian genes have specific loci on chromosomes, which undergo segregation and independent assortment.

c. The theory was proposed by Charles Darwin. It states the Mendelian genes have two alternate forms and undergo independent assortment. It helped increase understanding of linkage and recombination.

d. The theory was proposed by Boveri-Sutton. It describes the units of inheritance between parents and offspring as well as the processes by which those units control development in offspring.

8. In a test cross for two characteristics (dihybrid cross), can the predicted frequency of recombinant offspring be 60% ? Why or why not?

a. No. The predicted frequency of recombinant offspring ranges from 0% (for linked traits) to 50% (for unlinked traits) because of both parental and nonparental cases.

b. Yes. The predicted frequency of recombinant offspring can be 60% if genes are located very far from each other.

c. Yes. The predicted frequency can be 60% if crossing over occurs during every meiotic event.

d. No. The predicted frequency can never be 60% due to the presence of mutations such as deletions.

9. Choose the statement that best describes how nondisjunction (see **Figure 13.6**) can result in an aneuploid zygote.

a. Nondisjunction only occurs when homologous chromosomes do not separate during meiosis I, resulting in the formation of gametes containing n+1 and n-1 chromosomes.

b. Nondisjunction only occurs when sister chromatids do not separate in meiosis II, resulting in the formation of gametes containing n+1 and n-1 chromosomes.

c. Nondisjunction is the failure of homologous chromosomes to separate during meiosis I or the failure of sister chromatids to separate during meiosis II, leading to the formation of n+1/n-1/n chromosomes.

d. Nondisjunction occurs when the sister chromatids fail to separate during mitosis II, resulting in the formation of gametes containing n+1 and n-1/n chromosomes.

10. Select the answer that correctly identifies the various chromosomal aberrations and their respective genetic consequence.

a. nondisjunction - aneuploid gametes; duplication - physical and mental abnormalities; deletion - lethal to a diploid organism; inversion - chromosomal breaks in gene; translocations - effects depend on how positions of genes are altered

b. nondisjunction - physical and mental abnormalities; inversion - genetic imbalance; duplication - aneuploid gametes; translocations - chromosomal breaks in the gene; deletion - effects depend on how positions of genes are altered

c. deletion -aneuploid gametes; translocations - physical and mental abnormalities; duplication - effects depend on positions of genes; nondisjunction - causes genetic imbalance lethal to a diploid organism; aneuploidy - leads to various syndromes

d. nondisjunction - chromosomal breaks in gene; duplication - physical and mental abnormalities; deletion - genetic imbalance lethal to a diploid organism; inversion - aneuploid gametes; translocations - effects depend on positions of genes

TEST PREP FOR AP® COURSES

11.

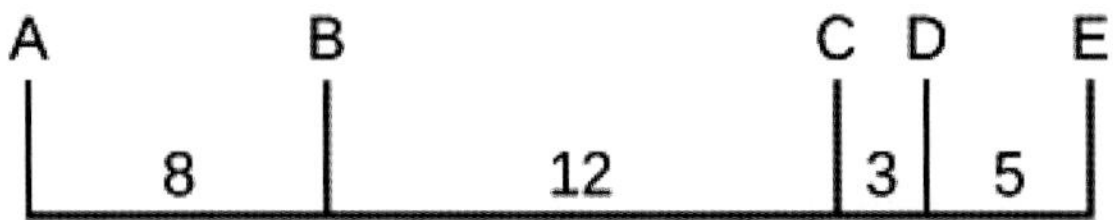

The figure represents a Drosophila linkage map for genes A-E. The numbers between the gene loci are the relative map units between each gene. Based on the linkage map, which two genes are most likely to segregate together?

a. A and B
b. B and C
c. C and D
d. D and E

12. A test cross was made between true-breeding EEWW flies and eeww flies. The resulting F_1 generation was then crossed with eeww flies. 100 offspring in the F_2 generation were examined, and it was discovered that the E and W genes were not linked. Which is the correct genotype of the F_2 offspring if the genes were linked and if the genes were not linked?

a. Linked: 50% EeWw and 50% eeww; not linked: 25% EeWw, 25% , Eeww 25% eeWw, and 25% eeww
b. Linked: 25% Eeww, 50% eeWw; not linked: parental genotypes EeWw and eeww.
c. Linked genotypes (EeWw and eeww) and recombinant genotypes (Eeww and eeWw) in the F2 generation are nearly the same irrespective of their linkage.
d. Linked: mostly with parental genotypes, Eeww and eeWw; unlinked: 25% EeWw and eeww with 75% Eeww and eeWw.

13.

	Number Observed			
F_2 Genotype	A	B	C	D
AaBb	46	4	25	50
Aabb	4	46	25	0
aaBb	4	46	25	0
Aabb	46	4	25	50

A cross was made with true-breeding AABB flies and true-breeding aabb flies. The resulting F_1 generation was then crossed with true-breeding aabb flies. Based on the linkage map, which of the following F_2 generation genotype ratios is most likely to be observed?

a. Number Observed: AaBb (46), Aabb (4), aaBb (4), Aabb (46)
b. Number Observed: AaBb (4), Aabb (46), aaBb (46), Aabb (4)
c. Number Observed: AaBb (25), Aabb (25), aaBb (25), Aabb (25)
d. Number Observed: AaBb (50), Aabb (0), aaBb (0), Aabb (50)

14.

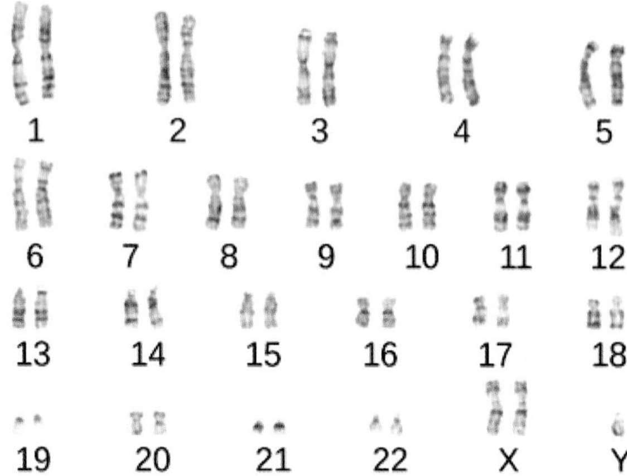

Which of the following symptoms is most likely associated with the disorder shown in the karyotype?

a. lethality
b. infertility
c. heart and bleeding defects
d. short stature and stunted growth

15.

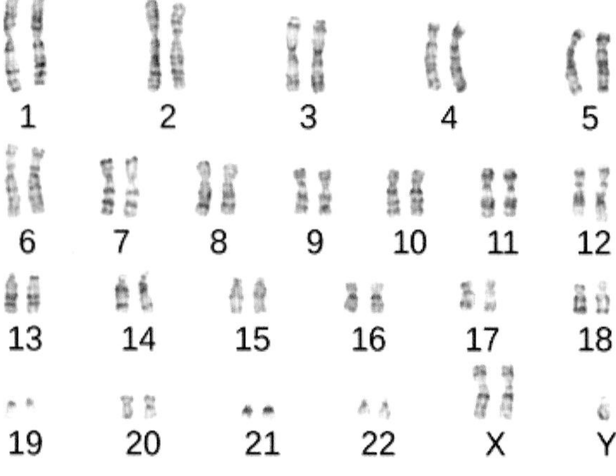

Choose the correct option amongst the following that describes the disorder shown in the karyotype and the social, ethical or medical issue related to the disorder.

a. Down syndrome (47 XY +21) causes intellectual disability, vision problems, congenital heart disease, and susceptibility to cancer. Healthcare providers often do not discuss the positive aspects of raising a child with Down syndrome and often provide out of date information.

b. Klinefelter syndrome (47 XY +21) causes intellectual disability, vision problems, congenital heart disease, and susceptibility to cancer. Arguments are often made against abortion of an affected fetus.

c. Klinefelter syndrome (47 XXY) causes sterility and reduced testosterone production. Arguments are often made against informing insurance companies about a diagnosis of this disease.

d. Down syndrome (47 XXY) causes sterility and lower testosterone production. Arguments are often made against informing insurance companies about a diagnosis of this disease.

16.

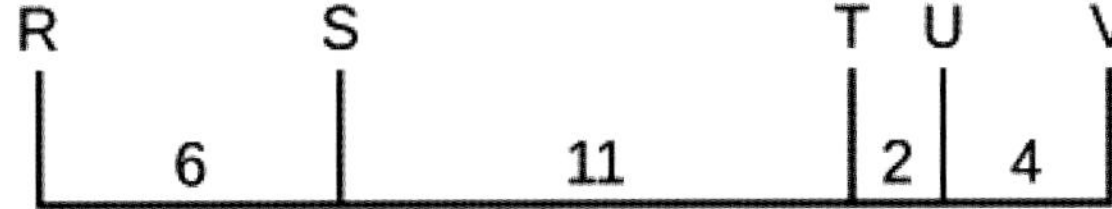

Which of the following gene orders is the most likely outcome of an inversion mutation in the chromosome shown?

a. RSTUV

b. RRSTUV

c. RSUV

d. RTSUV

17.

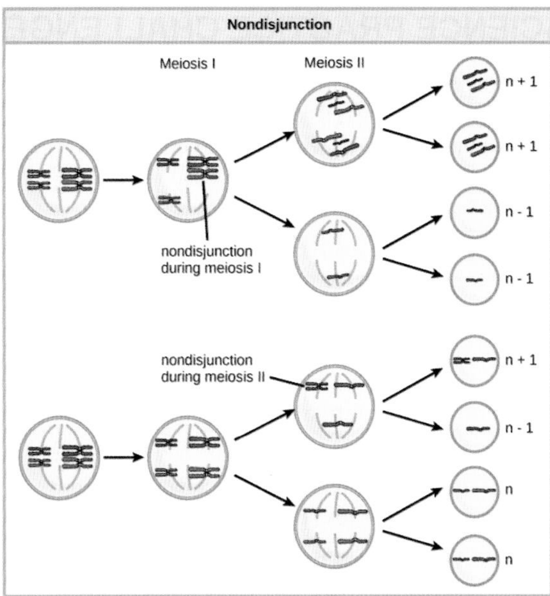

With the help the diagram given, choose the most appropriate statement describing nondisjunction and its genetic consequences.

a. Nondisjunction occurs when a homologous pair is unable to separate during meiosis I, resulting in the formation of gametes containing n+1 and n-1 chromosomes. This is called aneuploidy.

b. Nondisjunction occurs due to the inability of sister chromatids to separate during meiosis II, resulting in the formation of gametes containing n+1 and n-1 chromosomes. This results in heart and bleeding defects.

c. Nondisjunction is the failure of homologous chromosomes to separate during meiosis I or failure of sister chromatids to separate during meiosis II. This results in aneuploid gametes.

d. Nondisjunction occurs when a pair of homologous chromosomes fails to segregate during meiosis II resulting in the formation of gametes containing n+1, n-1, or n numbers of chromosomes. This results in abnormal growth patterns.

18. If the effects of Klinefelter syndrome are compared to the effects of Down Syndrome, this disorder is ______.

a. more severe than Down syndrome, due to gene deletions in this syndrome

b. more severe than Down syndrome, due to trisomy in Klinefelter syndrome

c. less severe than Down syndrome, due to monosomy in Down Syndrome

d. less severe than Down syndrome, due to X-inactivation in this disorder

SCIENCE PRACTICE CHALLENGE QUESTIONS

19. *Drosophila* that are true breeding for the traits straight wings (S) and red eyes (R) are crossed with flies that are true breeding for curved wings (s) and brown eyes (r). A test cross is then made between the offspring and the true-breeding ssrr flies.

A. Use the symbols S, s, R, and r to **construct a representation** of the parental genotypes in the test cross.

B. If these genes are located on different chromosomes, use a Punnett square to **construct a representation** of the offspring of the test cross.

C. **Predict** the distribution of genotypes and phenotypes resulting from the test cross.

D. As it happens, these genes are both on chromosome II as shown below. Use the symbols S, s, R, and r to **construct a representation** of the parental and recombinant genotypes in the test cross.

E. Suppose that 500 flies are produced in the test cross. **Apply mathematical methods** to calculate the expected number of recombinant offspring using the linear map units (LMU) shown in the diagram below.

Genetic Map of *D. melanogaster* Chromosome 2		
MUTANT		WILD TYPE
Short antennae	0	Long antennae
Dumpy wings	13	Long wings
Short legs	31	Long legs
Black body	48.5	Gray body
Vestigial wings	67	Long wings
Curved wings	75.5	Straight wings
Brown eyes	104.5	Red eyes
Values in linear map units (LMU)		

Figure 13.14

20. Studies like the one described in question AP12.1 were carried out by Morgan and Sturtevant beginning in 1911. The discovery of linkage was made by Bateson and Punnett in 1900. They crossed a true-breeding purple (P) plant with long seeds (L) with a true-breeding red (r) plant with round seeds (l). They then performed a self-cross between the F_1 generations. They obtained the F_2 data shown below.

Pheno-type	Geno-type(s)	Ob-served	Ex-pected
purple, long		4831	
purple, round		390	
red, long		393	
red, round		1338	
total		6952	

Table 13.1

A. Use the symbols P, p, L, and l to **construct a representation** of the F_2 genotypes and complete the second column in the table.

B. Complete the fourth column of the table above by recording the values of the **predicted** numbers of plants with each genotype.

C. Apply a c^2 test at the 95% confidence level to **evaluate the claim** that these data confirm linkage. The definition of the statistic $\chi^2 = \sum \frac{(o-e)^2}{e}$ and this table are provided in the AP Biology Exam.

D. At first, Bateson and Punnett did not see that these genes are located on the same chromosome and proceeded to measure the linkage distance between them, taking the first step toward creating a gene map. **Justify** the selection of data and the procedure from which data could be collected that would have provided the necessary evidence to confirm linkage and recombination.

21. Review the observations that provided researchers with evidence in support of the Chromosomal Theory of Inheritance.

A. **Evaluate** the dependence of these observations on improvements in a critical technology during the period from 1850 to 1940. **Identify** this technology and **describe** how this technology allowed scientists to make the connection between chromosomes and genes. (As a hint, the name “chromosome” is taken from the Greek word *chroma*, which means colored or stained.)

B. Mendel’s laws of inheritance are explained by the chromosomal theory. Use these observations to **justify**:

- the law of segregation
- the law of independent assortment

22. Errors in the transmission of genetic information to future generations are essential. Otherwise, organisms could not evolve over time. Some errors in the synthesis of new DNA during S phase in either meiosis or mitosis are not repaired. These errors usually involve single nucleotides. Errors that occur during prophase I of meiosis that are not corrected can involve the exchange of sequences between homologous chromosomes (duplications) or even nonhomologous chromosomes (translocations). Duplications are usually retained, and the organism remains viable without a change in phenotype. Translocations are usually lethal or significantly alter phenotype. In eukaryotes, duplications and the shuffling of parental genes through recombination are important sources of variation.

Construct an explanation of the role of duplication as a source of raw material for future mutations and selection and contrast this type of variation with recombination.

23. Bacteria and Archaea reproduce asexually, and genetic material is in a closed loop. In both domains, genetic material is transferred horizontally, and polyploidy is common. Polypoidy is common in plants and occurs in invertebrate animals but is less common in vertebrates. In all domains, multiple copies of genes (gene duplication) are common.

Based on this information, **compare and contrast** the mechanisms that provide genetic variation in the three domains: Bacteria, Archaea, and Eukarya.

14 | DNA STRUCTURE AND FUNCTION

Figure 14.1 Michael Morton went to jail in 1986 for the murder of this wife. Twenty-five years later, in 2011, he was exonerated of her murder by DNA evidence. (credit: Lauren Gerson)

Chapter Outline

Introduction

Each person's DNA is unique, and it is possible to detect differences among individuals within a species on the basis of these unique features. DNA analysis has many practical applications, including identifying criminals (forensics), determining paternity, tracing genealogy, identifying pathogens, researching archeological finds, tracing disease outbreaks, and studying human migration patterns. In the medical field, DNA is used in diagnostics, new vaccine development, and cancer therapy. It is often possible to determine predisposition to diseases by sequencing genes.

Sometimes an innocent person is erroneously convicted of a crime and sent to jail. Between 2000 and 2015, evidence from DNA was used to exonerate over 250 innocent people. Twenty of those people were on death row after being convicted of a murder they didn't commit. To learn more about the intense scientific and legal processes used to exonerate those wrongfully convicted, go to The Innocence Project website **here (http://www.openstaxcollege.org/l/32innocence)** .

14.1 | Historical Basis of Modern Understanding

In this section, you will explore the following questions:

- What is transformation of DNA? How do Griffith's experiments in 1928 relate to our modern understanding of DNA and how it works?
- What are key historic experiments that helped identify DNA as the genetic material?
- What are Chargaff's rules of nitrogenous base pairing?

Connection for AP® Courses

Today the three letters "DNA" have become synonymous with crime solving, paternity testing, human identification, and genetic testing. All of these procedures are possible because of the discovery, in the middle of the twentieth century, that DNA is the genetic material. The results of several classic experiments set the stage for an explosion of our knowledge about DNA and how it stores and transmits genetic information. DNA was first isolated from white blood cells by Miescher in the 1860s. Over fifty years later, Griffith's work transforming strains of the bacterium *Streptococcus pneumoniae* provided the first clue that DNA and not protein (as others argued) is the universal molecule of heredity. Griffith's conclusions were later supported by Avery, MacLeod, and McCarty.

Subsequent experiments by Hershey and Chase using the bacteriophage T2 proved decisively that DNA is the genetic material. Shortly thereafter, Chargaff determined the ratios of adenine, thymine, cytosine, and guanine in DNA, suggesting paired relationships (A = T and C = G). He also found that the percentages of A, T, C, and G are different for different species. All of these historically important experiments shaped our current understanding of DNA.

The content presented in this section supports the learning objectives outlined in Big Ideas 3 and 4 of the AP® Biology Curriculum Framework. The AP® learning objectives merge essential knowledge content with one or more of the seven science practices. These objectives provide a transparent foundation for the AP® Biology course, along with inquiry-based laboratory experiences, instructional activities, and AP® exam questions.

Big Idea 3	Living systems store, retrieve, transmit and respond to information essential to life processes.
Enduring Understanding 3.A	Heritable information provides for continuity of life.
Essential Knowledge	**3.A.1** DNA, and in some cases RNA, is the primary source of heritable information.
Science Practice	**6.5** The student can evaluate alternative scientific explanations.
Learning Objective	**3.1** The student is able to construct scientific explanations that use the structures and mechanisms of DNA to support the claim that DNA is the primary source of heritable information.
Essential Knowledge	**3.A.1** DNA, and in some cases RNA, is the primary source of heritable information.
Science Practice	**4.1** The student can justify the selection of the kind of data needed to answer a particular scientific question.
Learning Objective	**3.2** The student is able to justify the selection of data from historical investigations that support the claim that DNA is the source of heritable information.
Big Idea 4	Biological systems interact, and these systems and their interactions possess complex properties.

Enduring Understanding 4.A	Interactions within biological systems lead to complex properties.
Essential Knowledge	**4.A.1** The subcomponents of biological molecules and their sequence determine the properties of that molecule.
Science Practice	**7.1** The student can connect phenomena and models across spatial and temporal scales.
Learning Objective	**4.1** The student is able to explain the connection between the sequence and the subcomponents of a biological polymer and its properties.

The Science Practice Challenge Questions contain additional test questions for this section that will help you prepare for the AP exam. These questions address the following standards:
[APLO 3.2][APLO 3.28][APLO 1.11][APLO 1.16][APLO 3.1][APLO 4.1]

Modern understandings of DNA have evolved from the discovery of nucleic acid to the development of the double-helix model. In the 1860s, Friedrich Miescher (**Figure 14.2**), a physician by profession, was the first person to isolate phosphate-rich chemicals from white blood cells or leukocytes. He named these chemicals (which would eventually be known as RNA and DNA) nuclein because they were isolated from the nuclei of the cells.

Figure 14.2 Friedrich Miescher (1844–1895) discovered nucleic acids.

To see Miescher conduct an experiment step-by-step, click through this review (http://openstaxcollege.org/l/miescher_levene) of how he discovered the key role of DNA and proteins in the nucleus.

Why were Phoebus Levene's discoveries important to our current understanding of DNA?

a. Phoebus Levene believed that the four nucleotides in DNA are not linked or repeated in the same pattern and that they are held together by phosphodiester bonds.

b. He discovered that the nucleotides were held together by phosphodiester bonds, in which two phosphate groups bind two sugars together. This discovery led to our current understanding of DNA.

c. He believed that proteins were less likely the vehicles for hereditary information. Later he discovered the four nucleotides in DNA which were linked together and repeated in a wide variety of different ways.

d. He believed inaccurately that the four nucleotides in DNA repeated over in the same pattern. Also, he discovered that the nucleotides were held together by phosphodiester bonds in which the phosphate group binds two sugars together.

A half century later, British bacteriologist Frederick Griffith was perhaps the first person to show that hereditary information could be transferred from one cell to another "horizontally," rather than by descent. In 1928, he reported the first demonstration of bacterial **transformation**, a process in which external DNA is taken up by a cell, thereby changing morphology and physiology. He was working with *Streptococcus pneumoniae*, the bacterium that causes pneumonia. Griffith worked with two strains, rough (R) and smooth (S). The R strain is non-pathogenic (does not cause disease) and is called rough because its outer surface is a cell wall and lacks a capsule; as a result, the cell surface appears uneven under the microscope. The S strain is pathogenic (disease-causing) and has a capsule outside its cell wall. As a result, it has a smooth appearance under the microscope. Griffith injected the live R strain into mice and they survived. In another experiment, when he injected mice with the heat-killed S strain, they also survived. In a third set of experiments, a mixture of live R strain and heat-killed S strain were injected into mice, and—to his surprise—the mice died. Upon isolating the live bacteria from the dead mouse, only the S strain of bacteria was recovered. When this isolated S strain was injected into fresh mice, the mice died. Griffith concluded that something had passed from the heat-killed S strain into the live R strain and transformed it into the pathogenic S strain, and he called this the transforming principle (Figure 14.3). These experiments are now famously known as Griffith's transformation experiments.

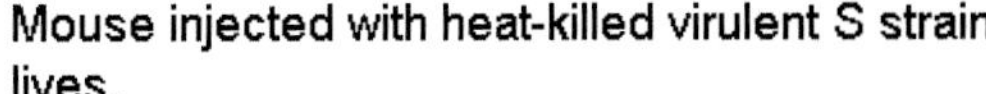

Mouse injected with heat-killed virulent S strain lives.

Mouse injected with both heat-killed S strain and live non-virulent R strain dies.

Figure 14.3 Two strains of *S. pneumoniae* were used in Griffith's transformation experiments. The R strain is non-pathogenic. The S strain is pathogenic and causes death. When Griffith injected a mouse with the heat-killed S strain and a live R strain, the mouse died. The S strain was recovered from the dead mouse. Thus, Griffith concluded that something had passed from the heat-killed S strain to the R strain, transforming the R strain into S strain in the process. (credit "living mouse": modification of work by NIH; credit "dead mouse": modification of work by Sarah Marriage)

Scientists Oswald Avery, Colin MacLeod, and Maclyn McCarty (1944) were interested in exploring this transforming principle further. They isolated the S strain from the dead mice and isolated the proteins and nucleic acids, namely RNA and DNA, as these were possible candidates for the molecule of heredity. They conducted a systematic elimination study. They used enzymes that specifically degraded each component and then used each mixture separately to transform the R strain. They found that when DNA was degraded, the resulting mixture was no longer able to transform the bacteria, whereas all of the other combinations were able to transform the bacteria. This led them to conclude that DNA was the transforming principle.

career CONNECTION

Forensic Scientists and DNA Analysis

DNA evidence was used for the first time to solve an immigration case. The story started with a teenage boy returning to London from Ghana to be with his mother. Immigration authorities at the airport were suspicious of him, thinking that he was traveling on a forged passport. After much persuasion, he was allowed to go live with his mother, but the immigration authorities did not drop the case against him. All types of evidence, including photographs, were provided to the authorities, but deportation proceedings were started nevertheless. Around the same time, Dr. Alec Jeffreys of Leicester University in the United Kingdom had invented a technique known as DNA fingerprinting. The immigration authorities approached Dr. Jeffreys for help. He took DNA samples from the mother and three of her children, plus an unrelated mother, and compared the samples with the boy's DNA. Because the biological father was not in the picture, DNA from the three children was compared with the boy's DNA. He found a match in the boy's DNA for both the mother and his three siblings. He concluded that the boy was indeed the mother's son.

Forensic scientists analyze many items, including documents, handwriting, firearms, and biological samples. They analyze the DNA content of hair, semen, saliva, and blood, and compare it with a database of DNA profiles of known criminals. Analysis includes DNA isolation, sequencing, and sequence analysis; most forensic DNA analysis involves polymerase chain reaction (PCR) amplification of short tandem repeat (STR) loci and electrophoresis to determine the length of the PCR-amplified fragment. Only mitochondrial DNA is sequenced for forensics. Forensic scientists are expected to appear at court hearings to present their findings. They are usually employed in crime labs of city and state government agencies. Geneticists experimenting with DNA techniques also work for scientific and research organizations, pharmaceutical industries, and college and university labs. Students wishing to pursue a career as a forensic scientist should have at least a bachelor's degree in chemistry, biology, or physics, and preferably some experience working in a laboratory.

science practices CONNECTION for AP® Courses

Activity *DNA Necklace.*

1) Using a molecular modeling kit (or an online virtual kit such as jmol), create a model of each of the 4 nucleotides in DNA, based on structural diagrams found in this chapter or elsewhere online.

2) Identify where each nucleotide hydrogen-bonds with its complementary base. Add these bonds to secure the two pairs of nucleotides together. How does the hydrogen bonding differ between the two pairs of complementary bases?

3) Now look at a structural diagram of a complete DNA molecule. Based on the diagram, connect your two pairs of nucleotides together along your DNA's sugar-phosphate backbone (depending on your model kit, you may have to first disconnect the hydrogen bonds between the complementary bases). Which atoms and molecules did you have to remove and add to create the sugar-phosphate backbone?

Think About It

Explain why radioactive sulfur and phosphorus were used to label T2 bacteriophages in the Hershey-Chase experiments. How did the results of these experiments contribute to the identification of DNA as the genetic material?

Experiments conducted by Martha Chase and Alfred Hershey in 1952 provided confirmatory evidence that DNA was the genetic material and not proteins. Chase and Hershey were studying a bacteriophage, which is a virus that infects bacteria. Viruses typically have a simple structure: a protein coat, called the capsid, and a nucleic acid core that contains the genetic material, either DNA or RNA. The bacteriophage infects the host bacterial cell by attaching to its surface, and then it injects its nucleic acids inside the cell. The phage DNA makes multiple copies of itself using the host machinery, and eventually the host cell bursts, releasing a large number of bacteriophages. Hershey and Chase labeled one batch of phage with radioactive sulfur, ^{35}S, to label the protein coat. Another batch of phage were labeled with radioactive phosphorus, ^{32}P. Because phosphorous is found in DNA, but not protein, the DNA and not the protein would be tagged with radioactive phosphorus.

Each batch of phage was allowed to infect the cells separately. After infection, the phage bacterial suspension was put in a blender, which caused the phage coat to be detached from the host cell. The phage and bacterial suspension was spun down in a centrifuge. The heavier bacterial cells settled down and formed a pellet, whereas the lighter phage particles stayed in the supernatant. In the tube that contained phage labeled with ^{35}S, the supernatant contained the radioactively labeled phage, whereas no radioactivity was detected in the pellet. In the tube that contained the phage labeled with ^{32}P, the radioactivity was detected in the pellet that contained the heavier bacterial cells, and no radioactivity was detected in the supernatant. Hershey and Chase concluded that it was the phage DNA that was injected into the cell and carried information to produce more phage particles, thus providing evidence that DNA was the genetic material and not proteins (**Figure 14.4**).

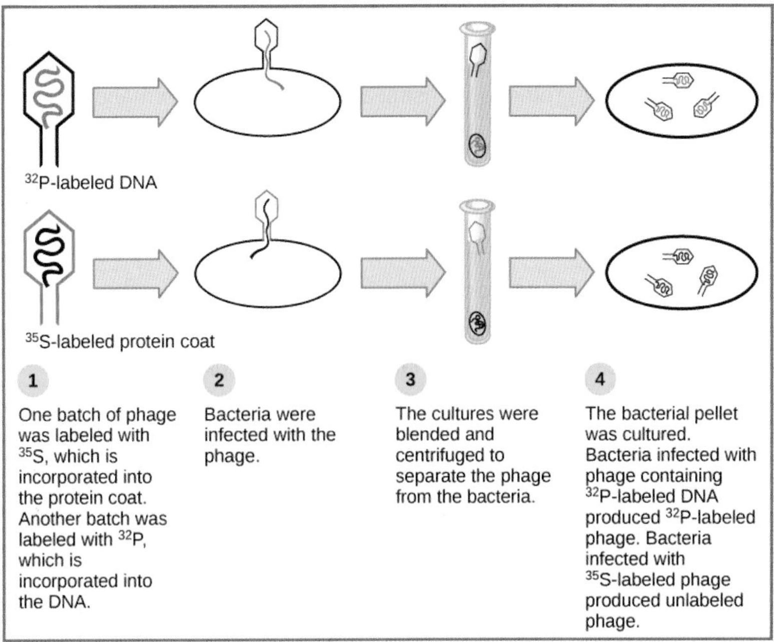

^{32}P-labeled DNA
^{35}S-labeled protein coat
1
One batch of phage was labeled with ^{35}S, which is incorporated into the protein coat. Another batch was labeled with ^{32}P, which is incorporated into the DNA.
2
Bacteria were infected with the phage.
3
The cultures were blended and centrifuged to separate the phage from the bacteria.
4
The bacterial pellet was cultured. Bacteria infected with phage containing ^{32}P-labeled DNA produced ^{32}P-labeled phage. Bacteria infected with ^{35}S-labeled phage produced unlabeled phage.

Figure 14.4 In Hershey and Chase's experiments, bacteria were infected with phage radiolabeled with either ^{35}S, which labels protein, or ^{32}P, which labels DNA. Only ^{32}P entered the bacterial cells, indicating that DNA is the genetic material.

Around this same time, Austrian biochemist Erwin Chargaff examined the content of DNA in different species and found that the amounts of adenine, thymine, guanine, and cytosine were not found in equal quantities, and that it varied from species to species, but not between individuals of the same species. He found that the amount of adenine equals the amount of thymine, and the amount of cytosine equals the amount of guanine, or A = T and G = C. This is also known as Chargaff's rules. This finding proved immensely useful when Watson and Crick were getting ready to propose their DNA double helix model.

14.2 | DNA Structure and Sequencing

In this section, you will explore the following questions:

- What is the molecular structure of DNA?
- What is the Sanger method of DNA sequencing? What is an application of DNA sequencing?
- What are the similarities and differences between eukaryotic and prokaryotic DNA?

Connection for AP® Courses

The currently accepted model of the structure of DNA was proposed in 1953 by Watson and Crick, who made their model after seeing a photograph of DNA that Franklin had taken using X-ray crystallography. The photo showed the molecule's double-helix shape and dimensions. The two strands that make up the double helix are complementary and anti-parallel in nature. That is, one strand runs in the 5' to 3' direction, whereas the complementary strand runs in the 3' to 5' direction. (The significance of directionality will be important when we explore how DNA copies itself.) DNA is a polymer of nucleotides that consists of deoxyribose sugar, a phosphate group, and one of four nitrogenous bases—A, T, C, and G—with a purine always pairing with a pyrimidine (as Chargaff found). The genetic "language" of DNA is found in sequences of the nucleotides. During cell division each daughter cell receives a copy of DNA in a process called replication. In the years since the discovery of the structure of DNA, many technologies, including DNA sequencing, have been developed that enable us to better understand DNA and its role in our genomes.

Information presented and the examples highlighted in the section support concepts outlined in Big Idea 3 of the AP® Biology Curriculum Framework. The Learning Objectives listed in the Curriculum Framework provide a transparent foundation for the AP® Biology course, an inquiry-based laboratory experience, instructional activities, and AP® exam questions. A Learning Objective merges required content with one or more of the seven science practices.

Big Idea 3	Living systems store, retrieve, transmit and respond to information essential to life processes.
Enduring Understanding 3.A	Heritable information provides for continuity of life.
Essential Knowledge	**3.A.1** DNA, and in some cases RNA, is the primary source of heritable information.
Science Practice	**6.5** The student can evaluate alternative scientific explanations.
Learning Objective	**3.1** The student is able to construct scientific explanations that use the structures and mechanisms of DNA to support the claim that DNA is the primary source of heritable information.
Essential Knowledge	**3.A.1** DNA, and in some cases RNA, is the primary source of heritable information.
Science Practice	**4.1** The student can justify the selection of the kind of data needed to answer a particular scientific question.
Learning Objective	**3.2** The student is able to justify the selection of data from historical investigations that support the claim that DNA is the source of heritable information.
Essential Knowledge	**3.A.1** DNA, and in some cases RNA, is the primary source of heritable information.
Science Practice	**6.4** The student can make claims and predictions about natural phenomena based on scientific theories and models.
Learning Objective	**3.5** The student can justify the claim that humans can manipulate heritable information by identifying *at least two* commonly used technologies.

The Science Practice Challenge Questions contain additional test questions for this section that will help you prepare for the AP exam. These questions address the following standards:
[APLO 3.3][APLO 3.5][APLO 3.13]

The building blocks of DNA are nucleotides. The important components of the nucleotide are a nitrogenous base, deoxyribose (5-carbon sugar), and a phosphate group (**Figure 14.5**). The nucleotide is named depending on the nitrogenous base. The nitrogenous base can be a purine such as adenine (A) and guanine (G), or a pyrimidine such as cytosine (C) and thymine (T).

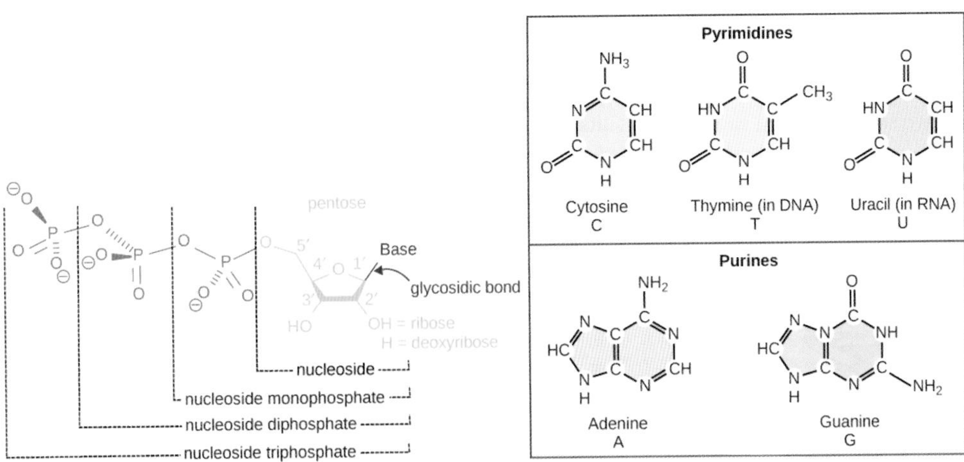

Figure 14.5 Each nucleotide is made up of a sugar, a phosphate group, and a nitrogenous base. The sugar is deoxyribose in DNA and ribose in RNA.

The nucleotides combine with each other by covalent bonds known as phosphodiester bonds or linkages. The purines have a double ring structure with a six-membered ring fused to a five-membered ring. Pyrimidines are smaller in size; they have a single six-membered ring structure. The carbon atoms of the five-carbon sugar are numbered 1', 2', 3', 4', and 5' (1' is read as "one prime"). The phosphate residue is attached to the hydroxyl group of the 5' carbon of one sugar of one nucleotide and the hydroxyl group of the 3' carbon of the sugar of the next nucleotide, thereby forming a 5'-3' phosphodiester bond.

In the 1950s, Francis Crick and James Watson worked together to determine the structure of DNA at the University of Cambridge, England. Other scientists like Linus Pauling and Maurice Wilkins were also actively exploring this field. Pauling had discovered the secondary structure of proteins using X-ray crystallography. In Wilkins' lab, researcher Rosalind Franklin was using X-ray diffraction methods to understand the structure of DNA. Watson and Crick were able to piece together the puzzle of the DNA molecule on the basis of Franklin's data because Crick had also studied X-ray diffraction (Figure 14.6). In 1962, James Watson, Francis Crick, and Maurice Wilkins were awarded the Nobel Prize in Medicine. Unfortunately, by then Franklin had died, and Nobel prizes are not awarded posthumously.

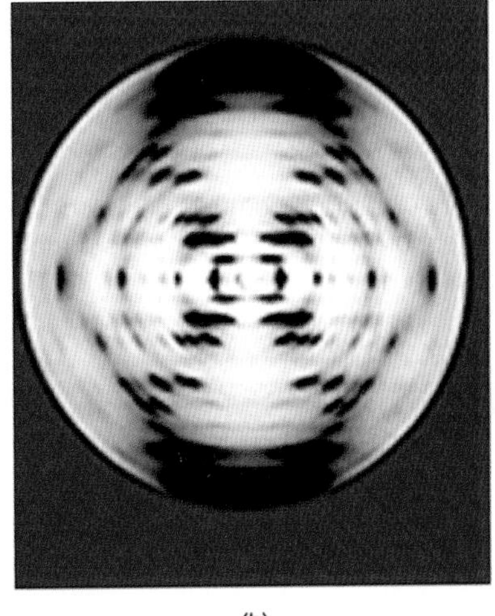

(a) (b)

Figure 14.6 The work of pioneering scientists (a) James Watson, Francis Crick, and Maclyn McCarty led to our present day understanding of DNA. Scientist Rosalind Franklin discovered (b) the X-ray diffraction pattern of DNA, which helped to elucidate its double helix structure. (credit a: modification of work by Marjorie McCarty, Public Library of Science)

Watson and Crick proposed that DNA is made up of two strands that are twisted around each other to form a right-handed helix. Base pairing takes place between a purine and pyrimidine; namely, A pairs with T and G pairs with C. Adenine and thymine are complementary base pairs, and cytosine and guanine are also complementary base pairs. The base pairs are stabilized by hydrogen bonds; adenine and thymine form two hydrogen bonds and cytosine and guanine form three hydrogen bonds. The two strands are anti-parallel in nature; that is, the 3' end of one strand faces the 5' end of the other strand. The sugar and phosphate of the nucleotides form the backbone of the structure, whereas the nitrogenous bases are stacked inside. Each base pair is separated from the other base pair by a distance of 0.34 nm, and each turn of the helix measures 3.4 nm. Therefore, ten base pairs are present per turn of the helix. The diameter of the DNA double helix is 2 nm, and it is uniform throughout. Only the pairing between a purine and pyrimidine can explain the uniform diameter. The twisting of the two strands around each other results in the formation of uniformly spaced major and minor grooves (Figure 14.7).

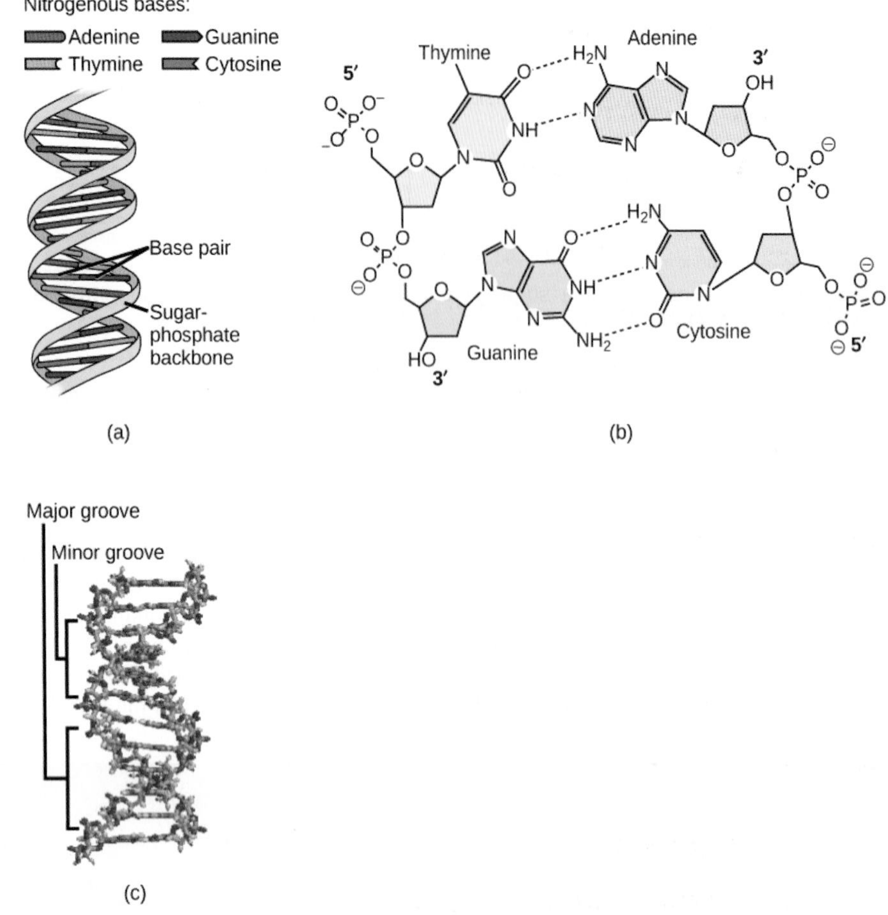

Figure 14.7 DNA has (a) a double helix structure and (b) phosphodiester bonds. The (c) major and minor grooves are binding sites for DNA binding proteins during processes such as transcription (the copying of RNA from DNA) and replication.

science practices CONNECTION for AP® Courses

Activity

Read Watson and Crick's original *Nature* article, "Molecular Structure of Nucleic Acids: A Structure for Deoxyribose Nucleic Acid," How did Watson and Crick's model build on the findings of Rosalind Franklin? How did their model of DNA build on the findings of Hershey and Chase, and others, showing that DNA can encode and pass information on to the next generation?

Think About It

Watson and Crick's work determined the structure of DNA. However, it was still relatively unknown how DNA encoded information into genes. Select one modern form of biotechnology and research its basic methods online. Examples include gene sequencing, DNA fingerprinting, PCR (polymerase chain reaction), genetically-modified food, etc. Briefly describe your chosen technology, and what benefits it provides us. Then describe how Watson and Crick's findings were vital to the development of your chosen technology.

DNA Sequencing Techniques

Until the 1990s, the sequencing of DNA (reading the sequence of DNA) was a relatively expensive and long process. Using radiolabeled nucleotides also compounded the problem through safety concerns. With currently available technology and automated machines, the process is cheap, safer, and can be completed in a matter of hours. Fred Sanger developed the sequencing method used for the human genome sequencing project, which is widely used today (Figure 14.8).

Visit this site (http://openstaxcollege.org/l/DNA_sequencing) to watch a video explaining the DNA sequence reading technique that resulted from Sanger's work.

Describe one advantage and a possible limitation to Sanger's method.

a. Sanger's method can be used to sequence more than one strand at a time which is less time consuming. Challenges of Sanger's method includes its decreased accuracy to sequence DNA strands.

b. Sanger's method is a reliable and accurate way of sequencing DNA strands. However, only one strand at a time can be sequenced at a time. Also, it can look for one base only at a time which can be time consuming.

c. Sanger's method is highly inexpensive and less accurate. However, it is not readily adaptable to commercial kits.

d. Sanger's method is less time consuming and highly accurate. However, it is more expensive than other methods available for sequencing.

The method is known as the dideoxy chain termination method. The sequencing method is based on the use of chain terminators, the dideoxynucleotides (ddNTPs). The dideoxynucleotides, or ddNTPSs, differ from the deoxynucleotides by the lack of a free 3' OH group on the five-carbon sugar. If a ddNTP is added to a growing a DNA strand, the chain is not extended any further because the free 3' OH group needed to add another nucleotide is not available. By using a predetermined ratio of deoxyribonucleotides to dideoxynucleotides, it is possible to generate DNA fragments of different sizes.

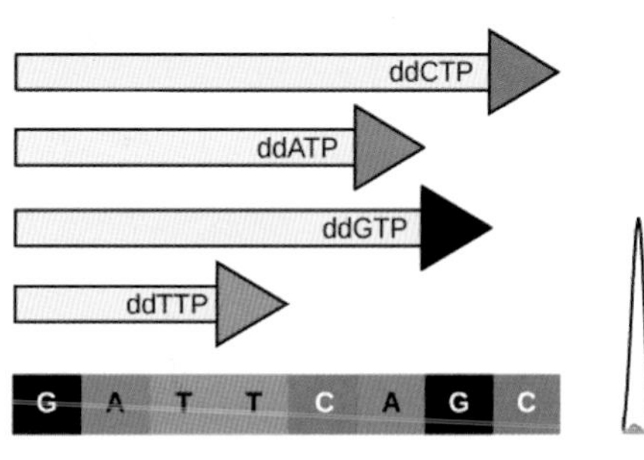

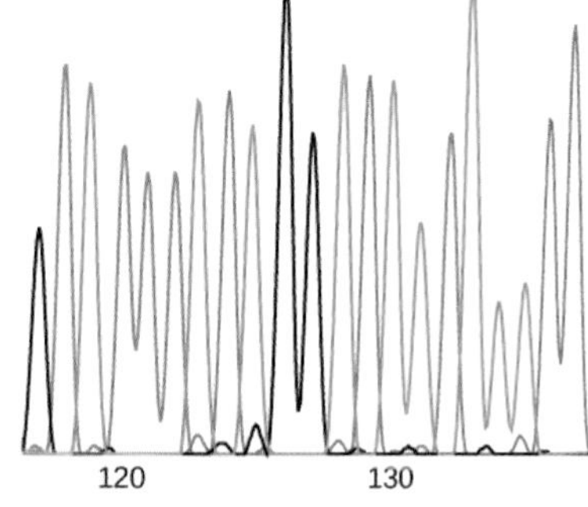

Figure 14.8 In Frederick Sanger's dideoxy chain termination method, dye-labeled dideoxynucleotides are used to generate DNA fragments that terminate at different points. The DNA is separated by capillary electrophoresis on the basis of size, and from the order of fragments formed, the DNA sequence can be read. The DNA sequence readout is shown on an electropherogram that is generated by a laser scanner.

The DNA sample to be sequenced is denatured or separated into two strands by heating it to high temperatures. The DNA is divided into four tubes in which a primer, DNA polymerase, and all four nucleotides (A, T, G, and C) are added. In addition to each of the four tubes, limited quantities of one of the four dideoxynucleotides are added to each tube respectively. The tubes are labeled as A, T, G, and C according to the ddNTP added. For detection purposes, each of the four dideoxynucleotides carries a different fluorescent label. Chain elongation continues until a fluorescent dideoxy nucleotide is incorporated, after which no further elongation takes place. After the reaction is over, electrophoresis is performed. Even a difference in length of a single base can be detected. The sequence is read from a laser scanner. For his work on DNA sequencing, Sanger received a Nobel Prize in chemistry in 1980.

Sanger's genome sequencing has led to a race to sequence human genomes at a rapid speed and low cost, often referred to as the $1000 in one day sequence. Learn more by selecting the Sequencing at Speed animation **here (http://openstaxcollege.org/l/DNA_and_genomes)** .

Explain how fast DNA sequencing can change the way doctors treat disease.

a. Faster genetic sequencing will help in quick analysis of the genetic makeup of bacteria that can cause diseases in humans for better and more efficient treatments. Also, sequencing of a cancerous cell's DNA can provide better ways to treat or prevent cancer.

b. Fast DNA sequencing can help us quickly analyze the genetic information of existing only bacteria (not new strains) only that cause disease in humans, which may lead to more efficient treatments.

c. Fast DNA sequencing can help doctors to treat and diagnose diseases which are not rare in populations.

d. Faster genetic sequencing can be used to treat and prevent a few types of cancers and thus increase the life expectancy of patients suffering from the diseases.

Gel **electrophoresis** is a technique used to separate DNA fragments of different sizes. Usually the gel is made of a chemical called agarose. Agarose powder is added to a buffer and heated. After cooling, the gel solution is poured into a casting tray. Once the gel has solidified, the DNA is loaded on the gel and electric current is applied. The DNA has a net negative charge and moves from the negative electrode toward the positive electrode. The electric current is applied for sufficient time to let the DNA separate according to size; the smallest fragments will be farthest from the well (where the DNA was loaded), and the heavier molecular weight fragments will be closest to the well. Once the DNA is separated, the gel is stained with a DNA-specific dye for viewing it (**Figure 14.9**).

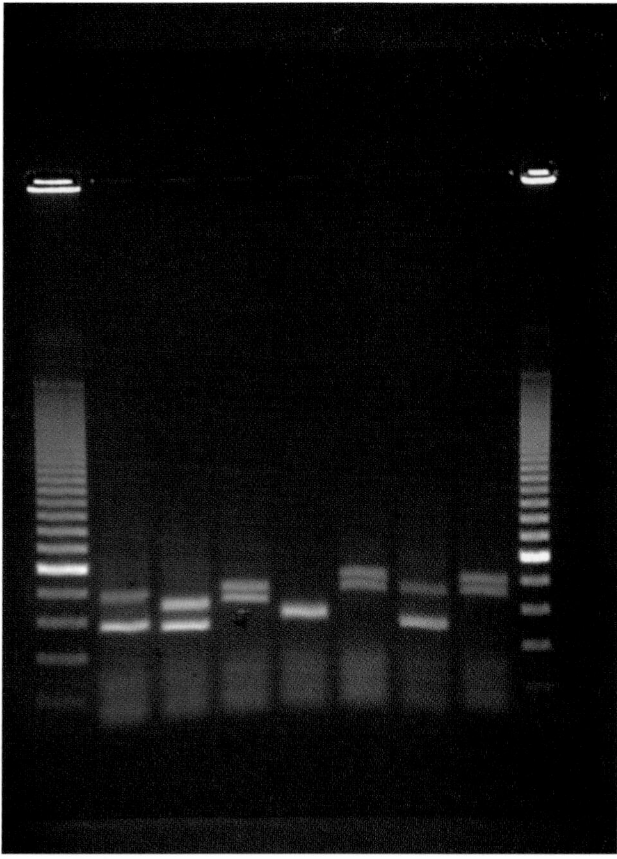

Figure 14.9 DNA can be separated on the basis of size using gel electrophoresis. (credit: James Jacob, Tompkins Cortland Community College)

Neanderthal Genome: How Are We Related?

The first draft sequence of the Neanderthal genome was recently published by Richard E. Green et al. in 2010.[1] Neanderthals are the closest ancestors of present-day humans. They were known to have lived in Europe and Western Asia before they disappeared from fossil records approximately 30,000 years ago. Green's team studied almost 40,000-year-old fossil remains that were selected from sites across the world. Extremely sophisticated means of sample preparation and DNA sequencing were employed because of the fragile nature of the bones and heavy microbial contamination. In their study, the scientists were able to sequence some four billion base pairs. The Neanderthal sequence was compared with that of present-day humans from across the world. After comparing the sequences, the researchers found that the Neanderthal genome had 2 to 3 percent greater similarity to people living outside Africa than to people in Africa. While current theories have suggested that all present-day humans can be traced to a small ancestral population in Africa, the data from the Neanderthal genome may contradict this view. Green and his colleagues also discovered DNA segments among people in Europe and Asia that are more similar to Neanderthal sequences than to other contemporary human sequences. Another interesting observation was that Neanderthals are as closely related to people from Papua New Guinea as to those from China or France. This is surprising because Neanderthal fossil remains have been located only in Europe and West Asia. Most likely, genetic exchange took place between Neanderthals and modern humans as modern humans emerged out of Africa, before the divergence of Europeans, East Asians, and Papua New Guineans.

Several genes seem to have undergone changes from Neanderthals during the evolution of present-day humans. These genes are involved in cranial structure, metabolism, skin morphology, and cognitive development. One of the genes that is of particular interest is *RUNX2*, which is different in modern day humans and Neanderthals. This gene is responsible for the prominent frontal bone, bell-shaped rib cage, and dental differences seen in Neanderthals. It is speculated that an evolutionary change in *RUNX2* was important in the origin of modern-day humans, and this affected the cranium and the upper body.

According to the passage, which statement best describes the relationship between humans and Neanderthals?

a. Early humans emerged from Africa, then spread out to populate different parts of the globe. An isolated population of these early humans interbred with Neanderthals.

b. Early humans interbred with Neanderthals, emerged from Africa, then spread out to populate different parts of the globe.

c. Early humans emerged from Africa, interbred with Neanderthals, then spread out to populate different parts of the globe.

d. Early humans did not interbreed with Neanderthals, but we have many genetic similarities because we share a common ancestor.

---

1. Richard E. Green et al., "A Draft Sequence of the Neandertal Genome," *Science* 328 (2010): 710-22.

Watch **Svante Pääbo's talk (http://openstaxcollege.org/l/neanderthal)** explaining the Neanderthal genome research at the 2011 annual TED (Technology, Entertainment, Design) conference.

Which of the statements gives the best explanation for the wider genetic variation in the human population in Africa than the rest of the world?

a. It has been suggested that all humans most likely descended from Africa. This is supported by the research that genetic variance in Africa was also found in the rest of the world.

b. The theory that humans descended from Africa was supported by the research that most of the human genomes tested outside of Africa had close ties to the genomes of people in Africa but a genetic variance in Africa was not found in the rest of the world.

c. Humans have most likely descended from Africa. This research is supported by the fact that all the human genomes tested outside of Africa had close ties to the genomes of people in Africa. Also, there is a genetic variance in Africa that was not found in the rest of the world.

d. The transition to modern humans occurred within Africa which was sudden. Thus, human genomes tested outside of Africa had close ties to the genomes of people in Africa.

DNA Packaging in Cells

When comparing prokaryotic cells to eukaryotic cells, prokaryotes are much simpler than eukaryotes in many of their features (**Figure 14.10**). Most prokaryotes contain a single, circular chromosome that is found in an area of the cytoplasm called the nucleoid.

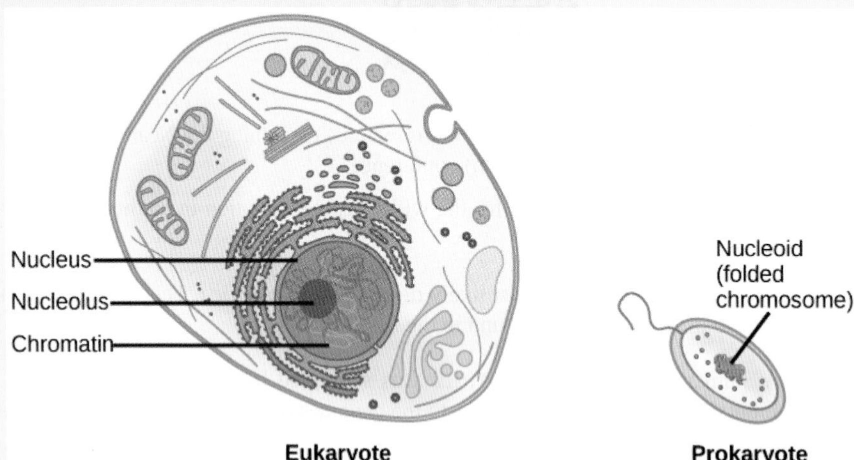

Figure 14.10 A eukaryote contains a well-defined nucleus, whereas in prokaryotes, the chromosome lies in the cytoplasm in an area called the nucleoid.

In eukaryotic cells, DNA and RNA synthesis occur in a separate compartment from protein synthesis. In prokaryotic cells, both processes occur together. What advantages might there be to separating the processes? What advantages might there be to having them occur together?

a. Compartmentalization in eukaryotic cells enables the building of more complex proteins and RNA products. In prokaryotes, the advantage is that RNA and protein synthesis occurs much more quickly because it occurs in a single compartment.
b. Compartmentalization in prokaryotic cells enables the building of more complex proteins and RNA products. In eukaryotes, the advantage is that RNA and protein synthesis occurs much more quickly because they occur in a single compartment.
c. Compartmentalization in eukaryotic cells enables the building of simpler proteins and RNA products. In prokaryotes, the advantage is only simpler proteins and RNA products because complex ones are not needed.
d. Compartmentalization in eukaryotic cells enables the building of more complex proteins and RNA products. In prokaryotes, the advantage is that RNA and protein synthesis takes more time because it occurs in a single compartment.

The size of the genome in one of the most well-studied prokaryotes, *E.coli*, is 4.6 million base pairs (approximately 1.1 mm, if cut and stretched out). So how does this fit inside a small bacterial cell? The DNA is twisted by what is known as supercoiling. Supercoiling means that DNA is either under-wound (less than one turn of the helix per 10 base pairs) or over-wound (more than 1 turn per 10 base pairs) from its normal relaxed state. Some proteins are known to be involved in the supercoiling; other proteins and enzymes such as DNA gyrase help in maintaining the supercoiled structure.

Eukaryotes, whose chromosomes each consist of a linear DNA molecule, employ a different type of packing strategy to fit their DNA inside the nucleus (Figure 14.11). At the most basic level, DNA is wrapped around proteins known as histones to form structures called nucleosomes. The histones are evolutionarily conserved proteins that are rich in basic amino acids and form an octamer. The DNA (which is negatively charged because of the phosphate groups) is wrapped tightly around the histone core. This nucleosome is linked to the next one with the help of a linker DNA. This is also known as the "beads on a string" structure. This is further compacted into a 30 nm fiber, which is the diameter of the structure. At the metaphase stage, the chromosomes are at their most compact, are approximately 700 nm in width, and are found in association with scaffold proteins.

In interphase, eukaryotic chromosomes have two distinct regions that can be distinguished by staining. The tightly packaged region is known as heterochromatin, and the less dense region is known as euchromatin. Heterochromatin usually contains genes that are not expressed, and is found in the regions of the centromere and telomeres. The euchromatin usually contains genes that are transcribed, with DNA packaged around nucleosomes but not further compacted.

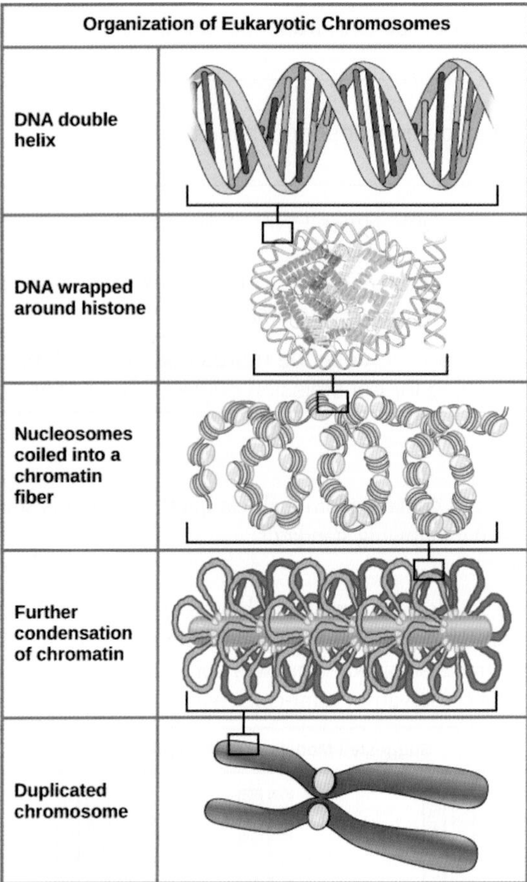

Figure 14.11 These figures illustrate the compaction of the eukaryotic chromosome.

14.3 | Basics of DNA Replication

In this section, you will explore the following questions:

- How does the structure of DNA provide for the process of replication?
- How did the Meselson and Stahl experiments support the semi-conservative nature of replication?

Connection for AP® Courses

The Watson and Crick model suggested a way in which DNA could be replicated during cell division. Basically, the two strands unwind and separate where the hydrogen bonds connect the nucleotides. Each parental strand then serves as a template for a new, complementary daughter strand. Replication is said to be semi-conservative because the original information encoded in each parental strand is conserved (kept) in the daughter molecules. Thus, a newly replicated molecule of DNA consists of one "old" strand and one "new" strand. Meselson and Stahl used density differences in nitrogen isotopes to investigate replication, and their experiments supported the semi-conservative model. However, the process of replication is more complex than their model's simple description.

Information presented and the examples highlighted in the section support concepts outlined in Big Idea 3 and Big Idea 4 of the AP® Biology Curriculum Framework. The Learning Objectives listed in the Curriculum Framework provide a transparent foundation for the AP® Biology course, an inquiry-based laboratory experience, instructional activities, and AP® exam questions. A Learning Objective merges required content with one or more of the seven Science Practices.

Big Idea 3	Living systems store, retrieve, transmit and respond to information essential to life processes.
Enduring Understanding 3.A	Heritable information provides for continuity of life.
Essential Knowledge	**3.A.1** DNA, and in some cases RNA, is the primary source of heritable information.
Science Practice	**1.2** The student can describe representations and models of natural or man-made phenomena and systems in the domain.
Learning Objective	**3.3** The student is able to describe representations and models that illustrate how genetic information is copied for transmission between generations.

The Science Practice Challenge Questions contain additional test questions for this section that will help you prepare for the AP exam. These questions address the following standards:
[APLO 2.34][APLO 3.3][APLO 4.1]

The elucidation of the structure of the double helix provided a hint as to how DNA divides and makes copies of itself. This model suggests that the two strands of the double helix separate during replication, and each strand serves as a template from which the new complementary strand is copied. What was not clear was how the replication took place. There were three models suggested (Figure 14.12): conservative, semi-conservative, and dispersive.

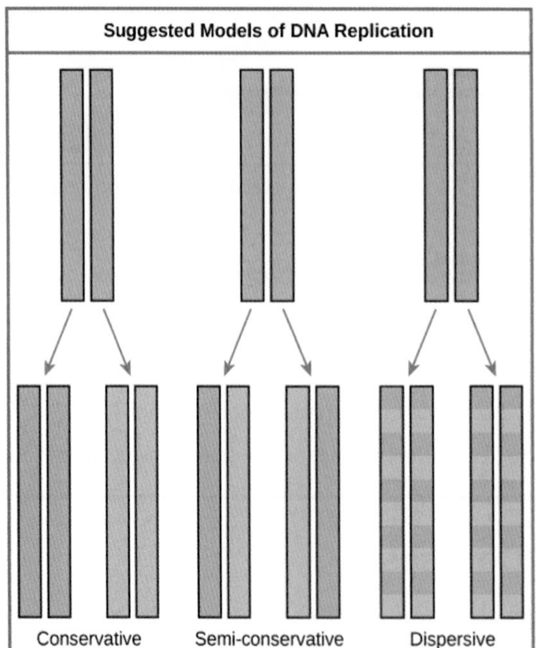

Figure 14.12 The three suggested models of DNA replication. Grey indicates the original DNA strands, and blue indicates newly synthesized DNA.

In conservative replication, the parental DNA remains together, and the newly formed daughter strands are together. The semi-conservative method suggests that each of the two parental DNA strands act as a template for new DNA to be synthesized; after replication, each double-stranded DNA includes one parental or "old" strand and one "new" strand. In the dispersive model, both copies of DNA have double-stranded segments of parental DNA and newly synthesized DNA interspersed.

Meselson and Stahl were interested in understanding how DNA replicates. They grew *E. coli* for several generations in a medium containing a "heavy" isotope of nitrogen (^{15}N) that gets incorporated into nitrogenous bases, and eventually into the DNA (Figure 14.13).

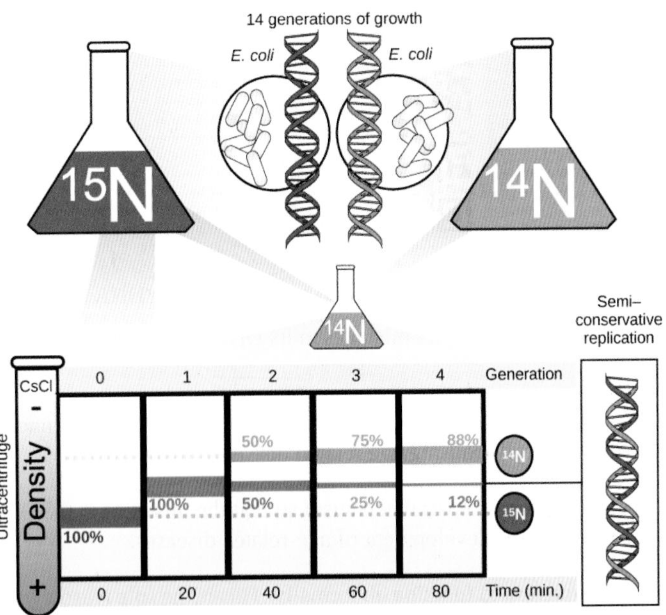

Figure 14.13 Meselson and Stahl experimented with *E. coli* grown first in heavy nitrogen (^{15}N) then in ^{14}N. DNA grown in ^{15}N (red band) is heavier than DNA grown in ^{14}N (orange band), and sediments to a lower level in cesium chloride solution in an ultracentrifuge. When DNA grown in ^{15}N is switched to media containing ^{14}N, after one round of cell division the DNA sediments halfway between the ^{15}N and ^{14}N levels, indicating that it now contains fifty percent ^{14}N. In subsequent cell divisions, an increasing amount of DNA contains ^{14}N only. This data supports the semi-conservative replication model. (credit: modification of work by Mariana Ruiz Villareal)

The *E. coli* culture was then shifted into medium containing ^{14}N and allowed to grow for one generation. The cells were harvested and the DNA was isolated. The DNA was centrifuged at high speeds in an ultracentrifuge. Some cells were allowed to grow for one more life cycle in ^{14}N and spun again. During the density gradient centrifugation, the DNA is loaded into a gradient (typically a salt such as cesium chloride or sucrose) and spun at high speeds of 50,000 to 60,000 rpm. Under these circumstances, the DNA will form a band according to its density in the gradient. DNA grown in ^{15}N will band at a higher density position than that grown in ^{14}N. Meselson and Stahl noted that after one generation of growth in ^{14}N after they had been shifted from ^{15}N, the single band observed was intermediate in position in between DNA of cells grown exclusively in ^{15}N and ^{14}N. This suggested either a semi-conservative or dispersive mode of replication. The DNA harvested from cells grown for two generations in ^{14}N formed two bands: one DNA band was at the intermediate position between ^{15}N and ^{14}N, and the other corresponded to the band of ^{14}N DNA. These results could only be explained if DNA replicates in a semi-conservative manner. Therefore, the other two modes were ruled out.

During DNA replication, each of the two strands that make up the double helix serves as a template from which new strands are copied. The new strand will be complementary to the parental or "old" strand. When two daughter DNA copies are formed, they have the same sequence and are divided equally into the two daughter cells.

Click through this tutorial (http://openstaxcollege.org/l/DNA_replicatio2) on DNA replication.

One theory of aging is that the body's ability to fix mistakes in its DNA decreases as we age. How can this affect DNA replication?

a. Aging causes accumulation of DNA mutations and DNA damage of only the nuclear DNA and the mistakes will be passed down to new cells causing age related diseases.

b. Aging results in ineffective DNA repair mechanism so that the mistakes in the DNA will be passed down to new cells. This could lead to the development of age-related diseases.

c. Aging causes DNA polymerase to function abnormally. This is the sole reason which causes defects in DNA replication.

d. DNA replication of only fast growing cells is affected by aging.

science practices CONNECTION for AP® Courses

Activity

Design (but do not implement) an experiment to test the three models of DNA replication. Summarize the results you would expect if each of the three models of DNA replication were correct. Assume you have access in a laboratory to the following: an experimental organism such as *E. coli*, an unlimited variety of isotopes, test tube and centrifuge, and organic growth media.

14.4 | DNA Replication in Prokaryotes

In this section, you will explore the following questions:

- How is DNA replicated in prokaryotes, and what are the roles of the leading and lagging strands and Okazaki fragments in the process?
- What is the role of DNA polymerase and other enzymes and proteins in supporting replication?

Connection for AP® Courses

As was stated previously, DNA replication is more complex than simply unzipping the double helix and making new complementary strands. Replication in prokaryotes starts from a sequence of nucleotides on the chromosome called the origin of replication—the point at which the DNA opens up or unzips. The enzyme helicase opens up the DNA at the point where hydrogen bonds connect the strands, resulting in the formation of a Y-shaped replication fork. Single-strand binding proteins keep the fork open. The enzyme primase synthesizes RNA primers to initiate DNA synthesis by DNA polymerase, which can add nucleotides only in the 5' to 3' direction. DNA polymerase recognizes the 3'-OH end as its landing site; thus, polymerase "reads" the template strand in the 3' to 5' direction and builds the complementary DNA polymer in the 5' to 3' direction. One strand—called the leading strand—is synthesized continuously in the direction of the replication fork (the direction in which helicase is separating the two strands), with polymerase adding new nucleotides one-by-one. However, replication of the other strand—called the lagging strand—occurs in a direction away from the replication fork, in short stretches of DNA known as Okazaki fragments. (Think of the activities on the lagging strand as analogous to trying to walk on a moving sidewalk that is moving in the opposite direction.) The RNA primers are replaced by DNA nucleotides, and ligase seals the DNA, creating phosphodiester bonds between the 3'-OH of one end and the 5'-phosphate of the other strand. The replicated DNA molecules now consist of one original template strand and one newly synthesized strand.

Information presented and the examples highlighted in the section support concepts outlined in Big Idea 3 of the AP® Biology Curriculum Framework. The Learning Objectives listed in the Curriculum Framework provide a transparent foundation for the AP® Biology course, an inquiry-based laboratory experience, instructional activities, and AP® exam questions. A Learning Objective merges required content with one or more of the seven Science Practices.

Big Idea 3	Living systems store, retrieve, transmit and respond to information essential to life processes.
Enduring Understanding 3.A	Heritable information provides for continuity of life.
Essential Knowledge	**3.A.1** DNA, and in some cases RNA, is the primary source of heritable information.
Science Practice	**1.2** The student can describe representations and models of natural or man-made phenomena and systems in the domain.
Learning Objective	**3.3** The student is able to describe representations and models that illustrate how genetic information is copied for transmission between generations.

The Science Practice Challenge Questions contain additional test questions for this section that will help you prepare for the AP exam. These questions address the following standards:
[APLO 4.3][APLO 1.18][APLO 1.21]

DNA replication has been extremely well studied in prokaryotes primarily because of the small size of the genome and the mutants that are available. *E. coli* has 4.6 million base pairs in a single circular chromosome and all of it gets replicated in approximately 42 minutes, starting from a single origin of replication and proceeding around the circle in both directions. This means that approximately 1000 nucleotides are added per second. The process is quite rapid and occurs without many mistakes.

DNA replication employs a large number of proteins and enzymes, each of which plays a critical role during the process. One of the key players is the enzyme DNA polymerase, also known as DNA pol, which adds nucleotides one by one to the growing DNA chain that are complementary to the template strand. The addition of nucleotides requires energy; this energy is obtained from the nucleotides that have three phosphates attached to them, similar to ATP which has three phosphate groups attached. When the bond between the phosphates is broken, the energy released is used to form the phosphodiester bond between the incoming nucleotide and the growing chain. In prokaryotes, three main types of polymerases are known: DNA pol I, DNA pol II, and DNA pol III. It is now known that DNA pol III is the enzyme required for DNA synthesis; DNA pol I and DNA pol II are primarily required for repair.

How does the replication machinery know where to begin? It turns out that there are specific nucleotide sequences called origins of replication where replication begins. In *E. coli*, which has a single origin of replication on its one chromosome (as do most prokaryotes), it is approximately 245 base pairs long and is rich in AT sequences. The origin of replication is recognized by certain proteins that bind to this site. An enzyme called **helicase** unwinds the DNA by breaking the hydrogen bonds between the nitrogenous base pairs. ATP hydrolysis is required for this process. As the DNA opens up, Y-shaped structures called **replication forks** are formed. Two replication forks are formed at the origin of replication and these get extended bi- directionally as replication proceeds. **Single-strand binding proteins** coat the single strands of DNA near the replication fork to prevent the single-stranded DNA from winding back into a double helix. DNA polymerase is able to add nucleotides only in the 5' to 3' direction (a new DNA strand can be only extended in this direction). It also requires a free 3'-OH group to which it can add nucleotides by forming a phosphodiester bond between the 3'-OH end and the 5' phosphate of the next nucleotide. This essentially means that it cannot add nucleotides if a free 3'-OH group is not available. Then how does it add the first nucleotide? The problem is solved with the help of a primer that provides the free 3'-OH end. Another enzyme, RNA **primase**, synthesizes an RNA primer that is about five to ten nucleotides long and complementary to the DNA. Because this sequence primes the DNA synthesis, it is appropriately called the **primer**. DNA polymerase can now extend this RNA primer, adding nucleotides one by one that are complementary to the template strand (Figure 14.14).

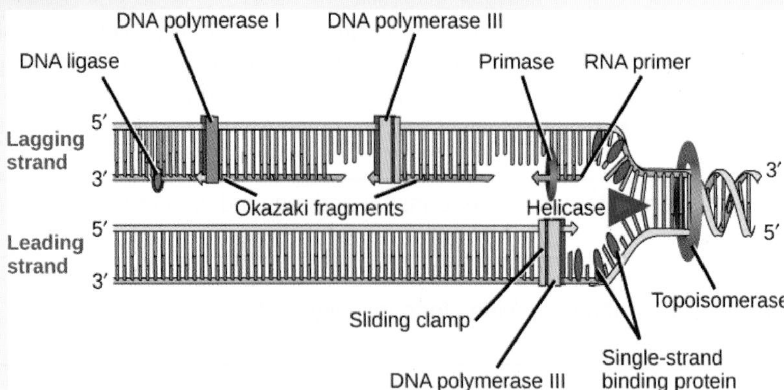

Figure 14.14 A replication fork is formed when helicase separates the DNA strands at the origin of replication. The DNA tends to become more highly coiled ahead of the replication fork. Topoisomerase breaks and reforms DNA's phosphate backbone ahead of the replication fork, thereby relieving the pressure that results from this supercoiling. Single-strand binding proteins bind to the single-stranded DNA to prevent the helix from re-forming. Primase synthesizes an RNA primer. DNA polymerase III uses this primer to synthesize the daughter DNA strand. On the leading strand, DNA is synthesized continuously, whereas on the lagging strand, DNA is synthesized in short stretches called Okazaki fragments. DNA polymerase I replaces the RNA primer with DNA. DNA ligase seals the gaps between the Okazaki fragments, joining the fragments into a single DNA molecule. (credit: modification of work by Mariana Ruiz Villareal)

You isolate a cell strain in which the joining together of Okazaki fragments is impaired and suspect that a mutation has occurred in an enzyme found at the replication fork. Which enzyme is most likely to be mutated?

a. DNA ligase
b. DNA polymerase III
c. helicase
d. topoisomerase

The replication fork moves at the rate of 1000 nucleotides per second. DNA polymerase can only extend in the 5' to 3' direction, which poses a slight problem at the replication fork. As we know, the DNA double helix is anti-parallel; that is, one strand is in the 5' to 3' direction and the other is oriented in the 3' to 5' direction. One strand, which is complementary to the 3' to 5' parental DNA strand, is synthesized continuously towards the replication fork because the polymerase can add nucleotides in this direction. This continuously synthesized strand is known as the **leading strand**. The other strand, complementary to the 5' to 3' parental DNA, is extended away from the replication fork, in small fragments known as **Okazaki fragments**, each requiring a primer to start the synthesis. Okazaki fragments are named after the Japanese scientist who first discovered them. The strand with the Okazaki fragments is known as the **lagging strand**.

The leading strand can be extended by one primer alone, whereas the lagging strand needs a new primer for each of the short Okazaki fragments. The overall direction of the lagging strand will be 3' to 5', and that of the leading strand 5' to 3'. A protein called the **sliding clamp** holds the DNA polymerase in place as it continues to add nucleotides. The sliding clamp is a ring-shaped protein that binds to the DNA and holds the polymerase in place. **Topoisomerase** prevents the over-winding of the DNA double helix ahead of the replication fork as the DNA is opening up; it does so by causing temporary nicks in the DNA helix and then resealing it. As synthesis proceeds, the RNA primers are replaced by DNA. The primers are removed by the exonuclease activity of DNA pol I, and the gaps are filled in by deoxyribonucleotides. The nicks that remain between the newly synthesized DNA (that replaced the RNA primer) and the previously synthesized DNA are sealed by the enzyme DNA **ligase** that catalyzes the formation of phosphodiester linkage between the 3'-OH end of one nucleotide and the 5' phosphate end of the other fragment.

Once the chromosome has been completely replicated, the two DNA copies move into two different cells during cell division. The process of DNA replication can be summarized as follows:

1. DNA unwinds at the origin of replication.

2. Helicase opens up the DNA-forming replication forks; these are extended bidirectionally.
3. Single-strand binding proteins coat the DNA around the replication fork to prevent rewinding of the DNA.
4. Topoisomerase binds at the region ahead of the replication fork to prevent supercoiling.
5. Primase synthesizes RNA primers complementary to the DNA strand.
6. DNA polymerase starts adding nucleotides to the 3'-OH end of the primer.
7. Elongation of both the lagging and the leading strand continues.
8. RNA primers are removed by exonuclease activity.
9. Gaps are filled by DNA pol by adding dNTPs.
10. The gap between the two DNA fragments is sealed by DNA ligase, which helps in the formation of phosphodiester bonds.

Table 14.1 summarizes the enzymes involved in prokaryotic DNA replication and the functions of each.

Prokaryotic DNA Replication: Enzymes and Their Functions

Enzyme/protein	Specific Function
DNA pol I	Exonuclease activity removes RNA primer and replaces with newly synthesized DNA
DNA pol II	Repair function
DNA pol III	Main enzyme that adds nucleotides in the 5'-3' direction
Helicase	Opens the DNA helix by breaking hydrogen bonds between the nitrogenous bases
Ligase	Seals the gaps between the Okazaki fragments to create one continuous DNA strand
Primase	Synthesizes RNA primers needed to start replication
Sliding Clamp	Helps to hold the DNA polymerase in place when nucleotides are being added
Topoisomerase	Helps relieve the stress on DNA when unwinding by causing breaks and then resealing the DNA
Single-strand binding proteins (SSB)	Binds to single-stranded DNA to avoid DNA rewinding back.

Table 14.1

Review the full process of DNA replication here (http://openstaxcollege.org/l/replication_DNA) .

Explain why errors in DNA replication are rare events in cells.

a. Errors in DNA replication are rare events in a cell due to the presence of DNA ligase enzyme which fixes mistakes in the copying process.

b. Polymerase I is solely responsible for proofreading and fixing mistakes in the copying process, which explains why so few mistakes are made.

c. Polymerase I and II are responsible for proofreading and fixing mistakes in the copying process which explains why errors in DNA replication are rare.

d. Errors in DNA replication are rare events in cells due to the action of DNA helicase.

science practices CONNECTION for AP® Courses

Activity

Use the model of DNA you constructed in Section 14.2 to demonstrate the process of replication in prokaryotes, showing how the activities differ on the leading and lagging strands. You need to add to your model by including enzymes and other proteins involved in the replication process.

Think About It

You isolate a DNA strand in which the joining together of Okazaki fragments is impaired and suspect that a mutation has occurred in an enzyme found at the replication fork. Which enzyme is most likely mutated?

14.5 | DNA Replication in Eukaryotes

In this section, you will explore the following questions:

- What are the similarities and differences between DNA replication in eukaryotes and prokaryotes?
- What is the role of telomerase in DNA replication?

Connection for AP® Courses

Concepts and examples described in this section are not in scope for AP. However, the roles of telomeres and telomerase in aging and cancer are informative and build on your knowledge of DNA replication in prokaryotes.

Eukaryotic genomes are much more complex and larger in size than prokaryotic genomes. The human genome has three billion base pairs per haploid set of chromosomes, and 6 billion base pairs are replicated during the S phase of the cell cycle. There are multiple origins of replication on the eukaryotic chromosome; humans can have up to 100,000 origins of replication. The rate of replication is approximately 100 nucleotides per second, much slower than prokaryotic replication.

In yeast, which is a eukaryote, special sequences known as Autonomously Replicating Sequences (ARS) are found on the chromosomes. These are equivalent to the origin of replication in *E. coli*.

The number of DNA polymerases in eukaryotes is much more than prokaryotes: 14 are known, of which five are known to have major roles during replication and have been well studied. They are known as pol α, pol β, pol γ, pol δ, and pol ε.

The essential steps of replication are the same as in prokaryotes. Before replication can start, the DNA has to be made available as template. Eukaryotic DNA is bound to basic proteins known as histones to form structures called nucleosomes. The chromatin (the complex between DNA and proteins) may undergo some chemical modifications, so that the DNA may be able to slide off the proteins or be accessible to the enzymes of the DNA replication machinery. At the origin of replication, a pre-replication complex is made with other initiator proteins. Other proteins are then recruited to start the replication process (Table 14.2).

A helicase using the energy from ATP hydrolysis opens up the DNA helix. Replication forks are formed at each replication origin as the DNA unwinds. The opening of the double helix causes over-winding, or supercoiling, in the DNA ahead of the replication fork. These are resolved with the action of topoisomerases. Primers are formed by the enzyme primase, and using the primer, DNA pol can start synthesis. While the leading strand is continuously synthesized by the enzyme pol δ, the lagging strand is synthesized by pol ε. A sliding clamp protein known as PCNA (Proliferating Cell Nuclear Antigen) holds the DNA pol in place so that it does not slide off the DNA. RNase H removes the RNA primer, which is then replaced with DNA nucleotides. The Okazaki fragments in the lagging strand are joined together after the replacement of the RNA primers with DNA. The gaps that remain are sealed by DNA ligase, which forms the phosphodiester bond.

Telomere Replication

Unlike prokaryotic chromosomes, eukaryotic chromosomes are linear. As you've learned, the enzyme DNA pol can add nucleotides only in the 5' to 3' direction. In the leading strand, synthesis continues until the end of the chromosome is reached. On the lagging strand, DNA is synthesized in short stretches, each of which is initiated by a separate primer. When the replication fork reaches the end of the linear chromosome, there is no place for a primer to be made for the DNA fragment to be copied at the end of the chromosome. These ends thus remain unpaired, and over time these ends may get progressively shorter as cells continue to divide.

The ends of the linear chromosomes are known as **telomeres**, which have repetitive sequences that code for no particular gene. In a way, these telomeres protect the genes from getting deleted as cells continue to divide. In humans, a six base pair sequence, TTAGGG, is repeated 100 to 1000 times. The discovery of the enzyme telomerase (Figure 14.16) helped in the understanding of how chromosome ends are maintained. The **telomerase** enzyme contains a catalytic part and a built-in RNA template. It attaches to the end of the chromosome, and complementary bases to the RNA template are added on the 3' end of the DNA strand. Once the 3' end of the lagging strand template is sufficiently elongated, DNA polymerase can add the nucleotides complementary to the ends of the chromosomes. Thus, the ends of the chromosomes are replicated.

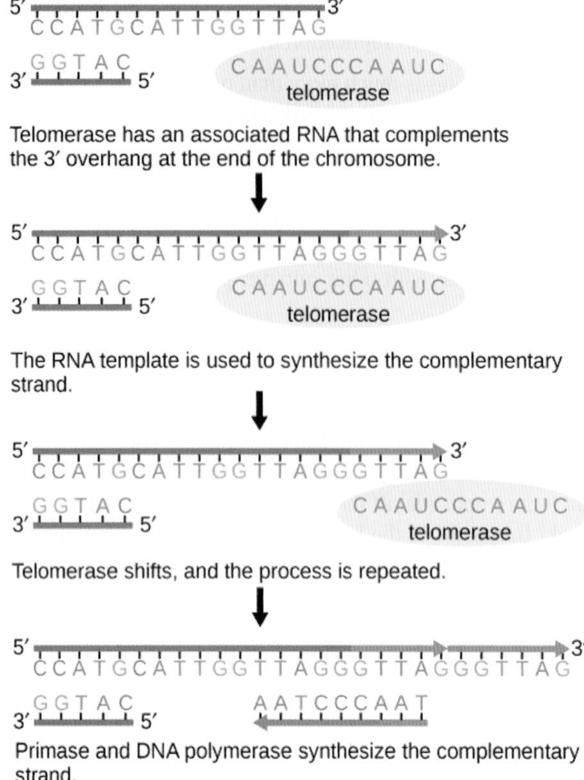

Figure 14.15 The ends of linear chromosomes are maintained by the action of the telomerase enzyme.

Telomerase is typically active in germ cells and adult stem cells. It is not active in adult somatic cells. For her discovery of telomerase and its action, Elizabeth Blackburn (Figure 14.16) received the Nobel Prize for Medicine and Physiology in 2009.

Figure 14.16 Elizabeth Blackburn, 2009 Nobel Laureate, is the scientist who discovered how telomerase works. (credit: US Embassy Sweden)

Telomerase and Aging

Cells that undergo cell division continue to have their telomeres shortened because most somatic cells do not make telomerase. This essentially means that telomere shortening is associated with aging. With the advent of modern medicine, preventative health care, and healthier lifestyles, the human life span has increased, and there is an increasing demand for people to look younger and have a better quality of life as they grow older.

In 2010, scientists found that telomerase can reverse some age-related conditions in mice. This may have potential in regenerative medicine.[2] Telomerase-deficient mice were used in these studies; these mice have tissue atrophy, stem cell depletion, organ system failure, and impaired tissue injury responses. Telomerase reactivation in these mice caused extension of telomeres, reduced DNA damage, reversed neurodegeneration, and improved the function of the testes, spleen, and intestines. Thus, telomere reactivation may have potential for treating age-related diseases in humans.

Cancer is characterized by uncontrolled cell division of abnormal cells. The cells accumulate mutations, proliferate uncontrollably, and can migrate to different parts of the body through a process called metastasis. Scientists have observed that cancerous cells have considerably shortened telomeres and that telomerase is active in these cells. Interestingly, only after the telomeres were shortened in the cancer cells did the telomerase become active. If the action of telomerase in these cells can be inhibited by drugs during cancer therapy, then the cancerous cells could potentially be stopped from further division.

Difference between Prokaryotic and Eukaryotic Replication

Property	Prokaryotes	Eukaryotes
Origin of replication	Single	Multiple
Rate of replication	1000 nucleotides/s	50 to 100 nucleotides/s
DNA polymerase types	5	14
Telomerase	Not present	Present
RNA primer removal	DNA pol I	RNase H
Strand elongation	DNA pol III	Pol δ, pol ε
Sliding clamp	Sliding clamp	PCNA

Table 14.2

14.6 | DNA Repair

In this section, you will explore the following questions:

- What are different types of mutations in DNA and the significance of mutations?
- What are examples of mechanisms that repair mutations in DNA?

Connection for AP® Courses

DNA polymerase is an efficient enzyme but it can make mistakes while adding nucleotides during replication. It edits the DNA by proofreading every newly added base. An incorrect base is removed and replaced by the correct base. If a base remains mismatched, special repair enzymes can often recognize the wrongly incorporated base, excise it from the DNA, and replace it with the correct base. Most mistakes are corrected, but if they are not they may result in a mutation, which is defined as a permanent change in a DNA sequence. A mutation can be passed to daughter cells through DNA replication and cell division. There are several types of DNA mutations, including substitution, deletion, insertion, and translocation. Mutations in repair genes may lead to serious consequences, such as cancer. Mutations can be induced by environmental factors, such as UV radiation, or they can occur spontaneously. (We will explore the effects of mutation in more detail in a later chapter. Remember that mutations are not always detrimental. They can be beneficial, too. Changes in DNA increase genetic variation—the foundation of evolution by natural selection.)

Information presented and the examples highlighted in the section support concepts outlined in Big Idea 3 of the AP® Biology Curriculum Framework. The Learning Objectives listed in the Curriculum Framework provide a transparent foundation for the AP® Biology course, an inquiry-based laboratory experience, instructional activities, and AP® exam questions. A Learning Objective merges required content with one or more of the seven Science Practices.

Big Idea 3 Living systems store, retrieve, transmit, and respond to information essential to life processes.

Enduring Understanding 3.C The processing of genetic information is imperfect and is a source of genetic variation.

2. Jaskelioff et al., "Telomerase reactivation reverses tissue degeneration in aged telomerase-deficient mice," *Nature* 469 (2011): 102-7.

Essential Knowledge	**3.C.1** Changes in genotype can result in changes in phenotype.
Science Practice	**6.4** The student can make claims and predictions about natural phenomena based on scientific theories and models.
Science Practice	**7.2** The student can connect concepts in and across domain(s) to generalize or extrapolate in and/or across enduring understandings and/or big ideas.
Learning Objective	**3.24** The student is able to predict how a change in genotype, when expressed as a phenotype, provides a variation that can be subject to natural selection.

Essential Knowledge	**3.C.1** Changes in genotype can result in changes in phenotype.
Science Practice	**1.1** The student can create representations and models of natural or man-made phenomena and systems in the domain.
Learning Objective	**3.25** The student can create a visual representation to illustrate how changes in a DNA nucleotide sequence can result in a change in the polypeptide produced.

Essential Knowledge	**3.C.2** Biological systems have multiple processes that increase genetic variation.
Science Practice	**6.2** The student can construct explanations of phenomena based on evidence produced through scientific practices.
Learning Objective	**3.28** The student is able to construct an explanation of the multiple processes that increase variation within a population.

DNA replication is a highly accurate process, but mistakes can occasionally occur, such as a DNA polymerase inserting a wrong base. Uncorrected mistakes may sometimes lead to serious consequences, such as cancer. Repair mechanisms correct the mistakes. In rare cases, mistakes are not corrected, leading to mutations; in other cases, repair enzymes are themselves mutated or defective.

Most of the mistakes during DNA replication are promptly corrected by DNA polymerase by proofreading the base that has been just added (Figure 14.17). In **proofreading**, the DNA pol reads the newly added base before adding the next one, so a correction can be made. The polymerase checks whether the newly added base has paired correctly with the base in the template strand. If it is the right base, the next nucleotide is added. If an incorrect base has been added, the enzyme makes a cut at the phosphodiester bond and releases the wrong nucleotide. This is performed by the exonuclease action of DNA pol III. Once the incorrect nucleotide has been removed, a new one will be added again.

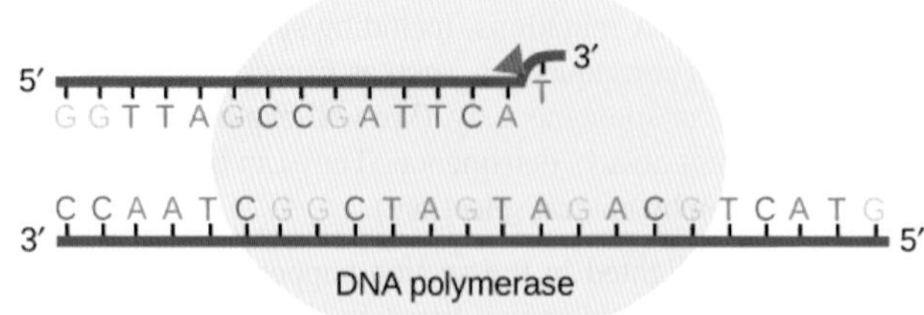

Figure 14.17 Proofreading by DNA polymerase corrects errors during replication.

Some errors are not corrected during replication, but are instead corrected after replication is completed; this type of repair is known as **mismatch repair** (Figure 14.18). The enzymes recognize the incorrectly added nucleotide and excise it; this is then replaced by the correct base. If this remains uncorrected, it may lead to more permanent damage. How do mismatch repair enzymes recognize which of the two bases is the incorrect one? In *E. coli*, after replication, the nitrogenous base adenine acquires a methyl group; the parental DNA strand will have methyl groups, whereas the newly synthesized strand lacks them. Thus, DNA polymerase is able to remove the wrongly incorporated bases from the newly synthesized, non-methylated strand. In eukaryotes, the mechanism is not very well understood, but it is believed to involve recognition of unsealed nicks in the new strand, as well as a short-term continuing association of some of the replication proteins with the new daughter strand after replication has completed.

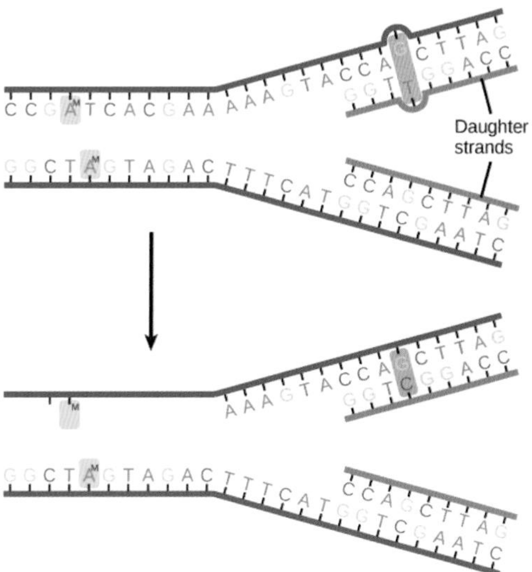

Figure 14.18 In mismatch repair, the incorrectly added base is detected after replication. The mismatch repair proteins detect this base and remove it from the newly synthesized strand by nuclease action. The gap is now filled with the correctly paired base.

In another type of repair mechanism, **nucleotide excision repair**, enzymes replace incorrect bases by making a cut on both the 3' and 5' ends of the incorrect base (Figure 14.19). The segment of DNA is removed and replaced with the correctly paired nucleotides by the action of DNA pol. Once the bases are filled in, the remaining gap is sealed with a phosphodiester linkage catalyzed by DNA ligase. This repair mechanism is often employed when UV exposure causes the formation of pyrimidine dimers.

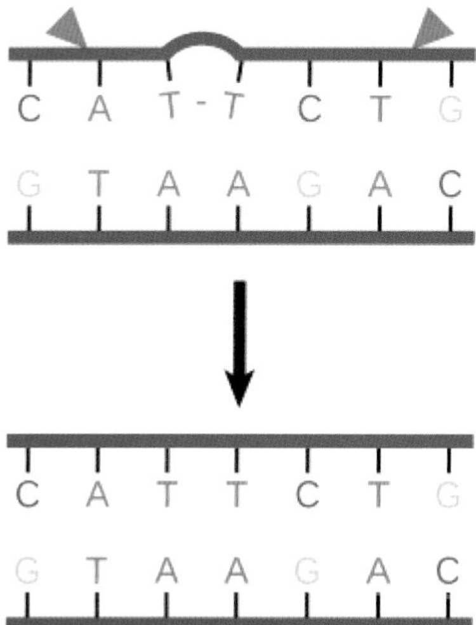

Figure 14.19 Nucleotide excision repairs thymine dimers. When exposed to UV, thymines lying adjacent to each other can form thymine dimers. In normal cells, they are excised and replaced.

A well-studied example of mistakes not being corrected is seen in people suffering from xeroderma pigmentosa (Figure 14.20). Affected individuals have skin that is highly sensitive to UV rays from the sun. When individuals are exposed to UV, pyrimidine dimers, especially those of thymine, are formed; people with xeroderma pigmentosa are not able to repair the damage. These are not repaired because of a defect in the nucleotide excision repair enzymes, whereas in normal individuals, the thymine dimers are excised and the defect is corrected. The thymine dimers distort the structure of the DNA double helix, and this may cause problems during DNA replication.

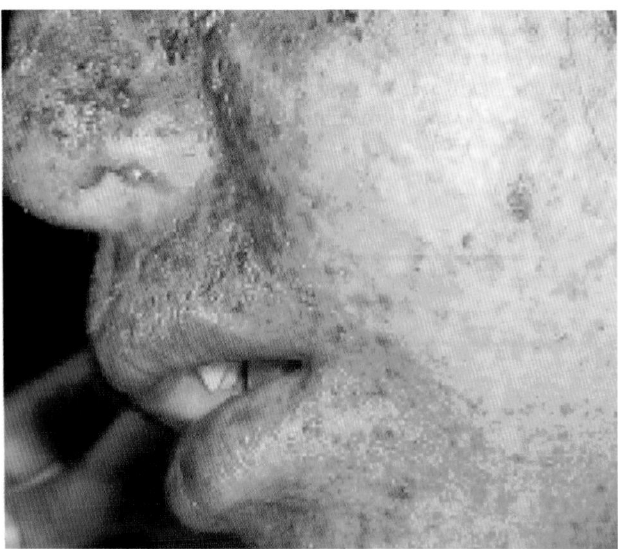

Figure 14.20 Xeroderma pigmentosa is a condition in which thymine dimerization from exposure to UV is not repaired. Exposure to sunlight results in skin lesions. (credit: James Halpern et al.)

Errors during DNA replication are not the only reason why mutations arise in DNA. **Mutations**, variations in the nucleotide sequence of a genome, can also occur because of damage to DNA. Such mutations may be of two types: induced or spontaneous. **Induced mutations** are those that result from an exposure to chemicals, UV rays, x-rays, or some other environmental agent. **Spontaneous mutations** occur without any exposure to any environmental agent; they are a result of natural reactions taking place within the body.

Mutations may have a wide range of effects. Some mutations are not expressed; these are known as **silent mutations**. **Point mutations** are those mutations that affect a single base pair. The most common nucleotide mutations are substitutions, in which one base is replaced by another. These can be of two types, either transitions or transversions. **Transition substitution** refers to a purine or pyrimidine being replaced by a base of the same kind; for example, a purine such as adenine may be replaced by the purine guanine. **Transversion substitution** refers to a purine being replaced by a pyrimidine, or vice versa; for example, cytosine, a pyrimidine, is replaced by adenine, a purine. Mutations can also be the result of the addition of a base, known as an insertion, or the removal of a base, also known as deletion. Sometimes a piece of DNA from one chromosome may get translocated to another chromosome or to another region of the same chromosome; this is also known as translocation. These mutation types are shown in Figure 14.22.

everyday CONNECTION for AP® Courses

Sometimes a nucleotide is overlooked by the DNA repair system for no known reason. This malignant melanoma is the result of DNA not undergoing repair after too much UV exposure.

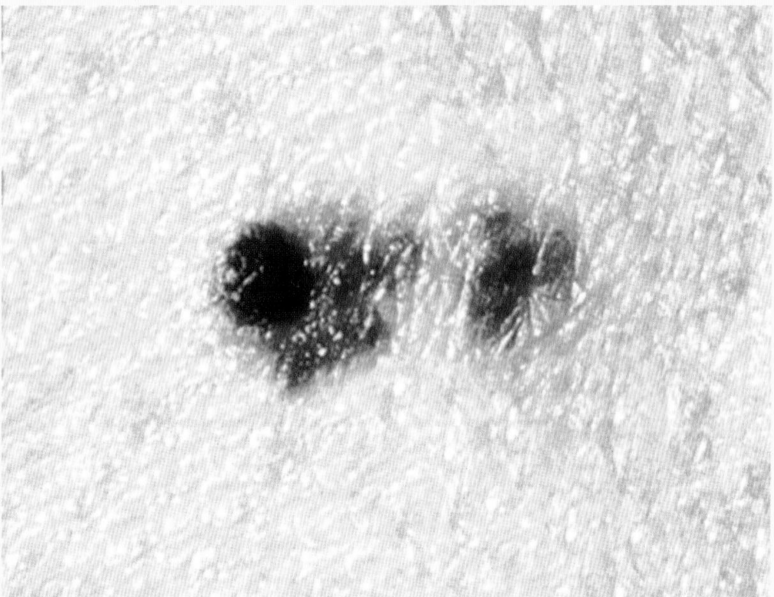

Figure 14.21

Which statement about the above malignant melanoma is most likely true?

a. it was the result of a spontaneous mutation
b. it was caused by thymine dimer formation
c. it was caused by a transition substitution
d. it was caused by a transversion substitution

visual CONNECTION

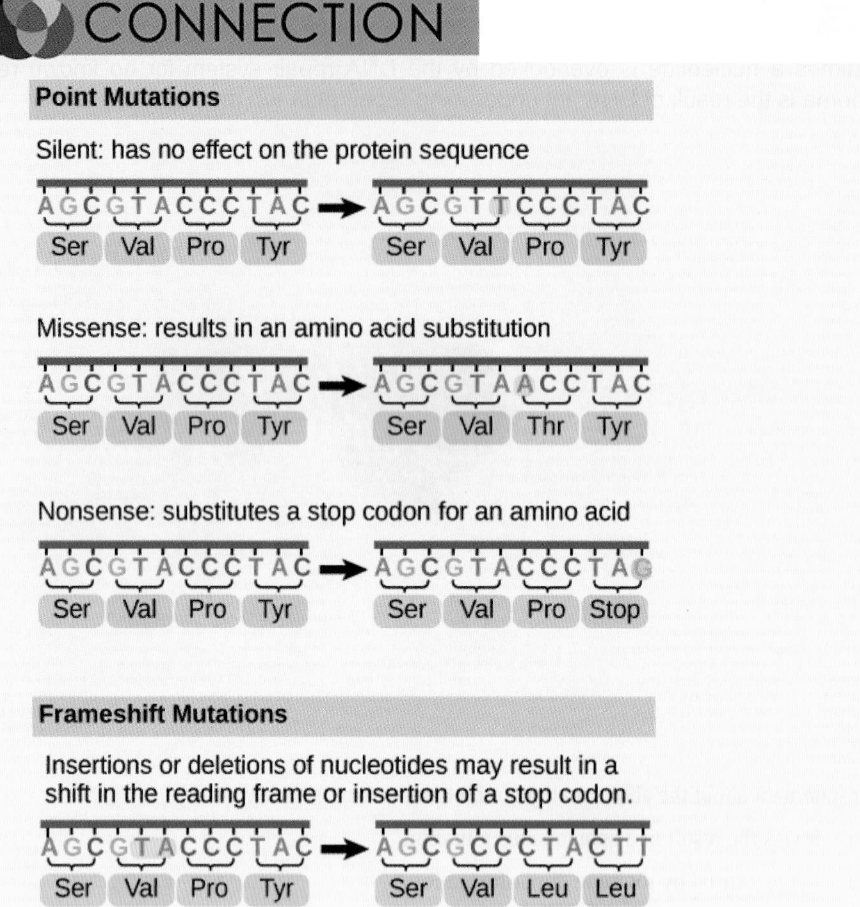

Figure 14.22 Mutations can lead to changes in the protein sequence encoded by the DNA.

A frameshift mutation that results in the insertion of three nucleotides is often less deleterious than a mutation that results in the insertion of one nucleotide. Why?

a. Addition of three nucleotides does not shift the reading frame.
b. Addition of three nucleotides shifts the reading frame.
c. Addition of three nucleotides incorporates two amino acids.
d. Addition of three nucleotides removes two amino acids.

Mutations in repair genes have been known to cause cancer. Many mutated repair genes have been implicated in certain forms of pancreatic cancer, colon cancer, and colorectal cancer. Mutations can affect either somatic cells or germ cells. If many mutations accumulate in a somatic cell, they may lead to problems such as the uncontrolled cell division observed in cancer. If a mutation takes place in germ cells, the mutation will be passed on to the next generation, as in the case of hemophilia and xeroderma pigmentosa.

science practices CONNECTION for AP® Courses

Think About It

Infertility can sometimes be explained by chromosome translocations. Explain how chromosome translocations can cause infertility. Are there times when a chromosome translocation might *not* result in infertility?

KEY TERMS

electrophoresis technique used to separate DNA fragments according to size

helicase during replication, this enzyme helps to open up the DNA helix by breaking the hydrogen bonds

induced mutation mutation that results from exposure to chemicals or environmental agents

lagging strand during replication, the strand that is replicated in short fragments and away from the replication fork

leading strand strand that is synthesized continuously in the 5'-3' direction which is synthesized in the direction of the replication fork

ligase enzyme that catalyzes the formation of a phosphodiester linkage between the 3' OH and 5' phosphate ends of the DNA

mismatch repair type of repair mechanism in which mismatched bases are removed after replication

mutation variation in the nucleotide sequence of a genome

nucleotide excision repair type of DNA repair mechanism in which the wrong base, along with a few nucleotides upstream or downstream, are removed

Okazaki fragment DNA fragment that is synthesized in short stretches on the lagging strand

point mutation mutation that affects a single base

primase enzyme that synthesizes the RNA primer; the primer is needed for DNA pol to start synthesis of a new DNA strand

primer short stretch of nucleotides that is required to initiate replication; in the case of replication, the primer has RNA nucleotides

proofreading function of DNA pol in which it reads the newly added base before adding the next one

replication fork Y-shaped structure formed during initiation of replication

silent mutation mutation that is not expressed

single-strand binding protein during replication, protein that binds to the single-stranded DNA; this helps in keeping the two strands of DNA apart so that they may serve as templates

sliding clamp ring-shaped protein that holds the DNA pol on the DNA strand

spontaneous mutation mutation that takes place in the cells as a result of chemical reactions taking place naturally without exposure to any external agent

telomerase enzyme that contains a catalytic part and an inbuilt RNA template; it functions to maintain telomeres at chromosome ends

telomere DNA at the end of linear chromosomes

topoisomerase enzyme that causes underwinding or overwinding of DNA when DNA replication is taking place

transformation process in which external DNA is taken up by a cell

transition substitution when a purine is replaced with a purine or a pyrimidine is replaced with another pyrimidine

transversion substitution when a purine is replaced by a pyrimidine or a pyrimidine is replaced by a purine

CHAPTER SUMMARY

14.1 Historical Basis of Modern Understanding

DNA was first isolated from white blood cells by Friedrich Miescher, who called it nuclein because it was isolated from nuclei. Frederick Griffith's experiments with strains of *Streptococcus pneumoniae* provided the first hint that DNA may be the transforming principle. Avery, MacLeod, and McCarty proved that DNA is required for the transformation of bacteria. Later experiments by Hershey and Chase using bacteriophage T2 proved that DNA is the genetic material. Chargaff found that the ratio of A = T and C = G, and that the percentage content of A, T, G, and C is different for different species.

14.2 DNA Structure and Sequencing

The currently accepted model of the double-helix structure of DNA was proposed by Watson and Crick. Some of the salient features are that the two strands that make up the double helix are complementary and anti-parallel in nature. Deoxyribose sugars and phosphates form the backbone of the structure, and the nitrogenous bases are stacked inside. The diameter of the double helix, 2 nm, is uniform throughout. A purine always pairs with a pyrimidine; A pairs with T, and G pairs with C. One turn of the helix has ten base pairs. During cell division, each daughter cell receives a copy of the DNA by a process known as DNA replication. Prokaryotes are much simpler than eukaryotes in many of their features. Most prokaryotes contain a single, circular chromosome. In general, eukaryotic chromosomes contain a linear DNA molecule packaged into nucleosomes, and have two distinct regions that can be distinguished by staining, reflecting different states of packaging and compaction.

14.3 Basics of DNA Replication

The model for DNA replication suggests that the two strands of the double helix separate during replication, and each strand serves as a template from which the new complementary strand is copied. In conservative replication, the parental DNA is conserved, and the daughter DNA is newly synthesized. The semi-conservative method suggests that each of the two parental DNA strands acts as template for new DNA to be synthesized; after replication, each double-stranded DNA includes one parental or "old" strand and one "new" strand. The dispersive mode suggested that the two copies of the DNA would have segments of parental DNA and newly synthesized DNA.

14.4 DNA Replication in Prokaryotes

Replication in prokaryotes starts from a sequence found on the chromosome called the origin of replication—the point at which the DNA opens up. Helicase opens up the DNA double helix, resulting in the formation of the replication fork. Single-strand binding proteins bind to the single-stranded DNA near the replication fork to keep the fork open. Primase synthesizes an RNA primer to initiate synthesis by DNA polymerase, which can add nucleotides only in the 5' to 3' direction. One strand is synthesized continuously in the direction of the replication fork; this is called the leading strand. The other strand is synthesized in a direction away from the replication fork, in short stretches of DNA known as Okazaki fragments. This strand is known as the lagging strand. Once replication is completed, the RNA primers are replaced by DNA nucleotides and the DNA is sealed with DNA ligase, which creates phosphodiester bonds between the 3'-OH of one end and the 5' phosphate of the other strand.

14.5 DNA Replication in Eukaryotes

Replication in eukaryotes starts at multiple origins of replication. The mechanism is quite similar to prokaryotes. A primer is required to initiate synthesis, which is then extended by DNA polymerase as it adds nucleotides one by one to the growing chain. The leading strand is synthesized continuously, whereas the lagging strand is synthesized in short stretches called Okazaki fragments. The RNA primers are replaced with DNA nucleotides; the DNA remains one continuous strand by linking the DNA fragments with DNA ligase. The ends of the chromosomes pose a problem as polymerase is unable to extend them without a primer. Telomerase, an enzyme with an inbuilt RNA template, extends the ends by copying the RNA template and extending one end of the chromosome. DNA polymerase can then extend the DNA using the primer. In this way, the ends of the chromosomes are protected.

14.6 DNA Repair

DNA polymerase can make mistakes while adding nucleotides. It edits the DNA by proofreading every newly added base. Incorrect bases are removed and replaced by the correct base, and then a new base is added. Most mistakes are corrected during replication, although when this does not happen, the mismatch repair mechanism is employed. Mismatch repair enzymes recognize the wrongly incorporated base and excise it from the DNA, replacing it with the correct base. In yet another type of repair, nucleotide excision repair, the incorrect base is removed along with a few bases on the 5' and 3' end, and these are replaced by copying the template with the help of DNA polymerase. The ends of the newly synthesized fragment are attached to the rest of the DNA using DNA ligase, which creates a phosphodiester bond.

Most mistakes are corrected, and if they are not, they may result in a mutation defined as a permanent change in the DNA sequence. Mutations can be of many types, such as substitution, deletion, insertion, and translocation. Mutations can be induced or may occur spontaneously.

REVIEW QUESTIONS

1. Who was the first person to isolate the material that came to be known as nucleic acids?

a. Frederick Griffith
b. Friedrich Miescher
c. James Watson
d. Oswald Avery

2. What is bacterial transformation?

a. The transformation of a bacterium occurs during replication.
b. It is the transformation of a bacterium into a pathogenic form.
c. Transformation of bacteria involves changes in its chromosome.
d. Transformation is a process in which external DNA is taken up by a cell, thereby changing morphology and physiology.

3. What type of nucleic acid material is analyzed the most frequently in forensics cases?

a. cytoplasmic rRNA
b. mitochondrial DNA
c. nuclear chromosomal DNA
d. nuclear mRNA

4. The experiments by Hershey and Chase helped confirm that DNA was the hereditary material on the basis of the finding of what?

a. Radioactive phages were found in the pellet.
b. Radioactive cells were found in the supernatant.
c. Radioactive sulfur was found inside the cell.
d. Radioactive phosphorus was found in the cell.

5. If DNA of a particular species was analyzed and it was found that it contains 27% A, what would be the percentage of C?

a. 23%
b. 27%
c. 30%
d. 54%

6. If the sequence of the 5’ to 3’ strand is AATGCTAC, then the complementary sequence has the following sequence:

a. 3’-AATGCTAC-5’
b. 3’-CATCGTAA-5’
c. 3’-TTACGATG-5’
d. 3’-GTAGCATT-5’

7. The DNA double helix does not have which of the following?

a. antiparallel configuration
b. complementary base pairing
c. major and minor grooves
d. uracil

8. What is a purine?

a. a double ring structure with a six-membered ring fused to a five-membered ring
b. a single six-membered ring
c. a six-membered ring
d. three phosphates covalently bonded by phosphodiester bonds

9. What is the name of the method developed by Fred Sanger to sequence DNA?

a. Dideoxy Chain Termination method
b. Double Helix Determination
c. Polymerase Chain Reaction
d. Polymer Gel Electrophoresis

10. What happens when a dideoxynucleotide is added to a developing DNA strand?

a. The chain extends to the end of the DNA strand.
b. The DNA stand is duplicated.
c. The chain is not extended any further.
d. The last codon is repeated.

11. In eukaryotes, what is DNA wrapped around?

a. histones
b. polymerase
c. single-stranded binding proteins
d. sliding clamp

12. Which enzyme is only found in prokaryotic organisms?

a. DNA gyrase
b. helicase
c. ligase
d. telomerase

13. Uracil is found where?

a. chromosomal DNA
b. helicase
c. mitochondrial DNA
d. mRNA

14. What prevents the further development of a DNA strand in Sanger sequencing?

a. the addition of DNA reductase
b. the addition of dideoxynucleotides
c. the elimination of DNA polymerase
d. the addition of uracil

15. Which of the following is not one of the proteins involved during the formation of the replication fork?

a. helicase
b. ligase
c. origin of replication
d. single-strand binding proteins

16. In which direction does DNA replication take place?

a. 5’ to 3’
b. 3’ to 5’
c. 5’
d. 3’

17. Meselson and Stahl’s experiments proved that DNA replicates by which mode?

a. conservative
b. converse
c. dispersive
d. semi-conservative

18. Which set of results was found in the Meselson and Stahl’s experiments?

a. The original chromosome was kept intact and a duplicate was made.
b. The original chromosome was split and half went to each duplicate.
c. The original chromosome was mixed with new material and each duplicate strand contained both old and new.
d. The original chromosome was used as a template for two new chromosomes and discarded.

19. Which enzyme initiates the splitting of the double DNA strand during replication?

a. DNA gyrase
b. helicase
c. ligase
d. telomerase

20. Which enzyme is most directly responsible for the main process of producing a new DNA strand?

a. DNA pol I
b. DNA pol II
c. DNA pol III
d. DNA pol I, DNA pol II, and DNA pol III

21. Which portion of a chromosome contains Okazaki fragments?

a. helicase
b. lagging strand
c. leading strand
d. primer

22. Which of the following does the enzyme primase synthesize?

a. DNA primer
b. Okazaki fragments
c. phosphodiester linkage
d. RNA primer

23. The ends of the linear chromosomes are maintained by what?

a. DNA polymerase
b. helicase
c. primase
d. telomerase

24. What is the difference in the rate of replication of nucleotides between prokaryotes and eukaryotes?

a. Eukaryotes are 50 times slower.
b. Eukaryotes are 20 times faster.
c. Prokaryotes are 100 times slower.
d. Prokaryotes are 10 times faster.

25. What are Autonomously Replicating Sequences (ARS)?

a. areas of prokaryotic chromosomes that initiate copying
b. portions of prokaryotic chromosomes that can be transferred from one organism to another
c. areas of eukaryotic chromosomes that are equivalent to the origin of replication in *E. coli*
d. portions of eukaryotic chromosomes that replicate independent of the parent chromosome

26. What type of body cell does not exhibit telomerase activity?

a. adult stem cells
b. embryonic cells
c. germ cells
d. liver cells

27. During proofreading, which of the following enzymes reads the DNA?

a. DNA polymerase
b. helicase
c. topoisomerase
d. primase

28. If a prokaryotic cell is replicating nucleotides at a rate of 100 per second, how fast would a eukaryotic cell be replicating nucleotides?

a. 1000 per second
b. 100 per second
c. 10 per second
d. 1 per second

29. Which type of point mutation would have no effect on gene expression?

a. frameshift
b. missense
c. nonsense
d. silent

30. Which type of point mutation would result in the substitution of a stop codon for an amino acid?

a. frameshift
b. missense
c. nonsense
d. silent

31. You have developed skin cancer and you are pregnant. You are worried that your child will be born with the cancer you have while carrying the baby. Should you be worried?

a. Yes, the cancer can spread to the baby.
b. No, the mutations causing the cancer are in somatic cells, not reproductive germ cells.
c. Yes, the mutations can be passed on to the child through the placenta.
d. No, UV light only affects adult, somatic cells.

32. What is the initial mechanism for repairing nucleotide errors in DNA?

a. DNA polymerase proofreading
b. mismatch repair
c. nucleotide excision repair
d. thymine dimers

33. Nucleotide excision repair is often employed when UV exposure causes the formation of what?

a. phosphodiester bonds
b. purine conjugates
c. pyrimidine dimers
d. tetrad disassembly

CRITICAL THINKING QUESTIONS

34. Explain Griffith's transformation experiments. What did he conclude from them?

a. Two strains of *S. pneumoniae* were used for the experiment. Griffith injected a mouse with heat-inactivated S strain (pathogenic) and R strain (non-pathogenic). The mouse died and S strain was recovered from the dead mouse. He concluded that external DNA is taken up by a cell that changed morphology and physiology.

b. Two strains of *Vibrio cholerae* were used for the experiment. Griffith injected a mouse with heat-inactivated S strain (pathogenic) and R strain (non-pathogenic). The mouse died and S strain was recovered from the dead mouse. He concluded that external DNA is taken up by a cell that changed morphology and physiology.

c. Two strains of *S. pneumoniae* were used for the experiment. Griffith injected a mouse with heat-inactivated S strain (pathogenic) and R strain (non-pathogenic). The mouse died and R strain was recovered from the dead mouse. He concluded that external DNA is taken up by a cell that changed morphology and physiology.

d. Two strains of *S. pneumoniae* were used for the experiment. Griffith injected a mouse with heat-inactivated S strain (pathogenic) and R strain (non-pathogenic). The mouse died and S strain was recovered from the dead mouse. He concluded that mutation occurred in the DNA of the cell that changed morphology and physiology.

35. Explain why radioactive sulfur and phosphorous were used to label bacteriophages in the Hershey and Chase experiments.

a. Protein was labeled with radioactive sulfur and DNA was labeled with radioactive phosphorous. Phosphorous is found in DNA, so it will be tagged by radioactive phosphorous.

b. Protein was labeled with radioactive phosphorous and DNA was labeled with radioactive sulfur. Phosphorous is found in DNA, so it will be tagged by radioactive phosphorous.

c. Protein was labeled with radioactive sulfur and DNA was labeled with radioactive phosphorous. Phosphorous is found in DNA, so DNA will be tagged by radioactive sulfur.

d. Protein was labeled with radioactive sulfur and DNA was labeled with radioactive phosphorous. Phosphorous is found in DNA, so DNA will be tagged by radioactive sulfur.

36. How can Chargaff's rules be used to identify different species?

a. The amount of adenine, thymine, guanine, and cytosine varies from species to species and are not found in equal quantities. They do not vary between individuals of the same species and can be used to identify different species.

b. The amount of adenine, thymine, guanine, and cytosine varies from species to species and is found in equal quantities. They do not vary between individuals of the same species and can be used to identify different species.

c. The amount of adenine and thymine is equal to guanine and cytosine and is found in equal quantities. They do not vary between individuals of the same species and can be used to identify different species.

d. The amount of adenine, thymine, guanine, and cytosine varies from species to species and they are not found in equal quantities. They vary between individuals of the same species and can be used to identify different species.

37. In the Avery, Macleod, and McCarty experiments, what conclusion would the scientists have drawn if the use of proteases prevented the transformation of R strain bacteria?

38. Describe the structure and complementary base pairing of DNA.

a. DNA is made up of two strands that are twisted around each other to form a helix. Adenine pairs up with thymine and cytosine pairs with guanine. The two strands are anti-parallel in nature; that is, the 3’ end of one strand faces the 5’ end of other strand. Sugar, phosphate and nitrogenous bases contribute to the DNA structure.

b. DNA is made up of two strands that are twisted around each other to form a helix. Adenine pairs up with cytosine and thymine pairs with guanine. The two strands are anti-parallel in nature; that is, the 3’ end of one strand faces the 5’ end of other strand. Sugar, phosphate and nitrogenous bases contribute to the DNA structure.

c. DNA is made up of two strands that are twisted around each other to form a helix. Adenine pairs up with thymine and cytosine pairs with guanine. The two strands are parallel in nature; that is, the 3’ end of one strand faces the 3’ end of other strand. Sugar, phosphate and nitrogenous bases contribute to the DNA structure.

d. DNA is made up of two strands that are twisted around each other to form a helix. Adenine pairs up with thymine and cytosine pairs with guanine. The two strands are anti-parallel in nature; that is, the 3’ end of one strand faces the 5’ end of other strand. Only sugar contributes to the DNA structure.

39. Provide a brief summary of the Sanger sequencing method.

a. Frederick Sanger’s sequencing is a chain termination method that is used to generate DNA fragments that terminate at different points using dye-labeled dideoxynucleotides. DNA is separated by electrophoresis on the basis of size. The DNA sequence can be read out on an electropherogram generated by a laser scanner.

b. Frederick Sanger’s sequencing is a chain elongation method that is used to generate DNA fragments that elongate at different points using dye-labeled dideoxynucleotides. DNA is separated by electrophoresis on the basis of size. The DNA sequence can be read out on an electropherogram generated by a laser scanner.

c. Frederick Sanger’s sequencing is a chain termination method that is used to generate DNA fragments that terminate at different points using dye-labeled dideoxynucleotides. DNA is joined together by electrophoresis on the basis of size. The DNA sequence can be read out on an electropherogram generated by a laser scanner.

d. Frederick Sanger’s sequencing is a chain termination method that is used to generate DNA fragments that terminate at different points using dye-labeled dideoxynucleotides. DNA is separated by electrophoresis on the basis of size. The DNA sequence can be read out on an electropherogram generated by a magnetic scanner.

40. Compare and contrast the similarities and differences between eukaryotic and prokaryotic DNA.

a. Eukaryotes have a single, circular chromosome, while prokaryotes have multiple, linear chromosomes. Prokaryotes pack their chromosomes by super coiling, managed by DNA gyrase. Eukaryote chromosomes are wrapped around histone proteins that create heterochromatin and euchromatin, which is not present in prokaryotes.

b. Prokaryotes have a single, circular chromosome, while eukaryotes have multiple, linear chromosomes. Prokaryotes pack their chromosomes by super coiling, managed by DNA gyrase. Eukaryote chromosomes are wrapped around histone proteins that could form heterochromatin, which is not present in prokaryotes.

c. Prokaryotes have a single, circular chromosome, while eukaryotes have multiple, linear chromosomes. Eukaryotes pack their chromosomes by super coiling, managed by DNA gyrase. Prokaryotes chromosomes are wrapped around histone proteins that could form heterochromatin, which is not present in eukaryotes.

d. Prokaryotes have a single, circular chromosome, while eukaryotes have multiple, linear chromosomes. Prokaryotes pack their chromosomes by super coiling, managed by DNA gyrase. Eukaryote chromosomes are wrapped around histone proteins that could form heterochromatin, which is present in prokaryotes.

41. DNA replication is bidirectional and discontinuous; explain your understanding of those concepts.

a. DNA polymerase reads the template strand in the 3' to 5' direction and adds nucleotides only in the 5' to 3' direction. The leading strand is synthesized in the direction of the replication fork. Replication on the lagging strand occurs in the direction away from the replication fork in short stretches of DNA called Okazaki fragments.

b. DNA polymerase reads the template strand in the 5' to 3' direction and adds nucleotides only in the 5' to 3' direction. The leading strand is synthesized in the direction of the replication fork. Replication on the lagging strand occurs in the direction away from the replication fork in short stretches of DNA called Okazaki fragments.

c. DNA polymerase reads the template strand in the 3' to 5' direction and adds nucleotides only in the 5' to 3' direction. The leading strand is synthesized in the direction away from the replication fork. Replication on the lagging strand occurs in the direction of the replication fork in short stretches of DNA called Okazaki fragments.

d. DNA polymerase reads the template strand in the 5' to 3' direction and adds nucleotides only in the 3' to 5' direction. The leading strand is synthesized in the direction of the replication fork. Replication on the lagging strand occurs in the direction away from the replication fork in long stretches of DNA called Okazaki fragments.

42. Discuss how the scientific community learned that DNA replication takes place in a semiconservative fashion.

a. Meselson and Stahl experimented with *E. coli*. DNA grown in ^{15}N was heavier than DNA grown in ^{14}N. When DNA in ^{15}N was switched to ^{14}N media, DNA sedimented halfway between the ^{15}N and ^{14}N levels after one round of cell division, indicating fifty percent presence of ^{14}N. This supports the semi-conservative replication model.

b. Meselson and Stahl experimented with *S. pneumonia*. DNA grown in ^{15}N was heavier than DNA grown in ^{14}N. When DNA in ^{15}N was switched to ^{14}N media, DNA sedimented halfway between the ^{15}N and ^{14}N levels after one round of cell division, indicating fifty percent presence of ^{14}N. This supports the semi-conservative replication model.

c. Meselson and Stahl experimented with *E. coli*. DNA grown in ^{14}N was heavier than DNA grown in ^{15}N. When DNA in ^{15}N was switched to ^{14}N media, DNA sedimented halfway between the ^{15}N and ^{14}N levels after one round of cell division, indicating fifty percent presence of ^{14}N. This supports the semi-conservative replication model.

d. Meselson and Stahl experimented with *S. pneumonia*. DNA grown in ^{15}N was heavier than DNA grown in ^{14}N. When DNA in ^{15}N was switched to ^{14}N media, DNA sedimented halfway between the ^{15}N and ^{14}N levels after one round of cell division, indicating complete presence of ^{14}N. This supports the semi-conservative replication model.

43. Explain why half of DNA is replicated in a discontinuous fashion.

a. Replication of the lagging strand occurs in the direction away from the replication fork in short stretches of DNA, since access to the DNA is always from the 5’ end. This results in pieces of DNA being replicated in a discontinuous fashion.

b. Replication of the leading strand occurs in the direction away from the replication fork in short stretches of DNA, since access to the DNA is always from the 5’ end. This results in pieces of DNA being replicated in a discontinuous fashion.

c. Replication of the lagging strand occurs in the direction of the replication fork in short stretches of DNA, since access to the DNA is always from the 5’ end. This results in pieces of DNA being replicated in a discontinuous fashion.

d. Replication of the lagging strand occurs in the direction away from the replication fork in short stretches of DNA, since access to the DNA is always from the 3’ end. This results in pieces of DNA being replicated in a discontinuous fashion.

44. Explain the events taking place at the replication fork. If the gene for helicase is mutated, what part of replication will be affected?

a. Helicase separates the DNA strands at the origin of replication. Topoisomerase breaks and reforms DNA's phosphate backbone ahead of the replication fork, thereby relieving the pressure. Single-stranded binding proteins prevent reforming of DNA. Primase synthesizes RNA primer which is used by DNA polymerase to form a daughter strand. If helicase is mutated, the DNA strands will not be separated at the beginning of replication.

b. Helicase joins the DNA strands together at the origin of replication. Topoisomerase breaks and reforms DNA's phosphate backbone after the replication fork, thereby relieving the pressure. Single-stranded binding proteins prevent reforming of DNA. Primase synthesizes RNA primer which is used by DNA polymerase to form a daughter strand. If helicase is mutated, the DNA strands will not be joined together at the beginning of replication.

c. Helicase separates the DNA strands at the origin of replication. Topoisomerase breaks and reforms DNA's sugar backbone ahead of the replication fork, thereby increasing the pressure. Single-stranded binding proteins prevent reforming of DNA. Primase synthesizes DNA primer which is used by DNA polymerase to form a daughter strand. If helicase is mutated, the DNA strands will be separated at the beginning of replication.

d. Helicase separates the DNA strands at the origin of replication. Topoisomerase breaks and reforms DNA's sugar backbone ahead of the replication fork, thereby relieving the pressure. Single-stranded binding proteins prevent reforming of DNA. Primase synthesizes DNA primer which is used by RNA polymerase to form a parent strand. If helicase is mutated, the DNA strands will be separated at the beginning of replication.

45. What are Okazaki fragments and how they are formed?

a. Okazaki fragments are short stretches of DNA on the lagging strand, which is synthesized in the direction away from the replication fork.

b. Okazaki fragments are long stretches of DNA on the lagging strand, which is synthesized in the direction of the replication fork.

c. Okazaki fragments are long stretches of DNA on the leading strand, which is synthesized in the direction away from the replication fork.

d. Okazaki fragments are short stretches of DNA on the leading strand, which is synthesized in the direction of the replication fork.

46. Compare and contrast the roles of DNA polymerase I and DNA ligase in DNA replication.

a. DNA polymerase I removes the RNA primers from the developing copy of DNA. DNA ligase seals the ends of the new segment, especially the Okazaki fragments.

b. DNA polymerase I adds the RNA primers to the already developing copy of DNA. DNA ligase separates the ends of the new segment, especially the Okazaki fragments.

c. DNA polymerase I seals the ends of the new segment, especially the Okazaki fragments. DNA ligase removes the RNA primers from the developing copy of DNA.

d. DNA polymerase I removes the enzyme primase from the developing copy of DNA. DNA ligase seals the ends of the old segment, especially the Okazaki fragments.

47. If the rate of replication in a particular prokaryote is 900 nucleotides per second, how long would it take to make two copies of a 1.2 million base pair genome?

a. 22.2 minutes

b. 44.4 minutes

c. 45.4 minutes

d. 54.4 minutes

48. How do the linear chromosomes in eukaryotes ensure that their ends are replicated completely?

a. The ends of the linear chromosomes are maintained by the activity of the telomerase enzyme.

b. The ends of the linear chromosomes are maintained by the formation of a replication fork.

c. The ends of the linear chromosomes are maintained by the continuous joining of Okazaki fragments.

d. The ends of the linear chromosomes are maintained by the action of the polymerase enzyme.

49. Compare and contrast prokaryotic and eukaryotic DNA replication.

a. A prokaryotic organism's rate of replication is ten times faster than that of eukaryotes. Prokaryotes have a single origin of replication and use five types of polymerases, while eukaryotes have multiple sites of origin and use fourteen polymerases. Telomerase is absent in prokaryotes. DNA pol I is the primer remover in prokaryotes, while in eukaryotes it is RNase H. DNA pol III performs strand elongation in prokaryotes and pol δ and pol ε do the same in eukaryotes.

b. A prokaryotic organism's rate of replication is ten times slower than that of eukaryotes. Prokaryotes have a single origin of replication and use five types of polymerases, while eukaryotes have multiple sites of origin and use fourteen polymerases. Telomerase is absent in eukaryotes. DNA pol I is the primer remover in prokaryotes, while in eukaryotes it is RNase H. DNA pol III performs strand elongation in prokaryotes and pol δ and pol ε do the same in eukaryotes.

c. A prokaryotic organism's rate of replication is ten times faster than that of eukaryotes. Prokaryotes have five origins of replication and use a single type of polymerase, while eukaryotes have a single site of origin and use fourteen polymerases. Telomerase is absent in prokaryotes. DNA pol I is the primer remover in prokaryotes, while in eukaryotes it is RNase H. DNA pol III performs strand elongation in prokaryotes and pol δ and pol ε do the same in eukaryotes.

d. A prokaryotic organism's rate of replication is ten times slower than that of eukaryotes. Prokaryotes have a single origin of replication and use five types of polymerases, while eukaryotes have multiple sites of origin and use fourteen polymerases. Telomerase is absent in prokaryotes. DNA pol I is the primer remover in eukaryotes, while in prokaryotes it is RNase H. DNA pol III performs strand elongation in prokaryotes and pol δ and pol ε do the same in eukaryotes.

50. What would be the consequence of a mutation in a mismatch repair enzyme? How will this affect the function of a gene?

a. Mismatch repair corrects the errors after the replication is completed by excising the incorrectly added nucleotide and adding the correct base. Any mutation in a mismatch repair enzyme would lead to more permanent damage.

b. Mismatch repair corrects the errors during the replication by excising the incorrectly added nucleotide and adding the correct base. Any mutation in the mismatch repair enzyme would lead to more permanent damage.

c. Mismatch repair corrects the errors after the replication is completed by excising the added nucleotides and adding more bases. Any mutation in the mismatch repair enzyme would lead to more permanent damage.

d. Mismatch repair corrects the errors after the replication is completed by excising the incorrectly added nucleotide and adding the correct base. Any mutation in the mismatch repair enzyme would lead to more temporary damage.

51. A mutation has occurred in the DNA and in the mRNA for a gene. Discuss which would have a more significant effect on gene expression. Why?

a. Both will result in the production of defective proteins. The DNA mutation, if not corrected, is permanent, while the mRNA mutation will only affect proteins made from that mRNA strand. Production of defective protein ceases when the mRNA strand deteriorates.

b. Both will result in the production of defective proteins. The DNA mutation, if not corrected, is permanent, while the mRNA mutation will not affect proteins made from that mRNA strand. Production of defective protein continues when the mRNA strand deteriorates.

c. Only DNA will result in the production of defective proteins. The DNA mutation, if not corrected, is permanent. Production of defective protein ceases when the DNA strand deteriorates.

d. Only mRNA will result in the production of defective proteins. The mRNA mutation will only affect proteins made from that mRNA strand. Production of defective protein ceases when the mRNA strand deteriorates.

52. Discuss the effects of point mutations on a DNA strand.

a. Mutations can cause a single change in an amino acid. A nonsense mutation can stop the replication or reading of that strand. Insertion or deletion mutations can cause a frame shift. This can result in non-functional proteins.

b. Mutations can cause a single change in amino acid. A missense mutation can stop the replication or reading of that strand. Insertion or deletion mutations can cause a frame shift. This can result in non-functional proteins.

c. Mutations can cause a single change in amino acid. A nonsense mutation can stop the replication or reading of that strand. Substitution mutations can cause a frame shift. This can result in non-functional proteins.

d. Mutations can cause a single change in amino acid. A nonsense mutation can stop the replication or reading of that strand. Insertion or deletion mutations can cause a frame shift. This can result in functional proteins.

53. Discuss the significance of mutations in tRNA and rRNA.

a. Mutations in tRNA and rRNA would lead to the production of defective proteins or no protein production.

b. Mutations in tRNA and rRNA would lead to changes in the semi-conservative mode of replication of DNA.

c. Mutations in tRNA and rRNA would lead to production of a DNA strand with a mutated single strand and normal other strand.

d. Mutations in tRNA and rRNA would lead to skin cancer in patients of xeroderma pigmentosa.

TEST PREP FOR AP® COURSES

54. What would Chase and Hershey have concluded if the supernatant contained radioactive labeled-phosphorus?

a. DNA was the primary source of heritable information.

b. RNA was the primary source of heritable information.

c. Protein was the primary source of heritable information.

d. Phages were the primary source of heritable information.

55. Which piece of evidence supports that the material Miescher discovered was DNA?

a. The precipitate contained sulfur.

b. The precipitate contained oxygen.

c. The precipitate contained phosphorus.

d. The precipitate contained protein.

56. Explain how forensic scientists are able to use DNA analysis to identify individuals.

a. Comparison of DNA from a known source or individual with analysis of the sequence of an unknown sample of DNA allows scientists to find out if both of them are similar or not.

b. DNA from the unknown sample is sequenced and analyzed. The result of the analysis is then matched with any random population. The matching individual then helps in forensics.

c. Comparison of DNA from a known source or individual with analysis of the sequence of bases in strands of an unknown sample of RNA allows scientists to find out if both of them are similar or not.

d. Comparison of DNA from a known source or individual with analysis of the sugars and phosphates in strands of an unknown sample of DNA allows scientists to find out if both of them are similar or not.

57. Discuss the contributions of Francis Crick, James Watson, and Rosalind Franklin to the discovery of the structure of DNA.

a. Rosalind Franklin used X-ray diffraction methods to demonstrate the helical nature of DNA, while Watson and Crick formulated the double stranded structural model of DNA.

b. Rosalind Franklin, Watson and Crick first employed the technique of X-ray diffraction to understand the storage of DNA. Since it did not work out, Watson and Crick then ran experiments to ascertain the DNA structure.

c. Rosalind Franklin, Watson and Crick used X-ray diffraction methods to demonstrate the helical nature of DNA, while Rosalind Franklin formulated the double stranded structural model of DNA.

d. Watson and Crick used X-ray diffraction methods to demonstrate the helical nature of DNA, while Rosalind Franklin formulated the double stranded structural model of DNA.

58. What do RNA and DNA have in common?

a. Both contain four different nucleotides.

b. Both are usually double-stranded molecules.

c. Both contain adenine and uracil.

d. Both contain ribose.

59. Which of the following would be a good application of plasmid transformation?

a. to make copies of DNA

b. to isolate a change in a single nucleotide

c. to separate DNA fragments

d. to sequence DNA

60. Explain how the components of DNA fit together.

a. DNA is composed of nucleotides, consisting of a 5 carbon sugar, a phosphate, and a nitrogenous base. DNA is a double helical structure in which complementary base pairing occurs. Adenine pairs with thymine and guanine pairs with cytosine. Adenine and thymine form two hydrogen bonds and cytosine and guanine form three hydrogen bonds. The two individual strands of DNA are held together by covalent bonds between the phosphate of one nucleotide and sugar of the next. The two strands run antiparallel to each other.

b. DNA is composed of nucleotides, consisting of a 5 carbon sugar, a phosphate, and a nitrogenous base. DNA is a double helical structure in which complementary base pairing occurs. Adenine pairs with cytosine and guanine pairs with thymine. Adenine and cytosine form two hydrogen bonds and guanine and thymine form three hydrogen bonds. The two individual strands of DNA are held together by covalent bonds between the phosphate of one nucleotide and sugar of the next. The two strands run antiparallel to each other.

c. DNA is composed of nucleotides, consisting of a 5 carbon sugar, a phosphate, and a nitrogenous base. DNA is a double helical structure in which complementary base pairing occurs. Adenine pairs with cytosine and guanine pairs with thymine. Adenine and cytosine form three hydrogen bonds and guanine and thymine form two hydrogen bonds. The two individual strands of DNA are held together by covalent bonds between the phosphate of one nucleotide and sugar of the next. The two strands run antiparallel to each other.

d. DNA is composed of nucleotides, consisting of a 5 carbon sugar, a phosphate, and a nitrogenous base. DNA is a double helical structure in which complementary base pairing occurs. Adenine pairs with cytosine and guanine pairs with thymine. Adenine and cytosine form three hydrogen bonds and guanine and thymine form two hydrogen bonds. The two individual strands of DNA are held together by covalent bonds between the phosphate of one nucleotide and sugar of the next. The two strands run parallel to each other.

61. Describe the Sanger DNA sequencing method used for the human genome sequencing project.

a. A DNA sample is denatured by heating and then put into four tubes. A primer, DNA polymerase and all four nucleotides are added. Limited quantities of one of the four dideoxynucleotides (ddNTPs) are added to each tube respectively. Each one of them carries a specific fluorescent label. Chain elongation continues until a fluorescent ddNTP is added to the growing chain, after which chain termination occurs. Gel electrophoresis is performed and the length of each base is detected by laser scanners with wavelengths specific to the four different ddNTPS's.

b. A DNA sample is denatured by heating and then put into four tubes. A primer, RNA polymerase and all four nucleotides are added. Limited quantities of one of the four dideoxynucleotides (ddNTPs) are added to each tube respectively. Each one of them carries a specific fluorescent label. Chain elongation continues until a fluorescent ddNTP is added to the growing chain, after which chain termination occurs. Gel electrophoresis is performed and the length of each base is detected by laser scanners with wavelengths specific to the four different ddNTPS's.

c. A DNA sample is denatured by heating and then put into four tubes. A primer, DNA polymerase and all four nucleotides are added. Limited quantities of one of the four dideoxynucleotides (ddNTPs) are added to each tube respectively. Each one of them carries a specific fluorescent label. Chain elongation continues until a fluorescent ddNTP is removed from the growing chain, after which chain termination occurs. Gel electrophoresis is performed and the length of each base is detected by laser scanners with wavelengths specific to the four different ddNTPS's.

d. A DNA sample is denatured by heating and then put into four tubes. A primer, DNA polymerase and all four nucleotides are added. Limited quantities of one of the four deoxynucleotides (dNTPs) are added to each tube respectively. Each one of them carries a specific fluorescent label. Chain elongation continues until a fluorescent dNTP is added the growing chain, after which chain termination occurs. Gel electrophoresis is performed and the length of each base is detected by laser scanners with wavelengths specific to the four different dNTPS's.

62. 

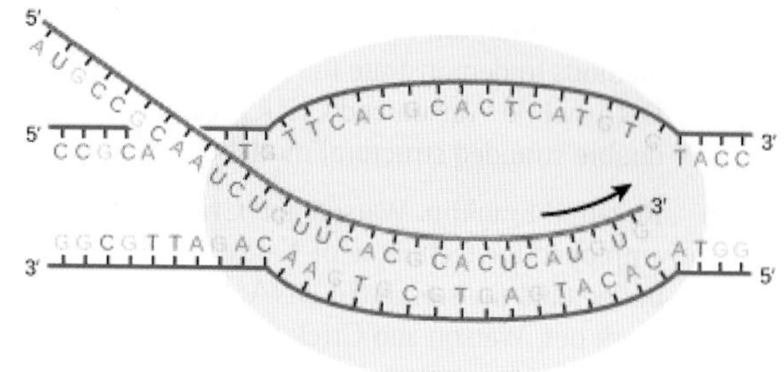

What process is illustrated in the figure?

a. transcription

b. mutation

c. excision

d. translation

63. Describe how the model of DNA replication illustrates the function of topoisomerase.

a. Topoisomerase relieves the pressure that results from supercoiling by breaking and reforming DNA's phosphate backbone ahead of the replication fork.

b. Topoisomerase increases the pressure to increase supercoiling by breaking and reforming DNA's phosphate backbone ahead of the replication fork.

c. Topoisomerase relieves the pressure that results from supercoiling by breaking and reforming DNA's nucleotide base pairs ahead of the replication fork.

d. Topoisomerase relieves the pressure that results from separation of DNA strands by breaking and reforming DNA's phosphate backbone ahead of the replication fork.

64. Flamingos have genotypes for white feathers yet often appear with pink feathers within the same population. What is most likely affecting the phenotype of some flamingos, causing their feathers to turn pink in an isolated population?

a. weather variations

b. dietary changes

c. DNA mutations

d. translation failure

65. What can be the result of DNA failing to undergo repair after too much UV exposure?

a. second degree burns

b. a malignant melanoma

c. a breakdown of deep layers of the skin

d. a sun burn

66. Identify the type of change that can occur in the DNA of a chromosome that is termed a chromosomal mutation.

a. substitution
b. translocation
c. missense
d. transversion

67. Explain why patients with Xeroderma Pigmentosa are more prone to cancer than the rest of the population.

a. Xeroderma Pigmentosa patients cannot employ the nucleotide excision repair mechanism. When these patients are exposed to UV light, thymine dimers are formed and they are not able to repair this defect. These dimers distort the structure of DNA and cause them to have a high risk of contracting skin cancer.
b. Xeroderma Pigmentosa patients can employ the nucleotide excision repair mechanism. When these patients are exposed to UV light, the thymine dimers are formed and they are able to repair this defect. These dimers do not distort the structure of DNA and they have moderate risk of contracting skin cancer.
c. Xeroderma Pigmentosa patients cannot employ the nucleotide excision repair mechanism. When these patients are exposed to UV light, the adjacent adenine forms dimers and they are not able to repair this defect. These dimers distort the structure of DNA and they have high risk of contracting skin cancer.
d. Xeroderma Pigmentosa patients cannot employ the nucleotide excision repair mechanism. When these patients are exposed to UV light, the adjacent thymine cannot form thymine dimers and they are not able to repair this defect. The non-formation of dimers distorts the structure of DNA and they have high risk of contracting skin cancer.

68. You are looking at two fragments of DNA. Both have the sequence CATTCTG on one strand and GTAAGAC on the other. One of the fragments is exposed to UV light, the other is not. What will happen to the fragments and how might these mutations be repaired?

a. The fragment exposed to UV light contains thymine dimers. Thymines lying adjacent to each other can form thymine dimers when exposed to UV light. They can be repaired by nucleotide excision.
b. The fragment exposed to UV light contains adenine dimers. Adenines lying adjacent to each other can form dimers when exposed to UV light. They can be repaired by nucleotide excision.
c. The fragment exposed to UV light contains thymine dimers. Thymines lying parallel to each other can form thymine dimers when exposed to UV light. They can be repaired by nucleotide excision.
d. The fragment exposed to UV light contains thymine dimers. Thymines lying adjacent to each other can form thymine dimers when exposed to UV light. They can be synthesized by nucleotide excision.

69. Discuss how mutations can increase variation within a population.

a. Substitution mutations may cause a different amino acid to be placed at a specific location, causing small changes in the protein. Frameshift mutations usually cause multiple amino acid changes, increasing chances that a new protein will form, leading to radically different characteristics in the offspring.
b. Substitution mutations may cause multiple amino acid changes, increasing chances that a new protein will form, leading to radically different characteristics in the offspring. Frameshift mutations may cause a different amino acid to be placed at a specific location, causing small changes in a protein.
c. Substitution mutations may cause a different amino acid to be placed at a specific location, resulting in major changes to the protein and leading to radically different characteristics in the offspring. Frameshift mutations cause multiple amino acid differences in a protein, leading to small changes in the protein.
d. Substitution mutations result in a different amino acid being placed at a specific position in a protein, causing small changes. Silent mutations could result in new characteristics possessed by an offspring when a stop codon is substituted for an amino acid.

SCIENCE PRACTICE CHALLENGE QUESTIONS

70. The proof that DNA, not protein, is the carrier of genetic information involved a number of historical experiments, including transformation or horizontal gene transfer (HGT), which is the uptake and expression of extracellular DNA.

A. As described in Figure 14.3, transformation or HGT

was first reported by Griffith in 1928 in an experiment in which the following occurred:

1. heat-treated, pathogenic bacteria recovered their pathogenicity when incubated with nonpathogenic bacteria
2. plasmids were transferred to nonpathogenic bacteria from pathogenic bacteria through conjugation
3. nonpathogenic bacteria acquired pathogenicity when incubated in a broth containing heat-treated, pathogenic bacteria
4. polysaccharide cell capsules from pathogenic bacteria were transferred to nonpathogenic bacteria

B. Griffith's experiment, however, left undetermined the identity of the cellular component that encoded genetic information. The identity of DNA as the carrier of genetic information was resolved through the experiments by Martha Chase and Alfred Hershey because they observed the following:

1. injections with a serum containing chemically isolated polysaccharides and nonpathogenic bacteria were not lethal
2. pathogenic bacterial DNA that was radioactively labeled using a phosphorus isotope was not present in mice that died
3. bacteriophages from a bacterial culture grown in a nutrient-containing medium and radioactively labeled using a sulfur isotope transferred the label to bacteria incubated in an unlabeled nutrient-containing medium
4. bacteriophages from a bacterial culture grown in a nutrient-containing medium and radioactively labeled using a sulfur isotope did not transfer the label to bacteria incubated in an unlabeled nutrient-containing medium

C. Transformation and transduction increase variation within populations of bacteria and archaebacteria by the following:

a. transferring DNA among different species

b. transferring free DNA across the cell membrane without energy expenditure

c. transferring DNA between different strains of the same species of bacteria

d. phagocytosis of bacteriophages

The evolution of antibiotic resistance via HGT poses a challenge to medical technology. On the other hand, transformation is often assayed by incorporating an antibiotic-resistance gene in the plasmid to be transferred into the host organism. In natural environments, bacterial and archaebacterial cells become competent (able to transport DNA through the cytoplasmic membrane) in response to stress such as UV radiation, high population density, or heat shock. Such conditions are often difficult to model in the laboratory, where competence can be induced by high concentrations of divalent cations, Ca^{+2} or Mg^{+2}, or electrical shock. In either setting, extracellular DNA can be transported into the cell, and (to a good approximation) uptake is proportional to the concentration of extracellular DNA.

D. **Identify** a factor that might affect transformation or HGT. Then, **design a plan** to evaluate the dependence of transformational efficiency (defined as the number of transformations per gram of extracellular DNA) of plasmids that transfer antibiotic resistance to a particular strain of *Escherichia coli* that is not resistant on that factor.

71. Prior to the work of Hershey and Chase, scientists thought that inheritance involved "nucleoproteins." The amount of information to be transmitted between generations did not seem consistent with the chemical simplicity of the few nucleotides found in polymers of deoxyribonucleic acids in comparison to the diversity of protein polymers. Briefly **explain**:

- the relationship between the structure of polymeric DNA and the information stored
- the relationship between the interactions between base pairs on complementary strands of the double helix and Chargaff's observation on the relative abundance of nucleotides in DNA
- the meaning of the statement from the *Nature* publication on the structure of DNA by Watson and Crick: "It has not escaped our notice that the specific pairing we have postulated immediately suggests a possible copying mechanism for the genetic material."

72. In 1977, Fred Sanger developed a method to determine the order of nucleotides in a strand of DNA. Sanger won a Nobel Prize for his work, and his method of sequencing based on dideoxy chain termination (Figure 14.8) has been foundational to the rapid development of more modern, rapid, and cheap methods of sequencing. The challenge of the $1,000 in one-day sequencing of the human genome was achieved in 2016 by next-generation sequencing (NGS), a "catch-all" term describing several sequencing methods.

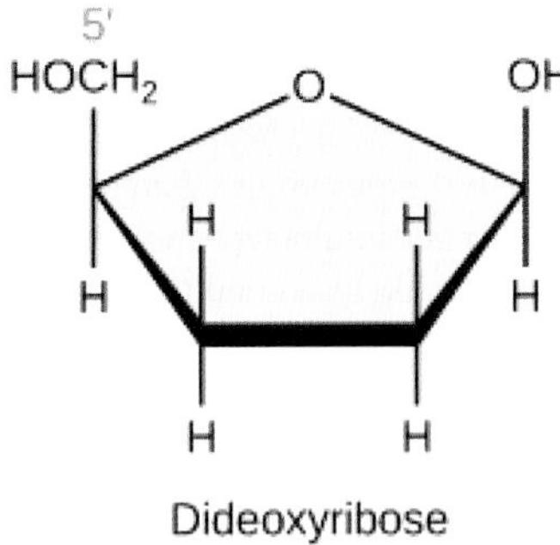

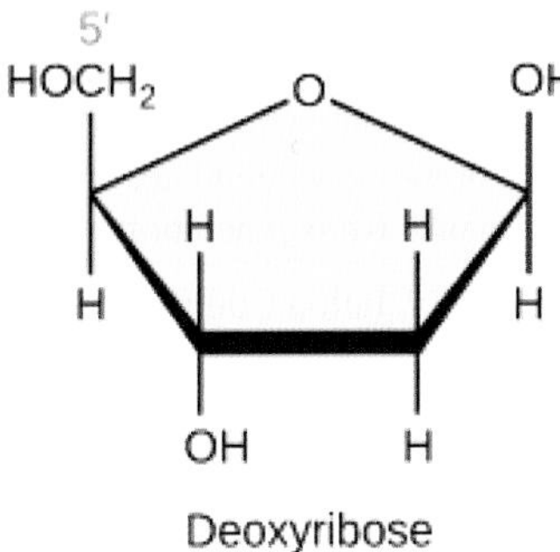

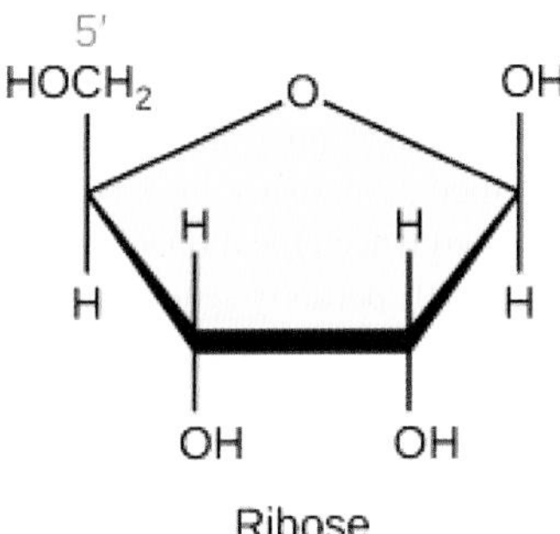

Figure 14.23

A. Using the diagrams shown above for reference, **explain** the effect of the addition of dideoxynucleotides on chain growth of the DNA strand that is copied during sequencing in terms of the structures of dideoxyribose and deoxyribose.

B. Suppose that a single strand to be sequenced is 5'CGAGTACG3'. In the presence of each of the four deoxynucleotides and the dideoxynucleotide ddCTP, **describe** the strands that would be formed from this template. Include in your description an annotation indicating the 3' and 5' ends of the fragments resulting from the procedure.

C. Next-generation sequencing makes termination technology very rapid and relatively inexpensive. All babies born in the U.S. are currently screened by state-mandated tests for several genetic conditions. The number of conditions tested ranges from 29 (GA and KS) to 59 (IL and MS). It is proposed that whole-genome sequencing should be mandatory for all newborns. The Genetic Information Nondiscrimination Act (2008) prevents health insurers from denying coverage or increasing costs of premiums based on genetic information. It also prohibits employers from making use of these data for hiring, firing, or promotion. The act passed in the House with a vote of 420 to 3, although it was lobbied against by organizations representing business (human resources, health insurance, and manufacturers), including the U.S. Chamber of Commerce. The act does not cover life, long-term care, or disability insurance. **Pose** three **questions** that are relevant to the use of whole-genome data.

73. Our understanding of the mechanisms of DNA replication is important to research on cancer and aging. Additionally, the molecular basis of Mendelian genetics was established.

A. The mechanism of DNA replication was investigated by Meselson and Stahl. The diagram below from their 1958 paper summarizes their findings. **Describe** how this representation illustrates the manner in which DNA is copied for transmission between generations.

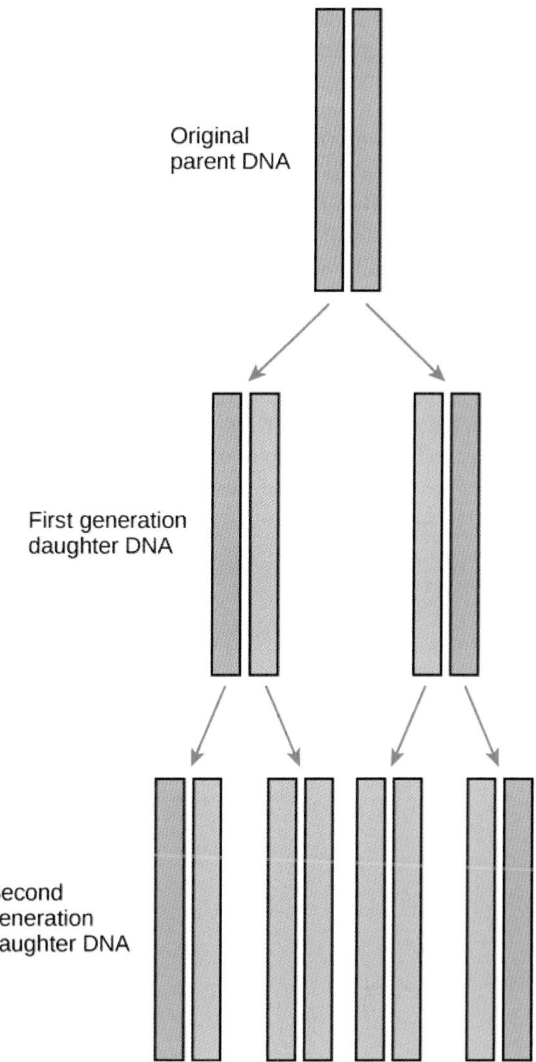

Figure 14.24

B. During the synthesis of new strands of DNA from the

parent strands, DNA polymerase can only add nucleotides at the terminal 3' of a growing strand. Using the diagram below, **describe** the similarities and differences between the DNA replication of both strands.

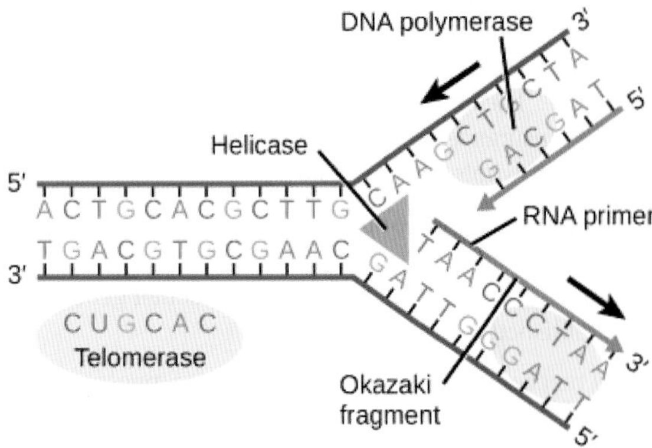

Figure 14.25

C. Shown at the left end of the upper parent strand is the six-base repeat sequence TTAGGG. In humans, this is the repeated, telomeric sequence that is attached to the telomere. The RNA primer in humans spans 10 base pairs, unlike in the drawing where it spans only three. In somatic cells, an enzyme called telomerase no longer functions. **Explain** the function of telomerase in the development of stem cells and cancer cells, and the inhibition of telomerase in programmed cell death or apoptosis.

74. The mitochondria of eukaryote cells contain their own circular DNA (mtDNA), consistent with their origin according to the theory of endosymbiosis. The mitochondrial genome is highly conserved in Eukarya. In humans, the 50 to 100 mitochondria in each of the cells in most tissues have 5 to 10 copies of the genome. Each has 37 genes that primarily encode proteins of the electron transport chain. Point mutations in which a single nucleotide is incorrectly placed is not repaired because the error-checking provided by DNA polymerase is not present in the mitochondria. The mutation rate for mtDNA is approximately 100 times higher than the mutation rate for nuclear DNA. The simultaneous existence of multiple alleles in each cell is likely, a condition called heteroplasmy. In mammals, sperm mitochondria are destroyed prior to fertilization.

A. **Explain** how point mutations in mtDNA can result in a loss of function in critical cellular components such as cytochrome c yet not be lethal to the cell.

B. Oocyte mitochondria are randomly segregated during meiosis, resulting in variation in the frequency of mtDNA mutations in offspring relative to the parent. **Explain** how a loss of function does not accumulate, lowering the metabolic performance from generation to generation.

As described in the Evolution Connection in this chapter of the text, a fossil fingertip found in a Siberian cave revealed an evolutionary link between Neanderthals and Denisovans. Fossils from 28 individuals were located in the "pit of bones," Sima de los Huesos, in Spain, thousands of miles from the Siberian cave. In 2013, mtDNA from a femur of one of these individuals was compared with mtDNA of Denisovans, Neanderthals, and modern humans. It was found that the Sima fossil shared many more alleles with Denisovans than with either Neanderthals or modern humans. In 2016, the same group of scientists who sequenced the mtDNA from the femur of one of the Sima fossils partially sequenced the DNA from that fossil, showing a clear connection to Neanderthals.

C. **Analyze** these data to draw alternative conclusions regarding the relatedness of the three fossils and support each with evidence.

D. **Design** a plan to differentiate or resolve these alternative conclusions.

15 | GENES AND PROTEINS

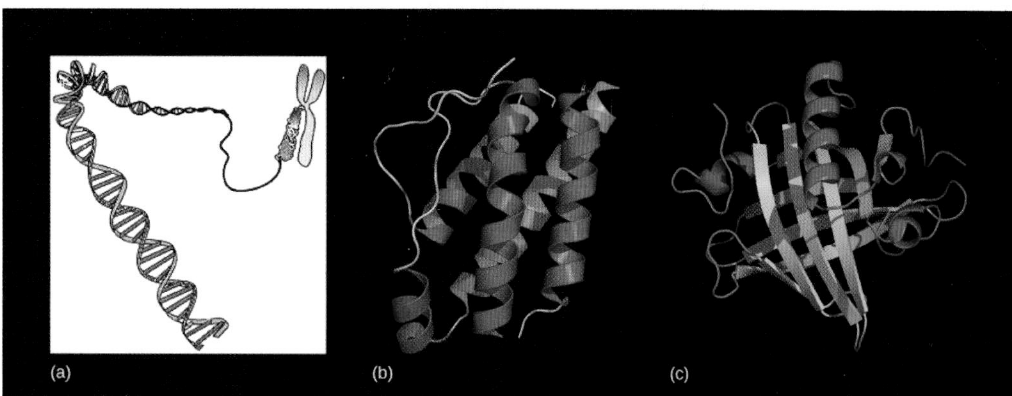

Figure 15.1 Genes, which are carried on (a) chromosomes, are linearly organized instructions for making the RNA and protein molecules that are necessary for all of processes of life. The (b) interleukin-2 protein and (c) alpha-2u-globulin protein are just two examples of the array of different molecular structures that are encoded by genes. (credit “chromosome: National Human Genome Research Institute; credit “interleukin-2”: Ramin Herati/Created from PDB 1M47 and rendered with Pymol; credit “alpha-2u-globulin”: Darren Logan/rendered with AISMIG)

Chapter Outline

Introduction

The definition of gene has progressed from being an abstract unit of heredity in Mendel’s time to our current concept of a tangible molecular entity capable of replication, expression, and mutation (Figure 15.1). Currently, we can perform tests for many genetic diseases, but these tests create ethical and legal issues. For example, would you want to be tested for a debilitating genetic disease if there was the possibility insurance companies could use that information to deny you coverage? Fortunately, the Genetic Information Nondiscrimination Act of 2008 protects American citizens from discrimination from both insurance companies and employers based on genetic information. More information about policy, legal, and ethical issues in genetic research can be found here (http://openstaxcollege.org/l/32genomegov) .

15.1 | The Genetic Code

In this section, you will explore the following questions:

- What is the “Central Dogma” of protein synthesis?
- What is the genetic code, and how does nucleotide sequence prescribe the amino acid and polypeptide sequence?

Connection for AP® Courses

Since the rediscovery of Mendel's work in the 1900s, scientists have learned much about how the genetic blueprints stored in DNA are capable of replication, expression, and mutation. Just as the 26 letters of the English alphabet can be arranged into what seems to be a limitless number of words, with new ones added to the dictionary every year, the four nucleotides of DNA—A, T, C, and G—can generate sequences of DNA called genes that specify tens of thousands of polymers of amino acids. In turn, these sequences can be transcribed into mRNA and translated into proteins which orchestrate nearly every function of the cell. The genetic code refers to the DNA alphabet (A, T, C, G), the RNA alphabet (A, U, C, G), and the polypeptide alphabet (20 amino acids). But how do genes located on a chromosome ultimately produce a polypeptide that can result in a physical phenotype such as hair or eye color—or a disease like cystic fibrosis or hemophilia?

The Central Dogma describes the normal flow of genetic information from DNA to mRNA to protein: DNA in genes specify sequences of mRNA which, in turn, specify amino acid sequences in proteins. The process requires two steps, transcription and translation. During transcription, genes are used to make messenger RNA (mRNA). In turn, the mRNA is used to direct the synthesis of proteins during the process of translation. Translation also requires two other types of RNA: transfer RNA (tRNA) and ribosomal RNA (rRNA). The genetic code is a triplet code, with each RNA codon consisting of three consecutive nucleotides that specify one amino acid or the release of the newly formed polypeptide chain; for example, the mRNA codon CAU specifies the amino acid histidine. The code is degenerate; that is, some amino acids are specified by more than one codon, like synonyms you study in your English class (different word, same meaning). For example, CCU, CCC, CCA, and CCG are all codons for proline. It is important to remember the same genetic code is universal to almost all organisms on Earth. Small variations in codon assignment exist in mitochondria and some microorganisms.

Deviations from the simple scheme of the central dogma are discovered as researchers explore gene expression with new technology. For example the human immunodeficiency virus (HIV) is a retrovirus which stores its genetic information in single stranded RNA molecules. Upon infection of a host cell, RNA is used as a template by the virally encoded enzyme, reverse transcriptase, to synthesize DNA. The viral DNA is later transcribed into mRNA and translated into proteins. Some RNA viruses such as the influenza virus never go through a DNA step. The RNA genome is replicated by an RNA dependent RNA polymerase which is virally encoded.

The content presented in this section supports the Learning Objectives outlined in Big Idea 1 and Big Idea 3 of the AP® Biology Curriculum Framework. The Learning Objectives merge Essential Knowledge content with one or more of the seven Science Practices. These Learning Objectives provide a transparent foundation for the AP® Biology course, along with inquiry-based laboratory experiences, instructional activities, and AP® Exam questions.

Big Idea 1	The process of evolution drives the diversity and unity of life.
Enduring Understanding 1.B	Organisms are linked by lines of descent from common ancestry.
Essential Knowledge	**1.B.1** Organisms share many conserved core processes and features that evolved and are widely distributed among organisms today.
Science Practice	**3.1** The student can pose scientific questions.
Science Practice	**7.2** The student can connect concepts in and across domain(s) to generalize or extrapolate in and/or across enduring understandings and/or big ideas.
Learning Objective	**1.15** The student is able to describe specific examples of conserved core biological processes and features shared by all domains or within one domain of life, and how these shared, conserved core processes and features support the concept of common ancestry for all organisms.
Big Idea 3	Living systems store, retrieve, transmit and respond to information essential to life processes.
Enduring Understanding 3.A	Heritable information provides for continuity of life.

Essential Knowledge	**3.A.1** DNA, and in some cases RNA, is the primary source of heritable information.
Science Practice	**6.5** The student can evaluate alternative scientific explanations.
Learning Objective	**3.1** The student is able to construct scientific explanations that use the structure and functions of DNA and RNA to support the claim that DNA and, in some cases, that RNA are the primary sources of heritable information.

The Science Practice Challenge Questions contain additional test questions for this section that will help you prepare for the AP exam. These questions address the following standards:
[APLO 3.4][APLO 3.25]

The cellular process of transcription generates messenger RNA (mRNA), a mobile molecular copy of one or more genes with an alphabet of A, C, G, and uracil (U). Translation of the mRNA template converts nucleotide-based genetic information into a protein product. Protein sequences consist of 20 commonly occurring amino acids; therefore, it can be said that the protein alphabet consists of 20 letters (Figure 15.2). Each amino acid is defined by a three-nucleotide sequence called the triplet codon. Different amino acids have different chemistries (such as acidic versus basic, or polar and nonpolar) and different structural constraints. Variation in amino acid sequence gives rise to enormous variation in protein structure and function.

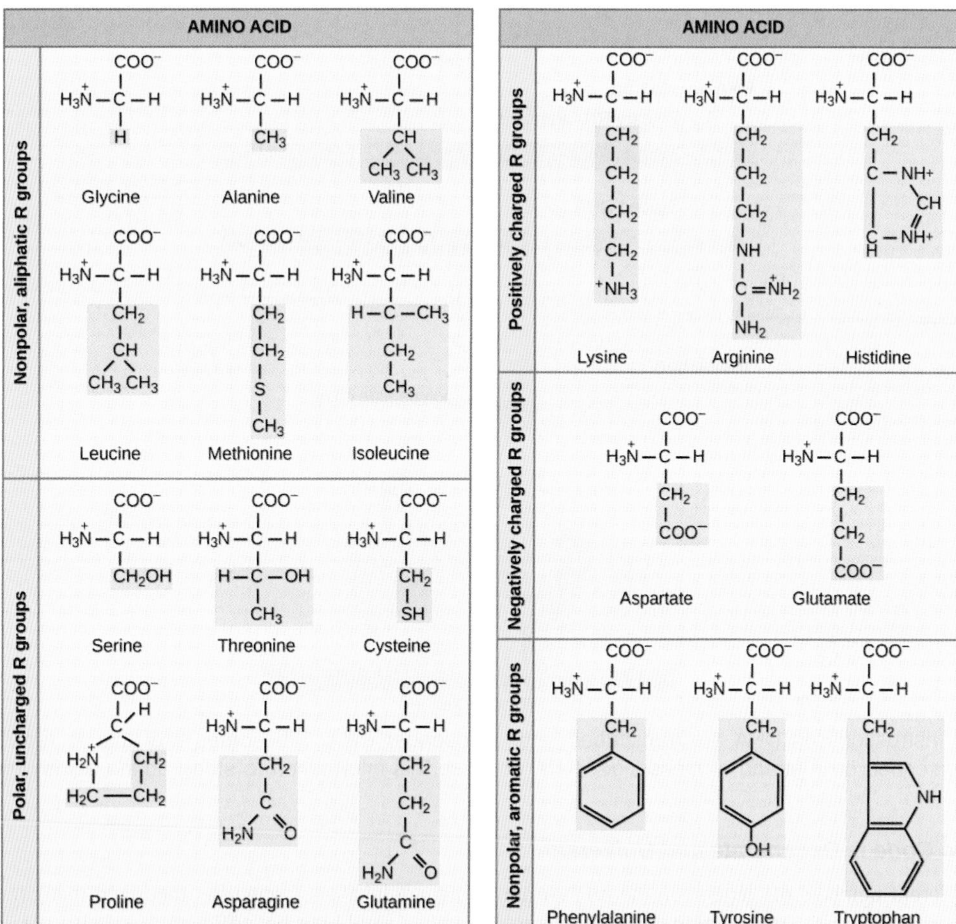

Figure 15.2 Structures of the 20 amino acids found in proteins are shown. Each amino acid is composed of an amino group (NH_3^+), a carboxyl group (COO^-), and a side chain (blue). The side chain may be nonpolar, polar, or charged, as well as large or small. It is the variety of amino acid side chains that gives rise to the incredible variation of protein structure and function.

The Central Dogma: DNA Encodes RNA; RNA Encodes Protein

The flow of genetic information in cells from DNA to mRNA to protein is described by the **Central Dogma** (Figure 15.3), which states that genes specify the sequence of mRNAs, which in turn specify the sequence of proteins. The decoding of one molecule to another is performed by specific proteins and RNAs. Because the information stored in DNA is so central to cellular function, it makes intuitive sense that the cell would make mRNA copies of this information for protein synthesis, while keeping the DNA itself intact and protected. The copying of DNA to RNA is relatively straightforward, with one nucleotide being added to the mRNA strand for every nucleotide read in the DNA strand. The translation to protein is a bit more complex because three mRNA nucleotides correspond to one amino acid in the polypeptide sequence. However, the translation to protein is still systematic and **colinear**, such that nucleotides 1 to 3 correspond to amino acid 1, nucleotides 4 to 6 correspond to amino acid 2, and so on.

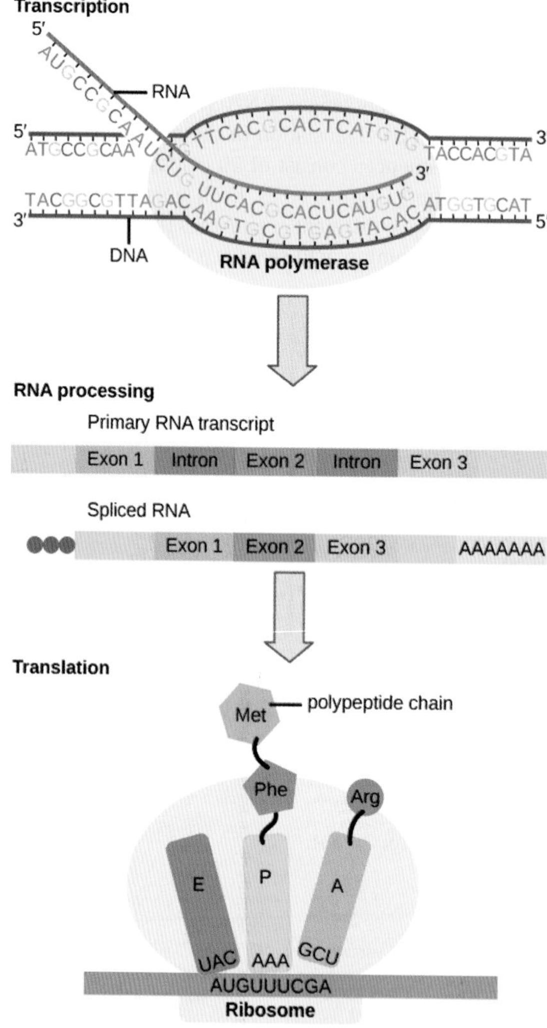

Figure 15.3 Instructions on DNA are transcribed onto messenger RNA. Ribosomes are able to read the genetic information inscribed on a strand of messenger RNA and use this information to string amino acids together into a protein.

The Genetic Code Is Degenerate and Universal

Given the different numbers of "letters" in the mRNA and protein "alphabets," scientists theorized that combinations of nucleotides corresponded to single amino acids. Nucleotide doublets would not be sufficient to specify every amino acid because there are only 16 possible two-nucleotide combinations (4^2). In contrast, there are 64 possible nucleotide triplets (4^3), which is far more than the number of amino acids. Scientists theorized that amino acids were encoded by nucleotide triplets and that the genetic code was **degenerate**. In other words, a given amino acid could be encoded by more than one nucleotide triplet. This was later confirmed experimentally; Francis Crick and Sydney Brenner used the chemical mutagen proflavin to insert one, two, or three nucleotides into the gene of a virus. When one or two nucleotides were inserted, protein synthesis was completely abolished. When three nucleotides were inserted, the protein was synthesized and functional. This demonstrated that three nucleotides specify each amino acid. These nucleotide triplets are called **codons**. The insertion of one or two nucleotides completely changed the triplet **reading frame**, thereby altering the message for every subsequent amino acid (Figure 15.4). Though insertion of three nucleotides caused an extra amino acid to be inserted during translation, the integrity of the rest of the protein was maintained.

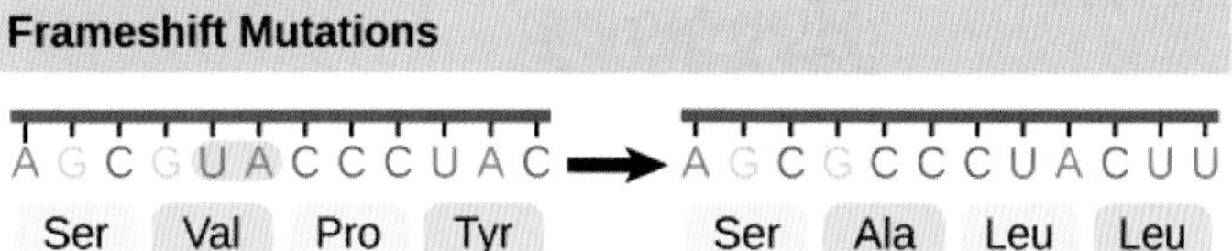

Figure 15.4 The deletion of two nucleotides shifts the reading frame of an mRNA and changes the entire protein message, creating a nonfunctional protein or terminating protein synthesis altogether.

Scientists painstakingly solved the genetic code by translating synthetic mRNAs in vitro and sequencing the proteins they specified (Figure 15.5).

First letter \ Second letter	U	C	A	G	Third letter
U	UUU } Phe UUC UUA } Leu UUG	UCU } Ser UCC UCA UCG	UAU } Tyr UAC **UAA Stop** **UAG Stop**	UGU } Cys UGC **UGA Stop** UGG Trp	U C A G
C	CUU } Leu CUC CUA CUG	CCU } Pro CCC CCA CCG	CAU } His CAC CAA } Gln CAG	CGU } Arg CGC CGA CGG	U C A G
A	AUU } Ile AUC AUA AUG Met	ACU } Thr ACC ACA ACG	AAU } Asn AAC AAA } Lys AAG	AGU } Ser AGC AGA } Arg AGG	U C A G
G	GUU } Val GUC GUA GUG	GCU } Ala GCC GCA GCG	GAU } Asp GAC GAA } Glu GAG	GGU } Gly GGC GGA GGG	U C A G

Figure 15.5 This figure shows the genetic code for translating each nucleotide triplet in mRNA into an amino acid or a termination signal in a nascent protein. (credit: modification of work by NIH)

In addition to instructing the addition of a specific amino acid to a polypeptide chain, three of the 64 codons terminate protein synthesis and release the polypeptide from the translation machinery. These triplets are called **nonsense codons**, or stop codons. Another codon, AUG, also has a special function. In addition to specifying the amino acid methionine, it also serves as the start codon to initiate translation. The reading frame for translation is set by the AUG start codon near the 5' end of the mRNA.

The genetic code is universal. With a few exceptions, virtually all species use the same genetic code for protein synthesis. Conservation of codons means that a purified mRNA encoding the globin protein in horses could be transferred to a tulip cell, and the tulip would synthesize horse globin. That there is only one genetic code is powerful evidence that all of life on Earth shares a common origin, especially considering that there are about 10^{84} possible combinations of 20 amino acids and 64 triplet codons.

Transcribe a gene and translate it to protein using complementary pairing and the genetic code at this site (http://openstaxcollege.org/l/create_protein) .

Some hereditary and age-related diseases are caused by translation errors. Explain why an error in translation may cause disease.

a. If there is an error in translation, the correct lipids will not be made for signaling, storage of energy or to perform vital functions. This can cause hereditary and age-related diseases.

b. Translation is the process in which a particular segment of DNA is copied into RNA (mRNA) by the enzyme RNA polymerase. Error in such copying can lead to various hereditary and age-related diseases.

c. Translation is the process used by ribosomes to synthesize proteins from amino acids. If there is an error in this process, the correct proteins will not be made to build important body tissue or perform vital functions thus leading to hereditary and age-related diseases.

d. Translation is the process Golgi bodies use to synthesize proteins from amino acids. If there is an error in this process, the correct proteins will not be made to build important body tissue or perform vital functions.

science practices CONNECTION for AP® Courses

Think About It

- A strand of DNA has the nucleotide sequence 3'......GCT GTC AAA TTC GAT......5'. What is the sequence of mRNA that is complementary to this DNA sequence? Using the chart of codons in the text, determine the sequence of amino acids which can be generated from this strand of DNA.
- How does degeneracy of the genetic code make cells less vulnerable to mutations? What is an advantage of degeneracy with respect to the negative impact of random mutations on natural selection and evolution?

Degeneracy is believed to be a cellular mechanism to reduce the negative impact of random mutations. Codons that specify the same amino acid typically only differ by one nucleotide. In addition, amino acids with chemically similar side chains are encoded by similar codons. This nuance of the genetic code ensures that a single-nucleotide substitution mutation might either specify the same amino acid but have no effect or specify a similar amino acid, preventing the protein from being rendered completely nonfunctional.

Which Has More DNA: A Kiwi or a Strawberry?

Figure 15.6 Do you think that a kiwi or a strawberry has more DNA per fruit? (credit “kiwi”: "Kelbv"/Flickr; credit: “strawberry”: Alisdair McDiarmid)

Question: Would a kiwifruit and strawberry that are approximately the same size (Figure 15.6) also have approximately the same amount of DNA?

Background: Genes are carried on chromosomes and are made of DNA. All mammals are diploid, meaning they have two copies of each chromosome. However, not all plants are diploid. The common strawberry is octoploid (8*n*) and the cultivated kiwi is hexaploid (6*n*). Research the total number of chromosomes in the cells of each of these fruits and think about how this might correspond to the amount of DNA in these fruits’ cell nuclei. Read about the technique of DNA isolation to understand how each step in the isolation protocol helps liberate and precipitate DNA.

Hypothesis: Hypothesize whether you would be able to detect a difference in DNA quantity from similarly sized strawberries and kiwis. Which fruit do you think would yield more DNA?

Test your hypothesis: Isolate the DNA from a strawberry and a kiwi that are similarly sized. Perform the experiment in at least triplicate for each fruit.

1. Prepare a bottle of DNA extraction buffer from 900 mL water, 50 mL dish detergent, and two teaspoons of table salt. Mix by inversion (cap it and turn it upside down a few times).
2. Grind a strawberry and a kiwifruit by hand in a plastic bag, or using a mortar and pestle, or with a metal bowl and the end of a blunt instrument. Grind for at least two minutes per fruit.
3. Add 10 mL of the DNA extraction buffer to each fruit, and mix well for at least one minute.
4. Remove cellular debris by filtering each fruit mixture through cheesecloth or porous cloth and into a funnel placed in a test tube or an appropriate container.
5. Pour ice-cold ethanol or isopropanol (rubbing alcohol) into the test tube. You should observe white, precipitated DNA.
6. Gather the DNA from each fruit by winding it around separate glass rods.

Record your observations: Because you are not quantitatively measuring DNA volume, you can record for each trial whether the two fruits produced the same or different amounts of DNA as observed by eye. If one or the other fruit produced noticeably more DNA, record this as well. Determine whether your observations are consistent with several pieces of each fruit.

Analyze your data: Did you notice an obvious difference in the amount of DNA produced by each fruit? Were your results reproducible?

Draw a conclusion: Given what you know about the number of chromosomes in each fruit, can you conclude that chromosome number necessarily correlates to DNA amount? Can you identify any drawbacks to this procedure? If you had access to a laboratory, how could you standardize your comparison and make it more quantitative?

15.2 | Prokaryotic Transcription

In this section, you will explore the following questions:

- What are the steps, in order, in prokaryotic transcription?
- How and when is transcription terminated?

Connection for AP® Courses

During transcription, the enzyme RNA polymerase moves along the DNA template, reading nucleotides in a 3′ to 5′ direction, with U pairing with A and C with G, and assembling the mRNA transcript in a 5′ to 3′ direction. In prokaryotes, mRNA synthesis is initiated at a promoter sequence on the DNA template. Transcription continues until RNA polymerase reaches a stop or terminator sequence at the end of the gene. Termination frees the mRNA and often occurs by the formation of an mRNA hairpin.

Information presented and the examples highlighted in the section support concepts outlined in Big Idea 3 of the AP® Biology Curriculum Framework. The Learning Objectives listed in the Curriculum Framework provide a transparent foundation for the AP® Biology course, an inquiry-based laboratory experience, instructional activities, and AP® Exam questions. A Learning Objective merges required content with one or more of the seven Science Practices.

Big Idea 3	Living systems store, retrieve, transmit and respond to information essential to life processes.
Enduring Understanding 3.A	Heritable information provides for continuity of life.
Essential Knowledge	**3.A.1** DNA, and in some cases RNA, is the primary source of heritable information.
Science Practice	**6.5** The student can evaluate alternative scientific explanations.
Learning Objective	**3.1** The student is able to construct scientific explanations that use the structures and mechanisms of DNA and RNA to support the claim that DNA and, in some cases, that RNA are the primary sources of heritable information.

The Science Practice Challenge Questions contain additional test questions for this section that will help you prepare for the AP exam. These questions address the following standards:
[APLO 2.23][APLO 3.28][APLO 4.8][APLO 4.24]

The prokaryotes, which include bacteria and archaea, are mostly single-celled organisms that, by definition, lack membrane-bound nuclei and other organelles. A bacterial chromosome is a covalently closed circle that, unlike eukaryotic chromosomes, is not organized around histone proteins. The central region of the cell in which prokaryotic DNA resides is called the nucleoid. In addition, prokaryotes often have abundant **plasmids**, which are shorter circular DNA molecules that may only contain one or a few genes. Plasmids can be transferred independently of the bacterial chromosome during cell division and often carry traits such as antibiotic resistance.

Transcription in prokaryotes (and in eukaryotes) requires the DNA double helix to partially unwind in the region of mRNA synthesis. The region of unwinding is called a **transcription bubble.** Transcription always proceeds from the same DNA strand for each gene, which is called the **template strand**. The mRNA product is complementary to the template strand and is almost identical to the other DNA strand, called the **nontemplate strand**. The only difference is that in mRNA, all of the T nucleotides are replaced with U nucleotides. In an RNA double helix, A can bind U via two hydrogen bonds, just as in A–T pairing in a DNA double helix.

The nucleotide pair in the DNA double helix that corresponds to the site from which the first 5' mRNA nucleotide is transcribed is called the +1 site, or the **initiation site**. Nucleotides preceding the initiation site are given negative numbers and are designated **upstream**. Conversely, nucleotides following the initiation site are denoted with "+" numbering and are called **downstream** nucleotides.

Initiation of Transcription in Prokaryotes

Prokaryotes do not have membrane-enclosed nuclei. Therefore, the processes of transcription, translation, and mRNA degradation can all occur simultaneously. The intracellular level of a bacterial protein can quickly be amplified by multiple transcription and translation events occurring concurrently on the same DNA template. Prokaryotic transcription often covers more than one gene and produces polycistronic mRNAs that specify more than one protein.

Our discussion here will exemplify transcription by describing this process in *Escherichia coli*, a well-studied bacterial species. Although some differences exist between transcription in *E. coli* and transcription in archaea, an understanding of *E. coli* transcription can be applied to virtually all bacterial species.

Prokaryotic RNA Polymerase

Prokaryotes use the same RNA polymerase to transcribe all of their genes. In *E. coli*, the polymerase is composed of five polypeptide subunits, two of which are identical. Four of these subunits, denoted α, α, β, and β' comprise the polymerase **core enzyme**. These subunits assemble every time a gene is transcribed, and they disassemble once transcription is complete. Each subunit has a unique role; the two α-subunits are necessary to assemble the polymerase on the DNA; the β-subunit binds to the ribonucleoside triphosphate that will become part of the nascent "recently born" mRNA molecule; and the β' binds the DNA template strand. The fifth subunit, σ, is involved only in transcription initiation. It confers transcriptional specificity such that the polymerase begins to synthesize mRNA from an appropriate initiation site. Without σ, the core enzyme would transcribe from random sites and would produce mRNA molecules that specified protein gibberish. The polymerase comprised of all five subunits is called the **holoenzyme**.

Prokaryotic Promoters

A **promoter** is a DNA sequence onto which the transcription machinery binds and initiates transcription. In most cases, promoters exist upstream of the genes they regulate. The specific sequence of a promoter is very important because it determines whether the corresponding gene is transcribed all the time, some of the time, or infrequently. Although promoters vary among prokaryotic genomes, a few elements are conserved. At the -10 and -35 regions upstream of the initiation site, there are two promoter **consensus** sequences, or regions that are similar across all promoters and across various bacterial species (Figure 15.7). The -10 consensus sequence, called the -10 region, is TATAAT. The -35 sequence, TTGACA, is recognized and bound by σ. Once this interaction is made, the subunits of the core enzyme bind to the site. The A–T-rich -10 region facilitates unwinding of the DNA template, and several phosphodiester bonds are made. The transcription initiation phase ends with the production of abortive transcripts, which are polymers of approximately 10 nucleotides that are made and released.

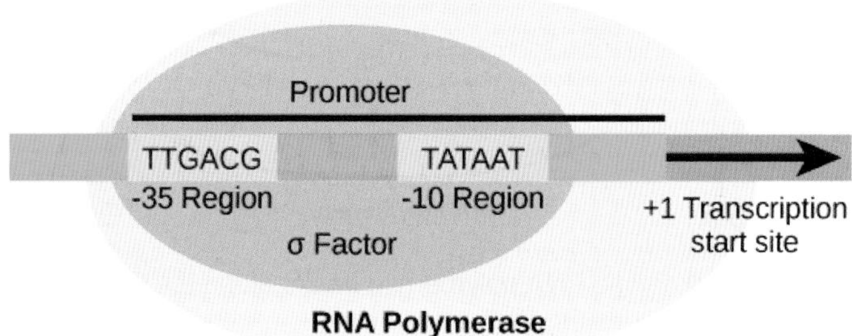

Figure 15.7 The σ subunit of prokaryotic RNA polymerase recognizes consensus sequences found in the promoter region upstream of the transcription start sight. The σ subunit dissociates from the polymerase after transcription has been initiated.

View this MolecularMovies animation (http://openstaxcollege.org/l/transcription) to see the first part of transcription and the base sequence repetition of the TATA box.

Mutations can occur in any part of the DNA. What can happen if there is a mutation in the promoter sequence?

a. All processes will carry on as usual. Nothing will be affected.

b. RNA polymerase will not be able to attach.

c. RNA polymerase will bind upstream of the promoter sequence.

d. RNA polymerase will bind downstream of the promoter sequence.

Elongation and Termination in Prokaryotes

The transcription elongation phase begins with the release of the σ subunit from the polymerase. The dissociation of σ allows the core enzyme to proceed along the DNA template, synthesizing mRNA in the 5' to 3' direction at a rate of approximately 40 nucleotides per second. As elongation proceeds, the DNA is continuously unwound ahead of the core enzyme and rewound behind it (Figure 15.8). The base pairing between DNA and RNA is not stable enough to maintain the stability of the mRNA synthesis components. Instead, the RNA polymerase acts as a stable linker between the DNA template and the nascent RNA strands to ensure that elongation is not interrupted prematurely.

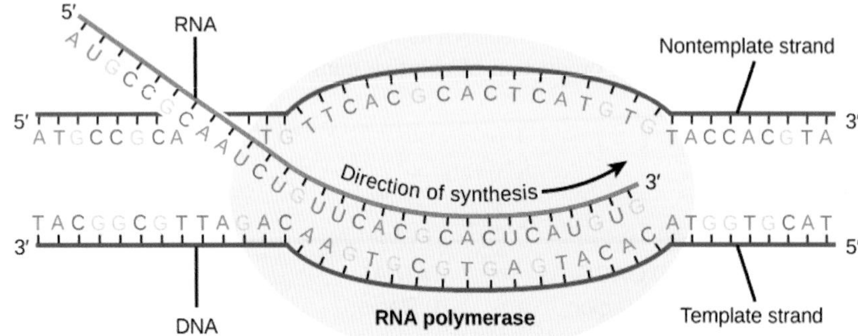

Figure 15.8 During elongation, the prokaryotic RNA polymerase tracks along the DNA template, synthesizes mRNA in the 5' to 3' direction, and unwinds and rewinds the DNA as it is read.

Prokaryotic Termination Signals

Once a gene is transcribed, the prokaryotic polymerase needs to be instructed to dissociate from the DNA template and liberate the newly made mRNA. Depending on the gene being transcribed, there are two kinds of termination signals. One is protein-based and the other is RNA-based. **Rho-dependent termination** is controlled by the rho protein, which tracks along behind the polymerase on the growing mRNA chain. Near the end of the gene, the polymerase encounters a run of G nucleotides on the DNA template and it stalls. As a result, the rho protein collides with the polymerase. The interaction with rho releases the mRNA from the transcription bubble.

Rho-independent termination is controlled by specific sequences in the DNA template strand. As the polymerase nears the end of the gene being transcribed, it encounters a region rich in C–G nucleotides. The mRNA folds back on itself, and the complementary C–G nucleotides bind together. The result is a stable **hairpin** that causes the polymerase to stall as soon as it begins to transcribe a region rich in A–T nucleotides. The complementary U–A region of the mRNA transcript forms only a weak interaction with the template DNA. This, coupled with the stalled polymerase, induces enough instability for the core enzyme to break away and liberate the new mRNA transcript.

Upon termination, the process of transcription is complete. By the time termination occurs, the prokaryotic transcript would already have been used to begin synthesis of numerous copies of the encoded protein because these processes can occur concurrently. The unification of transcription, translation, and even mRNA degradation is possible because all of these processes occur in the same 5' to 3' direction, and because there is no membranous compartmentalization in the prokaryotic cell (Figure 15.9). In contrast, the presence of a nucleus in eukaryotic cells precludes simultaneous transcription and translation.

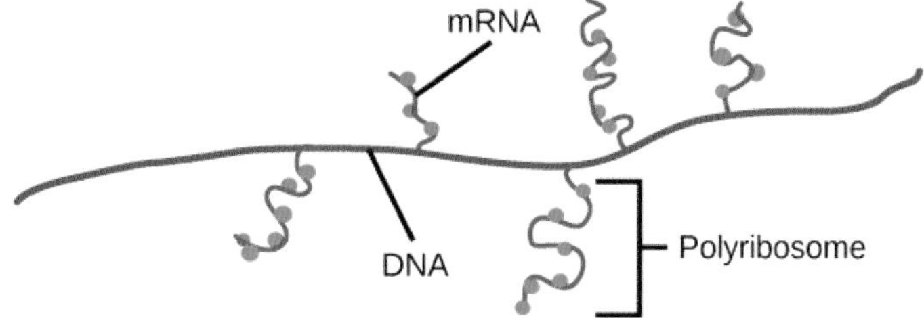

Figure 15.9 Multiple polymerases can transcribe a single bacterial gene while numerous ribosomes concurrently translate the mRNA transcripts into polypeptides. In this way, a specific protein can rapidly reach a high concentration in the bacterial cell.

Visit this BioStudio animation (http://openstaxcollege.org/l/transcription2) to see the process of prokaryotic transcription.

Why is the stop codon necessary for translation?

a. The stop codon is the first step in a series of steps to end translation.

b. The stop codon is necessary to initiate translation.

c. The stop codon ends translation which allows the polypeptide strand to be released.

d. The stop codon ends translation in order to initiate transcription.

science practices CONNECTION for AP® Courses

Activity

Working in small groups, use a model of DNA to demonstrate synthesis transcription of mRNA to other groups in your class. In your demonstration, be sure to distinguish the differences between DNA and RNA, the template and non-template strands of the DNA, the directionality of transcription, and the significance of promoters.

Think About It

If mRNA is complementary to the DNA template strand, and the DNA template strand is complementary to the DNA non-template strand, are the base sequences of mRNA and the DNA non-template strand ever identical? Justify your answer.

15.3 | Eukaryotic Transcription

In this section, you will explore the following questions:

- What are the steps in eukaryotic transcription?
- What are the structural and functional similarities and differences among the three RNA polymerases?

Connection for AP® Courses

As expected, transcription in eukaryotes is more complex than transcription in prokaryotes. First, transcription in eukaryotes involves one of three types of RNA polymerase, depending on the gene being transcribed. Second, the initiation of transcription involves the binding of several transcription factors to complex promoters which are usually located upstream of the gene being copied. Transcription factors can either activate or inhibit gene expression. Termination of transcription involves the RNA polymerases.

Information presented and the examples highlighted in the section support concepts outlined in Big Idea 3 of the AP® Biology Curriculum Framework. The Learning Objectives listed in the Curriculum Framework provide a transparent foundation for the AP® Biology course, an inquiry-based laboratory experience, instructional activities, and AP® Exam questions. A Learning Objective merges required content with one or more of the seven Science Practices.

Big Idea 3	Living systems store, retrieve, transmit and respond to information essential to life processes.
Enduring Understanding 3.A	Heritable information provides for continuity of life.
Essential Knowledge	**3.A.1** DNA, and in some cases RNA, is the primary source of heritable information.
Science Practice	**6.5** The student can evaluate alternative scientific explanations.
Learning Objective	**3.1** The student is able to construct scientific explanations that use the structures and mechanisms of DNA and RNA to support the claim that DNA and, in some cases, that RNA are the primary sources of heritable information.

The Science Practice Challenge Questions contain additional test questions for this section that will help you prepare for the AP exam. These questions address the following standards:
[APLO 3.3][APLO 3.22][APLO 2.36][APLO 1.14][APLO 2.22][APLO 4.5]

Prokaryotes and eukaryotes perform fundamentally the same process of transcription, with a few key differences. The most important difference between prokaryotes and eukaryotes is the latter's membrane-bound nucleus and organelles. With the genes bound in a nucleus, the eukaryotic cell must be able to transport its mRNA to the cytoplasm and must protect its mRNA from degrading before it is translated. Eukaryotes also employ three different polymerases that each transcribe a different subset of genes. Eukaryotic mRNAs are usually monogenic, meaning that they specify a single protein.

Initiation of Transcription in Eukaryotes

Unlike the prokaryotic polymerase that can bind to a DNA template on its own, eukaryotes require several other proteins, called transcription factors, to first bind to the promoter region and then help recruit the appropriate polymerase.

The Three Eukaryotic RNA Polymerases

The features of eukaryotic mRNA synthesis are markedly more complex those of prokaryotes. Instead of a single polymerase comprising five subunits, the eukaryotes have three polymerases that are each made up of 10 subunits or more. Each eukaryotic polymerase also requires a distinct set of transcription factors to bring it to the DNA template.

RNA polymerase I is located in the nucleolus, a specialized nuclear substructure in which ribosomal RNA (rRNA) is transcribed, processed, and assembled into ribosomes (Table 15.1). The rRNA molecules are considered structural RNAs because they have a cellular role but are not translated into protein. The rRNAs are components of the ribosome and are essential to the process of translation. RNA polymerase I synthesizes all of the rRNAs except for the 5S rRNA molecule. The "S" designation applies to "Svedberg" units, a nonadditive value that characterizes the speed at which a particle sediments during centrifugation.

Locations, Products, and Sensitivities of the Three Eukaryotic RNA Polymerases

RNA Polymerase	Cellular Compartment	Product of Transcription	α-Amanitin Sensitivity
I	Nucleolus	All rRNAs except 5S rRNA	Insensitive
II	Nucleus	All protein-coding nuclear pre-mRNAs	Extremely sensitive
III	Nucleus	5S rRNA, tRNAs, and small nuclear RNAs	Moderately sensitive

Table 15.1

RNA polymerase II is located in the nucleus and synthesizes all protein-coding nuclear pre-mRNAs. Eukaryotic pre-mRNAs undergo extensive processing after transcription but before translation. For clarity, this module's discussion of transcription and translation in eukaryotes will use the term "mRNAs" to describe only the mature, processed molecules that are ready to be translated. RNA polymerase II is responsible for transcribing the overwhelming majority of eukaryotic genes.

RNA polymerase III is also located in the nucleus. This polymerase transcribes a variety of structural RNAs that includes the 5S pre-rRNA, transfer pre-RNAs (pre-tRNAs), and **small nuclear** pre- **RNAs**. The tRNAs have a critical role in translation; they serve as the adaptor molecules between the mRNA template and the growing polypeptide chain. Small nuclear RNAs have a variety of functions, including "splicing" pre-mRNAs and regulating transcription factors.

A scientist characterizing a new gene can determine which polymerase transcribes it by testing whether the gene is expressed in the presence of a particular mushroom poison, α-amanitin (Table 15.1). Interestingly, α-amanitin produced by *Amanita phalloides*, the Death Cap mushroom, affects the three polymerases very differently. RNA polymerase I is completely insensitive to α-amanitin, meaning that the polymerase can transcribe DNA in vitro in the presence of this poison. In contrast, RNA polymerase II is extremely sensitive to α-amanitin, and RNA polymerase III is moderately sensitive. Knowing the transcribing polymerase can clue a researcher into the general function of the gene being studied. Because RNA polymerase II transcribes the vast majority of genes, we will focus on this polymerase in our subsequent discussions about eukaryotic transcription factors and promoters.

Structure of an RNA Polymerase II Promoter

Eukaryotic promoters are much larger and more complex than prokaryotic promoters, but both have a TATA box. For example, in the mouse thymidine kinase gene, the TATA box is located at approximately -30 relative to the initiation (+1) site (Figure 15.10). For this gene, the exact TATA box sequence is TATAAAA, as read in the 5' to 3' direction on the nontemplate strand. This sequence is not identical to the *E. coli* TATA box, but it conserves the A–T rich element. The thermostability of A–T bonds is low and this helps the DNA template to locally unwind in preparation for transcription.

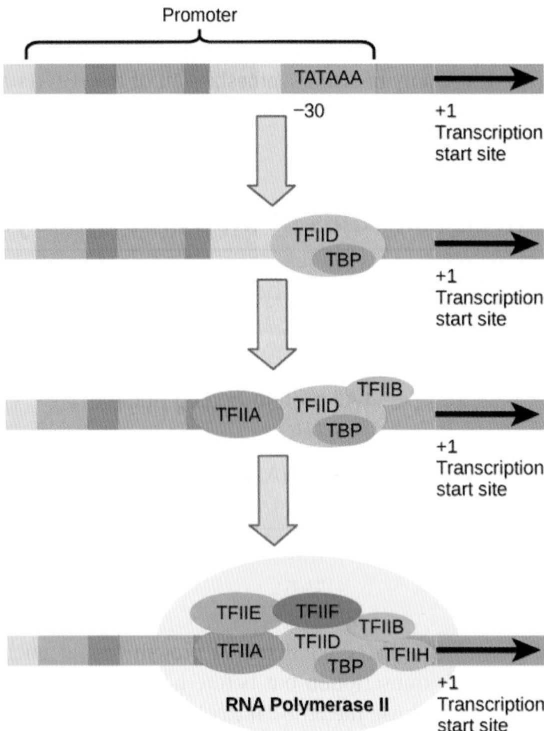

Figure 15.10 A generalized promoter of a gene transcribed by RNA polymerase II is shown. Transcription factors recognize the promoter. RNA polymerase II then binds and forms the transcription initiation complex.

visual CONNECTION

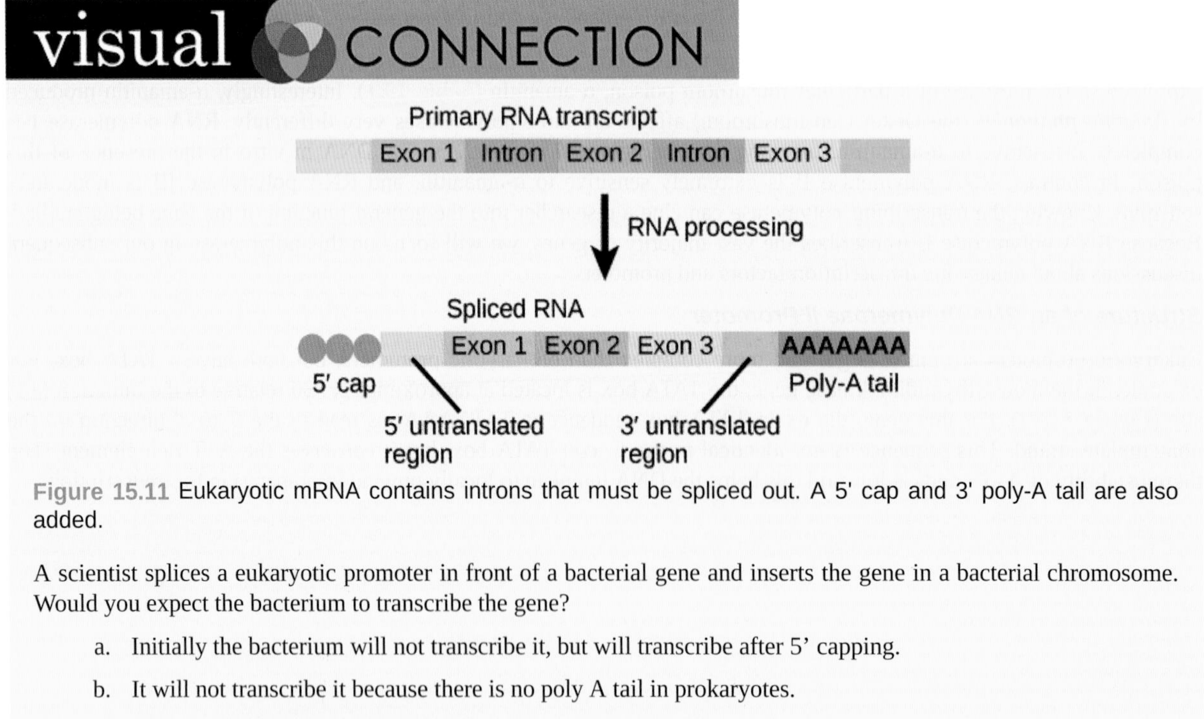

Figure 15.11 Eukaryotic mRNA contains introns that must be spliced out. A 5' cap and 3' poly-A tail are also added.

A scientist splices a eukaryotic promoter in front of a bacterial gene and inserts the gene in a bacterial chromosome. Would you expect the bacterium to transcribe the gene?

a. Initially the bacterium will not transcribe it, but will transcribe after 5’ capping.

b. It will not transcribe it because there is no poly A tail in prokaryotes.

c. No, prokaryotes use different promoters than eukaryotes.

d. Yes, the bacterium would transcribe the eukaryotic gene.

The mouse genome includes one gene and two pseudogenes for cytoplasmic thymidine kinase. Pseudogenes are genes that have lost their protein-coding ability or are no longer expressed by the cell. These pseudogenes are copied from mRNA and incorporated into the chromosome. For example, the mouse thymidine kinase promoter also has a conserved **CAAT box** (GGCCAATCT) at approximately -80. This sequence is essential and is involved in binding transcription factors. Further upstream of the TATA box, eukaryotic promoters may also contain one or more **GC-rich boxes** (GGCG) or **octamer boxes** (ATTTGCAT). These elements bind cellular factors that increase the efficiency of transcription initiation and are often identified in more “active” genes that are constantly being expressed by the cell.

Transcription Factors for RNA Polymerase II

The complexity of eukaryotic transcription does not end with the polymerases and promoters. An army of basal transcription factors, enhancers, and silencers also help to regulate the frequency with which pre-mRNA is synthesized from a gene. Enhancers and silencers affect the efficiency of transcription but are not necessary for transcription to proceed. Basal transcription factors are crucial in the formation of a **preinitiation complex** on the DNA template that subsequently recruits RNA polymerase II for transcription initiation.

The names of the basal transcription factors begin with “TFII” (this is the transcription factor for RNA polymerase II) and are specified with the letters A–J. The transcription factors systematically fall into place on the DNA template, with each one further stabilizing the preinitiation complex and contributing to the recruitment of RNA polymerase II.

The processes of bringing RNA polymerases I and III to the DNA template involve slightly less complex collections of transcription factors, but the general theme is the same. Eukaryotic transcription is a tightly regulated process that requires a variety of proteins to interact with each other and with the DNA strand. Although the process of transcription in eukaryotes involves a greater metabolic investment than in prokaryotes, it ensures that the cell transcribes precisely the pre-mRNAs that it needs for protein synthesis.

everyday CONNECTION for AP® Courses

During human embryonic development, a transcription factor encoded by the *SRY* gene starts a chain of events, causing the embryo to develop male sex characteristics. This gene is on the Y chromosome in humans and many other mammals. A deletion or mutation of the *SRY* gene can cause the human embryo to not develop into a male even though the individual has an XY genotype, a condition called Swyer syndrome.

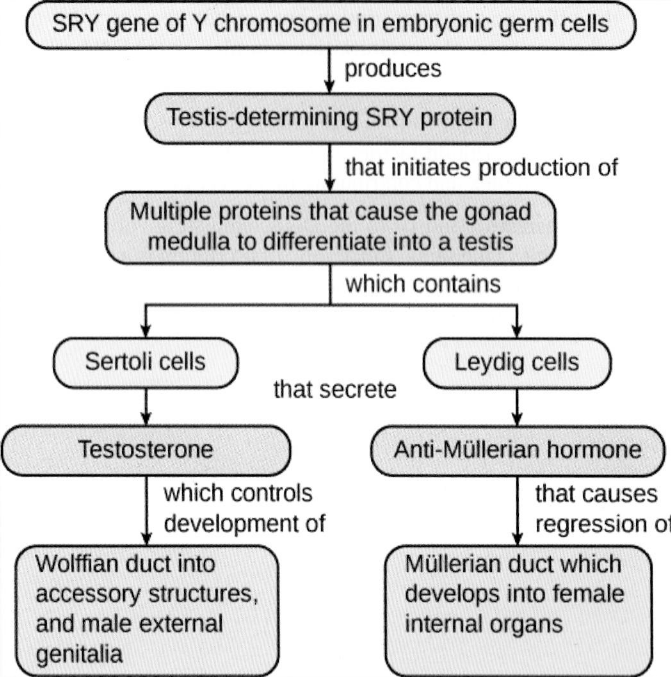

Figure 15.12 The SYR gene of the Y chromosome produces proteins that lead to the expression of primary sex characteristics, as shown.

The protein product of the SRY gene is a DNA binding protein. Together with a protein called SF1, the SRY protein acts as a transcription factor that "turns on" certain genes. Which of the following statements best describes how a change in these two proteins would affect male sexual development?

a. A mutation that abolished activity of SF1 would increase the effect of a SRY mutation, making the person more feminine.

b. A mutation that abolished activity of SF1 would cancel out a mutation in SRY, so if both mutations occur together male sex characteristics would develop normally.

c. A mutation in the SRY protein that abolished activity would result in abnormal development of male sex characteristics but a mutation of SF1 would not.

d. Both a mutation in the SRY protein and a mutation in SF1 that abolished activity would result in a lack of development of male sex characteristics.

The Evolution of Promoters

The evolution of genes may be a familiar concept. Mutations can occur in genes during DNA replication, and the result may or may not be beneficial to the cell. By altering an enzyme, structural protein, or some other factor, the process of mutation can transform functions or physical features. However, eukaryotic promoters and other gene regulatory sequences may evolve as well. For instance, consider a gene that, over many generations, becomes more valuable to the cell. Maybe the gene encodes a structural protein that the cell needs to synthesize in abundance for a certain function. If this is the case, it would be beneficial to the cell for that gene's promoter to recruit transcription factors more efficiently and increase gene expression.

Scientists examining the evolution of promoter sequences have reported varying results. In part, this is because it is difficult to infer exactly where a eukaryotic promoter begins and ends. Some promoters occur within genes; others are located very far upstream, or even downstream, of the genes they are regulating. However, when researchers limited their examination to human core promoter sequences that were defined experimentally as sequences that bind the preinitiation complex, they found that promoters evolve even faster than protein-coding genes.

It is still unclear how promoter evolution might correspond to the evolution of humans or other higher organisms. However, the evolution of a promoter to effectively make more or less of a given gene product is an intriguing alternative to the evolution of the genes themselves.[1]

According to this passage, which of the following has been shown to evolve faster than protein-coding genes?

a. core promoters that bind the preinitiation complex
b. core promoters that occur within genes
c. promoters that occur far upstream of the gene
d. promoters that occur downstream of a gene

Promoter Structures for RNA Polymerases I and III

In eukaryotes, the conserved promoter elements differ for genes transcribed by RNA polymerases I, II, and III. RNA polymerase I transcribes genes that have two GC-rich promoter sequences in the -45 to +20 region. These sequences alone are sufficient for transcription initiation to occur, but promoters with additional sequences in the region from -180 to -105 upstream of the initiation site will further enhance initiation. Genes that are transcribed by RNA polymerase III have upstream promoters or promoters that occur within the genes themselves.

Eukaryotic Elongation and Termination

Following the formation of the preinitiation complex, the polymerase is released from the other transcription factors, and elongation is allowed to proceed as it does in prokaryotes with the polymerase synthesizing pre-mRNA in the 5' to 3' direction. As discussed previously, RNA polymerase II transcribes the major share of eukaryotic genes, so this section will focus on how this polymerase accomplishes elongation and termination.

Although the enzymatic process of elongation is essentially the same in eukaryotes and prokaryotes, the DNA template is more complex. When eukaryotic cells are not dividing, their genes exist as a diffuse mass of DNA and proteins called chromatin. The DNA is tightly packaged around charged histone proteins at repeated intervals. These DNA–histone complexes, collectively called nucleosomes, are regularly spaced and include 146 nucleotides of DNA wound around eight histones like thread around a spool.

For polynucleotide synthesis to occur, the transcription machinery needs to move histones out of the way every time it encounters a nucleosome. This is accomplished by a special protein complex called **FACT**, which stands for "facilitates chromatin transcription." This complex pulls histones away from the DNA template as the polymerase moves along it. Once the pre-mRNA is synthesized, the FACT complex replaces the histones to recreate the nucleosomes.

The termination of transcription is different for the different polymerases. Unlike in prokaryotes, elongation by RNA polymerase II in eukaryotes takes place 1,000–2,000 nucleotides beyond the end of the gene being transcribed. This pre-mRNA tail is subsequently removed by cleavage during mRNA processing. On the other hand, RNA polymerases I and

1. H Liang et al., "Fast evolution of core promoters in primate genomes," *Molecular Biology and Evolution* 25 (2008): 1239–44.

III require termination signals. Genes transcribed by RNA polymerase I contain a specific 18-nucleotide sequence that is recognized by a termination protein. The process of termination in RNA polymerase III involves an mRNA hairpin similar to rho-independent termination of transcription in prokaryotes.

15.4 | RNA Processing in Eukaryotes

In this section, you will explore the following questions:

- What are the steps in eukaryotic transcription?
- What are the structural and functional similarities and differences among the three RNA polymerases?

Connection for AP® Courses

Scientists discovered a strand of mRNA translated into a sequence of amino acids (polypeptide) shorter than the mRNA molecule transcribed from DNA. Before the information in eukaryotic mRNA is translated into protein, it is modified or edited in several ways. A 5′ methylguanosine (or GTP) cap and a 3′ poly-A tail are added to protect mature mRNA from degradation and allow its export from the nucleus. Pre-mRNAs also undergo splicing, in which introns are removed and exons are reconnected. Exons can be reconnected in different sequences, a phenomenon referred to as alternative gene splicing, which allows a single eukaryotic gene to code for different proteins. (We will explore the significance of alternative gene splicing in more detail in other chapters.)

Information presented and the examples highlighted in the section support concepts outlined in Big Idea 3 of the AP® Biology Curriculum Framework. The Learning Objectives listed in the Curriculum Framework provide a transparent foundation for the AP® Biology course, an inquiry-based laboratory experience, instructional activities, and AP® Exam questions. A Learning Objective merges required content with one or more of the seven Science Practices.

Big Idea 3	Living systems store, retrieve, transmit and respond to information essential to life processes.
Enduring Understanding 3.A	Heritable information provides for continuity of life.
Essential Knowledge	**3.A.1** DNA, and in some cases RNA, is the primary source of heritable information.
Science Practice	**6.5** The student can evaluate alternative scientific explanations.
Learning Objective	**3.1** The student is able to construct scientific explanations that use the structures and mechanisms of DNA and RNA to support the claim that DNA and, in some cases, that RNA are the primary sources of heritable information.

After transcription, eukaryotic pre-mRNAs must undergo several processing steps before they can be translated. Eukaryotic (and prokaryotic) tRNAs and rRNAs also undergo processing before they can function as components in the protein synthesis machinery.

mRNA Processing

The eukaryotic pre-mRNA undergoes extensive processing before it is ready to be translated. The additional steps involved in eukaryotic mRNA maturation create a molecule with a much longer half-life than a prokaryotic mRNA. Eukaryotic mRNAs last for several hours, whereas the typical *E. coli* mRNA lasts no more than five seconds.

Pre-mRNAs are first coated in RNA-stabilizing proteins; these protect the pre-mRNA from degradation while it is processed and exported out of the nucleus. The three most important steps of pre-mRNA processing are the addition of stabilizing and signaling factors at the 5' and 3' ends of the molecule, and the removal of intervening sequences that do not specify the appropriate amino acids. In rare cases, the mRNA transcript can be “edited” after it is transcribed.

evolution CONNECTION

RNA Editing in Trypanosomes

The trypanosomes are a group of protozoa that include the pathogen *Trypanosoma brucei*, which causes sleeping sickness in humans (Figure 15.13). Trypanosomes, and virtually all other eukaryotes, have organelles called mitochondria that supply the cell with chemical energy. Mitochondria are organelles that express their own DNA and are believed to be the remnants of a symbiotic relationship between a eukaryote and an engulfed prokaryote. The mitochondrial DNA of trypanosomes exhibit an interesting exception to The Central Dogma: their pre-mRNAs do not have the correct information to specify a functional protein. Usually, this is because the mRNA is missing several U nucleotides. The cell performs an additional RNA processing step called **RNA editing** to remedy this.

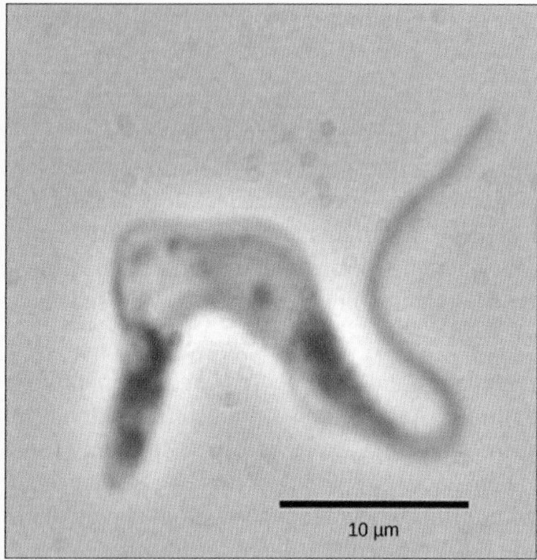

Figure 15.13 *Trypanosoma brucei* is the causative agent of sleeping sickness in humans. The mRNAs of this pathogen must be modified by the addition of nucleotides before protein synthesis can occur. (credit: modification of work by Torsten Ochsenreiter)

Other genes in the mitochondrial genome encode 40- to 80-nucleotide guide RNAs. One or more of these molecules interacts by complementary base pairing with some of the nucleotides in the pre-mRNA transcript. However, the guide RNA has more A nucleotides than the pre-mRNA has U nucleotides to bind with. In these regions, the guide RNA loops out. The 3' ends of guide RNAs have a long poly-U tail, and these U bases are inserted in regions of the pre-mRNA transcript at which the guide RNAs are looped. This process is entirely mediated by RNA molecules. That is, guide RNAs—rather than proteins—serve as the catalysts in RNA editing.

RNA editing is not just a phenomenon of trypanosomes. In the mitochondria of some plants, almost all pre-mRNAs are edited. RNA editing has also been identified in mammals such as rats, rabbits, and even humans. What could be the evolutionary reason for this additional step in pre-mRNA processing? One possibility is that the mitochondria, being remnants of ancient prokaryotes, have an equally ancient RNA-based method for regulating gene expression. In support of this hypothesis, edits made to pre-mRNAs differ depending on cellular conditions. Although speculative, the process of RNA editing may be a holdover from a primordial time when RNA molecules, instead of proteins, were responsible for catalyzing reactions.

In eukaryotes, pre-mRNAs are processed to form mature mRNAs. How does the mRNA editing that occurs in *Trypanosoma brucei* differ from mRNA processing that occurs in all eukaryotes?

a. mRNA editing changes the coding sequence of the mRNA, but mRNA processing does not.
b. mRNA editing splices out noncoding RNA, but mRNA processing does not.
c. mRNA editing adds a cap of 5'-methylguanosine to the mRNA, but mRNA processing does not.
d. mRNA editing adds a 3' poly-A tail, but mRNA processing does not.

5' Capping

While the pre-mRNA is still being synthesized, a **7-methylguanosine cap** is added to the 5' end of the growing transcript by a phosphate linkage. This moiety (functional group) protects the nascent mRNA from degradation. In addition, factors involved in protein synthesis recognize the cap to help initiate translation by ribosomes.

3' Poly-A Tail

Once elongation is complete, the pre-mRNA is cleaved by an endonuclease between an AAUAAA consensus sequence and a GU-rich sequence, leaving the AAUAAA sequence on the pre-mRNA. An enzyme called poly-A polymerase then adds a string of approximately 200 A residues, called the **poly-A tail**. This modification further protects the pre-mRNA from degradation and signals the export of the cellular factors that the transcript needs to the cytoplasm.

Pre-mRNA Splicing

Eukaryotic genes are composed of **exons**, which correspond to protein-coding sequences (*ex*-on signifies that they are *ex*pressed), and *int*ervening sequences called **introns** (*int*-ron denotes their *int*ervening role), which may be involved in gene regulation but are removed from the pre-mRNA during processing. Intron sequences in mRNA do not encode functional proteins.

The discovery of introns came as a surprise to researchers in the 1970s who expected that pre-mRNAs would specify protein sequences without further processing, as they had observed in prokaryotes. The genes of higher eukaryotes very often contain one or more introns. These regions may correspond to regulatory sequences; however, the biological significance of having many introns or having very long introns in a gene is unclear. It is possible that introns slow down gene expression because it takes longer to transcribe pre-mRNAs with lots of introns. Alternatively, introns may be nonfunctional sequence remnants left over from the fusion of ancient genes throughout evolution. This is supported by the fact that separate exons often encode separate protein subunits or domains. For the most part, the sequences of introns can be mutated without ultimately affecting the protein product.

All of a pre-mRNA's introns must be completely and precisely removed before protein synthesis. If the process errs by even a single nucleotide, the reading frame of the rejoined exons would shift, and the resulting protein would be dysfunctional. The process of removing introns and reconnecting exons is called **splicing** (Figure 15.14). Introns are removed and degraded while the pre-mRNA is still in the nucleus. Splicing occurs by a sequence-specific mechanism that ensures introns will be removed and exons rejoined with the accuracy and precision of a single nucleotide. The splicing of pre-mRNAs is conducted by complexes of proteins and RNA molecules called spliceosomes.

visual CONNECTION

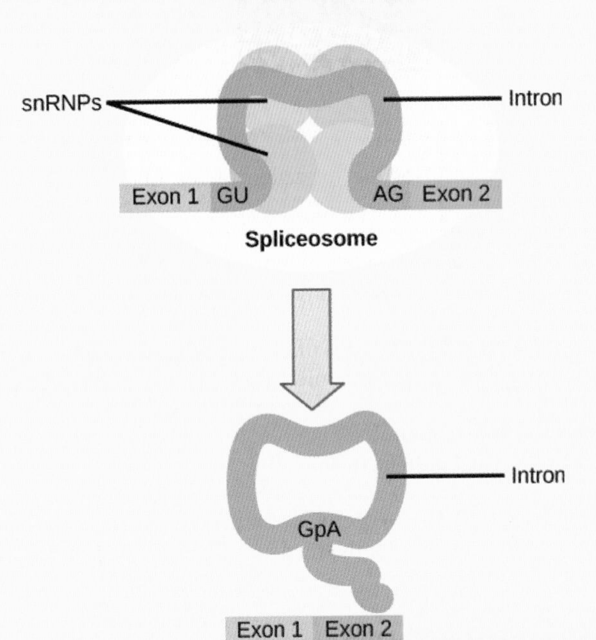

Figure 15.14 Pre-mRNA splicing involves the precise removal of introns from the primary RNA transcript. The splicing process is catalyzed by protein complexes called spliceosomes that are composed of proteins and RNA molecules called snRNAs. Spliceosomes recognize sequences at the 5' and 3' end of the intron.

Errors in splicing are implicated in cancers and other human diseases. What kinds of mutations might lead to splicing errors? Think of different possible outcomes if splicing errors occur.

a. Mutations in the spliceosome recognition sequence at each end of an intron, or in the proteins and RNAs that make up the spliceosome, may occur. Mutations may also add new spliceosome recognition sites.

b. Mutations in the spliceosome recognition sequence at each end of an exon, or in the proteins and RNAs that make up the spliceosome, may occur. Mutations may also add new spliceosome recognition sites.

c. Mutations in the spliceosome recognition sequence at each end of an intron, or in the proteins and RNAs that make up the spliceosome, may occur. Mutations may also delete existing spliceosome recognition sites.

d. Mutations at the each end of intron and exon, or in the proteins and RNAs that make up the spliceosome, may occur. Mutations may also add new spliceosome recognition sites and delete existing sites.

Note that more than 70 individual introns can be present, and each has to undergo the process of splicing—in addition to 5' capping and the addition of a poly-A tail—just to generate a single, translatable mRNA molecule.

See how introns are removed during RNA splicing at this website (http://openstaxcollege.org/l/RNA_splicing) .

Explain why helper proteins are necessary for the formation of the final protein during RNA splicing in higher organisms.

a. Helper proteins attach themselves to the ends of introns so that they can be spliced out during RNA splicing and coded areas are spliced together to form mRNA which then codes for the final protein.

b. Helper proteins attach themselves to the ends of exons so that they can be spliced out during RNA splicing and coded areas are spliced together to form mRNA which encodes the final protein.

c. Helper proteins attach themselves to mRNA in order to remove the non-coded areas and thus form the pre-mRNA which codes for the final protein.

d. Helper proteins help the pre-mRNA to recruit various other components which splice out the non-coded regions and form mRNA which codes for the final protein.

Processing of tRNAs and rRNAs

The tRNAs and rRNAs are structural molecules that have roles in protein synthesis; however, these RNAs are not themselves translated. Pre-rRNAs are transcribed, processed, and assembled into ribosomes in the nucleolus. Pre-tRNAs are transcribed and processed in the nucleus and then released into the cytoplasm where they are linked to free amino acids for protein synthesis.

Most of the tRNAs and rRNAs in eukaryotes and prokaryotes are first transcribed as a long precursor molecule that spans multiple rRNAs or tRNAs. Enzymes then cleave the precursors into subunits corresponding to each structural RNA. Some of the bases of pre-rRNAs are methylated; that is, a $-CH_3$ moiety (methyl functional group) is added for stability. Pre-tRNA molecules also undergo methylation. As with pre-mRNAs, subunit excision occurs in eukaryotic pre-RNAs destined to become tRNAs or rRNAs.

Mature rRNAs make up approximately 50 percent of each ribosome. Some of a ribosome's RNA molecules are purely structural, whereas others have catalytic or binding activities. Mature tRNAs take on a three-dimensional structure through intramolecular hydrogen bonding to position the amino acid binding site at one end and the **anticodon** at the other end (Figure 15.15). The anticodon is a three-nucleotide sequence in a tRNA that interacts with an mRNA codon through complementary base pairing.

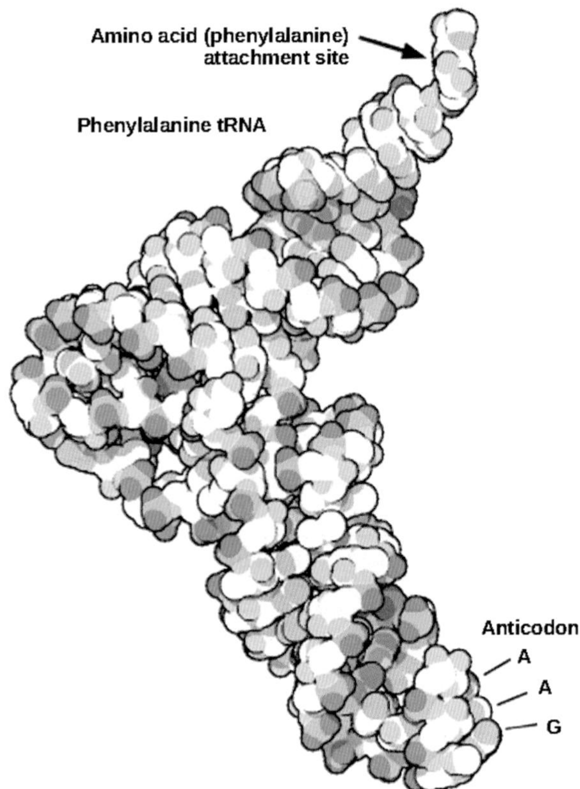

Figure 15.15 This is a space-filling model of a tRNA molecule that adds the amino acid phenylalanine to a growing polypeptide chain. The anticodon AAG binds the Codon UUC on the mRNA. The amino acid phenylalanine is attached to the other end of the tRNA.

15.5 | Ribosomes and Protein Synthesis

In this section, you will explore the following questions:

- What are the different sequential steps in protein synthesis?
- What is the role of ribosomes in protein synthesis?

Connection for AP® Courses

After the information in the gene has been transcribed to mRNA, it is ready to be translated to polypeptide. The players in translation include the mRNA template, ribosomes, tRNA molecules, amino acids, and various enzymes. Ribosomes consist of small and large subunits of protein and rRNA which bind with mRNA; many ribosomes can move along the same mRNA at a time. Translation begins at the initiating AUG on mRNA, specifying methionine, the first amino acid in any polypeptide. Each amino acid is carried to the ribosome by attaching to a specific molecule of tRNA. A tRNA molecule often is depicted as a cloverleaf, with an anticodon on one end, and the amino acid attachment site at the other. Amino-acid charging enzymes ensure that the correct amino acid is attached to the correct tRNA. The anticodons on tRNA are complementary to the codons on mRNA; for example, the anticodon AAA on tRNA corresponds to TTT on mRNA. Sequential amino acids are linked by peptide bonds. The mRNA is translated, elongating the polypeptide, until a STOP or nonsense codon is reached. When this happens, a release factor dissociates the components and frees the new polypeptide. Folding of the protein occurs during and after translation. Once a polypeptide is synthesized, its role as a protein is established, such as determining a physical phenotype of an organism.

Information presented and the examples highlighted in the section support concepts outlined in Big Idea 3 of the AP® Biology Curriculum Framework. The Learning Objectives listed in the Curriculum Framework provide a transparent foundation for the AP® Biology course, an inquiry-based laboratory experience, instructional activities, and AP® Exam questions. A Learning Objective merges required content with one or more of the seven Science Practices.

Big Idea 3	Living systems store, retrieve, transmit and respond to information essential to life processes.
Enduring Understanding 3.A	Heritable information provides for continuity of life.
Essential Knowledge	**3.A.1** DNA, and in some cases RNA, is the primary source of heritable information.
Science Practice	**1.2** The student can describe representations and models of natural or man-made phenomena and systems in the domain.
Learning Objective	**3.4** The student is able to describe representations and models illustrating how genetic information is translated into polypeptides.
Essential Knowledge	**3.A.1** DNA, and in some cases RNA, is the primary source of heritable information.
Science Practice	**6.4** The student can make claims and predictions about natural phenomena based on scientific theories and models.
Learning Objective	**3.6** The student can predict how a change in a specific DNA or RNA sequence can result in changes in gene expression.

The Science Practice Challenge Questions contain additional test questions for this section that will help you prepare for the AP exam. These questions address the following standards:
[APLO 1.16][APLO 4.22][APLO 3.6]

The synthesis of proteins consumes more of a cell's energy than any other metabolic process. In turn, proteins account for more mass than any other component of living organisms (with the exception of water), and proteins perform virtually every function of a cell. The process of translation, or protein synthesis, involves the decoding of an mRNA message into a polypeptide product. Amino acids are covalently strung together by interlinking peptide bonds in lengths ranging from approximately 50 amino acid residues to more than 1,000. Each individual amino acid has an amino group (NH_2) and a carboxyl (COOH) group. Polypeptides are formed when the amino group of one amino acid forms an amide (i.e., peptide) bond with the carboxyl group of another amino acid (Figure 15.16). This reaction is catalyzed by ribosomes and generates one water molecule.

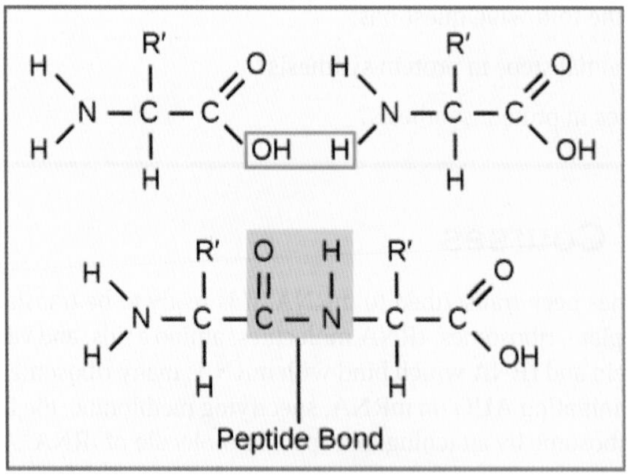

Figure 15.16 A peptide bond links the carboxyl end of one amino acid with the amino end of another, expelling one water molecule. For simplicity in this image, only the functional groups involved in the peptide bond are shown. The R and R' designations refer to the rest of each amino acid structure.

The Protein Synthesis Machinery

In addition to the mRNA template, many molecules and macromolecules contribute to the process of translation. The composition of each component may vary across species; for instance, ribosomes may consist of different numbers of rRNAs and polypeptides depending on the organism. However, the general structures and functions of the protein synthesis machinery are comparable from bacteria to human cells. Translation requires the input of an mRNA template, ribosomes, tRNAs, and various enzymatic factors.

Click through the steps of this PBS interactive (http://openstaxcollege.org/l/prokary_protein) to see protein synthesis in action.

A lack of protein in the diet can cause hair loss. Explain why this occurs.

a. Due to lack of protein in the diet, our body will not be able to form other proteins; thus, it will conserve the protein it has for critical use, leading to hair loss.

b. Lack of protein in the diet can weaken the immune system, thus leading to hair loss.

c. Due to lack of protein in the diet, energy will be lost, thus leading to hair loss.

d. Lack of protein in the diet will lead to breakage of disulfide bonds between proteins, thus leading to hair loss.

Ribosomes

Even before an mRNA is translated, a cell must invest energy to build each of its ribosomes. In *E. coli*, there are between 10,000 and 70,000 ribosomes present in each cell at any given time. A ribosome is a complex macromolecule composed of structural and catalytic rRNAs, and many distinct polypeptides. In eukaryotes, the nucleolus is completely specialized for the synthesis and assembly of rRNAs.

Ribosomes exist in the cytoplasm in prokaryotes and in the cytoplasm and rough endoplasmic reticulum in eukaryotes. Mitochondria and chloroplasts also have their own ribosomes in the matrix and stroma, which look more similar to prokaryotic ribosomes (and have similar drug sensitivities) than the ribosomes just outside their outer membranes in the cytoplasm. Ribosomes dissociate into large and small subunits when they are not synthesizing proteins and reassociate during the initiation of translation. In *E. coli*, the small subunit is described as 30S, and the large subunit is 50S, for a total of 70S (recall that Svedberg units are not additive). Mammalian ribosomes have a small 40S subunit and a large 60S subunit, for a total of 80S. The small subunit is responsible for binding the mRNA template, whereas the large subunit sequentially binds tRNAs. Each mRNA molecule is simultaneously translated by many ribosomes, all synthesizing protein in the same direction: reading the mRNA from 5' to 3' and synthesizing the polypeptide from the N terminus to the C terminus. The complete mRNA/poly-ribosome structure is called a **polysome**.

tRNAs

The tRNAs are structural RNA molecules that were transcribed from genes by RNA polymerase III. Depending on the species, 40 to 60 types of tRNAs exist in the cytoplasm. Serving as adaptors, specific tRNAs bind to sequences on the mRNA template and add the corresponding amino acid to the polypeptide chain. Therefore, tRNAs are the molecules that actually “translate” the language of RNA into the language of proteins.

Of the 64 possible mRNA codons—or triplet combinations of A, U, G, and C—three specify the termination of protein synthesis and 61 specify the addition of amino acids to the polypeptide chain. Of these 61, one codon (AUG) also encodes the initiation of translation. Each tRNA anticodon can base pair with one of the mRNA codons and add an amino acid or terminate translation, according to the genetic code. For instance, if the sequence CUA occurred on an mRNA template in the proper reading frame, it would bind a tRNA expressing the complementary sequence, GAU, which would be linked to the amino acid leucine.

As the adaptor molecules of translation, it is surprising that tRNAs can fit so much specificity into such a small package. Consider that tRNAs need to interact with three factors: 1) they must be recognized by the correct aminoacyl synthetase (see below); 2) they must be recognized by ribosomes; and 3) they must bind to the correct sequence in mRNA.

Aminoacyl tRNA Synthetases

The process of pre-tRNA synthesis by RNA polymerase III only creates the RNA portion of the adaptor molecule. The corresponding amino acid must be added later, once the tRNA is processed and exported to the cytoplasm. Through the process of tRNA “charging,” each tRNA molecule is linked to its correct amino acid by a group of enzymes called

aminoacyl tRNA synthetases. At least one type of aminoacyl tRNA synthetase exists for each of the 20 amino acids; the exact number of aminoacyl tRNA synthetases varies by species. These enzymes first bind and hydrolyze ATP to catalyze a high-energy bond between an amino acid and adenosine monophosphate (AMP); a pyrophosphate molecule is expelled in this reaction. The activated amino acid is then transferred to the tRNA, and AMP is released.

The Mechanism of Protein Synthesis

As with mRNA synthesis, protein synthesis can be divided into three phases: initiation, elongation, and termination. The process of translation is similar in prokaryotes and eukaryotes. Here we'll explore how translation occurs in *E. coli*, a representative prokaryote, and specify any differences between prokaryotic and eukaryotic translation.

Initiation of Translation

Protein synthesis begins with the formation of an initiation complex. In *E. coli*, this complex involves the small 30S ribosome, the mRNA template, three initiation factors (IFs; IF-1, IF-2, and IF-3), and a special **initiator tRNA**, called $\text{tRNA}_\text{f}^\text{Met}$. The initiator tRNA interacts with the **start codon** AUG (or rarely, GUG), links to a formylated methionine called fMet, and can also bind IF-2. Formylated methionine is inserted by $\text{fMet} - \text{tRNA}_\text{f}^\text{Met}$ at the beginning of every polypeptide chain synthesized by *E. coli*, but it is usually clipped off after translation is complete. When an in-frame AUG is encountered during translation elongation, a non-formylated methionine is inserted by a regular Met-tRNA^Met.

In *E. coli* mRNA, a sequence upstream of the first AUG codon, called the **Shine-Dalgarno sequence** (AGGAGG), interacts with the rRNA molecules that compose the ribosome. This interaction anchors the 30S ribosomal subunit at the correct location on the mRNA template. Guanosine triphosphate (GTP), which is a purine nucleotide triphosphate, acts as an energy source during translation—both at the start of elongation and during the ribosome's translocation.

In eukaryotes, a similar initiation complex forms, comprising mRNA, the 40S small ribosomal subunit, IFs, and nucleoside triphosphates (GTP and ATP). The charged initiator tRNA, called Met-tRNA_i, does not bind fMet in eukaryotes, but is distinct from other Met-tRNAs in that it can bind IFs.

Instead of depositing at the Shine-Dalgarno sequence, the eukaryotic initiation complex recognizes the 7-methylguanosine cap at the 5' end of the mRNA. A cap-binding protein (CBP) and several other IFs assist the movement of the ribosome to the 5' cap. Once at the cap, the initiation complex tracks along the mRNA in the 5' to 3' direction, searching for the AUG start codon. Many eukaryotic mRNAs are translated from the first AUG, but this is not always the case. According to **Kozak's rules**, the nucleotides around the AUG indicate whether it is the correct start codon. Kozak's rules state that the following consensus sequence must appear around the AUG of vertebrate genes: 5'-gccRccAUGG-3'. The R (for purine) indicates a site that can be either A or G, but cannot be C or U. Essentially, the closer the sequence is to this consensus, the higher the efficiency of translation.

Once the appropriate AUG is identified, the other proteins and CBP dissociate, and the 60S subunit binds to the complex of Met-tRNA_i, mRNA, and the 40S subunit. This step completes the initiation of translation in eukaryotes.

Translation, Elongation, and Termination

In prokaryotes and eukaryotes, the basics of elongation are the same, so we will review elongation from the perspective of *E. coli*. The 50S ribosomal subunit of *E. coli* consists of three compartments: the A (aminoacyl) site binds incoming charged aminoacyl tRNAs. The P (peptidyl) site binds charged tRNAs carrying amino acids that have formed peptide bonds with the growing polypeptide chain but have not yet dissociated from their corresponding tRNA. The E (exit) site releases dissociated tRNAs so that they can be recharged with free amino acids. There is one exception to this assembly line of tRNAs: in *E. coli*, $\text{fMet} - \text{tRNA}_\text{f}^\text{Met}$ is capable of entering the P site directly without first entering the A site. Similarly, the eukaryotic Met-tRNA_i, with help from other proteins of the initiation complex, binds directly to the P site. In both cases, this creates an initiation complex with a free A site ready to accept the tRNA corresponding to the first codon after the AUG.

During translation elongation, the mRNA template provides specificity. As the ribosome moves along the mRNA, each mRNA codon comes into register, and specific binding with the corresponding charged tRNA anticodon is ensured. If mRNA were not present in the elongation complex, the ribosome would bind tRNAs nonspecifically.

Elongation proceeds with charged tRNAs entering the A site and then shifting to the P site followed by the E site with each single-codon "step" of the ribosome. Ribosomal steps are induced by conformational changes that advance the ribosome by three bases in the 3' direction. The energy for each step of the ribosome is donated by an elongation factor that hydrolyzes GTP. Peptide bonds form between the amino group of the amino acid attached to the A-site tRNA and the carboxyl group of the amino acid attached to the P-site tRNA. The formation of each peptide bond is catalyzed by **peptidyl transferase**, an RNA-based enzyme that is integrated into the 50S ribosomal subunit. The energy for each peptide bond formation is derived from GTP hydrolysis, which is catalyzed by a separate elongation factor. The amino acid bound to the P-site tRNA is also linked to the growing polypeptide chain. As the ribosome steps across the mRNA, the former P-site tRNA enters the E site, detaches from the amino acid, and is expelled (**Figure 15.17**). Amazingly, the *E. coli* translation apparatus takes only 0.05 seconds to add each amino acid, meaning that a 200-amino acid protein can be translated in just 10 seconds.

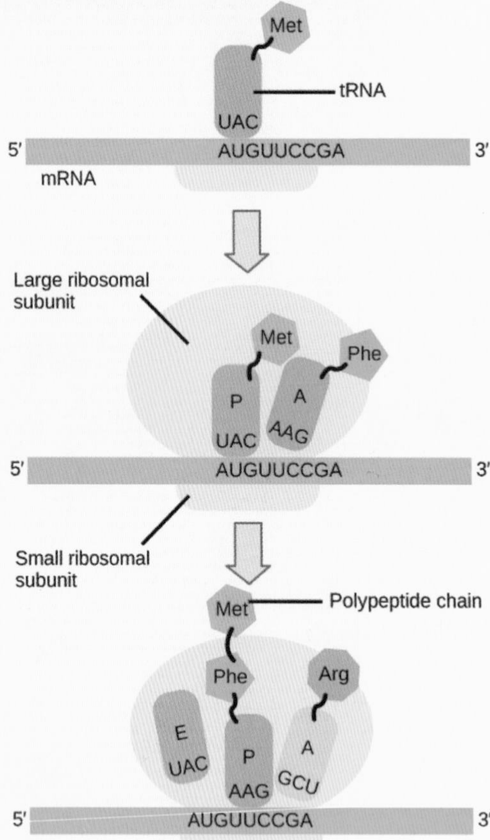

Figure 15.17 Translation begins when an initiator tRNA anticodon recognizes a codon on mRNA. The large ribosomal subunit joins the small subunit, and a second tRNA is recruited. As the mRNA moves relative to the ribosome, the polypeptide chain is formed. Entry of a release factor into the A site terminates translation and the components dissociate.

Many antibiotics inhibit bacterial protein synthesis. For example, tetracycline blocks the A site on the bacterial ribosome, and chloramphenicol blocks peptidyl transfer. What specific effect would you expect each of these antibiotics to have on protein synthesis?

Tetracycline would directly affect:

1. tRNA binding to the ribosome
2. Ribosome assembly
3. Growth of the protein chain

Chloramphenicol would directly affect:

1. tRNA binding to the ribosome
2. Ribosome assembly
3. Growth of the protein chain

   a. Tetracycline would directly affect tRNA binding to the ribosome. Chloramphenicol would affect the growth of the protein chain.

   b. Tetracycline would directly affect ribosome assembly. Chloramphenicol would affect the growth of the protein chain.

c. Tetracycline would directly affect the growth of the protein chain. Chloramphenicol would affect the tRNA binding to the ribosome.

d. Tetracycline would directly affect mRNA binding to the ribosome. Chloramphenicol would affect the ribosome assembly.

Termination of translation occurs when a nonsense codon (UAA, UAG, or UGA) is encountered. Upon aligning with the A site, these nonsense codons are recognized by release factors in prokaryotes and eukaryotes that instruct peptidyl transferase to add a water molecule to the carboxyl end of the P-site amino acid. This reaction forces the P-site amino acid to detach from its tRNA, and the newly made protein is released. The small and large ribosomal subunits dissociate from the mRNA and from each other; they are recruited almost immediately into another translation initiation complex. After many ribosomes have completed translation, the mRNA is degraded so the nucleotides can be reused in another transcription reaction.

Protein Folding, Modification, and Targeting

During and after translation, individual amino acids may be chemically modified, signal sequences may be appended, and the new protein "folds" into a distinct three-dimensional structure as a result of intramolecular interactions. A **signal sequence** is a short tail of amino acids that directs a protein to a specific cellular compartment. These sequences at the amino end or the carboxyl end of the protein can be thought of as the protein's "train ticket" to its ultimate destination. Other cellular factors recognize each signal sequence and help transport the protein from the cytoplasm to its correct compartment. For instance, a specific sequence at the amino terminus will direct a protein to the mitochondria or chloroplasts (in plants). Once the protein reaches its cellular destination, the signal sequence is usually clipped off.

Many proteins fold spontaneously, but some proteins require helper molecules, called chaperones, to prevent them from aggregating during the complicated process of folding. Even if a protein is properly specified by its corresponding mRNA, it could take on a completely dysfunctional shape if abnormal temperature or pH conditions prevent it from folding correctly.

science practices CONNECTION for AP® Courses

Activity

- Working in a small group, create a simple board game to model the key steps of transcription and translation and have classmates spend ten minutes playing the game.
- Provided with incomplete or incorrect diagrams illustrating transcription and translation in prokaryotes, have students refine or revise the diagrams and share the edited versions with classmates for critical review.

Think About It

- Many antibiotics inhibit protein synthesis. For example, tetracycline blocks the A site on the ribosome. What is the likely effect of tetracycline on protein synthesis?
- Using a chart of codons, transcribe and translate the following DNA sequence (non-template strand): 5′-ATGGCCGGTTATTAAGCA-3′. How can a single nucleotide change affect the protein produced from this sequence and its function?

KEY TERMS

7-methylguanosine cap modification added to the 5' end of pre-mRNAs to protect mRNA from degradation and assist translation

aminoacyl tRNA synthetase enzyme that "charges" tRNA molecules by catalyzing a bond between the tRNA and a corresponding amino acid

anticodon three-nucleotide sequence in a tRNA molecule that corresponds to an mRNA codon

CAAT box (GGCCAATCT) essential eukaryotic promoter sequence involved in binding transcription factors

Central Dogma states that genes specify the sequence of mRNAs, which in turn specify the sequence of proteins

codon three consecutive nucleotides in mRNA that specify the insertion of an amino acid or the release of a polypeptide chain during translation

colinear in terms of RNA and protein, three "units" of RNA (nucleotides) specify one "unit" of protein (amino acid) in a consecutive fashion

consensus DNA sequence that is used by many species to perform the same or similar functions

core enzyme prokaryotic RNA polymerase consisting of α, α, β, and β' but missing σ; this complex performs elongation

degeneracy (of the genetic code) describes that a given amino acid can be encoded by more than one nucleotide triplet; the code is degenerate, but not ambiguous

downstream nucleotides following the initiation site in the direction of mRNA transcription; in general, sequences that are toward the 3' end relative to a site on the mRNA

exon sequence present in protein-coding mRNA after completion of pre-mRNA splicing

FACT complex that "facilitates chromatin transcription" by disassembling nucleosomes ahead of a transcribing RNA polymerase II and reassembling them after the polymerase passes by

GC-rich box (GGCG) nonessential eukaryotic promoter sequence that binds cellular factors to increase the efficiency of transcription; may be present several times in a promoter

hairpin structure of RNA when it folds back on itself and forms intramolecular hydrogen bonds between complementary nucleotides

holoenzyme prokaryotic RNA polymerase consisting of α, α, β, β', and σ; this complex is responsible for transcription initiation

initiation site nucleotide from which mRNA synthesis proceeds in the 5' to 3' direction; denoted with a "+1"

initiator tRNA in prokaryotes, called $tRNA_f^{Met}$; in eukaryotes, called $tRNA_i$; a tRNA that interacts with a start codon, binds directly to the ribosome P site, and links to a special methionine to begin a polypeptide chain

intron non–protein-coding intervening sequences that are spliced from mRNA during processing

Kozak's rules determines the correct initiation AUG in a eukaryotic mRNA; the following consensus sequence must appear around the AUG: 5'-GCC(**purine**)CCAUG**G**-3'; the bolded bases are most important

nonsense codon one of the three mRNA codons that specifies termination of translation

nontemplate strand strand of DNA that is not used to transcribe mRNA; this strand is identical to the mRNA except that T nucleotides in the DNA are replaced by U nucleotides in the mRNA

Octamer box (ATTTGCAT) nonessential eukaryotic promoter sequence that binds cellular factors to increase the efficiency of transcription; may be present several times in a promoter

peptidyl transferase RNA-based enzyme that is integrated into the 50S ribosomal subunit and catalyzes the formation of peptide bonds

plasmid extrachromosomal, covalently closed, circular DNA molecule that may only contain one or a few genes; common in prokaryotes

poly-A tail modification added to the 3' end of pre-mRNAs to protect mRNA from degradation and assist mRNA export from the nucleus

polysome mRNA molecule simultaneously being translated by many ribosomes all going in the same direction

preinitiation complex cluster of transcription factors and other proteins that recruit RNA polymerase II for transcription of a DNA template

promoter DNA sequence to which RNA polymerase and associated factors bind and initiate transcription

reading frame sequence of triplet codons in mRNA that specify a particular protein; a ribosome shift of one or two nucleotides in either direction completely abolishes synthesis of that protein

Rho-dependent termination in prokaryotes, termination of transcription by an interaction between RNA polymerase and the rho protein at a run of G nucleotides on the DNA template

Rho-independent termination sequence-dependent termination of prokaryotic mRNA synthesis; caused by hairpin formation in the mRNA that stalls the polymerase

RNA editing direct alteration of one or more nucleotides in an mRNA that has already been synthesized

Shine-Dalgarno sequence (AGGAGG); initiates prokaryotic translation by interacting with rRNA molecules comprising the 30S ribosome

signal sequence short tail of amino acids that directs a protein to a specific cellular compartment

small nuclear RNA molecules synthesized by RNA polymerase III that have a variety of functions, including splicing pre-mRNAs and regulating transcription factors

splicing process of removing introns and reconnecting exons in a pre-mRNA

start codon AUG (or rarely, GUG) on an mRNA from which translation begins; always specifies methionine

TATA box conserved promoter sequence in eukaryotes and prokaryotes that helps to establish the initiation site for transcription

template strand strand of DNA that specifies the complementary mRNA molecule

transcription bubble region of locally unwound DNA that allows for transcription of mRNA

upstream nucleotides preceding the initiation site; in general, sequences toward the 5' end relative to a site on the mRNA

CHAPTER SUMMARY

15.1 The Genetic Code

The genetic code refers to the DNA alphabet (A, T, C, G), the RNA alphabet (A, U, C, G), and the polypeptide alphabet (20 amino acids). The Central Dogma describes the flow of genetic information in the cell from genes to mRNA to proteins. Genes are used to make mRNA by the process of transcription; mRNA is used to synthesize proteins by the process of translation. The genetic code is degenerate because 64 triplet codons in mRNA specify only 20 amino acids and three nonsense codons. Almost every species on the planet uses the same genetic code.

15.2 Prokaryotic Transcription

In prokaryotes, mRNA synthesis is initiated at a promoter sequence on the DNA template comprising two consensus sequences that recruit RNA polymerase. The prokaryotic polymerase consists of a core enzyme of four protein subunits and a σ protein that assists only with initiation. Elongation synthesizes mRNA in the 5' to 3' direction at a rate of 40 nucleotides per second. Termination liberates the mRNA and occurs either by rho protein interaction or by the formation of an mRNA hairpin.

15.3 Eukaryotic Transcription

Transcription in eukaryotes involves one of three types of polymerases, depending on the gene being transcribed. RNA polymerase II transcribes all of the protein-coding genes, whereas RNA polymerase I transcribes rRNA genes, and RNA polymerase III transcribes rRNA, tRNA, and small nuclear RNA genes. The initiation of transcription in eukaryotes involves the binding of several transcription factors to complex promoter sequences that are usually located upstream of the gene being copied. The mRNA is synthesized in the 5' to 3' direction, and the FACT complex moves and reassembles nucleosomes as the polymerase passes by. Whereas RNA polymerases I and III terminate transcription by protein- or RNA hairpin-dependent methods, RNA polymerase II transcribes for 1,000 or more nucleotides beyond the gene template and cleaves the excess during pre-mRNA processing.

15.4 RNA Processing in Eukaryotes

Eukaryotic pre-mRNAs are modified with a 5' methylguanosine cap and a poly-A tail. These structures protect the mature mRNA from degradation and help export it from the nucleus. Pre-mRNAs also undergo splicing, in which introns are removed and exons are reconnected with single-nucleotide accuracy. Only finished mRNAs that have undergone 5' capping, 3' polyadenylation, and intron splicing are exported from the nucleus to the cytoplasm. Pre-rRNAs and pre-tRNAs may be processed by intramolecular cleavage, splicing, methylation, and chemical conversion of nucleotides. Rarely, RNA editing is also performed to insert missing bases after an mRNA has been synthesized.

15.5 Ribosomes and Protein Synthesis

The players in translation include the mRNA template, ribosomes, tRNAs, and various enzymatic factors. The small ribosomal subunit forms on the mRNA template either at the Shine-Dalgarno sequence (prokaryotes) or the 5' cap (eukaryotes). Translation begins at the initiating AUG on the mRNA, specifying methionine. The formation of peptide bonds occurs between sequential amino acids specified by the mRNA template according to the genetic code. Charged tRNAs enter the ribosomal A site, and their amino acid bonds with the amino acid at the P site. The entire mRNA is translated in three-nucleotide "steps" of the ribosome. When a nonsense codon is encountered, a release factor binds and dissociates the components and frees the new protein. Folding of the protein occurs during and after translation.

REVIEW QUESTIONS

1. What is the flow of information for the synthesis of proteins according to the central dogma?

a. DNA to mRNA to protein
b. DNA to mRNA to tRNA to protein
c. DNA to protein to mRNA to protein
d. mRNA to DNA to mRNA to protein

2. The DNA of virus A is inserted into the protein coat of virus B. The combination virus is used to infect *E. coli*. The virus particles produced by the infection are analyzed for DNA and protein contents. What results would you expect?

a. DNA and protein from B
b. DNA and protein from A
c. DNA from A and protein from B
d. DNA from B and protein from A

3. The AUC and AUA codons in mRNA both specify isoleucine. What feature of the genetic code explains this?

a. Complementarity
b. Degeneracy
c. Nonsense codons
d. Universality

4. How many nucleotides are in 12 mRNA codons?

a. 12
b. 24
c. 36
d. 48

5. Which of the following molecules does not contain genetic information?

a. DNA
b. mRNA
c. Protein
d. RNA

6. Which molecule in the central dogma can be compared to a disposable photocopy of a book kept on reserve in the library?

a. DNA
b. mRNA
c. Protein
d. tRNA

7. Which subunit of the *E. coli* polymerase confers specificity to transcription?

a. α
b. β
c. β'
d. σ

8. Why are the -10 and -35 regions of prokaryotic promoters called consensus sequences?

a. They are identical in all bacterial species.
b. They are similar in all bacterial species.
c. They exist in all organisms.
d. They have the same function in all organisms.

9. The sequence that signals the end of transcription is called the:

a. promoter
b. stop codon
c. TATA box
d. terminator

10. If the ρ protein is missing, will a prokaryotic gene be terminated?

a. It depends on the gene.
b. No, the rho protein is essential.
c. Transcription termination is not required.
d. Yes, the rho protein is not involved in transcription.

11. Which feature of promoters can be found in both prokaryotes and eukaryotes?

a. GC box
b. octamer box
c. TATA box
d. -10 and -35 sequences

12. At what stage in the transcription of a eukaryotic gene would TFII factors be active?

a. elongation
b. initiation
c. processing
d. termination

13. Which polymerase is responsible for the synthesis of 5S rRNA?

a. polymerase I
b. polymerase II
c. polymerase III
d. ribonuclease I

14. What transcripts will be most affected by low levels of α-amanitin?

a. 18S and 28S rRNAs
b. 5S rRNAs and tRNAs
c. other small nuclear RNAs
d. pre-mRNAs

15. Which of the following features distinguishes eukaryotic transcription from bacterial transcription?

a. Eukaryotic transcription does not start at a consensus sequence.
b. Eukaryotic transcription does not require an initiation complex.
c. Eukaryotic transcription and translation do not take place at the same time.
d. Eukaryotic transcription does not require a termination sequence.

16. A poly-A sequence is added at the:

a. 5' end of a transcript in the nucleus
b. 3'-end of a transcript in the nucleus
c. 5' end of a transcript in the cytoplasm
d. 3'-end of a transcript in the cytoplasm

17. Which pre-mRNA processing step is important for initiating translation?

a. poly-A tail
b. RNA editing
c. splicing
d. 7-methylguanosine cap

18. Where are the RNA components of ribosomes synthesized?

a. cytoplasm
b. endoplasmic reticulum
c. nucleus
d. nucleolus

19. What processing step enhances the stability of pre-tRNAs and pre-rRNAs?

a. cleavage
b. methylation
c. nucleotide modification
d. splicing

20. What are introns?

a. DNA sequences to which polymerases bind
b. the processed mRNA
c. translated DNA sequences in a gene
d. untranslated DNA sequences in a gene

21. What is often the first amino acid added to a polypeptide chain?

a. adenine
b. leucine
c. methionine
d. thymine

22. In any given species, there are at least how many types of aminoacyl tRNA synthetases?

a. 20
b. 40
c. 100
d. 200

23. In prokaryotic cells, ribosomes are found in/on the:

a. cytoplasm
b. mitochondrion
c. nucleus
d. endoplasmic reticulum

24. The peptide bond synthesis in prokaryotic translation is catalyzed by:

a. a ribosomal protein
b. a cytoplasmic protein
c. mRNA itself
d. ribosomal RNA

25. What would happen if the 5' methyl guanosine was not added to an mRNA?

a. The transcript would degrade when the mRNA moves out of the nucleus to the cytoplasm.
b. The mRNA molecule would stabilize and start the process of translation within the nucleus of the cell.
c. The mRNA molecule would move out of the nucleus and create more copies of the mRNA molecule.
d. The mRNA molecule would not be able to add the poly-A tail on its strand at the 5' end.

26. Which of the following is associated with the docking of mRNA on a ribosome in eukaryotic cells?

a. Kozak's sequence
b. poly-A sequence
c. Shine-Dalgarno sequence
d. TATA box

CRITICAL THINKING QUESTIONS

27. If mRNA is complementary to the DNA template strand and the DNA template stand is complementary to the DNA non-template strand, why are base sequences of mRNA and the DNA non-template strand not identical? Could they ever be?

a. No, they cannot be identical because the T nucleotide in DNA is replaced with U nucleotide in RNA and AUG is the start codon.
b. No, they cannot be identical because the T nucleotide in RNA is replaced with U nucleotide in DNA.
c. They can be identical if methylation of the U nucleotide in RNA occurs and gives T nucleotide.
d. They can be identical if de-methylation of the U nucleotide in RNA occurs and gives T nucleotide.

28. Imagine if there were 200 commonly occurring amino acids instead of 20. Given what you know about the genetic code, what would be the shortest possible codon length? Explain.

a. Four
b. Five
c. Two
d. Three

29. What part of central dogma is not always followed in viruses?

a. The flow of information in HIV is from RNA to DNA, then back to RNA to proteins. Influenza viruses never go through DNA.
b. The flow of information is from protein to RNA in HIV virus, while the influenza virus converts DNA to RNA.
c. The flow of information is similar, but nucleic acids are synthesized as a result of translation in HIV and influenza viruses.
d. The flow of information is from RNA to protein. This protein is used to synthesize the DNA of the viruses in HIV and influenza.

30. Suppose a gene has the sequence ATGCGTTATCGGGAGTAG. A point mutation changes the gene to read ATGCGTTATGGGGAGTAG. How would the polypeptide product of this gene change?

31. Explain the initiation of transcription in prokaryotes. Include all proteins involved.

a. In prokaryotes the polymerase is composed of five polypeptide subunits, two of which are identical. Four of these subunits, denoted α, α, β, and β', comprise the polymerase core enzyme. The fifth subunit, σ, is involved only in transcription initiation. The polymerase comprised of all five subunits is called the holoenzyme.

b. In prokaryotes the polymerase is composed of four polypeptide subunits, two of which are identical. These subunits, denoted α, α, β, and β', comprise the polymerase core enzyme. There is a fifth subunit that is involved in translation initiation. The polymerase comprised of all four subunits is called the holoenzyme.

c. In prokaryotes the polymerase is composed of five polypeptide subunits, two of which are identical. Four of these subunits, denoted α, α, β, and β', comprise the polymerase holoenzyme. The fifth subunit, σ, is involved only in transcription initiation. The polymerase comprised of all five subunits is called the core enzyme.

d. In prokaryotes the polymerase is composed of five polypeptide subunits, two of which are identical. Four of these subunits, denoted α, α α, β, and β', comprise the polymerase core enzyme. The fifth subunit, σ, is involved only in termination. The polymerase comprised of all five subunits is called the holoenzyme.

32. In your own words, describe the difference between ρ-dependent and ρ-independent termination of transcription in prokaryotes.

a. Rho-dependent termination is controlled by rho protein and the polymerase stalls near the end of the gene at a run of G nucleotides on the DNA template. In rho-independent termination, when the polymerase encounters a region rich in C-G nucleotides the mRNA folds into a hairpin loop that causes the polymerase to stall.

b. Rho-independent termination is controlled by rho protein and the polymerase stalls near the end of the gene at a run of G nucleotides on the DNA template. In rho-dependent termination, when the polymerase encounters a region rich in C-G nucleotides, the mRNA folds into a hairpin loop that causes polymerase to stall.

c. Rho-dependent termination is controlled by rho protein and the polymerase begins near the end of the gene at a run of G nucleotides on the DNA template. In rho-independent termination, when the polymerase encounters a region rich in C-G nucleotides, the mRNA creates a hairpin loop that causes polymerase to stall.

d. Rho-dependent termination is controlled by rho protein and the polymerase stalls near the end of the gene at a run of G nucleotides on the DNA template. In rho-independent termination, when the polymerase encounters a region rich in A-T nucleotides, the mRNA creates a hairpin loop that causes polymerase to stall.

33. What is the main structure that differentiates between ρ-dependent and ρ-independent termination in prokaryotes?

a. Rho-independent termination involves the formation of a hairpin.

b. Rho-dependent termination involves the formation of a hairpin.

c. Rho-dependent termination stalls when the polymerase begins to transcribe a region rich in A-T nucleotides.

d. Rho-independent termination stalls when the polymerase begins to transcribe a region rich in G nucleotides.

34. Which step in the transcription of eukaryotic RNA differs the most from its prokaryotic counterpart?

a. The initiation step in eukaryotes requires an initiation complex with enhancers and transcription factors. Also, the separation of the DNA strand is different as histones are involved.

b. The initiation step in prokaryotes requires an initiation complex with enhancers and transcription factors. Also, the separation of the DNA strand is different as histones are involved.

c. The elongation step in eukaryotes requires an initiation complex with enhancers and transcription factors. Also, the separation of the DNA strand is different as histones are involved.

d. The initiation step in eukaryotes requires an initiation complex with enhancers and transcription factors. Also, the separation of the DNA strand is different as histones are not involved.

35. Would you be able to determine which RNA polymerase you isolated from a eukaryotic cell without analyzing its products?

a. No, because they have the same α-amanitin sensitivity in all products.

b. No, quantitative analysis of products is done to determine the type of polymerase.

c. Yes, they can be determined as they differ in α-amanitin sensitivity.

d. Yes, they can be determined by the number of molecules that bind to DNA.

36. Can you predict how alternative splicing may lead to an economy of genes? Do you need a different gene for every protein that the cell can produce?

a. Alternative splicing can lead to the synthesis of several polypeptides from a single gene.

b. Alternative splicing can lead to the synthesis of several forms of mRNA from a single gene.

c. Alternative splicing can lead to the synthesis of several forms of codons from a set of genes.

d. Alternative splicing can lead to the synthesis of several forms of ribosomes from a set of genes.

37. What is the major challenge in the production of RNA in eukaryotes compared to prokaryotes?

a. exporting the mRNA across the nuclear membrane

b. importing the mRNA across the nuclear membrane

c. the mRNA staying inside the nuclear membrane

d. the mRNA translating into proteins within seconds

38. What would happen if the 5' methyl guanosine was not added to an mRNA?

a. The transcript would degrade when the mRNA moves out of the nucleus to the cytoplasm.

b. The mRNA molecule would stabilize and start the process of translation within the nucleus of the cell.

c. The mRNA molecule would move out of the nucleus and create more copies of the mRNA molecule.

d. The mRNA molecule would not be able to add the poly-A tail on its strand at the 5' end.

39. Transcribe and translate the following DNA sequence (nontemplate strand): 5'-ATGGCCGGTTATTAAGCA-3'

a. The mRNA would be 5'-AUGGCCGGUUAUUAAGCA-3' and the protein will be MAGY.

b. The mRNA would be 3'-AUGGCCGGUUAUUAAGCA-5' and the protein will be MAGY.

c. The mRNA would be 5'-ATGGCCGGTTATTAAGCA-3' and the protein will be MAGY.

d. The mRNA would be 5'-AUGGCCGGUUAUUAAGCA-3' and the protein will be MACY.

40. The RNA world hypothesis proposes that the first complex molecule was RNA and it preceded protein formation. Which major function of the ribosomal RNA supports the hypothesis?

a. rRNA has catalytic properties in the large subunit and it assembles proteins.

b. rRNA is a protein molecule that helps in the synthesis of other proteins.

c. rRNA is essential for the transcription process.

d. rRNA plays a major role in post-translational processes.

41. A tRNA is chemically modified so that the amino acid bound is different than the one specified by its anticodon. Which codon in the mRNA would the tRNA recognize: the one specified by its anticodon or the one that matches the modified amino acid it carries?

a. The anticodon will match the codon in mRNA.

b. The anticodon will match with the modified amino acid it carries.

c. The anticodon will lose the specificity for the tRNA molecule.

d. The enzyme amino acyl tRNA synthetase would lose control over the amino acid.

TEST PREP FOR AP® COURSES

42. What characteristic of the genetic code points to a common ancestry for all organisms?

a. The code is degenerate
b. The code contains 64 codons.
c. The genetic code is almost universal.
d. The code contains stop codons

43. What process transfers heritable material to the next generation?

a. replication
b. splicing
c. transcription
d. translation

44. When comparing transcription of heritable information in prokaryotes and eukaryotes, which events are the same?

a. Transcription by polymerase, recognition of a consensus sequence in the promoter, and termination by a hairpin loop are conserved.
b. Translation by polymerase, recognition of a consensus sequence in the promoter, and termination by a hairpin loop are conserved.
c. Transcription by polymerase, recognition of a highly variable sequence in the promoter, and termination by a hairpin loop are conserved.
d. Transcription by polymerase, recognition of a consensus sequence in the promoter, and elongation by a hairpin loop are conserved.

45. Which of the following cell structures does not contain heritable information?

a. chloroplast
b. cytoplasmic membrane
c. mitochondria
d. nucleus

46. How does the enzyme reverse transcriptase violate the central dogma of molecular biology in HIV?

a. The enzyme reverse transcriptase reverse transcribes the RNA in the genome of HIV to DNA.
b. The enzyme reverse transcriptase translates the RNA of the HIV into protein and then back to DNA.
c. The enzyme reverse transcriptase transcribes the DNA straight into the protein molecules.
d. The enzyme reverse transcriptase transcribes DNA to RNA, then again to DNA. There is no protein synthesis.

47. Radioactive deoxythymidine triphosphate is supplied to the protist *Euglena*. After an interval of time, the cells are homogenized and different fractions are analyzed for radioactivity content in large nucleic acid molecules. Which fraction will not be labeled?

a. nucleus
b. mitochondrion
c. chloroplast
d. plasma membrane

48. You sequence a gene of interest and isolate the matching mRNA. You find that the mRNA is considerably shorter than the DNA sequence. Why is that?

a. There was an experimental mistake. The mRNA should have the same length as the gene.
b. The mRNA should be longer than the DNA sequence because the promoter is also transcribed.
c. The processed mRNA is shorter because introns were removed.
d. The mRNA is shorter because the signal sequence to cross the nuclear membrane was removed.

49. A mutation in the promoter region of the gene for the beta-globin can cause beta-thalassemia, a hereditary condition which causes anemia. Why would mutations in the promoter region lead to low levels of hemoglobin?

a. The globin chains produced are too long to form functional hemoglobin.
b. The globin chains are too short to form functional hemoglobin.
c. Fewer globin chains are synthesized because less mRNA is transcribed.
d. Globin chains do not fold properly and are non-functional.

50.

Codon on mRNA	Amino Acid
GCA	alanine
AAG	lysine
GUU	valine
AAU	asparagine
UGC	cysteine
UCG	serine
UCU	serine
UUA	leucine
UAA	stop

You are given three mRNA sequences:

1. 5'-UCG-GCA- AAU-UUA -GUU-3'
2. 5'-UCU-GCA- AAU-UUA -GUU-3'
3. 5'-UCU-GCA- AAU-UAA -GUU-3'

Using the table, write the peptide encoded by each of the mRNA sequences.

a. 1. Serine-alanine-asparagine-leucine-valine
   2. Serine-alanine-asparagine-leucine-valine
   3. Serine-alanine-asparagine(-stop)
b. 1. Serine-phenylalanine-asparagine-leucine-valine
   2. Serine-alanine-asparagine-leucine-valine
   3. Serine-alanine-asparagine (-stop)
c. 1. Serine-alanine-asparagine-leucine-valine
   2. Serine-alanine-asparagine (-stop)
   3. Serine-alanine-asparagine-leucine-valine
d. 1. Serine-alanine-asparagine-leucine-valine
   2. Serine-arginine-asparagine-leucine-valine
   3. Serine-alanine-asparagine(-stop)

51.

Codon on mRNA	Amino Acid
GCA	alanine
AAG	lysine
GUU	valine
AAU	asparagine
UGC	cysteine
UCG	serine
UCU	serine
UUA	leucine
UAA	stop

You are given three mRNA sequences:

1. 5'-UCG-GCA- AAU-UUA -GUU-3'
2. 5'-UCU-GCA- AAU-UUA -GUU-3'
3. 5'-UCU-GCA- AAU-UAA -GUU-3'

Using the peptide encoded by each of the above, compare the three peptides obtained. How are peptides 2 and 3 different from 1? What would be the consequence for the cell in each case?

a. There is a silent mutation in peptide 2 and peptide 3 has a stop codon due to mutation.
b. There is a silent mutation in peptide 3 and peptide 2 has a stop codon due to mutation.
c. There is a different amino acid in peptide 2 and peptide 3 has a stop codon due to mutation.
d. There isn't a mutation in peptide 2 and peptide 3 has a stop codon due to mutation.

SCIENCE PRACTICE CHALLENGE QUESTIONS

52. Gamow (1954) proposed that the structure of DNA deduced by Watson and Crick (1953) could be interpreted as a way of forming roughly 20 "words" of the common amino acids from the four "letters" A, T, C, and G that represent DNA nucleotides.

Crick and coworkers (1961) used a method developed by Benzer to induce mutations in the DNA of a virus by the insertion of a single nucleotide. The mutant could not infect the bacterium *Escherichia coli* and neither could viruses with a second insertion of a second DNA nucleotide. However, a third nucleotide insertion restored the ability of the virus to infect the bacterium.

In 1961, Nirenberg and Matthaei conducted a series of experiments to better understand the flow of genetic information from gene to protein. They discovered that in solutions containing the contents of ruptured *E. coli* bacterial cells from which DNA had been removed, polymers containing only one repeating amino acid, phenylalanine, would be synthesized if synthetic mRNA composed of only the single nucleotide, uracil (U), was added to the solution in which phenylalanine was also present. In solutions containing mRNA with only adenine (A) or cytosine (C) and the amino acids lysine or proline, polymers containing only these amino acids would be synthesized. The researchers found that when ribosomes were removed by filtration, these polymers did not form. Nirenberg and Leder (1964) extended this work to include other nucleotides.

A. Summarize the conclusions regarding the encoding and decoding of heritable information supported by these studies. Explain how these studies provided evidence to support the Triplet Code.

Khorana (1960) developed a technique for synthesizing RNA composed of predictable distributions of repeated pairs or triplets of nucleotides. He found, for example, that RNA synthesized when A and U were present in relative concentrations of 4:1, respectively, will produce RNA sequences with these distributions determined by their relative probabilities: AAU:AAA, AUA:AAA, and UAA:AAA; $0.8^2 \times 0.2/0.8^3 = 1/4$ [calculated as follows: i) 4/5 of the bases are A, so the likelihood of selecting A is 0.8; ii) the selection is repeated to determine the second letter of the three-letter codon; iii) the likelihood of selecting a U is 1 in 5; iv) the probability of selecting the set AUU is the product; v) similarly, the probability of AAA is $(4/5)^3$; and vi) the ratio of these probabilities is their relative likelihood]: AUU:AAA, UUA:AAA, and UAU:AAA; $0.8 \times 0.2^2/0.8^3 = 1/16$; and UUU:AAA; $0.2^3/0.8^3 = 1/64$.

B. Based on Khorana's findings, calculate the relative distributions of the following ratios of concentrations of RNA triplet sequences from mixtures in which the relative concentrations of guanine and cytosine, G:C, are 5:1.

Ratio	Relative Probabilities
GGC:GGG GCG:GGG CGG:GGG	
GCC:GGG CGC:GGG CCG:GGG	
CCC:GGG	

Table 15.2

C. Based on the work of Nirenberg, Matthaei, Leder, and Khorana, the following table was constructed (taken from Khorana's Nobel Prize address):

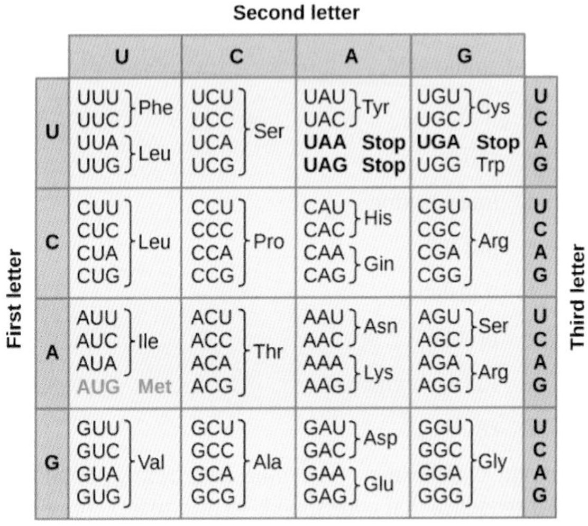

Second letter

First letter	U	C	A	G	Third letter
U	UUU, UUC Phe UUA, UUG Leu	UCU, UCC, UCA, UCG Ser	UAU, UAC Tyr **UAA Stop** **UAG Stop**	UGU, UGC Cys **UGA Stop** UGG Trp	U C A G
C	CUU, CUC, CUA, CUG Leu	CCU, CCC, CCA, CCG Pro	CAU, CAC His CAA, CAG Gln	CGU, CGC, CGA, CGG Arg	U C A G
A	AUU, AUC, AUA Ile AUG Met	ACU, ACC, ACA, ACG Thr	AAU, AAC Asn AAA, AAG Lys	AGU, AGC Ser AGA, AGG Arg	U C A G
G	GUU, GUC, GUA, GUG Val	GCU, GCC, GCA, GCG Ala	GAU, GAC Asp GAA, GAG Glu	GGU, GGC, GGA, GGG Gly	U C A G

Figure 15.18

A solution containing the amino acids shown in the table above and equal concentrations of the two nucleotides C and G is prepared. Predict the proteins that can be synthesized from this mixture in terms of each possible codon and their relative concentrations in terms of their amino acid repeat sequences.

D. Describe the effects of the codons UAA, UAG, and UGA on protein synthesis.

53. The yeast life cycle is usually dominated by haploid cells, each with a single set of unpaired chromosomes. The cell propagates asexually, and the genetic material is replicated through mitosis. Cell division occurs every 2–4 hours, leading to 60–100 generations in a single day. Yeast also reproduce sexually, particularly under adverse environmental conditions. When two haploid cells—with DNA containing complementary mating-type alleles—conjugate, a diploid zygote results. The diploid zygote can then complete the sexual segment of the life cycle through meiosis. After meiosis, four haploid spores are produced, which can germinate.

Researchers can grow yeast easily on nutrient-containing plates. Because both asexual and sexual reproduction is rapid, yeast has become an important organism for the experimental investigation of mutagenesis and evolution among eukaryotes. Environmental factors, such as chemicals or radiation, induce mutations. High-energy UV-c radiation of less than 1 minute in duration will result in many mutated yeast cells. UV-c can be used to mutate a strain of yeast in which the synthesis of adenine is blocked. This mutation is observable because the *ade-2* mutant has a red color when cultured on nutrient-containing plates. Exposure to uv-c also can result in additional mutations. In particular, one mutant, *ade-7*, changes the color of the *ade-2* mutant to white.

A. You have a uv-c lamp, culture plates, and growth chambers at 23 °C and 37 °C. You also have available known haploid strains that are (*ade-2*,+,+), where + denotes the wild type. **Design** a plan to determine the rate of uv-c-induced mutations in nutrient-containing plates inoculated with yeast.

Earth's ozone layer removes high-energy ultraviolet radiation, uv-c, from the solar radiation received at the surface. Lower-energy ultraviolet radiation, uv-b, strikes Earth's surface. Damage to DNA induced by ultraviolet radiation occurs with the formation of bonds between an adjacent pair of pyrimidine nucleotides, thymine and cytosine, on the same strand of DNA. A repair enzyme, photolyase, which is activated by visible light, is present in plants and most animals, but not in humans. In characterizing the relationship between environmental mutagens and cell damage, a useful assumption is often made and referred to as the linear hypothesis. This assumption states that the extent of damage is proportional to the amount of radiation received.

Mutation rates for a strain (*preac*) that does not produce photolyase and a wild-type (+) strain were studied. Cultures of the two strains of yeast were diluted, and nutrient-containing plates were inoculated in triplicate at 23 °C. The plates were exposed to bright sunlight for varying time intervals. After exposure, the plates were incubated in the dark at 23 °C. After incubation between 1 and 8 hours, data shown in the table below were collected by counting the density of living cells relative to the control, and averaging these among replicates.

B. Using the data table below, **graph** the average survival fraction, relative to the wild-type control. Predict the number of mutations in a sample of 1,000 cells of the *preac* type that are exposed to bright sunlight for 15 seconds.

Incu-bation Time(hr)	10-S Exposure	20-S Exposure	30-S Exposure	40-S Exposure	50-S Exposure
1	0.83	0.58	0.33	0.17	0.08
2	1.00	0.43	0.17	0.09	0.04
3	0.92	0.38	0.12	0.03	0.01
4	0.75	0.35	0.08	0.01	0.00
5	0.99	0.49	0.11	0.01	0.00
6	0.81	0.42	0.12	0.01	0.00
7	0.80	0.32	0.09	0.01	0.00
8	1.05	0.59	0.11	0.01	0.00
Mean	0.89	0.45	0.14	0.04	0.02
Standard Deviation	0.11	0.10	0.08	0.06	0.03

Figure 15.19 This is a 5 column table, showing Incubation time, in hours in the left most column, ranging from 1 to 8. A 10 second exposure has the following values for an incubation time of 1 to 8: 0.83, 1.00, 0.92, 0.75, 0.99, 0.81, 0.80, 1.05 and 0.89 with a standard deviation of 0.11. A 20 second exposure has the following values for an incubation time of 1 to 8: 0.58, 0.43, 0.38, 0.35, 0.49, 0.42, 0.32, 0.59, 0.45, with a standard deviation of 0.10. A 30 second exposure has the following values for an incubation time of 1 to 8: 0.33, 0.17, 0.12, 0.08, 0.11, 0.12, 0.09, 0.11, 0.14, with a standard deviation of 0.08. A 40 second exposure has the following values for an incubation time of 1 to 8: 0.17, 0.09, 0.03, 0.01, 0.01, 0.01, 0.01, 0.01, 0.04, with a standard deviation of .0.06. A 50 second exposure has the following values for an incubation time of 1 to 8: 0.08, 0.04, 0.01, 0.00, 0.00, 0.00, 0.00, 0.00, 0.02 with a standard deviation of 0.03

Yeast can also be used to study sexual reproduction, a somewhat puzzling phenomenon. Cloning of cells through mitosis is molecularly much less complex than meiosis, consumes less energy, and is less risky. Two alternative explanations for the evolution of sexual reproduction are popular. In one model, through assortment of genes, meiosis leads to an increase in the frequency of beneficial mutations. In the second model, detrimental mutations are purged from a population through sex. Studies using yeast (Gray and Goddard, *Evol. Biol.*, 2012 and McDonald et al., *Nature* 2012) have provided a mechanism to study these models. As shown below, the fitness (defined as the log of the ratio of the number of cells in successive generations) of yeast is graphed as a function of number of mitotic reproductions in yeast grown in low-stress and high-stress environments, and with and without alternating induction of sexual reproduction.

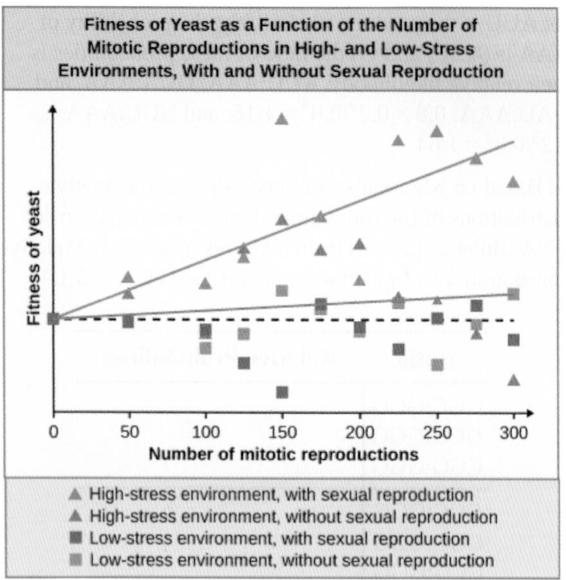

Figure 15.20

C. Based on these data, **evaluate** the merits of the alternative theories of the adaptive advantage provided by sexual reproduction.

54. A. **Describe** the storage and retrieval of genetic information with the following model. Use the list to fill in the blanks with the letter corresponding to the correct term.

a. amino acid
b. tRNA
c. DNA
d. transcription
e. mRNA
f. translation
g. protein
h. RNA polymerase
i. rRNA

Within the cytoplasm, __ is synthesized from __ bound to __ in a sequence that corresponds to information provided by __. This process is called __.

Within the nucleus, information originating in __ is encoded as a sequence of bases in __, which is synthesized by the enzyme __ that is embedded in the __. This process is called __.

B. During development, cell differentiation occurs, and the expression of genes is permanently switched off. Using the model summarized above, **explain** where information flow is most effectively blocked.

C. A chemical message is received by the cell regulating the timing of events controlled by gene expression. Using the model summarized above, **explain** where information flow is most effectively managed.

55. Structure and function in biology result from both the presence of genetic information and the expression of that information. Some genes are continually expressed, whereas the expression of most genes is regulated, commonly at the level of transcription. At the initiation of transcription, the TATA-binding protein (TBP) provides access to the DNA strand to be transcribed. The 5'TATAAA3' sequence called the TATA box is found in prokaryotes, archaebacteria, and eukaryotes. Even among eukarya, when the TATA box is not present among eukaryotes, the initiation of transcription involves TBP. Scientists attribute this common characteristic to the relative thermostability of the A-T interaction. Hydrogen bonds hold the two strands of the DNA double helix together. This type of bond has the smallest interaction energy of all intermolecular forces; as temperature increases, these bonds are broken.

A. **Explain** the advantage, in terms of the energy required, which is provided by an AT-rich region in the sequence where transcription is initiated.

B. The fact that the TATA box or the associated TBP are common to all domains provides evidence of common ancestry among all life. **Pose a scientific question** that would need to be addressed by a valid alternative explanation of this fact.

C. A whole-genome survey of prokaryotes (Zheng and Wu, *BMC Bioinformatics*, 2010) showed that the relative amounts of guanine and cytosine in DNA poorly predicted the temperature range conditions that are suitable for an organism. **Refine the question** posed in part B, taking this result into account.

56. Only a fraction of DNA encodes proteins. The noncoding portion of a gene is referred to as the intron. The intron fraction depends upon the gene. Introns are rare in prokaryotic and mitochondrial DNA; in human nuclear DNA, this fraction is about 95%. The intron is transcribed into mRNA, but this noncoding mRNA is edited out before translation of the coding portion, or exon, of a gene. The edited exon segments are then spliced together by a spliceosome, a very large and complex collection of RNAs and proteins.

Although introns do not encode proteins, they have functions. In particular, they amplify expression of the exon, although the mechanism is unknown. When introns are very long, which is common among mammalian genes with roles in development, they can significantly extend the time required to complete transcription. Analysis of genes common to different plant and animal species shows many shared intronic positions and base sequences, although in some organisms, such as yeast, many introns have been deleted. Because introns do not encode proteins, mutations can remain silent and accumulate.

A. As described above, introns are ancestral remnants that are replicated because they do not disadvantage the organism. Consider the claim that introns are "junk DNA." **Evaluate the claim** with supporting evidence.

B. Introns may be retained during transcription. **Explain** how the retention of a transcribed intron between two transcribed exons within a gene could do the following:

- block expression of one polypeptide sequence
- increase expression of a polypeptide
- alter the polypeptide expressed

16 | GENE REGULATION

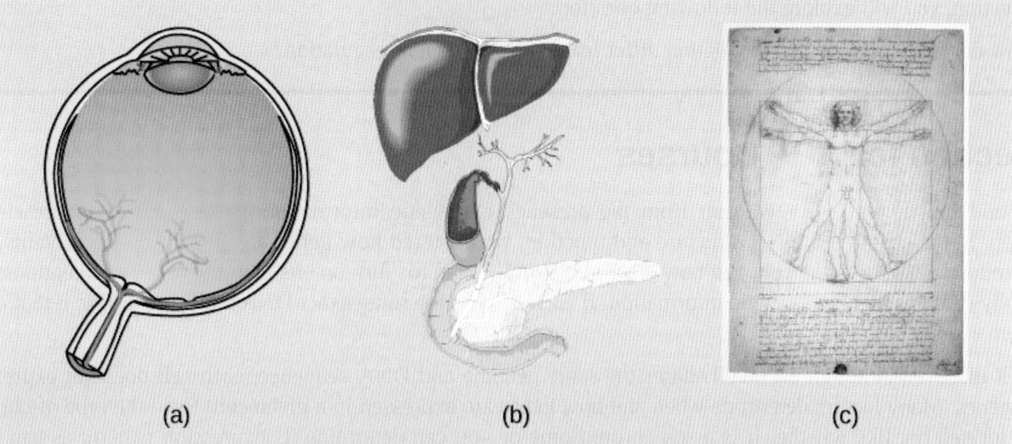

Figure 16.1 The genetic content of each somatic cell in an organism is the same, but not all genes are expressed in every cell. The control of which genes are expressed dictates whether a cell is (a) an eye cell or (b) a liver cell. It is the differential gene expression patterns that arise in different cells that give rise to (c) a complete organism.

Chapter Outline

Introduction

Most people know that regular exercise is important to maintain good health. It promotes cardiovascular health and helps to prevent obesity. Scientists have now discovered that long-term endurance training also changes how genes are expressed in muscle tissue. In a recent study, 23 healthy people each exercised one leg for 45 minutes four days a week while resting the other leg. After three months, muscles from participants' legs were biopsied, and scientists analyzed the activity level of over 20,000 genes in the tissue samples.

They found that for each participant the exercised leg had reduced inflammation and improved metabolism compared with the non-exercised leg. These differences were accompanied by changes in genes associated with metabolism and inflammation. However, the actual nucleotide sequences of the genes weren't changed. Instead, some genes were methylated, which simply means methyl groups were attached to certain nucleotides along the sequence. This, essentially, turned the genes "off" or otherwise changed how they were expressed. DNA methylation is an example of epigenetics, which is a process that alters genes without affecting the nucleotide sequence of the genes. The full research article can be found here (http://openstaxcollege.org/l/32endurance) .

16.1 | Regulation of Gene Expression

In this section, you will explore the following question:

- How does prokaryotic gene regulation differ from eukaryotic gene regulation?

Connection for AP® Courses

Structure and function in biology result from the presence of genetic information and the correct expression of this information. In the chapter on DNA structure and function, we explored how genes are translated into proteins, which in turn determine the nature of the cell. But how does a cell know when to "turn on" its DNA? With few exceptions, each cell in your body contains identical genetic information. If each cell has the same exact DNA make up, how is it that a liver cell differs from a nerve or muscle cell?

As we will discover, although each cell shares the same genome and DNA sequence, each cell does not express exactly the same genes. Many factors determine when and how genes are expressed in a given cell. Even the type of chromosome a gene is located on, like whether it is a sex chromosome or not, can determine its expression pattern, as can mutations or changes in DNA sequence and other external factors. In prokaryotes, gene expression is regulated primarily at the level of transcription, when DNA is copied into RNA. However, eukaryotes have evolved regulatory mechanisms in gene expression at multiple levels. In all cases, regulation of gene expression determines the type and amount of protein produced in the cell. Errors in regulatory processes can result in many human diseases and conditions, including cancer.

Gene expression regulation occurs at different points in prokaryotes and eukaryotes. Prokaryotic organisms express their entire genome in every cell, but not necessarily all at the same time. In general, a gene is expressed only when its specific protein product is needed. Remember that each cell in an organism carries the same DNA as every other cell. Yet cells of eukaryotic organisms each express a unique subset of DNA depending on cell type. To express a protein, DNA is first transcribed into RNA, which is then translated into proteins. In prokaryotic cells, transcription and translation occur almost simultaneously. In eukaryotic cells, transcription occurs in the nucleus, separate from the translation that occurs in the cytoplasm along ribosomes attached to endoplasmic reticulum. As stated above, gene expression in prokaryotes is regulated at the level of transcription, whereas in eukaryotes, gene expression is regulated at multiple levels, including the epigenetic (DNA), transcriptional, pre- and post-transcriptional, and translational levels.

The science of epigenetics studies heritable changes in the genome that do not affect the underlying DNA gene sequences.

The content presented in this section supports the learning objectives outlined in Big Idea 3 of the AP® Biology Curriculum Framework. The AP® learning objectives merge essential knowledge content with one or more of the seven science practices. These objectives provide a transparent foundation for the AP® Biology course, along with inquiry-based laboratory experiences, instructional activities, and AP® exam questions.

Big Idea 3	Living systems store, retrieve, transmit and respond to information essential to life processes.
Enduring Understanding 3.B	Expression of genetic information involves cellular and molecular mechanisms.
Essential Knowledge	**3.B.1** Gene regulation results in differential gene expression, leading to cell specialization
Science Practice	**7.1** The student can connect phenomena and models across spatial and temporal scales.
Learning Objective	**3.18** The student is able to describe the connection between the regulation of gene expression and observed differences between different kinds of organisms.

For a cell to function properly, necessary proteins must be synthesized at the proper time. All cells control or regulate the synthesis of proteins from information encoded in their DNA. The process of turning on a gene to produce RNA and protein is called **gene expression**. Whether in a simple unicellular organism or a complex multi-cellular organism, each cell controls when and how its genes are expressed. For this to occur, there must be a mechanism to control when a gene is expressed to make RNA and protein, how much of the protein is made, and when it is time to stop making that protein because it is no longer needed.

Although genetic differences between species and between individuals within a species are often responsible for phenotypic differences, another mechanism that can create phenotypic differences is differences in gene expression. For example, although every cell in an organism contains the same genes, the bone cells in the organism appears different from the fat cells due to differences in which genes are expressed by which cell. Similarly, although mice and humans share approximately 97.5% of their genes, they are very different organisms because different genes are turned on at different times during development and in different cells. Even organisms that share 100% identity in their genomes (a.k.a clones) can eventually appear different if they express their genes differently in response to different environmental conditions, for example. Even among humans, identical twins can possess different birthmarks, wrinkles, or other features that arise during development sometimes due to differential gene expression.

The regulation of gene expression conserves energy and space. It would require a significant amount of energy for an organism to express every gene at all times, so it is more energy efficient to turn on the genes only when they are required. In addition, only expressing a subset of genes in each cell saves space because DNA must be unwound from its tightly coiled structure to transcribe and translate the DNA. Cells would have to be enormous if every protein were expressed in every cell all the time.

The control of gene expression is extremely complex. Malfunctions in this process are detrimental to the cell and can lead to the development of many diseases.

Prokaryotic versus Eukaryotic Gene Expression

To understand how gene expression is regulated, we must first understand how a gene codes for a functional protein in a cell. The process occurs in both prokaryotic and eukaryotic cells, just in slightly different manners.

Prokaryotic organisms are single-celled organisms that lack a cell nucleus, and their DNA therefore floats freely in the cell cytoplasm. To synthesize a protein, the processes of transcription and translation occur almost simultaneously. When the resulting protein is no longer needed, transcription stops. As a result, the primary method to control what type of protein and how much of each protein is expressed in a prokaryotic cell is the regulation of DNA transcription. All of the subsequent steps occur automatically. When more protein is required, more transcription occurs. Therefore, in prokaryotic cells, the control of gene expression is mostly at the transcriptional level.

Eukaryotic cells, in contrast, have intracellular organelles that add to their complexity. In eukaryotic cells, the DNA is contained inside the cell's nucleus and there it is transcribed into RNA. The newly synthesized RNA is then transported out of the nucleus into the cytoplasm, where ribosomes translate the RNA into protein. The processes of transcription and translation are physically separated by the nuclear membrane; transcription occurs only within the nucleus, and translation occurs only outside the nucleus in the cytoplasm. The regulation of gene expression can occur at all stages of the process (Figure 16.2). Regulation may occur when the DNA is uncoiled and loosened from nucleosomes to bind transcription factors (**epigenetic** level), when the RNA is transcribed (transcriptional level), when the RNA is processed and exported to the cytoplasm after it is transcribed (**post-transcriptional** level), when the RNA is translated into protein (translational level), or after the protein has been made (**post-translational** level).

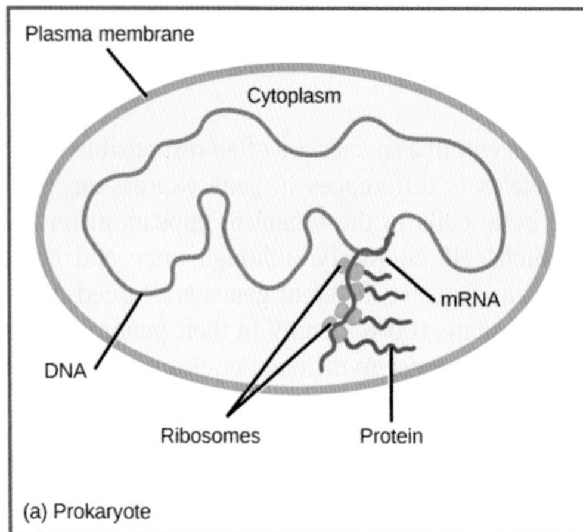

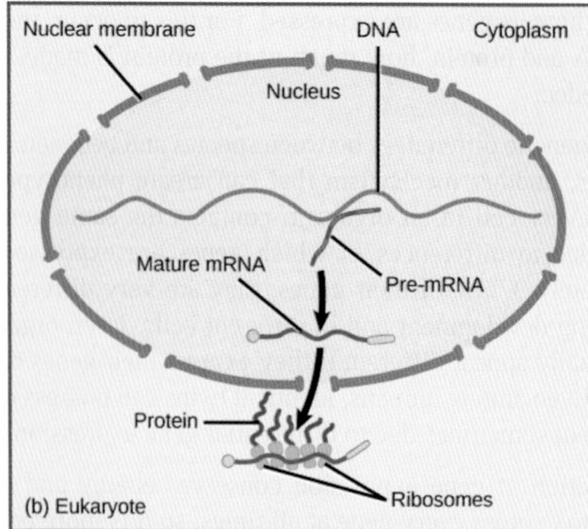

Figure 16.2 Prokaryotic transcription and translation occur simultaneously in the cytoplasm, and regulation occurs at the transcriptional level. Eukaryotic gene expression is regulated during transcription and RNA processing, which take place in the nucleus, and during protein translation, which takes place in the cytoplasm. Further regulation may occur through post-translational modifications of proteins.

The differences in the regulation of gene expression between prokaryotes and eukaryotes are summarized in Table 16.1. The regulation of gene expression is discussed in detail in subsequent modules.

Differences in the Regulation of Gene Expression of Prokaryotic and Eukaryotic Organisms

Prokaryotic organisms	Eukaryotic organisms
Lack nucleus	Contain nucleus
DNA is found in the cytoplasm	DNA is confined to the nuclear compartment
RNA transcription and protein formation occur almost simultaneously	RNA transcription occurs prior to protein formation, and it takes place in the nucleus. Translation of RNA to protein occurs in the cytoplasm.
Gene expression is regulated primarily at the transcriptional level	Gene expression is regulated at many levels (epigenetic, transcriptional, nuclear shuttling, post-transcriptional, translational, and post-translational)

Table 16.1

evolution CONNECTION

Prokaryotic cells can only regulate gene expression by controlling the amount of transcription. As eukaryotic cells evolved, the complexity of the control of gene expression increased. For example, with the evolution of eukaryotic cells came compartmentalization of important cellular components and cellular processes. A nuclear region that contains the DNA was formed. Transcription and translation were physically separated into two different cellular compartments. It therefore became possible to control gene expression by regulating transcription in the nucleus, and also by controlling the RNA levels and protein translation present outside the nucleus.

Some cellular processes arose from the need of the organism to defend itself. Cellular processes such as gene silencing developed to protect the cell from viral or parasitic infections. If the cell could quickly shut off gene expression for a short period of time, it would be able to survive an infection when other organisms could not. Therefore, the organism evolved a new process that helped it survive, and it was able to pass this new development to offspring.

Cytochrome c oxidase is a highly conserved protein found in bacteria and in the mitochondria of eukaryotes. Based on your knowledge of evolutionary relationships, which of the following statements would you expect to be true of the cytochrome c oxidase protein sequence?

a. The bacterial protein will be more similar to the human protein than the yeast protein.

b. The yeast protein will be more similar to the human protein than the bacterial protein.

c. The bacterial protein will be more similar to the yeast protein than the human protein.

d. The bacterial and yeast proteins will share a similar sequence, but the human protein will be unrelated.

science practices CONNECTION for AP® Courses

Think About It

How does controlling gene expression alter the overall protein level in the cell?

16.2 | Prokaryotic Gene Regulation

In this section, you will explore the following question:

- What are operons and what are the roles of activators, inducers, and repressors in regulating operons and gene expression?

Connection for AP® Courses

The regulation of gene expression in prokaryotic cells occurs at the transcriptional level. Simply stated, if a cell does not transcribe the DNA's message into mRNA, translation (protein synthesis), does not occur. Bacterial genes are often organized into common pathways or processes called operons for more coordinated regulation of expression. For example, in *E. coli*, genes responsible for lactose metabolism are located together on the bacterial chromosome. (The operon model includes several components, so when studying how the operon works, it is helpful to refer to a diagram of the model. See Figure 16.3 and Figure 16.4.) The operon includes a regulatory gene that codes for a repressor protein that binds to the operator, which prevents RNA polymerase from transcribing the gene(s) of interest. An example of this is seen in the structural genes for lactose metabolism. However, if the repressor is inactivated, RNA polymerase binds to the promoter, and transcription of the structural genes occurs.

There are three ways to control the transcription of an operon: inducible control, repressible control, and activator control.

The *lac* operon is an example of inducible control because the presence of lactose "turns on" transcription of the genes for its own metabolism. The *trp* operon is an example of repressible control because it uses proteins bound to the operator sequence to physically prevent the binding of RNA polymerase. If tryptophan is not needed by the cell, the genes necessary to produce it are turned off. Activator control (typified by the action of Catabolite Activator Protein) increases the binding ability of RNA polymerase to the promoter. Certain genes are continually expressed via this regulatory mechanism.

Information presented and the examples highlighted in the section support concepts outlined in Big Idea 3 of the AP® Biology Curriculum Framework. The learning objectives listed in the Curriculum Framework provide a transparent foundation for the AP® Biology course, an inquiry-based laboratory experience, instructional activities, and AP® exam questions. A learning objective merges required content with one or more of the seven science practices.

Big Idea 3	Living systems store, retrieve, transmit and respond to information essential to life processes.
Enduring Understanding 3.B	Expression of genetic information involves cellular and molecular mechanisms.
Essential Knowledge	**3.B.1** Gene regulation results in differential gene expression, leading to cell specialization
Science Practice	**1.4** The student can use representations and models to analyze situations or solve problems qualitatively and quantitatively
Learning Objective	**3.21** The student can use representations to describe how gene regulation influences cell products and function.
Essential Knowledge	**3.B.2** A variety of intercellular and intracellular signal transmissions mediate gene expression.
Science Practice	**1.4** The student can use representations and models to analyze situations or solve problems qualitatively and quantitatively.
Learning Objective	**3.23** The student can use representations to describe mechanisms of the regulation of gene expression.

The DNA of prokaryotes is organized into a circular chromosome supercoiled in the nucleoid region of the cell cytoplasm. Proteins that are needed for a specific function, or that are involved in the same biochemical pathway, are encoded together in blocks called **operons**. For example, all of the genes needed to use lactose as an energy source are coded next to each other in the lactose (or *lac*) operon.

In prokaryotic cells, there are three types of regulatory molecules that can affect the expression of operons: repressors, activators, and inducers. **Repressors** are proteins that suppress transcription of a gene in response to an external stimulus, whereas **activators** are proteins that increase the transcription of a gene in response to an external stimulus. Finally, inducers are small molecules that either activate or repress transcription depending on the needs of the cell and the availability of substrate.

The *trp* Operon: A Repressor Operon

Bacteria such as *E. coli* need amino acids to survive. **Tryptophan** is one such amino acid that *E. coli* can ingest from the environment. *E. coli* can also synthesize tryptophan using enzymes that are encoded by five genes. These five genes are next to each other in what is called the **tryptophan (*trp*) operon** (Figure 16.3). If tryptophan is present in the environment, then *E. coli* does not need to synthesize it and the switch controlling the activation of the genes in the *trp* operon is switched off. However, when tryptophan availability is low, the switch controlling the operon is turned on, transcription is initiated, the genes are expressed, and tryptophan is synthesized.

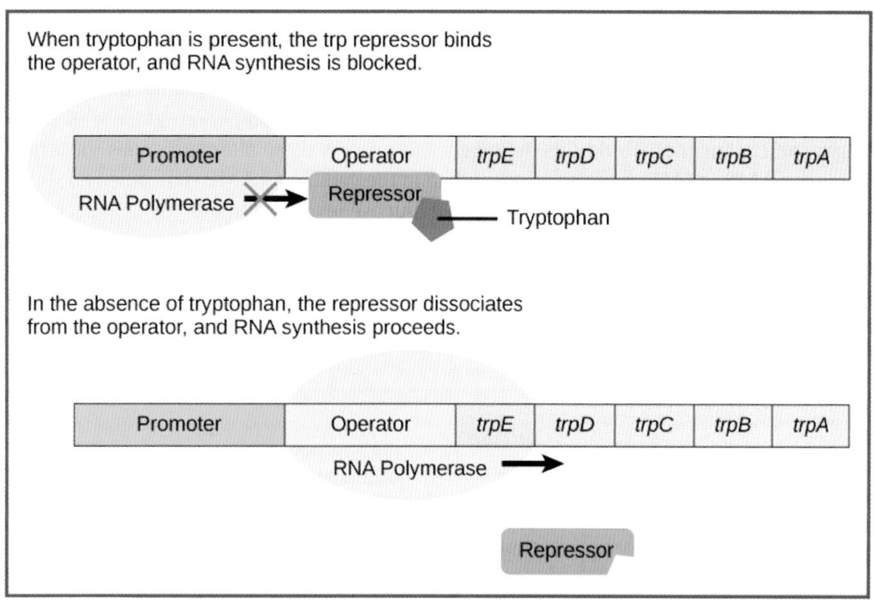

Figure 16.3 The five genes that are needed to synthesize tryptophan in *E. coli* are located next to each other in the *trp* operon. When tryptophan is plentiful, two tryptophan molecules bind the repressor protein at the operator sequence. This physically blocks the RNA polymerase from transcribing the tryptophan genes. When tryptophan is absent, the repressor protein does not bind to the operator and the genes are transcribed.

A DNA sequence that codes for proteins is referred to as the coding region. The five coding regions for the tryptophan biosynthesis enzymes are arranged sequentially on the chromosome in the operon. Just before the coding region is the **transcriptional start site**. This is the region of DNA to which RNA polymerase binds to initiate transcription. The promoter sequence is upstream of the transcriptional start site; each operon has a sequence within or near the promoter to which proteins (activators or repressors) can bind and regulate transcription.

A DNA sequence called the operator sequence is encoded between the promoter region and the first *trp* coding gene. This **operator** contains the DNA code to which the repressor protein can bind. When tryptophan is present in the cell, two tryptophan molecules bind to the *trp* repressor, which changes shape to bind to the *trp* operator. Binding of the tryptophan–repressor complex at the operator physically prevents the RNA polymerase from binding, and transcribing the downstream genes.

When tryptophan is not present in the cell, the repressor by itself does not bind to the operator; therefore, the operon is active and tryptophan is synthesized. Because the repressor protein actively binds to the operator to keep the genes turned off, the *trp* operon is negatively regulated and the proteins that bind to the operator to silence *trp* expression are **negative regulators**.

Watch this video (http://openstaxcollege.org/l/trp_operon) to learn more about the *trp* operon.

What would happen if bacteria did not have *trp* R?

a. The cell would not be able to break down tryptophan.

b. The cell will gradually produce more tryptophan over time.

c. The cell would not be able to make tryptophan.

d. The cell would make tryptophan when it was not needed.

Catabolite Activator Protein (CAP): An Activator Regulator

Just as the *trp* operon is negatively regulated by tryptophan molecules, there are proteins that bind to the operator sequences that act as a **positive regulator** to turn genes on and activate them. For example, when glucose is scarce, *E. coli* bacteria can turn to other sugar sources for fuel. To do this, new genes to process these alternate genes must be transcribed. When glucose levels drop, cyclic AMP (cAMP) begins to accumulate in the cell. The cAMP molecule is a signaling molecule that is involved in glucose and energy metabolism in *E. coli*. When glucose levels decline in the cell, accumulating cAMP binds to the positive regulator **catabolite activator protein (CAP)**, a protein that binds to the promoters of operons that control the processing of alternative sugars. When cAMP binds to CAP, the complex binds to the promoter region of the genes that are needed to use the alternate sugar sources (Figure 16.4). In these operons, a CAP binding site is located upstream of the RNA polymerase binding site in the promoter. This increases the binding ability of RNA polymerase to the promoter region and the transcription of the genes.

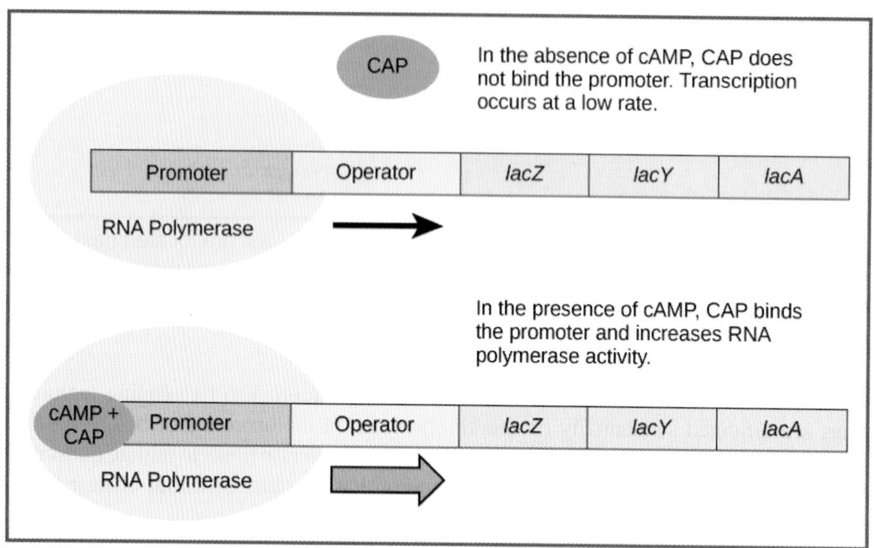

Figure 16.4 When glucose levels fall, *E. coli* may use other sugars for fuel but must transcribe new genes to do so. As glucose supplies become limited, cAMP levels increase. This cAMP binds to the CAP protein, a positive regulator that binds to an operator region upstream of the genes required to use other sugar sources.

The *lac* Operon: An Inducer Operon

The third type of gene regulation in prokaryotic cells occurs through **inducible operons**, which have proteins that bind to activate or repress transcription depending on the local environment and the needs of the cell. The *lac* operon is a typical inducible operon. As mentioned previously, *E. coli* is able to use other sugars as energy sources when glucose concentrations are low. To do so, the cAMP–CAP protein complex serves as a positive regulator to induce transcription. One such sugar source is lactose. The ***lac* operon** encodes the genes necessary to acquire and process the lactose from the local environment. CAP binds to the operator sequence upstream of the promoter that initiates transcription of the *lac* operon. However, for the *lac* operon to be activated, two conditions must be met. First, the level of glucose must be very low or non-existent. Second, lactose must be present. Only when glucose is absent and lactose is present will the *lac* operon be transcribed (Figure 16.5). This makes sense for the cell, because it would be energetically wasteful to create the proteins to process lactose if glucose was plentiful or lactose was not available.

visual CONNECTION

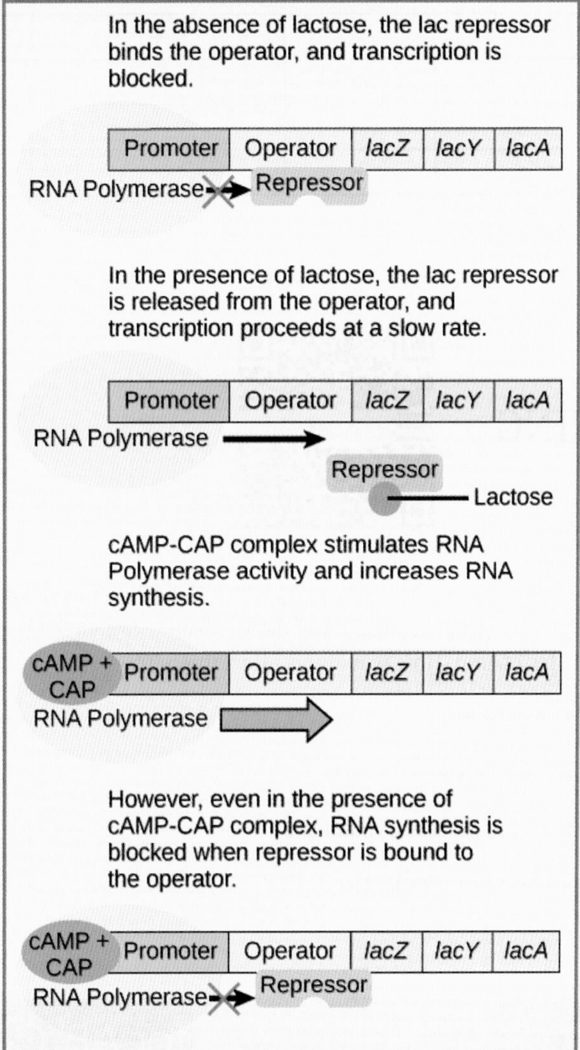
In the absence of lactose, the lac repressor binds the operator, and transcription is blocked.
Promoter
Operator
lacZ
lacY
lacA
RNA Polymerase
Repressor
In the presence of lactose, the lac repressor is released from the operator, and transcription proceeds at a slow rate.
Promoter
Operator
lacZ
lacY
lacA
RNA Polymerase
Repressor
Lactose
cAMP-CAP complex stimulates RNA Polymerase activity and increases RNA synthesis.
cAMP + CAP
Promoter
Operator
lacZ
lacY
lacA
RNA Polymerase
However, even in the presence of cAMP-CAP complex, RNA synthesis is blocked when repressor is bound to the operator.
cAMP + CAP
Promoter
Operator
lacZ
lacY
lacA
RNA Polymerase
Repressor

Figure 16.5 Transcription of the *lac* operon is carefully regulated so that its expression only occurs when glucose is limited and lactose is present to serve as an alternative fuel source.

In *E. coli*, the *trp* operon is on by default, while the *lac* operon is off. Why do you think that this is the case?

a. The trp operon is inducible and is positively regulated. Therefore it is ON by default whereas the lac operon is repressible and is OFF by default.

b. The trp operon synthesizes tryptophan which is essential for the cell and therefore remains ON, whereas the lac operon synthesizes enzymes for the breakdown of a sugar that is not always available and remains OFF by default.

c. The trp operon is constitutive and remains ON by default, whereas the lac operon is repressible and therefore is OFF by default.

d. The lac operon undergoes transcriptional attenuation and therefore is OFF by default, whereas the trp operon is not regulated by any such mechanism and is ON by default.

If glucose is absent, then CAP can bind to the operator sequence to activate transcription. If lactose is absent, then the repressor binds to the operator to prevent transcription. If either of these requirements is met, then transcription remains off.

Only when both conditions are satisfied is the *lac* operon transcribed (Table 16.2).

Signals that Induce or Repress Transcription of the *lac* Operon

Glucose	CAP binds	Lactose	Repressor binds	Transcription
+	-	-	+	No
+	-	+	-	Some
-	+	-	+	No
-	+	+	-	Yes

Table 16.2

Watch an animated tutorial (http://openstaxcollege.org/l/lac_operon) about the workings of *lac* operon here.

The *E. coli* bacteria can have several mutations that affect the lac operon system. One mutation inhibits the ability of RNA polymerase to bind to the lac operon. How would this affect the cell?

a. The cell would make more lactose.

b. There would be no lactose outside of the cell.

c. The cell would not be able to process tryptophan.

d. The cell would not be able to process lactose.

science practices CONNECTION for AP® Courses

Activity

Modeling the Operon. Use construction paper or more elaborate materials, such as Styrofoam noodles, electrical tape, and Velcro tabs, to create a model of the *lac* and *trp* operons that include a regulator, promoter, operator, and structural genes. Then use the model to show how the presence of substrate, e.g., allolactose or tryptophan, can change the activity of the operons. As an extension of the activity, use the model to make predictions about the effects of mutations in any of the regions on gene expression.

Think About It

In *E. coli*, the *trp* operon is on by default, while the *lac* operon is off by default. Why do you think this is the case?

16.3 | Eukaryotic Epigenetic Gene Regulation

In this section, you will explore the following question:

- What is the science of epigenetics and how is this process regulated?

Connection for AP® Courses

One reason that eukaryotic gene expression is more complex than prokaryotic gene expression is because the processes of transcription and translation are physically separated within the eukaryotic cell. Eukaryotic cells also package their genomes in a more sophisticated way compared with prokaryotic cells. Consequently, eukaryotic cells can regulate gene expression at multiple levels, beginning with control of access to DNA. Because genomic DNA is folded around histone proteins to create nucleosome complexes, nucleosomes physically regulate the access of proteins, such as transcription factors and enzymes, to the underlying DNA. Methylation of DNA and histones causes nucleosomes to pack tightly together, preventing transcription factors from binding to the DNA. Methylated nucleosomes contain DNA that is not expressed. On the other hand, histone acetylation results in loose packing of nucleosomes, allowing transcription factors to bind to DNA. Acetylated nucleosomes contain DNA that may be expressed.

Information presented and the examples highlighted in the section support concepts outlined in Big Idea 3 of the AP® Biology Curriculum Framework. The Learning Objectives listed in the Curriculum Framework provide a transparent foundation for the AP® Biology course, an inquiry-based laboratory experience, instructional activities, and AP® exam questions. A Learning Objective merges required content with one or more of the seven Science Practices.

Big Idea 3	Living systems store, retrieve, transmit and respond to information essential to life processes.
Enduring Understanding 3.B	Expression of genetic information involves cellular and molecular mechanisms.
Essential Knowledge	**3.B.1** Gene regulation results in differential gene expression, leading to cell specialization.
Science Practice	**7.1** The student can connect phenomena and models across spatial and temporal scales
Learning Objective	**3.19** The student is able to describe the connection between the regulation of gene expression and observed differences between individuals in a population

Epigenetic Control: Regulating Access to Genes within the Chromosome

As stated earlier, one reason why eukaryotic gene expression is more complex than prokaryotic gene expression is because the processes of transcription and translation are physically separated. Unlike prokaryotic cells, eukaryotic cells can regulate gene expression at many different levels. Eukaryotic gene expression begins with control of access to the DNA. This form of regulation, called epigenetic regulation, occurs even before transcription is initiated.

The human genome encodes over 20,000 genes; each of the 23 pairs of human chromosomes encodes thousands of genes. The DNA in the nucleus is precisely wound, folded, and compacted into chromosomes so that it will fit into the nucleus. It is also organized so that specific segments can be accessed as needed by a specific cell type.

The first level of organization, or packing, is the winding of DNA strands around histone proteins. Histones package and order DNA into structural units called nucleosome complexes, which can control the access of proteins to the DNA regions (Figure 16.6**a**). Under the electron microscope, this winding of DNA around histone proteins to form nucleosomes looks like small beads on a string (Figure 16.6**b**). These beads (histone proteins) can move along the string (DNA) and change the structure of the molecule.

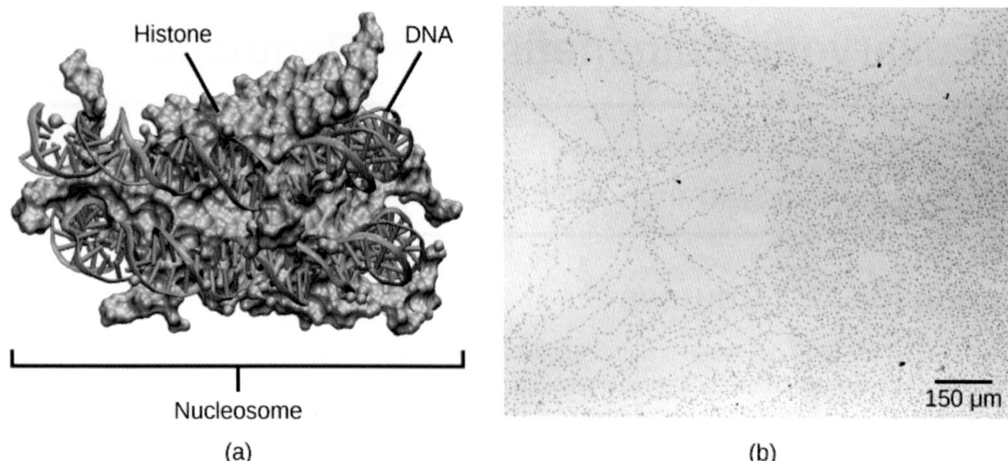

Figure 16.6 DNA is folded around histone proteins to create (a) nucleosome complexes. These nucleosomes control the access of proteins to the underlying DNA. When viewed through an electron microscope (b), the nucleosomes look like beads on a string. (credit "micrograph": modification of work by Chris Woodcock)

If DNA encoding a specific gene is to be transcribed into RNA, the nucleosomes surrounding that region of DNA can slide down the DNA to open that specific chromosomal region and allow for the transcriptional machinery (RNA polymerase) to initiate transcription (Figure 16.7). Nucleosomes can move to open the chromosome structure to expose a segment of DNA, but do so in a very controlled manner.

visual CONNECTION

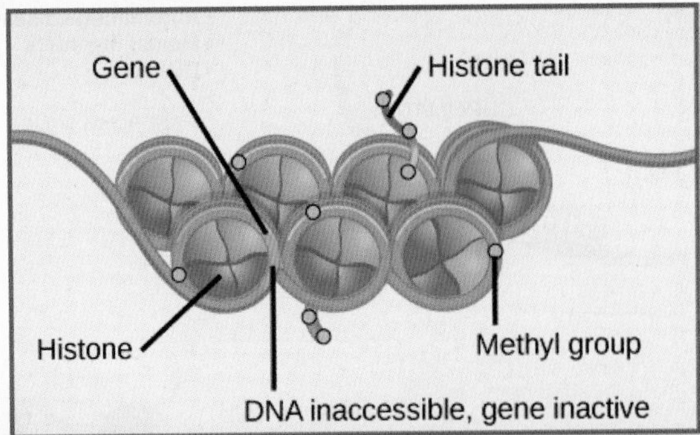

Methylation of DNA and histones causes nucleosomes to pack tightly together. Transcription factors cannot bind the DNA, and genes are not expressed.

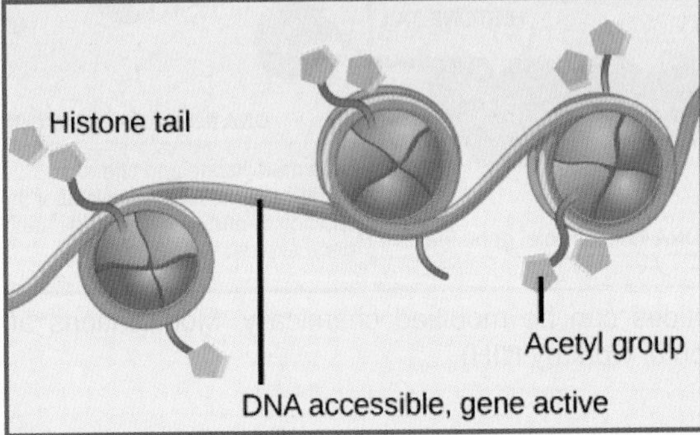

Histone acetylation results in loose packing of nucleosomes. Transcription factors can bind the DNA and genes are expressed.

Figure 16.7 Nucleosomes can slide along DNA. When nucleosomes are spaced closely together (top), transcription factors cannot bind and gene expression is turned off. When the nucleosomes are spaced far apart (bottom), the DNA is exposed. Transcription factors can bind, allowing gene expression to occur. Modifications to the histones and DNA affect nucleosome spacing.

In females, one of the two X chromosomes is inactivated during embryonic development because of epigenetic changes to the chromatin. What impact do you think these changes would have on nucleosome packing?

a. Methylation of DNA and hypo-acetylation of histones causes the nucleosomes to pack loosely together, inactivating one of the X chromosomes.

b. Methylation of histones and hyper-acetylation of DNA causes the nucleosomes to pack tightly together, inactivating one of the X chromosome due to transcriptional repression.

c. Methylation of DNA and hypo-acetylation of histones causes the nucleosomes to pack tightly together, inactivating one of the X chromosomes.

d. Acetylation of DNA and hyper-methylation of histones causes the nucleosomes to pack tightly together, inactivating one of the X chromosomes.

How the histone proteins move is dependent on signals found on both the histone proteins and on the DNA. These signals are tags added to histone proteins and DNA that tell the histones if a chromosomal region should be open or closed (Figure 16.8 depicts modifications to histone proteins and DNA). These tags are not permanent, but may be added or removed as needed. They are chemical modifications (phosphate, methyl, or acetyl groups) that are attached to specific amino acids in the protein or to the nucleotides of the DNA. The tags do not alter the DNA base sequence, but they do alter how tightly wound the DNA is around the histone proteins. DNA is a negatively charged molecule; therefore, changes in the charge of the histone will change how tightly wound the DNA molecule will be. When unmodified, the histone proteins have a large positive charge; by adding chemical modifications like acetyl groups, the charge becomes less positive.

The DNA molecule itself can also be modified. This occurs within very specific regions called CpG islands. These are stretches with a high frequency of cytosine and guanine dinucleotide DNA pairs (CG) found in the promoter regions of genes. When this configuration exists, the cytosine member of the pair can be methylated (a methyl group is added). This modification changes how the DNA interacts with proteins, including the histone proteins that control access to the region.

Highly methylated (hypermethylated) DNA regions with deacetylated histones are tightly coiled and transcriptionally inactive.

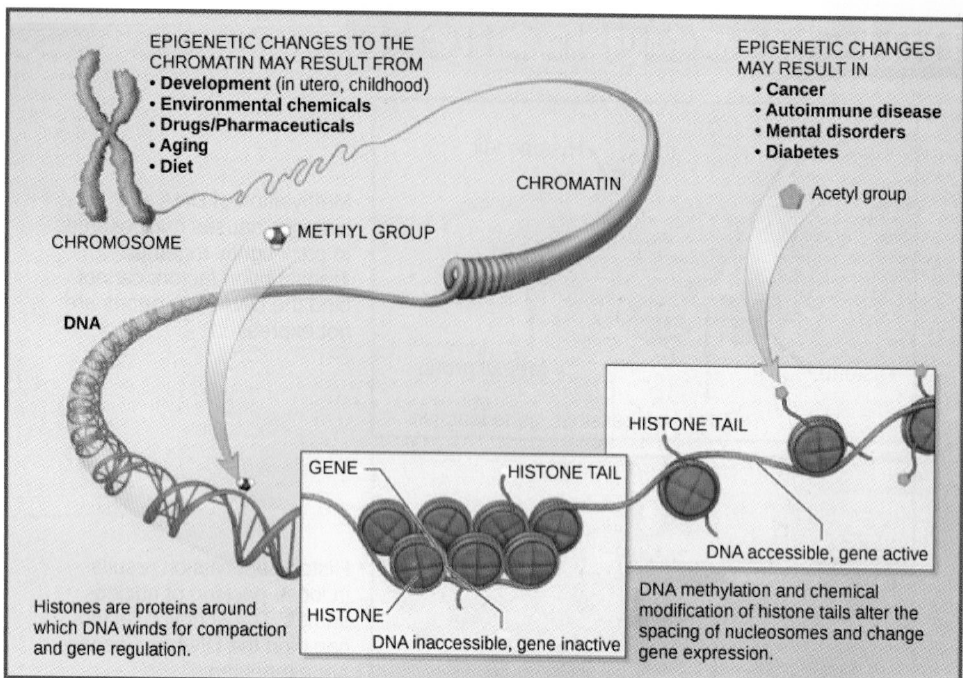

Figure 16.8 Histone proteins and DNA nucleotides can be modified chemically. Modifications affect nucleosome spacing and gene expression. (credit: modification of work by NIH)

This type of gene regulation is called epigenetic regulation. Epigenetic means "around genetics." The changes that occur to the histone proteins and DNA do not alter the nucleotide sequence and are not permanent. Instead, these changes are temporary (although they often persist through multiple rounds of cell division) and alter the chromosomal structure (open or closed) as needed. A gene can be turned on or off depending upon the location and modifications to the histone proteins and DNA. If a gene is to be transcribed, the histone proteins and DNA are modified surrounding the chromosomal region encoding that gene. This opens the chromosomal region to allow access for RNA polymerase and other proteins, called **transcription factors**, to bind to the promoter region, located just upstream of the gene, and initiate transcription. If a gene is to remain turned off, or silenced, the histone proteins and DNA have different modifications that signal a closed chromosomal configuration. In this closed configuration, the RNA polymerase and transcription factors do not have access to the DNA and transcription cannot occur (Figure 16.7).

science practices CONNECTION for AP® Courses

Think About It

In females, one of the two X chromosomes is inactivated during embryonic development because of epigenetic changes to the chromatin. What impact do you think these changes will have on nucleosome packaging and, consequently, gene expression?

View **this video (http://openstaxcollege.org/l/epigenetic_reg)** that describes how epigenetic regulation controls gene expression.

Explain how the study of epigenetics can lead to improved treatment of cancer.

a. Epigenetics would allow new body parts to be synthesized that could replace those damaged by cancer.

b. Epigenetics could change the genetic code of all cells in the body to prevent them from becoming cancerous.

c. New therapies could be made that changes the genetic code of harmful cancer genes.

d. New therapies could be made that do not require altering the cancer cell's DNA.

16.4 | Eukaryotic Transcriptional Gene Regulation

In this section, you will explore the following question:

- What is the role of transcription factors, enhancers, and repressors in gene regulation?

Connection for AP® Courses

To start transcription, general transcription factors must first bind to a specific area on the DNA called the TATA box and then recruit RNA polymerase to that location. In addition, other areas on the DNA called enhancer regions help augment transcription. Transcription factors can bind to enhancer regions to increase or prevent transcription.

Information presented and the examples highlighted in the section support concepts outlined in Big Idea 3 of the AP® Biology Curriculum Framework. The Learning Objectives listed in the Curriculum Framework provide a transparent foundation for the AP® Biology course, an inquiry-based laboratory experience, instructional activities, and AP® exam questions. A Learning Objective merges required content with one or more of the seven Science Practices

Big Idea 3	Living systems store, retrieve, transmit and respond to information essential to life processes.
Enduring Understanding 3.B	Expression of genetic information involves cellular and molecular mechanisms.
Essential Knowledge	**3.B.1** Gene regulation results in differential gene expression, leading to cell specialization
Science Practice	**7.1** The student can connect phenomena and models across spatial and temporal scales.
Learning Objective	**3.18** The student is able to describe the connection between the regulation of gene expression and observed differences between different kinds of organisms
Essential Knowledge	**3.B.1** Gene regulation results in differential gene expression, leading to cell specialization

Science Practice	**7.1** The student can connect phenomena and models across spatial and temporal scales
Learning Objective	**3.19** The student is able to describe the connection between the regulation of gene expression and observed differences between individuals in a population
Essential Knowledge	**3.B.1** Gene regulation results in differential gene expression, leading to cell specialization.
Science Practice	**6.2** The student can construct explanations of phenomena based on evidence produced through scientific practices
Learning Objective	**3.20** The student is able to explain how the regulation of gene expression is essential for the processes and structures that support efficient cell function.
Essential Knowledge	**3.B.1** 1 Gene regulation results in differential gene expression, leading to cell specialization.
Science Practice	**1.4** The student can use representations and models to analyze situations or solve problems qualitatively and quantitatively.
Learning Objective	**3.21** The student can use representations to describe how gene regulation influences cell products and function.

The Science Practice Challenge Questions contain additional test questions for this section that will help you prepare for the AP exam. These questions address the following standards:
[APLO 3.18]

Like prokaryotic cells, the transcription of genes in eukaryotes requires the actions of an RNA polymerase to bind to a sequence upstream of a gene to initiate transcription. However, unlike prokaryotic cells, the eukaryotic RNA polymerase requires other proteins, or transcription factors, to facilitate transcription initiation. Transcription factors are proteins that bind to the promoter sequence and other regulatory sequences to control the transcription of the target gene. RNA polymerase by itself cannot initiate transcription in eukaryotic cells. Transcription factors must bind to the promoter region first and recruit RNA polymerase to the site for transcription to be established.

The activity of transcription factors can regulate differential gene expression in cells, resulting in the development of different cell products and functions. For example, scientists have found that primary sexual characteristics is regulated by several genes Figure 16.9. In the fruit fly *Drosophila*, the *slx* gene determines sex. This gene is expressed when the organism has two copies of the X chromosome. The gene product for *slx* binds to the mRNA of the *tra* gene and regulates its splicing. In the presence of *slx, tra* is spliced into its female form and influences the expression of *dsx* and *fru* to result in female sexual characteristics. In the absence of *slx, tra* is spliced into its male form and male sexual characteristics result.

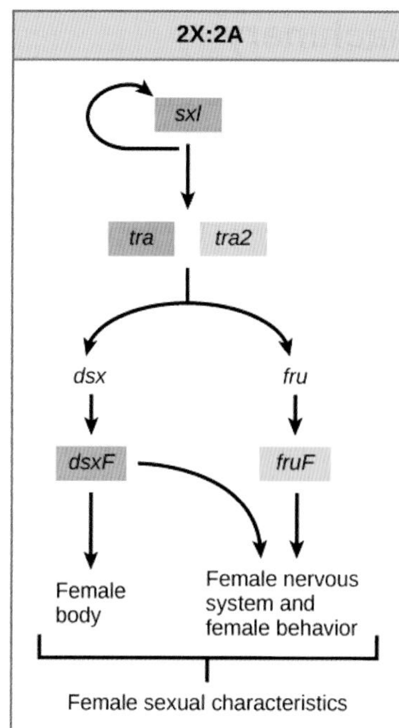

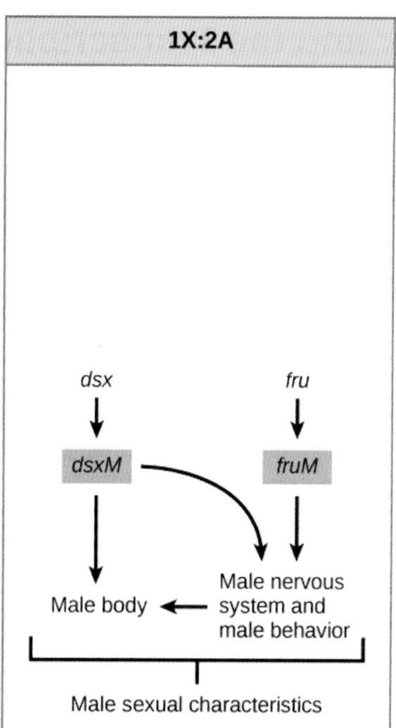

Figure 16.9 In *Drosophila melanogaster*, the sex is determined by a series of splicing events in sex determination genes on a cell-by-cell basis without any involvement of sex hormones (which circulate throughout the entire body). The primary sex-determination gene is *Sex lethal* (*Sxl*), which is transcribed only when the X/A ratio (the X chromosome-to-autosome ratio) equals or exceeds 1. As females have two X chromosomes and males have one, *Sxl* is transcribed only in females (see the figure, left part). Sxl is a splicing repressor and binds to its target, the primary RNA of the *transformer* (*tra*) gene, which undergoes differential splicing depending on the presence (female) or absence (male) of Sxl, yielding a protein-coding *tra* mRNA only in females. The Tra protein binds to the primary RNAs of *doublesex* (*dsx*) and *fruitless* (*fru*). In females, Tra promotes splicing to occur near its binding site, whereas in males it uses an alternative, default splice site. The *dsx* primary RNA thus produces female-specific mRNA and male-specific mRNA, both of which encode functional Dsx proteins, DsxF and DsxM, respectively. The presence (female) and absence (male) of Tra similarly results in female-type *fru* mRNA and male-type *fru* mRNA, but here, only the male-type *fru* mRNA encodes a functional protein.

View the process of transcription—the making of RNA from a DNA template—at this site (http://openstaxcollege.org/l/transcript_RNA) .

Describe the major events that occur during eukaryotic transcription.

a. DNA unwinds, transcription factors bind, the termination complex forms, and DNA polymerase adds nucleotides to the mRNA.

b. DNA unwinds, transcription factors bind, and RNA polymerase adds nucleotides to the mRNA.

c. The transcription complex forms, transcription factors add nucleotides to the forming mRNA, and the mRNA disconnects from the DNA.

d. Elongation occurs, followed by the formation of the transcription initiation complex and the disconnection of the mRNA strand from DNA.

The Promoter and the Transcription Machinery

Genes are organized to make the control of gene expression easier. The promoter region is immediately upstream of the coding sequence. This region can be short (only a few nucleotides in length) or quite long (hundreds of nucleotides long). The longer the promoter, the more available space for proteins to bind. This also adds more control to the transcription process. The length of the promoter is gene-specific and can differ dramatically between genes. Consequently, the level of control of gene expression can also differ quite dramatically between genes. The purpose of the promoter is to bind transcription factors that control the initiation of transcription.

Within the promoter region, just upstream of the transcriptional start site, resides the TATA box. This box is simply a repeat of thymine and adenine dinucleotides (literally, TATA repeats). RNA polymerase binds to the transcription initiation complex, allowing transcription to occur. To initiate transcription, a transcription factor (TFIID) is the first to bind to the TATA box. Binding of TFIID recruits other transcription factors, including TFIIB, TFIIE, TFIIF, and TFIIH to the TATA box. Once this complex is assembled, RNA polymerase can bind to its upstream sequence. When bound along with the transcription factors, RNA polymerase is phosphorylated. This releases part of the protein from the DNA to activate the transcription initiation complex and places RNA polymerase in the correct orientation to begin transcription; DNA-bending protein brings the enhancer, which can be quite a distance from the gene, in contact with transcription factors and mediator proteins (**Figure 16.10**).

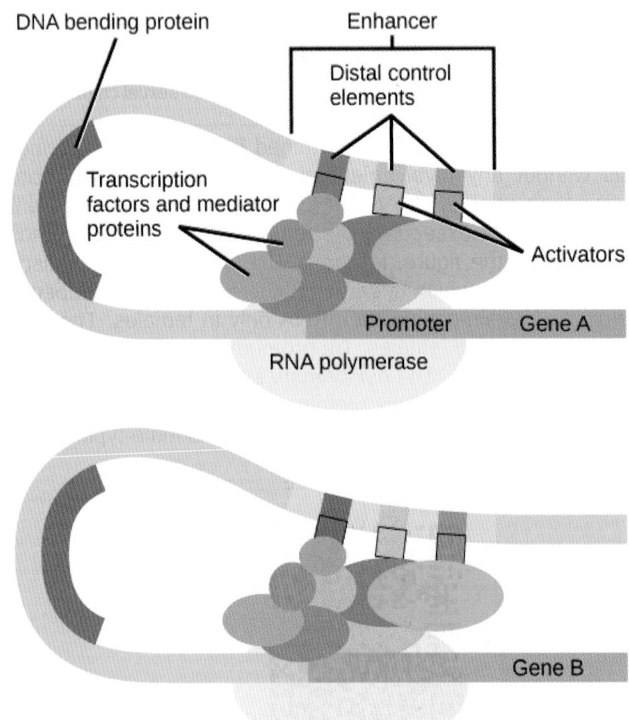

Figure 16.10 An enhancer is a DNA sequence that promotes transcription. Each enhancer is made up of short DNA sequences called distal control elements. Activators bound to the distal control elements interact with mediator proteins and transcription factors. Two different genes may have the same promoter but different distal control elements, enabling differential gene expression.

In addition to the general transcription factors, other transcription factors can bind to the promoter to regulate gene transcription. These transcription factors bind to the promoters of a specific set of genes. They are not general transcription factors that bind to every promoter complex, but are recruited to a specific sequence on the promoter of a specific gene. There are hundreds of transcription factors in a cell that each bind specifically to a particular DNA sequence motif. When transcription factors bind to the promoter just upstream of the encoded gene, it is referred to as a ***cis*-acting element**, because it is on the same chromosome just next to the gene. The region that a particular transcription factor binds to is called the **transcription factor binding site**. Transcription factors respond to environmental stimuli that cause the proteins to find their binding sites and initiate transcription of the gene that is needed.

Enhancers and Transcription

In some eukaryotic genes, there are regions that help increase or enhance transcription. These regions, called **enhancers**, are not necessarily close to the genes they enhance. They can be located upstream of a gene, within the coding region of the gene, downstream of a gene, or may be thousands of nucleotides away.

Enhancer regions are binding sequences, or sites, for transcription factors. When a DNA-bending protein binds, the shape of the DNA changes (Figure 16.10). This shape change allows for the interaction of the activators bound to the enhancers with the transcription factors bound to the promoter region and the RNA polymerase. Whereas DNA is generally depicted as a straight line in two dimensions, it is actually a three-dimensional object. Therefore, a nucleotide sequence thousands of nucleotides away can fold over and interact with a specific promoter.

Turning Genes Off: Transcriptional Repressors

Like prokaryotic cells, eukaryotic cells also have mechanisms to prevent transcription. Transcriptional repressors can bind to promoter or enhancer regions and block transcription. Like the transcriptional activators, repressors respond to external stimuli to prevent the binding of activating transcription factors.

science practices CONNECTION for AP® Courses

Think About It

How can cells in a multicellular eukaryotic organism be of different types given that they all share the same genome?

16.5 | Eukaryotic Post-transcriptional Gene Regulation

In this section, you will explore the following question:

- How is gene expression controlled through post-transcriptional modifications of RNA molecules?

Connection for AP® Courses

Post-transcriptional regulation can occur at any stage after transcription. One important post-transcriptional mechanism is RNA splicing. After RNA is transcribed, it is often modified to create a mature RNA that is ready to be translated. As we studied in previous chapters, processing messenger RNA involves the removal of introns that do not code for protein. Spliceosomes remove the introns and ligate the exons together, often in different sequences than their original order on the newly transcribed (immature) messenger RNA. A GTP cap is added to the 5'-end and a poly-A tail is added to the 3'-end. This mature messenger RNA then leaves the nucleus and enters the cytoplasm. Once in the cytoplasm, the length of time the messenger RNA resides there before being degraded—a characteristic lifespan or "shelf-life" of the molecule called RNA stability—can be altered to control the amount of protein that is synthesized. RNA stability is controlled by several factors, including microRNAs (miRNA or RNAi, RNA interference); miRNAs always decrease stability and promote decay of messenger RNA.

Information presented and the examples highlighted in the section support concepts outlined in Big Idea 3 of the AP® Biology Curriculum Framework. The learning objectives listed in the Curriculum Framework provide a transparent foundation for the AP® Biology course, an inquiry-based laboratory experience, instructional activities, and AP® exam questions. A learning objective merges required content with one or more of the seven science practices.

Big Idea 3	Living systems store, retrieve, transmit and respond to information essential to life processes.
Enduring Understanding 3.A	Heritable information provides for continuity of life.
Essential Knowledge	**3.A.1** DNA, and in some cases RNA, is the primary source of heritable information.

Science Practice	**6.5** The student can evaluate alternative scientific explanations.
Learning Objective	**3.1** The student is able to construct scientific explanations that use the structures and mechanisms of DNA and RNA to support the claim that DNA and, in some cases, RNA are the primary source of heritable information.
Essential Knowledge	**3.A.1** DNA, and in some cases RNA, is the primary source of heritable information.
Science Practice	**6.4** The student can make claims and predictions about natural phenomena based on scientific theories and models.
Learning Objective	**3.6** The student can predict how a change in a specific DNA or RNA sequence can result in changes in gene expression.

RNA is transcribed, but must be processed into a mature form before translation can begin. This processing after an RNA molecule has been transcribed, but before it is translated into a protein, is called post-transcriptional modification. As with the epigenetic and transcriptional stages of processing, this post-transcriptional step can also be regulated to control gene expression in the cell. If the RNA is not processed, shuttled, or translated, then no protein will be synthesized.

RNA Splicing, the First Stage of Post-transcriptional Control

In eukaryotic cells, the RNA transcript often contains regions, called introns, that are removed prior to translation. The regions of RNA that code for protein are called exons (Figure 16.11). After an RNA molecule has been transcribed, but prior to its departure from the nucleus to be translated, the RNA is processed and the introns are removed by splicing.

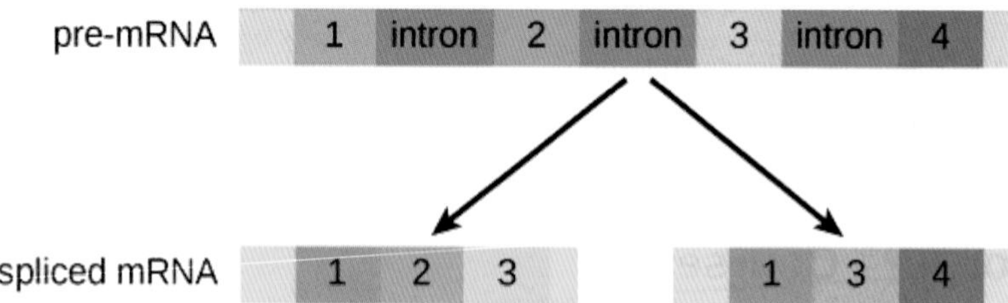

Figure 16.11 Pre-mRNA can be alternatively spliced to create different proteins.

Alternative RNA Splicing

In the 1970s, genes were first observed that exhibited alternative RNA splicing. Alternative RNA splicing is a mechanism that allows different protein products to be produced from one gene when different combinations of introns, and sometimes exons, are removed from the transcript (Figure 16.12). This alternative splicing can be haphazard, but more often it is controlled and acts as a mechanism of gene regulation, with the frequency of different splicing alternatives controlled by the cell as a way to control the production of different protein products in different cells or at different stages of development. Alternative splicing is now understood to be a common mechanism of gene regulation in eukaryotes; according to one estimate, 70 percent of genes in humans are expressed as multiple proteins through alternative splicing.

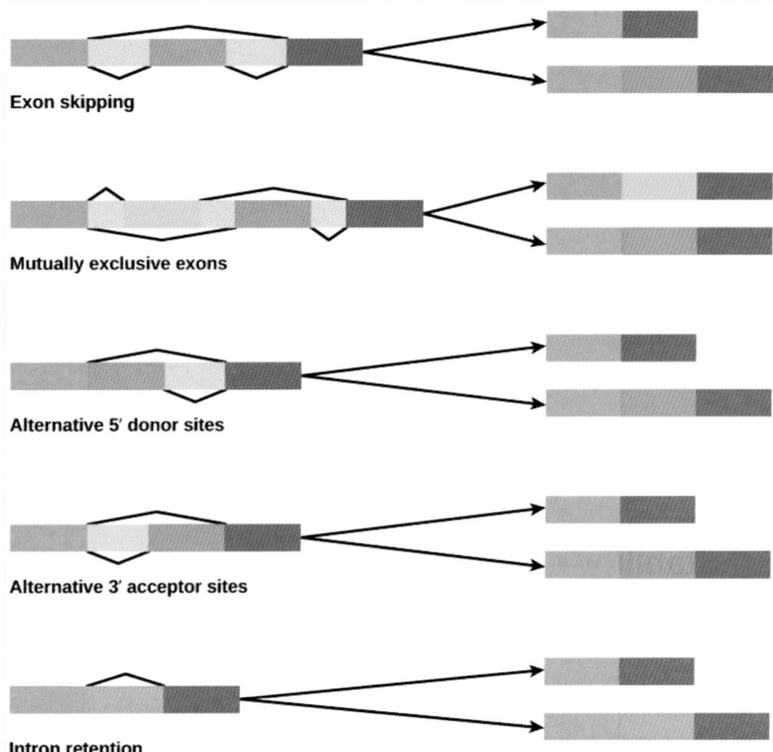

Figure 16.12 There are five basic modes of alternative splicing.

Does alternative gene splicing increase or decrease the flexibility of gene expression? Explain your answer.

a. Flexibility increases because mRNA can be altered after transcription is completed.

b. Flexibility increases because genes can be divided and recombined into new genes.

c. Flexibility decreases because the mRNA molecule becomes smaller.

d. Flexibility decreases because DNA is degraded during alternative splicing.

Visualize how mRNA splicing happens by watching the process in action in **this video (http://openstaxcollege.org/l/mRNA_splicing)** .

Several human diseases are caused by an error in mRNA splicing. Explain why this occurs.

a. Once an mRNA is spliced, the original mRNA cannot be created again.

b. Spliced RNA cannot produce proper proteins.

c. Splicing does not occur at all.

d. Splicing occurs in the wrong location on mRNA.

science practices CONNECTION for AP® Courses

Think About It

What is an evolutionary advantage of alternative gene splicing of introns during post-transcriptional modification of mRNA?

Control of RNA Stability

Before the mRNA leaves the nucleus, it is given two protective "caps" that prevent the end of the strand from degrading during its journey. The **5' cap**, which is placed on the 5' end of the mRNA, is usually composed of a methylated guanosine triphosphate molecule (GTP). The **poly-A tail**, which is attached to the 3' end, is usually composed of a series of adenine nucleotides. Once the RNA is transported to the cytoplasm, the length of time that the RNA resides there can be controlled. Each RNA molecule has a defined lifespan and decays at a specific rate. This rate of decay can influence how much protein is in the cell. If the decay rate is increased, the RNA will not exist in the cytoplasm as long, shortening the time for translation to occur. Conversely, if the rate of decay is decreased, the RNA molecule will reside in the cytoplasm longer and more protein can be translated. This rate of decay is referred to as the RNA stability. If the RNA is stable, it will be detected for longer periods of time in the cytoplasm.

Binding of proteins to the RNA can influence its stability. Proteins, called **RNA-binding proteins**, or RBPs, can bind to the regions of the RNA just upstream or downstream of the protein-coding region. These regions in the RNA that are not translated into protein are called the **untranslated regions**, or UTRs. They are not introns (those have been removed in the nucleus). Rather, these are regions that regulate mRNA localization, stability, and protein translation. The region just before the protein-coding region is called the **5' UTR**, whereas the region after the coding region is called the **3' UTR** (Figure 16.13). The binding of RBPs to these regions can increase or decrease the stability of an RNA molecule, depending on the specific RBP that binds.

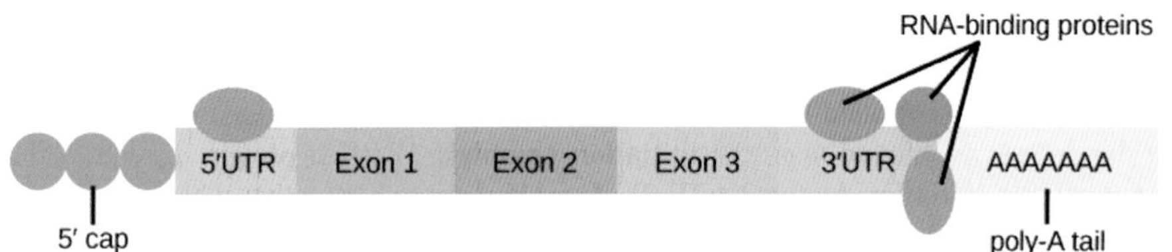

Figure 16.13 The protein-coding region of mRNA is flanked by 5' and 3' untranslated regions (UTRs). The presence of RNA-binding proteins at the 5' or 3' UTR influences the stability of the RNA molecule.

RNA Stability and microRNAs

In addition to RBPs that bind to and control (increase or decrease) RNA stability, other elements called microRNAs can bind to the RNA molecule. These **microRNAs**, or miRNAs, are short RNA molecules that are only 21–24 nucleotides in length. The miRNAs are made in the nucleus as longer pre-miRNAs. These pre-miRNAs are chopped into mature miRNAs by a protein called **dicer**. Like transcription factors and RBPs, mature miRNAs recognize a specific sequence and bind to the RNA; however, miRNAs also associate with a ribonucleoprotein complex called the **RNA-induced silencing complex (RISC)**. RISC binds along with the miRNA to degrade the target mRNA. Together, miRNAs and the RISC complex rapidly destroy the RNA molecule.

16.6 | Eukaryotic Translational and Post-translational Gene Regulation

In this section, you will explore the following question:

- What are different ways in which translational and post-translational control of gene expression take place?

Connection for AP® Courses

Changing the status of the RNA or the protein itself can affect the amount of protein produced, the function of the protein, or how long the protein resides in the cell. Modifications such as phosphorylation and environmental stimuli can affect the stability and function of the protein.

Information presented and the examples highlighted in the section support concepts outlined in Big Idea 4 of the AP® Biology Curriculum Framework. The Learning Objectives listed in the Curriculum Framework provide a transparent foundation for the AP® Biology course, an inquiry-based laboratory experience, instructional activities, and AP® exam questions. A Learning Objective merges required content with one or more of the seven Science Practices.

Big Idea 4	Biological systems interact, and these systems and their interactions possess complex properties.
Enduring Understanding 4.A	Interactions within biological systems lead to complex properties.
Essential Knowledge	**4.A.3** Interactions between external stimuli and regulated gene expression result in specialization of cells, tissues and organs.
Science Practice	**1.3** The student can refine representations and models of natural or man-made phenomena and systems in the domain.
Learning Objective	**4.7** The student is able to refine representations to illustrate how interactions between external stimuli and gene expression result in specialization of cells, tissues, and organs.

After the RNA has been transported to the cytoplasm, it is translated into protein. Control of this process is largely dependent on the RNA molecule. As previously discussed, the stability of the RNA will have a large impact on its translation into a protein. As the stability changes, the amount of time that it is available for translation also changes.

The Initiation Complex and Translation Rate

Like transcription, translation is controlled by proteins that bind and initiate the process. In translation, the complex that assembles to start the process is referred to as the **initiation complex**. The first protein to bind to the RNA to initiate translation is the **eukaryotic initiation factor-2 (eIF-2)**. The eIF-2 protein is active when it binds to the high-energy molecule **guanosine triphosphate (GTP)**. GTP provides the energy to start the reaction by giving up a phosphate and becoming **guanosine diphosphate (GDP)**. The eIF-2 protein bound to GTP binds to the small **40S ribosomal subunit**. When bound, the methionine initiator tRNA associates with the eIF-2/40S ribosome complex, bringing along with it the mRNA to be translated. At this point, when the initiator complex is assembled, the GTP is converted into GDP and energy is released. The phosphate and the eIF-2 protein are released from the complex and the large **60S ribosomal subunit** binds to translate the RNA. The binding of eIF-2 to the RNA is controlled by phosphorylation. If eIF-2 is phosphorylated, it undergoes a conformational change and cannot bind to GTP. Therefore, the initiation complex cannot form properly and translation is impeded (Figure 16.14). When eIF-2 remains unphosphorylated, it binds the RNA and actively translates the protein.

visual CONNECTION

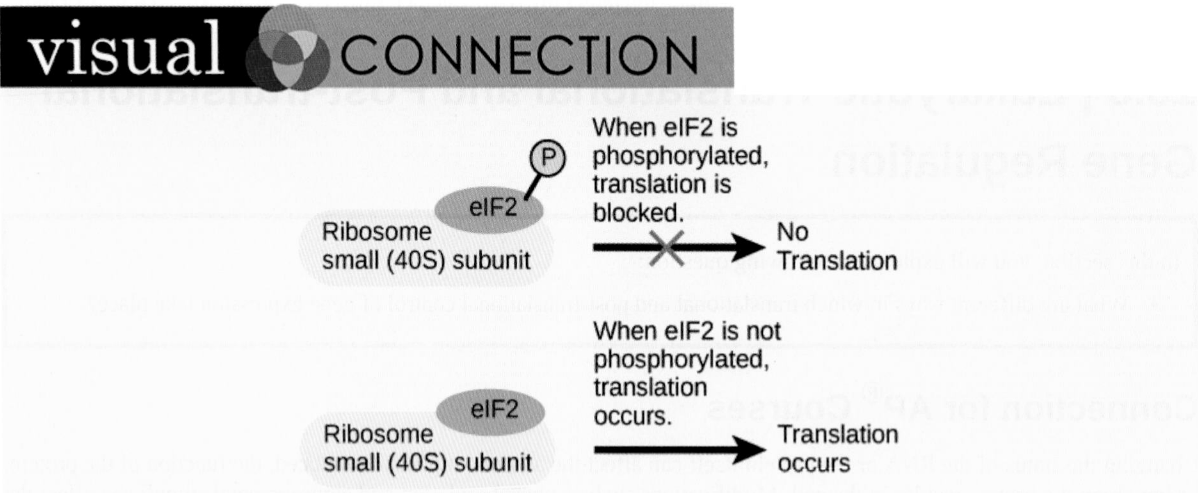

Figure 16.14 Gene expression can be controlled by factors that bind the translation initiation complex.

An increase in phosphorylation levels of eIF-2 has been observed in patients with neurodegenerative diseases such as Alzheimer's, Parkinson's and Huntington's. What impact do you think this might have on protein synthesis?

a. It will increase the rate of translation.
b. It will not affect the translation process.
c. It will block the translation of certain proteins.
d. It will produce multiple fragments of polypeptides.

Chemical Modifications, Protein Activity, and Longevity

Proteins can be chemically modified with the addition of groups including methyl, phosphate, acetyl, and ubiquitin groups. The addition or removal of these groups from proteins regulates their activity or the length of time they exist in the cell. Sometimes these modifications can regulate where a protein is found in the cell—for example, in the nucleus, the cytoplasm, or attached to the plasma membrane.

Chemical modifications occur in response to external stimuli such as stress, the lack of nutrients, heat, or ultraviolet light exposure. These changes can alter epigenetic accessibility, transcription, mRNA stability, or translation—all resulting in changes in expression of various genes. This is an efficient way for the cell to rapidly change the levels of specific proteins in response to the environment. Because proteins are involved in every stage of gene regulation, the phosphorylation of a protein (depending on the protein that is modified) can alter accessibility to the chromosome, can alter translation (by altering transcription factor binding or function), can change nuclear shuttling (by influencing modifications to the nuclear pore complex), can alter RNA stability (by binding or not binding to the RNA to regulate its stability), can modify translation (increase or decrease), or can change post-translational modifications (add or remove phosphates or other chemical modifications).

The addition of an ubiquitin group to a protein marks that protein for degradation. Ubiquitin acts like a flag indicating that the protein lifespan is complete. These proteins are moved to the **proteasome**, an organelle that functions to remove proteins, to be degraded (Figure 16.15). One way to control gene expression, therefore, is to alter the longevity of the protein.

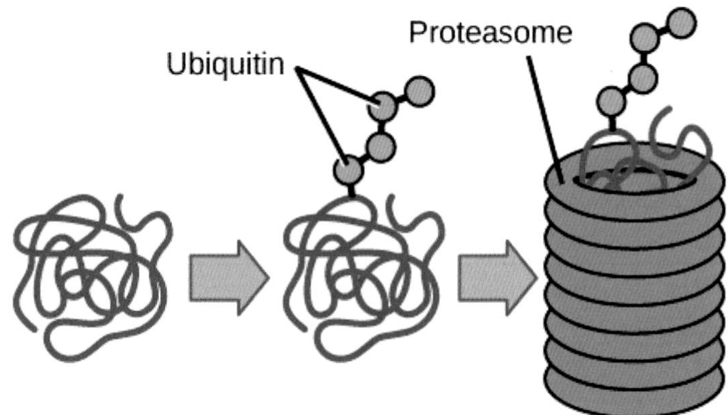

Figure 16.15 Proteins with ubiquitin tags are marked for degradation within the proteasome.

Think About It

How can environmental stimuli such as ultraviolet light exposure or nutrient deficiency modify gene expression?

16.7 | Cancer and Gene Regulation

In this section, you will explore the following questions:

- How can changes in gene expression cause cancer?
- How can changes to gene expression at different levels disrupt the cell cycle?

Connection for AP® Courses

Cancer is a disease of altered gene expression that can occur at every level of control, including at the levels of DNA methylation, histone acetylation, and activation of transcription factors. By understanding how each stage of gene regulation works in normal cells, we can understand what goes wrong in diseased states. For example, changes in the activity of the tumor suppressor gene *p53* can result in cancer. Phosphorylation and other protein modifications have also been implicated in cancer.

Information presented and the examples highlighted in the section support concepts outlined in Big Idea 3 of the AP® Biology Curriculum Framework. The learning objectives listed in the Curriculum Framework provide a transparent foundation for the AP® Biology course, an inquiry-based laboratory experience, instructional activities, and AP® exam questions. A Learning Objective merges required content with one or more of the seven Science Practices.

Big Idea 3	Living systems store, retrieve, transmit and respond to information essential to life processes.
Enduring Understanding 3.B	Expression of genetic information involves cellular and molecular mechanisms.

Essential Knowledge	**3.B.2** A variety of intercellular and intracellular signal transmissions mediate gene expression.
Science Practice	**6.2** The student can construct explanations of phenomena based on evidence produced through scientific practices.
Learning Objective	**3.22** The student is able to explain how signal pathways mediate gene expression, including how this process can affect protein production.
Essential Knowledge	**3.B.2** A variety of intercellular and intracellular signal transmissions mediate gene expression.
Science Practice	**1.4** The student can use representations and models to analyze situations or solve problems qualitatively and quantitatively.
Learning Objective	**3.23** The student can use representations to describe mechanisms of the regulation of gene expression.

Cancer is not a single disease but includes many different diseases. In cancer cells, mutations modify cell-cycle control and cells don't stop growing as they normally would. Mutations can also alter the growth rate or the progression of the cell through the cell cycle. One example of a gene modification that alters the growth rate is increased phosphorylation of cyclin B, a protein that controls the progression of a cell through the cell cycle and serves as a cell-cycle checkpoint protein.

For cells to move through each phase of the cell cycle, the cell must pass through checkpoints. This ensures that the cell has properly completed the step and has not encountered any mutation that will alter its function. Many proteins, including cyclin B, control these checkpoints. The phosphorylation of cyclin B, a post-translational event, alters its function. As a result, cells can progress through the cell cycle unimpeded, even if mutations exist in the cell and its growth should be terminated. This post-translational change of cyclin B prevents it from controlling the cell cycle and contributes to the development of cancer.

Cancer: Disease of Altered Gene Expression

Cancer can be described as a disease of altered gene expression. There are many proteins that are turned on or off (gene activation or gene silencing) that dramatically alter the overall activity of the cell. A gene that is not normally expressed in that cell can be switched on and expressed at high levels. This can be the result of gene mutation or changes in gene regulation (epigenetic, transcription, post-transcription, translation, or post-translation).

Changes in epigenetic regulation, transcription, RNA stability, protein translation, and post-translational control can be detected in cancer. While these changes don't occur simultaneously in one cancer, changes at each of these levels can be detected when observing cancer at different sites in different individuals. Therefore, changes in **histone acetylation** (epigenetic modification that leads to gene silencing), activation of transcription factors by phosphorylation, increased RNA stability, increased translational control, and protein modification can all be detected at some point in various cancer cells. Scientists are working to understand the common changes that give rise to certain types of cancer or how a modification might be exploited to destroy a tumor cell.

Tumor Suppressor Genes, Oncogenes, and Cancer

In normal cells, some genes function to prevent excess, inappropriate cell growth. These are tumor suppressor genes, which are active in normal cells to prevent uncontrolled cell growth. There are many tumor suppressor genes in cells. The most studied tumor suppressor gene is p53, which is mutated in over 50 percent of all cancer types. The p53 protein itself functions as a transcription factor. It can bind to sites in the promoters of genes to initiate transcription. Therefore, the mutation of p53 in cancer will dramatically alter the transcriptional activity of its target genes.

Watch **this animation (http://openstaxcollege.org/l/p53_cancer)** to learn more about the use of p53 in fighting cancer.

Treatment of cancer is often called a "fight against biology." Explain why the use of p53 supports this statement.

a. because normal cells are often negatively affected by cancer treatments, including p53

b. because cancer cells are always affected by current cancer treatments, including p53

c. because normal cells are often negatively affected by cancer treatments, with the exception of p53

d. because cancer cells often aren't affected by cancer treatments, with the exception of p53

Proto-oncogenes are positive cell-cycle regulators. When mutated, proto-oncogenes can become oncogenes and cause cancer. Overexpression of the oncogene can lead to uncontrolled cell growth. This is because oncogenes can alter transcriptional activity, stability, or protein translation of another gene that directly or indirectly controls cell growth. An example of an oncogene involved in cancer is a protein called myc. **Myc** is a transcription factor that is aberrantly activated in Burkett's Lymphoma, a cancer of the lymph system. Overexpression of myc transforms normal B cells into cancerous cells that continue to grow uncontrollably. High B-cell numbers can result in tumors that can interfere with normal bodily function. Patients with Burkett's lymphoma can develop tumors on their jaw or in their mouth that interfere with the ability to eat.

Cancer and Epigenetic Alterations

Silencing genes through epigenetic mechanisms is also very common in cancer cells. There are characteristic modifications to histone proteins and DNA that are associated with silenced genes. In cancer cells, the DNA in the promoter region of silenced genes is methylated on cytosine DNA residues in CpG islands. Histone proteins that surround that region lack the acetylation modification that is present when the genes are expressed in normal cells. This combination of DNA methylation and histone deacetylation (epigenetic modifications that lead to gene silencing) is commonly found in cancer. When these modifications occur, the gene present in that chromosomal region is silenced. Increasingly, scientists understand how epigenetic changes are altered in cancer. Because these changes are temporary and can be reversed—for example, by preventing the action of the histone deacetylase protein that removes acetyl groups, or by DNA methyl transferase enzymes that add methyl groups to cytosines in DNA—it is possible to design new drugs and new therapies to take advantage of the reversible nature of these processes. Indeed, many researchers are testing how a silenced gene can be switched back on in a cancer cell to help re-establish normal growth patterns.

Genes involved in the development of many other illnesses, ranging from allergies to inflammation to autism, are thought to be regulated by epigenetic mechanisms. As our knowledge of how genes are controlled deepens, new ways to treat diseases like cancer will emerge.

Cancer and Transcriptional Control

Alterations in cells that give rise to cancer can affect the transcriptional control of gene expression. Mutations that activate transcription factors, such as increased phosphorylation, can increase the binding of a transcription factor to its binding site in a promoter. This could lead to increased transcriptional activation of that gene that results in modified cell growth. Alternatively, a mutation in the DNA of a promoter or enhancer region can increase the binding ability of a transcription factor. This could also lead to the increased transcription and aberrant gene expression that is seen in cancer cells.

Researchers have been investigating how to control the transcriptional activation of gene expression in cancer. Identifying how a transcription factor binds, or a pathway that activates where a gene can be turned off, has led to new drugs and new ways to treat cancer. In breast cancer, for example, many proteins are overexpressed. This can lead to increased phosphorylation of key transcription factors that increase transcription. One such example is the overexpression of the epidermal growth factor receptor (EGFR) in a subset of breast cancers. The EGFR pathway activates many protein kinases that, in turn, activate many transcription factors that control genes involved in cell growth. New drugs that prevent the activation of EGFR have been developed and are used to treat these cancers.

Cancer and Post-transcriptional Control

Changes in the post-transcriptional control of a gene can also result in cancer. Recently, several groups of researchers have shown that specific cancers have altered expression of miRNAs. Because miRNAs bind to the 3' UTR of RNA molecules to degrade them, overexpression of these miRNAs could be detrimental to normal cellular activity. Too many miRNAs could dramatically decrease the RNA population leading to a decrease in protein expression. Several studies have demonstrated a change in the miRNA population in specific cancer types. It appears that the subset of miRNAs expressed in breast cancer cells is quite different from the subset expressed in lung cancer cells or even from normal breast cells. This suggests that alterations in miRNA activity can contribute to the growth of breast cancer cells. These types of studies also suggest that if some miRNAs are specifically expressed only in cancer cells, they could be potential drug targets. It would, therefore, be conceivable that new drugs that turn off miRNA expression in cancer could be an effective method to treat cancer.

Cancer and Translational/Post-translational Control

There are many examples of how translational or post-translational modifications of proteins arise in cancer. Modifications are found in cancer cells from the increased translation of a protein to changes in protein phosphorylation to alternative splice variants of a protein. An example of how the expression of an alternative form of a protein can have dramatically different outcomes is seen in colon cancer cells. The c-Flip protein, a protein involved in mediating the cell death pathway, comes in two forms: long (c-FLIPL) and short (c-FLIPS). Both forms appear to be involved in initiating controlled cell death mechanisms in normal cells. However, in colon cancer cells, expression of the long form results in increased cell growth instead of cell death. Clearly, the expression of the wrong protein dramatically alters cell function and contributes to the development of cancer.

New Drugs to Combat Cancer: Targeted Therapies

Scientists are using what is known about the regulation of gene expression in disease states, including cancer, to develop new ways to treat and prevent disease development. Many scientists are designing drugs on the basis of the gene expression patterns within individual tumors. This idea, that therapy and medicines can be tailored to an individual, has given rise to the field of personalized medicine. With an increased understanding of gene regulation and gene function, medicines can be designed to specifically target diseased cells without harming healthy cells. Some new medicines, called targeted therapies, have exploited the overexpression of a specific protein or the mutation of a gene to develop a new medication to treat disease. One such example is the use of anti-EGF receptor medications to treat the subset of breast cancer tumors that have very high levels of the EGF protein. Undoubtedly, more targeted therapies will be developed as scientists learn more about how gene expression changes can cause cancer.

Clinical Trial Coordinator

A clinical trial coordinator is the person managing the proceedings of the clinical trial. This job includes coordinating patient schedules and appointments, maintaining detailed notes, building the database to track patients (especially for long-term follow-up studies), ensuring proper documentation has been acquired and accepted, and working with the nurses and doctors to facilitate the trial and publication of the results. A clinical trial coordinator may have a science background, like a nursing degree, or other certification. People who have worked in science labs or in clinical offices are also qualified to become a clinical trial coordinator. These jobs are generally in hospitals; however, some clinics and doctor's offices also conduct clinical trials and may hire a coordinator.

science practices CONNECTION for AP® Courses

Think About It

New drugs are being developed that decrease DNA methylation and prevent the removal of acetyl groups from histone proteins. Explain how these drugs could affect gene expression to help kill tumor cells.

How can understanding the gene expression in a cancer cell tell you something about that specific form of cancer?

KEY TERMS

3' UTR 3' untranslated region; region just downstream of the protein-coding region in an RNA molecule that is not translated

5' cap a methylated guanosine triphosphate (GTP) molecule that is attached to the 5' end of a messenger RNA to protect the end from degradation

5' UTR 5' untranslated region; region just upstream of the protein-coding region in an RNA molecule that is not translated

activator protein that binds to prokaryotic operators to increase transcription

catabolite activator protein (CAP) protein that complexes with cAMP to bind to the promoter sequences of operons that control sugar processing when glucose is not available

***cis*-acting element** transcription factor binding sites within the promoter that regulate the transcription of a gene adjacent to it

dicer enzyme that chops the pre-miRNA into the mature form of the miRNA

DNA methylation epigenetic modification that leads to gene silencing; commonly found in cancer cells

enhancer segment of DNA that is upstream, downstream, perhaps thousands of nucleotides away, or on another chromosome that influence the transcription of a specific gene

epigenetic heritable changes that do not involve changes in the DNA sequence

eukaryotic initiation factor-2 (eIF-2) protein that binds first to an mRNA to initiate translation

gene expression processes that control the turning on or turning off of a gene

guanine diphosphate (GDP) molecule that is left after the energy is used to start translation

guanine triphosphate (GTP) energy-providing molecule that binds to eIF-2 and is needed for translation

histone acetylation epigenetic modification that leads to gene silencing; commonly found in cancer cells.

inducible operon operon that can be activated or repressed depending on cellular needs and the surrounding environment

initiation complex protein complex containing eIF2-2 that starts translation

lac operon operon in prokaryotic cells that encodes genes required for processing and intake of lactose

large 60S ribosomal subunit second, larger ribosomal subunit that binds to the RNA to translate it into protein

microRNA (miRNA) small RNA molecules (approximately 21 nucleotides in length) that bind to RNA molecules to degrade them

myc oncogene that causes cancer in many cancer cells

negative regulator protein that prevents transcription

operator region of DNA outside of the promoter region that binds activators or repressors that control gene expression in prokaryotic cells

operon collection of genes involved in a pathway that are transcribed together as a single mRNA in prokaryotic cells

poly-A tail a series of adenine nucleotides that are attached to the 3' end of an mRNA to protect the end from degradation

positive regulator protein that increases transcription

post-transcriptional control of gene expression after the RNA molecule has been created but before it is translated into protein

post-translational control of gene expression after a protein has been created

proteasome organelle that degrades proteins

repressor protein that binds to the operator of prokaryotic genes to prevent transcription

RISC protein complex that binds along with the miRNA to the RNA to degrade it

RNA stability how long an RNA molecule will remain intact in the cytoplasm

RNA-binding protein (RBP) protein that binds to the 3' or 5' UTR to increase or decrease the RNA stability

small 40S ribosomal subunit ribosomal subunit that binds to the RNA to translate it into protein

***trans*-acting element** transcription factor binding site found outside the promoter or on another chromosome that influences the transcription of a particular gene

transcription factor protein that binds to the DNA at the promoter or enhancer region and that influences transcription of a gene

transcription factor binding site sequence of DNA to which a transcription factor binds

transcriptional start site site at which transcription begins

trp operon series of genes necessary to synthesize tryptophan in prokaryotic cells

tryptophan amino acid that can be synthesized by prokaryotic cells when necessary

untranslated region segment of the RNA molecule that are not translated into protein. These regions lie before (upstream or 5') and after (downstream or 3') the protein-coding region

CHAPTER SUMMARY

16.1 Regulation of Gene Expression

While all somatic cells within an organism contain the same DNA, not all cells within that organism express the same proteins. Prokaryotic organisms express the entire DNA they encode in every cell, but not necessarily all at the same time. Proteins are expressed only when they are needed. Eukaryotic organisms express a subset of the DNA that is encoded in any given cell. In each cell type, the type and amount of protein is regulated by controlling gene expression. To express a protein, the DNA is first transcribed into RNA, which is then translated into proteins. In prokaryotic cells, these processes occur almost simultaneously. In eukaryotic cells, transcription occurs in the nucleus and is separate from the translation that occurs in the cytoplasm. Gene expression in prokaryotes is mostly regulated at the transcriptional level, whereas in eukaryotic cells, gene expression is regulated at the epigenetic, transcriptional, post-transcriptional, translational, and post-translational levels.

16.2 Prokaryotic Gene Regulation

The regulation of gene expression in prokaryotic cells occurs at the transcriptional level. There are three ways to control the transcription of an operon: repressive control, activator control, and inducible control. Repressive control, typified by the *trp* operon, uses proteins bound to the operator sequence to physically prevent the binding of RNA polymerase and the activation of transcription. Therefore, if tryptophan is not needed, the repressor is bound to the operator and transcription remains off. Activator control, typified by the action of CAP, increases the binding ability of RNA polymerase to the promoter when CAP is bound. In this case, low levels of glucose result in the binding of cAMP to CAP. CAP then binds the promoter, which allows RNA polymerase to bind to the promoter better. In the last example—the *lac* operon—two conditions must be met to initiate transcription. Glucose must not be present, and lactose must be available for the *lac* operon to be transcribed. If glucose is absent, CAP binds to the operator. If lactose is present, the repressor protein does not bind to its operator. Only when both conditions are met will RNA polymerase bind to the promoter to induce transcription.

16.3 Eukaryotic Epigenetic Gene Regulation

In eukaryotic cells, the first stage of gene expression control occurs at the epigenetic level. Epigenetic mechanisms control access to the chromosomal region to allow genes to be turned on or off. These mechanisms control how DNA is packed into the nucleus by regulating how tightly the DNA is wound around histone proteins. The addition or removal of chemical modifications (or flags) to histone proteins or DNA signals to the cell to open or close a chromosomal region. Therefore, eukaryotic cells can control whether a gene is expressed by controlling accessibility to transcription factors and the binding of RNA polymerase to initiate transcription.

16.4 Eukaryotic Transcriptional Gene Regulation

To start transcription, general transcription factors, such as TFIID, TFIIH, and others, must first bind to the TATA box and recruit RNA polymerase to that location. The binding of additional regulatory transcription factors to *cis*-acting elements will either increase or prevent transcription. In addition to promoter sequences, enhancer regions help augment transcription. Enhancers can be upstream, downstream, within a gene itself, or on other chromosomes. Transcription factors bind to enhancer regions to increase or prevent transcription.

16.5 Eukaryotic Post-transcriptional Gene Regulation

Post-transcriptional control can occur at any stage after transcription, including RNA splicing, nuclear shuttling, and RNA stability. Once RNA is transcribed, it must be processed to create a mature RNA that is ready to be translated. This involves the removal of introns that do not code for protein. Spliceosomes bind to the signals that mark the exon/intron border to remove the introns and ligate the exons together. Once this occurs, the RNA is mature and can be translated. RNA is created and spliced in the nucleus, but needs to be transported to the cytoplasm to be translated. RNA is transported to the cytoplasm through the nuclear pore complex. Once the RNA is in the cytoplasm, the length of time it resides there before being degraded, called RNA stability, can also be altered to control the overall amount of protein that is synthesized. The RNA stability can be increased, leading to longer residency time in the cytoplasm, or decreased, leading to shortened time and less protein synthesis. RNA stability is controlled by RNA-binding proteins (RPBs) and microRNAs (miRNAs). These RPBs and miRNAs bind to the 5' UTR or the 3' UTR of the RNA to increase or decrease RNA stability. Depending on the RBP, the stability can be increased or decreased significantly; however, miRNAs always decrease stability and promote decay.

16.6 Eukaryotic Translational and Post-translational Gene Regulation

Changing the status of the RNA or the protein itself can affect the amount of protein, the function of the protein, or how long it is found in the cell. To translate the protein, a protein initiator complex must assemble on the RNA. Modifications (such as phosphorylation) of proteins in this complex can prevent proper translation from occurring. Once a protein has been synthesized, it can be modified (phosphorylated, acetylated, methylated, or ubiquitinated). These post-translational modifications can greatly impact the stability, degradation, or function of the protein.

16.7 Cancer and Gene Regulation

Cancer can be described as a disease of altered gene expression. Changes at every level of eukaryotic gene expression can be detected in some form of cancer at some point in time. In order to understand how changes to gene expression can cause cancer, it is critical to understand how each stage of gene regulation works in normal cells. By understanding the mechanisms of control in normal, non-diseased cells, it will be easier for scientists to understand what goes wrong in disease states including complex ones like cancer.

REVIEW QUESTIONS

1. Control of gene expression in eukaryotic cells occurs at which level(s)?

a. only the transcriptional level

b. epigenetic and transcriptional levels

c. epigenetic and transcriptional and translational levels

d. epigenetic and transcriptional, translational, and post-translational levels

2.

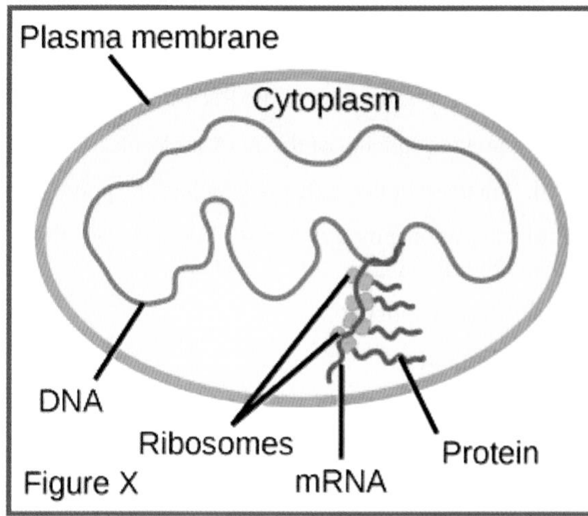

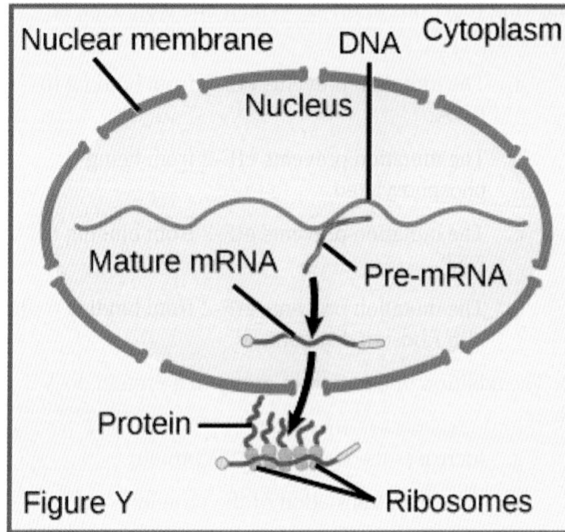

What do figures X and Y in the graphic illustrate?

a. Transcription and translation in a eukaryotic cell (figure X) and a prokaryotic cell (figure Y).
b. Transcription and translation in a prokaryotic cell (figure X) and a eukaryotic cell (figure Y).
c. Transcription in a eukaryotic cell (figure X) and translation in a prokaryotic cell (figure Y).
d. Transcription in a prokaryotic cell (figure X) and translation in a eukaryotic cell (figure Y)

3. If glucose is absent but lactose is present, the *lac* operon will be:

a. activated
b. repressed
c. partially activated
d. mutated

4. What would happen if the operator sequence of the *lac* operon contained a mutation that prevented the repressor protein from binding the operator?

a. In the presence of lactose, the lac operon will not be transcribed.
b. In the absence of lactose, the lac operon will be transcribed.
c. The cAMP-CAP complex will not increase RNA synthesis.
d. The RNA polymerase will not bind the promoter.

5. What would happen if the operator sequence of the *trp* operon contained a mutation that prevented the repressor protein from binding to the operator?

a. In the absence of tryptophan, the genes trpA-E will not be transcribed.
b. In the absence of tryptophan, only genes trpE and trpD will be transcribed.
c. In the presence of tryptophan, the genes trpA-E will be transcribed.
d. In the presence of tryptophan, the trpE gene will not be transcribed.

6. What are epigenetic modifications?

a. the addition of reversible changes to histone proteins and DNA
b. the removal of nucleosomes from the DNA
c. the addition of more nucleosomes to the DNA
d. mutation of the DNA sequence

7. Which of the following statements about epigenetic regulation is false?

a. Histone protein charge becomes more positive when acetyl groups are added.
b. DNA molecules are modified within CpG islands.
c. Methylation of DNA and histones causes nucleosomes to pack tightly together.
d. Histone acetylation results in the loose packing of nucleosomes.

8. Which of the following is true of epigenetic changes?

a. They only allow gene expression.
b. They allow movement of histones.
c. They change the DNA sequence.
d. They are always heritable.

9. The binding of what is required for transcription start?

a. a protein
b. DNA polymerase
c. RNA polymerase
d. a transcription factor

10. What would be the outcome of a mutation that prevented DNA binding proteins from being produced?

a. decreased transcription because transcription factors would not bind to transcription binding sites

b. decreased transcription because enhancers would not be able to bind to transcription factors

c. increased transcription because repressors would not be able to bind to promoter regions

d. increased transcription because RNA polymerase would be able to increase binding to promoter regions

11. What will result from the binding of a transcription factor to an enhancer region?

a. decreased transcription of an adjacent gene

b. increased transcription of a distant gene

c. alteration of the translation of an adjacent gene

d. initiation of the recruitment of RNA polymerase

12. Which of the following are involved in post-transcriptional control?

a. control of RNA splicing

b. ubiquitination

c. proteolytic cleavage

d. phosphorylation

13. Gene A is thought to be associated with color blindness. The protein corresponding to gene A is isolated. Analysis of the protein recovered shows there are actually two different proteins that differ in molecular weight that correspond to gene A. What is one reason why there may be two proteins corresponding to the gene?

a. One protein had a 5' cap and a poly-A tail in its mRNA, and the other protein did not.

b. One protein had a 5' UTR and a 3' UTR in its RNA, and the other protein did not.

c. The gene was alternatively spliced.

d. The gene produced mRNA molecules with differing stability.

14. Binding of an RNA binding protein will change the stability of the RNA molecule in what way?

a. increase

b. decrease

c. neither increase nor decrease

d. either increase or decrease

15. A mutation in the 5'UTR that prevents any proteins from binding to the region will:

a. increase or decrease the stability of the RNA molecule

b. prevent translation of the RNA molecule

c. prevent splicing of the RNA molecule

d. increase or decrease the length of the poly-A tail

16. Post-translational modifications of proteins can affect which of the following?

a. mRNA splicing

b. 5'capping

c. 3'polyadenylation

d. chemical modifications

17. A mutation is found in eIF-2 that impairs the initiation of translation. The mutation could affect all but one of the following functions of eIF-2. Which one would not be affected?

a. The mutation prevents eIF-2 from binding to RNA.

b. The mutation prevents eIF-2 from being phosphorylated.

c. The mutation prevents eIF-2 from binding to GTP.

d. The mutation prevents eIF-2 from binding to the 40S ribosomal subunit.

18. The addition of a ubiquitin group to a protein does what?

a. increases the stability of the protein

b. decreases translation of the protein

c. increases translation of the protein

d. marks the protein for degradation

19. What are cancer-causing genes called?

a. transformation genes

b. tumor suppressor genes

c. oncogenes

d. protooncogenes

20. Targeted therapies are used in patients with a certain gene expression pattern. A targeted therapy that prevents the activation of the estrogen receptor in breast cancer would be beneficial to what type of patient?

a. patients who express the EGFR receptor in normal cells

b. patients with a mutation that inactivates the estrogen receptor

c. patients with over-expression of ER alpha in their tumor cells

d. patients with over-expression of VEGF, which helps in tumor angiogenesis

21. In a new cancer treatment, a cold virus is genetically modified so that it binds to, enters, and is replicated in cells, causing them to burst. The modified cold virus cannot replicate when wildtype p53 protein is present in the cell. How does this treatment treat cancer without harming healthy cells?

a. The modified virus only infects and enters cancer cells.
b. The modified virus replicates in normal and cancer cells.
c. The modified virus only infects and enters normal cells.
d. The modified virus replicates only in cancer cells.

22. A drug designed to switch silenced genes back on in cancer cells would result in what?

a. prevent methylation of DNA and deacetylation of histones
b. prevent methylation of DNA and acetylation of histones
c. prevent deacetylation of DNA and methylation of histones
d. prevent acetylation of DNA and demethylation of histones

23. What are positive cell-cycle regulators that can cause cancer when mutated called?

a. transformation genes
b. tumor suppressor genes
c. oncogenes
d. mutated genes

CRITICAL THINKING QUESTIONS

24. Which best distinguishes prokaryotic and eukaryotic cells?

a. Prokaryotes possess a nucleus whereas eukaryotes do not, but eukaryotes show greater compartmentalization that allows for greater regulation of gene expression.
b. Eukaryotic cells contain a nucleus whereas prokaryotes do not, and eukaryotes show greater compartmentalization that allows for greater regulation of gene expression.
c. Prokaryotic cells are less complex and perform highly-regulated gene expression whereas eukaryotes perform less-regulated gene expression.
d. Eukaryotic cells are more complex and perform less-regulated gene expression whereas prokaryotic cells perform highly-regulated gene expression.

25. Which statement is correct regarding the distinction between prokaryotic and eukaryotic gene expression?

a. Prokaryotes regulate gene expression at the level of transcription whereas eukaryotes regulate at multiple levels including epigenetic, transcriptional and translational.
b. Prokaryotes regulate gene expression at the level of translation whereas eukaryotes regulate at the level of transcription to manipulate protein levels.
c. Prokaryotes regulate gene expression with the help of repressors and activators whereas eukaryotes regulate expression by degrading mRNA transcripts, thereby controlling protein levels.
d. Prokaryotes control protein levels using epigenetic modifications whereas eukaryotes control protein levels by regulating the rate of transcription and translation.

26. All the cells of one organisms share the genome. However, during development, some cells develop into skin cells while others develop into muscle cells. How can the same genetic instructions result in two different cell types in the same organism? Thoroughly explain your answer.

27. Which of the following statements describes prokaryotic transcription of the lac operon?

a. When lactose and glucose are present in the medium, transcription of the lac operon is induced.
b. When lactose is present but glucose is absent, the lac operon is repressed.
c. Lactose acts as an inducer of the lac operon when glucose is absent.
d. Lactose acts as an inducer of the lac operon when glucose is present.

28. The lac operon consists of regulatory regions such as the promoter as well as the structural genes lacZ, lacY, and lacA, which code for proteins involved in lactose metabolism. What would be the outcome of a mutation in one of the structural genes of the *lac* operon?

a. Mutation in structural genes will stop transcription.
b. Mutated lacY will produce an abnormal β galactosidase protein.
c. Mutated lacA will produce a protein that will transfer an acetyl group to β galactosidase.
d. Transcription will continue but lactose will not be metabolized properly.

29. In some diseases, alteration to epigenetic modifications turns off genes that are normally expressed. Hypothetically, how could you reverse this process to turn these genes back on?

30. Flowering Locus C (FLC) is a gene that is responsible for flowering in certain plants. FLC is expressed in new seedlings, which prevents flowering. Upon exposure to cold temperatures, FLC expression decreases and the plant flowers. FLC is regulated through epigenetic modifications. What type of epigenetic modifications are present in new seedlings and after cold exposure?

a. In new seedlings, histone acetylations are present; upon cold exposure, methylation occurs.
b. In new seedlings, histone deacetylations are present; upon cold exposure, methylation occurs.
c. In new seedlings, histone methylations are present; upon cold exposure, acetylation occurs.
d. In new seedlings, histone methylations are present; upon cold exposure, deacetylation occurs.

31. A mutation within the promoter region can alter gene transcription. Describe how this can happen.

a. Mutated promoters decrease the rate of transcription by altering the binding site for the transcription factor.
b. Mutated promoters increase the rate of transcription by altering the binding site for the transcription factor.
c. Mutated promoters alter the binding site for transcription factors to increase or decrease the rate of transcription.
d. Mutated promoters alter the binding site for transcription factors and thereby cease transcription of the adjacent gene.

32. What could happen if a cell had too much of an activating transcription factor present?

a. The transcription rate would increase, altering cell function.
b. The transcription rate would decrease, inhibiting cell functions.
c. The transcription rate decreases due to clogging of the transcription factors.
d. The transcription rate increases due to clogging of the transcription factors.

33. The *wnt* transcription pathway is responsible for key changes during animal development. Based on the transcription pathway shown below. In this diagram, arrows indicate the transformation of one substance into another. Square lines, or the lines with no arrowheads, indicate inhibition of the product below the line. Based on this, how would increased *wnt* gene expression affect the expression of Bar-1?

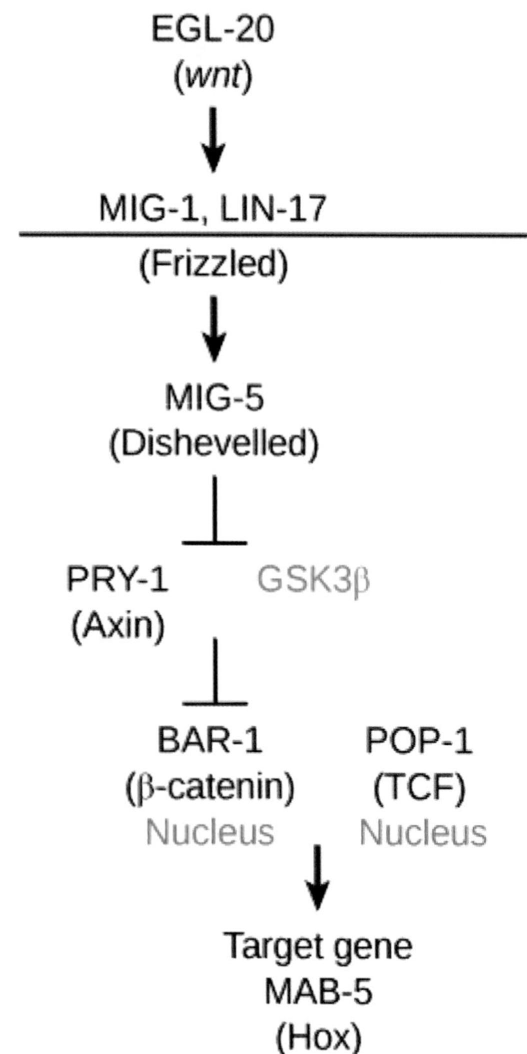

Figure 16.16

34. Describe how RBPs can prevent miRNAs from degrading an RNA molecule.

a. RBPs can bind first to the RNA, thus preventing the binding of miRNA, which degrades RNA.
b. RBPs bind the miRNA, thereby protecting the mRNA from degradation.
c. RBPs methylate miRNA to inhibit its function and thus stop mRNA degradation.
d. RBPs direct miRNA degradation with the help of a DICER protein complex.

35. How can external stimuli alter post-transcriptional control of gene expression?

a. UV rays can alter methylation and acetylation of proteins.
b. RNA binding proteins are modified through phosphorylation.
c. External stimuli can cause deacetylation and demethylation of the transcript.
d. UV rays can cause dimerization of the RNA binding proteins.

36. Protein modifications can alter gene expression in many ways. Describe how phosphorylation of proteins can alter gene expression.

a. Phosphorylation of proteins can alter translation, RNA shuttling, RNA stability or post transcriptional modification.
b. Phosphorylation of proteins can alter DNA replication, cell division, pathogen recognition and RNA stability.
c. Phosphorylated proteins affect only translation and can cause cancer by altering the p53 function.
d. Phosphorylated proteins affect only RNA shuttling, RNA stability, and post-translational modifications.

37. Changes in epigenetic modifications alter the accessibility and transcription of DNA. Describe how environmental stimuli, such as ultraviolet light exposure, could modify gene expression.

a. UV rays could cause methylation and deacetylation of the genes that could alter the accessibility and transcription of DNA.
b. The UV rays could cause phosphorylation and acetylation of the DNA and histones which could alter the transcriptional capabilities of the DNA.
c. UV rays could cause methylation and phosphorylation of the DNA bases which could become dimerized rendering no accessibility of DNA.
d. The UV rays can cause methylation and acetylation of histones making the DNA more tightly packed and leading to inaccessibility.

38. New drugs are being developed that decrease DNA methylation and prevent the removal of acetyl groups from histone proteins. Explain how these drugs could affect gene expression to help kill tumor cells.

a. These drugs maintain the demethylated and the acetylated forms of the DNA to keep transcription of necessary genes "on".
b. The demethylated and the acetylated forms of the DNA are reversed when the silenced gene is expressed.
c. The drug methylates and acetylates the silenced genes to turn them back "on".
d. Drugs maintain DNA methylation and acetylation to silence unimportant genes in cancer cells.

39. How can understanding the gene expression pattern in a cancer cell tell you something about that specific form of cancer?

a. Understanding gene expression patterns in cancer cells will identify the faulty genes, which is helpful in providing the relevant drug treatment.
b. Understanding gene expression will help diagnose tumor cells for antigen therapy.
c. Gene profiling would identify the target genes of the cancer-causing pathogens.
d. Breast cancer patients who do not express EGFR can respond to anti-EGFR therapy.

40. Explain what personalized medicine is and how it can be used to treat cancer.

a. Personalized medicines would vary based on the type of mutations and the gene's expression pattern.
b. The medicines are given based on the type of tumor found in the body of an individual.
c. The personalized medicines are provided based only on the symptoms of the patient.
d. The medicines tend to vary depending on the severity and the stage of the cancer.

TEST PREP FOR AP® COURSES

41. Which of the following is found in both prokaryotes and eukaryotes?

a. 3' poly-A tails
b. 5' caps
c. promoters
d. introns

42. The enzyme ployadenylate polymerase catalyzes the addition of adenosine monophosphate to the 3' ends of mRNAs to form a poly-A tail. If the enzyme were blocked so that it could not function, the result would be:

a. increased mRNA stability in eukaryotes, and decreased mRNA stability in prokaryotes
b. decreased mRNA stability in eukaryotes, and no effect in prokaryotes
c. no effect in eukaryotes, and increased mRNA stability in prokaryotes
d. no effect in eukaryotes, and decreased mRNA stability in prokaryotes

43. Describe two ways in which gene regulation differs and two ways in which it is similar in prokaryotes and eukaryotes.

a. Prokaryotes show co-transcriptional translation whereas eukaryotes perform transcription prior to translation; in both cell types, regulation occurs through the binding of transcription factors, activators, and repressors.
b. Prokaryotes perform transcription prior to translation whereas eukaryotes show co-transcriptional translation (the processes occur in the same organelle).
c. Prokaryotes show co-transcriptional translation that is regulated prior to translation whereas eukaryotes perform transcription prior to translation that is regulated only at the level of transcription. In both domains, transcription factors, activators, and repressors provide regulation.
d. Prokaryotes show co-transcriptional translation that occurs in the nucleus whereas eukaryotes show transcription prior to translation. In both cell types, regulation occurs using transcription factors, activators, and repressors.

44. Lactose digestion in *E. coli* begins with its hydrolysis by the enzyme β -galactosidase. The gene encoding β -galactosidase, lacZ, is part of a coordinately regulated operon containing other genes required for lactose utilization. Which of the following figures correctly depicts the interactions at the *lac* operon when lactose is not being utilized?

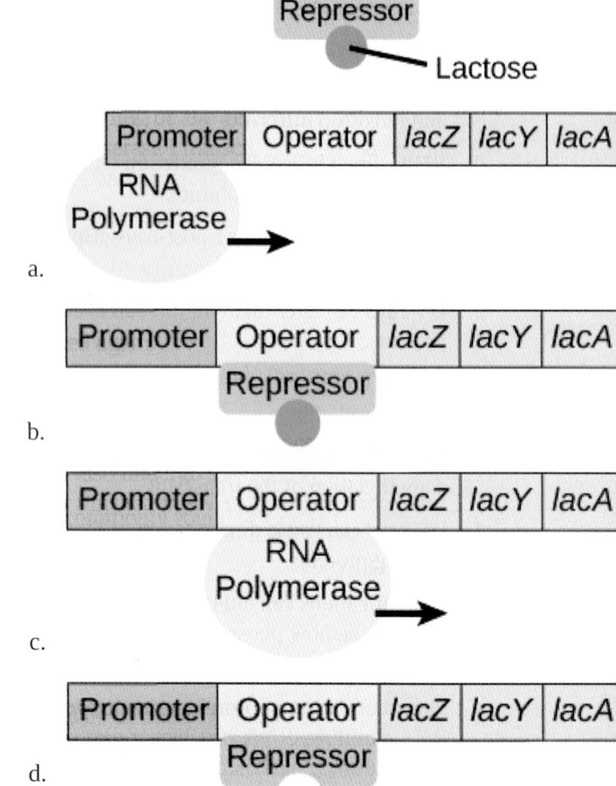

45. What would be the result of a mutation in the repressor protein that prevented it from binding lactose?

a. The repressor will bind to lactose when it is removed from the operator.
b. The repressor will bind the operator in the presence of lactose.
c. The repressor will not bind the operator in the presence of lactose.
d. The repressor will not bind the operator in the absence of lactose.

46. What type of modification might be observed in the GR gene in all newborn rats?

a. The DNA will have many methyl molecules.
b. The DNA will have many acetyl molecules.
c. The DNA will have few methyl groups.
d. The histones will have many acetyl groups.

47. What type of modification will be observed in the GR gene in the highly nurtured rats?

a. The DNA will have many methyl molecules.
b. The DNA will have many acetyl molecules.
c. The DNA will have few methyl groups.
d. The histones will have few acetyl groups.

48.

Normal gene

1 2 3 4 ++

Deletion 1

1 2 3 4 +++

Deletion 2

1 2 3 4 ++

Deletion 3

1 2 3 4 +

Deletion 4

1 2 3 4 ++

The level of transcription of a gene is tested by creating deletions in the gene as shown in the illustration. These modified genes are tested for their level of transcription: (++) normal transcription levels; (+) low transcription levels; (+++) high transcription levels. Which deletion is in an enhancer involved in regulating the gene?

a. deletion 1
b. deletion 2
c. deletion 3
d. deletion 4

49.

Normal gene

Deletion 1

Deletion 2

Deletion 3

Deletion 4

Which deletion is in a repressor involved in regulating the gene?

a. deletion 1
b. deletion 2
c. deletion 3
d. deletion 4

50.

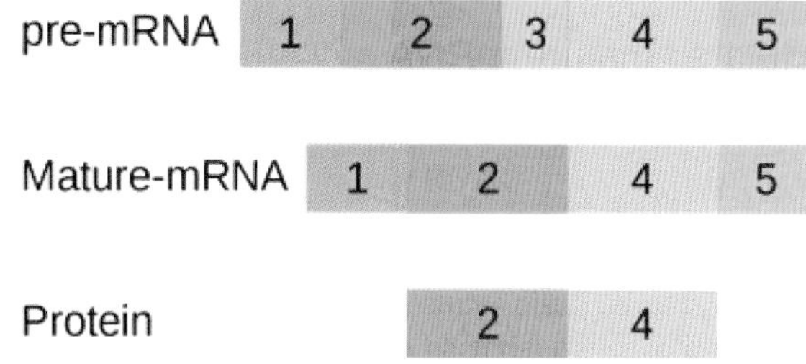

The diagram provided shows different regions (1-5) of a pre-mRNA molecule, a mature-mRNA molecule, and the protein corresponding to the mRNA. A mutation in which region is most likely to be damaging to the cell?

a. 1
b. 2
c. 3
d. 5

51.

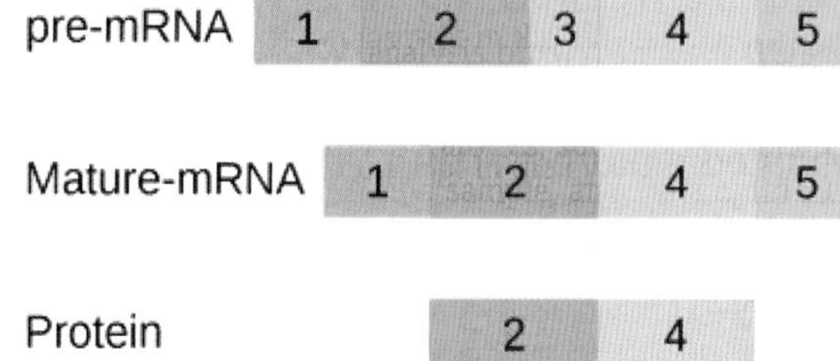

What do regions 1 and 5 correspond to?

a. exons
b. introns
c. promoters
d. untranslated regions

52.

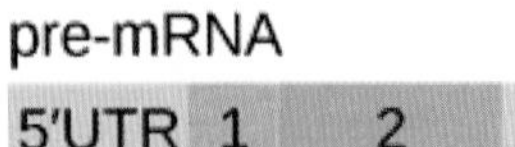

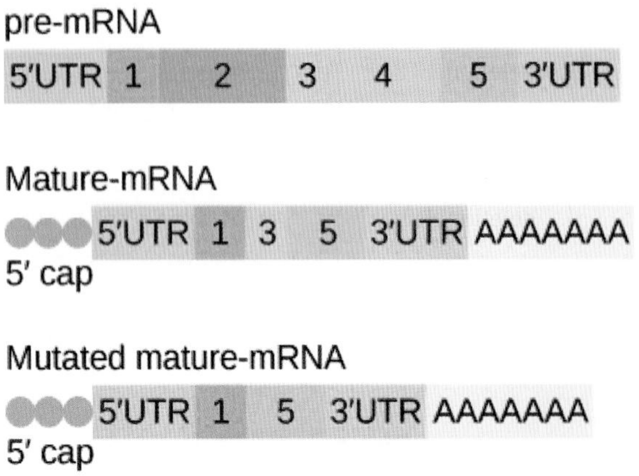

Mature-mRNA

5′UTR 1 3 5 3′UTR AAAAAAA

5′ cap

Mutated mature-mRNA

5′UTR 1 5 3′UTR AAAAAAA

5′ cap

What are regions 1 through 5 in the diagram?

a. 1, 3, and 5 are exons; 2 and 4 are introns.

b. 2 and 4 are exons; 1,3, and 5 are introns.

c. 1 and 5 are exons; 2, 3, and 4 are introns.

d. 2, 3, and 4 are exons; 1 and 5 are introns.

53.

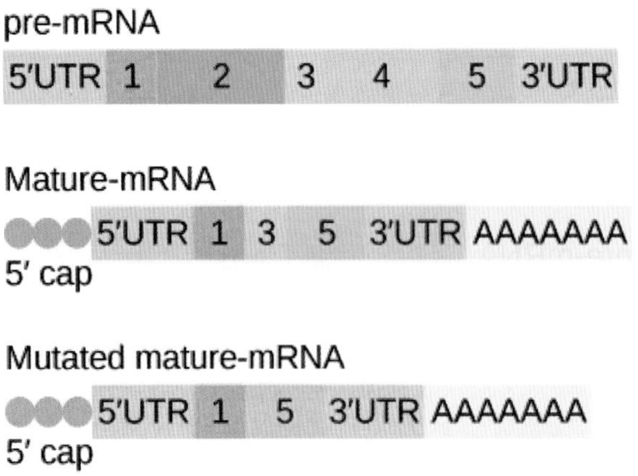

pre-mRNA

5′UTR 1 2 3 4 5 3′UTR

Mature-mRNA

5′UTR 1 3 5 3′UTR AAAAAAA

5′ cap

Mutated mature-mRNA

5′UTR 1 5 3′UTR AAAAAAA

5′ cap

A mutation results in the formation of the mutated mature-mRNA as indicated in the diagram. Describe what type of mutation occurred and what the likely outcome of the mutation is.

a. Mutation in the GU-AG sites of introns produced a non-functional protein.

b. A transversion mutation in the introns led to alternative splicing, producing a functional protein.

c. A transversion mutation in the GU-AG site mutated this mRNA, producing a non-functional protein.

d. Transition mutations in the introns could produce a functional protein.

54.

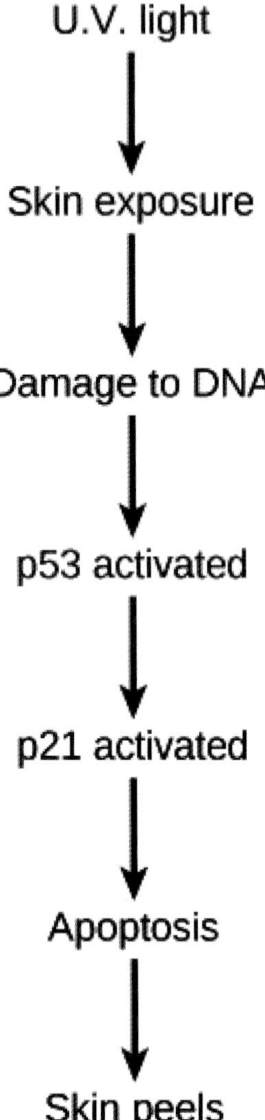

The diagram illustrates the role of p53 in response to UV exposure. What would be the result of a mutation in the p53 gene that inactivates it?

a. Skin will peel in response to UV exposure.

b. Apoptosis will occur in response to UV exposure.

c. No DNA damage will occur in response to UV exposure.

d. No peeling of skin will occur in response to UV exposure.

55. Which of the following will not occur in response to UV exposure if a p53 mutation inactivates the p53 protein?

1. Damage to DNA
2. p53 activation
3. p21 activation
4. Apoptosis

a. 1, 2, and 3
b. 3 and 4
c. 3
d. 2, 3, and 4

56.

What happens when tryptophan is present?

a. The repressor binds to the operator, and RNA synthesis is blocked.
b. RNA polymerase binds to the operator, and RNA synthesis is blocked.
c. Tryptophan binds to the repressor, and RNA synthesis proceeds.
d. Tryptophan binds to RNA polymerase, and RNA synthesis proceeds.

57.

Promoter	Operator	*trpE*	*trpD*	*trpC*	*trpB*	*trpA*

What happens in the absence of tryptophan?

a. RNA polymerase binds to the repressor
b. the repressor binds to the promoter
c. the repressor dissociates from the operator
d. RNA polymerase dissociates from the promoter

58.

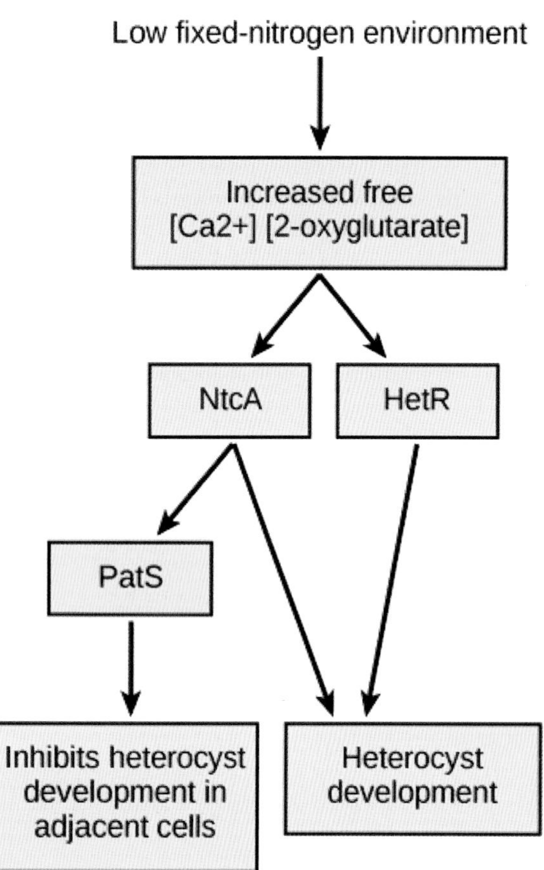

Anabaena is a simple multicellular photosynthetic cyanobacterium. In the absence of fixed nitrogen, certain newly developing cells along a filament express genes that code for nitrogen-fixing enzymes and become non-photosynthetic heterocysts. The specialization is advantageous because some nitrogen-fixing enzymes function best in the absence of oxygen. Heterocysts do not carry out photosynthesis but instead provides adjacent cells with fixed nitrogen and receives fixed carbon and reduced energy carriers in return. As shown in the diagram above, when there is low fixed nitrogen in the environment, an increase in the concentration of free calcium ions and 2-oxyglutarate stimulates the expression of genes that produce two transcription factors (NtcA and HetR) that promote the expression of genes responsible for heterocyst development. HetR also causes production of a signal, PatS, that prevents adjacent cells from developing as heterocysts. Based on your understanding of the ways in which signal transmission mediates cell function, which of the following predictions is most consistent with the information given above?

a. In an environment with low fixed nitrogen, treating the *Anabaena* cells with a calcium-binding compound should prevent heterocyst differentiation.
b. A strain that overexpresses the patS gene should develop many more heterocysts in a low nitrogen environment.
c. In an environment with abundant fixed nitrogen, free calcium levels should be high in all cells, preventing heterocysts from developing.
d. In environments with abundant fixed nitrogen, loss of the hetR gene should induce heterocyst development.

59.

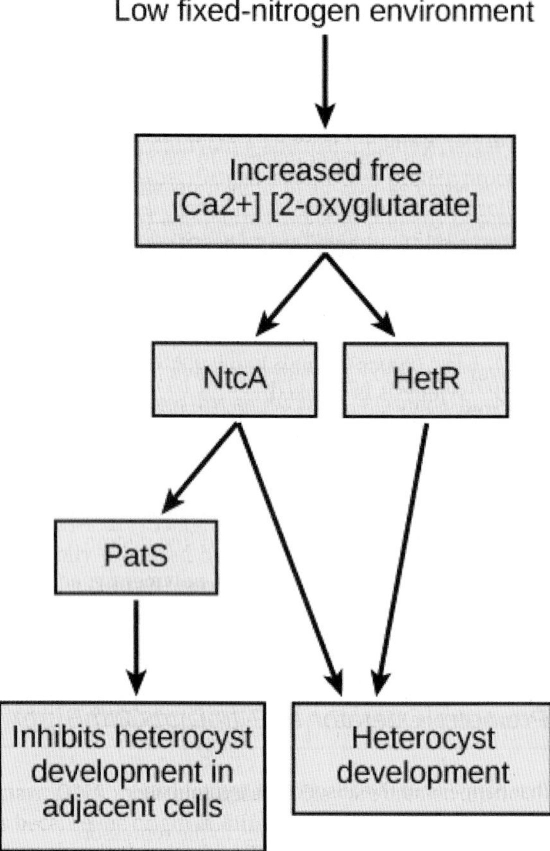

Which of the following statements about *Anabaena* is false?

a. Decreasing the concentration of free calcium ions will prevent heterocyst development.
b. In the presence of fixed nitrogen, NtcA will not be expressed.
c. Low fixed nitrogen levels result in increased PatS levels.
d. A mutation in NtcA that makes it nonfunctional will also allow adjacent cells to develop as heterocysts.

SCIENCE PRACTICE CHALLENGE QUESTIONS

60. The operon model describes expression in prokaryotes. **Describe** this model and the essential difference in the way in which expression is regulated in eukaryotes.

17 | BIOTECHNOLOGY AND GENOMICS

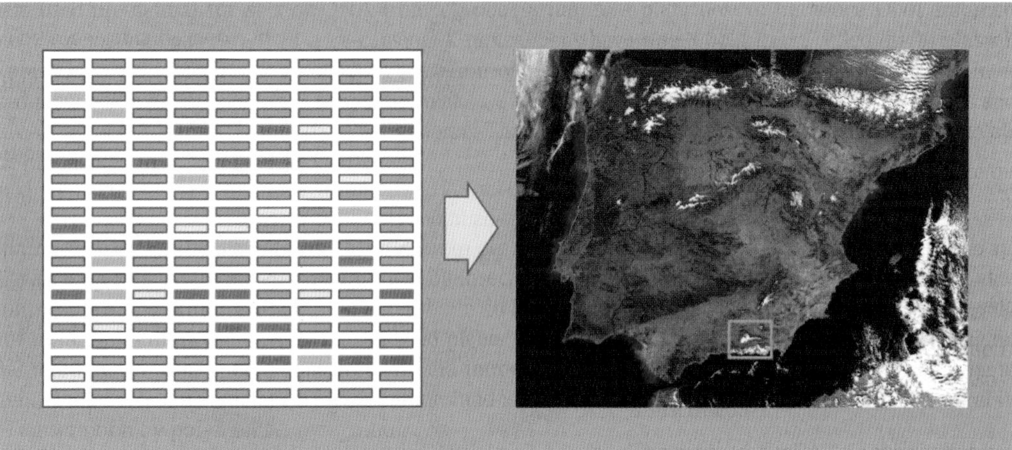

Figure 17.1 In genomics, the DNA of different organisms is compared, enabling scientists to create maps with which to navigate the DNA of different organisms. (credit "map": modification of photo by NASA)

Chapter Outline

Introduction

Some of the greatest accomplishments of biotechnology are in the fields of medicine and medical research. For example, intestinal failure due to missing or abnormal intestinal tissue is a frequent problem in premature babies. Intestinal problems are also common for people who have had parts of their small intestines removed for reasons , such as Crohn's Disease, cancer, and blockages. Complications from intestinal failure may include liver disease, bacterial overgrowth, dehydration, and malnutrition.

Scientists have recently developed a way to engineer human intestines from human cells using mice. Using a mixture of healthy mouse and human intestinal cells and placing it on scaffolding in the abdominal cavity of immunocompromised mice, functional human intestinal cells grow within four weeks. This could be the breakthrough needed to help patients suffering from intestinal failure. More details about this exciting research can be found **here (http://openstaxcollege.org/l/32grwinmouse)** .

17.1 | Biotechnology

In this section, you will explore the following questions:

- What are examples of basic techniques used to manipulate genetic material (DNA and RNA)?
- What is the difference between molecular and reproductive cloning?
- What are examples of uses of biotechnology in medicine and agriculture?

Connection for AP® Courses

Did you eat cereal for breakfast or tomatoes in your dinner salad? Do you know someone who has received gene therapy to treat a disease such as cancer? Should your school, health insurance provider, or employer have access to your genetic profile? Understanding how DNA works has allowed scientists to recombine DNA molecules, clone organisms, and produce mice that glow in the dark. We likely have eaten genetically modified foods and are familiar with how DNA analysis is used to solve crimes. Manipulation of DNA by humans has resulted in bacteria that can protect plants from insect pests and restore ecosystems. Biotechnologies also have been used to produce insulin, hormones, antibiotics, and medicine that dissolve blood clots. Comparative genomics yields new insights into relationships among species, and DNA sequences reveal our personal genetic make-up. However, manipulation of DNA comes with social and ethical responsibilities, raising questions about its appropriate uses.

Nucleic acids can be isolated from cells for analysis by lysing cell membranes and enzymatically destroying all other macromolecules. Fragmented or whole chromosomes can be separated on the basis of size (base pair length) by gel electrophoresis. Short sequences of DNA or RNA can be amplified using the polymerase chain reaction (PCR). Recombinant DNA technology can combine DNA from different sources using bacterial plasmids or viruses as vectors to carry foreign genes into host cells, resulting in genetically modified organisms (GMOs). Transgenic bacteria, agricultural plants such as corn and rice, and farm animals produce protein products such as hormones and vaccines that benefit humans. (It is important to remind ourselves that recombinant technology is possible because the genetic code is universal, and the processes of transcription and translation are fundamentally the same in all organisms.) Cloning produces genetically identical copies of DNA, cells, or even entire organisms (reproductive cloning). Genetic testing identifies disease-causing genes, and gene therapy can be used to treat or cure an inheritable disease. However, questions emerge from these technologies including the safety of GMOs and privacy issues.

Information presented and the examples highlighted in the section support concepts outlined in Big Idea 3 of the AP® Biology Curriculum Framework. The Learning Objectives listed in the Curriculum Framework provide a transparent foundation for the AP® Biology course, an inquiry-based laboratory experience, instructional activities, and AP® exam questions. A Learning Objective merges required content with one or more of the seven Science Practices.

Big Idea 3	Living systems store, retrieve, transmit and respond to information essential to life processes.
Enduring Understanding 3.A	Heritable information provides for continuity of life.
Essential Knowledge	**3.A.1** DNA, and in some cases RNA, is the primary source of heritable information.
Science Practice	**6.4** The student can make claims and predictions about natural phenomena based on scientific theories and models.
Learning Objective	**3.5** The student can justify the claim that humans can manipulate heritable information by identifying an example of a commonly used technology.
Big Idea 3	Living systems store, retrieve, transmit and respond to information essential to life processes.

Enduring Understanding 3.C	The processing of genetic information is imperfect and is a source of genetic variation.
Essential Knowledge	**3.C.1** Changes in genotype can result in changes in phenotype.
Science Practice	**7.2** The student can connect concepts in and across domain(s) to generalize or extrapolate in and/or across enduring understandings and/or big ideas.
Learning Objective	**3.24** The student is able to predict how a change in genotype, when expressed as a phenotype, provides a variation that can be subject to natural selection.

The Science Practice Challenge Questions contain additional test questions for this section that will help you prepare for the AP exam. These questions address the following standards:
[APLO 3.13][APLO 3.23][APLO 3.28][APLO 3.24][APLO 1.11][APLO 3.5][APLO 4.2][APLO 4.8]

Biotechnology is the use of biological agents for technological advancement. Biotechnology was used for breeding livestock and crops long before the scientific basis of these techniques was understood. Since the discovery of the structure of DNA in 1953, the field of biotechnology has grown rapidly through both academic research and private companies. The primary applications of this technology are in medicine (production of vaccines and antibiotics) and agriculture (genetic modification of crops, such as to increase yields). Biotechnology also has many industrial applications, such as fermentation, the treatment of oil spills, and the production of biofuels.

Basic Techniques to Manipulate Genetic Material (DNA and RNA)

To understand the basic techniques used to work with nucleic acids, remember that nucleic acids are macromolecules made of nucleotides (a sugar, a phosphate, and a nitrogenous base) linked by phosphodiester bonds. The phosphate groups on these molecules each have a net negative charge. An entire set of DNA molecules in the nucleus is called the genome. DNA has two complementary strands linked by hydrogen bonds between the paired bases. The two strands can be separated by exposure to high temperatures (DNA denaturation) and can be reannealed by cooling. The DNA can be replicated by the DNA polymerase enzyme. Unlike DNA, which is located in the nucleus of eukaryotic cells, RNA molecules leave the nucleus. The most common type of RNA that is analyzed is the messenger RNA (mRNA) because it represents the protein-coding genes that are actively expressed. However, RNA molecules present some other challenges to analysis, as they are often less stable than DNA.

DNA and RNA Extraction

To study or manipulate nucleic acids, the DNA or RNA must first be isolated or extracted from the cells. Various techniques are used to extract different types of DNA (Figure 17.2). Most nucleic acid extraction techniques involve steps to break open the cell and use enzymatic reactions to destroy all macromolecules that are not desired (such as degradation of unwanted molecules and separation from the DNA sample). Cells are broken using a **lysis buffer** (a solution which is mostly a detergent); lysis means “to split.” These enzymes break apart lipid molecules in the cell membranes and nuclear membranes. Macromolecules are inactivated using enzymes such as **proteases** that break down proteins, and **ribonucleases** (RNAses) that break down RNA. The DNA is then precipitated using alcohol. Human genomic DNA is usually visible as a gelatinous, white mass. The DNA samples can be stored frozen at –80°C for several years.

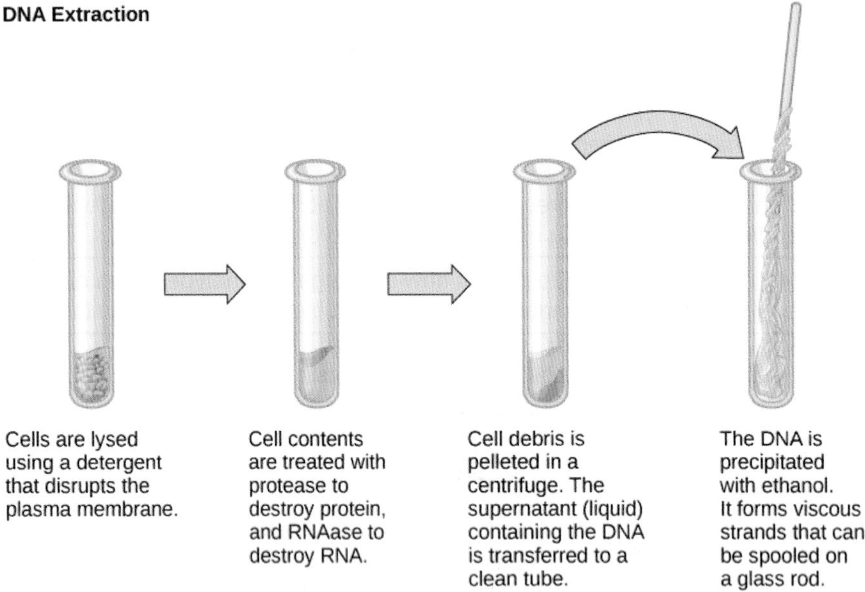

DNA Extraction
Cells are lysed using a detergent that disrupts the plasma membrane.
Cell contents are treated with protease to destroy protein, and RNAase to destroy RNA.
Cell debris is pelleted in a centrifuge. The supernatant (liquid) containing the DNA is transferred to a clean tube.
The DNA is precipitated with ethanol. It forms viscous strands that can be spooled on a glass rod.

Figure 17.2 This diagram shows the basic method used for extraction of DNA.

RNA analysis is performed to study gene expression patterns in cells. RNA is naturally very unstable because RNAses are commonly present in nature and very difficult to inactivate. Similar to DNA, RNA extraction involves the use of various buffers and enzymes to inactivate macromolecules and preserve the RNA.

Gel Electrophoresis

Because nucleic acids are negatively charged ions at neutral or basic pH in an aqueous environment, they can be mobilized by an electric field. **Gel electrophoresis** is a technique used to separate molecules on the basis of size, using this charge. The nucleic acids can be separated as whole chromosomes or fragments. The nucleic acids are loaded into a slot near the negative electrode of a semisolid, porous gel matrix and pulled toward the positive electrode at the opposite end of the gel. Smaller molecules move through the pores in the gel faster than larger molecules; this difference in the rate of migration separates the fragments on the basis of size. There are molecular weight standard samples that can be run alongside the molecules to provide a size comparison. Nucleic acids in a gel matrix can be observed using various fluorescent or colored dyes. Distinct nucleic acid fragments appear as bands at specific distances from the top of the gel (the negative electrode end) on the basis of their size (**Figure 17.3**). A mixture of genomic DNA fragments of varying sizes appear as a long smear, whereas uncut genomic DNA is usually too large to run through the gel and forms a single large band at the top of the gel.

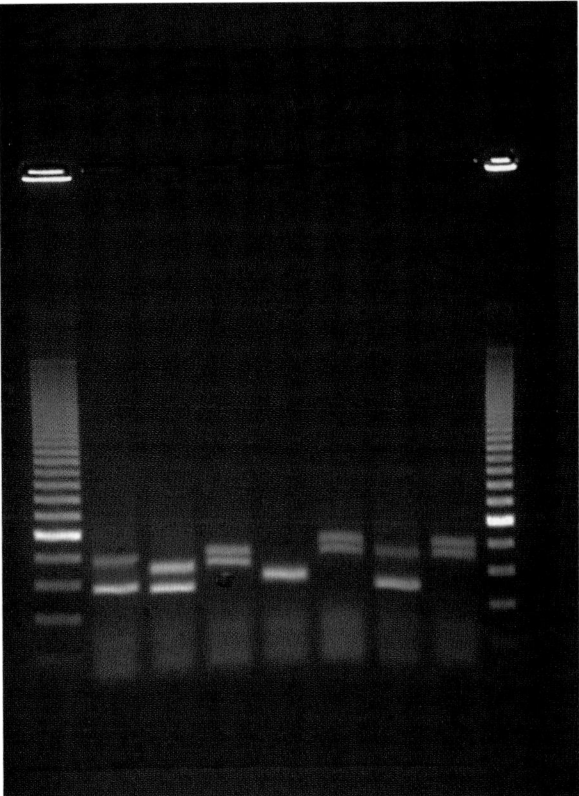

Figure 17.3 Shown are DNA fragments from seven samples run on a gel, stained with a fluorescent dye, and viewed under UV light. (credit: James Jacob, Tompkins Cortland Community College)

Amplification of Nucleic Acid Fragments by Polymerase Chain Reaction

Although genomic DNA is visible to the naked eye when it is extracted in bulk, DNA analysis often requires focusing on one or more specific regions of the genome. **Polymerase chain reaction** (**PCR**) is a technique used to amplify specific regions of DNA for further analysis (Figure 17.4). PCR is used for many purposes in laboratories, such as the cloning of gene fragments to analyze genetic diseases, identification of contaminant foreign DNA in a sample, and the amplification of DNA for sequencing. More practical applications include the detection of genetic diseases.

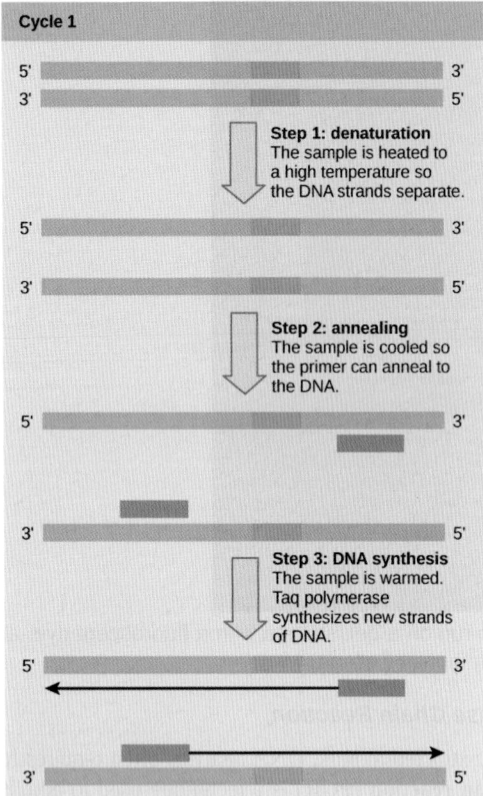
Polymerase Chain Reaction (PCR)
The PCR cycle consists of three steps—denaturation, annealing, and DNA synthesis—that occur at high, low, and intermediate temperatures, respectively. The cycle is repeated again and again, resulting in a doubling of DNA molecules each time. After several cycles, the vast majority of strands produced are the same length as the distance between the two primers.
Cycle 1
5'
3'
Step 1: denaturation
The sample is heated to a high temperature so the DNA strands separate.
Step 2: annealing
The sample is cooled so the primer can anneal to the DNA.
Step 3: DNA synthesis
The sample is warmed. Taq polymerase synthesizes new strands of DNA.

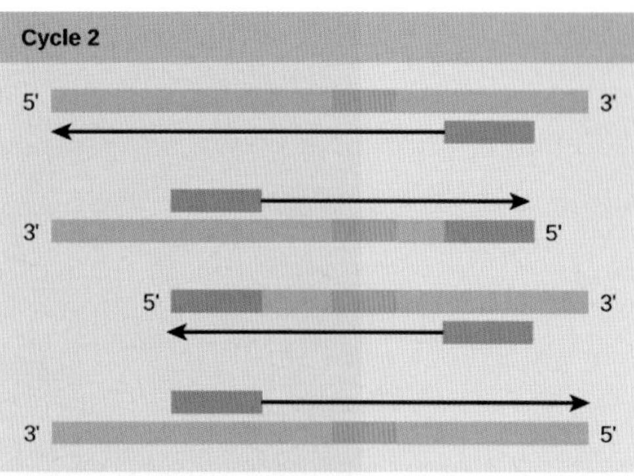
Cycle 2
5'
3'

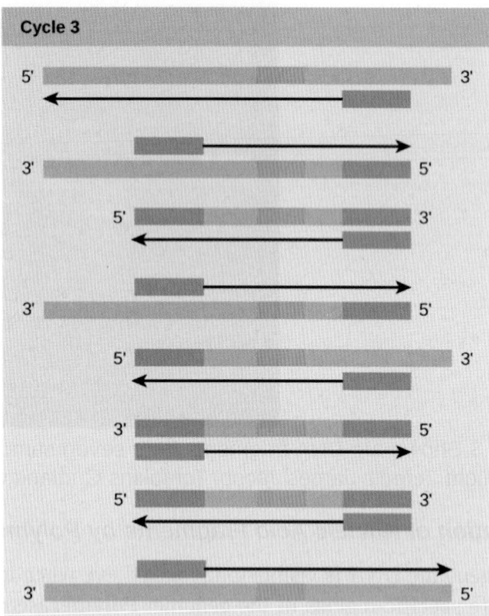
Cycle 3
5'
3'

Figure 17.4 Polymerase chain reaction, or PCR, is used to amplify a specific sequence of DNA. Primers—short pieces of DNA complementary to each end of the target sequence—are combined with genomic DNA, Taq polymerase, and deoxynucleotides. Taq polymerase is a DNA polymerase isolated from the thermostable bacterium *Thermus aquaticus* that is able to withstand the high temperatures used in PCR. *Thermus aquaticus* grows in the Lower Geyser Basin of Yellowstone National Park. Reverse transcriptase PCR (RT-PCR) is similar to PCR, but cDNA is made from an RNA template before PCR begins.

DNA fragments can also be amplified from an RNA template in a process called **reverse transcriptase PCR (RT-PCR)**. The first step is to recreate the original DNA template strand (called cDNA) by applying DNA nucleotides to the mRNA. This process is called reverse transcription. This requires the presence of an enzyme called reverse transcriptase. After the cDNA is made, regular PCR can be used to amplify it.

Deepen your understanding of the polymerase chain reaction by clicking through this interactive exercise (http://openstaxcollege.org/l/PCR) .

Explain an advantage the polymerase chain reaction (PCR) has for DNA research.

a. The process of PCR can isolate a particular piece of DNA for copying, which allows scientists to copy millions of strands of DNA in a short amount of time.

b. The process of PCR can purify a particular piece of DNA, and very small amounts of DNA can be used for purification.

c. The process of PCR separates and analyzes DNA and its fragments, which requires very little DNA.

d. The process of PCR anneals DNA molecules to complementary DNA strands, which maintains the same amount of DNA.

Hybridization, Southern Blotting, and Northern Blotting

Nucleic acid samples, such as fragmented genomic DNA and RNA extracts, can be probed for the presence of certain sequences. Short DNA fragments called **probes** are designed and labeled with radioactive or fluorescent dyes to aid detection. Gel electrophoresis separates the nucleic acid fragments according to their size. The fragments in the gel are then transferred onto a nylon membrane in a procedure called **blotting** (Figure 17.5). The nucleic acid fragments that are bound to the surface of the membrane can then be probed with specific radioactively or fluorescently labeled probe sequences. When DNA is transferred to a nylon membrane, the technique is called **Southern blotting**, and when RNA is transferred to a nylon membrane, it is called **northern blotting**. Southern blots are used to detect the presence of certain DNA sequences in a given genome, and northern blots are used to detect gene expression.

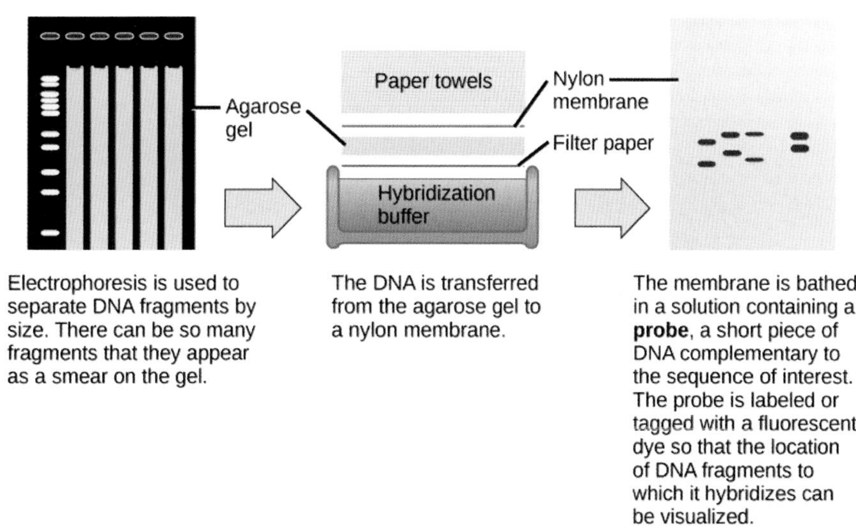

Figure 17.5 Southern blotting is used to find a particular sequence in a sample of DNA. DNA fragments are separated on a gel, transferred to a nylon membrane, and incubated with a DNA probe complementary to the sequence of interest. Northern blotting is similar to Southern blotting, but RNA is run on the gel instead of DNA. In western blotting, proteins are run on a gel and detected using antibodies.

Molecular Cloning

In general, the word “cloning” means the creation of a perfect replica; however, in biology, the re-creation of a whole organism is referred to as “reproductive cloning.” Long before attempts were made to clone an entire organism, researchers learned how to reproduce desired regions or fragments of the genome, a process that is referred to as molecular cloning.

Cloning small fragments of the genome allows for the manipulation and study of specific genes (and their protein products), or noncoding regions in isolation. A plasmid (also called a vector) is a small circular DNA molecule that replicates independently of the chromosomal DNA. In cloning, the plasmid molecules can be used to provide a "folder" in which to insert a desired DNA fragment. Plasmids are usually introduced into a bacterial host for proliferation. In the bacterial context, the fragment of DNA from the human genome (or the genome of another organism that is being studied) is referred to as **foreign DNA**, or a transgene, to differentiate it from the DNA of the bacterium, which is called the **host DNA**.

Plasmids occur naturally in bacterial populations (such as *Escherichia coli*) and have genes that can contribute favorable traits to the organism, such as **antibiotic resistance** (the ability to be unaffected by antibiotics). Plasmids have been repurposed and engineered as vectors for molecular cloning and the large-scale production of important reagents, such as insulin and human growth hormone. An important feature of plasmid vectors is the ease with which a foreign DNA fragment can be introduced via the **multiple cloning site (MCS)**. The MCS is a short DNA sequence containing multiple sites that can be cut with different commonly available restriction endonucleases. **Restriction endonucleases** recognize specific DNA sequences and cut them in a predictable manner; they are naturally produced by bacteria as a defense mechanism against foreign DNA. Many restriction endonucleases make staggered cuts in the two strands of DNA, such that the cut ends have a 2- or 4-base single-stranded overhang. Because these overhangs are capable of annealing with complementary overhangs, these are called “sticky ends.” Addition of an enzyme called DNA ligase permanently joins the DNA fragments via phosphodiester bonds. In this way, any DNA fragment generated by restriction endonuclease cleavage can be spliced between the two ends of a plasmid DNA that has been cut with the same restriction endonuclease (**Figure 17.6**).

Recombinant DNA Molecules

Plasmids with foreign DNA inserted into them are called **recombinant DNA** molecules because they are created artificially and do not occur in nature. They are also called chimeric molecules because the origin of different parts of the molecules can be traced back to different species of biological organisms or even to chemical synthesis. Proteins that are expressed from recombinant DNA molecules are called **recombinant proteins**. Not all recombinant plasmids are capable of expressing genes. The recombinant DNA may need to be moved into a different vector (or host) that is better designed for gene expression. Plasmids may also be engineered to express proteins only when stimulated by certain environmental factors, so that scientists can control the expression of the recombinant proteins.

visual CONNECTION

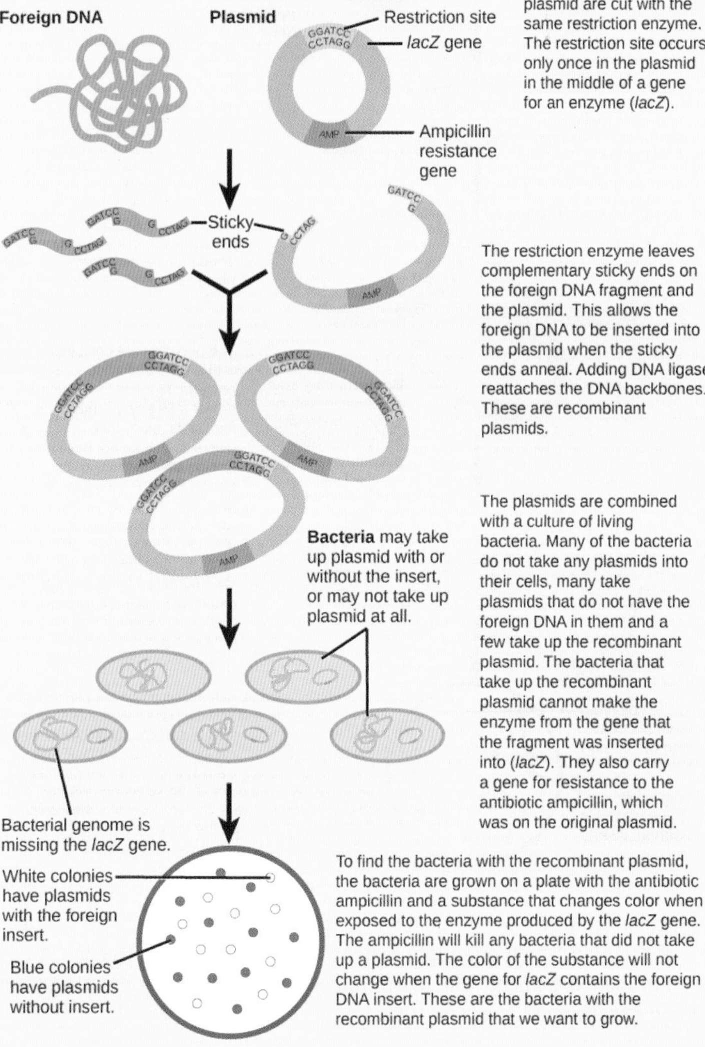

Foreign DNA
Plasmid
Restriction site
lacZ gene
Ampicillin resistance gene
Both foreign DNA and a plasmid are cut with the same restriction enzyme. The restriction site occurs only once in the plasmid in the middle of a gene for an enzyme (lacZ).
Sticky ends
The restriction enzyme leaves complementary sticky ends on the foreign DNA fragment and the plasmid. This allows the foreign DNA to be inserted into the plasmid when the sticky ends anneal. Adding DNA ligase reattaches the DNA backbones. These are recombinant plasmids.
Bacteria may take up plasmid with or without the insert, or may not take up plasmid at all.
The plasmids are combined with a culture of living bacteria. Many of the bacteria do not take any plasmids into their cells, many take plasmids that do not have the foreign DNA in them and a few take up the recombinant plasmid. The bacteria that take up the recombinant plasmid cannot make the enzyme from the gene that the fragment was inserted into (lacZ). They also carry a gene for resistance to the antibiotic ampicillin, which was on the original plasmid.
Bacterial genome is missing the lacZ gene.
White colonies have plasmids with the foreign insert.
Blue colonies have plasmids without insert.
To find the bacteria with the recombinant plasmid, the bacteria are grown on a plate with the antibiotic ampicillin and a substance that changes color when exposed to the enzyme produced by the lacZ gene. The ampicillin will kill any bacteria that did not take up a plasmid. The color of the substance will not change when the gene for lacZ contains the foreign DNA insert. These are the bacteria with the recombinant plasmid that we want to grow.

Figure 17.6 This diagram shows the steps involved in molecular cloning.

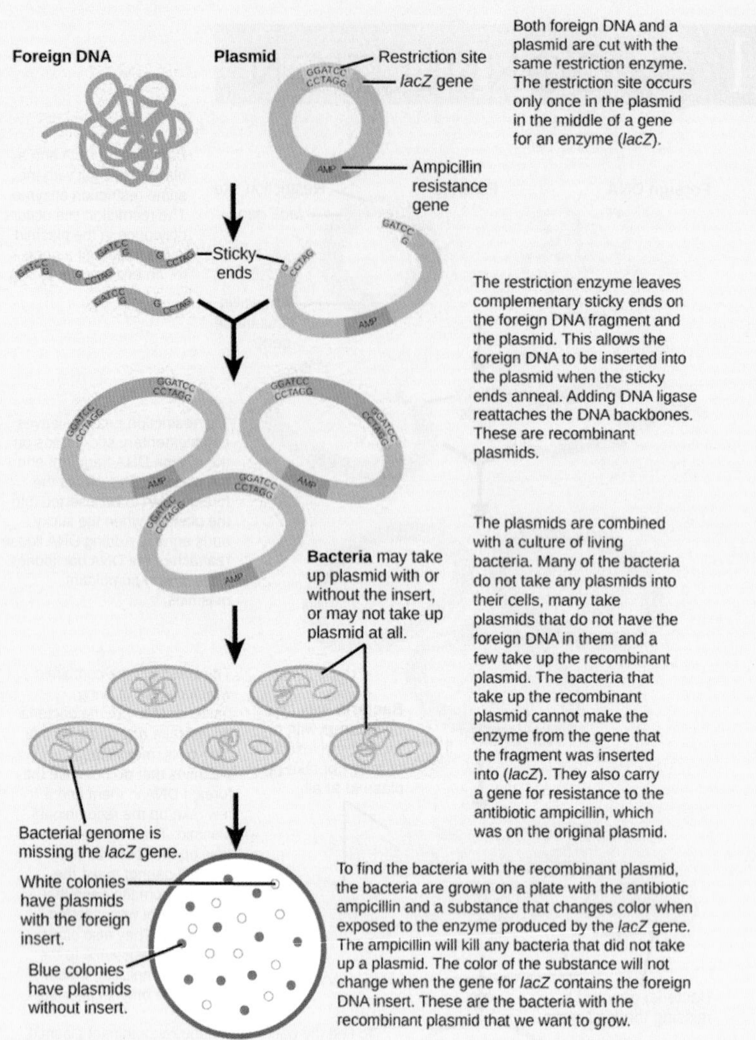
Foreign DNA
Plasmid
Restriction site
lacZ gene
Ampicillin resistance gene
Both foreign DNA and a plasmid are cut with the same restriction enzyme. The restriction site occurs only once in the plasmid in the middle of a gene for an enzyme (lacZ).
Sticky ends
The restriction enzyme leaves complementary sticky ends on the foreign DNA fragment and the plasmid. This allows the foreign DNA to be inserted into the plasmid when the sticky ends anneal. Adding DNA ligase reattaches the DNA backbones. These are recombinant plasmids.
Bacteria may take up plasmid with or without the insert, or may not take up plasmid at all.
The plasmids are combined with a culture of living bacteria. Many of the bacteria do not take any plasmids into their cells, many take plasmids that do not have the foreign DNA in them and a few take up the recombinant plasmid. The bacteria that take up the recombinant plasmid cannot make the enzyme from the gene that the fragment was inserted into (lacZ). They also carry a gene for resistance to the antibiotic ampicillin, which was on the original plasmid.
Bacterial genome is missing the lacZ gene.
White colonies have plasmids with the foreign insert.
Blue colonies have plasmids without insert.
To find the bacteria with the recombinant plasmid, the bacteria are grown on a plate with the antibiotic ampicillin and a substance that changes color when exposed to the enzyme produced by the lacZ gene. The ampicillin will kill any bacteria that did not take up a plasmid. The color of the substance will not change when the gene for lacZ contains the foreign DNA insert. These are the bacteria with the recombinant plasmid that we want to grow.

You are working in a molecular biology lab and, unbeknownst to you, your lab partner left the foreign genomic DNA you are planning to clone on the lab bench overnight instead of storing it in the freezer. As a result, it was degraded by nucleases, but still used in the experiment. The plasmid, on the other hand, is fine. What results would you expect from your molecular cloning experiment?

a. There will be no colonies on the bacterial plate.

b. There will be blue colonies only.

c. There will be blue and white colonies.

d. The will be white colonies only.

View an **animation of recombination in cloning (http://openstaxcollege.org/l/recombination)** from the DNA Learning Center.

What are the functions of the restriction enzymes and DNA ligase in recombination?

a. Restriction enzymes restrict the recombination process. DNA ligase ligates the products of recombination with each other.

b. DNA ligase splices DNA at a specific point, so the new piece of DNA can be inserted. Restriction enzymes stitch together the new gene to the existing piece of DNA.

c. Restriction enzymes splice DNA at a specific point, so the new piece of DNA can be inserted. DNA ligase stitches together the new foreign gene to the existing piece of DNA.

d. Restriction enzymes splice the existing piece of DNA only to accommodate the new piece of DNA. DNA ligase ligates the new DNA with the existing DNA.

science practices CONNECTION for AP® Courses

Activity

Cloning can be used to quickly replicate crop plants that have advantageous genes, such as greater disease resistance or greater fruit production. However, cloning also produces crop plants that have little genetic variation. In a group, discuss the advantages and disadvantages of using clones as human food sources in an era where the Earth is undergoing a period of climate change. How well will cloned populations of crop plants be able to adapt to climate change, compared to non-clone crop plants? Then, defend your group's position against those of other groups in a classroom debate.

Think About It

How would a scientist introduce a gene for herbicide resistance into a plant, such as corn?

Cellular Cloning

Unicellular organisms, such as bacteria and yeast, naturally produce clones of themselves when they replicate asexually by binary fission; this is known as **cellular cloning**. The nuclear DNA duplicates by the process of mitosis, which creates an exact replica of the genetic material.

Reproductive Cloning

Reproductive cloning is a method used to make a clone or an identical copy of an entire multicellular organism. Most multicellular organisms undergo reproduction by sexual means, which involves genetic hybridization of two individuals (parents), making it impossible for generation of an identical copy or a clone of either parent. Recent advances in biotechnology have made it possible to artificially induce asexual reproduction of mammals in the laboratory.

Parthenogenesis, or "virgin birth," occurs when an embryo grows and develops without the fertilization of the egg occurring; this is a form of asexual reproduction. An example of parthenogenesis occurs in species in which the female lays an egg and if the egg is fertilized, it is a diploid egg and the individual develops into a female; if the egg is not fertilized, it remains a haploid egg and develops into a male. The unfertilized egg is called a parthenogenic, or virgin, egg. Some insects and reptiles lay parthenogenic eggs that can develop into adults.

Sexual reproduction requires two cells; when the haploid egg and sperm cells fuse, a diploid zygote results. The zygote nucleus contains the genetic information to produce a new individual. However, early embryonic development requires the cytoplasmic material contained in the egg cell. This idea forms the basis for reproductive cloning. Therefore, if the haploid nucleus of an egg cell is replaced with a diploid nucleus from the cell of any individual of the same species (called a donor), it will become a zygote that is genetically identical to the donor. Somatic cell nuclear transfer is the technique of transferring a diploid nucleus into an enucleated egg. It can be used for either therapeutic cloning or reproductive cloning.

The first cloned animal was Dolly, a sheep who was born in 1996. The success rate of reproductive cloning at the time was very low. Dolly lived for seven years and died of respiratory complications (**Figure 17.7**). There is speculation that because the cell DNA belongs to an older individual, the age of the DNA may affect the life expectancy of a cloned individual. Since Dolly, several animals such as horses, bulls, and goats have been successfully cloned, although these individuals often exhibit facial, limb, and cardiac abnormalities. There have been attempts at producing cloned human embryos as sources of embryonic stem cells, sometimes referred to as cloning for therapeutic purposes. Therapeutic cloning produces stem cells to attempt to remedy detrimental diseases or defects (unlike reproductive cloning, which aims to reproduce an organism). Still, therapeutic cloning efforts have met with resistance because of bioethical considerations.

visual CONNECTION

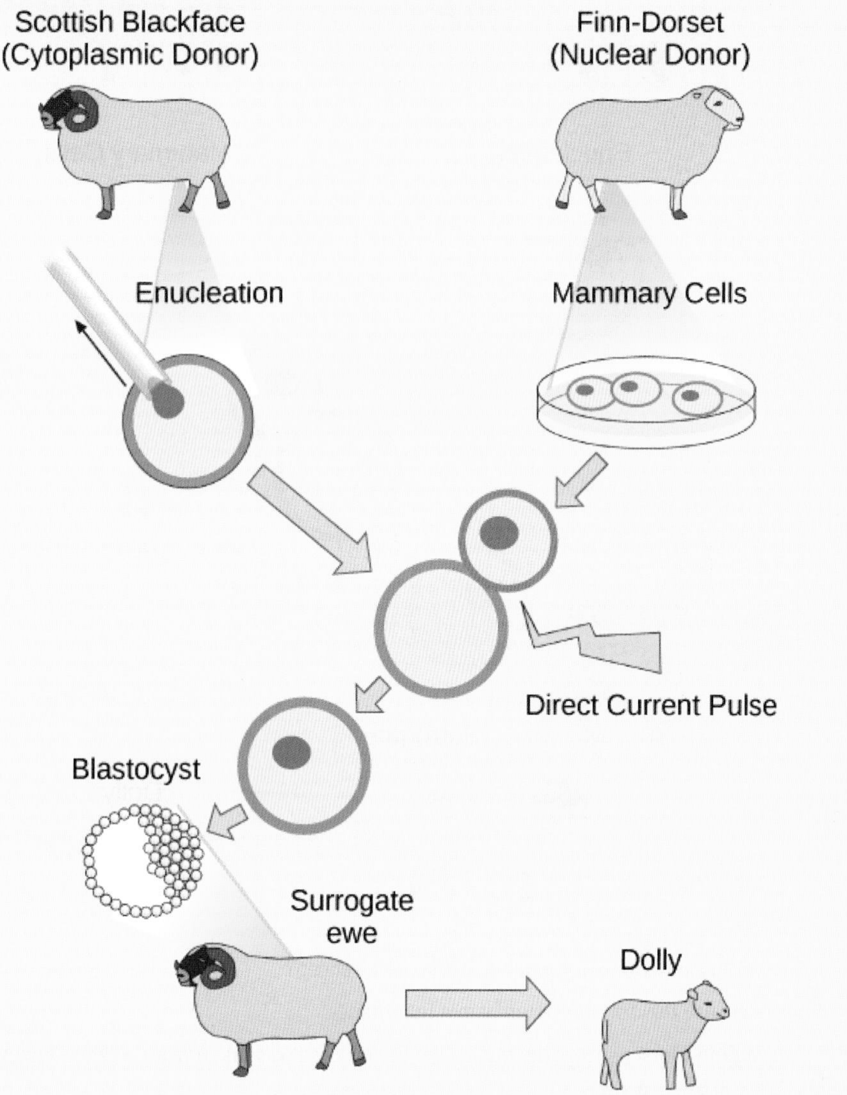

Figure 17.7 Dolly the sheep was the first mammal to be cloned. To create Dolly, the nucleus was removed from a donor egg cell. The nucleus from a second sheep was then introduced into the cell, which was allowed to divide to the blastocyst stage before being implanted in a surrogate mother. (credit: modification of work by "Squidonius"/Wikimedia Commons)

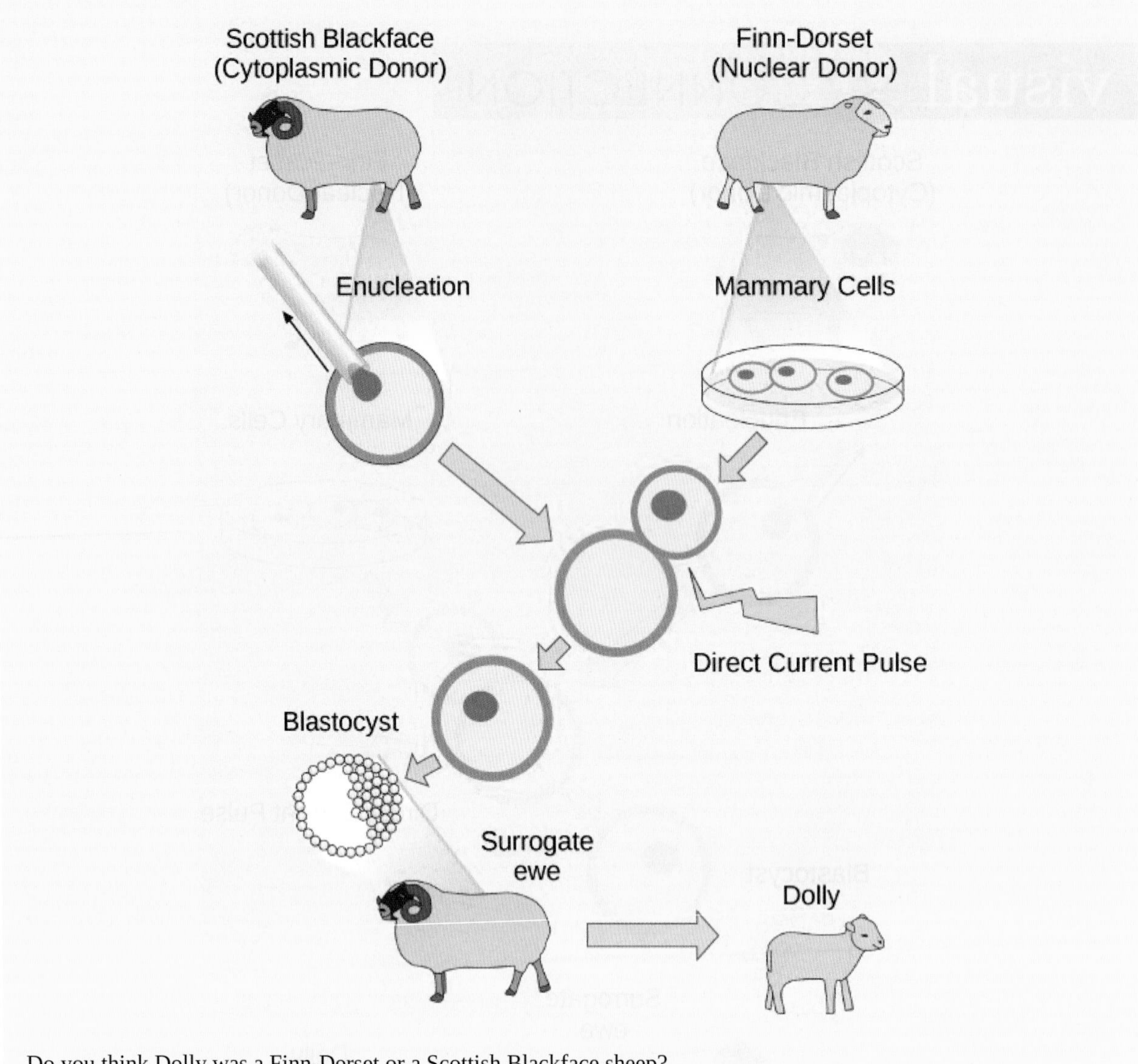

Do you think Dolly was a Finn-Dorset or a Scottish Blackface sheep?

a. Blackface because this follows cytoplasmic inheritance.
b. Dolly was a Finn-Dorset sheep; the nucleus in the process was taken from a Finn-Dorset mother.
c. Dorset sheep because this follows cytoplasmic inheritance.
d. Dolly the sheep was a Scottish blackface due to epigenetic inheritance.

Genetic Engineering

Genetic engineering is the alteration of an organism's genotype using recombinant DNA technology to modify an organism's DNA to achieve desirable traits. The addition of foreign DNA in the form of recombinant DNA vectors generated by molecular cloning is the most common method of genetic engineering. The organism that receives the recombinant DNA is called a **genetically modified organism** (GMO). If the foreign DNA that is introduced comes from a different species, the host organism is called **transgenic**. Bacteria, plants, and animals have been genetically modified since the early 1970s for academic, medical, agricultural, and industrial purposes. In the US, GMOs such as herbicide-resistant soybeans and borer-resistant corn are part of many common processed foods.

Gene Targeting

Although classical methods of studying the function of genes began with a given phenotype and determined the genetic basis of that phenotype, modern techniques allow researchers to start at the DNA sequence level and ask: "What does this gene or DNA element do?" This technique, called reverse genetics, has resulted in reversing the classic genetic methodology. This method would be similar to damaging a body part to determine its function. An insect that loses a wing cannot fly, which means that the function of the wing is flight. The classical genetic method would compare insects that cannot fly with insects that can fly, and observe that the non-flying insects have lost wings. Similarly, mutating or deleting genes provides researchers with clues about gene function. The methods used to disable gene function are collectively called gene targeting. **Gene targeting** is the use of recombinant DNA vectors to alter the expression of a particular gene, either by introducing mutations in a gene, or by eliminating the expression of a certain gene by deleting a part or all of the gene sequence from the genome of an organism.

Biotechnology in Medicine and Agriculture

It is easy to see how biotechnology can be used for medicinal purposes. Knowledge of the genetic makeup of our species, the genetic basis of heritable diseases, and the invention of technology to manipulate and fix mutant genes provides methods to treat the disease. Biotechnology in agriculture can enhance resistance to disease, pest, and environmental stress, and improve both crop yield and quality.

Genetic Diagnosis and Gene Therapy

The process of testing for suspected genetic defects before administering treatment is called **genetic diagnosis** by **genetic testing**. Depending on the inheritance patterns of a disease-causing gene, family members are advised to undergo genetic testing. For example, women diagnosed with breast cancer are usually advised to have a biopsy so that the medical team can determine the genetic basis of cancer development. Treatment plans are based on the findings of genetic tests that determine the type of cancer. If the cancer is caused by inherited gene mutations, other female relatives are also advised to undergo genetic testing and periodic screening for breast cancer. Genetic testing is also offered for fetuses (or embryos with in vitro fertilization) to determine the presence or absence of disease-causing genes in families with specific debilitating diseases.

Gene therapy is a genetic engineering technique used to cure disease. In its simplest form, it involves the introduction of a good gene at a random location in the genome to aid the cure of a disease that is caused by a mutated gene. The good gene is usually introduced into diseased cells as part of a vector transmitted by a virus that can infect the host cell and deliver the foreign DNA (Figure 17.8). More advanced forms of gene therapy try to correct the mutation at the original site in the genome, such as is the case with treatment of severe combined immunodeficiency (SCID).

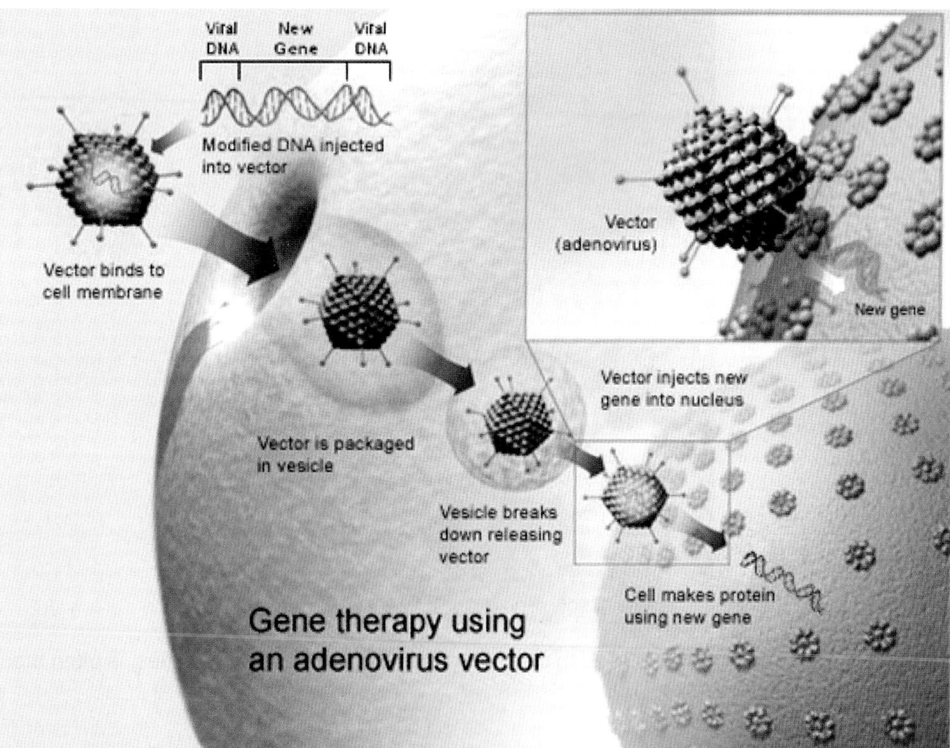

Figure 17.8 Gene therapy using an adenovirus vector can be used to cure certain genetic diseases in which a person has a defective gene. (credit: NIH)

Production of Vaccines, Antibiotics, and Hormones

Traditional vaccination strategies use weakened or inactive forms of microorganisms to mount the initial immune response.

Modern techniques use the genes of microorganisms cloned into vectors to mass produce the desired antigen. The antigen is then introduced into the body to stimulate the primary immune response and trigger immune memory. Genes cloned from the influenza virus have been used to combat the constantly changing strains of this virus.

Antibiotics are a biotechnological product. They are naturally produced by microorganisms, such as fungi, to attain an advantage over bacterial populations. Antibiotics are produced on a large scale by cultivating and manipulating fungal cells.

Recombinant DNA technology was used to produce large-scale quantities of human insulin in *E. coli* as early as 1978. Previously, it was only possible to treat diabetes with pig insulin, which caused allergic reactions in humans because of differences in the gene product. In addition, human growth hormone (HGH) is used to treat growth disorders in children. The HGH gene was cloned from a cDNA library and inserted into *E. coli* cells by cloning it into a bacterial vector.

Transgenic Animals

Although several recombinant proteins used in medicine are successfully produced in bacteria, some proteins require a eukaryotic animal host for proper processing. For this reason, the desired genes are cloned and expressed in animals, such as sheep, goats, chickens, and mice. Animals that have been modified to express recombinant DNA are called transgenic animals. Several human proteins are expressed in the milk of transgenic sheep and goats, and some are expressed in the eggs of chickens. Mice have been used extensively for expressing and studying the effects of recombinant genes and mutations.

Transgenic Plants

Manipulating the DNA of plants (i.e., creating GMOs) has helped to create desirable traits, such as disease resistance, herbicide and pesticide resistance, better nutritional value, and better shelf-life (Figure 17.9). Plants are the most important source of food for the human population. Farmers developed ways to select for plant varieties with desirable traits long before modern-day biotechnology practices were established.

Figure 17.9 Corn, a major agricultural crop used to create products for a variety of industries, is often modified through plant biotechnology. (credit: Keith Weller, USDA)

Plants that have received recombinant DNA from other species are called transgenic plants. Because they are not natural, transgenic plants and other GMOs are closely monitored by government agencies to ensure that they are fit for human consumption and do not endanger other plant and animal life. Because foreign genes can spread to other species in the environment, extensive testing is required to ensure ecological stability. Staples like corn, potatoes, and tomatoes were the first crop plants to be genetically engineered.

Transformation of Plants Using Agrobacterium tumefaciens

Gene transfer occurs naturally between species in microbial populations. Many viruses that cause human diseases act by incorporating their DNA into the human genome. In plants, tumors caused by the bacterium *Agrobacterium tumefaciens* occur by transfer of DNA from the bacterium to the plant. Although the tumors do not kill the plants, they make the plants stunted and more susceptible to harsh environmental conditions. Many plants, such as walnuts, grapes, nut trees, and beets, are affected by *A. tumefaciens*. The artificial introduction of DNA into plant cells is more challenging than in animal cells because of the thick plant cell wall.

Researchers used the natural transfer of DNA from *Agrobacterium* to a plant host to introduce DNA fragments of their choice into plant hosts. In nature, the disease-causing *A. tumefaciens* have a set of plasmids, called the **Ti plasmids** (tumor-inducing plasmids), that contain genes for the production of tumors in plants. DNA from the Ti plasmid integrates into the infected plant cell's genome. Researchers manipulate the Ti plasmids to remove the tumor-causing genes and insert the desired DNA fragment for transfer into the plant genome. The Ti plasmids carry antibiotic resistance genes to aid selection and can be propagated in *E. coli* cells as well.

The Organic Insecticide Bacillus thuringiensis

Bacillus thuringiensis (Bt) is a bacterium that produces protein crystals during sporulation that are toxic to many insect species that affect plants. Bt toxin has to be ingested by insects for the toxin to be activated. Insects that have eaten Bt toxin stop feeding on the plants within a few hours. After the toxin is activated in the intestines of the insects, death occurs within a couple of days. Modern biotechnology has allowed plants to encode their own crystal Bt toxin that acts against insects. The crystal toxin genes have been cloned from Bt and introduced into plants. Bt toxin has been found to be safe for the environment, non-toxic to humans and other mammals, and is approved for use by organic farmers as a natural insecticide.

Flavr Savr Tomato

The first GM crop was in 1994. It was a tomato that resisted rotting and maintained flavor for longer periods of time. Antisense RNA technology was used to slow down the process of softening and rotting caused by fungal infections, which led to increased shelf life of the GM tomatoes. Additional genetic modification improved the flavor of this tomato. This GM tomato did not successfully stay in the market because of problems maintaining and shipping the crop.

17.2 | Mapping Genomes

In this section, you will explore the following questions:

- What is genomics?
- What is a genetic map?
- What is an example of a genomic mapping method?

Connection for AP® Courses

Genome mapping is similar to solving a big, complicated puzzle with pieces of information collected from laboratories all over the world. Genetic maps provide an outline for the location of genes within a chromosome. Distances between genes and genetic markers are estimated on the basis of recombination (crossing over) frequencies during meiosis. The Human Genome Project helped researchers identify thousands of human genes and their protein products. Noncoding regions of DNA may be involved in regulating gene expression, and other sequences once considered "junk" may play an important role in genome evolution. Few differences exist between human DNA sequences and those of many other organisms.

Information presented and the examples highlighted in the section support concepts outlined in Big Idea 3 of the AP® Biology Curriculum Framework. The Learning Objectives listed in the Curriculum Framework provide a transparent foundation for the AP® Biology course, an inquiry-based laboratory experience, instructional activities, and AP® exam questions. A Learning Objective merges required content with one or more of the seven Science Practices.

Big Idea 3	Living systems store, retrieve, transmit and respond to information essential to life processes.

Enduring Understanding 3.A	Heritable information provides for continuity of life.
Essential Knowledge	**3.A.1** DNA, and in some cases RNA, is the primary source of heritable information.
Science Practice	**6.4** The student can make claims and predictions about natural phenomena based on scientific theories and models.
Learning Objective	**3.5** The student can justify the claim that humans can manipulate heritable information by identifying examples of commonly used technologies.
Essential Knowledge	**3.A.2** In eukaryotes, heritable information is passed to the next generation via processes that include the cell cycle and mitosis or meiosis.
Science Practice	**7.1** The student can connect phenomena and models across spatial and temporal scales.
Learning Objective	**3.10** The student is able to represent the connection between meiosis and increased genetic diversity necessary for evolution.
Essential Knowledge	**3.A.3** The chromosomal basis of inheritance provides an understanding of the pattern of passage (transmission) of genes from parent to offspring.
Science Practice	**1.1** The student can create representations and models of natural or man-made phenomena and systems in the domain.
Learning Objective	**7.2** The student can connect concepts in and across domain(s) to generalize or extrapolate in and/or across enduring understandings and/or big ideas.

Genomics is the study of entire genomes, including the complete set of genes, their nucleotide sequence and organization, and their interactions within a species and with other species. **Genome mapping** is the process of finding the locations of genes on each chromosome. The maps created by genome mapping are comparable to the maps that we use to navigate streets. A **genetic map** is an illustration that lists genes and their location on a chromosome. Genetic maps provide the big picture (similar to a map of interstate highways) and use genetic markers (similar to landmarks). A **genetic marker** is a gene or sequence on a chromosome that co-segregates (shows genetic linkage) with a specific trait. Early geneticists called this linkage analysis. Physical maps present the intimate details of smaller regions of the chromosomes (similar to a detailed road map). A **physical map** is a representation of the physical distance, in nucleotides, between genes or genetic markers. Both genetic linkage maps and physical maps are required to build a complete picture of the genome. Having a complete map of the genome makes it easier for researchers to study individual genes. Human genome maps help researchers in their efforts to identify human disease-causing genes related to illnesses like cancer, heart disease, and cystic fibrosis. Genome mapping can be used in a variety of other applications, such as using live microbes to clean up pollutants or even prevent pollution. Research involving plant genome mapping may lead to producing higher crop yields or developing plants that better adapt to climate change.

Genetic Maps

The study of genetic maps begins with **linkage analysis**, a procedure that analyzes the recombination frequency between genes to determine if they are linked or show independent assortment. The term *linkage* was used before the discovery of DNA. Early geneticists relied on the observation of phenotypic changes to understand the genotype of an organism. Shortly after Gregor Mendel (the father of modern genetics) proposed that traits were determined by what are now known as genes, other researchers observed that different traits were often inherited together, and thereby deduced that the genes were physically linked by being located on the same chromosome. The mapping of genes relative to each other based on linkage analysis led to the development of the first genetic maps.

Observations that certain traits were always linked and certain others were not linked came from studying the offspring of crosses between parents with different traits. For example, in experiments performed on the garden pea, it was discovered that the color of the flower and shape of the plant's pollen were linked traits, and therefore the genes encoding these traits were in close proximity on the same chromosome. The exchange of DNA between homologous pairs of chromosomes is called **genetic recombination**, which occurs by the crossing over of DNA between homologous strands of DNA, such as nonsister chromatids. Linkage analysis involves studying the recombination frequency between any two genes. The greater the distance between two genes, the higher the chance that a recombination event will occur between them, and the higher the recombination frequency between them. Two possibilities for recombination between two nonsister chromatids during meiosis are shown in Figure 17.10. If the recombination frequency between two genes is less than 50 percent, they are said to be linked.

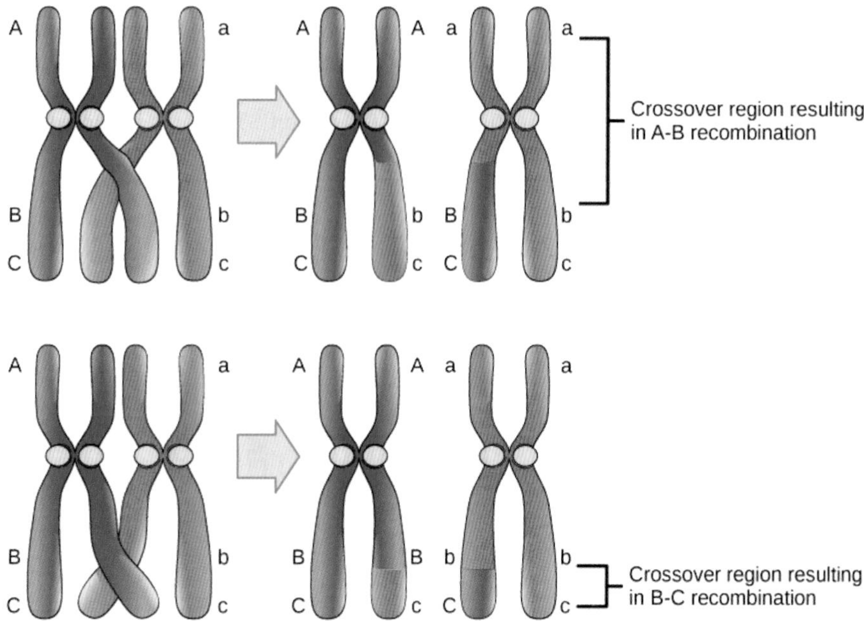

Figure 17.10 Crossover may occur at different locations on the chromosome. Recombination between genes *A* and *B* is more frequent than recombination between genes *B* and *C* because genes *A* and *B* are farther apart; a crossover is therefore more likely to occur between them.

The generation of genetic maps requires markers, just as a road map requires landmarks (such as rivers and mountains). Early genetic maps were based on the use of known genes as markers. More sophisticated markers, including those based on non-coding DNA, are now used to compare the genomes of individuals in a population. Although individuals of a given species are genetically similar, they are not identical; every individual has a unique set of traits. These minor differences in the genome between individuals in a population are useful for the purposes of genetic mapping. In general, a good genetic marker is a region on the chromosome that shows variability or polymorphism (multiple forms) in the population.

Some genetic markers used in generating genetic maps are **restriction fragment length polymorphisms** (RFLP), variable number of tandem repeats (VNTRs), **microsatellite polymorphisms**, and the **single nucleotide polymorphisms** (SNPs). RFLPs (sometimes pronounced "rif-lips") are detected when the DNA of an individual is cut with a restriction endonuclease that recognizes specific sequences in the DNA to generate a series of DNA fragments, which are then analyzed by gel electrophoresis. The DNA of every individual will give rise to a unique pattern of bands when cut with a particular set of restriction endonucleases; this is sometimes referred to as an individual's DNA "fingerprint." Certain regions of the chromosome that are subject to polymorphism will lead to the generation of the unique banding pattern. VNTRs are repeated sets of nucleotides present in the non-coding regions of DNA. Non-coding, or "junk," DNA has no known biological function; however, research shows that much of this DNA is actually transcribed. While its function is uncertain, it is certainly active, and it may be involved in the regulation of coding genes. The number of repeats may vary in individual organisms of a population. Microsatellite polymorphisms are similar to VNTRs, but the repeat unit is very small. SNPs are variations in a single nucleotide.

Because genetic maps rely completely on the natural process of recombination, mapping is affected by natural increases or decreases in the level of recombination in any given area of the genome. Some parts of the genome are recombination hotspots, whereas others do not show a propensity for recombination. For this reason, it is important to look at mapping information developed by multiple methods.

Physical Maps

A physical map provides detail of the actual physical distance between genetic markers, as well as the number of nucleotides. There are three methods used to create a physical map: cytogenetic mapping, radiation hybrid mapping, and sequence mapping. **Cytogenetic mapping** uses information obtained by microscopic analysis of stained sections of the chromosome (Figure 17.11). It is possible to determine the approximate distance between genetic markers using cytogenetic mapping, but not the exact distance (number of base pairs). **Radiation hybrid mapping** uses radiation, such as x-rays, to break the DNA into fragments. The amount of radiation can be adjusted to create smaller or larger fragments. This technique overcomes the limitation of genetic mapping and is not affected by increased or decreased recombination frequency. **Sequence mapping** resulted from DNA sequencing technology that allowed for the creation of detailed physical maps with distances measured in terms of the number of base pairs. The creation of **genomic libraries** and **complementary DNA (cDNA) libraries** (collections of cloned sequences or all DNA from a genome) has sped up the process of physical mapping. A genetic site used to generate a physical map with sequencing technology (a sequence-tagged site, or STS) is a unique sequence in the genome with a known exact chromosomal location. An **expressed sequence tag (EST)** and a single sequence length polymorphism (SSLP) are common STSs. An EST is a short STS that is identified with cDNA libraries, while SSLPs are obtained from known genetic markers and provide a link between genetic maps and physical maps.

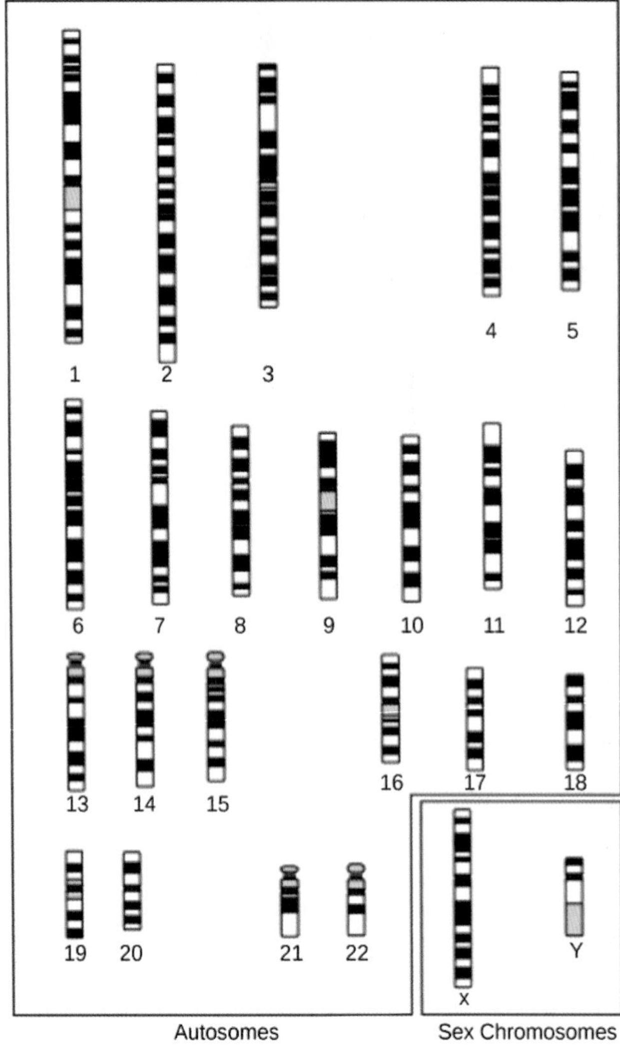

Figure 17.11 A cytogenetic map shows the appearance of a chromosome after it is stained and examined under a microscope. (credit: National Human Genome Research Institute)

Integration of Genetic and Physical Maps

Genetic maps provide the outline and physical maps provide the details. It is easy to understand why both types of genome mapping techniques are important to show the big picture. Information obtained from each technique is used in combination to study the genome. Genomic mapping is being used with different model organisms that are used for research. Genome mapping is still an ongoing process, and as more advanced techniques are developed, more advances are expected. Genome mapping is similar to completing a complicated puzzle using every piece of available data. Mapping information generated in laboratories all over the world is entered into central databases, such as GenBank at the National Center for Biotechnology Information (NCBI). Efforts are being made to make the information more easily accessible to researchers and the general public. Just as we use global positioning systems instead of paper maps to navigate through roadways, NCBI has created a genome viewer tool to simplify the data-mining process.

How to Use a Genome Map Viewer

Problem statement: Do the human, macaque, and mouse genomes contain common DNA sequences?

Develop a hypothesis.

To test the hypothesis, click this **link (http://openstaxcollege.org/l/32mapview)** .

In Search box on the left panel, type any gene name or phenotypic characteristic, such as iris pigmentation (eye color). Select the species you want to study, and then press Enter. The genome map viewer will indicate which chromosome encodes the gene in your search. Click each hit in the genome viewer for more detailed information. This type of search is the most basic use of the genome viewer; it can also be used to compare sequences between species, as well as many other complicated tasks.

Is the hypothesis correct? Why or why not?

Online Mendelian Inheritance in Man (OMIM) is a searchable online catalog of human genes and genetic disorders. This website shows genome mapping information, and also details the history and research of each trait and disorder. Click this **link (http://openstaxcollege.org/l/OMIM)** to search for traits (such as handedness) and genetic disorders (such as diabetes).

How can this database help to support and guide research for rare genetic conditions, like progeria?

a. The database provides information related to the prevention of a genetic disease.

b. The database provides all the information about genes for genetic diseases, their inheritance and their expression. It also provides suggestions for some treatments.

c. The database provides information about the symptoms of the disease.

d. The database provides information only about the early reported cases.

science practices CONNECTION for AP® Courses

Think About It

Why is so much effort being poured into genome mapping applications? How could a genetic map of the human genome help find a treatment for genetically based cancers?

17.3 | Whole-Genome Sequencing

In this section, you will explore the following questions:

- What are three types of gene sequencing?
- What is whole-genome sequencing?

Connection for AP® Courses

Information presented in section is not in scope for AP®. However, you can study information in the section as optional or illustrative material.

Although there have been significant advances in the medical sciences in recent years, doctors are still confounded by some diseases, and they are using whole-genome sequencing to get to the bottom of the problem. **Whole-genome sequencing** is a process that determines the DNA sequence of an entire genome. Whole-genome sequencing is a brute-force approach to problem solving when there is a genetic basis at the core of a disease. Several laboratories now provide services to sequence, analyze, and interpret entire genomes.

Whole-exome sequencing is a lower-cost alternative to whole genome sequencing. In exome sequencing, only the coding, exon-producing regions of the DNA are sequenced. In 2010, whole-exome sequencing was used to save a young boy whose intestines had multiple mysterious abscesses. The child had several colon operations with no relief. Finally, whole-exome sequencing was performed, which revealed a defect in a pathway that controls apoptosis (programmed cell death). A bone-marrow transplant was used to overcome this genetic disorder, leading to a cure for the boy. He was the first person to be successfully treated based on a diagnosis made by whole-exome sequencing.

The Science Practice Challenge Questions contain additional test questions related to the material in this section that will help you prepare for the AP exam. These questions address the following standards:
[APLO 2.23][APLO 3.5][APLO 3.20][APLO 3.21]

Strategies Used in Sequencing Projects

The basic sequencing technique used in all modern day sequencing projects is the chain termination method (also known as the dideoxy method), which was developed by Fred Sanger in the 1970s. The chain termination method involves DNA replication of a single-stranded template with the use of a primer and a regular **deoxynucleotide** (dNTP), which is a monomer, or a single unit, of DNA. The primer and dNTP are mixed with a small proportion of fluorescently labeled **dideoxynucleotides** (ddNTPs). The ddNTPs are monomers that are missing a hydroxyl group (–OH) at the site at which another nucleotide usually attaches to form a chain (Figure 17.12). Each ddNTP is labeled with a different color of fluorophore. Every time a ddNTP is incorporated in the growing complementary strand, it terminates the process of DNA replication, which results in multiple short strands of replicated DNA that are each terminated at a different point during replication. When the reaction mixture is processed by gel electrophoresis after being separated into single strands, the multiple newly replicated DNA strands form a ladder because of the differing sizes. Because the ddNTPs are fluorescently labeled, each band on the gel reflects the size of the DNA strand and the ddNTP that terminated the reaction. The different colors of the fluorophore-labeled ddNTPs help identify the ddNTP incorporated at that position. Reading the gel on the basis of the color of each band on the ladder produces the sequence of the template strand (Figure 17.13).

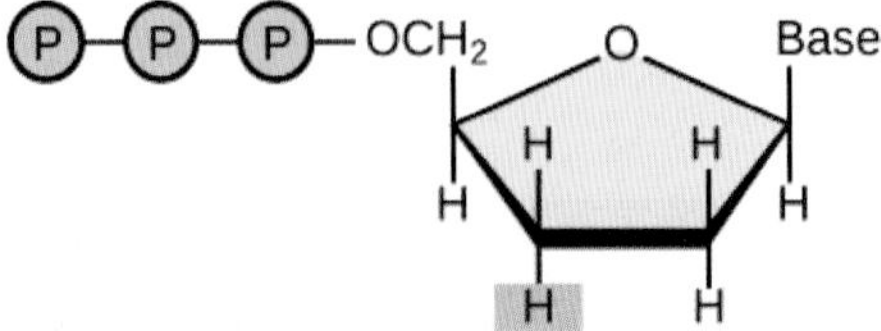

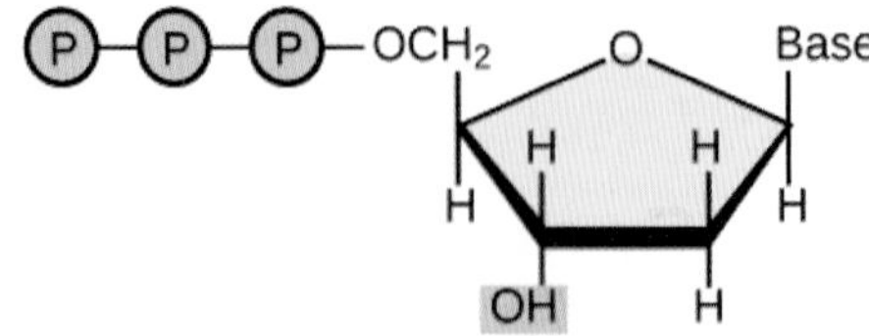

Figure 17.12 A dideoxynucleotide is similar in structure to a deoxynucleotide, but is missing the 3' hydroxyl group (indicated by the box). When a dideoxynucleotide is incorporated into a DNA strand, DNA synthesis stops.

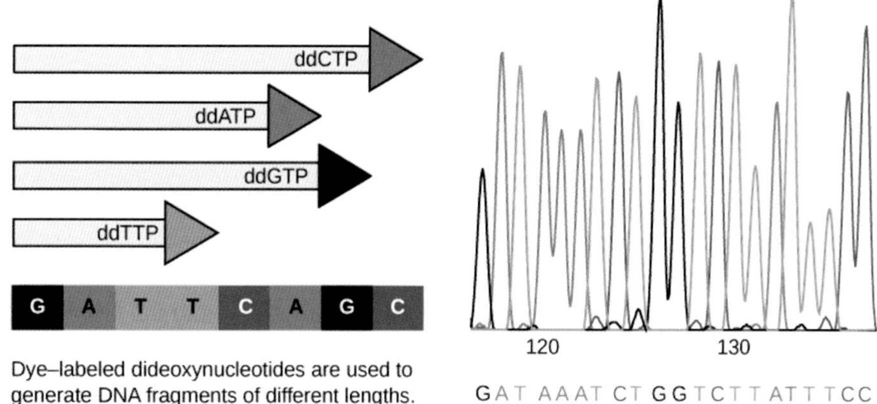

Figure 17.13 Frederick Sanger's dideoxy chain termination method is illustrated. Using dideoxynucleotides, the DNA fragment can be terminated at different points. The DNA is separated on the basis of size, and these bands, based on the size of the fragments, can be read.

Early Strategies: Shotgun Sequencing and Pair-Wise End Sequencing

In **shotgun sequencing** method, several copies of a DNA fragment are cut randomly into many smaller pieces (somewhat like what happens to a round shot cartridge when fired from a shotgun). All of the segments are then sequenced using the chain-sequencing method. Then, with the help of a computer, the fragments are analyzed to see where their sequences overlap. By matching up overlapping sequences at the end of each fragment, the entire DNA sequence can be reformed. A larger sequence that is assembled from overlapping shorter sequences is called a **contig**. As an analogy, consider that someone has four copies of a landscape photograph that you have never seen before and know nothing about how it should appear. The person then rips up each photograph with their hands, so that different size pieces are present from each copy. The person then mixes all of the pieces together and asks you to reconstruct the photograph. In one of the smaller pieces you see a mountain. In a larger piece, you see that the same mountain is behind a lake. A third fragment shows only the lake, but it reveals that there is a cabin on the shore of the lake. Therefore, from looking at the overlapping information in these three fragments, you know that the picture contains a mountain behind a lake that has a cabin on its shore. This is the principle behind reconstructing entire DNA sequences using shotgun sequencing.

Originally, shotgun sequencing only analyzed one end of each fragment for overlaps. This was sufficient for sequencing small genomes. However, the desire to sequence larger genomes, such as that of a human, led to the development of double-barrel shotgun sequencing, more formally known as **pairwise-end sequencing**. In pairwise-end sequencing, both ends of each fragment are analyzed for overlap. Pairwise-end sequencing is, therefore, more cumbersome than shotgun sequencing, but it is easier to reconstruct the sequence because there is more available information.

Next-generation Sequencing

Since 2005, automated sequencing techniques used by laboratories are under the umbrella of **next-generation sequencing**, which is a group of automated techniques used for rapid DNA sequencing. These automated low-cost sequencers can generate sequences of hundreds of thousands or millions of short fragments (25 to 500 base pairs) in the span of one day. These sequencers use sophisticated software to get through the cumbersome process of putting all the fragments in order.

Comparing Sequences

A sequence alignment is an arrangement of proteins, DNA, or RNA; it is used to identify regions of similarity between cell types or species, which may indicate conservation of function or structures. Sequence alignments may be used to construct phylogenetic trees. The following website uses a software program called BLAST (basic local alignment search tool) (http://openstaxcollege.org/l/32blast) .

Under "Basic Blast," click "Nucleotide Blast." Input the following sequence into the large "query sequence" box: ATTGCTTCGATTGCA. Below the box, locate the "Species" field and type "human" or "Homo sapiens". Then click "BLAST" to compare the inputted sequence against known sequences of the human genome. The result is that this sequence occurs in over a hundred places in the human genome. Scroll down below the graphic with the horizontal bars and you will see short description of each of the matching hits. Pick one of the hits near the top of the list and click on "Graphics". This will bring you to a page that shows where the sequence is found within the entire human genome. You can move the slider that looks like a green flag back and forth to view the sequences immediately around the selected gene. You can then return to your selected sequence by clicking the "ATG" button.

Cytochrome c oxidase is a highly conserved protein found in bacteria and in the mitochondria of eukaryotes. Based on your knowledge of evolutionary relationships, which of the following statements would you expect to be true of the cytochrome c oxidase protein sequence?

a. The bacterial protein will be more similar to the human protein than the yeast protein.
b. The yeast protein will be more similar to the human protein than the bacterial protein.
c. The bacterial protein will be more similar to the yeast protein than the human protein.
d. The bacterial and yeast protein will share a similar sequence, but the human protein will be unrelated.

Use of Whole-Genome Sequences of Model Organisms

The first genome to be completely sequenced was of a bacterial virus, the bacteriophage fx174 (5368 base pairs); this was accomplished by Fred Sanger using shotgun sequencing. Several other organelle and viral genomes were later sequenced. The first organism whose genome was sequenced was the bacterium *Haemophilus influenzae*; this was accomplished by Craig Venter in the 1980s. Approximately 74 different laboratories collaborated on the sequencing of the genome of the yeast *Saccharomyces cerevisiae*, which began in 1989 and was completed in 1996, because it was 60 times bigger than any other genome that had been sequenced. By 1997, the genome sequences of two important model organisms were available: the bacterium *Escherichia coli* K12 and the yeast *Saccharomyces cerevisiae*. Genomes of other model organisms, such as the mouse *Mus musculus*, the fruit fly *Drosophila melanogaster*, the nematode *Caenorhabditis. elegans*, and humans *Homo sapiens* are now known. A lot of basic research is performed in model organisms because the information can be applied to genetically similar organisms. A **model organism** is a species that is studied as a model to understand the biological processes in other species represented by the model organism. Having entire genomes sequenced helps with the research efforts in these model organisms. The process of attaching biological information to gene sequences is called **genome annotation**. Annotation of gene sequences helps with basic experiments in molecular biology, such as designing PCR primers and RNA targets.

Click through each step of genome sequencing at this site (http://openstaxcollege.org/l/DNA_sequence) .

How is deep sequencing an improvement on Sanger sequencing?

a. Deep sequencing allows for much faster sequencing of short strands of DNA as compared to Sanger sequencing which, reads only short sequences of DNA at a slow rate. Also, there is a high risk of chain termination and problems with separation during Sanger sequencing.

b. Sequence coverage is higher in Sanger sequencing as compared to deep sequencing.

c. Sanger sequencing is suitable when there is only one nucleotide different between chains whereas deep sequencing is suitable when there is one or more than one nucleotide different between chains.

d. Sanger sequencing reads and sequences a genome multiple times whereas deep sequencing accurately sequences the whole genome in a single time.

Uses of Genome Sequences

DNA microarrays are methods used to detect gene expression by analyzing an array of DNA fragments that are fixed to a glass slide or a silicon chip to identify active genes and identify sequences. Almost one million genotypic abnormalities can be discovered using microarrays, whereas whole-genome sequencing can provide information about all six billion base pairs in the human genome. Although the study of medical applications of genome sequencing is interesting, this discipline tends to dwell on abnormal gene function. Knowledge of the entire genome will allow future onset diseases and other genetic disorders to be discovered early, which will allow for more informed decisions to be made about lifestyle, medication, and having children. Genomics is still in its infancy, although someday it may become routine to use whole-genome sequencing to screen every newborn to detect genetic abnormalities.

In addition to disease and medicine, genomics can contribute to the development of novel enzymes that convert biomass to biofuel, which results in higher crop and fuel production, and lower cost to the consumer. This knowledge should allow better methods of control over the microbes that are used in the production of biofuels. Genomics could also improve the methods used to monitor the impact of pollutants on ecosystems and help clean up environmental contaminants. Genomics has allowed for the development of agrochemicals and pharmaceuticals that could benefit medical science and agriculture.

It sounds great to have all the knowledge we can get from whole-genome sequencing; however, humans have a responsibility to use this knowledge wisely. Otherwise, it could be easy to misuse the power of such knowledge, leading to discrimination based on a person's genetics, human genetic engineering, and other ethical concerns. This information could also lead to legal issues regarding health and privacy.

17.4 | Applying Genomics

In this section, you will explore the following questions:

- What is pharmacogenomics?
- What is an example of a polygenic human disease?

Connection for AP® Courses

Information presented in section is not in scope for AP®. However, you can study information in the section as optional or illustrative material.

The introduction of DNA sequencing and whole genome sequencing projects, particularly the Human Genome project, has expanded the applicability of DNA sequence information. Genomics is now being used in a wide variety of fields, such as metagenomics, pharmacogenomics, and mitochondrial genomics. The most commonly known application of genomics is to understand and find cures for diseases.

Predicting Disease Risk at the Individual Level

Predicting the risk of disease involves screening currently healthy individuals by genome analysis at the individual level. Intervention with lifestyle changes and drugs can be recommended before disease onset. However, this approach is most applicable when the problem resides within a single gene defect. Such defects only account for approximately 5 percent of diseases in developed countries. Most of the common diseases, such as heart disease, are multi-factored or **polygenic**, which is a phenotypic characteristic that involves two or more genes, and also involve environmental factors such as diet. In April 2010, scientists at Stanford University published the genome analysis of a healthy individual (Stephen Quake, a scientist at Stanford University, who had his genome sequenced); the analysis predicted his propensity to acquire various diseases. A risk assessment was performed to analyze Quake's percentage of risk for 55 different medical conditions. A rare genetic mutation was found, which showed him to be at risk for sudden heart attack. He was also predicted to have a 23 percent risk of developing prostate cancer and a 1.4 percent risk of developing Alzheimer's. The scientists used databases and several publications to analyze the genomic data. Even though genomic sequencing is becoming more affordable and analytical tools are becoming more reliable, ethical issues surrounding genomic analysis at a population level remain to be addressed.

visual CONNECTION

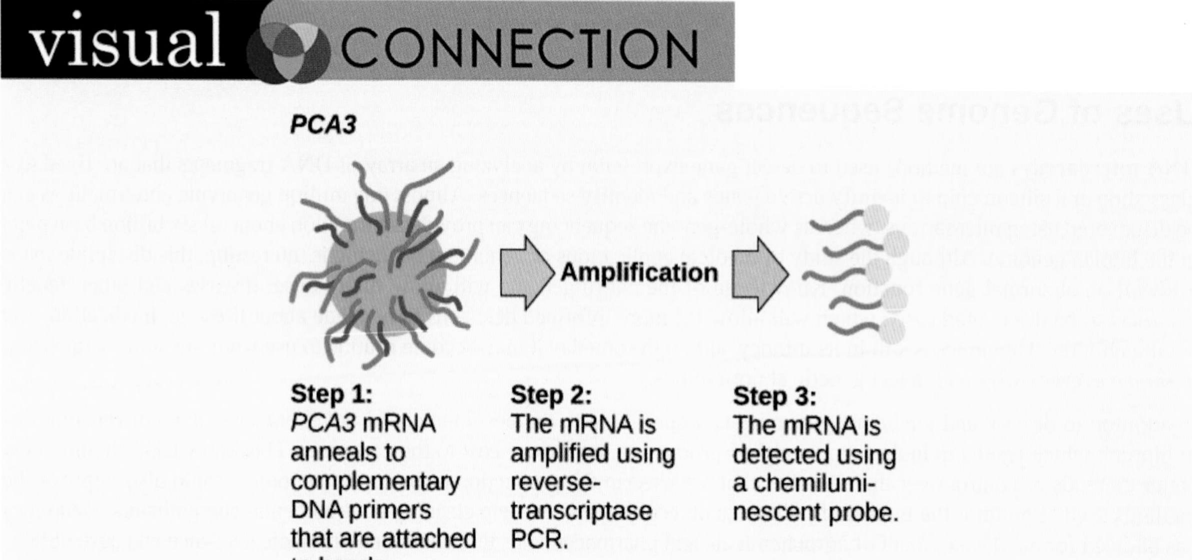

Figure 17.14 *PCA3* is a gene that is expressed in prostate epithelial cells and overexpressed in cancerous cells. A high concentration of *PCA3* in urine is indicative of prostate cancer. The *PCA3* test is considered to be a better indicator of cancer than the more well know PSA test, which measures the level of PSA (prostate-specific antigen) in the blood.

In 2011, the United States Preventative Services Task Force recommended against using the PSA test to screen healthy men for prostate cancer. Their recommendation is based on evidence that screening does not reduce the risk of death from prostate cancer. Prostate cancer often develops very slowly and does not cause problems, while the cancer treatment can have severe side effects. The PCA3 test is considered to be more accurate, but screening may still result in men who would not have been harmed by the cancer itself suffering side effects from treatment. What do you think? Should all healthy men be screened for prostate cancer using the PCA3 or PSA test? Should people in general be screened to find out if they have a genetic risk for cancer or other diseases?

a. In general, all men should be screened as it is necessary to take the risk.

b. In general, all men should be given treatment irrespective of the presence or absence of cancer symptoms.

c. In general, only men suspecting cancer should be screened.

d. There is no requirement of any screening, as cancer shows no problems.

Pharmacogenomics and Toxicogenomics

Pharmacogenomics, also called toxicogenomics, involves evaluating the effectiveness and safety of drugs on the basis of information from an individual's genomic sequence. Genomic responses to drugs can be studied using experimental animals (such as laboratory rats or mice) or live cells in the laboratory before embarking on studies with humans. Studying changes in gene expression could provide information about the transcription profile in the presence of the drug, which can be used as an early indicator of the potential for toxic effects. For example, genes involved in cellular growth and controlled cell death, when disturbed, could lead to the growth of cancerous cells. Genome-wide studies can also help to find new genes involved in drug toxicity. Personal genome sequence information can be used to prescribe medications that will be most effective and least toxic on the basis of the individual patient's genotype. The gene signatures may not be completely accurate, but can be tested further before pathologic symptoms arise.

Microbial Genomics: Metagenomics

Traditionally, microbiology has been taught with the view that microorganisms are best studied under **pure culture** conditions, which involves isolating a single type of cell and culturing it in the laboratory. Because microorganisms can go through several generations in a matter of hours, their gene expression profiles adapt to the new laboratory environment very quickly. In addition, the vast majority of bacterial species resist being cultured in isolation. Most microorganisms do not live as isolated entities, but in microbial communities known as biofilms. For all of these reasons, pure culture is not always the best way to study microorganisms. **Metagenomics** is the study of the collective genomes of multiple species that grow and interact in an environmental niche. Metagenomics can be used to identify new species more rapidly and to analyze the effect of pollutants on the environment (Figure 17.15).

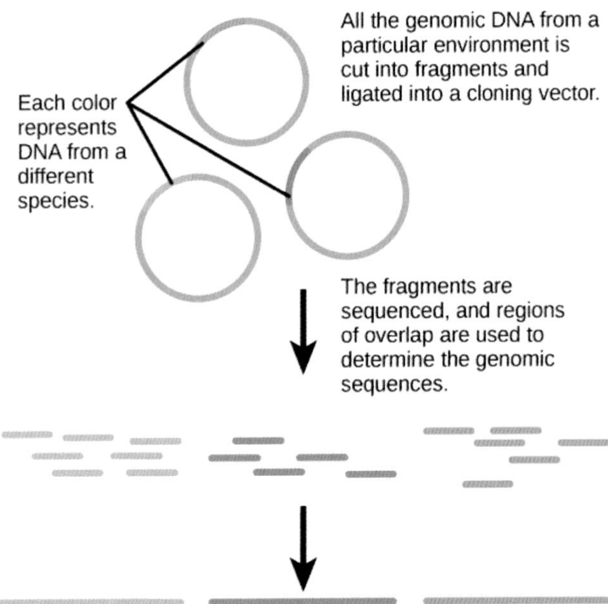

Figure 17.15 Metagenomics involves isolating DNA from multiple species within an environmental niche.

Microbial Genomics: Creation of New Biofuels

Knowledge of the genomics of microorganisms is being used to find better ways to harness biofuels from algae and cyanobacteria. The primary sources of fuel today are coal, oil, wood, and other plant products, such as ethanol. Although plants are renewable resources, there is still a need to find more alternative renewable sources of energy to meet our population's energy demands. The microbial world is one of the largest resources for genes that encode new enzymes and produce new organic compounds, and it remains largely untapped. Microorganisms are used to create products, such as enzymes that are used in research, antibiotics, and other anti-microbial mechanisms. Microbial genomics is helping to develop diagnostic tools, improved vaccines, new disease treatments, and advanced environmental cleanup techniques.

Mitochondrial Genomics

Mitochondria are intracellular organelles that contain their own DNA. Mitochondrial DNA mutates at a rapid rate and is often used to study evolutionary relationships. Another feature that makes studying the mitochondrial genome interesting is that the mitochondrial DNA in most multicellular organisms is passed on from the mother during the process of fertilization.

For this reason, mitochondrial genomics is often used to trace genealogy.

Information and clues obtained from DNA samples found at crime scenes have been used as evidence in court cases, and genetic markers have been used in forensic analysis. Genomic analysis has also become useful in this field. In 2001, the first use of genomics in forensics was published. It was a collaborative attempt between academic research institutions and the FBI to solve the mysterious cases of anthrax communicated via the US Postal Service. Using microbial genomics, researchers determined that a specific strain of anthrax was used in all the mailings.

Genomics in Agriculture

Genomics can reduce the trials and failures involved in scientific research to a certain extent, which could improve the quality and quantity of crop yields in agriculture. Linking traits to genes or gene signatures helps to improve crop breeding to generate hybrids with the most desirable qualities. Scientists use genomic data to identify desirable traits, and then transfer those traits to a different organism. Scientists are discovering how genomics can improve the quality and quantity of agricultural production. For example, scientists could use desirable traits to create a useful product or enhance an existing product, such as making a drought-sensitive crop more tolerant of the dry season.

17.5 | Genomics and Proteomics

In this section, you will explore the following questions:

- What is a proteome?
- What is a protein signature and what is its relevance to cancer screening?

Connection for AP® Courses

Information presented in section is not in scope for AP®. However, you can study information in the section as optional or illustrative material.

Proteins are the final products of genes, which help perform the function encoded by the gene. Proteins are composed of amino acids and play important roles in the cell. All enzymes (except ribozymes) are proteins that act as catalysts to affect the rate of reactions. Proteins are also regulatory molecules, and some are hormones. Transport proteins, such as hemoglobin, help transport oxygen to various organs. Antibodies that defend against foreign particles are also proteins. In the diseased state, protein function can be impaired because of changes at the genetic level or because of direct impact on a specific protein.

A **proteome** is the entire set of proteins produced by a cell type. Proteomes can be studied using the knowledge of genomes because genes code for mRNAs, and the mRNAs encode proteins. Although mRNA analysis is a step in the right direction, not all mRNAs are translated into proteins. The study of the function of proteomes is called **proteomics**. Proteomics complements genomics and is useful when scientists want to test their hypotheses that were based on genes. Even though all cells of a multicellular organism have the same set of genes, the set of proteins produced in different tissues is different and dependent on gene expression. Thus, the genome is constant, but the proteome varies and is dynamic within an organism. In addition, RNAs can be alternately spliced (cut and pasted to create novel combinations and novel proteins) and many proteins are modified after translation by processes such as proteolytic cleavage, phosphorylation, glycosylation, and ubiquitination. There are also protein-protein interactions, which complicate the study of proteomes. Although the genome provides a blueprint, the final architecture depends on several factors that can change the progression of events that generate the proteome.

Metabolomics is related to genomics and proteomics. **Metabolomics** involves the study of small molecule metabolites found in an organism. The **metabolome** is the complete set of metabolites that are related to the genetic makeup of an organism. Metabolomics offers an opportunity to compare genetic makeup and physical characteristics, as well as genetic makeup and environmental factors. The goal of metabolome research is to identify, quantify, and catalogue all of the metabolites that are found in the tissues and fluids of living organisms.

Basic Techniques in Protein Analysis

The ultimate goal of proteomics is to identify or compare the proteins expressed from a given genome under specific conditions, study the interactions between the proteins, and use the information to predict cell behavior or develop drug targets. Just as the genome is analyzed using the basic technique of DNA sequencing, proteomics requires techniques for protein analysis. The basic technique for protein analysis, analogous to DNA sequencing, is mass spectrometry. Mass spectrometry is used to identify and determine the characteristics of a molecule. Advances in spectrometry have allowed researchers to analyze very small samples of protein. X-ray crystallography, for example, enables scientists to determine the three-dimensional structure of a protein crystal at atomic resolution. Another protein imaging technique, nuclear magnetic resonance (NMR), uses the magnetic properties of atoms to determine the three-dimensional structure of proteins in aqueous solution. Protein microarrays have also been used to study interactions between proteins. Large-scale adaptations of the basic two-hybrid screen (Figure 17.16) have provided the basis for protein microarrays. Computer software is used to analyze the vast amount of data generated for proteomic analysis.

Genomic- and proteomic-scale analyses are part of systems biology. **Systems biology** is the study of whole biological systems (genomes and proteomes) based on interactions within the system. The European Bioinformatics Institute and the Human Proteome Organization (HUPO) are developing and establishing effective tools to sort through the enormous pile of systems biology data. Because proteins are the direct products of genes and reflect activity at the genomic level, it is natural to use proteomes to compare the protein profiles of different cells to identify proteins and genes involved in disease processes. Most pharmaceutical drug trials target proteins. Information obtained from proteomics is being used to identify novel drugs and understand their mechanisms of action.

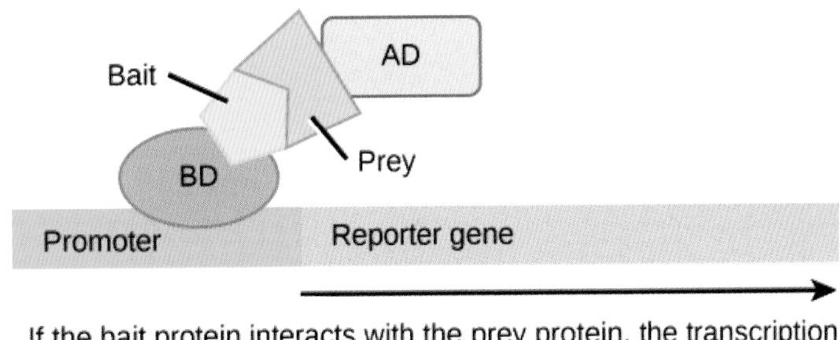

If the bait protein interacts with the prey protein, the transcription factor's activator domain binds to the binding domain, and transcription occurs.

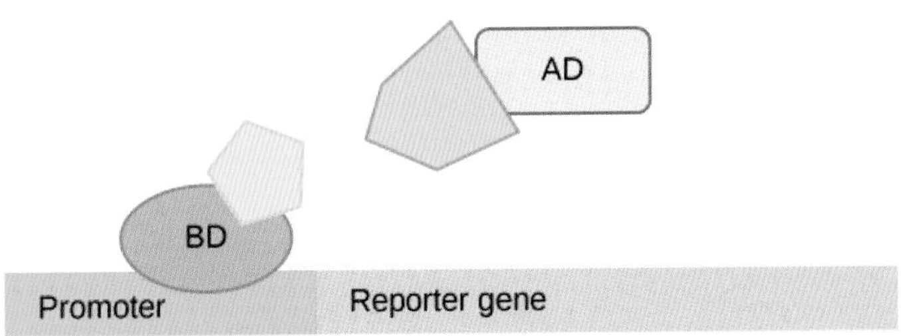

If the prey doesn't catch the bait, no transcription occurs.

Figure 17.16 Two-hybrid screening is used to determine whether two proteins interact. In this method, a transcription factor is split into a DNA-binding domain (BD) and an activator domain (AD). The binding domain is able to bind the promoter in the absence of the activator domain, but it does not turn on transcription. A protein called the bait is attached to the BD, and a protein called the prey is attached to the AD. Transcription occurs only if the prey "catches" the bait.

The challenge of techniques used for proteomic analyses is the difficulty in detecting small quantities of proteins. Although mass spectrometry is good for detecting small amounts of proteins, variations in protein expression in diseased states can be difficult to discern. Proteins are naturally unstable molecules, which makes proteomic analysis much more difficult than genomic analysis.

Cancer Proteomics

Genomes and proteomes of patients suffering from specific diseases are being studied to understand the genetic basis of the disease. The most prominent disease being studied with proteomic approaches is cancer. Proteomic approaches are being used to improve screening and early detection of cancer; this is achieved by identifying proteins whose expression is affected by the disease process. An individual protein is called a **biomarker**, whereas a set of proteins with altered expression levels is called a **protein signature**. For a biomarker or protein signature to be useful as a candidate for early screening and detection of a cancer, it must be secreted in body fluids, such as sweat, blood, or urine, such that large-scale screenings can be performed in a non-invasive fashion. The current problem with using biomarkers for the early detection of cancer is the high rate of false-negative results. A **false negative** is an incorrect test result that should have been positive. In other words, many cases of cancer go undetected, which makes biomarkers unreliable. Some examples of protein biomarkers used in cancer detection are CA-125 for ovarian cancer and PSA for prostate cancer. Protein signatures may be more reliable than biomarkers to detect cancer cells. Proteomics is also being used to develop individualized treatment plans, which involves the prediction of whether or not an individual will respond to specific drugs and the side effects that the individual may experience. Proteomics is also being used to predict the possibility of disease recurrence.

The National Cancer Institute has developed programs to improve the detection and treatment of cancer. The Clinical Proteomic Technologies for Cancer and the Early Detection Research Network are efforts to identify protein signatures specific to different types of cancers. The Biomedical Proteomics Program is designed to identify protein signatures and design effective therapies for cancer patients.

KEY TERMS

antibiotic resistance ability of an organism to be unaffected by the actions of an antibiotic

biomarker individual protein that is uniquely produced in a diseased state

biotechnology use of biological agents for technological advancement

cDNA library collection of cloned cDNA sequences

cellular cloning production of identical cell populations by binary fission

chain termination method method of DNA sequencing using labeled dideoxynucleotides to terminate DNA replication; it is also called the dideoxy method or the Sanger method

clone exact replica

contig larger sequence of DNA assembled from overlapping shorter sequences

cytogenetic mapping technique that uses a microscope to create a map from stained chromosomes

deoxynucleotide individual monomer (single unit) of DNA

dideoxynucleotide individual monomer of DNA that is missing a hydroxyl group (–OH)

DNA microarray method used to detect gene expression by analyzing an array of DNA fragments that are fixed to a glass slide or a silicon chip to identify active genes and identify sequences

expressed sequence tag (EST) short STS that is identified with cDNA

false negative incorrect test result that should have been positive

foreign DNA DNA that belongs to a different species or DNA that is artificially synthesized

gel electrophoresis technique used to separate molecules on the basis of size using electric charge

gene targeting method for altering the sequence of a specific gene by introducing the modified version on a vector

gene therapy technique used to cure inheritable diseases by replacing mutant genes with good genes

genetic diagnosis diagnosis of the potential for disease development by analyzing disease-causing genes

genetic engineering alteration of the genetic makeup of an organism

genetic map outline of genes and their location on a chromosome

genetic marker gene or sequence on a chromosome with a known location that is associated with a specific trait

genetic recombination exchange of DNA between homologous pairs of chromosomes

genetic testing process of testing for the presence of disease-causing genes

genetically modified organism (GMO) organism whose genome has been artificially changed

genome annotation process of attaching biological information to gene sequences

genome mapping process of finding the location of genes on each chromosome

genomic library collection of cloned DNA which represents all of the sequences and fragments from a genome

genomics study of entire genomes including the complete set of genes, their nucleotide sequence and organization, and their interactions within a species and with other species

host DNA DNA that is present in the genome of the organism of interest

linkage analysis procedure that analyzes the recombination of genes to determine if they are linked

lysis buffer solution used to break the cell membrane and release cell contents

metabolome complete set of metabolites which are related to the genetic makeup of an organism

metabolomics study of small molecule metabolites found in an organism

metagenomics study of the collective genomes of multiple species that grow and interact in an environmental niche

microsatellite polymorphism variation between individuals in the sequence and number of repeats of microsatellite DNA

model organism species that is studied and used as a model to understand the biological processes in other species represented by the model organism

molecular cloning cloning of DNA fragments

multiple cloning site (MCS) site that can be recognized by multiple restriction endonucleases

next-generation sequencing group of automated techniques used for rapid DNA sequencing

northern blotting transfer of RNA from a gel to a nylon membrane

pharmacogenomics study of drug interactions with the genome or proteome; also called toxicogenomics

physical map representation of the physical distance between genes or genetic markers

polygenic phenotypic characteristic caused by two or more genes

polymerase chain reaction (PCR) technique used to amplify DNA

probe small DNA fragment used to determine if the complementary sequence is present in a DNA sample

protease enzyme that breaks down proteins

protein signature set of uniquely expressed proteins in the diseased state

proteome entire set of proteins produced by a cell type

proteomics study of the function of proteomes

pure culture growth of a single type of cell in the laboratory

radiation hybrid mapping information obtained by fragmenting the chromosome with x-rays

recombinant DNA combination of DNA fragments generated by molecular cloning that does not exist in nature; also known as a chimeric molecule

recombinant protein protein product of a gene derived by molecular cloning

reproductive cloning cloning of entire organisms

restriction endonuclease enzyme that can recognize and cleave specific DNA sequences

restriction fragment length polymorphism (RFLP) variation between individuals in the length of DNA fragments generated by restriction endonucleases

reverse genetics method of determining the function of a gene by starting with the gene itself instead of starting with the gene product

reverse transcriptase PCR (RT-PCR) PCR technique that involves converting RNA to DNA by reverse transcriptase

ribonuclease enzyme that breaks down RNA

sequence mapping mapping information obtained after DNA sequencing

shotgun sequencing method used to sequence multiple DNA fragments to generate the sequence of a large piece of DNA

single nucleotide polymorphism (SNP) variation between individuals in a single nucleotide

Southern blotting transfer of DNA from a gel to a nylon membrane

systems biology study of whole biological systems (genomes and proteomes) based on interactions within the system

Ti plasmid plasmid system derived from *Agrobacterium tumifaciens* that has been used by scientists to introduce foreign DNA into plant cells

transgenic organism that receives DNA from a different species

variable number of tandem repeats (VNTRs) variation in the number of tandem repeats between individuals in the population

whole-genome sequencing process that determines the DNA sequence of an entire genome

CHAPTER SUMMARY

17.1 Biotechnology

Nucleic acids can be isolated from cells for the purposes of further analysis by breaking open the cells and enzymatically destroying all other major macromolecules. Fragmented or whole chromosomes can be separated on the basis of size by gel electrophoresis. Short stretches of DNA or RNA can be amplified by PCR. Southern and northern blotting can be used to detect the presence of specific short sequences in a DNA or RNA sample. The term “cloning” may refer to cloning small DNA fragments (molecular cloning), cloning cell populations (cellular cloning), or cloning entire organisms (reproductive cloning). Genetic testing is performed to identify disease-causing genes, and gene therapy is used to cure an inheritable disease.

Transgenic organisms possess DNA from a different species, usually generated by molecular cloning techniques. Vaccines, antibiotics, and hormones are examples of products obtained by recombinant DNA technology. Transgenic plants are usually created to improve characteristics of crop plants.

17.2 Mapping Genomes

Genome mapping is similar to solving a big, complicated puzzle with pieces of information coming from laboratories all over the world. Genetic maps provide an outline for the location of genes within a genome, and they estimate the distance between genes and genetic markers on the basis of recombination frequencies during meiosis. Physical maps provide detailed information about the physical distance between the genes. The most detailed information is available through sequence mapping. Information from all mapping and sequencing sources is combined to study an entire genome.

17.3 Whole-Genome Sequencing

Whole-genome sequencing is the latest available resource to treat genetic diseases. Some doctors are using whole-genome sequencing to save lives. Genomics has many industrial applications including biofuel development, agriculture, pharmaceuticals, and pollution control. The basic principle of all modern-day sequencing strategies involves the chain termination method of sequencing.

Although the human genome sequences provide key insights to medical professionals, researchers use whole-genome sequences of model organisms to better understand the genome of the species. Automation and the decreased cost of whole-genome sequencing may lead to personalized medicine in the future.

17.4 Applying Genomics

Imagination is the only barrier to the applicability of genomics. Genomics is being applied to most fields of biology; it is being used for personalized medicine, prediction of disease risks at an individual level, the study of drug interactions before the conduct of clinical trials, and the study of microorganisms in the environment as opposed to the laboratory. It is also being applied to developments such as the generation of new biofuels, genealogical assessment using mitochondria, advances in forensic science, and improvements in agriculture.

17.5 Genomics and Proteomics

Proteomics is the study of the entire set of proteins expressed by a given type of cell under certain environmental conditions. In a multicellular organism, different cell types will have different proteomes, and these will vary with changes in the environment. Unlike a genome, a proteome is dynamic and in constant flux, which makes it both more complicated and more useful than the knowledge of genomes alone.

Proteomics approaches rely on protein analysis; these techniques are constantly being upgraded. Proteomics has been used to study different types of cancer. Different biomarkers and protein signatures are being used to analyze each type of cancer. The future goal is to have a personalized treatment plan for each individual.

REVIEW QUESTIONS

1. How are GMOs created?

a. introducing recombinant DNA into an organism by any means
b. in vitro fertilization methods
c. mutagenesis
d. plant breeding techniques

2. Which technique used to manipulate genetic material results in a significant increase in DNA or RNA fragments?

a. gel electrophoresis
b. nucleic acid extraction
c. nuclear hybridization
d. polymerase chain reaction (PCR)

3. What is the role of the plasmid in molecular cloning?

a. They are used to create clones.
b. They are used as vectors to insert genes into bacteria.
c. They are a functional part of binary fission.
d. They contain the circular chromosome of prokaryotic organisms.

4. What is meant by a recombinant DNA molecule?

a. chimeric molecules
b. bacteria transformed into another species
c. molecules that have been through the PCR process
d. the result of crossing over during cell reproduction

5. Bt toxin is considered to be what?

a. a gene for modifying insect DNA
b. an organic insecticide produced by bacteria
c. useful for humans to fight against insects
d. a recombinant protein

6. What is one trait of the Flavr Savr Tomato?

a. has a better shelf life
b. is not a variety of vine-ripened tomato in the supermarket
c. was not created to have better flavor
d. undergoes soft rot

7. What is the first step in isolating DNA?

a. generating genomic DNA fragments with restriction endonucleases
b. introducing recombinant DNA into an organism by any means
c. overexpressing proteins in *E. coli*
d. lysing the cells in the sample

8. What is genomics?

a. Genomics is the study of entire genomes, including the complete set of genes, their nucleotide sequence and organization, and their interactions within a species and with other species.
b. Genomics is the process of finding the locations of genes on each chromosome.
c. Genomics is an illustration that lists genes and their location on a chromosome.
d. Genomics is a genetic marker, a gene or sequence on a chromosome that co-segregates (shows genetic linkage) with a specific trait.

9. What is required in addition to a genetic linkage map to build a complete picture of the genome?

a. a genetic marker
b. a physical map
c. linkage analysis of chromosomes
d. plasmids

10. Genetic recombination occurs by which process?

a. crossing over

b. chromosome segregation

c. independent assortment

d. sister chromatids

11. Individual genetic maps in a given species are ________.

a. genetically similar

b. genetically identical

c. genetically dissimilar

d. not useful in species analysis

12. Information obtained by microscopic analysis of stained chromosomes is used in what procedure?

a. cytogenetic mapping

b. radiation hybrid mapping

c. RFLP mapping

d. sequence mapping

13. Which of the following is true about linkage analysis?

a. It is used to create a physical map.

b. It is based on the natural recombination process.

c. It involves the breaking and re-joining of DNA artificially.

d. It requires radiation hybrid mapping.

14. The chain termination method of sequencing uses what?

a. labeled ddNTPs

b. only dideoxynucleotides

c. only deoxynucleotides

d. labeled dNTPs

15. What sequencing technique is used to identify regions of similarity between cell types or species?

a. dideoxy chain termination

b. proteins, DNA, or RNA sequence alignment

c. shotgun sequencing

d. whole-exome sequencing

16. Whole-genome sequencing can be used for advances in what field?

a. bioinformatics

b. iron industry

c. multimedia

d. the medical field

17. Sequencing an individual person's genome ______.

a. is currently impossible

b. helps in predicting faulty genes in diseases

c. will not lead to legal issues regarding discrimination and privacy

d. will not help make informed choices about medical treatment

18. Genomics can be used in agriculture to do what?

a. generate new hybrid strains

b. improve disease resistance

c. improve yield

d. improve yield and resistance and generate hybrids

19. What are the uses of metagenomics?

a. identification of biofuels

b. testing for multiple drug susceptibility in a population

c. use in increasing agricultural yields

d. identifying new species more rapidly and analyzing the effect of pollutants on the environment

20. Genomics can be used on a personal level to do what?

a. determine the risks of genetic diseases for an individual's children

b. increase transplant rejection

c. predict protein profile of a person

d. produce antibodies for an antigen

21. What is the percentage of single gene defects causing disease in developed countries?

a. 0.05

b. 0.1

c. 0.2

d. 0.4

22. The rapid identification of new species and the analysis of the effect of pollutants on the environment is a function of what?

a. metagenomics

b. linkage analysis

c. genomics

d. shotgun sequencing

23. The risks of genetic diseases for an individual's children can be determined through ______.

a. metagenomics
b. linkage analysis
c. genomics
d. shotgun sequencing

24. What is a biomarker?

a. the color coding of different genes
b. a protein uniquely produced in a diseased state
c. a molecule in the genome or proteome
d. a marker that is genetically inherited

25. What is a metabolome?

a. a provisional listing of the genome of a species
b. a unique metabolite used to identify an individual
c. a method used for protein analysis
d. the complete set of metabolites related to the genetic makeup of an organism

26. How would you describe a set of proteins with altered expression levels?

a. a group of biomarkers
b. a protein signature
c. the result of a defect in mRNA transcription
d. the results of crossing over during cell replication

27. What is a protein signature?

a. a protein expressed on the cell surface
b. a unique set of proteins present in a diseased state
c. the path followed by a protein after it is synthesized in the nucleus
d. the path followed by a protein in the cytoplasm

28. What describes a protein that is uniquely produced in a diseased state?

a. a genomic protein
b. a genetic defect
c. a chimeric molecule
d. a biomarker

29. The metabolites that results from the anabolic and catabolic reactions of an organisms is called what?

a. genetic metabolic profile
b. metabolic signature
c. metabolome
d. metagenomics

CRITICAL THINKING QUESTIONS

30. Describe the process of Southern blotting.

a. Southern Blotting is used to find DNA sequences. Fragments are separated on gel, incubated with probes to check for the sequence of interest, and transferred to a nylon membrane.
b. Southern blotting is used to find DNA sequences. Fragments are separated on gel, transferred to a nylon membrane, and incubated with probes to check for the sequence of interest.
c. When RNA is used, the process is called Northern blotting.
d. Southern blotting is used to find RNA sequences. Fragments are separated on gel, incubated with probes to check for the sequence of interest, and transferred to a nylon membrane.

31. A researcher wants to study cancer cells from a patient with breast cancer. Is cloning the cancer cells an option?

a. The cancer cells should be cloned along with a biomarker for better detection and study.
b. The cells should be screened first in order to assure their carcinogenic nature.
c. The cancer cells, being clones of each other already, should directly be grown in a culture media and then studied.
d. The cancer cells should be extracted using the specific antibodies.

32. Discuss the uses of genome mapping.

a. Genome mapping is useful in identifying human disease-causing genes, developing microbes to clean up pollutants, and increasing crop yield.
b. Genome mapping is directly required to produce recombinants, in FISH detection, and detecting the methylated parts of genetic material.
c. Genome mapping is useful for knowing the pedigree of diseases in humans and tracing the movement of transposons in plants.
d. Genome mapping identifies human disease-causing genes only.

33. If you had a chance to get your genome sequenced, what are some questions you might be able to have answered about yourself?

a. One can determine the drugs that can rectify a disease, symptoms of the disease and its severity.

b. One can determine the ancestry and genetic origin of diseases and their susceptibility to drugs.

c. One can predict the symptoms of a disease, the vectors to be used in gene therapy and the causal organism of the disease.

d. One can determine the pedigree of a disease, produce recombinants and detect the presence of extracellular genes using FISH.

34. Describe an example of a genomic mapping method

a. The radiation mapping method is an example which uses radiation to break the DNA and is affected by changes in recombination frequency.

b. Cytogenetic mapping obtains information from microscopic analysis of stained chromosomes. It can estimate the approximate distance between markers.

c. In restriction mapping, the DNA fragments are cut by using the restriction enzymes and then stained fragments are viewed on gel.

d. Cytogenetic mapping obtains information from microscopic analysis of stained chromosomes. It can estimate the exact base pair distance between markers.

35. Describe three methods of gene sequencing.

a. Chain termination method - automated sequencers are used to generate sequences of short fragments; Shotgun sequencing method - incorporation of ddNTP during DNA replication; Next-generation sequencing - cutting DNA into random fragments, sequencing using chain termination, and assembling overlapping sequences

b. Chain termination method - incorporation of ddNTP during DNA replication; Shotgun sequencing method - cutting DNA into random fragments, sequencing using chain termination, and assembling overlapping sequences; Next-generation sequencing - automated sequencers are used to generate sequences of short fragments

c. Chain termination method - incorporation of ddNTP during DNA replication; Shotgun sequencing method - automated sequencers are used to generate sequences of short fragments; Next-generation sequencing - cutting DNA into random fragments, sequencing using chain termination, and assembling overlapping sequences

d. Chain termination method - automated sequencers are used to generate sequences of short fragments; Shotgun sequencing method - cutting DNA into random fragments, sequencing using chain termination, and assembling overlapping sequences; Next-generation sequencing - incorporation of ddNTP during DNA replication

36. What is the greatest challenge facing genome sequencing?

a. the lack of resources and use of chemicals for the sequencing of the DNA fragments

b. the ethical issues such as discrimination based on person's genetics

c. the use of chemicals during the sequencing methods that could incorporate mutations

d. the scientific issues, like conserving the human genome sequences

37. How is shotgun sequencing performed?

a. The DNA is cut into fragments, sequencing is done using the chain termination method, fragments are analyzed to see the overlapping sequences, and the entire fragment is reformed.

b. The DNA is cut into fragments, overlapping sequences are analyzed using a computer, sequencing is done using the chain termination method, and the DNA fragment is reformed.

c. The DNA is cut into fragments, stained with fluorescent dye, sequenced using the chain termination method, fragments are analyzed to see the overlapping sequences, and the entire DNA fragment is reformed.

d. The DNA is cut into fragments, sequencing is done using the chain termination method, the DNA is stained with fluorescent dye, and a computer is used to analyze and reform the entire DNA fragment.

38. Coumadin is a drug frequently given to prevent excessive blood clotting in stroke or heart attack patients, which could lead to another stroke or heart attack. Administration of the drug also can result in an overdose in some patients, depending on the liver function of a patient. How could pharmacogenomics be used to assist these patients?

a. Pharmacogenomics will be able to provide a counter-acting drug to decrease the effect of Coumadin.

b. Pharmacogenomics will test every patient for their sensitivity to the drug.

c. Pharmacogenomics will not be able to provide any help to patients highly sensitive to the drug.

d. Pharmacogenomics will provide an overdose to each patient to test for the symptoms of the drug.

39. Why is so much effort being poured into genome mapping applications?

a. Genome mapping is necessary to know the base pair difference between the markers.

b. The mapping would help scientists understand the role of proteins in specific organelles.

c. The mapping technique identifies the role of transposons.

d. Genome mapping helps identify faulty alleles, which could cause diseases.

40. What is the reason for studying mitochondrial genomics that is most directly important for humans?

a. Mitochondria evolved from bacteria; therefore, their genome is important to study.

b. Mitochondria undergo rapid mutation and it is essential that this pattern be studied.

c. Mitochondria contain DNA, and it is passed on from mother to offspring, which renders it helpful in tracing genealogy.

d. Mitochondria are the only ATP-producing organelles of the cell, thus their genome is important.

41. How can proteomics complement genomics?

a. The genes are responsible to produce proteins and this implies that proteomics complements genomics.

b. Genomics is responsible to decide the structure of the proteins, and, thereby, the result of proteomic studies.

c. The genome is constant but the proteome is dynamic as different tissues possess the same genes but express different genes, thereby complementing genomics.

d. The study of genes is incomplete without the study of their respective proteins and thus they complement each other.

42. How could a proteomic map of the human genome help find a cure for cancer?

a. A genetic map could help in identifying genes that could counteract the cause of cancer.

b. Metabolomics can be used to study the genes producing metabolites during cancer.

c. Proteomics detects biomarkers whose expression is affected by the disease process.

d. The mapping helps in analyzing the inheritance of cancer-causing genes.

43. What contributions have been made through the use of microbial genomics?

a. Microbial genomics has provided various tools to study the psychological behaviors of organisms.

b. Microbial genomics has been useful in producing antibiotics, enzymes, improved vaccines, disease treatments and advanced cleanup techniques.

c. Microbial genomics has contributed resistance in other bacteria by horizontal and lateral gene transfer mechanisms.

d. Microbial genomics has contributed to fighting global warming.

TEST PREP FOR AP® COURSES

44. In separating DNA for genomic analysis, it is important to consider RNA contaminating the sample during the cell lysis step of a DNA extraction. Which is likely to cause what to occur?

a. DNA separates into the supernatant.
b. DNA is destroyed by the protease.
c. DNA is unaffected by the RNA.
d. DNA combines with the RNA.

45. There are many techniques for investigating human genomic disorders. Western blotting looks for protein, Eastern blotting looks for post-translational changes, Northern blotting looks at mRNA, and Southern blotting looks at DNA. If you were to look at sickle cell anemia, a disorder affecting hemoglobin produced in red blood cells, which technique would be the most useful in detecting polymorphism in a sample?

a. Northern blotting
b. Southern blotting
c. Western blotting
d. Eastern blotting

46. A population of insects were formally distinguished by a mix of colors on their thorax and legs. This population now appears to be split into 2 sub-groups, purple and orange-legged. Researchers hypothesize that the purple-legged group may be increasingly resistant to the Bt (*Bacillus thuringiensis*) toxin. Which idea supports this observation?

a. transgenesis
b. natural selection
c. hybridization
d. recombination

47. Describe the process of molecular cloning.

a. The foreign DNA and plasmid are cut with the same restriction enzyme and DNA is inserted within the lacZ gene, whose product metabolizes lactose. The foreign DNA and vector are allowed to anneal. The vector is transferred to a bacterial host that is ampicillin sensitive and those with a disrupted lacZ gene show inability to metabolize X-gal.
b. The foreign DNA and plasmid are denatured using high heat, and DNA is inserted within the lacZ gene, whose product metabolizes glucose. The foreign DNA and vector are allowed to anneal. The vector is transferred to a bacterial host that is ampicillin sensitive and disrupted lacZ gene will metabolize X-gal
c. The foreign DNA and plasmid are cut with the same restriction enzyme and DNA is inserted randomly in the plasmid. The foreign DNA and vector are allowed to anneal. The vector is transferred to a bacterial host that is ampicillin sensitive and the disrupted lacZ gene shows inability to synthesize X-gal.
d. The foreign DNA and plasmid are cut with the same restriction enzyme and DNA is inserted within the lacZ gene, whose product metabolizes lactose. The foreign DNA and vector are allowed to anneal. The vector is transformed into a viral host that is ampicillin sensitive and the disrupted lacZ gene show inability to synthesize X-gal.

48. There are three methods of creating maps to evaluate genomes: cytogenetic (staining chromosomes); radiation hybrid maps (fragments with x-rays); and sequence maps (comparing DNA sequences). Which of the following accurately describes the three methods?

a. Cytogenetic mapping - stained sections of chromosomes are analyzed using microscope, the distance between genetic markers can be found; Radiation hybrid mapping - breaks DNA using radiation and is affected by recombination frequency; Sequence mapping - DNA sequencing technology used to create physical maps.

b. Cytogenetic mapping - stained sections of chromosomes are analyzed using microscope, the approximate distance between genetic markers can be found; Radiation hybrid mapping - breaks DNA using radiation and is unaffected by recombination frequency; Sequence mapping - DNA sequencing technology used to create physical maps.

c. Cytogenetic mapping - stained sections of chromosomes are analyzed using microscope, the distance in base pairs between genetic markers can be found; Radiation hybrid mapping - breaks DNA using radiation and is unaffected by recombination frequency; Sequence mapping - DNA sequencing technology used to create physical maps.

d. Cytogenetic mapping - stained sections of chromosomes are analyzed using a telescope, the distance between genetic markers can be found; Radiation hybrid mapping - breaks DNA using radiation and is affected by recombination frequency; Sequence mapping - DNA sequencing technology used to create physical maps.

49. How many cells with different genetic variations are possible after a single round of meiosis?

a. two

b. three

c. four

d. eight

SCIENCE PRACTICE CHALLENGE QUESTIONS

50. Prokaryotes have an adaptive strategy to identify and respond to viral infections. This strategy uses segments of the cyclic DNA called CRISPRs and genes encoding CRISPR-associated (cas) proteins. When a virus enters the cell, a strand of viral DNA is excised by a cas protein and inserted into the bacterial DNA in a CRISPR region. When the same viral DNA is encountered subsequently, this foreign DNA is targeted by cas proteins that carry RNA markers transcribed from the inserted segment. The cas proteins cleave the viral DNA. The bacteria “remember” the infectious agent, providing a form of immunity.

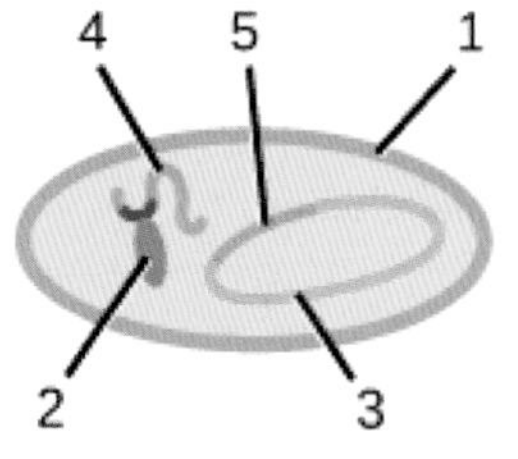

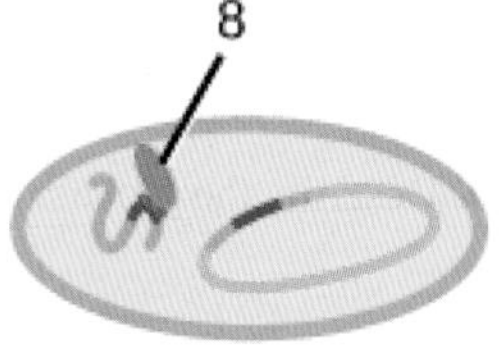

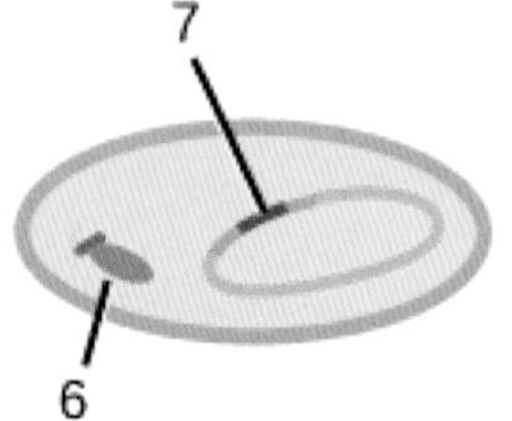

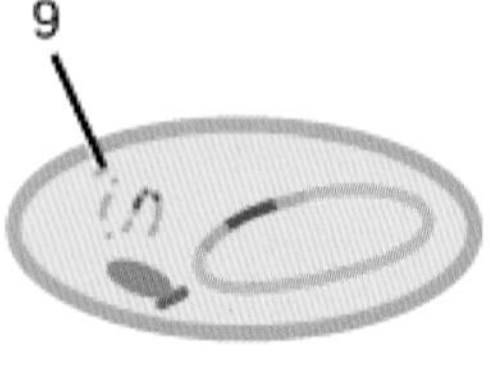

Figure 17.17

A. Use the diagram above to identify the components of a transcript-based response of bacteria to the presence of viral DNA by placing the corresponding number next to each feature of the diagram:

___ viral DNA ___ degraded viral DNA ___ cell membrane

___ cellular DNA ___ cas protein ___ stored viral DNA template

___ excised viral DNA ___ cas protein-RNA complex

___ cas protein-RNA-viral DNA complex

The CRISPR system was discovered in cultures of yogurt in 2002. Subsequently, researchers developed a technology based on the manipulation of this system. The code for the prokaryotic CRISPR/cas system is highly conserved and is found in the human genome. DNA sequences are known to encode proteins responsible for many heritable diseases. CRISPR/cas is a technology that allows DNA to be cleaved at the boundaries of a nucleotide sequence, making the protein dysfunctional. The break in the strand is then recognized and replaced with the code for the functional protein. If the editing is done with zygote-forming cells, the change is inherited. Not only the patient, but all progeny of the patient, are cured. This technology is the first to easily make genomic modifications of a germ line. In the words of a prominent molecular biologist, this technology, which was recognized as the *Breakthrough of 2015* in the journal *Science*, "democratizes genetic engineering." Just as PCR became a standard, widely used tool, any molecular biology lab is now able to apply this technology.

B. **Pose three questions**—whose pursuit would require an understanding of genetics—regarding the ethical and social issues that accompany the use of this medical technology.

C. **Explain** the value of genetic variation within a population. **Predict** a possible effect that this technology could have, if unregulated, on human genetic variation.

51. Gel electrophoresis of polymers and polymer fragments is an important element in many investigations. Samples of a solution are pipetted into the wells of a gel. The gel is placed in a solution that maintains a constant pH, and an electric field is applied over the length of the gel. Separated components are transferred to a substrate where they can be visualized and identified by comparison with samples of standards. Application of this method to DNA is called a Southern blot, named for the inventor of the technology. The method's application to RNA is called a northern blot, another demonstration that biologist have fun (there are also western, eastern, and far-eastern blots, but these techniques are *not* named for their inventors).

A. Consider the three amino acids shown below and **explain** how, when pipetted into a gel and subjected to an electric field, the amino acids move; how the amino acids are separated as they move; and which amino acid moves furthest.

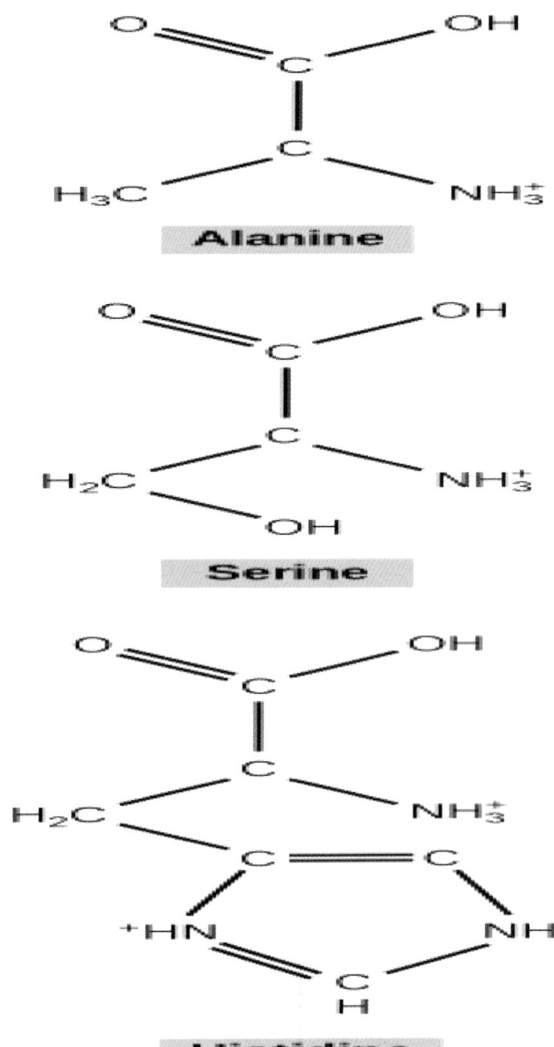

Figure 17.18

B. A biologist wants to determine whether a new protocol is successful in constructing and amplifying a molecular clone of a segment of DNA introduced as a plasmid. After the procedure is complete, the bacterial cells containing the plasmid with the inserted segment are lysed, and a gel is run into which samples of the lysate and the sequences to be cloned have been pipetted. Use the data displayed in the developed gel shown below to **evaluate the question** of whether the protocol was successful.

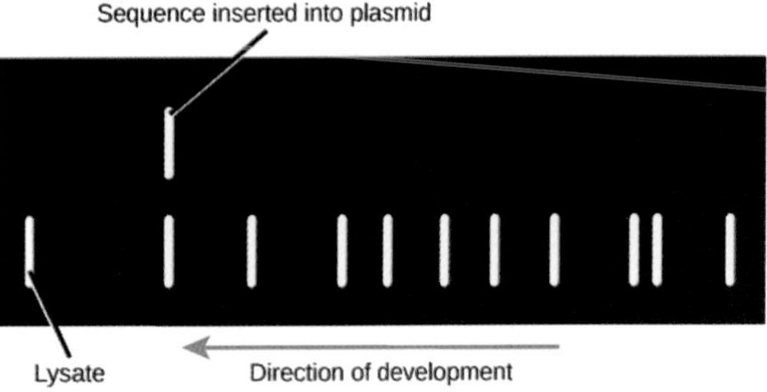

Figure 17.19

C. **Design a plan** to answer the question of whether the new DNA has been incorporated into the DNA of the host organism.

52. Genetic engineering can be applied to heritable information to produce what is referred to as a "knockdown organism." Biotechnology also can be applied to produce nonheritable changes in a "knockdown gene." Post-transcriptional strategies target the mRNA product of a gene. One such strategy uses the conserved genes that encode RNA interference (RNAi) proteins for the regulation of levels of mRNA transcription.

Some viral RNA is double stranded (dsRNA). A cell responds to the presence of double-stranded RNA by the attachment of the enzyme DICER, which cuts dsRNA into short fragments. One strand of the fragment is transferred to the RNA-induced silencing complex (RISC), which searches for an mRNA with a sequence matching that of the fragment strand. When detected, this mRNA is degraded.

A. Common in cancer cells is a mutation of the gene that encodes the protein p53, whose role is to detect and repair errors in DNA; if repairs cannot be made, p53 initiates apoptosis. **Create a visual representation** to **explain** how the DICER-RISC system within the cell can be used to suppress the translation of a mutated form of the gene encoding p53, potentially destroying a tumor.

B. Whole-genome sequences provide a library of potentially expressed proteins, but they do not provide information on the functions of each protein. In an approach called reverse genetics, investigations attempt to determine the function of the gene, often by silencing the gene using RNAi technology. Assume that you have the ability to synthesize dsRNA from a DNA segment taken from an organism whose whole genome has been determined. **Design a plan** for collecting data that could be used to assign a function to the protein encoded by this sequence. (Hint: Don't worry about the number of experiments that might need to be conducted to implement your plan. An automated technique called high-throughput screening robotically supports thousands of simultaneous experiments.)

18 | EVOLUTION AND ORIGIN OF SPECIES

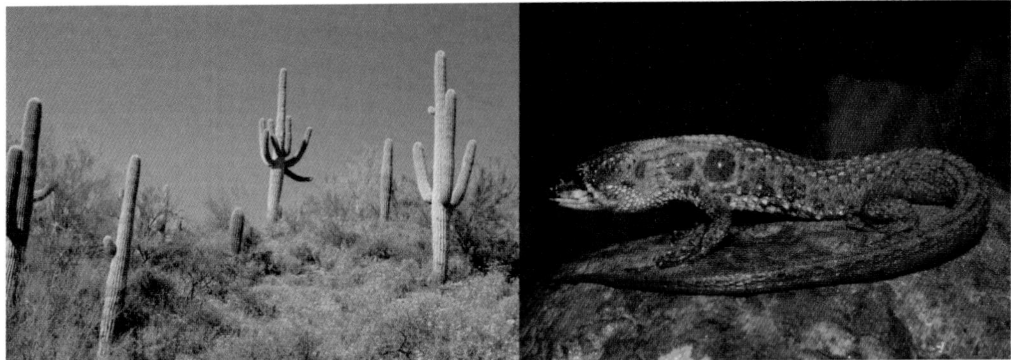

Figure 18.1 All organisms are products of evolution adapted to their environment. (a) Saguaro (*Carnegiea gigantea*) can soak up 750 liters of water in a single rain storm, enabling these cacti to survive the dry conditions of the Sonora desert in Mexico and the Southwestern United States. (b) The Andean semiaquatic lizard (*Potamites montanicola*) discovered in Peru in 2010 lives between 1,570 to 2,100 meters in elevation, and, unlike most lizards, is nocturnal and swims. Scientists still do no know how these ectotherms, which rely on external sources of body heat, are able to move in the cold (10 to 15°C) temperatures of the Andean night. (credit a: modification of work by Gentry George, U.S. Fish and Wildlife Service; credit b: modification of work by Germán Chávez and Diego Vásquez, *ZooKeys*)

Chapter Outline

Introduction

The field of biology is a diverse one that includes the study of organisms from the small and simple to the large and complex. From biological molecules to biomes, the one theme that remains consistent is evolution. All **species** of living organisms are descended from a common ancestor. Although it may seem that living things today stay much the same, this is not the case. Evolution is actually an ongoing process. Additionally, new species are discovered regularly. For example, scientists have used a method called fluorescent *in situ* hybridization, which uses fluorescent probes to locate specific genes on chromosomes, to discover a green sea slug that can perform photosynthesis just like a plant.[1] The slug obtains genes related to photosynthesis from the algae it eats through a process called horizontal gene transfer. In this process, genes can be transferred directly from one cell to another. The algal genes code for products that repair and maintain chloroplasts eaten by the slug. You can read more about it at this website (http://openstaxcollege.org/l/32slug) .

1. Biol. Bull. 227: 300–312. (December 2014)

18.1 | Understanding Evolution

In this section, you will explore the following questions:

- How was the present-day theory of evolution developed?
- What is adaptation, and how does adaptation relate to natural selection?
- What are the differences between convergent and divergent evolution, and what are examples of each that support evolution by natural selection?
- What are examples of homologous and vestigial structures, and what evidence do these structures provide to support patterns of evolution?
- What are common misconceptions about the theory of evolution?

Connection for AP® Courses

Millions of species, from bacteria to blueberries to baboons, currently call Earth their home, but these organisms evolved from different species. Furthermore, scientists estimate that several million more species will become extinct before they have been classified and studied. But why don't polar bears naturally inhabit deserts or rain forests, except, perhaps, in movies? Why do humans possess traits, such as opposable thumbs, that are unique to primates but not other mammals? How did observations of finches by Charles Darwin visiting the Galapagos Islands in the 1800s provide the foundation for our modern understanding of evolution?

The **theory of evolution** as proposed by Darwin is the unifying theory of biology. The tenet that all life has evolved and diversified from a common ancestor is the foundation from which we approach all questions in biology. As we learned in our exploration of the structure and function of DNA, variations in individuals within a population occur through mutation, allowing more desirable traits to be passed to the next generation. Due to competition for resources and other environmental pressures, individuals possessing more favorable adaptive characteristics are more likely to survive and reproduce, passing those characteristics to the next generation with increased frequency. When environments change, what was once an unfavorable trait may become a favorable one. Organisms may evolve in response to their changing environment by the accumulation of favorable traits in succeeding generations. Thus, evolution by **natural selection** explains both the unity and diversity of life.

Convergent evolution occurs when similar traits with the same function evolve in multiple species exposed to similar selection pressure, such as the wings of bats and insects. In **divergent evolution**, two species evolve in different directions from a common point, such as the forelimbs of humans, dogs, birds, and whales. Although Darwin's theory was revolutionary for its time because it contrasted with long-held ideas (for example, Lamarck proposed the inheritance of **acquired characteristics**), evidence drawn from many scientific disciplines, including the fossil record, the existence of homologous and vestigial structures, mathematics, and DNA analysis supports evolution through natural selection. It is also important to understand that evolution continues to occur; for example, bacteria that evolve resistance to antibiotics or plants that become resistant to pesticides provide evidence for continuing change.

Information presented and the examples highlighted in this section support concepts outlined in Big Idea 1 of the AP® Biology Curriculum Framework. The AP® Learning Objectives listed in the Curriculum Framework provide a transparent foundation for the AP® Biology course, an inquiry-based laboratory experience, instructional activities, and AP® exam questions. A learning objective merges required content with one or more of the seven science practices.

Big Idea 1	The process of evolution drives the diversity and unity of life.
Enduring Understanding 1.A	Change in the genetic makeup of a population over time is evolution.
Essential Knowledge	**1.A.1** Natural selection is a major mechanism of evolution.

Science Practice	**5.3** The student can evaluate the evidence provided by data sets in relation to a particular scientific question.
Learning Objective	**1.9** The student is able to evaluate evidence provided by data from many scientific disciplines that support biological evolution.
Essential Knowledge	**1.A.2** Natural selection acts on phenotypic variations in populations.
Science Practice	**1.2** The student can describe representations and models of natural or man-made phenomena and systems in the domain.
Learning Objective	**1.5** The student is able to connect evolutionary changes in a population over time to a change in the environment.
Essential Knowledge	**1.A.4** Biological evolution is supported by scientific evidence from many disciplines, including mathematics.
Science Practice	**2.2** The student can apply mathematical routines to quantities that describe natural phenomena.
Learning Objective	**1.2** The student is able to evaluate evidence provided by data to qualitatively and quantitatively investigate the role of natural selection in evolution.
Essential Knowledge	**1.A.4** Biological evolution is supported by scientific evidence from many disciplines, including mathematics.
Science Practice	**5.3** The student can evaluate the evidence provided by data sets in relation to a particular scientific question.
Learning Objective	**1.12** The student is able to connect scientific evidence from many scientific disciplines to support the modern concept of evolution.
Essential Knowledge	**1.A.4** Biological evolution is supported by scientific evidence from many disciplines, including mathematics.
Science Practice	**5.2** The student can refine observations and measurements based on data analysis.
Learning Objective	**1.10** The student is able to refine evidence based on data from many scientific disciplines that support biological evolution.
Enduring Understanding 1.C	Life continues to evolve within a changing environment.
Essential Knowledge	**1.C.3** Populations of organisms continue to evolve.
Science Practice	**7.1** The student can connect phenomena and models across spatial and temporal scales.
Learning Objective	**1.26** The student is able to evaluate given data sets that illustrate evolution as an ongoing processes.
Essential Knowledge	**1.C.3** Populations of organisms continue to evolve.
Science Practice	**7.1** The student can connect phenomena and models across spatial and temporal scales.
Learning Objective	**1.25** The student is able to describe a model that represents evolution within a population.
Essential Knowledge	**1.C.3** Populations of organisms continue to evolve.
Science Practice	**7.1** The student can connect phenomena and models across spatial and temporal scales.
Learning Objective	**1.4** The student is able to evaluate data-based evidence that describes evolutionary changes in the genetic makeup of a population over time.

The Science Practice Challenge Questions contain additional test questions for this section that will help you prepare for the AP exam. These questions address the following standards:
[APLO 1.10][APLO 1.12][APLO 1.13][APLO 1.31][APLO 1.32][APLO 1.27][APLO 1.28][APLO 1.30][APLO 1.14][APLO 1.29][APLO 1.26][APLO 4.8]

The Origin of Life

Humans have adopted many theories regarding the origin of life over the course of our time on Earth. Early civilizations believed that life was created by supernatural forces. Organisms were "hand-made" to be perfectly adapted to their environment and, therefore, did not change over time. Some early thinkers, such as the Greek philosopher Aristotle, believed that organisms belonged to a ladder of increasing complexity. Based on this understanding, scientists such as Carolus Linnaeus attempted to organize all living things into classification schemes that demonstrated an increasing complexity of life.

Over time, however, scientists came to understand that life was constantly evolving on Earth. Georges Cuvier found that fossilized remains or organisms changed as he dug into deeper rock layers (strata), indicating that the organisms present in the area had changed over time. This observation led Jean-Baptiste de Lamarck to hypothesize that organisms adapted to their environment by changing over time. As organisms used different parts of their body, those parts improved, and these changes were passed down to their offspring. Ultimately, these theories were disproven by scientists, but their development contributed to the theory of evolution that was finally formulated by Charles Darwin.

Charles Darwin and Natural Selection

In the mid-nineteenth century, the actual mechanism for evolution was independently conceived of and described by two naturalists: Charles Darwin and Alfred Russel Wallace. Importantly, each naturalist spent time exploring the natural world on expeditions to the tropics. From 1831 to 1836, Darwin traveled around the world on *H.M.S. Beagle*, including stops in South America, Australia, and the southern tip of Africa. Wallace traveled to Brazil to collect insects in the Amazon rainforest from 1848 to 1852 and to the Malay Archipelago from 1854 to 1862. Darwin's journey, like Wallace's later journeys to the Malay Archipelago, included stops at several island chains, the last being the Galápagos Islands west of Ecuador. On these islands, Darwin observed species of organisms on different islands that were clearly similar, yet had distinct differences. For example, the ground finches inhabiting the Galápagos Islands comprised several species with a unique beak shape (Figure 18.2). The species on the islands had a graded series of beak sizes and shapes with very small differences between the most similar. He observed that these finches closely resembled another finch species on the mainland of South America. Darwin imagined that the island species might be species modified from one of the original mainland species. Upon further study, he realized that the varied beaks of each finch helped the birds acquire a specific type of food. For example, seed-eating finches had stronger, thicker beaks for breaking seeds, and insect-eating finches had spear-like beaks for stabbing their prey.

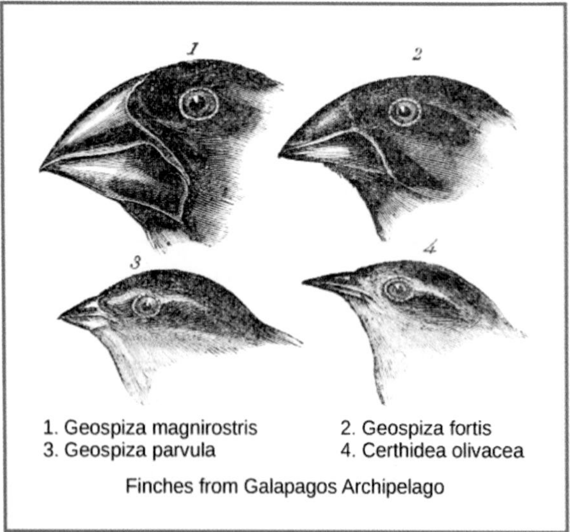

Figure 18.2 Darwin observed that beak shape varies among finch species. He postulated that the beak of an ancestral species had adapted over time to equip the finches to acquire different food sources.

Wallace and Darwin both observed similar patterns in other organisms and they independently developed the same explanation for how and why such changes could take place. Darwin called this mechanism natural selection. **Natural**

selection, also known as "survival of the fittest," is the more prolific reproduction of individuals with favorable traits that survive environmental change because of those traits; this leads to evolutionary change.

For example, a population of giant tortoises found in the Galapagos Archipelago was observed by Darwin to have longer necks than those that lived on other islands with dry lowlands. These tortoises were "selected" because they could reach more leaves and access more food than those with short necks. In times of drought when fewer leaves would be available, those that could reach more leaves had a better chance to eat and survive than those that couldn't reach the food source. Consequently, long-necked tortoises would be more likely to be reproductively successful and pass the long-necked trait to their offspring. Over time, only long-necked tortoises would be present in the population.

Natural selection, Darwin argued, was an inevitable outcome of three principles that operated in nature. First, most characteristics of organisms are inherited, or passed from parent to offspring. Although no one, including Darwin and Wallace, knew how this happened at the time, it was a common understanding. Second, more offspring are produced than are able to survive, so resources for survival and reproduction are limited. The capacity for reproduction in all organisms outstrips the availability of resources to support their numbers. Thus, there is competition for those resources in each generation. Both Darwin and Wallace's understanding of this principle came from reading an essay by the economist Thomas Malthus who discussed this principle in relation to human populations. Third, offspring vary among each other in regard to their characteristics and those variations are inherited. Darwin and Wallace reasoned that offspring with inherited characteristics which allow them to best compete for limited resources will survive and have more offspring than those individuals with variations that are less able to compete. Because characteristics are inherited, these traits will be better represented in the next generation. This will lead to change in populations over generations in a process that Darwin called descent with modification. Ultimately, natural selection leads to greater adaptation of the population to its local environment; it is the only mechanism known for adaptive evolution.

Papers by Darwin and Wallace (Figure 18.3) presenting the idea of natural selection were read together in 1858 before the Linnean Society in London. The following year Darwin's book, *On the Origin of Species*, was published. His book outlined in considerable detail his arguments for evolution by natural selection.

Figure 18.3 Both (a) Charles Darwin and (b) Alfred Wallace wrote scientific papers on natural selection that were presented together before the Linnean Society in 1858.

Demonstrations of evolution by natural selection are time consuming and difficult to obtain. One of the best examples has been demonstrated in the very birds that helped to inspire Darwin's theory: the Galápagos finches. Peter and Rosemary Grant and their colleagues have studied Galápagos finch populations every year since 1976 and have provided important demonstrations of natural selection. The Grants found changes from one generation to the next in the distribution of beak shapes with the medium ground finch on the Galápagos island of Daphne Major. The birds have inherited variation in the bill shape with some birds having wide deep bills and others having thinner bills. During a period in which rainfall was higher than normal because of an El Niño, the large hard seeds that large-billed birds ate were reduced in number; however, there was an abundance of the small soft seeds which the small-billed birds ate. Therefore, survival and reproduction were much better in the following years for the small-billed birds. In the years following this El Niño, the Grants measured beak sizes in the population and found that the average bill size was smaller. Since bill size is an inherited trait, parents with smaller bills had more offspring and the size of bills had evolved to be smaller. As conditions improved in 1987 and larger seeds became more available, the trend toward smaller average bill size ceased.

career CONNECTION

Field Biologist

Many people hike, explore caves, scuba dive, or climb mountains for recreation. People often participate in these activities hoping to see wildlife. Experiencing the outdoors can be incredibly enjoyable and invigorating. What if your job was to be outside in the wilderness? Field biologists by definition work outdoors in the "field." The term field in this case refers to any location outdoors, even under water. A field biologist typically focuses research on a certain species, group of organisms, or a single habitat (Figure 18.4).

Figure 18.4 A field biologist tranquilizes a polar bear for study. (credit: Karen Rhode)

One objective of many field biologists includes discovering new species that have never been recorded. Not only do such findings expand our understanding of the natural world, but they also lead to important innovations in fields such as medicine and agriculture. Plant and microbial species, in particular, can reveal new medicinal and nutritive knowledge. Other organisms can play key roles in ecosystems or be considered rare and in need of protection. When discovered, these important species can be used as evidence for environmental regulations and laws.

Processes and Patterns of Evolution

Natural selection can only take place if there is **variation**, or differences, among individuals in a population. Importantly, these differences must have some genetic basis; otherwise, the selection will not lead to change in the next generation. This is critical because variation among individuals can be caused by non-genetic reasons such as an individual being taller because of better nutrition rather than different genes.

Genetic diversity in a population comes from two main mechanisms: mutation and sexual reproduction. Mutation, a change in DNA, is the ultimate source of new alleles, or new genetic variation in any population. The genetic changes caused by mutation can have one of three outcomes on the phenotype. A mutation can affect the phenotype of the organism in a way that gives it reduced fitness—lower likelihood of survival or fewer offspring. Alternatively, a mutation may produce a phenotype with a beneficial effect on fitness. And, many mutations will also have no effect on the fitness of the phenotype; these are called neutral mutations. Mutations may also have a whole range of effect sizes on the fitness of the organism that expresses them in their phenotype, from a small effect to a great effect. Sexual reproduction also leads to genetic diversity: when two parents reproduce, unique combinations of alleles assemble to produce the unique genotypes and thus phenotypes in each of the offspring.

A heritable trait that helps the survival and reproduction of an organism in its present environment is called an **adaptation**. Scientists describe groups of organisms becoming adapted to their environment when a change in the range of genetic variation occurs over time that increases or maintains the "fit" of the population to its environment. The webbed feet of platypuses are an adaptation for swimming. The snow leopards' thick fur is an adaptation for living in the cold. The cheetahs' fast speed is an adaptation for catching prey.

These adaptations can occur through the rearrangements of entire genomes or can be caused by the mutation of a single gene. For example, dogs have 78 chromosomes while cats have 38. A large number of the characteristics that distinguish dogs from cats arose from chromosomal rearrangements that have occurred since both groups diverged from their last common ancestor. On the other hand, certain mice are white and other mice are black. The difference in fur color occurs through the mutation of a single gene. Thus, as a result of a single mutation, a mouse population can become more adapted to survive in snowy environments versus a dark, forest floor.

Whether or not a trait is favorable depends on the environmental conditions at the time. The same traits are not always selected because environmental conditions can change. For example, consider a species of plant that grew in a moist climate and did not need to conserve water. Large leaves were selected because they allowed the plant to obtain more energy from the sun. Large leaves require more water to maintain than small leaves, and the moist environment provided favorable conditions to support large leaves. After thousands of years, the climate changed, and the area no longer had excess water. The direction of natural selection shifted so that plants with small leaves were selected because those populations were able to conserve water to survive the new environmental conditions.

The evolution of species has resulted in enormous variation in form and function. Sometimes, evolution gives rise to groups of organisms that become tremendously different from each other. When two species evolve in diverse directions from a common point, it is called divergent evolution. Such divergent evolution can be seen in the forms of the reproductive organs of flowering plants which share the same basic anatomies; however, they can look very different as a result of selection in different physical environments and adaptation to different kinds of pollinators (Figure 18.5).

Figure 18.5 Flowering plants evolved from a common ancestor. Notice that the (a) dense blazing star (*Liatrus spicata*) and the (b) purple coneflower (*Echinacea purpurea*) vary in appearance, yet both share a similar basic morphology. (credit a: modification of work by Drew Avery; credit b: modification of work by Cory Zanker)

In other cases, similar phenotypes evolve independently in distantly related species. For example, flight has evolved in both bats and insects, and they both have structures we refer to as wings, which are adaptations to flight. However, the wings of bats and insects have evolved from very different original structures. This phenomenon is called convergent evolution, where similar traits evolve independently in species that do not share a common ancestry. The two species came to the same function, flying, but did so separately from each other.

These physical changes occur over enormous spans of time and help explain how evolution occurs. Natural selection acts on individual organisms, which in turn can shape an entire species. Although natural selection may work in a single generation on an individual, it can take thousands or even millions of years for the genotype of an entire species to evolve. It is over these large time spans that life on earth has changed and continues to change.

Evidence of Evolution

The evidence for evolution is compelling and extensive. Looking at every level of organization in living systems, biologists see the signature of past and present evolution. Darwin dedicated a large portion of his book, *On the Origin of Species*, to identifying patterns in nature that were consistent with evolution, and since Darwin, our understanding has become clearer and broader.

Fossils

Fossils provide solid evidence that organisms from the past are not the same as those found today, and fossils show a progression of evolution. Scientists determine the age of fossils and categorize them from all over the world to determine when the organisms lived relative to each other. The resulting fossil record tells the story of the past and shows the evolution of form over millions of years (Figure 18.6). For example, scientists have recovered highly detailed records showing the evolution of humans and horses.

Figure 18.6 In this (a) display, fossil hominids are arranged from oldest (bottom) to newest (top). As hominids evolved, the shape of the skull changed. An artist's rendition of (b) extinct species of the genus *Equus* reveals that these ancient species resembled the modern horse (*Equus ferus*) but varied in size.

Anatomy and Embryology

Another type of evidence for evolution is the presence of structures in organisms that share the same basic form. For example, the bones in the appendages of a human, dog, bird, and whale all share the same overall construction (Figure 18.7) resulting from their origin in the appendages of a common ancestor. Over time, evolution led to changes in the shapes and sizes of these bones in different species, but they have maintained the same overall layout. Scientists call these synonymous parts **homologous structures**.

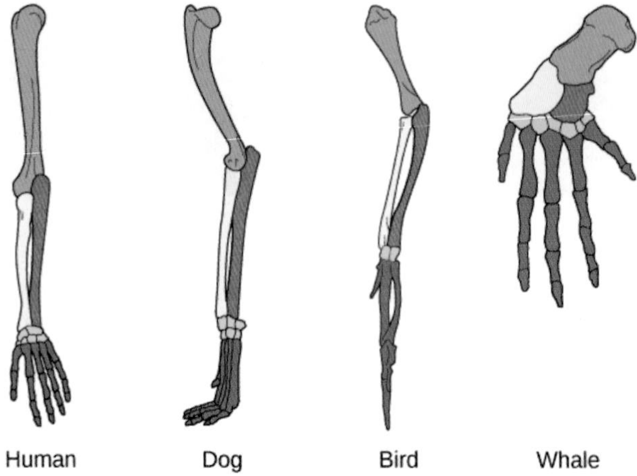

Figure 18.7 The similar construction of these appendages indicates that these organisms share a common ancestor.

Some structures exist in organisms that have no apparent function at all, and appear to be residual parts from a past common ancestor. These unused structures without function are called **vestigial structures**. Examples of vestigial structures include wings on flightless birds, leaves on some cacti, and hind leg bones in whales.

Visit this interactive site (http://openstaxcollege.org/l/bone_structures) to guess which bones structures are homologous and which are analogous, and see examples of evolutionary adaptations to illustrate these concepts.

What is the basic difference between things that are homologous and things that are analogous?

a. Things that are analogous look similar and things that are homologous do not.

b. Things that are analogous have the same function and things that are homologous have different functions.

c. Things that are analogous are not a result of evolution, whereas things that are homologous are.

d. Things that are analogous result from convergence and things that are homologous result from common ancestry

Another evidence of evolution is the convergence of form in organisms that share similar environments. For example, species of unrelated animals, such as the arctic fox and ptarmigan, living in the arctic region have been selected for seasonal white phenotypes during winter to blend with the snow and ice (Figure 18.8**ab**). These similarities occur not because of common ancestry, but because of similar selection pressures—the benefits of not being seen by predators.

Figure 18.8 The white winter coat of the (a) arctic fox and the (b) ptarmigan's plumage are adaptations to their environments. (credit a: modification of work by Keith Morehouse)

Embryology, the study of the development of the anatomy of an organism to its adult form, also provides evidence of relatedness between now widely divergent groups of organisms. Mutational tweaking in the embryo can have such magnified consequences in the adult that embryo formation tends to be conserved. As a result, structures that are absent in some groups often appear in their embryonic forms and disappear by the time the adult or juvenile form is reached. For example, all vertebrate embryos, including humans, exhibit gill slits and tails at some point in their early development. These disappear in the adults of terrestrial groups but are maintained in adult forms of aquatic groups such as fish and some amphibians. Great ape embryos, including humans, have a tail structure during their development that is lost by the time of birth.

Biogeography

The geographic distribution of organisms on the planet follows patterns that are best explained by evolution in conjunction with the movement of tectonic plates over geological time. Broad groups that evolved before the breakup of the supercontinent Pangaea (about 200 million years ago) are distributed worldwide. Groups that evolved since the breakup appear uniquely in regions of the planet, such as the unique flora and fauna of northern continents that formed from the supercontinent Laurasia and of the southern continents that formed from the supercontinent Gondwana. The presence of members of the plant family Proteaceae in Australia, southern Africa, and South America, for example, is best explained by their presence prior to the southern supercontinent Gondwana breaking up.

The great diversification of marsupials in Australia and the absence of other mammals reflect Australia's long isolation. Australia has an abundance of endemic species—species found nowhere else—which is typical of islands whose isolation by expanses of water prevents species from migrating. Over time, these species diverge evolutionarily into new species that look very different from their ancestors that may exist on the mainland. The marsupials of Australia, the finches on the Galápagos, and many species on the Hawaiian Islands are all unique to their one point of origin, yet they display distant relationships to ancestral species on mainlands.

Molecular Biology

Like anatomical structures, the structures of the molecules of life reflect descent with modification. Evidence of a common ancestor for all of life is reflected in the universality of DNA as the genetic material and in the near universality of the genetic code and the machinery of DNA replication and expression. Fundamental divisions in life between the three domains are reflected in major structural differences in otherwise conservative structures such as the components of ribosomes and the structures of membranes. In general, the relatedness of groups of organisms is reflected in the similarity of their DNA sequences—exactly the pattern that would be expected from descent and diversification from a common ancestor.

DNA sequences have also shed light on some of the mechanisms of evolution. For example, it is clear that the evolution of new functions for proteins commonly occurs after gene duplication events that allow the free modification of one copy by mutation, selection, or drift (changes in a population's gene pool resulting from chance), while the second copy continues to produce a functional protein.

Direct Observations

Scientists have also observed evolution occurring in both the laboratory and in the wild. A common example of this is the spread of antibiotic resistant genes in a population of bacteria. When bacteria are exposed to antibiotics, alleles that help the organism survive increase in frequency Figure 18.9. This is because individuals that cannot resist the antibacterial die off, leaving only individuals with the resistance gene to reproduce.

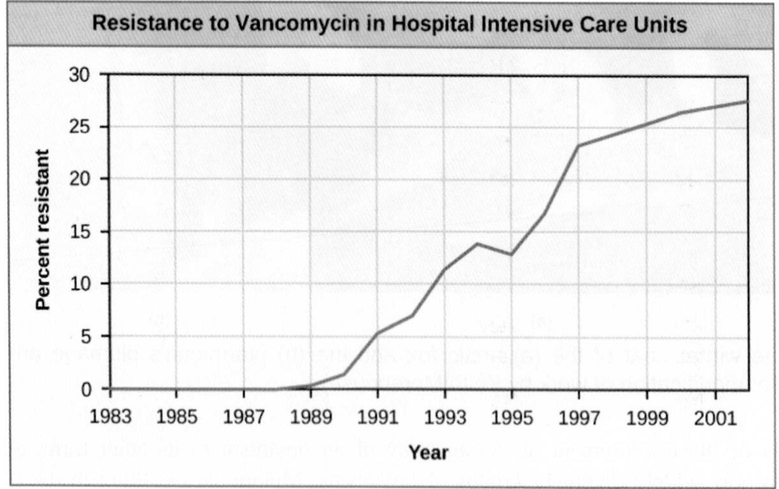

Figure 18.9

Adaptations for homeostasis

One major reason that organisms adapt is to maintain homeostasis, one of the main characteristics of life. All organisms have likely descended from a single common ancestor, which is why so many organisms share anatomical, morphological, and molecular features. However, each organism has adapted these similar features to suit their environment and adapt to environmental changes over time. For example, all organisms use DNA polymerase to replicate their genomes. However, whereas organisms with small genomes can get away with just a single polymerase molecule working at one point in the genome at time, organisms with larger genomes replicate many points of the genome simultaneously. Other organisms that live in extremely hot environments, such as deep-sea thermal vents, have specialized polymerase molecules that can withstand the heat that would quickly denature the polymerases in land-based animals. Although the basis for each of these different DNA polymerase molecules is the same, each one has been adapted to function in the organism's environmental niche.

Misconceptions of Evolution

Although the theory of evolution generated some controversy when it was first proposed, it was almost universally accepted by biologists, particularly younger biologists, within 20 years after publication of *On the Origin of Species*. Nevertheless, the theory of evolution is a difficult concept and misconceptions about how it works abound.

This site (http://openstaxcollege.org/l/misconceptions) addresses some of the main misconceptions associated with the theory of evolution.

Select one misconception about evolution and explain what you might say to someone to dispel it.

a. Misconception: Evolution is not a well-founded theory. Correction: Although evolution cannot be observed occurring today, there is strong evidence in the fossil record and in shared DNA sequences to support the theory

b. Misconception: Humans are not currently evolving. Correction: The environmental pressures humans face are different than the ones they faced several thousands of years ago, but they are still there, and they are still producing (slowly!) evolutionary change.

c. Misconception: Evolution produces individuals that are perfectly fit to their environment. Correction: Evolution produces random changes in the genetic code that sometimes lead to adaptations

d. Misconception: Evolution is a random process. Correction: evolution is a force that makes animals adapt to perfectly fit the environment they are living in

Evolution Is Just a Theory

Critics of the theory of evolution dismiss its importance by purposefully confounding the everyday usage of the word "theory" with the way scientists use the word. In science, a "theory" is understood to be a body of thoroughly tested and verified explanations for a set of observations of the natural world. Scientists have a theory of the atom, a theory of gravity, and the theory of relativity, each of which describes understood facts about the world. In the same way, the theory of evolution describes facts about the living world. As such, a theory in science has survived significant efforts to discredit it by scientists. In contrast, a "theory" in common vernacular is a word meaning a guess or suggested explanation; this meaning is more akin to the scientific concept of "hypothesis." When critics of evolution say evolution is "just a theory," they are implying that there is little evidence supporting it and that it is still in the process of being rigorously tested. This is a mischaracterization.

Individuals Evolve

Evolution is the change in genetic composition of a population over time, specifically over generations, resulting from differential reproduction of individuals with certain alleles. Individuals do change over their lifetime, obviously, but this is called development and involves changes programmed by the set of genes the individual acquired at birth in coordination with the individual's environment. When thinking about the evolution of a characteristic, it is probably best to think about the change of the average value of the characteristic in the population over time. For example, when natural selection leads to bill-size change in medium-ground finches in the Galápagos, this does not mean that individual bills on the finches are changing. If one measures the average bill size among all individuals in the population at one time and then measures the average bill size in the population several years later, this average value will be different as a result of evolution. Although some individuals may survive from the first time to the second, they will still have the same bill size; however, there will be many new individuals that contribute to the shift in average bill size.

Evolution Explains the Origin of Life

It is a common misunderstanding that evolution includes an explanation of life's origins. Conversely, some of the theory's critics believe that it cannot explain the origin of life. The theory does not try to explain the origin of life. The theory of evolution explains how populations change over time and how life diversifies the origin of species. It does not shed light on the beginnings of life including the origins of the first cells, which is how life is defined. The mechanisms of the origin of life on Earth are a particularly difficult problem because it occurred a very long time ago, and presumably it just occurred once. Importantly, biologists believe that the presence of life on Earth precludes the possibility that the events that led to life on Earth can be repeated because the intermediate stages would immediately become food for existing living things.

However, once a mechanism of inheritance was in place in the form of a molecule like DNA either within a cell or pre-cell, these entities would be subject to the principle of natural selection. More effective reproducers would increase in frequency at the expense of inefficient reproducers. So while evolution does not explain the origin of life, it may have something to say about some of the processes operating once pre-living entities acquired certain properties.

Organisms Evolve on Purpose

Statements such as "organisms evolve in response to a change in an environment" are quite common, but such statements can lead to two types of misunderstandings. First, the statement must not be understood to mean that individual organisms evolve. The statement is shorthand for "a population evolves in response to a changing environment." However, a second misunderstanding may arise by interpreting the statement to mean that the evolution is somehow intentional. A changed environment results in some individuals in the population, those with particular phenotypes, benefiting and therefore producing proportionately more offspring than other phenotypes. This results in change in the population if the characteristics are genetically determined.

It is also important to understand that the variation that natural selection works on is already in a population and does not arise in response to an environmental change. For example, applying antibiotics to a population of bacteria will, over time, select a population of bacteria that are resistant to antibiotics. The resistance, which is caused by a gene, did not arise by mutation because of the application of the antibiotic. The gene for resistance was already present in the gene pool of the bacteria, likely at a low frequency. The antibiotic, which kills the bacterial cells without the resistance gene, strongly selects individuals that are resistant, since these would be the only ones that survived and divided. Experiments have demonstrated that mutations for antibiotic resistance do not arise as a result of antibiotic.

In a larger sense, evolution is not goal directed. Species do not become "better" over time; they simply track their changing environment with adaptations that maximize their reproduction in a particular environment at a particular time. Evolution has no goal of making faster, bigger, more complex, or even smarter species, despite the commonness of this kind of language in popular discourse. What characteristics evolve in a species are a function of the variation present and the environment, both of which are constantly changing in a non-directional way. What trait is fit in one environment at one time may well be fatal at some point in the future. This holds equally well for a species of insect as it does the human species.

Activity

Using information from a book or online resource such as Jonathan Weiner's *The Beak of the Finch*, explain how contemporary evidence drawn from multiple scientific disciplines supports the observations of Charles Darwin regarding evolution by natural selection. Then, in small groups or as a whole class discussion or debate, present an argument to dispel misconceptions about evolution and how it works.

Lab Investigation

AP® Biology Investigative Labs: Inquiry-Based, Investigation 8: Biotechnology: Bacterial Transformation. You will explore how genetic engineering techniques can be used to manipulate heritable information by inserting plasmids into bacterial cells.

Think About It

What selection pressures may affect the survival and reproduction of a group of pea seeds scattered by a person along the ground?

18.2 | Formation of New Species

In this section, you will explore the following questions:

- What defines a species, and how can different species be distinguished from each other?
- How does genetic variation lead to speciation?
- What is the role of pre-zygotic and post-zygotic reproductive barriers in speciation?
- What is the difference between allopatric speciation and sympatric speciation?
- How does adaptive radiation explain the diversification?

Connection for AP® Courses

Speciation explains the diversity of organisms that inhabit the Earth. Although all life shares various genetic similarities, only certain organisms combine genetic information by sexual reproduction and produce viable and fertile offspring that, in turn, can successfully reproduce. Scientists call such organisms members of a biological species. As we will study in later, changes in allele frequencies within a population over generations result in microevolution. However, macroevolution leads to the evolution of new species when populations diverge from a common ancestor and, for one reason or another, become reproductively isolated from the original population.

Speciation occurs along two main pathways: geographic separation (**allopatric speciation**) and through mechanisms that occur within a shared habitat (**sympatric speciation**). In both cases, populations become reproductively isolated. When populations become geographically isolated, the free-flow of alleles is prevented. Over time—and because of different selective pressures—the populations diverge and become genetically independent species. **Prezygotic barriers** block reproduction prior to formation of a zygote, whereas **postzygotic barriers** block reproduction after fertilization occurs. Obviously, if two populations are separated by a vast ocean, they will not come in contact with each other to reproduce. However, if speciation has occurred, even when brought back together, they will retain their species identity. There are many examples of this in nature, including Darwin's finches, northern and Mexican spotted owls, and Hawaiian honeycreeper. **Adaptive radiation** occurs when a single ancestral species gives rise to many new species. This may occur, for example, when new habitats become available. It can also be seen historically in the rise of mammals following the extinction of dinosaurs. Other examples of prezygotic isolating mechanisms include mating seasons and unique courtship behaviors. Sometimes mating occurs between two different species, resulting in a **hybrid** such as the mule, which is a cross between a horse and a donkey. However, most hybrids are inviable or sterile.

Sympatric speciation does not require a geographic barrier and explains how many different species can inhabit the same area. One form of sympatric speciation begins with a serious chromosomal error during cell division. As you recall from our exploration of meiosis, sometimes errors occur in the separation of chromosomes or chromatids, resulting in gametes with extra chromosomes (**polyploidy**). This type of speciation is more common in plants than in animals, though some examples in animals exist. For example, two groups of cichlid fish in Africa's Lake Victoria, which have distinct morphologies and diets, may be in the early stage of sympatric speciation without polyploidy, as genetic differences arise between the two groups.

Information presented and the examples highlighted in this section support concepts outlined in Big Idea 1 and Big Idea 3 of the AP® Biology Curriculum Framework. The AP® Learning Objectives listed in the Curriculum Framework provide a transparent foundation for the AP® Biology course, an inquiry-based laboratory experience, instructional activities, and AP® exam questions. A learning objective merges required content with one or more of the seven science practices.

Big Idea 1	The process of evolution drives the diversity and unity of life.
Enduring Understanding 1.C	Life continues to evolve within a changing environment.
Essential Knowledge	**1.C.1** Speciation and extinction have occurred throughout the Earth's history.
Science Practice	**5.1** The student can analyze data to identify patterns or relationships.
Learning Objective	**1.20** The student is able to analyze data related to questions of speciation and extinction throughout the Earth's history.
Essential Knowledge	**1.C.1** Speciation and extinction have occurred throughout the Earth's
Science Practice	**4.2** The student can design a plan for collecting data to answer a particular scientific question.
Learning Objective	**1.21** The student is able to design a plan for collecting data to investigate the scientific claim that speciation and extinction have occurred throughout the Earth's history.
Essential Knowledge	**1.C.2** Speciation may occur when two populations become reproductively isolated from each other.
Science Practice	**6.4** The student can make claims and predictions about natural phenomena based on scientific theories and models.
Learning Objective	**1.22** The student is able to use data from a real or simulated population(s), based on graphs or models of types of selection, to predict what will happen to the population in the future.
Essential Knowledge	**1.C.2** Speciation may occur when two populations become reproductively isolated from each other.
Science Practice	**4.1** The student can justify the selection of the kind of data needed to answer a particular scientific question.
Learning Objective	**1.23** The student is able to justify the selection of data that address questions related to reproductive isolation and speciation.
Essential Knowledge	**1.C.2** Speciation may occur when two populations become reproductively isolated from each other.
Science Practice	**6.4** The student can make claims and predictions about natural phenomena based on scientific theories and models.
Learning Objective	**1.24** The student is able to describe speciation in an isolated population and connect it to change in gene frequency, change in environment, natural selection, and/or genetic drift.
Big Idea 3	Living systems store, retrieve, transmit and respond to information essential to life processes.

Enduring Understanding 3.C	The processing of genetic information is imperfect and is a source of genetic variation.
Essential Knowledge	**3.C.1** Changes in genotype can result in changes in phenotype.
Science Practice	**6.4** The student can make claims and predictions about natural phenomena based on scientific theories and models.
Learning Objective	**3.24** The student is able to predict how a change in genotype, when expressed as a phenotype, provides a variation that can be subject to natural selection.
Essential Knowledge	**3.C.1** Changes in genotype can result in changes in phenotype.
Science Practice	**7.2** The student can connect concepts in and across domain(s) to generalize or extrapolate in and/or across enduring understandings and/or big ideas.
Learning Objective	**3.26** The student is able to explain the connection between genetic variations in organisms and phenotypic variations in populations.

The Science Practice Challenge Questions contain additional test questions for this section that will help you prepare for the AP exam. These questions address the following standards:
[APLO 2.27][APLO 1.8][APLO 1.23]

Species and the Ability to Reproduce

A species is a group of individual organisms that interbreed and produce fertile, viable offspring. According to this definition, one species is distinguished from another when, in nature, it is not possible for matings between individuals from each species to produce fertile offspring.

Members of the same species share both external and internal characteristics, which develop from their DNA. The closer relationship two organisms share, the more DNA they have in common, just like people and their families. People's DNA is likely to be more like their father or mother's DNA than their cousin or grandparent's DNA. Organisms of the same species have the highest level of DNA alignment and therefore share characteristics and behaviors that lead to successful reproduction.

Species' appearance can be misleading in suggesting an ability or inability to mate. For example, even though domestic dogs (*Canis lupus familiaris*) display phenotypic differences, such as size, build, and coat, most dogs can interbreed and produce viable puppies that can mature and sexually reproduce (Figure 18.10).

(a)

(b)

(c)

Figure 18.10 The (a) poodle and (b) cocker spaniel can reproduce to produce a breed known as (c) the cockapoo. (credit a: modification of work by Sally Eller, Tom Reese; credit b: modification of work by Jeremy McWilliams; credit c: modification of work by Kathleen Conklin)

In other cases, individuals may appear similar although they are not members of the same species. For example, even though bald eagles (*Haliaeetus leucocephalus*) and African fish eagles (*Haliaeetus vocifer*) are both birds and eagles, each belongs to a separate species group (Figure 18.11). If humans were to artificially intervene and fertilize the egg of a bald eagle with the sperm of an African fish eagle and a chick did hatch, that offspring, called a hybrid (a cross between two species), would probably be infertile—unable to successfully reproduce after it reached maturity. Different species may have different genes that are active in development; therefore, it may not be possible to develop a viable offspring with two different sets of directions. Thus, even though hybridization may take place, the two species still remain separate.

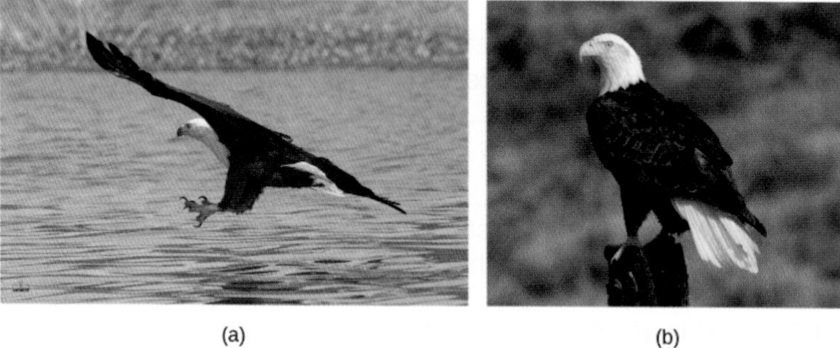

(a) (b)

Figure 18.11 The (a) African fish eagle is similar in appearance to the (b) bald eagle, but the two birds are members of different species. (credit a: modification of work by Nigel Wedge; credit b: modification of work by U.S. Fish and Wildlife Service)

Populations of species share a gene pool: a collection of all the variants of genes in the species. Again, the basis to any changes in a group or population of organisms must be genetic for this is the only way to share and pass on traits. When variations occur within a species, they can only be passed to the next generation along two main pathways: asexual reproduction or sexual reproduction. The change will be passed on asexually simply if the reproducing cell possesses the changed trait. For the changed trait to be passed on by sexual reproduction, a gamete, such as a sperm or egg cell, must possess the changed trait. In other words, sexually-reproducing organisms can experience several genetic changes in their body cells, but if these changes do not occur in a sperm or egg cell, the changed trait will never reach the next generation. Only heritable traits can evolve. Therefore, reproduction plays a paramount role for genetic change to take root in a population or species. In short, organisms must be able to reproduce with each other to pass new traits to offspring.

everyday CONNECTION for AP® Courses

Until recently, these three species of short-tailed pythons, *Python curtus, Python brongersmai* (middle), and *Python breitensteini* were considered one species. However, due to the different locations in which they are found, they have become three distinct species.

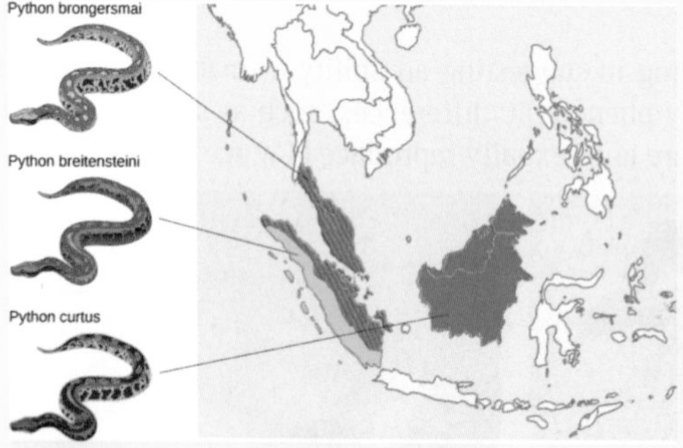

Figure 18.12

Until recently, these three species of short-tailed pythons, *Python curtus*, *Python brongersmai* (middle), and *Python breitensteini* were considered one species. However, due to the different locations in which they are found, they have become three distinct species. What is this an example of?

a. divergent evolution

b. sympatric speciation

c. allopatric speciation

d. variation

Speciation

The biological definition of species, which works for sexually reproducing organisms, is a group of actually or potentially interbreeding individuals. There are exceptions to this rule. Many species are similar enough that hybrid offspring are possible and may often occur in nature, but for the majority of species this rule generally holds. In fact, the presence in nature of hybrids between similar species suggests that they may have descended from a single interbreeding species, and the speciation process may not yet be complete.

Given the extraordinary diversity of life on the planet there must be mechanisms for **speciation**: the formation of two species from one original species. Darwin envisioned this process as a branching event and diagrammed the process in the only illustration found in *On the Origin of Species* (Figure 18.13**a**). Compare this illustration to the diagram of elephant evolution (Figure 18.13**b**), which shows that as one species changes over time, it branches to form more than one new species, repeatedly, as long as the population survives or until the organism becomes extinct.

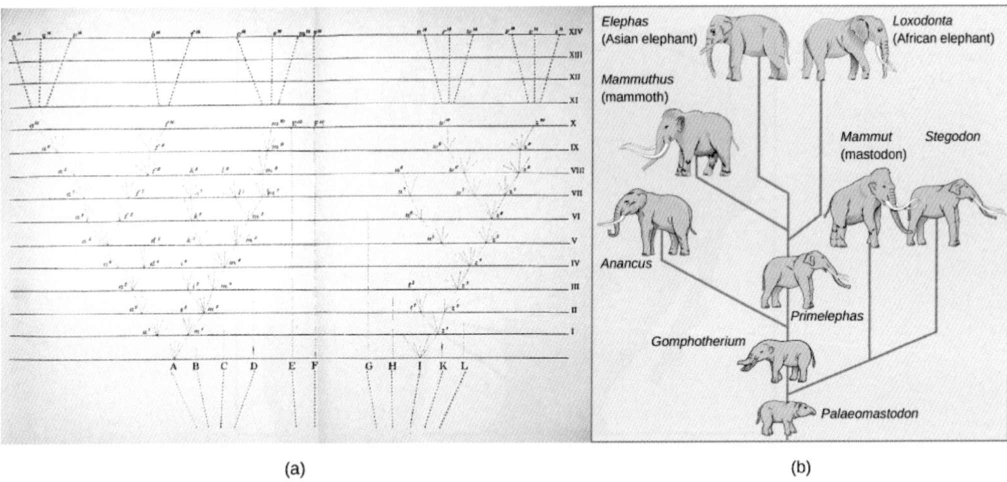

Figure 18.13 The only illustration in Darwin's *On the Origin of Species* is (a) a diagram showing speciation events leading to biological diversity. The diagram shows similarities to phylogenetic charts that are drawn today to illustrate the relationships of species. (b) Modern elephants evolved from the *Palaeomastodon*, a species that lived in Egypt 35–50 million years ago.

For speciation to occur, two new populations must be formed from one original population and they must evolve in such a way that it becomes impossible for individuals from the two new populations to interbreed. Biologists have proposed mechanisms by which this could occur that fall into two broad categories. Allopatric speciation (allo- = "other"; -patric = "homeland") involves geographic separation of populations from a parent species and subsequent evolution. Sympatric speciation (sym- = "same"; -patric = "homeland") involves speciation occurring within a parent species remaining in one location.

Biologists think of speciation events as the splitting of one ancestral species into two descendant species. There is no reason why there might not be more than two species formed at one time except that it is less likely and multiple events can be conceptualized as single splits occurring close in time.

Allopatric Speciation

A geographically continuous population has a gene pool that is relatively homogeneous. Gene flow, the movement of alleles across the range of the species, is relatively free because individuals can move and then mate with individuals in their new location. Thus, the frequency of an allele at one end of a distribution will be similar to the frequency of the allele at the other end. When populations become geographically discontinuous, that free-flow of alleles is prevented. When that separation lasts for a period of time, the two populations are able to evolve along different trajectories. Thus, their allele frequencies at numerous genetic loci gradually become more and more different as new alleles independently arise by mutation in each population. Typically, environmental conditions, such as climate, resources, predators, and competitors for the two populations will differ causing natural selection to favor divergent adaptations in each group.

Isolation of populations leading to allopatric speciation can occur in a variety of ways: a river forming a new branch, erosion forming a new valley, a group of organisms traveling to a new location without the ability to return, or seeds floating over the ocean to an island. The nature of the geographic separation necessary to isolate populations depends entirely on the biology of the organism and its potential for dispersal. If two flying insect populations took up residence in separate nearby valleys, chances are, individuals from each population would fly back and forth continuing gene flow. However, if two rodent populations became divided by the formation of a new lake, continued gene flow would be unlikely; therefore, speciation would be more likely.

Biologists group allopatric processes into two categories: dispersal and vicariance. **Dispersal** is when a few members of a species move to a new geographical area, and **vicariance** is when a natural situation arises to physically divide organisms.

Scientists have documented numerous cases of allopatric speciation taking place. For example, along the west coast of the United States, two separate sub-species of spotted owls exist. The northern spotted owl has genetic and phenotypic differences from its close relative: the Mexican spotted owl, which lives in the south (Figure 18.14).

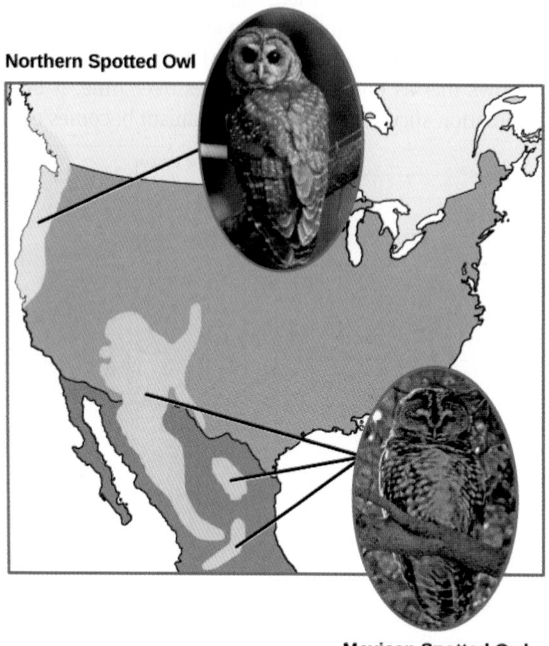

Figure 18.14 The northern spotted owl and the Mexican spotted owl inhabit geographically separate locations with different climates and ecosystems. The owl is an example of allopatric speciation. (credit "northern spotted owl": modification of work by John and Karen Hollingsworth; credit "Mexican spotted owl": modification of work by Bill Radke)

Additionally, scientists have found that the farther the distance between two groups that once were the same species, the more likely it is that speciation will occur. This seems logical because as the distance increases, the various environmental factors would likely have less in common than locations in close proximity. Consider the two owls: in the north, the climate is cooler than in the south; the types of organisms in each ecosystem differ, as do their behaviors and habits; also, the hunting habits and prey choices of the southern owls vary from the northern owls. These variances can lead to evolved differences in the owls, and speciation likely will occur.

Adaptive Radiation

In some cases, a population of one species disperses throughout an area, and each population finds a distinct niche or isolated habitat. Over time, the varied demands of their new lifestyles lead to multiple speciation events originating from a single species. This is called adaptive radiation because many adaptations evolve from a single point of origin; thus, causing the species to radiate into several new ones. Island archipelagos like the Hawaiian Islands provide an ideal context for adaptive radiation events because water surrounds each island which leads to geographical isolation for many organisms. The Hawaiian honeycreeper illustrates one example of adaptive radiation. From a single species, called the founder species, numerous species have evolved, including the six shown in Figure 18.15.

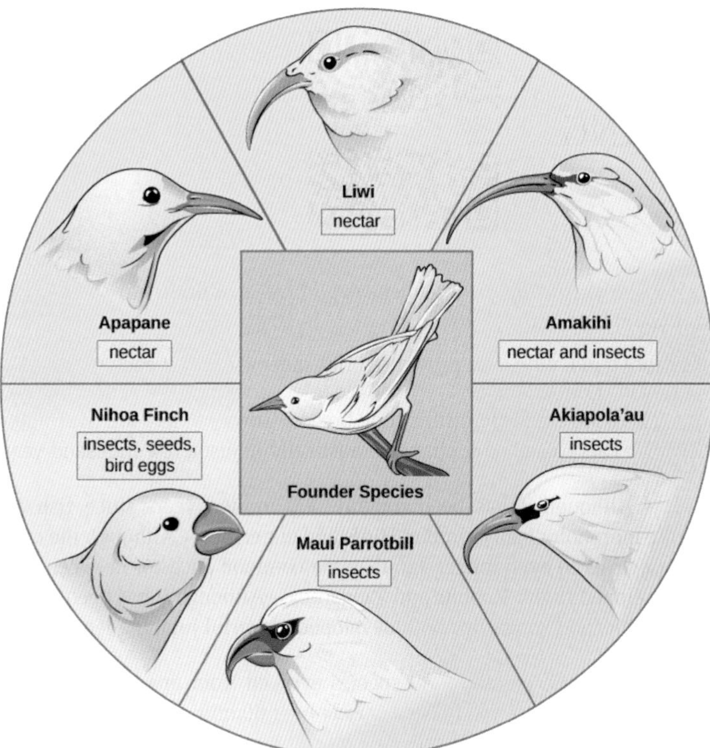

Figure 18.15 The honeycreeper birds illustrate adaptive radiation. From one original species of bird, multiple others evolved, each with its own distinctive characteristics.

Notice the differences in the species' beaks in **Figure 18.15**. Evolution in response to natural selection based on specific food sources in each new habitat led to evolution of a different beak suited to the specific food source. The seed-eating bird has a thicker, stronger beak which is suited to break hard nuts. The nectar-eating birds have long beaks to dip into flowers to reach the nectar. The insect-eating birds have beaks like swords, appropriate for stabbing and impaling insects. Darwin's finches are another example of adaptive radiation in an archipelago.

Click through this interactive site (http://openstaxcollege.org/l/bird_evolution) to see how island birds evolved in evolutionary increments from 5 million years ago to today.

Name three examples of adaptive radiation, and provide a brief statement about each one.

a. Domestic dogs – There are over 300 distinct dog breeds. Cows – There are over 800 cow breeds recognized worldwide. Domestic cats – Cats have changed drastically in just a few thousand years.

b. Whales and fish – Although it has been roughly 400 million years since fish and mammals diverged, whales and fish are morphologically similar. Birds and butterflies – Although the common ancestor between vertebrates and insects lived even longer ago than the common ancestor between whales and fish, birds and butterflies both developed flight. Rabbits and kangaroos – Although it has been over 150 million years since their divergence, rabbits and kangaroos both developed powerful jumping legs.

c. Hawaiian silverswords-There are about 30 species evolved from one parent species. Madagascar lemurs-Their common ancestor likely arrived to Madagascar over 60 million years ago. Hawaiian fruit fly-There are 500 species of fruit fly from one parent species.

d. Beetles – There are about 350,000 species of beetles that we know of. Birds – There are almost 10,000 species of birds in existence. Frogs – There are almost 5,000 species of frogs worldwide.

Sympatric Speciation

Can divergence occur if no physical barriers are in place to separate individuals who continue to live and reproduce in the same habitat? The answer is yes. The process of speciation within the same space is called sympatric speciation; the prefix "sym" means same, so "sympatric" means "same homeland" in contrast to "allopatric" meaning "other homeland." A number of mechanisms for sympatric speciation have been proposed and studied.

One form of sympatric speciation can begin with a serious chromosomal error during cell division. In a normal cell division event chromosomes replicate, pair up, and then separate so that each new cell has the same number of chromosomes. However, sometimes the pairs separate and the end cell product has too many or too few individual chromosomes in a condition called **aneuploidy** (Figure 18.16).

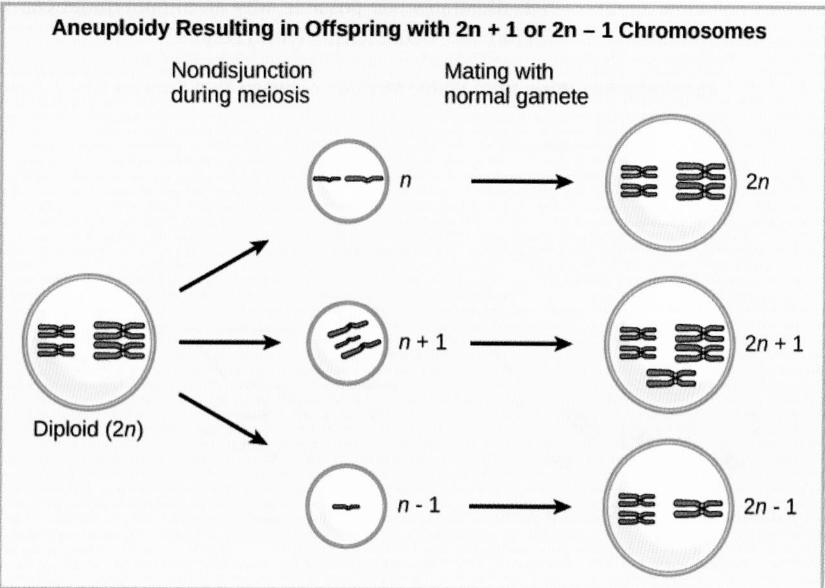

Figure 18.16 Aneuploidy results when the gametes have too many or too few chromosomes due to nondisjunction during meiosis. In the example shown here, the resulting offspring will have $2n+1$ or $2n-1$ chromosomes

In your own words, define aneuploidy.

a. Aneuploidy is a mutation that causes the genome of a cell to break down.
b. neuploidy is the condition of having too many or too few chromosomes as a result of an error during cell division
c. Aneuploidy is the condition of having an extra copy of every chromosome in the genome.
d. Aneuploidy is a prezygotic barrier in which the gametes of two distinct species will not fertilize each other.

Polyploidy is a condition in which a cell or organism has an extra set, or sets, of chromosomes. Scientists have identified two main types of polyploidy that can lead to reproductive isolation of an individual in the polyploidy state. Reproductive isolation is the inability to interbreed. In some cases, a polyploid individual will have two or more complete sets of chromosomes from its own species in a condition called **autopolyploidy** (Figure 18.17). The prefix "auto-" means "self," so the term means multiple chromosomes from one's own species. Polyploidy results from an error in meiosis in which all of the chromosomes move into one cell instead of separating.

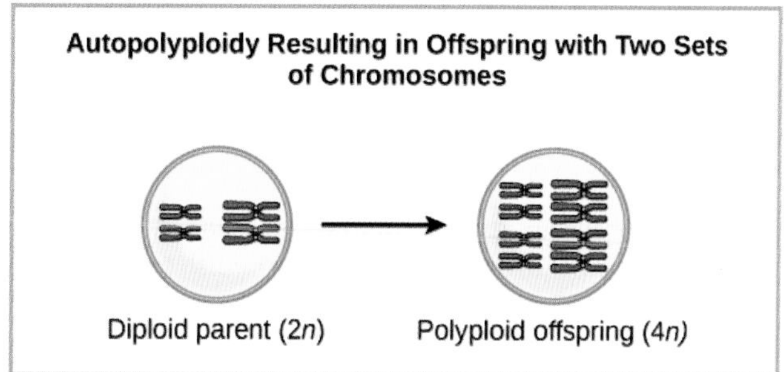

Figure 18.17 Autopolyploidy results when mitosis is not followed by cytokinesis.

For example, if a plant species with $2n = 6$ produces autopolyploid gametes that are also diploid ($2n = 6$, when they should be $n = 3$), the gametes now have twice as many chromosomes as they should have. These new gametes will be incompatible with the normal gametes produced by this plant species. However, they could either self-pollinate or reproduce with other autopolyploid plants with gametes having the same diploid number. In this way, sympatric speciation can occur quickly by forming offspring with 4*n* called a tetraploid. These individuals would immediately be able to reproduce only with those of this new kind and not those of the ancestral species.

The other form of polyploidy occurs when individuals of two different species reproduce to form a viable offspring called an **allopolyploid**. The prefix "allo-" means "other" (recall from allopatric): therefore, an allopolyploid occurs when gametes from two different species combine. Figure 18.18 illustrates one possible way an allopolyploid can form. Notice how it takes two generations, or two reproductive acts, before the viable fertile hybrid results.

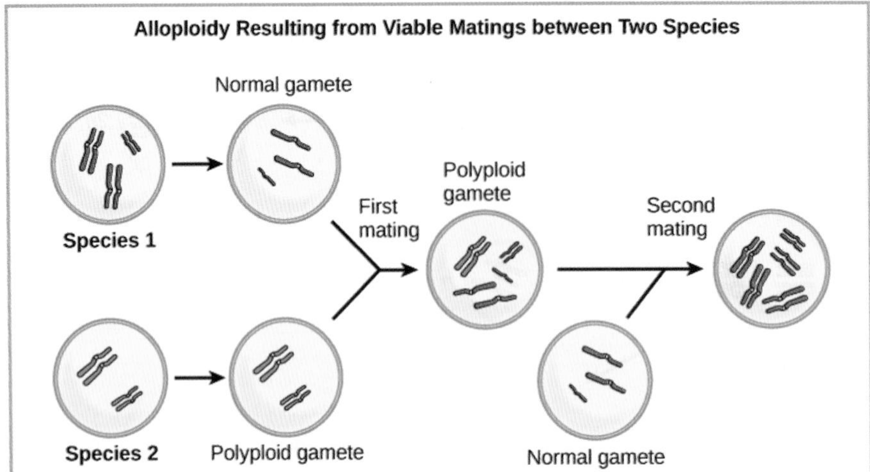

Figure 18.18 Alloploidy results when two species mate to produce viable offspring. In the example shown, a normal gamete from one species fuses with a polyploidy gamete from another. Two matings are necessary to produce viable offspring.

The cultivated forms of wheat, cotton, and tobacco plants are all allopolyploids. Although polyploidy occurs occasionally in animals, it takes place most commonly in plants. (Animals with any of the types of chromosomal aberrations described here are unlikely to survive and produce normal offspring.) Scientists have discovered more than half of all plant species studied relate back to a species evolved through polyploidy. With such a high rate of polyploidy in plants, some scientists hypothesize that this mechanism takes place more as an adaptation than as an error.

science practices CONNECTION for AP® Courses

Activity

Create a visual representation such as a diagram with annotation to explain how island chains provide ideal conditions for allopatric speciation and adaptive radiation to occur. Then design a plan for collecting data to support the claim that speciation has occurred.

Think About It

- Two species of fish had recently undergone sympatric speciation. The males of each species had a different coloring through which the females could identify and choose a partner from her own species. After some time, pollution made the lake so cloudy that it was hard for females to distinguish colors. What might take place in this situation?
- In a lake where most fish of a single species exhibit colorful stripes, a few individual animals have muted colors. The local fisherman receives a large order to catch the most colorful fish for a local aquarium store. The fisherman casts wide nets across the lake to catch a large number of the fish. He then keeps the colorful fish for the aquarium and throws back the dull colored fish. How will this single event change the make-up of the fish population?

Reproductive Isolation

Given enough time, the genetic and phenotypic divergence between populations will affect characters that influence reproduction: if individuals of the two populations were to be brought together, mating would be less likely, but if mating occurred, offspring would be non-viable or infertile. Many types of diverging characters may affect the **reproductive isolation** (the inability to interbreed) of the two populations.

Reproductive isolation can take place in a variety of ways. Scientists organize them into two groups: prezygotic barriers and postzygotic barriers. Recall that a zygote is a fertilized egg: the first cell of the development of an organism that reproduces sexually. Therefore, a prezygotic barrier is a mechanism that blocks reproduction from taking place; this includes barriers that prevent fertilization when organisms attempt reproduction. A postzygotic barrier occurs after zygote formation; this includes organisms that don't survive the embryonic stage and those that are born sterile.

Some types of prezygotic barriers prevent reproduction entirely. Many organisms only reproduce at certain times of the year, often just annually. Differences in breeding schedules, called **temporal isolation**, can act as a form of reproductive isolation. For example, two species of frogs inhabit the same area, but one reproduces from January to March, whereas the other reproduces from March to May (**Figure 18.19**).

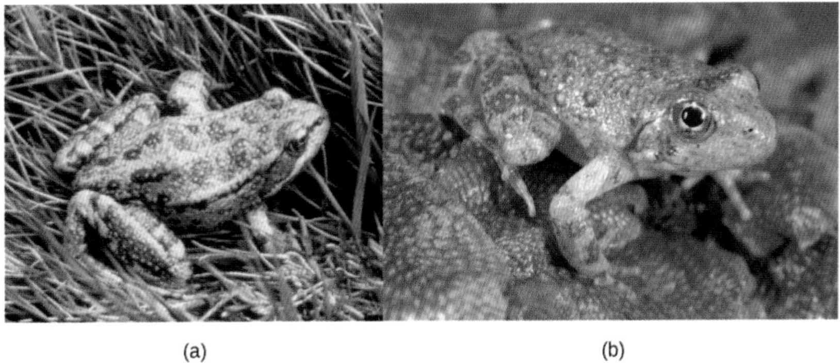
(a)
(b)

Figure 18.19 These two related frog species exhibit temporal reproductive isolation. (a) *Rana aurora* breeds earlier in the year than (b) *Rana boylii*. (credit a: modification of work by Mark R. Jennings, USFWS; credit b: modification of work by Alessandro Catenazzi)

In some cases, populations of a species move or are moved to a new habitat and take up residence in a place that no longer overlaps with the other populations of the same species. This situation is called **habitat isolation**. Reproduction with the parent species ceases, and a new group exists that is now reproductively and genetically independent. For example, a cricket population that was divided after a flood could no longer interact with each other. Over time, the forces of natural selection, mutation, and genetic drift will likely result in the divergence of the two groups (**Figure 18.20**).

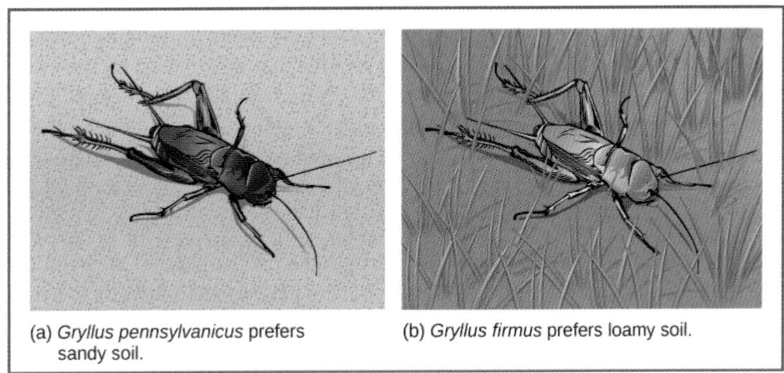
(a) *Gryllus pennsylvanicus* prefers sandy soil.
(b) *Gryllus firmus* prefers loamy soil.

Figure 18.20 Speciation can occur when two populations occupy different habitats. The habitats need not be far apart. The cricket (a) *Gryllus pennsylvanicus* prefers sandy soil, and the cricket (b) *Gryllus firmus* prefers loamy soil. The two species can live in close proximity, but because of their different soil preferences, they became genetically isolated.

Behavioral isolation occurs when the presence or absence of a specific behavior prevents reproduction from taking place. For example, male fireflies use specific light patterns to attract females. Various species of fireflies display their lights differently. If a male of one species tried to attract the female of another, she would not recognize the light pattern and would not mate with the male.

Other prezygotic barriers work when differences in their gamete cells (eggs and sperm) prevent fertilization from taking place; this is called a **gametic barrier**. Similarly, in some cases closely related organisms try to mate, but their reproductive structures simply do not fit together. For example, damselfly males and females of different species have differently shaped reproductive organs. If one species tries to mate with another, their body parts simply do not fit together. (**Figure 18.21**).

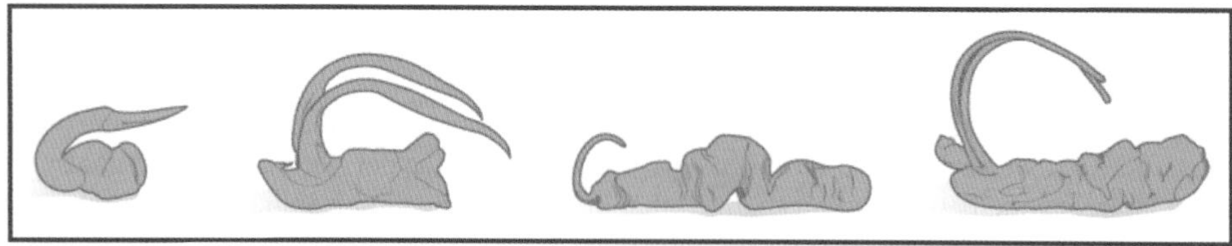

Figure 18.21 The shape of the male reproductive organ varies among male damselfly species, and is only compatible with the female of the same species. Reproductive organ incompatibility keeps each species reproductively isolated.

In plants, certain structures aimed to attract one type of pollinator simultaneously prevent a different pollinator from accessing the pollen. The tunnel through which an animal must access nectar can vary widely in length and diameter, which prevents the plant from being cross-pollinated with a different species (Figure 18.22).

(a) Honeybee drinking nectar from a foxglove flower
(b) Ruby-throated hummingbird drinking nectar from a trumpet creeper flower

Figure 18.22 Some flowers have evolved to attract certain pollinators. The (a) wide foxglove flower is adapted for pollination by bees, while the (b) long, tube-shaped trumpet creeper flower is adapted for pollination by hummingbirds.

When fertilization takes place and a zygote forms, postzygotic barriers can prevent reproduction. Hybrid individuals in many cases cannot form normally in the womb and simply do not survive past the embryonic stages. This is called **hybrid inviability** because the hybrid organisms simply are not viable. In another postzygotic situation, reproduction leads to the birth and growth of a hybrid that is sterile and unable to reproduce offspring of their own; this is called hybrid sterility.

Habitat Influence on Speciation

Sympatric speciation may also take place in ways other than polyploidy. For example, consider a species of fish that lives in a lake. As the population grows, competition for food also grows. Under pressure to find food, suppose that a group of these fish had the genetic flexibility to discover and feed off another resource that was unused by the other fish. What if this new food source was found at a different depth of the lake? Over time, those feeding on the second food source would interact more with each other than the other fish; therefore, they would breed together as well. Offspring of these fish would likely behave as their parents: feeding and living in the same area and keeping separate from the original population. If this group of fish continued to remain separate from the first population, eventually sympatric speciation might occur as more genetic differences accumulated between them.

This scenario does play out in nature, as do others that lead to reproductive isolation. One such place is Lake Victoria in Africa, famous for its sympatric speciation of cichlid fish. Researchers have found hundreds of sympatric speciation events in these fish, which have not only happened in great number, but also over a short period of time. Figure 18.23 shows this type of speciation among a cichlid fish population in Nicaragua. In this locale, two types of cichlids live in the same geographic location but have come to have different morphologies that allow them to eat various food sources.

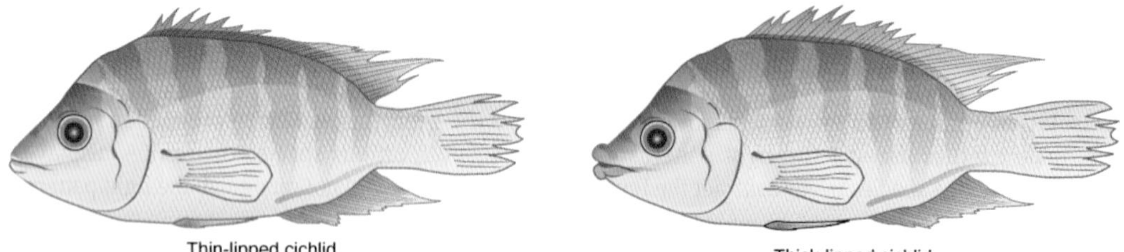

Figure 18.23 Cichlid fish from Lake Apoyeque, Nicaragua, show evidence of sympatric speciation. Lake Apoyeque, a crater lake, is 1800 years old, but genetic evidence indicates that the lake was populated only 100 years ago by a single population of cichlid fish. Nevertheless, two populations with distinct morphologies and diets now exist in the lake, and scientists believe these populations may be in an early stage of speciation.

18.3 | Reconnection and Rates of Speciation

In this section, you will explore the following questions:

- What are the pathways of species evolution in hybrid zones?
- What are the two major theories on rates of speciation?

Connection for AP® Courses

Speciation can both occur gradually over time in small steps or in bursts of change known as punctuated equilibrium. With punctuated equilibrium, a species may remain unchanged for long periods of time. The primary influencing factor on changes in speciation rate is environmental change.

Information presented and the examples highlighted in the section support concepts outlined in Big Idea 1 of the AP® Biology Curriculum Framework. The AP® Learning Objectives listed in the Curriculum Framework provide a transparent foundation for the AP® Biology course, an inquiry-based laboratory experience, instructional activities, and AP® exam questions. A learning objective merges required content with one or more of the seven science practices.

Big Idea 1	The process of evolution drives the diversity and unity of life.
Enduring Understanding 1.C	Life continues to evolve within a changing environment.
Essential Knowledge	**1.C.1** Speciation and extinction have occurred throughout Earth's history.
Science Practice	**5.1** The student can analyze data to identify patterns or relationships.
Learning Objective	**1.20** The student is able to analyze data related to questions of speciation and extinction throughout the Earth's history.

Speciation occurs over a span of evolutionary time, so when a new species arises, there is a transition period during which the closely related species continue to interact.

Reconnection

After speciation, two species may continue interacting indefinitely or even recombine. Individual organisms will mate with any nearby individual who they are capable of breeding with. An area where two closely related species continue to interact and reproduce, forming hybrids, is called a **hybrid zone**. Over time, the hybrid zone may change depending on the fitness of the hybrids and the reproductive barriers (Figure 18.24). If the hybrids are less fit than the parents, reinforcement of speciation occurs, and the species continue to diverge until they can no longer mate and produce viable offspring. If reproductive barriers weaken, fusion occurs and the two species become one. Barriers remain the same if hybrids are fit and reproductive: stability may occur and hybridization continues.

visual CONNECTION

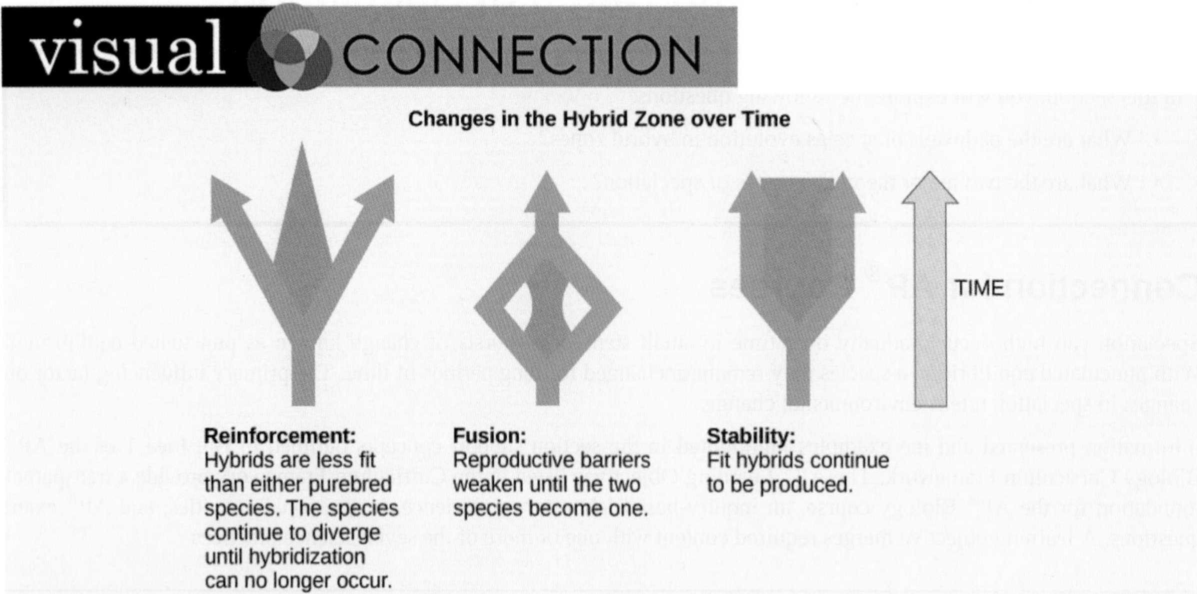

Figure 18.24 After speciation has occurred, the two separate but closely related species may continue to produce offspring in an area called the hybrid zone. Reinforcement, fusion, or stability may result, depending on reproductive barriers and the relative fitness of the hybrids.

What are three different pathways that species evolution may take in hybrid zones?

a. stability, fusion, reinforcement

b. allopatric speciation, sympatric speciation, fusion

c. convergent evolution, divergent evolution, no evolution

d. natural selection, genetic drift, gene flow

Hybrids can be either less fit than the parents, more fit, or about the same. Usually hybrids tend to be less fit; therefore, such reproduction diminishes over time, nudging the two species to diverge further in a process called **reinforcement**. This term is used because the low success of the hybrids reinforces the original speciation. If the hybrids are as fit or more fit than the parents, the two species may fuse back into one species (**Figure 18.25**). Scientists have also observed that sometimes two species will remain separate but also continue to interact to produce some hybrid individuals; this is classified as stability because no real net change is taking place.

Varying Rates of Speciation

Scientists around the world study speciation, documenting observations both of living organisms and those found in the fossil record. As their ideas take shape and as research reveals new details about how life evolves, they develop models to help explain rates of speciation. In terms of how quickly speciation occurs, two patterns are currently observed: gradual speciation model and punctuated equilibrium model.

In the **gradual speciation model**, species diverge gradually over time in small steps. In the **punctuated equilibrium** model, a new species undergoes changes quickly from the parent species, and then remains largely unchanged for long periods of time afterward (**Figure 18.25**). This early change model is called punctuated equilibrium, because it begins with a punctuated or periodic change and then remains in balance afterward. While punctuated equilibrium suggests a faster tempo, it does not necessarily exclude gradualism.

visual CONNECTION

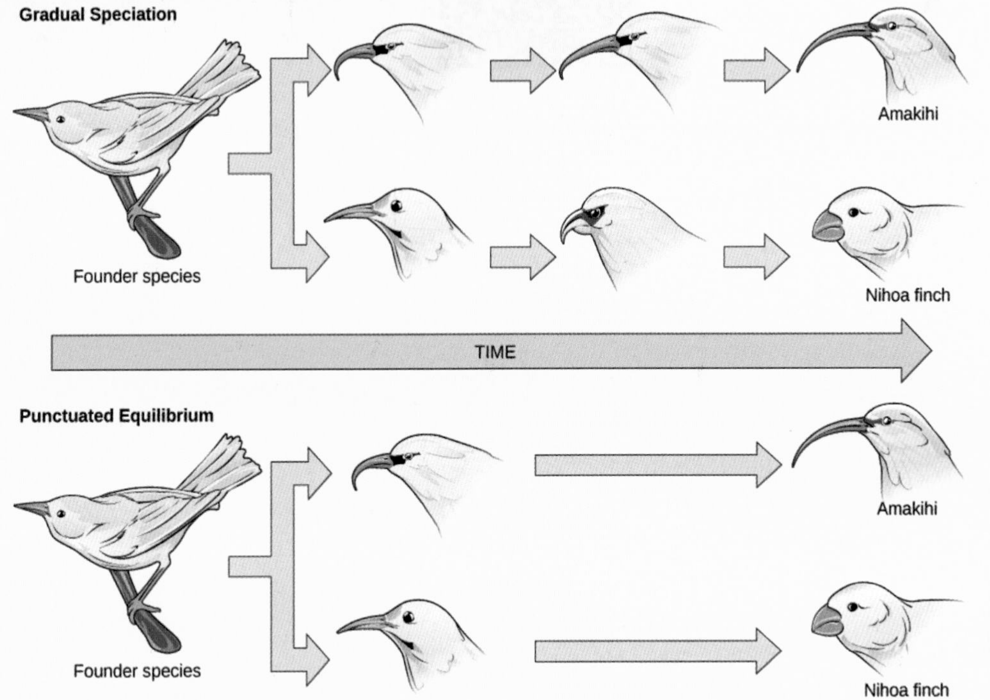

Figure 18.25 In (a) gradual speciation, species diverge at a slow, steady pace as traits change incrementally. In (b) punctuated equilibrium, species diverge quickly and then remain unchanged for long periods of time.

Describe a situation in which punctuated equilibrium is more likely to take place.

a. There is a significant change in the environment over time, such as the breakup of a supercontinent due to tectonic activity.
b. A species that has a competitor outcompetes it and drives it to extinction, freeing up more resources.
c. There is a sudden and significant change in the environment, such as a volcanic eruption that divides a population that once shared a habitat.
d. There is a stable and unchanging environment in which a species can flourish.

The primary influencing factor on changes in speciation rate is environmental conditions. Under some conditions, selection occurs quickly or radically. Consider a species of snails that had been living with the same basic form for many thousands of years. Layers of their fossils would appear similar for a long time. When a change in the environment takes place—such as a drop in the water level—a small number of organisms are separated from the rest in a brief period of time, essentially forming one large and one tiny population. The tiny population faces new environmental conditions. Because its gene pool quickly became so small, any variation that surfaces and that aids in surviving the new conditions becomes the predominant form.

Visit this website (http://openstaxcollege.org/l/snails) to continue the speciation story of the snails.

KEY TERMS

acquired characteristics modifications caused by an individual's environment that can be inherited by its offspring

adaptation heritable trait or behavior in an organism that aids in its survival and reproduction in its present environment

adaptive radiation speciation when one species radiates out to form several other species

allopatric speciation speciation that occurs via geographic separation

allopolyploid polyploidy formed between two related, but separate species

aneuploidy condition of a cell having an extra chromosome or missing a chromosome for its species

autopolyploid polyploidy formed within a single species

behavioral isolation type of reproductive isolation that occurs when a specific behavior or lack of one prevents reproduction from taking place

convergent evolution process by which groups of organisms independently evolve to similar forms

dispersal allopatric speciation that occurs when a few members of a species move to a new geographical area

divergent evolution process by which groups of organisms evolve in diverse directions from a common point

gametic barrier prezygotic barrier occurring when closely related individuals of different species mate, but differences in their gamete cells (eggs and sperm) prevent fertilization from taking place

gradual speciation model model that shows how species diverge gradually over time in small steps

habitat isolation reproductive isolation resulting when populations of a species move or are moved to a new habitat, taking up residence in a place that no longer overlaps with the other populations of the same species

homologous structures parallel structures in diverse organisms that have a common ancestor

hybrid offspring of two closely related individuals, not of the same species

hybrid zone area where two closely related species continue to interact and reproduce, forming hybrids

natural selection reproduction of individuals with favorable genetic traits that survive environmental change because of those traits, leading to evolutionary change

polyploidy gametes with extra chromosomes

postzygotic barrier reproductive isolation mechanism that occurs after zygote formation

prezygotic barrier reproductive isolation mechanism that occurs before zygote formation

punctuated equilibrium model for rapid speciation that can occur when an event causes a small portion of a population to be cut off from the rest of the population

reinforcement continued speciation divergence between two related species due to low fitness of hybrids between them

reproductive isolation situation that occurs when a species is reproductively independent from other species; this may be brought about by behavior, location, or reproductive barriers

speciation formation of a new species

species group of populations that interbreed and produce fertile offspring

sympatric speciation speciation that occurs in the same geographic space

temporal isolation differences in breeding schedules that can act as a form of prezygotic barrier leading to reproductive isolation

theory of evolution explains how populations change over time and how life diversifies the origin of species

variation genetic differences among individuals in a population

vestigial structure physical structure present in an organism but that has no apparent function and appears to be from a functional structure in a distant ancestor

vicariance allopatric speciation that occurs when something in the environment separates organisms of the same species into separate groups

CHAPTER SUMMARY

18.1 Understanding Evolution

Evolution is the process of adaptation through mutation which allows more desirable characteristics to be passed to the next generation. Over time, organisms evolve more characteristics that are beneficial to their survival. For living organisms to adapt and change to environmental pressures, genetic variation must be present. With genetic variation, individuals have differences in form and function that allow some to survive certain conditions better than others. These organisms pass their favorable traits to their offspring. Eventually, environments change, and what was once a desirable, advantageous trait may become an undesirable trait and organisms may further evolve. Evolution may be convergent with similar traits evolving in multiple species or divergent with diverse traits evolving in multiple species that came from a common ancestor. Evidence of evolution can be observed by means of DNA code and the fossil record, and also by the existence of homologous and vestigial structures.

18.2 Formation of New Species

Speciation occurs along two main pathways: geographic separation (allopatric speciation) and through mechanisms that occur within a shared habitat (sympatric speciation). Both pathways isolate a population reproductively in some form. Mechanisms of reproductive isolation act as barriers between closely related species, enabling them to diverge and exist as genetically independent species. Prezygotic barriers block reproduction prior to formation of a zygote, whereas postzygotic barriers block reproduction after fertilization occurs. For a new species to develop, something must cause a breach in the reproductive barriers. Sympatric speciation can occur through errors in meiosis that form gametes with extra chromosomes (polyploidy). Autopolyploidy occurs within a single species, whereas allopolyploidy occurs between closely related species.

18.3 Reconnection and Rates of Speciation

Speciation is not a precise division: overlap between closely related species can occur in areas called hybrid zones. Organisms reproduce with other similar organisms. The fitness of these hybrid offspring can affect the evolutionary path of the two species. Scientists propose two models for the rate of speciation: one model illustrates how a species can change slowly over time; the other model demonstrates how change can occur quickly from a parent generation to a new species. Both models continue to follow the patterns of natural selection.

REVIEW QUESTIONS

1. Which scientific concept did Charles Darwin and Alfred Wallace independently discover?

a. mutation

b. natural selection

c. overbreeding

d. sexual reproduction

2. Which of these statements about a natural principle that points to the inevitability of natural selection is false?

a. Most characteristics of organisms are inherited.

b. Offspring vary among each other in regard to their characteristics.

c. Some generations of offspring do not need to compete for resources.

d. Certain traits will be better represented in the next generation.

3. Which is the best definition of adaptation?

a. a trait or behavior that aids an organism's survival and reproduction
b. a heritable trait or behavior that aids an organism's survival and reproduction
c. a trait or behavior that aids a population's survival and reproduction
d. a heritable trait or behavior that aids a population's survival and reproduction

4. Which is an example of an adaptation?

a. The better nutrition of a human helps her grow taller.
b. The webbed feet of a duck help it swim.
c. The urban location of a raccoon helps it find food.
d. The large leaves of a desert plant require more water.

5. Which of the processes described is divergent evolution?

a. Groups of organisms evolve in different directions from a common point.
b. A new species develops rapidly when an event cuts off a portion of a population.
c. Groups of organisms independently evolve to similar forms.
d. A species evolves when a few members move to a new geographical area.

6. Which situation is most likely an example of convergent evolution?

a. Some fish that live in total darkness have eyes.
b. Hawks and other birds have feathers.
c. Worms and snakes both move without legs.
d. Flowers that look very different have the same reproductive organs.

7. What are homologous structures?

a. physical structures that have no apparent function
b. parallel structures in diverse organisms
c. physical structures that are used only occasionally
d. similar structures in diverse organisms

8. Which of the following are two examples of vestigial structures?

a. gills in fish and parts of the throat in humans
b. butterfly wings and dragonfly wings
c. hind leg bones in whales and leaves on some cacti
d. shark fins and dolphin fins

9. Which statement best describes the relationship between the theory of evolution and the origin of life?

a. The theory includes an explanation of life's origins.
b. The theory cannot explain the origin of life.
c. The theory does not try to explain the origin of life.
d. The theory does not contribute understanding to pre-life processes.

10. Which best describes what happens when an antibiotic is applied to a population of bacteria?

a. The bacteria develops resistance to the antibiotic in direct response to its application.
b. The bacteria's genetic material mutates in response to the antibiotic, resulting in resistance.
c. A gene for resistance, already present in the population, decreases in frequency.
d. A gene for resistance, already present in the population, increases in frequency.

11. Which is the best definition of species?

a. A group of individual organisms with significant genetic similarities
b. a group of individual organisms with significant genetic similarities that share external and internal characteristics
c. a group of individual organisms that interbreed
d. a group of individual organisms that interbreed and produce viable, fertile offspring

12. What do scientists focus on to distinguish between species?

a. ecological niches
b. morphological differences
c. reproductive barriers
d. genetic changes

13. Which are two primary sources of genetic variation?

a. mutations and sexual reproduction
b. isolation and sexual reproduction
c. sexual reproduction and asexual reproduction
d. migration and sexual reproduction

14. Which statement best describes the relationship between genetic variation and speciation?

a. Without genetic variation, speciation would occur more slowly.
b. Without genetic variation, speciation would not be possible.
c. Genetic variation influences sympatric speciation, but not allopatric speciation.
d. There is no relationship between genetic variation and any form of speciation.

15. Which statement about postzygotic barriers is false?

a. They occur after fertilization.
b. They include hybrids that are sterile.
c. They include hybrid organisms that don't survive the embryonic stage.
d. They include reproductive organ incompatibility.

16. Which situation is an example of a prezygotic barrier?

a. Two species of fish produce sterile offspring.
b. Two species of flowers attract different pollinators.
c. Two species of insects mate, but the zygote does not survive.
d. Two species of lizards mate, but the offspring dies before reproducing.

17. Which situation would most likely lead to allopatric speciation?

a. A flood causes the formation of a new lake
b. A storm causes several large trees to fall down.
c. A mutation causes a new trait to develop.
d. An injury causes an organism to seek out a new food source.

18. What is the main difference between an autopolyploid individual and a allopolyploid individual?

a. number of extra chromosomes
b. functionality of extra chromosomes
c. source of extra chromosomes
d. number of mutations in the extra chromosomes

19. What is unique about speciation due to adaptive radiation?

a. It leads to multiple species forming from one parent species.
b. It only occurs on or around island archipelagos.
c. It requires a population to disperse from its parent species.
d. It is a special kind of sympatric speciation.

20. Which is least likely to be a factor that increases the probability of speciation by adaptive radiation?

a. There are vacant ecological niches nearby.
b. Genetic drift in a population increases.
c. There are isolated regions with suitable habitats.
d. There are few competitor species.

21. In a hybrid zone, in addition to interacting, what else do two closely related species do?

a. compete
b. reproduce
c. transition
d. fuse

22. Which situation means reinforcement is more likely to occur in the hybrid zone?

a. The hybrid offspring are more fit than the parent species.
b. Reproductive barriers weaken.
c. The hybrid offspring are about as fit as the parent species.
d. Reproductive barriers strengthen.

23. Which of the following statements is false?

a. Graudal speciation and punctuated equilibrium both result in the divergence of species.
b. Punctuated equilibrium is most likely to occur in a large population in a stable environment.
c. In the punctuated equilibrium model, gradualism is not excluded.
d. In the gradual speciation model, traits change incrementally.

24. Which component of speciation would be least likely to be a part of punctuated equilibrium?

a. a division in populations
b. a change in environmental conditions
c. ongoing gene flow
d. a number of mutations occuring at once

CRITICAL THINKING QUESTIONS

25. What conclusions can you draw about the relationship between the way in which the present-day theory of evolution developed and the credibility of the theory? Explain your thinking.

a. When the theory of evolution was first proposed, it met with a lot of criticism and disbelief, but it is widely supported today. Theories that have withstood a larger amount of criticism are more credible than those that are accepted easily
b. The theory of evolution has its foundation in both biological and geological observations, making it a more credible theory because it can explain more about the world
c. The theory of evolution relies on the heritability of traits, but the mechanism of this inheritance was not understood when the theory was developed. This reduces the credibility of the theory because the people who created it did not understand how it worked
d. It is meaningful that two naturalists working independently from each other offered the same explanation for the same set of phenomena. When two people independently look at the same evidence and come to the same conclusion, this reinforces the credibility of that conclusion

26. Describe how an adaptation, such as better running speed, relates to natural selection.

a. Natural selection produces beneficial adaptations, such as better running speed, in individuals that run more frequently
b. Natural selection randomly mutates individuals' genetic code until it produces beneficial adaptations, such as better running speed
c. Natural selection produces adaptations, such as better running speed, to help individuals survive and reproduce
d. Natural selection reproduces individuals with favorable genetic traits-such as the adaptation of better running speed-over time.

27. Give an example of convergent evolution and explain how it supports the theory of evolution by natural selection.

a. An example of convergent evolution is the development of the same function, swimming, in organisms that live in different parts of the globe, such as Arctic beluga whales and Antarctic right whales. The fact that organisms that do not come in contact with each other have developed the same traits suggests that natural selection can produce similar adaptations in organisms who share a similar environment
b. An example of convergent evolution is the set of adaptations, such as better running speed or more efficient hunting, developed by a species in response to competition with a new species that moves into the same region. The fact that a species adapts after it comes into contact with a competitor suggests that natural selection works more quickly with higher selective pressures.
c. An example of convergent evolution is the development of an ancestral structure, a limb, into two different modern structures, such as a hand and a flipper. The fact that natural selection can cause a structure to develop down two different pathways due to different environmental conditions supports the theory of evolution
d. An example of convergent evolution is the development of the same function, flying, in organisms that do not share a recent common ancestry, such as insects and birds. The fact that wings that allow flight have developed from very different original structures suggests that the process of natural selection can produce similar adaptations in two very different types of organisms who share a similar environment

28. Why do scientists consider vestigial structures evidence for evolution?

a. Vestigial structures are the result of convergent evolution, so they are good evidence that natural selection act similarly in similar environmental conditions.
b. Vestigial structures are the result of common ancestry, so they are good evidence that different populations of organisms evolved from a common point.
c. Vestigial structures are the result of convergent evolution, so they are good evidence for an end goal to evolution.
d. Vestigial structures are the result of common ancestry, so they are good evidence for a common origin of all life.

29. Reproduction in sexually-reproducing organisms occurs when two sex cells, or gametes, fuse. In fish, this occurs when sperm swim through the water to find the ovum. In flowers, pollen is dispersed through the air and carried to another flower. Explain what evolutionary adaptations for reproduction occur in humans, based on the fact that we are land-based animals.

30. While examining the human genome, you find a gene that is not homologous to any other organisms known to man. You conclude that this gene must be unique to the human species and could not have evolved from another organism. Would this discovery suggest that humans do not share a common ancestor with all other organisms on Earth? Explain your answer.

31. Mutations in the glucose 6-phosphate dehydrogenase (G6PD) gene can cause a rare anemia when inherited. However, homozygotes with this mutation are less prone to malaria infection, a disease that historically was the most widespread deadly disease among humans. Predict how this mutation would affect the fitness of individuals living in countries where malaria is endemic.

32. How does the scientific meaning of "theory" differ from the common vernacular meaning?

a. A scientific theory is a hypothesis that needs to be tested, whereas people often use theory to mean a simple guess.

b. A scientific theory is a statement that has been proven correct, while people often use it to mean a statement that has not yet been verified.

c. A scientific theory is a thoroughly tested set of explanations for a body of observations of nature, while people often use it to mean a guess or speculation.

d. A scientific theory is a random guess, while people often use it to mean a statement that is somewhat based in fact.

33. Why is having a way of defining species and distinguishing between them important for the study of evolution?

a. A distinction between species allows scientists to understand the common origin of all species.

b. A common definition of species allows scientists to agree on all aspects of the theory of evolution.

c. Divergence can only occur at the species level: it does not occur to larger taxa. Therefore it is important to know which groups are distinct species.

d. In the study of evolution, the species is the unit over which change is measured.

34. If a population stopped reproducing sexually, but still reproduced asexually, how would its genetic variation be affected over time? Could speciation occur in this situation? Explain your ideas.

a. Genetic variation would increase and speciation would be possible

b. Genetic variation would increase and speciation would not be possible.

c. Genetic variation would decrease and speciation would be possible.

d. Genetic variation would decrease and speciation would not be possible.

35. What role do prezygotic and postzygotic barriers play in speciation?

a. Prezygotic and postzygotic barriers allow for the formation of less-fit hybrids that reinforces speciation.

b. Prezygotic and postzygotic barriers prevent interbreeding of species such that there is no gene flow between them.

c. Prezygotic and postzygotic barriers prevent migration of the two species, causing them to remain in contact with each other and begin to interbreed.

d. Prezygotic and postzygotic barriers are present only in newly-formed species, allowing scientists to identify the time of divergence of the species.

36. A population of flowers was separated into two subpopulations when a new river cut through the plain in which they were growing. The number of interbreeding events per year for the two subpopulations of flowers is shown in the graph below. Twenty-four years after they were separated, can you conclude that the two subpopulations of flowers have become new species? Why or why not?

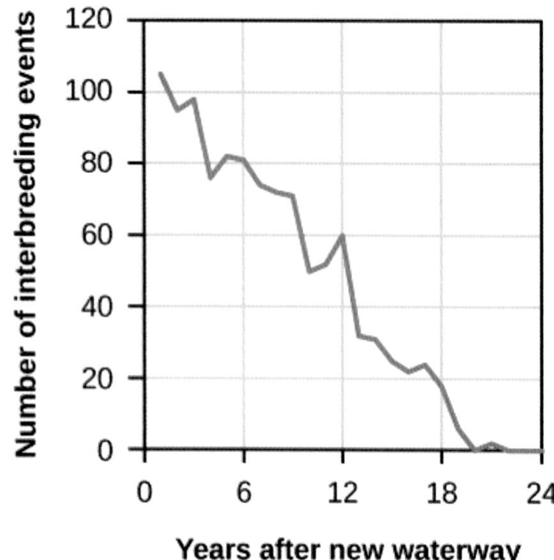

Figure 18.26

37. Which type of speciation, allopatric or sympatric, is more common? Why?

a. Allopatric speciation is more common because it prevents gene flow between the species.
b. Allopatric speciation is more common because it involves stronger prezygotic barriers.
c. Sympatric speciation is more common because it prevents gene flow between the species.
d. Sympatric speciation is more common because it involves stronger prezygotic barriers.

38. Use adaptive radiation to explain the diversification of the finches Darwin observed in the Galapagos.

a. The finches likely shared a common ancestor when they came to the island, but exhibited different traits. Each species of finch settled the island where its particular traits would be the most adaptive.
b. The finches likely originated as one parent species, but over time mutations caused them to develop reproductive barriers and separate into different species. To reduce competition, the species then radiated out to inhabit different islands.
c. The finches likely dispersed from one parent species, and natural selection based on different food sources in differing habitats led to adaptive changes, evidenced in the different beak shapes of the different species-each suited to a different food type.
d. It is likely that a series of cataclysmic events caused an original finch species to diverge into the many finch species that inhabited the islands when Darwin observed them. The different species then radiated out to the different islands and adapted to the different conditions on each.

39. Describe a situation where hybrid reproduction would cause two species to fuse into one.

a. Separate species cannot interbreed, so hybrid reproduction does not occur in nature
b. If the hybrid offspring are more fit than the parents, reproduction would likely continue between both species and the hybrids, eventually bringing all organisms under the umbrella of one species
c. Two species that have recently diverged from each other can reproduce with each other, creating hybrid individuals that belong to the species of the parents' common ancestor.
d. If two species occupy the same niche in the same area, they can either compete or they can collaborate and reproduce with each other, eventually fusing into a single species

40. What do both rate of speciation models have in common? Explain.

a. Both models ignore the influence of gene flow for simplicity's sake.
b. Both models apply only to island chains.
c. Both models require the influence of cataclysmic events which precipitate rapid adaptation and speciation
d. Both models conform to the rules of natural selection and the influences of gene flow, genetic drift, and mutation

41. Describe a situation where hybrid reproduction would cause two species to continue divergence.

a. f two closely related species continue to produce hybrids, the hybrids will compete with both species, causing them to find new niches which will further their divergence
b. If two closely related species continue to produce hybrids, they will develop reproductive barriers to prevent production of hybrids, to ensure that they remain separate species.
c. If two closely related species continue to produce hybrids that are less fit than the parent species, there would be reinforcement of divergence.
d. f two closely related species continue to produce hybrids they will always converge into a single species

TEST PREP FOR AP® COURSES

42. Prior to 1800 in England, the typical moth of the species *Biston betularia* (peppered moth) had a light pattern. Dark colored moths were rare. By the late 19th century, the light-colored moths were rare, and the moths with dark patterns were abundant.

The cause of this change was hypothesized to be selective predation by birds (J.W. Tutt, 1896). During the industrial revolution, soot and other wastes from industrial processes killed tree lichens and darkened tree trunks. Thus, prior to the pollution of the industrial revolution, dark moths stood out on light-colored trees and were vulnerable to predators. With the rise of pollution, however, the coloring of moths vulnerable to predators changed to light.

Which of the following aspects of Darwin's theory of

evolution does the story of the peppered moth most clearly illustrate?

a. There is competition for resources in an overbred population.

b. There is great variability among members of a population.

c. There is differential reproduction of individuals with favorable traits.

d. The majority of characteristics of organisms are inherited.

43. Prior to 1800 in England, the typical moth of the species *Biston betularia* (peppered moth) had a light pattern. Dark colored moths were rare. By the late 19th century, the light-colored moths were rare, and the moths with dark patterns were abundant.

The cause of this change was hypothesized to be selective predation by birds (J.W. Tutt, 1896). During the industrial revolution, soot and other wastes from industrial processes killed tree lichens and darkened tree trunks. Thus, prior to the pollution of the industrial revolution, dark moths stood out on light-colored trees and were vulnerable to predators. With the rise of pollution, however, the coloring of moths vulnerable to predators changed to light.

In the late 1900s, England cleaned up its air, and pollution decreased. The bark of trees went from dark to light.

Which of the following outcomes to the populations of peppered moth would you expect given this environmental change?

a. An increase in the number of dark moths and a decrease in the number of light moths

b. an increase in the number of moths overall

c. an approximately equal number of light moths and dark moths

d. an increase in the number of light moths and a decrease in the number of dark moths

44. Prior to 1800 in England, the typical moth of the species *Biston betularia* (peppered moth) had a light pattern. Dark colored moths were rare. By the late 19th century, the light-colored moths were rare, and the moths with dark patterns were abundant.

The cause of this change was hypothesized to be selective predation by birds (J.W. Tutt, 1896). During the industrial revolution, soot and other wastes from industrial processes killed tree lichens and darkened tree trunks. Thus, prior to the pollution of the industrial revolution, dark moths stood out on light-colored trees and were vulnerable to predators. With the rise of pollution, however, the coloring of moths vulnerable to predators changed to light.

Commonly used in biology textbooks, the peppered moth is a classic example of evolutionary change in action. The example describes changes in a population's allele frequencies-a small-scale change, evolutionarily speaking. The presence of both light and dark forms within the gene pool is demonstrated by the story, but the peppered moth stays a peppered moth.

Which scenario, if it were to occur, would be a model for large-scale evolutionary change?

a. Conditions change such that the dark form of the moth is favored and the light form is diminished in the population due to predation. Conditions change again, the dark form is vulnerable, and the light form returns to prevalence.

b. Conditions change such that the dark form of the moth is favored and the light form is eradicated in the population due to predation. Conditions change again, the dark form is vulnerable, and the dark form is eradicated due to predation.

c. Conditions change such that dark form of the moth is favored and the light form is diminished in the population due to predation. Conditions change again, and both forms have equal prevalence.

d. Conditions change such that dark form of the moth is favored and the light form is eradicated in the population due to predation. Conditions change again, the dark form is vulnerable. It develops an adaptation that shields it from predation.

45. Given your understanding of evolutionary theory and the relationship between evolution and the genetic makeup of populations, which statement is false?

a. Homologous characteristics that have evolved more recently are shared only within smaller groups of organisms.

b. The genetic code is a homologous characteristic shared by all species because they share a common ancestor in the deep past.

c. DNA sequence data would likely support any evolutionary tree drawn from anatomical data sets.

d. The degree of relatedness between groups of organisms is only sometimes reflected in the similarity of their DNA sequences.

46. Each of the following observations comes from a different scientific discipline. Which is the best support for Darwin's concept of descent with modification?

a. Geologists provide evidence that earthquakes reshape life by causing mass extinctions.
b. Botanists provide evidence that South American temperate plants have more in common with South American tropical plants than temperate plants from Europe.
c. Zoologists provide evidence that fewer animal species live on islands than on nearby mainlands.
d. Ecologists provide evidence that species diversity increases closer to the equator.

47. Paleontologists have recovered a fossil for an organisms named *Archaeopteryx*. It has many features in common with reptiles, but, like birds, shows evidence of feathers. For what aspect of evolutionary theory does this piece of evidence suggest support?

a. Modern species are distinct natural entities.
b. Modern species are not currently evolving.
c. Modern species share a common ancestor.
d. Modern species have both convergent and divergent traits.

48. Which of the following pieces of evidence illustrates evolution as an ongoing process?

a. Some genes from the bacterium *E. coli* have sequences that are similar to genes found in humans.
b. Marsupial mammals live in just a few places in the world today-Australia, South America, and part of North America.
c. The fossil record shows that Rodhocetus, an aquatic mammal related to whales, had a type of ankle bone that is otherwise unique to a group of land animals.
d. In the 1940s, infections by the bacterium *Staphylococcus aureus* could be treated with penicillin; today populations exist that are completely resistant.

49. The process of mutation, which generates genetic variation, is random. Thus, life has evolved, and continues to evolve, randomly. Which statement is an appropriately evidence-based refinement of the above?

a. The process of mutation, which generates genetic variation, is random. However, the process of natural selection, which results in adaptations like the fit between a flower and its pollinator, favors variants which are better able to survive and reproduce. Natural selection is not random, so the overall process of evolution is not random, either.
b. The process of mutation, which generates genetic variation, is random. However, the process of migration, which results in gene flow between populations, also generates genetic variation. Migration is not random, so the overall process of evolution is not random, either.
c. The process of mutation, which generates genetic variation, is random. However, the process of sexual reproduction, which also introduces genetic variance, is not random. Because sexual reproduction is not random, the overall process of evolution is not random, either.
d. The process of mutation, which generates genetic variation, is random. Whether mutations have a positive, negative, or neutral effect in terms of selective advantage is also random. Mutations and their effects are random, so the overall process of evolution is random.

50. The selective breeding of plants and animals that possess desired traits is a process called artificial selection. For example, broccoli, cabbage, and kale are all vegetables that have been selected from one species of wild mustard. How is artificial selection both similar to and different from Darwin's conception of natural selection? Does artificial selection provide evidence for evolution by natural selection? Explain.

a. Both artificial selection and natural selection are the differential reproduction of individual organisms with favored traits. In artificial selection, humans have actively modified plants and animals by selecting and breeding individuals with traits deemed desirable. In natural selection, the most successful individuals in a species are selected by the species to reproduce

b. Both artificial selection and natural selection are processes that result in better-adapted individuals within a species. In artificial selection, humans have actively modified plants and animals by selecting beneficial genes from other organisms and inserting them into the target organisms. In natural selection, natural processes such as mutations and viruses introduce new genes to a population

c. Both artificial selection and natural selection are processes that cause organisms to be better adapted over time. In artificial selection, humans have trained animals to be more successful in completing tasks that the humans want completed. In natural selection, organisms train the functions that they will need to survive and reproduce

d. Both artificial selection and natural selection are the differential reproduction of individual organisms with favored traits. In artificial selection, humans have actively modified plants and animals by selecting and breeding individuals with traits deemed desirable. In natural selection, individuals are selected naturally as its traits deem it more fit for survival and reproduction

51. Genes important in the embryonic development of animals have been relatively well conserved during evolution. This means they are more similar among different species than many other genes. What explains this genetic conservation across animal species?

a. Changes in the genes that are important to embryonic development have been relatively minor because there are no selective pressures on an individual before it is born

b. Changes in the genes that are important to embryonic development have been relatively minor because not much time has elapsed since the divergence of the various animal taxa.

c. Changes in the genes that are important to embryonic development have been relatively minor because early embryos are very fragile and even small mutations can result in death

d. Changes in the genes that are important to embryonic development have been relatively minor because mutational tweaking in the embryo has magnified consequences in the adult

52. The upper forelimbs of humans and cats have fairly similar structures. In contrast, the upper forelimbs of whales (their flippers) have bones with a different shape and proportion from both cats and humans. Interestingly, genetic data suggests that all three organisms have a common ancestor from about the same point in time. What is a likely explanation for these data?

a. Cats and humans are more closely related to each other than either are to whales.

b. The shape of the whale forelimb arose a result of disadvantageous mutations

c. The whale flipper is an adaptive characteristic unique to its water environment.

d. The whale flipper is a vestigial structure.

53. Biogeography is the study of biological species as they relate to geographical space and geological time. The fossil record shows that dinosaurs originated about 200 to 250 million years ago. Would you expect the geographic distribution of early dinosaur fossils to be broad (on many continents) or narrow (on one or a few continents)? Explain.

a. broad because dinosaurs originated before the breakup of Pangaea

b. broad because some dinosaurs could fly between continents

c. narrow because they went extinct too quickly to disperse very far

d. narrow because they lived so long ago that the fossils have mostly broken down or disappeared

54. The term microevolution describes evolution on its smallest scale: the change in allele frequencies in a population over generations. DDT is a pesticide that was widely in use in the United States from the 1940s until 1972. The table below summarizes a particular allele frequency in laboratory strains of the common fruit fly, *Drosophila melanogaster*.

	Strains collected from flies in the wild in the 1930s	**Strains collected from flies in the wild in the 1960s**
Frequency of allele conferring DDT resistance	0%	40%

Using this information, describe a model in which natural selection improved the match between *D. mealanogaster* and its environment through microevolution.

a. DDT killed off a large proportion of the population, and the alleles present in the surviving fruit flies differed from those in the original population
b. Mutations from the application of DDT caused the allele conferring DDT resistance to appear in the population.
c. Female mosquitoes chose to mate with male mosquitoes that had the allele conferring DDT resistance because it would make their offspring more fit.
d. The wide use of DDT meant that fruit flies with DDT resistance were more evolutionarily fit than their counterparts without DDT resistance.

55. In 1795, a Scottish geologist named Charles Hutton suggested that Earth's geologic features could be explained by gradual processes that were still operating. This was in direct contrast to other scientific thought at the time, which included well-accepted proposals that geologic layers were representative of catastrophic events caused by processes no longer operating in the present time. Hutton proposed geologic features as the result of slow and consistent change, such as valleys formed by rivers wearing through rock. Hutton's ideas were incorporated in the work of Charles Lyell, a geologist working in Darwin's time. Lyell advocated a principle called uniformitarianism, the consistency of mechanisms of change over time. In other words, Lyell argued that the same geologic processes operating in the present had operated in the past, and at the same rate.

The ideas of Hutton and Lyell influenced the work of Charles Darwin. How do Hutton's and Lyell's ideas connect to and provide support for Darwin's theory of evolutionary change?

a. The idea that the same processes that operate in the present also operated in the past, and at the same rate, supported Darwin's hypothesis of natural selection because humans could select for desirable traits and produce change very rapidly, so natural selection would also be fast enough to produce the full range of diversity in living organisms.
b. The idea that the same processes that operate in the present also operated in the past, and at the same rate, connects to Darwin's hypothesis of natural selection because he had observed it happening in the present
c. The idea that geologic change is the result of slow, continuous processes rather than sudden, substantial change connects to Darwin's support of gradualism rather than punctuated equilibrium as the process that guided evolution.
d. The idea that geologic change is the result of slow, continuous processes rather than sudden, substantial change connects directly to Darwin's hypothesis that, given enough time, slow and subtle processes could produce substantial biological change.

56. The human immunodeficiency virus (HIV) reproduces very quickly. A single virus can replicate itself a billion times in one 24-hour period. In a hypothetical treatment situation, a patient's HIV population consists entirely of drug-resistant viruses after just a few weeks of treatment. How can this treatment result best be explained? How does this explanation illustrate that evolution is an ongoing process?

a. The resistant viruses passed their genes to the non-resistant viruses so that 100% of the viruses became resistant. This illustrates evolution as an ongoing process because the genes of the population changed in real time.
b. The non-resistant viruses died, and the resistant ones survived and rapidly reproduced. This illustrates evolution as an ongoing process because the change in the HIV population is the result of natural selection.
c. The viruses developed resistance to the drug after repeated exposure to it. This illustrates evolution as an ongoing process because the viruses were able to adapt to changing conditions.
d. The drug-resistant viruses were more fit than their non-resistant counterparts to begin with, and over time they dominated the population. This illustrates evolution as an ongoing process because natural selection favored one phenotype over another.

57. A friend says: "Natural selection is about the survival of the very fittest in a population. The fittest are those that are strongest, largest, fastest."

Would you agree with that statement? Explain. What evidence from scientific disciplines can you offer to support your agreement or your disagreement?

a. The statement is true. If an organism is not strong and fast, it will not survive long enough to reproduce and pass on its genes, and if it is not large and fitter than the other individuals around it then it will not be able to compete for a mate. Many seal species, for example, have only a single male who gets to mate. He must be the very fittest seal to win all the females.

b. The very fittest organisms are not necessarily the ones that survive. Sometimes it is the least fit organisms that survive and reproduce. For example, in one generation the mice who are bad at foraging for seeds may reproduce prolifically and dominate the mice who are good at foraging. In this case, natural selection will select for the less-fit phenotype and spread it in the population.

c. The definition of fitness is not correct. The strongest and fastest organisms are more fit than the weaker and slower ones, but large individuals are often at a disadvantage to smaller ones because they are easily spotted by predators. For example, a large rabbit will stick out on a field more than a small one and will get eaten by a hawk.

d. What is meant by "fittest" is not necessarily strong, large, and fast. Fitness, as defined in evolutionary terms, has to do with survival and the reproduction of genetic material. For example, a small but showy male bird may be selected by female birds to reproduce, while a large but less colorful one is not.

58. A student placed 20 tobacco seeds of the same species on moist paper towels in each of two petri dishes. Dish A was wrapped completely in an opaque cover to exclude all light. Dish B was not wrapped. The dishes were placed equidistant from a light source set to a cycle of 14 hours of light and 10 hours of dark. All other conditions were the same for both dishes. The dishes were examined after 7 days, and the opaque cover was permanently removed from dish A. Both dishes were returned to the light and examined again at 14 days. The following data were obtained:

	Dish A	
	Day 7 covered	Day 14 uncovered
Germinated seeds	12	20
Green-leaved seedlings	0	14
Yellow-leaved seedlings	12	6
Mean stem length below first set of leaves	8 mm	9 mm

	Dish B	
	Day 7 uncovered	Day 14 covered
Germinated seeds	20	20
Green-leaved seedlings	15	15
Yellow-leaved seedlings	5	5
Mean stem length below first set of leaves	3 mm	3 mm

Figure 18.27

Which of the following best supports the hypothesis that the difference in leaf color is genetically controlled?

a. the number of yellow-leaved seedlings in dish A on day 7

b. the number of germinated seeds in dish A on days 7 and 14

c. the death of all the yellow-leaved seedings

d. the existence of yellow-leaved seedlings as well as green-leaved ones on day 14 in dish B

59. Use the data from Figure 18.27 to answer the question. Which best describes the usefulness of the yellow-leaved phenotype as a variation subject to natural selection?

a. the yellow-leaved phenotype can germinate in environments without light

b. the germination of the yellow-leaved phenotype is unaffected by light intensity

c. the germination of the yellow-leaved phenotype is accelerated as compared to the green-leaved phenotype

d. the yellow-leaved phenotype cannot germinate in environments with light

60. Use the data from Figure 18.27 to answer the question. Yellow-leaved seedlings are unable to convert light energy to chemical energy. Which observation is most likely to be made on day 21?

a. a few yellow-leaved seedlings alive in dish A, but none in dish B

b. a few yellow-leaved seedlings alive in dish B, but none in dish A

c. no yellow-leaved seedlings alive in dish A or dish B

d. a few yellow-leaved seedlings alive in dish A and dish B

61. Populations of a nocturnal toad live along a long river. On the other side of a band of territory that is about 10 kilometers wide, there are populations of a toad that appear similar. Which of the following data would provide compelling evidence that the two populations represent different species?

a. The populations of toads on the other side of the banded territory are not completely nocturnal.

b. Fertile hybrid populations of toads are found between the two other populations.

c. There appear to be some hybrid toads between the two populations, but they are few and frail.

d. The two populations of toads enact very different mating behaviors.

62.

Mass Extinction	Time of Extinction	Organisms Greatly Reduced or Made Extinct
End of the Ordovician period	443 million years ago	Trilobites, brachiopods, echinoderms, and corals
End of the Devonian period	354 million years ago	Marine families on tropical reefs, corals, brachiopods, and bivalves
End of the Permian period	248 million years ago	Trilobites, mollusks, brachiopods, and many vertebrates
End of the Triassic period	206 million years ago	Mollusks, sponges, marine vertebrates, and large amphibians
End of the Cretaceous period	65 million years ago	Ammonites, dinosaurs, brachiopods, bivalves, and echinoderms

>

a. searching horizontal rock layers in any class of rock and trying to find those that contain the greatest number of fossils

b. collecting fossils from rock layers deposited prior to the Permian period that contain some early vertebrate bones

c. looking in sedimentary layers next to bodies of water in order to find marine fossils of bivalves and trilobites

d. using relative dating techniques to determine the geological ages of the fossils found so they can calculate the rate of speciation of early organisms

63. Populations of a plant species have been found growing in the mountains at altitudes above 2,500 meters. Populations of a plant that appears similar, with slight differences, have been found in the same mountains at altitudes below 2,300 meters.

Describe a plan for collecting two kinds of data that could provide a direct answer to the question: do the populations growing above 2,500 meters and the populations growing below 2,300 meters represent a single species?

a. Scientists could take the genetic code of a plant from each altitude and determine whether the two sets of DNA are identical. They could also insert genes from one plant into the cells from the other and see if the cells survive

b. Scientists could look in the fossil record to find the plants' most recent common ancestor. They could also check the surrounding mountains to determine if the most recent common ancestor is still living.

c. Scientists could breed the two groups in the same environment and observe whether, over several generations, they begin to look more similar. They could also switch the groups, growing the high-altitude plants at low altitude and the low-altitude plants at high altitude, and observe whether the former begin to look like low-altitude plants and the latter begin to look like high-altitude plants.

d. Scientists could collect seeds and test whether they might be cross-pollinated to produce fertile offspring. They could also investigate the area between 2,500 meters and 2,300 meters to see if fertile hybrid populations might be found living between the two other populations of plants.

64. Populations of a plant species have been found growing in the mountains at altitudes above 2,500 meters. Populations of a plant that appears similar, with slight differences, have been found in the same mountains at altitudes below 2,300 meters.

Explain how the two types of data you suggested provide a direct answer to the question of whether speciation has taken place.

a. If the plants become more similar when grown in the same environment, or if the high-altitude plants respond to low altitude in the same way that low-altitude plants have, and low-altitude plants respond to high altitude the same way that high-altitude plants have, then the two groups have the same underlying genetic structure and belong to one species.
b. If the seeds from the plants can be cross fertilized and developed into fertile offspring, the two populations are not yet reproductively isolated and remain one species. If hybrid forms are found, the two populations are not reproductively isolated and hybrids are both viable and successful.
c. If the genetic codes of the two plants are identical, then they must belong to the same species. Also, if genes transplanted between the plants function successfully, then the plants must be similar enough to each other to belong to the same species.
d. If scientists are able to find the common ancestor of the two groups in the fossil record or in neighboring communities, then they can determine whether the plants have diverged into separate species or remain a single species.

65. Assuming a population that has genetic variation and is under the influence of natural selection, place the following events in the order in which they would occur:

- Genetic frequencies within the population change.
- A change occurs in the population's environment.
- Phenotypic variations shift.
- Individuals who are well-adapted leave more offspring than individuals who are poorly adapted.
- Individuals who are poorly adapted do not survive at the same rate as individuals who are well adapted.

a.
1. A change occurs in the population's environment.
2. Individuals who are poorly adapted do not survive at the same rate as individuals who are well adapted.
3. Individuals who are well-adapted leave more offspring than individuals who are poorly adapted.
4. Genetic frequencies within the population change.
5. Phenotypic variations shift.

b.
1. A change occurs in the population's environment.
2. Genetic frequencies within the population change.
3. Phenotypic variations shift.
4. Individuals who are poorly adapted do not survive at the same rate as individuals who are well adapted.
5. Individuals who are well-adapted leave more offspring than individuals who are poorly adapted.

c.
1. Phenotypic variations shift.
2. A change occurs in the population's environment.
3. Genetic frequencies within the population change.
4. Individuals who are poorly adapted do not survive at the same rate as individuals who are well adapted.
5. Individuals who are well-adapted leave more offspring than individuals who are poorly adapted.

d.
1. Individuals who are well-adapted leave more offspring than individuals who are poorly adapted.
2. Individuals who are poorly adapted do not survive at the same rate as individuals who are well adapted.
3. Phenotypic variations shift.
4. Genetic frequencies within the population change.
5. A change occurs in the population's environment.

66. A biologist studies a population of voles for 20 years. During almost the entire research period, the population stays between 50 and 75 individuals. Additionally, fewer than half of the voles born do not survive to reproduce, due to predation and competition for food. Then, in one generation, 80% of the voles born live to reproduce. The population increases to 110 individuals. What inferences about food and predation can you make for the singular generation in which 80% of offspring survived? What prediction can you make about the genetic and phenotypic variation of future populations for this group of voles?

a. Either there was fewer food available or the degree of predation increased. The future generations of this group of voles should evidence fewer genetic variation.

b. Either there was fewer food available or the degree of predation increased. The future generations of this group of voles should evidence greater genetic variation.

c. Either there was more food available or the degree of predation decreased. The future generations of this group of voles should evidence less genetic variation.

d. Either there was more food available or the degree of predation decreased. The future generations of this group of voles should evidence greater genetic variation.

67. There are years of drought in a small, relatively isolated community. During the drought, small seeds with thin shells become rare. Large seeds with hard cases become increasingly common. The large, tough seeds are successfully eaten by birds with large and broad beaks. Assuming that the drought continues and the population of birds in the community stays isolated, what predictions for the population can you make under the influence of natural selection?

a. The birds with small, thin beaks will grow larger, broader beaks to be able to eat the larger seeds. This will result in subsequent generations having a higher percentage of birds with large, broad beaks.

b. There will be more birds with small, thin beaks dying and more birds with large, broad beaks surviving. Differential reproduction of birds with large, broad beaks will result in subsequent generations having a higher percentage of birds with large, broad beaks.

c. The species will diverge into two species, one with small, thin beaks and one with large, broad beaks. The two species will then compete for resources.

d. There will be neither phenotypic nor genotypic changes in the population.

68. At one time, avian researchers in the Sulawesi region of Indonesia described the Flowerpecker populations on the mainland and the Wakatobi archipelago as one species. A recent reassessment of the Wakatobi populations resulted in the suggested reclassification of these populations as a distinct species, the Wakatobi Flowerpecker. Which of the following pieces of evidence, if true, would be cause for this reclassification?

a. The populations have become dependent on the island food sources.

b. The populations have become morphologically distinct from the mainland species.

c. The populations have become adapted to the island habitat.

d. The populations have become reproductively isolated from the mainland species.

69. What pattern in the fossil record would you expect to see to support the model of gradual speciation? How would you expect this pattern to differ from a pattern in the fossil record that supports the model of punctuated equilibrium? Explain.

a. In the case of gradual speciation, the fossil record would show only a few hybrid individuals, followed by individuals of the two distinct species. For the case of punctuated equilibrium, the fossil record would show many hybrid individuals persisting through several geological layers.

b. In the case of gradual speciation, the fossil record would show the parent species in a single location, such that the newly diverged species remained in contact with each other. For the case of punctuated equilibrium, the fossil record would show a geographic divide within the parent species that caused it to diverge into multiple new species.

c. In the case of gradual speciation, the fossil record would show many intermediate forms. For the case of punctuated equilibrium, the fossil record would show new forms that persist essentially unchanged through several geological layers, then disappear just as a new form appears.

d. Gradual speciation would be undetectable in the fossil record. For the case of punctuated equilibrium, the fossil record would show a steady progression of distinct forms.

70. Until recently, these three species of short-tailed pythons, *Python curtus*, *Python brongersmai* (middle), and *Python breitensteini* were considered one species. However, due to the different locations in which they are found, they have become three distinct species. What is this an example of?

a. divergent evolution

b. sympatric speciation

c. allopatric speciation

d. variation

71. Consider two species of birds that diverged while separated geographically but resumed their contact before reproductive isolation was complete. Which describes the first step in what would happen over time if the two species mated extensively and their hybrid offspring survived and reproduced more poorly than offspring from intra-species matings?

a. Natural selection would cause prezygotic barriers to reproduction between the parent species to strengthen over time.

b. The production of unfit hybrids would increase and the speciation process would complete.

c. The extensive mating between the species would continue to produce large numbers of hybrids.

d. The gene pools of the parent species would fuse over time, reversing the speciation process.

SCIENCE PRACTICE CHALLENGE QUESTIONS

72. In addition to biology, evidence drawn from many different disciplines, including chemistry, geology, and mathematics, supports models of the origin of life on Earth. In order to determine when the first forms of life likely formed, the rate of radioactive decay can be used to determine the age of the oldest rocks (see optional problems C and D, below) exposed on Earth's surface. These are found to be approximately 3.5 billion years old. The age of rocks can be correlated to fossils of the earliest forms of life.

A. The graph compares times of divergence from the last common ancestor based on the fossil record with a "molecular time" constructed by comparing sequences of conserved proteins to determine a mutation rate (after Hedges and Kumar, *Trends in Genetics*, 2003). **Explain** how such a molecular clock could be refined to infer time for the evolution of prokaryotes.

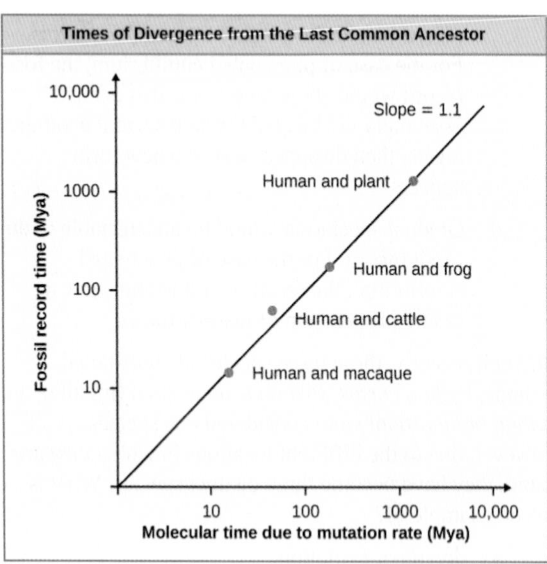

Figure 18.28

B. Using a molecular clock constructed from 32 conserved proteins, Hedges and colleagues (Battistuzzi et al., *BMC Evol. Biol*. 2004) estimated the times during which key biological processes evolved. A diagram based on their work is shown. **Connect** the time of the origin of life inferred from this diagram with the age of the oldest fossil stromatolites and the age of the oldest exposed rock to show how evidence from different scientific disciplines provides support for the concept of evolution. **Evaluate** the legitimacy of claims drawn from these different disciplines (biology, geology, and mathematics) regarding the origin of life on Earth.

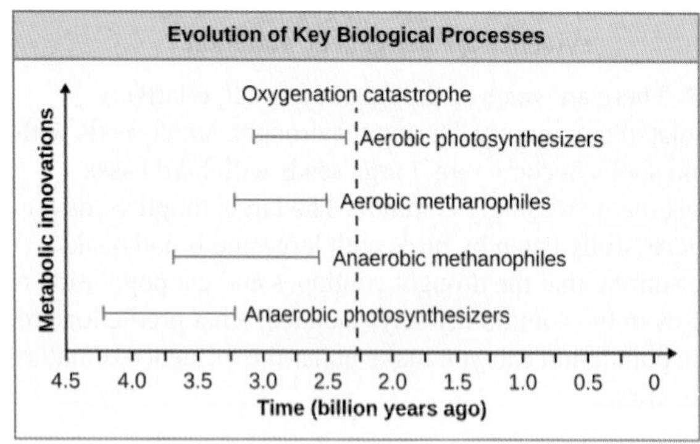

Figure 18.29

The oldest known rocks are exposed at three locations: Greenland, Australia, and Swaziland. The following application of mathematical methods provides the essential evidence of the minimum age of Earth. The mathematics is appropriate for students who have completed a second year of algebra. However, it is not illustrative of the type of item that could appear on the AP Biology Exam.

The exposed rocks contain a radioactive isotope of rubidium, ^{87}Rb, which decays into a stable isotope of strontium, ^{87}Sr. An ^{87}Rb atom with 37 protons and 50 neutrons decays when a proton is converted into a neutron to produce an atom, ^{87}Sr, with 36 protons and 51 neutrons. As time passed, the number of each isotope changed from its initial value. When a crystal containing ^{87}Rb atoms formed from the molten surface of the hot, early Earth during the Hadean eon, the number of these atoms at that initial time can be represented as $N_{87Rb,0}$. As time passed, the number of atoms of this isotope changed to N_{87Rb}.

C. **Justify** the relationship between the number of each isotope at any time and the number of each at the time that the molten rock solidified (denoted by the subscript 0):

$$N_{^{87}Sr} = N_{^{87}Sr,\,0} + N_{^{87}Rb,\,0} - N_{^{87}Rb}$$

The decay of unstable radioisotopes is exponential with a half-life of $T_{1/2}$, which for ^{87}Rb is 4.88×10^{10} years:

$$N_{87_{Rb}} = N_{87_{Rb,\,0}} e^{-0.693t / T_{1/2}}$$

This can be used to replace the initial number of ^{87}Rb atoms, which cannot be measured, with the present-day value:

$$\frac{N_{87_{sr}}}{N_{86_{sr}}} = \frac{N_{87_{sr,\,0}}}{N_{86_{sr}}} + (e^{-0.693t / T_{1/2}} - 1)\frac{N_{87_{Rb}}}{N_{86_{sr}}}$$

When the measurements of the numbers of ^{87}Rb and ^{87}Sr were made (Moorbath et al., *Nature*, 1972), measurements of a second stable isotope of strontium, ^{86}Sr, were also made. The ratio of the initial number of ^{87}Sr and ^{86}Sr atoms is the same as today, since the isotopes are both stable. The value of this ratio is 0.71.

This is a linear equation in the form $y = ax + b$, where a is the term in parenthesis containing the half-life of ^{87}Rb. If $Y = N_{87_{Sr}} / N_{86_{Sr}}$ is graphed versus $N_{87_{Rb}} / N_{86_{Sr}}$, the slope can be used to determine the time, t, that has passed since the rock formed from melting:

$a = e^{0.683t / T_{1/2}} - 1$, so

$t = \ln(a + 1) \bullet T_{1/2} / 0.693$

D. Data on the rubidium and strontium isotopes at Isua in Greenland are provided in the table. **Analyze** these data to obtain the age of formation of these rocks.

N 87_{Rb} / N 86_{Sr}	N 87_{Sr} / N 86_{Sr}
.212	.711
.214	.711
.223	.712
.259	.714
.268	.714
.267	.715
.290	.716
.394	.720
.434	.723

Table 18.1

The solidification of the molten surface of Earth at the end of the Hadean eon (4 to 4.6 billion years ago) and the condensation of liquid oceans provided a medium from which life emerged. The most ancient fossils are colonial, photosynthetic cyanobacteria called stromatolites. As climate change melted the perennial snow covering Greenland, new geologic evidence of the time of that origin was obtained (Nutman et al., *Nature* 2016) with the discovery of the most ancient stromatolites. These fossils record communities of photosynthetic bacteria embedded in Isua sediments 3.7 billion years ago. Worldwide stromatolite fossils show a decline between 1 and 1.3 billion years ago.

73. In 1952, the Miller-Urey experiment showed that an electrical discharge in a gas-phase mixture of ammonia, hydrogen, methane, and water produced five amino acids. When the experiment was conducted, evidence indicated that this mixture was representative of the Hadean (early Earth) atmosphere. The experiment was repeated in the presence of jets of hot steam, simulating Hadean volcanic eruptions and producing an even larger variety of amino acids.

A. Consider the following criticisms of the "organic soup" model and **justify the selection of data** that other experiments might provide regarding the origin of life on Earth.

- Biopolymers on Earth have a left-hand symmetry at the carbon adjacent to the carboxylic acid carbon, and these experiments produced mixtures of both left- and right-hand symmetries.
- No peptide bonds between amino acids were observed.
- Early Earth's atmospheric oxygen concentration is known to have been very low, implying the absence of an ozone layer to filter high-energy ultraviolet (uv) radiation.
- Ammonia decomposes when it absorbs high-energy uv radiation, but diatomic nitrogen does not.

Models of the abiotic synthesis of biomolecules suffer from a "chicken and egg" dilemma. Proteins are needed to synthesize DNA and RNA, and DNA and RNA are needed to synthesize proteins. Which molecules came first?

B. In light of the following observations, **evaluate the hypothesis** that nucleotides arose from a prebiotic mixture.

- Nuclei acids are not found in experiments like those of Miller and Urey.
- Purines and pyrimidines decompose at high temperature, and Earth was bombarded by meteors and comets during the Hadean eon.
- Bonds in the purine and pyrimidine rings of nucleic acids are broken by high-energy uv radiation.
- Carl Sagan and colleagues synthesized ATP from a mixture of adenosine, ribose, and phosphate when exposed to uv radiation.
- Ribose has never been synthesized in experiments like those conducted by Miller and Urey.
- Ribose has a left/right symmetry, and the right-handed form occurs in Earth organisms.

Continuing with the analogy, if neither the chicken nor the egg came first, then both must have arisen together. Some regard simultaneous innovations in both catalysis and information storage and retrieval as too improbable. In samples of meteorites, both amino acids and nucleic acids have been found. The amino acids are mixtures of left- and right-handed symmetries, although some have shown a significant bias toward the left-handed form (J. Elisa et al., *ACS Central Science*, 2016). The arrival from space of the seeds of biomolecules is called panspermia. Carl Sagan (1966) and Francis Crick (1973), one of the first to describe the structure of DNA, regarded panspermia as the only plausible origin of life on Earth. In fact, their belief was in directed panspermia, the intentional seeding by intelligent aliens.

C. **Describe** the questions that must be addressed for panspermia to be a scientific hypothesis about the origin of life on Earth and **describe** the reasons for the directed panspermia revision of this hypothesis.

To avoid the conflicting chicken-and-egg claims that "protein catalyst was first" and "DNA information storage was first," two alternatives have emerged regarding the origin of life on Earth. Consider two simple ideas: 1) water blocks uv radiation, and cracks in the ocean floor (hot vents) provide a temperature difference that generates a source of entropy; and 2) ribosomes are composed of RNA.

D. **Describe** one of the following as a hypothesis concerning the origin of life on Earth:

- Reactions among molecules in the vicinity of hot vents became organized in space and time, eventually developing structures that foreshadow the proton gradient upon which metabolism is based. This alternative is the basis for what is referred to as the metabolism-first hypothesis.
- The catalytic properties of the ribosome reflect the self-catalytic polymerization of nucleotides with sequential structures conserved in modern DNA, the catalytic properties conserved in proteins, and the catalytic properties of the ribosome whose core structure is RNA. This alternative is the basis for what is referred to as the RNA-first hypothesis.

74. The radiant energy emitted by a star gradually increases after its birth. During the Hadean eon, while the molten Earth cooled and life emerged, the Sun provided approximately 25% less radiant energy than it does now. Ignoring effects due to differences in the composition of Earth's atmosphere between then and now, this means that the average surface temperature of the surface would be about 25 °C below the freezing temperature of water. Evidence of liquid water on Earth during the Hadean eon is provided by geologic structures known only to form in liquid water, such as lava pillows and the stromatolites that are the fossilized layers of photosynthetic cyanobacteria.

Pose a scientific question that guides inquiry into early Earth conditions that supported the innovation of photosynthesis.

75. Connect the techniques of radiometric measurement, anatomy, and molecular biology to the supporting evidence of the theory of evolution provided.

76. Describe reasons for the revision of scientific hypotheses of the origin of life on Earth.

77. Directed evolution is an inquiry strategy that is usually used to investigate gene expression or the function of proteins that are expressed. The investigator imposes a selection pressure and observes the evolution of a population. In one investigation, unicellular yeast were allowed to sediment in a column of a nutrient-containing solution. Individuals that traveled furthest towards the bottom of the column were removed and placed in a new column. After 60 generations of repeated selection, yeast became multicellular. In this experiment, selection was acting on the collection of cells and not on the individual. To test the claim that selection was acting on the multicellular system and not just individual cells, the investigators compared the effects on a population of yeast that had acquired multicellularity by strong selection (allowing only 5 minutes to settle) and weak selection (allowing 25 minutes to settle). A strong selection increased cluster size, and a weak selection decreased cluster size.

A. **Evaluate** the claim that the use of both a strong and weak selection demonstrates that evolution is an ongoing process that, under artificially imposed conditions, led to the emergence of multicellularity in a single-celled organism.

B. In this directed evolution study, the selection pressure imposed by the investigators led to a new phenotype. Consider a situation in which there is a vertical variation in the density of nutritional resources. Analyze the advantages and disadvantages of cooperative behavior, including changes in the likelihood of replication of the individual and population genomes.

78. Selection processes in changing and unchanging environments differ. **Connect** the effects of negative and positive selection pressures to changes in the environment.

79. In biology, the word "race" is rarely used. It could be imagined to be synonymous with a subspecies. Species is well defined, at least when horizontal gene transfer is not taken into account, by reproductive isolation. Speciation may arise through geographic isolation.

A. Aside from geographic isolation leading to reproductive isolation, **predict** two other mechanisms of speciation in a population and how these mechanisms can lead to a scientific definition of a subspecies.

The use of the term "race" with regard to human populations might be a reference to cultural or socioeconomic isolation, and has often been mistaken to have biological significance. Rosenberg et al. (*Science*, 2002) sampled the genes of 1,056 people from 52 populations. They compared genetic variations within each population to variations among populations. They found that differences between individuals in two different populations were, on average, roughly 20 times smaller than differences between two individuals in the same population.

B. Groups of humans have often been geographically isolated for long periods of time until isolation is broken by invasion, enslavement, migration, or another similar event. Invaders have traditionally been male. **Predict** the effect of invasion on the differential inheritance of genes in X- and autosomal chromosomes.

19 | THE EVOLUTION OF POPULATIONS

Figure 19.1 Living things may be single-celled or complex, multicellular organisms. They may be plants, animals, fungi, bacteria, or archaea. This diversity results from evolution. (credit "wolf": modification of work by Gary Kramer; credit "coral": modification of work by William Harrigan, NOAA; credit "river": modification of work by Vojtěch Dostál; credit "fish" modification of work by Christian Mehlführer; credit "mushroom": modification of work by Cory Zanker; credit "tree": modification of work by Joseph Kranak; credit "bee": modification of work by Cory Zanker)

Chapter Outline

Introduction

Evolutionary medicine is an emerging field that applies evolutionary theory to modern medicine. Rather than just seeking answers to how illness occurs, evolutionary medicine also asks why illness occurs. This approach to medicine has led to many important advances. For example, endogenous retroviruses (ERVs) are pieces of retroviruses that began invading mammalian genomes over 100 million years ago. While studying why smaller mammals tend to get cancer more frequently than larger mammals, scientists discovered that larger mammals have had fewer ERVs invade their genome. Because retroviral integration is associated with cancer, results from this research suggest the possibility that larger mammals are able to control EVR replication until they reach post-reproductive age.[1] More on this research can be found on the PLOS Pathogens website (http://openstaxcollege.org/l/32mammalcancer) .

1. Katzourakis A, Magiorkinis G, Lim AG, Gupta S, Belshaw R, et al. (2014) Larger Mammalian Body Size Leads to Lower Retroviral Activity. PLoS Pathog10(7): e1004214. doi: 10.1371/journal.ppat.1004214

19.1 | Population Evolution

In this section, you will explore the following questions:

- What is population genetics and how is population genetics a synthesis of Mendelian inheritance and Darwinian evolution?
- What is the Hardy–Weinberg principle, and how can it be applied to microevolution?

The mechanisms of inheritance, or genetics, were not understood at the time Charles Darwin and Alfred Russel Wallace were developing their idea of natural selection. This lack of understanding was a stumbling block to understanding many aspects of evolution. In fact, the predominant (and incorrect) genetic theory of the time, blending inheritance, made it difficult to understand how natural selection might operate. Darwin and Wallace were unaware of the genetics work by Austrian monk Gregor Mendel, which was published in 1866, not long after publication of Darwin's book, *On the Origin of Species*. Mendel's work was rediscovered in the early twentieth century at which time geneticists were rapidly coming to an understanding of the basics of inheritance. Initially, the newly discovered particulate nature of genes made it difficult for biologists to understand how gradual evolution could occur. But over the next few decades genetics and evolution were integrated in what became known as the **modern synthesis**—the coherent understanding of the relationship between natural selection and genetics that took shape by the 1940s and is generally accepted today. In sum, the modern synthesis describes how evolutionary processes, such as natural selection, can affect a population's genetic makeup, and, in turn, how this can result in the gradual evolution of populations and species. The theory also connects this change of a population over time, called **microevolution**, with the processes that gave rise to new species and higher taxonomic groups with widely divergent characters, called **macroevolution**.

Connection for AP® Courses

Population genetics studies microevolution by measuring changes in a population's allele frequencies over time. (Remember that we studied genotypes and allele frequencies when we explored inheritance patterns proposed by Mendel.) For example, scientists examining allele frequencies in a pesticide resistance gene in mosquitoes at Equatorial Guinea found that the frequency of one resistance allele was 6.3%, while a second resistance allele's frequency was 74.6%, and the non-resistance allele's frequency was 19.0%. These three frequencies add up to 100%.[2] A population's **gene pool** is the sum of all the alleles. If these frequencies do not change over time, the population is said to be in **Hardy–Weinberg principle of equilibrium**—a stable, non-evolving state. However, if a phenotype is favored by natural selection, allele frequencies can change. If this is the case, the population is evolving. Sometimes allele frequencies within a population change randomly with no advantage to the population over existing allele frequencies. This phenomenon is called **genetic drift**. An event that initiates an allele frequency change in an isolated part of the population, which is not typical of the original population, is called the **founder effect**. In Population Genetics, we will explore how natural selection, random drift, and founder effects can lead to significant changes in the genome of a population.

Hardy–Weinberg equilibrium reflects a state of constancy in a population's gene pool. In other words, allele frequencies remain stable from generation to generation if certain conditions are met: no mutations, no gene flow, random mating, no genetic drift, and no selection. Because these conditions are rarely met, allele frequencies are typically changing, reflecting evolution. The Hardy–Weinberg principle is represented by the mathematical equation $p^2 + 2pq + q^2 = 1$, where p represents the frequency of the dominant allele and q represents the frequency of the recessive allele. Deviations from Hardy–Weinberg equilibrium allow us to measure microevolutionary shifts in a population when one or more of the Hardy–Weinberg parameters change. For example, if we go back to the study of the frequencies of alleles in a pesticide resistance gene, after an area was treated with pesticides for two years, the resistance alleles increased to 11.1% and 83.3%, respectively, while the non-resistance allele decreased to 5.6%. This indicates that microevolution was occurring.

Information presented and the examples highlighted in the section support concepts outlined in Big Idea 1 of the AP® Biology Curriculum Framework. The AP® Learning Objectives listed in the Curriculum Framework provide a transparent foundation for the AP® Biology course, an inquiry-based laboratory experience, instructional activities, and AP® exam questions. A learning objective merges required content with one or more of the seven science practices.

2. Reddy, M. R., Godoy, A., Dion, K., Matias, A., Callender, K., Kiszewski, A. E., Slotman, M. A. (2013). Insecticide Resistance Allele Frequencies in *Anopheles gambiae* before and after Anti-Vector Interventions in Continental Equatorial Guinea. *The American Journal of Tropical Medicine and Hygiene, 88*(5), 897–907. doi:10.4269/ajtmh.12-0467

Big Idea 1	The process of evolution drives the diversity and unity of life.
Enduring Understanding 1.A	Change in the genetic makeup of a population over time is evolution.
Essential Knowledge	**1.A.1** Natural selection is a major mechanism of evolution.
Science Practice	**1.5** The student can re-express key elements of natural phenomena across multiple representations in the domain.
Science Practice	**1.1** The student is able to convert a data set from a table of numbers that reflect a change in the genetic makeup of a population over time and to apply mathematical methods and conceptual understandings to investigate the cause(s) and effect(s) of this change.
Learning Objective	**1.1** The student is able to convert a data set from a table of numbers that reflect a change in the genetic makeup of a population over time and to apply mathematical methods and conceptual understandings to investigate the cause(s) and effect(s) of this change.
Essential Knowledge	**1.A.1** Natural selection is a major mechanism of evolution.
Science Practice	**2.2** The student can apply mathematical routines to quantities that describe natural phenomena.
Learning Objective	**1.2** The student is able to evaluate evidence provided by data to qualitatively and quantitatively investigate the role of natural selection in evolution.
Essential Knowledge	**1.A.1** Natural selection is a major mechanism of evolution.
Science Practice	**5.3** The student can evaluate the evidence provided by data sets in relation to a particular scientific question.
Learning Objective	**1.3** The student is able to apply mathematical methods to data from a real or simulated population to predict what will happen to the population in the future.

The Science Practice Challenge Questions contain additional test questions for this section that will help you prepare for the AP exam. These questions address the following standards:
[APLO 1.1]

everyday CONNECTION for AP® Courses

Evolution and Flu Vaccines

Every fall, the media starts reporting on flu vaccinations and potential outbreaks. Scientists, health experts, and institutions determine recommendations for different parts of the population, predict optimal production and inoculation schedules, create vaccines, and set up clinics to provide inoculations. You may think of the annual flu shot as a lot of media hype, an important health protection, or just a briefly uncomfortable prick in your arm. But do you think of it in terms of evolution?

The media hype of annual flu shots is scientifically grounded in our understanding of evolution. Each year, scientists across the globe strive to predict the flu strains that they anticipate being most widespread and harmful in the coming year. This knowledge is based in how flu strains have evolved over time and over the past few flu seasons. Scientists then work to create the most effective vaccine to combat those selected strains. Hundreds of millions of doses are produced in a short period in order to provide vaccinations to key populations at the optimal time.

Because viruses, like the flu, evolve very quickly (especially in evolutionary time), this poses quite a challenge. Viruses mutate and replicate at a fast rate, so the vaccine developed to protect against last year's flu strain may not provide the protection needed against the coming year's strain. Evolution of these viruses means continued adaptions to ensure survival, including adaptations to survive previous vaccines.

Population genetics is the study of what?

a. How selective forces change the allele frequencies in a population over time.

b. The genetic basis of genetic traits within individuals.

c. Whether traits have a genetic basis.

d. The degree of inbreeding in a population.

Population Genetics

Recall that a gene for a particular character may have several alleles, or variants, that code for different traits associated with that character. For example, in the ABO blood type system in humans, three alleles determine the particular blood-type protein on the surface of red blood cells. Each individual in a population of diploid organisms can only carry two alleles for a particular gene, but more than two may be present in the individuals that make up the population. Mendel followed alleles as they were inherited from parent to offspring. In the early twentieth century, biologists in a field of study known as population genetics began to study how selective forces change a population through changes in allele and genotypic frequencies.

The **allele frequency** (or gene frequency) is the proportion of a specific allele within a population, relative to all other alleles of that gene that are present in the population. Until now we have discussed evolution as a change in the characteristics of a population of organisms, but behind that phenotypic change is genetic change. In population genetics, the term evolution is defined as a change in the frequency of an allele in a population. Using the ABO blood type system as an example, the frequency of one of the alleles, I^A, is the number of copies of that allele divided by all the copies of the ABO gene in the population. For example, a study in Jordan[3] found a frequency of I^A to be 26.1 percent. The I^B and I^0 alleles made up 13.4 percent and 60.5 percent of the alleles respectively, and all of the frequencies added up to 100 percent. A change in this frequency over time would constitute evolution in the population.

The allele frequency within a given population can change depending on environmental factors; therefore, certain alleles become more widespread than others during the process of natural selection. Natural selection can alter the population's genetic makeup; for example, if a given allele confers a phenotype that allows an individual to better survive or have more offspring. Because many of those offspring will also carry the beneficial allele, and often the corresponding phenotype, they will have more offspring of their own that also carry the allele, thus, perpetuating the cycle. Over time, the allele will spread throughout the population. Some alleles will quickly become fixed in this way, meaning that every individual of the population will carry the allele, while detrimental mutations may be swiftly eliminated if derived from a dominant allele from the gene pool. The gene pool is the sum of all the alleles in a population.

3. Sahar S. Hanania, Dhia S. Hassawi, and Nidal M. Irshaid, "Allele Frequency and Molecular Genotypes of ABO Blood Group System in a Jordanian Population," *Journal of Medical Sciences* 7 (2007): 51-58, doi:10.3923/jms.2007.51.58.

Sometimes, allele frequencies within a population change randomly with no advantage to the population over existing allele frequencies. This phenomenon is called genetic drift. Natural selection and genetic drift usually occur simultaneously in populations and are not isolated events. It is hard to determine which process dominates because it is often nearly impossible to determine the cause of change in allele frequencies at each occurrence. An event that initiates an allele frequency change in an isolated part of the population, which is not typical of the original population, is called the founder effect. Natural selection, random drift, and founder effects can lead to significant changes in the genome of a population.

Hardy–Weinberg Principle of Equilibrium

In the early twentieth century, English mathematician Godfrey Hardy and German physician Wilhelm Weinberg stated the principle of equilibrium to describe the genetic makeup of a population. The theory, which later became known as the Hardy–Weinberg principle of equilibrium, states that a population's allele and **genotype frequencies** are inherently stable—unless some kind of evolutionary force is acting upon the population, neither the allele nor the genotypic frequencies would change. The Hardy–Weinberg principle assumes conditions with no mutations, migration, emigration, or selective pressure for or against genotype, plus an infinite population; while no population can satisfy those conditions, the principle offers a useful model against which to compare real population changes.

Working under this theory, population geneticists represent different alleles as different variables in their mathematical models. The variable p, for example, typically represents the frequency of the dominant allele, say Y for the trait of yellow in Mendel's peas. The variable q represents the frequency of the recessive allele, in this case y, that confers the color green. If these are the only two possible alleles for a given locus in the population, $p + q = 1$. In other words, all the p alleles and all the q alleles make up all of the alleles for that locus that are found in the population.

But what ultimately interests most biologists is not the frequencies of different alleles, but the frequencies of the resulting genotypes, known as the population's **genetic structure**, from which scientists can surmise the distribution of phenotypes. If the phenotype is observed, only the genotype of the homozygous recessive alleles can be known; the calculations provide an estimate of the remaining genotypes. Since each individual carries two alleles per gene, if the allele frequencies (p and q) are known, predicting the frequencies of these genotypes is a simple mathematical calculation to determine the probability of getting these genotypes if two alleles are drawn at random from the gene pool. So in the above scenario, an individual pea plant could be pp (YY), and thus produce yellow peas; pq (Yy), also yellow; or qq (yy), and thus producing green peas (Figure 19.2). In other words, the frequency of pp individuals is simply p^2; the frequency of pq individuals is 2pq; and the frequency of qq individuals is q^2. And, again, if p and q are the only two possible alleles for a given trait in the population, these genotypes frequencies will sum to one: $p^2 + 2pq + q^2 = 1$.

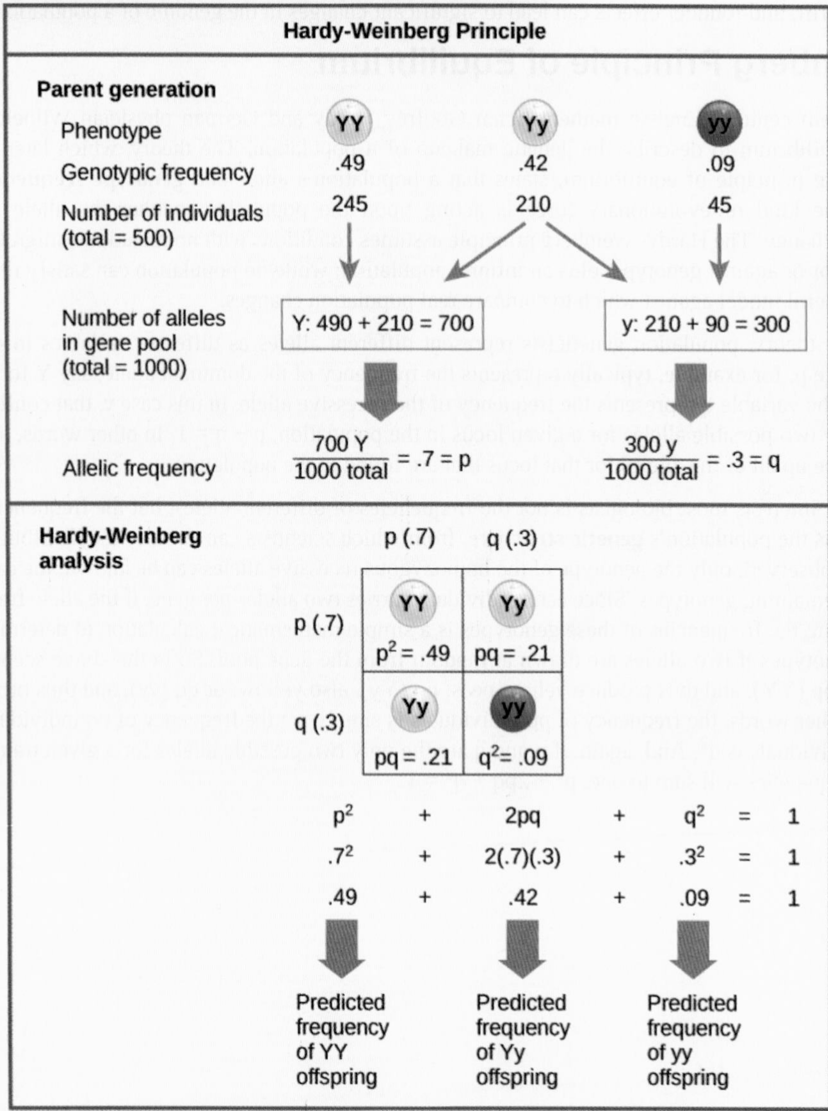

Figure 19.2 When populations are in the Hardy–Weinberg equilibrium, the allelic frequency is stable from generation to generation and the distribution of alleles can be determined from the Hardy–Weinberg equation. If the allelic frequency measured in the field differs from the predicted value, scientists can make inferences about what evolutionary forces are at play.

In plants, violet flower color (V) is dominant over white (v). If $p = 0.8$ and $q = 0.2$ in a population of 500 plants, how many individuals would you expect to be homozygous dominant (VV), heterozygous (Vv), and homozygous recessive (vv)? How many plants would you expect to have violet flowers, and how many would have white flowers?

a. homozygous dominant: 320 heterozygous: 160 homozygous recessive: 20 violet: 480 white: 20

b. homozygous dominant: 320 heterozygous: 80 homozygous recessive: 20 violet: 400 white: 20

c. homozygous dominant: 400 heterozygous: 0 homozygous recessive: 100 violet: 400 white: 100

d. homozygous dominant: 480 heterozygous: 0 homozygous recessive: 20 violet: 480 white: 20

In theory, if a population is at equilibrium—that is, there are no evolutionary forces acting upon it—generation after generation would have the same gene pool and genetic structure, and these equations would all hold true all of the time.

Of course, even Hardy and Weinberg recognized that no natural population is immune to evolution. Populations in nature are constantly changing in genetic makeup due to drift, mutation, possibly migration, and selection. As a result, the only way to determine the exact distribution of phenotypes in a population is to go out and count them. But the Hardy–Weinberg principle gives scientists a mathematical baseline of a non-evolving population to which they can compare evolving populations and thereby infer what evolutionary forces might be at play. If the frequencies of alleles or genotypes deviate from the value expected from the Hardy–Weinberg equation, then the population is evolving.

Use this **online calculator (http://openstaxcollege.org/l/hardy-weinberg)** to determine the genetic structure of a population.

What would violate the conditions of Hardy-Weinberg equilibrium?

a. random mating

b. mutations

c. large population

d. no natural selection

science practices CONNECTION for AP® Courses

Lab Investigation

AP® Biology Investigative Labs: Inquiry-Based Approach, Investigation 2: Mathematical Modeling: Hardy–Weinberg. In this lab investigation, you apply the Hardy–Weinberg equation and create a spreadsheet to study changes in allele frequencies in a population and to examine possible causes for these changes.

Think About It

Imagine you are trying to determine if a population of flowers is undergoing microevolution. You suspect there is selection pressure on the color of the flower because bees seem to cluster around red flowers more often than blue flowers. In a separate experiment, you discover that blue flower color is dominant to red flower color. In a field, you count 600 blue flowers and 200 red flowers. Based on the H-W equation, what are the expected allele frequencies for flower color?

Two years later, you revisit the same field and discover that out of 1,000 flowers, 650 are blue. Use the H–W equation to determine if the population of flowers is undergoing evolution.

19.2 | Population Genetics

In this section, you will explore the following questions:

- What are the different types of variation in a population?
- Why can only heritable variation be acted upon by natural selection?
- How can genetic drift, the bottleneck effect, and the founder effect influence allele frequencies in a population?
- How can gene flow, mutation, nonrandom mating, and environmental variance affect allele frequencies in a population?

Connection for AP® Courses

Take a look at your classmates. Individuals of a population often display different phenotypes, or express different alleles of a particular gene. These differences are called **polymorphisms**. The distribution of phenotypes among individuals, known as **population variation**, is influenced by several factors, including the population's genetic structure and the environment (Figure 19.3). Understanding the sources of phenotypic variation is important for determining how a population will evolve in response to different evolutionary pressures. Only those variations that are encoded in an individual's genes can be passed to its offspring and be a target of natural selection.

Figure 19.3 The distribution of phenotypes in this litter of kittens illustrates population variation. (credit: Pieter Lanser)

As you learn in the chapter that discusses the evolution and origin of species, natural selection works by selecting for phenotypes—and the alleles that determine them—that confer beneficial traits or behaviors. Deleterious qualities are selected against. Genetic drift stems from the chance occurrence that some individuals have more offspring than others and, thus, will pass on more of their genes to the next generation. Small and isolated populations are more susceptible to genetic drift. Natural events, such as wildfires or hurricanes, can magnify genetic drift when a large portion of the population is killed. Because a fire does not distinguish between the genotypes of various organisms, no particular genotype survives the fire better than another. Therefore, the genetic structure of the surviving population may be very different from the genetic structure of the original population. This is called the bottleneck effect. Another scenario in which populations might experience a strong influence of genetic drift occurs when some portion of the population leaves to start a new population in a new location or gets separated by a physical barrier of some kind. In this situation, those individuals are unlikely to be representative of the entire population, a phenomenon called the founder effect. Both the bottleneck effect and the founder effect reduce genetic variation within a population—and genetic variation is the basis for natural selection. When individuals leave or join a population, they carry their alleles with them, resulting in changes in the population's allele frequencies. Allele frequencies also can change due to mutation in DNA and when individuals do not randomly mate with others; when an individual selects a mate based on phenotype, the genotype is also selected. In summary, any of these conditions can result in deviations from the Hardy–Weinberg equilibrium—and lead to the microevolution of a population.

Information presented and the examples highlighted in the section support concepts outlined in Big Idea 1 of the AP® Biology Curriculum Framework. The AP® Learning Objectives listed in the Curriculum Framework provide a transparent foundation for the AP® Biology course, an inquiry-based laboratory experience, instructional activities, and AP® exam questions. A learning objective merges required content with one or more of the seven science practices.

Big Idea 1	The process of evolution drives the diversity and unity of life.
Enduring Understanding 1.A	Change in the genetic makeup of a population over time is evolution.
Essential Knowledge	**1.A.1** Natural selection is a major mechanism of evolution.
Science Practice	**2.2** The student can apply mathematical routines to quantities that describe natural phenomena.
Learning Objective	**1.2** The student is able to evaluate evidence provided by data to qualitatively and quantitatively investigate the role of natural selection in evolution.
Essential Knowledge	**1.A.2** Natural selection acts on phenotypic variations in populations.
Science Practice	**6.4** The student can make claims and predictions about natural phenomena based on scientific theories and models.
Learning Objective	**1.3** The student is able to apply mathematical methods to data from a real or simulated population to predict what will happen to the population in the future.
Essential Knowledge	**1.A.2** Natural selection acts on phenotypic variations in populations.
Science Practice	**5.3** The student can evaluate the evidence provided by data sets in relation to a particular scientific question.
Learning Objective	**1.4** The student is able to evaluate data-based evidence that describes evolutionary changes in the genetic makeup of a population over time.
Essential Knowledge	**1.A.3** Evolutionary change is also driven by random processes.
Science Practice	**6.4** The student can make claims and predictions about natural phenomena based on scientific theories and models.
Learning Objective	**1.8** The student is able to make predictions about the effects of genetic drift, migration, and artificial selection on the genetic makeup of a population.
Essential Knowledge	**1.A.3** Evolutionary change is also driven by random processes.
Science Practice	**1.4** The student can use representatives and models to analyze situations or solve problems qualitatively and quantitatively.
Science Practice	**2.1** The student can justify the selection of a mathematical routine to solve problems.
Learning Objective	**1.6** The student is able to use data from mathematical models based on the Hardy–Weinberg equilibrium to analyze genetic drift and the effects of selection in the evolution of specific populations.
Essential Knowledge	**1.A.3** Evolutionary change is also driven by random processes.
Science Practice	**2.1** The student can justify the selection of a mathematical routine to solve problems.
Learning Objective	**1.7** The student is able to justify data from mathematical models based on the Hardy–Weinberg equilibrium to analyze genetic drift and the effects of selection in the evolution of specific populations.

The Science Practice Challenge Questions contain additional test questions for this section that will help you prepare for the AP exam. These questions address the following standards:
[APLO 1.1][APLO 1.3][APLO 1.4][APLO 1.8][APLO 1.23][APLO 1.24][APLO 1.25][APLO 1.6][APLO 1.7][APLO 1.22]

Genetic Variance

Natural selection and some of the other evolutionary forces can only act on heritable traits, namely an organism's genetic code. Because alleles are passed from parent to offspring, those that confer beneficial traits or behaviors may be selected for, while deleterious alleles may be selected against. Acquired traits, for the most part, are not heritable. For example, if an athlete works out in the gym every day, building up muscle strength, the athlete's offspring will not necessarily grow up to be a body builder. If there is a genetic basis for the ability to run fast, on the other hand, this may be passed to a child.

Before Darwinian evolution became the prevailing theory of the field, French naturalist Jean-Baptiste Lamarck theorized that acquired traits could, in fact, be inherited; while this hypothesis has largely been unsupported, scientists have recently begun to realize that Lamarck was not completely wrong. Visit this **site (http://openstaxcollege.org/l/epigenetic)** to learn more.

Explain naturalist Jean-Baptiste Lamarck's theory on heritability.

a. Lamarck theorized that individuals more fit to their environment would me more likely to survive, reproduce, and pass on their genes.

b. Lamarck theorized that traits that parents acquired in their lifetime could be inherited by offspring in an attempt to improve.

c. Lamarck theorized that traits in offspring were a blend of traits from the two parents.

d. Lamarck theorized that inbreeding would lead to higher proportions of homozygous recessive genotypes, potentially conferring recessive diseases onto offspring.

Heritability is the fraction of phenotype variation that can be attributed to genetic differences, or genetic variance, among individuals in a population. The greater the hereditability of a population's phenotypic variation, the more susceptible it is to the evolutionary forces that act on heritable variation.

The diversity of alleles and genotypes within a population is called **genetic variance**. When scientists are involved in the breeding of a species, such as with animals in zoos and nature preserves, they try to increase a population's genetic variance to preserve as much of the phenotypic diversity as they can. This also helps reduce the risks associated with **inbreeding**, the mating of closely related individuals, which can have the undesirable effect of bringing together deleterious recessive mutations that can cause abnormalities and susceptibility to disease. For example, a disease that is caused by a rare, recessive allele might exist in a population, but it will only manifest itself when an individual carries two copies of the allele. Because the allele is rare in a normal, healthy population with unrestricted habitat, the chance that two carriers will mate is low, and even then, only 25 percent of their offspring will inherit the disease allele from both parents. While it is likely to happen at some point, it will not happen frequently enough for natural selection to be able to swiftly eliminate the allele from the population, and as a result, the allele will be maintained at low levels in the gene pool. However, if a family of carriers begins to interbreed with each other, this will dramatically increase the likelihood of two carriers mating and eventually producing diseased offspring, a phenomenon known as **inbreeding depression**.

Changes in allele frequencies that are identified in a population can shed light on how it is evolving. In addition to natural selection, there are other evolutionary forces that could be in play: genetic drift, gene flow, mutation, nonrandom mating, and environmental variances.

Genetic Drift

The theory of natural selection stems from the observation that some individuals in a population are more likely to survive longer and have more offspring than others; thus, they will pass on more of their genes to the next generation. A big, powerful male gorilla, for example, is much more likely than a smaller, weaker one to become the population's silverback, the pack's leader who mates far more than the other males of the group. The pack leader will father more offspring, who share half of his genes, and are likely to also grow bigger and stronger like their father. Over time, the genes for bigger size will increase in frequency in the population, and the population will, as a result, grow larger on average. That is, this would occur if this particular **selection pressure**, or driving selective force, were the only one acting on the population. In other examples, better camouflage or a stronger resistance to drought might pose a selection pressure.

Another way a population's allele and genotype frequencies can change is genetic drift (**Figure 19.4**), which is simply the effect of chance. By chance, some individuals will have more offspring than others—not due to an advantage conferred by some genetically-encoded trait, but just because one male happened to be in the right place at the right time (when the receptive female walked by) or because the other one happened to be in the wrong place at the wrong time (when a fox was hunting).

visual CONNECTION

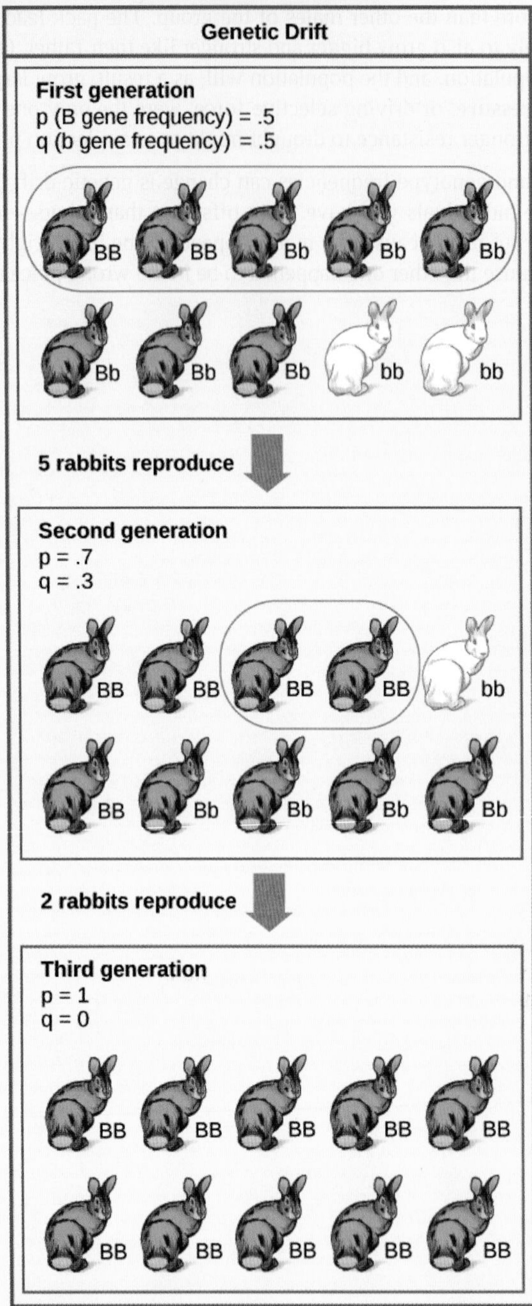

Figure 19.4 Genetic drift occurs when the gene frequency of a population shifts by random chance (i.e. without a selective pressure). Over time, genetic drift can completely eliminate an allele from the population. For example, in the first generation here, the two alleles *B* and *b* occur with equal frequency, so $p = q = 0.5$. If only half the individuals reproduce, and by chance most of the reproducing alleles of are of *B*, then the second generation results in $p = 0.7$ and $q = 0.3$. In the second generation, only two individuals, both of whom are homozygote in *B*, reproduce. This leads to a loss of *b* from the third generation.

As seen from the table, the frequency of the *b* allele is reduced as a percentage of the population due to genetic drift.

Generation	Individuals with genotype *BB*	Individuals with genotype *Bb*	Individuals with genotype *bb*
1	22	53	25
2	108	118	25
3	633	0	0

Table 19.1 Genotypic frequencies of rabbit populations undergoing genetic drift

Explain why small populations are more vulnerable to the forces of genetic drift than large populations.

a. The fewer individuals in a population, the more room there is for new individuals to migrate into it.
b. The more individuals in a population, the more alleles are present in its gene pool.
c. The fewer individuals in a population, the more likely it is to go extinct.
d. The more individuals in a population, the larger and more stable is its gene pool.

Small populations are more susceptible to the forces of genetic drift. Large populations, on the other hand, are buffered against the effects of chance. If one individual of a population of 10 individuals happens to die at a young age before it leaves any offspring to the next generation, all of its genes—1/10 of the population's gene pool—will be suddenly lost. In a population of 100, that's only 1 percent of the overall gene pool; therefore, it is much less impactful on the population's genetic structure.

Go to this site (http://openstaxcollege.org/l/genetic_drift) to watch an animation of random sampling and genetic drift in action.

Describe an example of genetic drift.

a. Immigration of new individuals can cause genetic drift. For example, if several white rabbits migrate into a population of mostly brown rabbits, the allele for white fur will increase within the population.

b. Introduction of new alleles through mutation can cause genetic drift. For example, if there are two alleles for fur color in a rabbit population, and a mutation in one of them produces a third allele, the gene pool changes to incorporate the new allele.

c. Chance events such as a natural disasters can cause genetic drift. For example, if the only white rabbits in a population get killed by a storm, the allele for white fur will diminish or disappear in the population.

d. Differential survival and reproduction can cause genetic drift. For example, if all the white rabbits in a population get eaten by wolves because their white fur stands out and is more visible, the proportion of the allele for white fur in the population will decrease.

Genetic drift can also be magnified by natural events, such as a natural disaster that kills—at random—a large portion of the population. Known as the bottleneck effect, it results in a large portion of the genome suddenly being wiped out (Figure 19.5). In one fell swoop, the genetic structure of the survivors becomes the genetic structure of the entire population, which may be very different from the pre-disaster population.

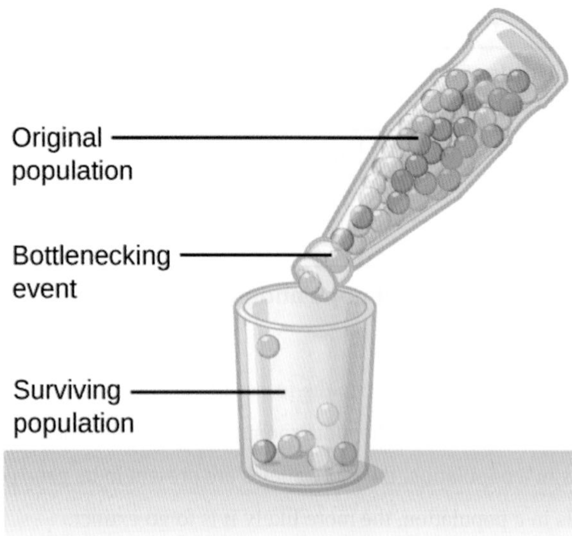

Figure 19.5 A chance event or catastrophe can reduce the genetic variability within a population.

Another scenario in which populations might experience a strong influence of genetic drift is if some portion of the population leaves to start a new population in a new location or if a population gets divided by a physical barrier of some kind. In this situation, those individuals are unlikely to be representative of the entire population, which results in the founder effect. The founder effect occurs when the genetic structure changes to match that of the new population's founding fathers and mothers. The founder effect is believed to have been a key factor in the genetic history of the Afrikaner population of Dutch settlers in South Africa, as evidenced by mutations that are common in Afrikaners but rare in most other populations. This is likely due to the fact that a higher-than-normal proportion of the founding colonists carried these mutations. As a result, the population expresses unusually high incidences of Huntington's disease (HD) and Fanconi anemia (FA), a genetic disorder known to cause blood marrow and congenital abnormalities.

Watch this short **video (http://openstaxcollege.org/l/founder_bottle)** to learn more about the founder and bottleneck effects.

Compare and contrast the bottleneck and founder effects.

a. Both the bottleneck and founder effect are examples of gene flow. However, the bottleneck effect occurs after a cataclysmic event, whereas the founder effect occurs when mutations introduce new alleles into a population.

b. Both the bottleneck and founder effect are examples of genetic drift. However, the bottleneck effect is a process in which a large portion of a genome is wiped out, whereas the founder effect occurs when members of a larger population migrate to establish their own population.

c. Both the bottleneck and founder effect change the genetic structure of a population. However, the bottleneck effect reduces or eliminates alleles within a population, whereas the founder effect introduces or increases alleles.

d. Both the bottleneck and founder effect change the genetic structure of a population. However, the bottleneck effect occurs when inbreeding depression kills off part of a population, whereas the founder effect relies on nonrandom mating.

scientific method CONNECTION

Testing the Bottleneck Effect

Question: How do natural disasters affect the genetic structure of a population?

Background: When much of a population is suddenly wiped out by an earthquake or hurricane, the individuals that survive the event are usually a random sampling of the original group. As a result, the genetic makeup of the population can change dramatically. This phenomenon is known as the bottleneck effect.

Hypothesis: Repeated natural disasters will yield different population genetic structures; therefore, each time this experiment is run, the results will vary.

Test the hypothesis: Count out the original population using different colored beads. For example, red, blue, and yellow beads might represent red, blue, and yellow individuals. After recording the number of each individual in the original population, place them all in a bottle with a narrow neck that will only allow a few beads out at a time. Then, pour 1/3 of the bottle's contents into a bowl. This represents the surviving individuals after a natural disaster kills a majority of the population. Count the number of the different colored beads in the bowl, and record it. Then, place all of the beads back in the bottle and repeat the experiment four more times.

Analyze the data: Compare the five populations that resulted from the experiment. Do the populations all contain the same number of different colored beads, or do they vary? Remember, these populations all came from the same exact parent population.

Form a conclusion: Most likely, the five resulting populations will differ quite dramatically. This is because natural disasters are not selective—they kill and spare individuals at random. Now think about how this might affect a real population. What happens when a hurricane hits the Mississippi Gulf Coast? How do the seabirds that live on the beach fare?

Gene Flow

Another important evolutionary force is **gene flow**: the flow of alleles in and out of a population due to the migration of individuals or gametes (Figure 19.6). While some populations are fairly stable, others experience more flux. Many plants, for example, send their pollen far and wide, by wind or by bird, to pollinate other populations of the same species some distance away. Even a population that may initially appear to be stable, such as a pride of lions, can experience its fair share of immigration and emigration as developing males leave their mothers to seek out a new pride with genetically unrelated females. This variable flow of individuals in and out of the group not only changes the gene structure of the population, but it can also introduce new genetic variation to populations in different geological locations and habitats.

Figure 19.6 Gene flow can occur when an individual travels from one geographic location to another.

Mutation

Mutations are changes to an organism's DNA and are an important driver of diversity in populations. Species evolve because of the accumulation of mutations that occur over time. The appearance of new mutations is the most common way to introduce novel genotypic and phenotypic variance. Some mutations are unfavorable or harmful and are quickly eliminated from the population by natural selection. Others are beneficial and will spread through the population. Whether or not a mutation is beneficial or harmful is determined by whether it helps an organism survive to sexual maturity and reproduce. Some mutations do not do anything and can linger, unaffected by natural selection, in the genome. Some can have a dramatic effect on a gene and the resulting phenotype.

Nonrandom Mating

If individuals nonrandomly mate with their peers, the result can be a changing population. There are many reasons **nonrandom mating** occurs. One reason is simple mate choice; for example, female peahens may prefer peacocks with bigger, brighter tails. Traits that lead to more matings for an individual become selected for by natural selection. One common form of mate choice, called **assortative mating**, is an individual's preference to mate with partners who are phenotypically similar to themselves.

Another cause of nonrandom mating is physical location. This is especially true in large populations spread over large geographic distances where not all individuals will have equal access to one another. Some might be miles apart through woods or over rough terrain, while others might live immediately nearby.

Environmental Variance

Genes are not the only players involved in determining population variation. Phenotypes are also influenced by other factors, such as the environment (Figure 19.7). For example, sun exposure is an environmental factor, as a person who spends more time in the sun will likely have darker skin than a person who spends most of their time indoors (assuming both people had similarly-colored skin to start with). Some major characteristics, such as sex, are determined by the environment for some species. For example, some turtles and other reptiles have temperature-dependent sex determination (TSD). TSD means that individuals develop into males if their eggs are incubated within a certain temperature range, or females at a different temperature range.

Figure 19.7 The sex of the American alligator (*Alligator mississippiensis*) is determined by the temperature at which the eggs are incubated. Eggs incubated at 30°C produce females, and eggs incubated at 33°C produce males. (credit: Steve Hillebrand, USFWS)

Geographic separation between populations can lead to differences in the phenotypic variation between those populations. Such **geographical variation** is seen between most populations and can be significant. One type of geographic variation, called a **cline**, can be seen as populations of a given species vary gradually across an ecological gradient. Species of warm-blooded animals, for example, tend to have larger bodies in the cooler climates closer to the earth's poles, allowing them to better conserve heat. This is considered a latitudinal cline. Alternatively, flowering plants tend to bloom at different times depending on where they are along the slope of a mountain, known as an altitudinal cline.

If there is gene flow between the populations, the individuals will likely show gradual differences in phenotype along the cline. Restricted gene flow, on the other hand, can lead to abrupt differences, even speciation.

science practices CONNECTION for AP® Courses

Lab Investigation

AP® Biology Investigative Labs: Inquiry-Based Approach, Investigation 1: Artificial Selection. Using Wisconsin Fast Plants, you explore evolution by conducting an artificial selection investigation to increase or decrease genetic variation in a population and then determine if extreme selection can change the expression of a quantitative trait.

Think About It

- Do you think genetic drift would happen more quickly on an island or on the mainland? Provide reasoning for your answer.
- Consider the population of red and blue flowers you analyzed in Section 1 to determine if they were undergoing microevolution. Recall that you counted 600 blue flowers and 200 red flowers.
- Imagine that you return four years after your initial visit, and the flowers at the site have been split into two different populations by a newly formed river, which isolates the two populations. In the population 1, you counted 125 blue flowers and 10 red flowers. In the population 2, you counted 450 blue flowers and 300 red flowers. Did genetic drift or natural selection likely cause these change in allele frequencies in population 1? What about population 2? Explain how you know for each population.

19.3 | Adaptive Evolution

In this section, you will explore the following questions:

- What are different ways in which natural selection can shape populations?
- How can these different forces lead to different outcomes in terms of population variation?

Connections for AP® Courses

As we have learned, natural selection acts on the level of the individual, selecting those with a higher overall **fitness** (reproductive success) compared to the rest of the population. In other words, natural selection favors the most adaptive variation for a given environment. If the fit phenotypes are evolving in a stable environment, natural selection results in **stabilizing selection**, resulting in an overall decrease in the population's variation. However, if environmental conditions change, **directional selection** shifts a population's variance toward a new and more favorable phenotype. **Diversifying selection** results in increased variance by selecting for two or more distinct phenotypes.

Sexual selection results when one sex has more reproductive success than the other; as a result, males and females experience different selective pressures, which often lead to distinct phenotypic differences, or **sexual dimorphisms**, between the two. For example, male birds often exhibit more colorful plumage than female birds of the same species.

What is most important to recognize is that there is no perfect organism. Natural selection acts on existing variations in the population; it does not create anything from scratch. Although natural selection selects the fittest individuals, other forces of evolution, including genetic drift and gene flow, often introduce deleterious alleles to the population's gene pool. Evolution has no purpose; it is simply the sum of various forces that influence the genetic and phenotypic variation of a population.

Information presented and the examples highlighted in the section support concepts outlined in Big Idea 1 of the AP® Biology Curriculum Framework. The AP® Learning Objectives listed in the Curriculum Framework provide a transparent foundation for the AP® Biology course, an inquiry-based laboratory experience, instructional activities, and AP® exam questions. A learning objective merges required content with one or more of the seven science practices.

Big Idea 1	The process of evolution drives the diversity and unity of life.

Enduring Understanding 1.A	Change in the genetic makeup of a population over time is evolution.
Essential Knowledge	**1.A.1** Natural selection is a major mechanism of evolution.
Science Practice	**2.2** The student can apply mathematical routines to quantities that describe natural phenomena.
Science Practice	**5.3** The student can evaluate the evidence provided by data sets in relation to a particular scientific question.
Learning Objective	**1.2** The student is able to evaluate evidence provided by data to qualitatively and quantitatively investigate the role of natural selection in evolution.
Essential Knowledge	**1.A.2** Natural selection acts on phenotypic variations in populations.
Science Practice	**7.1** The student can connect phenomena and models across spatial and temporal scales.
Learning Objective	**1.5** The student is able to connect evolutionary changes in a population over time to a change in the environment.

Natural selection only acts on the population's heritable traits: selecting for beneficial alleles and thus increasing their frequency in the population, while selecting against deleterious alleles and thereby decreasing their frequency—a process known as **adaptive evolution**. Natural selection does not act on individual alleles, however, but on entire organisms. An individual may carry a very beneficial genotype with a resulting phenotype that, for example, increases the ability to reproduce (fecundity), but if that same individual also carries an allele that results in a fatal childhood disease, that fecundity phenotype will not be passed on to the next generation because the individual will not live to reach reproductive age. Natural selection acts at the level of the individual; it selects for individuals with greater contributions to the gene pool of the next generation, known as an organism's **evolutionary (Darwinian) fitness**.

Fitness is often quantifiable and is measured by scientists in the field. However, it is not the absolute fitness of an individual that counts, but rather how it compares to the other organisms in the population. This concept, called **relative fitness**, allows researchers to determine which individuals are contributing additional offspring to the next generation, and thus, how the population might evolve.

There are several ways selection can affect population variation: stabilizing selection, directional selection, diversifying selection, frequency-dependent selection, and sexual selection. As natural selection influences the allele frequencies in a population, individuals can either become more or less genetically similar and the phenotypes displayed can become more similar or more disparate.

Stabilizing Selection

If natural selection favors an average phenotype, selecting against extreme variation, the population will undergo stabilizing selection (Figure 19.9). In a population of mice that live in the woods, for example, natural selection is likely to favor individuals that best blend in with the forest floor and are less likely to be spotted by predators. Assuming the ground is a fairly consistent shade of brown, those mice whose fur is most closely matched to that color will be most likely to survive and reproduce, passing on their genes for their brown coat. Mice that carry alleles that make them a bit lighter or a bit darker will stand out against the ground and be more likely to fall victim to predation. As a result of this selection, the population's genetic variance will decrease.

Directional Selection

When the environment changes, populations will often undergo directional selection (Figure 19.9), which selects for phenotypes at one end of the spectrum of existing variation. A classic example of this type of selection is the evolution of the peppered moth in eighteenth- and nineteenth-century England. Prior to the Industrial Revolution, the moths were predominately light in color, which allowed them to blend in with the light-colored trees and lichens in their environment. But as soot began spewing from factories, the trees became darkened, and the light-colored moths became easier for predatory birds to spot. Over time, the frequency of the melanic form of the moth increased because they had a higher survival rate in habitats affected by air pollution because their darker coloration blended with the sooty trees.

Scientist can observe directional selection. Suppose populations of rabbits that eat flowers is introduced into an environment with flowering plants. Once the flowers are eaten, the plants cannot reproduce. Over time, the height of the flowers will shift higher so that the rabbits cannot reach them ???.

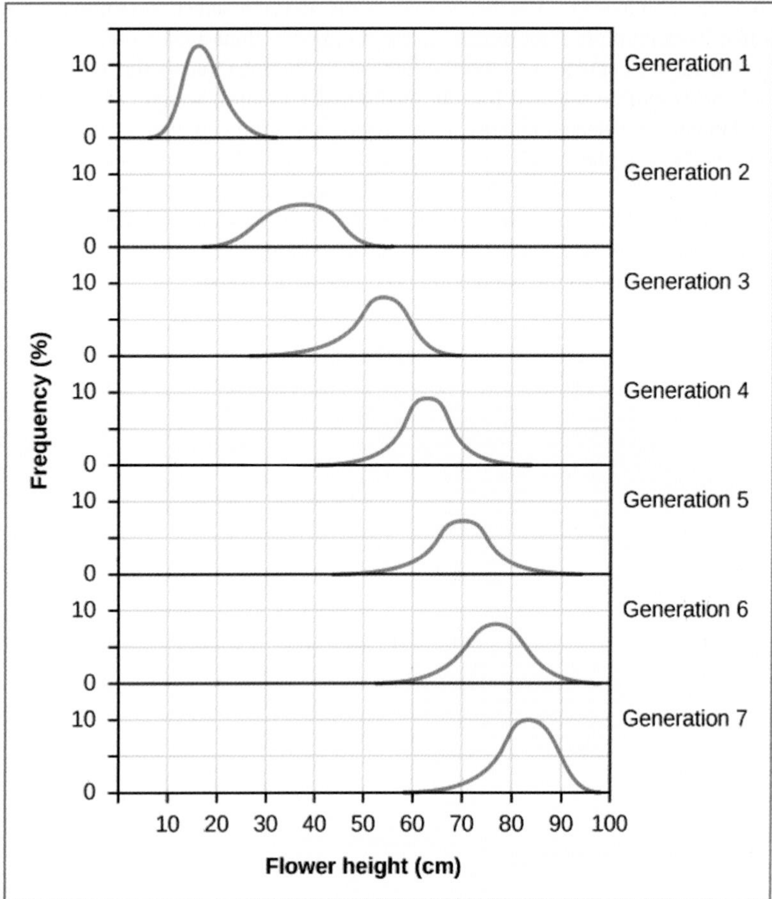

Figure 19.8 The introduction of small herbivores that eat flowers often results in directional selection for increased flower height.

In science, sometimes things are believed to be true, and then new information comes to light that changes our understanding. The story of the peppered moth is an example: the facts behind the selection toward darker moths have recently been called into question. Read this article (http://openstaxcollege.org/l/peppered_moths) to learn more.

What is fitness the measure of?

a. the frequency of beneficial alleles

b. the effect of chance on a population's gene pool

c. successful reproduction

d. the abnormalities in a population

Diversifying Selection

Sometimes two or more distinct phenotypes can each have their advantages and be selected for by natural selection, while the intermediate phenotypes are, on average, less fit. Known as diversifying selection (**Figure 19.9**), this is seen in many populations of animals that have multiple male forms. Large, dominant alpha males obtain mates by brute force, while small males can sneak in for furtive copulations with the females in an alpha male's territory. In this case, both the alpha males and the "sneaking" males will be selected for, but medium-sized males, which can't overtake the alpha males and are too big to sneak copulations, are selected against. Diversifying selection can also occur when environmental changes favor individuals on either end of the phenotypic spectrum. Imagine a population of mice living at the beach where there is light-colored sand interspersed with patches of tall grass. In this scenario, light-colored mice that blend in with the sand would be favored, as well as dark-colored mice that can hide in the grass. Medium-colored mice, on the other hand, would not blend in with either the grass or the sand, and would thus be more likely to be eaten by predators. The result of this type of selection is increased genetic variance as the population becomes more diverse.

visual CONNECTION

(a) **Stabilizing selection**

Original population

Population after natural selection

Robins typically lay four eggs, an example of stabilizing selection. Larger clutches may result in malnourished chicks, while smaller clutches may result in no viable offspring.

(b) **Directional selection**

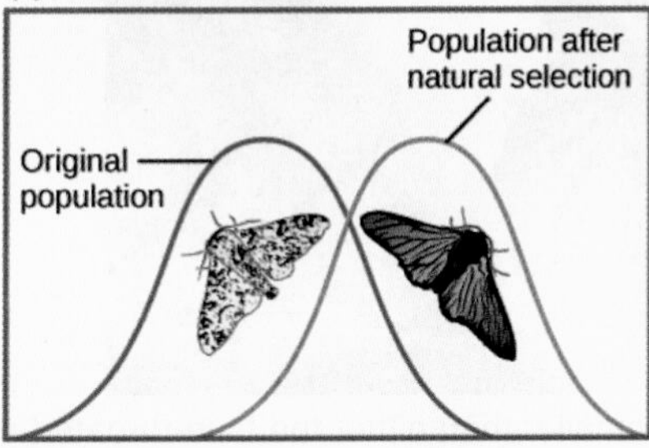

Light-colored peppered moths are better camouflaged against a pristine environment; likewise, dark-colored peppered moths are better camouflaged against a sooty environment. Thus, as the Industrial Revolution progressed in nineteenth-century England, the color of the moth population shifted from light to dark, an example of directional selection.

(c) **Diversifying selection**

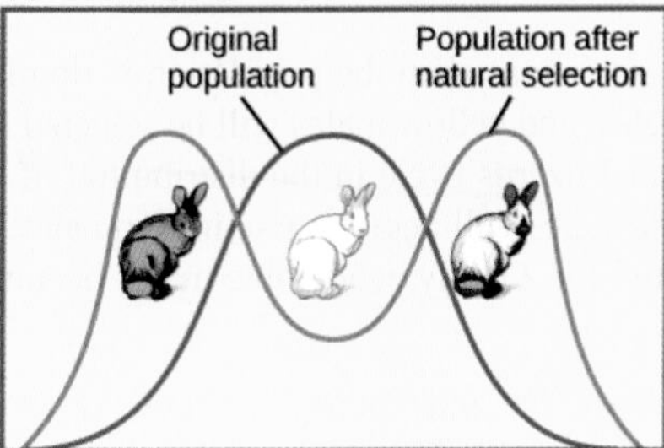

In a hyphothetical population, gray and Himalayan (gray and white) rabbits are better able to blend with a rocky environment than white rabbits, resulting in diversifying selection.

Figure 19.9 Different types of natural selection can impact the distribution of phenotypes within a population. In (a) stabilizing selection, an average phenotype is favored. In (b) directional selection, a change in the environment shifts the spectrum of phenotypes observed. In (c) diversifying selection, two or more extreme phenotypes are selected for, while the average phenotype is selected against.

Before the Industrial revolution light-colored moths were able to blend in with the environment and better avoid predators. Since the Industrial Revolution, dark-colored moths are better camouflaged than light-colored moths. The number of dark-colored moths has increased to be the most common color. This is an example of what?

a. directional selection
b. stabilizing selection
c. frequency-dependent selection
d. diversifying selection

Frequency-dependent Selection

Another type of selection, called **frequency-dependent selection**, favors phenotypes that are either common (positive frequency-dependent selection) or rare (negative frequency-dependent selection). An interesting example of this type of selection is seen in a unique group of lizards of the Pacific Northwest. Male common side-blotched lizards come in three throat-color patterns: orange, blue, and yellow. Each of these forms has a different reproductive strategy: orange males are the strongest and can fight other males for access to their females; blue males are medium-sized and form strong pair bonds with their mates; and yellow males (Figure 19.10) are the smallest, and look a bit like females, which allows them to sneak copulations. Like a game of rock-paper-scissors, orange beats blue, blue beats yellow, and yellow beats orange in the competition for females. That is, the big, strong orange males can fight off the blue males to mate with the blue's pair-bonded females, the blue males are successful at guarding their mates against yellow sneaker males, and the yellow males can sneak copulations from the potential mates of the large, polygynous orange males.

Figure 19.10 A yellow-throated side-blotched lizard is smaller than either the blue-throated or orange-throated males and appears a bit like the females of the species, allowing it to sneak copulations. (credit: "tinyfroglet"/Flickr)

In this scenario, orange males will be favored by natural selection when the population is dominated by blue males, blue males will thrive when the population is mostly yellow males, and yellow males will be selected for when orange males are the most populous. As a result, populations of side-blotched lizards cycle in the distribution of these phenotypes—in one generation, orange might be predominant, and then yellow males will begin to rise in frequency. Once yellow males make up a majority of the population, blue males will be selected for. Finally, when blue males become common, orange males will once again be favored.

Negative frequency-dependent selection serves to increase the population's genetic variance by selecting for rare phenotypes, whereas positive frequency-dependent selection usually decreases genetic variance by selecting for common phenotypes.

Sexual Selection

Males and females of certain species are often quite different from one another in ways beyond the reproductive organs. Males are often larger, for example, and display many elaborate colors and adornments, like the peacock's tail, while females tend to be smaller and duller in decoration. Such differences are known as sexual dimorphisms (Figure 19.11), which arise from the fact that in many populations, particularly animal populations, there is more variance in the reproductive success of the males than there is of the females. That is, some males—often the bigger, stronger, or more decorated males—get the vast majority of the total matings, while others receive none. This can occur because the males are better at fighting off other males, or because females will choose to mate with the bigger or more decorated males. In either case, this variation in reproductive success generates a strong selection pressure among males to get those matings, resulting in the evolution of bigger body size and elaborate ornaments to get the females' attention. Females, on the other hand, tend to get a handful of selected matings; therefore, they are more likely to select more desirable males.

Sexual dimorphism varies widely among species, of course, and some species are even sex-role reversed. In such cases, females tend to have a greater variance in their reproductive success than males and are correspondingly selected for the bigger body size and elaborate traits usually characteristic of males.

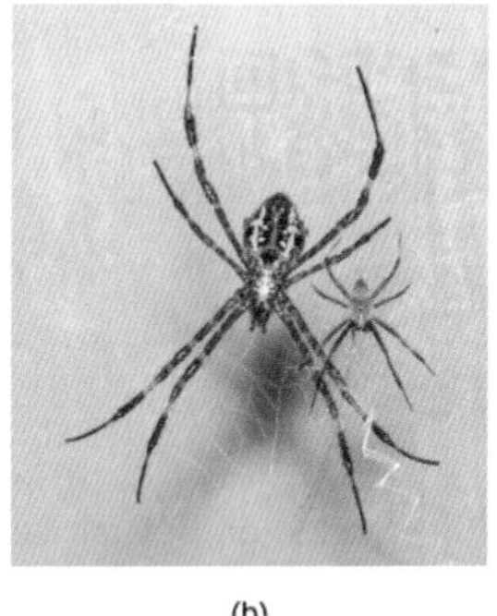
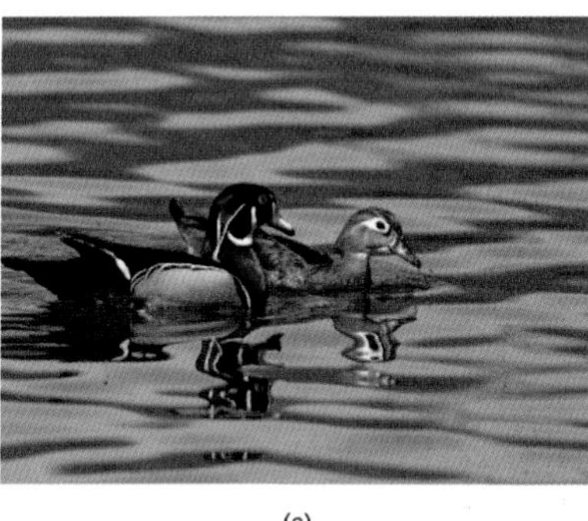

(a) (b) (c)

Figure 19.11 Sexual dimorphism is observed in (a) peacocks and peahens, (b) *Argiope appensa* spiders (the female spider is the large one), and in (c) wood ducks. (credit “spiders”: modification of work by “Sanba38”/Wikimedia Commons; credit “duck”: modification of work by Kevin Cole)

The selection pressures on males and females to obtain matings is known as sexual selection; it can result in the development of secondary sexual characteristics that do not benefit the individual’s likelihood of survival but help to maximize its reproductive success. Sexual selection can be so strong that it selects for traits that are actually detrimental to the individual’s survival. Think, once again, about the peacock’s tail. While it is beautiful and the male with the largest, most colorful tail is more likely to win the female, it is not the most practical appendage. In addition to being more visible to predators, it makes the males slower in their attempted escapes. There is some evidence that this risk, in fact, is why females like the big tails in the first place. The speculation is that large tails carry risk, and only the best males survive that risk: the bigger the tail, the more fit the male. This idea is known as the **handicap principle**.

The **good genes hypothesis** states that males develop these impressive ornaments to show off their efficient metabolism or their ability to fight disease. Females then choose males with the most impressive traits because it signals their genetic superiority, which they will then pass on to their offspring. Though it might be argued that females should not be picky because it will likely reduce their number of offspring, if better males father more fit offspring, it may be beneficial. Fewer, healthier offspring may increase the chances of survival more than many, weaker offspring.

In 1915, biologist Ronald Fisher proposed another model of sexual selection: the **Fisherian runaway model (http://openstaxcollege.org/l/sexual_select)** , which suggests that selection of certain traits is a result of sexual preference.

Explain the handicap principle.

a. The peacock's tail is an example of the handicap principle. Having a healthy, beautiful tail discourages predation, helping in survival. This means that those individuals are most likely to survive and produce offspring.

b. The peacock's tail is an example of the handicap principle. It appears that the tail makes the males more visible to predators and less able to escape, making it a disadvantage to the birds' survival. However, traits cannot evolve in a population if they serve as a handicap to the individuals that express that trait. Therefore, the tail must actually be an advantage.

c. The peacock's tail is an example of the handicap principle. The tail makes the males more visible to predators and less able to escape, so the birds with the longest and most extravagant tails get eaten and do not reproduce. This causes the average tail length for males within the population to decrease over time due to natural selection.

d. The peacock's tail is an example of the handicap principle. The tail, which makes the males more visible to predators and less able to escape, is clearly a disadvantage to the birds' survival. But because it is a disadvantage, only the most fit males should be able to survive with it. Thus, the tail serves as an honest signal of quality to the females of the population; therefore, the male will earn more matings and greater reproductive success.

In both the handicap principle and the good genes hypothesis, the trait is said to be an **honest signal** of the males' quality, thus giving females a way to find the fittest mates— males that will pass the best genes to their offspring.

No Perfect Organism

Natural selection is a driving force in evolution and can generate populations that are better adapted to survive and successfully reproduce in their environments. But natural selection cannot produce the perfect organism. Natural selection can only select on existing variation in the population; it does not create anything from scratch. Thus, it is limited by a population's existing genetic variance and whatever new alleles arise through mutation and gene flow.

Natural selection is also limited because it works at the level of individuals, not alleles, and some alleles are linked due to their physical proximity in the genome, making them more likely to be passed on together (linkage disequilibrium). Any given individual may carry some beneficial alleles and some unfavorable alleles. It is the net effect of these alleles, or the organism's fitness, upon which natural selection can act. As a result, good alleles can be lost if they are carried by individuals that also have several overwhelmingly bad alleles; likewise, bad alleles can be kept if they are carried by individuals that have enough good alleles to result in an overall fitness benefit.

Furthermore, natural selection can be constrained by the relationships between different polymorphisms. One morph may confer a higher fitness than another, but may not increase in frequency due to the fact that going from the less beneficial to the more beneficial trait would require going through a less beneficial phenotype. Think back to the mice that live at the beach. Some are light-colored and blend in with the sand, while others are dark and blend in with the patches of grass. The dark-colored mice may be, overall, more fit than the light-colored mice, and at first glance, one might expect the light-colored mice be selected for a darker coloration. But remember that the intermediate phenotype, a medium-colored coat, is very bad for the mice—they cannot blend in with either the sand or the grass and are more likely to be eaten by predators. As a result, the light-colored mice would not be selected for a dark coloration because those individuals that began moving in that direction (began being selected for a darker coat) would be less fit than those that stayed light.

Finally, it is important to understand that not all evolution is adaptive. While natural selection selects the fittest individuals and often results in a more fit population overall, other forces of evolution, including genetic drift and gene flow, often do the opposite: introducing deleterious alleles to the population's gene pool. Evolution has no purpose—it is not changing a population into a preconceived ideal. It is simply the sum of the various forces described in this chapter and how they influence the genetic and phenotypic variance of a population.

Think About It

In recent years, factories have been cleaner, and less soot is released into the environment. What impact do you think this has had on the distribution of moth color in the population?

KEY TERMS

adaptive evolution increase in frequency of beneficial alleles and decrease in deleterious alleles due to selection

allele frequency (also, gene frequency) rate at which a specific allele appears within a population

assortative mating when individuals tend to mate with those who are phenotypically similar to themselves

bottleneck effect magnification of genetic drift as a result of natural events or catastrophes

cline gradual geographic variation across an ecological gradient

directional selection selection that favors phenotypes at one end of the spectrum of existing variation

diversifying selection selection that favors two or more distinct phenotypes

evolutionary fitness (also, Darwinian fitness) individual's ability to survive and reproduce

fitness measure of successful reproduction, the passing on alleles to the next generation

founder effect event that initiates an allele frequency change in part of the population, which is not typical of the original population

frequency-dependent selection selection that favors phenotypes that are either common (positive frequency-dependent selection) or rare (negative frequency-dependent selection)

gene flow flow of alleles in and out of a population due to the migration of individuals or gametes

gene pool all of the alleles carried by all of the individuals in the population

genetic drift effect of chance on a population's gene pool

genetic structure distribution of the different possible genotypes in a population

genetic variance diversity of alleles and genotypes in a population

genotype frequency the proportion of a specific genotype in a population relative to all other genotypes for those genes that are present in the population

geographical variation differences in the phenotypic variation between populations that are separated geographically

good genes hypothesis theory of sexual selection that argues individuals develop impressive ornaments to show off their efficient metabolism or ability to fight disease

handicap principle theory of sexual selection that argues only the fittest individuals can afford costly traits

Hardy–Weinberg principle of equilibrium a stable, non-evolving state of a population in which allelic frequencies are stable over time

heritability fraction of population variation that can be attributed to its genetic variance

honest signal trait that gives a truthful impression of an individual's fitness

inbreeding mating of closely related individuals

inbreeding depression increase in abnormalities and disease in inbreeding populations

macroevolution broader scale evolutionary changes seen over paleontological time

microevolution changes in a population's genetic structure

modern synthesis overarching evolutionary paradigm that took shape by the 1940s and is generally accepted today

nonrandom mating changes in a population's gene pool due to mate choice or other forces that cause individuals to mate with certain phenotypes more than others

polymorphisms variations in phenotype within individuals of a population

population genetics study of how selective forces change the allele frequencies in a population over time

population variation distribution of phenotypes in a population

relative fitness individual's ability to survive and reproduce relative to the rest of the population

selective pressure environmental factor that causes one phenotype to be better than another

sexual dimorphism phenotypic difference between the males and females of a population

stabilizing selection selection that favors average phenotypes

CHAPTER SUMMARY

19.1 Population Evolution

The modern synthesis of evolutionary theory grew out of the cohesion of Darwin's, Wallace's, and Mendel's thoughts on evolution and heredity, along with the more modern study of population genetics. It describes the evolution of populations and species, from small-scale changes among individuals to large-scale changes over paleontological time periods. To understand how organisms evolve, scientists can track populations' allele frequencies over time. If they differ from generation to generation, scientists can conclude that the population is not in Hardy–Weinberg equilibrium, and is thus evolving.

19.2 Population Genetics

Both genetic and environmental factors can cause phenotypic variation in a population. Different alleles can confer different phenotypes, and different environments can also cause individuals to look or act differently. Only those differences encoded in an individual's genes, however, can be passed to its offspring and, thus, be a target of natural selection. Natural selection works by selecting for alleles that confer beneficial traits or behaviors, while selecting against those for deleterious qualities. Genetic drift stems from the chance occurrence that some individuals in the germ line have more offspring than others. When individuals leave or join the population, allele frequencies can change as a result of gene flow. Mutations to an individual's DNA may introduce new variation into a population. Allele frequencies can also be altered when individuals do not randomly mate with others in the group.

19.3 Adaptive Evolution

Because natural selection acts to increase the frequency of beneficial alleles and traits while decreasing the frequency of deleterious qualities, it is adaptive evolution. Natural selection acts at the level of the individual, selecting for those that have a higher overall fitness compared to the rest of the population. If the fit phenotypes are those that are similar, natural selection will result in stabilizing selection, and an overall decrease in the population's variation. Directional selection works to shift a population's variance toward a new, fit phenotype, as environmental conditions change. In contrast, diversifying selection results in increased genetic variance by selecting for two or more distinct phenotypes.

Other types of selection include frequency-dependent selection, in which individuals with either common (positive frequency-dependent selection) or rare (negative frequency-dependent selection) are selected for. Finally, sexual selection results from the fact that one sex has more variance in the reproductive success than the other. As a result, males and females experience different selective pressures, which can often lead to the evolution of phenotypic differences, or sexual dimorphisms, between the two.

REVIEW QUESTIONS

1. What is the ultimate source of all variation in and among populations?

a. genetic mutations that result in viable offspring
b. natural selection
c. diverse habitats
d. factors in the environment that may affect development

2. When male lions reach sexual maturity, they are thrown out of their group, or pride, and must live on their own or with other males until they can take over their own pride. This can alter the allele frequencies of the population through which of the following mechanisms?

a. natural selection
b. gene flow
c. random mating
d. genetic drift

3. Which of the following populations has violated the conditions of Hardy-Weinberg Equilibrium?

a. an infinitely large population
b. a population in which the allele frequencies do not change over time
c. a population in which the Hardy-Weinberg equation is equal to 1
d. a population undergoing natural selection

4. What is the difference between micro and macroevolution?

a. Microevolution describes the evolution of small organisms, such as insects, while macroevolution describes the evolution of large organisms, like people and elephants.
b. Microevolution describes the evolution of microscopic entities, such as molecules and proteins, while macroevolution describes the evolution of whole organisms.
c. Microevolution describes the evolution of organisms in populations, while macroevolution describes the evolution of species over long periods of time.
d. Microevolution describes the evolution of organisms over their lifetimes, while macroevolution describes the evolution of organisms over multiple generations.

5. Which of the following would be supported by Lamarck?

a. Natural selection leads to changes in organisms over time
b. The strong arms of a gorilla are the result of its parents constantly climbing, lifting and fighting.
c. Lack of resources led to the death of three of four fox cubs.
d. The founder effect is when a few individuals in a population are separated from the original population.

6. What is population variance influenced by?

a. genetic structure
b. environment
c. diet composition
d. All of the above

7. What is genetic variance?

a. the change in a population's genetic structure
b. the effect of chance on a population's gene pool
c. the diversity of alleles and genotypes within a population
d. the magnification of genetic drift as a result of natural events or catastrophes

8. When closely related individuals mate with each other, or inbreed, the offspring are often not as fit as the offspring of two unrelated individuals. Why?

a. Inbreeding causes normally silent alleles to be expressed.
b. The DNA of close relatives reacts negatively in the offspring.
c. Inbreeding can bring together rare, deleterious mutations that lead to harmful phenotypes
d. Close relatives are genetically incompatible.

9. What could cause genetic drift to occur within a population?

a. accidental deaths
b. predators
c. disease
d. lack of gene flow

10. What is the evolutionary mechanism that alters allele frequencies by chance called?

a. genetic drift
b. natural selection
c. inbreeding
d. migration

11. What is assortative mating?

a. when individuals mate with those who are similar to themselves
b. when individuals mate with those who are dissimilar to themselves
c. when individuals mate with those who are most fit in the population
d. when individuals mate with those who are least fit in the population

12. What is an example of a cline?

a. a random fluctuation in a species gene frequencies
b. a mutation that spreads across the ecological range of a species
c. the females of a species preferring males that are orange in coloration instead of white
d. a species having greater cold tolerance in the colder parts of its range than in the warmer parts of its range

13. Which type of selection results in greater genetic variance in a population?

a. stabilizing selection
b. directional selection
c. diversifying selection
d. positive frequency-dependent selection

14. What types of phenotypes does negative frequency-dependent selection favor?

a. advantageous
b. rare
c. common
d. disadvantageous

15. The good genes hypothesis is a theory that explains what?

a. why more fit individuals are more likely to have more offspring
b. why alleles that confer beneficial traits or behaviors are selected for by natural selection
c. why some deleterious mutations are maintained in the population
d. why individuals of one sex develop impressive ornament traits

16. Which of the following describes when males and females of a population look or act differently/

a. sexual selection
b. diversifying selection
c. sexual dimorphism
d. a cline

CRITICAL THINKING QUESTIONS

17. Describe natural selection and give an example of natural selection at work in a population.

a. The process in which genes flow from one population to another. The beak size of Darwin's finches changing as the availability of different-sized seeds changes.
b. The process in which genes flow from one population to another. The Founder Effect occurring among humans immigrating to a new country.
c. The process in which better-adapted organisms are able to survive and reproduce; The beak size of Darwin's finches changing as the availability of different-sized seeds changes.
d. The process in which better-adapted organisms are able to survive and reproduce; The Founder Effect occurring among humans immigrating to a new country.

18. Imagine you are trying to test whether a population of flowers is undergoing evolution. You suspect there is selection pressure on the color of the flower: bees seem to cluster around the red flowers more often than the blue flowers. In a separate experiment, you discover that blue flower color is dominant to red flower color. In a field, you count 600 blue flowers and 200 red flowers. What would you expect the genetic structure of the flowers to be?

a. You would expect 300 homozygous dominant blue flowers, 300 heterozygous blue flowers, and 200 homozygous recessive red flowers.
b. You would expect 200 homozygous dominant blue flowers, 400 heterozygous blue flowers, and 200 homozygous recessive red flowers.
c. You would expect 100 homozygous dominant red flowers, 100 heterozygous red flowers, and 600 homozygous recessive blue flowers.
d. You would expect 14 homozygous dominant red flowers, 186 heterozygous blue flowers, and 600 homozygous recessive blue flowers.

19. What must occur in order for a new trait to appear in a population and then reach a steady, high frequency within that population?

a. New traits appear through gene mutations or through genetic drift. In order to reach a steady, high frequency in the population, there must be many mutagens, such as UV radiation, in the environment to produce many mutations.
b. New traits appear through gene mutations or through genetic drift. In order to reach a steady, high frequency in the population, there must be a consistent source of immigrant individuals with the allele.
c. New traits appear through gene mutations or through evolution. In order to reach a steady, high frequency in the population, the allele must code for a favorable adaptation.
d. New traits appear through gene mutations or through gene flow. In order to reach a steady, high frequency in the population, the trait associated with the gene must be favored by either natural or sexual selection.

20. Define and identify an example of population variation.

a. Population variation is a description of the diversity of different forms of life. An example of population variation would be the different forms and functions of prokaryotes versus eukaryotes.
b. Population variation is the geographic distribution of different phenotypes in a population. An example of population variation would be the fact that warm-blooded mammals that live near the poles tend to be larger than their southern counterparts to conserve heat.
c. Population variation is the distribution of phenotypes in a population. An example of population variation would be the many different fur colors and patterns found in domestic dogs.
d. Population variation is the distribution of genotypes in a population. An example of population variation would be Mendel's pea plants that were homozygous dominant, heterozygous and homozygous recessive for various traits.

21. People who breed domesticated animals try to avoid inbreeding even though most domesticated animals are indiscriminate. Evaluate why this is a good practice.

a. A breeder would not allow close relatives to mate because inbreeding increases the likelihood of fatal mutations in offspring.
b. A breeder would not allow close relatives to mate because inbreeding prevents gene flow which can bring new, successful genes into the population.
c. A breeder would not allow close relatives to mate because inbreeding causes diversifying selection, which dilutes the breeder's desired genes in the population.
d. A breeder would not allow close relatives to mate because inbreeding can bring together deleterious recessive mutations that can cause abnormalities and susceptibility to disease.

22. Explain the founder effect and identify the best example.

a. The founder effect is an event that isolates part of a population, generating an allele frequency which is not typical of the original population. An example of the founder effect is the Amish population. The Amish population was established from about 200 German immigrants. Individuals of this founding population carried gene mutations that cause inherited disorders such as Ellis-van Creveld syndrome. This form of dwarfism is found in a large concentration in the Amish population today because the immigrants that established the population had a high concentration of the disorder in a very small population.

b. The founder effect is an event that kills off a significant proportion of a population, generating an allele frequency which is not typical of the original population. An example of the founder effect is the Northern elephant seal. At one point, hunting of these seals had reduced their numbers to less than 50 individuals. The population has since rebounded, but still contains less genetic variation than the related Southern elephant seal due to the loss of some alleles.

c. The founder effect is when only a few males within a population are selected by females to reproduce, generating an allele frequency which is different from the original population. An example of the founder effect is the reproductive pattern of mountain gorillas. Mountain gorillas tend to have a single dominant male, the silverback, who gets the vast majority of the matings in the population. This leads to the next generation expressing mainly genes from the silverback and very few genes from the other males, changing the genetic structure of the population.

d. The founder effect occurs when the selective pressure on a trait varies depending on the alleles expressed within the population, generating varying allele frequencies based on the genetic makeup of the original population. An example of the founder effect is the cyclical dominance of three throat-color patterns in side-blotched lizards.

23. Explain what a cline is and identify an example.

a. A cline is a type of geographic variation that is seen in populations of a given species that vary gradually across an ecological gradient. For example, endothermic animals tend to have larger bodies in the cooler climates closer to the earth's poles, allowing them to better conserve heat.

b. A cline is a change in ecological conditions over a geographic distance. For example, a latitudinal cline is the decrease in temperature towards the Earth's poles, and an altitudinal cline is the decrease in temperature with increase in altitude.

c. A cline is the specific set of traits in a population of a given species that have been influenced by the local environment. For example, a population of warm-blooded animals that lived in a cooler climate closer to the North Pole would have larger bodies, allowing them to better conserve heat.

d. A cline is the specific set of ecological conditions in a geographic region. For example, towards the North Pole it is cold and there is little precipitation. This will influence the traits of the organisms that live there.

24. The table below shows data for a small population of mice. The mice are either brown or white. Based on the data, is the population experiencing genetic drift? Explain.

Generation	Brown mice	Black mice
1	14	32
2	20	26
3	24	22
4	21	28
5	19	30
6	24	29

Table 19.2

25. The large alpha male elephant seal is constantly fending off the advances of medium sized males. Small males are then able to sneak copulation with females and successfully pass on their genes. What is this an example of? Explain.

a. This is an example of sexual selection. The females are selecting the small males over the large male.

b. This is an example of genetic drift. Because there are so many medium-sized males to compete with the large alpha male, the small males are able to mate and cause the gene pool to shift towards smaller individuals.

c. This is an example of positive frequency-dependent selection, which is selection that favors phenotypes that are either common or rare. The sneaky males (rare) are favored in this case.

d. This is an eample of directional selection. Because only the smallest males are mating, the next generation will have a higher proportion of alleles for small size, making the seals smaller over time.

26. Explain why there is no perfect organism despite natural selection.

a. Because natural selection works on a geographic level.

b. Because natural selection works in a random manner like mutations.

c. Because of limitations due to a population's existing variation in genes.

d. Because natural selection is limited to sexual dimorphism.

27. A new predator invades the habitat of a population of field mice. Individuals with larger body size are easier for the predator to capture then individuals with smaller body size. Draw a histogram of body sizes with two plot lines, one showing the former population and another showing the new population that indicates how this population will likely evolve. On your histogram, also indicate what type of natural selection is occurring here.

28. Quinine is an antimalarial drug that is used to treat malaria in the Western Hemisphere. Scientists have noticed that this drug has become less effective over time. Based on the data below, what type of selection is being exerted on the malaria population?

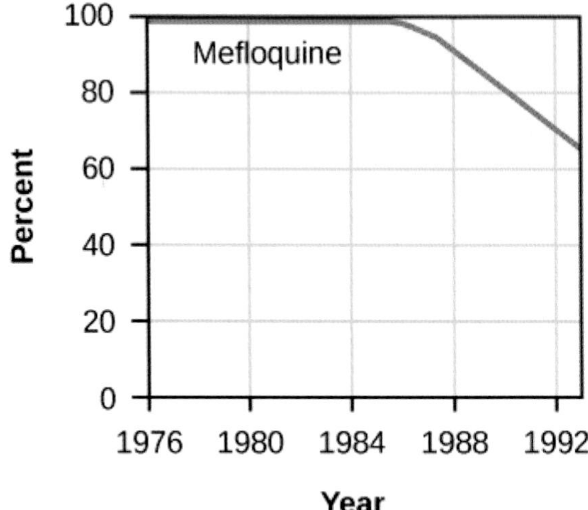

Figure 19.12

TEST PREP FOR AP® COURSES

29. A scientist is studying the genetics of a population of plants that she suspects is undergoing natural selection. After examining samples of the population's DNA over several years, she finds the following data:

Year	Allele A Frequency	Allele B Frequency
1	0.80	0.2
2	0.72	0.28
3	0.66	0.34
4	0.52	0.48
5	0.45	0.55
6	0.39	0.61

Does this provide evidence of natural selection in this population? Why or why not?

a. No, because the genotype frequencies, not allele frequencies, have to change for evolution to occur.

b. No, because the allele frequencies are changing randomly, suggesting that genetic drift is occurring, not natural selection.

c. Yes, because it shows that the previously favorable or neutral allele A is now being selected against in favor of allele B.

d. Yes, because it is showing that the frequency of both alleles are changing over time.

30. A scientist is studying two large populations of deer that are centralized in nearby forests. She takes blood samples from all of the deer in each population and records in how many individuals she finds allele A. She then computes the frequency of the alleles in each population. The frequencies observed over five years are shown in the tables below.

	Population A	
Year	Allele A Frequency	Allele B Frequency
1	0.69	0.20
2	0.71	0.29
3	0.73	0.27
4	0.75	0.25
5	0.81	0.19
6	0.84	0.16

	Population B	
Year	Allele A Frequency	Allele B Frequency
1	0.00	1.00
2	0.00	1.00
3	0.10	0.90
4	0.16	0.84
5	0.21	0.79
6	0.25	0.75

Which forms of evolution are most likely occurring in populations A and B? Explain your answer.

a. In population A, genetic drift is likely occurring, causing allele A to become more prevalent than allele B. In population B, mutation apparently occurred, introducing allele A to population B. Allele A also appears to be increasing due to genetic drift in population B.

b. In population A, natural selection is likely occurring, with allele A being favored over allele B. In population B, gene flow apparently occurred, allowing allele A to become established in population B. Allele A also appears to be favored by selection in population B.

c. In population A, gene flow apparently occurred, allowing allele B to become established in population A. Allele A also appears to be favored by selection in population A. In population B genetic drift is likely occurring, causing allele A to become more prevalent than allele B.

d. In population A, mutation apparently occurred, introducing allele B to population A. Allele A also appears to be increasing due to genetic drift in population A. In population B natural selection is likely occurring, with allele A being favored over allele B.

31. A land manager mows a section of annual grass. Over the years, he recorded the date of flowering from the mown field as well as a similar grass field that was not mown. What is the most likely explanation for this trend?

Year	Mowed field flowering date	Unmowed field flowering date
2010	7/29	7/28
2011	7/20	7/26
2012	7/13	8/1
2013	7/8	7/29
2014	7/1	8/2
2015	6/29	7/26

a. The grass population is adapting to the mowing, so it can flower for longer before being mowed.

b. Mowing stabilizes the flowering time, which follows a steady trend in the mowed field but not in the unmowed field.

c. The mowing is preventing the grass from reproducing, causing the mowed field to adapt by flowering earlier.

d. The grass typically flowers earlier and earlier every year as it becomes older with each passing year.

32. A scientist observed two populations of insects for 10 years. They took data on the length, in mm , of the insect's mouthparts. Their data is shown in the graphs below. How is this population evolving and what agent of evolution is most likely at work?

Distribution of Insect Mouthpart Lengths Throughout the Population Years 1 and 10

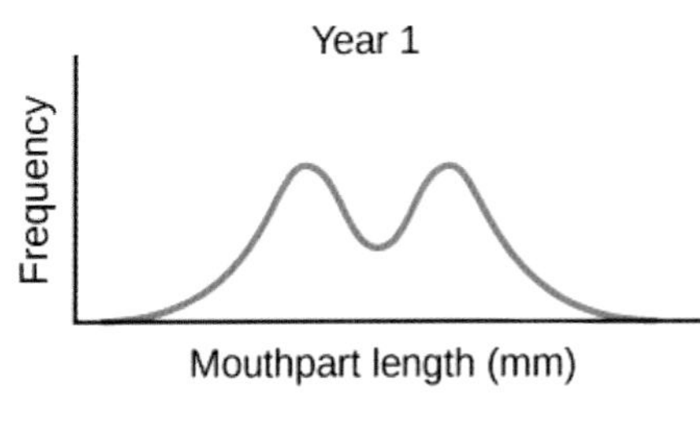

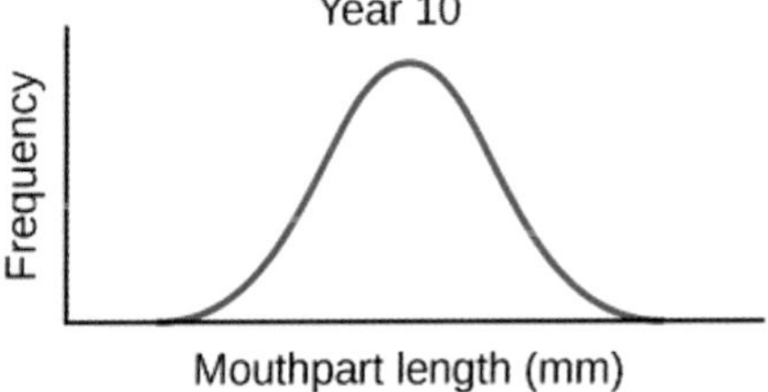

a. inbreeding, because the gene distributions are becoming less similar among the population
b. genetic drift, as the distribution of traits has become more random
c. gene flow, as the population has likely gained new mouthpart traits through immigration
d. natural selection, as insects that have mid-sized mouthparts are being favored

33. A pond is stocked with 250 fish, all of the same species. At that time, the researchers tested the fish to determine if they were genetically predisposed to a certain disease. The gene tested has two alleles, A and a. They found that 58 of the fish possessed allele A, while the rest of the fish possessed allele a. They plan to reassess the fish 5 years later. A computer model predicts that the population will likely increase to 850 fish and have 403 heterozygote (Aa) individuals. Will the future population have evolved? State how you know.

a. Evolution has not occurred, because the frequency of the heterozygotes is different 5 years later compared with the original population.
b. Evolution has not occurred, because the frequency of the heterozygotes is different 5 years later as in the original population.
c. Evolution has not occurred, because the frequency of the heterozygotes is the same 5 years later as in the original population.
d. Evolution has occurred, because the frequency of the heterozygotes is different 5 years later compared with the original population.

34. Heterozygote advantage is a condition in which heterozygotes are favored by natural selection. How would the value of $2pq$ likely change if the population was undergoing heterozygote advantage?

a. It would remain in equilibrium because the value of p and q would remain the same.
b. It would remain in equilibrium because the value of $2pq$ would remain the same.
c. It would not remain in equilibrium because the value of $2pq$ would likely increase.
d. It would not remain in equilibrium because the value of $2pq$ would likely decrease.

35. The graph below shows the change in gene frequency of the two alleles of a gene: A and a. The population being studies has no emigration or immigration. Which type of evolution is likely occurring here and is the allele selected for, neutral, or selected against by natural selection?

Distribution of Insect Mouthpart Lengths Throughout the Population Years 1 and 10

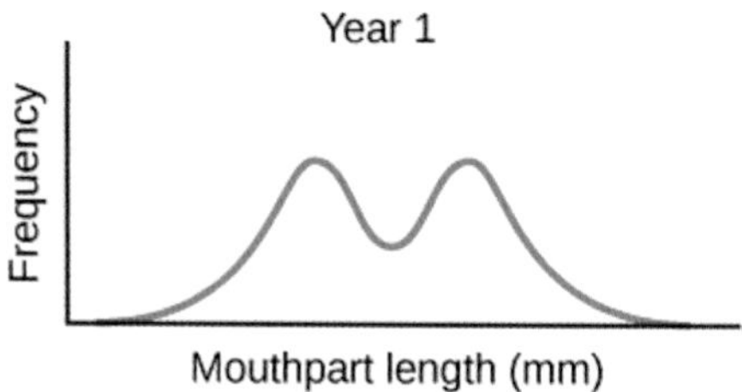

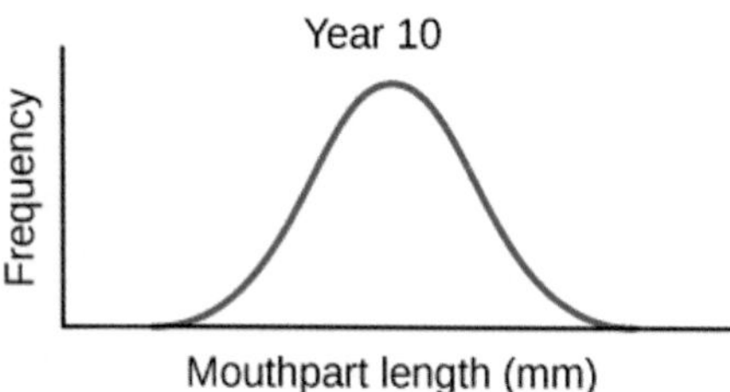

a. non-random mating; both alleles are favored
b. gene flow; allele A is favored
c. genetic drift; both alleles are neutral
d. natural selection; allele a is not favored

36. The graph below shows the change in gene frequency of the two alleles: A and B. These alleles are located on separate genes that do not influence each other in any way. The population being studied has no emigration or immigration. Which type of evolution is likely occurring here, if at all? Explain how you know.

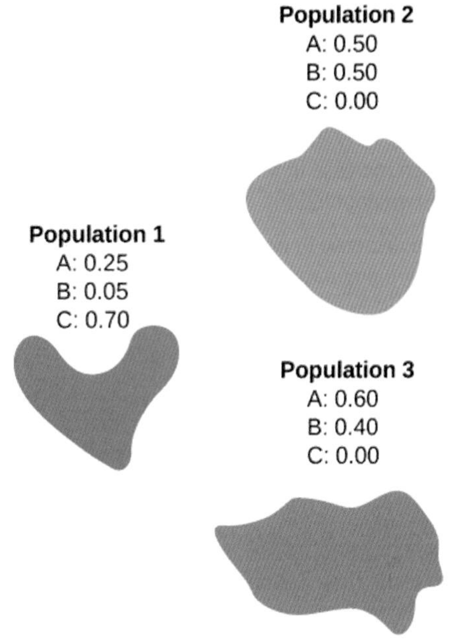

Prevailing wind direction

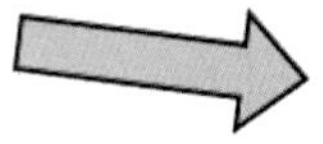

a. no multiple choice available

b. no multiple choice available

37. The graph below shows the current frequencies of two genotypes of the same gene: AA and aa. What would most likely happen to the frequencies of A and a if heterozygous individuals were favored by natural selection?

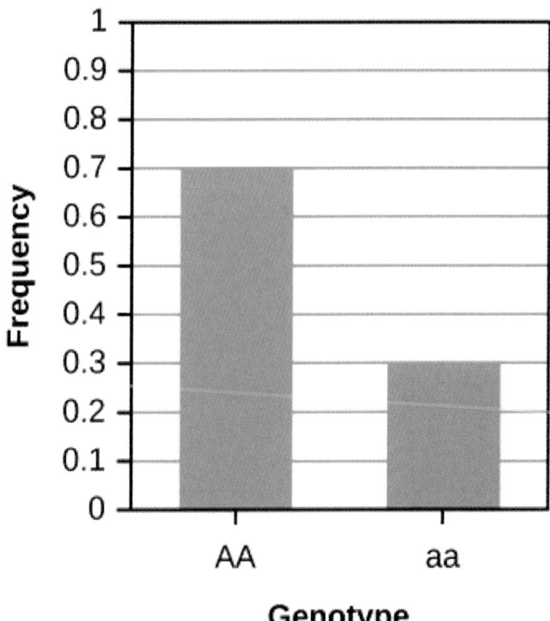

a. Both AA and aa will drop in frequency by the same amount.

b. Both AA and aa will drop, but aa will drop more.

c. AA will increase in frequency and aa will drop in frequency.

d. aa will increase in frequency and AA will drop in frequency.

38. The diagram below shows the frequency of alleles on two species of wind-pollinated plants, as well as the prevailing wind direction. These frequencies have been fairly stable for around 10 years. However, climate change has created a new prevailing wind direction, as shown in the diagram. How will the two populations likely evolve in the future?

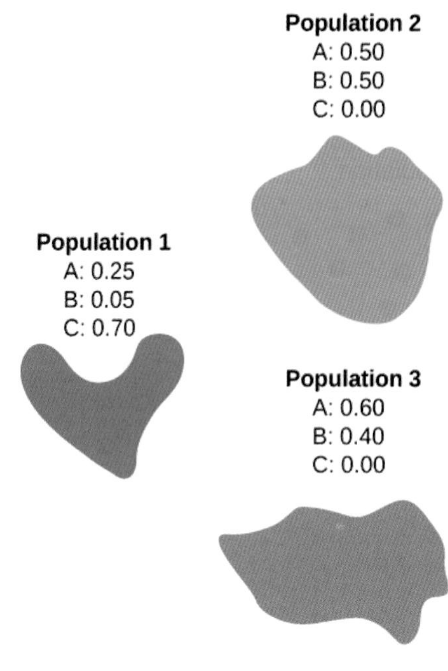

Prevailing wind direction

a. natural selection will cause the frequency of B to increase in population 1

b. gene flow will cause the frequencies of A and B to drop in population 3

c. genetic drift will cause the frequencies of A and C to increase in population 1 and 2

d. inbreeding will reduce the frequency of allele B in population 2 and 3

39. The diagram below shows two populations of organisms that have been long-separated by a river which prevents interbreeding. The two populations differ in coloration, as shown in the diagram. Recent human activity has caused the river to dry, however, resulting in the two populations shown in the lower diagram. What is the most likely explanation for this change?

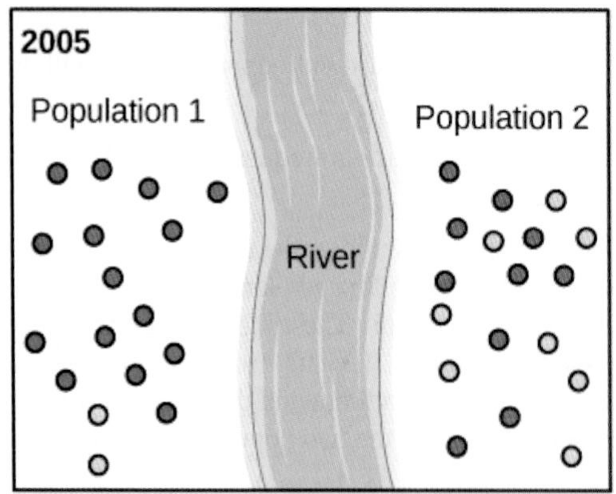

Human disturbance of river 2005

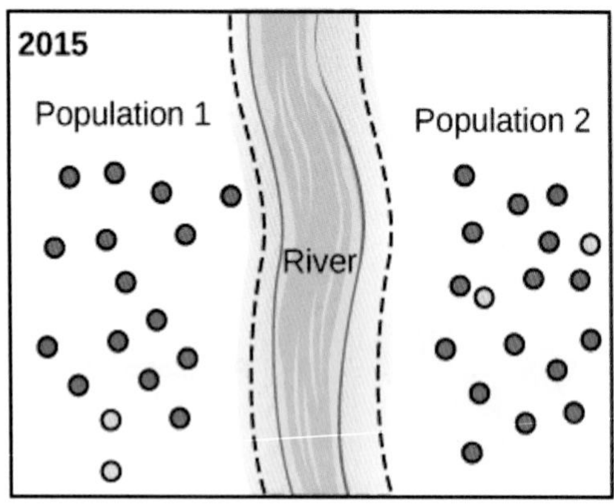

Purple coloration

Yellow coloration

Blue coloration

a. an increase in gene flow between the two populations

b. a decrease in gene flow between the two populations

c. an increase in non-random mating between the two populations

d. a decrease in non-random mating between the two populations

40. Antibiotics are medicines that are designed to kill disease-causing organisms, or pathogens. However, some pathogens evolve antibiotic resistance, where they gain traits that allow them to survive in the presence of antibiotics. The ability of bacteria to adapt to antibiotics so quickly has created a huge concern over whether antibiotics are being overused. What form of evolution is antibiotic resistance an example of, and why?

a. Gene flow because the bacteria are passing on the resistant trait within their populations.

b. Natural selection, because the bacteria is adapting to a new environmental condition - the presence of the antibiotic.

c. Genetic drift because medical workers cannot follow the randomly-fluctuating gene frequencies of bacterial populations

d. Mutation, because each bacteria must mutate to an antibody resistant form in order to survive.

SCIENCE PRACTICE CHALLENGE QUESTIONS

41. Consider a polymorphic gene with three alleles: A, B, and C.

A. If the frequencies of the alleles A and B are 0.2 and 0.3, the frequency of allele C is closest to ___.

a. 0.25

b. 0.5

c. 0.2

d. 0.3

Consider a gene with only two alleles: dominant A and recessive a. In a population of 1,000 organisms, the fraction expressing the homozygous recessive phenotype is 0.37.

B. The calculated allele frequencies p and q have values that are closest to ___.

a. 0.69 and 0.31

b. 0.31 and 0.69

c. 0.37 and 0.63

d. 0.63 and 0.37

Genotype	C_1 C_1	C_2 C_2	C_3 C_3	C_1 C_2	C_1 C_3	C_2 C_3	Total
Observed	120	230	112	175	198	165	1,000

Table 19.3

C. The calculated number of individuals in this population that are heterozygotes is closest to ___.

a. 240

b. 230

c. 430

d. 476

Mountain pine beetles (*Dendroctonus ponderosae*) were collected from a one-acre tract of lodge pole pine trees (*Pinus contorta*) in a region of British Columbia where the forests are under temperature stress. The beetles were crushed, and a cellulase enzyme was extracted. Three polymorphs of the enzyme were observed when separated by gel electrophoresis. The three proteins observed correspond to alleles labeled C_1, C_2, and C_3. The numbers of beetles with each allele are shown in the following table.

D. The calculated allelic frequencies p_{C1}, p_{C2}, and p_{C3} are closest to ___.

a. $p_{C1} = 0.57$ $p_{C2} = 0.57$ $p_{C3} = 0.59$

b. $p_{C1} = 0.29$ $p_{C2} = 0.29$ $p_{C3} = 0.42$

c. $p_{C1} = 0.61$ $p_{C2} = 0.80$ $p_{C3} = 0.59$

d. $p_{C1} = 0.31$ $p_{C2} = 0.40$ $p_{C3} = 0.29$

E. In order to investigate the presence of selection at the cellulase locus due to changing temperature, a biologist should:

a. calculate the values of the sums $p_{C1} + p_{C2} + p_{C3}$ and $(p_{C1} + p_{C2} + p_{C3})^2$. If these numbers are not equal to 1, the gene is not in Hardy-Weinberg equilibrium, and the gene is evolving.

b. return next year and repeat this examination of the enzyme, calculating frequencies of each allele each year. Then calculate the values of the sums $p_{C1} + p_{C2} + p_{C3}$ and $(p_{C1} + p_{C2} + p_{C3})^2$. If these numbers are not the same each year, the gene is not in Hardy-Weinberg equilibrium, and the gene is evolving.

c. return each year for several years and repeat this examination of the enzyme, calculating frequencies of each allele each year. If the allele frequencies are changing, the gene is not in Hardy-Weinberg equilibrium, and temperature is exerting a selection pressure.

d. return each year for several years and repeat this examination of the enzyme, calculating frequencies of each allele each year. If the allele frequencies are changing, the gene is not in Hardy-Weinberg equilibrium. Analysis of the dependence of allele frequencies on temperature could indicate selection.

42. *Calamus finmarchicus* is the dominant copepod in the Gulf of Maine. The polymorphic aminopeptidase locus, Lap-1, has been shown to be useful for the genetic differentiation of populations of this organism. By examining the population dynamics of copepods, the dynamics of the fin fish on which they feed can be predicted. The aerial photograph shows a landmass separating two coastal estuarine habits, the mud flats of Egypt Bay and the Mount Desert Narrows. For the past 40 years, transport between the two habits has been hindered by a dam over the Carrying Place Inlet. However, small volumes of water occasionally crest the dam.

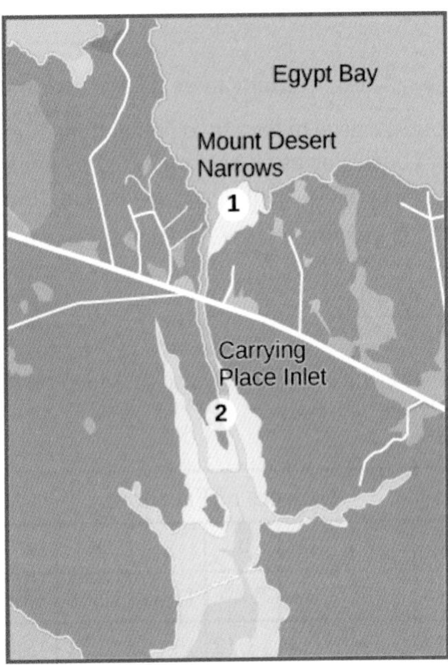

Figure 19.13

To evaluate the geographic isolation of invertebrate populations in these two habitats, copepods are sampled at the points labeled 1 and 2 on the photograph. These points lie at either ends of the Carrying Place Inlet. Enzymes encoded by three alleles, labeled A, B, and C, were determined by gel electrophoresis of equal numbers of the organisms collected at the two sites. Numbers of each genotype are given in the following table:

Site	1	2
AA	82	96
AB	114	108
AC	102	92
BB	74	54
BC	98	110
CC	30	40
Total	500	500

Table 19.4

A. Calculate the frequencies, f, of each allele and complete the following table:

Site	f(A)	f(B)	f(C)
1			
2			

Table 19.5

B. Using a χ^2 test, **evaluate** these data to determine if the aminopeptidase gene in these two populations is evolving. State your conclusion as claims supported by evidence at both the 95% and 99% confidence levels. The formula for the χ^2 test is provided on the AP Biology Exam.

$$\chi^2 = \sum \frac{(o-e)^2}{e}$$

This table of critical p values is also provided on the AP Biology Exam.

	Degrees of Freedom							
p	1	2	3	4	5	6	7	8
0.05	3.84	5.99	7.82	9.49	11.07	12.59	14.07	15.51
0.01	6.64	9.32	11.34	13.28	15.09	16.81	18.48	20.09

Table 19.6

C. Based on these data, **predict**, with justification, changes over time in the aminopeptidase enzyme for these populations.

D. The B form of this aminopeptidase is slightly more efficient at extracting nutritional leucine from a protein than the A and C forms but slightly less efficient at extracting valine and serine. **Describe** an investigation of the two habitats that could suggest a causal relationship between changes in allele frequency and characteristics of the environment.

E. Single-nucleotide mutations are neutral when they encode changes in proteins that result in no significant differential selection. If differences in environmental factors between sites 1 and 2 are not observed, **predict** what other factors could result in departures from Hardy-Weinberg equilibrium for aminopeptidase.

43. Bioluminescence is an example of convergent evolution; 30 distinct lineages have acquired this characteristic, and all involve some form of a class of molecules called luciferins. Sexual selection pressures are strong for light-emitting organisms. Ellis and Oakley (*Curr Biol*, 2016) examined the number of species that lack luminosity in groups of closest evolutionary relation (sister linear) with those species that are luminous. Similarly, scientists made the same comparison between groups that use luminosity for concealment (counter-illumination) and their sister lineages. The graphs summarize their results, comparing the natural logarithm of the number of species in each lineage.

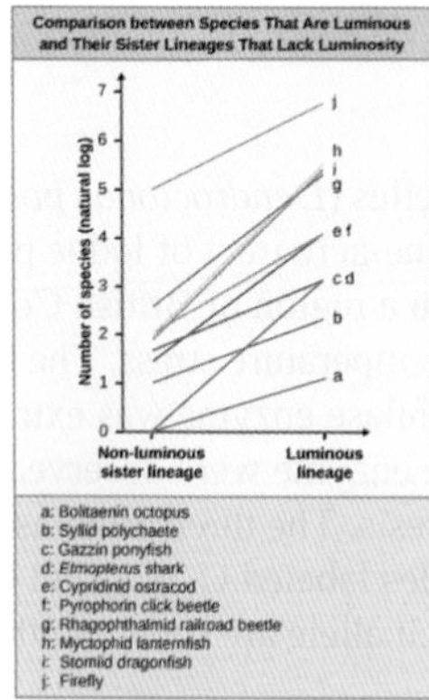

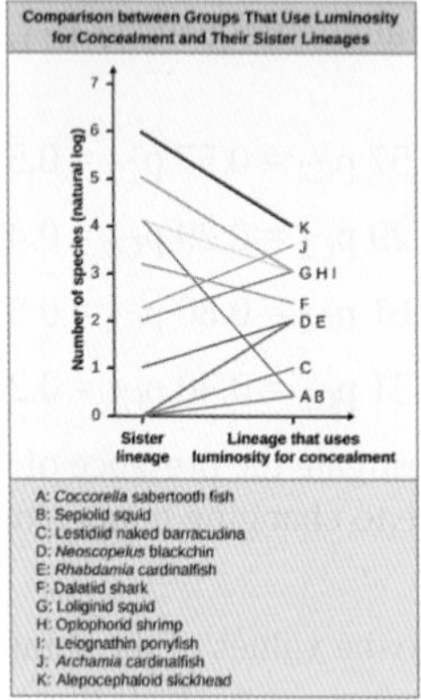

Figure 19.14

Based on the data shown in the graphs, **describe** a model that can account for the increased speciation of bioluminescent lineages, including the mechanism of speciation.

44.

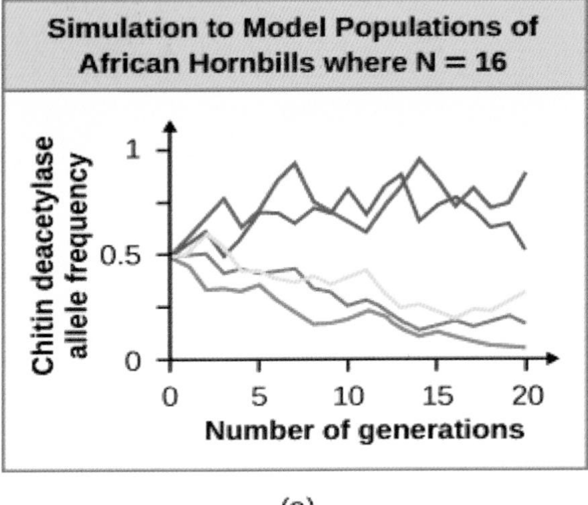

(a)

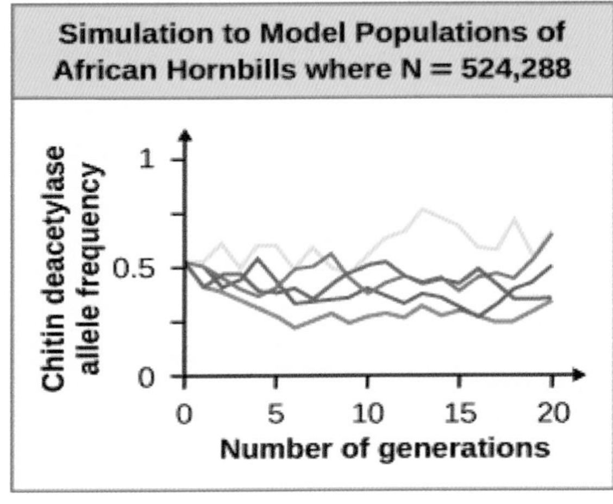

(b)

Figure 19.15 A biologist is using a simulation to model populations of African hornbills (*Bycanistes* spp. and *Ceratogymna* spp.), a keystone species of the savanna. Populations of the birds are declining due to habitat loss. The hornbill's diet consists primarily of termites and fruit. A critical component of termite digestion is chitin deacetylase, an enzyme whose mutation rate is a model parameter. The other model parameter is population size, N. In the results of the simulation study shown above, there is no selection, and the mutation rate is fixed. Although both population size and mutation rate are fixed, randomness results in the five different outcomes shown in each graph above.

A. **Select** the graph displaying the results that are closer to Hardy-Weinberg equilibrium. Justify the selection of the graph.

B. Based on these simulations, **predict** the future heterozygosity, 2pq, of the smaller populations, as shown in graph A.

C. **Justify** the use of a simulation study with no selection under environmental conditions in which the availability of both termites and fruit is high.

D. If a change in the environment occurs suddenly, such as an increase in average temperature, where fruit production declines, **analyze** the effect of the change on allele frequency in the large and small populations.

20 | PHYLOGENIES AND THE HISTORY OF LIFE

Figure 20.1 The life of a bee is very different from the life of a flower, but the two organisms are related. Both are members of the domain Eukarya and have cells containing many similar organelles, genes, and proteins. (credit: modification of work by John Beetham)

Chapter Outline

Introduction

This bee and *Echinacea* flower (Figure 20.1) could not look more different, yet they are related, as are all living organisms on Earth. By following pathways of similarities and changes—both visible and genetic—scientists seek to map the evolutionary past of how life developed from single-celled organisms to the tremendous variety of creatures that have germinated, crawled, floated, swam, flown, and walked on this planet.

New species are discovered with frequent regularity, but it's not too common to discover a new large mammal. However, that's what scientists did in Australia when they named a new species of cetacean the Australian humpback dolphin, *Souse sahulensis*. The dolphin had originally been classified as another closely related species, but a closer look at its coloration, skeletal structure, habitat, and DNA determined that it was in fact a separate species.

For more information, read the research article (http://openstaxcollege.org/l/32dolphin) yourself.

20.1 | Organizing Life on Earth

In this section, you will explore the following questions:

- Why do scientists need a comprehensive classification system to study living organisms?
- What are the different levels of the taxonomic classification system?
- How are systematics and taxonomy related to phylogeny?
- What are the components and purpose of a phylogenetic tree?

Connection for AP® Courses

In prior chapters we explored how all organisms on Earth, extant and extinct, evolved from common ancestry. Supporting this claim are core features and processes, such as a common genetic code and metabolic pathways, which evolved billions of years ago and are widely distributed among organisms living today. The evolutionary history and relationship of an organism or a group of organisms is called **phylogeny**. Scientists often construct **phylogenetic trees** based on evidence drawn from multiple disciplines to illustrate evolutionary pathways and connections among organisms.

Scientists historically organized Earth's millions of species into a hierarchical **taxonomic classification system** from the most inclusive category to the most specific: domain, kingdom, phylum, class, order, family, genus, and species. The traditional five-kingdom system that you might have studied in middle school was expanded (and reorganized) to include three domains: Bacteria, Archaea, and Eukarya, with prokaryotes divided between Bacteria or Archaea depending on their molecular genetic machinery, and protists, fungi, plants, and animals grouped in Eukarya. Today, however, phylogenetic trees provide more specific information about evolutionary history and relationships among organisms. (For the purpose of AP®, you do not have to memorize the taxonomic levels. However, it is important to reiterate that taxonomy is a tool to organize the millions of organisms on Earth, similar to how items in a grocery store or mall shop are organized into different departments. Like new products, organisms are often shifted among their taxonomic groups!)

Information presented and the examples highlighted in the section support concepts outlined in Big Idea 1 of the AP® Biology Curriculum Framework. The AP® Learning Objectives listed in the Curriculum Framework provide a transparent foundation for the AP® Biology course, an inquiry-based laboratory experience, instructional activities, and AP® exam questions. A learning objective merges required content with one or more of the seven science practices.

Big Idea 1	The process of evolution drives the diversity and unity of life.
Enduring Understanding 1.B	Organisms are linked by lines of descent from common ancestry.
Essential Knowledge	**1.B.1** Organisms share many conserved core processes and features that evolved and are widely distributed among organisms today.
Science Practice	**3.1** The student can pose scientific questions.
Learning Objective	**1.14** The student is able to pose scientific questions that correctly identify essential properties of shared, core life processes that provide insight into the history of life on Earth.
Essential Knowledge	**1.B.1** Phylogenetic trees and cladograms are graphical representations (models) of evolutionary history that can be tested.
Science Practice	**7.2** The student can connect concepts in and across domain(s) to generalize or extrapolate in and/or across enduring understandings and/or big ideas.
Learning Objective	**1.15** The student is able to describe specific examples of conserved core biological processes and features shared by all domains or within one domain of life, and how these shared, conserved core processes and features support the concept of common ancestry for all organisms.

Essential Knowledge	**1.B.1** Organisms share many conserved core processes and features that evolved and are widely distributed among organisms today.
Science Practice	**6.1** The student can justify claims with evidence.
Learning Objective	**1.16** The student is able to justify the scientific claim that organisms share many conserved core processes and features that evolved and are widely distributed among organisms today.
Essential Knowledge	**1.B.2** Phylogenetic trees and cladograms are graphical representations (models) of evolutionary history that can be tested.
Science Practice	**3.1** The student can pose scientific questions.
Learning Objective	**1.17** The student is able to pose scientific questions about a group of organisms whose relatedness is described by a phylogenetic tree or cladogram.

The Science Practice Challenge Questions contain additional test questions for this section that will help you prepare for the AP exam. These questions address the following standards:
[APLO 1.20][APLO 1.26]

Phylogenetic Trees

Scientists use a tool called a phylogenetic tree to show the evolutionary pathways and connections among organisms. A phylogenetic tree is a diagram used to reflect evolutionary relationships among organisms or groups of organisms. Scientists consider phylogenetic trees to be a hypothesis of the evolutionary past since one cannot go back to confirm the proposed relationships. In other words, a "tree of life" can be constructed to illustrate when different organisms evolved and to show the relationships among different organisms (Figure 20.2).

Unlike a taxonomic classification diagram, a phylogenetic tree can be read like a map of evolutionary history. Many phylogenetic trees have a single lineage at the base representing a common ancestor. Scientists call such trees **rooted**, which means there is a single ancestral lineage (typically drawn from the bottom or left) to which all organisms represented in the diagram relate. Notice in the rooted phylogenetic tree that the three domains— Bacteria, Archaea, and Eukarya—diverge from a single point and branch off. The small branch that plants and animals (including humans) occupy in this diagram shows how recent and miniscule these groups are compared with other organisms. Unrooted trees don't show a common ancestor but do show relationships among species.

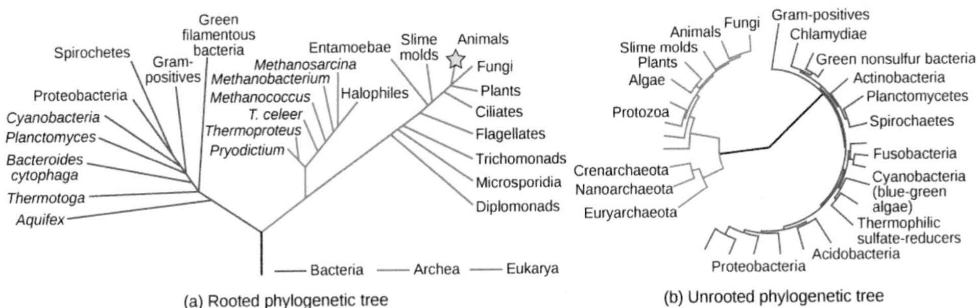

Figure 20.2 Both of these phylogenetic trees shows the relationship of the three domains of life—Bacteria, Archaea, and Eukarya—but the (a) rooted tree attempts to identify when various species diverged from a common ancestor while the (b) unrooted tree does not. (credit a: modification of work by Eric Gaba)

In a rooted tree, the branching indicates evolutionary relationships (Figure 20.3). The point where a split occurs, called a **branch point**, represents where a single lineage evolved into a distinct new one. A lineage that evolved early from the root and remains unbranched is called **basal taxon**. When two lineages stem from the same branch point, they are called **sister taxa**. A branch with more than two lineages is called a **polytomy** and serves to illustrate where scientists have not definitively determined all of the relationships. It is important to note that although sister taxa and polytomy do share an ancestor, it does not mean that the groups of organisms split or evolved from each other. Organisms in two taxa may have split apart at a specific branch point, but neither taxa gave rise to the other.

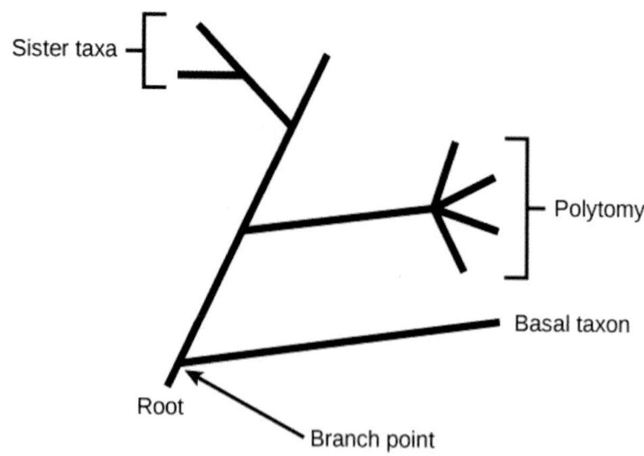

Figure 20.3 The root of a phylogenetic tree indicates that an ancestral lineage gave rise to all organisms on the tree. A branch point indicates where two lineages diverged. A lineage that evolved early and remains unbranched is a basal taxon. When two lineages stem from the same branch point, they are sister taxa. A branch with more than two lineages is a polytomy.

The diagrams above can serve as a pathway to understanding evolutionary history. The pathway can be traced from the origin of life to any individual species by navigating through the evolutionary branches between the two points. Also, by starting with a single species and tracing back towards the "trunk" of the tree, one can discover that species' ancestors, as well as where lineages share a common ancestry. In addition, the tree can be used to study entire groups of organisms.

Another point to mention on phylogenetic tree structure is that rotation at branch points does not change the information. For example, if a branch point was rotated and the taxon order changed, this would not alter the information because the evolution of each taxon from the branch point was independent of the other.

Many disciplines within the study of biology contribute to understanding how past and present life evolved over time; these disciplines together contribute to building, updating, and maintaining the “tree of life.” Information is used to organize and classify organisms based on evolutionary relationships in a scientific field called **systematics**. Data may be collected from fossils, from studying the structure of body parts or molecules used by an organism, and by DNA analysis. By combining data from many sources, scientists can put together the phylogeny of an organism; since phylogenetic trees are hypotheses, they will continue to change as new types of life are discovered and new information is learned.

Limitations of Phylogenetic Trees

It may be easy to assume that more closely related organisms look more alike, and while this is often the case, it is not always true. If two closely related lineages evolved under significantly varied surroundings or after the evolution of a major new adaptation, it is possible for the two groups to appear more different than other groups that are not as closely related. For example, the phylogenetic tree in Figure 20.4 shows that lizards and rabbits both have amniotic eggs, whereas frogs do not; yet lizards and frogs appear more similar than lizards and rabbits.

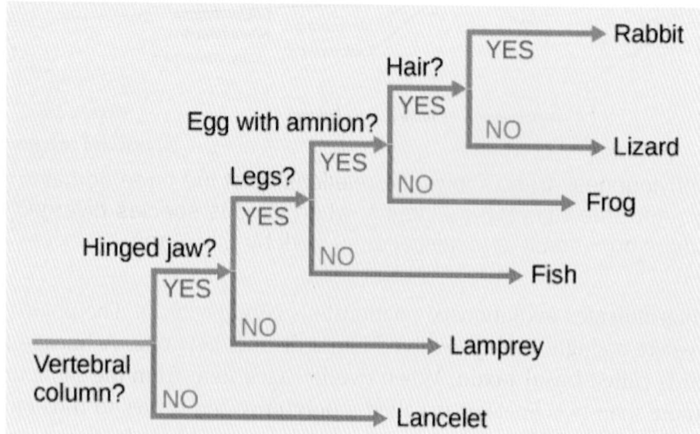

Figure 20.4 This ladder-like phylogenetic tree of vertebrates is rooted by an organism that lacked a vertebral column. At each branch point, organisms with different characters are placed in different groups based on the characteristics they share.

Another aspect of phylogenetic trees is that, unless otherwise indicated, the branches do not account for length of time, only the evolutionary order. In other words, the length of a branch does not typically mean more time passed, nor does a short branch mean less time passed— unless specified on the diagram. For example, in Figure 20.4, the tree does not indicate how much time passed between the evolution of amniotic eggs and hair. What the tree does show is the order in which things took place. Again using Figure 20.4, the tree shows that the oldest trait is the vertebral column, followed by hinged jaws, and so forth. Remember that any phylogenetic tree is a part of the greater whole, and like a real tree, it does not grow in only one direction after a new branch develops. So, for the organisms in Figure 20.4, just because a vertebral column evolved does not mean that invertebrate evolution ceased, it only means that a new branch formed. Also, groups that are not closely related, but evolve under similar conditions, may appear more phenotypically similar to each other than to a close relative.

Head to this website (http://openstaxcollege.org/l/tree_of_life) to see interactive exercises that allow you to explore the evolutionary relationships among species.

What is the main function of the ITOL (Interactive Tree of Life) website?

a. iTOL is a website that provides the history about the Tree of Life.

b. iTOL is a website that provides guidelines for researching data to create a phylogenetic tree.

c. iTOL is an online tool that provides the display and manipulation of pre-computed phylogenetic trees, and you can upload and display your own trees and data.

d. iTOL is a website that explains the evolutionary relationships among species.

science practices CONNECTION for AP® Courses

Think About It

How does a phylogenetic tree relate to the passing of time? What other questions about the evolutionary history of an organism and its relatedness to other organisms can a phylogenetic tree answer?

The Levels of Classification

Taxonomy (which literally means “arrangement law”) is the science of classifying organisms to construct internationally shared classification systems with each organism placed into more and more inclusive groupings. Think about how a grocery store is organized. One large space is divided into departments, such as produce, dairy, and meats. Then each department further divides into aisles, then each aisle into categories and brands, and then finally a single product. This organization from larger to smaller, more specific categories is called a hierarchical system.

The taxonomic classification system (also called the Linnaean system after its inventor, Carl Linnaeus, a Swedish botanist, zoologist, and physician) uses a hierarchical model. Moving from the point of origin, the groups become more specific, until one branch ends as a single species. For example, after the common beginning of all life, scientists divide organisms into three large categories called a domain: Bacteria, Archaea, and Eukarya. Within each domain is a second category called a **kingdom**. After kingdoms, the subsequent categories of increasing specificity are: **phylum**, **class**, **order**, **family**, **genus**, and **species** (Figure 20.5).

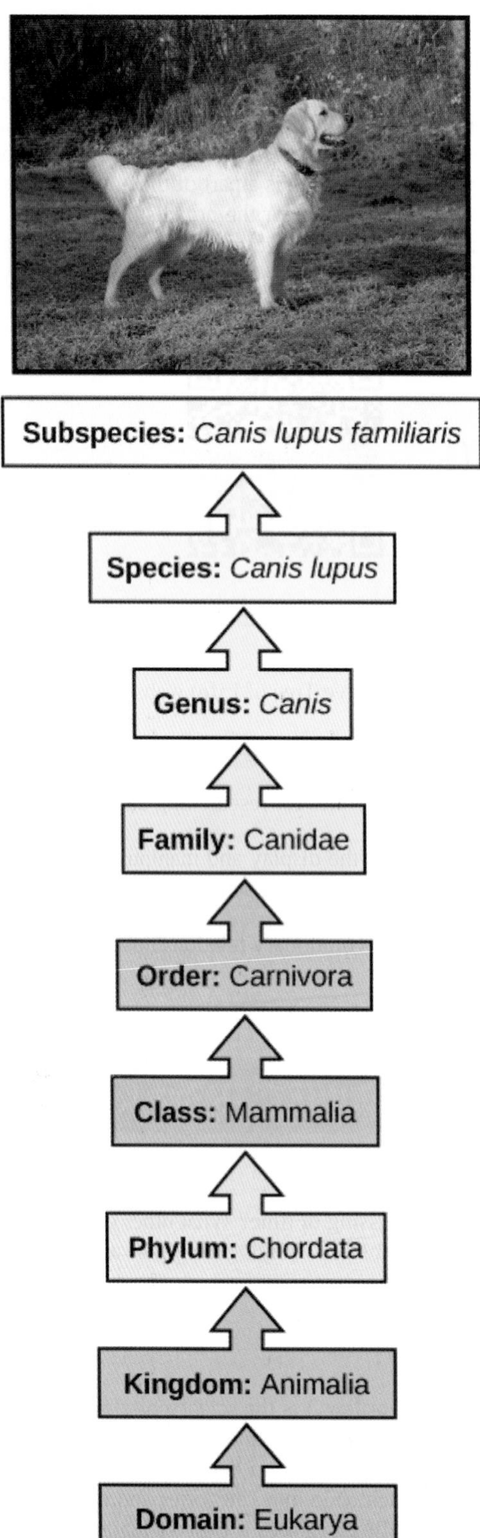

Figure 20.5 The taxonomic classification system uses a hierarchical model to organize living organisms into increasingly specific categories. The common dog, *Canis lupus familiaris*, is a subspecies of *Canis lupus*, which also includes the wolf and dingo. (credit "dog": modification of work by Janneke Vreugdenhil)

The kingdom Animalia stems from the Eukarya domain. For the common dog, the classification levels would be as shown in Figure 20.5. Therefore, the full name of an organism technically has eight terms. For the dog, it is: Eukarya, Animalia, Chordata, Mammalia, Carnivora, Canidae, *Canis*, and *lupus*. Notice that each name is capitalized except for species, and the genus and species names are italicized. Scientists generally refer to an organism only by its genus and species, which is its two-word scientific name, in what is called **binomial nomenclature**. Therefore, the scientific name of the dog is *Canis lupus*. The name at each level is also called a **taxon**. In other words, dogs are in order Carnivora. Carnivora is the name of the taxon at the order level; Canidae is the taxon at the family level, and so forth. Organisms also have a common name that people typically use, in this case, dog. Note that the dog is additionally a subspecies: the "*familiaris*" in *Canis lupus familiaris*. Subspecies are members of the same species that are capable of mating and reproducing viable offspring, but they are considered separate subspecies due to geographic or behavioral isolation or other factors.

Figure 20.6 shows how the levels move toward specificity with other organisms. Notice how the dog shares a domain with the widest diversity of organisms, including plants and butterflies. At each sublevel, the organisms become more similar because they are more closely related. Historically, scientists classified organisms using characteristics, but as DNA technology developed, more precise phylogenies have been determined.

visual CONNECTION

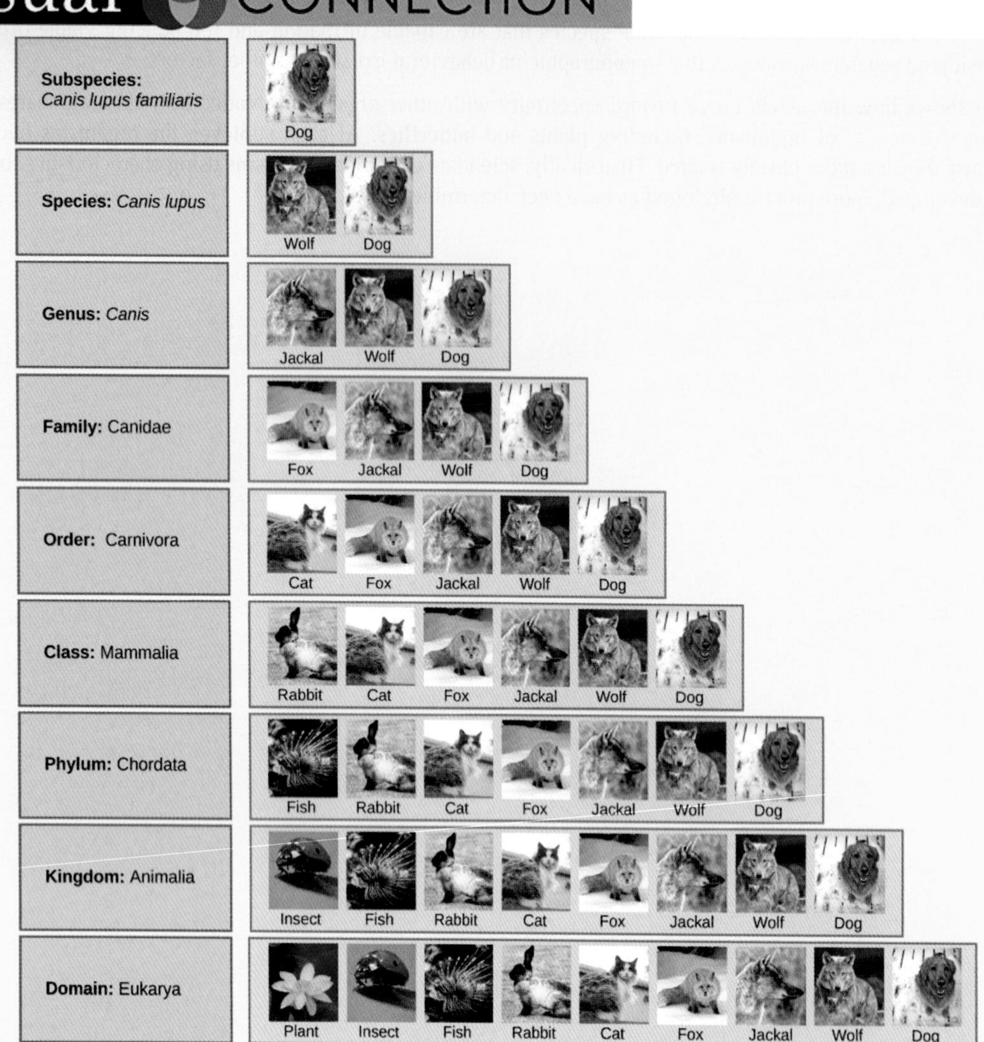

Figure 20.6 At each sublevel in the taxonomic classification system, organisms become more similar. Dogs and wolves are the same species because they can breed and produce viable offspring, but they are different enough to be classified as different subspecies. (credit "plant": modification of work by "berduchwal"/Flickr; credit "insect": modification of work by Jon Sullivan; credit "fish": modification of work by Christian Mehlführer; credit "rabbit": modification of work by Aidan Wojtas; credit "cat": modification of work by Jonathan Lidbeck; credit "fox": modification of work by Kevin Bacher, NPS; credit "jackal": modification of work by Thomas A. Hermann, NBII, USGS; credit "wolf": modification of work by Robert Dewar; credit "dog": modification of work by "digital_image_fan"/Flickr)

At what levels are cats and dogs considered to be part of the same group?

a. Cats and dogs are only found together in the Domain level.
b. Cats and dogs are in the same group beginning at the Domain level and including the sublevels Kingdom, Phylum, Class, and Order.
c. Cats and dogs are in the same group beginning at the Family level.
d. Cats and dogs are part of the same group beginning with the Order: Carnivora level.

Visit this website (http://openstaxcollege.org/l/classify_life) to classify three organisms—bear, orchid, and sea cucumber—from kingdom to species. To launch the game, under Classifying Life, click the picture of the bear or the Launch Interactive button.

Using the taxonomic classification system, which Kingdom category best describes a bear?

a. Plantae: Multicellular organisms that get their energy through photosynthesis.

b. Animalia: Multicellular organismsthat get their energy through ingesting other organisms.

c. Fungi: Single-celled and multi-celled organisms that get their energy mainly by absorbing nutrients from their surroundings and not through photosynthesis.

Recent genetic analysis and other advancements have found that some earlier phylogenetic classifications do not align with the evolutionary past; therefore, changes and updates must be made as new discoveries occur. Recall that phylogenetic trees are hypotheses and are modified as data becomes available. In addition, classification historically has focused on grouping organisms mainly by shared characteristics and does not necessarily illustrate how the various groups relate to each other from an evolutionary perspective. For example, despite the fact that a hippopotamus resembles a pig more than a whale, the hippopotamus may be the closest living relative of the whale.

20.2 | Determining Evolutionary Relationships

- What is the difference between homologous and analogous traits? How are these traits used when determining evolutionary relatedness?
- What is cladistics? How does a cladogram differ from a phylogenetic tree?
- What is parsimony?

Connection for AP® Courses

To build phylogenetic trees, scientists must collect accurate information that allows them to make evolutionary connections among organisms. Using morphological and molecular data, scientists identify both homologous and analogous characteristics and genes. (In a prior chapter we explored the differences between homologous and analogous traits and how they relate to convergent and divergent evolution.) Similarities among organisms stem either from shared ancestral history (homologies) or from separate evolutionary paths (analogies). **Cladograms** are constructed by using shared derived traits to distinguish different groups of species from one another. For example, lizards, rabbits and humans all descended from a common ancestor that had an amniotic egg; thus, lizards, rabbits, and humans all belong to the same clade. Vertebrata is a larger clade that also includes fish, lamprey, and lancelets. The closer two species or groups are located to each on a phylogenetic tree or cladogram, they more recently they shared a common ancestor. With the influx of new information, scientists can revise phylogenetic trees; for example, computer programs, such as one called BLAST, which helps determine relatedness using DNA sequencing. Typically, a phylogenetic tree is constructed with the simplest explanation of evolutionary history (maximum **parsimony**) and the fewest number of evolutionary steps.

Understanding phylogeny extends far beyond understanding the evolutionary history of species on Earth. For botanists, phylogeny acts as a guide to discovering new plants that can be used to make food, medicine, and clothing. For doctors, phylogenies provide information about the origin of diseases and how to treat them, for example, HIV/AIDS.

Information presented and the examples highlighted in the section support concepts outlined in Big Idea 1 of the AP® Biology Curriculum Framework. The AP® Learning Objectives listed in the Curriculum Framework provide a transparent foundation for the AP® Biology course, an inquiry-based laboratory experience, instructional activities, and AP® exam questions. A learning objective merges required content with one or more of the seven science practices.

Big Idea 1	The process of evolution drives the diversity and unity of life.
Enduring Understanding 1.A	Change in the genetic makeup of a population over time is evolution.
Essential Knowledge	**1.A.4** Biological evolution is supported by scientific evidence from many disciplines, including mathematics.
Science Practice	**5.3** The student can evaluate the evidence provided by data sets in relation to a particular scientific question.
Learning Objective	**1.9** The student is able to evaluate evidence provided by data from many scientific disciplines that support biological evolution.
Essential Knowledge	**1.A.4** Biological evolution is supported by scientific evidence from many disciplines, including mathematics.
Science Practice	**5.2** The student can refine observations and measurements based on data analysis.
Learning Objective	**1.10** The student is able to refine evidence based on data from many scientific disciplines that support biological evolution.
Essential Knowledge	**1.A.4** Biological evolution is supported by scientific evidence from many disciplines, including mathematics.
Science Practice	**4.2** The student can design a plan for collecting data to answer a particular scientific question.
Learning Objective	**1.11** The student is able to design a plan to answer scientific questions regarding how organisms have changed over time using information from morphology, biochemistry, and geology.
Essential Knowledge	**1.A.4** Biological evolution is supported by scientific evidence from many disciplines, including mathematics.
Science Practice	**7.1** The student can connect phenomena and models across spatial and temporal scales.
Learning Objective	**1.12** The student is able to connect scientific evidence from many scientific disciplines to support the modern concept of evolution.
Essential Knowledge	**1.A.4** Biological evolution is supported by scientific evidence from many disciplines, including mathematics.
Science Practice	**1.1** The student can create representations and models of natural or man-made phenomena and systems in the domain.
Science Practice	**2.1** The student can justify the selection of a mathematical routine to solve problems.
Learning Objective	**1.13** The student is able to construct and/or justify mathematical models, diagrams or simulations that represent processes of biological evolution.
Big Idea 1	The process of evolution drives the diversity and unity of life.
Enduring Understanding 1.B	Organisms are linked by lines of descent from common ancestry.
Essential Knowledge	**1.B.1** Organisms share many conserved core processes and features that evolved and are widely distributed among organisms today.

Science Practice	**3.1** The student can pose scientific questions.
Learning Objective	**1.14** The student is able to pose scientific questions that correctly identify essential properties of shared, core life processes that provide insight into the history of life on Earth.
Essential Knowledge	**1.B.1** Organisms share many conserved core processes and features that evolved and are widely distributed among organisms today.
Science Practice	**7.2** The student can connect concepts in and across domain(s) to generalize or extrapolate in and/or across enduring understandings and/or big ideas.
Learning Objective	**1.15** The student is able to describe specific examples of conserved core biological processes and features shared by all domains or within one domain of life, and how these shared, conserved core processes and features support the concept of common ancestry for all organisms.
Essential Knowledge	**1.B.1** Organisms share many conserved core processes and features that evolved and are widely distributed among organisms today.
Science Practice	**6.1** The student can justify claims with evidence.
Learning Objective	**1.16** The student is able to justify the scientific claim that organisms share many conserved core processes and features that evolved and are widely distributed among organisms today.
Essential Knowledge	**1.B.2** Phylogenetic trees and cladograms are graphical representations (models) of evolutionary history that can be tested.
Science Practice	**3.1** The student can pose scientific questions.
Learning Objective	**1.17** The student is able to pose scientific questions about a group of organisms whose relatedness is described by a phylogenetic tree or cladogram.
Essential Knowledge	**1.B.2** Phylogenetic trees and cladograms are graphical representations (models) of evolutionary history that can be tested.
Science Practice	**5.3** The student can evaluate the evidence provided by data sets in relation to a particular scientific question.
Learning Objective	**1.18** The student is able to evaluate evidence provided by a data set in conjunction with a phylogenetic tree or simple cladogram to determine evolutionary history and speciation.
Essential Knowledge	**1.B.2** Phylogenetic trees and cladograms are graphical representations (models) of evolutionary history that can be tested.
Science Practice	**1.1** The student can create representations and models of natural or man-made phenomena and systems in the domain.
Science Practice	**2.1** The student can justify the selection of a mathematical routine to solve problems.
Learning Objective	**1.19** The student is able to create a phylogenetic tree or simple cladogram that correctly represents evolutionary history and speciation from a provided data set.

The Science Practice Challenge Questions contain additional test questions for this section that will help you prepare for the AP exam. These questions address the following standards:
[APLO 1.15][APLO 1.16][APLO 1.18][APLO 1.17][APLO 1.19][APLO 1.26]

Two Options for Similarities

In general, organisms that share similar physical features and genomes tend to be more closely related than those that do not. Such features that overlap both morphologically (in form) and genetically are referred to as homologous structures; they stem from developmental similarities that are based on evolution. For example, the bones in the wings of bats and birds have homologous structures (**Figure 20.7**).

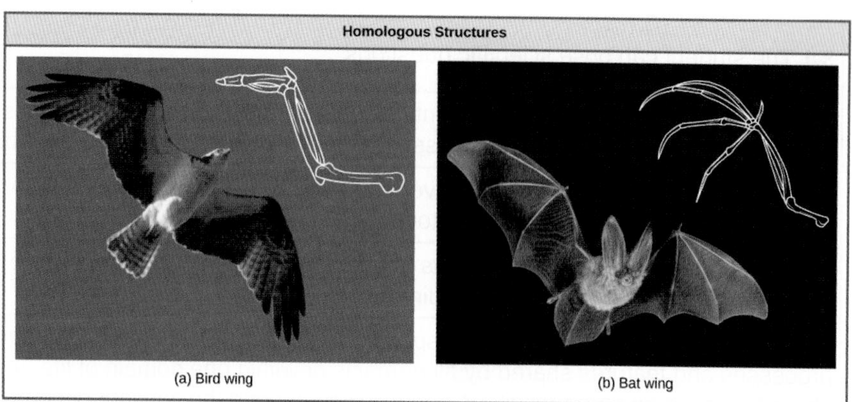

Figure 20.7 Bat and bird wings are homologous structures, indicating that bats and birds share a common evolutionary past. (credit a: modification of work by Steve Hillebrand, USFWS; credit b: modification of work by U.S. DOI BLM)

Notice it is not simply a single bone, but rather a grouping of several bones arranged in a similar way. The more complex the feature, the more likely any kind of overlap is due to a common evolutionary past. Imagine two people from different countries both inventing a car with all the same parts and in exactly the same arrangement without any previous or shared knowledge. That outcome would be highly improbable. However, if two people both invented a hammer, it would be reasonable to conclude that both could have the original idea without the help of the other. The same relationship between complexity and shared evolutionary history is true for homologous structures in organisms.

Misleading Appearances

Some organisms may be very closely related, even though a minor genetic change caused a major morphological difference to make them look quite different. Similarly, unrelated organisms may be distantly related, but appear very much alike. This usually happens because both organisms were in common adaptations that evolved within similar environmental conditions. When similar characteristics occur because of environmental constraints and not due to a close evolutionary relationship, it is called an **analogy** or homoplasy. For example, insects use wings to fly like bats and birds, but the wing structure and embryonic origin is completely different. These are called analogous structures (Figure 20.8).

Similar traits can be either homologous or analogous. Homologous structures share a similar embryonic origin; analogous organs have a similar function. For example, the bones in the front flipper of a whale are homologous to the bones in the human arm. These structures are not analogous. The wings of a butterfly and the wings of a bird are analogous but not homologous. Some structures are both analogous and homologous: the wings of a bird and the wings of a bat are both homologous and analogous. Scientists must determine which type of similarity a feature exhibits to decipher the phylogeny of the organisms being studied.

(a) Bat wing

(b) Bird wing

(c) Insect wing

Figure 20.8 The (c) wing of a honeybee is similar in shape to a (b) bird wing and (a) bat wing, and it serves the same function. However, the honeybee wing is not composed of bones and has a distinctly different structure and embryonic origin. These wing types (insect versus bat and bird) illustrate an analogy—similar structures that do not share an evolutionary history. (credit a: modification of work by Steve Hillebrand, USFWS; credit b: modification of work by U.S. DOI BLM; credit c: modification of work by Jon Sullivan)

This website (http://openstaxcollege.org/l/relationships) has several examples to show how appearances can be misleading in understanding the phylogenetic relationships of organisms.

James Lake of the UCLA/NASA Astrobiology Institute presented new evidence regarding the evolution of eukaryotic cells. He hypothesized that eukaryotes developed from an endosymbiotic gene fusion between the two other domains of life. What kind of genetic evidence would best support this hypothesis?

a. Their mitochondrial DNA resembles that of other eukaryotes.

b. The chloroplasts of eukaryotes contain a double cell layer.

c. All eukaryotic genes are identical to either Archaea or Bacteria.

d. Some eukaryotic genes resemble those of Archaea, while some resemble those of Bacteria and some are unlike the genes of either domain.

Molecular Comparisons

With the advancement of DNA technology, the area of **molecular systematics**, which describes the use of information on the molecular level including DNA analysis, has blossomed. New computer programs not only confirm many earlier classified organisms, but also uncover previously made errors. As with physical characteristics, even the DNA sequence can be tricky to read in some cases. For some situations, two very closely related organisms can appear unrelated if a mutation occurred that caused a shift in the genetic code. An insertion or deletion mutation would move each nucleotide base over one place, causing two similar codes to appear unrelated.

Sometimes two segments of DNA code in distantly related organisms randomly share a high percentage of bases in the same locations, causing these organisms to appear closely related when they are not. For both of these situations, computer technologies have been developed to help identify the actual relationships, and, ultimately, the coupled use of both morphologic and molecular information is more effective in determining phylogeny.

evolution CONNECTION

Why Does Phylogeny Matter?

Evolutionary biologists could list many reasons why understanding phylogeny is important to everyday life in human society. For botanists, phylogeny acts as a guide to discovering new plants that can be used to benefit people. Think of all the ways humans use plants—food, medicine, and clothing are a few examples. If a plant contains a compound that is effective in treating diseases, scientists might want to examine all of the relatives of that plant for other useful drugs.

A research team in China identified a segment of DNA thought to be common to some medicinal plants in the family Fabaceae (the legume family) and worked to identify which species had this segment (Figure 20.9). After testing plant species in this family, the team found a DNA marker (a known location on a chromosome that enabled them to identify the species) present. Then, using the DNA to uncover phylogenetic relationships, the team could identify whether a newly discovered plant was in this family and assess its potential medicinal properties.

Figure 20.9 *Dalbergia sissoo (D. sissoo)* is in the Fabaceae, or legume family. Scientists found that *D. sissoo* shares a DNA marker with species within the Fabaceae family that have antifungal properties. Subsequently, *D. sissoo* was shown to have fungicidal activity, supporting the idea that DNA markers can be used to screen for plants with potential medicinal properties.

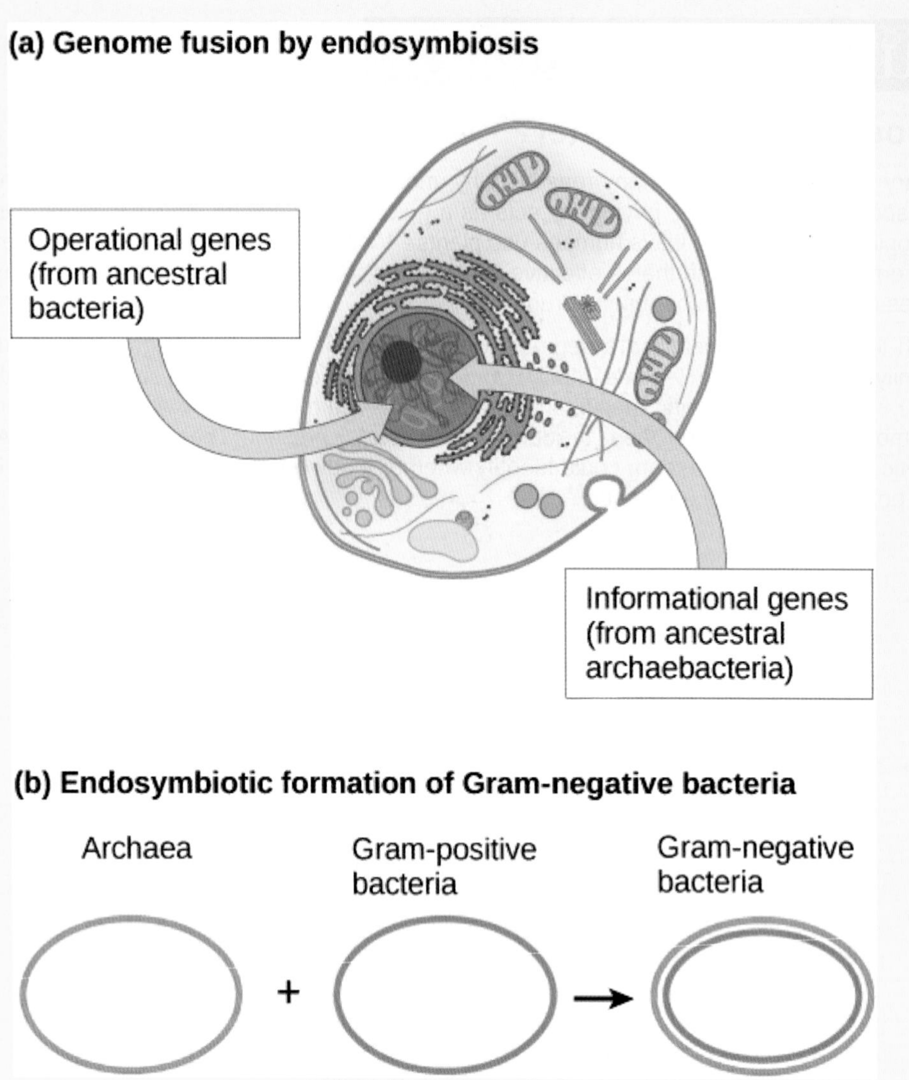

Part b of the figure shows a hypothetical model of the evolution of the cell membrane of gram-negative bacteria, which has a double membrane. If this hypothesis is true, what does it suggest about the evolution of mitochondria and chloroplasts in eukaryotic cells and why?

a. Chloroplasts and mitochondria did not come about through endosymbiosis with gram-negative bacteria because these organelles have a single membrane.
b. Chloroplasts and mitochondria likely evolved later in eukaryotic cells, as these organelles show no similarities to prokaryotes.
c. Chloroplasts and mitochondria came about through endosymbiosis with Archaea and gram positive bacteria because these organelles have prokaryote-like DNA.
d. Chloroplasts and mitochondria came about through endosymbiosis with gram-negative bacteria because these organelles have a double membrane.

Building Phylogenetic Trees

How do scientists construct phylogenetic trees? After the homologous and analogous traits are sorted, scientists often organize the homologous traits using a system called **cladistics**. This system sorts organisms into clades: groups of organisms that descended from a single ancestor. For example, in Figure 20.10, all of the organisms in the orange region evolved from a single ancestor that had amniotic eggs. Consequently, all of these organisms also have amniotic eggs and make a single clade, also called a **monophyletic group**. Clades must include all of the descendants from a branch point.

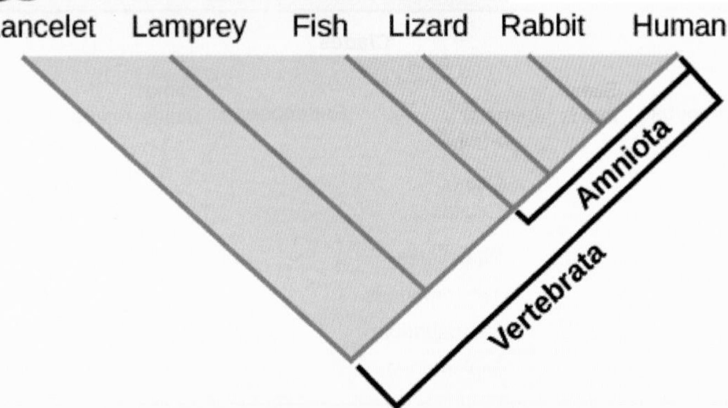

Figure 20.10 Lizards, rabbits, and humans all descend from a common ancestor that had an amniotic egg. Thus, lizards, rabbits, and humans all belong to the clade Amniota. Vertebrata is a larger clade that also includes fish and lamprey.

Eukaryotic mitochondria contain their own DNA, known as mitochondrial DNA, or mtDNA. Nuclear and mitochondrial DNA are thought to be of different (separate) evolutionary origin, with the mitochondrial DNA being derived from the circular chromosomes of bacteria that were engulfed by ancient prokaryotic cells. Does the presence of mitochondrial DNA suggest that organisms share many conserved core processes and features that evolved and are widely distributed among organisms today? Why or why not?

a. Yes, because it shows the prokaryotes and eukaryotes use similar organelles, namely, mitochondria.
b. Yes, because it suggests the eukaryotes possess traits that were likely conserved from prokaryotic ancestors.
c. No, because mitochondrial DNA is very different from the DNA within a eukaryote's nucleus.
d. No, because mitochondrial DNA is not used by the eukaryotic cells.

Clades can vary in size depending on which branch point is being referenced. The important factor is that all of the organisms in the clade or monophyletic group stem from a single point on the tree. This can be remembered because monophyletic breaks down into "mono," meaning one, and "phyletic," meaning evolutionary relationship. Figure 20.11 shows various examples of clades. Notice how each clade comes from a single point, whereas the non-clade groups show branches that do not share a single point.

visual CONNECTION

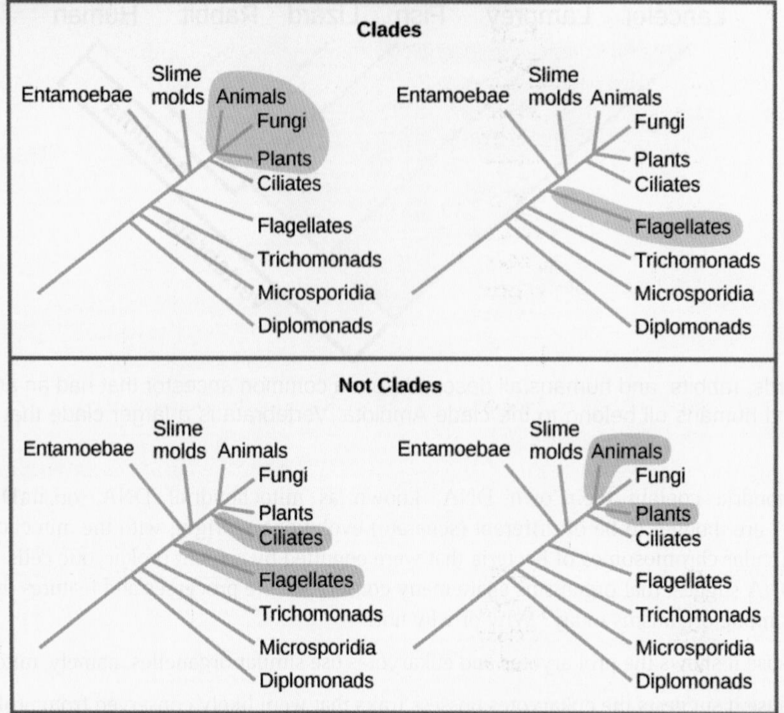

Figure 20.11 All the organisms within a clade stem from a single point on the tree. A clade may contain multiple groups, as in the case of animals, fungi and plants, or a single group, as in the case of flagellates. Groups that diverge at a different branch point, or that do not include all groups in a single branch point, are not considered clades.

Glycolysis, or the breakdown of glucose, is a process used by almost all organisms as a way to release energy stored within glucose molecules. This energy can then be stored in cells as ATP, which powers cell processes when needed. What does this show, in terms of the evolutionary history of cells using glycolysis?

a. Glycolysis has been conserved despite the independent evolution of the three domains of life.
b. Prokaryotes would likely not benefit from the Krebs cycle or the ETC.
c. Prokaryotes likely evolved after eukaryotes.
d. Glycolysis is the only way in which living things can break down glucose.

Shared Characteristics

Organisms evolve from common ancestors and then diversify. Scientists use the phrase “descent with modification” because even though related organisms have many of the same characteristics and genetic codes, changes occur. This pattern repeats over and over as one goes through the phylogenetic tree of life:

1. A change in the genetic makeup of an organism leads to a new trait which becomes prevalent in the group.
2. Many organisms descend from this point and have this trait.
3. New variations continue to arise: some are adaptive and persist, leading to new traits.
4. With new traits, a new branch point is determined (go back to step 1 and repeat).

If a characteristic is found in the ancestor of a group, it is considered a **shared ancestral character** because all of the organisms in the taxon or clade have that trait. The vertebrate in Figure 20.10 is a shared ancestral character. Now consider the amniotic egg characteristic in the same figure. Only some of the organisms in Figure 20.10 have this trait, and to those that do, it is called a **shared derived character** because this trait derived at some point but does not include all of the ancestors in the tree.

The tricky aspect to shared ancestral and shared derived characters is the fact that these terms are relative. The same trait can be considered one or the other depending on the particular diagram being used. Returning to **Figure 20.10**, note that the amniotic egg is a shared ancestral character for the Amniota clade, while having hair is a shared derived character for some organisms in this group. These terms help scientists distinguish between clades in the building of phylogenetic trees.

Choosing the Right Relationships

Imagine being the person responsible for organizing all of the items in a department store properly—an overwhelming task. Organizing the evolutionary relationships of all life on Earth proves much more difficult: scientists must span enormous blocks of time and work with information from long-extinct organisms. Trying to decipher the proper connections, especially given the presence of homologies and analogies, makes the task of building an accurate tree of life extraordinarily difficult. Add to that the advancement of DNA technology, which now provides large quantities of genetic sequences to be used and analyzed. Taxonomy is a subjective discipline: many organisms have more than one connection to each other, so each taxonomist will decide the order of connections.

To aid in the tremendous task of describing phylogenies accurately, scientists often use a concept called maximum parsimony, which means that events occurred in the simplest, most obvious way. For example, if a group of people entered a forest preserve to go hiking, based on the principle of maximum parsimony, one could predict that most of the people would hike on established trails rather than forge new ones.

For scientists deciphering evolutionary pathways, the same idea is used: the pathway of evolution probably includes the fewest major events that coincide with the evidence at hand. Starting with all of the homologous traits in a group of organisms, scientists look for the most obvious and simple order of evolutionary events that led to the occurrence of those traits.

Head to this **website (http://openstaxcollege.org/l/32species)** to learn how maximum parsimony is used to create phylogenetic trees.

What do phylogenetic relationships refer to?

a. the similarities among organisms

b. the differences among organisms

c. the evolution of the shape, size and number of body parts

d. the relative times in the past that species shared common ancestors

These tools and concepts are only a few of the strategies scientists use to tackle the task of revealing the evolutionary history of life on Earth. Recently, newer technologies have uncovered surprising discoveries with unexpected relationships, such as the fact that people seem to be more closely related to fungi than fungi are to plants. Sound unbelievable? As the information about DNA sequences grows, scientists will become closer to mapping the evolutionary history of all life on Earth.

science practices CONNECTION for AP® Courses

Activity

Using a data set provided by your teacher or other sources, construct a phylogenetic tree or cladogram to reflect the evolutionary history among a group of organisms based on shared characteristics. Then share the phylogenetic tree or cladogram with peers for review and revision.

Lab Investigation

AP® Biology Investigative Labs: Inquiry-Based Approach, Investigation 3: Comparing DNA Sequences to Understand Evolutionary Relationships with BLAST. Students will learn to use a common tool, BLAST, to compare several genes from different organisms and then use this information to construct a cladogram to determine evolutionary relatedness among species. Then students will use BLAST to track a gene(s) of choice through several species. Bioinformatics has many applications, including understanding genetic disease.

Think About It

Why must scientists distinguish between homologous and analogous characteristics before building phylogenetic trees? Do more closely related organisms share homologous or analogous traits? Which type of trait is used to support convergent or divergent evolution?

20.3 | Perspectives on the Phylogenetic Tree

In this section, you will explore the following questions:

- What is horizontal gene transfer and its significance in constructing phylogenetic trees?
- How do prokaryotes and eukaryotes transfer genes horizontally?
- What are other models of phylogenetic relationships and how do they differ from the original phylogenetic tree concept?

Connection for AP® Courses

Newer technologies have uncovered surprising discoveries with unexpected relationships among organisms, such as the fact that humans seems to be more closely related to fungi than fungi are to plants. (Think about that the next time you see a mushroom). As the information about DNA sequences grows, scientists will become closer to mapping a more accurate evolutionary history of all life on Earth.

What makes phylogeny difficult, especially among prokaryotes, is the transfer of genes horizontally (**horizontal gene transfer**, or **HGT**) between unrelated species. Like mutations, HGT introduces genetic variation into the bacterial population. This passing of genes between species adds a layer of complexity to understanding relatedness.

Information presented and the examples highlighted in the section support concepts outlined in Big Idea 3 of the AP® Biology Curriculum Framework. The AP® Learning Objectives listed in the Curriculum Framework provide a transparent foundation for the AP® Biology course, an inquiry-based laboratory experience, instructional activities, and AP® exam questions. A learning objective merges required content with one or more of the seven science practices.

Big Idea 1	The process of evolution drives the diversity and unity of life.

Enduring Understanding 1.B	Organisms are linked by lines of descent from common ancestry.
Essential Knowledge	**1.B.1** Organisms share many conserved core processes and features that evolved and are widely distributed among organisms today.
Science Practice	**3.1** The student can pose scientific questions.
Learning Objective	**1.14** The student is able to pose scientific questions that correctly identify essential properties of shared, core life processes that provide insight into the history of life on Earth.
Essential Knowledge	**1.B.1** Organisms share many conserved core processes and features that evolved and are widely distributed among organisms today.
Science Practice	**7.2** The student can connect concepts in and across domain(s) to generalize or extrapolate in and/or across enduring understandings and/or big ideas.
Learning Objective	**1.15** The student is able to describe specific examples of conserved core biological processes and features shared by all domains or within one domain of life, and how these shared, conserved core processes and features support the concept of common ancestry for all organisms.
Big Idea 3	Living systems store, retrieve, transmit and respond to information essential to life processes.
Enduring Understanding 3.C	The processing of genetic information is imperfect and is a source of genetic variation.
Essential Knowledge	**3.C.2** Biological systems have multiple processes that increase genetic variation.
Science Practice	**6.2** The student can construct explanations of phenomena based on evidence produced through scientific practices.
Learning Objective	**3.27** The student is able to construct an explanation of processes that increase variation within a population.

The concepts of phylogenetic modeling are constantly changing. It is one of the most dynamic fields of study in all of biology. Over the last several decades, new research has challenged scientists' ideas about how organisms are related. New models of these relationships have been proposed for consideration by the scientific community.

Many phylogenetic trees have been shown as models of the evolutionary relationship among species. Phylogenetic trees originated with Charles Darwin, who sketched the first phylogenetic tree in 1837 (**Figure 20.12a**), which served as a pattern for subsequent studies for more than a century. The concept of a phylogenetic tree with a single trunk representing a common ancestor, with the branches representing the divergence of species from this ancestor, fits well with the structure of many common trees, such as the oak (**Figure 20.12b**). However, evidence from modern DNA sequence analysis and newly developed computer algorithms has caused skepticism about the validity of the standard tree model in the scientific community.

Figure 20.12 The (a) concept of the "tree of life" goes back to an 1837 sketch by Charles Darwin. Like an (b) oak tree, the "tree of life" has a single trunk and many branches. (credit b: modification of work by "Amada44"/Wikimedia Commons)

Limitations to the Classic Model

Classical thinking about prokaryotic evolution, included in the classic tree model, is that species evolve clonally. That is, they produce offspring themselves with only random mutations causing the descent into the variety of modern-day and extinct species known to science. This view is somewhat complicated in eukaryotes that reproduce sexually, but the laws of Mendelian genetics explain the variation in offspring, again, to be a result of a mutation within the species. The concept of genes being transferred between unrelated species was not considered as a possibility until relatively recently. Horizontal gene transfer (HGT), also known as lateral gene transfer, is the transfer of genes between unrelated species. HGT has been shown to be an ever-present phenomenon, with many evolutionists postulating a major role for this process in evolution, thus complicating the simple tree model. Genes have been shown to be passed between species which are only distantly related using standard phylogeny, thus adding a layer of complexity to the understanding of phylogenetic relationships.

The various ways that HGT occurs in prokaryotes is important to understanding phylogenies. Although at present HGT is not viewed as important to eukaryotic evolution, HGT does occur in this domain as well. Finally, as an example of the ultimate gene transfer, theories of genome fusion between symbiotic or endosymbiotic organisms have been proposed to explain an event of great importance—the evolution of the first eukaryotic cell, without which humans could not have come into existence.

Horizontal Gene Transfer

Horizontal gene transfer (HGT) is the introduction of genetic material from one species to another species by mechanisms other than the vertical transmission from parent(s) to offspring. These transfers allow even distantly related species to share genes, influencing their phenotypes. It is thought that HGT is more prevalent in prokaryotes, but that only about 2% of the prokaryotic genome may be transferred by this process. Some researchers believe such estimates are premature: the actual importance of HGT to evolutionary processes must be viewed as a work in progress. As the phenomenon is investigated more thoroughly, it may be revealed to be more common. Many scientists believe that HGT and mutation appear to be (especially in prokaryotes) a significant source of genetic variation, which is the raw material for the process of natural selection. These transfers may occur between any two species that share an intimate relationship (Table 20.1).

Summary of Mechanisms of Prokaryotic and Eukaryotic HGT

	Mechanism	Mode of Transmission	Example
Prokaryotes	transformation	DNA uptake	many prokaryotes
	transduction	bacteriophage (virus)	bacteria
	conjugation	pilus	many prokaryotes

Table 20.1

Summary of Mechanisms of Prokaryotic and Eukaryotic HGT

	Mechanism	Mode of Transmission	Example
	gene transfer agents	phage-like particles	purple non-sulfur bacteria
Eukaryotes	from food organisms	unknown	aphid
	jumping genes	transposons	rice and millet plants
	epiphytes/parasites	unknown	yew tree fungi
	from viral infections		

Table 20.1

HGT in Prokaryotes

The mechanism of HGT has been shown to be quite common in the prokaryotic domains of Bacteria and Archaea, significantly changing the way their evolution is viewed. The majority of evolutionary models, such as in the Endosymbiont Theory, propose that eukaryotes descended from multiple prokaryotes, which makes HGT all the more important to understanding the phylogenetic relationships of all extant and extinct species.

The fact that genes are transferred among common bacteria is well known to microbiology students. These gene transfers between species are the major mechanism whereby bacteria acquire resistance to antibiotics. Classically, this type of transfer has been thought to occur by three different mechanisms:

1. Transformation: naked DNA is taken up by a bacteria
2. Transduction: genes are transferred using a virus
3. Conjugation: the use a hollow tube called a pilus to transfer genes between organisms

More recently, a fourth mechanism of gene transfer between prokaryotes has been discovered. Small, virus-like particles called **gene transfer agents (GTAs)** transfer random genomic segments from one species of prokaryote to another. GTAs have been shown to be responsible for genetic changes, sometimes at a very high frequency compared to other evolutionary processes. The first GTA was characterized in 1974 using purple, non-sulfur bacteria. These GTAs, which are thought to be bacteriophages that lost the ability to reproduce on their own, carry random pieces of DNA from one organism to another. The ability of GTAs to act with high frequency has been demonstrated in controlled studies using marine bacteria. Gene transfer events in marine prokaryotes, either by GTAs or by viruses, have been estimated to be as high as 10^{13} per year in the Mediterranean Sea alone. GTAs and viruses are thought to be efficient HGT vehicles with a major impact on prokaryotic evolution.

As a consequence of this modern DNA analysis, the idea that eukaryotes evolved directly from Archaea has fallen out of favor. While eukaryotes share many features that are absent in bacteria, such as the TATA box (found in the promoter region of many genes), the discovery that some eukaryotic genes were more homologous with bacterial DNA than Archaea DNA made this idea less tenable. Furthermore, the fusion of genomes from Archaea and Bacteria by endosymbiosis has been proposed as the ultimate event in eukaryotic evolution.

HGT in Eukaryotes

Although it is easy to see how prokaryotes exchange genetic material by HGT, it was initially thought that this process was absent in eukaryotes. After all, prokaryotes are but single cells exposed directly to their environment, whereas the sex cells of multicellular organisms are usually sequestered in protected parts of the body. It follows from this idea that the gene transfers between multicellular eukaryotes should be more difficult. Indeed, it is thought that this process is rarer in eukaryotes and has a much smaller evolutionary impact than in prokaryotes. In spite of this fact, HGT between distantly related organisms has been demonstrated in several eukaryotic species, and it is possible that more examples will be discovered in the future.

In plants, gene transfer has been observed in species that cannot cross-pollinate by normal means. Transposons or "jumping genes" have been shown to transfer between rice and millet plant species. Furthermore, fungal species feeding on yew trees, from which the anti-cancer drug paclitaxel is derived from the bark, have acquired the ability to make paclitaxel themselves, a clear example of gene transfer.

In animals, a particularly interesting example of HGT occurs within the aphid species (**Figure 20.13**). Aphids are insects that vary in color based on carotenoid content. Carotenoids are pigments made by a variety of plants, fungi, and microbes, and they serve a variety of functions in animals, who obtain these chemicals from their food. Humans require carotenoids to synthesize vitamin A, and we obtain them by eating orange fruits and vegetables: carrots, apricots, mangoes, and sweet potatoes. On the other hand, aphids have acquired the ability to make the carotenoids on their own. According to DNA analysis, this ability is due to the transfer of fungal genes into the insect by HGT, presumably as the insect consumed fungi for food. A carotenoid enzyme called a desaturase is responsible for the red coloration seen in certain aphids, and it has been further shown that when this gene is inactivated by mutation, the aphids revert back to their more common green color (Figure 20.13).

Figure 20.13 (a) Red aphids get their color from red carotenoid pigment. Genes necessary to make this pigment are present in certain fungi, and scientists speculate that aphids acquired these genes through HGT after consuming fungi for food. If genes for making carotenoids are inactivated by mutation, the aphids revert back to (b) their green color. Red coloration makes the aphids a lot more conspicuous to predators, but evidence suggests that red aphids are more resistant to insecticides than green ones. Thus, red aphids may be more fit to survive in some environments than green ones. (credit a: modification of work by Benny Mazur; credit b: modification of work by Mick Talbot)

everyday CONNECTION for AP® Courses

Barbara McClintock (1902–1992) discovered transposons while working on maize genetics.

Figure 20.14

What does the Eukaryote-first hypothesis suggest?

a. that mitochondria were first established in a prokaryotic host which acquired a nucleus to become the first eukaryotic cell
b. that the nucleus evolved in prokaryotes first followed by fusion of the new eukaryote with bacteria that became mitochondria
c. that prokaryotes actually evolved from eukaryotes by losing genes and complexity
d. that eukaryotes developed Golgi before mitochondria

Genome Fusion and the Evolution of Eukaryotes

Scientists believe the ultimate in HGT occurs through **genome fusion** between different species of prokaryotes when two symbiotic organisms become endosymbiotic. This occurs when one species is taken inside the cytoplasm of another species, which ultimately results in a genome consisting of genes from both the endosymbiont and the host. This mechanism is an aspect of the Endosymbiont Theory, which is accepted by a majority of biologists as the mechanism whereby eukaryotic cells obtained their mitochondria and chloroplasts. However, the role of endosymbiosis in the development of the nucleus is more controversial. Nuclear and mitochondrial DNA are thought to be of different (separate) evolutionary origin, with the mitochondrial DNA being derived from the circular genomes of bacteria that were engulfed by ancient prokaryotic cells. Mitochondrial DNA can be regarded as the smallest chromosome. Interestingly enough, mitochondrial DNA is inherited only from the mother. The mitochondrial DNA degrades in sperm when the sperm degrades in the fertilized egg or in other instances when the mitochondria located in the flagellum of the sperm fails to enter the egg.

Within the past decade, the process of genome fusion by endosymbiosis has been proposed by James Lake of the UCLA/NASA Astrobiology Institute to be responsible for the evolution of the first eukaryotic cells (Figure 20.15**a**). Using DNA analysis and a new mathematical algorithm called conditioned reconstruction (CR), his laboratory proposed that eukaryotic cells developed from an endosymbiotic gene fusion between two species, one an Archaea and the other a Bacteria. As mentioned, some eukaryotic genes resemble those of Archaea, whereas others resemble those from Bacteria. An endosymbiotic fusion event, such as Lake has proposed, would clearly explain this observation. On the other hand, this work is new and the CR algorithm is relatively unsubstantiated, which causes many scientists to resist this hypothesis.

More recent work by Lake (Figure 20.15**b**) proposes that gram-negative bacteria, which are unique within their domain in that they contain two lipid bilayer membranes, indeed resulted from an endosymbiotic fusion of archaeal and bacterial species. The double membrane would be a direct result of the endosymbiosis, with the endosymbiont picking up the second membrane from the host as it was internalized. This mechanism has also been used to explain the double membranes found in mitochondria and chloroplasts. Lake's work is not without skepticism, and the ideas are still debated within the biological science community. In addition to Lake's hypothesis, there are several other competing theories as to the origin of eukaryotes. How did the eukaryotic nucleus evolve? One theory is that the prokaryotic cells produced an additional membrane that surrounded the bacterial chromosome. Some bacteria have the DNA enclosed by two membranes; however, there is no evidence of a nucleolus or nuclear pores. Other proteobacteria also have membrane-bound chromosomes. If the eukaryotic nucleus evolved this way, we would expect one of the two types of prokaryotes to be more closely related to eukaryotes.

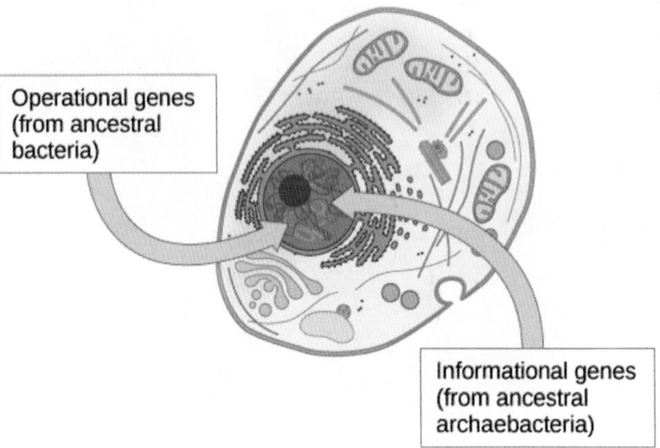

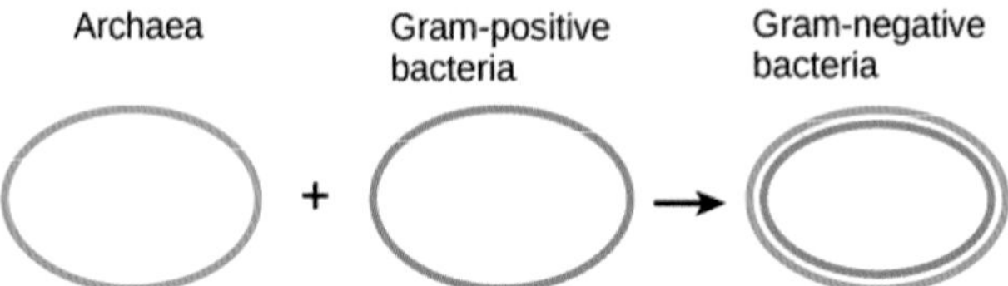

Figure 20.15 The theory that mitochondria and chloroplasts are endosymbiotic in origin is now widely accepted. More controversial is the proposal that (a) the eukaryotic nucleus resulted from the fusion of archaeal and bacterial genomes, and that (b) Gram-negative bacteria, which have two membranes, resulted from the fusion of Archaea and Gram-positive bacteria, each of which has a single membrane.

The **nucleus-first** hypothesis proposes that the nucleus evolved in prokaryotes first (Figure 20.16**a**), followed by a later fusion of the new eukaryote with bacteria that became mitochondria. The **mitochondria-first** hypothesis proposes that mitochondria were first established in a prokaryotic host (Figure 20.16**b**), which subsequently acquired a nucleus, by fusion or other mechanisms, to become the first eukaryotic cell. Most interestingly, the **eukaryote-first** hypothesis proposes that prokaryotes actually evolved from eukaryotes by losing genes and complexity (Figure 20.16**c**). All of these hypotheses are testable. Only time and more experimentation will determine which hypothesis is best supported by data.

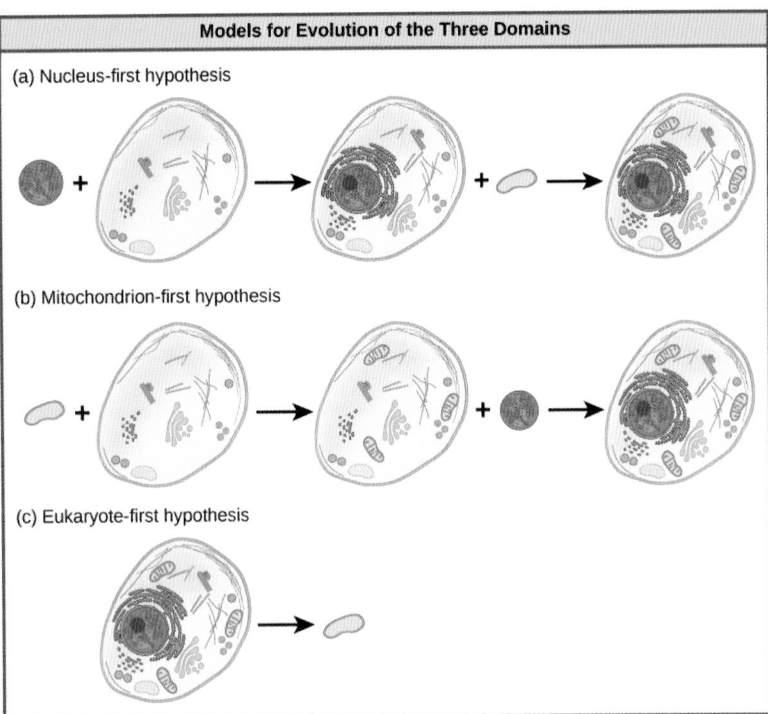

Figure 20.16 Three alternate hypotheses of eukaryotic and prokaryotic evolution are (a) the nucleus-first hypothesis, (b) the mitochondrion-first hypothesis, and (c) the eukaryote-first hypothesis.

Web and Network Models

The recognition of the importance of HGT, especially in the evolution of prokaryotes, has caused some to propose abandoning the classic "tree of life" model. In 1999, W. Ford Doolittle proposed a phylogenetic model that resembles a web or a network more than a tree. The hypothesis is that eukaryotes evolved not from a single prokaryotic ancestor, but from a pool of many species that were sharing genes by HGT mechanisms. As shown in Figure 20.17**a**, some individual prokaryotes were responsible for transferring the bacteria that caused mitochondrial development to the new eukaryotes, whereas other species transferred the bacteria that gave rise to chloroplasts. This model is often called the "**web of life**." In an effort to save the tree analogy, some have proposed using the *Ficus* tree (Figure 20.17**b**) with its multiple trunks as a phylogenetic to represent a diminished evolutionary role for HGT.

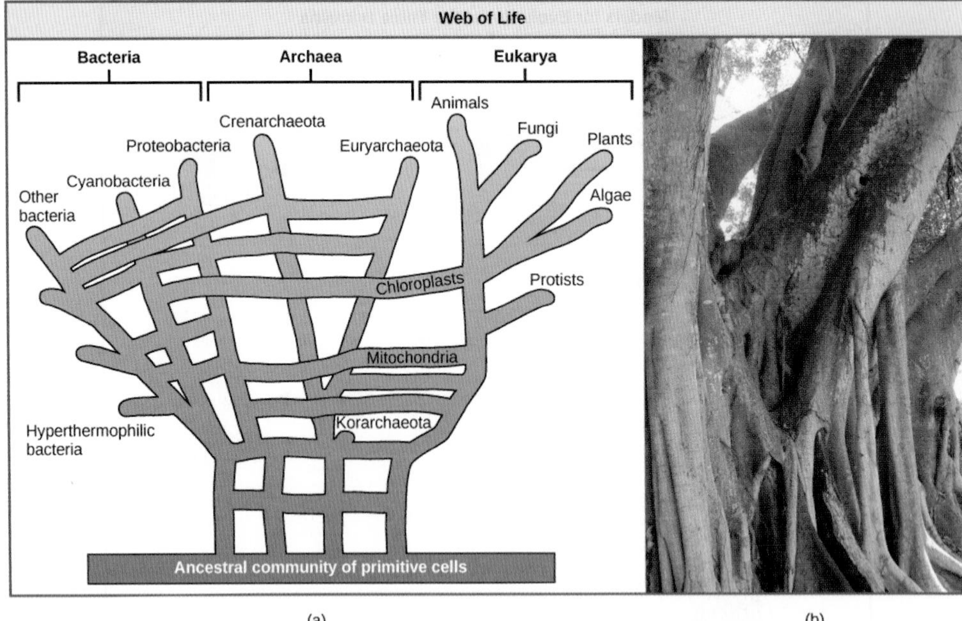

Figure 20.17 In the (a) phylogenetic model proposed by W. Ford Doolittle, the "tree of life" arose from a community of ancestral cells, has multiple trunks, and has connections between branches where horizontal gene transfer has occurred. Visually, this concept is better represented by (b) the multi-trunked **Ficus** than by the single trunk of the oak similar to the tree drawn by Darwin Figure 20.12. (credit b: modification of work by "psyberartist"/Flickr)

Ring of Life Models

Others have proposed abandoning any tree-like model of phylogeny in favor of a ring structure, the so-called "**ring of life**" (Figure 20.18); a phylogenetic model where all three domains of life evolved from a pool of primitive prokaryotes. Lake, again using the conditioned reconstruction algorithm, proposes a ring-like model in which species of all three domains—Archaea, Bacteria, and Eukarya—evolved from a single pool of gene-swapping prokaryotes. His laboratory proposes that this structure is the best fit for data from extensive DNA analyses performed in his laboratory, and that the ring model is the only one that adequately takes HGT and genomic fusion into account. However, other phylogeneticists remain highly skeptical of this model.

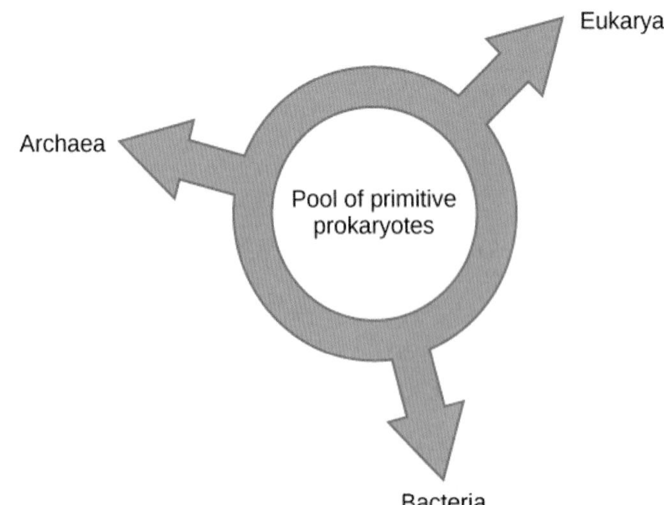

Figure 20.18 According to the "ring of life" phylogenetic model, the three domains of life evolved from a pool of primitive prokaryotes.

In summary, the "tree of life" model proposed by Darwin must be modified to include HGT. Does this mean abandoning the tree model completely? Even Lake argues that all attempts should be made to discover some modification of the tree model to allow it to accurately fit his data, and only the inability to do so will sway people toward his ring proposal.

This doesn't mean a tree, web, or a ring will correlate completely to an accurate description of phylogenetic relationships of life. A consequence of the new thinking about phylogenetic models is the idea that Darwin's original conception of the phylogenetic tree is too simple, but made sense based on what was known at the time. However, the search for a more useful model moves on: each model serving as hypotheses to be tested with the possibility of developing new models. This is how science advances. These models are used as visualizations to help construct hypothetical evolutionary relationships and understand the massive amount of data being analyzed.

KEY TERMS

analogy (also, homoplasy) characteristic that is similar between organisms by convergent evolution, not due to the same evolutionary path

basal taxon branch on a phylogenetic tree that has not diverged significantly from the root ancestor

binomial nomenclature system of two-part scientific names for an organism, which includes genus and species names

branch point node on a phylogenetic tree where a single lineage splits into distinct new ones

cladistics system used to organize homologous traits to describe phylogenies

cladograms visual representations of evolutionary relationships between organisms

class division of phylum in the taxonomic classification system

eukaryote-first hypothesis proposal that prokaryotes evolved from eukaryotes

family division of order in the taxonomic classification system

gene transfer agent (GTA) bacteriophage-like particle that transfers random genomic segments from one species of prokaryote to another

genome fusion fusion of two prokaryotic genomes, presumably by endosymbiosis

genus division of family in the taxonomic classification system; the first part of the binomial scientific name

horizontal gene transfer (HGT) (also, lateral gene transfer) transfer of genes between unrelated species

kingdom division of domain in the taxonomic classification system

maximum parsimony applying the simplest, most obvious way with the least number of steps

mitochondria-first hypothesis proposal that prokaryotes acquired a mitochondrion first, followed by nuclear development

molecular systematics technique using molecular evidence to identify phylogenetic relationships

monophyletic group (also, clade) organisms that share a single ancestor

nucleus-first hypothesis proposal that prokaryotes acquired a nucleus first, and then the mitochondrion

order division of class in the taxonomic classification system

parsimony the simplest, most straightforward way of constructing phylogenetic and evolutionary relationships between organisms

phylogenetic tree diagram used to reflect the evolutionary relationships among organisms or groups of organisms

phylogeny evolutionary history and relationship of an organism or group of organisms

phylum (plural: phyla) division of kingdom in the taxonomic classification system

polytomy branch on a phylogenetic tree with more than two groups or taxa

ring of life phylogenetic model where all three domains of life evolved from a pool of primitive prokaryotes

rooted single ancestral lineage on a phylogenetic tree to which all organisms represented in the diagram relate

shared ancestral character describes a characteristic on a phylogenetic tree that is shared by all organisms on the tree

shared derived character describes a characteristic on a phylogenetic tree that is shared only by a certain clade of organisms

sister taxa two lineages that diverged from the same branch point

systematics field of organizing and classifying organisms based on evolutionary relationships

taxon (plural: taxa) single level in the taxonomic classification system

taxonomic classification system hierarchical system of classifying organisms, including the classification of domain, kingdom, phylum, class, order, family, genus, and species

taxonomy science of classifying organisms

web of life phylogenetic model that attempts to incorporate the effects of horizontal gene transfer on evolution

CHAPTER SUMMARY

20.1 Organizing Life on Earth

Scientists continually gain new information that helps understand the evolutionary history of life on Earth. Each group of organisms went through its own evolutionary journey, called its phylogeny. Each organism shares relatedness with others, and based on morphologic and genetic evidence, scientists attempt to map the evolutionary pathways of all life on Earth. Historically, organisms were organized into a taxonomic classification system. However, today many scientists build phylogenetic trees to illustrate evolutionary relationships.

20.2 Determining Evolutionary Relationships

To build phylogenetic trees, scientists must collect accurate information that allows them to make evolutionary connections between organisms. Using morphologic and molecular data, scientists work to identify homologous characteristics and genes. Similarities between organisms can stem either from shared evolutionary history (homologies) or from separate evolutionary paths (analogies). Newer technologies can be used to help distinguish homologies from analogies. After homologous information is identified, scientists use cladistics to organize these events as a means to determine an evolutionary timeline. Scientists apply the concept of maximum parsimony, which states that the order of events probably occurred in the most obvious and simple way with the least amount of steps. For evolutionary events, this would be the path with the least number of major divergences that correlate with the evidence.

20.3 Perspectives on the Phylogenetic Tree

The phylogenetic tree, first used by Darwin, is the classic "tree of life" model describing phylogenetic relationships among species, and the most common model used today. New ideas about HGT and genome fusion have caused some to suggest revising the model to resemble webs or rings.

REVIEW QUESTIONS

1. Who devised a commonly used classification system?

a. Carl Linnaeus
b. Darwin
c. Plato
d. Aristotle

2. Which of the following uses a hierarchial model to classify organisms?

a. analogy
b. taxonomic classification system
c. Order
d. systematics

3. Correctly list the hierarchy of taxonomy.

a. Kingdom, Domain, Phylum, Order, Class, Family, Genus, species
b. Domain, Kingdom, Class, Phylum, Order, Family, Genus, species
c. Domain, Kingdom, Phylum, Class, Order, Family, Genus, species
d. Domain, Kingdom, Class, Phylum, Order, Family, Genus, species

4. Which of category, below the level of Kingdom, would have the next largest number of organisms?

a. Order
b. Phylum
c. Family
d. Class

5. How is systematics related to phylogeny?

a. Systematics provides guidelines that scientists use to describe the relationships of organisms.
b. Scientists use systematics programs to put together the phylogeny of an organism.
c. In systematics, scientists use combined data based on evolutionary relationships from many sources to put together the phylogeny of an organism.
d. Systematics is a process used to put together the phylogeny of an organism.

6. Which of the following is the best explanation of what systematists do?

a. Scientists in the field of systematics organize organisms by characteristics.
b. Scientists in the field of systematics provide information on how organisms are similar or different.
c. Scientists in the field of systematics contribute to building, updating, and maintaining the "tree of life."
d. Scientists in the field of systematics collect data from fossils.

7. What is the purpose of a phylogenetic tree?

a. to organize and name organisms into specific categories
b. The taxonomy is used to organize and name organisms into specific categories.
c. to show the evolutionary pathways and connections among organisms
d. to show geographic or behavioral factors

8. What does the term "rooted" mean on a phylogenetic tree diagram?

a. relationships among species do not show
b. all organisms represented in the diagram relate to a single ancestral lineage
c. a single lineage evolved into a distinct new one
d. A lineage evolved early from the root and remains unbranched.

9. Phylogeny is important to everyday life in human society. How did the research team in China use phylogeny as a guide to discover new plants that can be used to benefit people?

a. The research team used DNA to uncover phylogenetic relationships in the legume family, and they found a compound in the plant that is effective in treating cancer.
b. The research team used DNA to uncover phylogenetic relationships in the legume family, and then they identified a newly discovered plant as Dalbergia sissoo.
c. The research team used DNA to uncover phylogenetic relationships in the legume family, and they found a DNA marker that can be used to screen for plants with potential medicinal properties.
d. The research team searched all the relatives of the newly discovered plant Dlabergia sissoo to find antifungal properties.

10. Which animals in the figure belong to a clade that includes animals with hair? Which evolved first, hair or the amniotic egg?

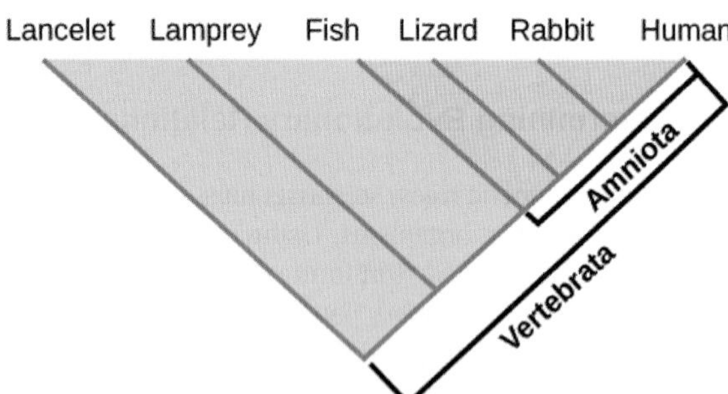

a. Rabbit and Human-Hair evolved before the amniotic egg.
b. Rabbit-Hair evolved before the amniotic egg.
c. Rabbit and Human-Amniotic egg evolved before hair.
d. Lancelet-Hair evolved before the amniotic egg.

11. What is the largest clade in the preceding diagram?

a. Animals, Fungi, and Plants
b. Fungi
c. Diplomonads
d. Flagellates

12. Why is it important for scientists to distinguish between homologous and analogous characteristics before building phylogenetic trees?

a. Phylogenetic trees are based on evolutionary connections, so scientists can use the analogous characteristics to build the phylogenetic trees.

b. Phylogenetic trees are based on evolutionary connections, so scientists can use the homologous characteristics to build the phylogenetic trees.

c. Phylogenetic trees are based on similar functions, so scientists can use the homologous characteristics to build the phylogenetic trees.

d. Phylogenetic trees are based on similar functions, so scientists can use the homologous characteristics to build the phylogenetic trees.

13. Describe an analogous structure.

a. A penguin and a seagull both have wings. The penguin uses wings to swim while the seagull uses wings to fly.

b. Lizards and whales have similar skeleton structures, but they have a different habitat and lifestyle.

c. Birds and butterflies have wings with similar characteristics for flight even though their wings do not share an evolutionary relationship.

d. The bone structure in leg of a cat is very similar to the bone structure in the arm of a human, but the functions of the limbs are very different.

14. What is the ring of life?

a. a phylogenetic model where all three domains of life evolved from a pool of primitive prokaryotes

b. an evolutionary history and relationship of an organism or group of organisms

c. a phylogenetic model that attempts to incorporate the effects of horizontal gene transfer on evolution

d. a field of organizing and classifying organisms based on evolutionary relationships

15. Some individual prokaryotes were responsible for transferring the bacteria that caused mitochondrial development to the new eukaryotes, whereas other species transferred the bacteria that gave rise to chloroplasts. This statement best describes which model?

a. ring of life

b. tree of life

c. branches of life

d. web of life

16. Explain why the classic tree model needs to be revised.

a. The model is unable to incorporate DNA evidence.

b. The model is erroneously based on many analogous traits, which have no basis in evolutionary relationships.

c. The model cannot be experimentally verified.

d. The model does not consider the possibility that genes could be transferred between unrelated species.

17. Compare three different ways that eukaryotic cells may have evolved.

a. Some hypotheses propose that mitochondria were acquired first. Others propose that the nucleus evolved first. Still others hypothesize that prokaryotes descended from eukaryotes by the loss of genes and complexity.

b. Some hypotheses propose that eukaryotic cells are a combination of bacterial and archaeal cells. Others propose that eukaryotic cells are a combination of bacterial and fungal cells. Still others hypothesize that eukaryotic and prokaryotic cells developed independently.

c. Some hypotheses propose that mitochondria developed from bacterial cells. Others propose that they developed from archaeal cells. Still others hypothesize that bacteria developed from mitochondria that had been released from eukaryotic cells.

d. Some hypotheses propose that eukaryotic cells developed from gram-negative bacteria. Others propose that they developed from gram-positive bacteria. Still others hypothesize that both gram-positive and gram-negative bacteria contributed to the eukaryotic genome through horizontal gene transfer.

18. Explain the ring of life model.

a. The ring of life model is a phylogenetic model where the three domains of life started as distinct groups that could swap genes horizontally with each other in all directions.

b. The ring of life model is a phylogenetic model where all three domains of life are said to have developed from a pool of primitive prokaryotes.

c. The ring of life model is a phylogenetic model where bacterial and archaeal cells fused to form eukaryotic cells.

d. The ring of life model is a phylogenetic model where there is only a single domain of life due to modern DNA analysis.

19.

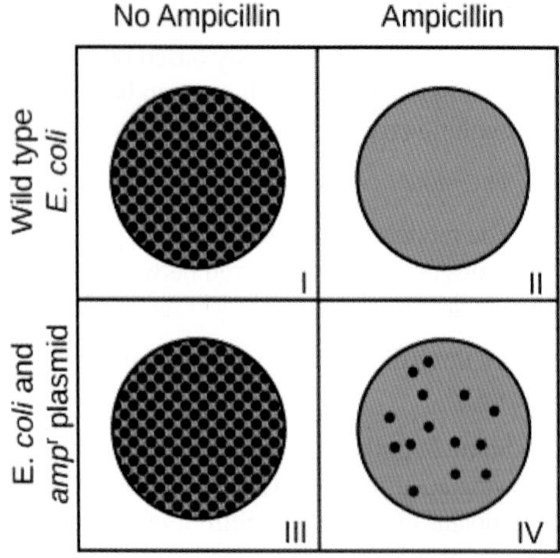

In a transformation experiment, a sample of E. coli bacteria was mixed with a plasmid containing the gene for resistance to the antibiotic ampicillin (ampr). Plasmid was not added to the second sample. Samples were plated on nutrient agar plates, some of which were supplemented with the antibiotic ampicillin. The results of E. coli growth are summarized below. The shaded area represents extensive growth of bacteria; dots represent individual colonies of bacteria. Plates that have only ampicillin resistant bacteria include which of the following?

a. I only
b. III only
c. IV only
d. I and II

CRITICAL THINKING QUESTIONS

20. Describe how organisms are classified in the taxonomic classification system.

a. The taxonomic classification system uses a hierarchical model to organize living organisms. At each sublevel, the organisms are more similar.
b. The taxonomic classification system uses a hierarchical model to organize living organisms. At each sublevel, the number of organisms increases.
c. The categories in the taxonomic classification system are organized from smaller, more specific categories to larger categories.
d. In the hierarchal model for the taxonomic classification system, from the point of origin, the groups become less specific.

21. What is the correct way to format a two-word scientific name?

a. Italicize both words. Both words are lower case.
b. Italicize both words. The first word should be capitalized. The second word should be lower case.
c. Italicize both words. Capitalize both words.
d. Underline both words. Capitalize both words.

22. Some organisms that appear very closely related may not actually be closely related. Why is this?

a. There are cases where organisms used to be closely related but diverged from each other and no longer look closely related.
b. There are cases where organisms can interbreed making them look like a single species, when in fact they are not closely related at all.
c. There are cases where organisms evolved through convergence and appear closely related but are not.
d. There are cases when extremely distant taxa can recombine into a single group.

23. How does a phylogenetic tree relate to the passing of time?

a. A phylogenetic tree relates to the passing of time because species branch off from each other at regular time intervals.
b. A phylogenetic tree is not related to the passing of time because speciation is based on geographic changes.
c. The phylogenetic tree only shows the order in which things took place.
d. A phylogenetic tree relates to the passing of time when the diagram also shows how long ago the divergence from the common ancestor occurred.

24. Judeo-Christian religious texts explain that the Earth and all the organisms on Earth were created in seven days. Why is this not a valid scientific hypothesis?

25. Scientists use the cladistics system to organize what?

a. homologous traits
b. homoplasies
c. analogous traits
d. monophyletic groups

26. Describe how a clade relates to monophyletic group.

a. Clades vary in size depending on the number of branches.
b. All the organisms within a clade stem from a single point on the phylogenetic tree.
c. A clade shows branches that do not share a single point.
d. A clade shows groups that diverge at a different branch point.

27. Scientists apply the concept of maximum parsimony to do what?

a. describe phylogenies accurately
b. eliminate analogous traits
c. identify mutations to DNA codes
d. locate homoplasies

28. You discover a new species of animal in the rainforest. What characteristics could you use to distinguish this organism from the other organisms in the same clade based on Figure 20.11?

29. Based on the phylogenetic tree below, is the Jungle cat likely closer related to a tiger or a cougar? Why?

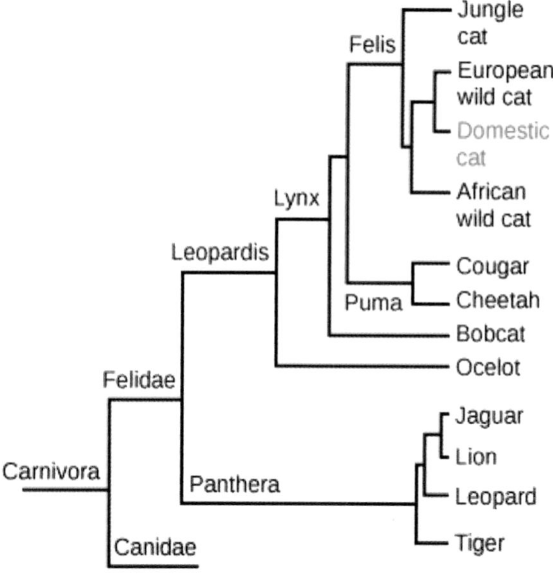

Figure 20.19

30. Two cultures of bacteria are separated by a filter that blocks the movement of cells but allows free exchange of anything smaller than a bacterial cell. On one side of the filter, a sample of penicillin resistant cells in culture broth is added, on the second side of the tube, a culture of penicillin sensitive cells in culture is added. After 24 hours, resistant cells appear on the side with the cells sensitive to penicillin. Which three genetic mechanisms can account for appearance of the penicillin resistant cells?

a. transformation, transduction, and conjugation
b. transformation, transduction, and mutation
c. transformation, conjugation, and mutation
d. transduction, conjugation, and mutation

TEST PREP FOR AP® COURSES

31. What evolutionary question is better addressed by the fig-shaped evolutionary tree in Figure 20.17, as opposed to the more typical, single-trunk phylogenetic tree in Figure 20.2?

a. What was the single organism from which all other forms of life on Earth arose?
b. Did animals evolve from fungi?
c. In which species of eukaryote did chloroplasts first appear?
d. Were chloroplasts and mitochondria transferred to eukaryotic cells through horizontal gene transfer?

32.

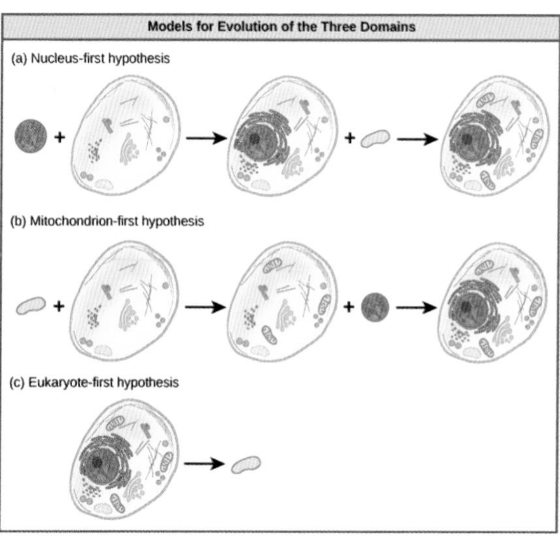

Which question, relating to the endosymbiotic hypothesis and the evolution of eukaryotes, is not answered by the eukaryote-first hypothesis, based on the figures?

a. Which evolved first, the nucleus or prokaryotes?
b. Which evolved first, mitochondria or prokaryotes?
c. How and when did the nucleus evolve in eukaryotes?
d. How and when did prokaryotes evolve?

33.

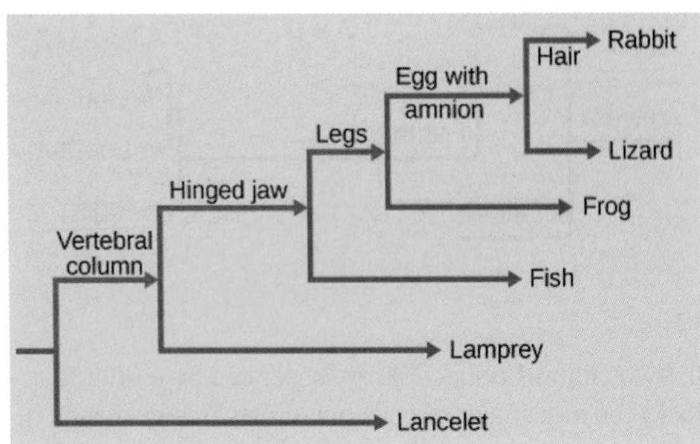

The phylogeny above shows the evolution of traits in vertebrates. Based on this phylogeny, a student asks "Does this mean that lizards, frogs and rabbits all possessed hair and an egg with amnion at some point in their evolution?" Based on the phylogeny, how should you respond to the student?

a. Hair and an amniotic egg were both possessed by all three species at some point in their evolution.
b. Hair is only a characteristic found in the rabbit evolutionary history. The amniotic egg was possessed by both the rabbit and lizard, but not frogs, at some point in their evolutionary history.
c. Hair is a characteristic only found in the rabbit evolutionary history. The amniotic egg was possessed by all three species at some point in their evolutionary history.
d. Hair was possessed by all three species at some point in their evolutionary history. The amniotic egg was possessed by both the lizard and frog, but not the rabbit at some point in their evolutionary history.

34.

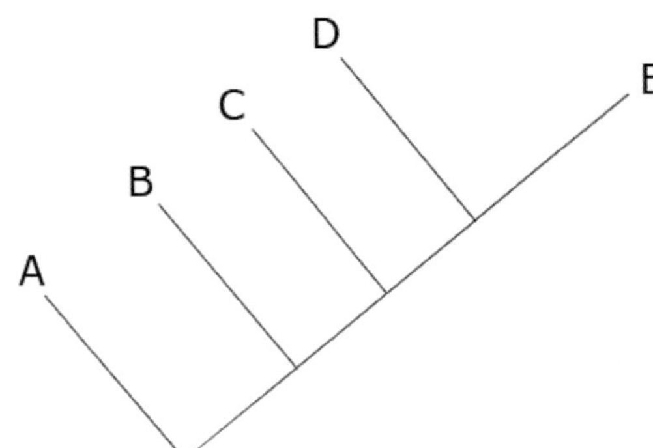

The tree above shows the phylogenetic relationships between four species. A scientist wishes to perform a genetic analysis on all four species in which she determines the number of genetic similarities between all four species. What would she likely find regarding the genetic similarities between species A, B, D and E?

a. Species D and E would share more genetic similarities with each other than with species A and B, and vice versa.
b. Species A and E would share more genetic similarities with each other than with species B and D, and vice versa.
c. Species D and A would share more genetic similarities with each other than with species A and B, and vice versa.
d. Species D and B would share more genetic similarities with each other than with species A and E.

35. What is the aim of scientists applying the maximum parsimony concept when creating phylogenetic trees?

a. The scientists spend more time creating the phylogenetic table.
b. Scientists find the shortest tree with the smallest number of changes.
c. A complex, detailed phylogenetic tree diagram is created.
d. The scientists spend more time researching the data for evolutionary connections.

36. Dolphins and fish have similar body shapes. Is this feature more likely a homologous or analogous trait? Explain your answer.

a. Analogous-Dolphins are mammals and fish are not, thus their evolutionary paths are quite separate. They have similar body shapes because of their similar environment.

b. Analogous-Dolphins and fish are both vertebrates, thus they share an evolutionary history, causing them to have similar body shapes.

c. Homologous-Dolphins and fish are both vertebrates, thus they have a similar recent evolutionary history, causing them to have similar body shapes.

d. Homologous-Dolphins are mammals and fish are not, thus their evolutionary paths are quite separate. They have similar body shapes because of their similar environment.

37. What effect has the advancement of DNA technology had on determining phylogeny?

a. Morphologic and molecular information often disagree.

b. Scientists are struggling with molecular systematics.

c. Information is not reliable because organisms appear to be closely related when they are not.

d. Computer programs help determine relatedness using DNA sequencing, and morphologic and molecular information is more effective in determining phylogeny.

38. Describe what maximum parsimony is used for in evolutionary biology.

a. Maximum parsimony hypothesizes that organisms that share the most traits are the most likely to share a common ancestor.

b. Maximum parsimony hypothesizes that organisms that share a common ancestor are more likely to have many traits in common.

c. Maximum parsimony hypothesizes that events occurred in the simplest, most obvious way, and the pathway of evolution probably includes the fewest major events that coincide with the evidence at hand.

d. Maximum parsimony hypothesizes that organisms that display homologous structures are closely related, while organisms that display analogous structures must have diverged much farther in the past.

39. The emu in Australia and ostrich in Africa are flightless birds that look similar. One proposed hypothesis was the birds descend from an early common ancestor that spread when the continents were connected. DNA analysis shows that emus and ostriches share more genetic homology with flying birds which live in the same region than with each other. What is the best explanation for these findings?

a. This is an example of an early shared ancestor.

b. This is an example of convergent evolution.

c. This is an example of random DNA homology.

d. This is an example of divergent evolution.

40. A scientist decides to investigate the evolutionary connection between closely related bacteria. Which gene would be a good choice to use for establishing relatedness, a very well conserved gene or a poorly conserved sequence? Explain your reasoning.

a. A very well conserved gene would be a good choice, because well conserved genes undergo sufficient changes during relatively short times, which allows for the study of recent evolutionary events. Well-conserved genes do not undergo changes during short durations.

b. A poorly conserved gene would be a good choice, because poorly conserved genes show sequence similarity, which is used as evidence of evolutionary relationships between sequences.

c. A poorly conserved gene would be a good choice, because poorly conserved genes undergo sufficient changes during relatively short times, which allows for the study of recent evolutionary events.

d. A very well conserved gene would be a good choice, because well conserved genes show sequence similarity, which is used as evidence of evolutionary relationships between sequences.

41.

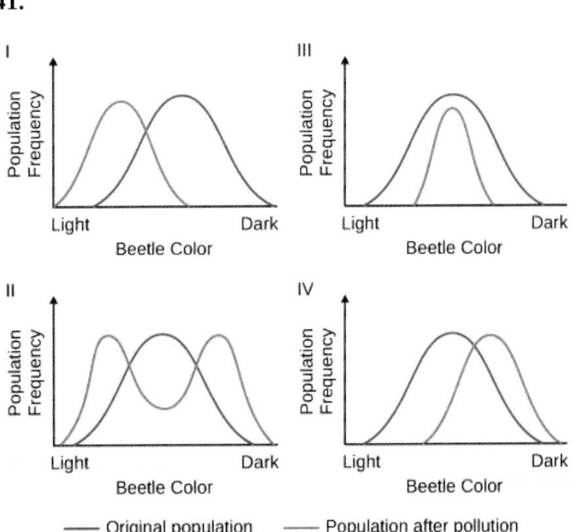

In a hypothetical population of beetles, there is a wide variety of color, matching the range of coloration of the tree trunks on which the beetles hide from predators. The graphs below illustrate four possible changes in the beetle population as a result of a change in the environment due to pollution that darkened the tree trunks. What would be the most likely change in the coloration of the beetle population after pollution and why?

a. The coloration range shifted toward more light-colored beetles, as in diagram I. The pollution helped the predators find the darkened tree trunks.
b. The coloration in the population split into two extremes, as in diagram II. Both the light-colored and the dark-colored beetles were able to hide on the darker tree trunks.
c. The coloration range became narrower, as in diagram III. The predators selected beetles at the color extremes.
d. The coloration in the population shifted toward more dark-colored beetles, as in diagram IV. The light-colored beetles were found more easily by the predators than were the dark-colored beetles.

42. A population of rodents settles on the shore of an island close to the Arctic Circle. The landscape consists mainly of rocks. If the individuals are too large, they cannot hide in crevices to escape hawks. On the other hand, small bodies do not maintain internal temperature in cold weather. Show diagrammatically the change in the population and explain what selective pressures took place.

a. directional selection
b. stabilizing selection
c. disruptive selection
d. diversifying selection

43. Five new species of bacteria were discovered in Antarctic ice core samples. The nucleotide (base sequences of rRNA subunits were determined for the new species. The table below shows the number of nucleotide differences between the species.

Species	1	2	3	4	5
1	-	3	19	18	27
2		-	19	18	26
3			-	1	27
4				-	27

Which of the following phylogenetic trees is most consistent with the data?

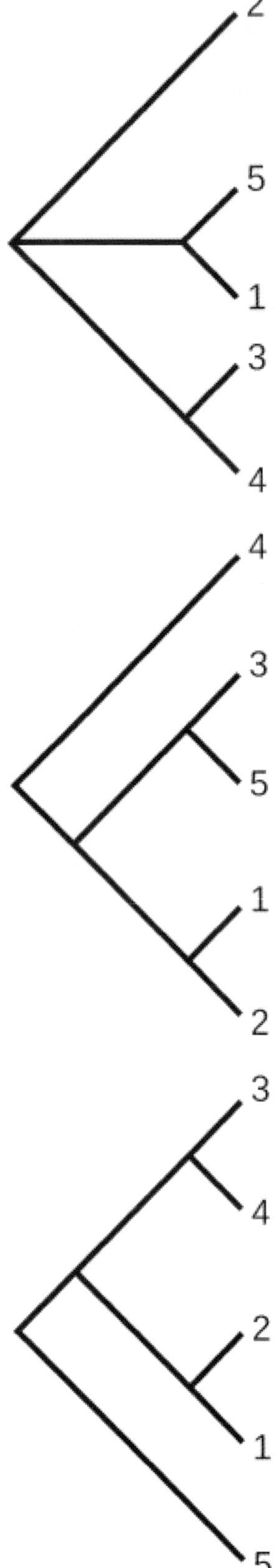

d. 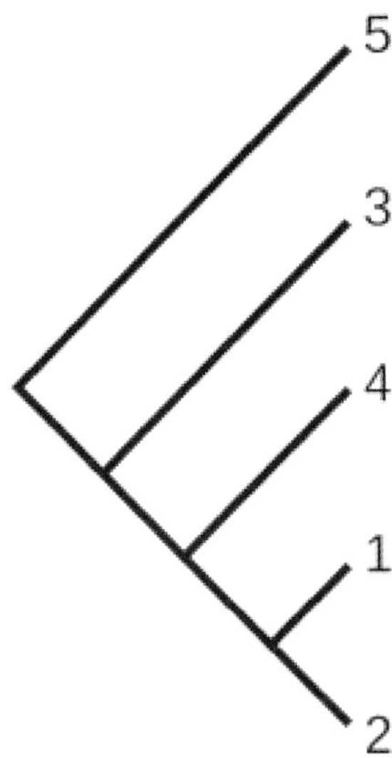

44. Draw the phylogenetic tree for the species below. Identify where on the tree each feature evolved.

	Amniotic Egg	Endotherm	Feathers	Lungs	Vertebrae	Notochord
Snake	Y	N	N	Y	Y	Y
Ostrich	Y	Y	Y	Y	Y	Y
Shark	N	N	N	N	Y	Y
Frog	N	N	N	Y	Y	Y
Lancelet	N	N	N	N	N	Y

Figure 20.20

a. The ostrich branched off first, followed by the snake, then the frog, then the shark and then the lancelet.
b. The shark branched off first, followed by the lancelet, then the frog, then the ostrich and then the snake.
c. The lancelet branched off first, followed by the shark, then the frog, then the snake and then the ostrich.
d. The lancelet branched off first, followed by the shark, then the ostrich, then the snake and then the frog.

45. Barbara McClintock discovered transposons while working on maize genetics. What are the transposons composed of when they are able to shift from one location to another?

a. segments of RNA
b. Plasmids
c. segments of DNA
d. proteins

46. What is Horizontal Gene Transfer (HGT)?

a. the proposal that eukaryotes developed a nucleus first, and then their mitochondrion
b. the transmission of genetic material from one species to another through mechanisms other than from parent to offspring
c. the fusion of two prokaryotic genomes
d. the division of kingdom in the taxonomic classification

47. What is referred to as the transfer of genes by a mechanism that does not involve asexual reproduction?

a. web of life
b. meiosis
c. gene fusion
d. horizontal gene transfer

48. Which of the following describes small, virus-like particles that act as a mechanism of gene transfer between prokaryotes?

a. gene transfer agents
b. horizontal gene transfer
c. vertical gene transfer
d. basal taxon

SCIENCE PRACTICE CHALLENGE QUESTIONS

49.

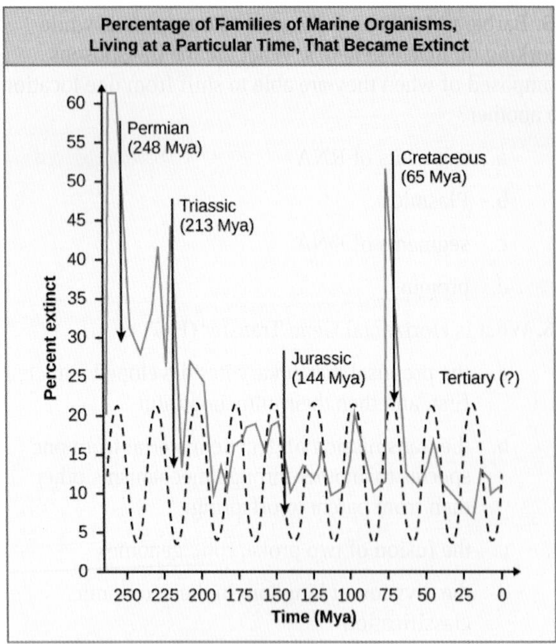

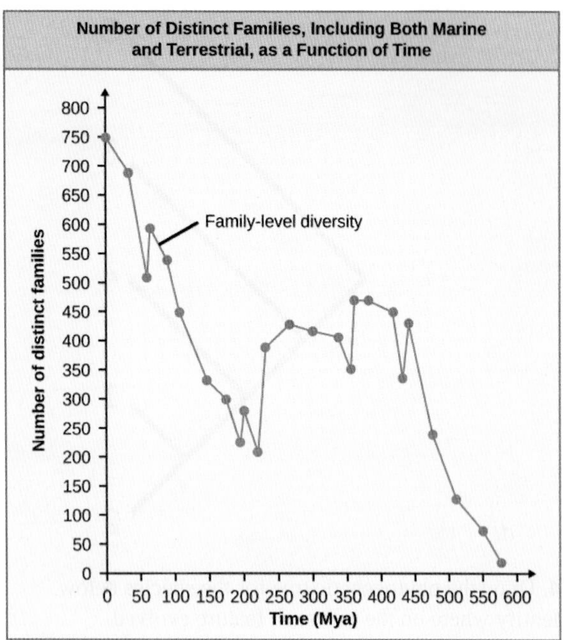

The figure shows a plot of the fraction, as a percentage, of families of marine organisms, living at a particular point in time that became extinct (vanished from the fossil record) in the next geological moment. These mass extinctions mark the ends of geologic periods. For example, the Triassic period ended around 213 million years ago (Mya).

A. The fact that evolution is an ongoing process is illustrated by these data. Whether the process displays a pattern involving regular intervals is a question that has been raised. Of those who believe periodicity is present, a period of 26 million years is favored. A wave with this periodicity is drawn on the figure. **Evaluate** the evidence provided in terms of agreement and disagreement with the marine extinction record.

The Cretaceous and Jurassic were periods of warm landmasses covered by a shallow sea. The ends of these periods are known to be due to asteroids that left a sedimentary trace. At the end of the Triassic, there is no evidence of an asteroid impact. Instead, there was massive volcanism associated with the opening of the Atlantic Ocean, a four-fold increase in carbon dioxide, and a 3–6 °C temperature rise (A. Marzoli et al., *Science*, 1999). Macrofossil, spore, and pollen data show that marine animal species declined much more than marine plant species (L. Mander et al., *Proc Natl Acad Sci*, 2010). The cause of the end of the Permian period is less uncertain, but an 8-°C temperature rise has been established (McElwain and Punyasena, *Trends in Ecology and Evolution*, 2007). Both terrestrial and marine taxa were affected.

The graph estimates the number of distinct families, including both marine and terrestrial, as a function of time before the present. Note that the time scale for this graph is much longer than that of the previous graph.

Figure 20.21

B. **Analyze** this graph by:

- identifying times of mass extinctions
- posing a question regarding any difference between the graph of extinctions of marine life and the graph of family-level diversity
- explaining the slope of the graph of family diversity following a mass extinction event

50.

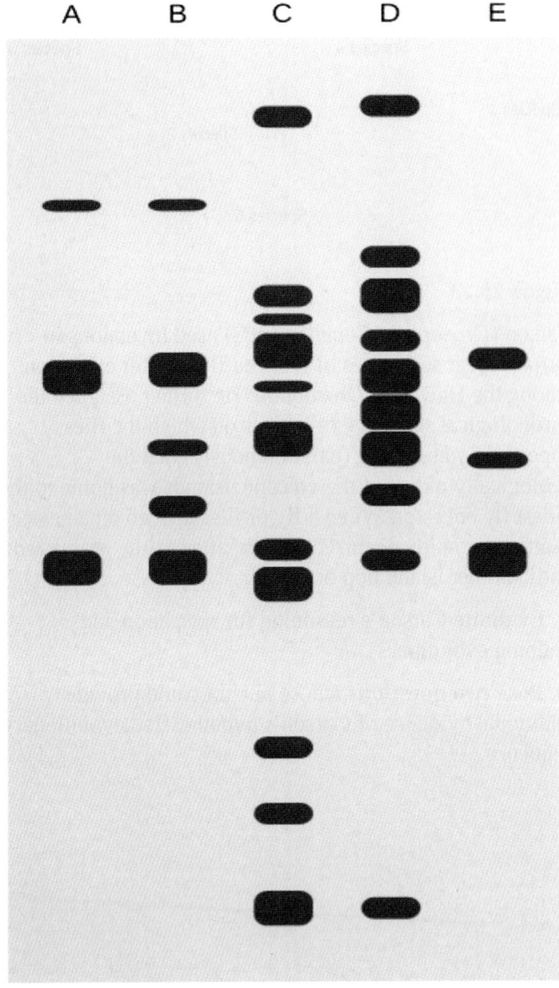

Lactate dehydrogenase, an enzyme involved in glycolysis, from several species are compared using a Southern blot technique in the figure on the left: (A) yeast; (B) snail; (C) mouse; (D) rat; and (E) human (after K. Webster, *Journal of Experimental Biology* 2003).

A. **Justify** the claim that these data provide evidence that supports glycolysis as a conserved core property.

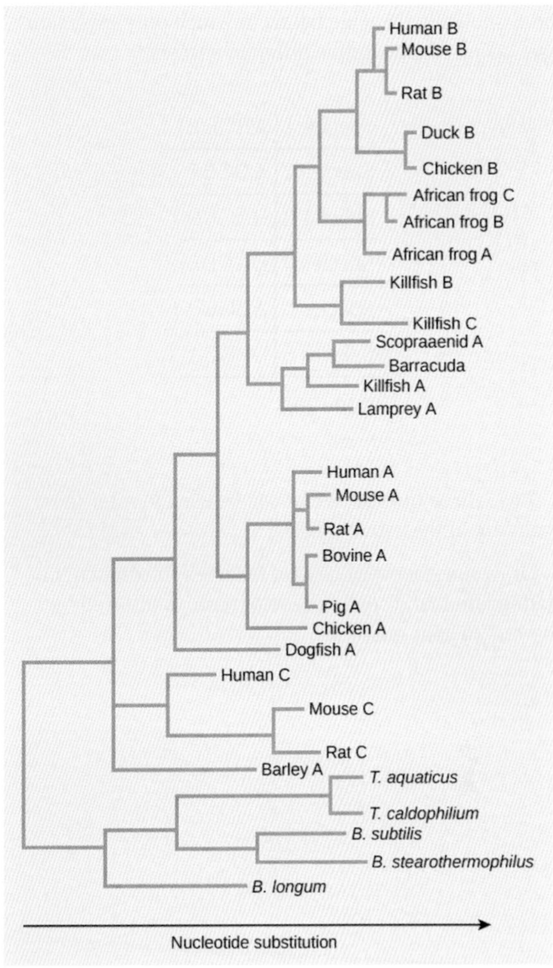

Figure 20.22

There are three forms of lactate dehydrogenase whose roles vary within an organism: LDH-A, -B, and -C. The question arises as to the origins of each. The cladogram on the right (after S. Tsuji et al., *Proc Natl Acad Sci* 1994) displays a proposed relatedness of variations in LDHs over many species.

B. Based on these data, **describe** the differences between the likely evolutionary sequences of LDH-A, -B, and -C in the African frog and in humans.

C. **Evaluate** the claim that in both species (African frog and human), LDH-C is the most recently evolved form of the enzyme.

51. Nucleotide-repeat sequences often occur within the intron, and sequence variation is neutral, that is, there is no selection. For example, the nucleotide-repeat sequence labeled A might be ACGGGC, and the repeat sequence labeled B might be ACTGGT. Repeat sequences evolve by single-step duplication, deletion, and inversion, rather than by single-nucleotide substitution. Because these repeat sequences can be used to infer phylogeny, a phylogenetic tree can be hypothesized based on the principle of parsimony—the simplest explanation is the best explanation. Consider the repeat sequences A, B, C, D, and E shown in the table below in which only inversions have occurred among five different species.

Species 1	ABCDE
Species 2	ADCBE
Species 3	BACED
Species 4	DACBE
Species 5	ABCED
Species 6	DEBCA

Table 20.2

A. **Pose three questions** that can be used to infer the evolution of these five species.

B. Draw lines between nearest relatives **to construct a cladogram** that displays the relationships inferred by answers to your questions.

Figure 20.23

Carson (*Drosophila Genetics* 1983) used inversions in intron-repeat sequences of the fruit fly to infer evolution among the Hawaiian *Drosophila*. He further assigned the chronological sequence of islands on which the flies appeared by assuming (parsimoniously) that the geologically oldest of the volcanic islands was home to the oldest fly ancestor. When a fly or flies arrived on a newer island, speciation occurred, which, after a time, stabilized until another island hop occurred.

C. **Evaluate** Carson's reasoning for speciation and ongoing evolution.

D. **Pose two questions** whose pursuit could provide additional evidence of Carson's hypothesized evolutionary sequence.

21 | VIRUSES

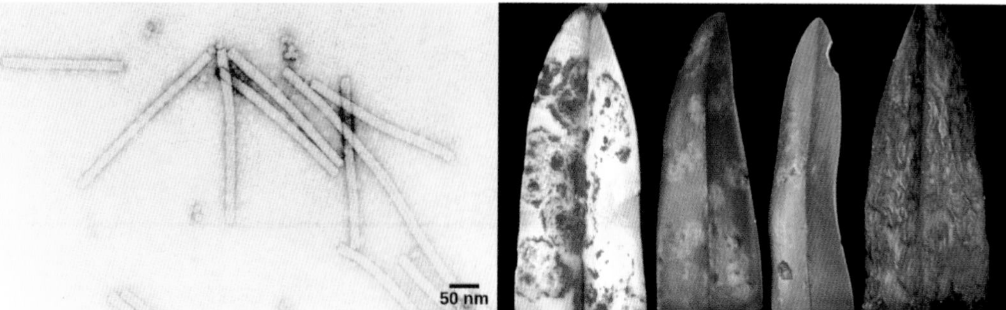

Figure 21.1 The tobacco mosaic virus (left), seen here by transmission electron microscopy, was the first virus to be discovered. The virus causes disease in tobacco and other plants, such as the orchid (right). (credit a: USDA ARS; credit b: modification of work by USDA Forest Service, Department of Plant Pathology Archive North Carolina State University; scale-bar data from Matt Russell)

Chapter Outline

Introduction

Have you ever had the measles? Like many other diseases, it begins with a fever, runny nose, and sore throat. Soon after, a rash begins to cover the body. In about 30% of measles cases other complications develop, such as pneumonia, encephalitis (swelling of the brain), and even death. Though the first recorded account of the measles was in the 9th century, it was not until 1912 that healthcare providers in the United States began reporting cases. Between 1912 and 1922, there were over 6,000 deaths related to the measles. This trend continued until 1963, when the first measles vaccine became available. The measles was declared eliminated from the United States in 2000 primarily due to the fact that the vast majority of children were receiving two doses of the vaccine. On January 23, 2015, the Center for Disease Control issued a health advisory about an outbreak of measles in several states . The outbreak originated at a popular theme park in California in December 2014 when an infected tourist from another country visited the theme park. Many of the people who became infected were not vaccinated or had not received the second dose of the vaccination. You can read more about the health advisory at the CDC website (http://Openstaxcollege.org/l/32measles) .

No one knows exactly when viruses emerged or from where they came, since viruses do not leave historical footprints such as fossils. Modern viruses are thought to be a mosaic of bits and pieces of nucleic acids picked up from various sources along their respective evolutionary paths. Viruses are **acellular**, parasitic entities that are not classified within any kingdom. Unlike most living organisms, viruses are not cells and cannot divide. Instead, they infect a host cell and use the host's replication processes to produce identical progeny virus particles. Viruses infect organisms as diverse as bacteria, plants, and animals. They exist in a netherworld between a living organism and a nonliving entity. Living things grow, metabolize, and reproduce. Viruses replicate, but to do so, they are entirely dependent on their host cells. They do not metabolize or grow, but are assembled in their mature form.

21.1 | Viral Evolution, Morphology, and Classification

In this section, you will explore the following questions:

- How were viruses first discovered and how are they detected?
- What three hypotheses describe the evolution of viruses?
- What is the basic structure of a virus?
- How are viruses classified?

Connection for AP® Courses

The first organisms that originated about 3.5 billion years ago were prokaryotes that possessed the structures and metabolic processes associated with cells (refer to the Cell Structure chapter). As discussed in the chapter on cell structure, prokaryotic cells are much smaller than eukaryotic cells and inhabit just about every square inch of our planet, from the most inhospitable environments to the surface of the skin. Viruses are much smaller than prokaryotes and much simpler in structure. They must reproduce inside a host cell. Their origin is still a mystery to us, but we do know that they can make us very sick.

Viruses have a basic structure: a DNA or RNA core surrounded by an outer capsid of proteins. Some viruses have an outer phospholipid envelope. As we will explore in more detail, many viruses use some sort of glycoprotein to attach to their host cells. Viruses infect all known cell types and use the host cell's replication proteins and metabolic machinery to replicate. Classification of viruses is challenging, but one method categorizes them based on how they produce their mRNA. Retroviruses (also called RNA viruses) use the enzyme reverse transcriptase to transcribe DNA from RNA. (In the Genes and Proteins chapter we learned that the usual flow of genetic information is from DNA to RNA to protein.) Common viruses include bacteriophage T4, adenovirus, and HIV retrovirus.

Information presented and the examples highlighted in the section support concepts outlined in Big Idea 3 of the AP® Biology Curriculum Framework. The AP® Learning Objectives listed in the Curriculum Framework provide a transparent foundation for the AP® Biology course, an inquiry-based laboratory experience, instructional activities, and AP® exam questions. A learning objective merges required content with one or more of the seven science practices.

Big Idea 3	Living systems store, retrieve, transmit and respond to information essential to life processes.
Enduring Understanding 3.A	Heritable information provides for continuity of life.
Essential Knowledge	**3.A.1** DNA, and in some cases RNA, is the primary source of heritable information.
Science Practice	**6.5** The student can evaluate alternative scientific explanations.
Learning Objective	**3.1** The student is able to construct scientific explanations that use the structures and mechanisms of DNA and RNA to support the claim that DNA and, in some cases, that RNA are the primary sources of heritable information.

The Science Practice Challenge Questions contain additional test questions for this section that will help you prepare for the AP exam. These questions address the following standards:
[APLO 2.20][APLO 3.3][APLO 3.29][APLO 3.30][APLO 2.22][APLO 2.26][APLO 1.31][APLO 1.27][APLO 1.30]

Discovery and Detection

Viruses were first discovered after the development of a porcelain filter, called the Chamberland-Pasteur filter, which could remove all bacteria visible in the microscope from any liquid sample. In 1886, Adolph Meyer demonstrated that a disease of tobacco plants, tobacco mosaic disease, could be transferred from a diseased plant to a healthy one via liquid plant extracts. In 1892, Dmitri Ivanowski showed that this disease could be transmitted in this way even after the Chamberland-Pasteur filter had removed all viable bacteria from the extract. Still, it was many years before it was proven that these "filterable" infectious agents were not simply very small bacteria but were a new type of very small, disease-causing particle.

Virions, single virus particles, are very small, about 20–250 nanometers in diameter. These individual virus particles are the infectious form of a virus outside the host cell. Unlike bacteria (which are about 100-times larger), we cannot see viruses with a light microscope, with the exception of some large virions of the poxvirus family. It was not until the development of the electron microscope in the late 1930s that scientists got their first good view of the structure of the tobacco mosaic virus (TMV) (Figure 21.1) and other viruses (Figure 21.2). The surface structure of virions can be observed by both scanning and transmission electron microscopy, whereas the internal structures of the virus can only be observed in images from a transmission electron microscope. The use of these technologies has allowed for the discovery of many viruses of all types of living organisms. They were initially grouped by shared morphology. Later, groups of viruses were classified by the type of nucleic acid they contained, DNA or RNA, and whether their nucleic acid was single- or double-stranded. More recently, molecular analysis of viral replicative cycles has further refined their classification.

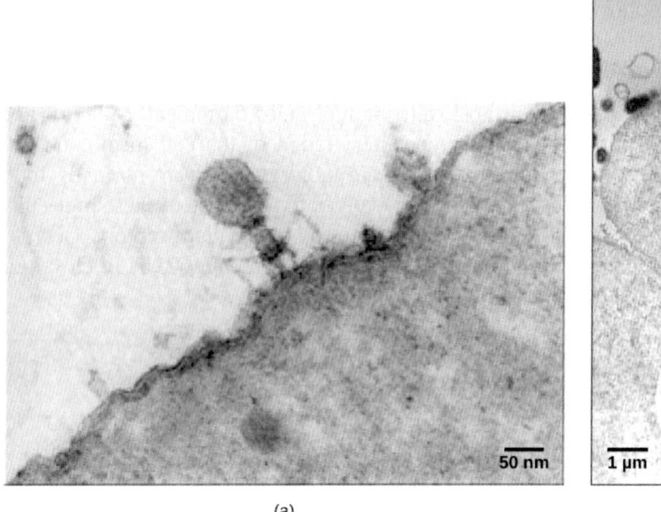

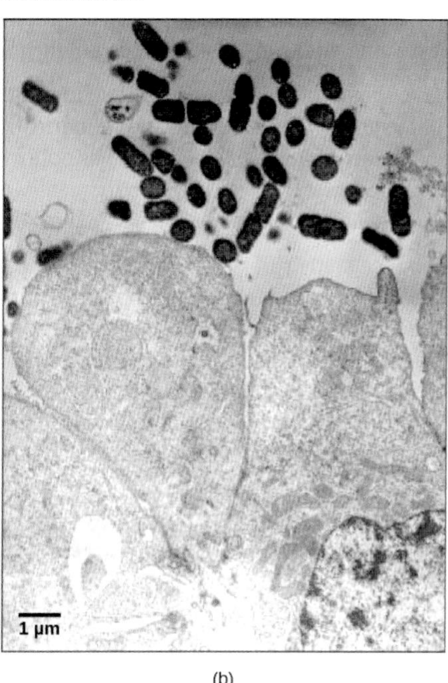

(a) (b)

Figure 21.2 In these transmission electron micrographs, (a) a virus is dwarfed by the bacterial cell it infects, while (b) these *E. coli* cells are dwarfed by cultured colon cells. (credit a: modification of work by U.S. Dept. of Energy, Office of Science, LBL, PBD; credit b: modification of work by J.P. Nataro and S. Sears, unpub. data, CDC; scale-bar data from Matt Russell)

Evolution of Viruses

Although biologists have accumulated a significant amount of knowledge about how present-day viruses evolve, much less is known about how viruses originated in the first place. When exploring the evolutionary history of most organisms, scientists can look at fossil records and similar historic evidence. However, viruses do not fossilize, so researchers must conjecture by investigating how today's viruses evolve and by using biochemical and genetic information to create speculative virus histories.

While most findings agree that viruses don't have a single common ancestor, scholars have yet to find a single hypothesis about virus origins that is fully accepted in the field. One such hypothesis, called devolution or the regressive hypothesis, proposes to explain the origin of viruses by suggesting that viruses evolved from free-living cells. However, many components of how this process might have occurred are a mystery. A second hypothesis (called escapist or the progressive hypothesis) accounts for viruses having either an RNA or a DNA genome and suggests that viruses originated from RNA and DNA molecules that escaped from a host cell. A third hypothesis posits a system of self-replication similar to that of other self-replicating molecules, likely evolving alongside the cells they rely on as hosts; studies of some plant pathogens support this hypothesis.

As technology advances, scientists may develop and refine further hypotheses to explain the origin of viruses. The emerging field called virus molecular systematics attempts to do just that through comparisons of sequenced genetic material. These researchers hope to one day better understand the origin of viruses, a discovery that could lead to advances in the treatments for the ailments they produce.

Viral Morphology

Viruses are acellular, meaning they are biological entities that do not have a cellular structure. They therefore lack most of the components of cells, such as organelles, ribosomes, and the plasma membrane. A virion consists of a nucleic acid core, an outer protein coating or **capsid**, and sometimes an outer **envelope** made of protein and phospholipid membranes derived from the host cell. Viruses may also contain additional proteins, such as enzymes. The most obvious difference between members of viral families is their morphology, which is quite diverse. An interesting feature of viral complexity is that the complexity of the host does not correlate with the complexity of the virion. Some of the most complex virion structures are observed in bacteriophages, viruses that infect the simplest living organisms, bacteria.

Morphology

Viruses come in many shapes and sizes, but these are consistent and distinct for each viral family. All virions have a nucleic acid genome covered by a protective layer of proteins, called a capsid. The capsid is made up of protein subunits called **capsomeres**. Some viral capsids are simple polyhedral "spheres," whereas others are quite complex in structure.

In general, the shapes of viruses are classified into four groups: filamentous, isometric (or icosahedral), enveloped, and head and tail. Filamentous viruses are long and cylindrical. Many plant viruses are filamentous, including TMV. Isometric viruses have shapes that are roughly spherical, such as poliovirus or herpesviruses. Enveloped viruses have membranes surrounding capsids. Animal viruses, such as HIV, are frequently enveloped. Head and tail viruses infect bacteria and have a head that is similar to icosahedral viruses and a tail shape like filamentous viruses.

Many viruses use some sort of glycoprotein to attach to their host cells via molecules on the cell called **viral receptors** (Figure 21.3). For these viruses, attachment is a requirement for later penetration of the cell membrane, so they can complete their replication inside the cell. The receptors that viruses use are molecules that are normally found on cell surfaces and have their own physiological functions. Viruses have simply evolved to make use of these molecules for their own replication. For example, HIV uses the CD4 molecule on T lymphocytes as one of its receptors. CD4 is a type of molecule called a cell adhesion molecule, which functions to keep different types of immune cells in close proximity to each other during the generation of a T lymphocyte immune response.

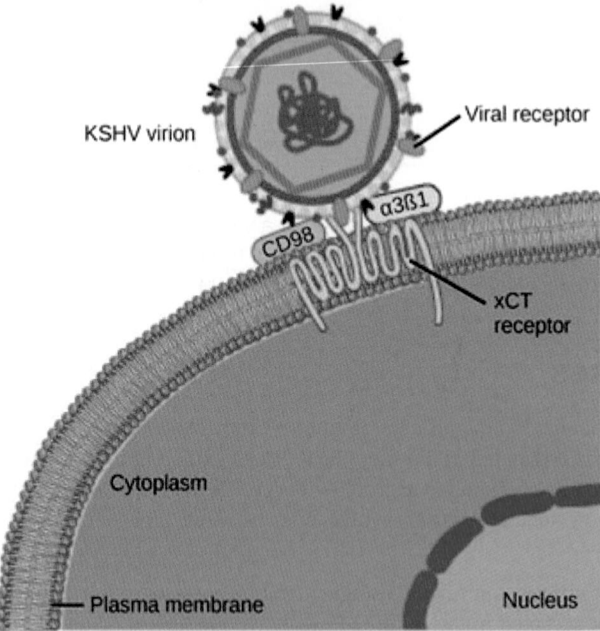

Figure 21.3 The KSHV virus binds the xCT receptor on the surface of human cells. xCT receptors protect cells against stress. Stressed cells express more xCT receptors than non-stressed cells. The KSHV virion causes cells to become stressed, thereby increasing expression of the receptor to which it binds. (credit: modification of work by NIAID, NIH)

Among the most complex virions known, the T4 bacteriophage, which infects the *Escherichia coli* bacterium, has a tail structure that the virus uses to attach to host cells and a head structure that houses its DNA.

Adenovirus, a non-enveloped animal virus that causes respiratory illnesses in humans, uses glycoprotein spikes protruding from its capsomeres to attach to host cells. Non-enveloped viruses also include those that cause polio (poliovirus), plantar warts (papillomavirus), and hepatitis A (hepatitis A virus).

Enveloped virions like HIV, the causative agent in AIDS, consist of nucleic acid (RNA in the case of HIV) and capsid proteins surrounded by a phospholipid bilayer envelope and its associated proteins. Glycoproteins embedded in the viral envelope are used to attach to host cells. Other envelope proteins are the **matrix proteins** that stabilize the envelope and often play a role in the assembly of progeny virions. Chicken pox, influenza, and mumps are examples of diseases caused by viruses with envelopes. Because of the fragility of the envelope, non-enveloped viruses are more resistant to changes in temperature, pH, and some disinfectants than enveloped viruses.

Overall, the shape of the virion and the presence or absence of an envelope tell us little about what disease the virus may cause or what species it might infect, but they are still useful means to begin viral classification (Figure 21.4).

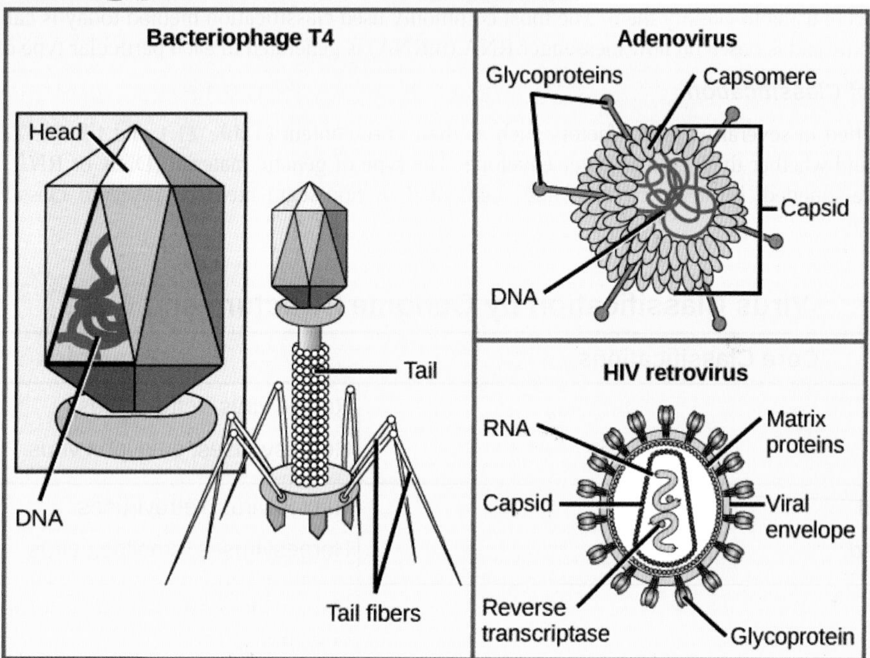

Figure 21.4 Viruses can be either complex in shape or relatively simple. This figure shows three relatively complex virions: the bacteriophage T4, with its DNA-containing head group and tail fibers that attach to host cells; adenovirus, which uses spikes from its capsid to bind to host cells; and HIV, which uses glycoproteins embedded in its envelope to bind to host cells. Notice that HIV has proteins called matrix proteins, internal to the envelope, which help stabilize virion shape. (credit "bacteriophage, adenovirus": modification of work by NCBI, NIH; credit "HIV retrovirus": modification of work by NIAID, NIH)

Which of the following statements about viral structure is true?

a. Viruses are very similar in structure.
b. The capsomere is made up of small protein subunits called capsids.
c. DNA is the genetic material in all viruses.
d. Glycoproteins help the virus attach to the host cell.

Types of Nucleic Acid

Unlike nearly all living organisms that use DNA as their genetic material, viruses may use either DNA or RNA as theirs. The **virus core** contains the genome or total genetic content of the virus. Viral genomes tend to be small, containing only those genes that encode proteins that the virus cannot get from the host cell. This genetic material may be single- or double-stranded. It may also be linear or circular. While most viruses contain a single nucleic acid, others have genomes that have several, which are called segments.

In DNA viruses, the viral DNA directs the host cell's replication proteins to synthesize new copies of the viral genome and to transcribe and translate that genome into viral proteins. DNA viruses cause human diseases such as chickenpox and hepatitis B.

RNA viruses contain only RNA as their genetic material. To replicate their genomes in the host cell, the RNA viruses encode enzymes that can replicate RNA into DNA, which cannot be done by the host cell. These RNA polymerase enzymes are more likely to make copying errors than DNA polymerases, and therefore often make mistakes during transcription. For this reason, mutations in RNA viruses occur more frequently than in DNA viruses. This causes them to change and adapt more rapidly to their host. Human diseases caused by RNA viruses include hepatitis C, measles, and rabies.

Virus Classification

To understand the features shared among different groups of viruses, a classification scheme is necessary. As most viruses are not thought to have evolved from a common ancestor, however, the methods that scientists use to classify living things are not very useful. Biologists have used several classification systems in the past, based on the morphology and genetics of the different viruses. However, these earlier classification methods grouped viruses differently, based on which features of the virus they were using to classify them. The most commonly used classification method today is called the Baltimore classification scheme and is based on how messenger RNA (mRNA) is generated in each particular type of virus.

Past Systems of Classification

Viruses are classified in several ways: by factors such as their core content (Table 21.1 and Figure 21.3), the structure of their capsids, and whether they have an outer envelope. The type of genetic material (DNA or RNA) and its structure (single- or double-stranded, linear or circular, and segmented or non-segmented) are used to classify the virus core structures.

Virus Classification by Genome Structure and Core

Core Classifications	Examples
RNA DNA	Rabies virus, retroviruses Herpesviruses, smallpox virus
Single-stranded Double-stranded	Rabies virus, retroviruses Herpesviruses, smallpox virus
Linear Circular	Rabies virus, retroviruses, herpesviruses, smallpox virus Papillomaviruses, many bacteriophages
Non-segmented: genome consists of a single segment of genetic material Segmented: genome is divided into multiple segments	Parainfluenza viruses Influenza viruses

Table 21.1

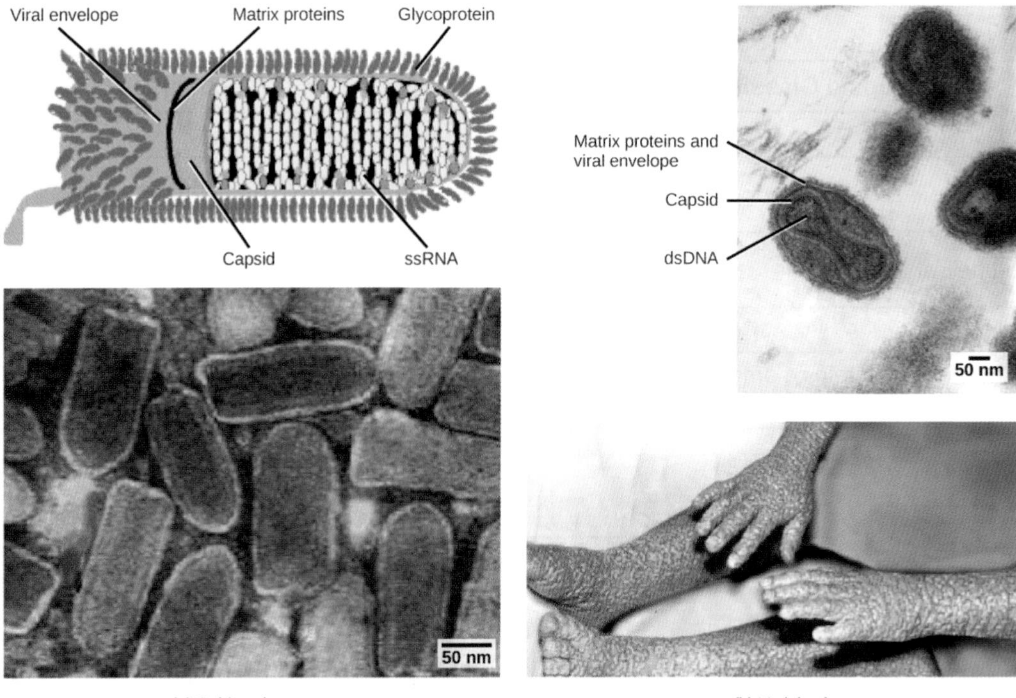

Figure 21.5 Viruses are classified based on their core genetic material and capsid design. (a) Rabies virus has a single-stranded RNA (ssRNA) core and an enveloped helical capsid, whereas (b) variola virus, the causative agent of smallpox, has a double-stranded DNA (dsDNA) core and a complex capsid. Rabies transmission occurs when saliva from an infected mammal enters a wound. The virus travels through neurons in the peripheral nervous system to the central nervous system where it impairs brain function, and then travels to other tissues. The virus can infect any mammal, and most die within weeks of infection. Smallpox is a human virus transmitted by inhalation of the variola virus, localized in the skin, mouth, and throat, which causes a characteristic rash. Before its eradication in 1979, infection resulted in a 30–35 percent mortality rate. (credit "rabies diagram": modification of work by CDC; "rabies micrograph": modification of work by Dr. Fred Murphy, CDC; credit "small pox micrograph": modification of work by Dr. Fred Murphy, Sylvia Whitfield, CDC; credit "smallpox photo": modification of work by CDC; scale-bar data from Matt Russell)

Viruses can also be classified by the design of their capsids (Figure 21.4 and Figure 21.5). Capsids are classified as naked icosahedral, enveloped icosahedral, enveloped helical, naked helical, and complex (Figure 21.6 and Figure 21.7). The type of genetic material (DNA or RNA) and its structure (single- or double-stranded, linear or circular, and segmented or non-segmented) are used to classify the virus core structures (Table 21.2).

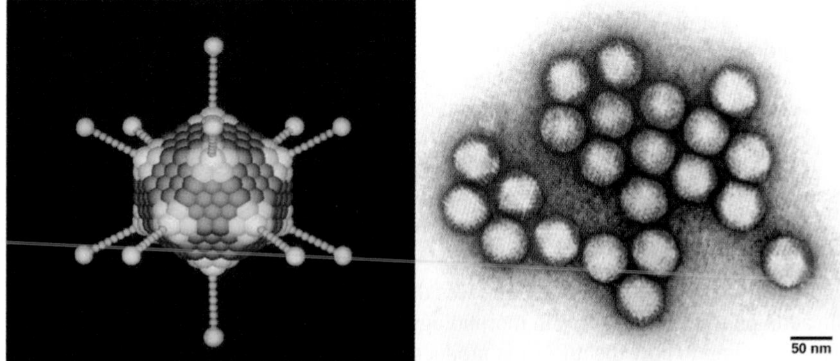

Figure 21.6 Adenovirus (left) is depicted with a double-stranded DNA genome enclosed in an icosahedral capsid that is 90–100 nm across. The virus, shown clustered in the micrograph (right), is transmitted orally and causes a variety of illnesses in vertebrates, including human eye and respiratory infections. (credit "adenovirus": modification of work by Dr. Richard Feldmann, National Cancer Institute; credit "micrograph": modification of work by Dr. G. William Gary, Jr., CDC; scale-bar data from Matt Russell)

Virus Classification by Capsid Structure

Capsid Classification	Examples
Naked icosahedral	Hepatitis A virus, polioviruses
Enveloped icosahedral	Epstein-Barr virus, herpes simplex virus, rubella virus, yellow fever virus, HIV-1
Enveloped helical	Influenza viruses, mumps virus, measles virus, rabies virus
Naked helical	Tobacco mosaic virus
Complex with many proteins; some have combinations of icosahedral and helical capsid structures	Herpesviruses, smallpox virus, hepatitis B virus, T4 bacteriophage

Table 21.2

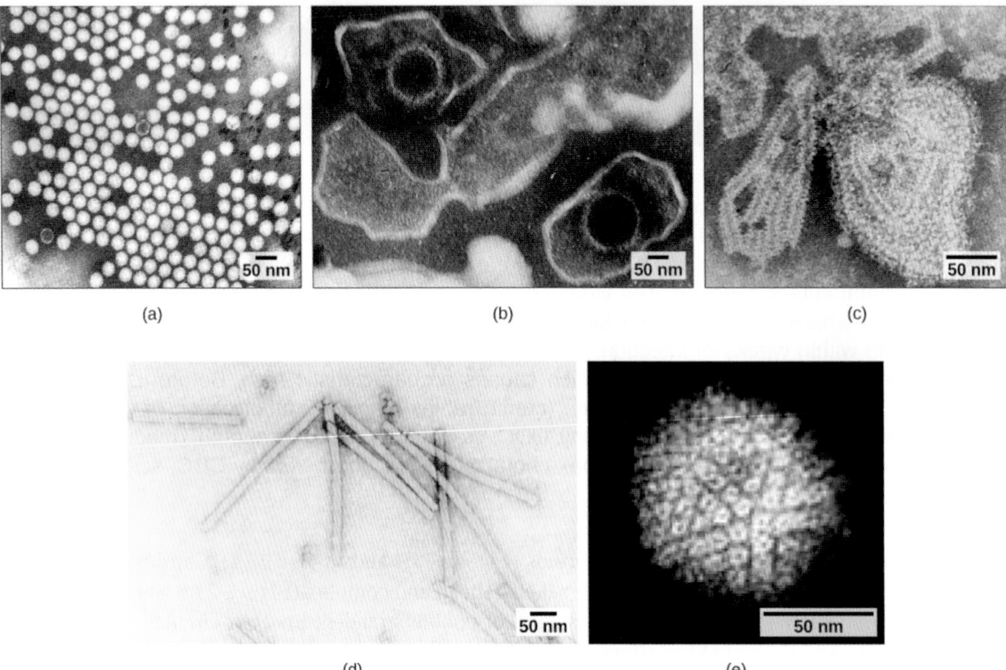

Figure 21.7 Transmission electron micrographs of various viruses show their structures. The capsid of the (a) polio virus is naked icosahedral; (b) the Epstein-Barr virus capsid is enveloped icosahedral; (c) the mumps virus capsid is an enveloped helix; (d) the tobacco mosaic virus capsid is naked helical; and (e) the herpesvirus capsid is complex. (credit a: modification of work by Dr. Fred Murphy, Sylvia Whitfield; credit b: modification of work by Liza Gross; credit c: modification of work by Dr. F. A. Murphy, CDC; credit d: modification of work by USDA ARS; credit e: modification of work by Linda Stannard, Department of Medical Microbiology, University of Cape Town, South Africa, NASA; scale-bar data from Matt Russell)

Baltimore Classification

The most commonly used system of virus classification was developed by Nobel Prize-winning biologist David Baltimore in the early 1970s. In addition to the differences in morphology and genetics mentioned above, the Baltimore classification scheme groups viruses according to how the mRNA is produced during the replicative cycle of the virus.

Group I viruses contain double-stranded DNA (dsDNA) as their genome. Their mRNA is produced by transcription in much the same way as with cellular DNA. **Group II** viruses have single-stranded DNA (ssDNA) as their genome. They convert their single-stranded genomes into a dsDNA intermediate before transcription to mRNA can occur. **Group III** viruses use dsRNA as their genome. The strands separate, and one of them is used as a template for the generation of mRNA using the RNA-dependent RNA polymerase encoded by the virus. **Group IV** viruses have ssRNA as their genome with a positive polarity. **Positive polarity** means that the genomic RNA can serve directly as mRNA. Intermediates of dsRNA, called **replicative intermediates**, are made in the process of copying the genomic RNA. Multiple, full-length RNA strands of negative polarity (complementary to the positive-stranded genomic RNA) are formed from these intermediates, which may then serve as templates for the production of RNA with positive polarity, including both full-length genomic RNA and shorter viral mRNAs. **Group V** viruses contain ssRNA genomes with a **negative polarity**, meaning that their sequence is complementary to the mRNA. As with Group IV viruses, dsRNA intermediates are used to make copies of the genome and produce mRNA. In this case, the negative-stranded genome can be converted directly to mRNA. Additionally, full-length positive RNA strands are made to serve as templates for the production of the negative-stranded genome. **Group VI** viruses have diploid (two copies) ssRNA genomes that must be converted, using the enzyme **reverse transcriptase**, to dsDNA; the dsDNA is then transported to the nucleus of the host cell and inserted into the host genome. Then, mRNA can be produced by transcription of the viral DNA that was integrated into the host genome. **Group VII** viruses have partial dsDNA genomes and make ssRNA intermediates that act as mRNA, but are also converted back into dsDNA genomes by reverse transcriptase, necessary for genome replication. The characteristics of each group in the Baltimore classification are summarized in Table 21.3 with examples of each group.

Baltimore Classification

Group	Characteristics	Mode of mRNA Production	Example
I	Double-stranded DNA	mRNA is transcribed directly from the DNA template	Herpes simplex (herpesvirus)
II	Single-stranded DNA	DNA is converted to double-stranded form before RNA is transcribed	Canine parvovirus (parvovirus)
III	Double-stranded RNA	mRNA is transcribed from the RNA genome	Childhood gastroenteritis (rotavirus)
IV	Single stranded RNA (+)	Genome functions as mRNA	Common cold (pircornavirus)
V	Single stranded RNA (-)	mRNA is transcribed from the RNA genome	Rabies (rhabdovirus)
VI	Single stranded RNA viruses with reverse transcriptase	Reverse transcriptase makes DNA from the RNA genome; DNA is then incorporated in the host genome; mRNA is transcribed from the incorporated DNA	Human immunodeficiency virus (HIV)
VII	Double stranded DNA viruses with reverse transcriptase	The viral genome is double-stranded DNA, but viral DNA is replicated through an RNA intermediate; the RNA may serve directly as mRNA or as a template to make mRNA	Hepatitis B virus (hepadnavirus)

Table 21.3

21.2 | Virus Infection and Hosts

In this section, you will explore the following questions:

- What are the steps in viral replication, and what events occur in each?
- What is the difference between the lytic and lysogenic cycles of virus replication?
- How are plant and animal viruses transmitted, what are examples of virus-caused diseases in plants and animals, and what are the economic impacts of plant viruses?

Connection for AP® Courses

Viruses differ from other organisms in their method of replication. Viruses replicate within a living host cell, producing changes in the cell that often result in the death of the infected cell. Thus, viruses are considered intracellular parasites. Viral replication involves several steps: attachment, penetration, replication, assembly, and release. Viruses are host-specific because they only can attach to and infect cells of certain organisms. Cells that a virus may use to replicate are called **permissive**. The virus attacks the host cell by first attaching to a specific receptor site on the membrane of the host cell. Next, the viral nucleic acid, either DNA or RNA, enters the host cell, either naked, leaving the protein capsid behind, or with the capsid. If the capsid enters the cell, an additional uncoating step is needed. Viral nucleic acid then becomes available for replication and transcription. The last stage of viral replication is the release of the new virions produced by the host that are able to infect other cells. Depending on the type of virus, the replication cycle facilitates the transfer of genetic information through the **lytic** and **lysogenic** cycles.

Bacteriophages, such as T4 are viruses that infect bacterial cells, can enter both the lytic and lysogenic cycles. Animal viruses cause a variety of infections, for example, hepatitis C, herpes, HPV, colds, and flu. Occasionally, viruses can "hide" and remain latent (dormant) in cells such as nerve or liver cells for months, or even years; for example, the varicella-zoster virus that causes chickenpox in children can reactivate in adults to cause the painful condition known as "shingles." Oncogenic viruses in animals can cause cancer by interfering with the regulation of the host cell cycle. Plant viruses can cause considerable economic damage caused by poor crop quality and quantity globally.

Information presented and the examples highlighted in the section support concepts outlined in Big Idea 3 of the AP® Biology Curriculum Framework. The AP® Learning Objectives listed in the Curriculum Framework provide a transparent foundation for the AP® Biology course, an inquiry-based laboratory experience, instructional activities, and AP® exam questions. A learning objective merges required content with one or more of the seven science practices.

Big Idea 3	Living systems store, retrieve, transmit and respond to information essential to life processes.
Enduring Understanding 3.C	The processing of genetic information is imperfect and is a source of genetic variation.
Essential Knowledge	**3.C.3** Viral replication results in genetic variation, and viral infection can introduce genetic variation into the hosts.
Science Practice	**6.2** The student can construct explanations of phenomena based on evidence produced through scientific practices.
Learning Objective	**3.29** The student is able to construct an explanation of how viruses introduce genetic variation in host organisms.
Essential Knowledge	**3.C.3** Viral replication results in genetic variation, and viral infection can introduce genetic variation into the hosts.
Science Practice	**1.4** The student can use representations and models to analyze situations or solve problems qualitatively and quantitatively.
Learning Objective	**3.30** The student is able to use representations and appropriate models to describe how viral replication introduces genetic variation in the viral population.

The Science Practice Challenge Questions contain additional test questions for this section that will help you prepare for the AP exam. These questions address the following standards:
[APLO 3.1][APLO 3.27][APLO 3.29][APLO 1.3][APLO 2.38][APLO 3.40][APLO 3.30]

Steps of Virus Infections

A virus must use cell processes to replicate. The viral replication cycle can produce dramatic biochemical and structural changes in the host cell, which may cause cell damage. These changes, called **cytopathic** (causing cell damage) effects, can change cell functions or even destroy the cell. Some infected cells, such as those infected by the common cold virus known as rhinovirus, die through **lysis** (bursting) or apoptosis (programmed cell death), releasing all progeny virions at once. The symptoms of viral diseases result from the immune response to the virus, which attempts to control and eliminate the virus from the body, and from cell damage caused by the virus. Many animal viruses leave the infected cells of the immune system by a process known as **budding**, where virions leave the cell individually. During the budding process, the cell does not undergo lysis and is not immediately killed. However, the damage to the cells that the virus infects may make it impossible for the cells to function normally, even though the cells remain alive for a period of time. Most productive viral infections follow similar steps in the virus replication cycle: attachment, penetration, uncoating, replication, assembly, and release (Figure 21.8).

Attachment

A virus attaches to a specific receptor site on the host cell membrane through attachment proteins in the capsid or via glycoproteins embedded in the viral envelope. The specificity of this interaction determines the host—and the cells within the host—that can be infected by a particular virus. This can be illustrated by thinking of several keys and several locks, where each key will fit only one specific lock.

This video (http://openstaxcollege.org/l/influenza) explains how influenza attacks the body.

The video shows how viruses replicate in our body. Using the terminology provided in the video, explain how a virus attaches to a cell in our body?

a. When the virus capsule makes contact with the cell, it bursts, and then the virions attach to the cell.

b. If a key on the virus fits a lock on the surface of the cell, the virus will attach to the cell.

c. The keys automatically attach to all the locks.

d. The welcoming committee interlocks with the virus.

Entry

The nucleic acid of bacteriophages enters the host cell naked, leaving the capsid outside the cell. Plant and animal viruses can enter through endocytosis, in which the cell membrane surrounds and engulfs the entire virus. Some enveloped viruses enter the cell when the viral envelope fuses directly with the cell membrane. Once inside the cell, the viral capsid is degraded, and the viral nucleic acid is released, which then becomes available for replication and transcription.

Replication and Assembly

The replication mechanism depends on the viral genome. DNA viruses usually use host cell proteins and enzymes to make additional DNA that is transcribed to messenger RNA (mRNA), which is then used to direct protein synthesis. RNA viruses usually use the RNA core as a template for synthesis of viral genomic RNA and mRNA. The viral mRNA directs the host cell to synthesize viral enzymes and capsid proteins, and assemble new virions. Of course, there are exceptions to this pattern. If a host cell does not provide the enzymes necessary for viral replication, viral genes supply the information to direct synthesis of the missing proteins. **Retroviruses** have an RNA genome that must be reverse transcribed into DNA, which then is incorporated into the host cell genome. They are within group VI of the Baltimore classification scheme. To convert RNA into DNA, retroviruses must contain genes that encode the virus-specific enzyme reverse transcriptase that transcribes an RNA template to DNA. Reverse transcription never occurs in uninfected host cells—the needed enzyme reverse transcriptase is only derived from the expression of viral genes within the infected host cells. The fact that some retroviruses produces some of its own enzymes not found in the host has allowed researchers to develop drugs that inhibit these enzymes. These drugs inhibit replication by reducing the activity of the enzyme without affecting the host's metabolism. This approach has led to the development of a variety of drugs used to treat these viruses and has been effective at reducing the number of infectious virions (copies of viral RNA) in the blood to non-detectable levels in people affected with the virus.

Egress

The last stage of viral replication is the release of the new virions produced in the host organism, where they are able to infect adjacent cells and repeat the replication cycle. As you've learned, some viruses are released when the host cell dies, and other viruses can leave infected cells by budding through the membrane without directly killing the cell.

visual CONNECTION

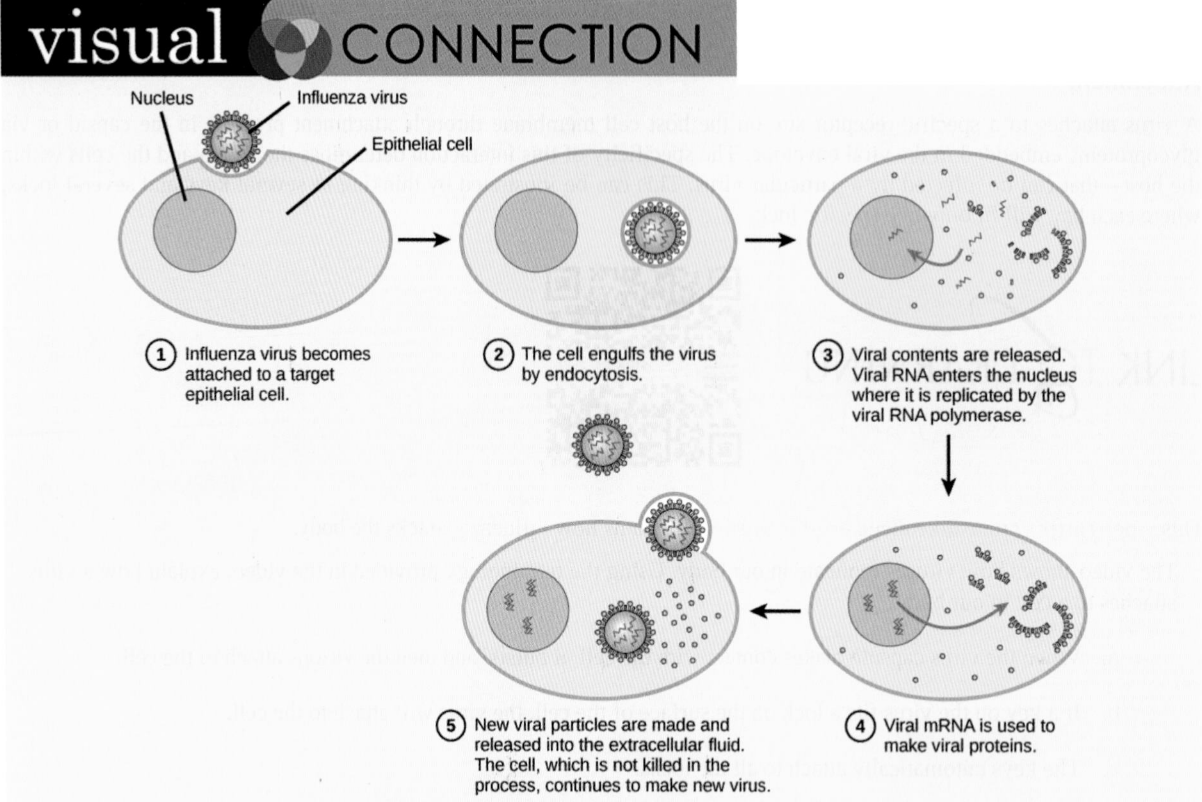

Figure 21.8 In influenza virus infection, glycoproteins attach to a host epithelial cell. As a result, the virus is engulfed. RNA and proteins are made and assembled into new virions.

Influenza virus is packaged in a viral envelope that fuses with the plasma membrane. This way, the virus can exit the host cell without killing it. What advantage does the virus gain by keeping the host cell alive?

a. The virus can live dormant in the host cell.
b. The virus capsid is upgraded.
c. Lysis causes the host cell to die.
d. The host cell can continue to make new virus particles.

Visit this website (http://openstaxcollege.org/l/32virusrep) to learn about viral replication.

How do viruses get inside a host cell?

a. To get inside the host cell, the virus forces the cell to lyse, or break open.

b. To get inside a host cell, he virus produces proteins and copies its genome.

c. To get inside a host cell, the virus attaches to a specific receptor site on the host cell.

d. To get inside a host cell, the virus can fuse the membrane of the cell.

Different Hosts and Their Viruses

As you've learned, viruses are often very specific as to which hosts and which cells within the host they will infect. This feature of a virus makes it specific to one or a few species of life on Earth. On the other hand, so many different types of viruses exist on Earth that nearly every living organism has its own set of viruses that tries to infect its cells. Even the smallest and simplest of cells, prokaryotic bacteria, may be attacked by specific types of viruses.

Bacteriophages

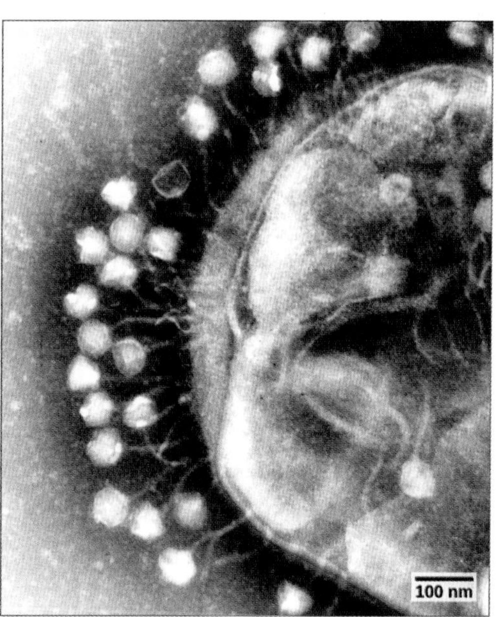

Figure 21.9 This transmission electron micrograph shows bacteriophages attached to a bacterial cell. (credit: modification of work by Dr. Graham Beards; scale-bar data from Matt Russell)

Bacteriophages are viruses that infect bacteria (Figure 21.9). When infection of a cell by a bacteriophage results in the production of new virions, the infection is said to be **productive**. If the virions are released by bursting the cell, the virus replicates by means of a lytic cycle (Figure 21.10). An example of a lytic bacteriophage is T4, which infects *Escherichia coli* found in the human intestinal tract. Sometimes, however, a virus can remain within the cell without being released. For example, when a temperate bacteriophage infects a bacterial cell, it replicates by means of a lysogenic cycle (Figure 21.10), and the viral genome is incorporated into the genome of the host cell. When the phage DNA is incorporated into the host cell genome, it is called a **prophage**. An example of a lysogenic bacteriophage is the λ (lambda) virus, which also infects the *E. coli* bacterium. Viruses that infect plant or animal cells may also undergo infections where they are not producing virions for long periods. An example is the animal herpesviruses, including herpes simplex viruses, the cause of herpes in humans. In a process called **latency**, these viruses can exist in nervous tissue for long periods of time without producing new virions, only to leave latency periodically and cause lesions in the skin where the virus replicates. Even though there are similarities between lysogeny and latency, the term lysogenic cycle is usually reserved to describe bacteriophages. Latency will be described in more detail below.

visual CONNECTION

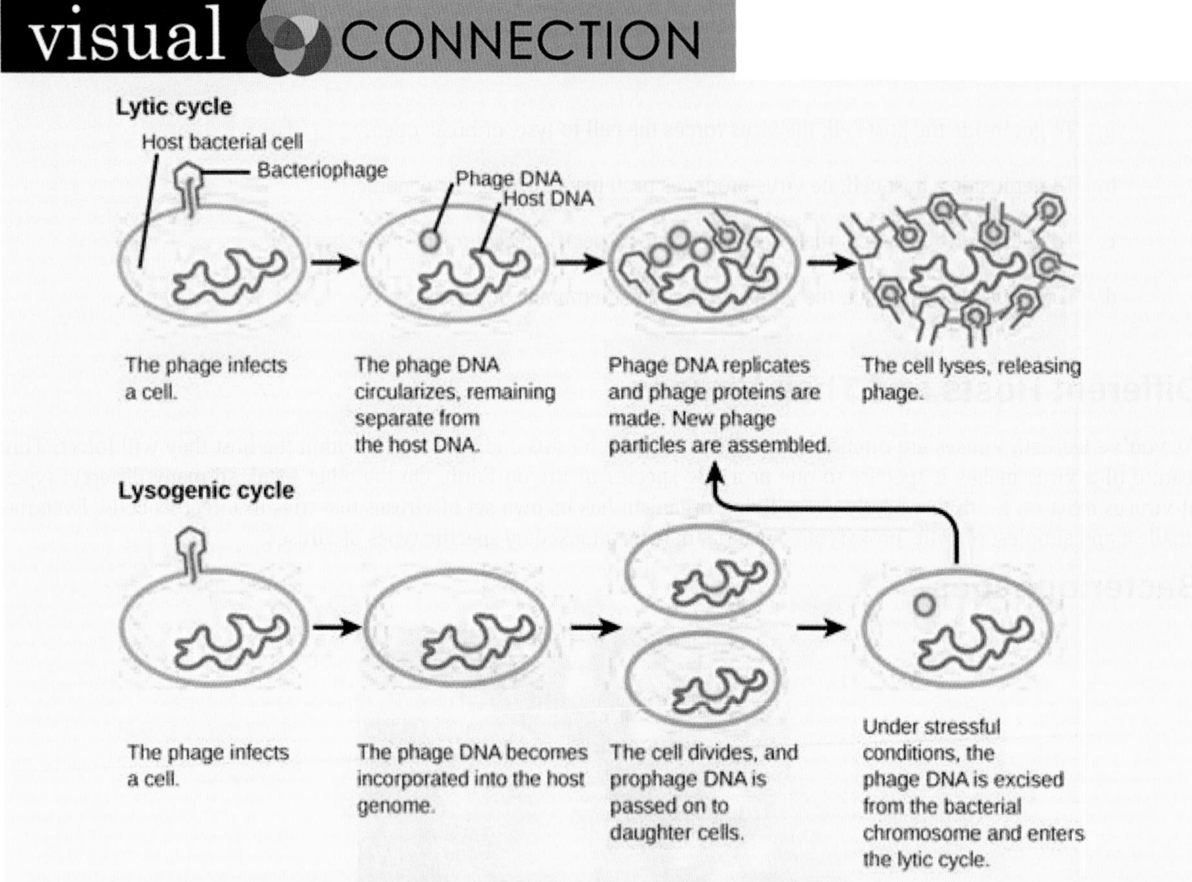

Figure 21.10 A temperate bacteriophage has both lytic and lysogenic cycles. In the lytic cycle, the phage replicates and lyses the host cell. In the lysogenic cycle, phage DNA is incorporated into the host genome, where it is passed on to subsequent generations. Environmental stressors such as starvation or exposure to toxic chemicals may cause the prophage to excise and enter the lytic cycle.

Which of the following statements is false?

a. In the lytic cycle, new phage are produced and released into the environment.
b. An environmental stressor can cause the phage to initiate the lysogenic cycle.
c. In the lysogenic cycle, phage DNA is incorporated into the host genome.
d. Bacteriophage is a viruses that infects bacteria.

Animal Viruses

Animal viruses, unlike the viruses of plants and bacteria, do not have to penetrate a cell wall to gain access to the host cell. Non-enveloped or "naked" animal viruses may enter cells in two different ways. As a protein in the viral capsid binds to its receptor on the host cell, the virus may be taken inside the cell via a vesicle during the normal cell process of receptor-mediated endocytosis. An alternative method of cell penetration used by non-enveloped viruses is for capsid proteins to undergo shape changes after binding to the receptor, creating channels in the host cell membrane. The viral genome is then "injected" into the host cell through these channels in a manner analogous to that used by many bacteriophages. Enveloped viruses also have two ways of entering cells after binding to their receptors: receptor-mediated endocytosis, or **fusion**. Many enveloped viruses enter the cell by receptor-mediated endocytosis in a fashion similar to some non-enveloped viruses. On the other hand, fusion only occurs with enveloped virions. These viruses, which include HIV among others, use special fusion proteins in their envelopes to cause the envelope to fuse with the plasma membrane of the cell, thus releasing the genome and capsid of the virus into the cell cytoplasm.

After making their proteins and copying their genomes, animal viruses complete the assembly of new virions and exit the cell Enveloped animal viruses may bud from the cell membrane as they assemble themselves, taking a piece of the cell's plasma membrane in the process. On the other hand, non-enveloped viral progeny, such as rhinoviruses, accumulate in infected cells until there is a signal for lysis or apoptosis, and all virions are released together.

As you will learn in the next module, animal viruses are associated with a variety of human diseases. Some of them follow the classic pattern of **acute disease**, where symptoms get increasingly worse for a short period followed by the elimination of the virus from the body by the immune system and eventual recovery from the infection. Examples of acute viral diseases are the common cold and influenza. Other viruses cause long-term **chronic infections**, such as the virus causing hepatitis C, whereas others, like herpes simplex virus, only cause **intermittent** symptoms. Still other viruses, such as human herpesviruses 6 and 7, which in some cases can cause the minor childhood disease roseola, often successfully cause productive infections without causing any symptoms at all in the host, and thus we say these patients have an **asymptomatic infection**.

In hepatitis C infections, the virus grows and reproduces in liver cells, causing low levels of liver damage. The damage is so low that infected individuals are often unaware that they are infected, and many infections are detected only by routine blood work on patients with risk factors. On the other hand, since many of the symptoms of viral diseases are caused by immune responses, a lack of symptoms is an indication of a weak immune response to the virus. This allows for the virus to escape elimination by the immune system and persist in individuals for years, all the while producing low levels of progeny virions in what is known as a chronic viral disease.

As already discussed, herpes simplex virus can remain in a state of latency in nervous tissue for months, even years. As the virus "hides" in the tissue and makes few if any viral proteins, there is nothing for the immune response to act against, and immunity to the virus slowly declines. Under certain conditions, including various types of physical and psychological stress, the latent herpes simplex virus may be reactivated and undergo a lytic replication cycle in the skin, causing the lesions associated with the disease. Once virions are produced in the skin and viral proteins are synthesized, the immune response is again stimulated and resolves the skin lesions in a few days by destroying viruses in the skin. As a result of this type of replicative cycle, appearances of cold sores outbreaks only occur intermittently, even though the viruses remain in the nervous tissue for life. Latent infections are common with other herpesviruses as well, including the varicella-zoster virus that causes chickenpox. After having a chickenpox infection in childhood, the varicella-zoster virus can remain latent for many years and reactivate in adults to cause the painful condition known as "shingles" (Figure 21.11**ab**).

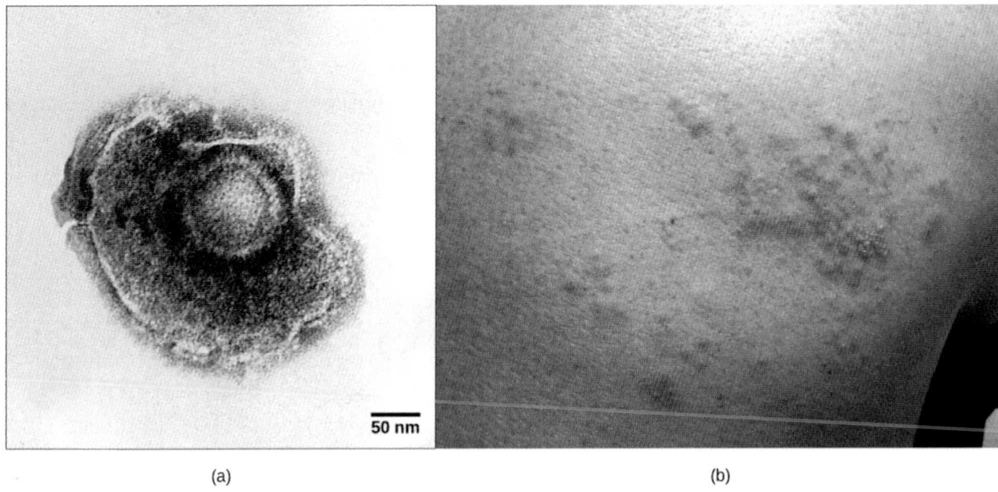

Figure 21.11 (a) Varicella-zoster, the virus that causes chickenpox, has an enveloped icosahedral capsid visible in this transmission electron micrograph. Its double-stranded DNA genome becomes incorporated in the host DNA and can reactivate after latency in the form of (b) shingles, often exhibiting a rash. (credit a: modification of work by Dr. Erskine Palmer, B. G. Martin, CDC; credit b: modification of work by "rosmary"/Flickr; scale-bar data from Matt Russell)

Some animal-infecting viruses, including the hepatitis C virus discussed above, are known as **oncogenic viruses**: They have the ability to cause cancer. These viruses interfere with the normal regulation of the host cell cycle either by either introducing genes that stimulate unregulated cell growth (oncogenes) or by interfering with the expression of genes that inhibit cell growth. Oncogenic viruses can be either DNA or RNA viruses. Cancers known to be associated with viral infections include cervical cancer caused by human papillomavirus (HPV) (Figure 21.12), liver cancer caused by hepatitis B virus, T-cell leukemia, and several types of lymphoma.

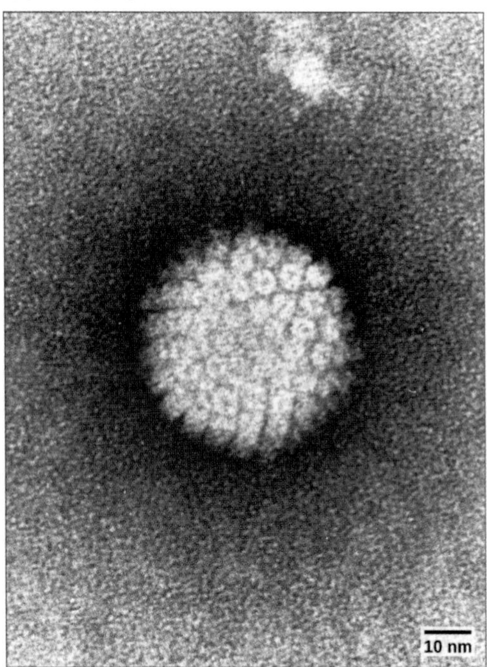

Figure 21.12 HPV, or human papillomavirus, has a naked icosahedral capsid visible in this transmission electron micrograph and a double-stranded DNA genome that is incorporated into the host DNA. The virus, is oncogenic and can lead to cervical cancer. (credit: modification of work by NCI, NIH; scale-bar data from Matt Russell)

Visit the interactive **animations (http://openstaxcollege.org/l/animal_viruses)** showing the various stages of the replicative cycles of animal viruses and click on the flash animation links.

Before a virus can replicate in a host cell, the capsid or envelope must be released. This process is sometimes referred to as _____.

a. viral attachment or adsorption

b. viral entry

c. uncoating

d. viral replication

Plant Viruses

Plant viruses, like other viruses, contain a core of either DNA or RNA. You have already learned about one of these, the tobacco mosaic virus. As plant cells have a cell wall to protect their cells, these viruses do not use receptor-mediated endocytosis to enter host cells as is seen with animal viruses. For many plant viruses to be transferred from plant to plant, damage to some of the plants' cells must occur to allow the virus to enter a new host. This damage is often caused by weather, insects, animals, fire, or human activities like farming or landscaping. Additionally, plant offspring may inherit viral diseases from parent plants. Plant viruses can be transmitted by a variety of vectors, through contact with an infected plant's sap, by living organisms such as insects and nematodes, and through pollen. When plants viruses are transferred between different plants, this is known as **horizontal transmission**, and when they are inherited from a parent, this is called **vertical transmission**.

Symptoms of viral diseases vary according to the virus and its host (Table 21.4). One common symptom is **hyperplasia**, the abnormal proliferation of cells that causes the appearance of plant tumors known as **galls**. Other viruses induce **hypoplasia**, or decreased cell growth, in the leaves of plants, causing thin, yellow areas to appear. Still other viruses affect the plant by directly killing plant cells, a process known as **cell necrosis**. Other symptoms of plant viruses include malformed leaves, black streaks on the stems of the plants, altered growth of stems, leaves, or fruits, and ring spots, which are circular or linear areas of discoloration found in a leaf.

Some Common Symptoms of Plant Viral Diseases

Symptom	Appears as
Hyperplasia	Galls (tumors)
Hypoplasia	Thinned, yellow splotches on leaves
Cell necrosis	Dead, blackened stems, leaves, or fruit
Abnormal growth patterns	Malformed stems, leaves, or fruit
Discoloration	Yellow, red, or black lines, or rings in stems, leaves, or fruit

Table 21.4

Plant viruses can seriously disrupt crop growth and development, significantly affecting our food supply. They are responsible for poor crop quality and quantity globally, and can bring about huge economic losses annually. Others viruses may damage plants used in landscaping. Some viruses that infect agricultural food plants include the name of the plant they infect, such as tomato spotted wilt virus, bean common mosaic virus, and cucumber mosaic virus. In plants used for landscaping, two of the most common viruses are peony ring spot and rose mosaic virus. There are far too many plant viruses to discuss each in detail, but symptoms of bean common mosaic virus result in lowered bean production and stunted, unproductive plants. In the ornamental rose, the rose mosaic disease causes wavy yellow lines and colored splotches on the leaves of the plant.

everyday CONNECTION for AP® Courses

Plant viruses can be spread through sap, insects, organisms living in the soil, seeds, and pollen. They cause damage to fruit, leaves, and stems, which has a large economic impact. For example, estimated yields from barley infected with the barley stripe mosaic virus as pictured below, can be 35–40% less. This virus is transmitted by a parasite that lives in the plant's roots.

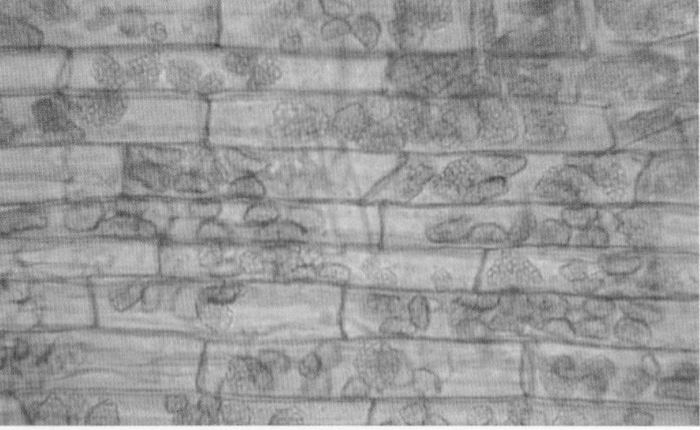

Figure 21.13 (credit: H.J. Larsen, Wikimedia Commons)

What symptoms of plant viral diseases do you see in this light micrograph of the cells of a plant root?

a. hyperplasia
b. abnormal growth patterns
c. discoloration
d. hypoplasia

science practices CONNECTION for AP® Courses

Activity

Create a visual representation to describe how viruses differ from bacteria in their modes of reproduction. What characteristics do viruses share with living organisms? How do they differ? What evidence supports the claim that viruses do not fit our usual definition of life?

Think About It

The influenza virus that causes seasonal "flu" is packaged in a viral envelope that fuses with the plasma membrane. This way, the virus can exit the host cell without killing it. What advantage does the virus gain by keeping the host alive?

21.3 | Prevention and Treatment of Viral Infections

In this section, you will explore the following questions:

- What are examples of major viral illnesses that affect humans?
- How do vaccinations differ from antiviral drugs as medical approaches to viruses?

Connection for AP® Courses

The majority of content described in this section is not within the scope for AP®. We explore some of these concepts when we study the immune system. However, because all of us will fight viral infections and will receive vaccinations against many diseases, including seasonal flu shots, the content in this section is relevant to our lives outside the classroom. While studying, think about why there are many different antibiotics available for treating bacterial infections but relatively few drugs available to treat viral infections. How do viruses differ from bacteria in both structure and activity?

Viruses cause a variety of diseases in animals, including humans, ranging from the common cold to potentially fatal illnesses like meningitis (Figure 21.14). These diseases can be treated by antiviral drugs or by vaccines, but some viruses are capable of both avoiding the immune response and mutating to become resistant to antiviral drugs.

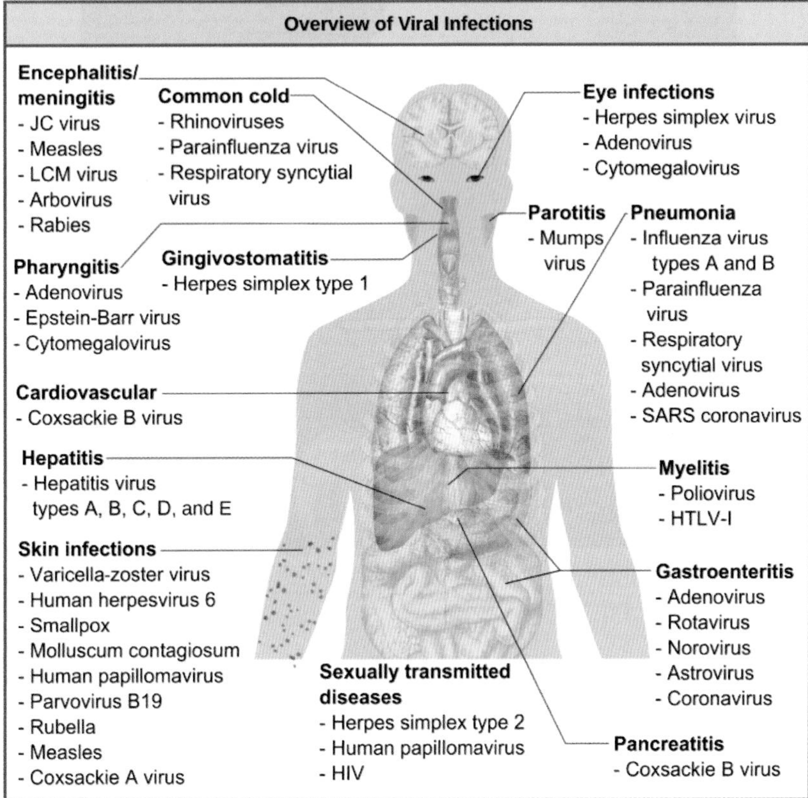

Figure 21.14 Viruses can cause dozens of ailments in humans, ranging from mild illnesses to serious diseases. (credit: modification of work by Mikael Häggström)

Vaccines for Prevention

While we do have limited numbers of effective antiviral drugs, such as those used to treat influenza, the primary method of controlling viral disease is by vaccination, which is intended to prevent outbreaks by building immunity to a virus or virus family (Figure 21.15). **Vaccines** may be prepared using live viruses, killed viruses, or molecular subunits of the virus. The killed viral vaccines and subunit viruses are both incapable of causing disease.

Live viral vaccines are designed in the laboratory to cause few symptoms in recipients while giving them protective immunity against future infections. Polio was one disease that represented a milestone in the use of vaccines. Mass immunization campaigns in the 1950s (killed vaccine) and 1960s (live vaccine) significantly reduced the incidence of the disease, which caused muscle paralysis in children and generated a great amount of fear in the general population when regional epidemics occurred. The success of the polio vaccine paved the way for the routine dispensation of childhood vaccines against measles, mumps, rubella, chickenpox, and other diseases.

The danger of using live vaccines, which are usually more effective than killed vaccines, is the low but significant danger that these viruses will revert to their disease-causing form by **back mutations**. Live vaccines are usually made by **attenuating** (weakening) the “wild-type” (disease-causing) virus by growing it in the laboratory in tissues or at temperatures different from what the virus is accustomed to in the host. Adaptations to these new cells or temperatures induce mutations in the genomes of the virus, allowing it to grow better in the laboratory while inhibiting its ability to cause disease when reintroduced into conditions found in the host. These attenuated viruses thus still cause infection, but they do not grow very well, allowing the immune response to develop in time to prevent major disease. Back mutations occur when the vaccine undergoes mutations in the host such that it readapts to the host and can again cause disease, which can then be spread to other humans in an epidemic. This type of scenario happened as recently as 2007 in Nigeria where mutations in a polio vaccine led to an epidemic of polio in that country.

Some vaccines are in continuous development because certain viruses, such as influenza, have a high mutation rate compared to other viruses and normal host cells. With influenza, mutations in the surface molecules of the virus help the organism evade the protective immunity that may have been obtained in a previous influenza season, making it necessary for individuals to get vaccinated every year. Other viruses, such as those that cause the childhood diseases measles, mumps, and rubella, mutate so infrequently that the same vaccine is used year after year.

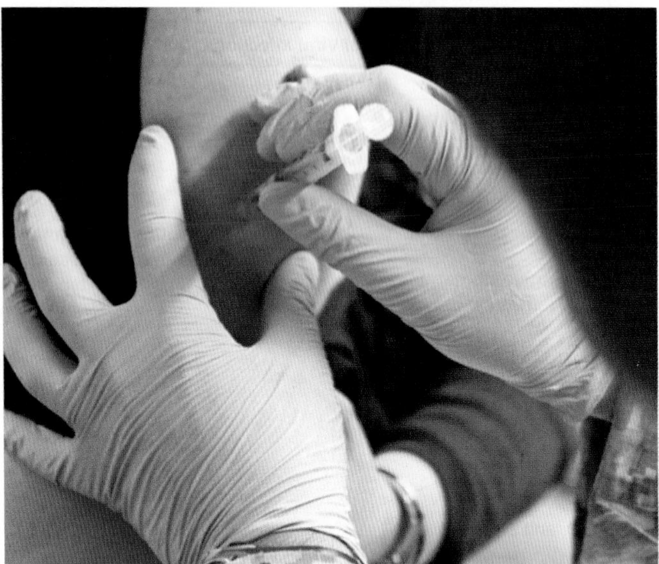

Figure 21.15 Vaccinations are designed to boost immunity to a virus to prevent infection. (credit: USACE Europe District)

Watch this NOVA **video (http://openstaxcollege.org/l/1918_flu)** to learn how microbiologists are attempting to replicate the deadly 1918 Spanish influenza virus so they can understand more about virology.

The Avian virus and the 1918 Spanish influenza virus both infect the _____ system.

a. nervous

b. respiratory

c. cardio vascular

d. digestive

Vaccines and Antiviral Drugs for Treatment

In some cases, vaccines can be used to treat an active viral infection. The concept behind this is that by giving the vaccine, immunity is boosted without adding more disease-causing virus. In the case of rabies, a fatal neurological disease transmitted via the saliva of rabies virus-infected animals, the progression of the disease from the time of the animal bite to the time it enters the central nervous system may be 2 weeks or longer. This is enough time to vaccinate an individual who suspects that they have been bitten by a rabid animal, and their boosted immune response is sufficient to prevent the virus from entering nervous tissue. Thus, the potentially fatal neurological consequences of the disease are averted, and the individual only has to recover from the infected bite. This approach is also being used for the treatment of Ebola, one of the fastest and most deadly viruses on earth. Transmitted by bats and great apes, this disease can cause death in 70–90 percent of infected humans within 2 weeks. Using newly developed vaccines that boost the immune response in this way, there is hope that affected individuals will be better able to control the virus, potentially saving a greater percentage of infected persons from a rapid and very painful death.

Another way of treating viral infections is the use of antiviral drugs. These drugs often have limited success in curing viral disease, but in many cases, they have been used to control and reduce symptoms for a wide variety of viral diseases. For most viruses, these drugs can inhibit the virus by blocking the actions of one or more of its proteins. It is important that the targeted proteins be encoded by viral genes and that these molecules are not present in a healthy host cell. In this way, viral growth is inhibited without damaging the host. There are large numbers of antiviral drugs available to treat infections, some specific for a particular virus and others that can affect multiple viruses.

Antivirals have been developed to treat herpes and influenza. For herpes, drugs such as acyclovir can reduce the number and duration of episodes of active viral disease, during which patients develop viral lesions in their skin cells. As the virus remains latent in nervous tissue of the body for life, this drug is not curative but can make the symptoms of the disease more manageable. For influenza, drugs like oseltamivir (Figure 21.16) can reduce the duration of “flu” symptoms by 1 or 2 days, but the drug does not prevent symptoms entirely. Oseltamivir works by inhibiting an enzyme (viral neuraminidase) that allows new virions to leave their infected cells. Thus, Oseltamivir inhibits the spread of virus from infected to uninfected cells. Other antiviral drugs, such as Ribavirin, have been used to treat a variety of viral infections, although its mechanism of action against certain viruses remains unclear.

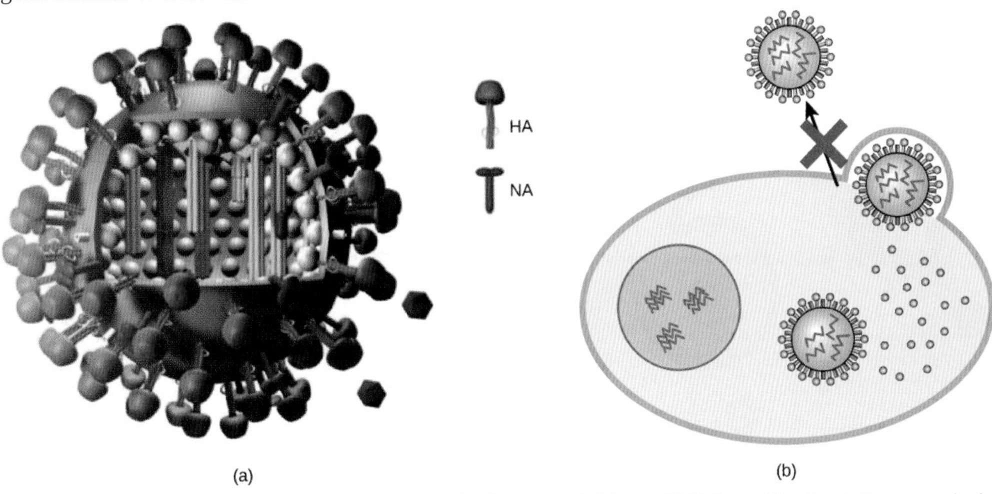

Figure 21.16 (a) Oseltamivir inhibits a viral enzyme called neuraminidase (NA) found in the influenza viral envelope. (b) Neuraminidase cleaves the connection between viral hemagglutinin (HA), also found in the viral envelope, and glycoproteins on the host cell surface. Inhibition of neuraminidase prevents the virus from detaching from the host cell, thereby blocking further infection. (credit a: modification of work by M. Eickmann)

By far, the most successful use of antivirals has been in the treatment of the retrovirus HIV, which causes a disease that, if untreated, is usually fatal within 10–12 years after infection. Anti-HIV drugs have been able to control viral replication to the point that individuals receiving these drugs survive for a significantly longer time than the untreated.

Anti-HIV drugs inhibit viral replication at many different phases of the HIV replicative cycle (Figure 21.17). Drugs have been developed that inhibit the fusion of the HIV viral envelope with the plasma membrane of the host cell (fusion inhibitors), the conversion of its RNA genome into double-stranded DNA (reverse transcriptase inhibitors), the integration of the viral DNA into the host genome (integrase inhibitors), and the processing of viral proteins (protease inhibitors).

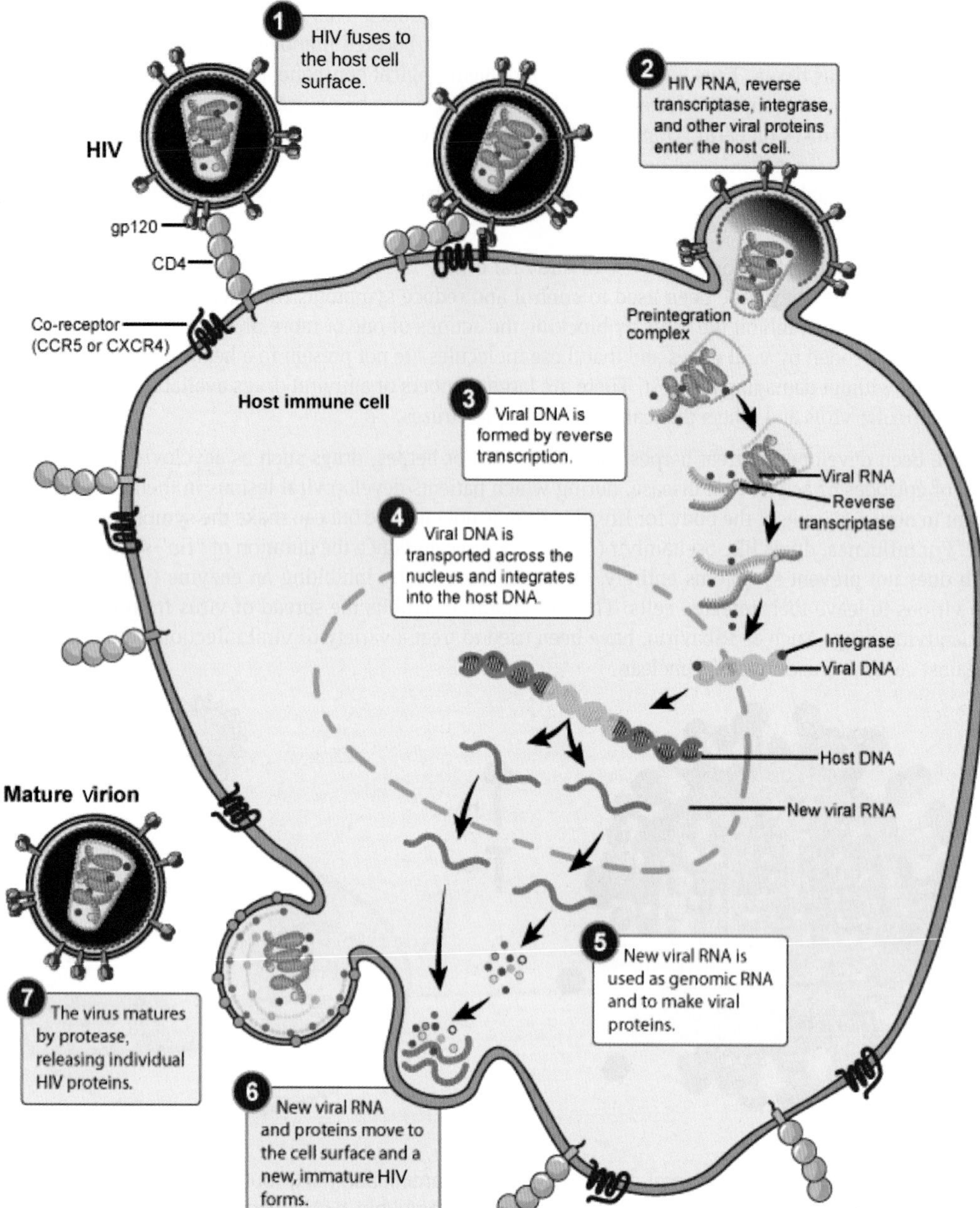

Figure 21.17 HIV, an enveloped, icosahedral virus, attaches to the CD4 receptor of an immune cell and fuses with the cell membrane. Viral contents are released into the cell, where viral enzymes convert the single-stranded RNA genome into DNA and incorporate it into the host genome. (credit: NIAID, NIH)

When any of these drugs are used individually, the high mutation rate of the virus allows it to easily and rapidly develop resistance to the drug, limiting the drug's effectiveness. The breakthrough in the treatment of HIV was the development of HAART, highly active antiretroviral therapy, which involves a mixture of different drugs, sometimes called a drug "cocktail." By attacking the virus at different stages of its replicative cycle, it is much more difficult for the virus to develop resistance to multiple drugs at the same time. Still, even with the use of combination HAART therapy, there is concern that, over time, the virus will develop resistance to this therapy. Thus, new anti-HIV drugs are constantly being developed with the hope of continuing the battle against this highly fatal virus.

everyday CONNECTION

Applied Virology

The study of viruses has led to the development of a variety of new ways to treat non-viral diseases. Viruses have been used in **gene therapy**. Gene therapy is used to treat genetic diseases such as severe combined immunodeficiency (SCID), a heritable, recessive disease in which children are born with severely compromised immune systems. One common type of SCID is due to the lack of an enzyme, adenosine deaminase (ADA), which breaks down purine bases. To treat this disease by gene therapy, bone marrow cells are taken from a SCID patient and the ADA gene is inserted. This is where viruses come in, and their use relies on their ability to penetrate living cells and bring genes in with them. Viruses such as adenovirus, an upper respiratory human virus, are modified by the addition of the ADA gene, and the virus then transports this gene into the cell. The modified cells, now capable of making ADA, are then given back to the patients in the hope of curing them. Gene therapy using viruses as carrier of genes (viral vectors), although still experimental, holds promise for the treatment of many genetic diseases. Still, many technological problems need to be solved for this approach to be a viable method for treating genetic disease.

Another medical use for viruses relies on their specificity and ability to kill the cells they infect. **Oncolytic viruses** are engineered in the laboratory specifically to attack and kill cancer cells. A genetically modified adenovirus known as H101 has been used since 2005 in clinical trials in China to treat head and neck cancers. The results have been promising, with a greater short-term response rate to the combination of chemotherapy and viral therapy than to chemotherapy treatment alone. This ongoing research may herald the beginning of a new age of cancer therapy, where viruses are engineered to find and specifically kill cancer cells, regardless of where in the body they may have spread.

A third use of viruses in medicine relies on their specificity and involves using bacteriophages in the treatment of bacterial infections. Bacterial diseases have been treated with antibiotics since the 1940s. However, over time, many bacteria have developed resistance to antibiotics. A good example is methicillin-resistant *Staphylococcus aureus* (MRSA, pronounced "mersa"), an infection commonly acquired in hospitals. This bacterium is resistant to a variety of antibiotics, making it difficult to treat. The use of bacteriophages specific for such bacteria would bypass their resistance to antibiotics and specifically kill them. Although **phage therapy** is in use in the Republic of Georgia to treat antibiotic-resistant bacteria, its use to treat human diseases has not been approved in most countries. However, the safety of the treatment was confirmed in the United States when the U.S. Food and Drug Administration approved spraying meats with bacteriophages to destroy the food pathogen *Listeria.* As more and more antibiotic-resistant strains of bacteria evolve, the use of bacteriophages might be a potential solution to the problem, and the development of phage therapy is of much interest to researchers worldwide.

How can viruses be used in gene therapy?

a. Viruses are used to attack and kill specific cells.

b. Bacteriophages are used to treat bacterial infections.

c. Viruses are used to transport a gene into a cell.

d. Viruses are used to destroy the food pathogen Listeria.

21.4 | Other Acellular Entities: Prions and Viroids

In this section, you will explore the following questions:

- What are prions and how do they cause disease?
- What are viroids and their targets of infection?

Connection for AP® Courses

The content described in this section is outside the scope for AP®. However, it's interesting to note that prions and viroids—pathogens that are far simpler in structure than viruses—can produce deadly diseases, including mad cow disease and Creutzfeldt–Jakob disease. Prions are infectious proteins, whereas viroids are single-stranded RNA **pathogens** (agents with the ability to cause disease) that infect plants.

Prions

Prions, so-called because they are proteinaceous, are infectious particles—smaller than viruses—that contain no nucleic acids (neither DNA nor RNA). Historically, the idea of an infectious agent that did not use nucleic acids was considered impossible, but pioneering work by Nobel Prize-winning biologist Stanley Prusiner has convinced the majority of biologists that such agents do indeed exist.

Fatal neurodegenerative diseases, such as kuru in humans and bovine spongiform encephalopathy (BSE) in cattle (commonly known as "mad cow disease") were shown to be transmitted by prions. The disease was spread by the consumption of meat, nervous tissue, or internal organs between members of the same species. Kuru, native to humans in Papua New Guinea, was spread from human to human via ritualistic cannibalism. BSE, originally detected in the United Kingdom, was spread between cattle by the practice of including cattle nervous tissue in feed for other cattle. Individuals with kuru and BSE show symptoms of loss of motor control and unusual behaviors, such as uncontrolled bursts of laughter with kuru, followed by death. Kuru was controlled by inducing the population to abandon its ritualistic cannibalism.

On the other hand, BSE was initially thought to only affect cattle. Cattle dying of the disease were shown to have developed lesions or "holes" in the brain, causing the brain tissue to resemble a sponge. Later on in the outbreak, however, it was shown that a similar encephalopathy in humans known as variant Creutzfeldt-Jakob disease (CJD) could be acquired from eating beef from animals with BSE, sparking bans by various countries on the importation of British beef and causing considerable economic damage to the British beef industry (Figure 21.18). BSE still exists in various areas, and although a rare disease, individuals that acquire CJD are difficult to treat. The disease can be spread from human to human by blood, so many countries have banned blood donation from regions associated with BSE.

The cause of spongiform encephalopathies, such as kuru and BSE, is an infectious structural variant of a normal cellular protein called PrP (prion protein). It is this variant that constitutes the prion particle. PrP exists in two forms, **PrP^c**, the normal form of the protein, and **PrP^{sc}**, the infectious form. Once introduced into the body, the PrP^{sc} contained within the prion binds to PrP^c and converts it to PrP^{sc}. This leads to an exponential increase of the PrP^{sc} protein, which aggregates. PrP^{sc} is folded abnormally, and the resulting conformation (shape) is directly responsible for the lesions seen in the brains of infected cattle. Thus, although not without some detractors among scientists, the prion seems likely to be an entirely new form of infectious agent, the first one found whose transmission is not reliant upon genes made of DNA or RNA.

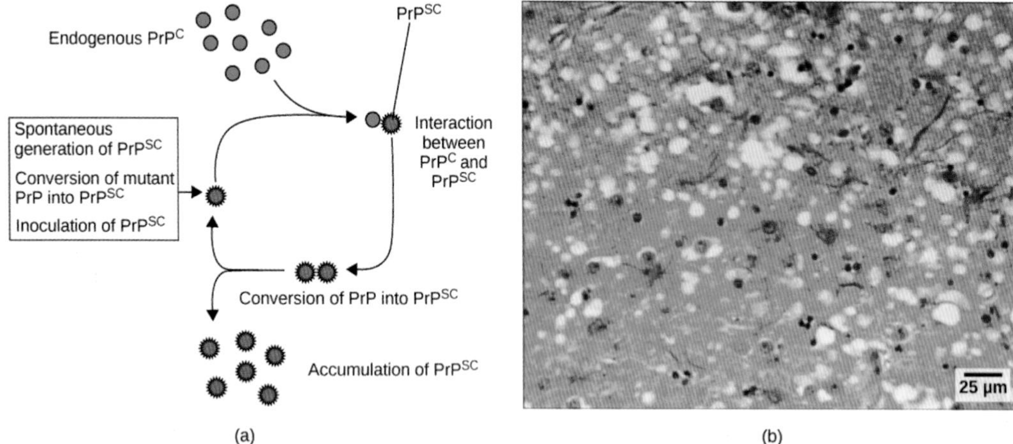

Figure 21.18 (a) Endogenous normal prion protein (PrP^c) is converted into the disease-causing form (PrP^{sc}) when it encounters this variant form of the protein. PrP^{sc} may arise spontaneously in brain tissue, especially if a mutant form of the protein is present, or it may occur via the spread of misfolded prions consumed in food into brain tissue. (b) This prion-infected brain tissue, visualized using light microscopy, shows the vacuoles that give it a spongy texture, typical of transmissible spongiform encephalopathies. (credit b: modification of work by Dr. Al Jenny, USDA APHIS; scale-bar data from Matt Russell)

Viroids

Viroids are plant pathogens: small, single-stranded, circular RNA particles that are much simpler than a virus. They do not have a capsid or outer envelope, but like viruses can reproduce only within a host cell. Viroids do not, however, manufacture any proteins, and they only produce a single, specific RNA molecule. Human diseases caused by viroids have yet to be identified.

Viroids are known to infect plants (Figure 21.19) and are responsible for crop failures and the loss of millions of dollars in agricultural revenue each year. Some of the plants they infect include potatoes, cucumbers, tomatoes, chrysanthemums, avocados, and coconut palms.

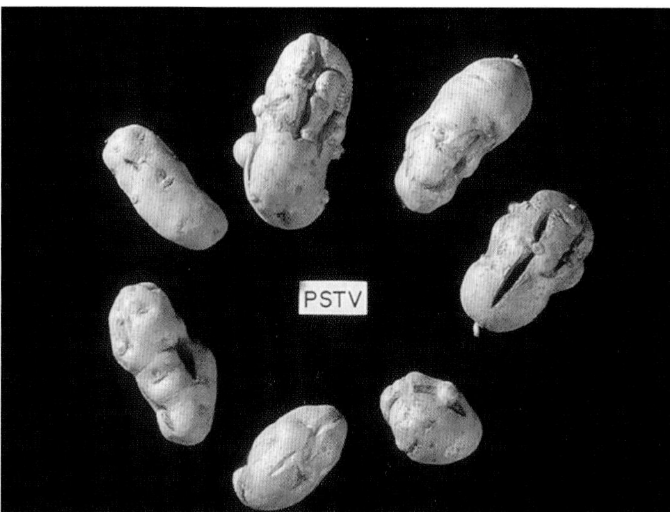

Figure 21.19 These potatoes have been infected by the potato spindle tuber viroid (PSTV), which is typically spread when infected knives are used to cut healthy potatoes, which are then planted. (credit: Pamela Roberts, University of Florida Institute of Food and Agricultural Sciences, USDA ARS)

career CONNECTION

Virologist

Virology is the study of viruses, and a virologist is an individual trained in this discipline. Training in virology can lead to many different career paths. Virologists are actively involved in academic research and teaching in colleges and medical schools. Some virologists treat patients or are involved in the generation and production of vaccines. They might participate in epidemiologic studies (Figure 21.20) or become science writers, to name just a few possible careers.

Figure 21.20 This virologist is engaged in fieldwork, sampling eggs from this nest for avian influenza. (credit: Don Becker, USGS EROS, U.S. Fish and Wildlife Service)

If you think you may be interested in a career in virology, find a mentor in the field. Many large medical centers have departments of virology, and smaller hospitals usually have virology labs within their microbiology departments. Volunteer in a virology lab for a semester or work in one over the summer. Discussing the profession and getting a first-hand look at the work will help you decide whether a career in virology is right for you. The American Society of Virology's website (http://openstaxcollege.org/l/asv) is a good resource for information regarding training and careers in virology.

KEY TERMS

acellular lacking cells

acute disease disease where the symptoms rise and fall within a short period of time

asymptomatic disease disease where there are no symptoms and the individual is unaware of being infected unless lab tests are performed

attenuation weakening of a virus during vaccine development

AZT anti-HIV drug that inhibits the viral enzyme reverse transcriptase

back mutation when a live virus vaccine reverts back to it disease-causing phenotype

bacteriophage virus that infects bacteria

budding method of exit from the cell used in certain animal viruses, where virions leave the cell individually by capturing a piece of the host plasma membrane

capsid protein coating of the viral core

capsomere protein subunit that makes up the capsid

cell necrosis cell death

chronic infection describes when the virus persists in the body for a long period of time

cytopathic causing cell damage

envelope lipid bilayer that envelopes some viruses

fusion method of entry by some enveloped viruses, where the viral envelope fuses with the plasma membrane of the host cell

gall appearance of a plant tumor

gene therapy treatment of genetic disease by adding genes, using viruses to carry the new genes inside the cell

group I virus virus with a dsDNA genome

group II virus virus with a ssDNA genome

group III virus virus with a dsRNA genome

group IV virus virus with a ssRNA genome with positive polarity

group V virus virus with a ssRNA genome with negative polarity

group VI virus virus with a ssRNA genomes converted into dsDNA by reverse transcriptase

group VII virus virus with a single-stranded mRNA converted into dsDNA for genome replication

horizontal transmission transmission of a disease from parent to offspring

hyperplasia abnormally high cell growth and division

hypoplasia abnormally low cell growth and division

intermittent symptom symptom that occurs periodically

latency virus that remains in the body for a long period of time but only causes intermittent symptoms

lysis bursting of a cell

lysogenic cycle type of virus replication in which the viral genome is incorporated into the genome of the host cell

lytic cycle type of virus replication in which virions are released through lysis, or bursting, of the cell

matrix protein envelope protein that stabilizes the envelope and often plays a role in the assembly of progeny virions

negative polarity ssRNA viruses with genomes complementary to their mRNA

oncogenic virus virus that has the ability to cause cancer

oncolytic virus virus engineered to specifically infect and kill cancer cells

pathogen agent with the ability to cause disease

permissive cell type that is able to support productive replication of a virus

phage therapy treatment of bacterial diseases using bacteriophages specific to a particular bacterium

positive polarity ssRNA virus with a genome that contains the same base sequences and codons found in their mRNA

prion infectious particle that consists of proteins that replicate without DNA or RNA

productive viral infection that leads to the production of new virions

prophage phage DNA that is incorporated into the host cell genome

PrP^c normal prion protein

PrP^{sc} infectious form of a prion protein

replicative intermediate dsRNA intermediate made in the process of copying genomic RNA

retrovirus virus with an RNA genome that must be reverse transcribed into DNA before being incorporated into the host cell genome

reverse transcriptase enzyme found in Baltimore groups VI and VII that converts single-stranded RNA into double-stranded DNA

vaccine weakened solution of virus components, viruses, or other agents that produce an immune response

vertical transmission transmission of disease from parent to offspring

viral receptor glycoprotein used to attach a virus to host cells via molecules on the cell

virion individual virus particle outside a host cell

viroid plant pathogen that produces only a single, specific RNA

virus core contains the virus genome

CHAPTER SUMMARY

21.1 Viral Evolution, Morphology, and Classification

Viruses are tiny, acellular entities that can usually only be seen with an electron microscope. Their genomes contain either DNA or RNA—never both—and they replicate using the replication proteins of a host cell. Viruses are diverse, infecting archaea, bacteria, fungi, plants, and animals. Viruses consist of a nucleic acid core surrounded by a protein capsid with or without an outer lipid envelope. The capsid shape, presence of an envelope, and core composition dictate some elements of the classification of viruses. The most commonly used classification method, the Baltimore classification, categorizes viruses based on how they produce their mRNA.

21.2 Virus Infection and Hosts

Viral replication within a living cell always produces changes in the cell, sometimes resulting in cell death and sometimes slowly killing the infected cells. There are six basic stages in the virus replication cycle: attachment, penetration, uncoating, replication, assembly, and release. A viral infection may be productive, resulting in new virions, or nonproductive, which means that the virus remains inside the cell without producing new virions. Bacteriophages are viruses that infect bacteria. They have two different modes of replication: the lytic cycle, where the virus replicates and bursts out of the bacteria, and the lysogenic cycle, which involves the incorporation of the viral genome into the bacterial host genome. Animal viruses cause a variety of infections, with some causing chronic symptoms (hepatitis C), some intermittent symptoms (latent viruses such a herpes simplex virus 1), and others that cause very few symptoms, if any (human herpesviruses 6 and 7). Oncogenic viruses in animals have the ability to cause cancer by interfering with the regulation of the host cell cycle. Viruses of plants are responsible for significant economic damage in both agriculture and plants used for ornamentation.

21.3 Prevention and Treatment of Viral Infections

Viruses cause a variety of diseases in humans. Many of these diseases can be prevented by the use of viral vaccines, which stimulate protective immunity against the virus without causing major disease. Viral vaccines may also be used in active viral infections, boosting the ability of the immune system to control or destroy the virus. A series of antiviral drugs that target enzymes and other protein products of viral genes have been developed and used with mixed success. Combinations of anti-HIV drugs have been used to effectively control the virus, extending the lifespans of infected individuals. Viruses have many uses in medicines, such as in the treatment of genetic disorders, cancer, and bacterial infections.

21.4 Other Acellular Entities: Prions and Viroids

Prions are infectious agents that consist of protein, but no DNA or RNA, and seem to produce their deadly effects by duplicating their shapes and accumulating in tissues. They are thought to contribute to several progressive brain disorders, including mad cow disease and Creutzfeldt-Jakob disease. Viroids are single-stranded RNA pathogens that infect plants. Their presence can have a severe impact on the agriculture industry.

REVIEW QUESTIONS

1. Viruses were first discovered after the development of the porcelain filter, called the Chamberland-Pasteur filter. How did the porcelain filter enable scientists to discover viruses?

a. The porcelain filter removed diseases from a liquid sample.

b. The porcelain filter removed virions from a liquid sample.

c. The porcelain filter removed bacteria from a liquid sample.

d. The porcelain filter removed a disease from tobacco plants.

2. In the late 1930s, scientists got their first good view of viruses. How did this happen?

a. The development of the light microscope helped scientists discover many viruses of all types of living organisms.

b. The development of the viral receptor helped scientists discover many viruses of all types of living organisms.

c. The development of the porcelain filter helped scientists discover many viruses of all types of living organisms.

d. The development of the electron microscope helped scientists discover many viruses of all types of living organisms.

3. Determining the origins of viruses is challenging. The _____ hypothesis proposes to explain the origin of viruses by suggesting that viruses evolved from free-living cells.

a. escapist or the progressive

b. system of self-replication

c. devolution or the regressive

d. virus molecular systematics

4. Which statement best describes what biologists know about the evolution of viruses?

a. Scientists can look at fossil records and similar historic evidence.
b. Much about virus origins and evolution remains unknown.
c. Biologists have accumulated a significant amount of knowledge about how viruses originated.
d. Biologists know exactly when viruses emerged and from where they came.

5. A(n) _____ is an individual virus particle outside a host cell that consists of a nucleic acid core, an outer protein coating, and sometimes an outer envelope.

a. capsid
b. virion
c. capsomere
d. viral receptor

6. For many viruses to penetrate the cell membrane and complete their replication inside the cell, the virus must attach to their host cells. Describe how a virus attaches to a host cell.

a. A virus uses its cellular structure to attach to a host cell.
b. A virus uses a plasma membrane to connect to a host cell.
c. A virus uses matrix proteins to attach to a host cell.
d. Viruses use viral receptors to attach to a host cell.

7. _____ means that the genomic RNA can function as mRNA.

a. double-stranded
b. negative polarity
c. positive polarity
d. replica intermediates

8. Viruses are often classified based on the type of genetic material and its structure. In the Baltimore classification scheme, the _____ virus has a single-stranded RNA (–) genome.

a. human immunodeficiency virus (HIV)
b. rabies (rhabdovirus)
c. canine parvovirus (parvovirus)
d. common cold (pircornavirus)

9. To get a visual look at the internal structure of virions, scientists must use a(n) ____.

a. scanning electron microscope
b. transmission electron microscope
c. porcelain filter
d. light microscope

10. Which of the following statements about the viral replication cycle is accurate?

a. The viral replication cycle does not affect the structure of the host cell.
b. The viral replication cycle cannot affect genetic material of the host cell.
c. The viral replication cycle has seven basic steps.
d. The viral replication cycle can change cell functions or even destroy the host cell.

11. What happens in the replication cycle?

a. During the budding process, virions leave the host cell individually
b. During the budding process, the host cell bursts.
c. During the budding process, the virus connects with a permissive host cell.
d. During the budding process, the host cell dies immediately.

12. In the _____ cycle, the virus replicates and bursts out of the host cell.

a. lytic
b. lysogenic
c. cytopathic
d. latency

13. How is the lytic cycle different from the lysogenic cycle?

a. The phage infects a cell in the lytic cycle.
b. The lytic cycle contains the formation of a prophage.
c. In the lytic cycle, new phages are produced; immediately in the lysogenic cycle phage DNA is merged into the host genome.
d. The phages move on to infect other cells in the lysogenic phase.

14. Which of the following statements is false?

a. Enveloped viruses and naked viruses both may enter cells using the fusion method.
b. Many enveloped viruses enter the cell by receptor-mediated endocytosis.
c. Naked viruses enter the cell by receptor-mediated endocytosis.
d. Undergoing shape changes and creating channels in the host cell membrane is an alternative method of cell penetration used by naked viruses.

15. An apple tree has yellow splotches on the leaves. This is a symptom of _____.

a. cell necrosis
b. discoloration
c. hyperplasia
d. hypoplasia

16. What happens during the release step in the viral replication cycle?

a. During the release step, genetic information is transferred through the lytic and lysogenic cycles.
b. During the release step, DNA is transcribed to messenger RNA.
c. During the release step, the nucleic acid is released from the viral capsid or envelope.
d. During the release step, the new virions are able to infect adjacent cells and repeat the replication cycle.

17. Why does the HIV virus use reverse transcriptase in the replication process?

a. The HIV virus uses reverse transcriptase to replicate cells and build proteins.
b. The HIV virus uses reverse transcriptase to erase mutated virions.
c. The HIV virus uses reverse transcriptase because it is a retrovirus.
d. The HIV virus uses reverse transcriptase because it has a DNA genome.

18. What are the symptoms of the herpes simplex virus?

a. The herpes simplex virus causes eye infections.
b. The herpes simplex virus causes pneumonia.
c. The herpes simplex virus causes pancreatitis.
d. The herpes simplex virus can cause septicemia.

19. Which of the following statements accurately describes the measles virus?

a. The measles virus causes nasal and lung infections.
b. The measles virus causes pancreas and liver infections.
c. The measles virus causes mouth and gum infections.
d. The measles virus causes brain and skin infections.

20. Which of the following statements best describes vaccines?

a. Vaccines kill viruses.
b. Vaccines stimulate an immune response against future infections.
c. Vaccines inhibit the virus by blocking the action of key viral proteins.
d. Vaccines control and reduce symptoms.

21. Which kind of therapy attacks a stage of the virus replicative cycle?

a. phage therapy
b. anti-retroviral
c. gene therapy
d. cancer therapy

22. Which virus causes parotitis?

a. measles virus
b. norovirus
c. HIV
d. mumps virus

23. Which of the following statements about prions is true?

a. Prions are larger than viruses.
b. Prions contain DNA and RNA.
c. The PrPCis the normal form of the protein.
d. The PrPSCis folded abnormally.

24. Kuru is a prion disease that affects both humans and animals. How is Kuru spread?

a. Kuru disease is spread between cattle.
b. Kuru is passed from person to person.
c. Kuru is passed from cows with BSE to humans.
d. Kuru is a viroid that infects plants.

25. Which of the following statements about viroids is true?

a. Viroids are single-stranded RNA particles.
b. Viroids reproduce only outside of the cell.
c. Viroids produce proteins.
d. Viroids affect both plants and animals.

26. On which industry can viroids have a severe impact?

a. dairy
b. poultry
c. avocado
d. livestock

27. Which of the following statements best explains how infected prions cause disease?

a. Infected prions cause disease by transmitting nucleic acids to normal prion proteins.
b. Infected prions cause disease by converting DNA to RNA in normal prion proteins.
c. Infected prions cause disease by converting the shapes of normal proteins.
d. Infected prions cause disease by replicating the normal form of the protein.

CRITICAL THINKING QUESTIONS

28. How did the development of a porcelain filter, called the Chamberland-Pasteur filter, help scientists discover viruses?

a. After filtering a liquid plant extract, the scientists could see the virions using the light microscope.
b. After filtering a liquid plant extract, the disease was still transferred to a healthy plant.
c. After filtering a liquid plant extract, the virus cells multiplied.
d. After filtering a liquid plant extract, scientists were able to trace historical footprints.

29. Scientists have a few hypotheses about virus origins. Why might they develop and refine further hypotheses to explain the origin of viruses?

a. Advances in technology provide historic evidence.
b. Biochemical and genetic information provide historic evidence.
c. Advances in technology provide new information for scientists.
d. Advances in technology have proven that viruses have a single common ancestor.

30. Why don't dogs catch the measles?

a. Measles is a DNA virus, and DNA viruses cause human diseases.
b. Dogs do not have glycoproteins.
c. The virus can't attach to dog cells.
d. Dogs do not get RNA viruses.

31. The Baltimore classification system groups viruses according to how the mRNA is produced. When classified this way, the viruses in each group _____.

a. behave in a similar manner
b. look very similar
c. connect with living things
d. are based on the type of disease they cause

32. Researchers have been able to develop a variety of anti-HIV drugs, such as the drug AZT. How does the drug AZT work?

a. AZT blocks the enzyme called HIV protease, which the virus uses to reproduce itself.
b. AZT blocks the HIV integrase enzyme, which the virus uses to insert its viral DNA into the DNA of the host cell.
c. AZT prevents reverse transcriptase and HIV protease enzyme from functioning inside the body.
d. AZT prevents reverse transcriptase from making DNA from the viral RNA genome.

33. Compare the lytic and lysogenic cycles and explain which cycle has the potential to produce the most virions.

a. The lytic cycle can theoretically produce more virions as the viral genome is incorporated into the host cell's genome replicating along with the host cell.
b. The lysogenic cycle can theoretically produce more virions as the reproductive cycle of viruses undergoing lysogeny is much faster than the reproductive cycle of viruses following lytic cycle.
c. The lysogenic cycle can theoretically produce more virions as the viral genome is incorporated into the host cell's genome replicating along with the host cell.
d. The lytic cycle can theoretically produce more virions as the prophage following lysogenic cycle ultimately gets excised from the host cell's genome and enter the lytic cycle.

34. Would a person who has never been in contact with the varicella-zoster virus be at risk of developing chickenpox or shingles if they come in close contact with a person with shingles? Explain your reasoning.

a. The person is at risk of developing chickenpox. Chickenpox is the first infection with the virus before it enters latency in the host.

b. The person is at risk of developing shingles. Shingles is the first infection with the virus before it enters latency in the host.

c. The person is at risk of developing chickenpox. Chickenpox is the first infection with the virus that is already latent in the body.

d. The person is at risk of developing shingles. The virus enters the person and gets activated when a person with shingles comes in close contact.

35. Which step in the replication cycle of viruses do you think is most critical for the virus to infect cells? Explain why.

a. The attachment step is the most critical, as infection cannot begin if virus does not attach to the host cell.

b. The replication step is the most critical as this step directs protein synthesis.

c. The assembly step is the most critical because new virions are assembled to infect cells.

d. The entry step is the most critical as nucleic acid of virus needs to enter the host cell naked, leaving the capsid outside.

36. For most people, the measles virus does not cause a serious illness. Symptoms include fever and a rash, but the symptoms are usually gone in about a week. However, for some, the measles virus can be much more serious. How can the measles virus cause a potentially fatal illness?

a. Measles can cause meningococcal disease, which causes severe headaches, seizures and in severe cases can be life-threatening.

b. Measles can cause variant Creutzfeldt–Jakob disease, which causes severe headaches, seizures and in severe cases can be life-threatening.

c. Measles can cause encephalitis/meningitis, which causes severe headaches, seizures and in severe cases can be life-threatening.

d. Measles can cause Legionnaires' disease, which causes severe headaches, seizures and in severe cases can be life-threatening.

37. Why is immunization after being bitten by a rabid animal so effective and why aren't people vaccinated for rabies like dogs and cats are?

a. It takes a month for the virus to travel from the site of the bite to the central nervous system. People are not vaccinated beforehand as routine vaccination of domestic animals makes it unlikely that humans will contract rabies from an animal bite.

b. It takes a week for the virus to travel from the site of the bite to the peripheral nervous system. People are not vaccinated beforehand as routine vaccination of domestic animals makes it unlikely that humans will contract rabies from an animal bite.

c. It takes a week for the virus to travel from the site of the bite to the central nervous system. People are not vaccinated beforehand as routine vaccination of domestic animals makes it unlikely that humans will contract rabies from an animal bite, and also.

d. It takes a week for the virus to travel from the site of the bite to the central nervous system. People are not vaccinated beforehand, as routine vaccination of domestic animals makes it fully sure that humans will contract rabies from an animal bite, and also.

38. Why don't dogs and cats catch human colds from humans?

a. As cats and dogs have different proteins than humans, the virus that causes colds in humans cannot find receptors in dogs and cats.

b. As cats and dogs have different receptors than humans, the virus that causes colds in humans cannot find receptors in dogs and cats.

c. As cats and dogs' immune system attacks the virus unlike humans, so the virus that causes colds in humans cannot find receptors in dogs and cats.

d. As natural killer cells of cats and dogs attack the virus, the virus that causes colds in humans cannot find receptors in dogs and cats.

39. Prions are responsible for variant CJD (Creutzfeldt Jakob Disease). How has this disease been documented to spread from human to human?

a. Surgery with instruments previously used in a patient with vCJD that were not adequately sterilized and contaminated pineal growth hormones taken from human pineal glands from infected cadavers.

b. Through human consumption of infected meat and contaminated pituitary growth hormones taken from human pituitary glands from infected cadavers.

c. Surgery with instruments previously used in a patient with vCJD that were not adequately sterilized and contaminated pituitary growth hormones taken from human pituitary glands from unwell individuals.

d. Surgery with instruments previously used in a patient with vCJD that were not adequately sterilized and contaminated pituitary growth hormones taken from human pituitary glands from infected cadavers.

40. What characteristics do viroids and viruses have in common?

a. They both replicate within a host cell and contain nucleic acids.

b. They both replicate within a host cell and do not contain nucleic acids.

c. They both replicate within a host cell and contain proteins.

d. They both replicate within a host cell and contain only RNA.

41. Why is the transmission of a prion not reliant upon genes made of DNA or RNA?

a. DNA or RNA, though present, is not transmitted when a prion causes infection.

b. The prion does not contain DNA or RNA.

c. Only parts of DNA or RNA are transmitted in a prion.

d. More of protein and less of DNA or RNA is transmitted.

TEST PREP FOR AP® COURSES

42. The table below shows the Baltimore Classification used to classify viruses based on their genetic material. What is the difference between how Group I and Group III viruses reproduce?

Baltimore classification	
Group	**Characteristics**
I	Double-stranded DNA
II	Single-stranded DNA
III	Double-stranded RNA
IV	Single-stranded RNA (+)
V	Single-stranded RNA (–)
VI	Single-stranded RNA with reverse transcriptase
VII	Double-stranded DNA with reverse transcriptase

a. In Group I, RNA is transcribed from an RNA genome while in Group III, RNA is transcribed from a DNA genome.

b. In Group I, RNA is transcribed from a DNA genome while in Group III, RNA is transcribed from an RNA genome.

c. In Group I, DNA is transcribed from a DNA genome while in Group III, RNA is transcribed from an RNA genome.

d. In Group I, DNA is transcribed from an RNA genome while in Group III, RNA is transcribed from a DNA genome.

43. The table below shows the Baltimore Classification used to classify viruses based on their genetic material. What is a similar or different between the genome of Group I and Group VI, as well as how the two virus types reproduce?

Baltimore classification	
Group	**Characteristics**
I	Double-stranded DNA
II	Single-stranded DNA
III	Double-stranded RNA
IV	Single-stranded RNA (+)
V	Single-stranded RNA (–)
VI	Single-stranded RNA with reverse transcriptase
VII	Double-stranded DNA with reverse transcriptase

a. Group I and VI viruses use RNA as their genome. Group I viruses reproduce by transcribing RNA from their DNA genome, while Group VI viruses first synthesize their RNA genome using reverse transcriptase before they can reproduce.

b. Group I and VI viruses use DNA as their genome. Group I viruses reproduce by transcribing RNA from their DNA genome while group VI viruses first synthesize their DNA genome using reverse transcriptase before they can reproduce.

c. Group I and VI viruses use DNA as their genome. Group I viruses reproduce by transcribing RNA from their DNA genome, while group VI viruses first synthesize RNA genome using reverse transcriptase before they can reproduce.

d. Group I viruses use DNA as their genome while group VI use RNA. Group I viruses reproduce by transcribing RNA from their DNA genome while group VI viruses synthesize DNA from RNA using reverse transcriptase before they can reproduce.

44. The diagram below shows the stages during which a virus infects a host cell. During which of the numbered steps does the amount of viral genetic material begin to change within the host cell and why?

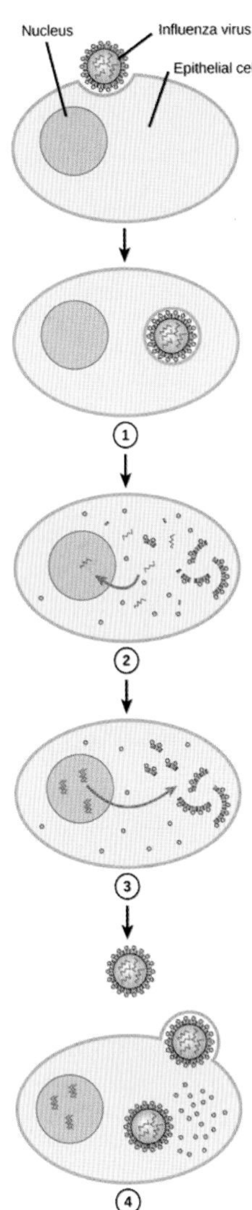

a. 1; virus enters the cell

b. 2; virus RNA enters the nucleus

c. 3; new viruses assemble within the cell

d. 4; viruses leave the cell

45. The diagram below shows the stages during which a virus infects a host cell. How could the influenza virus change the function of a host cell? Which has the potential to produce the most copies of the virus?

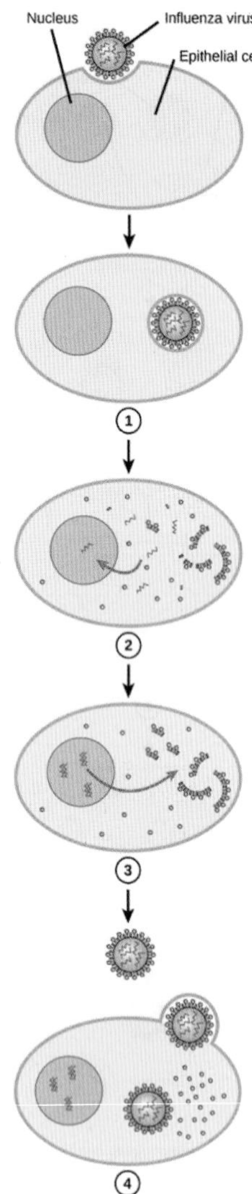

a. Because it replicates its DNA within the cell and reproduces, which could interfere with cell processes.

b. Because it replicates RNA within the cell and reproduces which could interfere with cell processes.

c. Because it attacks the immune system of the host cell, which would in turn interfere with cell processes.

d. Because it replicates its protein within the cell and reproduces, which could interfere with cell processes.

46. The diagrams below model the lytic and lysogenic reproductive cycles of viruses. Which cycle would maintain the DNA of the virus over several generations, and why?

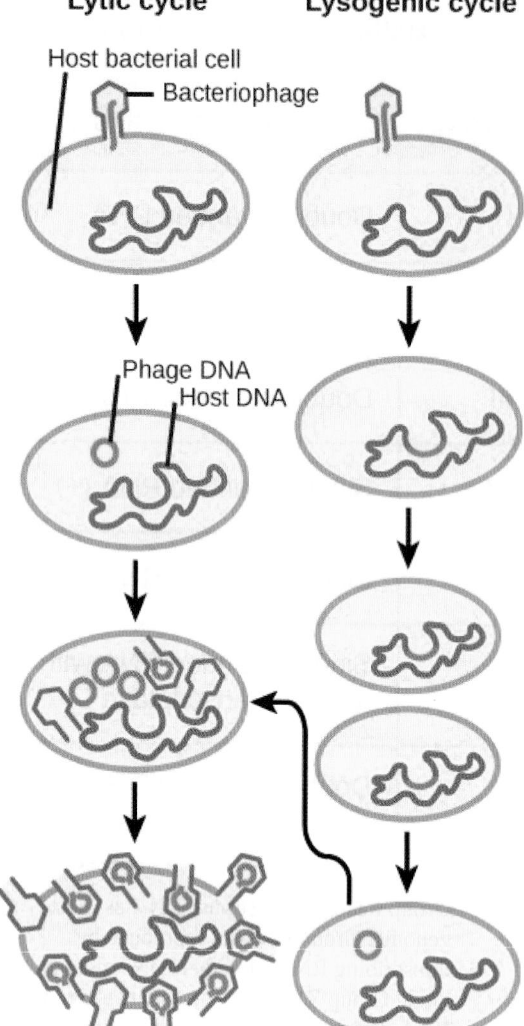

a. Lysogenic, because the viral DNA can be excised from the host cell's DNA when under stress.

b. Lytic, because the viral DNA can be excised from the host cell's DNA when under stress.

c. Lytic, because the viral DNA can be passed on when the host cell replicates.

d. Lysogenic, because the viral DNA can be passed on when the host cell replicates.

47. The diagrams below model the lytic and lysogenic reproductive cycles of viruses. Based on the diagram, identify whether the following statement is true or false, and explain why or why not: "The lysogenic cycle allows viruses to preserve their genome during unfavorable conditions."

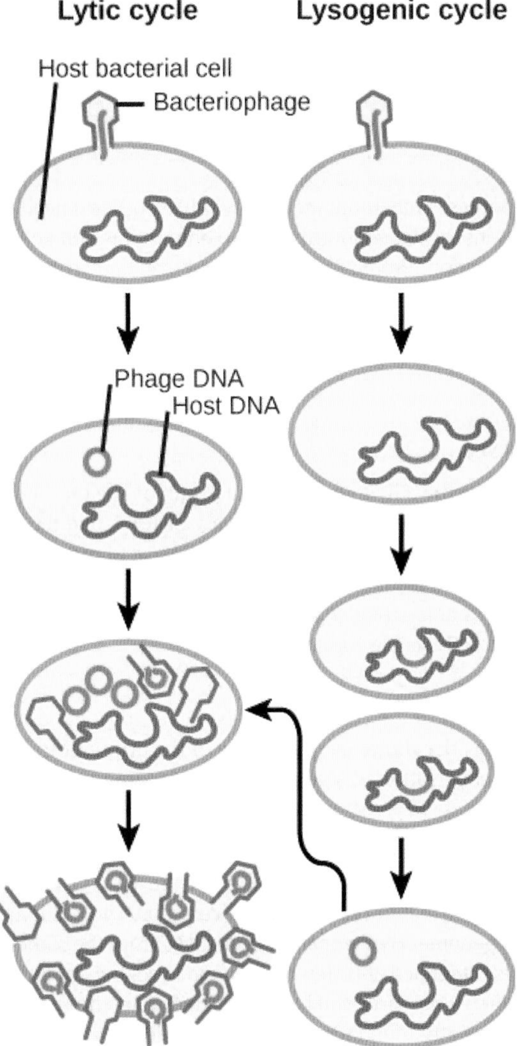

a. True. Because when the host cell experiences unfavorable conditions, it stops dividing and stays in the same state.
b. True. Because the host cell in both the replication stage and during unfavorable conditions stays in the lysogenic cycle as it is more preferable over the lytic cycle.
c. False. Because when the host cell experiences unfavorable conditions, the prophage exits the genome and enters the lytic cycle.
d. False. Because when the host cell experiences unfavorable conditions, the virus enters latency period.

SCIENCE PRACTICE CHALLENGE QUESTIONS

48. Influenza A virus is the most pathogenic of the human influenza viruses. Its envelope encloses a protein complex (vRNP) and eight, single-stranded, negative RNA (the complement of a positive RNA strand that can be transcribed by a ribosome) segments (vRNA). Each segment encodes one or two proteins that support viral replication. On the outer surface of the envelope are proteins that recognize and bind to host receptors.

A. Annotate the representation below to briefly **describe** each process associated with a numbered label.

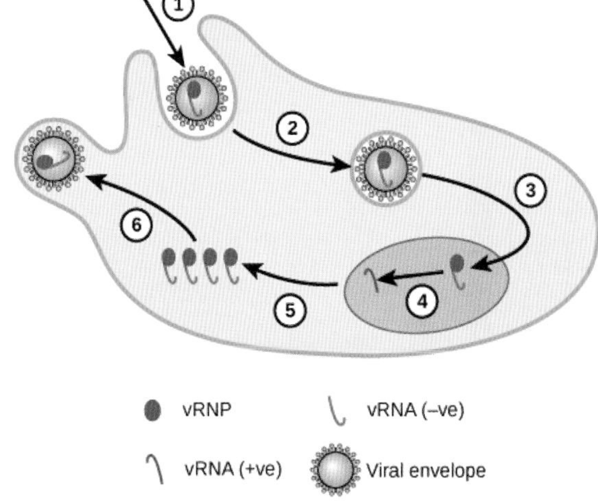

Figure 21.21

B. **Describe** influenza A viral replication as a process regulated by either positive or negative feedback and

justify your selection.

The human-acquired immunodeficiency syndrome (AIDS) and many cancers are cause by double-stranded RNA retroviruses.

C. **Contrast** the processes of viral replication of HIV and influenza A virus.

D. **Explain** the difference in the effects of infection by HIV and influenza A virus on host genetic variability.

E. Measured mutation rates for influenza A virus and HIV are nearly identical (Sanjuan et al., *Jour. Virology*, 2010). **Explain** this observation even though host error-checking operates in one of these replication modes.

49. Three-dimensional (3D) structures, or folding, of proteins have been shown to contain more information about evolutionary relationships than the sequences of DNA nucleotides that encode the proteins. Amino acid sequences of rabbit skeletal muscle actin (375 amino acids) and bovine ATPase (386 amino acids) have only 39 locations in common. However, the 3D structure of these proteins are nearly identical (Flaherty et al., *Proc. Natl. Acad. Sci. USA*, 1991). As information about the 3D folding of proteins and the number of sequenced whole genomes has increased, folding has been shown to be an evolutionarily conserved property.

A. **Analyze** these data to **refine** the following model: The evolutionary history of life on Earth can be inferred from variations over time of the nucleotide sequence of a gene.

By applying a classification scheme based on protein folding, Nasir and Caetano-Anollés (*Sci. Adv.* 2015) have determined the number of folding families that viruses share with the three domains. Approximately 60% of the folding patterns found in viruses were common to all three domains, as shown below. Fewer than 10% were unique to viruses.

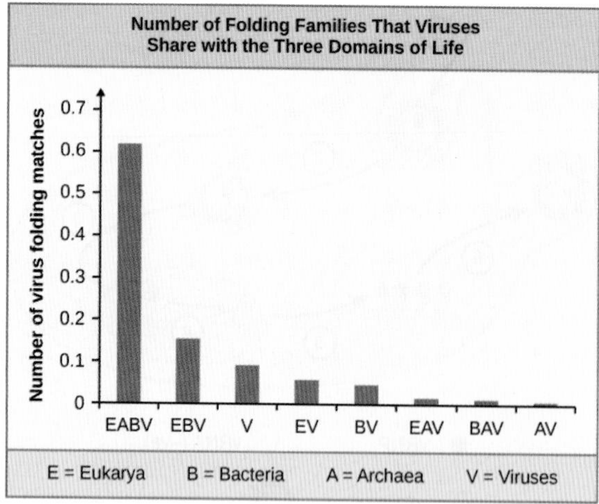

Figure 21.22

Viruses are acellular, and, consequently, they lie outside of the three domains of cellular life. However, their exclusion is increasingly challenged. Since 2012, several very large viruses have been discovered, each a double-stranded DNA virus with more than one million bases, with some encoding nucleotides and amino acids. However, none encode ribosomes, so these viruses are still dependent on a marine bacteriovore (amoeba or flagellate) host for replication.

Hypotheses regarding the origin of life on Earth need to account for the relationship between proteins and genetic information. Proteins are required to read and write genetic information, but genetic information is required to synthesize proteins. Which of these systems evolved first, and if neither came first, how could they evolve simultaneously? The RNA-first model is based on the idea that ribosomal RNA both encodes and synthesizes proteins.

B. **Describe** a hypothesis for the origin of life on Earth that combines the dual functionality of RNA and the function of retroviral reverse transcriptase to propose a mechanism leading to an ancient, acellular lineage of very large, double-stranded DNA viruses and a first DNA-based cellular life form.

C. Like viruses, the nucleus of a eukaryote uses the machinery of the cell to transcribe DNA and synthesize proteins. **Evaluate** the possibility of the origin of Eukarya by specialization of a very large double-stranded DNA virus.

50. Viruses evolve but leave no fossil evidence that can be used to construct phylogenies. However, viral DNA, especially that of retroviruses, is commonly found in the host genome. By comparing sequences from the same virus integrated at different points in time, the evolutionary history of the virus can be constructed. The viral genomes are typically found incomplete, in segments, and interrupted by stop codons. In jawed vertebrates, retroviral sequences or sequences that have been derived from them are a significant fraction of the whole genome.

A. **Explain** why retroviral DNA rather than the genomes of single-stranded or double-stranded DNA or single-stranded RNA viruses are found in host DNA.

Exaptation occurs when gene expression provides a function that is independent of the selection pressures that have acted on the gene. For example, a pigment that provided selective advantage by reducing damage from solar radiation becomes an element of mating behavior. Feathers that evolved under selection to prevent heat loss become a means of flight.

In a study of viral evolution within host genomes of primates, Katzuorakis and Gifford (*PLOS Genetics*, 2010) found that viral genomes within the host were surprisingly stable; with computer simulation, they estimated the probability of such constancy at 1 in 100,000.

B. **Explain** in terms of selection how viral genetic information that no longer replicates the virus is maintained by the host.

Distemper is an incurable disease of cats, dogs, and their

sister lineages caused by a parvovirus. The virus exploits the host's transferrin, a membrane-bound protein used for iron transport, to attach to the cell. The phylogeny of the *Parvoviridae* family has been constructed (J. Kaebler, *PLOS Pathogens*, 2012). That study revealed the evolution of both the virus and the host protein through selection to resist infection. About 54 million years ago when the lineage of cats (*Feliformia*) diverged from that of dogs (*Caniformia*), the parvovirus envelope diverged as well, conforming to changes in the host's transferrin. In 1978, a worldwide disease in dogs due to a parvovirus suddenly appeared.

C. **Explain** how this pandemic could have originated in the cat population.

51. A simple calculation of the rate of spread of a pox virus (virion) led researchers at Imperial College London to a new insight. Virions communicate with other virions. The researchers observed that the radius of an approximately circular plaque of infected cells grew to 1.45 mm in just 3 days. They measured the distance between adjacent cells to be 0.037 mm to obtain the apparent time for the lytic cycle (from infection to lysis). They compared this time to the actual rate at which new virions are formed: 5 to 6 hours.

A. **Predict** the radius of infection if the infection process involved a sequence of entry, replication, lysis, and infection of an adjacent cell.

To account for this discrepancy between observed and predicted growth rates, the researchers examined the viral entry process and discovered that the actin protein on the host cell's surface that provided the viral receptor was modified by attachment. They then found a mutant virus that did not modify the cell surface protein. The dependence of the growth of plaque radius on time for the wild type and mutant are shown in the graph.

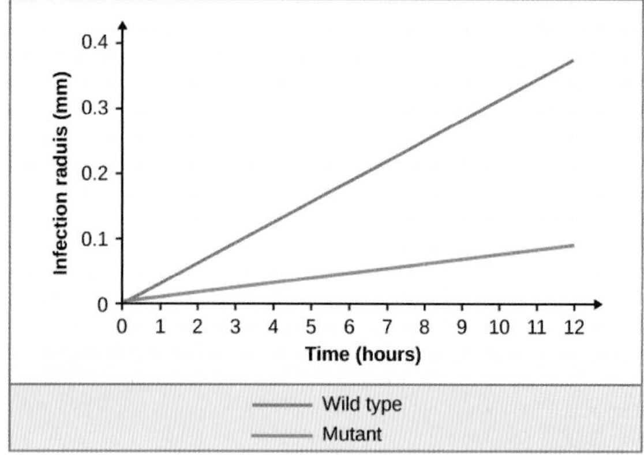

Figure 21.23

B. **Analyze** these data and compare the infection rates calculated with those predicted in part A.

C. Use the results of this experiment to **support the claim** that responses to information and communication of information affect natural selection.

52. Describe how viral replication introduces genetic variation in the viral population.

22 | PROKARYOTES: BACTERIA AND ARCHAEA

Figure 22.1 Certain prokaryotes can live in extreme environments such as the Morning Glory pool, a hot spring in Yellowstone National Park. The spring's vivid blue color is from the prokaryotes that thrive in its very hot waters. (credit: modification of work by Jon Sullivan)

Chapter Outline

Introduction

Most people think of bacteria as disease-causing organisms. Although some bacteria are pathogens, many are not. For example, the commensal bacteria that inhabit our skin and gastrointestinal tract do a host of good things for us. They protect us from pathogens, help us digest our food, and produce some of our vitamins and other nutrients. These activities have been known for a long time. More recently, scientists have gathered evidence that these bacteria may also help regulate our moods, influence our activity levels, and even help control weight by affecting our food choices and absorption patterns. The Human Microbiome Project has begun the process of cataloging our normal bacteria (and archaea) so we can better understand these functions. You can learn more about the Human Microbiome Project here (http://openstaxcollege.org/l/32microbiome) .

22.1 | Prokaryotic Diversity

In this section, you will explore the following questions:

- What is the evolutionary history of prokaryotes?
- What are distinguishing features of extremophiles?
- Why is it difficult to culture prokaryotes for study purposes?

Connection for AP® Courses

In the recent past, scientists grouped living organisms into five kingdoms based on several criteria, including the absence or presence of a nucleus and other membrane-bound organelles, the absence or presence of cell walls, multicellularity, and so on. As we learned earlier, prokaryotes were the first cells to evolve on Earth 3.5 to 4.5 millions of years ago and lacked a nucleus and cytoplasmic organelles. In the late 20th century, scientists compared sequences of small-subunit ribosomal RNA, which resulted in a more fundamental way to group organisms on Earth. Based on the differences in the structure of the cell membranes and in rRNA, Carl Woese and his colleagues proposed the three domain system. The domain Bacteria comprises all organisms in the kingdom Eubacteria (bacteria), the domain Archaea comprises the rest of the prokaryotes, and the domain Eukarya comprises all eukaryotes, including protists, fungi, plants, and animals. Prokaryotes exhibit great diversity in form and function and are abundant and ubiquitous. In addition to inhabiting moderate environments like the human digestive system, prokaryotes are found in extreme conditions (**extremophiles**), from boiling hot springs to the Great Salt Lake and to frozen environments in Antarctica.

Because prokaryotes inhabit many different environments, they have evolved multiple strategies for meeting their energy demands, including chemosynthesis, photosynthesis, anaerobic cellular respiration, and aerobic cellular respiration. Hot springs and hydrothermal vents may have been the environments in which life began, and there is fossil evidence of the presence of microbial mats about 3.5 billion years ago. During the first two billion years of Earth's history, the atmosphere lacked sufficient quantities of oxygen, and only anaerobic organisms were able to live. Cyanobacteria evolved from early phototrophs and began the oxygenation of the atmosphere. The increase in oxygen concentration allows the evolution of other life forms with other metabolic processes. Most prokaryotes prefer to live in communities, often forming biofilms.

Information presented and the examples highlighted in the section support concepts outlined in Big Idea 1 of the AP® Biology Curriculum Framework. The AP® Learning Objectives listed in the Curriculum Framework provide a transparent foundation for the AP® Biology course, an inquiry-based laboratory experience, instructional activities, and AP® exam questions. A learning objective merges required content with one or more of the seven science practices.

Big Idea 1	The process of evolution drives the diversity and unity of life.
Enduring Understanding 1.D	The origin of living systems is explained by natural processes.
Essential Knowledge	**1.D.1** There are several hypotheses about the natural origin of life on Earth, each with supporting scientific evidence.
Science Practice	**6.3** The student can articulate the reasons that scientific explanations and theories are refined or replaced.
Learning Objective	**1.29** The student is able to describe the reasons for revisions of scientific hypotheses of the origin of life on Earth.
Essential Knowledge	**1.D.1** There are several hypotheses about the natural origin of life on Earth, each with supporting scientific evidence.
Science Practice	**6.5** The student can evaluate alternative scientific explanations.
Learning Objective	**1.30** The student is able to evaluate scientific hypotheses about the origin of life on Earth.

Essential Knowledge	**1.D.1** There are several hypotheses about the natural origin of life on Earth, each with supporting scientific evidence.
Science Practice	**4.4** The student can evaluate sources of data to answer a particular scientific question.
Learning Objective	**1.31** The student is able to evaluate the accuracy and legitimacy of data to answer scientific questions about the origin of life on Earth.
Essential Knowledge	**1.D.2** Life on Earth evolved between 3.5 and 4.5 billion years ago.
Science Practice	**4.1** The student can justify the selection of the kind of data needed to answer a particular scientific question.
Learning Objective	**1.32** The student is able to justify the selection of geological, physical, and chemical data that reveal early Earth conditions.

The Science Practice Challenge Questions contain additional test questions for this section that will help you prepare for the AP exam. These questions address the following standards:
[APLO 2.35][APLO 2.36][APLO 2.37]

Prokaryotes are ubiquitous. They cover every imaginable surface where there is sufficient moisture, and they live on and inside of other living things. In the typical human body, prokaryotic cells outnumber human body cells by about ten to one. They comprise the majority of living things in all ecosystems. Some prokaryotes thrive in environments that are inhospitable for most living things. Prokaryotes recycle **nutrients**—essential substances (such as carbon and nitrogen)—and they drive the evolution of new ecosystems, some of which are natural and others man-made. Prokaryotes have been on Earth since long before multicellular life appeared.

Prokaryotes, the First Inhabitants of Earth

When and where did life begin? What were the conditions on Earth when life began? Prokaryotes were the first forms of life on Earth, and they existed for billions of years before plants and animals appeared. The Earth and its moon are thought to be about 4.54 billion years old. This estimate is based on evidence from radiometric dating of meteorite material together with other substrate material from Earth and the moon. Early Earth had a very different atmosphere (contained less molecular oxygen) than it does today and was subjected to strong radiation; thus, the first organisms would have flourished where they were more protected, such as in ocean depths or beneath the surface of the Earth. At this time too, strong volcanic activity was common on Earth, so it is likely that these first organisms—the first prokaryotes—were adapted to very high temperatures. Early Earth was prone to geological upheaval and volcanic eruption, and was subject to bombardment by mutagenic radiation from the sun. The first organisms were prokaryotes that could withstand these harsh conditions.

Microbial Mats

Microbial mats or large biofilms may represent the earliest forms of life on Earth; there is fossil evidence of their presence starting about 3.5 billion years ago. A **microbial mat** is a multi-layered sheet of prokaryotes (Figure 22.2) that includes mostly bacteria, but also archaea. Microbial mats are a few centimeters thick, and they typically grow where different types of materials interface, mostly on moist surfaces. The various types of prokaryotes that comprise them carry out different metabolic pathways, and that is the reason for their various colors. Prokaryotes in a microbial mat are held together by a glue-like sticky substance that they secrete called extracellular matrix.

The first microbial mats likely obtained their energy from chemicals found near hydrothermal vents. A **hydrothermal vent** is a breakage or fissure in the Earth's surface that releases geothermally heated water. With the evolution of photosynthesis about 3 billion years ago, some prokaryotes in microbial mats came to use a more widely available energy source—sunlight—whereas others were still dependent on chemicals from hydrothermal vents for energy and food.

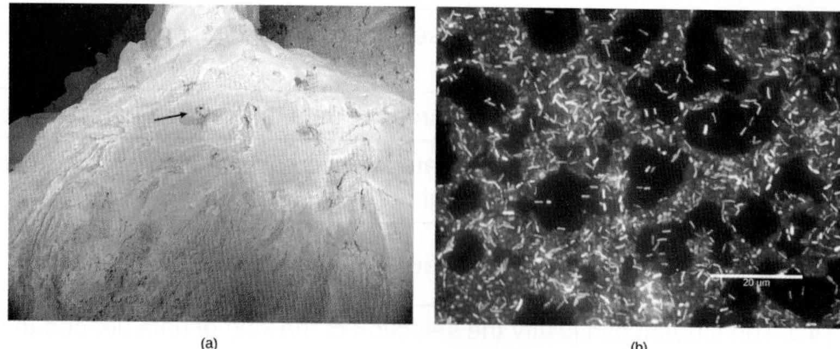

Figure 22.2 This (a) microbial mat, about one meter in diameter, grows over a hydrothermal vent in the Pacific Ocean in a region known as the "Pacific Ring of Fire." The mat helps retain microbial nutrients. Chimneys such as the one indicated by the arrow allow gases to escape. (b) In this micrograph, bacteria are visualized using fluorescence microscopy. (credit a: modification of work by Dr. Bob Embley, NOAA PMEL, Chief Scientist; credit b: modification of work by Ricardo Murga, Rodney Donlan, CDC; scale-bar data from Matt Russell)

Stromatolites

Fossilized microbial mats represent the earliest record of life on Earth. A **stromatolite** is a sedimentary structure formed when minerals are precipitated out of water by prokaryotes in a microbial mat (Figure 22.3). Stromatolites form layered rocks made of carbonate or silicate. Although most stromatolites are artifacts from the past, there are places on Earth where stromatolites are still forming. For example, growing stromatolites have been found in the Anza-Borrego Desert State Park in San Diego County, California.

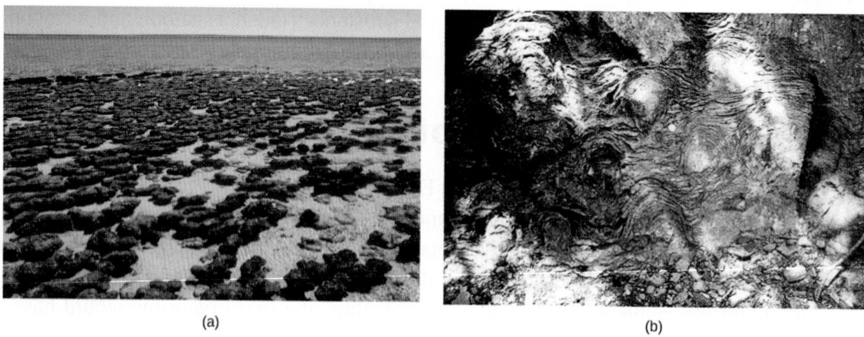

Figure 22.3 (a) These living stromatolites are located in Shark Bay, Australia. (b) These fossilized stromatolites, found in Glacier National Park, Montana, are nearly 1.5 billion years old. (credit a: Robert Young; credit b: P. Carrara, NPS)

The Ancient Atmosphere

Evidence indicates that during the first two billion years of Earth's existence, the atmosphere was **anoxic**, meaning that there was no molecular oxygen. Therefore, only those organisms that can grow without oxygen—**anaerobic** organisms—were able to live. Autotrophic organisms that convert solar energy into chemical energy are called **phototrophs**, and they appeared within one billion years of the formation of Earth. Then, **cyanobacteria**, also known as blue-green algae, evolved from these simple phototrophs one billion years later. Cyanobacteria (Figure 22.4) began the oxygenation of the atmosphere. Increased atmospheric oxygen allowed the development of more efficient O_2-utilizing catabolic pathways. It also opened up the land to increased colonization, because some O_2 is converted into O_3 (ozone) and ozone effectively absorbs the ultraviolet light that would otherwise cause lethal mutations in DNA. Ultimately, the increase in O_2 concentrations allowed the evolution of other life forms.

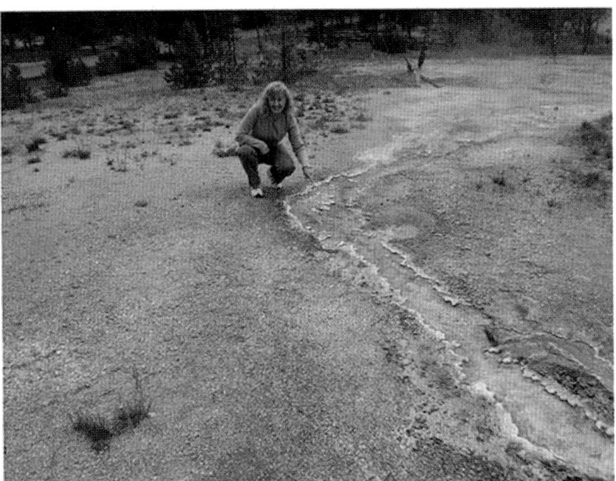

Figure 22.4 This hot spring in Yellowstone National Park flows toward the foreground. Cyanobacteria in the spring are green, and as water flows down the gradient, the intensity of the color increases as cell density increases. The water is cooler at the edges of the stream than in the center, causing the edges to appear greener. (credit: Graciela Brelles-Mariño)

science practices CONNECTION for AP® Courses

Early Earth was inhospitable to most life as we know it today, with a substantial amount of geological upheaval, volcanic activity, and an anoxic atmosphere (which means it lacked oxygen). Therefore, the origin of life on Earth is of great interest to scientists.

One of the earliest hypotheses of how life originated on Earth was by panspermia, which dates back to the 5th century BC. Panspermia is the idea that life is distributed to different parts of the universe on objects such as meteoroids and asteroids. If this were to occur, organic compounds and microorganisms would be able to survive the extreme conditions of space.

However, in the 1960s, scientists Stanley Miller and Harold Urey conducted laboratory experiments that showed it was possible for organic compounds, including amino acids, to be formed under certain conditions from inorganic molecules and energy, both of which would have been present in the early conditions of Earth. Subsequently, fossilized evidence of microbial mats by deep sea hydrothermal vents that dates back 3.5 billion years was discovered. Consequently, there are now several hypotheses regarding how life could have evolved on Earth.

Activity

Perform internet research using reliable webpages containing current scientific evidence supporting the ideas that 1) life originated on Earth, and 2) that life arrived on Earth from an extraterrestrial object, such as an asteroid or comet. Then decide which idea has more supporting evidence. Be able to justify your conclusion.

Think About It

If organic compounds, which eventually formed organisms, could have formed both extraterrestrially and on Earth, why would it be less complicated, and thus more likely, that life formed on Earth?

Think About It

Even though Miller and Urey showed that organic molecules could be produced from conditions of early Earth, why are there still different hypotheses about how life could have originated on Earth?

Microbes Are Adaptable: Life in Moderate and Extreme Environments

Some organisms have developed strategies that allow them to survive harsh conditions. Prokaryotes thrive in a vast array of environments: Some grow in conditions that would seem very normal to us, whereas others are able to thrive and grow under conditions that would kill a plant or animal. Almost all prokaryotes have a cell wall, a protective structure that allows them to survive in both hyper- and hypo-osmotic conditions. Some soil bacteria are able to form endospores that resist heat and drought, thereby allowing the organism to survive until favorable conditions recur. These adaptations, along with others, allow bacteria to be the most abundant life form in all terrestrial and aquatic ecosystems.

Other bacteria and archaea are adapted to grow under extreme conditions and are called **extremophiles**, meaning "lovers of extremes." Extremophiles have been found in all kinds of environments: the depth of the oceans, hot springs, the Artic and the Antarctic, in very dry places, deep inside Earth, in harsh chemical environments, and in high radiation environments (Figure 22.5), just to mention a few. These organisms give us a better understanding of prokaryotic diversity and open up the possibility of finding new prokaryotic species that may lead to the discovery of new therapeutic drugs or have industrial applications. Because they have specialized adaptations that allow them to live in extreme conditions, many extremophiles cannot survive in moderate environments. There are many different groups of extremophiles: They are identified based on the conditions in which they grow best, and several habitats are extreme in multiple ways. For example, a soda lake is both salty and alkaline, so organisms that live in a soda lake must be both alkaliphiles and halophiles (Table 22.1). Other extremophiles, like **radioresistant** organisms, do not prefer an extreme environment (in this case, one with high levels of radiation), but have adapted to survive in it (Figure 22.5).

Extremophiles and Their Preferred Conditions

Extremophile Type	Conditions for Optimal Growth
Acidophiles	pH 3 or below
Alkaliphiles	pH 9 or above
Thermophiles	Temperature 60–80 °C (140–176 °F)
Hyperthermophiles	Temperature 80–122 °C (176–250 °F)
Psychrophiles	Temperature of -15-10 °C (5-50 °F) or lower
Halophiles	Salt concentration of at least 0.2 M
Osmophiles	High sugar concentration

Table 22.1

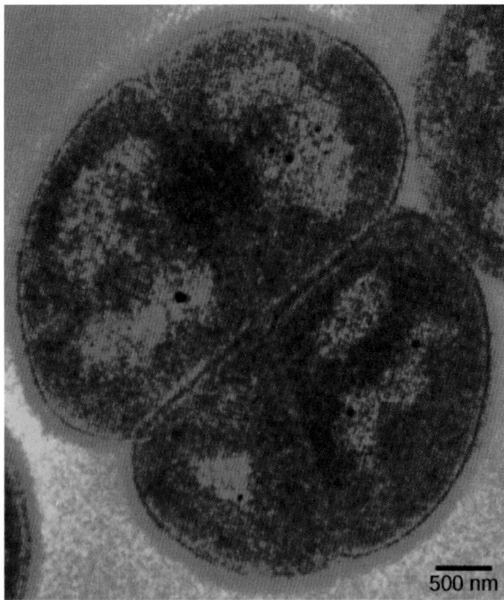

Figure 22.5 *Deinococcus radiodurans*, visualized in this false color transmission electron micrograph, is a prokaryote that can tolerate very high doses of ionizing radiation. It has developed DNA repair mechanisms that allow it to reconstruct its chromosome even if it has been broken into hundreds of pieces by radiation or heat. (credit: modification of work by Michael Daly; scale-bar data from Matt Russell)

Prokaryotes in the Dead Sea

One example of a very harsh environment is the Dead Sea, a hypersaline basin that is located between Jordan and Israel. Hypersaline environments are essentially concentrated seawater. In the Dead Sea, the sodium concentration is 10 times higher than that of seawater, and the water contains high levels of magnesium (about 40 times higher than in seawater) that would be toxic to most living things. Iron, calcium, and magnesium, elements that form divalent ions (Fe^{2+}, Ca^{2+}, and Mg^{2+}), produce what is commonly referred to as "hard" water. Taken together, the high concentration of divalent cations, the acidic pH (6.0), and the intense solar radiation flux make the Dead Sea a unique, and uniquely hostile, ecosystem[1] (Figure 22.6).

What sort of prokaryotes do we find in the Dead Sea? The extremely salt-tolerant bacterial mats include *Halobacterium*, *Haloferax volcanii* (which is found in other locations, not only the Dead Sea), *Halorubrum sodomense*, and *Halobaculum gomorrense*, and the archaea *Haloarcula marismortui*, among others.

(a)

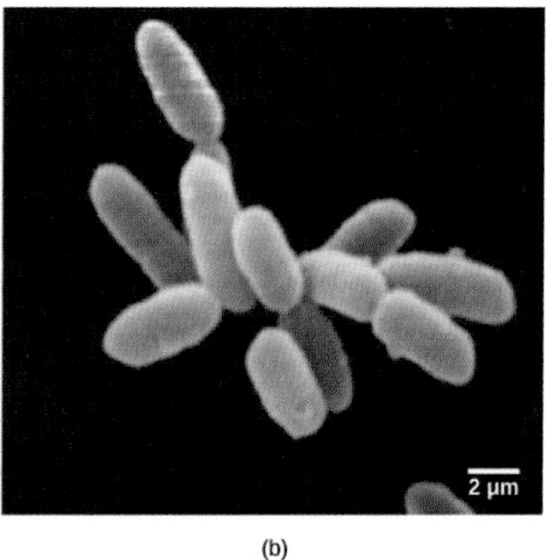

(b)

Figure 22.6 (a) The Dead Sea is hypersaline. Nevertheless, salt-tolerant bacteria thrive in this sea. (b) These halobacteria cells can form salt-tolerant bacterial mats. (credit a: Julien Menichini; credit b: NASA; scale-bar data from Matt Russell)

Unculturable Prokaryotes and the Viable-but-Non-Culturable State

Microbiologists typically grow prokaryotes in the laboratory using an appropriate culture medium containing all the nutrients needed by the target organism. The medium can be liquid, broth, or solid. After an incubation time at the right temperature, there should be evidence of microbial growth (Figure 22.7). The process of culturing bacteria is complex

1. Bodaker, I, Itai, S, Suzuki, MT, Feingersch, R, Rosenberg, M, Maguire, ME, Shimshon, B, and others. Comparative community genomics in the Dead Sea: An increasingly extreme environment. *The ISME Journal* 4 (2010): 399–407, doi:10.1038/ismej.2009.141. published online 24 December 2009.

and is one of the greatest discoveries of modern science. German physician Robert Koch is credited with discovering the techniques for pure culture, including staining and using growth media. His assistant Julius Petri invented the Petri dish whose use persists in today's laboratories. Koch worked primarily with the *Mycobacterium tuberculosis* bacterium that causes tuberculosis and developed postulates to identify disease-causing organisms that continue to be widely used in the medical community. Koch's postulates include that an organism can be identified as the cause of disease when it is present in all infected samples and absent in all healthy samples, and it is able to reproduce the infection after being cultured multiple times. Today, cultures remain a primary diagnostic tool in medicine and other areas of molecular biology.

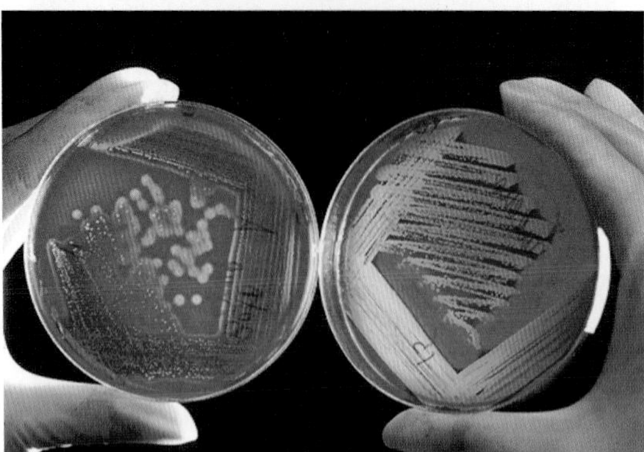

Figure 22.7 In these agar plates, the growth medium is supplemented with red blood cells. Blood agar becomes transparent in the presence of hemolytic *Streptococcus*, which destroys red blood cells and is used to diagnose *Streptococcus* infections. The plate on the left is inoculated with non-hemolytic *Staphylococcus* (large white colonies), and the plate on the right is inoculated with hemolytic *Streptococcus* (tiny clear colonies). If you look closely at the right plate, you can see that the agar surrounding the bacteria has turned clear. (credit: Bill Branson, NCI)

Some prokaryotes, however, cannot grow in a laboratory setting. In fact, over 99 percent of bacteria and archaea are unculturable. For the most part, this is due to a lack of knowledge as to what to feed these organisms and how to grow them; they have special requirements for growth that remain unknown to scientists, such as needing specific micronutrients, pH, temperature, pressure, co-factors, or co-metabolites. Some bacteria cannot be cultured because they are obligate intracellular parasites and cannot be grown outside a host cell.

In other cases, culturable organisms become unculturable under stressful conditions, even though the same organism could be cultured previously. Those organisms that cannot be cultured but are not dead are in a **viable-but-non-culturable** (VBNC) state. The VBNC state occurs when prokaryotes respond to environmental stressors by entering a dormant state that allows their survival. The criteria for entering into the VBNC state are not completely understood. In a process called **resuscitation**, the prokaryote can go back to "normal" life when environmental conditions improve.

Is the VBNC state an unusual way of living for prokaryotes? In fact, most of the prokaryotes living in the soil or in oceanic waters are non-culturable. It has been said that only a small fraction, perhaps one percent, of prokaryotes can be cultured under laboratory conditions. If these organisms are non-culturable, then how is it known whether they are present and alive? Microbiologists use molecular techniques, such as the polymerase chain reaction (PCR), to amplify selected portions of DNA of prokaryotes, demonstrating their existence. Recall that PCR can make billions of copies of a DNA segment in a process called amplification.

The Ecology of Biofilms

Until a couple of decades ago, microbiologists used to think of prokaryotes as isolated entities living apart. This model, however, does not reflect the true ecology of prokaryotes, most of which prefer to live in communities where they can interact. A **biofilm** is a microbial community (Figure 22.8) held together in a gummy-textured matrix that consists primarily of polysaccharides secreted by the organisms, together with some proteins and nucleic acids. Biofilms grow attached to surfaces. Some of the best-studied biofilms are composed of prokaryotes, although fungal biofilms have also been described as well as some composed of a mixture of fungi and bacteria.

Biofilms are present almost everywhere: they can cause the clogging of pipes and readily colonize surfaces in industrial settings. In recent, large-scale outbreaks of bacterial contamination of food, biofilms have played a major role. They also colonize household surfaces, such as kitchen counters, cutting boards, sinks, and toilets, as well as places on the human body, such as the surfaces of our teeth.

Interactions among the organisms that populate a biofilm, together with their protective exopolysaccharidic (EPS) environment, make these communities more robust than free-living, or planktonic, prokaryotes. The sticky substance that holds bacteria together also excludes most antibiotics and disinfectants, making biofilm bacteria hardier than their planktonic counterparts. Overall, biofilms are very difficult to destroy because they are resistant to many common forms of sterilization.

visual CONNECTION

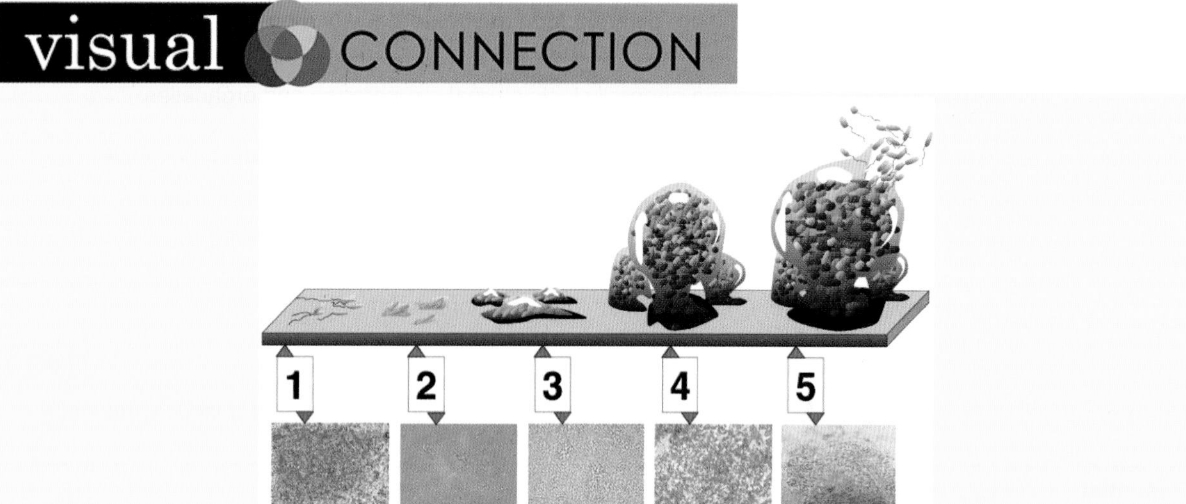

Figure 22.8 Five stages of biofilm development are shown. During stage 1, initial attachment, bacteria adhere to a solid surface via weak van der Waals interactions. During stage 2, irreversible attachment, hairlike appendages called pili permanently anchor the bacteria to the surface. During stage 3, maturation I, the biofilm grows through cell division and recruitment of other bacteria. An extracellular matrix composed primarily of polysaccharides holds the biofilm together. During stage 4, maturation II, the biofilm continues to grow and takes on a more complex shape. During stage 5, dispersal, the biofilm matrix is partly broken down, allowing some bacteria to escape and colonize another surface. Micrographs of a *Pseudomonas aeruginosa* biofilm in each of the stages of development are shown. (credit: D. Davis, Don Monroe, PLoS)

22.2 | Structure of Prokaryotes

In this section, you will explore the following questions:

- What are similarities in the structures of the prokaryotes, Archaea and Bacteria?
- What are examples of structural differences between Archaea and Bacteria?

Connection for AP® Courses

Domains Archaea and Bacteria contain single-celled organisms lacking a nucleus and other membrane-bound organelles. The two groups have substantial biochemical and structural differences. Most have a cell wall external to the plasma cell membrane, the composition of which can vary among groups, and many have additional structures such as flagella and pili. Prokaryotes also have ribosomes, where protein synthesis occurs. For the purpose of AP®, you do not have to memorize the various groups of bacteria. You should, however, be able to distinguish between prokaryotes and eukaryotes and know the domains.

Information presented and the examples highlighted in the section support concepts outlined in Big Idea 2 and Big Idea 3 of the AP® Biology Curriculum Framework. The AP® Learning Objectives listed in the Curriculum Framework provide a transparent foundation for the AP® Biology course, an inquiry-based laboratory experience, instructional activities, and AP® exam questions. A learning objective merges required content with one or more of the seven science practices.

Big Idea 2	Biological systems utilize free energy and molecular building blocks to grow, to reproduce, and to maintain dynamic homeostasis.
Enduring Understanding 2.B	Growth, reproduction and dynamic homeostasis require that cell create and maintain internal environments that are different form their external environment.
Essential Knowledge	**2.B.3** Archaea and Bacteria generally lack internal membranes and organelles.
Science Practice	**1.4** The student can use representations and models to analyze situations or solve problems qualitatively and quantitatively.
Learning Objective	**2.14** The student is able to use representations and models to describe differences in prokaryotic and eukaryotic cells.
Big Idea 3	Living systems store, retrieve, transmit and respond to information essential to life processes.
Enduring Understanding 3.C	The processing of genetic information is imperfect and is a source of genetic variation.
Essential Knowledge	**3.C.2** Prokaryotes contain circular chromosomes and plasmid DNA.
Science Practice	**6.2** The student can construct explanations of phenomena based on evidence produced through scientific practices.
Learning Objective	**3.27** The student is able to compare and contrast processes by which genetic variation is produced and maintained in organisms from multiple domains.
Essential Knowledge	**3.C.2** Prokaryotes contain circular chromosomes and plasmid DNA.
Science Practice	**7.2** The student can connect concepts in and across domain(s) to generalize or extrapolate in and/or across enduring understandings and/or big ideas.
Learning Objective	**3.28** The student is able to construct an explanation of the multiple processes that increase variation within a population.

The Science Practice Challenge Questions contain additional test questions for this section that will help you prepare for the AP exam. These questions address the following standards:
[APLO 2.5][APLO 2.13][APLO 2.14][APLO 4.9]

There are many differences between prokaryotic and eukaryotic cells. However, all cells have four common structures: the plasma membrane, which functions as a barrier for the cell and separates the cell from its environment; the cytoplasm, a jelly-like substance inside the cell; nucleic acids, the genetic material of the cell; and ribosomes, where protein synthesis takes place. Prokaryotes come in various shapes, but many fall into three categories: cocci (spherical), bacilli (rod-shaped), and spirilli (spiral-shaped) (**Figure 22.9**).

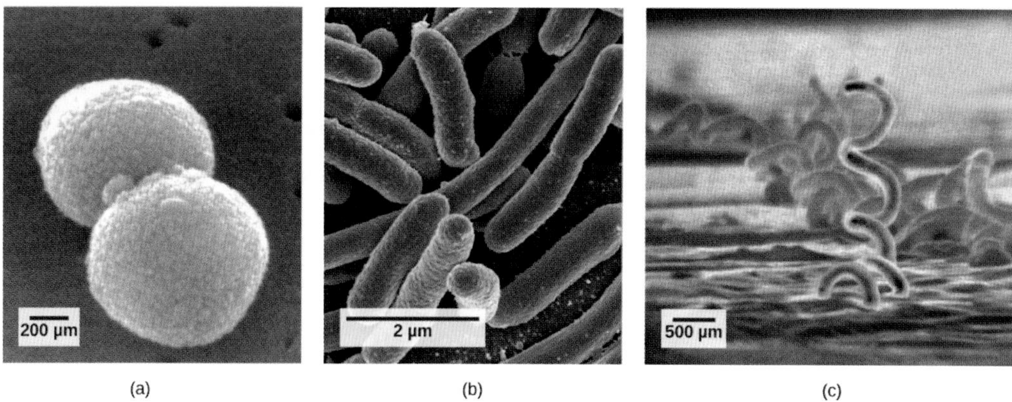

Figure 22.9 Prokaryotes fall into three basic categories based on their shape, visualized here using scanning electron microscopy: (a) cocci, or spherical (a pair is shown); (b) bacilli, or rod-shaped; and (c) spirilli, or spiral-shaped. (credit a: modification of work by Janice Haney Carr, Dr. Richard Facklam, CDC; credit c: modification of work by Dr. David Cox; scale-bar data from Matt Russell)

The Prokaryotic Cell

Recall that prokaryotes (Figure 22.10) are unicellular organisms that lack organelles or other internal membrane-bound structures. Therefore, they do not have a nucleus but instead generally have a single chromosome—a piece of circular, double-stranded DNA located in an area of the cell called the nucleoid. Most prokaryotes have a cell wall outside the plasma membrane.

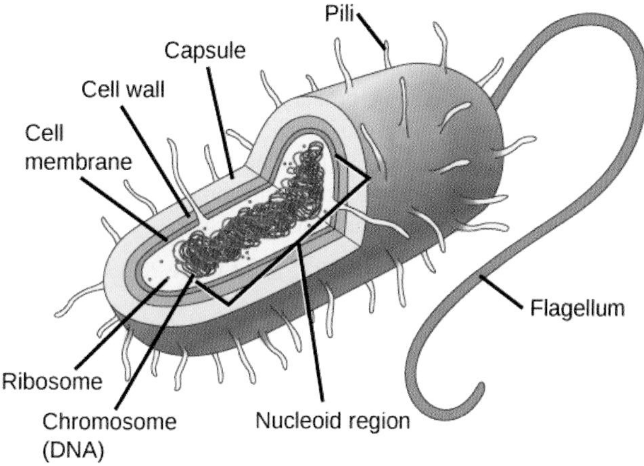

Figure 22.10 The features of a typical prokaryotic cell are shown.

Recall that prokaryotes are divided into two different domains, Bacteria and Archaea, which together with Eukarya, comprise the three domains of life (Figure 22.11).

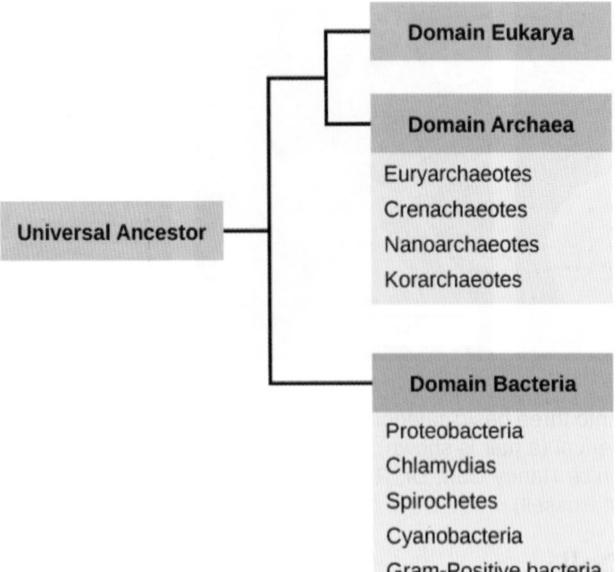

Figure 22.11 Bacteria and Archaea are both prokaryotes but differ enough to be placed in separate domains. An ancestor of modern Archaea is believed to have given rise to Eukarya, the third domain of life. Archaeal and bacterial phyla are shown; the evolutionary relationship between these phyla is still open to debate.

The composition of the cell wall differs significantly between the domains Bacteria and Archaea. The composition of their cell walls also differs from the eukaryotic cell walls found in plants (cellulose) or fungi and insects (chitin). The cell wall functions as a protective layer, and it is responsible for the organism's shape. Some bacteria have an outer **capsule** outside the cell wall. Other structures are present in some prokaryotic species, but not in others (Table 22.2). For example, the capsule found in some species enables the organism to attach to surfaces, protects it from dehydration and attack by phagocytic cells, and makes pathogens more resistant to our immune responses. Some species also have flagella (singular, flagellum) used for locomotion, and **pili** (singular, pilus) used for attachment to surfaces. Plasmids, which consist of extra-chromosomal DNA, are also present in many species of bacteria and archaea.

Characteristics of phyla of Bacteria are described in Figure 22.12 and Figure 22.13; Archaea are described in Figure 22.14.

Bacteria of Phylum Proteobacteria		
Class	**Representative organisms**	**Representative micrograph**
Alpha Proteobacteria Some species are photoautotrophic but some are symbionts of plants and animals and others are pathogens. Eukaryotic mitochondria are thought be derived from bacteria in this group.	*Rhizobium* Nitrogen-fixing endosymbiont associated with the roots of legumes *Rickettsia* Obligate intracellular parasite that causes typhus and Rocky Mountain Spotted Fever (but not rickets, which is caused by Vitamin C deficiency)	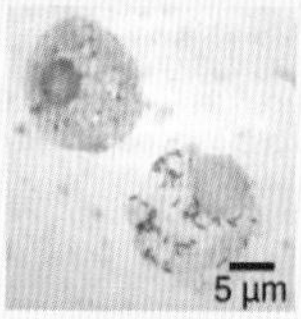 5 µm *Rickettsia rickettsia*, stained red, grow inside a host cell.
Beta Proteobacteria This group of bacteria is diverse. Some species play an important role in the nitrogen cycle.	*Nitrosomas* Species from this group oxidize ammonia into nitrite. *Spirillum minus* Causes rat-bite fever	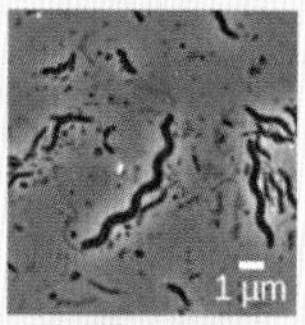 1 µm *Spirillum minus*
Gamma Proteobacteria Many are beneficial symbionts that populate the human gut, but others are familiar human pathogens. Some species from this subgroup oxidize sulfur compounds.	*Escherichia coli* Normally beneficial microbe of the human gut, but some strains cause disease *Salmonella* Certain strains cause food poisoning or typhoid fever *Yersinia pestis* Causative agent of Bubonic plague *Psuedomonas aeruginosa* Causes lung infections *Vibrio cholera* Causative agent of cholera *Chromatium* Sulfur-producing bacteria that oxidize sulfur, producing H_2S	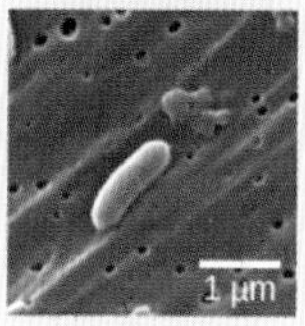 1 µm *Vibrio cholera*
Delta Proteobacteria Some species generate a spore-forming fruiting body in adverse conditions. Others reduce sulfate and sulfur.	*Myxobacteria* Generate spore-forming fruiting bodies in adverse conditions *Desulfovibrio vulgaris* Aneorobic, sulfate-reducing bacterium	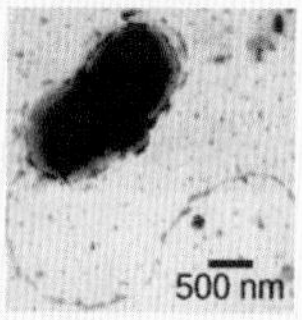 500 nm *Desulfovibrio vulgaris*
Epsilon Proteobacteria Many species inhabit the digestive tract of animals as symbionts or pathogens. Bacteria from this group have been found in deep-sea hydrothermal vents and cold seep habitats.	*Campylobacter* Causes blood poisoning and intestinal inflammation *Heliobacter pylori* Causes stomach ulcers	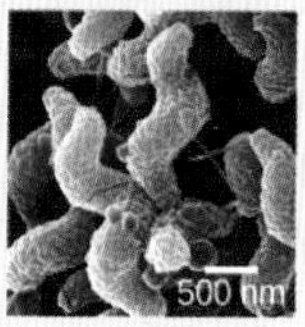 500 nm *Campylobacter*

Figure 22.12 Phylum Proteobacteria is one of up to 52 bacteria phyla. Proteobacteria is further subdivided into five classes, Alpha through Epsilon. (credit "Rickettsia rickettsia": modification of work by CDC; credit "Spirillum minus": modification of work by Wolframm Adlassnig; credit "Vibrio cholera": modification of work by Janice Haney Carr, CDC; credit "Desulfovibrio vulgaris": modification of work by Graham Bradley; credit "Campylobacter": modification of work by De Wood, Pooley, USDA, ARS, EMU; scale-bar data from Matt Russell)

Bacteria: Chlamydia, Spirochaetae, Cyanobacteria, and Gram-positive		
Phylum	**Representative organisms**	**Representative micrograph**
Chlamydias All members of this group are obligate intracellular parasites of animal cells. Cells walls lack peptidoglycan.	*Chlamydia trachomatis* Common sexually transmitted disease that can lead to blindness	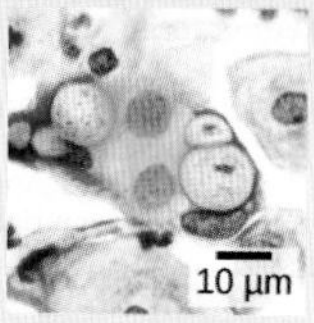 10 µm In this pap smear, *Chlamydia trachomatis* appear as pink inclusions inside cells.
Spirochetes Most members of this species, which has spiral-shaped cells, are free-living aneaerobes, but some are pathogenic. Flagella run lengthwise in the periplasmic space between the inner and outer membrane.	*Treponema pallidum* Causative agent of syphilis *Borrelia burgdorferi* Causative agent of Lyme disease	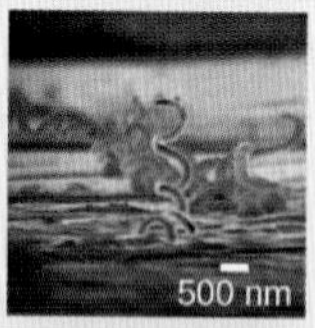 500 nm *Treponema pallidum*
Cyanobacteria Also known as blue-green algae, these bacteria obtain their energy through photosynthesis. They are ubiquitous, found in terrestrial, marine, and freshwater environments. Eukaryotic chloroplasts are thought be derived from bacteria in this group.	*Prochlorococcus* Believed to be the most abundant photosynthetic organism on earth; responsible for generating half the world's oxygen	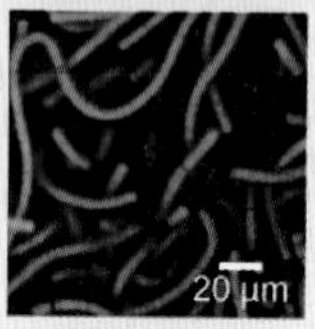 20 µm *Phormidium*
Gram-positive Bacteria Soil-dwelling members of this subgroup decompose organic matter. Some species cause disease. They have a thick cell wall and lack an outer membrane.	*Bacillus anthracis* Causes anthrax *Clostridium botulinum* Causes Botulism *Clostridium difficile* Causes diarrhea during antibiotic therapy *Streptomyces* Many antibiotics, including streptomyocin, are derived from these bacteria. *Mycoplasmas* These tiny bacteria, the smallest known, lack a cell wall. Some are free-living, and some are pathogenic.	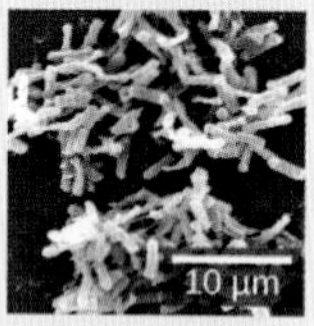 10 µm *Clostridium difficile*

Figure 22.13 Chlamydia, Spirochetes, Cyanobacteria, and Gram-positive bacteria are described in this table. Note that bacterial shape is not phylum-dependent; bacteria within a phylum may be cocci, rod-shaped, or spiral. (credit "Chlamydia trachomatis": modification of work by Dr. Lance Liotta Laboratory, NCI; credit "Treponema pallidum": modification of work by Dr. David Cox, CDC; credit "Phormidium": modification of work by USGS; credit "Clostridium difficile": modification of work by Lois S. Wiggs, CDC; scale-bar data from Matt Russell)

Archaea		
Phylum	**Representative organisms**	**Representative micrograph**
Euryarchaeota This phylum includes methanogens, which produce methane as a metabolic waste product, and halobacteria, which live in an extreme saline environment.	*Methanogens* Methane production causes flatulence in humans and other animals. *Halobacteria* Large blooms of this salt-loving archaea appear reddish due to the presence of bacterirhodopsin in the membrane. Bacteriorhodopsin is related to the retinal pigment rhodopsin.	2 µm *Halobacterium* strain NRC-1
Crenarchaeota Members of the ubiquitous phylum play an important role in the fixation of carbon. Many members of this group are sulfur-dependent extremophiles. Some are thermophilic or hyperthermophilic.	*Sulfolobus* Members of this genus grow in volcanic springs at temperatures between 75° and 80°C and at a pH between 2 and 3.	1 µm *Sulfolobus* being infected by bacteriophage
Nanoarchaeota This group currently contains only one species, *Nanoarchaeum equitans.*	*Nanoarchaeum equitans* This species was isolated from the bottom of the Atlantic Ocean and from a hydrothermal vent at Yellowstone National Park. It is an obligate symbiont with *Ignicoccus*, another species of archaea.	1 µm *Nanoarchaeum equitans* (small dark spheres) are in contact with their larger host, *Ignicoccus.*
Korarchaeota Members of this phylum, considered to be one of the most primitive forms of life, have only been found in the Obsidian Pool, a hot spring at Yellowstone National Park.	No members of this species have been cultivated.	1 µm This image shows a variety of korarchaeota species from the Obsidian Pool at Yellowstone National Park.

Figure 22.14 Archaea are separated into four phyla: the Korarchaeota, Euryarchaeota, Crenarchaeota, and Nanoarchaeota. (credit "Halobacterium": modification of work by NASA; credit "Nanoarchaeotum equitans": modification of work by Karl O. Stetter; credit "korarchaeota": modification of work by Office of Science of the U.S. Dept. of Energy; scale-bar data from Matt Russell)

The Plasma Membrane

The plasma membrane is a thin lipid bilayer (6 to 8 nanometers) that completely surrounds the cell and separates the inside from the outside. Its selectively permeable nature keeps ions, proteins, and other molecules within the cell and prevents them from diffusing into the extracellular environment, while other molecules may move through the membrane. Recall that the general structure of a cell membrane is a phospholipid bilayer composed of two layers of lipid molecules. In archaeal cell membranes, isoprene (phytanyl) chains linked to glycerol replace the fatty acids linked to glycerol in bacterial membranes. Some archaeal membranes are lipid monolayers instead of bilayers (Figure 22.14).

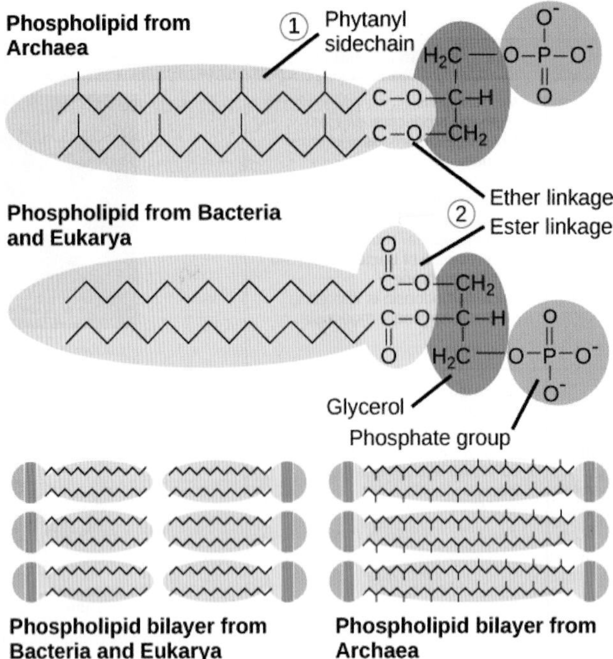

Figure 22.15 Archaeal phospholipids differ from those found in Bacteria and Eukarya in two ways. First, they have branched phytanyl sidechains instead of linear ones. Second, an ether bond instead of an ester bond connects the lipid to the glycerol.

The Cell Wall

The cytoplasm of prokaryotic cells has a high concentration of dissolved solutes. Therefore, the osmotic pressure within the cell is relatively high. The cell wall is a protective layer that surrounds some cells and gives them shape and rigidity. It is located outside the cell membrane and prevents osmotic lysis (bursting due to increasing volume). The chemical composition of the cell walls varies between archaea and bacteria, and also varies between bacterial species.

Bacterial cell walls contain **peptidoglycan**, composed of polysaccharide chains that are cross-linked by unusual peptides containing both L- and D-amino acids including D-glutamic acid and D-alanine. Proteins normally have only L-amino acids; as a consequence, many of our antibiotics work by mimicking D-amino acids and therefore have specific effects on bacterial cell wall development. There are more than 100 different forms of peptidoglycan. **S-layer** (surface layer) proteins are also present on the outside of cell walls of both archaea and bacteria.

Bacteria are divided into two major groups: **Gram positive** and **Gram negative**, based on their reaction to Gram staining. Note that all Gram-positive bacteria belong to one phylum; bacteria in the other phyla (Proteobacteria, Chlamydias, Spirochetes, Cyanobacteria, and others) are Gram-negative. The Gram staining method is named after its inventor, Danish scientist Hans Christian Gram (1853–1938). The different bacterial responses to the staining procedure are ultimately due to cell wall structure. Gram-positive organisms typically lack the outer membrane found in Gram-negative organisms (Figure 22.15). Up to 90 percent of the cell wall in Gram-positive bacteria is composed of peptidoglycan, and most of the rest is composed of acidic substances called **teichoic acids**. Teichoic acids may be covalently linked to lipids in the plasma membrane to form lipoteichoic acids. Lipoteichoic acids anchor the cell wall to the cell membrane. Gram-negative bacteria have a relatively thin cell wall composed of a few layers of peptidoglycan (only 10 percent of the total cell wall), surrounded by an outer envelope containing lipopolysaccharides (LPS) and lipoproteins. This outer envelope is sometimes referred to as a second lipid bilayer. The chemistry of this outer envelope is very different, however, from that of the typical lipid bilayer that forms plasma membranes.

visual CONNECTION

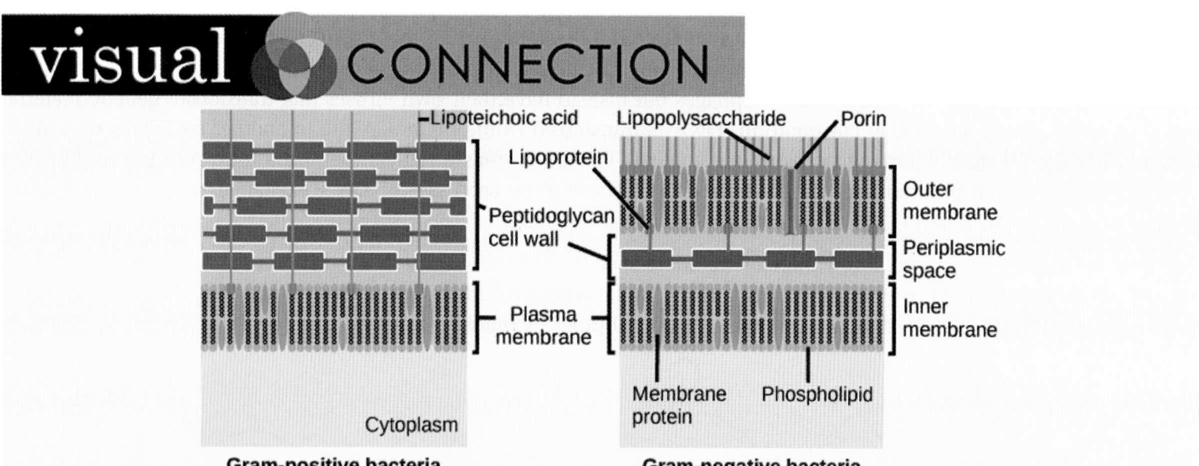

Figure 22.16 Bacteria are divided into two major groups: Gram positive and Gram negative. Both groups have a cell wall composed of peptidoglycan: in Gram-positive bacteria, the wall is thick, whereas in Gram-negative bacteria, the wall is thin. In Gram-negative bacteria, the cell wall is surrounded by an outer membrane that contains lipopolysaccharides and lipoproteins. Porins are proteins in this cell membrane that allow substances to pass through the outer membrane of Gram-negative bacteria. In Gram-positive bacteria, lipoteichoic acid anchors the cell wall to the cell membrane. (credit: modification of work by "Franciscosp2"/Wikimedia Commons)

Which of the following statements is true?

a. Gram-positive bacteria have a cell wall anchored to the cell membrane by lipoteichoic acid.
b. Porins allow entry of substances into both Gram-positive and Gram-negative bacteria.
c. The cell wall of Gram-negative bacteria is thick, and the cell wall of Gram-positive bacteria is thin.
d. Gram-negative bacteria have a cell wall made of peptidoglycan, whereas Gram-positive bacteria have a cell wall made of lipoteichoic acid.

Archaean cell walls do not have peptidoglycan. There are four different types of Archaean cell walls. One type is composed of **pseudopeptidoglycan**, which is similar to peptidoglycan in morphology but contains different sugars in the polysaccharide chain. The other three types of cell walls are composed of polysaccharides, glycoproteins, or pure protein.

Structural Differences and Similarities between Bacteria and Archaea

Structural Characteristic	Bacteria	Archaea
Cell type	Prokaryotic	Prokaryotic
Cell morphology	Variable	Variable
Cell wall	Contains peptidoglycan	Does not contain peptidoglycan
Cell membrane type	Lipid bilayer	Lipid bilayer or lipid monolayer
Plasma membrane lipids	Fatty acids	Phytanyl groups

Table 22.2

Reproduction

Reproduction in prokaryotes is asexual and usually takes place by binary fission. Recall that the DNA of a prokaryote exists as a single, circular chromosome. Prokaryotes do not undergo mitosis. Rather the chromosome is replicated and the two resulting copies separate from one another, due to the growth of the cell. The prokaryote, now enlarged, is pinched inward at its equator and the two resulting cells, which are clones, separate. Binary fission does not provide an opportunity for genetic recombination or genetic diversity, but prokaryotes can share genes by three other mechanisms.

In **transformation**, the prokaryote takes in DNA found in its environment that is shed by other prokaryotes. If a nonpathogenic bacterium takes up DNA for a toxin gene from a pathogen and incorporates the new DNA into its own chromosome, it too may become pathogenic. In **transduction**, bacteriophages, the viruses that infect bacteria, sometimes also move short pieces of chromosomal DNA from one bacterium to another. Transduction results in a recombinant organism. Archaea are not affected by bacteriophages but instead have their own viruses that translocate genetic material from one individual to another. In **conjugation**, DNA is transferred from one prokaryote to another by means of a pilus, which brings the organisms into contact with one another. The DNA transferred can be in the form of a plasmid or as a hybrid, containing both plasmid and chromosomal DNA. These three processes of DNA exchange are shown in Figure 22.17.

Reproduction can be very rapid: a few minutes for some species. This short generation time coupled with mechanisms of genetic recombination and high rates of mutation result in the rapid evolution of prokaryotes, allowing them to respond to environmental changes (such as the introduction of an antibiotic) very quickly.

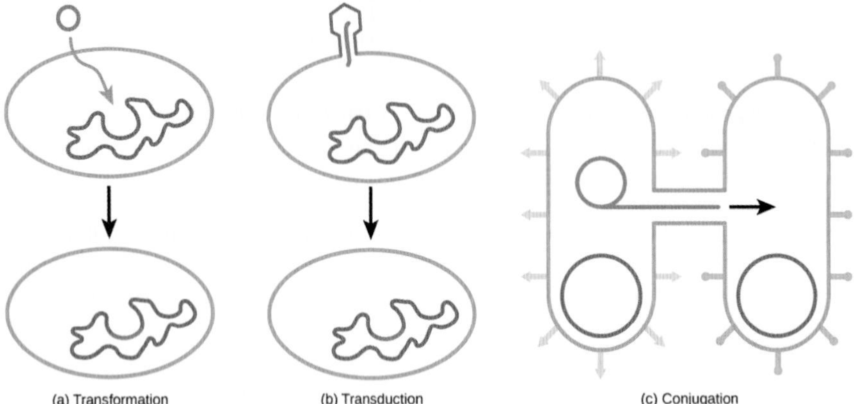

Figure 22.17 Besides binary fission, there are three other mechanisms by which prokaryotes can exchange DNA. In (a) transformation, the cell takes up prokaryotic DNA directly from the environment. The DNA may remain separate as plasmid DNA or be incorporated into the host genome. In (b) transduction, a bacteriophage injects DNA into the cell that contains a small fragment of DNA from a different prokaryote. In (c) conjugation, DNA is transferred from one cell to another via a mating bridge that connects the two cells after the sex pilus draws the two bacteria close enough to form the bridge.

The Evolution of Prokaryotes

How do scientists answer questions about the evolution of prokaryotes? Unlike with animals, artifacts in the fossil record of prokaryotes offer very little information. Fossils of ancient prokaryotes look like tiny bubbles in rock. Some scientists turn to genetics and to the principle of the molecular clock, which holds that the more recently two species have diverged, the more similar their genes (and thus proteins) will be. Conversely, species that diverged long ago will have more genes that are dissimilar.

Scientists at the NASA Astrobiology Institute and at the European Molecular Biology Laboratory collaborated to analyze the molecular evolution of 32 specific proteins common to 72 species of prokaryotes.[2] The model they derived from their data indicates that three important groups of bacteria—Actinobacteria, *Deinococcus*, and Cyanobacteria (which the authors call *Terrabacteria*)—were the first to colonize land. (Recall that *Deinococcus* is a genus of prokaryote—a bacterium—that is highly resistant to ionizing radiation.) Cyanobacteria are photosynthesizers, while Actinobacteria are a group of very common bacteria that include species important in decomposition of organic wastes.

The timelines of divergence suggest that bacteria (members of the domain Bacteria) diverged from common ancestral species between 2.5 and 3.2 billion years ago, whereas archaea diverged earlier: between 3.1 and 4.1 billion years ago. Eukarya later diverged off the Archaean line. Stromatolites are some of the oldest fossilized organisms on Earth at around 3.5 million years ago. There is evidence that these prokaryotes were also some of the first photosynthesizes on Earth. In fact, bacterial prokaryotes were likely responsible for the first accumulation of oxygen in our atmosphere through photosynthesis. The group Terrabacteria possessed many adaptations for living on land, such as resistance to drying. Some of these adaptations were also related to photosynthesis, such as compounds that protect cells from excess light. These early prokaryotic pathways related to photosynthesis were the foundation for photosynthesis in eukaryotic cells. This is evidenced by the similarity in structure and function between some photosynthetic prokaryotes and eukaryotic chloroplasts.

science practices CONNECTION for AP® Courses

Think About It

What features and metabolic processes do all cells, both prokaryotes and eukaryotes, have in common? How do prokaryotes and eukaryotes differ?

22.3 | Prokaryotic Metabolism

In this section, you will explore the following questions:

- What are examples of macronutrients needs by prokaryotes, and what is their importance?
- How do prokaryotes obtain free energy and carbon for life processes?
- What are the roles of prokaryotes in the carbon and nitrogen cycles?

Connection for AP® Courses

Because prokaryotes are metabolically diverse organisms, they can flourish in many different environments using a wide

2. Battistuzzi, FU, Feijao, A, and Hedges, SB. A genomic timescale of prokaryote evolution: Insights into the origin of methanogenesis, phototrophy, and the colonization of land. *BioMed Central: Evolutionary Biology* 4 (2004): 44, doi:10.1186/1471-2148-4-44.

range of energy and carbon sources. Some are decomposers that are essential to the cycling of nutrients in ecosystems, for example, carbon and nitrogen cycles. (Later, we will explore in more depth the role of these cycles in ecosystems.) Many bacteria form symbiotic relationships with other organisms; for example, nitrogen-fixing bacteria live on the roots of legumes. Other bacteria are disease-causing pathogens or parasites.

Like all cells, prokaryotes require macronutrients (including carbon, hydrogen, nitrogen, oxygen, phosphorus, and sulfur) and micronutrients, such as metallic elements from growth and enzyme function.

Information presented and the examples highlighted in the section support concepts outlined in Big Idea 2 of the AP® Biology Curriculum Framework. The AP® Learning Objectives listed in the Curriculum Framework provide a transparent foundation for the AP® Biology course, an inquiry-based laboratory experience, instructional activities, and AP® exam questions. A learning objective merges required content with one or more of the seven science practices.

Big Idea 2	Biological systems utilize free energy and molecular building blocks to grow, to reproduce, and to maintain dynamic homeostasis.
Enduring Understanding 2.A	Growth, reproduction and maintenance of living systems require free energy and matter.
Essential Knowledge	**2.A.2** Prokaryotes have evolved multiple energy-capturing strategies, and photosynthesis first evolved in prokaryotes and was responsible for the production of an oxygenated atmosphere.
Science Practice	**1.4** The student can use representations and models to analyze situations or solve problems qualitatively and quantitatively.
Science Practice	**3.1** The student can pose scientific questions.
Learning Objective	**2.4** The student is able to use representations to pose scientific questions about what mechanisms and structural features allow organisms to capture, store and use free energy.
Enduring Understanding 2.A	Growth, reproduction and maintenance of living systems require free energy and matter.
Essential Knowledge	**2.A.2** Prokaryotes have evolved multiple energy-capturing strategies, and photosynthesis first evolved in prokaryotes and was responsible for the production of an oxygenated atmosphere.
Science Practice	**6.2** The student can construct explanations of phenomena based on evidence produced through scientific practices.
Learning Objective	**2.5** The student is able to construct explanations of the mechanisms and structural features of cells that allow organisms to capture, store or use free energy.

The Science Practice Challenge Questions contain additional test questions for this section that will help you prepare for the AP exam. These questions address the following standards:
[APLO 4.7][APLO 4.10][APLO 4.23][APLO 2.28]

Needs of Prokaryotes

The diverse environments and ecosystems on Earth have a wide range of conditions in terms of temperature, available nutrients, acidity, salinity, and energy sources. Prokaryotes are very well equipped to make their living out of a vast array of nutrients and conditions. To live, prokaryotes need a source of energy, a source of carbon, and some additional nutrients.

Macronutrients

Cells are essentially a well-organized assemblage of macromolecules and water. Recall that macromolecules are produced by the polymerization of smaller units called monomers. For cells to build all of the molecules required to sustain life, they need certain substances, collectively called **nutrients**. When prokaryotes grow in nature, they obtain their nutrients from the environment. Nutrients that are required in large amounts are called macronutrients, whereas those required in smaller or trace amounts are called micronutrients. Just a handful of elements are considered macronutrients—carbon, hydrogen, oxygen, nitrogen, phosphorus, and sulfur. (A mnemonic for remembering these elements is the acronym *CHONPS*.)

Why are these macronutrients needed in large amounts? They are the components of organic compounds in cells, including water. Carbon is the major element in all macromolecules: carbohydrates, proteins, nucleic acids, lipids, and many other compounds. Carbon accounts for about 50 percent of the composition of the cell. Nitrogen represents 12 percent of the total dry weight of a typical cell and is a component of proteins, nucleic acids, and other cell constituents. Most of the nitrogen available in nature is either atmospheric nitrogen (N_2) or another inorganic form. Diatomic (N_2) nitrogen, however, can be converted into an organic form only by certain organisms, called nitrogen-fixing organisms. Both hydrogen and oxygen are part of many organic compounds and of water. Phosphorus is required by all organisms for the synthesis of nucleotides and phospholipids. Sulfur is part of the structure of some amino acids such as cysteine and methionine, and is also present in several vitamins and coenzymes. Other important macronutrients are potassium (K), magnesium (Mg), calcium (Ca), and sodium (Na). Although these elements are required in smaller amounts, they are very important for the structure and function of the prokaryotic cell.

Micronutrients

In addition to these macronutrients, prokaryotes require various metallic elements in small amounts. These are referred to as micronutrients or trace elements. For example, iron is necessary for the function of the cytochromes involved in electron-transport reactions. Some prokaryotes require other elements—such as boron (B), chromium (Cr), and manganese (Mn)—primarily as enzyme cofactors.

The Ways in Which Prokaryotes Obtain Energy

Prokaryotes can use different sources of energy to assemble macromolecules from smaller molecules. **Phototrophs** (or phototrophic organisms) obtain their energy from sunlight. **Chemotrophs** (or chemosynthetic organisms) obtain their energy from chemical compounds. Chemotrophs that can use organic compounds as energy sources are called chemoorganotrophs. Those that can also use inorganic compounds as energy sources are called chemolithotrophs.

The Ways in Which Prokaryotes Obtain Carbon

Prokaryotes not only can use different sources of energy but also different sources of carbon compounds. Recall that organisms that are able to fix inorganic carbon are called autotrophs. Autotrophic prokaryotes synthesize organic molecules from carbon dioxide. In contrast, heterotrophic prokaryotes obtain carbon from organic compounds. To make the picture more complex, the terms that describe how prokaryotes obtain energy and carbon can be combined. Thus, photoautotrophs use energy from sunlight, and carbon from carbon dioxide and water, whereas chemoheterotrophs obtain energy and carbon from an organic chemical source. Chemolitoautotrophs obtain their energy from inorganic compounds, and they build their complex molecules from carbon dioxide. The table below (Table 22.3) summarizes carbon and energy sources in prokaryotes.

Carbon and Energy Sources in Prokaryotes

Energy Sources			Carbon Sources	
Light	Chemicals		Carbon dioxide	Organic compounds
Phototrophs	Chemotrophs		Autotrophs	Heterotrophs
	Organic chemicals	Inorganic chemicals		
	Chemo-organotrophs	Chemolithotrophs		

Table 22.3

Role of Prokaryotes in Ecosystems

Prokaryotes are ubiquitous: There is no niche or ecosystem in which they are not present. Prokaryotes play many roles in the environments they occupy. The roles they play in the carbon and nitrogen cycles are vital to life on Earth.

Prokaryotes and the Carbon Cycle

Carbon is one of the most important macronutrients, and prokaryotes play an important role in the carbon cycle (Figure 22.18). Carbon is cycled through Earth's major reservoirs: land, the atmosphere, aquatic environments, sediments and rocks, and biomass. The movement of carbon is via carbon dioxide, which is removed from the atmosphere by land plants and marine prokaryotes, and is returned to the atmosphere via the respiration of chemoorganotrophic organisms, including prokaryotes, fungi, and animals. Although the largest carbon reservoir in terrestrial ecosystems is in rocks and sediments, that carbon is not readily available.

A large amount of available carbon is found in land plants. Plants, which are producers, use carbon dioxide from the air to synthesize carbon compounds. Related to this, one very significant source of carbon compounds is humus, which is a mixture of organic materials from dead plants and prokaryotes that have resisted decomposition. Consumers such as animals use organic compounds generated by producers and release carbon dioxide to the atmosphere. Then, bacteria and fungi, collectively called **decomposers**, carry out the breakdown (decomposition) of plants and animals and their organic compounds. The most important contributor of carbon dioxide to the atmosphere is microbial decomposition of dead material (dead animals, plants, and humus) that undergo respiration.

In aqueous environments and their anoxic sediments, there is another carbon cycle taking place. In this case, the cycle is based on one-carbon compounds. In anoxic sediments, prokaryotes, mostly archaea, produce methane (CH_4). This methane moves into the zone above the sediment, which is richer in oxygen and supports bacteria called methane oxidizers that oxidize methane to carbon dioxide, which then returns to the atmosphere.

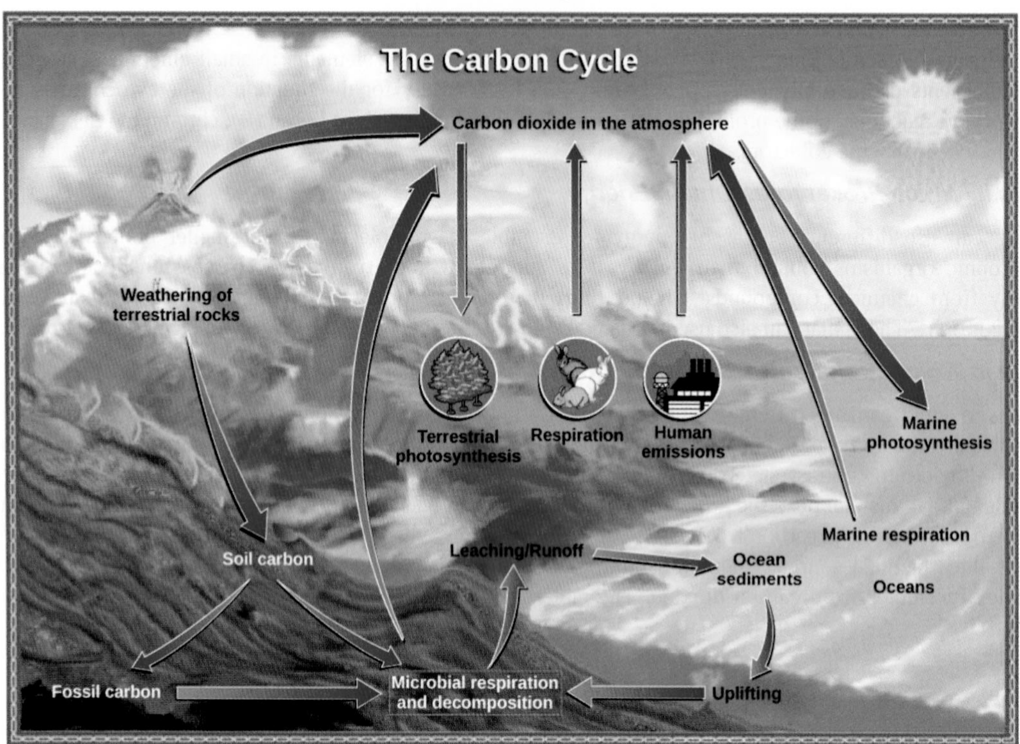

Figure 22.18 Prokaryotes play a significant role in continuously moving carbon through the biosphere. (credit: modification of work by John M. Evans and Howard Perlman, USGS)

Prokaryotes and the Nitrogen Cycle

Nitrogen is a very important element for life because it is part of proteins and nucleic acids. It is a macronutrient, and in nature, it is recycled from organic compounds to ammonia, ammonium ions, nitrate, nitrite, and nitrogen gas by myriad processes, many of which are carried out only by prokaryotes. As illustrated in Figure 22.19, prokaryotes are key to the nitrogen cycle. The largest pool of nitrogen available in the terrestrial ecosystem is gaseous nitrogen from the air, but this nitrogen is not usable by plants, which are primary producers. Gaseous nitrogen is transformed, or "fixed" into more readily available forms such as ammonia through the process of **nitrogen fixation**. Ammonia can be used by plants or converted to other forms.

Another source of ammonia is **ammonification**, the process by which ammonia is released during the decomposition of nitrogen-containing organic compounds. Ammonia released to the atmosphere, however, represents only 15 percent of the total nitrogen released; the rest is as N_2 and N_2O. Ammonia is catabolized anaerobically by some prokaryotes, yielding N_2 as the final product. **Nitrification** is the conversion of ammonium to nitrite and nitrate. Nitrification in soils is carried out by bacteria belonging to the genera *Nitrosomas*, *Nitrobacter*, and *Nitrospira*. The bacteria performs the reverse process, the reduction of nitrate from the soils to gaseous compounds such as N_2O, NO, and N_2, a process called **denitrification**.

visual CONNECTION

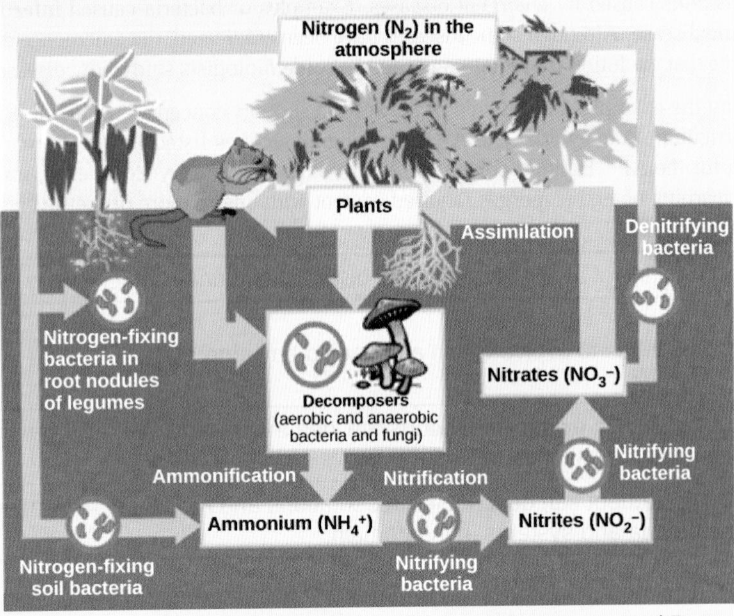

Figure 22.19 Prokaryotes play a key role in the nitrogen cycle. (credit: Environmental Protection Agency)

Which of the following statements about the nitrogen cycle is false?

a. Nitrogen-fixing bacteria exist on the root nodules of legumes and in the soil.
b. Denitrifying bacteria convert nitrates (NO3-) into nitrogen gas (N2).
c. Ammonification is the process by which ammonium ion (NH4+) is released from decomposing organic compounds.
d. Nitrification is the process by which nitrites (NO2-) are converted to ammonium ion (NH4+).

science practices CONNECTION for AP® Courses

Think About It

Prokaryotes inhabit many diverse environments. Think about the conditions (temperature, light, pressure, and organic and inorganic materials) that you may find in a deep-sea hydrothermal vent. What types of prokaryotes, in terms of their metabolic needs (autotrophs, phototrophs, chemotrophs, and so on) would expect to find there? What features of these prokaryotes would make it possible for them to inhabit such an extreme environment?

22.4 | Bacterial Diseases in Humans

In this section, you will explore the following questions:

- What are examples of bacterial diseases that caused historically important plagues and epidemics?
- What are links between bacteria, especially in biofilms, and foodborne diseases?
- How can the overuse of antibiotics create "super bugs" such as MRSA?

Connection for AP® Courses

Although many bacteria participate in mutualistic relationships with their hosts, others exist in parasitic relationships, causing disease. Many bacteria have evolved resistance to antibiotics, and scientists are developing new antibiotics that are effective against infections caused by emergent diseases. Examples of bacteria-caused infections include pneumonia, plague, typhoid, and Lyme disease. Although some diseases have been eradicated, the emergence of new infections, such as MRSA, provides evidence that evolution is an ongoing process. Epidemiologists study how disease affects a population.

Information presented and the examples highlighted in the section support concepts outlined in Big Idea 1 and Big Idea 3 of the AP® Biology Curriculum Framework. The AP® Learning Objectives listed in the Curriculum Framework provide a transparent foundation for the AP® Biology course, an inquiry-based laboratory experience, instructional activities, and AP® exam questions. A learning objective merges required content with one or more of the seven science practices.

Big Idea 1	The process of evolution drives the diversity and unity of life.
Enduring Understanding 1.C	Life continues to evolve within a changing environment.
Essential Knowledge	**1.C.3** Scientific evidence supports the idea that evolution in all organisms, including prokaryotes, continues to occur.
Science Practice	**1.2** The student can describe representations and models of natural or man-made phenomena and systems in the domain.
Learning Objective	**1.25** The student is able to describe a model that represents evolution within a population.
Essential Knowledge	**1.C.3** Scientific evidence supports the idea that evolution in all organisms, including prokaryotes, continues to occur.
Science Practice	**5.3** The student can evaluate the evidence provided by data sets in relation to a particular scientific question.
Learning Objective	**1.26** The student is able to evaluate given data sets that illustrate evolution as an ongoing process.
Big Idea 3	Living systems store, retrieve, transmit and respond to information essential to life processes.
Enduring Understanding 2.C	Organisms use feedback mechanisms to regulate growth and reproduction, and to maintain dynamic homeostasis.
Essential Knowledge	**3.C.1** Genetic changes that affect phenotypes are subject to selection.
Science Practice	**6.4** The student can make claims and predictions about natural phenomena based on scientific theories and models.
Science Practice	**7.2** The student can connect concepts in and across domain(s) to generalize or extrapolate in and/or across enduring understandings and/or big ideas.
Learning Objective	**3.24** The student is able to predict how a change in genotype, when expressed as a phenotype, provides a variation that is subject to natural selection.

The Science Practice Challenge Questions contain additional test questions for this section that will help you prepare for the AP exam. These questions address the following standards:
[APLO 3.3][APLO 3.27][APLO 2.8][APLO 2.9][APLO 2.24][APLO 4.14][APLO 4.21]

Devastating pathogen-borne diseases and plagues, both viral and bacterial in nature, have affected humans since the beginning of human history. The true cause of these diseases was not understood at the time, and some people thought that diseases were a spiritual punishment. Over time, people came to realize that staying apart from afflicted persons, and disposing of the corpses and personal belongings of victims of illness, reduced their own chances of getting sick.

Epidemiologists study how diseases affect a population. An **epidemic** is a disease that occurs in an unusually high number of individuals in a population at the same time. A **pandemic** is a widespread, usually worldwide, epidemic. An **endemic disease** is a disease that is constantly present, usually at low incidence, in a population.

Long History of Bacterial Disease

There are records about infectious diseases as far back as 3000 B.C. A number of significant pandemics caused by bacteria have been documented over several hundred years. Some of the most memorable pandemics led to the decline of cities and nations.

In the 21st century, infectious diseases remain among the leading causes of death worldwide, despite advances made in medical research and treatments in recent decades. A disease spreads when the pathogen that causes it is passed from one person to another. For a pathogen to cause disease, it must be able to reproduce in the host's body and damage the host in some way.

The Plague of Athens

In 430 B.C., the Plague of Athens killed one-quarter of the Athenian troops that were fighting in the great Peloponnesian War and weakened Athens' dominance and power. The plague impacted people living in overcrowded Athens as well as troops aboard ships that had to return to Athens. The source of the plague may have been identified recently when researchers from the University of Athens were able to use DNA from teeth recovered from a mass grave. The scientists identified nucleotide sequences from a pathogenic bacterium, *Salmonella enterica* serovar Typhi (Figure 22.20), which causes typhoid fever.[3] This disease is commonly seen in overcrowded areas and has caused epidemics throughout recorded history.

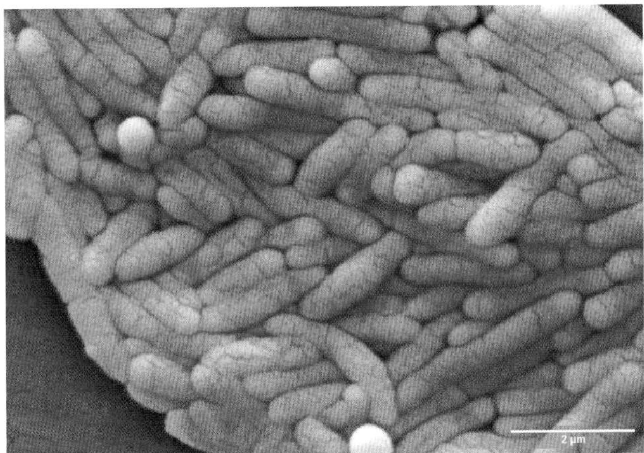

Figure 22.20 *Salmonella enterica* serovar Typhi, the causative agent of Typhoid fever, is a Gram-negative, rod-shaped gamma protobacterium. Typhoid fever, which is spread through feces, causes intestinal hemorrhage, high fever, delirium and dehydration. Today, between 16 and 33 million cases of this re-emerging disease occur annually, resulting in over 200,000 deaths. Carriers of the disease can be asymptomatic. In a famous case in the early 1900s, a cook named Mary Mallon unknowingly spread the disease to over fifty people, three of whom died. Other *Salmonella* serotypes cause food poisoning. (credit: modification of work by NCI, CDC)

Bubonic Plagues

From 541 to 750, an outbreak of what was likely a bubonic plague (the Plague of Justinian), eliminated one-quarter to one-half of the human population in the eastern Mediterranean region. The population in Europe dropped by 50 percent during this outbreak. Bubonic plague would strike Europe more than once.

One of the most devastating pandemics was the **Black Death** (1346 to 1361) that is believed to have been another outbreak of bubonic plague caused by the bacterium *Yersinia pestis*. It is thought to have originated initially in China and spread along the Silk Road, a network of land and sea trade routes, to the Mediterranean region and Europe, carried by rat fleas living on black rats that were always present on ships. The Black Death reduced the world's population from an estimated 450 million to about 350 to 375 million. Bubonic plague struck London hard again in the mid-1600s (Figure 22.21). In modern times, approximately 1,000 to 3,000 cases of plague arise globally each year. Although contracting bubonic plague before antibiotics meant almost certain death, the bacterium responds to several types of modern antibiotics, and mortality rates from plague are now very low.

3. Papagrigorakis MJ, Synodinos PN, and Yapijakis C. Ancient typhoid epidemic reveals possible ancestral strain of *Salmonella enterica* serovar Typhi. *Infect Genet Evol* 7 (2007): 126–7, Epub 2006 Jun.

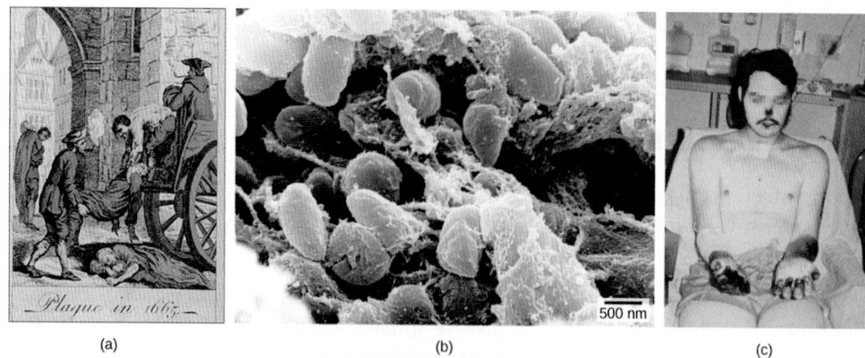

Figure 22.21 The (a) Great Plague of London killed an estimated 200,000 people, or about twenty percent of the city's population. The causative agent, the (b) bacterium *Yersinia pestis*, is a Gram-negative, rod-shaped bacterium from the class Gamma Proteobacteria. The disease is transmitted through the bite of an infected flea, which is infected by a rodent. Symptoms include swollen lymph nodes, fever, seizure, vomiting of blood, and (c) gangrene. (credit b: Rocky Mountain Laboratories, NIAID, NIH; scale-bar data from Matt Russell; credit c: Textbook of Military Medicine, Washington, D.C., U.S. Dept. of the Army, Office of the Surgeon General, Borden Institute)

Watch a video (http://openstaxcollege.org/l/black_death) on the modern understanding of the Black Death—bubonic plague in Europe during the 14th century.

How were researchers able to use modern science to determine the agent of disease for the bubonic plague of the 14th century?

a. The amino acid sequence of proteins, extracted from the samples taken from skeletons buried in a cemetery from the 14th century, was constructed and compared to that of modern strain of the bacterium *Y. enterocolitica* and found a close match.

b. The genomic sequence of the DNA, extracted from the samples taken from skeletons buried in a cemetery from the 14th century, was constructed and compared to that of modern strain of the bacterium *Y. enterocolitica* and found a close match.

c. The gene sequence of 16S rRNA, extracted from the samples taken from skeletons buried in a cemetery from the 14th century, was constructed and compared to that of modern strain of the bacterium *Y. pestis* and found a close match.

d. The genomic sequence of the DNA, extracted from the samples taken from skeletons buried in a cemetery from the 14th century, was constructed and compared to that of modern strain of the bacterium *Y. pestis* and found a close match.

Migration of Diseases to New Populations

Over the centuries, Europeans tended to develop genetic immunity to endemic infectious diseases, but when European conquerors reached the western hemisphere, they brought with them disease-causing bacteria and viruses, which triggered epidemics that completely devastated populations of Native Americans, who had no natural resistance to many European diseases. It has been estimated that up to 90 percent of Native Americans died from infectious diseases after the arrival of Europeans, making conquest of the New World a foregone conclusion.

Emerging and Re-emerging Diseases

The distribution of a particular disease is dynamic. Therefore, changes in the environment, the pathogen, or the host population can dramatically impact the spread of a disease. According to the World Health Organization (WHO) an **emerging disease** (Figure 22.22) is one that has appeared in a population for the first time, or that may have existed previously but is rapidly increasing in incidence or geographic range. This definition also includes re-emerging diseases that were previously under control. Approximately 75 percent of recently emerging infectious diseases affecting humans are zoonotic diseases, **zoonoses**, diseases that primarily infect animals and are transmitted to humans; some are of viral origin and some are of bacterial origin. Brucellosis is an example of a prokaryotic zoonosis that is re-emerging in some regions, and necrotizing fasciitis (commonly known as flesh-eating bacteria) has been increasing in virulence for the last 80 years for unknown reasons.

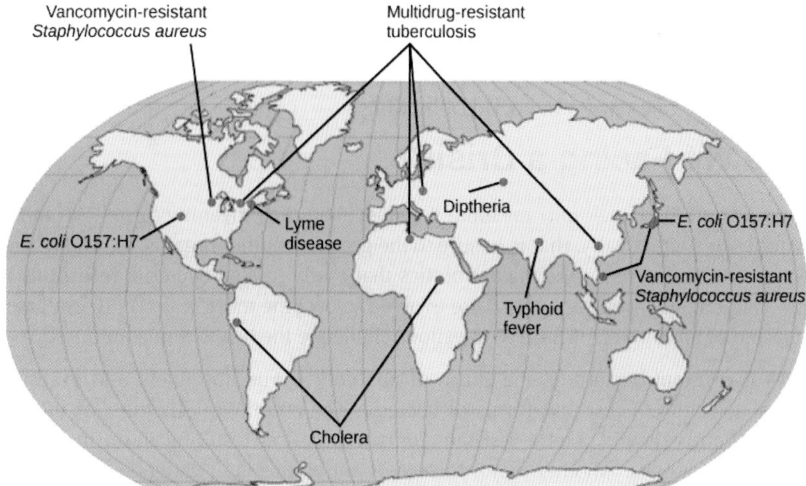

Figure 22.22 The map shows regions where bacterial diseases are emerging or reemerging. (credit: modification of work by NIH)

Some of the present emerging diseases are not actually new, but are diseases that were catastrophic in the past (Figure 22.23). They devastated populations and became dormant for a while, just to come back, sometimes more virulent than before, as was the case with bubonic plague. Other diseases, like tuberculosis, were never eradicated but were under control in some regions of the world until coming back, mostly in urban centers with high concentrations of immunocompromised people. The WHO has identified certain diseases whose worldwide re-emergence should be monitored. Among these are two viral diseases (dengue fever and yellow fever), and three bacterial diseases (diphtheria, cholera, and bubonic plague). The war against infectious diseases has no foreseeable end.

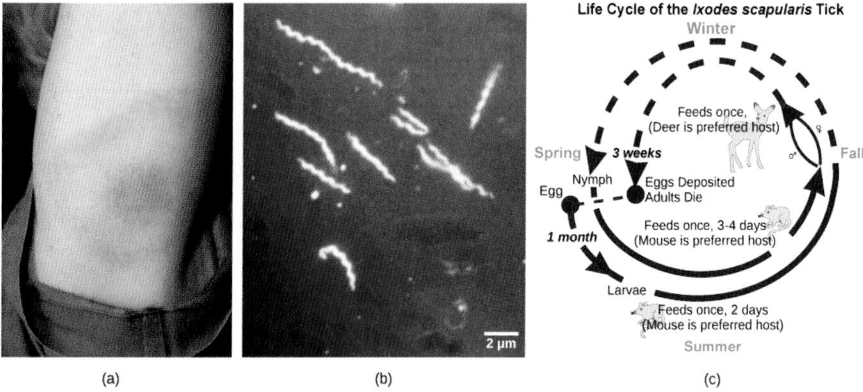

Figure 22.23 Lyme disease often, but not always, results in (a) a characteristic bullseye rash. The disease is caused by a (b) Gram-negative spirochete bacterium of the genus *Borrelia*. The bacteria (c) infect ticks, which in turns infect mice. Deer are the preferred secondary host, but the ticks also may feed on humans. Untreated, the disease causes chronic disorders in the nervous system, eyes, joints, and heart. The disease is named after Lyme, Connecticut, where an outbreak occurred in 1995 and has subsequently spread. The disease is not new, however. Genetic evidence suggests that Ötzi the Iceman, a 5,300-year-old mummy found in the Alps, was infected with *Borrelia*. (credit a: James Gathany, CDC; credit b: CDC; scale-bar data from Matt Russell)

Biofilms and Disease

Recall that biofilms are microbial communities that are very difficult to destroy. They are responsible for diseases such as infections in patients with cystic fibrosis, Legionnaires' disease, and otitis media. They produce dental plaque and colonize catheters, prostheses, transcutaneous and orthopedic devices, contact lenses, and internal devices such as pacemakers. They also form in open wounds and burned tissue. In healthcare environments, biofilms grow on hemodialysis machines, mechanical ventilators, shunts, and other medical equipment. In fact, 65 percent of all infections acquired in the hospital (nosocomial infections) are attributed to biofilms. Biofilms are also related to diseases contracted from food because they colonize the surfaces of vegetable leaves and meat, as well as food-processing equipment that isn't adequately cleaned.

Biofilm infections develop gradually; sometimes, they do not cause symptoms immediately. They are rarely resolved by host defense mechanisms. Once an infection by a biofilm is established, it is very difficult to eradicate, because biofilms tend to be resistant to most of the methods used to control microbial growth, including antibiotics. Biofilms respond poorly or only temporarily to antibiotics; it has been said that they can resist up to 1,000 times the antibiotic concentrations used to kill the same bacteria when they are free-living or planktonic. An antibiotic dose that large would harm the patient; therefore, scientists are working on new ways to get rid of biofilms.

Antibiotics: Are We Facing a Crisis?

The word *antibiotic* comes from the Greek *anti* meaning "against" and *bios* meaning "life." An **antibiotic** is a chemical, produced either by microbes or synthetically, that is hostile to the growth of other organisms. Today's news and media often address concerns about an antibiotic crisis. Are the antibiotics that easily treated bacterial infections in the past becoming obsolete? Are there new "superbugs"—bacteria that have evolved to become more resistant to our arsenal of antibiotics? Is this the beginning of the end of antibiotics? All these questions challenge the healthcare community.

One of the main causes of resistant bacteria is the abuse of antibiotics. The imprudent and excessive use of antibiotics has resulted in the natural selection of resistant forms of bacteria. The antibiotic kills most of the infecting bacteria, and therefore only the resistant forms remain. These resistant forms reproduce, resulting in an increase in the proportion of resistant forms over non-resistant ones. Another major misuse of antibiotics is in patients with colds or the flu, for which antibiotics are useless. Another problem is the excessive use of antibiotics in livestock. The routine use of antibiotics in animal feed promotes bacterial resistance as well. In the United States, 70 percent of the antibiotics produced are fed to animals. These antibiotics are given to livestock in low doses, which maximize the probability of resistance developing, and these resistant bacteria are readily transferred to humans.

Visit **this site (http://openstaxcollege.org/l/antibiotics)** to learn more about the problem of routine antibiotic administration to livestock and antibiotic-resistant bacteria.

In your own words, what is the problem with administering antibiotics to livestock when they are not in need of them?

a. Development of antibiotic-susceptible bacteria that can be transferred to humans, and their presence makes treatment of disease with antibiotics (in animals or humans) much more difficult.

b. Development of antibiotic-resistant bacteria that cannot be transferred to humans, and their presence makes treatment of disease with antibiotics (in animals or humans) much more difficult.

c. Development of antibiotic-resistant bacteria that can be transferred to humans, and their presence makes treatment of disease with antibiotics (in animals or humans) much more difficult.

d. Development of antibiotic-susceptible bacteria that cannot be transferred to humans, and their presence makes treatment of disease with antibiotics (in animals or humans) much more difficult.

One of the Superbugs: MRSA

The imprudent use of antibiotics has paved the way for bacteria to expand populations of resistant forms. For example, *Staphylococcus aureus*, often called "staph," is a common bacterium that can live in the human body and is usually easily treated with antibiotics. A very dangerous strain, however, **methicillin-resistant *Staphylococcus aureus* (MRSA)** has made the news over the past few years (Figure 22.24). This strain is resistant to many commonly used antibiotics, including methicillin, amoxicillin, penicillin, and oxacillin. MRSA can cause infections of the skin, but it can also infect the bloodstream, lungs, urinary tract, or sites of injury. While MRSA infections are common among people in healthcare facilities, they have also appeared in healthy people who haven't been hospitalized but who live or work in tight populations (like military personnel and prisoners). Researchers have expressed concern about the way this latter source of MRSA targets a much younger population than those residing in care facilities. *The Journal of the American Medical Association* reported that, among MRSA-afflicted persons in healthcare facilities, the average age is 68, whereas people with "community-associated MRSA" (**CA-MRSA**) have an average age of 23.[4]

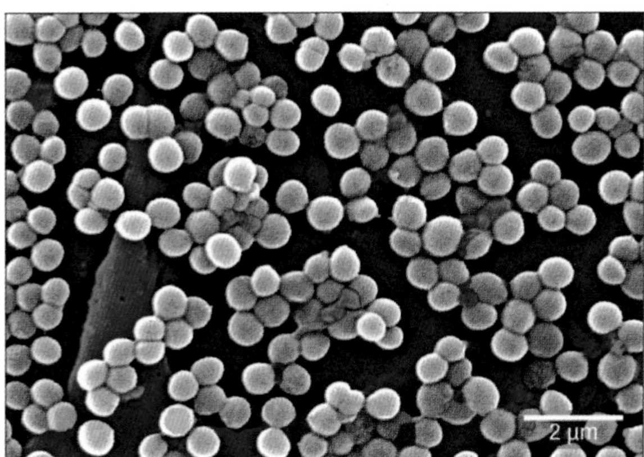

Figure 22.24 This scanning electron micrograph shows methicillin-resistant *Staphylococcus aureus* bacteria, commonly known as MRSA. *S. aureus* is not always pathogenic, but can cause diseases such as food poisoning and skin and respiratory infections. (credit: modification of work by Janice Haney Carr; scale-bar data from Matt Russell)

In summary, the medical community is facing an antibiotic crisis. Some scientists believe that after years of being protected from bacterial infections by antibiotics, we may be returning to a time in which a simple bacterial infection could again devastate the human population. Researchers are developing new antibiotics, but it takes many years to of research and clinical trials, plus financial investments in the millions of dollars, to generate an effective and approved drug.

Foodborne Diseases

Prokaryotes are everywhere: They readily colonize the surface of any type of material, and food is not an exception. Most of the time, prokaryotes colonize food and food-processing equipment in the form of a biofilm. Outbreaks of bacterial infection related to food consumption are common. A **foodborne disease** (colloquially called "food poisoning") is an illness resulting from the consumption the pathogenic bacteria, viruses, or other parasites that contaminate food. Although the United States has one of the safest food supplies in the world, the U.S. Centers for Disease Control and Prevention (CDC) has reported that "76 million people get sick, more than 300,000 are hospitalized, and 5,000 Americans die each year from foodborne illness."

The characteristics of foodborne illnesses have changed over time. In the past, it was relatively common to hear about sporadic cases of **botulism**, the potentially fatal disease produced by a toxin from the anaerobic bacterium *Clostridium botulinum*. Some of the most common sources for this bacterium were non-acidic canned foods, homemade pickles, and processed meat and sausages. The can, jar, or package created a suitable anaerobic environment where *Clostridium* could grow. Proper sterilization and canning procedures have reduced the incidence of this disease.

While people may tend to think of foodborne illnesses as associated with animal-based foods, most cases are now linked to produce. There have been serious, produce-related outbreaks associated with raw spinach in the United States and with vegetable sprouts in Germany, and these types of outbreaks have become more common. The raw spinach outbreak in 2006 was produced by the bacterium *E. coli* serotype O157:H7. A **serotype** is a strain of bacteria that carries a set of similar antigens on its cell surface, and there are often many different serotypes of a bacterial species. Most *E. coli* are not particularly dangerous to humans, but serotype O157:H7 can cause bloody diarrhea and is potentially fatal.

All types of food can potentially be contaminated with bacteria. Recent outbreaks of *Salmonella* reported by the CDC occurred in foods as diverse as peanut butter, alfalfa sprouts, and eggs. A deadly outbreak in Germany in 2010 was caused by *E. coli* contamination of vegetable sprouts (Figure 22.25). The strain that caused the outbreak was found to be a new serotype not previously involved in other outbreaks, which indicates that *E. coli* is continuously evolving.

---

4. Naimi, TS, LeDell, KH, Como-Sabetti, K, et al. Comparison of community- and health care-associated methicillin-resistant *Staphylococcus aureus* infection. *JAMA* 290 (2003): 2976–84, doi: 10.1001/jama.290.22.2976.

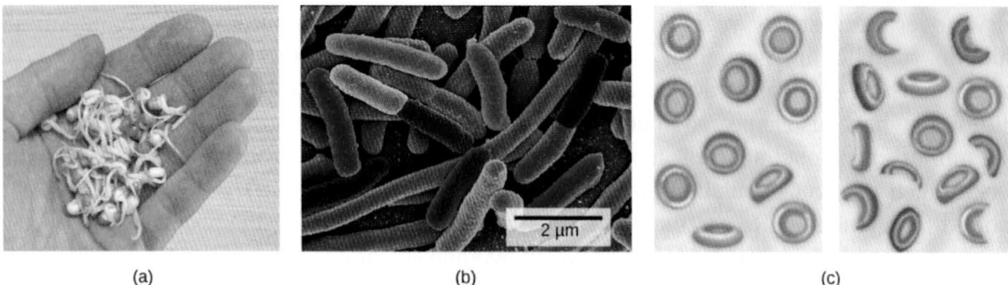

Figure 22.25 (a) Vegetable sprouts grown at an organic farm were the cause of an (b) *E. coli* outbreak that killed 32 people and sickened 3,800 in Germany in 2011. The strain responsible, *E. coli* O104:H4, produces Shiga toxin, a substance that inhibits protein synthesis in the host cell. The toxin (c) destroys red blood cells resulting in bloody diarrhea. Deformed red blood cells clog the capillaries of the kidney, which can lead to kidney failure, as happened to 845 patients in the 2011 outbreak. Kidney failure is usually reversible, but some patients experience kidney problems years later. (credit c: NIDDK, NIH)

career CONNECTION

Epidemiologist

Epidemiology is the study of the occurrence, distribution, and determinants of health and disease in a population. It is, therefore, part of public health. An epidemiologist studies the frequency and distribution of diseases within human populations and environments.

Epidemiologists collect data about a particular disease and track its spread to identify the original mode of transmission. They sometimes work in close collaboration with historians to try to understand the way a disease evolved geographically and over time, tracking the natural history of pathogens. They gather information from clinical records, patient interviews, surveillance, and any other available means. That information is used to develop strategies, such as vaccinations (Figure 22.26), and design public health policies to reduce the incidence of a disease or to prevent its spread. Epidemiologists also conduct rapid investigations in case of an outbreak to recommend immediate measures to control it.

An epidemiologist has a bachelor's degree, plus a master's degree in public health (MPH). Many epidemiologists are also physicians (and have an M.D.), or they have a Ph.D. in an associated field, such as biology or microbiology.

Figure 22.26 Vaccinations can slow the spread of communicable diseases. (credit: modification of work by Daniel Paquet)

Think About It

How can a strain of bacteria that was previously sensitive to an antibiotic become resistant to the same antibiotic? Why has this become a major global problem?

22.5 | Beneficial Prokaryotes

In this section, you will explore the following questions:

- What is the need for nitrogen fixation and how is it accomplished?
- What are examples of foods for which prokaryotes are used in processing?
- What is bioremediation and how do prokaryotes play a role in this process?

Connection for AP® Courses

We commonly think of pathogens when we think of prokaryotes, focusing on their relationship with disease. However, most prokaryotes do not cause disease and they play a wide range of other roles in ecosystems. Nitrogen needed to synthesize proteins and nucleic acids is often the most limiting element in ecosystems and bacteria are able to "fix" nitrogen into forms that can be used by eukaryotes. Microbes also are used to remove pollutants from environments, a process called **bioremediation**. Microbes that call us home are necessary for our survival. They help us digest our food, produce crucial nutrients, protect us from pathogenic microbes, and help train our immune system to function correctly. In addition, without prokaryotes we wouldn't have cheese, bread, wine, beer, and yogurt.

Information presented and the examples highlighted in the section support concepts outlined in Big Idea 4 of the AP® Biology Curriculum Framework. The AP® Learning Objectives listed in the Curriculum Framework provide a transparent foundation for the AP® Biology course, an inquiry-based laboratory experience, instructional activities, and AP® exam questions. A learning objective merges required content with one or more of the seven science practices.

Big Idea 4	Biological systems interact, and these systems and their interactions possess complex properties.
Enduring Understanding 4.B	Competition and cooperation are important aspects of biological systems.
Essential Knowledge	**4.B.2** Interactions among prokaryotes and between prokaryotes and other organisms lead to increased efficiency and utilization of energy and matter.
Science Practice	**1.4** The student can use representations and models to analyze situations or solve problems qualitatively and quantitatively.
Learning Objective	**4.18** The student is able to use representations and models to analyze how cooperative interactions within organisms promote efficiency in the use of energy and matter.

The Science Practice Challenge Questions contain additional test questions for this section that will help you prepare for the AP exam. These questions address the following standards:
[APLO 2.6][APLO 2.28][APLO 2.42][APLO 4.9][APLO 4.1]

Not all prokaryotes are pathogenic. On the contrary, pathogens represent only a very small percentage of the diversity of the microbial world. In fact, our life would not be possible without prokaryotes. Just think about the role of prokaryotes in biogeochemical cycles.

Cooperation between Bacteria and Eukaryotes: Nitrogen Fixation

Nitrogen is a very important element to living things, because it is part of nucleotides and amino acids that are the building blocks of nucleic acids and proteins, respectively. Nitrogen is usually the most limiting element in terrestrial ecosystems, with atmospheric nitrogen, N_2, providing the largest pool of available nitrogen. However, eukaryotes cannot use atmospheric, gaseous nitrogen to synthesize macromolecules. Fortunately, nitrogen can be "fixed," meaning it is converted into ammonia (NH_3) either biologically or abiotically. Abiotic nitrogen fixation occurs as a result of lightning or by industrial processes.

Biological nitrogen fixation (BNF) is exclusively carried out by prokaryotes: soil bacteria, cyanobacteria, and *Frankia* spp. (filamentous bacteria interacting with actinorhizal plants such as alder, bayberry, and sweet fern). After photosynthesis, BNF is the second most important biological process on Earth. The equation representing the process is as follows

$$N_2 + 16ATP + 8e^- + 8H^+ \rightarrow 2NH_3 + 16ADP + 16Pi + H_2$$

where Pi stands for inorganic phosphate. The total fixed nitrogen through BNF is about 100 to 180 million metric tons per year. Biological processes contribute 65 percent of the nitrogen used in agriculture.

Cyanobacteria are the most important nitrogen fixers in aquatic environments. In soil, members of the genus *Clostridium* are examples of free-living, nitrogen-fixing bacteria. Other bacteria live symbiotically with legume plants, providing the most important source of BNF. Symbionts may fix more nitrogen in soils than free-living organisms by a factor of 10. Soil bacteria, collectively called rhizobia, are able to symbiotically interact with legumes to form **nodules**, specialized structures where nitrogen fixation occurs (Figure 22.27). Nitrogenase, the enzyme that fixes nitrogen, is inactivated by oxygen, so the nodule provides an oxygen-free area for nitrogen fixation to take place. This process provides a natural and inexpensive plant fertilizer, as it reduces atmospheric nitrogen to ammonia, which is easily usable by plants. The use of legumes is an excellent alternative to chemical fertilization and is of special interest to sustainable agriculture, which seeks to minimize the use of chemicals and conserve natural resources. Through symbiotic nitrogen fixation, the plant benefits from using an endless source of nitrogen: the atmosphere. Bacteria benefit from using photosynthates (carbohydrates produced during photosynthesis) from the plant and having a protected niche. Additionally, the soil benefits from being naturally fertilized. Therefore, the use of rhizobia as biofertilizers is a sustainable practice.

Why are legumes so important? Some, like soybeans, are key sources of agricultural protein. Some of the most important grain legumes are soybean, peanuts, peas, chickpeas, and beans. Other legumes, such as alfalfa, are used to feed cattle.

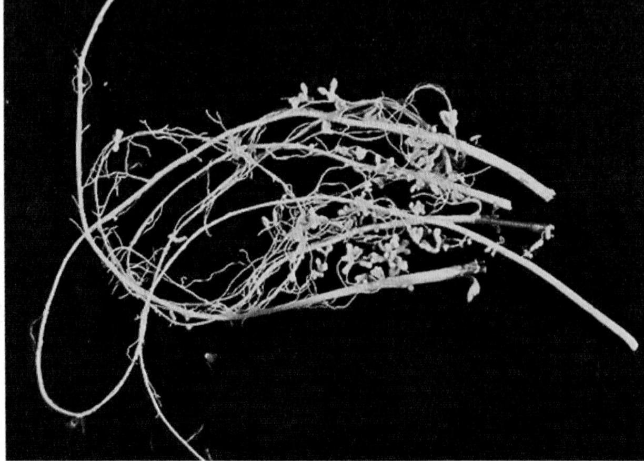

Figure 22.27 Soybean (*Glycine max*) is a legume that interacts symbiotically with the soil bacterium *Bradyrhizobium japonicum* to form specialized structures on the roots called nodules where nitrogen fixation occurs. (credit: USDA)

Early Biotechnology: Cheese, Bread, and Yogurt

According to the United Nations Convention on Biological Diversity, **biotechnology** is "any technological application that uses biological systems, living organisms, or derivatives thereof, to make or modify products or processes for specific use."[5] The concept of "specific use" involves some sort of commercial application. Genetic engineering, artificial selection, antibiotic production, and cell culture are current topics of study in biotechnology. However, humans have used prokaryotes before the term biotechnology was even coined. In addition, some of the goods and services are as simple as cheese, bread, and yogurt, which employ both bacteria and other microbes, such as yeast, a fungus.

---

5. http://www.cbd.int/convention/articles/?a=cbd-02, United Nations Convention on Biological Diversity: Article 2: Use of Terms.

Cheese production began around 4,000–7,000 years ago when humans began to breed animals and process their milk. Fermentation in this case preserves nutrients: Milk will spoil relatively quickly, but when processed as cheese, it is more stable Evidence suggests that cultured milk products, like yogurt, have existed for at least 4,000 years.

Using Prokaryotes to Clean up Our Planet: Bioremediation

Microbial **bioremediation** is the use of prokaryotes (or microbial metabolism) to remove pollutants. Bioremediation has been used to remove agricultural chemicals (pesticides, fertilizers) that leach from soil into groundwater and the subsurface. Certain toxic metals and oxides, such as selenium and arsenic compounds, can also be removed from water by bioremediation. The reduction of SeO_4^{-2} to SeO_3^{-2} and to Se^0 (metallic selenium) is a method used to remove selenium ions from water. Mercury is an example of a toxic metal that can be removed from an environment by bioremediation. As an active ingredient of some pesticides, mercury is used in industry and is also a by-product of certain processes, such as battery production. Methyl mercury is usually present in very low concentrations in natural environments, but it is highly toxic because it accumulates in living tissues. Several species of bacteria can carry out the biotransformation of toxic mercury into nontoxic forms. These bacteria, such as *Pseudomonas aeruginosa*, can convert Hg^{+2} into Hg^0, which is nontoxic to humans.

One of the most useful and interesting examples of the use of prokaryotes for bioremediation purposes is the cleanup of oil spills. The importance of prokaryotes to petroleum bioremediation has been demonstrated in several oil spills in recent years, such as the Exxon Valdez spill in Alaska (1989) (Figure 22.28), the Prestige oil spill in Spain (2002), the spill into the Mediterranean from a Lebanon power plant (2006), and more recently, the Deepwater Horizon oil spill in the Gulf of Mexico (2010). To clean up these spills, bioremediation is promoted by the addition of inorganic nutrients that help bacteria to grow. Hydrocarbon-degrading bacteria feed on hydrocarbons in the oil droplet, breaking down the hydrocarbons. Some species, such as *Alcanivorax borkumensis*, produce surfactants that solubilize the oil, whereas other bacteria degrade the oil into carbon dioxide. In the case of oil spills in the ocean, ongoing, natural bioremediation tends to occur, inasmuch as there are oil-consuming bacteria in the ocean prior to the spill. In addition to naturally occurring oil-degrading bacteria, humans select and engineer bacteria that possess the same capability with increased efficacy and spectrum of hydrocarbon compounds that can be processed. Under ideal conditions, it has been reported that up to 80 percent of the nonvolatile components in oil can be degraded within one year of the spill. Other oil fractions containing aromatic and highly branched hydrocarbon chains are more difficult to remove and remain in the environment for longer periods of time.

(a)

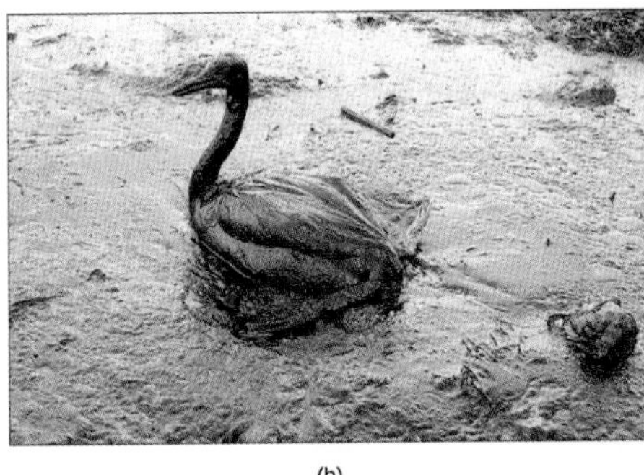

(b)

Figure 22.28 (a) Cleaning up oil after the Valdez spill in Alaska, workers hosed oil from beaches and then used a floating boom to corral the oil, which was finally skimmed from the water surface. Some species of bacteria are able to solubilize and degrade the oil. (b) One of the most catastrophic consequences of oil spills is the damage to fauna. (credit a: modification of work by NOAA; credit b: modification of work by GOLUBENKOV, NGO: Saving Taman)

everyday CONNECTION for AP® Courses

A particularly fascinating example of our normal flora relates to our digestive systems. People who take high doses of antibiotics tend to lose many of their normal gut bacteria, allowing a naturally antibiotic-resistant species called *Clostridium difficile* to overgrow and cause severe gastric problems, especially chronic diarrhea. Obviously, trying to treat this problem with antibiotics only makes it worse. However, it has been successfully treated by giving the patients fecal transplants from healthy donors to reestablish the normal intestinal microbial community. Scientists are also discovering that the absence of certain key microbes from our intestinal tract may set us up for a variety of problems including obesity, insulin resistance, and autoimmune disorders. Pictured here is a scanning electron micrograph of *Clostridium difficile*, a Gram-positive, rod-shaped bacterium that causes severe diarrhea. Infection commonly occurs after the normal gut fauna is eradicated by antibiotics.

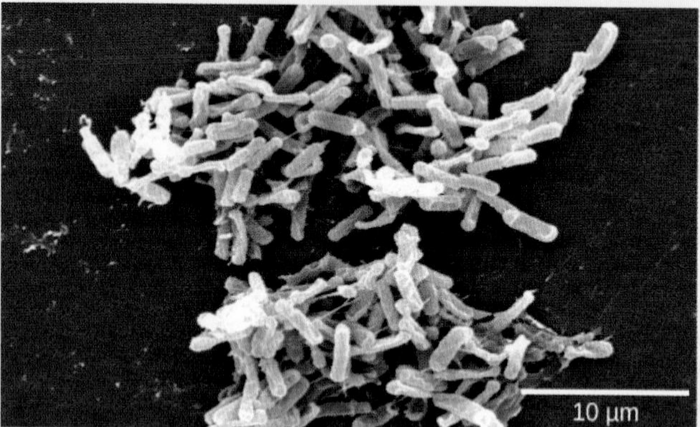

Figure 22.29 (credit: modification of work by CDC, HHS; scale-bar data from Matt Russell)

What treatment is possible for people who have too much C. difficile in their digestive system?

a. By taking antibiotics like metronidazole as treatment.
b. They can have a fecal transplant from a healthy donor.
c. They can have urine transplant from a healthy donor.
d. By taking probiotic supplements to restore microbial intestinal community.

science practices CONNECTION for AP® Courses

Think About It

One of your classmates claims that prokaryotes are always detrimental and pathogenic. How would you explain to him that his claim is incorrect?

KEY TERMS

acidophile organism with optimal growth pH of three or below

alkaliphile organism with optimal growth pH of nine or above

ammonification process by which ammonia is released during the decomposition of nitrogen-containing organic compounds

anaerobic refers to organisms that grow without oxygen

anoxic without oxygen

antibiotic biological substance that, in low concentration, is antagonistic to the growth of prokaryotes

biofilm microbial community that is held together by a gummy-textured matrix

biological nitrogen fixation conversion of atmospheric nitrogen into ammonia exclusively carried out by prokaryotes

bioremediation use of microbial metabolism to remove pollutants

biotechnology any technological application that uses living organisms, biological systems, or their derivatives to produce or modify other products

Black Death devastating pandemic that is believed to have been an outbreak of bubonic plague caused by the bacterium *Yersinia pestis*

botulism disease produce by the toxin of the anaerobic bacterium *Clostridium botulinum*

CA-MRSA MRSA acquired in the community rather than in a hospital setting

capsule external structure that enables a prokaryote to attach to surfaces and protects it from dehydration

chemotroph organism that obtains energy from chemical compounds

conjugation process by which prokaryotes move DNA from one individual to another using a pilus

cyanobacteria bacteria that evolved from early phototrophs and oxygenated the atmosphere; also known as blue-green algae

decomposer organism that carries out the decomposition of dead organisms

denitrification transformation of nitrate from soil to gaseous nitrogen compounds such as N_2O, NO and N_2

emerging disease disease making an initial appearance in a population or that is increasing in incidence or geographic range

endemic disease disease that is constantly present, usually at low incidence, in a population

epidemic disease that occurs in an unusually high number of individuals in a population at the same time

extremophile organism that grows under extreme or harsh conditions

foodborne disease any illness resulting from the consumption of contaminated food, or of the pathogenic bacteria, viruses, or other parasites that contaminate food

Gram negative bacterium whose cell wall contains little peptidoglycan but has an outer membrane

Gram positive bacterium that contains mainly peptidoglycan in its cell walls

halophile organism that require a salt concentration of at least 0.2 M

hydrothermal vent fissure in Earth's surface that releases geothermally heated water

hyperthermophile organism that grows at temperatures between 80–122 °C

microbial mat multi-layered sheet of prokaryotes that may include bacteria and archaea

MRSA (methicillin-resistant *Staphylococcus aureus*) very dangerous *Staphylococcus aureus* strain resistant to multiple antibiotics

nitrification conversion of ammonium into nitrite and nitrate in soils

nitrogen fixation process by which gaseous nitrogen is transformed, or "fixed" into more readily available forms such as ammonia

nodule novel structure on the roots of certain plants (legumes) that results from the symbiotic interaction between the plant and soil bacteria, is the site of nitrogen fixation

nutrient essential substances for growth, such as carbon and nitrogen

osmophile organism that grows in a high sugar concentration

pandemic widespread, usually worldwide, epidemic disease

peptidoglycan material composed of polysaccharide chains cross-linked to unusual peptides

phototroph organism that is able to make its own food by converting solar energy to chemical energy

pilus surface appendage of some prokaryotes used for attachment to surfaces including other prokaryotes

pseudopeptidoglycan component of archaea cell walls that is similar to peptidoglycan in morphology but contains different sugars

psychrophile organism that grows at temperatures of –15 °C or lower

radioresistant organism that grows in high levels of radiation

resuscitation process by which prokaryotes that are in the VBNC state return to viability

S-layer surface-layer protein present on the outside of cell walls of archaea and bacteria

serotype strain of bacteria that carries a set of similar antigens on its cell surface, often many in a bacterial species

stromatolite layered sedimentary structure formed by precipitation of minerals by prokaryotes in microbial mats

teichoic acid polymer associated with the cell wall of Gram-positive bacteria

thermophile organism that lives at temperatures between 60–80 °C

transduction process by which a bacteriophage moves DNA from one prokaryote to another

transformation process by which a prokaryote takes in DNA found in its environment that is shed by other prokaryotes

viable-but-non-culturable (VBNC) state survival mechanism of bacteria facing environmental stress conditions

zoonosis disease that primarily infects animals that is transmitted to humans

CHAPTER SUMMARY

22.1 Prokaryotic Diversity

Prokaryotes existed for billions of years before plants and animals appeared. Hot springs and hydrothermal vents may have been the environments in which life began. Microbial mats are thought to represent the earliest forms of life on Earth, and there is fossil evidence of their presence about 3.5 billion years ago. A microbial mat is a multi-layered sheet of prokaryotes that grows at interfaces between different types of material, mostly on moist surfaces. During the first 2 billion years, the atmosphere was anoxic and only anaerobic organisms were able to live. Cyanobacteria evolved from early phototrophs and began the oxygenation of the atmosphere. The increase in oxygen concentration allowed the evolution of other life forms. Fossilized microbial mats are called stromatolites and consist of laminated organo-sedimentary structures formed by precipitation of minerals by prokaryotes. They represent the earliest fossil record of life on Earth.

Bacteria and archaea grow in virtually every environment. Those that survive under extreme conditions are called extremophiles (extreme lovers). Some prokaryotes cannot grow in a laboratory setting, but they are not dead. They are in the viable-but-non-culturable (VBNC) state. The VBNC state occurs when prokaryotes enter a dormant state in response to environmental stressors. Most prokaryotes are social and prefer to live in communities where interactions take place. A biofilm is a microbial community held together in a gummy-textured matrix.

22.2 Structure of Prokaryotes

Prokaryotes (domains Archaea and Bacteria) are single-celled organisms lacking a nucleus. They have a single piece of circular DNA in the nucleoid area of the cell. Most prokaryotes have a cell wall that lies outside the boundary of the plasma membrane. Some prokaryotes may have additional structures such as a capsule, flagella, and pili. Bacteria and Archaea differ in the lipid composition of their cell membranes and the characteristics of the cell wall. In archaeal membranes, phytanyl units, rather than fatty acids, are linked to glycerol. Some archaeal membranes are lipid monolayers instead of bilayers.

The cell wall is located outside the cell membrane and prevents osmotic lysis. The chemical composition of cell walls varies between species. Bacterial cell walls contain peptidoglycan. Archaean cell walls do not have peptidoglycan, but they may have pseudopeptidoglycan, polysaccharides, glycoproteins, or protein-based cell walls. Bacteria can be divided into two major groups: Gram positive and Gram negative, based on the Gram stain reaction. Gram-positive organisms have a thick cell wall, together with teichoic acids. Gram-negative organisms have a thin cell wall and an outer envelope containing lipopolysaccharides and lipoproteins.

22.3 Prokaryotic Metabolism

Prokaryotes are the most metabolically diverse organisms; they flourish in many different environments with various carbon energy and carbon sources, variable temperature, pH, pressure, and water availability. Nutrients required in large amounts are called macronutrients, whereas those required in trace amounts are called micronutrients or trace elements. Macronutrients include C, H, O, N, P, S, K, Mg, Ca, and Na. In addition to these macronutrients, prokaryotes require various metallic elements for growth and enzyme function. Prokaryotes use different sources of energy to assemble macromolecules from smaller molecules. Phototrophs obtain their energy from sunlight, whereas chemotrophs obtain energy from chemical compounds.

Prokaryotes play roles in the carbon and nitrogen cycles. Carbon is returned to the atmosphere by the respiration of animals and other chemoorganotrophic organisms. Consumers use organic compounds generated by producers and release carbon dioxide into the atmosphere. The most important contributor of carbon dioxide to the atmosphere is microbial decomposition of dead material. Nitrogen is recycled in nature from organic compounds to ammonia, ammonium ions, nitrite, nitrate, and nitrogen gas. Gaseous nitrogen is transformed into ammonia through nitrogen fixation. Ammonia is anaerobically catabolized by some prokaryotes, yielding N_2 as the final product. Nitrification is the conversion of ammonium into nitrite. Nitrification in soils is carried out by bacteria. Denitrification is also performed by bacteria and transforms nitrate from soils into gaseous nitrogen compounds, such as N_2O, NO, and N_2.

22.4 Bacterial Diseases in Humans

Devastating diseases and plagues have been among us since early times. There are records about microbial diseases as far back as 3000 B.C. Infectious diseases remain among the leading causes of death worldwide. Emerging diseases are those rapidly increasing in incidence or geographic range. They can be new or re-emerging diseases (previously under control). Many emerging diseases affecting humans, such as brucellosis, are zoonoses. The WHO has identified a group of diseases whose re-emergence should be monitored: Those caused by bacteria include bubonic plague, diphtheria, and cholera.

Biofilms are considered responsible for diseases such as bacterial infections in patients with cystic fibrosis, Legionnaires' disease, and otitis media. They produce dental plaque; colonize catheters, prostheses, transcutaneous, and orthopedic devices; and infect contact lenses, open wounds, and burned tissue. Biofilms also produce foodborne diseases because they colonize the surfaces of food and food-processing equipment. Biofilms are resistant to most of the methods used to control microbial growth. The excessive use of antibiotics has resulted in a major global problem, since resistant forms of bacteria have been selected over time. A very dangerous strain, methicillin-resistant *Staphylococcus aureus* (MRSA), has wreaked havoc recently. Foodborne diseases result from the consumption of contaminated food, pathogenic bacteria, viruses, or parasites that contaminate food.

22.5 Beneficial Prokaryotes

Pathogens are only a small percentage of all prokaryotes. In fact, our life would not be possible without prokaryotes. Nitrogen is usually the most limiting element in terrestrial ecosystems; atmospheric nitrogen, the largest pool of available nitrogen, is unavailable to eukaryotes. Nitrogen can be “fixed,” or converted into ammonia (NH_3) either biologically or abiotically. Biological nitrogen fixation (BNF) is exclusively carried out by prokaryotes. After photosynthesis, BNF is the second most important biological process on Earth. The most important source of BNF is the symbiotic interaction between soil bacteria and legume plants.

Microbial bioremediation is the use of microbial metabolism to remove pollutants. Bioremediation has been used to remove agricultural chemicals that leach from soil into groundwater and the subsurface. Toxic metals and oxides, such as selenium and arsenic compounds, can also be removed by bioremediation. Probably one of the most useful and interesting examples of the use of prokaryotes for bioremediation purposes is the cleanup of oil spills.

Human life is only possible due to the action of microbes, both those in the environment and those species that call us home. Internally, they help us digest our food, produce crucial nutrients for us, protect us from pathogenic microbes, and help train our immune systems to function correctly.

REVIEW QUESTIONS

1. Which is the best evidence that prokaryotes evolved about 3 billion years ago?

a. Scientists believe photosynthesis evolved about 3.0 billion years ago.
b. There is fossil evidence of mammalian forms going back about 4.0 billion years.
c. Earth and its moon are thought to be about 4.5 billion years old.
d. There is fossil evidence of microbial mats—large multi-layered sheets of prokaryotes—starting about 3.5 billion years ago.

2. Which statement describing the environment of early Earth is false?

a. The atmosphere contained much less molecular oxygen.
b. Strong volcanic activity was common.
c. It was subject to mutagenic radiation from the Sun.
d. There was little to no geologic activity.

3. Which type of extremophile grows optimally at temperatures of –15 to 10 °C or lower?

a. alkaliphiles
b. thermophiles
c. hyperthermophiles
d. psychrophiles

4. Which is an example of a relatively moderate environmental condition to which some prokaryotes are adapted and can survive as spores?

a. extremely low temperature
b. hypersalinity
c. high doses of radiation
d. normal drought

5. Over _____ percent of bacteria and archaea cannot be successfully cultured in a laboratory setting.

a. 9
b. 19
c. 91
d. 99

6. The most substantial difficulty in culturing prokaryotes in laboratory settings is related to _____.

a. the lack of knowledge about their needs for growth
b. growth requirements that are too difficult to meet
c. inefficient methods for resuscitation of viable but nonculturable (VBNC) organisms
d. the expense of techniques such as polymerase chain reaction (PCR)

7. Which of the following represents the earliest forms of life on Earth?

a. hydrothermal vent
b. microbial mat
c. meteorite
d. stromatolite

8. Which best summarizes the conditions of early Earth at the time that life first evolved?

a. The atmosphere of early Earth was very different from today's atmosphere, but most other conditions (such as geologic upheaval and volcanic activity) were very much the same.
b. The atmosphere of early Earth was very much like today's atmosphere, but many other conditions (such as geologic upheaval and volcanic activity) were very different.
c. Early Earth had a very different atmosphere, was subject to extreme radiation, and had a lot of geologic upheaval and volcanic activity.
d. Early Earth had a very different atmosphere and was subject to extreme radiation, but there was very little geologic upheaval or volcanic activity.

9. Halophiles prefer conditions in which there is a _____.

a. high sugar concentration
b. salt concentration of at least 0.2 M
c. pH of 3 or below
d. high level of radiation

10. The presence of a membrane-enclosed nucleus is a characteristic of ____.

a. prokaryotic cells
b. eukaryotic cells
c. all cells
d. viruses

11. All prokaryotic and eukaryotic cells have four structures in common: the plasma membrane, the cytoplasm, nucleic acid, and ____.

a. the cell wall
b. ribosomes
c. the nucleus
d. organelles

12. Which statement comparing the prokaryotes Bacteria and Archaea is false?

a. The cytoplasm of both bacterial and archaean prokaryotic cells has a high concentration of dissolved solutes.
b. Osmotic pressure in both types of prokaryotic cells is relatively high.
c. The domains Bacteria and Archaea differ in the use of fatty acids versus phytanal groups in their cell membranes.
d. The domains Bacteria and Archaea have very similar cell wall structure.

13. Pseudopeptidoglycan is a characteristic of the walls of some _____.

a. eukaryotic cells
b. bacterial prokaryotic cells
c. archaean prokaryotic cells
d. bacterial and archaean prokaryotic cells

14. The cell wall, a feature of most prokaryotes, is _______.

a. interior to the cell membrane
b. exterior to the cell membrane
c. a part of the cell membrane
d. interior or exterior, depending on the particular cell

15. Which statement summarizes what is known about macronutrient needs of prokaryotes?

a. Boron is required in small amounts by some prokaryotic organisms.
b. Manganese is required in small amounts by some prokaryotic organisms.
c. Iron is required in small amounts by some prokaryotic organisms.
d. Sulfur is needed in large amounts by prokaryotic organisms. It is part of the structure of some amino acids and is also present in some vitamins and coenzymes.

16. Which statement about the importance of particular nutrients is false?

a. Carbon is a macronutrient and major element in all macromolecules.
b. Nitrogen is a macronutrient and necessary component of proteins and nucleic acids.
c. Hydrogen is a macronutrient and key component of many organic compounds, including water.
d. Iron is a macronutrient necessary for the function of cytochromes.

17. What are prokaryotes that obtain their energy from chemical compounds called?

a. phototrophs
b. autotrophs
c. chemotrophs
d. heterotrophs

18. What uses organic compounds as both an energy source and as a carbon source?

a. chemolithotrophs
b. photoautotrophs
c. photoheterotrophs
d. chemoorganotrophs

19. A primary role of many prokaryotes in the carbon cycle is that of ____.

a. producers
b. decomposers
c. fixers
d. synthesizers

20. Ammonification is the process by which ____.

a. ammonia is released during the decomposition of nitrogen-containing organic compounds
b. ammonium is converted to nitrite and nitrate in soils
c. nitrate from soil is transformed to gaseous nitrogen compounds
d. gaseous nitrogen is fixed to yield ammonia

21. Which is a macronutrient needed by prokaryotes?

a. phosphorus
b. iron
c. chromium
d. boron

22. A disease that is constantly present in a population is called _______.

a. pandemic
b. endemic
c. emerging
d. re-emerging

23. Which set of terms names diseases caused by bacteria?

a. diptheria, bubonic plague, yellow fever
b. yellow fever, dengue fever, bubonic plague
c. bubonic plague, diptheria, cholera
d. cholera, diptheria, dengue fever

24. Which of the following health issues is caused by biofilm colonization?

a. dental plaque
b. dry scalp
c. skin rash
d. prosthetic discomfort

25. Which of the statements about the loci of biofilm-related disease is false?

a. Biofilms are related to foodborne illnesses because they colonize food surfaces and food-processing equipment.
b. In healthcare environments, biofilms grow on ventilators, shunts, and other medical equipment.
c. Biofilms tend to colonize medical devices such as prostheses, contact lenses, and catheters.
d. Biofilms form in open wounds, burned tissue, or internal medical devices such as pacemakers.

26. Which best describes the crisis related to antibiotics?

a. It is becoming too expensive to manufacture effective antibiotics.
b. It takes too much time to develop effective antibiotics; infections spread before treatment is available.
c. Bacteria are increasingly resistant to antibiotics used to treat and eradicate infections.
d. People are increasingly allergic to antibiotics commonly used in treatment.

27. Which statement about the cause of resistant bacteria is false?

a. The excessive use of antibiotics has resulted in the natural selection of resistant forms of bacteria.
b. Antibiotics are used by patients with colds or the flu, the treatment for which antibiotics are useless.
c. There is excessive use of antibiotics in livestock and in animal feed.
d. Antibiotics are used by patients of different ages and the fact that their ages differ increases resistance.

28. Which statement about diseases is false?

a. An epidemic is a disease that occurs in a high number of individuals in a population at a time.
b. A pandemic is a widespread, usually worldwide, epidemic.
c. An endemic disease is a disease that is constantly present, usually at high incidence, in a population.
d. An emerging disease is a disease that has appeared in a population for the first time.

29. Which statement best explains which organisms need nitrogen fixation and why?

a. Prokaryotes cannot use gaseous nitrogen to synthesize macromolecules, so it must be converted into ammonia.
b. Prokaryotes cannot use ammonia to synthesize macromolecules, so it must be converted into gaseous nitrogen.
c. Eukaryotes cannot use ammonia to synthesize macromolecules, so it must be converted into gaseous nitrogen.
d. Eukaryotes cannot use gaseous nitrogen to synthesize macromolecules, so it must be converted into ammonia.

30. Which statement about nitrogen fixation is false?

a. It can be accomplished abiotically, as a result of lightning.
b. It can be accomplished abiotically, as a result of industrial processes.
c. It can be accomplished biologically, by algae.
d. It can be accomplished biologically, by cyanobacteria.

31. Which are three foods for which prokaryotes are used in their processing?

a. cheese, yogurt, and milk
b. cheese, yogurt, and bread
c. wine, bread, and butter
d. milk, wine, and beer

32. What was the initial benefit for humans in processing foods with prokaryotes?

a. The foods taste better.
b. Nutrients are preserved.
c. The food is less stable.
d. Nutrients were safer.

33. Which best defines bioremediation?

a. the use of microbial metabolism to clean up oil spills
b. the use of microbial metabolism to ferment food
c. the use of microbial metabolism to remove pollutants
d. the use of microbial metabolism to fix nitrogen

34. Which statement about bioremediation is false?

a. It includes removing agricultural chemicals.
b. It includes removing industrial by-products.
c. It includes cleaning up oil spills.
d. It includes cleaning up ammonia in soil.

35. Nitrogen is an essential element that is widely available in the atmosphere. Because eukaryotes cannot use nitrogen in its gaseous form, they benefit from prokaryotes' conversion of gaseous nitrogen to ____.

a. nitrates, a form of nitrogen they can use
b. phosphate, a different essential element they can use
c. ammonia, a form of nitrogen they can use
d. hydrogen, a different essential element they can use

CRITICAL THINKING QUESTIONS

36. Explain the relationship between Earth's ancient atmosphere and the evolution of some of the first life forms on Earth. Use the terms anaerobicandphototrophic, and explain the effect of cyanobacteria on the atmosphere.

a. Phototrophic organisms appeared during the first two billion years of Earth's existence. Anaerobic organisms appeared within one billion years of Earth's formation. From these organisms evolved the cyanobacteria which produce oxygen as a by-product of photosynthesis, leading to the oxygenation of the atmosphere.

b. For the first two billion years of Earth's existence, the atmosphere had no molecular oxygen. Thus, the first organisms were anaerobic. Cyanobacteria appeared within one billion years of Earth's formation. From these evolved the phototrophic organisms which produce oxygen as a by-product of photosynthesis, leading to the oxygenation of the atmosphere.

c. For the first two billion years of Earth's existence, the atmosphere had no molecular oxygen. Thus, the first organisms were anaerobic. Phototrophic organisms appeared within one billion years of Earth's formation. From these organisms evolved the cyanobacteria, which produce oxygen as a by-product of photosynthesis, leading to the oxygenation of the atmosphere.

d. For the first two billion years of Earth's existence, the atmosphere had no molecular oxygen. Thus, the first organisms were anaerobic. Cyanobacteria which produce oxygen as a by-product of photosynthesis, leading to the oxygenation of the atmosphere, appeared within one billion years of Earth's formation. From these organisms evolved phototrophic organisms.

37. Extremophiles are considered an important area for research in the development of therapeutic drugs or industrial applications. Why do you think this is so?

a. Extremophiles can be altered genetically in vitro to allow them to live in extreme conditions and this capability of alteration can be used to help humans. For example, some water-resistant prokaryotes have developed DNA repair mechanisms. Also, they could be developed and used in the treatment of human disease.

b. Extremophiles have specialized adaptations that allow them to live in extreme conditions. These adaptations can be mobilized to help humans. For example, some water-resistant prokaryotes have developed DNA repair mechanisms. Also, they could be developed and used in the treatment of human disease.

c. Extremophiles can be altered genetically in vitro to allow them to live in extreme conditions and this capability of alteration can be used to help humans. For example, some radiation-resistant prokaryotes have developed DNA repair mechanisms. Also, they could be developed and used in the treatment of human disease.

d. Extremophiles have specialized adaptations that allow them to live in extreme conditions. These adaptations can be mobilized to help humans. For example, some radiation-resistant prokaryotes have developed DNA repair mechanisms. Also, they could be developed and used in the treatment of human disease.

38. Describe briefly how you would detect the presence of a non culturable prokaryote in an environmental sample.

a. Recombinant DNA techniques are used to detect the presence of a non-culturable prokaryote in an environmental sample. Polymerase chain reaction is used to amplify selected portions of prokaryotic DNA.

b. Molecular biology techniques are used to detect the presence of a non-culturable prokaryote in an environmental sample. Electrophoresis is used to amplify selected portions of prokaryotic DNA.

c. Molecular biology techniques are used to detect the presence of a non-culturable prokaryote in an environmental sample. Polymerase chain reaction is used to amplify selected portions of prokaryotic DNA.

d. Recombinant DNA techniques are used to detect the presence of a non-culturable prokaryote in an environmental sample. Electrophoresis is used to amplify selected portions of prokaryotic DNA.

39. Why do scientists believe that the first organisms on Earth were extremophiles?

a. Earth's early environment was full of extreme places with much oxygen in the atmosphere, no ozone to shield Earth's surface from mutagenic radiation, much geologic upheaval and volcanic activity. Extremophiles are bacteria and archaea that are adapted to grow in extreme environments.

b. Earth's early environment was full of extreme places with little oxygen in the atmosphere, no ozone to shield Earth's surface from mutagenic radiation, much geologic upheaval and volcanic activity. Extremophiles are bacteria and archaea that are adapted to grow in extreme environments.

c. Earth's early environment was full of extreme places with little oxygen in the atmosphere, no ozone to shield Earth's surface from mutagenic radiation, less geologic upheaval and volcanic activity. Extremophiles are bacteria and archaea that are adapted to grow in extreme environments.

d. For the first two billion years of Earth's existence, the atmosphere had no molecular oxygen.

40. Describe a typical prokaryotic cell.

a. It has a cell wall enclosing cell membrane, cytoplasm, ribosomes and nucleoid region with genetic material. It may have a protective capsule, flagellum, pili and plasmids.

b. It has a cell wall enclosing cell membrane, cytoplasm, ribosomes and nucleus containing genetic material. It may have a protective capsule, flagellum, pili and plasmids.

c. It has a cell wall enclosing nuclear membrane, cytoplasm, ribosomes and nucleoid region with genetic material. It may have a protective capsule, flagellum, pili and plasmids.

d. It has a cell wall enclosing nuclear membrane, cytoplasm, mitochondria, vacuoles and nucleoid region with genetic material. It may have a protective capsule, flagellum, pili and plasmids.

41. Explain the statement that both Archaea and Bacteria have the same basic structures, but these structures are built from different chemical components.

a. Typical cells in Archaea and Bacteria contain a cell wall, cell membrane, nucleoid region, ribosomes, and often a capsule, flagellum, and pili. However, these are sometimes made from different chemical compounds. Cell walls of Bacteria contain peptidoglycan while Archaea do not. Plasma membrane lipids of Bacteria are fatty acids while those of Archaea are phytanyl groups.

b. Typical cells in Archaea and Bacteria contain a cell wall, cell membrane, nucleoid region and often a capsule, flagellum, and pili but in some instances different chemical compounds make them. Cell walls of Bacteria contain peptidoglycan while Archaea do not. Bacteria contain 70S ribosomes while Archaea contain 80S ribosomes.

c. Typical cells in Archaea and Bacteria contain a cell wall, nuclear membranes, nucleoid region and often a capsule, flagellum, and pili but in some instances different chemical compounds make them. Cell walls of Bacteria contain peptidoglycan while Archaea do not. Plasma membrane lipids of bacteria are fatty acids, while the plasma membrane lipids of Archaea are phytanyl groups.

d. Typical cells in Archaea and Bacteria contain a cell wall, cell membrane, nucleoid region and often a capsule, flagellum, and pili but in some instances different chemical compounds make them. Cell walls of Bacteria contain peptidoglycan while Archaea do not. Plasma membrane lipids of Bacteria are phytanyl groups, while the plasma membrane lipids of Archaea are fatty acids.

42. Three basic prokaryotic categories are cocci, spirilli, and bacilli. Describe the basic structural features of each category.

a. These three prokaryote groups have similar basic structural features. They typically have cell walls enclosing nuclear membranes, cytoplasm, ribosomes, mitochondria and nucleoid region with genetic material. They may have a protective capsule, flagellum, pili and plasmids.

b. Cocci and spirilli have similar basic structural features. They typically have cell walls enclosing cell membranes, a flagellum for locomotion and pili for attachment. Bacilli are rod shaped which contain ribosomes and a nucleoid region with genetic material.

c. These three prokaryote groups have similar basic structural features. They typically have cell walls enclosing cell membranes, cytoplasm, ribosomes and a nucleoid region with chromosomes. They may have a protective capsule, flagellum, pili and plasmids.

d. Bacilli and spirilli have similar basic structural features. They typically have cell walls enclosing nuclear membranes, a flagellum for locomotion and pili for attachment. Cocci are spherical containing ribosomes and a nucleoid region with genetic material.

43. Which macronutrient do you think is most important? What evidence can you offer to support your choice?

a. Carbon because it represents 12 percent of the total dry weight of a typical cell and is a component of all macromolecules.

b. Oxygen because it is necessary and is a major component for all macromolecules. It also accounts for 50% of the total composition of a cell.

c. Carbon because it is necessary and is a major component for all macromolecules. It also accounts for 50% of the total composition of a cell.

d. Nitrogen because it is necessary and is a major component for all macromolecules. It also accounts for 50% of the total composition of a cell.

44. A bacterium requires only a particular amino acid as an organic nutrient and lives in a completely lightless environment. What mode of nutrition (free energy and carbon) does it use? Justify your response.

a. Chemoheterotroph, as it must rely on chemical sources of energy living in a lightless environment and a heterotroph if it uses organic compounds for its carbon source.

b. Chemoorganotroph, as it must rely on chemical sources of energy living in a lightless environment and an organotroph if it uses organic compounds other than carbon dioxide for its carbon source.

c. Chemolitoautotroph, as it must rely on chemical sources of energy living in a lightless environment and an autotroph if it uses organic compounds other than carbon dioxide for its carbon source.

d. Chemoheterotroph, as it must rely on chemical sources of energy living in a lightless environment and a heterotroph if it uses organic compounds other than carbon dioxide for its carbon source.

45. Assuming that you could synthesize all of the nitrogen-containing compounds needed if you had nitrogen, what might you eat for a typical meal if you could fix nitrogen like some prokaryotes?

a. My meal might be fruits or vegetables and water as nitrogen is present in the highest amount in water.

b. My meal might be fruits or vegetables, water and air as atmospheric nitrogen could be simply absorbed.

c. My meal might be fruits or vegetables, cheese, meat, water, and air as atmospheric nitrogen could be simply absorbed.

d. My meal might be cheese or meat, water, and air as atmospheric nitrogen could be simply absorbed.

46. Which are more important: macronutrients or micronutrients? Explain your reasoning.

a. Neither are important, as cells can survive as well as carry out essential functions without both types of nutrients.

b. Micronutrients, even though they are required in lesser amounts, without them cells cannot survive and carry out functional processes.

c. Macronutrients, as they are required in larger amounts by cells and thus are more essential than micronutrients.

d. Neither is more important as both types of nutrients are absolutely necessary for prokaryotic cell structure and function.

47. Identify and discuss a bacterial disease that caused a historically important plague or epidemic. What is the modern distribution of this disease?

a. Bubonic plague caused by *Yersinia pestis* was a pandemic that occurred in the 14th century. In modern times, there are only about 100 cases of bubonic plague each year. The bacterium responds well to modern antibiotics.

b. Bubonic plague caused by *Yersinia enterocolitica* was a pandemic that occurred in the 14th century. In modern times, there are about 1,000 to 3,000 cases of bubonic plague each year. The bacterium responds well to modern antibiotics.

c. Pneumonic plague caused by *Yersinia pestis* was a pandemic that occurred in the 14th century. In modern times, there are about 1,000 to 3,000 cases of pneumonic plague each year. The bacterium responds well to modern antibiotics.

d. Bubonic plague caused by *Yersinia pestis* was a pandemic that occurred in the 14th century. In modern times, there are about 1,000 to 3,000 cases of bubonic plague each year. The bacterium responds well to modern antibiotics.

48. Have foodborne illnesses related to biofilms changed over time? Explain.

a. Yes, better sterilization and canning procedures have reduced the incidence of botulism. Most cases of foodborne illness now are related to small-scale food production.

b. No, better sterilization and canning procedures have reduced the incidence of botulism. Most cases of foodborne illness now are related to small-scale food production.

c. No, better sterilization and canning procedures have increased the incidence of botulism. Most cases of foodborne illnesses now are related to large-scale food production.

d. Yes, better sterilization and canning procedures have reduced the incidence of botulism. Most cases of foodborne illnesses now are related to large-scale food production.

49. What is the relationship between MRSA and the problem of antibiotic resistance?

a. Indiscriminate use of antibiotics results in the population growth of resistant bacteria like MRSA.

b. Infrequent use of antibiotics results in the population growth of resistant bacteria like MRSA.

c. Indiscriminate use of antibiotics results in the population decline of resistant bacteria like MRSA.

d. Infrequent use of antibiotics results in the population stability of resistant bacteria like MRSA.

50. What was the Plague of Athens? What is the modern distribution of this disease?

a. The Plague of Athens was a disease caused by *Yersinia pestis* that killed one-quarter of Athenian troops in 430 BC. Between 10 and 15 million cases of typhoid fever occur today, resulting in over 10, 000 deaths annually.

b. The Plague of Athens was a disease caused by *Salmonella entericaserovar typhi* that killed one-quarter of Athenian troops in 430 BC. Between 5 and 10 million cases of typhoid fever occur today, resulting in over 20, 000 deaths annually.

c. The Plague of Athens was a disease caused by *Yersinia pestis* that killed one-quarter of Athenian troops in 430 BC. Between 16 and 33 million cases of typhoid fever occur today, resulting in over 200,000 deaths annually.

d. The Plague of Athens was a disease caused by *Salmonella entericaserovar typhi* that killed one-quarter of Athenian troops in 430 BC. Between 16 and 33 million cases of typhoid fever occur today, resulting in over 200,000 deaths annually.

51. Identify three beneficial results of symbiotic nitrogen fixation.

a. Plants benefit from an endless supply of nitrogen; soils benefit from being naturally fertilized; and bacteria benefit from using potassium from plants.

b. Plants benefit from a limited supply of nitrogen; soils benefit from being naturally fertilized, and bacteria benefit from using photosynthates from plants.

c. Plants benefit from an endless supply of carbon; soils benefit from being naturally fertilized; and bacteria benefit from using photosynthates from plants.

d. Plants benefit from an endless supply of nitrogen; soils benefit from being naturally fertilized; and bacteria benefit from using photosynthates from plants.

52. Why is the processing of foods with prokaryotes considered an example of early biotechnology?

a. Prokaryotes have been used to only make specific food products like cheese, wine, bread, beer and yogurt since before the term biotechnology was coined.

b. Prokaryotes have been used to make and alter specific food products like cheese, wine, single cell proteins, beer and yogurt since before the term biotechnology was coined.

c. As prokaryotes have been used to make and alter specific food products like cheese, wine, bread, beer and yogurt since before the term biotechnology was coined.

d. As prokaryotes have been used to alter specific food products like cheese, wine, bread, beer and yogurt since before the term biotechnology was coined.

53. On what does the success of bioremediation of oil spills depend?

a. Success depends on the presence of only aromatic and highly branched hydrocarbon chain compounds and the temperature.

b. Success depends on the presence of less nonvolatile and more aromatic and highly branched hydrocarbon chain compounds and the temperature.

c. Success depends on the type of oil compounds, the presence of naturally-occurring oil-solubilizing prokaryotes in the ocean, and the type of water body.

d. Success depends on the type of oil compounds, the presence of naturally-occurring oil-solubilizing prokaryotes in the ocean and the temperature.

54. Why is the relationship between sustainable agriculture and nitrogen fixers called a mutualism?

a. Due to agrobacterium which are nitrogen fixers, plants benefit from an endless supply of nitrogen; soils benefit from being naturally fertilized and bacteria benefit from using photosynthates from plants.

b. Due to rhizobia, which are nitrogen fixers, plants benefit from an endless supply of nitrogen; soils benefit from being naturally fertilized and bacteria benefit from using photosynthates from plants.

c. Due to rhizobia, which are nitrogen fixers, plants benefit from an endless supply of nitrogen; soils benefit from being naturally fertilized and bacteria benefit from using potassium from plants.

d. Due to rhizobia, which are nitrogen fixers, plants benefit from a limited supply of nitrogen; soils benefit from being naturally fertilized and bacteria benefit from using potassium from plants.

TEST PREP FOR AP® COURSES

55. Which of the following pieces of evidence is the BEST support for the alternative scenario of early life formation, in which organic compounds on early Earth formed near submerged volcanoes?

a. Some prokaryotes that live near deep-sea vents today use hydrogen as an energy source.

b. Fossilized stromatolites that are 3.5 billion years old are found near deep-sea vents.

c. Extremophiles that exist today live in a variety of extreme environments, including those that are high in salinity.

d. The chemical composition of water around deep-sea vents is the same as it was on early Earth.

56. Stanley Miller and Harold Urey conducted experiments which demonstrated that several organic compounds could be formed spontaneously by simulating the conditions of Earth's early atmosphere. When Miller and Urey repeated their experiment without the electrical discharge, no organic compounds were found. Hypothesize what might explain this result. Consider your answer in the context of the conditions of early Earth.

a. The lack of organic compounds without the sparks indicates that organic components are formed from biotic components.

b. The first trial of the experiment must have been done incorrectly.

c. Abiotic molecules can only develop into organic molecules in the presence of oxygen, so oxygen should be added.

d. Lightning, or some form of energy, is needed for the inorganic molecules in the atmosphere to interact with each other. This indicates that a similar energy source was present on early Earth which stimulates the interaction and development.

57. Laboratory experiments have demonstrated that the abiotic synthesis of organic molecules in condition similar to those of early Earth is possible. Which of the following provides additional support for the idea of abiotic synthesis of organic compounds?

a. Analysis of the chemical composition of meteorites sometimes yields amino acids.
b. A hydrothermal vent in the Sea of Cortés releases hydrogen sulfide and iron sulfide.
c. Researchers have dripped solutions of amino acids onto hot surfaces to produce amino acid polymers.
d. Some present-day prokaryotes live and reproduce in very extreme and unforgiving environments, such as the Arctic.

58. Which of the following cell types does Figure 22.10 illustrate?

a. Plant cell
b. Animal cell
c. Bacterial cell
d. Fungal cell

59. Which option best describes the function and presence of cell organelles among prokaryotes and eukaryotes?

a. Ribosomes are the sites of protein synthesis found in prokaryotic and eukaryotic cells. Cell wall is a protective layer, typical in prokaryotic cells and in some eukaryotes. Chromosomal DNA, the genetic material of the cell is present in a nucleoid region in prokaryotes while enclosed in a nucleus in eukaryotes.
b. Ribosomes are the sites of protein synthesis found in prokaryotic and eukaryotic cells. The cell wall is a protective layer found in some prokaryotic and eukaryotic cells. Chromosomal DNA is the genetic material of the cell present in a nucleoid region in prokaryotes while in eukaryotes, it is enclosed in a nucleus.
c. Ribosomes are sites of ATP production found in both prokaryotic and eukaryotic cells. The cell wall is a protective layer, typically found in prokaryotic cells and in some eukaryotes. Chromosomal DNA is present in a nucleoid region while enclosed in a nucleus in eukaryotes. It is the genetic material of the cell.
d. Ribosomes are the sites of protein synthesis found in prokaryotic and eukaryotic cells. The cell wall is a protective layer, typically found in prokaryotic cells and in some eukaryotes. Chromosomal DNA, the genetic material of the cell is present in a nucleus in prokaryotes while it is enclosed in a nucleoid region in eukaryotes.

60. A nonpathogenic bacterium acquires resistance to antibiotics. Which of the following scenarios describing how this strain could pose a health risk to people is false?

a. Genes for antibiotic resistance are transferred from the nonpathogenic bacterium to a pathogenic bacterium via transduction.
b. Genes for antibiotic resistance are transferred from the nonpathogenic bacterium to a pathogenic bacterium via transformation.
c. Genes for antibiotic resistance are transferred from the nonpathogenic bacterium to a pathogenic bacterium via conjugation.
d. Genes for antibiotic resistance are transferred from the nonpathogenic bacterium to a pathogenic bacterium via binary fission.

61. In a rapidly changing environment, which prokaryotic population would you hypothesize likely to be more successful: one that included individuals capable of conjugation or one that did not?

a. A population including individuals capable of conjugation would be more successful because all of its members would form recombinant cells having new gene combinations advantageous in a new environment.
b. A population including individuals capable of conjugation would be more successful as some members could form recombinant cells having new gene combinations advantageous in a new environment.
c. A population including individuals not capable of conjugation would be more successful as the members undergoing conjugation would form new recombinant cells having gene combinations lethal in the new environment.
d. A population including individuals not capable of conjugation would be more successful because conjugation will result in an increase in genetic diversity of the prokaryotic population which will be disadvantageous in a new population.

62. Plates that have only ampicillin-resistant bacteria growing include which of the following?

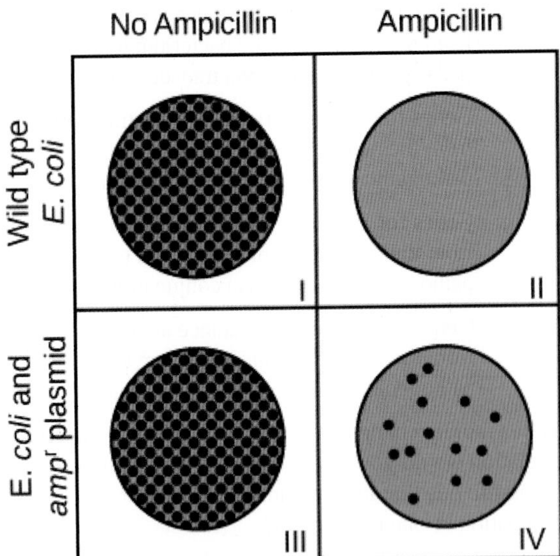

a. I only
b. III only
c. IV only
d. I and II

63. Given your understanding of the experiment and of bacterial genetic recombination, explain why there are fewer colonies on plate IV than on plate III.

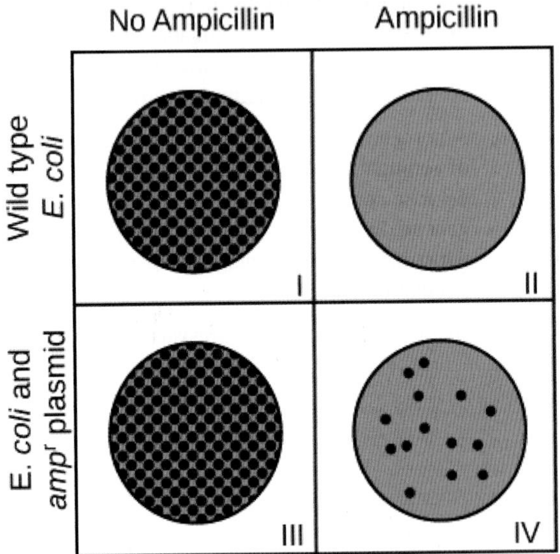

a. All *E. coli* cells were not successfully transformed on plate IV.
b. The nutrient agar medium inhibited the growth of some bacteria on plate IV.
c. All *E. coli* cells were successfully transformed on plate IV.
d. The bacteria in plate III were naturally resistant to ampicillin.

64. Which of the labeled structures in the diagram allows you to positively identify the cell as a prokaryote?

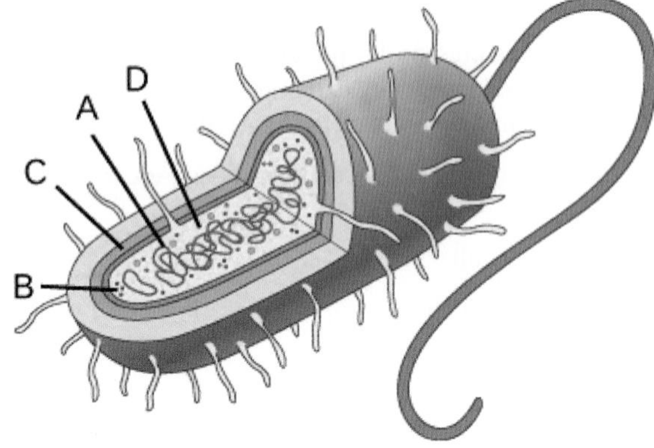

a. A, circular DNA
b. B, ribosome
c. C, cell wall
d. D, cytoplasm

65. A bacterial species that is a methanogen is discovered. If you wanted to build on this discovery to better understand the evolution of mechanisms related to the ability to capture, store, and use free energy in prokaryotes, which question would you pose to answer?

a. Have metabolic pathways evolved separately in Bacteria and Archaea?
b. Should all methanogens be classed as Archaea in evolutionary phylogeny?
c. Have methanogens evolved to live in both moderate and extreme environments?
d. Did the methanogenic bacteria species also evolve as a strict anaerobe?

66. What is another question you might pose to learn more about the structural features that allow for the capture, storage, and use of free energy by archaean methanogens?

a. Do archaean methanogens differ from other Archaea structurally, and if so, in what way? Is one or more of these structural differences related to these methanogens' ability to use H_2 to oxidize CO_2?

b. Do archaean methanogens differ from other Bacteria structurally, and if so, in what way? Is one or more of these structural differences related to these methagens' ability to use CO_2 to oxidize H_2?

c. Do archaean methanogens differ from other Archaea structurally, and if so, in what way? Is one or more of these structural differences related to these methagens' ability to use CO_2 to oxidize H_2?

d. Do archaean methanogens differ from other Archaea structurally, and if so, in what way? Is one or more of these structural differences related to these methagens' ability to use H_2O to oxidize H_2?

67. Which set of phrases related to nutritional and metabolic adaptations best fits the organisms described?

a. chemoautotrophs, obligate anaerobes

b. chemoautotrophs, faculative anaerobes

c. chemoheterotrophs, faculative anaerobes

d. chemoheterotrophs, obligate anaerobes

68. In an experiment, researchers grew plant seedlings in soils to which one of two strains of bacteria were added. A control group had no bacteria added to the soil. The seedlings' uptake of the nutrient potassium increased dramatically in the soil with Strain 1 and decreased dramatically in the soil with Strain 2. What specific and broad inferences about the relationship between the bacteria, the seedlings, and available nutrients can you make?

a. The Strain 2 bacteria increased the availability of potassium in the soil and this nutrient was needed and used by the seedlings in the soil. The Strain 1 bacteria decreased the availability of potassium in the soil.

b. The soil with Strain 1 bacteria must have had more potassium in comparison to soil with Strain 2 bacteria. The seedlings took up more potassium in Soil 1 than in 2 due to this.

c. The Strain 1 bacteria increased the availability of potassium in the soil and this nutrient was needed and used by the seedlings in the soil. The Strain 2 bacteria decreased the availability of potassium in the soil.

d. The Strain 1 bacteria decreased the availability of potassium in the soil and this nutrient was needed and used by the seedlings in the soil. The Strain 2 bacteria increased the availability of potassium in the soil.

69. In a hypothetical research situation, scientists discover bacterial endospores in silt at the bottom of a marsh that has been contaminated with a pollutant for 25 years. The silt of the marsh was deposited in annual layers. The age of the endospores can be estimated, then, by identifying the layer of silt in which the endospores are found. In flask A, researchers place 20-year-old endospores along with growth medium and the pollutant. In flask B, researchers place 100-year-old endospores along with growth medium and the pollutant. Which statement describes the results you would expect to see in the growth of the flasks?

a. The growth in flask A will exceed that of flask B.

b. The growth in flask B will exceed that of flask A.

c. The growth each flask will be about equal.

d. There will be little to no growth in each flask.

70. In a hypothetical research situation, scientists discover bacterial endospores in silt at the bottom of a marsh that has been contaminated with a pollutant for 25 years. The silt of the marsh was deposited in annual layers. The age of the endospores can be estimated, then, by identifying the layer of silt in which the endospores are found. In flask A, researchers place 20-year-old endospores along with growth medium and the pollutant. In flask B, researchers place 100-year-old endospores along with growth medium and the pollutant. Explain why you would expect to see more growth in one particular flask than in the other.

a. Because endospores formed 20 years ago would be more dormant compared to endospores formed 100 years ago, before the marsh was polluted.

b. Because endospores formed 20 years ago would be less adapted to polluted conditions compared to endospores formed 100 years ago, before the marsh was polluted.

c. Because endospores formed 20 years ago would be more adapted to polluted conditions compared to endospores formed 100 years ago, before the marsh was polluted.

d. Because endospores formed 20 years ago would be less dormant compared to endospores formed 100 years ago, before the marsh was polluted.

71. In a hypothetical research situation, scientists discover bacterial endospores in silt at the bottom of a marsh that has been contaminated with a pollutant for 25 years. The silt of the marsh was deposited in annual layers. The age of the endospores can be estimated, then, by identifying the layer of silt in which the endospores are found. In flask A, researchers place 20-year-old endospores along with growth medium and the pollutant. In flask B, researchers place 100-year-old endospores along with growth medium and the pollutant. Suppose the researchers observe the flasks for a while, continuing to replenish growth medium and pollutant as necessary. Which statement describes the results you would expect to see in the growth of the flasks after some time?

a. The growth in flask A will continue to exceed that of flask B.

b. The growth in flask B will exceed continue to exceed that of flask A.

c. Eventually, the difference in the growth in each flask will lessen.

d. Eventually, will be little to no growth in each flask.

72. In a hypothetical research situation, scientists discover bacterial endospores in silt at the bottom of a marsh that has been contaminated with a pollutant for 25 years. The silt of the marsh was deposited in annual layers. The age of the endospores can be estimated, then, by identifying the layer of silt in which the endospores are found. In flask A, researchers place 20-year-old endospores along with growth medium and the pollutant. In flask B, researchers place 100-year-old endospores along with growth medium and the pollutant. Suppose the researchers observe the flasks for a while, continuing to replenish growth medium and pollutant as necessary. If the difference in the growth in each flask lessened after some time, which statement explains why?

a. Because the endospores formed 100 years ago, before the marsh was polluted, they would evolve resistance to the pollutant fairly quickly. The bacteria in flask B would then grow more prolifically, and the difference in population size of each flask would lessen.

b. Because the endospores formed 20 years ago would lose their resistance to the pollutant. The bacteria in flask A would die, and the difference in population size of each flask would lessen.

c. Because the endospores formed 100 years ago, before the marsh was polluted, they would lose their resistance to the pollutant. The bacteria in flask B would then grow more prolifically, and the difference in population size of each flask would lessen.

d. Because the endospores formed 20 years ago would evolve resistance to the pollutant fairly quickly. The bacteria in flask A would die, and the difference in population size of each flask would lessen.

73. How does resistance spread in bacteria?

a. By undergoing genetic recombination through conjugation, transduction, and transformation.

b. By undergoing reproduction through binary fission.

c. By undergoing genetic recombination through conjugation and transformation only.

d. Reproduction among bacteria through any mechanism results in the spread of antibiotic resistance genes.

74. Health officials worldwide are concerned about antibiotic resistance in bacteria that cause disease. In patients infected with nonresistant strains of the bacterium that causes tuberculosis, antibiotics can relieve symptoms fast—in as short of a time as a few weeks. However, it takes much longer to stop infection entirely, and patients may discontinue treatment once symptoms are abated. In a hypothetical study, researchers found a much higher incidence of recurrent tuberculosis infection in patients who discontinued treatment once symptoms were relieved, but before the planned course of treatment was complete. Which statement best explains this result?

a. The wrong course of antibiotics was used on the patient, so the infection was never treated.

b. Not all of the bacteria were killed, and the remaining ones reproduced and bring back the symptoms of infection.

c. The antibiotics were not prescribed for a long enough time to treat the infection.

d. The infection was actually viral in nature, and so the antibiotics were a useless treatment.

75. Human intestines are home to hundreds of species of

bacteria. One of these, *Bacteriodes thetaiotaomicron*, has the capability of digesting complex plant materials that human enzymes cannot digest. Its presence in the human guts makes a significant contribution to human metabolic processes.Which term best describes the relationship between humans and *B. thetaiotaomicron*?

a. commensalistic
b. mutualistic
c. parasitic
d. pathogenic

76. If you suddenly and dramatically changed your diet, how might this affect the diversity of prokaryotic species that live in your intestine?

a. The diversity would not get altered and would remain the same.
b. Species abundance and relative distribution may increase.
c. Species abundance and relative distribution may get affected.
d. Species abundance and relative distribution may decrease.

77. More than 100 bacterial species live on the surface of the human body. Bacteria cover portions of human skin in concentrations of up to 8 million cells per square centimeter. In particular, human sebaceous glands support the growth of the bacterium *Propionibacterium acnes*, which uses oil from the glands for food. Two strains of *P. acnes* are associated with the development of acne on human skin, but other strains are associated with healthy skin. Which statement best describes the relationship between humans and *P. acnes*?

a. In some cases it is commensal and in others it is parasitic.
b. In some cases it is mutualistic and in others it is commensalistic.
c. It is almost always parasitic.
d. It is almost always mutualistic.

SCIENCE PRACTICE CHALLENGE QUESTIONS

78. That the uniformity of cell size in prokaryotes is independent of the conditions of cell growth has long been a puzzle. Suppose that cells grew for a random period of time and then divided. The largest and smallest, by sometimes dividing to make even larger or smaller cells, would be expected to broaden the distribution of cell sizes, as shown in the diagram on the left for a time, t_2, after a time t_1. Competing claims are made to explain the fact, however, that the distribution does not broaden: 1) There is a “timer” that initiates cell division, and 2) there is a volume threshold that, when reached, initiates cell division. Recently (Amir, *Phys. Rev. Lett*, 2014), a third model was suggested: From the end of the last cell division to the next, the cell volume increases by a constant value.

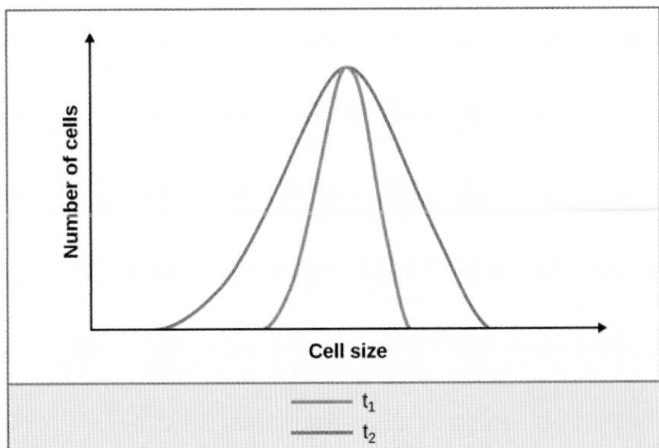

Figure 22.30

A. **Justify the claim** of the third model by i) rejecting the two alternative claims, using the fact that growth rate depends on the availability of resources and considering that regulation of expression at a critical volume would require measurement of total volume by the cell, and ii) arguing that adding a constant volume before each cell division would narrow the cell size distribution.

B. **Design a plan** to test both the most recent model and the timer model.

79. Gram-negative bacteria have an inner cytoplasmic membrane separated by a peptidoglycan layer from a second outer membrane. In addition, transport proteins called efflux pumps span this double membrane and actively eliminate chemicals such as antibiotics that pass through porins on the outer membrane. These efflux pumps can confer multi-drug resistance, a situation that is threatening human health.

A. **Explain** how combining a drug that disrupts ATP synthesis in bacteria with antibiotics is a possible strategy for the treatment of bacterial infections caused by antibiotic-resistant gram-negative bacteria.

ATP synthesis in prokaryotes is accomplished by a protein that connects the extracellular space to the cytoplasm. In gram-negative bacteria, the proton gradient that supplies the free energy to convert ADP into ATP is established across the inner membrane.

B. **Predict** differences in the interactions of eukaryotic and prokaryotic cells with a drug molecule that successfully targets ATP synthesis and provide reasoning for your predictions.

In gram-positive bacteria, ATP synthesis is accomplished by a protein that spans the single membrane and the outer cell wall. During the production of yogurt and wine, which rely on gram-positive bacteria, the pH is controlled. Sodium bicarbonate secretions from the pancreas maintain the pH of the human intestine, where many beneficial methanogens are gram-positive bacteria.

C. **Explain** why homeostasis for gram-positive bacteria requires control of extracellular pH.

80. Cyanobacteria are single-celled organisms with the capacity to fix nitrogen, N_2. Some cyanobacteria cooperatively aggregate as filaments, and heterocysts may form at intervals along the filament between a pair of vegetative (actively growing) cells. Heterocysts are specialized cells that express certain genes when nitrogen becomes limiting. The nitrogenase complex converts the nitrogen in N_2 into NH_3 (ammonia). This enzyme functions only under anaerobic conditions that are, in part, enforced by an O_2 barrier surrounding the cytoplasm of the heterocyst, as shown below.

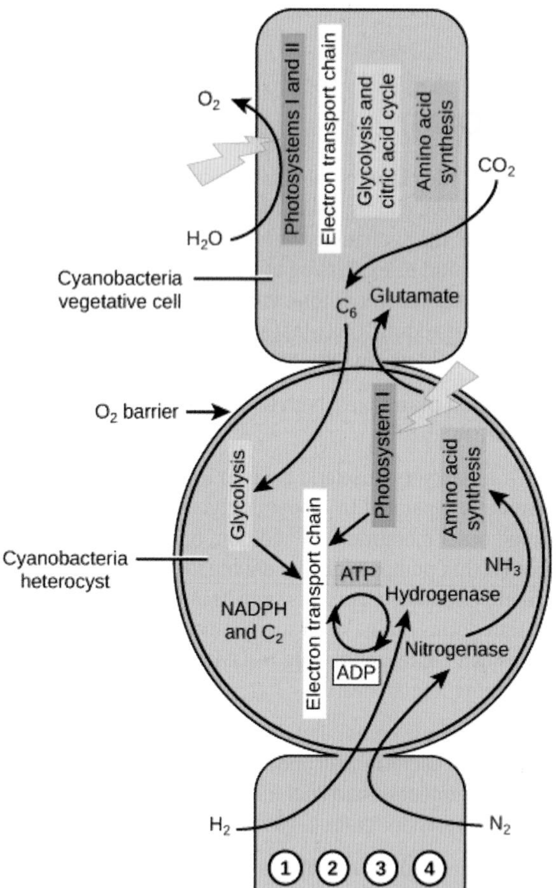

Figure 22.31

A. Other modifications displayed in the diagram maintain an anaerobic state and synthesize ammonia from N_2. Identify four modifications of vegetative cells, either by their addition to or omission from the heterocyst. **Refine the representation** by drawing a line between each of the three numbered circles and the feature.

B. Further **refine the representation** by providing a brief description of the role of each modification in either regulating oxygen or synthesizing ammonia.

The Krebs cycle in prokaryotes and eukaryotes differs. In prokaryotes, the Krebs cycle occurs in the cytoplasm and the intermediate 2-oxoglutarate (?-ketoglutarate) is absent.

C. **Construct a representation** of the regulation of genes encoding the nitrogen fixation system using the elements below. The irregular shapes are either metabolites or transcription factors, NtcA, HetR, and PatS. In your representation, label each shape using the names on the left in the figure below. Your representation must account for these observations:

- when nitrogen is limiting, 2-oxoglutarate concentration in the cytoplasm increases
- HetR is transcribed when 2-oxoglutarate concentrations are low
- PatS is transcribed when 2-oxoglutarate concentrations are low
- nitrogenase is transcribed when HetR concentrations are high and PatS concentrations are low
- when PatS concentrations are high, nifX genes are not transcribed

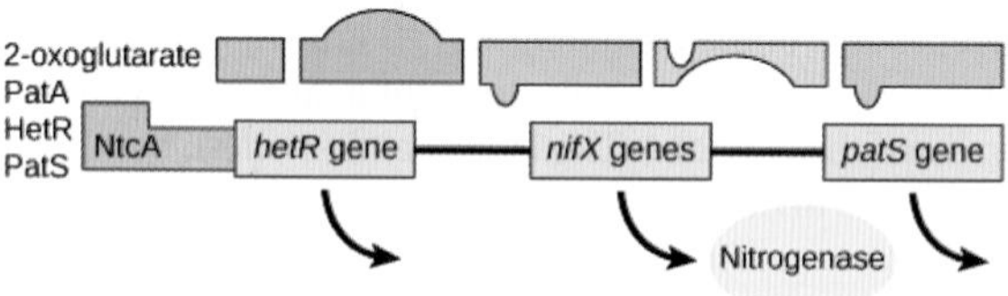

Figure 22.32

D. Heterocysts form along the filament separated by a fixed number of vegetative cells. Based on your model of the regulation of heterocyst development, **make and support a claim** that accounts for this pattern.

81. *Escherichia coli* Strain A is able to grow in a minimal medium only when supplemented with methionine and biotin. Strain B is able to grow in a minimal medium only when supplemented with threonine, leucine, and thiamine. The two strains are incubated together in a medium containing each supplement. They are then transferred to a minimal medium with no supplements, and each strain is able to grow under these conditions.

A. **Describe** the evidence that supports information exchange between Strain A and Strain B, and the mechanisms that can account for this behavior demonstrated by Lederberg and Tatum (*Nature*, 1946).

Colistin is regarded as a last-resort antibiotic in the treatment of multi-drug-resistant, gram-negative bacteria. The MCR-1 gene that confers colistin resistance was recently detected in a plasmid found in *E. coli* from the intestines of human patients (Liu et al, *Lancet Infect. Dis.*, 2016). Colistin is cheap to produce, is often used as a feed supplement for domesticated animals (12,000 metric tons per year in 2015), and its use is increasing. Colistin is also unstable in water (Healan et al., *Antimicrob. Agents Chemother*, 2012).

B. **Describe** the possible biological consequences of an immediate ban on the use of colistin in agriculture.

82. Life on Earth is sustained by four processes that are unique to prokaryotes: 1) methanogens reduce hydrogen or carbon atoms to produce methane; 2) methanotrophs combine methane with oxygen to form formaldehyde; 3) nitrogen fixation converts N_2 into ammonia; and 4) nitrification converts ammonia into nitrates. These processes recycle matter, maintaining the carbon (1 and 2) and nitrogen (3 and 4) cycles.

Methanogens are strictly anaerobic. Estimates of global fluxes of methane from major sources (Kirschke, *Nature Geoscience*, 2013, in units of 10^{12} g C/year) are shown in the figure below. Agricultural sources are predominately the microbiomes of ruminants (cows, goats, etc.) and rice cultivated in shallow ponds where anoxic compost and crop residues promote methanogen growth on roots. Other major human activities that contribute to atmospheric methane levels are landfills and natural gas drilling.

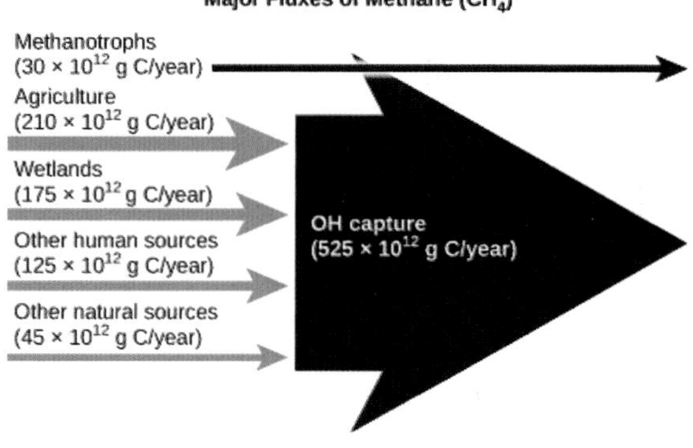

Figure 22.33

The fate of this methane is also shown. Most reacts with OH in the lower atmosphere to make formic acid, which then decomposes into carbon dioxide and water. Methanotrophs consume the remaining methane.

Methane is a component of the carbon cycle, but it is much less significant than carbon dioxide, whose major fluxes are shown in units of 10^{15} g C/year (*NASA*, 2015). Oceanic uptake and loss of CO_2 are primarily abiotic. Prokaryotic marine organisms account for approximately 50% of the biotic exchanges.

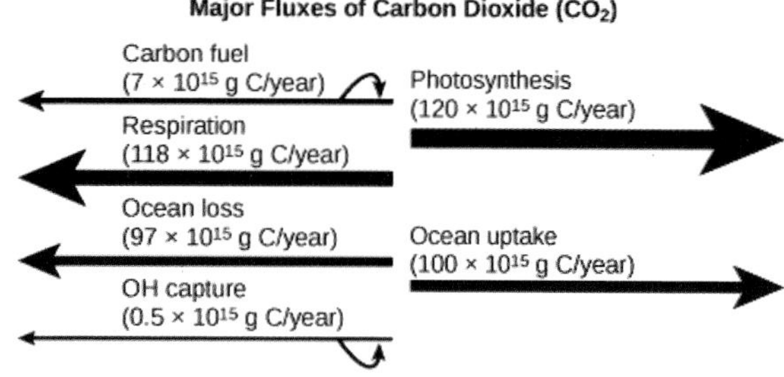

Figure 22.34

A. **Compare** quantitatively the rates of carbon cycling as methane between the biosphere and atmosphere. **Calculate** the percentage of methane production that is anthropocentric (due to human actions).

B. Assuming that the rates of carbon dioxide exchange shown in the diagram are accurate, **analyze** these data to **identify** a missing contribution to the carbon budget.

Recently, it was discovered that ruminants fed nitrooxypropanoic acid reduced their methane release from digestion by approximately 50% and increased the rate of meat production by as much as 80% (E. Duin et al., *Proc. Natl. Acad. Sci*, 2016).

C. Since methane is a greenhouse gas, its release into the atmosphere further increases global temperatures. It has been claimed that a feed supplement program will reduce the effects of climate change. **Predict** the consequences of such a program and provide reasoning for your prediction.

A vertical profile of methane and oxygen below the surface of a rice paddy are shown in the graph below (Lee et al., *Front. Microbiol*, 25, 2015). Also shown are estimates of the relative abundance of all genera of methanotrophs (red line) and methanogens (blue line) as a function of depth. Rice paddies are the largest contributor to agricultural methane production. The estimates were based on extraction and analysis of ribosomal RNA from the soil.

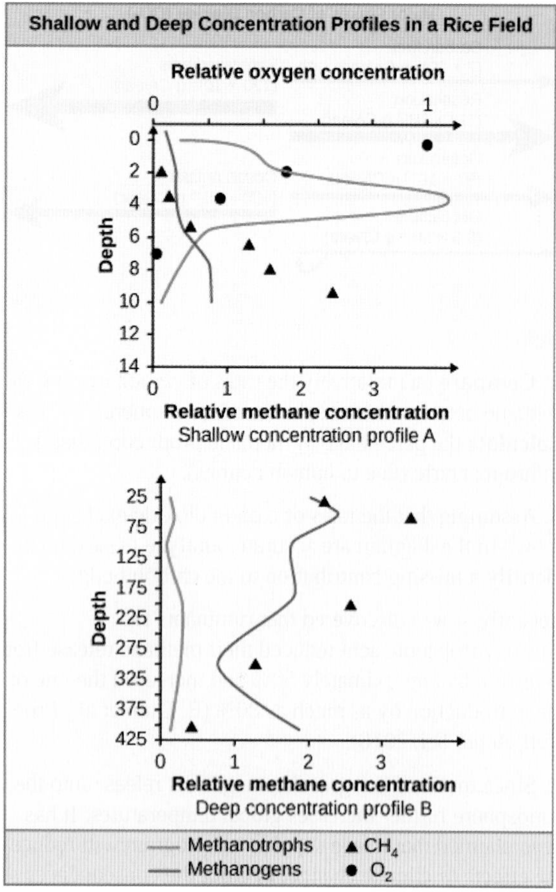

Figure 22.35

D. **Justify** the **selection** of these measurements of the concentrations of two types of microbes and the gases that are consumed or produced to the development of a quantitative understanding of the habitat range of both groups and the control of methane release from rice fields.

83. The human gut provides a habitat for approximately 100 trillion bacteria. Some sources claim that the surface area of the cells lining the small and large intestines is between 150 and 300 square meters and compare this area to that of a tennis court. Recent measurements, however, show that the surface area of the gut is closer to that of a studio apartment (Helander and Fandriks, *Jour. Gastro*, 2014) and is roughly 50 square meters.

A. **Calculate** the cellular surface area of the 100 trillion (10^{14}) microbes in the typical human gut, assuming that the cells are spherical with an average radius of 0.001 mm. Use this calculated surface area to **predict** the relative rates of procurement of nutrients by both microbes and the host cells lining the large and small intestines.

Humans compete with microbes for nutrients, but the relationship is mutually beneficial. Between 10 and 30% of ingested food remains undigested before reaching the large intestine. Some microbial waste products, particularly H_2 and CH_4, are not resources for the host. But short-chain fatty acids like acetic, propionic, and butyric acids are resources that microbes extract from the undigested fraction. The large intestine of the adult human has a length of approximately 1.5 meters with a volume between 6 and 7 liters. The total volume of gut microbes is just a few hundred milliliters.

B. **Predict** the length of a large intestine with equivalent recovery of resources and the same transit times through the bowel if, rather than 100 trillion organisms with a total volume of 1 L, there were 100 billion (10^{11}) organisms, each with a volume of 10^{-8} mL (the approximate volume of the epithelial cells lining the intestine).

The relationship between gut microbes and their host is more complex than simple resource recovery, as shown in the figure of the microbiome below. PYY is a hormone that works with the enteric nervous system lining the intestinal wall to cause changes in the period of contractions of muscles (motility) that push material through the intestine.

C. Based on the diagram, **summarize** the regulation of appetite by the microbiome and the elimination of waste by the host in terms of feedback loops and chemical signaling.

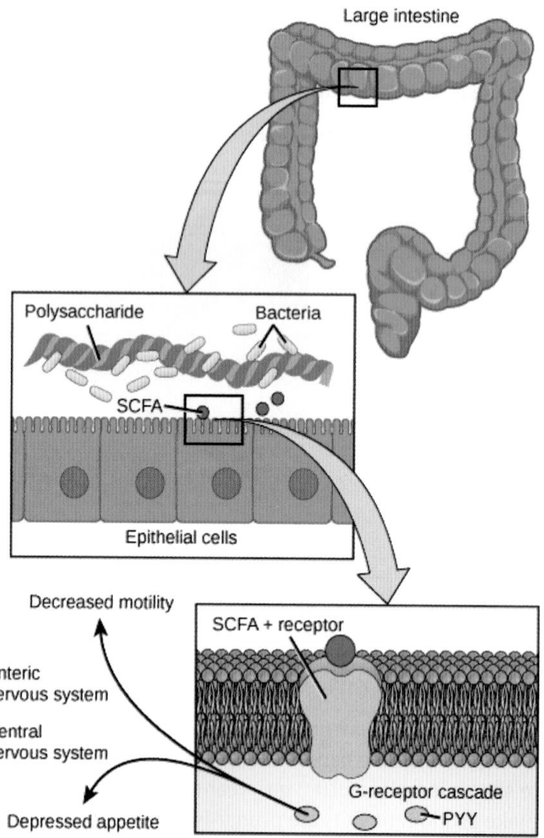

Figure 22.36

The microbial population of the intestine is referred to as the microbiome. Undernutrition and obesity are both symptoms of malnutrition, and populations of the microbiome vary with the type of malnutrition (Brown et al., *Nutr Clin Pract*, 2012). The microbiome of humans can be transplanted into germ-free (GF) mice to observe the effects of diet in a controlled experiment of relatively short duration. The microbiomes of healthy and undernourished 6-month-old children were transplanted into GF mice whose growth is graphed below. Growth in both length and weight were reduced when the source of the microbiome was the undernourished child (after Blanton et al., *Science*, 2016). Both groups of mice were provided with the same nutritional resources.

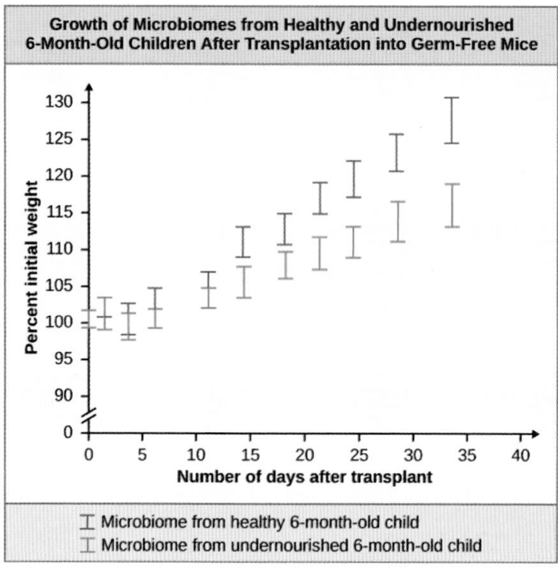

Figure 22.37

D. **Pose** two scientific **questions** that, when investigated, could lead to a solution for the stunting of growth caused by undernourishment in early infancy that affects millions of children.

Human growth hormone stimulates the release of insulin-like growth factor 1 (IGF-1). IGF-1 is a messenger that activates the production of bone cells called osteocytes. The data (after Schwarzer et al., *Science*, 2016) show concentrations of this growth factor in mice with no microbiome (GF), wild-type mice whose microbiome and growth provide a control (WT), and mice whose microbiome population is composed entirely of *Lactobacillus plantarum* (two strains labeled L1 and L2). *Lactobacillus* is one of many hundred genera of microbial inhabitants of a healthy human intestine.

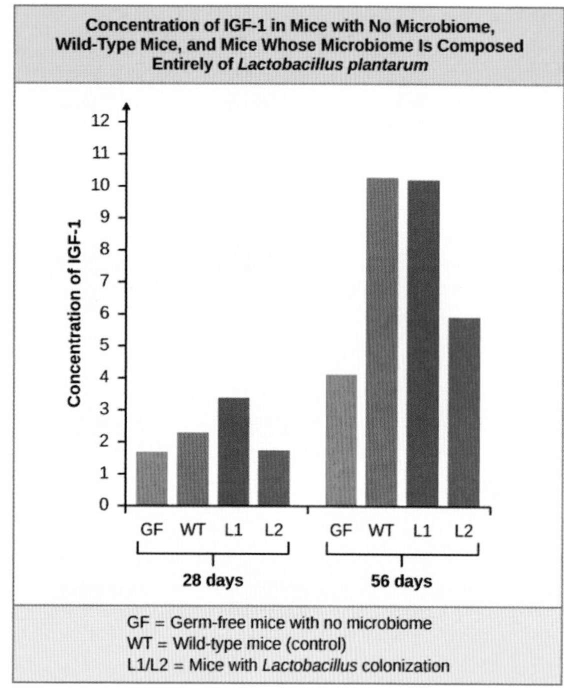

Figure 22.38

E. **Analyze** these data in terms of the potential for disruption of human bone growth due to loss or reduction in diversity of the microbiome.

23 | PLANT FORM AND PHYSIOLOGY

Figure 23.1 A locust leaf consists of leaflets arrayed along a central midrib. Each leaflet is a complex photosynthetic machine, exquisitely adapted to capture sunlight and carbon dioxide. An intricate vascular system supplies the leaf with water and minerals, and exports the products of photosynthesis. (credit: modification of work by Todd Petit)

Chapter Outline

Introduction

Plants are as essential to human existence as land, water, and air. Without plants, our day-to-day lives would be impossible because without oxygen from photosynthesis, aerobic life cannot be sustained. From providing food and shelter to serving as a source of medicines, oils, perfumes, and industrial products, plants provide humans with numerous valuable resources.

When you think of plants, those that first come to mind are likely to be vascular plants. These plants have tissues that conduct food and water (the word "vascular" means "having vessels"). While each vascular plant species is unique, all are made up of a plant body consisting of stems, roots, and leaves. They also all transport water, minerals, and sugars produced through photosynthesis through the plant body using the same mechanism, and they all respond to environmental factors, such as light, gravity, competition, temperature, and predation. Scientists recently discovered that two plants, the giant goldenrod and spicebush, each make five different compounds that disrupt the life cycles of insect pests. Further investigation into the chemicals could lead to a new class of pesticides.[1] You can read more about it in ScienceNews magazine (http://openstaxcollege.org/l/32pest) .

1. Seok-Hee Lee, Hyun-Woo Oh, Ying Fang, Saes-Byeol An, Doo-Sang Park, Hyuk-Hwan Song, Sei-Ryang Oh, Soo-Young Kim, Seonghyun Kim, Namjung Kim, Alexander S. Raikhel, Yeon Ho Je, and Sang Woon Shin. "Identification of Plant Compounds that Disrupt the Insect Juvenile Hormone Receptor Complex." PNAS 112.6 (2015) : 1733–1738; published ahead of print January 26, 2015, doi: 10.1073/pnas.1424386112

23.1 | The Plant Body

In this section, you will explore the following questions:

- What are differences between the shoot organ system and the root organ system?
- What are differences between meristematic tissues and permanent tissues?
- What are the three regions where plant growth occurs?
- What are the role of dermal tissues, vascular tissues, and ground tissues?
- What is the difference between simple plant tissues and complex plant tissues?

Connection for AP® Courses

Much of the content in this chapter is not within the scope of AP®, including information about the different kinds of tissues that comprise the plant body. However, the evolution of vascular tissue made possible the transition of plants from aquatic to terrestrial environments. Xylem and phloem transport water, minerals, and sugars produced through photosynthesis through the plant body (see the **Transport of Water and Solutes in Plants** module). In addition all plant species respond to environmental factors, such as light, gravity, competition, temperature, and predation (see the **Plant Sensory Systems and Reponses** module). Like animals, plants contain cells with organelles, in which specific metabolic activities occur, and specialized tissues and organs. Unlike animals, plant use energy from sunlight to synthesize sugars during photosynthesis—creating the food that supports life on this planet. Without plants, life on Earth could not exist.

With the exception of vascular tissue—which we will explore in detail in the **Transport of Water and Solutes in Plants** module—information presented in this section, and the examples highlighted, does *not* align to the content and AP® Learning Objectives outlined in the AP® Curriculum Framework.

The Science Practice Challenge Questions contain additional test questions for this section that will help you prepare for the AP exam. These questions address the following standards:
[APLO 2.3][APLO 2.4][APLO 2.28][APLO 4.15][APLO 4.14][APLO 4.21]

Like eukaryotes, plants contain cells with organelles in which specific metabolic activities take place. Unlike animals, however, plants use energy from sunlight to form sugars during photosynthesis. In addition, plant cells have cell walls, plastids, and a large central vacuole: structures that are not found in animal cells. Each of these cellular structures plays a specific role in plant structure and function.

Watch **Botany Without Borders (http://openstaxcollege.org/l/botany_wo_bord)** , a video produced by the Botanical Society of America about the importance of plants.

When the link opens to the page “Botany Without Borders” click on the menu item, “Plants Are Cool Too!” View the videoAngiosperms: The Secrets of Flowers, by Botanical Society of America (BSA) member Kate March, and answer the question below.Which group of plants dominates the landscape on Earth?

a. conifers

b. mosses

c. ferns

d. flowering plants

Plant Organ Systems

In plants, just as in animals, similar cells working together form a tissue. When different types of tissues work together to perform a unique function, they form an organ; organs working together form organ systems. Vascular plants have two distinct organ systems: a shoot system, and a root system. The **shoot system** consists of two portions: the vegetative (non-reproductive) parts of the plant, such as the leaves and the stems, and the reproductive parts of the plant, which include flowers and fruits. The shoot system generally grows above ground, where it absorbs the light needed for photosynthesis. The **root system**, which supports the plants and absorbs water and minerals, is usually underground. Figure 23.2 shows the organ systems of a typical plant.

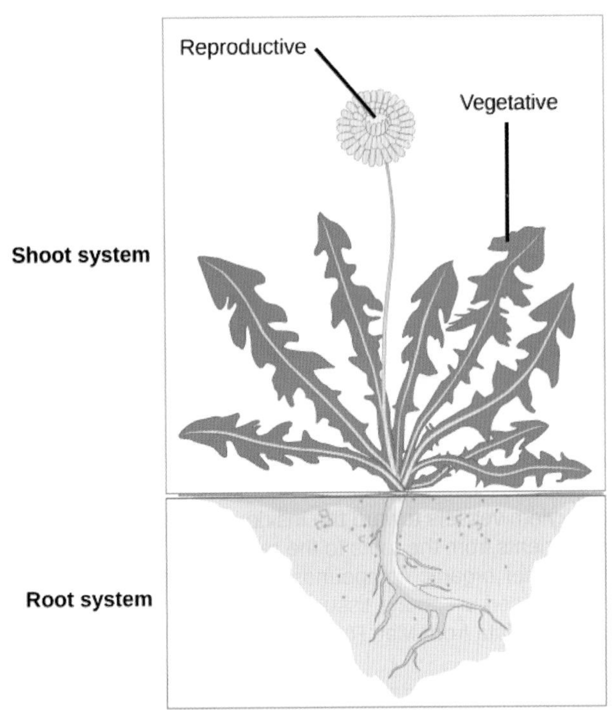

Figure 23.2 The shoot system of a plant consists of leaves, stems, flowers, and fruits. The root system anchors the plant while absorbing water and minerals from the soil.

Plant Tissues

Plants are multicellular eukaryotes with tissue systems made of various cell types that carry out specific functions. Plant tissue systems fall into one of two general types: meristematic tissue, and permanent (or non-meristematic) tissue. Cells of the meristematic tissue are found in **meristems**, which are plant regions of continuous cell division and growth. **Meristematic tissue** cells are either undifferentiated or incompletely differentiated, and they continue to divide and contribute to the growth of the plant. In contrast, **permanent tissue** consists of plant cells that are no longer actively dividing.

Meristematic tissues consist of three types, based on their location in the plant. **Apical meristems** contain meristematic tissue located at the tips of stems and roots, which enable a plant to extend in length. **Lateral meristems** facilitate growth in thickness or girth in a maturing plant. **Intercalary meristems** occur only in monocots, at the bases of leaf blades and at nodes (the areas where leaves attach to a stem). This tissue enables the monocot leaf blade to increase in length from the leaf base; for example, it allows lawn grass leaves to elongate even after repeated mowing.

Meristems produce cells that quickly differentiate, or specialize, and become permanent tissue. Such cells take on specific roles and lose their ability to divide further. They differentiate into three main types: dermal, vascular, and ground tissue. **Dermal tissue** covers and protects the plant, and **vascular tissue** transports water, minerals, and sugars to different parts of the plant. **Ground tissue** serves as a site for photosynthesis, provides a supporting matrix for the vascular tissue, and helps to store water and sugars.

Secondary tissues are either simple (composed of similar cell types) or complex (composed of different cell types). Dermal tissue, for example, is a simple tissue that covers the outer surface of the plant and controls gas exchange. Vascular tissue is an example of a complex tissue, and is made of two specialized conducting tissues: xylem and phloem. Xylem tissue transports water and nutrients from the roots to different parts of the plant, and includes three different cell types: vessel elements and tracheids (both of which conduct water), and xylem parenchyma. Phloem tissue, which transports organic compounds from the site of photosynthesis to other parts of the plant, consists of four different cell types: sieve cells (which conduct photosynthates), companion cells, phloem parenchyma, and phloem fibers. Unlike xylem conducting cells, phloem conducting cells are alive at maturity. The xylem and phloem always lie adjacent to each other (Figure 23.3). In stems, the xylem and the phloem form a structure called a **vascular bundle**; in roots, this is termed the **vascular stele** or **vascular cylinder**.

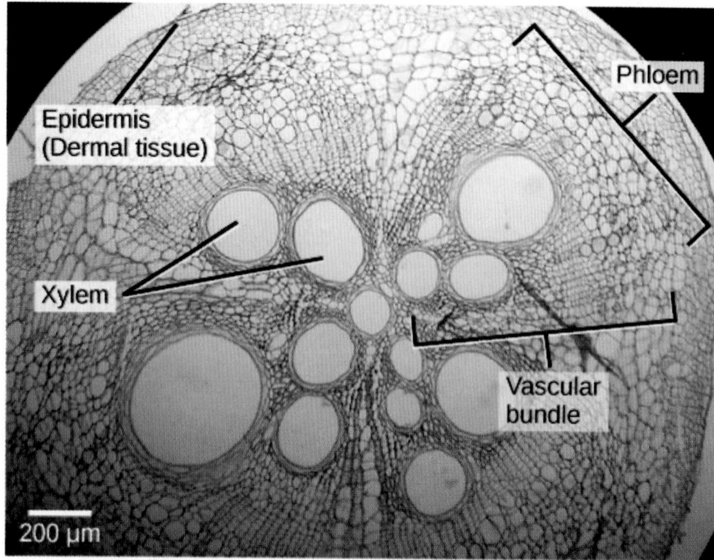

Figure 23.3 This light micrograph shows a cross section of a squash (*Curcurbita maxima*) stem. Each teardrop-shaped vascular bundle consists of large xylem vessels toward the inside and smaller phloem cells toward the outside. Xylem cells, which transport water and nutrients from the roots to the rest of the plant, are dead at functional maturity. Phloem cells, which transport sugars and other organic compounds from photosynthetic tissue to the rest of the plant, are living. The vascular bundles are encased in ground tissue and surrounded by dermal tissue. (credit: modification of work by "(biophotos)"/Flickr; scale-bar data from Matt Russell)

23.2 | Stems

In this section, you will explore the following questions:

- What is the main function and basic structure of a plant stem?
- What are the roles of dermal tissues, vascular tissues, and ground tissues?
- What is the difference between primary growth and secondary growth in stems?
- What is the origin of annual rings in stems? How are annual rings used to approximate the age of a tree?
- What are examples of modified stems?

Connection for AP® Courses

Much content described in this section is not within the scope of AP®. You are not required to memorize the different types of tissues that comprise the plant stem. However, in the Transport of Water and Solutes in Plants module we will explore in detail the roles vascular tissues (xylem and phloem), epidermal guard cells, **stomata**, and trichomes play in **transpiration**, the uptake of carbon dioxide and the release of oxygen and water vapor. **Trichomes**—hair-like structures on the epidermal surface—also defend leaves against predation (see the Plant Sensory Systems and Reponses module).

Except for the concepts described in the AP® Connection, information presented in this module, and the examples highlighted, does *not* align to the content and AP® Learning Objectives outlined in the AP® Curriculum Framework.

Stems are a part of the shoot system of a plant. They may range in length from a few millimeters to hundreds of meters, and also vary in diameter, depending on the plant type. Stems are usually above ground, although the stems of some plants, such as the potato, also grow underground. Stems may be herbaceous (soft) or woody in nature. Their main function is to provide support to the plant, holding leaves, flowers and buds; in some cases, stems also store food for the plant. A stem may be unbranched, like that of a palm tree, or it may be highly branched, like that of a magnolia tree. The stem of the plant connects the roots to the leaves, helping to transport absorbed water and minerals to different parts of the plant. It also helps to transport the products of photosynthesis, namely sugars, from the leaves to the rest of the plant.

Plant stems, whether above or below ground, are characterized by the presence of nodes and internodes (Figure 23.4). **Nodes** are points of attachment for leaves, aerial roots, and flowers. The stem region between two nodes is called an **internode**. The stalk that extends from the stem to the base of the leaf is the petiole. An **axillary bud** is usually found in the axil—the area between the base of a leaf and the stem—where it can give rise to a branch or a flower. The apex (tip) of the shoot contains the apical meristem within the **apical bud**.

Figure 23.4 Leaves are attached to the plant stem at areas called nodes. An internode is the stem region between two nodes. The petiole is the stalk connecting the leaf to the stem. The leaves just above the nodes arose from axillary buds.

Stem Anatomy

The stem and other plant organs arise from the ground tissue, and are primarily made up of simple tissues formed from three types of cells: parenchyma, collenchyma, and sclerenchyma cells.

Parenchyma cells are the most common plant cells (Figure 23.5). They are found in the stem, the root, the inside of the leaf, and the pulp of the fruit. Parenchyma cells are responsible for metabolic functions, such as photosynthesis, and they help repair and heal wounds. Some parenchyma cells also store starch.

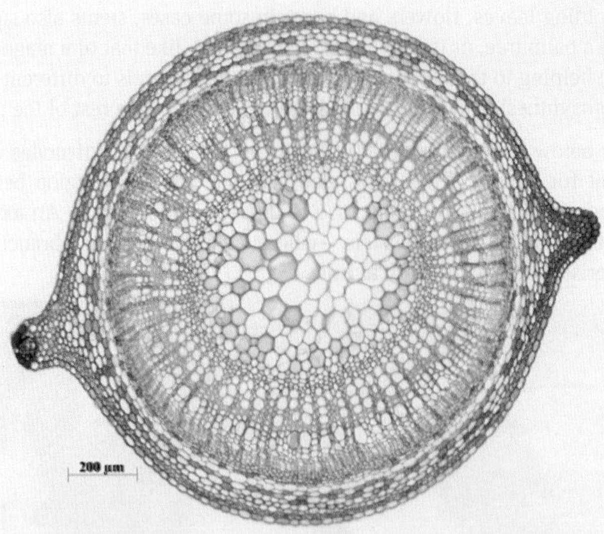

Figure 23.5 The stem of common St John's Wort (*Hypericum perforatum*) is shown in cross section in this light micrograph. The central pith (greenish-blue, in the center) and peripheral cortex (narrow zone 3–5 cells thick just inside the epidermis) are composed of parenchyma cells. Vascular tissue composed of xylem (red) and phloem tissue (green, between the xylem and cortex) surrounds the pith. (credit: Rolf-Dieter Mueller)

Collenchyma cells are elongated cells with unevenly thickened walls (Figure 23.6). They provide structural support, mainly to the stem and leaves. These cells are alive at maturity and are usually found below the epidermis. The "strings" of a celery stalk are an example of collenchyma cells.

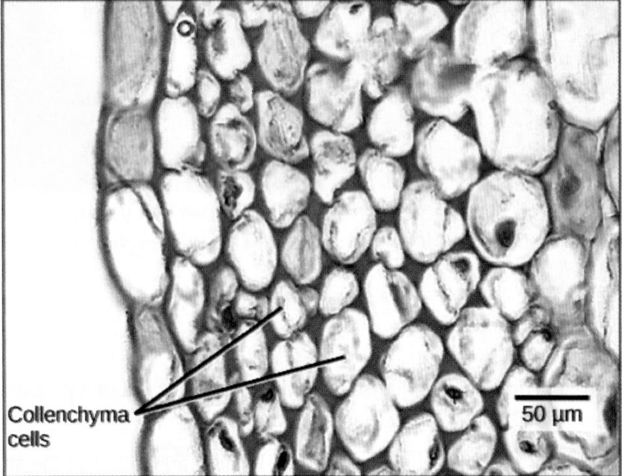

Figure 23.6 Collenchyma cell walls are uneven in thickness, as seen in this light micrograph. They provide support to plant structures. (credit: modification of work by Carl Szczerski; scale-bar data from Matt Russell)

Sclerenchyma cells also provide support to the plant, but unlike collenchyma cells, many of them are dead at maturity. There are two types of sclerenchyma cells: fibers and sclereids. Both types have secondary cell walls that are thickened with deposits of lignin, an organic compound that is a key component of wood. Fibers are long, slender cells; sclereids are smaller-sized. Sclereids give pears their gritty texture. Humans use sclerenchyma fibers to make linen and rope (Figure 23.7).

visual CONNECTION

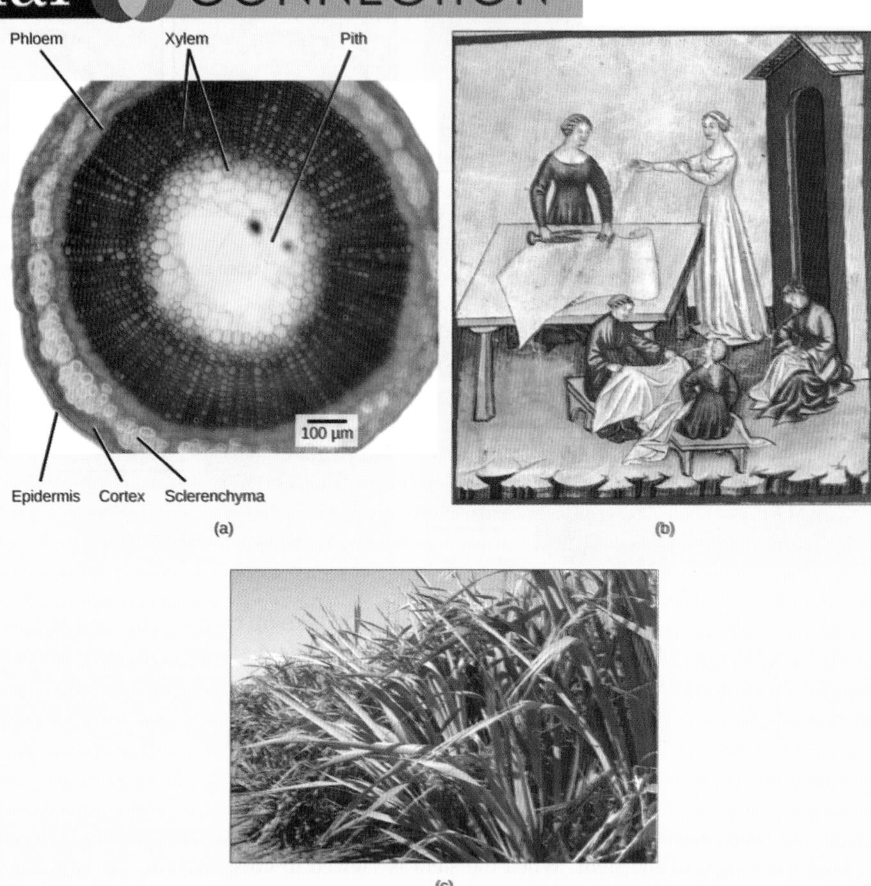

Figure 23.7 The central pith and outer cortex of the (a) flax stem are made up of parenchyma cells. Inside the cortex is a layer of sclerenchyma cells, which make up the fibers in flax rope and clothing. Humans have grown and harvested flax for thousands of years. In (b) this drawing, fourteenth-century women prepare linen. The (c) flax plant is grown and harvested for its fibers, which are used to weave linen, and for its seeds, which are the source of linseed oil. (credit a: modification of work by Emmanuel Boutet based on original work by Ryan R. MacKenzie; credit c: modification of work by Brian Dearth; scale-bar data from Matt Russell)

Students are examining stem cross-sections under the microscope and sketching their observations. As they are labeling the different tissues, they realize that they labeled different parts of the stem as parenchyma. Which part of the stem is made of parenchyma cells?

a. The cortex and pith are made of parenchyma cells.
b. The companion cells of the phloem are parenchyma cells.
c. Fiber cells of the sclerenchyma
d. Sieve elements and tracheids of the xylem

Like the rest of the plant, the stem has three tissue systems: dermal, vascular, and ground tissue. Each is distinguished by characteristic cell types that perform specific tasks necessary for the plant's growth and survival.

Dermal Tissue

The dermal tissue of the stem consists primarily of **epidermis**, a single layer of cells covering and protecting the underlying tissue. Woody plants have a tough, waterproof outer layer of cork cells commonly known as **bark**, which further protects the plant from damage. Epidermal cells are the most numerous and least differentiated of the cells in the epidermis. The epidermis of a leaf also contains openings known as stomata, through which the exchange of gases takes place (**Figure**

23.8). Two cells, known as **guard cells**, surround each leaf stoma, controlling its opening and closing and thus regulating the uptake of carbon dioxide and the release of oxygen and water vapor. Trichomes are hair-like structures on the epidermal surface. They help to reduce transpiration (the loss of water by aboveground plant parts), increase solar reflectance, and store compounds that defend the leaves against predation by herbivores.

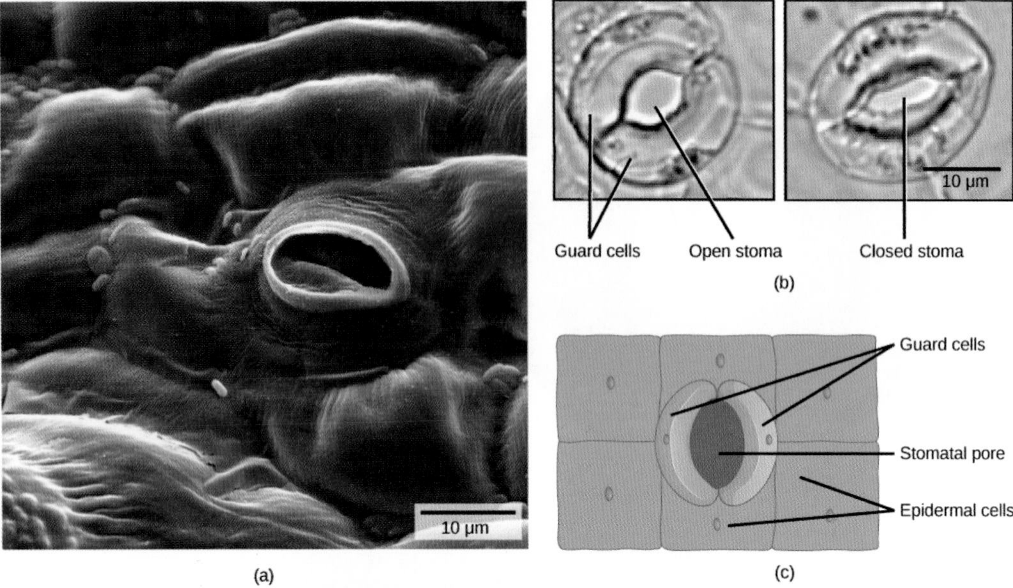

Figure 23.8 Openings called stomata (singular: stoma) allow a plant to take up carbon dioxide and release oxygen and water vapor. The (a) colorized scanning-electron micrograph shows a closed stoma of a dicot. Each stoma is flanked by two guard cells that regulate its (b) opening and closing. The (c) guard cells sit within the layer of epidermal cells (credit a: modification of work by Louisa Howard, Rippel Electron Microscope Facility, Dartmouth College; credit b: modification of work by June Kwak, University of Maryland; scale-bar data from Matt Russell)

Vascular Tissue

The xylem and phloem that make up the vascular tissue of the stem are arranged in distinct strands called vascular bundles, which run up and down the length of the stem. When the stem is viewed in cross section, the vascular bundles of dicot stems are arranged in a ring. In plants with stems that live for more than one year, the individual bundles grow together and produce the characteristic growth rings. In monocot stems, the vascular bundles are randomly scattered throughout the ground tissue (Figure 23.9).

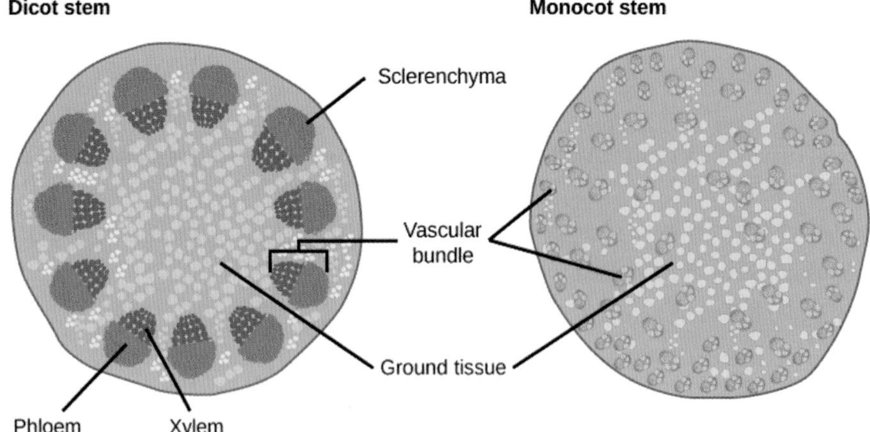

Figure 23.9 In (a) dicot stems, vascular bundles are arranged around the periphery of the ground tissue. The xylem tissue is located toward the interior of the vascular bundle, and phloem is located toward the exterior. Sclerenchyma fibers cap the vascular bundles. In (b) monocot stems, vascular bundles composed of xylem and phloem tissues are scattered throughout the ground tissue.

Xylem tissue has three types of cells: xylem parenchyma, tracheids, and vessel elements. The latter two types conduct water and are dead at maturity. **Tracheids** are xylem cells with thick secondary cell walls that are lignified. Water moves from one tracheid to another through regions on the side walls known as pits, where secondary walls are absent. **Vessel elements** are xylem cells with thinner walls; they are shorter than tracheids. Each vessel element is connected to the next by means of a perforation plate at the end walls of the element. Water moves through the perforation plates to travel up the plant.

Phloem tissue is composed of sieve-tube cells, companion cells, phloem parenchyma, and phloem fibers. A series of **sieve-tube cells** (also called sieve-tube elements) are arranged end to end to make up a long sieve tube, which transports organic substances such as sugars and amino acids. The sugars flow from one sieve-tube cell to the next through perforated sieve plates, which are found at the end junctions between two cells. Although still alive at maturity, the nucleus and other cell components of the sieve-tube cells have disintegrated. **Companion cells** are found alongside the sieve-tube cells, providing them with metabolic support. The companion cells contain more ribosomes and mitochondria than the sieve-tube cells, which lack some cellular organelles.

Ground Tissue

Ground tissue is mostly made up of parenchyma cells, but may also contain collenchyma and sclerenchyma cells that help support the stem. The ground tissue towards the interior of the vascular tissue in a stem or root is known as **pith**, while the layer of tissue between the vascular tissue and the epidermis is known as the **cortex**.

Growth in Stems

Growth in plants occurs as the stems and roots lengthen. Some plants, especially those that are woody, also increase in thickness during their life span. The increase in length of the shoot and the root is referred to as **primary growth**, and is the result of cell division in the shoot apical meristem. **Secondary growth** is characterized by an increase in thickness or girth of the plant, and is caused by cell division in the lateral meristem. Figure 23.10 shows the areas of primary and secondary growth in a plant. Herbaceous plants mostly undergo primary growth, with hardly any secondary growth or increase in thickness. Secondary growth or "wood" is noticeable in woody plants; it occurs in some dicots, but occurs very rarely in monocots.

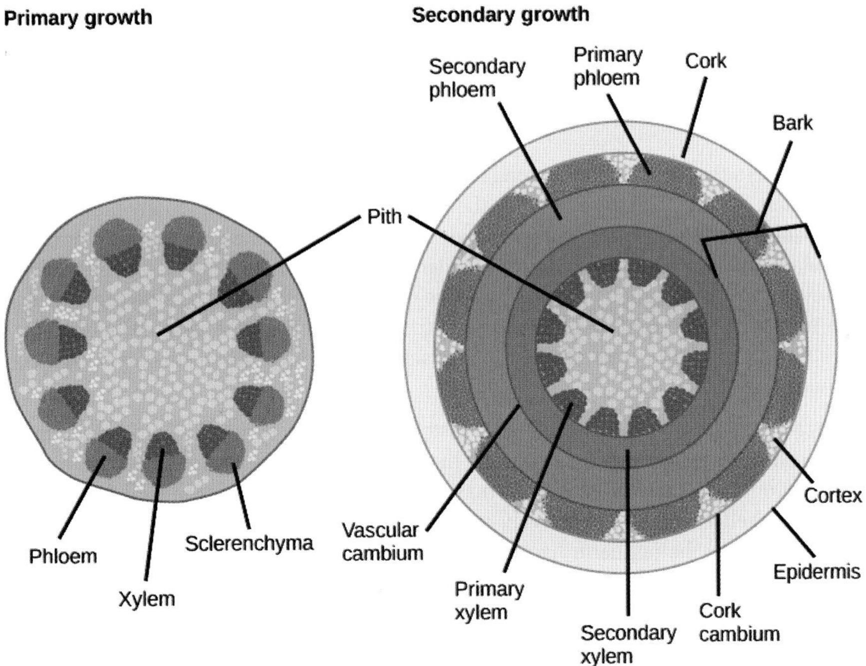

Figure 23.10 In woody plants, primary growth is followed by secondary growth, which allows the plant stem to increase in thickness or girth. Secondary vascular tissue is added as the plant grows, as well as a cork layer. The bark of a tree extends from the vascular cambium to the epidermis.

Some plant parts, such as stems and roots, continue to grow throughout a plant's life: a phenomenon called indeterminate growth. Other plant parts, such as leaves and flowers, exhibit determinate growth, which ceases when a plant part reaches a particular size.

Primary Growth

Most primary growth occurs at the apices, or tips, of stems and roots. Primary growth is a result of rapidly dividing cells in the apical meristems at the shoot tip and root tip. Subsequent cell elongation also contributes to primary growth. The growth of shoots and roots during primary growth enables plants to continuously seek water (roots) or sunlight (shoots).

The influence of the apical bud on overall plant growth is known as apical dominance, which diminishes the growth of axillary buds that form along the sides of branches and stems. Most coniferous trees exhibit strong apical dominance, thus producing the typical conical Christmas tree shape. If the apical bud is removed, then the axillary buds will start forming lateral branches. Gardeners make use of this fact when they prune plants by cutting off the tops of branches, thus encouraging the axillary buds to grow out, giving the plant a bushy shape.

Watch this **BBC Nature video (http://openstaxcollege.org/l/motion_plants)** showing how time-lapse photography captures plant growth at high speed.

The video you watched showed time lapse photography of the growth of a stem. Which of these is a fast response in a plant that was not recorded in the video?

a. opening of a flower

b. tendrils looping around a support

c. growth of an apical bud

d. closing of leaflets on a lightly touched mimosa leaf

Secondary Growth

The increase in stem thickness that results from secondary growth is due to the activity of the lateral meristems, which are lacking in herbaceous plants. Lateral meristems include the vascular cambium and, in woody plants, the cork cambium (see **Figure 23.10**). The vascular cambium is located just outside the primary xylem and to the interior of the primary phloem. The cells of the vascular cambium divide and form secondary xylem (tracheids and vessel elements) to the inside, and secondary phloem (sieve elements and companion cells) to the outside. The thickening of the stem that occurs in secondary growth is due to the formation of secondary phloem and secondary xylem by the vascular cambium, plus the action of cork cambium, which forms the tough outermost layer of the stem. The cells of the secondary xylem contain lignin, which provides hardiness and strength.

In woody plants, cork cambium is the outermost lateral meristem. It produces cork cells (bark) containing a waxy substance known as suberin that can repel water. The bark protects the plant against physical damage and helps reduce water loss. The cork cambium also produces a layer of cells known as phelloderm, which grows inward from the cambium. The cork cambium, cork cells, and phelloderm are collectively termed the **periderm**. The periderm substitutes for the epidermis in mature plants. In some plants, the periderm has many openings, known as **lenticels**, which allow the interior cells to exchange gases with the outside atmosphere (**Figure 23.11**). This supplies oxygen to the living and metabolically active cells of the cortex, xylem and phloem.

Figure 23.11 Lenticels on the bark of this cherry tree enable the woody stem to exchange gases with the surrounding atmosphere. (credit: Roger Griffith)

Annual Rings

The activity of the vascular cambium gives rise to annual growth rings. During the spring growing season, cells of the secondary xylem have a large internal diameter and their primary cell walls are not extensively thickened. This is known as early wood, or spring wood. During the fall season, the secondary xylem develops thickened cell walls, forming late wood, or autumn wood, which is denser than early wood. This alternation of early and late wood is due largely to a seasonal decrease in the number of vessel elements and a seasonal increase in the number of tracheids. It results in the formation of an annual ring, which can be seen as a circular ring in the cross section of the stem (Figure 23.12). An examination of the number of annual rings and their nature (such as their size and cell wall thickness) can reveal the age of the tree and the prevailing climatic conditions during each season.

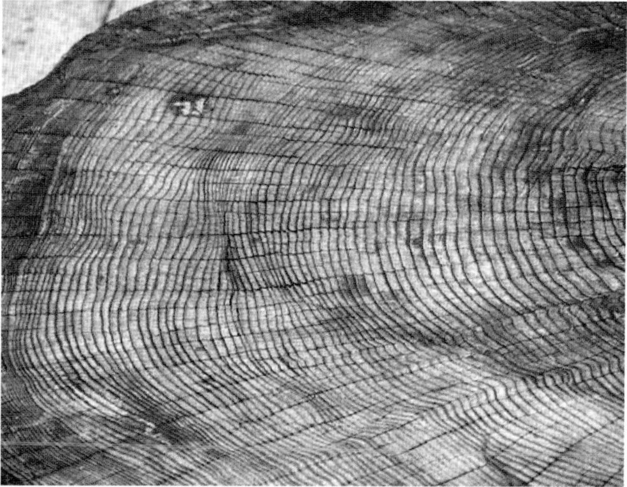

Figure 23.12 The rate of wood growth increases in summer and decreases in winter, producing a characteristic ring for each year of growth. Seasonal changes in weather patterns can also affect the growth rate—note how the rings vary in thickness. (credit: Adrian Pingstone)

Stem Modifications

Some plant species have modified stems that are especially suited to a particular habitat and environment (Figure 23.13). A **rhizome** is a modified stem that grows horizontally underground and has nodes and internodes. Vertical shoots may arise from the buds on the rhizome of some plants, such as ginger and ferns. **Corms** are similar to rhizomes, except they are more rounded and fleshy (such as in gladiolus). Corms contain stored food that enables some plants to survive the winter. **Stolons** are stems that run almost parallel to the ground, or just below the surface, and can give rise to new plants at the nodes. **Runners** are a type of stolon that runs above the ground and produces new clone plants at nodes at varying intervals: strawberries are an example. **Tubers** are modified stems that may store starch, as seen in the potato (*Solanum* sp.). Tubers arise as swollen ends of stolons, and contain many adventitious or unusual buds (familiar to us as the "eyes" on potatoes). A **bulb**, which functions as an underground storage unit, is a modification of a stem that has the appearance of enlarged fleshy leaves emerging from the stem or surrounding the base of the stem, as seen in the iris.

Figure 23.13 Stem modifications enable plants to thrive in a variety of environments. Shown are (a) ginger (*Zingiber officinale*) rhizomes, (b) a carrion flower (*Amorphophallus titanum*) corm (c) Rhodes grass (*Chloris gayana*) stolons, (d) strawberry (*Fragaria ananassa*) runners, (e) potato (*Solanum tuberosum*) tubers, and (f) red onion (*Allium*) bulbs. (credit a: modification of work by Maja Dumat; credit c: modification of work by Harry Rose; credit d: modification of work by Rebecca Siegel; credit e: modification of work by Scott Bauer, USDA ARS; credit f: modification of work by Stephen Ausmus, USDA ARS)

Watch botanist Wendy Hodgson, of Desert Botanical Garden in Phoenix, Arizona, explain how agave plants were cultivated for food hundreds of years ago in the Arizona desert in this **video: (http://openstaxcollege.org/l/ancient_crop)** *Finding the Roots of an Ancient Crop.*

Agave plants were cultivated for hundreds of years by Pre-Columbian American populations. The sap was considered a good source of _____.

a. sweetener for drinks and cooking

b. proteins to supplement the daily diet

c. lipids for cooking and baking

d. starch for thickening desserts and stews

Some aerial modifications of stems are tendrils and thorns (Figure 23.14). **Tendrils** are slender, twining strands that enable a plant (like a vine or pumpkin) to seek support by climbing on other surfaces. **Thorns** are modified branches appearing as sharp outgrowths that protect the plant; common examples include roses, Osage orange and devil's walking stick.

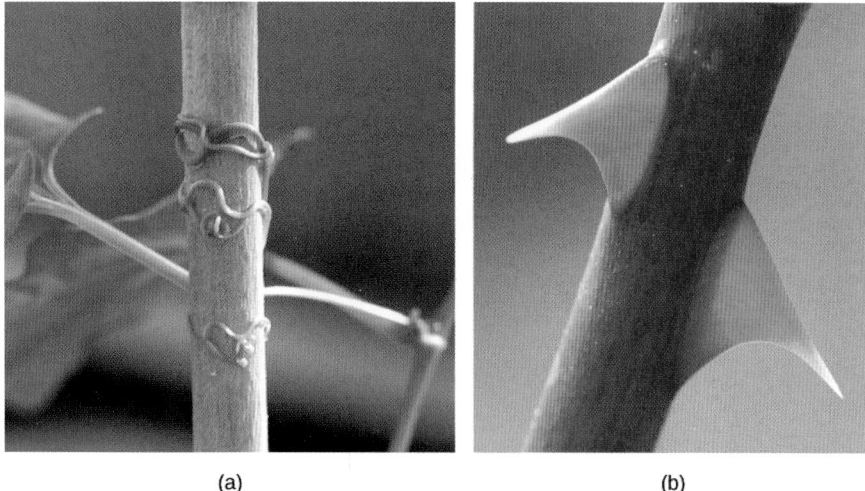

Figure 23.14 Found in southeastern United States, (a) buckwheat vine (*Brunnichia ovata*) is a weedy plant that climbs with the aid of tendrils. This one is shown climbing up a wooden stake. (b) Thorns are modified branches. (credit a: modification of work by Christopher Meloche, USDA ARS; credit b: modification of work by "macrophile"/Flickr)

23.3 | Roots

In this section, you will explore the following questions:

- What are the two types of root system?
- What are the three zones of the root tip and what is the role of each in root growth?
- What is the structure of the root?
- What are examples of modified roots?

Connection for AP® Courses

Much content described in this section, specifically root anatomy, is not within the scope of AP®. However, in the Transport of Water and Solutes in Plants module, we will explore the role of roots in absorbing water necessary for photosynthesis, transporting minerals and other nutrients, and storing carbohydrates.

When we explored mitosis in the Cell Reproduction chapter, you may have examined a root meristem under the microscope. The meristem is comprised of actively dividing cells. However, just like animal organs and organ systems, plant structures, including roots, interact to provide specific functions. For example, water is absorbed through the root system and travels upward through xylem to the leaves, where it is used in photosynthesis. (See the Transport of Water and Solutes in Plants module.)

With the exceptions described in the AP® Connection, information presented in this section, and the examples highlighted, does *not* align to the content and AP® Learning Objectives outlined in the AP® Curriculum Framework.

The roots of seed plants have three major functions: anchoring the plant to the soil, absorbing water and minerals and transporting them upwards, and storing the products of photosynthesis. Some roots are modified to absorb moisture and exchange gases. Most roots are underground. Some plants, however, also have **adventitious roots**, which emerge above the ground from the shoot.

Types of Root Systems

Root systems are mainly of two types (Figure 23.15). Dicots have a tap root system, while monocots have a fibrous root system. A **tap root system** has a main root that grows down vertically, and from which many smaller lateral roots arise. Dandelions are a good example; their tap roots usually break off when trying to pull these weeds, and they can regrow another shoot from the remaining root). A tap root system penetrates deep into the soil. In contrast, a **fibrous root system** is located closer to the soil surface, and forms a dense network of roots that also helps prevent soil erosion (lawn grasses are a good example, as are wheat, rice, and corn). Some plants have a combination of tap roots and fibrous roots. Plants that grow in dry areas often have deep root systems, whereas plants growing in areas with abundant water are likely to have shallower root systems.

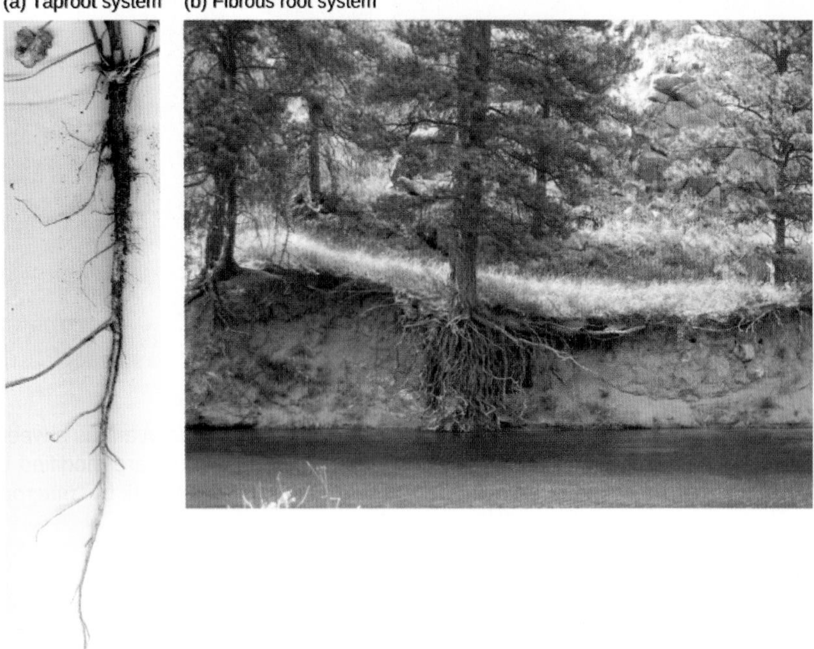

Figure 23.15 (a) Tap root systems have a main root that grows down, while (b) fibrous root systems consist of many small roots. (credit b: modification of work by "Austen Squarepants"/Flickr)

Root Growth and Anatomy

Root growth begins with seed germination. When the plant embryo emerges from the seed, the radicle of the embryo forms the root system. The tip of the root is protected by the **root cap**, a structure exclusive to roots and unlike any other plant structure. The root cap is continuously replaced because it gets damaged easily as the root pushes through soil. The root tip can be divided into three zones: a zone of cell division, a zone of elongation, and a zone of maturation and differentiation (Figure 23.16). The zone of cell division is closest to the root tip; it is made up of the actively dividing cells of the root meristem. The zone of elongation is where the newly formed cells increase in length, thereby lengthening the root. Beginning at the first root hair is the zone of cell maturation where the root cells begin to differentiate into special cell types. All three zones are in the first centimeter or so of the root tip.

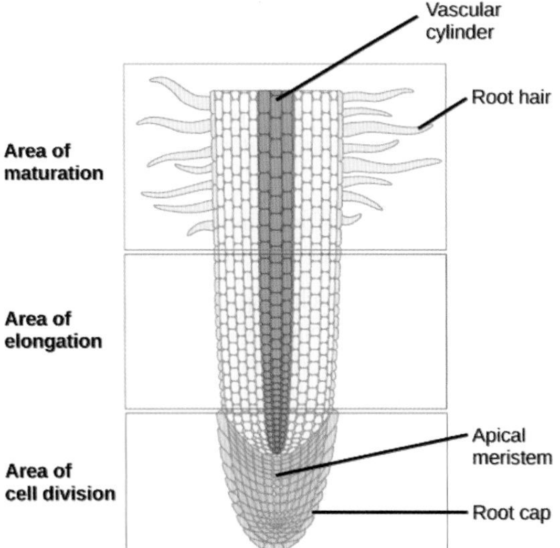

Figure 23.16 A longitudinal view of the root reveals the zones of cell division, elongation, and maturation. Cell division occurs in the apical meristem.

The root has an outer layer of cells called the epidermis, which surrounds areas of ground tissue and vascular tissue. The epidermis provides protection and helps in absorption. **Root hairs**, which are extensions of root epidermal cells, increase the surface area of the root, greatly contributing to the absorption of water and minerals.

Inside the root, the ground tissue forms two regions: the cortex and the pith (Figure 23.17). Compared to stems, roots have lots of cortex and little pith. Both regions include cells that store photosynthetic products. The cortex is between the epidermis and the vascular tissue, whereas the pith lies between the vascular tissue and the center of the root.

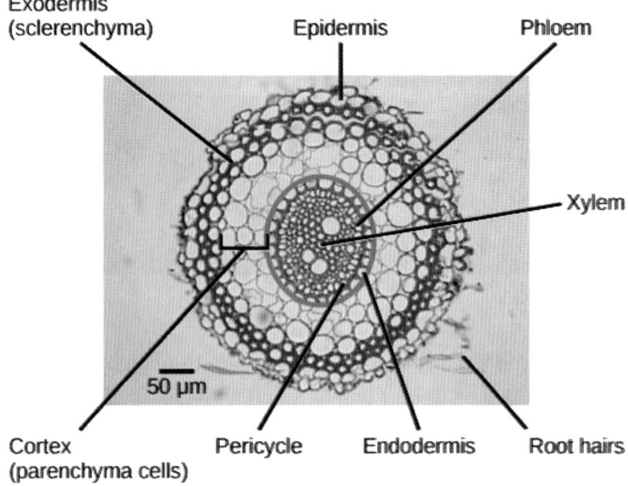

Figure 23.17 Staining reveals different cell types in this light micrograph of a wheat (*Triticum*) root cross section. Sclerenchyma cells of the exodermis and xylem cells stain red, and phloem cells stain blue. Other cell types stain black. The stele, or vascular tissue, is the area inside endodermis (indicated by a green ring). Root hairs are visible outside the epidermis. (credit: scale-bar data from Matt Russell)

The vascular tissue in the root is arranged in the inner portion of the root, which is called the **stele** (Figure 23.18). A layer of cells known as the **endodermis** separates the stele from the ground tissue in the outer portion of the root. The endodermis is exclusive to roots, and serves as a checkpoint for materials entering the root's vascular system. A waxy substance called suberin is present on the walls of the endodermal cells. This waxy region, known as the **Casparian strip**, forces water and solutes to cross the plasma membranes of endodermal cells instead of slipping between the cells. This ensures that only materials required by the root pass through the endodermis, while toxic substances and pathogens are generally excluded. The outermost cell layer of the root's vascular tissue is the **pericycle**, an area that can give rise to lateral roots. In dicot roots, the xylem and phloem of the stele are arranged alternately in an X shape, whereas in monocot roots, the vascular tissue is arranged in a ring around the pith.

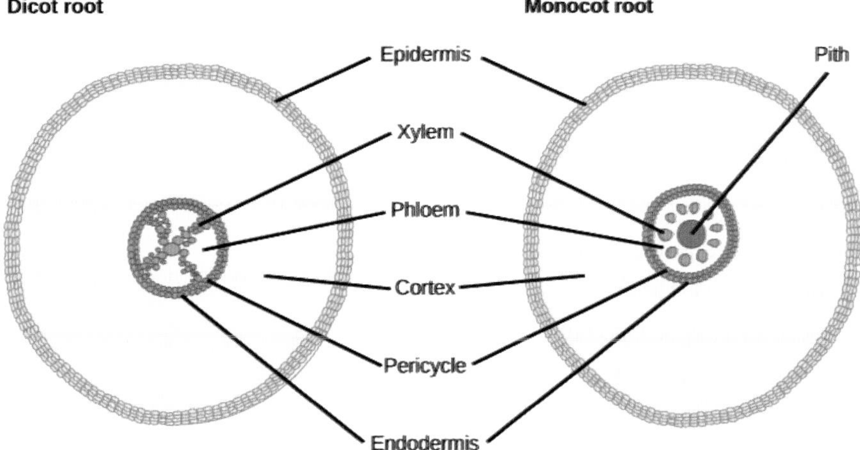

Figure 23.18 In (left) typical dicots, the vascular tissue forms an X shape in the center of the root. In (right) typical monocots, the phloem cells and the larger xylem cells form a characteristic ring around the central pith.

Root Modifications

Root structures may be modified for specific purposes. For example, some roots are bulbous and store starch. Aerial roots and prop roots are two forms of aboveground roots that provide additional support to anchor the plant. Tap roots, such as carrots, turnips, and beets, are examples of roots that are modified for food storage (Figure 23.19).

Figure 23.19 Many vegetables are modified roots.

Epiphytic roots enable a plant to grow on another plant. For example, the epiphytic roots of orchids develop a spongy tissue to absorb moisture. The banyan tree (*Ficus* sp.) begins as an epiphyte, germinating in the branches of a host tree; aerial roots develop from the branches and eventually reach the ground, providing additional support (Figure 23.20). In screwpine (*Pandanus* sp.), a palm-like tree that grows in sandy tropical soils, aboveground prop roots develop from the nodes to provide additional support.

Figure 23.20 The (a) banyan tree, also known as the strangler fig, begins life as an epiphyte in a host tree. Aerial roots extend to the ground and support the growing plant, which eventually strangles the host tree. The (b) screwpine develops aboveground roots that help support the plant in sandy soils. (credit a: modification of work by "psyberartist"/Flickr; credit b: modification of work by David Eikhoff)

23.4 | Leaves

In this section, you will explore the following questions:

- What are the parts of a typical leaf?
- What is the internal structure and function of a leaf?
- What are differences between simple leaves and compound leaves? Similarities?
- What are examples of modified leaves?

Connection for AP® Courses

Plants have specialized leaves adapted to their particular environments. For example, the leaves of plants growing in tropical rainforests have a larger surface area than cacti growing in the desert or in very cold conditions, whose smaller surface area minimizes water loss through transpiration. A waxy **cuticle** covers the surface of all plant species to reduce the rate of water loss from the leaf surface. Other leaves may have small hairs called trichomes on the leaf surface; not only do trichomes also help reduce water loss; they also protect the leaf from herbivory by restricting insect movements or by storing toxic or bad-tasting chemicals.

The information presented in this module does not align to the content and AP® Learning Objectives outlined in the AP® Curriculum Framework. The role of stomata, guard cells, and trichomes in transpiration are explored in the Transport of Water and Solutes in Plants module.

Leaves are the main sites for photosynthesis: the process by which plants synthesize food. Most leaves are usually green, due to the presence of chlorophyll in the leaf cells. However, some leaves may have different colors, caused by other plant pigments that mask the green chlorophyll.

The thickness, shape, and size of leaves are adapted to the environment. Each variation helps a plant species maximize its chances of survival in a particular habitat. Usually, the leaves of plants growing in tropical rainforests have larger surface areas than those of plants growing in deserts or very cold conditions, which are likely to have a smaller surface area to minimize water loss.

Structure of a Typical Leaf

Each leaf typically has a leaf blade called the **lamina**, which is also the widest part of the leaf. Some leaves are attached to the plant stem by a **petiole**. Leaves that do not have a petiole and are directly attached to the plant stem are called **sessile** leaves. Small green appendages usually found at the base of the petiole are known as **stipules**. Most leaves have a midrib, which travels the length of the leaf and branches to each side to produce veins of vascular tissue. The edge of the leaf is called the margin. Figure 23.21 shows the structure of a typical eudicot leaf.

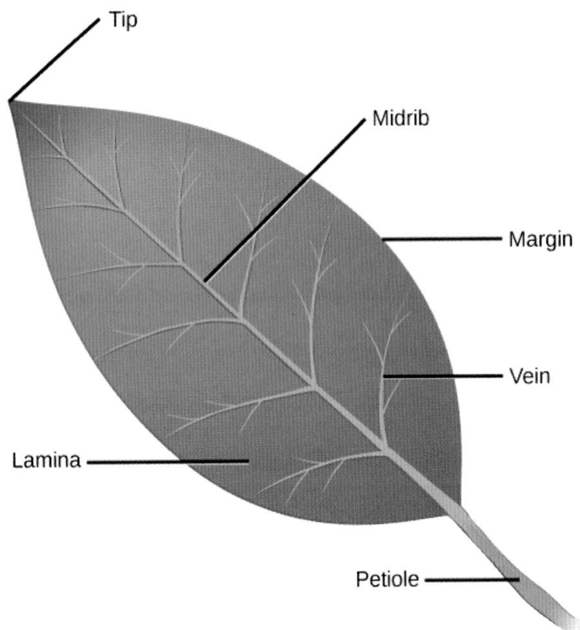

Figure 23.21 Deceptively simple in appearance, a leaf is a highly efficient structure.

Within each leaf, the vascular tissue forms veins. The arrangement of veins in a leaf is called the **venation** pattern. Monocots and dicots differ in their patterns of venation (Figure 23.22). Monocots have parallel venation; the veins run in straight lines across the length of the leaf without converging at a point. In dicots, however, the veins of the leaf have a net-like appearance, forming a pattern known as reticulate venation. One extant plant, the *Ginkgo biloba*, has dichotomous venation where the veins fork.

Figure 23.22 (a) Tulip (*Tulipa*), a monocot, has leaves with parallel venation. The netlike venation in this (b) linden (*Tilia cordata*) leaf distinguishes it as a dicot. The (c) *Ginkgo biloba* tree has dichotomous venation. (credit a photo: modification of work by "Drewboy64"/Wikimedia Commons; credit b photo: modification of work by Roger Griffith; credit c photo: modification of work by "geishaboy500"/Flickr; credit abc illustrations: modification of work by Agnieszka Kwiecień)

Leaf Arrangement

The arrangement of leaves on a stem is known as **phyllotaxy**. The number and placement of a plant's leaves will vary depending on the species, with each species exhibiting a characteristic leaf arrangement. Leaves are classified as either alternate, spiral, or opposite. Plants that have only one leaf per node have leaves that are said to be either alternate—meaning the leaves alternate on each side of the stem in a flat plane—or spiral, meaning the leaves are arrayed in a spiral along the stem. In an opposite leaf arrangement, two leaves arise at the same point, with the leaves connecting opposite each other along the branch. If there are three or more leaves connected at a node, the leaf arrangement is classified as **whorled**.

Leaf Form

Leaves may be simple or compound (Figure 23.23). In a **simple leaf**, the blade is either completely undivided—as in the banana leaf—or it has lobes, but the separation does not reach the midrib, as in the maple leaf. In a **compound leaf**, the leaf blade is completely divided, forming leaflets, as in the locust tree. Each leaflet may have its own stalk, but is attached to the rachis. A **palmately compound leaf** resembles the palm of a hand, with leaflets radiating outwards from one point Examples include the leaves of poison ivy, the buckeye tree, or the familiar houseplant *Schefflera* sp. (common name "umbrella plant"). **Pinnately compound leaves** take their name from their feather-like appearance; the leaflets are arranged along the midrib, as in rose leaves (*Rosa* sp.), or the leaves of hickory, pecan, ash, or walnut trees.

Figure 23.23 Leaves may be simple or compound. In simple leaves, the lamina is continuous. The (a) banana plant (*Musa* sp.) has simple leaves. In compound leaves, the lamina is separated into leaflets. Compound leaves may be palmate or pinnate. In (b) palmately compound leaves, such as those of the horse chestnut (*Aesculus hippocastanum*), the leaflets branch from the petiole. In (c) pinnately compound leaves, the leaflets branch from the midrib, as on a scrub hickory (*Carya floridana*). The (d) honey locust has double compound leaves, in which leaflets branch from the veins. (credit a: modification of work by "BazzaDaRambler"/Flickr; credit b: modification of work by Roberto Verzo; credit c: modification of work by Eric Dion; credit d: modification of work by Valerie Lykes)

Leaf Structure and Function

The outermost layer of the leaf is the epidermis; it is present on both sides of the leaf and is called the upper and lower epidermis, respectively. Botanists call the upper side the adaxial surface (or adaxis) and the lower side the abaxial surface (or abaxis). The epidermis helps in the regulation of gas exchange. It contains stomata (Figure 23.24): openings through which the exchange of gases takes place. Two guard cells surround each stoma, regulating its opening and closing.

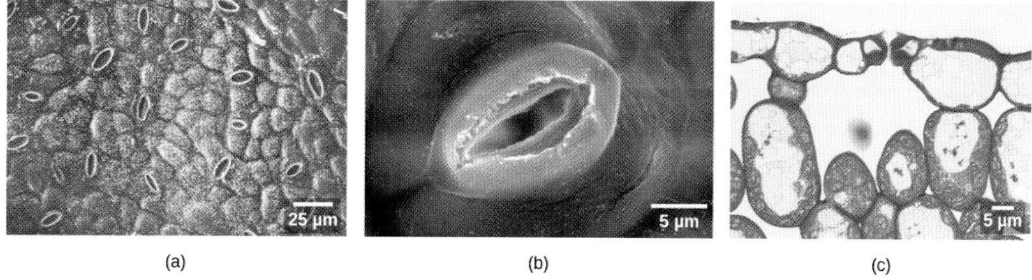

Figure 23.24 Visualized at 500x with a scanning electron microscope, several stomata are clearly visible on (a) the surface of this sumac (*Rhus glabra*) leaf. At 5,000x magnification, the guard cells of (b) a single stoma from lyre-leaved sand cress (*Arabidopsis lyrata)* have the appearance of lips that surround the opening. In this (c) light micrograph cross-section of an *A. lyrata* leaf, the guard cell pair is visible along with the large, sub-stomatal air space in the leaf. (credit: modification of work by Robert R. Wise; part c scale-bar data from Matt Russell)

The epidermis is usually one cell layer thick; however, in plants that grow in very hot or very cold conditions, the epidermis may be several layers thick to protect against excessive water loss from transpiration. A waxy layer known as the cuticle covers the leaves of all plant species. The cuticle reduces the rate of water loss from the leaf surface. Other leaves may have small hairs (trichomes) on the leaf surface. Trichomes help to deter herbivory by restricting insect movements, or by storing toxic or bad-tasting compounds; they can also reduce the rate of transpiration by blocking air flow across the leaf surface (Figure 23.25).

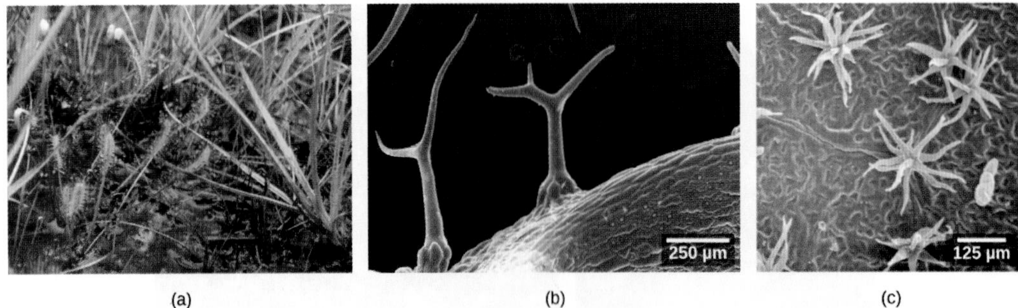

Figure 23.25 Trichomes give leaves a fuzzy appearance as in this (a) sundew (*Drosera* sp.). Leaf trichomes include (b) branched trichomes on the leaf of *Arabidopsis lyrata* and (c) multibranched trichomes on a mature *Quercus marilandica* leaf. (credit a: John Freeland; credit b, c: modification of work by Robert R. Wise; scale-bar data from Matt Russell)

Below the epidermis of dicot leaves are layers of cells known as the mesophyll, or "middle leaf." The mesophyll of most leaves typically contains two arrangements of parenchyma cells: the palisade parenchyma and spongy parenchyma (Figure 23.26). The palisade parenchyma (also called the palisade mesophyll) has column-shaped, tightly packed cells, and may be present in one, two, or three layers. Below the palisade parenchyma are loosely arranged cells of an irregular shape. These are the cells of the spongy parenchyma (or spongy mesophyll). The air space found between the spongy parenchyma cells allows gaseous exchange between the leaf and the outside atmosphere through the stomata. In aquatic plants, the intercellular spaces in the spongy parenchyma help the leaf float. Both layers of the mesophyll contain many chloroplasts. Guard cells are the only epidermal cells to contain chloroplasts.

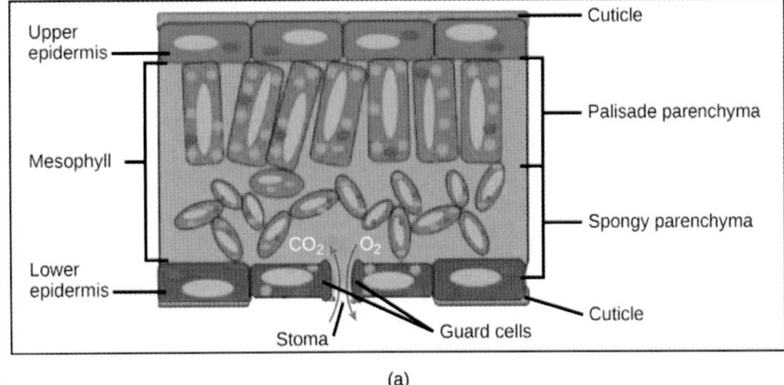

(a)

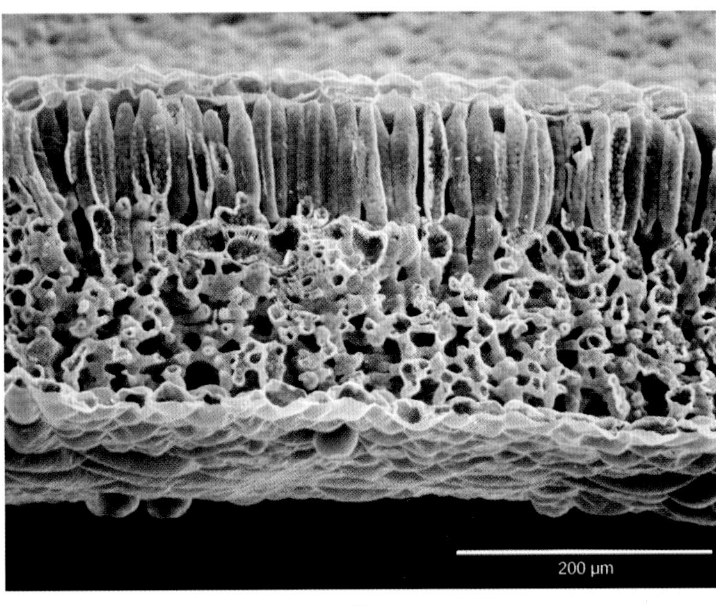

(b)

Figure 23.26 In the (a) leaf drawing, the central mesophyll is sandwiched between an upper and lower epidermis. The mesophyll has two layers: an upper palisade layer comprised of tightly packed, columnar cells, and a lower spongy layer, comprised of loosely packed, irregularly shaped cells. Stomata on the leaf underside allow gas exchange. A waxy cuticle covers all aerial surfaces of land plants to minimize water loss. These leaf layers are clearly visible in the (b) scanning electron micrograph. The numerous small bumps in the palisade parenchyma cells are chloroplasts. Chloroplasts are also present in the spongy parenchyma, but are not as obvious. The bumps protruding from the lower surface of the leave are glandular trichomes, which differ in structure from the stalked trichomes in Figure 23.25. (credit b: modification of work by Robert R. Wise)

Like the stem, the leaf contains vascular bundles composed of xylem and phloem (Figure 23.27). The xylem consists of tracheids and vessels, which transport water and minerals to the leaves. The phloem transports the photosynthetic products from the leaf to the other parts of the plant. A single vascular bundle, no matter how large or small, always contains both xylem and phloem tissues.

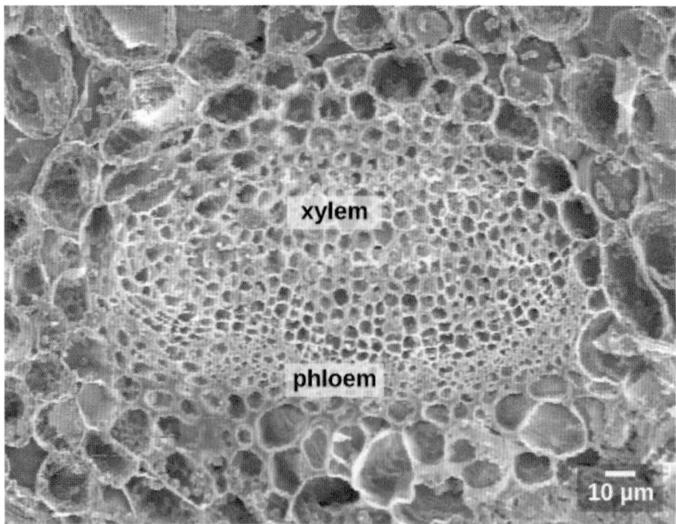

Figure 23.27 This scanning electron micrograph shows xylem and phloem in the leaf vascular bundle from the lyre-leaved sand cress (*Arabidopsis lyrata*). (credit: modification of work by Robert R. Wise; scale-bar data from Matt Russell)

Leaf Adaptations

Coniferous plant species that thrive in cold environments, like spruce, fir, and pine, have leaves that are reduced in size and needle-like in appearance. These needle-like leaves have sunken stomata and a smaller surface area: two attributes that aid in reducing water loss. In hot climates, plants such as cacti have leaves that are reduced to spines, which in combination with their succulent stems, help to conserve water. Many aquatic plants have leaves with wide lamina that can float on the surface of the water, and a thick waxy cuticle on the leaf surface that repels water.

Watch "The Pale Pitcher Plant" episode of the video (http://openstaxcollege.org/l/plants_cool_too) series *Plants Are Cool, Too*, a Botanical Society of America video about a carnivorous plant species found in Louisiana.

How do pale pitcher plants (Sarracinia alata) make sure that insects do not escape after consuming the nectar that attracted them?

a. The insects are skewered on spikes and thorns that rim the funnel-shaped leaf.

b. The insects ingest narcotics secreted by the leaf and fall into the funnel-shaped leaf.

c. The insects are poisoned by lethal compounds in the nectar.

d. The insects are immobilized by sticky substances on the rim of the funnel-shaped leaf.

Plant Adaptations in Resource-Deficient Environments

Roots, stems, and leaves are structured to ensure that a plant can obtain the required sunlight, water, soil nutrients, and oxygen resources. Some remarkable adaptations have evolved to enable plant species to thrive in less than ideal habitats, where one or more of these resources is in short supply.

In tropical rainforests, light is often scarce, since many trees and plants grow close together and block much of the sunlight from reaching the forest floor. Many tropical plant species have exceptionally broad leaves to maximize the capture of sunlight. Other species are epiphytes: plants that grow on other plants that serve as a physical support. Such plants are able to grow high up in the canopy atop the branches of other trees, where sunlight is more plentiful. Epiphytes live on rain and minerals collected in the branches and leaves of the supporting plant. Bromeliads (members of the pineapple family), ferns, and orchids are examples of tropical epiphytes (Figure 23.28). Many epiphytes have specialized tissues that enable them to efficiently capture and store water.

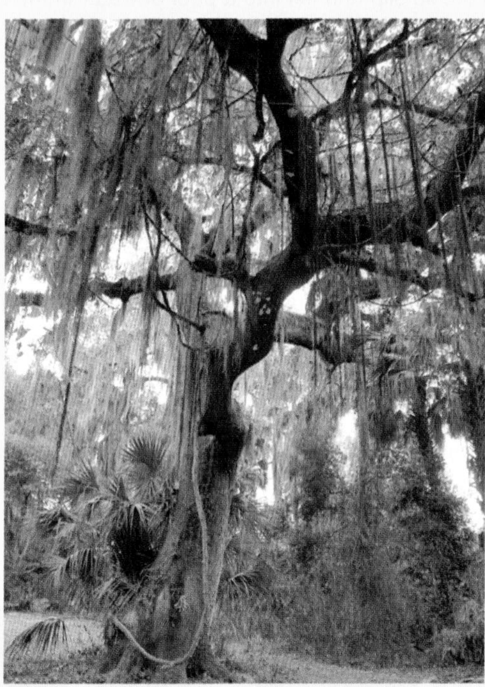

Figure 23.28 One of the most well known bromeliads is Spanish moss (*Tillandsia usneoides*), seen here in an oak tree. (credit: Kristine Paulus)

Some plants have special adaptations that help them to survive in nutrient-poor environments. Carnivorous plants, such as the Venus flytrap and the pitcher plant (Figure 23.29), grow in bogs where the soil is low in nitrogen. In these plants, leaves are modified to capture insects. The insect-capturing leaves may have evolved to provide these plants with a supplementary source of much-needed nitrogen.

Figure 23.29 The (a) Venus flytrap has modified leaves that can capture insects. When an unlucky insect touches the trigger hairs inside the leaf, the trap suddenly closes. The opening of the (b) pitcher plant is lined with a slippery wax. Insects crawling on the lip slip and fall into a pool of water in the bottom of the pitcher, where they are digested by bacteria. The plant then absorbs the smaller molecules. (credit a: modification of work by Peter Shanks; credit b: modification of work by Tim Mansfield)

Many swamp plants have adaptations that enable them to thrive in wet areas, where their roots grow submerged underwater. In these aquatic areas, the soil is unstable and little oxygen is available to reach the roots. Trees such as mangroves (*Rhizophora* sp.) growing in coastal waters produce aboveground roots that help support the tree (Figure 23.30). Some species of mangroves, as well as cypress trees, have pneumatophores: upward-growing roots containing pores and pockets of tissue specialized for gas exchange. Wild rice is an aquatic plant with large air spaces in the root cortex. The air-filled tissue—called aerenchyma—provides a path for oxygen to diffuse down to the root tips, which are embedded in oxygen-poor bottom sediments.

How do pale pitcher plants (Sarracinia alata) make sure that insects do not escape after consuming the nectar that attracted them?

a. The insects are skewered on spikes and thorns that rim the funnel-shaped leaf.

b. The insects ingest narcotics secreted by the leaf and fall into the funnel-shaped leaf.

c. The insects are poisoned by lethal compounds in the nectar.

d. The insects are immobilized by sticky substances on the rim of the funnel-shaped leaf.

Figure 23.30 The branches of (a) mangrove trees develop aerial roots, which descend to the ground and help to anchor the trees. (b) Cypress trees and some mangrove species have upward-growing roots called pneumatophores that are involved in gas exchange. Aquatic plants such as (c) wild rice have large spaces in the root cortex called aerenchyma, visualized here using scanning electron microscopy. (credit a: modification of work by Roberto Verzo; credit b: modification of work by Duane Burdick; credit c: modification of work by Robert R. Wise)

Watch Venus Flytraps: Jaws of Death (http://openstaxcollege.org/l/venus_flytrap) , an extraordinary BBC close-up of the Venus flytrap in action.

Why do many ornamental plants that thrive indoors originate on the floor of tropical rainforest, where they grow under the canopy of trees?

a. Growing under the rainforest's canopy made these plants adapt to less water and nutrients.

b. With their narrow leaves, these plants are adapted to grow in low light.

c. With their broad leaves, these plants are adapted to grow in low light, like that usually found indoors.

d. Growing under the rainforest's canopy provides the plants with more water and nutrients, which they also need as indoor plants.

23.5 | Transport of Water and Solutes in Plants

In this section, you will explore the following questions:

- What is water potential, and how is it influenced by solutes, pressures, gravity, and the matric potential?
- How do water potential, evapotranspiration, and stomatal regulation influence how water is transported in plants?
- How are photosynthates transported in plants?

Connection for AP® Courses

Information in this section applies to concepts we explored in previous chapters by connecting them to the transport of water and solutes through a plant, showing ways that plants take up and transport materials. These concepts include the processes of photosynthesis and cellular respiration, the chemical and physical properties of water, and the coevolution of plants with mutualistic bacteria and fungi. The vascular system of terrestrial plants allows the efficient absorption and delivery of water through the cells that comprise xylem, whereas phloem delivers sugars produced in photosynthesis to all parts of the plant, including the roots for storage. The physical separation of xylem and phloem permits plants to move different nutrients simultaneously from roots to shoots and vice versa. Nearly all plants use related mechanisms of osmoregulation, and we will focus on the transport of water and other nutrients.

You likely remember the concept of **water potential** (Ψ) from our exploration of diffusion and osmosis in the chapter where we discuss the structure and function of plasma membranes. Water potential is a measure of the differences in potential energy between a water sample with solutes and pure water. Water moves via osmosis from an area of higher water potential (more water molecules, less solute) to an area of lower water potential (less water, more solutes). The water potential in plant solutions is influenced by solute concentration, pressure, gravity, and other factors (matrix effects). Water potential and transpiration influence how water is transported through the xylem.

Carbohydrates synthesized in photosynthesis, primarily sucrose, move from sources to sinks through the plant's phloem. Sucrose produced in the Calvin cycle is loaded into the sieve-tube elements of the phloem, and the increased solute concentration causes water to move by osmosis from the xylem into the phloem.

Information presented and the examples highlighted in the section support concepts outlined in Big Idea 2 and Big Idea 4 of the AP® Biology Curriculum Framework. The AP® Learning Objectives listed in the Curriculum Framework provide a transparent foundation for the AP® Biology course, an inquiry-based laboratory experience, instructional activities, and

AP® exam questions. A learning objective merges required content with one or more of the seven science practices.

Big Idea 2	Biological systems utilize free energy and molecular building blocks to grow, to reproduce, and to maintain dynamic homeostasis.
Enduring Understanding 2.A	Growth, reproduction and maintenance of living systems require free energy and matter.
Essential Knowledge	**2.A.3** Molecules and atoms from the environment are necessary to build new molecules; the movement of water in a plant depends on the properties of water.
Science Practice	**4.1:** The student can justify the selection of the kind of data needed to answer a particular scientific question.
Learning Objective	**2.8** The student is able to justify the selection of data regarding the types of molecules that an animal, plant or bacterium will take up as necessary building blocks and excrete as waste products.
Big Idea 2	Biological systems utilize free energy and molecular building blocks to grow, to reproduce, and to maintain dynamic homeostasis.
Enduring Understanding 2.A	Growth, reproduction and maintenance of living systems require free energy and matter.
Essential Knowledge	**2.A.3** Molecules and atoms from the environment are necessary to build new molecules; the movement of water in a plant depends on the properties of water.
Science Practice	**1.1:** The student can create representations and models of natural or man-made phenomena and systems in the domain.
Science Practice	**1.4:** The student can use representations and models to analyze situations or solve problems qualitatively and quantitatively.
Learning Objective	**2.9** The student is able to represent graphically or model quantitatively (or qualitatively) the exchange of molecules between an organism and its environment, and the subsequent use of these molecules to building new molecules that facilitate dynamic homeostasis, growth and reproduction.
Big Idea 4	Biological systems interact, and these systems and their interactions possess complex properties.
Enduring Understanding 4.A	Interactions within biological systems lead to complex properties.
Essential Knowledge	**4.A.4** Interactions and coordination between organs and organ systems provide essential biological activities.
Science Practice	**3.3:** The student can evaluate scientific questions.
Learning Objective	**4.8** The student is able to evaluate scientific questions concerning organisms that exhibit complex properties due to the interaction of their constituent parts.
Big Idea 4	Biological systems interact, and these systems and their interactions possess complex properties.
Enduring Understanding 4.A	Interactions within biological systems lead to complex properties.
Essential Knowledge	**4.A.4** Interactions and coordination between organs and organ systems provide essential biological activities.

Science Practice	**3.3:** The student can evaluate scientific questions.
Learning Objective	**4.9** The student is able to predict the effects of a change in the component(s) of a biological system on the functionality of an organism(s).
Big Idea 4	Biological systems interact, and these systems and their interactions possess complex properties.
Enduring Understanding 4.A	Interactions within biological systems lead to complex properties.
Essential Knowledge	**4.A.4** Interactions and coordination between organs and organ systems provide essential biological activities.
Science Practice	**1.3:** The student can refine representations and models of natural or man-made phenomena and systems in the domain.
Science Practice	**6.4:** The student can make claims and predictions about natural phenomena based on scientific theories and models.
Learning Objective	**4.10** The student is able to refine representations and models to illustrate biocomplexity due to interactions of the constituent parts.

The Practice Challenge Questions contain additional test questions for this section that will help you prepare for the AP exam. These questions address the following standards:
[APLO 2.40][APLO 4.12][APLO 2.1][APLO 2.8][APLO 2.9][APLO 2.41][APLO 1.2][APLO 1.22][APLO 1.25][APLO 2.19][APLO 2.32]

The structure of plant roots, stems, and leaves facilitates the transport of water, nutrients, and photosynthates throughout the plant. The phloem and xylem are the main tissues responsible for this movement. Water potential, evapotranspiration, and stomatal regulation influence how water and nutrients are transported in plants. To understand how these processes work, we must first understand the energetics of water potential.

Water Potential

Plants are phenomenal hydraulic engineers. Using only the basic laws of physics and the simple manipulation of potential energy, plants can move water to the top of a 116-meter-tall tree (Figure 23.31**a**). Plants can also use hydraulics to generate enough force to split rocks and buckle sidewalks (Figure 23.31**b**). Plants achieve this because of water potential.

(a)

(b)

Figure 23.31 With heights nearing 116 meters, (a) coastal redwoods (*Sequoia sempervirens*) are the tallest trees in the world. Plant roots can easily generate enough force to (b) buckle and break concrete sidewalks, much to the dismay of homeowners and city maintenance departments. (credit a: modification of work by Bernt Rostad; credit b: modification of work by Pedestrians Educating Drivers on Safety, Inc.)

Water potential is a measure of the potential energy in water. Plant physiologists are not interested in the energy in any one particular aqueous system, but are very interested in water movement between two systems. In practical terms, therefore, water potential is the difference in potential energy between a given water sample and pure water (at atmospheric pressure and ambient temperature). Water potential is denoted by the Greek letter Ψ (*psi*) and is expressed in units of pressure (pressure is a form of energy) called **megapascals** (MPa). The potential of pure water ($\Psi_w^{\text{pure H2O}}$) is, by convenience of definition, designated a value of zero (even though pure water contains plenty of potential energy, that energy is ignored). Water potential values for the water in a plant root, stem, or leaf are therefore expressed relative to $\Psi_w^{\text{pure H2O}}$.

The water potential in plant solutions is influenced by solute concentration, pressure, gravity, and factors called matrix effects. Water potential can be broken down into its individual components using the following equation:

$$\Psi_{\text{system}} = \Psi_{\text{total}} = \Psi_s + \Psi_p + \Psi_g + \Psi_m$$

where Ψ_s, Ψ_p, Ψ_g, and Ψ_m refer to the solute, pressure, gravity, and matric potentials, respectively. “System” can refer to the water potential of the soil water (Ψ^{soil}), root water (Ψ^{root}), stem water (Ψ^{stem}), leaf water (Ψ^{leaf}) or the water in the atmosphere ($\Psi^{\text{atmosphere}}$): whichever aqueous system is under consideration. As the individual components change, they raise or lower the total water potential of a system. When this happens, water moves to equilibrate, moving from the system or compartment with a higher water potential to the system or compartment with a lower water potential. This brings the difference in water potential between the two systems (ΔΨ) back to zero (ΔΨ = 0). Therefore, for water to move through the plant from the soil to the air (a process called transpiration), Ψ^{soil} must be $> \Psi^{\text{root}} > \Psi^{\text{stem}} > \Psi^{\text{leaf}} > \Psi^{\text{atmosphere}}$.

Water only moves in response to ΔΨ, not in response to the individual components. However, because the individual components influence the total Ψ_{system}, by manipulating the individual components (especially Ψ_s), a plant can control water movement.

Solute Potential

Solute potential (Ψ_s), also called osmotic potential, is negative in a plant cell and zero in distilled water. Typical values for cell cytoplasm are –0.5 to –1.0 MPa. Solutes reduce water potential (resulting in a negative Ψ_w) by consuming some of the potential energy available in the water. Solute molecules can dissolve in water because water molecules can bind to them via hydrogen bonds; a hydrophobic molecule like oil, which cannot bind to water, cannot go into solution. The energy in the hydrogen bonds between solute molecules and water is no longer available to do work in the system because it is tied up in the bond. In other words, the amount of available potential energy is reduced when solutes are added to an aqueous system. Thus, Ψ_s decreases with increasing solute concentration. Because Ψ_s is one of the four components of Ψ_{system} or Ψ_{total}, a decrease in Ψ_s will cause a decrease in Ψ_{total}. The internal water potential of a plant cell is more negative than pure water because of the cytoplasm’s high solute content (**Figure 23.32**). Because of this difference in water potential water will move from the soil into a plant’s root cells via the process of osmosis. This is why solute potential is sometimes called osmotic potential.

Plant cells can metabolically manipulate Ψ_s (and by extension, Ψ_{total}) by adding or removing solute molecules. Therefore, plants have control over Ψ_{total} via their ability to exert metabolic control over Ψ_s.

visual CONNECTION

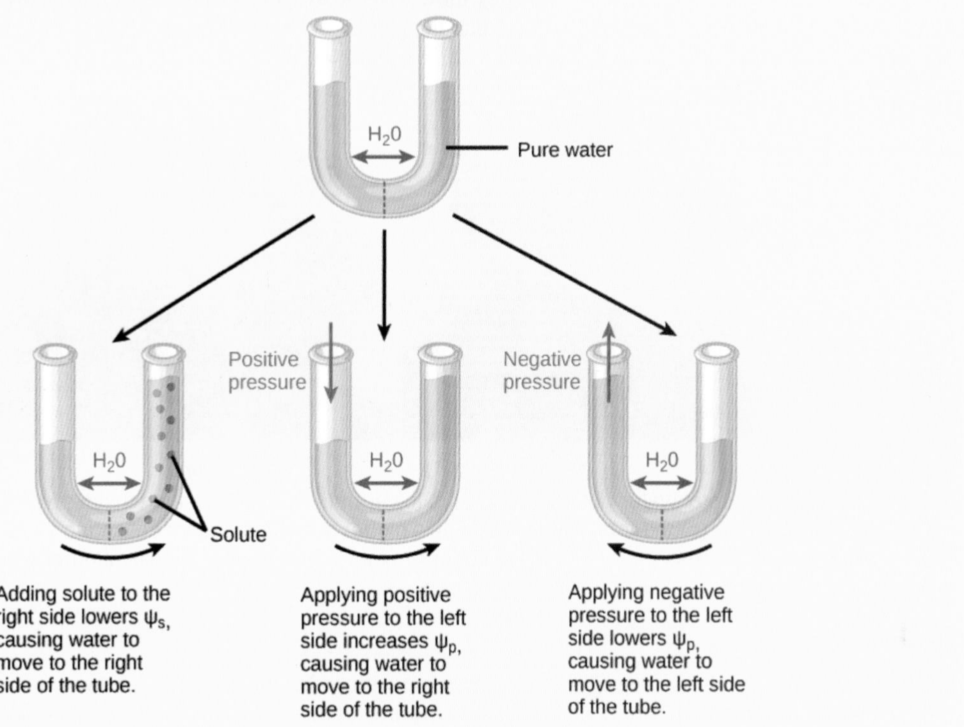

Figure 23.32 In this example with a semipermeable membrane between two aqueous systems, water will move from a region of higher to lower water potential until equilibrium is reached. Solutes (Ψ_s), pressure (Ψ_p), and gravity (Ψ_g) influence total water potential for each side of the tube ($\Psi_{total}{}^{\text{right or left}}$), and therefore, the difference between Ψ_{total} on each side ($\Delta\Psi$). (Ψ_m , the potential due to interaction of water with solid substrates, is ignored in this example because glass is not especially hydrophilic). Water moves in response to the difference in water potential between two systems (the left and right sides of the tube).

Positive water potential is applied on the left side of a tube by increasing Ψp so that the water level rises on the right side. The equation for water potential is: Ψsystem = Ψtotal = Ψs + Ψp + Ψg + Ψm where Ψs, Ψp, Ψg, and Ψm refer to the solute, pressure, gravity, and matric potentials, respectively. Could you equalize the water level on each side of the tube by adding solute?

a. Yes, water level can be equalized by adding solute to the right side of the tube so that water moves toward the left until the water levels are equal.
b. No, water level cannot be equalized on both sides of the tubes by adding solutes with no other action.
c. Yes, water level can be equalized by adding solute to the left side of the tube so that water moves toward the left until the water levels are equal.
d. No, water level cannot be equalized by adding solutes because solutes are always pulled down by gravity, thereby not letting water equalize.

Pressure Potential

Pressure potential (Ψ_p), also called turgor potential, may be positive or negative (**Figure 23.32**). Because pressure is an expression of energy, the higher the pressure, the more potential energy in a system, and vice versa. Therefore, a positive Ψ_p (compression) increases Ψ_{total}, and a negative Ψ_p (tension) decreases Ψ_{total}. Positive pressure inside cells is contained by the cell wall, producing turgor pressure. Pressure potentials are typically around 0.6–0.8 MPa, but can reach as high as 1.5 MPa in a well-watered plant. A Ψ_p of 1.5 MPa equates to 210 pounds per square inch (1.5 MPa x 140 lb in^{-2} MPa^{-1} = 210 lb/in^{-2}). As a comparison, most automobile tires are kept at a pressure of 30–34 psi. An example of the effect of turgor pressure is the wilting of leaves and their restoration after the plant has been watered (**Figure 23.33**). Water is lost from the leaves via transpiration (approaching $\Psi_p = 0$ MPa at the wilting point) and restored by uptake via the roots.

A plant can manipulate Ψ_p via its ability to manipulate Ψ_s and by the process of osmosis. If a plant cell increases the cytoplasmic solute concentration, Ψ_s will decline, Ψ_{total} will decline, the $\Delta\Psi$ between the cell and the surrounding tissue will decline, water will move into the cell by osmosis, and Ψ_p will increase. Ψ_p is also under indirect plant control via the opening and closing of stomata. Stomatal openings allow water to evaporate from the leaf, reducing Ψ_p and Ψ_{total} of the leaf and increasing $\Delta\Psi$ between the water in the leaf and the petiole, thereby allowing water to flow from the petiole into the leaf.

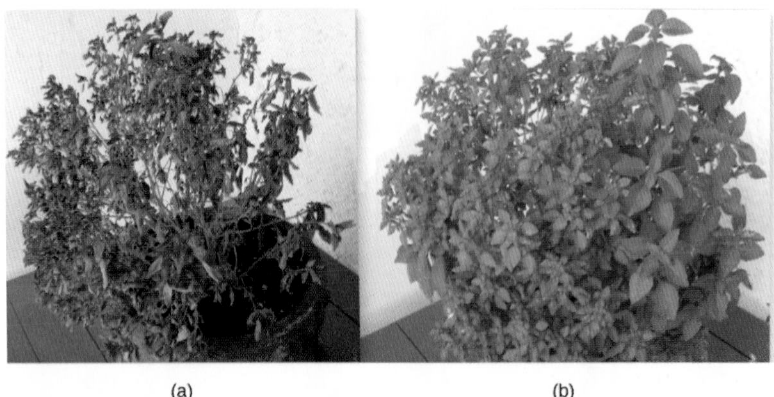

Figure 23.33 When (a) total water potential (Ψ_{total}) is lower outside the cells than inside, water moves out of the cells and the plant wilts. When (b) the total water potential is higher outside the plant cells than inside, water moves into the cells, resulting in turgor pressure (Ψ_p) and keeping the plant erect. (credit: modification of work by Victor M. Vicente Selvas)

Gravity Potential

Gravity potential (Ψ_g) is always negative to zero in a plant with no height. It always removes or consumes potential energy from the system. The force of gravity pulls water downwards to the soil, reducing the total amount of potential energy in the water in the plant (Ψ_{total}). The taller the plant, the taller the water column, and the more influential Ψ_g becomes. On a cellular scale and in short plants, this effect is negligible and easily ignored. However, over the height of a tall tree like a giant coastal redwood, the gravitational pull of –0.1 MPa m^{-1} is equivalent to an extra 1 MPa of resistance that must be overcome for water to reach the leaves of the tallest trees. Plants are unable to manipulate Ψ_g.

Matric Potential

Matric potential (Ψ_m) is always negative to zero. In a dry system, it can be as low as –2 MPa in a dry seed, and it is zero in a water-saturated system. The binding of water to a matrix always removes or consumes potential energy from the system. Ψ_m is similar to solute potential because it involves tying up the energy in an aqueous system by forming hydrogen bonds between the water and some other component. However, in solute potential, the other components are soluble, hydrophilic solute molecules, whereas in Ψ_m, the other components are insoluble, hydrophilic molecules of the plant cell wall. Every plant cell has a cellulosic cell wall and the cellulose in the cell walls is hydrophilic, producing a matrix for adhesion of water: hence the name matric potential. Ψ_m is very large (negative) in dry tissues such as seeds or drought-affected soils. However, it quickly goes to zero as the seed takes up water or the soil hydrates. Ψ_m cannot be manipulated by the plant and is typically ignored in well-watered roots, stems, and leaves.

Movement of Water and Minerals in the Xylem

Solutes, pressure, gravity, and matric potential are all important for the transport of water in plants. Water moves from an area of higher total water potential (higher Gibbs free energy) to an area of lower total water potential. Gibbs free energy is the energy associated with a chemical reaction that can be used to do work. This is expressed as $\Delta\Psi$.

Transpiration is the loss of water from the plant through evaporation at the leaf surface. It is the main driver of water movement in the xylem. Transpiration is caused by the evaporation of water at the leaf–atmosphere interface; it creates negative pressure (tension) equivalent to –2 MPa at the leaf surface. This value varies greatly depending on the vapor pressure deficit, which can be negligible at high relative humidity (RH) and substantial at low RH. Water from the roots is pulled up by this tension. At night, when stomata shut and transpiration stops, the water is held in the stem and leaf by the adhesion of water to the cell walls of the xylem vessels and tracheids, and the cohesion of water molecules to each other. This is called the cohesion–tension theory of sap ascent.

Inside the leaf at the cellular level, water on the surface of mesophyll cells saturates the cellulose microfibrils of the primary cell wall. The leaf contains many large intercellular air spaces for the exchange of oxygen for carbon dioxide, which is required for photosynthesis. The wet cell wall is exposed to this leaf internal air space, and the water on the surface of the cells evaporates into the air spaces, decreasing the thin film on the surface of the mesophyll cells. This decrease creates a greater tension on the water in the mesophyll cells (Figure 23.34), thereby increasing the pull on the water in the xylem vessels. The xylem vessels and tracheids are structurally adapted to cope with large changes in pressure. Rings in the vessels maintain their tubular shape, much like the rings on a vacuum cleaner hose keep the hose open while it is under pressure. Small perforations between vessel elements reduce the number and size of gas bubbles that can form via a process called cavitation. The formation of gas bubbles in xylem interrupts the continuous stream of water from the base to the top of the plant, causing a break termed an embolism in the flow of xylem sap. The taller the tree, the greater the tension forces needed to pull water, and the more cavitation events. In larger trees, the resulting embolisms can plug xylem vessels, making them non-functional.

visual CONNECTION

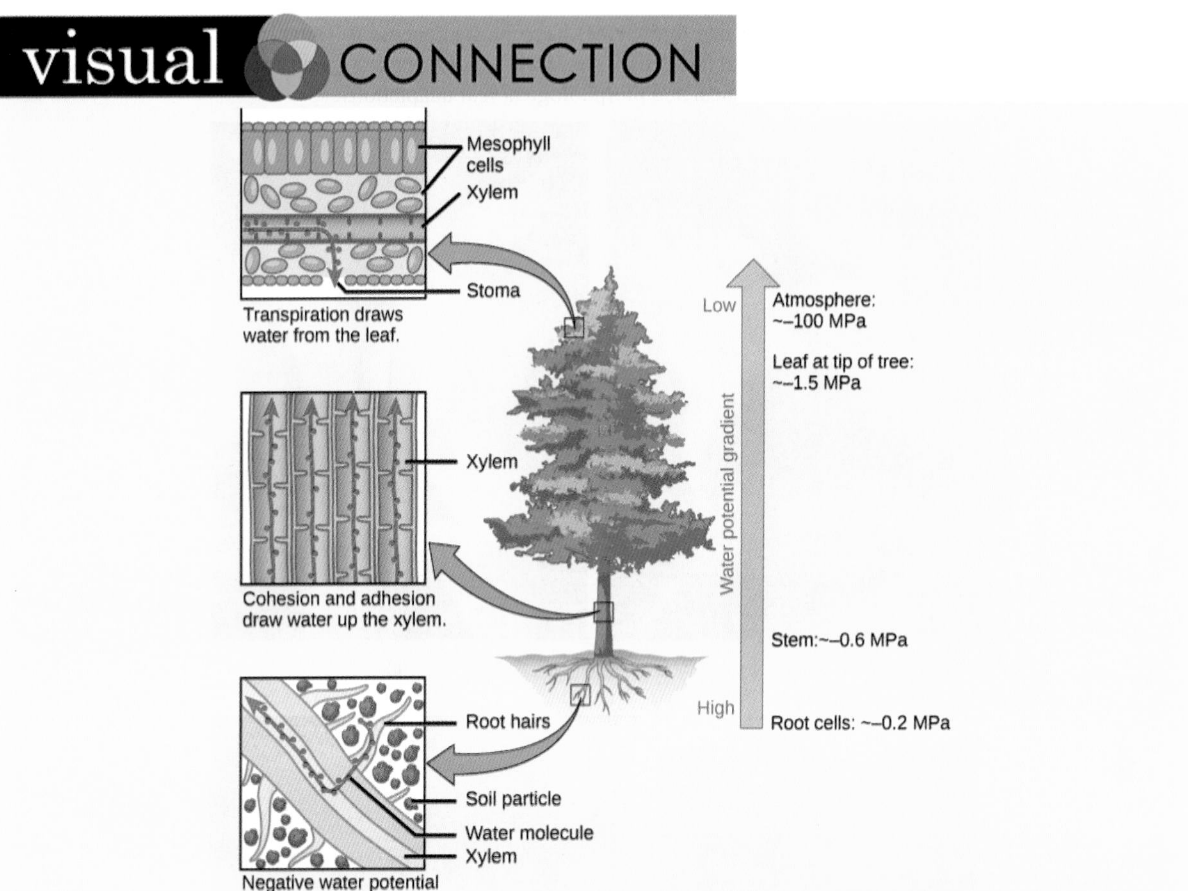

Figure 23.34 The cohesion–tension theory of sap ascent is shown. Evaporation from the mesophyll cells produces a negative water potential gradient that causes water to move upwards from the roots through the xylem.

Which statement is false?

a. Negative water potential draws water into the root hairs, cohesion and adhesion draw water up the xylem, and transpiration draws water from the leaf.
b. Negative water potential draws water into the root hairs, cohesion and adhesion draw water up the phloem, and transpiration draws water from the leaf.
c. Water potential decreases from the roots to the top of the plant.
d. Water enters the plant through the root hairs and exits through stomata.

Transpiration—the loss of water vapor to the atmosphere through stomata—is a passive process, meaning that metabolic energy in the form of ATP is not required for water movement. The energy driving transpiration is the difference in energy between the water in the soil and the water in the atmosphere. However, transpiration is tightly controlled.

Control of Transpiration

The atmosphere to which the leaf is exposed drives transpiration, but also causes massive water loss from the plant. Up to 90 percent of the water taken up by roots may be lost through transpiration.

Leaves are covered by a waxy **cuticle** on the outer surface that prevents the loss of water. Regulation of transpiration, therefore, is achieved primarily through the opening and closing of stomata on the leaf surface. Stomata are surrounded by two specialized cells called guard cells, which open and close in response to environmental cues such as light intensity and quality, leaf water status, and carbon dioxide concentrations. Stomata must open to allow air containing carbon dioxide and oxygen to diffuse into the leaf for photosynthesis and respiration. When stomata are open, however, water vapor is lost to the external environment, increasing the rate of transpiration. Therefore, plants must maintain a balance between efficient photosynthesis and water loss.

Plants have evolved over time to adapt to their local environment and reduce transpiration(Figure 23.35). Desert plants (xerophytes) and plants that grow on other plants (epiphytes) have limited access to water. Such plants usually have a much thicker waxy cuticle than those growing in more moderate, well-watered environments (mesophytes). Aquatic plants (hydrophytes) also have their own set of anatomical and morphological leaf adaptations.

Figure 23.35 Plants are suited to their local environment. (a) Xerophytes, like this prickly pear cactus (*Opuntia sp.*) and (b) epiphytes such as this tropical *Aeschynanthus perrottetii* have adapted to very limited water resources. The leaves of a prickly pear are modified into spines, which lowers the surface-to-volume ratio and reduces water loss. Photosynthesis takes place in the stem, which also stores water. (b) *A. perottetii* leaves have a waxy cuticle that prevents water loss. (c) Goldenrod (*Solidago sp.*) is a mesophyte, well suited for moderate environments. (d) Hydrophytes, like this fragrant water lily (*Nymphaea odorata*), are adapted to thrive in aquatic environments. (credit a: modification of work by Jon Sullivan; credit b: modification of work by L. Shyamal/Wikimedia Commons; credit c: modification of work by Huw Williams; credit d: modification of work by Jason Hollinger)

Xerophytes and epiphytes often have a thick covering of trichomes or of stomata that are sunken below the leaf's surface. Trichomes are specialized hair-like epidermal cells that secrete oils and substances. These adaptations impede air flow across the stomatal pore and reduce transpiration. Multiple epidermal layers are also commonly found in these types of plants.

Transportation of Photosynthates in the Phloem

Plants need an energy source to grow. In seeds and bulbs, food is stored in polymers (such as starch) that are converted by metabolic processes into sucrose for newly developing plants. Once green shoots and leaves are growing, plants are able to produce their own food by photosynthesizing. The products of photosynthesis are called photosynthates, which are usually in the form of simple sugars such as sucrose.

Structures that produce photosynthates for the growing plant are referred to as **sources**. Sugars produced in sources, such as leaves, need to be delivered to growing parts of the plant via the phloem in a process called **translocation**. The points of sugar delivery, such as roots, young shoots, and developing seeds, are called **sinks**. Seeds, tubers, and bulbs can be either a source or a sink, depending on the plant's stage of development and the season.

The products from the source are usually translocated to the nearest sink through the phloem. For example, the highest leaves will send photosynthates upward to the growing shoot tip, whereas lower leaves will direct photosynthates downward to the roots. Intermediate leaves will send products in both directions, unlike the flow in the xylem, which is always unidirectional (soil to leaf to atmosphere). The pattern of photosynthate flow changes as the plant grows and develops. Photosynthates are directed primarily to the roots early on, to shoots and leaves during vegetative growth, and to seeds and fruits during reproductive development. They are also directed to tubers for storage.

Translocation: Transport from Source to Sink

Photosynthates, such as sucrose, are produced in the mesophyll cells of photosynthesizing leaves. From there they are translocated through the phloem to where they are used or stored. Mesophyll cells are connected by cytoplasmic channels called plasmodesmata. Photosynthates move through these channels to reach phloem sieve-tube elements (STEs) in the vascular bundles. From the mesophyll cells, the photosynthates are loaded into the phloem STEs. The sucrose is actively transported against its concentration gradient (a process requiring ATP) into the phloem cells using the electrochemical potential of the proton gradient. This is coupled to the uptake of sucrose with a carrier protein called the sucrose-H^+ symporter.

Phloem STEs have reduced cytoplasmic contents, and are connected by a sieve plate with pores that allow for pressure-driven bulk flow, or translocation, of phloem sap. Companion cells are associated with STEs. They assist with metabolic activities and produce energy for the STEs (Figure 23.36).

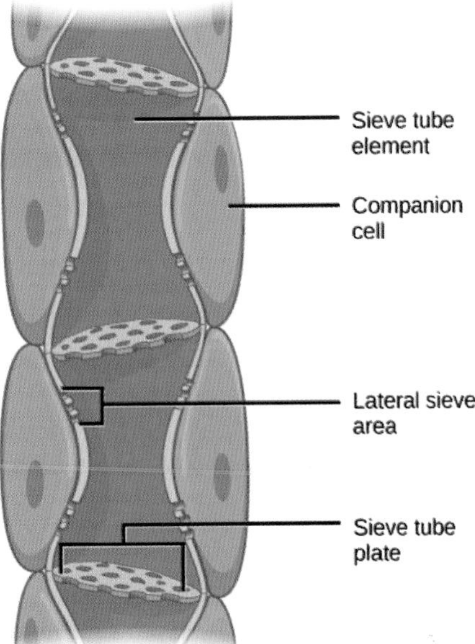

Figure 23.36 Phloem is comprised of cells called sieve-tube elements. Phloem sap travels through perforations called sieve tube plates. Neighboring companion cells carry out metabolic functions for the sieve-tube elements and provide them with energy. Lateral sieve areas connect the sieve-tube elements to the companion cells.

Once in the phloem, the photosynthates are translocated to the closest sink. Phloem sap is an aqueous solution that contains up to 30 percent sugar, minerals, amino acids, and plant growth regulators. The high percentage of sugar decreases Ψ_s, which decreases the total water potential and causes water to move by osmosis from the adjacent xylem into the phloem tubes, thereby increasing pressure. This increase in total water potential causes the bulk flow of phloem from source to sink (Figure 23.37). Sucrose concentration in the sink cells is lower than in the phloem STEs because the sink sucrose has been metabolized for growth, or converted to starch for storage or other polymers, such as cellulose, for structural integrity. Unloading at the sink end of the phloem tube occurs by either diffusion or active transport of sucrose molecules from an area of high concentration to one of low concentration. Water diffuses from the phloem by osmosis and is then transpired or recycled via the xylem back into the phloem sap.

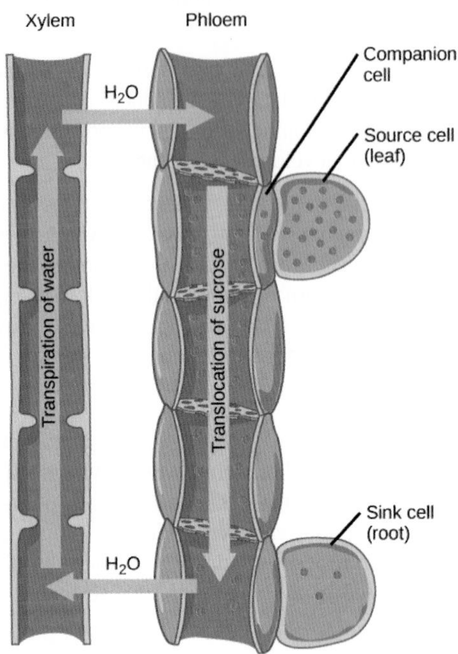

Figure 23.37 Sucrose is actively transported from source cells into companion cells and then into the sieve-tube elements. This reduces the water potential, which causes water to enter the phloem from the xylem. The resulting positive pressure forces the sucrose-water mixture down toward the roots, where sucrose is unloaded. Transpiration causes water to return to the leaves through the xylem vessels.

science practices CONNECTION for AP® Courses

Activity

Based on water's molecular properties, create a visual diagram/model to illustrate how water travels up a 300-foot California redwood tree through xylem.

Lab Investigation

AP® Biology Investigative Labs: Inquiry-Based, Investigation 11: Transpiration. Design and conduct a series of experiments to investigate the effects of environmental variables on transpiration rates.

Think About It

Desert travelers claim that cactus juice tastes sweeter during the day than at night. Based on your understanding of photosynthesis, transpiration, and the regulation of stomata by guard cells in response to environmental conditions, is there any validity to this claim?

23.6 | Plant Sensory Systems and Responses

In this section, you will explore the following questions:

- How do red and blue light affect plant growth and metabolic activities?
- What is gravitropism?
- What are examples of plant hormones, and how do they affect plant growth and development?
- What are the differences between thigmotropism, thigmonastism, and thigmogenesis?
- How do plants defend themselves against predators and respond to wounds?

Connection for AP® Courses

Why do some flowering plants bloom in the spring, whereas others bloom in the summer or fall? Why do the stems of plants grow upward and bend toward light, while roots grow downward? Why do the leaves of deciduous plants in northern climates turn colors in the fall and eventually fall off, while evergreens keep their needles all year around? Is it true that putting an unripe avocado in a paper bag will hasten the ripening process? Can the same tactic work on bananas?

Like most other organisms, plants have the ability to detect and respond to environmental change; this ability is an adaptation favored by natural selection. Flowering plants react to light, gravity, infection by pathogens, drought, and, as with the Venus flytrap, touch. Animals have two systems on which they can rely to detect and respond to stimuli: the nervous and endocrine systems. Plants, however, only have chemical control mechanisms at their disposal. In addition to the phytochromes, plants evolved hormones that allow them to respond to environmental changes. Like animal hormones, plant hormones are chemical signaling molecules that trigger a cellular response through a signal transduction pathway.

Although you do not have to memorize a laundry list of plant hormones and their activities, you should understand the basic mechanism of how they trigger a response. Examples that we'll learn about in this chapter include auxins, which cause plant stems to grow and bend toward light, and gibberellins, which stimulate cell growth and breaks seed dormancy. Plants also produce other chemicals to protect against biotic stimuli, including herbivory and parasitism. The fact that plants produce chemicals should not be surprising; our pharmaceutical industry depends on these substances. For example, species of the foxglove plant produce digitalis, a powerful heart medicine, whereas the opium from the poppy is the source of many narcotics.

Information presented and the examples highlighted in the section support concepts outlined in Big Idea 2 and Big Idea 3 of the AP® Biology Curriculum Framework. The AP® Learning Objectives listed in the Curriculum Framework provide a transparent foundation for the AP® Biology course, an inquiry-based laboratory experience, instructional activities, and AP® exam questions. A learning objective merges required content with one or more of the seven science practices.

Big Idea 2	Biological systems utilize free energy and molecular building blocks to grow, to reproduce, and to maintain dynamic homeostasis.
Enduring Understanding 2.C	Organisms use feedback mechanisms to regulate growth and reproduction, and to maintain dynamic homeostasis.
Essential Knowledge	**2.C.1** Plants use negative and positive feedback mechanisms to maintain their internal environments and respond to external environmental changes.
Science Practice	**4.2** The student can design a plan for collecting data to answer a particular scientific question.
Science Practice	**5.3** The student can evaluate the evidence provided by data sets in relation to a particular scientific question.
Science Practice	**6.1** The student can justify claims with evidence.

Learning Objective	**2.17** The student is able to evaluate data that show the effect(s) of changes in concentrations of key molecules on negative feedback mechanisms.
Big Idea 2	Biological systems utilize free energy and molecular building blocks to grow, to reproduce, and to maintain dynamic homeostasis.
Enduring Understanding 2.C	Organisms use feedback mechanisms to regulate growth and reproduction, and to maintain dynamic homeostasis.
Essential Knowledge	**2.C.1** Plants use negative and positive feedback mechanisms to maintain their internal environments and respond to external environmental changes.
Science Practice	**1.1** The student can create representations and models of natural or man-made phenomena and systems in the domain.
Science Practice	**6.4** The student can make claims and predictions about natural phenomena based on scientific theories and models.
Science Practice	**7.2** The student can connect concepts in and across domain(s) to generalize or extrapolate in and/or across enduring understandings and/or big ideas.
Learning Objective	**2.18** The student can make predictions about how organisms use negative feedback mechanisms to maintain their internal environments.
Big Idea 2	Biological systems utilize free energy and molecular building blocks to grow, to reproduce, and to maintain dynamic homeostasis.
Enduring Understanding 2.D	Growth and dynamic homeostasis of a biological system are influenced by changes in the system's environment.
Essential Knowledge	**2.D.1** Cellular activity in plants is affected by interactions with biotic and abiotic factors.
Science Practice	**1.1** The student can create representations and models of natural or man-made phenomena and systems in the domain.
Science Practice	**1.2** The student can describe representations and models of natural or man-made phenomena and systems in the domain.
Science Practice	**6.4** The student can make claims and predictions about natural phenomena based on scientific theories and models.
Science Practice	**7.2** The student can connect concepts in and across domain(s) to generalize or extrapolate in and/or across enduring understandings and/or big ideas.
Learning Objective	**2.22** The student is able to refine scientific models and questions about the effect of complex biotic and abiotic interactions on all biological systems, from cells and organisms to populations, communities, and ecosystems.
Big Idea 2	Biological systems utilize free energy and molecular building blocks to grow, to reproduce, and to maintain dynamic homeostasis.
Enduring Understanding 2.D	Growth and dynamic homeostasis of a biological system are influenced by changes in the system's environment.
Essential Knowledge	**2.D.4** Plants have nonspecific immune responses to defend against infections and other threats.
Science Practice	**1.1** The student can create representations and models of natural or man-made phenomena and systems in the domain.
Science Practice	**1.2** The student can describe representations and models of natural or man-made phenomena and systems in the domain.

Science Practice	**7.2** The student can connect concepts in and across domain(s) to generalize or extrapolate in and/or across enduring understandings and/or big ideas.
Learning Objective	**2.30** The student can create representations or models to describe nonspecific immune defenses in plants and animals.
Big Idea 2	Biological systems utilize free energy and molecular building blocks to grow, to reproduce, and to maintain dynamic homeostasis.
Big Idea 2	Biological systems utilize free energy and molecular building blocks to grow, to reproduce, and to maintain dynamic homeostasis.
Enduring Understanding 2.E	Many biological processes involved in growth, reproduction and dynamic homeostasis include temporal regulation and coordination.
Essential Knowledge	**2.E.3** Organisms use feedback mechanisms to maintain their internal environments and respond to external environmental changes.
Science Practice	**4.2** The student can design a plan for collecting data to answer a particular scientific question.
Science Practice	**5.3** The student can evaluate the evidence provided by data sets in relation to a particular scientific question.
Science Practice	**6.1** The student can justify claims with evidence.
Science Practice	**7.2** The student can connect concepts in and across domain(s) to generalize or extrapolate in and/or across enduring understandings and/or big ideas.
Learning Objective	**2.39** The student is able to justify scientific claims, using evidence, to describe how timing and coordination of behavioral events in organisms are regulated by several mechanisms.
Big Idea 2	Biological systems utilize free energy and molecular building blocks to grow, to reproduce, and to maintain dynamic homeostasis.
Enduring Understanding 2.E	Many biological processes involved in growth, reproduction and dynamic homeostasis include temporal regulation and coordination.
Essential Knowledge	**2.E.3** Plant responses to stimuli are adaptations favored by natural selection.
Science Practice	**7.2** The student can connect concepts in and across domain(s) to generalize or extrapolate in and/or across enduring understandings and/or big ideas.
Learning Objective	**2.40** The student is able to connect concepts in and across domain(s) to predict how environmental factors affect responses to information and change behavior.
Big Idea 3	Living systems store, retrieve, transmit and respond to information essential to life processes.
Enduring Understanding 3.B	Expression of genetic information involves cellular and molecular mechanisms.
Essential Knowledge	**3.B.2** Signal transmission within and between plant cells mediates gene expression.
Science Practice	**6.2** The student can construct explanations of phenomena based on evidence produced through scientific practices.
Learning Objective	**3.22** The student is able to explain how signal pathways mediate gene expression, including how this process can affect protein production.

The Science Practice Challenge Questions contain additional test questions for this section that will help you prepare for

the AP exam. These questions address the following standards:
[APLO 2.29][APLO 2.30]

Animals can respond to environmental factors by moving to a new location. Plants, however, are rooted in place and must respond to the surrounding environmental factors. Plants have sophisticated systems to detect and respond to light, gravity, temperature, and physical touch. Receptors sense environmental factors and relay the information to effector systems—often through intermediate chemical messengers—to bring about plant responses.

Plant Responses to Light

Plants have a number of sophisticated uses for light that go far beyond their ability to photosynthesize low-molecular-weight sugars using only carbon dioxide, light, and water. **Photomorphogenesis** is the growth and development of plants in response to light. It allows plants to optimize their use of light and space. **Photoperiodism** is the ability to use light to track time. Plants can tell the time of day and time of year by sensing and using various wavelengths of sunlight. **Phototropism** is a directional response that allows plants to grow towards, or even away from, light.

The sensing of light in the environment is important to plants; it can be crucial for competition and survival. The response of plants to light is mediated by different photoreceptors, which are comprised of a protein covalently bonded to a light-absorbing pigment called a **chromophore**. Together, the two are called a chromoprotein.

The red/far-red and violet-blue regions of the visible light spectrum trigger structural development in plants. Sensory photoreceptors absorb light in these particular regions of the visible light spectrum because of the quality of light available in the daylight spectrum. In terrestrial habitats, light absorption by chlorophylls peaks in the blue and red regions of the spectrum. As light filters through the canopy and the blue and red wavelengths are absorbed, the spectrum shifts to the far-red end, shifting the plant community to those plants better adapted to respond to far-red light. Blue-light receptors allow plants to gauge the direction and abundance of sunlight, which is rich in blue–green emissions. Water absorbs red light, which makes the detection of blue light essential for algae and aquatic plants.

The Phytochrome System and the Red/Far-Red Response

The **phytochromes** are a family of chromoproteins with a linear tetrapyrrole chromophore, similar to the ringed tetrapyrrole light-absorbing head group of chlorophyll. Phytochromes have two photo-interconvertible forms: Pr and Pfr. Pr absorbs red light (~667 nm) and is immediately converted to Pfr. Pfr absorbs far-red light (~730 nm) and is quickly converted back to Pr. Absorption of red or far-red light causes a massive change to the shape of the chromophore, altering the conformation and activity of the phytochrome protein to which it is bound. Pfr is the physiologically active form of the protein; therefore, exposure to red light yields physiological activity. Exposure to far-red light inhibits phytochrome activity. Together, the two forms represent the phytochrome system (Figure 23.38).

The phytochrome system acts as a biological light switch. It monitors the level, intensity, duration, and color of environmental light. The effect of red light is reversible by immediately shining far-red light on the sample, which converts the chromoprotein to the inactive Pr form. Additionally, Pfr can slowly revert to Pr in the dark, or break down over time. In all instances, the physiological response induced by red light is reversed. The active form of phytochrome (Pfr) can directly activate other molecules in the cytoplasm, or it can be trafficked to the nucleus, where it directly activates or represses specific gene expression.

Once the phytochrome system evolved, plants adapted it to serve a variety of needs. Unfiltered, full sunlight contains much more red light than far-red light. Because chlorophyll absorbs strongly in the red region of the visible spectrum, but not in the far-red region, any plant in the shade of another plant on the forest floor will be exposed to red-depleted, far-red-enriched light. The preponderance of far-red light converts phytochrome in the shaded leaves to the Pr (inactive) form, slowing growth. The nearest non-shaded (or even less-shaded) areas on the forest floor have more red light; leaves exposed to these areas sense the red light, which activates the Pfr form and induces growth. In short, plant shoots use the phytochrome system to grow away from shade and towards light. Because competition for light is so fierce in a dense plant community, the evolutionary advantages of the phytochrome system are obvious.

In seeds, the phytochrome system is not used to determine direction and quality of light (shaded versus unshaded). Instead, is it used merely to determine if there is any light at all. This is especially important in species with very small seeds, such as lettuce. Because of their size, lettuce seeds have few food reserves. Their seedlings cannot grow for long before they run out of fuel. If they germinated even a centimeter under the soil surface, the seedling would never make it into the sunlight and would die. In the dark, phytochrome is in the Pr (inactive form) and the seed will not germinate; it will only germinate if exposed to light at the surface of the soil. Upon exposure to light, Pr is converted to Pfr and germination proceeds.

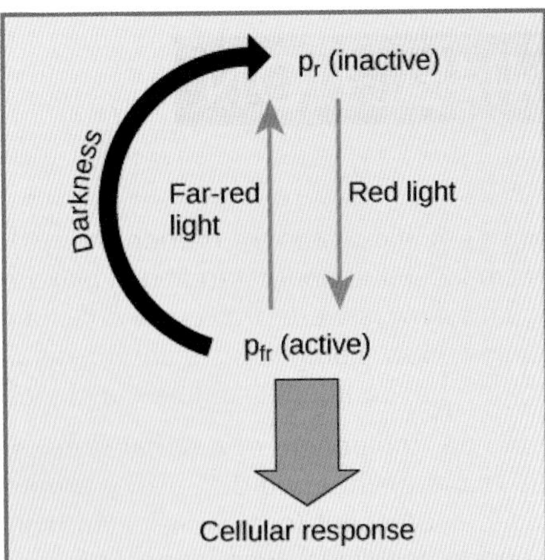

Figure 23.38 The biologically inactive form of phytochrome (Pr) is converted to the biologically active form Pfr under illumination with red light. Far-red light and darkness convert the molecule back to the inactive form.

Plants also use the phytochrome system to sense the change of season. Photoperiodism is a biological response to the timing and duration of day and night. It controls flowering, setting of winter buds, and vegetative growth. Detection of seasonal changes is crucial to plant survival. Although temperature and light intensity influence plant growth, they are not reliable indicators of season because they may vary from one year to the next. Day length is a better indicator of the time of year.

As stated above, unfiltered sunlight is rich in red light but deficient in far-red light. Therefore, at dawn, all the phytochrome molecules in a leaf quickly convert to the active Pfr form, and remain in that form until sunset. In the dark, the Pfr form takes hours to slowly revert back to the Pr form. If the night is long (as in winter), all of the Pfr form reverts. If the night is short (as in summer), a considerable amount of Pfr may remain at sunrise. By sensing the Pr/Pfr ratio at dawn, a plant can determine the length of the day/night cycle. In addition, leaves retain that information for several days, allowing a comparison between the length of the previous night and the preceding several nights. Shorter nights indicate springtime to the plant; when the nights become longer, autumn is approaching. This information, along with sensing temperature and water availability, allows plants to determine the time of the year and adjust their physiology accordingly. Short-day (long-night) plants use this information to flower in the late summer and early fall, when nights exceed a critical length (often eight or fewer hours). Long-day (short-night) plants flower during the spring, when darkness is less than a critical length (often eight to 15 hours). Not all plants use the phytochrome system in this way. Flowering in day-neutral plants is not regulated by daylength.

Horticulturist

The word "horticulturist" comes from the Latin words for garden (*hortus*) and culture (*cultura*). This career has been revolutionized by progress made in the understanding of plant responses to environmental stimuli. Growers of crops, fruit, vegetables, and flowers were previously constrained by having to time their sowing and harvesting according to the season. Now, horticulturists can manipulate plants to increase leaf, flower, or fruit production by understanding how environmental factors affect plant growth and development.

Greenhouse management is an essential component of a horticulturist's education. To lengthen the night, plants are covered with a blackout shade cloth. Long-day plants are irradiated with red light in winter to promote early flowering. For example, fluorescent (cool white) light high in blue wavelengths encourages leafy growth and is excellent for starting seedlings. Incandescent lamps (standard light bulbs) are rich in red light, and promote flowering in some plants. The timing of fruit ripening can be increased or delayed by applying plant hormones. Recently, considerable progress has been made in the development of plant breeds that are suited to different climates and resistant to pests and transportation damage. Both crop yield and quality have increased as a result of practical applications of the knowledge of plant responses to external stimuli and hormones.

Horticulturists find employment in private and governmental laboratories, greenhouses, botanical gardens, and in the production or research fields. They improve crops by applying their knowledge of genetics and plant physiology. To prepare for a horticulture career, students take classes in botany, plant physiology, plant pathology, landscape design, and plant breeding. To complement these traditional courses, horticulture majors add studies in economics, business, computer science, and communications.

The Blue Light Responses

Phototropism—the directional bending of a plant toward or away from a light source—is a response to blue wavelengths of light. Positive phototropism is growth towards a light source (**Figure 23.39**), while negative phototropism (also called skototropism) is growth away from light.

The aptly-named **phototropins** are protein-based receptors responsible for mediating the phototropic response. Like all plant photoreceptors, phototropins consist of a protein portion and a light-absorbing portion, called the chromophore. In phototropins, the chromophore is a covalently-bound molecule of flavin; hence, phototropins belong to a class of proteins called flavoproteins.

Other responses under the control of phototropins are leaf opening and closing, chloroplast movement, and the opening of stomata. However, of all responses controlled by phototropins, phototropism has been studied the longest and is the best understood.

In their 1880 treatise *The Power of Movements in Plants*, Charles Darwin and his son Francis first described phototropism as the bending of seedlings toward light. Darwin observed that light was perceived by the tip of the plant (the apical meristem), but that the response (bending) took place in a different part of the plant. They concluded that the signal had to travel from the apical meristem to the base of the plant.

Figure 23.39 Azure bluets (*Houstonia caerulea*) display a phototropic response by bending toward the light. (credit: Cory Zanker)

In 1913, Peter Boysen-Jensen demonstrated that a chemical signal produced in the plant tip was responsible for the bending at the base. He cut off the tip of a seedling, covered the cut section with a layer of gelatin, and then replaced the tip. The seedling bent toward the light when illuminated. However, when impermeable mica flakes were inserted between the tip and the cut base, the seedling did not bend. A refinement of the experiment showed that the signal traveled on the shaded side of the seedling. When the mica plate was inserted on the illuminated side, the plant did bend towards the light. Therefore, the chemical signal was a growth stimulant because the phototropic response involved faster cell elongation on the shaded side than on the illuminated side. We now know that as light passes through a plant stem, it is diffracted and generates phototropin activation across the stem. Most activation occurs on the lit side, causing the plant hormone indole acetic acid (IAA) to accumulate on the shaded side. Stem cells elongate under influence of IAA.

Cryptochromes are another class of blue-light absorbing photoreceptors that also contain a flavin-based chromophore. Cryptochromes set the plants 24-hour activity cycle, also know as its circadian rhythem, using blue light cues. There is some evidence that cryptochromes work together with phototropins to mediate the phototropic response.

Use the navigation menu in the left panel of this website (http://openstaxcollege.org/l/plnts_n_motion) to view images of plants in motion.

If green light was used rather than white light to irradiate a sunflower seedling, what would happen?

a. Green light is absorbed by the plant. The seedling would not bend, but it would grow tall and spindly as if grown in the dark.

b. Green light is not absorbed by the plant. The seedling would not bend, but it would grow tall and spindly as if grown in the dark.

c. Green light is not absorbed by the plant. The seedling would not grow tall and spindly, but it would bend.

d. Green light is absorbed by the plant. The seedling would not grow tall and spindly, but it would bend.

Plant Responses to Gravity

Whether or not they germinate in the light or in total darkness, shoots usually sprout up from the ground, and roots grow downward into the ground. A plant laid on its side in the dark will send shoots upward when given enough time. Gravitropism ensures that roots grow into the soil and that shoots grow toward sunlight. Growth of the shoot apical tip upward is called **negative gravitropism**, whereas growth of the roots downward is called **positive gravitropism**.

Amyloplasts (also known as **statoliths**) are specialized plastids that contain starch granules and settle downward in response to gravity. Amyloplasts are found in shoots and in specialized cells of the root cap. When a plant is tilted, the statoliths drop to the new bottom cell wall. A few hours later, the shoot or root will show growth in the new vertical direction.

The mechanism that mediates gravitropism is reasonably well understood. When amyloplasts settle to the bottom of the gravity-sensing cells in the root or shoot, they physically contact the endoplasmic reticulum (ER), causing the release of calcium ions from inside the ER. This calcium signaling in the cells causes polar transport of the plant hormone IAA to the bottom of the cell. In roots, a high concentration of IAA inhibits cell elongation. The effect slows growth on the lower side of the root, while cells develop normally on the upper side. IAA has the opposite effect in shoots, where a higher concentration at the lower side of the shoot stimulates cell expansion, causing the shoot to grow up. After the shoot or root begin to grow vertically, the amyloplasts return to their normal position. Other hypotheses—involving the entire cell in the gravitropism effect—have been proposed to explain why some mutants that lack amyloplasts may still exhibit a weak gravitropic response.

Growth Responses

A plant's sensory response to external stimuli relies on chemical messengers (hormones). Plant hormones affect all aspects of plant life, from flowering to fruit setting and maturation, and from phototropism to leaf fall. Potentially every cell in a plant can produce plant hormones. They can act in their cell of origin or be transported to other portions of the plant body, with many plant responses involving the synergistic or antagonistic interaction of two or more hormones. In contrast, animal hormones are produced in specific glands and transported to a distant site for action, and they act alone.

Plant hormones are a group of unrelated chemical substances that affect plant morphogenesis. Five major plant hormones are traditionally described: auxins (particularly IAA), cytokinins, gibberellins, ethylene, and abscisic acid. In addition, other nutrients and environmental conditions can be characterized as growth factors.

Auxins

The term auxin is derived from the Greek word *auxein*, which means "to grow." **Auxins** are the main hormones responsible for cell elongation in phototropism and gravitropism. They also control the differentiation of meristem into vascular tissue, and promote leaf development and arrangement. While many synthetic auxins are used as herbicides, IAA is the only naturally occurring auxin that shows physiological activity. Apical dominance—the inhibition of lateral bud formation—is triggered by auxins produced in the apical meristem. Flowering, fruit setting and ripening, and inhibition of **abscission** (leaf falling) are other plant responses under the direct or indirect control of auxins. Auxins also act as a relay for the effects of the blue light and red/far-red responses.

Commercial use of auxins is widespread in plant nurseries and for crop production. IAA is used as a rooting hormone to promote growth of adventitious roots on cuttings and detached leaves. Applying synthetic auxins to tomato plants in greenhouses promotes normal fruit development. Outdoor application of auxin promotes synchronization of fruit setting and dropping to coordinate the harvesting season. Fruits such as seedless cucumbers can be induced to set fruit by treating unfertilized plant flowers with auxins.

Cytokinins

The effect of cytokinins was first reported when it was found that adding the liquid endosperm of coconuts to developing plant embryos in culture stimulated their growth. The stimulating growth factor was found to be **cytokinin**, a hormone that promotes cytokinesis (cell division). Almost 200 naturally occurring or synthetic cytokinins are known to date. Cytokinins are most abundant in growing tissues, such as roots, embryos, and fruits, where cell division is occurring. Cytokinins are known to delay senescence in leaf tissues, promote mitosis, and stimulate differentiation of the meristem in shoots and roots. Many effects on plant development are under the influence of cytokinins, either in conjunction with auxin or another hormone. For example, apical dominance seems to result from a balance between auxins that inhibit lateral buds, and cytokinins that promote bushier growth.

Gibberellins

Gibberellins (GAs) are a group of about 125 closely related plant hormones that stimulate shoot elongation, seed germination, and fruit and flower maturation. GAs are synthesized in the root and stem apical meristems, young leaves, and seed embryos. In urban areas, GA antagonists are sometimes applied to trees under power lines to control growth and reduce the frequency of pruning.

GAs break dormancy (a state of inhibited growth and development) in the seeds of plants that require exposure to cold or light to germinate. Other effects of GAs include gender expression, seedless fruit development, and the delay of senescence in leaves and fruit. Seedless grapes are obtained through standard breeding methods and contain inconspicuous seeds that fail to develop. Because GAs are produced by the seeds, and because fruit development and stem elongation are under GA control, these varieties of grapes would normally produce small fruit in compact clusters. Maturing grapes are routinely treated with GA to promote larger fruit size, as well as looser bunches (longer stems), which reduces the instance of mildew infection (Figure 23.40).

Figure 23.40 In grapes, application of gibberellic acid increases the size of fruit and loosens clustering. (credit: Bob Nichols, USDA)

Abscisic Acid

The plant hormone **abscisic acid** (ABA) was first discovered as the agent that causes the abscission or dropping of cotton bolls. However, more recent studies indicate that ABA plays only a minor role in the abscission process. ABA accumulates as a response to stressful environmental conditions, such as dehydration, cold temperatures, or shortened day lengths. Its activity counters many of the growth-promoting effects of GAs and auxins. ABA inhibits stem elongation and induces dormancy in lateral buds.

ABA induces dormancy in seeds by blocking germination and promoting the synthesis of storage proteins. Plants adapted to temperate climates require a long period of cold temperature before seeds germinate. This mechanism protects young plants from sprouting too early during unseasonably warm weather in winter. As the hormone gradually breaks down over winter, the seed is released from dormancy and germinates when conditions are favorable in spring. Another effect of ABA is to promote the development of winter buds; it mediates the conversion of the apical meristem into a dormant bud. Low soil moisture causes an increase in ABA, which causes stomata to close, reducing water loss in winter buds.

Ethylene

Ethylene is associated with fruit ripening, flower wilting, and leaf fall. Ethylene is unusual because it is a volatile gas (C_2H_4). Hundreds of years ago, when gas street lamps were installed in city streets, trees that grew close to lamp posts developed twisted, thickened trunks and shed their leaves earlier than expected. These effects were caused by ethylene volatilizing from the lamps.

Aging tissues (especially senescing leaves) and nodes of stems produce ethylene. The best-known effect of the hormone, however, is the promotion of fruit ripening. Ethylene stimulates the conversion of starch and acids to sugars. Some people store unripe fruit, such as avocadoes, in a sealed paper bag to accelerate ripening; the gas released by the first fruit to mature will speed up the maturation of the remaining fruit. Ethylene also triggers leaf and fruit abscission, flower fading and dropping, and promotes germination in some cereals and sprouting of bulbs and potatoes.

Ethylene is widely used in agriculture. Commercial fruit growers control the timing of fruit ripening with application of the gas. Horticulturalists inhibit leaf dropping in ornamental plants by removing ethylene from greenhouses using fans and ventilation.

Nontraditional Hormones

Recent research has discovered a number of compounds that also influence plant development. Their roles are less understood than the effects of the major hormones described so far.

Jasmonates play a major role in defense responses to herbivory. Their levels increase when a plant is wounded by a predator, resulting in an increase in toxic secondary metabolites. They contribute to the production of volatile compounds that attract natural enemies of predators. For example, chewing of tomato plants by caterpillars leads to an increase in jasmonic acid levels, which in turn triggers the release of volatile compounds that attract predators of the pest.

Oligosaccharins also play a role in plant defense against bacterial and fungal infections. They act locally at the site of injury, and can also be transported to other tissues. **Strigolactones** promote seed germination in some species and inhibit lateral apical development in the absence of auxins. Strigolactones also play a role in the establishment of mycorrhizae, a mutualistic association of plant roots and fungi. Brassinosteroids are important to many developmental and physiological processes. Signals between these compounds and other hormones, notably auxin and GAs, amplifies their physiological effect. Apical dominance, seed germination, gravitropism, and resistance to freezing are all positively influenced by hormones. Root growth and fruit dropping are inhibited by steroids.

Plant Responses to Wind and Touch

The shoot of a pea plant winds around a trellis, while a tree grows on an angle in response to strong prevailing winds. These are examples of how plants respond to touch or wind.

The movement of a plant subjected to constant directional pressure is called **thigmotropism**, from the Greek words *thigma* meaning “touch,” and *tropism* implying “direction.” Tendrils are one example of this. The meristematic region of tendrils is very touch sensitive; light touch will evoke a quick coiling response. Cells in contact with a support surface contract, whereas cells on the opposite side of the support expand (Figure 23.14). Application of jasmonic acid is sufficient to trigger tendril coiling without a mechanical stimulus.

A **thigmonastic** response is a touch response independent of the direction of stimulus Figure 23.24. In the Venus flytrap, two modified leaves are joined at a hinge and lined with thin fork-like tines along the outer edges. Tiny hairs are located inside the trap. When an insect brushes against these trigger hairs, touching two or more of them in succession, the leaves close quickly, trapping the prey. Glands on the leaf surface secrete enzymes that slowly digest the insect. The released nutrients are absorbed by the leaves, which reopen for the next meal.

everyday CONNECTION for AP® Courses

The mimosa plant is also known as the sensitive plant, because its leaves are sensitive to touch and will fold inward and droop. Leaves in their normal state are shown on the left.

Figure 23.41

Thigmomorphogenesis is a slow developmental change in the shape of a plant subjected to continuous mechanical stress. When trees bend in the wind, for example, growth is usually stunted and the trunk thickens. Strengthening tissue, especially xylem, is produced to add stiffness to resist the wind’s force. Researchers hypothesize that mechanical strain induces growth and differentiation to strengthen the tissues. Ethylene and jasmonate are likely involved in thigmomorphogenesis.

Use the menu at the left to navigate to three short movies: (http://openstaxcollege.org/l/nastic_mvmt) a Venus fly trap capturing prey, the progressive closing of sensitive plant leaflets, and the twining of tendrils.

A Venus fly trap response is triggered by touching the leaves __.

a. anywhere, because the whole surface of the leaf responds to touch

b. only on the margins of the leaves where insects usually land

c. in the center of the leaf, where the touch-sensitive hairs are located

d. on the petiole followed by the center of leaf which signal the presence of a wandering insect

Defense Responses against Herbivores and Pathogens

Plants face two types of enemies: herbivores and pathogens. Herbivores both large and small use plants as food, and actively chew them. Pathogens are agents of disease. These infectious microorganisms, such as fungi, bacteria, and nematodes, live off of the plant and damage its tissues. Plants have developed a variety of strategies to discourage or kill attackers.

The first line of defense in plants is an intact and impenetrable barrier. Bark and the waxy cuticle can protect against predators. Other adaptations against herbivory include thorns, which are modified branches, and spines, which are modified leaves. They discourage animals by causing physical damage and inducing rashes and allergic reactions. A plant's exterior protection can be compromised by mechanical damage, which may provide an entry point for pathogens. If the first line of defense is breached, the plant must resort to a different set of defense mechanisms, such as toxins and enzymes.

Secondary metabolites are compounds that are not directly derived from photosynthesis and are not necessary for respiration or plant growth and development. Many metabolites are toxic, and can even be lethal to animals that ingest them. Some metabolites are alkaloids, which discourage predators with noxious odors (such as the volatile oils of mint and sage) or repellent tastes (like the bitterness of quinine). Other alkaloids affect herbivores by causing either excessive stimulation (caffeine is one example) or the lethargy associated with opioids. Some compounds become toxic after ingestion; for instance, glycol cyanide in the cassava root releases cyanide only upon ingestion by the herbivore.

Mechanical wounding and predator attacks activate defense and protection mechanisms both in the damaged tissue and at sites farther from the injury location. Some defense reactions occur within minutes: others over several hours. The infected and surrounding cells may die, thereby stopping the spread of infection.

Long-distance signaling elicits a systemic response aimed at deterring the predator. As tissue is damaged, jasmonates may promote the synthesis of compounds that are toxic to predators. Jasmonates also elicit the synthesis of volatile compounds that attract parasitoids, which are insects that spend their developing stages in or on another insect, and eventually kill their host. The plant may activate abscission of injured tissue if it is damaged beyond repair.

science practices CONNECTION for AP® Courses

Think About It

1. Owners and managers of plant nurseries have to plan a lighting schedule for a long-day plant that will flower in February. What lighting periods will be most effective?
2. Storage facilities for fruits and vegetables are usually refrigerated and well ventilated. Why are these conditions advantageous?
3. Stomata close in response to bacterial infection. Create a diagram to illustrate how this is a defense mechanism for the plant.

KEY TERMS

abscisic acid (ABA) plant hormone that induces dormancy in seeds and other organs

abscission physiological process that leads to the fall of a plant organ (such as leaf or petal drop)

adventitious root aboveground root that arises from a plant part other than the radicle of the plant embryo

apical bud bud formed at the tip of the shoot

apical meristem meristematic tissue located at the tips of stems and roots; enables a plant to extend in length

auxin plant hormone that influences cell elongation (in phototropism), gravitropism, apical dominance and root growth

axillary bud bud located in the axil: the stem area where the petiole connects to the stem

bark tough, waterproof, outer epidermal layer of cork cells

bulb modified underground stem that consists of a large bud surrounded by numerous leaf scales

Casparian strip waxy coating that forces water to cross endodermal plasma membranes before entering the vascular cylinder, instead of moving between endodermal cells

chromophore molecule that absorbs light

collenchyma cell elongated plant cell with unevenly thickened walls; provides structural support to the stem and leaves

companion cell phloem cell that is connected to sieve-tube cells; has large amounts of ribosomes and mitochondrion

compound leaf leaf in which the leaf blade is subdivided to form leaflets, all attached to the midrib

corm rounded, fleshy underground stem that contains stored food

cortex ground tissue found between the vascular tissue and the epidermis in a stem or root

cryptochrome protein that absorbs light in the blue and ultraviolet regions of the light spectrum

cuticle waxy protective layer on the leaf surface

cuticle waxy covering on the outside of the leaf and stem that prevents the loss of water

cytokinin plant hormone that promotes cell division

dermal tissue protective plant tissue covering the outermost part of the plant; controls gas exchange

endodermis layer of cells in the root that forms a selective barrier between the ground tissue and the vascular tissue, allowing water and minerals to enter the root while excluding toxins and pathogens

epidermis single layer of cells found in plant dermal tissue; covers and protects underlying tissue

ethylene volatile plant hormone that is associated with fruit ripening, flower wilting, and leaf fall

fibrous root system type of root system in which the roots arise from the base of the stem in a cluster, forming a dense network of roots; found in monocots

gibberellin (GA) plant hormone that stimulates shoot elongation, seed germination, and the maturation and dropping of fruit and flowers

ground tissue plant tissue involved in photosynthesis; provides support, and stores water and sugars

guard cells paired cells on either side of a stoma that control stomatal opening and thereby regulate the movement of gases and water vapor

intercalary meristem meristematic tissue located at nodes and the bases of leaf blades; found only in monocots

internode region between nodes on the stem

jasmonates small family of compounds derived from the fatty acid linoleic acid

lamina leaf blade

lateral meristem meristematic tissue that enables a plant to increase in thickness or girth

lenticel opening on the surface of mature woody stems that facilitates gas exchange

megapascal (MPa) pressure units that measure water potential

meristem plant region of continuous growth

meristematic tissue tissue containing cells that constantly divide; contributes to plant growth

negative gravitropism growth away from Earth's gravity

node point along the stem at which leaves, flowers, or aerial roots originate

oligosaccharin hormone important in plant defenses against bacterial and fungal infections

palmately compound leaf leaf type with leaflets that emerge from a point, resembling the palm of a hand

parenchyma cell most common type of plant cell; found in the stem, root, leaf, and in fruit pulp; site of photosynthesis and starch storage

pericycle outer boundary of the stele from which lateral roots can arise

periderm outermost covering of woody stems; consists of the cork cambium, cork cells, and the phelloderm

permanent tissue plant tissue composed of cells that are no longer actively dividing

petiole stalk of the leaf

photomorphogenesis growth and development of plants in response to light

photoperiodism occurrence of plant processes, such as germination and flowering, according to the time of year

phototropin blue-light receptor that promotes phototropism, stomatal opening and closing, and other responses that promote photosynthesis

phototropism directional bending of a plant toward a light source

phyllotaxy arrangement of leaves on a stem

phytochrome plant pigment protein that exists in two reversible forms (Pr and Pfr) and mediates morphologic changes in response to red light

pinnately compound leaf leaf type with a divided leaf blade consisting of leaflets arranged on both sides of the midrib

pith ground tissue found towards the interior of the vascular tissue in a stem or root

positive gravitropism growth toward Earth's gravitational center

primary growth growth resulting in an increase in length of the stem and the root; caused by cell division in the shoot or root apical meristem

rhizome modified underground stem that grows horizontally to the soil surface and has nodes and internodes

root cap protective cells covering the tip of the growing root

root hair hair-like structure that is an extension of epidermal cells; increases the root surface area and aids in absorption of water and minerals

root system belowground portion of the plant that supports the plant and absorbs water and minerals

runner stolon that runs above the ground and produces new clone plants at nodes

sclerenchyma cell plant cell that has thick secondary walls and provides structural support; usually dead at maturity

secondary growth growth resulting in an increase in thickness or girth; caused by the lateral meristem and cork cambium

sessile leaf without a petiole that is attached directly to the plant stem

shoot system aboveground portion of the plant; consists of non-reproductive plant parts, such as leaves and stems, and reproductive parts, such as flowers and fruits

sieve-tube cell phloem cell arranged end to end to form a sieve tube that transports organic substances such as sugars and amino acids

simple leaf leaf type in which the lamina is completely undivided or merely lobed

sink growing parts of a plant, such as roots and young leaves, which require photosynthate

source organ that produces photosynthate for a plant

statolith (also, **amyloplast**) plant organelle that contains heavy starch granules

stele inner portion of the root containing the vascular tissue; surrounded by the endodermis

stipule small green structure found on either side of the leaf stalk or petiole

stolon modified stem that runs parallel to the ground and can give rise to new plants at the nodes

strigolactone hormone that promotes seed germination in some species and inhibits lateral apical development in the absence of auxins

tap root system type of root system with a main root that grows vertically with few lateral roots; found in dicots

tendril modified stem consisting of slender, twining strands used for support or climbing

thigmomorphogenesis developmental response to touch

thigmonastic directional growth of a plant independent of the direction in which contact is applied

thigmotropism directional growth of a plant in response to constant contact

thorn modified stem branch appearing as a sharp outgrowth that protects the plant

tracheid xylem cell with thick secondary walls that helps transport water

translocation mass transport of photosynthates from source to sink in vascular plants

transpiration loss of water vapor to the atmosphere through stomata

trichome hair-like structure on the epidermal surface

tuber modified underground stem adapted for starch storage; has many adventitious buds

vascular bundle strands of stem tissue made up of xylem and phloem

vascular stele strands of root tissue made up of xylem and phloem

vascular tissue tissue made up of xylem and phloem that transports food and water throughout the plant

venation pattern of veins in a leaf; may be parallel (as in monocots), reticulate (as in dicots), or dichotomous (as in *Gingko biloba*)

vessel element xylem cell that is shorter than a tracheid and has thinner walls

water potential (Ψ_w) the potential energy of a water solution per unit volume in relation to pure water at atmospheric pressure and ambient temperature

whorled pattern of leaf arrangement in which three or more leaves are connected at a node

CHAPTER SUMMARY

23.1 The Plant Body

A vascular plant consists of two organ systems: the shoot system and the root system. The shoot system includes the aboveground vegetative portions (stems and leaves) and reproductive parts (flowers and fruits). The root system supports the plant and is usually underground. A plant is composed of two main types of tissue: meristematic tissue and permanent tissue. Meristematic tissue consists of actively dividing cells found in root and shoot tips. As growth occurs, meristematic tissue differentiates into permanent tissue, which is categorized as either simple or complex. Simple tissues are made up of similar cell types; examples include dermal tissue and ground tissue. Dermal tissue provides the outer covering of the plant. Ground tissue is responsible for photosynthesis; it also supports vascular tissue and may store water and sugars. Complex tissues are made up of different cell types. Vascular tissue, for example, is made up of xylem and phloem cells.

23.2 Stems

The stem of a plant bears the leaves, flowers, and fruits. Stems are characterized by the presence of nodes (the points of attachment for leaves or branches) and internodes (regions between nodes).

Plant organs are made up of simple and complex tissues. The stem has three tissue systems: dermal, vascular, and ground tissue. Dermal tissue is the outer covering of the plant. It contains epidermal cells, stomata, guard cells, and trichomes. Vascular tissue is made up of xylem and phloem tissues and conducts water, minerals, and photosynthetic products. Ground tissue is responsible for photosynthesis and support and is composed of parenchyma, collenchyma, and sclerenchyma cells.

Primary growth occurs at the tips of roots and shoots, causing an increase in length. Woody plants may also exhibit secondary growth, or increase in thickness. In woody plants, especially trees, annual rings may form as growth slows at the end of each season. Some plant species have modified stems that help to store food, propagate new plants, or discourage predators. Rhizomes, corms, stolons, runners, tubers, bulbs, tendrils, and thorns are examples of modified stems.

23.3 Roots

Roots help to anchor a plant, absorb water and minerals, and serve as storage sites for food. Taproots and fibrous roots are the two main types of root systems. In a taproot system, a main root grows vertically downward with a few lateral roots. Fibrous root systems arise at the base of the stem, where a cluster of roots forms a dense network that is shallower than a taproot. The growing root tip is protected by a root cap. The root tip has three main zones: a zone of cell division (cells are actively dividing), a zone of elongation (cells increase in length), and a zone of maturation (cells differentiate to form different kinds of cells). Root vascular tissue conducts water, minerals, and sugars. In some habitats, the roots of certain plants may be modified to form aerial roots or epiphytic roots.

23.4 Leaves

Leaves are the main site of photosynthesis. A typical leaf consists of a lamina (the broad part of the leaf, also called the blade) and a petiole (the stalk that attaches the leaf to a stem). The arrangement of leaves on a stem, known as phyllotaxy, enables maximum exposure to sunlight. Each plant species has a characteristic leaf arrangement and form. The pattern of leaf arrangement may be alternate, opposite, or spiral, while leaf form may be simple or compound. Leaf tissue consists of the epidermis, which forms the outermost cell layer, and mesophyll and vascular tissue, which make up the inner portion of the leaf. In some plant species, leaf form is modified to form structures such as tendrils, spines, bud scales, and needles.

23.5 Transport of Water and Solutes in Plants

Water potential (Ψ) is a measure of the difference in potential energy between a water sample and pure water. The water potential in plant solutions is influenced by solute concentration, pressure, gravity, and matric potential. Water potential and transpiration influence how water is transported through the xylem in plants. These processes are regulated by stomatal opening and closing. Photosynthates (mainly sucrose) move from sources to sinks through the plant's phloem. Sucrose is actively loaded into the sieve-tube elements of the phloem. The increased solute concentration causes water to move by osmosis from the xylem into the phloem. The positive pressure that is produced pushes water and solutes down the pressure gradient. The sucrose is unloaded into the sink, and the water returns to the xylem vessels.

23.6 Plant Sensory Systems and Responses

Plants respond to light by changes in morphology and activity. Irradiation by red light converts the photoreceptor phytochrome to its far-red light-absorbing form—Pfr. This form controls germination and flowering in response to length of day, as well as triggers photosynthesis in dormant plants or those that just emerged from the soil. Blue-light receptors, cryptochromes, and phototropins are responsible for phototropism. Amyloplasts, which contain heavy starch granules, sense gravity. Shoots exhibit negative gravitropism, whereas roots exhibit positive gravitropism. Plant hormones—naturally occurring compounds synthesized in small amounts—can act both in the cells that produce them and in distant tissues and organs. Auxins are responsible for apical dominance, root growth, directional growth toward light, and many other growth responses. Cytokinins stimulate cell division and counter apical dominance in shoots. Gibberellins inhibit dormancy of seeds and promote stem growth. Abscisic acid induces dormancy in seeds and buds, and protects plants from excessive water loss by promoting stomatal closure. Ethylene gas speeds up fruit ripening and dropping of leaves. Plants respond to touch by rapid movements (thigmotropy and thigmonasty) and slow differential growth (thigmomorphogenesis). Plants have evolved defense mechanisms against predators and pathogens. Physical barriers like bark and spines protect tender tissues. Plants also have chemical defenses, including toxic secondary metabolites and hormones, which elicit additional defense mechanisms.

REVIEW QUESTIONS

1. Students are sketching diagrams of the shoot system of angiosperms for a plant anatomy class. These lists describe diagrams made by four students. Which diagram represents the shoot system incorrectly?

a. leaves, stem, fruit, flowers
b. stem, fruit, leaves, branches
c. flowers, leaves, branches, stem
d. stem, hair roots, leaves, flowers, branches

2. An herbicide causes roots to shrivel and die. What is the most direct consequence for a plant treated with the herbicide?

a. The plant will grow normally but will not bloom.
b. The plant will dry out because water is not reaching all its organs.
c. New leaves will form to compensate for the dying of roots
d. The plant will grow normally but will not produce fruit

3. Scientists label cells in the lateral meristem of a sapling with a dye to follow the developmental fate of the cells. After several weeks, sections are prepared from the sapling and observed under the microscope. Which tissues are most likely to be stained by the dye that was injected into the lateral meristem?

a. Vascular tissue to transport nutrients and water
b. The tip of plant to promote growth of plant
c. Secondary xylem to increase girth of stem
d. Epidermis to cover the plant

4. A lab technician is looking for a slide that shows an example of permanent tissue. Which slide is the best choice?

a. a slide of the apical bud of a stem
b. a slide obtained from the intercalary meristems
c. lateral meristem in the vascular cambium
d. secondary xylem

5. Which region of a plant is most likely to contribute to an increase in its length?

a. tip of leaves
b. dermal layer
c. vascular bundles
d. tip of the root

6. You are measuring the effect of a new fertilizer on the growth of lawns. Which of the following tissues should be the target of the fertilizer?

a. apical meristem
b. lateral meristem
c. intercalary meristem
d. vascular bundle

7. The dermal tissue of a plant provides __ for the plant.

a. transport of water

b. transport of minerals

c. support

d. protection

8. A branch of celery is soaked in a glass of water containing food dye. Soon, the tough fibers in celery branch are colored. What tissue do the tough fibers contain?

a. dermal tissue

b. xylem

c. phloem

d. ground tissue

9. A plant biologist is examining sections of plant tissue under the microscope. The slides are not labeled and the biologist is interested in simple tissues. Which of the following slides is a sample of a simple tissue?

a. cells dividing rapidly in a stem

b. root cambium showing different types of cells

c. parenchyma showing only one type of cell

d. leaf displaying the vascular bundle where diverse types of cells are involved in transport

10. Students are asked to sort tissue slides into simple and complex tissues. How should they recognize a complex tissue through the microscope?

a. Complex tissue has a variety of cell types that fulfill different functions.

b. Only complex tissue is observed in adult plants.

c. Complex tissue appears only in lateral roots and branches.

d. Complex tissues contain cells that are strikingly different in appearance but perform the same function.

11. Students are sketching diagrams of the reproductive system of angiosperms for a plant anatomy class. These lists describe diagrams made by four students. Which diagram represents the reproductive system correctly?

a. hair roots, lateral roots, and taproot

b. stem, branches, and leaves

c. flowers and fruit

d. leaves, petioles, and branches

12. Plant scientists are interested in isolating meristematic tissue for an experiment. They sample several regions of a plant. Which sample is most likely to contain meristematic tissue?

a. the thin epidermis that covers an onion bulb

b. a sample of fruit tissue

c. a sample of actively dividing cells located at the tip of an onion root

d. a region of the mesenchyme

13.

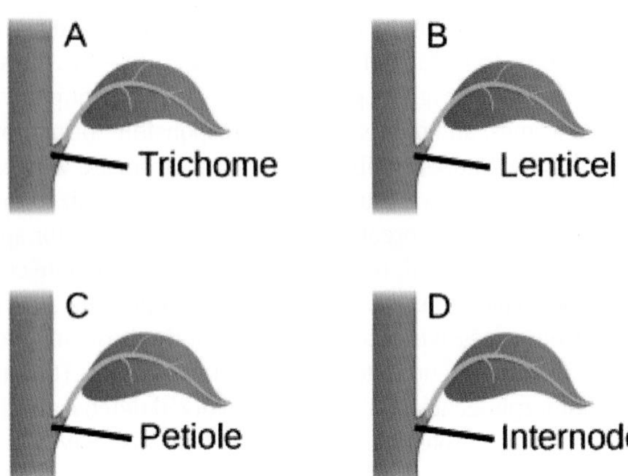

This sketch of a stem shows the region to which leaves are attached. Which version of the sketch is correctly labeled?

a. version A

b. version B

c. version C

d. version D

14. A student examines a plant part and concludes that it is part of a stem. The presence of _____fully justifies the student's conclusion.

a. vascular tissue

b. nodes and internodes

c. epidermal layer

d. stored carbohydrates

15. A student reported vascular tissue while inspecting a cross-section of a plant stem under the microscope. Which cells would allow the student to identify vascular tissue?

a. tracheids, vessel elements, sieve-tube cells, and companion cells

b. cells actively dividing at the apex of the stem

c. parenchyma cells at the center of the section

d. cells covered by a cuticle at the outside edge of the section

16. While using a microscope to observe a stem section stained with a dye that binds lignin, a student notices that some cells with thick cell walls and large hollow centers are preferentially stained. He concludes that those cells belong to the ____.

a. meristematic tissue
b. vascular tissue
c. ground tissue
d. dermal tissue

17. Scientists are cataloguing slides of plant cross-sections. They are interested in finding examples of secondary growth. Which example contributes to secondary growth?

a. apical meristem, which contributes to increase in length
b. vascular cambium, which contributes to increase in thickness or girth
c. root region, which shows an increase in root hairs
d. stems, which show an increase in number of leaves

18. Where is the vascular cambium located in an established woody plant?

a. between the primary xylem and the primary phloem
b. between the secondary xylem and the primary phloem
c. between the secondary xylem and the secondary phloem
d. between the primary xylem and the secondary phloem

19. Dendrochronology is the science of dating the age of a tree by counting the annual rings in a tree trunk. If scientists are determining the age of a tree by dendrochronology, what tissue are they looking at?

a. primary xylem
b. secondary xylem
c. primary phloem
d. vascular cambium

20. While examining the stump of a recently cut tree, you count four thick rings alternating with four rings that are much narrower and appear denser. From this observation, you should conclude that the tree is __.

a. two years old, because each ring corresponds to a season
b. three years old, because the first ring you observe is the primary xylem
c. four years old, because secondary xylem grows only in the spring and fall of each year
d. eight years old, because there are eight rings in all

21. Many forms of modified organs exist in plants. What is a rhizome?

a. an underground stem with fleshy leaves modified for food storage as in onions
b. a solid, underground stem covered with scales formed by some plants such as crocuses
c. an aboveground stem with buds as seen in strawberry plants
d. a modified horizontal stem that grows underground as seen in irises

22. Modified organs are part of survival strategies of plants. Which of these plants has a flattened, photosynthetic stem that could be mistaken for a leaf?

a. fern
b. cactus
c. potato
d. iris

23. Analyzing cross-sections of different parts of a plant in a plant anatomy class, students categorized the most frequently encountered types of cells in plant tissues. Which student gave the most accurate report?

a. Student A reported that meristematic cells were the most abundant.
b. Student B tallied mostly collenchyma cells.
c. Student C noticed mostly sclerenchyma cells.
d. Student D observed that parenchyma cells were the most abundant.

24. A carrot is an example of a tap root. Which of these can also be classified as a tap root?

a. the large network of superficial roots of a cactus
b. a dandelion anchored by a long main root that penetrates deep into the soil
c. a banyan tree’s system of roots that dangle from the branches
d. a round organ that stores carbohydrates

25. Some weeds are anchored by taproots. They cause problems to gardeners because they are ___.

a. easy to pull up because the root system is shallow
b. difficult to pull up because their taproots penetrate deep into the soil
c. difficult to pull up because they are anchored by an extensive network of roots
d. easy to pull up because there is not a large network to anchor the plant

26. One of the major concepts of biology is that form follows function. If that is so, what can be deduced from the shape and location of the root cap?

a. It provides protection to the root tip.
b. It absorbs water and minerals.
c. It acts as a storage tissue.
d. It replicates actively to elongate the root.

27. A technician is preparing microscope slides that will display the different stages of mitosis from root samples. He compares sections from several areas of the root. Which is the best prediction of his observation?

a. The technician will see mostly mitotic cells in the root cap.
b. The technician will observe mitotic figures in the meristematic tissue below the cap.
c. The technician will observe cell division in the elongation zone.
d. The technician will see that most mitotic cells are in the maturation zone.

28. Selective uptake of minerals in the root is measured and the results are analyzed. If you analyze the data, what should you see?

a. Pericycle is the tissue where selectivity takes place.
b. The endodermis acts as a selective barrier for minerals taken up by the root.
c. The epidermis acts as a selective barrier for minerals.
d. The root cap functions as a selective barrier for minerals taken up by the root.

29. Sudan Red dye stains primarily waxy, hydrophobic material. A root is soaked in Sudan Red and analyzed for stain retention. What is a scientist observing sections of the root under a microscope likely to see?

a. The cells in the cortex show the deepest stain.
b. The tracheids in the xylem contain mostly lipid droplets stained with Sudan Red.
c. The Casparian strip will show the deepest coloring.
d. The sieve elements in the phloem show staining with Sudan Red because of transported oil droplets.

30. In environments where light is scarce, some plants grow on other plants to reach light. Which root system would best support this mode of life?

a. Epiphytic root system in the air
b. Prop roots that support the trees to stand in muddy soil
c. Adventitious roots that grow above ground
d. Taproots that penetrate the soil

31. A section of buttercup root is stained with iodine, which stains starch blue. Where would you expect to find the blue granules indicative of starch?

a. parenchymal cells of the cortex
b. cells of phloem
c. cells of the epidermis
d. cells of the endodermis and pericycle

32. Which of the following best describes a fibrous root system?

a. covers a limited surface and contains few roots
b. consists of a single main root with adjacent smaller roots
c. covers a large area and contains an extensive network of roots
d. contains several major, interconnected roots

33. Ethylene promotes the fall of leaves by triggering the death of cells and abscission. What region of the leaf responds to ethylene?

a. the lamina, where photosynthesis takes place
b. the vein, which carries nutrients and water in and out of the leaf
c. the petiole, which attaches the leaf to the stem
d. the margin, which is serrated and may be sharp

34. A horticulture student is classifying plants as dicots or monocots according to their leaf structure. How is a dicot leaf recognizable?

a. It does not have stipules
b. The veins form a network pattern.
c. The veins are parallel.
d. The veins form forks and fan out.

35. Multiple leaves attached to the same node are fairly unusual. One example is found on the macadamia nut tree. The leaf arrangement in the macadamia tree is best characterized as ___.

a. whorled
b. opposite
c. tripled
d. alternate

36. You picked leaves while on a hike. One specimen appears to show an opposite arrangement. On closer inspection, you notice that those are not leaves, but leaflets attached to a midrib vein. What type of leaf arrangement are you observing?

a. palmately compound
b. pinnately compound
c. simple whorled
d. simple spiral

37. Chlorophyll, the primary photosynthetic pigment,

emits light in the red region of the visible spectrum. The presence of chlorophyll correlates with photosynthetic capacity. Under a fluorescent microscope, what part of a leaf would fluoresce in the red region of the spectrum?

a. vascular bundle
b. epidermis
c. mesophyll
d. cuticle

38. A pulse of radioactive carbon dioxide (CO_2) is provided to isolated leaves. In which tissue would you expect to see radioactive glucose appear first?

a. in the cells of the mesophyll
b. in the sieve elements of the phloem
c. epidermis
d. vessels of the xylem

39. Which adaptation is most likely to be found in a desert environment?

a. broad leaves to capture sunlight
b. spines instead of leaves
c. needle-like leaves
d. wide, flat leaves that can float

40. In the collection of a botanical garden, plants are classified according to the environments in which they thrive. What plant would have large leaves covered with a thick upper cuticle and wide flat blades and possess large air spaces (chambers) within its mesophyll tissue?

a. a water lily floating on water
b. a pine tree growing in the cold and dry taiga
c. a cactus growing in a hot, sunny, and dry environment
d. an orchid hanging from a tree in a tropical forest

41. If a gardener trims leaves off of the stem of a rose, which part of the leaf is cut?

a. petiole
b. lamina
c. stipule
d. midrib

42. On a field trip, students collect a few samples to analyze back in their classroom. One student picks a blade of grass in the field and identifies it as a dicot leaf, but his partner thinks it is a monocot. Which explanation supports his partner's opinion?

a. The leaf displays a thin lamina.
b. There is no petiole.
c. The margins are serrated.
d. The venation is parallel.

43. Which of the following physical components of the total water potential cannot be manipulated by the plant because it represents the interaction between water and hydrophilic molecules lining the vessels and tracheids?

a. pressure
b. solute concentration
c. gravity
d. matric potential

44. If the concentration of solute increases in a cell, the water potential will ________ **inside the cell and water will move** ________ the cell.

a. increase; out of
b. increase; into
c. decrease; into
d. decrease; out of

45. Plants can modify their water potential by opening and closing their stomata to modulate the rate of respiration according to environmental conditions. Which of the following environmental conditions would cause the stomata to close?

a. increased temperature
b. high oxygen concentration
c. high relative humidity
d. high light levels

46. Plants regulate their internal water potential by opening and closing stomata. Which events take place when stomata open?

a. Water vapor is lost to the external environment, increasing the rate of transpiration.
b. Water vapor is lost to the external environment, decreasing the rate of transpiration.
c. Water vapor enters the spaces in the mesophyll, increasing the rate of transpiration.
d. The rate of photosynthesis drops when stomata open.

47. A pulse of sugars labelled with a fluorescent dye is supplied to leaves of young plants. After a brief interval, tissue sections are obtained from the plant and examined under the fluorescence microscope. Tissues are scored for the presence of fluorescence and ranked from very high to low fluorescence. Which cells would contain the most fluorescence?

a. xylem
b. companion cells
c. sieve elements
d. epidermis

48. Sugars produced in the leaf are distributed throughout the plant body. An experimenter supplies plants with a pulse of radiolabeled CO_2 in a control chamber. The movement of radioactively labeled sugar is monitored in the plant by analyzing different cells content over time. Where will the radiolabeled sugar appear immediately after detection in the leaf cells?

a. tracheids and vessel elements
b. tracheids and companion cells
c. vessel elements and companion cells
d. sieve-tube elements and companion cells

49. Solute potential decreases when solutes are added to a cell. The consequence is to draw water into the cell. Which of these terms corresponds to solute potential?

a. water potential
b. pressure potential
c. osmotic potential
d. negative potential

50.

Photoreceptor	Active Region of the Spectrum
Phototropin	Blue
Phytochrome	Red–far red
Carotenoids	Blue
Chlorophyll	Blue–red

Plants have many light responses, including photosynthesis, photoperiodism, and phototropism (growing toward a light source). Specific wavelengths of light absorbed by different photoreceptors trigger responses. This table shows some of the most common photoreceptors and pigments and the major regions of the spectrum in which they are active. Research shows that plants bend toward blue light. Even mutant plants that lack carotenoids will bend toward blue light. The photoreceptor is likely _____.

a. phytochrome
b. chlorophyll
c. phototropin
d. carotenoids

51. Plant flowering is an example of photoperiodism, the response to the length of nights or periods of darkness. A plant that responds to short nights followed by increasingly longer nights will most likely flower in _____.

a. spring
b. summer
c. autumn
d. winter

52. Gravitropism is plant growth in response to gravity. A dahlia stem was toppled by the wind and is lying lies on the ground. After a few days, you would likely notice that ________ .

a. the stem is growing by curving toward the roots
b. the stem is growing by trailing on the ground
c. the stem is growing by curving upward
d. the plant is wilting

53. Plants most likely detect gravity by sensing the direction in which some components respond to gravity. A mutant plant has roots that grow in all directions. Which organelle would you expect to be missing in the cell?

a. mitochondria
b. amyloplast
c. chloroplast
d. nucleus

54.

Plate	Hormone
A	Abscisic acid
B	Cytokinin
C	Ethylene
D	Gibberellic acid

In an experiment to release seeds from dormancy, several hormones were applied to seeds and germination rates were computed. Which plate likely showed the highest rate of germination?

a. abscisic acid
b. cytokinin
c. ethylene
d. gibberellic acid

55. Green bananas or unripe avocadoes can be kept in a

brown bag to ripen faster. What hormone is involved?

a. cytokinin
b. abscisic acid
c. ethylene
d. gibberellic acid

56. A lab teacher wants to demonstrate thigmonastic behavior of a plant. Which of these experiments is the best choice?

a. Observe flowering of a plant after a brief red light irradiation in the middle of a dark period.
b. Observe whether seedlings bend towards blue light.
c. Observe whether a tree grows bent in the direction of the prevailing wind.
d. Touch the plant Mimosa pudicaand observe the closing of the leaflets.

57. A lab teacher wants to demonstrate thigmotropic behavior of a plant. Which of these experiments is the best choice?

a. roots growing downwards
b. venus fly trap snapping on an insect
c. seedling germinating under a stone and growing upward and away from the stone
d. plant growing towards a shaded area

58. Which is a protection against microbial pathogens?

a. thorns and spines
b. cutin and suberin
c. neurotoxic compounds
d. bitter-tasting alkaloids

59. Many secondary alkaloids are poisonous to the nervous system. What organisms are targeted by the alkaloids?

a. bacteria
b. herbivores
c. fungi
d. viruses

60. Red light converts phytochrome red (Pr) to __.

a. an inactive form of Pr
b. a breakdown product
c. the far red light absorbing form called Pfr
d. cryptochrome

61. Circadian rhythm refers to a pattern of behavior that recurs on a daily schedule in the absence of an external stimulus. Flowers open and close according to a circadian rhythm. If a plant is transferred to a dark environment, what will happen?

a. Flowers will stay closed.
b. Flowers will stay open.
c. Flowers will open and close every day at the same time.
d. Flowers will open and close at random times.

CRITICAL THINKING QUESTIONS

62. Why are plants with shallow roots more easily damaged by some herbivores?

a. Shallow roots do not anchor the plant to the ground and can be easily uprooted. Once the plant is no longer in the ground, the roots are unable to grow back.
b. Plants with shallow roots do not anchor the plant to the ground; meristems can be easily damaged and cannot grow back when not in the ground.
c. Shallow roots do not anchor the plant to the ground and can be easily uprooted. Once the plant is no longer in the ground, roots take a long time to grow back.
d. Shallow roots anchor the plant to the ground strongly but can be easily uprooted, and they grow back very slowly.

63. A researcher intends to test the effects of several growth factors on the differentiation of plant tissue. What would be the best choice of experimental tissue?

a. dermal tissue
b. meristematic tissue
c. vascular tissue
d. ground tissue

64. How do the locations and the functions of the three types of meristematic tissues compare?

a. Apical meristems found in the tip of stems and roots promote growth by elongation; lateral meristems found at nodes and bases of leaf blades promote increase in length and intercalary meristems found in the vascular and cork cambia promote increase in girth.

b. Apical meristems found at nodes and bases of leaf blades promote growth by elongation; lateral meristems found in the vascular and cork cambia promote increase in girth and intercalary meristems found in the tip of stems and roots promote increase in length.

c. Apical meristems found in the tip of stems and roots promote growth by elongation; lateral meristems found in the vascular and cork cambia promote increase in girth and intercalary meristems found at nodes and bases of leaf blades promote increase in length.

d. Apical meristems found in the tip of stems and roots promote growth by elongation; lateral meristems found in the vascular and cork cambia promote increase in length and intercalary meristems found at nodes and bases of leaf blades promote increase in length.

65. In an experiment on transport in plants, seedlings are exposed to radiolabeled minerals. In a second experiment, plants are provided with CO2 that is labeled with 14C. At the end of each experiment, tissue slices are analyzed for the presence of radiolabeled minerals and radioactive sucrose. Which plant tissue would show the presence of labeled minerals and which would show the presence of radioactive sucrose?

a. Phloem tissue would show the presence of labeled minerals and xylem tissue would show the presence of radioactive sucrose.

b. Xylem tissue would show the presence of labeled minerals and phloem tissue would show the presence of radioactive sucrose.

c. Parenchyma would show the presence of labeled minerals and sclerenchyma would show the presence of radioactive sucrose.

d. Sclerenchyma would show the presence of labeled minerals and parenchyma would show the presence of radioactive sucrose.

66. How could the morphology of cells observed microscopically indicate that the specimen is probably simple tissue?

a. Simple tissue is made of cells that have different shapes, so the specimen will show oval, polygonal, and other shapes.

b. Simple tissue is made of cells that have intercellular spaces, so the specimen will contain spaces.

c. Simple tissue is made of cells that are elongated and tapered, so the specimen will show elongated cells.

d. Simple tissue is made of cells that are morphologically similar, so the specimen will appear uniform.

67. Which statements list two advantages of a taproot?

a. It anchors the plant, so that it is not easily uprooted by predators or wind. It is a sink for proteins that is protected from herbivores by being underground.

b. It anchors the plant, so that it is not easily uprooted by predators or wind. It is a source of starches that is protected from herbivores by being underground.

c. It anchors the plant, so that it cannot be uprooted by predators or wind. It is a sink for starches that is protected from herbivores by being underground.

d. It anchors the plant, so that it is not easily uprooted by predators or wind. It is a sink for starches that is protected from herbivores by being underground.

68. Students observe several slides of tissue cross-sections under the microscope. They are asked to develop a key system to classify the slides as coming from either monocot or dicots. What key system should the students develop?

a. In monocots, the vascular bundles form a distinct ring. In dicots, the vascular bundles are scattered in the ground tissue.

b. In monocots, the vascular tissue forms a characteristic X shape in the center. In dicots, the phloem and xylem cells are scattered in the pith.

c. In monocots, the vascular bundles are scattered in the ground tissue. In dicots the vascular bundles form a distinct ring.

d. In monocot roots, the pith is absent or very small. In dicots, the pith is large and well developed.

69. What are the functions of stomata and guard cells, and what would happen to a plant if these cells did not function correctly?

a. Guard cells allow carbon dioxide to enter and exit the plant. Stomata regulate the opening and closing of guard cells. If the cells didn't function, photosynthesis and transpiration would cease, which would interfere with the necessary continuous flow of water upward from roots to leaves.

b. Stomata allow oxygen to enter and exit the plant. Guard cells regulate the opening and closing of stomata. If the cells didn't function, photosynthesis would continue but transpiration would cease, which would interfere with the necessary continuous flow of water upward from roots to leaves.

c. Guard cells allow carbon dioxide to enter and exit the plant. Stomata regulate the opening and closing of guard cells. Transpiration and in turn, photosynthesis would not occur which is necessary to maintain a continuous flow of water upwards from the roots to the leaves.

d. Stomata allow gases to enter and exit the plant. Guard cells regulate the opening and closing of stomata. Photosynthesis and, in turn, transpiration, would not occur which is necessary to maintain a continuous flow of water upwards from the roots to the leaves.

70. An herbicide is developed that impairs the function of the cork cambium in woody plants. Which changes in the plant should be monitored to gauge the effectiveness of the herbicide?

a. Cork will not be produced and the plant will not increase in girth.

b. Excess cork will be produced and annual rings will not be formed.

c. Cork will not be produced and the plant will not be able to exchange gases.

d. Excess cork will be produced and the plant will not increase in girth.

71. Besides the age of a tree, what additional information can annual rings reveal?

a. Annual rings can also indicate the height of the tree.

b. Annual rings can also indicate the climatic conditions that prevailed during each growing season.

c. Annual rings can also indicate in which season the tree was sown.

d. Annual rings can also give an estimation of how long a particular tree is going to live.

72. Modified stems give an advantage to plants. What advantage do rhizomes, stolons, and runners provide? What advantages do corms, tubers, and bulbs provide?

a. Rhizomes, stolons and runners give rise to new plants that are the clones of the parents and they store food. Corms, tubers, and bulbs can also produce new plants.

b. Rhizomes, stolons, and runners give rise to new plants that are the different from the parents. Corms, tubers, and bulbs can also produce new plants as well as store food.

c. Rhizomes, stolons and runners give rise to new plants that are the clones of the parents. Corms, tubers, and bulbs can also produce new plants as well as store food.

d. Rhizomes, stolons and runners give rise to new plants that are similar to the parents but show genetic variability. Corms, tubers, and bulbs can also produce new plants as well as store food.

73. A time course is developed to follow the fate of the vascular bundles in the stem of dicots. Sections along the stem are fixed, stained, and observed under a microscope. What happens to the vascular bundles in the stem of a dicot as the plant matures?

a. The vascular bundles join to form growth rings.

b. The vascular bundles divide into primary xylem and primary phloem.

c. The vascular bundles divide into secondary xylem and primary phloem.

d. The vascular bundles die out.

74. Which description correctly compares a tap root system with a fibrous root system?

a. A tap root system, such as that of carrots, has a single main root that grows down. A fibrous root system, such as that of wheat, forms a dense network of roots that is closer to the soil surface. Fibrous root systems are found in monocots and tap root systems are found in dicots.

b. A fibrous root system, such as that of a carrot, has a single main root that grows down. A taproot system, such as that of wheat, forms a dense network of roots that is closer to the soil surface. Fibrous root systems are found in monocots and tap root systems are found in dicots.

c. A taproot system, such as that of rice, has a single main root that grows down. A fibrous root system, such as that of a carrot, forms a dense network of roots that is closer to the soil surface. Fibrous root systems are found in monocots and tap root systems are found in dicots.

d. A taproot system, such as that of a carrot, has a single main root that grows down. A fibrous root system, such as that of wheat, forms a dense network of roots that is closer to the soil surface. Taproot systems are found in monocots and fibrous root systems are found in dicots.

75. What is the advantage of a root cap covering the apical meristem of a root?

a. It provides protection and helps in absorption.

b. It increases the surface area of root for absorption of water and minerals.

c. It protects meristem against injury and provides lubrication for the growing root to dig through soil.

d. It protects the meristem against injury and helps in absorption.

76. How does selective uptake of water and mineral take place in a root?

a. Water and minerals must follow entirely a path between cells, where selectivity occurs.

b. Water and minerals must follow entirely a path between cells, where no selectivity occurs.

c. Water and minerals must cross the endodermis.

d. Water and minerals must cross the tracheids of the xylem.

77. What are the advantages to a plant of storing a food reserve underground?

a. Food reserves are more nutritious underground. The soil conditions make these food reserves abundant.

b. Food reserves underground are hidden from potential predators. The soil conditions make these food reserves abundant.

c. Food reserves are more nutritious underground. The soil conditions such as moisture and temperature are less variable.

d. Food reserves underground are hidden from potential predators. Soil conditions such as moisture and temperature are less variable.

78. Some desert plants have taproots that extend up to 20-30 feet underground. Others have fibrous root systems that cover wide areas. What are the advantages of a deep taproot and the advantages of a fibrous root system in a desert?

a. A deep taproot can reach the deeper soil regions that stay moist after several rainfalls. A shallow fibrous system provides additional support to anchor the plant in the desert.

b. A deep taproot provides additional support to anchor the plant in the desert. A shallow fibrous system increases the amount of water that can be absorbed after a light rainfall when the soil dries quickly in the desert.

c. A deep taproot increases the amount of water that can be absorbed after a light rainfall when the soil dries quickly in the desert. A shallow fibrous system can reach the deeper soil regions that stay moist after several rainfalls.

d. A deep taproot can reach the deeper soil regions that stay moist after several rainfalls. A shallow fibrous system increases the amount of water that can be absorbed after a light rainfall when the soil dries quickly in the desert.

79. Samples of leaves from monocots and dicots are piled on the table in a laboratory and students are sorting the leaves. What information will help them know which leaves to identify as monocots?

a. Bulliform cells are usually absent from monocots whereas they are present on the upper epidermis of dicot leaves.

b. Monocots have leaves with parallel venation and dicot leaves have reticulate, net-like venation.

c. Dorsiventral symmetry is observed in monocot leaves whereas isobilateral symmetry is observed in dicot leaves.

d. Monocots have leaves with reticulate, net-like venation and dicot leaves have parallel venation.

80. How does a compound leaf give a selective advantage to avoid herbivory?

a. Compound leaves produce certain types of chemical compounds that are harmful to herbivores.
b. It is more efficient for large herbivores to eat large, simple leaves.
c. Compound leaves are thicker than simple leaves.
d. It is more efficient for large herbivores to eat the small leaflets of compound leaves.

81. Stomata are usually found in higher numbers on the abaxial or bottom surface of a leaf. What is the advantage of such an arrangement?

a. Presence of stomata on the abaxial or bottom surface ensures that no, or very little, water is lost due to guttation.
b. The abaxial or bottom surface receives more sunlight and water evaporates faster by transpiration.
c. Herbivores do not prefer to eat leaves with stomata on the abaxial or bottom surface.
d. The adaxial or upper surface receives more sunlight and water evaporates faster by transpiration.

82. Which plants have leaves that are adapted to cold temperatures?

a. Conifers such as spruce, fir, and pine have oval-shaped leaves with sunken stomata, helping to reduce water loss.
b. Succulents such as aloes and agaves have waxy cuticles with sunken stomata, helping to reduce water loss.
c. Conifers such as spruce, orchids, and pine have needle-shaped leaves with sunken stomata, helping to reduce water loss.
d. Conifers such as spruce, fir, and pine have needle-shaped leaves with sunken stomata, helping to reduce water loss.

83. How is a leaf different from a leaflet?

a. A leaf petiole attaches directly to the stem at a bud node, whereas a leaflet petiole is attached to the main petiole or the midrib, not the stem.
b. A leaf has reticulate venation whereas leaflets show parallel venation.
c. A leaf petiole attaches to the main petiole or the midrib, not the stem, whereas a leaflet petiole attaches directly to the stem at a bud node.
d. A leaf has parallel venation whereas leaflets show reticulate venation.

84. Scientists on a new project to restore a damaged salt marsh are investigating several plants that could be introduced. Plant X is considered a possible candidate. Before the decision is made, the following data are examined. Assume that the contribution of gravity and matric potential are negligible and can be ignored. Recall that the overall water potential for a system is represented by the equation: Ψsystem = Ψtotal = Ψs + Ψp + Ψg + Ψm

overall Ψ of the soil: -2.1MPa solute potential of the plant's cell contents: -0.12MPa pressure potential (Ψp) of the plant's cells: -2.3 MPa

Is Plant X a good candidate for introduction to the salt marsh?

a. Yes, because the overall water potential of the plant is less negative than the water potential of the soil.
b. No, because the overall water potential of the plant is less negative than the water potential of the soil.
c. Yes, because the overall water potential of the plant is more negative than the water potential of the soil.
d. No, because the overall water potential of the plant is more negative than the water potential of the soil.

85. What organs in humans are similar in function to the vascular tissues of vascular plants?

86. Apoptosis, or programmed cell death, is an important step in the development of xylem. How does apoptosis contribute to xylem development?

87. A florist decided to paint the leaves of poinsettia with a gold paint to embellish them. The plant soon wilted and the leaves drooped. What explains this damage?

a. The paint clogged the stomata. Without photosynthesis, the plant could not pull water from the soil.
b. The paint clogged the stomata. Without transpiration, the plant could not pull water from the soil.
c. The paint clogged the hydathodes. Without transpiration, the plant could not pull water from the soil.
d. The paint clogged the stomata. Without guttation, the plant could not pull water from the soil.

88. The process of bulk flow transports fluids in a plant. What are the two main bulk flow processes?

a. Movement of water up the xylem and movement of solutes up and down the phloem
b. Movement of water up the phloem and movement of solutes up and down the xylem.
c. Movement of water up and down the xylem and movement of solutes up the phloem
d. Movement of solutes up the xylem and movement of water up and down the phloem

89. During a severe drought, the soil becomes dry and its water potential decreases. Many plants will wilt in such an environment. Consider that the overall water potential for a system is represented by the equation: Ψsystem = Ψtotal = Ψs + Ψp + Ψg + Ψm What is one reason that plants are unable to draw water from the soil?

a. The water potential of the soil becomes lower than the water potential of the plants.
b. The water potential of the soil becomes lower than the solute potential of the plants.
c. The water potential of the soil becomes higher than the water potential of the plants.
d. The solute potential of the soil becomes lower than the water potential of the plants.

90. A botanist compares the number of stomata between two plants. One plant, a eucalyptus, has stomata equally distributed on both sides of the leaf. The other plant has most of its stomata on the underside of the leaf. What does the positioning of the stomata indicate about which leaf surfaces on the two plants receive light in their natural environment?

a. The first plant receives light only on the upper surface of the leaves whereas the leaves of the second plant are equally exposed to sunlight.
b. The first plant receives light only on the lower surface whereas the second plant receives light only on the upper surface.
c. The first plant receives light only on the upper surface whereas the second plant receives light only on the lower surface.
d. The first plant has leaves that are equally exposed to sunlight whereas the second plant receives light only on the upper surface.

91. In the Northern Hemisphere, owners and managers of plant nurseries have to plan lighting schedules for a long-day plant that will flower in February. What lighting periods and color will be most effective?

a. Long periods of illumination with light enriched in the red range of the spectrum
b. Short periods of illumination with light enriched in the red range of the spectrum
c. Long periods of illumination with light enriched in the far-red range of the spectrum
d. Short periods of illumination with light enriched in the far-red range of the spectrum

92. Why do plants that cannot detect gravity show stunted growth with tangled roots and trailing stems?

a. Without gravitropism, both roots and seedlings would grow upward.
b. Without gravitropism, roots would grow in all directions and seedlings would grow upward.
c. Without gravitropism, roots would grow upward but seedlings would not grow upward toward the surface.
d. Without gravitropism, roots would grow in all directions but seedlings would not grow upward toward the surface.

93. Storage facilities for fruits and vegetables are usually refrigerated and well ventilated. Why are these conditions advantageous?

a. Refrigeration slows chemical reactions, including fruit ripening. Ventilation adds the ethylene gas that speeds up fruit maturation.
b. Refrigeration slows chemical reactions, including fruit maturation. Ventilation removes the ethylene gas that reduces fruit ripening.
c. Refrigeration slows chemical reactions, including fruit maturation. Ventilation removes the ethylene gas that speeds up fruit ripening.
d. Refrigeration removes the ethylene gas that speeds up fruit ripening. Ventilation slows chemical reactions, including fruit maturation.

94. A Venus fly trap has a very low sensitivity threshold, yet it can tell the difference between the light touch of an insect and a drop of rainwater or wind. How can the Venus fly trap differentiate between a random stimulus and an actual prey?

a. Hair-like appendages on the surface of the leaves respond to repeated contact.
b. Hair-like appendages on the surface of the leaves respond to a single contact.
c. Hair-like appendages on the surface of the leaves respond to chemical stimulus from the insect.
d. Hair-like appendages on the surface of the leaves respond to the electrical stimulus from the insect.

95. Stomata close in response to bacterial infection. This response is a defense mechanism because it ________ **, and the hormone involved is** ________ .

a. restricts the entry of O_2; gibberellin
b. restricts the entry of CO_2; abscisic acid
c. prevents further entry of pathogens; auxin
d. prevents further entry of pathogens; abscisic acid

96. Why is shade avoidance an important survival mechanism for plants? Would you expect seeds with large energy storage to display as strong a response of shade avoidance as small seeds with limited reserves?

a. A seedling growing in the shade of a mature plant will not have enough light to promote meristematic growth. A seed with large storage will be able to sustain growth until its seedling can reach enough light for photosynthesis.
b. A seedling growing in the shade of a mature plant will not have enough light to promote photosynthesis. Small seeds with limited reserve will be able to sustain growth until seedlings can reach enough light for photosynthesis.
c. A seedling growing in the shade of a mature plant will not have enough light to promote photosynthesis. A seed with large storage will be able to sustain growth until its seedling can reach enough light for photosynthesis.
d. A seedling growing in the shade of a mature plant will not have enough light to promote respiration. Small seeds with limited reserve will be able to sustain growth until their seedlings can reach enough light for photosynthesis.

TEST PREP FOR AP® COURSES

97. A plant has a measured pressure potential Ψp = 0.21MPa and a solute potential Ψs =-3.50MPa. The soil is saturated with water because it rained. How will the water move? After three months of dry weather, the soil has dried out. How will the water potential of the soil compare to the water potential measured immediately before the rain? How will the stomata respond to the change in weather?

a. The water will move from the plant to the soil. Dry soil has a lower water potential than wet soil. Under drought conditions, the stomata close to conserve water and leaves may also be shed if the drought continues.
b. The water will move from the soil to the plant. Dry soil has a higher water potential than wet soil. Under drought conditions, the stomata close to conserve water and leaves may also be shed if the drought continues.
c. The water will move from the soil to the plant. Dry soil has a lower water potential than wet soil. Under drought conditions, the stomata open its pores wider in order to perform a better rate of transpiration.
d. The water will move from the soil to the plant. Dry soil has a lower water potential than wet soil. Under drought conditions, the stomata close to conserve water and leaves may also be shed if the drought continues.

98.

	Transpiration rate versus temperature				
Temperature (°C)	20	23	27	28	30
Transpiration rate ($mmol/m^2sec$)	1.5	3	5	4.5	4

Plants lose water from their aboveground surfaces in the process of transpiration. Most of this water is lost from stomata. Excess loss of water has severe consequences and may be fatal for the plant. The table shows data collected on a sunny day. What is the best explanation for the transpiration rates leveling off and declining at temperature higher than 27°C?

a. The plant ran out of water.
b. The plant needs less water as temperature increases, so transpiration slows down to limit water uptake by the roots.
c. Stomata close to conserve water, slowing down transpiration.
d. The amount of water in the leaves decreases at high temperature and less is available for evaporation.

99. Humidity is an environmental factor that affects transpiration rate. Which statement accurately explains the shape of the curve obtained when increasing humidity is plotted against constant temperature to find the rate of transcription?

a. Increasing humidity leads to reduced evaporation rates due to increased difference in water vapor pressure between leaf and atmosphere.
b. Increasing humidity leads to reduced evaporation rates due to decreased difference in water vapor pressure between leaf and soil.
c. Increasing humidity leads to reduced evaporation rates due to decreased difference in water vapor pressure between leaf and atmosphere.
d. Increasing humidity leads to increased evaporation rates due to decreased difference in water vapor pressure between leaf and atmosphere.

100.

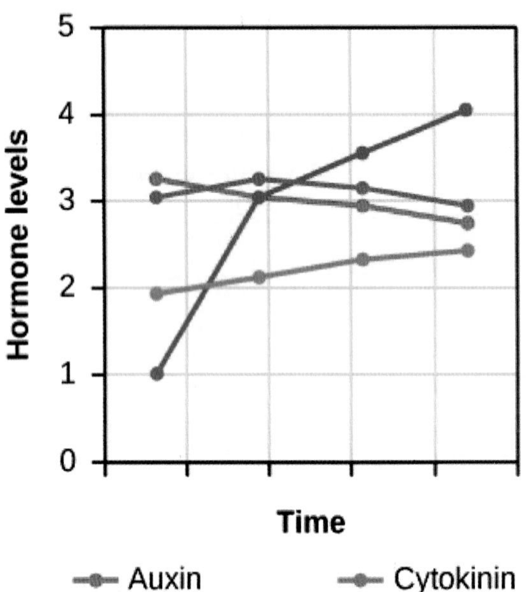

Plants sense drought through the decrease in water potential in the ground. This graph shows concentrations of several hormones that were measured during a drought period and plotted versus time. According to the data in the graph, which hormone shows the strongest response to drought?

a. auxin
b. abscisic acid
c. cytokinin
d. gibberellins

101.

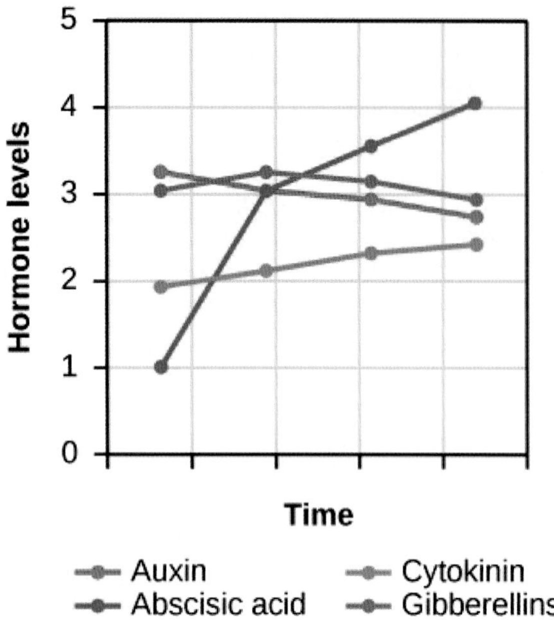

When drought conditions are forecast, fields are sprayed with a hormone that will promote a stress response. According to the graph, which hormone should be sprayed and why?

a. Gibberellins, to promote plant growth before the plants are damaged
b. Abscisic acid, to promote plant growth before the plants are damaged
c. Abscisic acid, to promote protective response to drought before the plants are damaged.
d. Gibberellins, to promote protective response to drought before the plants are damaged.

102.

	Plate A	Plate B	Plate C
Percentage germination	95%	50%	52%

Seeds were germinated in the dark on three plates. Plate A was irradiated with a short pulse of red light; plate B was irradiated with a short pulse of red light followed by a pulse of far-red light; and plate C was the control and was maintained in the dark. After three days, the plates were scored for percentage of germination, as shown in this table. What conclusion can be drawn from the experiment?

a. Darkness inhibits germination.

b. Red light promotes germination.

c. Far-red light promotes germination.

d. Germination is independent from light irradiation.

103.

	Plate A	Plate B	Plate C	Plate D
Percentage germination	95%	50%	96%	52%

Seeds were germinated in the dark on three plates. Plate A was irradiated with a short pulse of red light; plate B was irradiated with a short pulse of red light followed immediately by a pulse of far-red light; plate D was irradiated by a short pulse of red light followed one hour later by a pulse of far-red light; and plate C was the control and was maintained in the dark. After three days, the plates were scored for percentage of germination, as shown in this table. What hypothesis do the results suggest about the mechanism of action of red light?

a. Red light converts the phytochrome to its active form Pr which can be converted to the inactive form Pfr by far red light. After one hour, cascade of events initiated by Pfr has already begun promoting germination and hence, it cannot be reversed even by the pulse of far light.

b. Red light converts the phytochrome to its active form Pfr, which can be converted to the inactive form Pr by far-red light. After one hour, cascade of events initiated by Pr has already begun promoting germination and, hence, it cannot be reversed even by the pulse of far light.

c. Far red light converts the phytochrome to its active form Pfr, which can be converted to the inactive form Pr by red light. After one hour, the cascade of events initiated by Pr has already begun promoting germination and, hence, it cannot be reversed even by the pulse of far light.

d. Red light converts the phytochrome to its active form Pfr which can be converted to the inactive form Pr by far red light. After one hour, the cascade of events initiated by Pfr has already begun promoting germination and, hence, it cannot be reversed even by the pulse of far light.

104. After branches of woody saplings were trimmed, half of the cuts were covered with a sealant and the other half were left untouched. The plants with sealed cuts fared much better after several weeks. What is the likely reason?

a. The sealant stopped evaporation.

b. The plants with sealed cuts grew new branches.

c. The plants with unsealed cuts were infected by pathogens that entered through the cuts.

d. The plants with unsealed cuts lost photosynthates through bleeding of sap.

105.

	Mutant plants (*Ja*$^-$)	Normal plants (*Ja*$^+$)
Average size of wound from fungal infection	10 mm	4 mm
Weight of moth larvae	80 mg	55 mg

Jasmonate is produced in plants as a response to injury. Researchers compared the response to infection of mutant plants that were unable to produce jasmonate (Ja-) with the response of normal plants (Ja+) from the same species. Leaves were inoculated with spores from pathogenic molds. The size of the wounds was examined 48 hours after application. The plants were also infected with moths and the weight of the larvae was determined aafter 48 hours. This table shows the results. According to the results of the experiment, what conclusion can the researchers draw about the specificity of jasmonate protection?

a. Jasmonate protects against infection from a variety of pathogens.

b. Jasmonate protects against infection from one pathogen.

c. Jasmonate cannot provide protection against infection.

d. Jasmonate provides specific defense in winters and the defense is non-specific in summers.

106. In the Northern Hemisphere, a florist grows shrubs of the same species of woody plant under two different light schedules for three weeks. The first set is maintained under 15 hours of light and 9 hours of dark daily. The second set is maintained under 9 hours of light followed by 14 hours of dark daily. The first set of plants does not form flowers, but the second set of plants blooms. What can you conclude about these plants?

a. This species of shrub does not flower if the day is short.
b. They bloom early in the year (around February).
c. They bloom mid-summer (around June).
d. The critical dark period is 9 hours.

107.

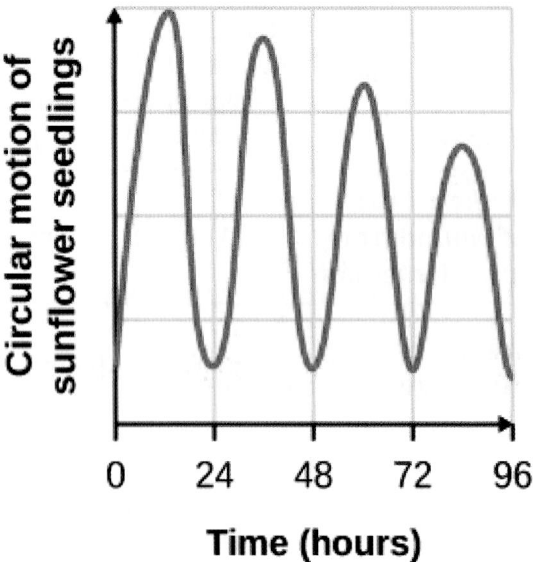

Heliotropism is the description of a response to the light of the sun. Seedlings of sunflowers were exposed to sunlight for 15 days. Following the 15 days of exposure to sunlight, the seedlings were transferred to complete darkness and their movement was monitored. This graph plots the movement of the seedlings in the dark versus time. What conclusion can be drawn about the light dependence of the movement of sunflowers from the graph?

a. The movement does require light once it is set but it will eventually slow down, suggesting that a "clock" molecule is degraded over time.
b. The movement does not require light once it is set and it will keep showing this upward and downward trend in the same manner.
c. The movement does not require light once it is set and it will eventually slow down, suggesting that a "clock" molecule never degrades.
d. The movement does not require light once it is set and it will eventually slow down, suggesting that a "clock" molecule is degraded over time.

108.

	Dish A	Dish B
Germinated seeds	12	20
Green-leaved seedlings	0	15
Yellow-leaved seedlings	12	5
Mean length of stem below 1st leaves	8 mm	3 mm

A student randomly chose 40 tobacco seeds of the same species from a packet. He placed 20 seeds on moist paper towels in each of two petri dishes. He wrapped dish A completely in an opaque cover to exclude all light. He did not wrap dish B. He placed the dishes equidistant from a light source set to a cycle of 14 hours of light and 10 hours of dark. All other conditions were the same for the two dishes. He examined the dishes after 7 days, and permanently removed the opaque cover from dish A. This table shows the student's data. The most probable cause for the difference in mean stem length between plants in dish A and plants in dish B is ____.

a. shortening of cells in the stem in response to the lack of light
b. elongation of the stem in response to the lack of light
c. enhancement of stem elongation by light
d. genetic differences between the seeds

109.

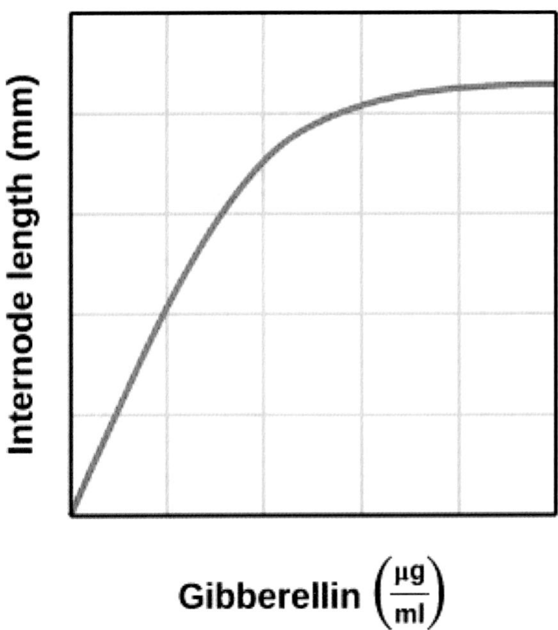

Groups of 20 seedlings from the same plant species were treated with gibberellins. Each group received a different concentration of hormone. The seedlings were grown under the same environmental conditions. After 15 days of growth, the internode distances between the first and second sets of leaves were measured in each group of seedlings. On this graph, the mean internode distance for each group is plotted against the concentration of gibberellins that the group received. According to the results, why is this effect of gibberellins on internode length used in agriculture to spray grapes with oversized fruit?

a. to lengthen the internode distance and accommodate larger fruit
b. to shorten the internode distance and accommodate larger fruit
c. to lengthen the internode distance and accommodate more flowers
d. to shorten the internode distance and accommodate smaller fruit

SCIENCE PRACTICE CHALLENGE QUESTIONS

110. The net photosynthetic production rate (NPP) is the difference between the rate of carbon fixation by photosynthesis (P) and the respiration rate (R). Each of these rates can be expressed in units of grams of carbon per day (gC/d). Vascular plants convert fixed carbon that is not released as carbon dioxide into biomass with a growth rate (G).

A. **Draw** areas within the box to represent the rates of growth (G) and respiration (R) to show the limit of each on the overall growth rate. The area of the box represents the rate of photosynthesis (P).

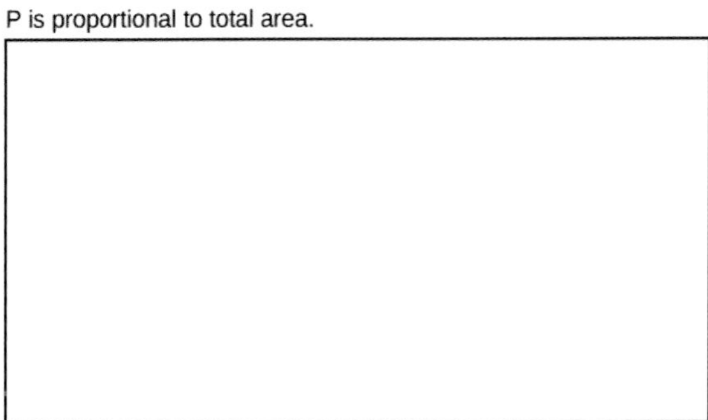

Figure 23.42

When the dependences on temperature of photosynthetic and respiration rates of a vascular plant are measured, the results depend on the species but have the general form shown in the figure. In these measurements, the temperature is maintained for several hours. The plant is then returned to 25 °C for several hours before the next set of measurements is made at a slightly higher temperature.

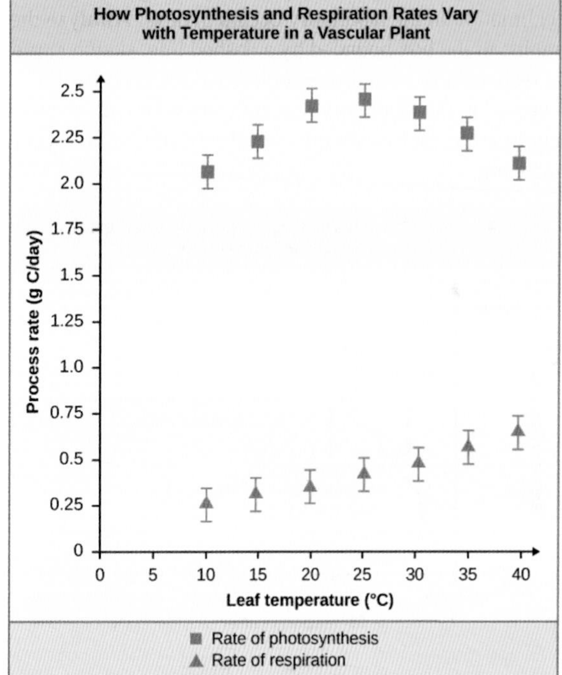

Figure 23.43

B. **Evaluate** these data to approximately **predict** the quantitative effect on the NPP and free energy availability in a deciduous forest ecosystem with a 3–5-°C increase in temperature. This is the expected temperature increase by the year 2100. Assume the current average summer temperature of the forest ecosystem is 25 °C.

In other experiments, rather than returning the plants to 25 °C, the plant is grown for several days at a constant higher temperature. Under these conditions, the maximum photosynthetic rate shifts towards the temperature of the new growing conditions. However, there is little change in the temperature dependence of respiration rate. This is referred to as temperature acclimation, an effect of great importance to predictions of future climate change.

C. **Pose** two **scientific questions** whose pursuit could lead to either an improved understanding of the mechanisms of temperature acclimation or improvements in models of atmospheric carbon dioxide concentrations that control temperature.

According to the graph, growth is predicted to increase when acclimation is taken into account and the average temperature increases of Earth's surface increases by the expected 3-5°C. Growth enhancement may be reduced, however, if respiration increases more rapidly than photosynthesis, particularly under periods of drought and stress. Thus, climate warming may result in positive, negative, or potentially no effect on the free energy availability in forest ecosystems.

D. In the figure below, the response to temperate change in terms of the rates of photosynthesis and respiration are sketched as a function of time from the very short-term (seconds) to the longer-term (decades) changes. Acclimation in the laboratory occurs in days. **Analyze** the graphs; in the box bounded by a dashed line, sketch curves for responses of both processes beyond the acclimation observed in the laboratory that are consistent with a neutral effect on free energy availability and provide your reasoning.

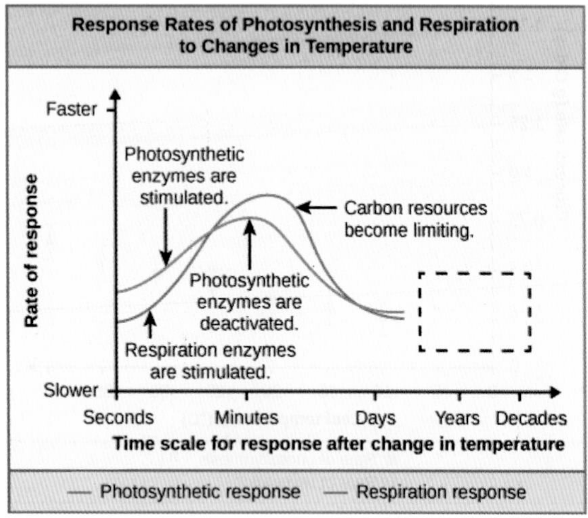

Figure 23.44

E. **Analyze** the long-term effect of a rate of respiration that exceeds the rate of photosynthesis in terms of dynamic homeostasis.

111. A disruption of dynamic homeostasis in the relationship between vascular plants and insects is occurring as global climate changes. The reduction in the yield of soybeans is plotted against leaf area removed by two insects, beetles and aphids. Soybean blooms begin to develop in the week of 13 July. Prior to that time, there is no effect of leaf removal on yield, even with complete loss of leaves. In the week of 18 August, plants are beginning to form seeds, and loss of leaves can be devastating.

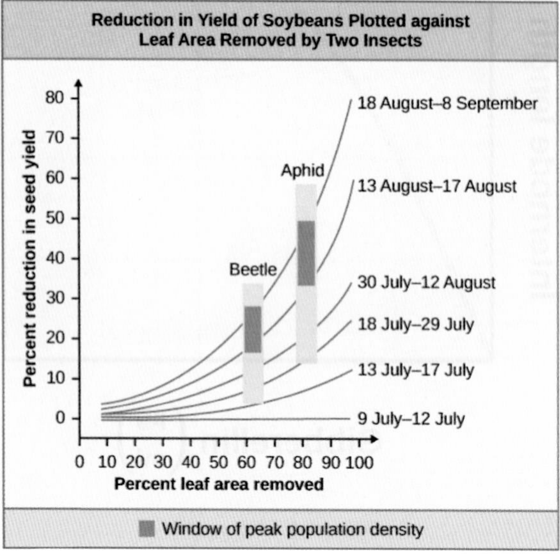

Figure 23.45

A. One observed effect of climate change is the shift toward earlier development in many insects. Quantitatively **describe** the worst possible consequences for yield, assuming plant developmental timing is not altered by warming temperatures, if the peak abundance of Japanese beetles is shifted from 18 July to 13 July, and 80% of leaf area is lost.

The expression of genes involved in seed development is temperature dependent, unlike the scenario suggested in part A. More than 90% of soybean seeds planted in 2015 in the soybean-corn ecosystem of the central United States are the herbicide-resistant, genetically modified "Roundup Ready" variety. The seed has a patented genome. It produces seeds that are sterile and must be purchased each spring from the patent holder.

B. **Predict** how the use of Roundup Ready seeds affects the selection of expression regulated in response to increasing temperature.

Roundup is an herbicide whose active chemical component is glyphosphate. This molecule disrupts the synthesis of phenylalanine, tyrosine, and tryptophan. By inserting a gene from *Agrobacteria*, a Roundup Ready seed can synthesize these amino acids in the presence of the herbicide.

C. **Pose** two **scientific questions** that must be considered to estimate the long-term effectiveness of this strategy for weed management.

112. By increasing the photosynthetic surface area, a plant increases the rate of capture of free energy. For every carbon atom fixed into carbohydrates, between 200 and 400 water molecules are released through stomata to the atmosphere. A simple geometric model can be used to estimate the minimum number of leaves on a tree, as shown.

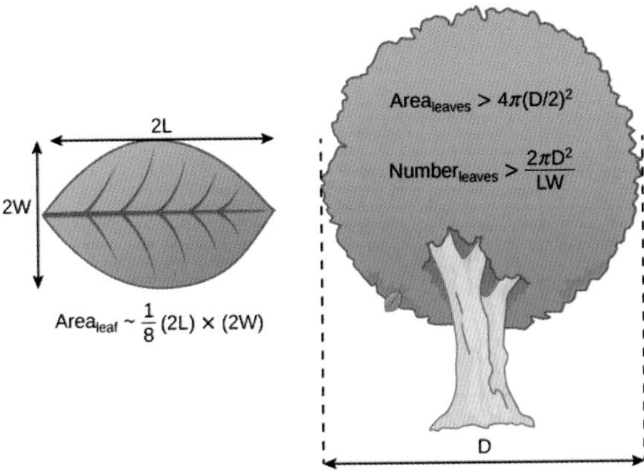

Figure 23.46

A. **Identify and justify the data** needed to describe the relationship between the free energy captured and the water transpired by a tree with dimensions D, L, and W. Use these data to **construct a mathematical model** of the relationship between transpiration rate and the rate of free energy captured when a single carbon atom is fixed.

The diversity of vascular plants decreases with increasing latitude. Equatorial ecosystems have greater plant diversity than do ecosystems further south or north. One of several explanations offered to account for this observation is the energy-equivalence model—as free energy increases, population size increases. As population size increases, mutations increase. One bit of evidence for the energy-equivalence model is the correlation of family-level diversity with actual evapotranspiration, the sum of water transferred by both transpiration and evaporation of surface water. This property is reported in mm of water per square meter of surface area.

B. **Explain** the relationship between free energy exchange and latitude that is the basis of the energy-equivalence model.

Shared ancestry is indicated by taxonomic classification in which a family of organisms contains many genera, and within each genus there are many species. A survey of tree flora (Latham and Ricklefs, *Oikos*, 67, 1993) at comparable latitudes in a temperate eastern Asia forest ecosystem (729 species in 177 genera and 67 families) and an eastern North America forest ecosystem (253 species in 90 genera and 46 families) had no species in common, but there were 20 common genera and 40 common families. Actual evapotranspiration for the two ecosystems are 850 ± 200 mm (eastern North America) and 730 ± 160 mm (eastern Asia).

C. **Analyze** these data to test the validity of the energy-equivalence model.

113. The evolution of vascular plants followed the colonization of terrestrial habitats by ancestors of *Chlorophyta*, green algae, during the Devonian period (which began about 400 million years ago). The three most significant structural innovations in that process are responses to selection through the availability of water resources: 1) the cuticle, a waxy covering of the epidermis that retains water; 2) stomata, openings that penetrate the cuticle through which water and carbon dioxide are transported; and 3) a vascular system, plant tissues through which water moves.

Measurements of gases trapped in ice cores provide atmospheric concentrations of the distant, as well as the recent, past. Life must adapt to changes in the environment. Woodward examined samples from the Cambridge herbarium of several trees (*Nature*, 327, 1987) to determine the stomatal index (percentage of epidermal cells that contain a stoma). In 1720, when the herbarium samples were collected, the carbon dioxide concentration in Earth's atmosphere was 225 ppm. In the year of the study, 1987, it was 340 ppm (it is 370 ppm in 2016). The following table presents some of Woodward's reported results.

Tree Genus	CO_2 (ppm)	Stomatal Index (%)
Acer	225	14.9 ± 0.8
	340	6.7 ± 1.1
Quercus	225	17.4 ± 1.1
	340	9.6 ± 1
Rumex	225	15.5 ± 0.7
	340	11.8 ± 0.9

Table 23.1

Teng and co-workers (PLoS ONE, 2009) followed the dependence of *Arabidopsis*, a member of the *Brassica* family of vascular plants, grown under a range of elevated CO_2 concentrations for 15 generations. They found elevated stomatal densities for each generation that were not heritable.

Engineer and co-workers (*Nature*, 513, 2014) discovered a mutant *Arabidopsis* in which stomatal density increases as CO_2 concentration increases. Measurements of a component of the set of mRNA molecules for epidermal patterning factor 2 (EPF2), responsible for stomatal density, are shown for plants grown in low and high CO_2 concentrations.

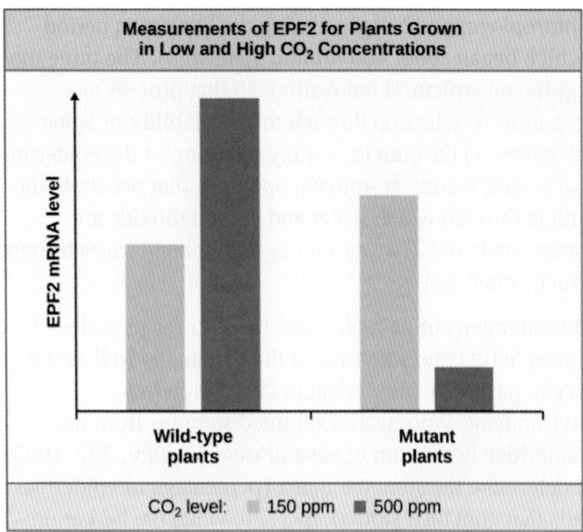

Figure 23.47

A. **Analyze** these data in terms of the likelihood that the effect of carbon dioxide concentration on stomatal density involves negative feedback at the level of i) translation, ii) post-transcription, or iii) changes in genotype.

B. Changes in precipitation patterns are expected to accompany an increase in atmospheric carbon dioxide. **Predict** the effect on a forest where trees that have matured over decades are suddenly under drought stress. **Justify** your prediction in terms of positive or negative feedback where stomatal density is high and a drought occurs.

In a favorable environment, trees continue to accumulate biomass and increase in height until the flow rate of water through the xylem (plant vascular tissue that transports water and minerals from roots to shoots) is no longer sufficient to support the negative water potential at the interface between root and soil. Fluid dynamic models predict that increasing the diameter, d, of the xylem greatly increases the rate of flow of water, leading to greater productivity when water is abundant. Under conditions of drought stress, the water potential is reduced, and an air bubble can disrupt the flow of water in that vessel entirely. A larger stem diameter permits a larger number of small vessels.

C. **Describe a model** of the evolution of xylem in trees in terms of selection under conditions of unlimited and limited water resources.

Olson and Rosell (*New Phytologist*, 197, 2013) investigated the question of whether xylem diameter was determined by water availability or by plant height and, consequently, stem diameter. A summary of their data is shown with lines of best fit through data with the corresponding color.

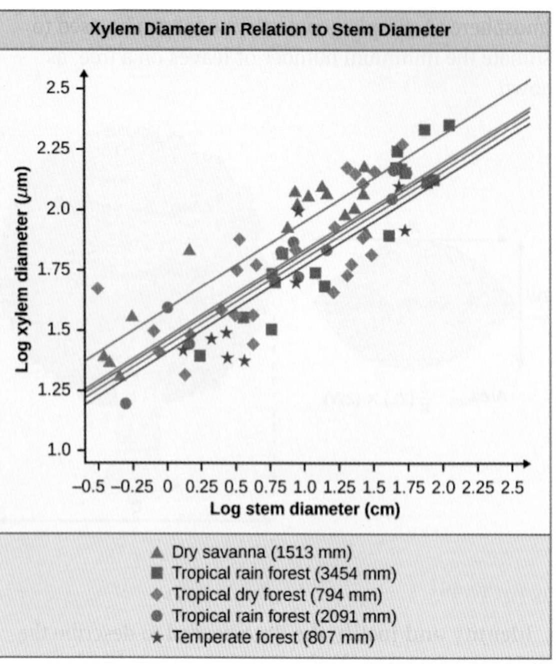

Figure 23.48

D. **Analyze** these data and summarize the pattern that addresses their question. Note: As x increases, log(x) increases.

114. Like the animal intestine, the organ system principally responsible for nutrient and water uptake, the plant root system, is home to a microbiome upon which the host depends. One important role for the root microbiome is innate immunity. Wheat take-all is a disease caused by the fungus *Gaeumannomyces graminis* that attacks plant roots and blocks root water channels. When a major outbreak occurs in a wheat field, susceptibility remains high in the following year. But after four to six continued crops of wheat in the same field, susceptibility to the disease declines. This resistance can be transferred with the soil. Burning the soil surface or rotation with another crop returns susceptibility to the next wheat crop. The *Fusarium* (a fungus) wilt disease of strawberries and potato scab caused by *Streptomyces scabies* (a bacteria) show a similar disease progression and transferability of resistance (Weller, *Ann. Rev. Plant Phytopath*, 26, 1988).

A. Plants, like animals, have immune defenses that may involve cooperative interactions between organisms. **Describe** a **model** of immune response that accounts for these behaviors.

In plants, the first line of defense is the cell wall. Animal cells lack this protective barrier. Adaptive immunity of vertebrates to pathogens uses specific defenses that are transportable within the organism, such as T-cells, and retains information about earlier infections, such as T-cell receptors. Unlike adaptive immunity, the innate responses of plants are much less effective in defending against necrotrophic (colonizing dead tissue) than against biotrophic (infecting living tissue) pathogens. In animal tissue, the response to infection is inflammation, the recruitment of resources to protect the tissue. In plant tissue, the response is apoptosis.

B. **Describe** contrasting models of defense strategies for plants and animals that express each of these differences in terms of these strategies: cell boundary, immunological memory, and tissue repair.

24 | THE ANIMAL BODY: BASIC FORM AND FUNCTION

Figure 24.1 An arctic fox is a complex animal, well adapted to its environment. It changes coat color with the seasons, and has longer fur in winter to trap heat. (credit: modification of work by Keith Morehouse, USFWS)

Chapter Outline

Introduction

The structures of animals consist of primary tissues that make up more complex organs and organ systems. Homeostasis allows an animal to maintain a balance between its internal and external environments.

The arctic fox is an example of a complex animal that is well adapted to its environment and illustrates the relationships between an animal's form and function. According to researchers, animals living millions of years ago in the Himalayan Mountains of Tibet are ancestors to many of today's cold-adapted animals. For example, a type of Tibetan fox from 3–5 million years ago is the ancestor to the arctic fox.[1] More about this research can be found at the Science Daily website (http://openstaxcollege.org/l/32arcticfox) .

1. Xiaoming Wang, Zhijie Jack Tseng, Qiang Li, Gary T. Takeuchi, Guangpu Xie, From 'third pole' to north pole: a Himalayan origin for the arctic fox. *Proceedings of the Royal Society B: Biological Sciences. June 11, 2014.*

24.1 | Animal Form and Function

In this section, you will explore the following questions:

- What are the various types of body plans that occur in animals?
- What are the limits on animal size and shape?
- How do bioenergetics relate to body size, levels of activity, and the environment?

Connection for AP® Courses

As you have learned, specialized cells in the animal body are organized into tissues, organs, and organ systems, which efficiently localize functions, such as the digestion of food and the elimination of wastes. As we explore the information in this section, our primary focus is **homeostasis**—the ability to maintain dynamic equilibrium around a **set point**. Animals need to maintain their "normal" internal environments while also responding to external environmental changes.

In our study of biology thus far, we have seen numerous examples of structure-function relationships, and the design of the animal body is no exception. Specialization in multicellular animals contributes to efficiency in cell processes. For example, animals must be able to procure nutrients and eliminate wastes, and cells that line the small intestine allow for diffusion. Furthermore, the relationship between metabolic rate and body mass is typically an inverse one: The smaller the animal, the higher its metabolism, with mice having a higher metabolic rate than, for example, elephants. Because mice have a greater surface area-to-volume ratio for their mass than larger animals, they lose heat at a faster rate and, consequently, require more energy to maintain constant body temperature.

Speaking of temperature, we learned that the body temperature of ectothermic animals varies according to environmental temperatures. When snakes need to warm up, they bask in the sun; when they need to cool down, they go into the shade. Other animals, including mice, kangaroos and humans, are endothermic because they are able to maintain a fairly constant internal body temperature despite environmental temperatures; for example, shivering generates heat, whereas sweating returns our body temperature to its normal set point of 37°C. We will explore the control of these responses in more detail in the Homeostasis section.

The information presented and the examples highlighted in the section support concepts outlined in Big Idea 2 of the AP® Biology Curriculum Framework. The AP® Learning Objectives listed in the Curriculum Framework provide a transparent foundation for the AP® Biology course, an inquiry-based laboratory experience, instructional activities, and AP® exam questions. A learning objective merges required content with one or more of the seven Science Practices.

Big Idea 2	Biological systems utilize free energy and molecular building blocks to grow, to reproduce, and to maintain dynamic homeostasis.
Enduring Understanding 2.A	Growth, reproduction and maintenance of living systems require free energy and matter.
Essential Knowledge	**2.A.1** All living systems require constant input of free energy.
Science Practice	**6.2** The student can construct explanations of phenomena based on evidence produced through scientific practices.
Learning Objective	**2.1** The student is able to explain how biological systems use free energy based on empirical data that all organisms require constant energy input to maintain organization, to grow and to reproduce.
Essential Knowledge	**2.A.1** All living systems require constant input of free energy.
Science Practice	**6.1:** The student can justify claims with evidence.

Learning Objective	**2.2** The student is able to justify a scientific claim that free energy is required for living systems to maintain organization, to grow or to reproduce, but that multiple strategies exist in different living systems.
Essential Knowledge	**2.A.1** All living systems require constant input of free energy.
Science Practice	**4.2** The student can design a plan for collecting data to answer a particular scientific question.
Learning Objective	**2.35** The student is able to design a plan for collecting data to support the scientific claim that timing and coordination of physiological events involve regulation
Essential Knowledge	**2.A.1** All living systems require constant input of free energy.
Science Practice	**6.1** The student can justify claims with evidence.
Learning Objective	**2.36** The student is able to justify scientific claims with evidence to show how timing and coordination of physiological events involve regulation.
Essential Knowledge	**2.A.1** All living systems require constant input of free energy.
Science Practice	**7.2** The student can connect concepts in and across domain(s) to generalize or extrapolate in and/or across enduring understandings and/or big ideas.
Learning Objective	**2.37** The student is able to connect concepts that describe mechanisms that regulate the timing and coordination of physiological events.

Animals vary in form and function. From a sponge to a worm to a goat, an organism has a distinct body plan that limits its size and shape. Animals' bodies are also designed to interact with their environments, whether in the deep sea, a rainforest canopy, or the desert. Therefore, a large amount of information about the structure of an organism's body (anatomy) and the function of its cells, tissues and organs (physiology) can be learned by studying that organism's environment.

Body Plans

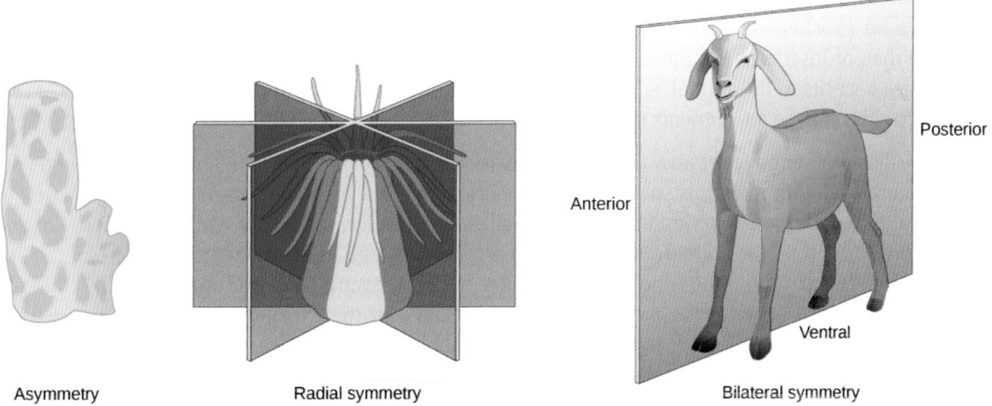

Figure 24.2 Animals exhibit different types of body symmetry. The sponge is asymmetrical, the sea anemone has radial symmetry, and the goat has bilateral symmetry.

Animal body plans follow set patterns related to symmetry. They are asymmetrical, radial, or bilateral in form as illustrated in Figure 24.2. **Asymmetrical** animals are animals with no pattern or symmetry; an example of an asymmetrical animal is a sponge. Radial symmetry, as illustrated in Figure 24.2, describes when an animal has an up-and-down orientation: any plane cut along its longitudinal axis through the organism produces equal halves, but not a definite right or left side. This plan is found mostly in aquatic animals, especially organisms that attach themselves to a base, like a rock or a boat, and extract their food from the surrounding water as it flows around the organism. Bilateral symmetry is illustrated in the same figure by a goat. The goat also has an upper and lower component to it, but a plane cut from front to back separates the animal into definite right and left sides. Additional terms used when describing positions in the body are anterior (front), posterior (rear), dorsal (toward the back), and ventral (toward the stomach). Bilateral symmetry is found in both land-based and aquatic animals; it enables a high level of mobility.

Limits on Animal Size and Shape

Animals with bilateral symmetry that live in water tend to have a **fusiform** shape: this is a tubular shaped body that is tapered at both ends. This shape decreases the drag on the body as it moves through water and allows the animal to swim at high speeds. Table 24.1 lists the maximum speed of various animals. Certain types of sharks can swim at fifty kilometers an hour and some dolphins at 32 to 40 kilometers per hour. Land animals frequently travel faster, although the tortoise and snail are significantly slower than cheetahs. Another difference in the adaptations of aquatic and land-dwelling organisms is that aquatic organisms are constrained in shape by the forces of drag in the water since water has higher viscosity than air. On the other hand, land-dwelling organisms are constrained mainly by gravity, and drag is relatively unimportant. For example, most adaptations in birds are for gravity not for drag.

Maximum Speed of Assorted Land Marine Animals

Animal	Speed (kmh)	Speed (mph)
Cheetah	113	70
Quarter horse	77	48
Fox	68	42
Shortfin mako shark	50	31
Domestic house cat	48	30
Human	45	28
Dolphin	32–40	20–25
Mouse	13	8
Snail	0.05	0.03

Table 24.1

Most animals have an exoskeleton, including insects, spiders, scorpions, horseshoe crabs, centipedes, and crustaceans. Scientists estimate that, of insects alone, there are over 30 million species on our planet. The exoskeleton is a hard covering or shell that provides benefits to the animal, such as protection against damage from predators and from water loss (for land animals); it also provides for the attachments of muscles.

As the tough and resistant outer cover of an arthropod, the exoskeleton may be constructed of a tough polymer such as chitin and is often biomineralized with materials such as calcium carbonate. This is fused to the animal's epidermis. Ingrowths of the exoskeleton, called **apodemes**, function as attachment sites for muscles, similar to tendons in more advanced animals (Figure 24.3). In order to grow, the animal must first synthesize a new exoskeleton underneath the old one and then shed or molt the original covering. This limits the animal's ability to grow continually, and may limit the individual's ability to mature if molting does not occur at the proper time. The thickness of the exoskeleton must be increased significantly to accommodate any increase in weight. It is estimated that a doubling of body size increases body weight by a factor of eight. The increasing thickness of the chitin necessary to support this weight limits most animals with an exoskeleton to a relatively small size. The same principles apply to endoskeletons, but they are more efficient because muscles are attached on the outside, making it easier to compensate for increased mass.

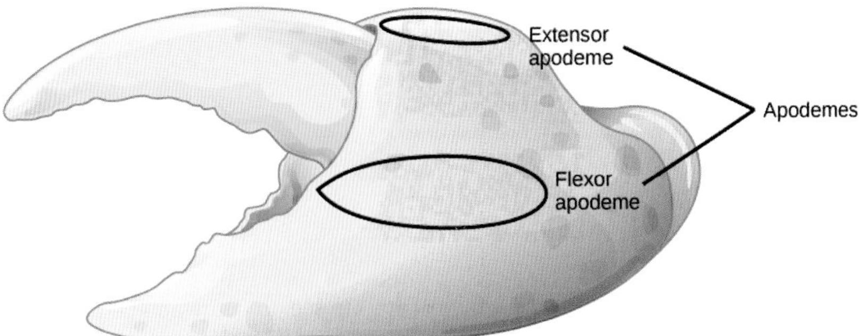

Figure 24.3 Apodemes are ingrowths on arthropod exoskeletons to which muscles attach. The apodemes on this crab leg are located above and below the fulcrum of the claw. Contraction of muscles attached to the apodemes pulls the claw closed.

An animal with an endoskeleton has its size determined by the amount of skeletal system it needs in order to support the other tissues and the amount of muscle it needs for movement. As the body size increases, both bone and muscle mass increase. The speed achievable by the animal is a balance between its overall size and the bone and muscle that provide support and movement.

Limiting Effects of Diffusion on Size and Development

The exchange of nutrients and wastes between a cell and its watery environment occurs through the process of diffusion. All living cells are bathed in liquid, whether they are in a single-celled organism or a multicellular one. Diffusion is effective over a specific distance and limits the size that an individual cell can attain. If a cell is a single-celled microorganism, such as an amoeba, it can satisfy all of its nutrient and waste needs through diffusion. If the cell is too large, then diffusion is ineffective and the center of the cell does not receive adequate nutrients nor is it able to effectively dispel its waste.

An important concept in understanding how efficient diffusion is as a means of transport is the surface area to volume ratio. Recall that any three-dimensional object has a surface area and volume; the ratio of these two quantities is the surface-to-volume ratio. Consider a cell shaped like a perfect sphere: it has a surface area of $4\pi r^2$, and a volume of $(4/3)\pi r^3$. The surface-to-volume ratio of a sphere is 3/r; as the cell gets bigger, its surface area to volume ratio decreases, making diffusion less efficient. The larger the size of the sphere, or animal, the less surface area for diffusion it possesses.

The solution to producing larger organisms is for them to become multicellular. Specialization occurs in complex organisms, allowing cells to become more efficient at doing fewer tasks. For example, circulatory systems bring nutrients and remove waste, while respiratory systems provide oxygen for the cells and remove carbon dioxide from them. Other organ systems have developed further specialization of cells and tissues and efficiently control body functions. Moreover, surface area-to-volume ratio applies to other areas of animal development, such as the relationship between muscle mass and cross-sectional surface area in supporting skeletons, and in the relationship between muscle mass and the generation of dissipation of heat.

Visit this interactive site (http://openstaxcollege.org/l/nanoscopy) to see an entire animal (a zebrafish embryo) at the cellular and sub-cellular level. Use the zoom and navigation functions for a virtual nanoscopy exploration.

Zebrafish have bilateral symmetry. What does that mean?

a. Bilaterally symmetric means that a plane cut from the front to back of the organism produces distinct left and right sides that are mirror images of each other.

b. Bilaterally symmetric means that a plane cut from the top to the bottom of the organism produces distinct left and right sides that are mirror images of each other.

c. Bilaterally symmetric means that a plane cut from the front to back of the organism produces distinct left and right sides that are not mirror images of each other.

d. Bilaterally symmetric means that a plane cut along its longitudinal axis produces equal halves, but not definite right or left sides.

Animal Bioenergetics

All animals must obtain their energy from food they ingest or absorb. These nutrients are converted to adenosine triphosphate (ATP) for short-term storage and use by all cells. Some animals store energy for slightly longer times as glycogen, and others store energy for much longer times in the form of triglycerides housed in specialized adipose tissues. No energy system is one hundred percent efficient, and an animal's metabolism produces waste energy in the form of heat. If an animal can conserve that heat and maintain a relatively constant body temperature, it is classified as a warm-blooded animal and called an **endotherm**. The insulation used to conserve the body heat comes in the forms of fur, fat, or feathers. The absence of insulation in **ectothermic** animals increases their dependence on the environment for body heat.

The amount of energy expended by an animal over a specific time is called its metabolic rate. The rate is measured variously in joules, calories, or kilocalories (1000 calories). Carbohydrates and proteins contain about 4.5 to 5 kcal/g, and fat contains about 9 kcal/g. Metabolic rate is estimated as the **basal metabolic rate (BMR)** in endothermic animals at rest and as the **standard metabolic rate (SMR)** in ectotherms. Human males have a BMR of 1600 to 1800 kcal/day, and human females have a BMR of 1300 to 1500 kcal/day. Even with insulation, endothermal animals require extensive amounts of energy to maintain a constant body temperature. An ectotherm such as an alligator has an SMR of 60 kcal/day.

Energy Requirements Related to Body Size

Smaller endothermic animals have a greater surface area for their mass than larger ones (Figure 24.4). Therefore, smaller animals lose heat at a faster rate than larger animals and require more energy to maintain a constant internal temperature. This results in a smaller endothermic animal having a higher BMR, per body weight, than a larger endothermic animal.

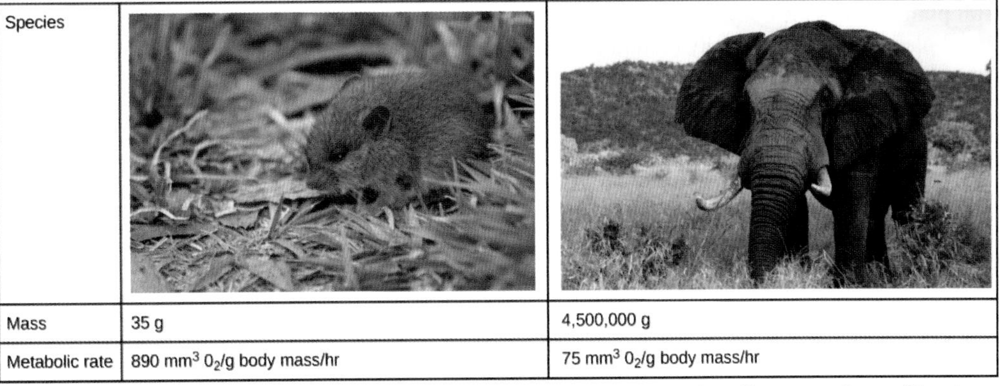

Species		
Mass	35 g	4,500,000 g
Metabolic rate	890 mm^3 0_2/g body mass/hr	75 mm^3 0_2/g body mass/hr

Figure 24.4 The mouse has a much higher metabolic rate than the elephant. (credit "mouse": modification of work by Magnus Kjaergaard; credit "elephant": modification of work by "TheLizardQueen"/Flickr)

Energy Requirements Related to Levels of Activity

The more active an animal is, the more energy is needed to maintain that activity, and the higher its BMR or SMR. The average daily rate of energy consumption is about two to four times an animal's BMR or SMR. Humans are more sedentary than most animals and have an average daily rate of only 1.5 times the BMR. The diet of an endothermic animal is determined by its BMR. For example: the type of grasses, leaves, or shrubs that an herbivore eats affects the number of calories that it takes in. The relative caloric content of herbivore foods, in descending order, is tall grasses > legumes > short grasses > forbs (any broad-leaved plant, not a grass) > subshrubs > annuals/biennials.

Energy Requirements Related to Environment

Animals adapt to extremes of temperature or food availability through torpor. **Torpor** is a process that leads to a decrease in activity and metabolism and allows animals to survive adverse conditions. Torpor can be used by animals for long periods, such as entering a state of **hibernation** during the winter months, in which case it enables them to maintain a reduced body temperature. During hibernation, ground squirrels can achieve an abdominal temperature of 0° C (32° F), while a bear's internal temperature is maintained higher at about 37° C (99° F).

If torpor occurs during the summer months with high temperatures and little water, it is called **estivation**. Some desert animals use this to survive the harshest months of the year. Torpor can occur on a daily basis; this is seen in bats and hummingbirds. While endothermy is limited in smaller animals by surface to volume ratio, some organisms can be smaller and still be endotherms because they employ daily torpor during the part of the day that is coldest. This allows them to conserve energy during the colder parts of the day, when they consume more energy to maintain their body temperature.

science practices CONNECTION for AP® Courses

Activity

Read about how scientists developed a method using today's technology to collect data on heart rates in hibernating bears at this website (http://openstaxcollege.org/l/32bears) . Design an experiment that would allow you to collect body temperature and heart rate at the same time. Discuss how combining data on body temperature with heart rate can give you information on the animal's overall metabolism.

Think About It

- Small mammals, such as squirrels need to eat at least once a week during hibernation. Why is it impossible for them to go through the entire winter without eating, as bears do? Also, why must smaller mammals, like squirrels, store food for the winter while larger mammals, like bears, do not?
- Hummingbirds lower their metabolic rate and body temperature at night, an example of torpor. What advantage does torpor provide hummingbirds on a nightly basis? Think about the high metabolic rates of hummingbirds.

Animal Body Planes and Cavities

A standing vertebrate animal can be divided by several planes. A **sagittal plane** divides the body into right and left portions.

A **midsagittal plane** divides the body exactly in the middle, making two equal right and left halves. A **frontal plane** (also called a coronal plane) separates the belly (ventral) or stomach from the back (dorsal). A **transverse plane** (or, horizontal plane) is perpendicular to the sagittal planes and the long axis of the body. This is sometimes called a cross section, and, if the transverse cut is at an angle, it is called an oblique plane. Figure 24.5 illustrates these planes on a goat (a four-legged animal) and a human being.

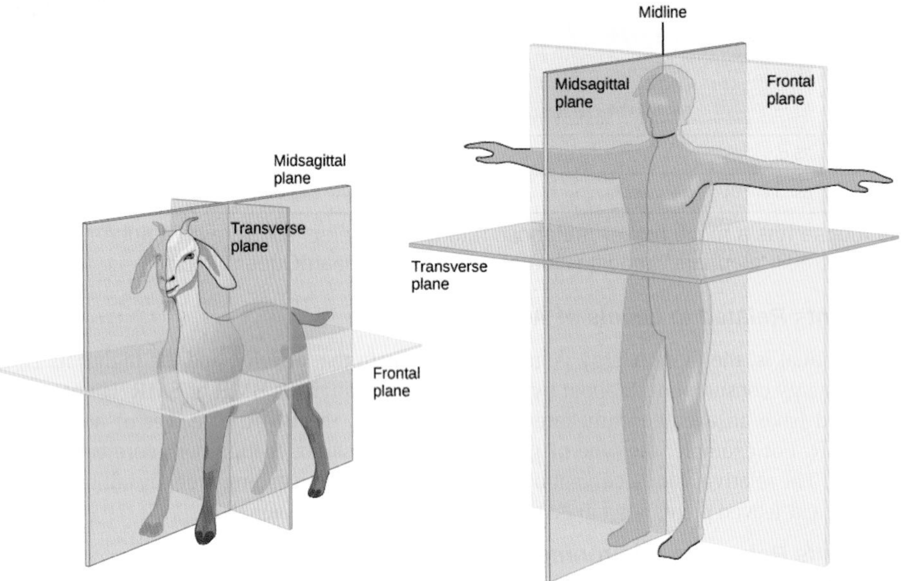

Figure 24.5 Shown are the planes of a quadruped goat and a bipedal human. The midsagittal plane divides the body exactly in half, into right and left portions. The frontal plane divides the front and back, and the transverse plane divides the body into upper and lower portions.

Vertebrate animals have a number of defined body cavities, as illustrated in Figure 24.6. Two of these are major cavities that contain smaller cavities within them. The **dorsal cavity** contains the cranial and the vertebral (or spinal) cavities. The **ventral cavity** contains the thoracic cavity, which in turn contains the pleural cavity around the lungs and the pericardial cavity, which surrounds the heart. The ventral cavity also contains the abdominopelvic cavity, which can be separated into the abdominal and the pelvic cavities.

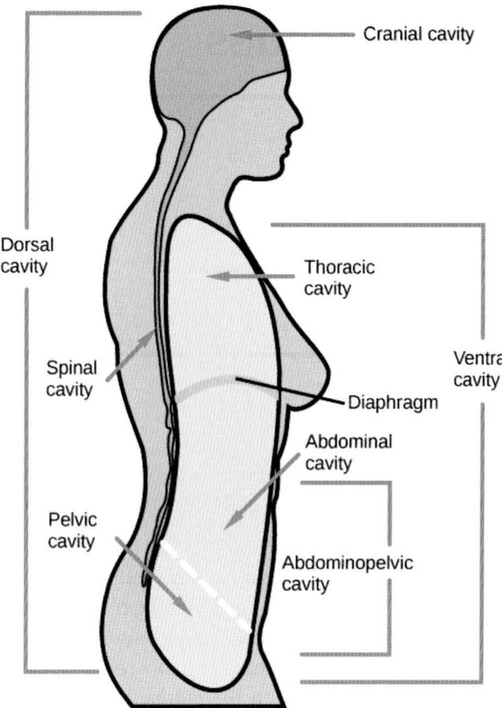

Figure 24.6 Vertebrate animals have two major body cavities. The dorsal cavity, indicated in green, contains the cranial and the spinal cavity. The ventral cavity, indicated in yellow, contains the thoracic cavity and the abdominopelvic cavity. The thoracic cavity is separated from the abdominopelvic cavity by the diaphragm. The thoracic cavity is separated into the abdominal cavity and the pelvic cavity by an imaginary line parallel to the pelvis bones. (credit: modification of work by NCI)

career CONNECTION

Physical Anthropologist

Physical anthropologists study the adaption, variability, and evolution of human beings, plus their living and fossil relatives. They can work in a variety of settings, although most will have an academic appointment at a university, usually in an anthropology department or a biology, genetics, or zoology department.

Non-academic positions are available in the automotive and aerospace industries where the focus is on human size, shape, and anatomy. Research by these professionals might range from studies of how the human body reacts to car crashes to exploring how to make seats more comfortable. Other non-academic positions can be obtained in museums of natural history, anthropology, archaeology, or science and technology. These positions involve educating students from grade school through graduate school. Physical anthropologists serve as education coordinators, collection managers, writers for museum publications, and as administrators. Zoos employ these professionals, especially if they have an expertise in primate biology; they work in collection management and captive breeding programs for endangered species. Forensic science utilizes physical anthropology expertise in identifying human and animal remains, assisting in determining the cause of death, and for expert testimony in trials.

24.2 | Animal Primary Tissues

In this section, you will explore the following questions:

- What are characteristics of epithelial tissues?
- What are the different types of connective tissues in animals?
- What are differences among the three types of muscle tissue?
- What are characteristics of nervous tissue?

Connection for AP® Courses

The content described in this section is not within the scope of AP®. However, we have already learned that the relationship between structure and function includes the cellular level, and we will continue to reinforce that when we explore the nervous system later.

The tissues of multicellular, complex animals are four primary types: epithelial, connective, muscle, and nervous. Recall that tissues are groups of similar cells group of similar cells carrying out related functions. These tissues combine to form organs—like the skin or kidney—that have specific, specialized functions within the body. Organs are organized into organ systems to perform functions; examples include the circulatory system, which consists of the heart and blood vessels, and the digestive system, consisting of several organs, including the stomach, intestines, liver, and pancreas. Organ systems come together to create an entire organism.

Epithelial Tissues

Epithelial tissues cover the outside of organs and structures in the body and line the lumens of organs in a single layer or multiple layers of cells. The types of epithelia are classified by the shapes of cells present and the number of layers of cells. Epithelia composed of a single layer of cells is called **simple epithelia**; epithelial tissue composed of multiple layers is called **stratified epithelia**. Table 24.2 summarizes the different types of epithelial tissues.

Different Types of Epithelial Tissues

Cell shape	Description	Location
squamous	flat, irregular round shape	simple: lung alveoli, capillaries stratified: skin, mouth, vagina
cuboidal	cube shaped, central nucleus	glands, renal tubules
columnar	tall, narrow, nucleus toward base tall, narrow, nucleus along cell	simple: digestive tract pseudostratified: respiratory tract
transitional	round, simple but appear stratified	urinary bladder

Table 24.2

Squamous Epithelia

Squamous epithelial cells are generally round, flat, and have a small, centrally located nucleus. The cell outline is slightly irregular, and cells fit together to form a covering or lining. When the cells are arranged in a single layer (simple epithelia), they facilitate diffusion in tissues, such as the areas of gas exchange in the lungs and the exchange of nutrients and waste at blood capillaries.

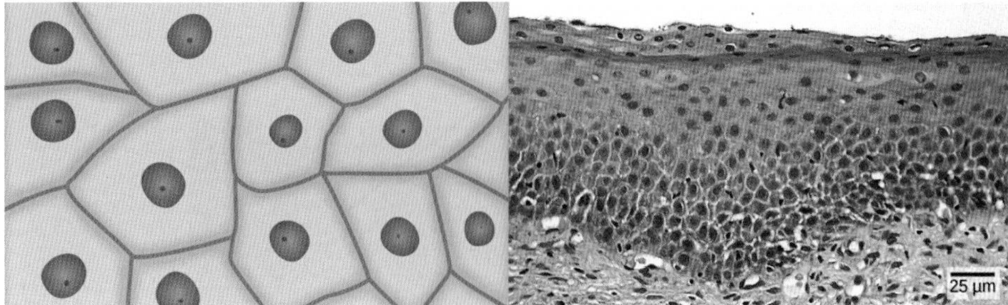

Figure 24.7 Squamous epithelia cells (a) have a slightly irregular shape, and a small, centrally located nucleus. These cells can be stratified into layers, as in (b) this human cervix specimen. (credit b: modification of work by Ed Uthman; scale-bar data from Matt Russell)

Figure 24.7**a** illustrates a layer of squamous cells with their membranes joined together to form an epithelium. Image Figure 24.7**b** illustrates squamous epithelial cells arranged in stratified layers, where protection is needed on the body from outside abrasion and damage. This is called a stratified squamous epithelium and occurs in the skin and in tissues lining the mouth and vagina.

Cuboidal Epithelia

Cuboidal epithelial cells, shown in Figure 24.8, are cube-shaped with a single, central nucleus. They are most commonly found in a single layer representing a simple epithelia in glandular tissues throughout the body where they prepare and secrete glandular material. They are also found in the walls of tubules and in the ducts of the kidney and liver.

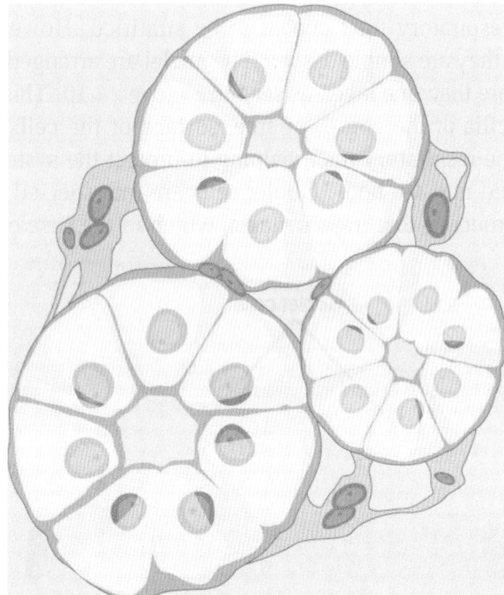

Figure 24.8 Simple cuboidal epithelial cells line tubules in the mammalian kidney, where they are involved in filtering the blood.

Columnar Epithelia

Columnar epithelial cells are taller than they are wide: they resemble a stack of columns in an epithelial layer, and are most commonly found in a single-layer arrangement. The nuclei of columnar epithelial cells in the digestive tract appear to be lined up at the base of the cells, as illustrated in Figure 24.9. These cells absorb material from the lumen of the digestive tract and prepare it for entry into the body through the circulatory and lymphatic systems.

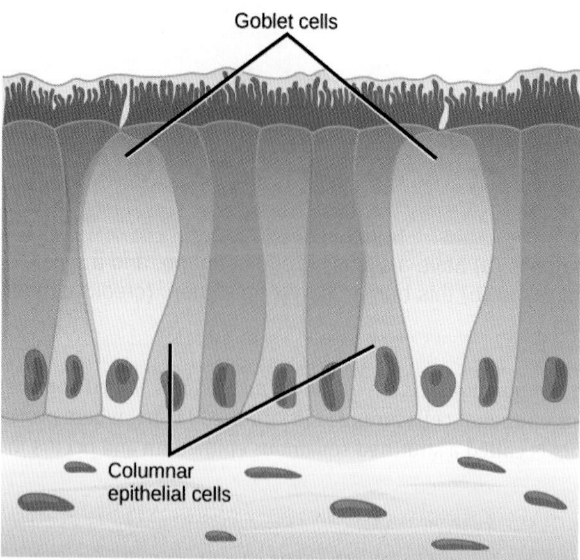

Figure 24.9 Simple columnar epithelial cells absorb material from the digestive tract. Goblet cells secret mucous into the digestive tract lumen.

Columnar epithelial cells lining the respiratory tract appear to be stratified. However, each cell is attached to the base membrane of the tissue and, therefore, they are simple tissues. The nuclei are arranged at different levels in the layer of cells, making it appear as though there is more than one layer, as seen in Figure 24.10. This is called **pseudostratified**, columnar epithelia. This cellular covering has cilia at the apical, or free, surface of the cells. The cilia enhance the movement of mucous and trapped particles out of the respiratory tract, helping to protect the system from invasive microorganisms and harmful material that has been breathed into the body. Goblet cells are interspersed in some tissues (such as the lining of the trachea). The goblet cells contain mucous that traps irritants, which in the case of the trachea keep these irritants from getting into the lungs.

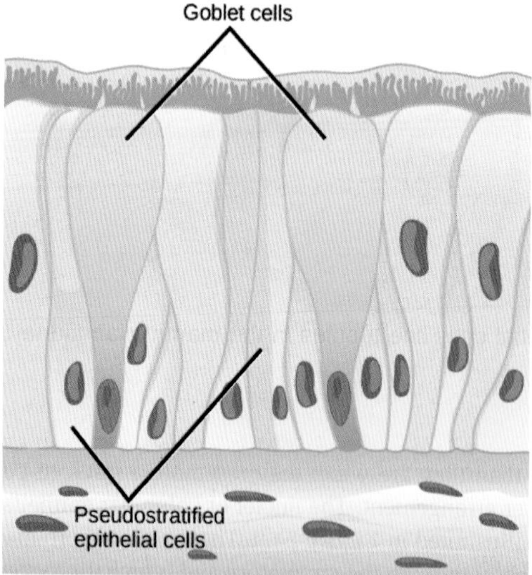

Figure 24.10 Pseudostratified columnar epithelia line the respiratory tract. They exist in one layer, but the arrangement of nuclei at different levels makes it appear that there is more than one layer. Goblet cells interspersed between the columnar epithelial cells secrete mucous into the respiratory tract.

Transitional Epithelia

Transitional or uroepithelial cells appear only in the urinary system, primarily in the bladder and ureter. These cells are arranged in a stratified layer, but they have the capability of appearing to pile up on top of each other in a relaxed, empty bladder, as illustrated in Figure 24.11. As the urinary bladder fills, the epithelial layer unfolds and expands to hold the volume of urine introduced into it. As the bladder fills, it expands and the lining becomes thinner. In other words, the tissue transitions from thick to thin.

visual CONNECTION

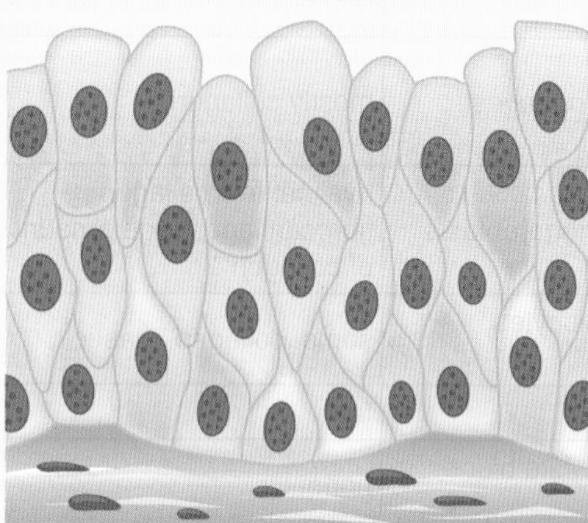

Figure 24.11 Transitional epithelia of the urinary bladder undergo changes in thickness depending on how full the bladder is.

An empty bladder is composed of piled up transitional cells with a folded epithelial lining. What would you predict happens to those cells as the bladder fills with urine?

a. The epithelial lining unfolds and becomes thicker.
b. The epithelial lining remains folded with the cells piled up.
c. The epithelial lining unfolds and becomes thinner.
d. The epithelial lining unfolds, but remains the same thickness.

Connective Tissues

Connective tissues are made up of a matrix consisting of living cells and a non-living substance, called the ground substance. The ground substance is made of an organic substance (usually a protein) and an inorganic substance (usually a mineral or water). The principal cell of connective tissues is the fibroblast. This cell makes the fibers found in nearly all of the connective tissues. Fibroblasts are motile, able to carry out mitosis, and can synthesize whichever connective tissue is needed. Macrophages, lymphocytes, and, occasionally, leukocytes can be found in some of the tissues. Some tissues have specialized cells that are not found in the others. The **matrix** in connective tissues gives the tissue its density. When a connective tissue has a high concentration of cells or fibers, it has proportionally a less dense matrix.

The organic portion or protein fibers found in connective tissues are either collagen, elastic, or reticular fibers. Collagen fibers provide strength to the tissue, preventing it from being torn or separated from the surrounding tissues. Elastic fibers are made of the protein elastin; this fiber can stretch to one and one half of its length and return to its original size and shape. Elastic fibers provide flexibility to the tissues. Reticular fibers are the third type of protein fiber found in connective tissues. This fiber consists of thin strands of collagen that form a network of fibers to support the tissue and other organs to which it is connected. The various types of connective tissues, the types of cells and fibers they are made of, and sample locations of the tissues is summarized in Table 24.3.

Connective Tissues

Tissue	Cells	Fibers	Location
loose/areolar	fibroblasts, macrophages, some lymphocytes, some neutrophils	few: collagen, elastic, reticular	around blood vessels; anchors epithelia
dense, fibrous connective tissue	fibroblasts, macrophages,	mostly collagen	irregular: skin regular: tendons, ligaments
cartilage	chondrocytes, chondroblasts	hyaline: few collagen fibrocartilage: large amount of collagen	shark skeleton, fetal bones, human ears, intervertebral discs
bone	osteoblasts, osteocytes, osteoclasts	some: collagen, elastic	vertebrate skeletons
adipose	adipocytes	few	adipose (fat)
blood	red blood cells, white blood cells	none	blood

Table 24.3

Loose/Areolar Connective Tissue

Loose connective tissue, also called areolar connective tissue, has a sampling of all of the components of a connective tissue. As illustrated in Figure 24.12, loose connective tissue has some fibroblasts; macrophages are present as well. Collagen fibers are relatively wide and stain a light pink, while elastic fibers are thin and stain dark blue to black. The space between the formed elements of the tissue is filled with the matrix. The material in the connective tissue gives it a loose consistency similar to a cotton ball that has been pulled apart. Loose connective tissue is found around every blood vessel and helps to keep the vessel in place. The tissue is also found around and between most body organs. In summary, areolar tissue is tough, yet flexible, and comprises membranes.

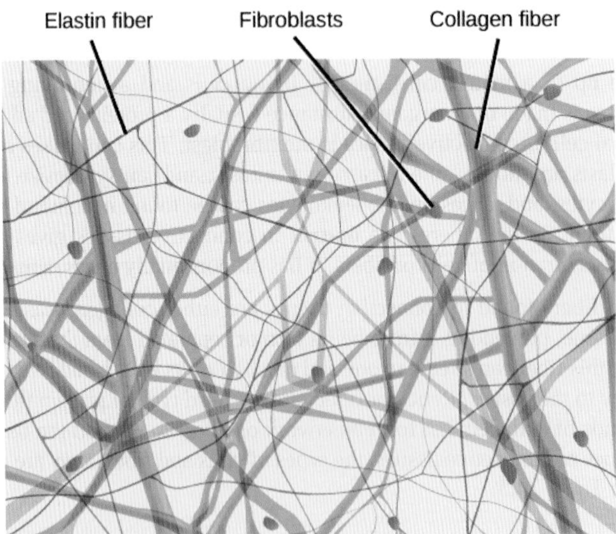

Figure 24.12 Loose connective tissue is composed of loosely woven collagen and elastic fibers. The fibers and other components of the connective tissue matrix are secreted by fibroblasts.

Fibrous Connective Tissue

Fibrous connective tissues contain large amounts of collagen fibers and few cells or matrix material. The fibers can be arranged irregularly or regularly with the strands lined up in parallel. Irregularly arranged fibrous connective tissues are found in areas of the body where stress occurs from all directions, such as the dermis of the skin. Regular fibrous connective tissue, shown in Figure 24.13, is found in tendons (which connect muscles to bones) and ligaments (which connect bones to bones).

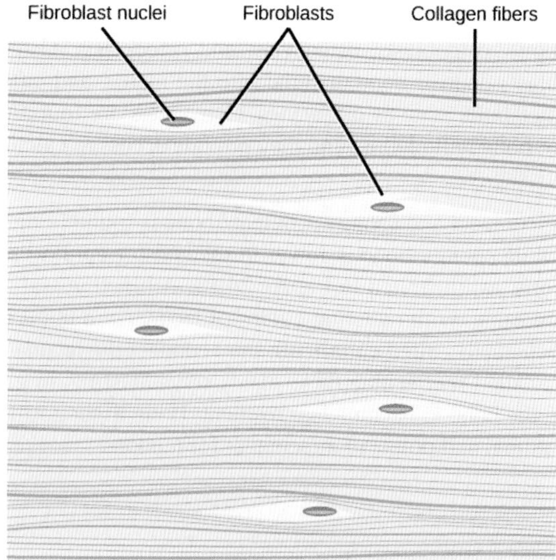

Figure 24.13 Fibrous connective tissue from the tendon has strands of collagen fibers lined up in parallel.

Cartilage

Cartilage is a connective tissue with a large amount of the matrix and variable amounts of fibers. The cells, called **chondrocytes**, make the matrix and fibers of the tissue. Chondrocytes are found in spaces within the tissue called **lacunae**.

A cartilage with few collagen and elastic fibers is hyaline cartilage, illustrated in Figure 24.14. The lacunae are randomly scattered throughout the tissue and the matrix takes on a milky or scrubbed appearance with routine histological stains. Sharks have cartilaginous skeletons, as does nearly the entire human skeleton during a specific pre-birth developmental stage. A remnant of this cartilage persists in the outer portion of the human nose. Hyaline cartilage is also found at the ends of long bones, reducing friction and cushioning the articulations of these bones.

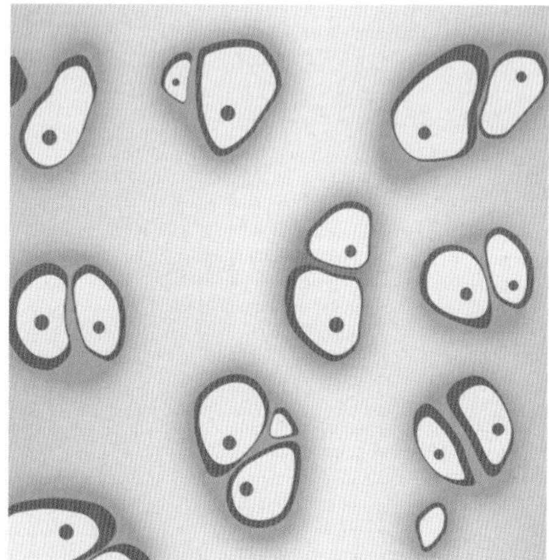

Figure 24.14 Hyaline cartilage consists of a matrix with cells called chondrocytes embedded in it. The chondrocytes exist in cavities in the matrix called lacunae.

Elastic cartilage has a large amount of elastic fibers, giving it tremendous flexibility. The ears of most vertebrate animals contain this cartilage as do portions of the larynx, or voice box. Fibrocartilage contains a large amount of collagen fibers, giving the tissue tremendous strength. Fibrocartilage comprises the intervertebral discs in vertebrate animals. Hyaline cartilage found in movable joints such as the knee and shoulder becomes damaged as a result of age or trauma. Damaged hyaline cartilage is replaced by fibrocartilage and results in the joints becoming "stiff."

Bone

Bone, or osseous tissue, is a connective tissue that has a large amount of two different types of matrix material. The organic matrix is similar to the matrix material found in other connective tissues, including some amount of collagen and elastic fibers. This gives strength and flexibility to the tissue. The inorganic matrix consists of mineral salts—mostly calcium salts—that give the tissue hardness. Without adequate organic material in the matrix, the tissue breaks; without adequate inorganic material in the matrix, the tissue bends.

There are three types of cells in bone: osteoblasts, osteocytes, and osteoclasts. Osteoblasts are active in making bone for growth and remodeling. Osteoblasts deposit bone material into the matrix and, after the matrix surrounds them, they continue to live, but in a reduced metabolic state as osteocytes. Osteocytes are found in lacunae of the bone. Osteoclasts are active in breaking down bone for bone remodeling, and they provide access to calcium stored in tissues. Osteoclasts are usually found on the surface of the tissue.

Bone can be divided into two types: compact and spongy. Compact bone is found in the shaft (or diaphysis) of a long bone and the surface of the flat bones, while spongy bone is found in the end (or epiphysis) of a long bone. Compact bone is organized into subunits called **osteons**, as illustrated in Figure 24.15. A blood vessel and a nerve are found in the center of the structure within the Haversian canal, with radiating circles of lacunae around it known as lamellae. The wavy lines seen between the lacunae are microchannels called **canaliculi**; they connect the lacunae to aid diffusion between the cells. Spongy bone is made of tiny plates called **trabeculae** these plates serve as struts to give the spongy bone strength. Over time, these plates can break causing the bone to become less resilient. Bone tissue forms the internal skeleton of vertebrate animals, providing structure to the animal and points of attachment for tendons.

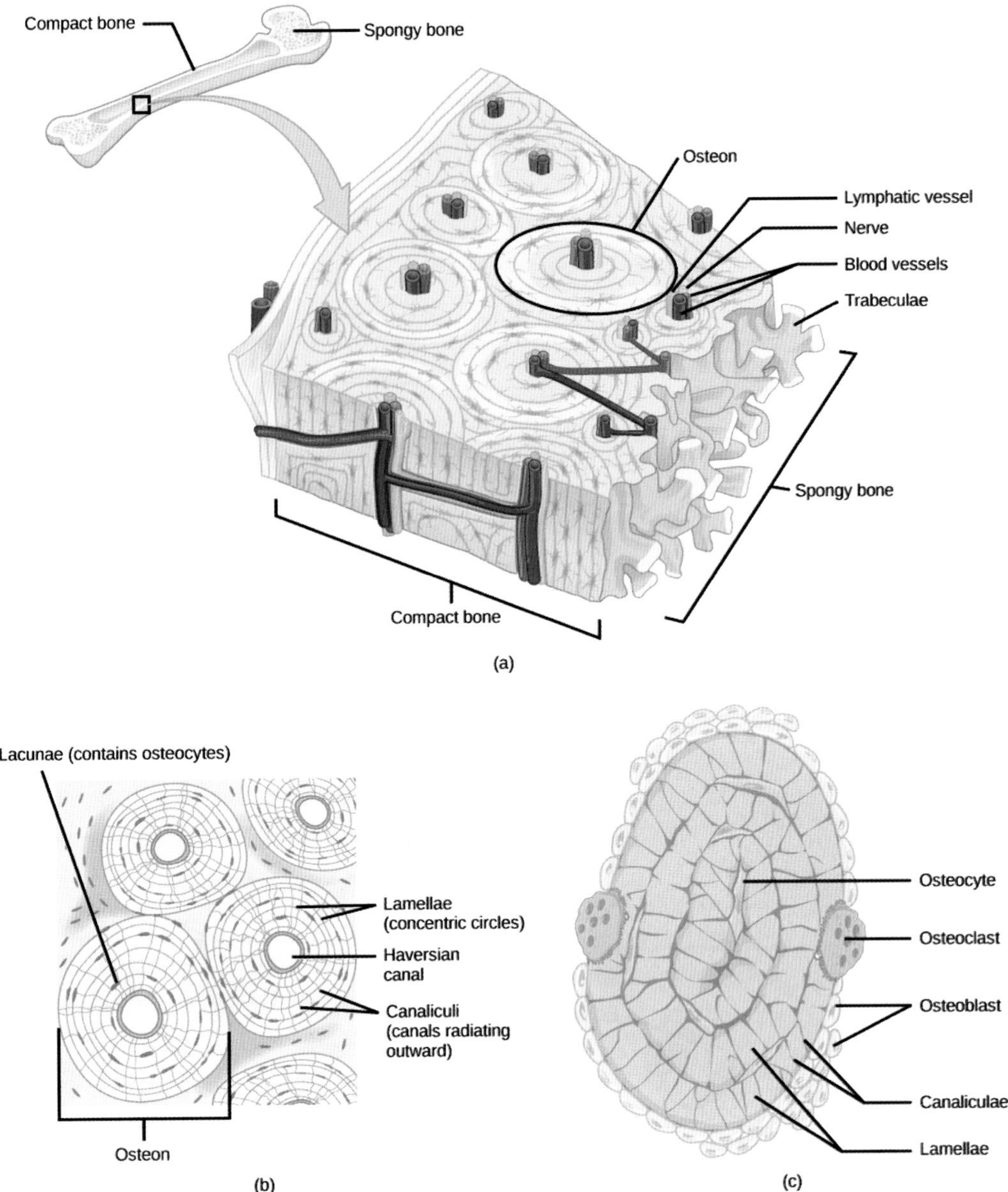

Figure 24.15 (a) Compact bone is a dense matrix on the outer surface of bone. Spongy bone, inside the compact bone, is porous with web-like trabeculae. (b) Compact bone is organized into rings called osteons. Blood vessels, nerves, and lymphatic vessels are found in the central Haversian canal. Rings of lamellae surround the Haversian canal. Between the lamellae are cavities called lacunae. Canaliculi are microchannels connecting the lacunae together. (c) Osteoblasts surround the exterior of the bone. Osteoclasts bore tunnels into the bone and osteocytes are found in the lacunae.

Adipose Tissue

Adipose tissue, or fat tissue, is considered a connective tissue even though it does not have fibroblasts or a real matrix and only has a few fibers. Adipose tissue is made up of cells called adipocytes that collect and store fat in the form of triglycerides, for energy metabolism. Adipose tissues additionally serve as insulation to help maintain body temperatures, allowing animals to be endothermic, and they function as cushioning against damage to body organs. Under a microscope, adipose tissue cells appear empty due to the extraction of fat during the processing of the material for viewing, as seen in Figure 24.16. The thin lines in the image are the cell membranes, and the nuclei are the small, black dots at the edges of the cells.

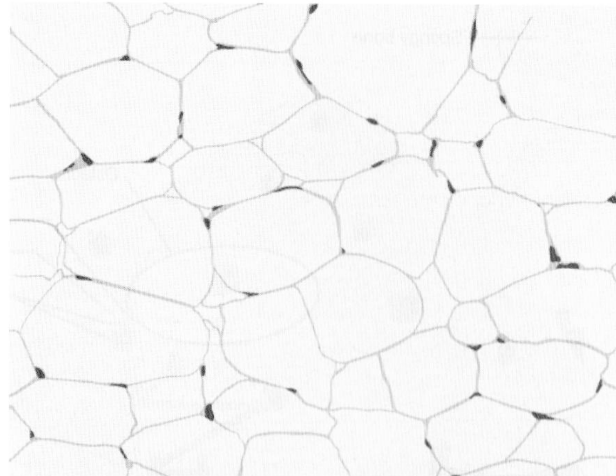

Figure 24.16 Adipose is a connective tissue is made up of cells called adipocytes. Adipocytes have small nuclei localized at the cell edge.

Blood

Blood is considered a connective tissue because it has a matrix, as shown in Figure 24.17. The living cell types are red blood cells (RBC), also called erythrocytes, and white blood cells (WBC), also called leukocytes. The fluid portion of whole blood, its matrix, is commonly called plasma.

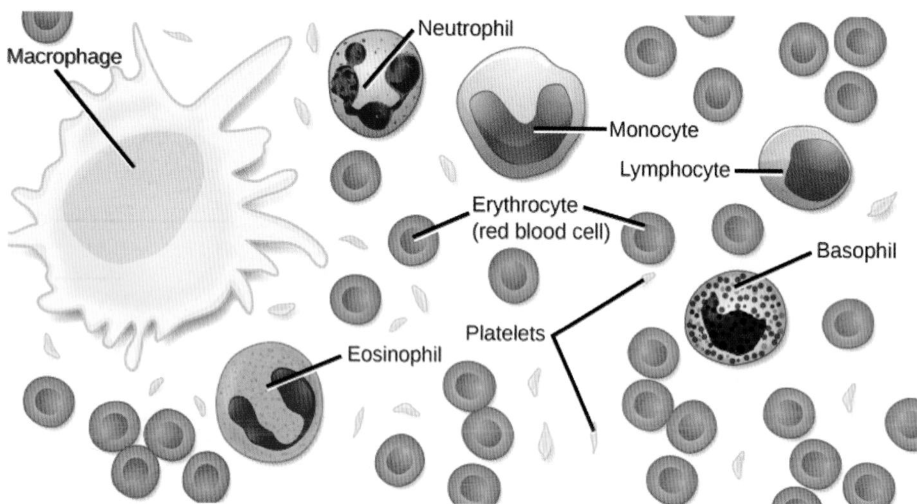

Figure 24.17 Blood is a connective tissue that has a fluid matrix, called plasma, and no fibers. Erythrocytes (red blood cells), the predominant cell type, are involved in the transport of oxygen and carbon dioxide. Also present are various leukocytes (white blood cells) involved in immune response.

The cell found in greatest abundance in blood is the erythrocyte. Erythrocytes are counted in millions in a blood sample: the average number of red blood cells in primates is 4.7 to 5.5 million cells per microliter. Erythrocytes are consistently the same size in a species, but vary in size between species. For example, the average diameter of a primate red blood cell is 7.5 um, a dog is close at 7.0 um, but a cat's RBC diameter is 5.9 um. Sheep erythrocytes are even smaller at 4.6 um. Mammalian erythrocytes lose their nuclei and mitochondria when they are released from the bone marrow where they are made. Fish, amphibian, and avian red blood cells maintain their nuclei and mitochondria throughout the cell's life. The principal job of an erythrocyte is to carry and deliver oxygen to the tissues.

Leukocytes are the predominant white blood cells found in the peripheral blood. Leukocytes are counted in the thousands in the blood with measurements expressed as ranges: primate counts range from 4,800 to 10,800 cells per µl, dogs from 5,600 to 19,200 cells per µl, cats from 8,000 to 25,000 cells per µl, cattle from 4,000 to 12,000 cells per µl, and pigs from 11,000 to 22,000 cells per µl.

Lymphocytes function primarily in the immune response to foreign antigens or material. Different types of lymphocytes make antibodies tailored to the foreign antigens and control the production of those antibodies. Neutrophils are phagocytic cells and they participate in one of the early lines of defense against microbial invaders, aiding in the removal of bacteria that has entered the body. Another leukocyte that is found in the peripheral blood is the monocyte. Monocytes give rise to phagocytic macrophages that clean up dead and damaged cells in the body, whether they are foreign or from the host animal. Two additional leukocytes in the blood are eosinophils and basophils—both help to facilitate the inflammatory response.

The slightly granular material among the cells is a cytoplasmic fragment of a cell in the bone marrow. This is called a platelet or thrombocyte. Platelets participate in the stages leading up to coagulation of the blood to stop bleeding through damaged blood vessels. Blood has a number of functions, but primarily it transports material through the body to bring nutrients to cells and remove waste material from them.

Muscle Tissues

There are three types of muscle in animal bodies: smooth, skeletal, and cardiac. They differ by the presence or absence of striations or bands, the number and location of nuclei, whether they are voluntarily or involuntarily controlled, and their location within the body. Table 24.4 summarizes these differences.

Types of Muscles

Type of Muscle	Striations	Nuclei	Control	Location
smooth	no	single, in center	involuntary	visceral organs
skeletal	yes	many, at periphery	voluntary	skeletal muscles
cardiac	yes	single, in center	involuntary	heart

Table 24.4

Smooth Muscle

Smooth muscle does not have striations in its cells. It has a single, centrally located nucleus, as shown in Figure 24.18. Constriction of smooth muscle occurs under involuntary, autonomic nervous control and in response to local conditions in the tissues. Smooth muscle tissue is also called non-striated as it lacks the banded appearance of skeletal and cardiac muscle. The walls of blood vessels, the tubes of the digestive system, and the tubes of the reproductive systems are composed of mostly smooth muscle.

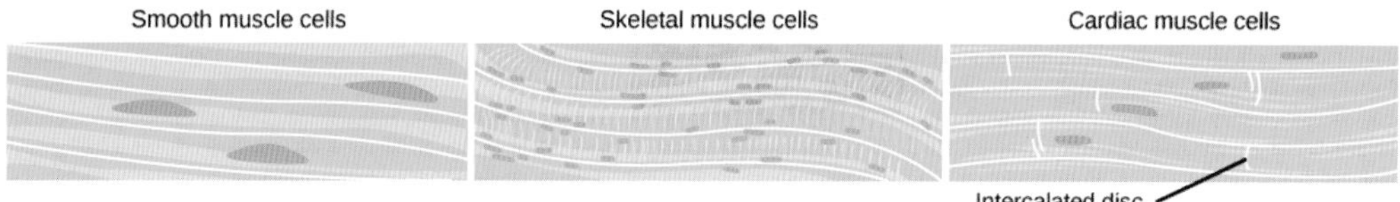

Figure 24.18 Smooth muscle cells do not have striations, while skeletal muscle cells do. Cardiac muscle cells have striations, but, unlike the multinucleate skeletal cells, they have only one nucleus. Cardiac muscle tissue also has intercalated discs, specialized regions running along the plasma membrane that join adjacent cardiac muscle cells and assist in passing an electrical impulse from cell to cell.

Skeletal Muscle

Skeletal muscle has striations across its cells caused by the arrangement of the contractile proteins actin and myosin. These muscle cells are relatively long and have multiple nuclei along the edge of the cell. Skeletal muscle is under voluntary, somatic nervous system control and is found in the muscles that move bones. Figure 24.18 illustrates the histology of skeletal muscle.

Cardiac Muscle

Cardiac muscle, shown in Figure 24.18, is found only in the heart. Like skeletal muscle, it has cross striations in its cells, but cardiac muscle has a single, centrally located nucleus. Cardiac muscle is not under voluntary control but can be influenced by the autonomic nervous system to speed up or slow down. An added feature to cardiac muscle cells is a line than extends along the end of the cell as it abuts the next cardiac cell in the row. This line is called an intercalated disc: it assists in passing electrical impulse efficiently from one cell to the next and maintains the strong connection between neighboring cardiac cells.

Nervous Tissues

Nervous tissues are made of cells specialized to receive and transmit electrical impulses from specific areas of the body and to send them to specific locations in the body. The main cell of the nervous system is the neuron, illustrated in Figure

24.19. The large structure with a central nucleus is the cell body of the neuron. Projections from the cell body are either dendrites specialized in receiving input or a single axon specialized in transmitting impulses. Some glial cells are also shown. Astrocytes regulate the chemical environment of the nerve cell, and oligodendrocytes insulate the axon so the electrical nerve impulse is transferred more efficiently. Other glial cells that are not shown support the nutritional and waste requirements of the neuron. Some of the glial cells are phagocytic and remove debris or damaged cells from the tissue. A nervous tissue consists of neurons and glial cells.

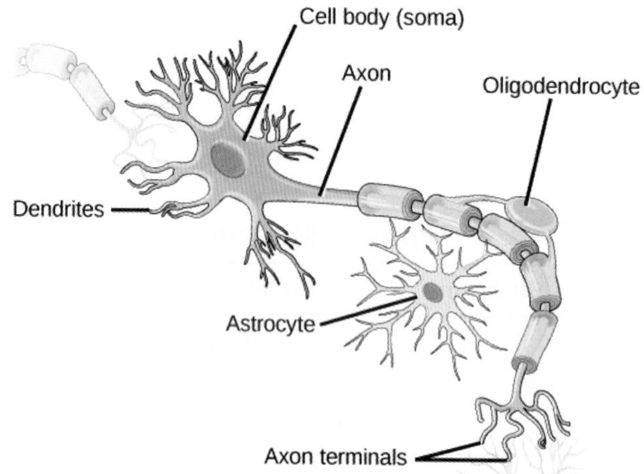

Figure 24.19 The neuron has projections called dendrites that receive signals and projections called axons that send signals. Also shown are two types of glial cells: astrocytes regulate the chemical environment of the nerve cell, and oligodendrocytes insulate the axon so the electrical nerve impulse is transferred more efficiently.

Click through the interactive review (http://openstaxcollege.org/l/tissues) to learn more about epithelial tissues.

Why would a single layer of flat epithelial cells rather than cuboidal cells (cube-shaped) cells function more efficiently in diffusion?

a. As a single layer of flat epithelia are more tightly knit than cuboidal cells.

b. As diffusion of nutrients and gas is easier across a single layer of flat epithelial cells than cuboidal cells.

c. As diffusion of only gases is easier across a single layer of flat epithelial cells than cuboidal cells.

d. As active transport of nutrients and gas is easier across a single layer of flat epithelial cells than cuboidal cells.

Pathologist

A pathologist is a medical doctor or veterinarian who has specialized in the laboratory detection of disease in animals, including humans. These professionals complete medical school education and follow it with an extensive post-graduate residency at a medical center. A pathologist may oversee clinical laboratories for the evaluation of body tissue and blood samples for the detection of disease or infection. They examine tissue specimens through a microscope to identify diseases. Some pathologists perform autopsies to determine the cause of death and the progression of disease.

24.3 | Homeostasis

In this section, you will explore the following questions:

- What is homeostasis?
- What factors affect homeostasis?
- What are differences between negative and positive feedback mechanisms used in homeostasis?
- What are differences between thermoregulation mechanisms in endothermic and ectothermic animals?

Connection for AP® Courses

Animals must be able to maintain homeostasis—the ability to maintain dynamic equilibrium around a set point—while also being able to respond to changing conditions. For example, as an endotherm, your body temperature remains fairly constant around 37°C or 98.6°F. If your temperature climbs above the set point, you sweat to cool off; if your temperature drops below the set point, you shiver to warm up. Your blood glucose levels also remain fairly constant because the liver removes glucose from the blood and converts it to glycogen; when the body cells require glucose, glycogen is broken down. (You can probably hypothesize how your liver will respond if you eat a dozen jelly donuts!) The failure to maintain homeostasis can be detrimental and can even cause death. Consequently, **negative** and/or **positive feedback loops** regulate homeostasis.

Negative feedback mechanisms result in slight fluctuations above and below the set point. For example, if you were to consume a dozen jelly donuts, your blood sugar level would rise, and your pancreas would release insulin, a hormone involved in the conversion of glucose to glycogen, thus returning your blood glucose level to its appropriate set point. By comparison, **positive feedback** amplifies responses in the same direction, with the variable initiating the response moving the system even further away from the set point. There are fewer examples of positive feedback, but one is the onset of labor in childbirth when uterine contractions increase in strength with the secretion of oxytocin, another hormone. However, the loss of internal equilibrium due to positive feedback can be detrimental; for example, a small area of damaged heart tissue can precipitate a heart attack which, in turn, damages even more cardiac muscle.

Information presented and the examples highlighted in the section support concepts outlined in Big Idea 2 of the AP Biology® Curriculum Framework. The AP® Learning Objectives listed in the Curriculum Framework provide a transparent foundation for the AP® Biology course, an inquiry-based laboratory experience, instructional activities, and AP® exam questions. A learning objective merges required content with one or more of the seven Science Practices.

Big Idea 2	Biological systems utilize free energy and molecular building blocks to grow, to reproduce, and to maintain dynamic homeostasis.
Enduring Understanding 2.C	Organisms use feedback mechanisms to regulate growth and reproduction, and to maintain dynamic homeostasis.

Essential Knowledge	**2.C.1** Organisms use feedback mechanisms to maintain their internal environments and respond to external environmental changes.
Science Practice	**7.2** The student can connect concepts in and across domain(s) to generalize or extrapolate in and/or across enduring understandings and/or big ideas.
Learning Objective	**2.16** The student is able to connect how organisms use negative feedback to maintain their internal environments.
Essential Knowledge	**2.C.1** Organisms use feedback mechanisms to maintain their internal environments and respond to external environmental changes.
Science Practice	**5.3** The student can evaluate the evidence provided by data sets in relation to a particular scientific question.
Learning Objective	**2.17** The student is able to evaluate data that show the effect(s) of changes in concentrations of key molecules on negative feedback mechanisms.
Essential Knowledge	**2.C.1** Organisms use feedback mechanisms to maintain their internal environments and respond to external environmental changes.
Science Practice	**6.4** The student can make claims and predictions about natural phenomena based on scientific theories and models.
Learning Objective	**2.18** The student is able to make predictions about how organisms use negative feedback mechanisms to maintain their international environments.
Essential Knowledge	**2.C.1** Organisms use feedback mechanisms to maintain their internal environments and respond to external environmental changes.
Science Practice	**6.4** The student can make claims and predictions about natural phenomena based on scientific theories and models.
Learning Objective	**2.19** The student is able to make predictions about how positive feedback mechanisms amplify activities and processes in organisms based on scientific theories and models.
Essential Knowledge	**2.C.1** Organisms use feedback mechanisms to maintain their internal environments and respond to external environmental changes.
Science Practice	**6.1** The student can justify claims with evidence.
Learning Objective	**2.20** The student is able to justify that positive feedback mechanisms amplify responses in organisms.

Animal organs and organ systems constantly adjust to internal and external changes through a process called homeostasis ("steady state"). These changes might be in the level of glucose or calcium in blood or in external temperatures. Homeostasis means to maintain dynamic equilibrium in the body. It is dynamic because it is constantly adjusting to the changes that the body's systems encounter. It is equilibrium because body functions are kept within specific ranges. Even an animal that is apparently inactive is maintaining this homeostatic equilibrium.

Homeostatic Process

The goal of homeostasis is the maintenance of equilibrium around a point or value called a set point. While there are normal fluctuations from the set point, the body's systems will usually attempt to go back to this point. A change in the internal or external environment is called a stimulus and is detected by a receptor; the response of the system is to adjust the deviation parameter toward the set point. For instance, if the body becomes too warm, adjustments are made to cool the animal. If the blood's glucose rises after a meal, adjustments are made to lower the blood glucose level by getting the nutrient into tissues that need it or to store it for later use.

Control of Homeostasis

When a change occurs in an animal's environment, an adjustment must be made. The receptor senses the change in the environment, then sends a signal to the control center (in most cases, the brain) which in turn generates a response that is signaled to an effector. The effector is a muscle (that contracts or relaxes) or a gland that secretes. Homeostatsis is maintained by negative feedback loops. Positive feedback loops actually push the organism further out of homeostasis, but may be necessary for life to occur. Homeostasis is controlled by the nervous and endocrine system of mammals.

Negative Feedback Mechanisms

Any homeostatic process that changes the direction of the stimulus is a negative feedback loop. It may either increase or decrease the stimulus, but the stimulus is not allowed to continue as it did before the receptor sensed it. In other words, if a level is too high, the body does something to bring it down, and conversely, if a level is too low, the body does something to make it go up. Hence the term negative feedback. An example is animal maintenance of blood glucose levels. When an animal has eaten, blood glucose levels rise. This is sensed by the nervous system. Specialized cells in the pancreas sense this, and the hormone insulin is released by the endocrine system. Insulin causes blood glucose levels to decrease, as would be expected in a negative feedback system, as illustrated in Figure 24.20. However, if an animal has not eaten and blood glucose levels decrease, this is sensed in another group of cells in the pancreas, and the hormone glucagon is released causing glucose levels to increase. This is still a negative feedback loop, but not in the direction expected by the use of the term "negative." Another example of an increase as a result of the feedback loop is the control of blood calcium. If calcium levels decrease, specialized cells in the parathyroid gland sense this and release parathyroid hormone (PTH), causing an increased absorption of calcium through the intestines and kidneys and, possibly, the breakdown of bone in order to liberate calcium. The effects of PTH are to raise blood levels of the element. Negative feedback loops are the predominant mechanism used in homeostasis.

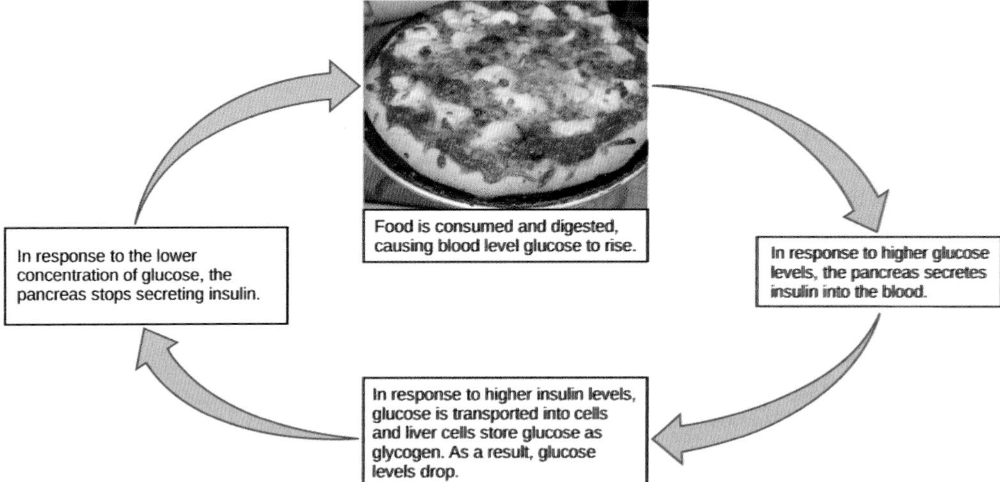

Figure 24.20 Blood sugar levels are controlled by a negative feedback loop. (credit: modification of work by Jon Sullivan)

Positive Feedback Loop

A positive feedback loop maintains the direction of the stimulus, possibly accelerating it. Few examples of positive feedback loops exist in animal bodies, but one is found in the cascade of chemical reactions that result in blood clotting, or coagulation. As one clotting factor is activated, it activates the next factor in sequence until a fibrin clot is achieved. The direction is maintained, not changed, so this is positive feedback. Another example of positive feedback is uterine contractions during childbirth, as illustrated in Figure 24.21. The hormone oxytocin, made by the endocrine system, stimulates the contraction of the uterus. This produces pain sensed by the nervous system. Instead of lowering the oxytocin and causing the pain to subside, more oxytocin is produced until the contractions are powerful enough to produce childbirth.

visual CONNECTION

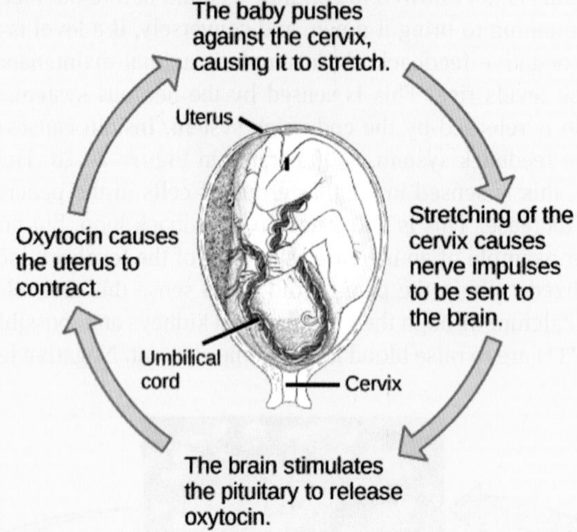
The baby pushes against the cervix, causing it to stretch.
Uterus
Stretching of the cervix causes nerve impulses to be sent to the brain.
Oxytocin causes the uterus to contract.
Umbilical cord
Cervix
The brain stimulates the pituitary to release oxytocin.

Figure 24.21 The birth of a human infant is the result of positive feedback.

State whether each of the following processes is regulated by a positive or negative feedback loop.

a. A person feels satiated after eating a large meal.

b. The blood has plenty of red blood cells. As a result, erythropoietin, a hormone that stimulates the production of new red blood cells, is no longer released from the kidney.

a. a. This is regulated by a positive feedback loop as the stimulus (hunger) has changed direction in response to a signal (fullness).
   b. This is regulated by a positive feedback loop as the stimulus (red blood cell release) has changed direction in response to a signal (presence of enough red blood cells).
b. a. This is regulated by a negative feedback loop as the stimulus (hunger) has changed direction in response to a signal (fullness).
   b. This is regulated by a positive feedback loop as the direction of the stimulus has been maintained.
c. a. This is regulated by a positive feedback loop as the stimulus (hunger) has changed direction in response to a signal (fullness).
   b. This is regulated by a negative feedback loop as the stimulus (red blood cell release) has changed direction in response to a signal (presence of enough red blood cells).
d. a. This is regulated by a negative feedback loop as the stimulus (hunger) changed direction in response to a signal (fullness).
   b. This is regulated by a negative feedback loop as the stimulus (red blood cell release) changed direction in response to a signal (presence of enough red blood cells).

Set Point

It is possible to adjust a system's set point. When this happens, the feedback loop works to maintain the new setting. An example of this is blood pressure: over time, the normal or set point for blood pressure can increase as a result of continued increases in blood pressure. The body no longer recognizes the elevation as abnormal and no attempt is made to return to the lower set point. The result is the maintenance of an elevated blood pressure that can have harmful effects on the body. Medication can lower blood pressure and lower the set point in the system to a more healthy level. This is called a process of **alteration** of the set point in a feedback loop.

Changes can be made in a group of body organ systems in order to maintain a set point in another system. This is called **acclimatization**. This occurs, for instance, when an animal migrates to a higher altitude than it is accustomed to. In order to adjust to the lower oxygen levels at the new altitude, the body increases the number of red blood cells circulating in the blood to ensure adequate oxygen delivery to the tissues. Another example of acclimatization is animals that have seasonal changes in their coats: a heavier coat in the winter ensures adequate heat retention, and a light coat in summer assists in keeping body temperature from rising to harmful levels.

Feedback mechanisms can be understood in terms of driving a race car along a track: watch a short **video lesson (http://openstaxcollege.org/l/feedback_loops)** on positive and negative feedback loops.

Voltage-gated sodium channels occur in the cell membranes of nerve cells. They open in response to sodium entering the cell, which in turn, allows more sodium to enter the cell. Is this a positive or negative feedback loop and why?

a. This is a positive feedback loop as voltage-gated sodium channels open in response to sodium influx and then close when enough sodium has entered through the channels.

b. This is a negative feedback loop as voltage-gated sodium channels open in response to sodium influx and then close when enough sodium has entered through the channels.

c. This is a positive feedback loop as voltage-gated sodium channels open in response to sodium influx, which allows more sodium to go in through the channels.

d. This is a negative feedback loop as voltage-gated sodium channels open in response to sodium influx, which allows more sodium to go in through the channels.

science practices CONNECTION for AP® Courses

Think About It

How are negative feedback loops used to regulate body homeostasis? How is a condition such as diabetes a good example of the failure of a set point in humans? Hypothesize and draw a diagram that shows what you think is the feedback failure for a person with diabetes.

Homeostasis: Thermoregulation

Body temperature affects body activities. Generally, as body temperature rises, enzyme activity rises as well. For every ten degree centigrade rise in temperature, enzyme activity doubles, up to a point. Body proteins, including enzymes, begin to denature and lose their function with high heat (around 50°C for mammals). Enzyme activity will decrease by half for every ten degree centigrade drop in temperature, to the point of freezing, with a few exceptions. Some fish can withstand freezing solid and return to normal with thawing.

Watch this **Discovery Channel video (http://openstaxcollege.org/l/thermoregulate)** on thermoregulation to see illustrations of this process in a variety of animals.

How does the loose skin of an elephant help it regulate body temperature?

a. Loose skin is thicker, which allows the excess heat to dissipate quickly through the skin.

b. Loose skin brings more heat and blood to the body surface, facilitating heat loss.

c. Loose skin contains greater skin area, which allows excess heat to dissipate as heat loss occurs through the skin.

d. Loose skin has smaller skin area, which allows excess heat to dissipate as heat loss occurs through the skin.

Endotherms and Ectotherms

Animals can be divided into two groups: some maintain a constant body temperature in the face of differing environmental temperatures, while others have a body temperature that is the same as their environment and thus varies with the environment. Animals that do not control their body temperature are ectotherms. This group has been called cold-blooded, but the term may not apply to an animal in the desert with a very warm body temperature. In contrast to ectotherms, which rely on external temperatures to set their body temperatures, poikilotherms are animals with constantly varying internal temperatures. An animal that maintains a constant body temperature in the face of environmental changes is called a homeotherm. Endotherms are animals that rely on internal sources for body temperature but which can exhibit extremes in temperature. These animals are able to maintain a level of activity at cooler temperature, which an ectotherm cannot due to differing enzyme levels of activity.

Heat can be exchanged between an animal and its environment through four mechanisms: radiation, evaporation, convection, and conduction (**Figure 24.22**). Radiation is the emission of electromagnetic "heat" waves. Heat comes from the sun in this manner and radiates from dry skin the same way. Heat can be removed with liquid from a surface during evaporation. This occurs when a mammal sweats. Convection currents of air remove heat from the surface of dry skin as the air passes over it. Heat will be conducted from one surface to another during direct contact with the surfaces, such as an animal resting on a warm rock.

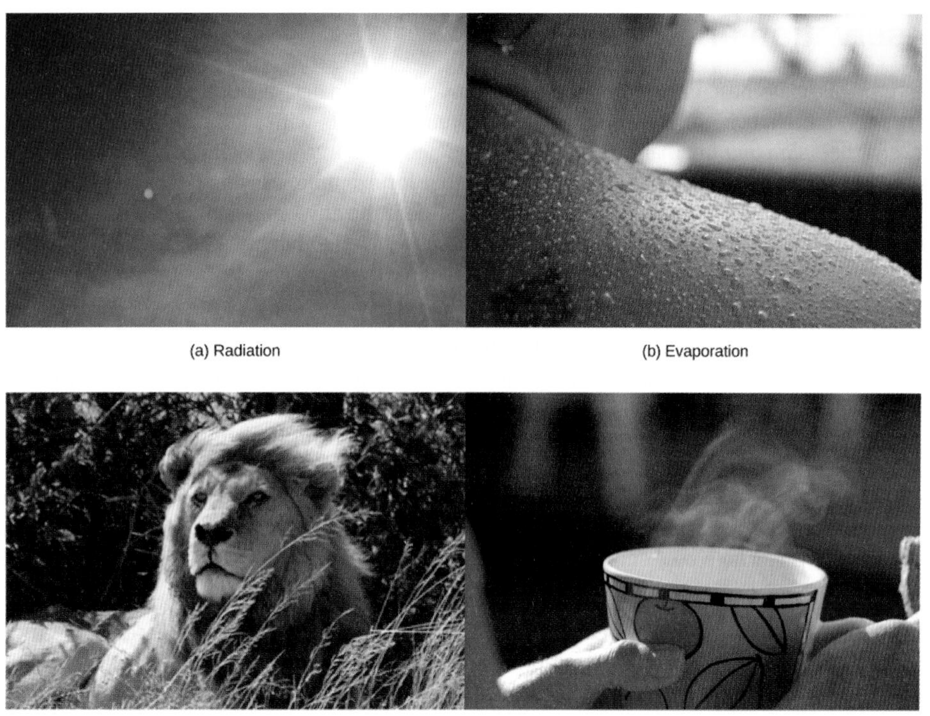

Figure 24.22 Heat can be exchanged by four mechanisms: (a) radiation, (b) evaporation, (c) convection, or (d) conduction. (credit b: modification of work by "Kullez"/Flickr; credit c: modification of work by Chad Rosenthal; credit d: modification of work by "stacey.d"/Flickr)

everyday CONNECTION for AP® Courses

Figure 24.23 The body temperature of ectotherms varies with the environment. For that reason, reptiles, such as this American alligator, bask in the sun to warm themselves.

If an American alligator has been basking but gets too hot, how might the alligator cool itself?

a. increase vasodilation

b. sweat

c. move into shade

d. increase metabolic rate

Heat Conservation and Dissipation

Animals conserve or dissipate heat in a variety of ways. In certain climates, endothermic animals have some form of insulation, such as fur, fat, feathers, or some combination thereof. Animals with thick fur or feathers create an insulating layer of air between their skin and internal organs. Polar bears and seals live and swim in a subfreezing environment and yet maintain a constant, warm, body temperature. The arctic fox, for example, uses its fluffy tail as extra insulation when it curls up to sleep in cold weather. Mammals have a residual effect from shivering and increased muscle activity: arrector pili muscles cause "goose bumps," causing small hairs to stand up when the individual is cold; this has the intended effect of increasing body temperature. Mammals use layers of fat to achieve the same end. Loss of significant amounts of body fat will compromise an individual's ability to conserve heat.

Endotherms use their circulatory systems to help maintain body temperature. Vasodilation brings more blood and heat to the body surface, facilitating radiation and evaporative heat loss, which helps to cool the body. Vasoconstriction reduces blood flow in peripheral blood vessels, forcing blood toward the core and the vital organs found there, and conserving heat. Some animals have adaptions to their circulatory system that enable them to transfer heat from arteries to veins, warming blood returning to the heart. This is called a countercurrent heat exchange; it prevents the cold venous blood from cooling the heart and other internal organs. This adaption can be shut down in some animals to prevent overheating the internal organs. The countercurrent adaption is found in many animals, including dolphins, sharks, bony fish, bees, and hummingbirds. In contrast, similar adaptations can help cool endotherms when needed, such as dolphin flukes and elephant ears.

Some ectothermic animals use changes in their behavior to help regulate body temperature. For example, a desert ectothermic animal may simply seek cooler areas during the hottest part of the day in the desert to keep from getting too warm. The same animals may climb onto rocks to capture heat during a cold desert night. Some animals seek water to aid evaporation in cooling them, as seen with reptiles. Other ectotherms use group activity such as the activity of bees to warm a hive to survive winter.

Many animals, especially mammals, use metabolic waste heat as a heat source. When muscles are contracted, most of the energy from the ATP used in muscle actions is wasted energy that translates into heat. Severe cold elicits a shivering reflex that generates heat for the body. Many species also have a type of adipose tissue called brown fat that specializes in generating heat.

Neural Control of Thermoregulation

The nervous system is important to **thermoregulation**, as illustrated in Figure 24.22. The processes of homeostasis and temperature control are centered in the hypothalamus of the advanced animal brain.

visual CONNECTION

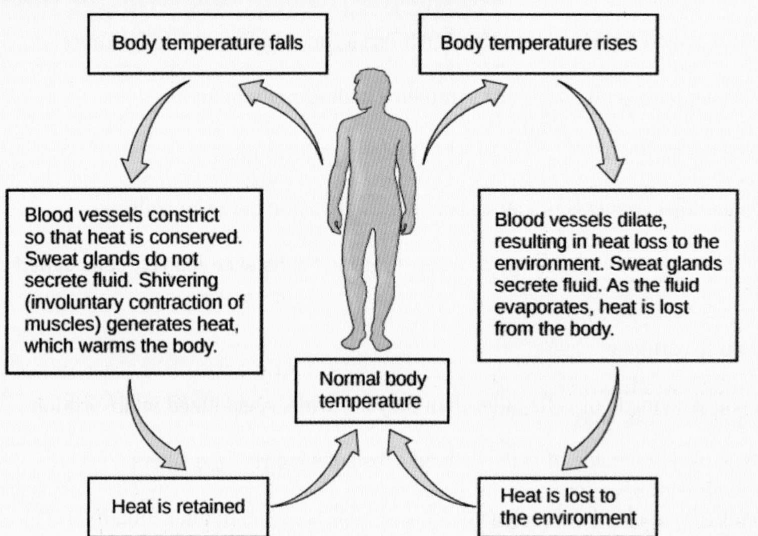

Figure 24.24 The body is able to regulate temperature in response to signals from the nervous system.

When bacteria are destroyed by leukocytes, pyrogens are released into the blood. Pyrogens reset the body's thermostat to a higher temperature, resulting in fever. How do pyrogens cause body temperature to rise?

a. Pyrogens circulate to the hypothalamus to reset the body's "thermostat," causing a rise in temperature.
b. Pyrogens circulate to the thalamus to reset the body's "thermostat," causing a rise in temperature.
c. Pyrogens cause an increase in the activity of the animal's enzymes, which results in the temperature rise.
d. Pyrogens entering the blood release some lipid substances, which ultimately cause the rise in temperature.

The hypothalamus maintains the set point for body temperature through reflexes that cause vasodilation and sweating when the body is too warm, or vasoconstriction and shivering when the body is too cold. It responds to chemicals from the body. When a bacterium is destroyed by phagocytic leukocytes, chemicals called endogenous pyrogens are released into the blood. These pyrogens circulate to the hypothalamus and reset the thermostat. This allows the body's temperature to increase in what is commonly called a fever. An increase in body temperature causes iron to be conserved, which reduces a nutrient needed by bacteria. An increase in body heat also increases the activity of the animal's enzymes and protective cells while inhibiting the enzymes and activity of the invading microorganisms. Finally, heat itself may also kill the pathogen. A fever that was once thought to be a complication of an infection is now understood to be a normal defense mechanism.

KEY TERMS

acclimatization alteration in a body system in response to environmental change

alteration change of the set point in a homeostatic system

apodeme ingrowth of an animal's exoskeleton that functions as an attachment site for muscles

asymmetrical describes animals with no axis of symmetry in their body pattern

basal metabolic rate (BMR) metabolic rate at rest in endothermic animals

canaliculus microchannel that connects the lacunae and aids diffusion between cells

cartilage type of connective tissue with a large amount of ground substance matrix, cells called chondrocytes, and some amount of fibers

chondrocyte cell found in cartilage

columnar epithelia epithelia made of cells taller than they are wide, specialized in absorption

connective tissue type of tissue made of cells, ground substance matrix, and fibers

cuboidal epithelia epithelia made of cube-shaped cells, specialized in glandular functions

dorsal cavity body cavity on the posterior or back portion of an animal; includes the cranial and vertebral cavities

ectotherm animal incapable of maintaining a relatively constant internal body temperature

endotherm animal capable of maintaining a relatively constant internal body temperature

epithelial tissue tissue that either lines or covers organs or other tissues

estivation torpor in response to extremely high temperatures and low water availability

fibrous connective tissue type of connective tissue with a high concentration of fibers

frontal (coronal) plane plane cutting through an animal separating the individual into front and back portions

fusiform animal body shape that is tubular and tapered at both ends

hibernation torpor over a long period of time, such as a winter

homeostasis dynamic equilibrium maintaining appropriate body functions

lacuna space in cartilage and bone that contains living cells

loose (areolar) connective tissue type of connective tissue with small amounts of cells, matrix, and fibers; found around blood vessels

matrix component of connective tissue made of both living and non-living (ground substances) cells

midsagittal plane plane cutting through an animal separating the individual into even right and left sides

negative feedback loop feedback to a control mechanism that increases or decreases a stimulus instead of maintaining it

osteon subunit of compact bone

positive feedback loop feedback to a control mechanism that continues the direction of a stimulus

pseudostratified layer of epithelia that appears multilayered, but is a simple covering

sagittal plane plane cutting through an animal separating the individual into right and left sides

set point midpoint or target point in homeostasis

simple epithelia single layer of epithelial cells

squamous epithelia type of epithelia made of flat cells, specialized in aiding diffusion or preventing abrasion

standard metabolic rate (SMR) metabolic rate at rest in ectothermic animals

stratified epithelia multiple layers of epithelial cells

thermoregulation regulation of body temperature

torpor decrease in activity and metabolism that allows an animal to survive adverse conditions

trabecula tiny plate that makes up spongy bone and gives it strength

transitional epithelia epithelia that can transition for appearing multilayered to simple; also called uroepithelial

transverse (horizontal) plane plane cutting through an animal separating the individual into upper and lower portions

ventral cavity body cavity on the anterior or front portion of an animal that includes the thoracic cavities and the abdominopelvic cavities

CHAPTER SUMMARY

24.1 Animal Form and Function

Animal bodies come in a variety of sizes and shapes. Limits on animal size and shape include impacts to their movement. Diffusion affects their size and development. Bioenergetics describes how animals use and obtain energy in relation to their body size, activity level, and environment.

24.2 Animal Primary Tissues

The basic building blocks of complex animals are four primary tissues. These are combined to form organs, which have a specific, specialized function within the body, such as the skin or kidney. Organs are organized together to perform common functions in the form of systems. The four primary tissues are epithelia, connective tissues, muscle tissues, and nervous tissues.

24.3 Homeostasis

Homeostasis is a dynamic equilibrium that is maintained in body tissues and organs. It is dynamic because it is constantly adjusting to the changes that the systems encounter. It is in equilibrium because body functions are kept within a normal range, with some fluctuations around a set point for the processes.

REVIEW QUESTIONS

1. The pleural cavity is part of which cavity?

a. dorsal
b. thoracic
c. abdominal
d. pericardial

2. A plane that divides an animal into dorsal and ventral portions is the _____ plane.

a. sagittal
b. midsagittal
c. frontal
d. transverse

3. What is the term for a hard covering or shell that provides protection and muscle attachment?

a. apodeme
b. fusiform
c. exoskeleton
d. endotherm

4. Which organism has a fusiform shape?

a. elephant
b. dolphin
c. spider
d. human

5. Which type of animal maintains a constant internal body temperature?

a. endotherm
b. ectotherm
c. poikilotherm
d. fusiform

6. Smaller endothermic animals have _______ surface area for their mass compared with larger endothermic animals.

a. equal
b. greater
c. less
d. no

7. What is the term for epithelial cells that are composed of multiple layers?

a. simple
b. stratified
c. squamous
d. transitional

8. Which type of epithelial cell is best adapted to aid diffusion?

a. squamous
b. cuboidal
c. columnar
d. transitional

9. Why do osteoclasts need to break down bone?

a. to deposit bone material into the bone matrix
b. to facilitate osteoclast persistence without using excess energy
c. to provide access to calcium in the tissue
d. to facilitate compact bone structure

10. Plasma is the ____.

a. fibers in the blood
b. matrix of the blood
c. cell that phagocytizes bacteria
d. cell that functions in response to antigens

11. Why is it necessary for most muscle cells to be under voluntary control?

a. to facilitate response to local conditions of tissues
b. to facilitate movement of bone
c. to speed up or slow down the autonomic nervous system
d. to facilitate movement of internal organs

12. Cardiac muscle contains specialized regions along the plasma membrane called intercalated discs. What is the role of intercalated discs?

a. efficiently pass electrical impulses between cardiac cells
b. facilitate immune response to foreign antigens
c. cushion body organs from damage
d. keeps blood vessels in place

13. The part of a neuron that contains the nucleus is the ____.

a. axon
b. dendrite
c. cell body
d. oligodendrocyte

14. Schwann cells or oligodendrocytes manufacture a lipid called myelin. Which statement best describes the function of this lipid?

a. regulates the chemical environment
b. sends input
c. receives input
d. improves signal transfer efficiency

15. Animals maintain an overall steady state of internal conditions by ___.

a. ectothermy
b. homeostasis
c. basal metabolic rate
d. standard metabolic rate

16. To what does the term “equilibrium” refer in the context of organismal homeostasis?

a. control mechanisms that amplify a response
b. control mechanisms that increase or decrease a stimulus
c. the target point in homeostasis
d. body functions are maintained within a given range

17. What type of feedback loop pushes an organism’s physiology further away from it normal setpoints?

a. positive feedback loop
b. negative feedback loop
c. set point
d. receptor

18. When faced with a sudden drop in environmental temperature, an endothermic animal will ____.

a. experience a substantial drop in its body temperature
b. find a warm rock on which to bask
c. increase muscle activity to generate heat
d. increase fur or fat to increase insulation

19. Homeostasis is primarily controlled by _______ feedback loops.

a. positive
b. negative
c. acclimatization
d. receptor

20. Which is an example of negative feedback?

a. lowering of blood glucose after a meal
b. blood clotting after an injury
c. lactation during nursing
d. uterine contractions during labor

21. Which method of heat exchange occurs during direct contact between the source and the animal?

a. radiation
b. evaporation
c. convection
d. conduction

22. Which of the following is a strategy that may be employed by an ectotherm to immediately increase body temperature?

a. Consume more food to increase fat as insulation.
b. Increase amount of vasodilation.
c. Increase amount of muscle contraction.
d. Sit on a warm rock.

CRITICAL THINKING QUESTIONS

23. How does an asymmetrical body plan differ from radial or bilateral body plans?

a. Asymmetrical organisms can produce equal halves if cut along a certain plane, whereas radially and bilaterally symmetric organisms have no distinct pattern.
b. Asymmetrical organisms have no distinct pattern, whereas radially and bilaterally symmetric organisms can produce equal halves if cut along a certain plane.
c. Asymmetrical organisms produce equal halves if cut along a certain plane with no definite right or left side, whereas radially and bilaterally symmetric organisms can produce equal halves.
d. Asymmetrical organisms produce equal halves if cut along a certain plane with definite right and left sides, whereas radially and bilaterally symmetric organisms can produce equal halves.

24. Why are most organisms with exoskeletons relatively small?

a. Increases in body weight increase body size by a factor of eight, and the chitin thickness of the exoskeleton has to significantly decrease to accommodate increase in body size.
b. Doubling of body size increases body weight by a factor of eight, and the chitin thickness of the exoskeleton has to significantly decrease to accommodate weight increase.
c. Increases in body weight increase body size by a factor of eight, and the chitin thickness of the exoskeleton has to significantly increase to accommodate increase in body size.
d. Doubling of body size increases body weight by a factor of eight, and the chitin thickness of the exoskeleton has to significantly increase to accommodate weight increase.

25. What is the relationship between basal metabolic rate (BMR) and body size? Why?

a. BMR decreases with body size, because larger animals require more energy to maintain their size. However, smaller animals have relatively higher BMRs per body weight because they have greater surface area.
b. BMR increases with body size, because smaller animals require more energy to maintain their size. However, larger animals have relatively higher BMRs per body weight because they have greater surface area.
c. BMR increases with body size, because larger animals require more energy to maintain their size. However, smaller animals have relatively higher BMRs per body weight because they have greater surface area for their mass.
d. BMR decreases with body size, because smaller animals require more energy to maintain their size. However, larger animals have relatively higher BMRs per body weight because they have greater surface area for their mass.

26. Radial symmetry is typically found in aquatic organisms. What is radial symmetry and why is it advantageous to certain aquatic organisms?

a. Radially symmetric means that a plane cut from the front to back of the organism produces distinct left and right sides that are mirror images of each other. It helps certain aquatic organisms to extract food from surrounding environments.
b. Radially symmetric means that a plane cut from the front to back of the organism produces distinct left and right sides that are mirror images of each other. It helps certain aquatic organisms to perform photosynthesis.
c. Radially symmetric means that a plane cut along its longitudinal axis will produce equal halves, and there is no distinct left or right. It helps certain aquatic organisms to perform photosynthesis.
d. Radially symmetric means that a plane cut along its longitudinal axis to produce equal halves, and there is no distinct left or right. It helps certain aquatic organisms to extract food from surrounding environments.

27. Columnar epithelial cells, which are typically found in a single-layer arrangement, are found along the digestive tract. What is the role of columnar epithelial cells in digestion?

a. Columnar epithelial cells absorb material from the lumen of the digestive tract to prepare the material for entry into the body.
b. Columnar epithelial cells release mucus for lubrication as well as antimicrobial agents in the digestive tract.
c. Columnar epithelial cells secrete enzymes like salivary amylase which aid in digestion by the breakdown of carbohydrates in the body.
d. Columnar epithelial cells help in the propulsion of food by peristalsis in the digestive tract of the body.

28. In vertebrates, cartilage is found in fetal bones, ears, and intervertebral discs, whereas bone is found in the skeleton. What are the similarities between cartilage and bone?

a. Both are types of connective tissue in the body and cells of both are known as chondrocytes.
b. Both are types of connective tissue in the body and have non-vascular organic matrix material that provides strength and flexibility.
c. Both are types of connective tissue in the body and have organic matrix material that provides strength and flexibility.
d. Both consist of bone marrow and have organic matrix material that provides strength and flexibility.

29. A friend sneaks up behind you and scares you, speeding up your heart rate. How and why did this event influence cardiac muscle contraction?

a. Muscle contraction speed increases as the enteric nervous system responds to local conditions and makes muscle contraction speed up or slow down.
b. Muscle contraction speed increases as the autonomic nervous system responds to local conditions and makes muscle contraction speed up or slow down.
c. Muscle contraction speed increases as the somatic nervous system responds to local conditions and makes muscle contraction speed up or slow down.
d. Muscle contraction speed increases as the central nervous system responds to local conditions and makes muscle contraction speed up or slow down.

30. Neurons have several specialized structures, including dendrites. What might happen if an individual has malformed dendrites?

a. The individual's neurons would not be able to receive input properly.
b. The individual's neurons would not be able to synthesize proteins.
c. The individual's neurons would not be able to communicate with target neurons.
d. The individual's neurons would not be able to carry nerve signals.

31. How can squamous epithelia, which have a high surface area-to-volume ratio, both facilitate diffusion and prevent damage from abrasion?

a. Single layers of squamous epithelia facilitate gas, nutrient or waste exchange, whereas stratified layers provide protection but are not replaceable following damage.
b. Stratified layers of squamous epithelia facilitate gas, nutrient or waste exchange, whereas single layers provide protection and are replaceable following damage.
c. Single layers of squamous epithelia facilitate gas, nutrient or waste exchange whereas stratified layers provide protection and are replaceable following damage.
d. Single layers of squamous epithelia facilitate only exchange of gases by diffusion, whereas stratified layers provide protection and are replaceable following damage.

32. What is homeostasis and how does it help maintain equilibrium of various body functions throughout the body?

a. Homeostasis is the process of achieving stability, which occurs through behavioral changes. Equilibrium is maintained by that ensuring body functions remain within a certain range.
b. Homeostasis is the process by which constant adjustments to changes in the body occur, and equilibrium is maintained by ensuring that body functions remain within a certain range.
c. Homeostasis is the process that prevents blood loss from circulation when a blood vessel is ruptured, and equilibrium is maintained by ensuring that circulation of blood is kept within a normal range.
d. Homeostasis is the process by which constant adjustment to changes in the body occurs, and equilibrium is maintained as body functions remain within a certain range without any fluctuations.

33. How can an environmental change result in an alteration of gland secretion?

a. A receptor detects change, sends a signal to the control center, which sends a signal to the gland to inhibit the gland secretions.
b. A receptor detects change, sends a signal to the control center, which sends a signal to the gland to increase the secretions of the gland.
c. A receptor detects change and sends a signal to the effector directly ,which in this case is the gland.
d. A receptor detects change, sends a signal to the control center, which in turn sends a signal to the effector, which in this case is the gland.

34. How is a condition such as diabetes a good example of the failure of a set point in humans?

a. A negative feedback loop cannot proceed in diabetic individuals, as they do not produce enough functional insulin to lower blood sugar.
b. Negative feedback loop cannot proceed in diabetic individuals, as they do not produce enough functional insulin to increase the blood sugar.
c. Positive feedback loop cannot proceed in diabetic individuals, as they do not produce enough functional insulin to lower blood sugar.
d. Positive feedback loop cannot proceed in diabetic individuals, as they do not produce enough functional insulin to increase the blood sugar.

35. What are the roles of vasodilation and vasoconstriction in maintaining body temperature?

a. Vasodilation allows for radiation and evaporative heat loss, and vasoconstriction brings blood to the core to conserve heat by vital organs.
b. Vasodilation brings blood to the core to conserve heat by vital organs, and vasoconstriction results in radiation and evaporative heat loss.
c. Vasodilation results in the formation of an insulating layer between skin and internal organs causing heat conservation and brings blood to the core to conserve heat.
d. Vasodilation results in radiation and evaporative heat loss, and vasoconstriction transfers heat from arteries to veins to warm blood returning to the heart.

TEST PREP FOR AP® COURSES

36. Maintaining body heat is important for maintaining body functions in animals. Which of the following statements provides an example of how an animal can actively generate body heat?

a. Triglycerides are used to store energy for later use.

b. An animal produces metabolic waste energy in the form of heat.

c. An animal has insulation, which helps it maintain a constant body temperature.

d. An animal eats a large amount of high-fat foods to produce adipose tissue.

37. Ectotherms and endotherms have different strategies for generating and maintaining body heat. Explain why ectotherms are more dependent on the environment for body heat than endotherms and how endotherms are able to generate and maintain body temperature.

a. Ectotherms use external thermal heat whereas endotherms use metabolically generated heat to help regulate and maintain body temperatures.

b. Ectotherms use external heat to help regulate and maintain body temperatures whereas endotherms have constantly varying internal temperatures.

c. Ectotherms use metabolically-generated heat to maintain a constant body temperature whereas endotherms use metabolically generated heat to regulate body temperature within a wider range.

d. Ectotherms use external thermal energy to help regulate and maintain body temperatures whereas endotherms maintain a constant body temperature.

38. Which of the following statements most directly supports the claim that different species of organisms use different metabolic strategies to meet their energy requirements for growth, reproduction, and homeostasis?

a. During cold periods, pond-dwelling animals can increase the number of unsaturated fatty acids in their cell membranes, while some plants make antifreeze proteins to prevent ice crystal formation in tissues.

b. Bacteria lack introns, while many eukaryotic genes contain many of these intervening sequences.

c. Carnivores have more teeth that are specialized for grinding food.

d. Plants generally use starch molecules for storage while animals use glycogen and fats for storage.

39. The body sizes of organisms vary and tends to be correlated with the region in which the organisms are found. Why do organisms at different latitudes tend to have different body sizes, and what is the relationship between heat loss and body size in an organism?

a. Temperature varies by latitude, and body size affects heat retention and loss. Smaller organisms lose heat at a slower rate than larger organisms because they have a smaller surface area for their mass.

b. Temperature varies by latitude, and body size affects heat retention and loss. Smaller organisms lose heat at a faster rate than larger organisms because they have a greater surface area for their mass.

c. Temperature varies by latitude, and body size affects heat retention and loss. Larger organisms lose heat at a faster rate than smaller organisms because they have a greater surface area for their mass.

d. Temperature varies by latitude, and body size affects heat retention and loss. Smaller organisms lose heat at a faster rate than larger organisms because they have a smaller surface area for their mass.

40. If an American alligator has been basking but gets too hot, how might the alligator cool itself?

a. increase vasodilation

b. sweat

c. move into shade

d. increase metabolic rate

41.

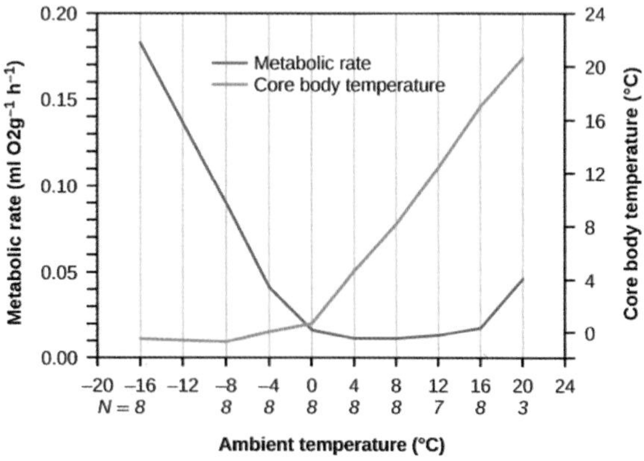

During torpor, arctic ground squirrels reduce their energy requirements by reducing their core body temperature and metabolic rate. Why would an active ground squirrel's ATP synthesis also increase in proportion to metabolic rate when temperatures fall below 0°?

a. Colder temperatures causes ATP to degrade.

b. ATP is synthesized through cellular respiration, which provides body heat.

c. ATP synthesis is needed to provide more oxygen to the cells.

d. ATP is consumed by the cells to generate body heat.

42. Why is hibernation not a good option for small animals like the hummingbirds to help reduce its metabolic rate and conserve its need for food?

a. Hummingbirds have a fast metabolic rate and a large surface area to volume ratio.
b. Hummingbirds are unable to lower their metabolic rate and body temperature to enter hibernation.
c. Hummingbirds migrate south for the winter.
d. Hummingbirds live a short life.

43. How does hibernation differ in small animals such as ground squirrels and larger animals such as bears?

a. Smaller animals can engage in torpor while larger animals cannot.
b. Larger animals can engage in torpor while smaller animals cannot.
c. Smaller animals cannot remain inactive throughout the entire winter while larger animals can.
d. Larger animals cannot remain inactive throughout the entire winter while smaller animals can.

44.

	Bear	Marmot	Honey possum	Hummingbird	Shrew
BM (g)	80,000	4,000	10	4	2
CD (min)	8,307	1,766	80	59	35
WU (min)	741	237	24	17	13
NBT (°C)	37	40	37	40	34
BTH (°C)	33	18	5	2	2

In the data, BM = body mass, CD = cool-down time; WU = warm-up time, NBT = normal body temperature and BTH = body temperature during hibernation. What can you conclude from the data collected on five different animals as shown in the table above?

a. The time it takes for animals to change body temperature is directly related to body size.
b. The time it takes for animals to change their body temperature is indirectly related to their size.
c. Larger animals hibernate for longer periods of time.
d. Smaller animals hibernate for shorter periods of time

45.

	Bear	Marmot	Honey opposum	Hummingbird	Shrew
BM (g)	80,000	4,000	10	4	2
CD (min)	8,307	1,766	80	59	35
WU (min)	741	237	24	17	13
NBT (°C)	37	40	37	40	34
BTH (°C)	33	18	5	2	2

In the data, BM = body mass, CD = cool-down time; WU = warm-up time, NBT = normal body temperature and BTH = body temperature during hibernation. What can you conclude from about the time it takes to cool down versus the time it takes to warm up?

a. Larger animals consume more energy to maintain their body temperatures.
b. Smaller animals can survive hibernation with less food reserves than larger animals.
c. Smaller animals require more time to alter their body temperature.
d. Larger animals require more time to alter their body temperature.

46. The endocrine system incorporates feedback mechanisms that maintain homeostasis. Which of the following demonstrates negative feedback by the endocrine system?

a. During labor, the fetus exerts pressure on the uterine wall, inducing the production of oxytocin, which stimulates uterine wall contraction. The contractions cause the fetus to further push on the wall, increasing the production of oxytocin.
b. After a meal, blood glucose levels become elevated, stimulating beta cells of the pancreas to release insulin into the blood. Excess glucose is then converted to glycogen in the liver, reducing blood glucose levels.
c. At high elevation, atmospheric oxygen is scarcer. In response to signals that oxygen is low, the brain decreases an individual's rate of respiration to compensate for the difference.
d. A transcription factor binds to the regulating region of a gene, blocking the binding of another transcription factor required for expression.

47.

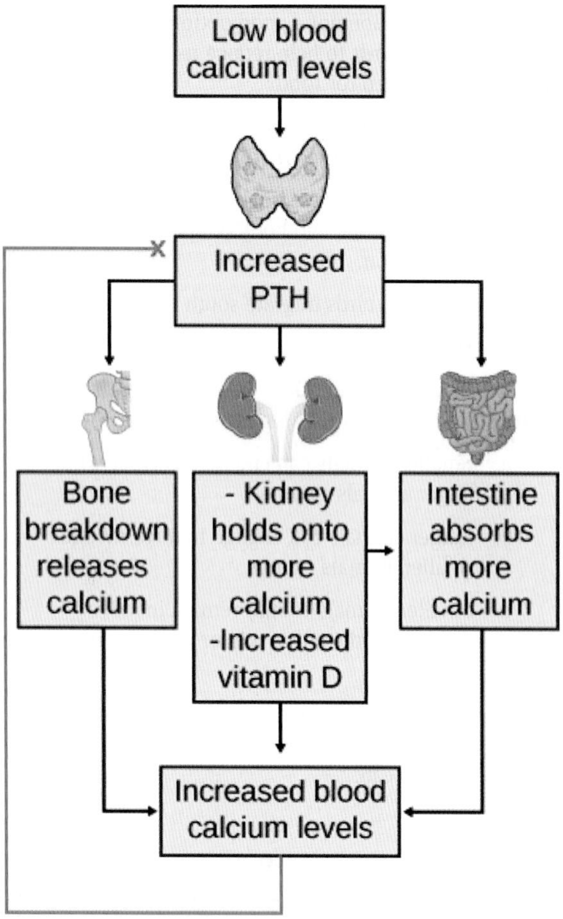

Low blood calcium levels
Increased PTH
Bone breakdown releases calcium
- Kidney holds onto more calcium -Increased vitamin D
Intestine absorbs more calcium
Increased blood calcium levels

This figure depicts the process of calcium homeostasis. Describe how blood calcium control is an example of a negative feedback loop.

a. Cells in parathyroid gland sense calcium decrease causing parathyroid hormone release and stimulating calcium absorption. Bone may also break down to release calcium.
b. Cells in parathyroid gland sense calcium decrease causing calcitonin release and stimulating calcium absorption. Bone may also break down to release calcium.
c. Cells in thyroid gland sense calcium decrease causing calcitonin release and stimulating calcium absorption. Bone may also break down to release calcium.
d. Cells in parathyroid gland sense calcium increase causing parathyroid hormone release and stimulating calcium absorption. Bone may also break down to release calcium.

48. In organisms, homeostasis of various bodily processes, such as body temperature, blood glucose levels, and blood calcium levels, is essential for the maintenance of proper body functions. What role does insulin play in homeostasis?

a. When a fetus pushes against the uterine wall, insulin is released by the brain to stimulate uterine contractions.

b. In the presence of decreased blood glucose levels, insulin is produced by the parathyroid to increase calcium absorption.

c. Insulin activation activates other clotting factors until a fibrin clot is produced.

d. Insulin is secreted by the pancreas in response to elevated blood glucose levels to remove glucose from the blood.

49. Proper blood glucose levels are necessary to maintain cellular function, because glucose is fuel for cells. Glucagon is an important component of blood glucose homeostasis, which is maintained by a negative feedback loop. Describe the role of glucagon in blood glucose homeostasis.

a. When blood sugar is low, glucose and ATP produce glycogen. Excess blood sugar stimulates the release of glucagon, which in turn stimulates glycogen release to increase blood glucose levels.

b. When there is excess blood sugar, excess glucose and ATP produce glucagon. A drop in blood glucose level stimulates the release of glycogen, which in turn stimulates glycogen release to increase blood glucose levels.

c. When there is excess blood sugar, the excess glucose and ATP produce glycogen. A drop in blood glucose level stimulates the release of glucagon, which in turn stimulates the release of glycogen to increase blood glucose levels.

d. When there is excess blood sugar, the excess glucose and ATP produce glycogen. A drop in blood glucose level stimulates the release of glucagon, which in turn releases more glucagon to increase blood glucose levels.

50. One process that is under the control of a negative feedback loop is red blood cell production. These cells carry oxygen to all of the body cells, and remove some carbon dioxide. What would most likely happen if an individual had a sufficient number of red blood cells?

a. The individual would have increased red blood cell production.

b. The individual's body would start destroying the red blood cells.

c. The individual's body would cease production of new red blood cells.

d. The individual would produce the same amount of red blood cells.

51. Diabetes results when either insulin cannot be produced or does not function properly. Consequently, diabetes can produce complications such as blindness, heart disease, and kidney disease. To help manage diabetes, a patient can get insulin injections. How do insulin injections promote a negative feedback loop to help maintain blood glucose production?

a. Insulin injections allow transport and storage of glucose to increase blood glucose levels after consuming a large or high-glucose meal.

b. Insulin injections allow only storage of glucose to decrease blood glucose levels after consuming a large or high-glucose meal.

c. Insulin injections allow transport and storage of glucose to increase blood glucose levels before consuming a meal.

d. Insulin injections allow transport and storage of glucose to decrease blood glucose levels after consuming a large or high-glucose meal.

52. Positive feedback loops amplify processes in organisms. Which of the following statements describes the role of the hormone oxytocin in a positive feedback loop for childbirth?

a. Oxytocin halts uterine contractions when the fetus pushes on the uterine wall.

b. Oxytocin maintains pain levels as the child is pushed through the birth canal.

c. Oxytocin stimulates uterine contractions when the fetus pushes on the uterine wall.

d. Oxytocin decreases pain levels as the child is pushed through the birth canal.

53. Birth is one of the few positive feedback loops observed in humans and is essential for the proper delivery of babies. Describe how a baby pushing against a pregnant woman's cervix stimulates a positive feedback loop.

a. Stretching stimulates nerve impulses to be sent to the brain, which releases oxytocin from the pituitary, which in turn causes uterine contractions.

b. Stretching stimulates nerve impulses to be sent to the brain, which releases estrogen from the pituitary, which in turn causes uterine contractions.

c. Stretching stimulates nerve impulses to be sent to the brain, which releases oxytocin from the parathyroid gland, which in turn causes uterine contractions.

d. Stretching stimulates nerve impulses to be sent to the brain which releases progesterone from the pituitary, which in turn causes uterine contractions

54. Negative feedback mechanisms are far more prevalent in the human body than positive feedback loops because they help regulate homeostasis. However, there are some instances of positive feedback loops that can be observed in animals. Regulation of which of the following is an example of a positive feedback loop?

a. When body temperature gets too high, signals are sent to reduce body temperature.
b. Increased blood glucose levels stimulate insulin production, which in turn sequesters glucose from the blood.
c. Decreased calcium levels stimulate increased calcium absorption.
d. Activation of one clotting factor stimulates production of other clotting factors until a fibrin clot is produced.

55. Both negative and positive feedback loops are essential for maintaining proper body functions. Blood calcium and blood clotting are under the control of different feedback loops. Which of these processes is maintained by a positive feedback loop and why?

a. Blood clotting is maintained by a positive feedback loop, as clotting is amplified in response by increasing the amount of clotting factors when clotting factors are present.
b. Blood clotting is maintained by a positive feedback loop, as clotting factors are maintained in a specific range and a positive loop helps return the conditions to the set point.
c. Blood calcium is maintained by a positive feedback loop, as calcium levels are amplified in response by increasing the amount of calcium levels when calcium is present.
d. Blood calcium is maintained by a positive feedback loop, as calcium levels are maintained in a specific range and a positive feedback loop helps return the conditions to the set point.

25 | ANIMAL NUTRITION AND THE DIGESTIVE SYSTEM

Figure 25.1 For humans, fruits and vegetables are important in maintaining a balanced diet. (credit: modification of work by Julie Rybarczyk)

Chapter Outline

Introduction

All living organisms need nutrients to survive. Animals obtain their nutrients by the consumption of other organisms. At the cellular level, the biological molecules necessary for animal function are amino acids, lipid molecules, nucleotides, and simple sugars. However, the food consumed consists of protein, fat, and complex carbohydrates. Animals must convert these macromolecules into the simple molecules required for maintaining cellular functions, such as assembling new molecules, cells, and tissues. The conversion of the food consumed to the nutrients required is a multi-step process involving digestion and absorption. During digestion, food particles are broken down into smaller components; later, they are absorbed by the body.

One of the challenges in human nutrition is maintaining a balance between food intake, storage, and energy expenditure. Imbalances can have serious health consequences. For example, eating too much food while not expending much energy

leads to obesity; this in turn will increase the risk of developing illnesses such as type-2 diabetes and cardiovascular disease. The recent rise in obesity and related diseases makes understanding the role of diet and nutrition in maintaining good health all the more important. Many health experts believe that nutrition education will improve the overall health of the entire population. In fact, one nutrition education program, the Supplemental Nutrition Assistance Program (SNAP),[1] focused on preschool-aged children enrolled in a low-cost childcare setting and found that participating children were significantly more likely to eat more vegetables at home. You can read more about SNAP **here (http://openstaxcollege.org/l/32SNAP)**
.

25.1 | Digestive Systems

In this section, you will explore the following questions:

- What are the differences between digestion and absorption?
- What are different types of digestive systems in invertebrates and vertebrates?
- What are the specialized functions of the organs involved in processing food in the human body?
- How do organs work together to digest food and absorb nutrients?

Connection for AP® Courses

Much information in this chapter is not within the scope of AP®. However, the chapter provides us with the opportunity to review concepts we've explored previously, including structure and function, macromolecules, energy production, transport of substances across membranes, and enzyme activity. All living organisms require a source of energy and molecules needed to build cells, tissues, and organs. During digestion, food is broken down into smaller molecules for absorption and distribution to all cells of the body. Nutrients are required to carry out cellular processes and maintain homeostasis, and digestion and absorption require the participation of several organs. Different animals have evolved different types of digestive systems specialized to meet their dietary needs. You do not need to memorize details about the different types of animal digestive systems, but you might find it interesting to explore the evolution of the system through a few groups of animals, from intracellular digestion in simple invertebrates to a digestive tract and accessory organs in complex vertebrates. Using a human eating a turkey sandwich as an example, food is ingested through the mouth. The mouth is the location where both mechanical (chewing) and chemical breakdown of food begins via the enzyme amylase, which breaks down carbohydrates into simpler sugars. The food bolus then travels by peristalsis (alternating waves of contraction) down the pharynx and esophagus to the stomach. In the stomach, pepsinogen mixes with hydrochloric acid to form pepsin, which begins digesting proteins, such as turkey, into smaller chains of amino acids. Mucus in the stomach protects its lining from damage by acidity, and the tightening of a sphincter prevents stomach contents from regurgitating into the esophagus. Further digestion of the ingredients of the sandwich occurs in the small intestine aided by a variety of enzymes; for example, bile salts and pancreatic amylase dumped into the small intestine from the gallbladder and pancreas, respectively, help emulsify fats. Once the ingredients of the sandwich have been broken down into smaller nutrient molecules, including amino acids, glucose, and fatty acids, they are absorbed from the small intestine into the circulatory and lymphatic systems. The walls of the small intestine contain small, finger-like projections called villi and microvilli that increase surface area for absorption of nutrients by diffusion. The large intestine or colon does not produce digestive enzymes but functions to absorb water, salts, and some vitamins. Any nutrients from the sandwich are stored in the liver, and wastes are eliminated.

Information presented and the examples highlighted in the section support concepts outlined in Big Idea 2 and Big Idea 4 of the AP® Biology Curriculum Framework. The AP® Learning Objectives listed in the Curriculum Framework provide a transparent foundation for the AP® Biology course, an inquiry-based laboratory experience, instructional activities, and AP® exam questions. A Learning Objective merges required content with one or more of the seven Science Practices.

Big Idea 2	Biological systems utilize free energy and molecular building blocks to grow, to reproduce, and to maintain dynamic homeostasis.

1. P. A. Williams et al. **Nutrition-education program improves preschoolers' at-home diet: a group randomized trial**. *Journal of the Academy of Nutrition and Dietetics*, 2014; 114 (7): 1001.

Enduring Understanding 2.A	Growth, reproduction and maintenance of living systems require free energy and matter.
Essential Knowledge	**2.A.3** Organisms must exchange matter with the environment to grow, reproduce and maintain organization.
Science Practice	**2.2** The student can apply mathematical routines to quantities that describe natural phenomena.
Learning Objective	**2.6** The student is able to use calculated surface area-to-volume ratios to predict which cell(s) might eliminate wastes or procure nutrients faster by diffusion.
Essential Knowledge	**2.A.3** Organisms must exchange matter with the environment to grow, reproduce and maintain organization.
Science Practice	**6.2** The student can construct explanations of phenomena based on evidence produced through scientific practices.
Learning Objective	**2.7** The student will be able to explain how cell size and shape affects the overall rate of nutrient intake and the rate of waste elimination.
Big Idea 4	Biological systems interact, and these systems and their interactions possess complex properties.
Enduring Understanding 4.A	Interactions within biological systems lead to complex properties.
Essential Knowledge	**4.A.4** Organisms exhibit complex properties due to interactions between their constituent parts.
Science Practice	**3.3** The student can evaluate scientific questions.
Learning Objective	**4.8** The student is able to evaluate scientific questions concerning organisms that exhibit complex properties due to the interaction of their constituent parts.
Essential Knowledge	**4.A.4** Organisms exhibit complex properties due to interactions between their constituent parts.
Science Practice	**6.4** The student can make claims and predictions about natural phenomena based on scientific theories and models.
Learning Objective	**4.9** The student is able to predict the effects of a change in a component(s) of a biological system on the functionality of an organism(s).
Essential Knowledge	**4.A.4** Organisms exhibit complex properties due to interactions between their constituent parts.
Science Practice	**1.3** The student can refine representations and models of natural or man-made phenomena and systems in the domain.
Learning Objective	**4.10** The student is able to refine representations and models to illustrate biocomplexity due to interactions of the constituent parts.
Enduring Understanding 4.B	Competition and cooperation are important aspects of biological systems.
Essential Knowledge	**4.B.2** Cooperative interactions within organisms promote efficiency in the use of energy and matter.
Science Practice	**1.4** The student can use representations and models to analyze situations or solve problems qualitatively and quantitatively.
Learning Objective	**4.18** The student is able to use representations and models to analyze how cooperative interactions within organisms promote efficiency in the use of matter and energy.

Animals obtain their nutrition by consuming other organisms. Depending on their diet, animals can be classified into the following categories: plant eaters (herbivores), meat eaters (carnivores), and those that eat both plants and animals (omnivores). The nutrients and macromolecules present in food are not immediately accessible to the cells. There are a number of processes that modify food within the animal body to make the nutrients and organic molecules accessible for cellular function. As animals evolved in complexity of form and function, their digestive systems have also evolved to accommodate their various dietary needs.

Herbivores, Omnivores, and Carnivores

Herbivores are animals whose primary food source is plant-based. Examples of herbivores, as shown in Figure 25.2 include vertebrates like deer, koalas, and some bird species, as well as invertebrates such as crickets and caterpillars. These animals have evolved digestive systems capable of handling large amounts of plant material. Herbivores can be further classified into frugivores (fruit-eaters), granivores (seed eaters), nectivores (nectar feeders), and folivores (leaf eaters).

Figure 25.2 Herbivores, like this (a) mule deer and (b) monarch caterpillar, eat primarily plant material. (credit a: modification of work by Bill Ebbesen; credit b: modification of work by Doug Bowman)

Carnivores are animals that eat other animals. The word carnivore is derived from Latin and literally means "meat eater." Wild cats such as lions, shown in Figure 25.3**a** and tigers are examples of vertebrate carnivores, as are snakes and sharks, while invertebrate carnivores include sea stars, spiders, and ladybugs, shown in Figure 25.3**b**. Obligate carnivores are those that rely entirely on animal flesh to obtain their nutrients; examples of obligate carnivores are members of the cat family, such as lions and cheetahs. Facultative carnivores are those that also eat non-animal food in addition to animal food. Note that there is no clear line that differentiates facultative carnivores from omnivores; dogs would be considered facultative carnivores.

(a)

(b)

Figure 25.3 Carnivores like the (a) lion eat primarily meat. The (b) ladybug is also a carnivore that consumes small insects called aphids. (credit a: modification of work by Kevin Pluck; credit b: modification of work by Jon Sullivan)

Omnivores are animals that eat both plant- and animal-derived food. In Latin, omnivore means to eat everything. Humans, bears (shown in Figure 25.4**a**), and chickens are example of vertebrate omnivores; invertebrate omnivores include cockroaches and crayfish (shown in Figure 25.4**b**).

(a)

(b)

Figure 25.4 Omnivores like the (a) bear and (b) crayfish eat both plant and animal based food. (credit a: modification of work by Dave Menke; credit b: modification of work by Jon Sullivan)

Invertebrate Digestive Systems

Animals have evolved different types of digestive systems to aid in the digestion of the various foods they consume. The simplest example is that of a **gastrovascular cavity** and is found in organisms with only one opening for digestion. Platyhelminthes (flatworms), Ctenophora (comb jellies), and Cnidaria (coral, jelly fish, and sea anemones) use this type of digestion. Gastrovascular cavities, as shown in Figure 25.5**a**, are typically a blind tube or cavity with only one opening, the "mouth", which also serves as an "anus". Ingested material enters the mouth and passes through a hollow, tubular cavity. Cells within the cavity secrete digestive enzymes that break down the food. The food particles are engulfed by the cells lining the gastrovascular cavity.

The **alimentary canal**, shown in Figure 25.5**b**, is a more advanced system: it consists of one tube with a mouth at one end and an anus at the other. Earthworms are an example of an animal with an alimentary canal. Once the food is ingested through the mouth, it passes through the esophagus and is stored in an organ called the crop; then it passes into the gizzard where it is churned and digested. From the gizzard, the food passes through the intestine, the nutrients are absorbed, and the waste is eliminated as feces, called castings, through the anus.

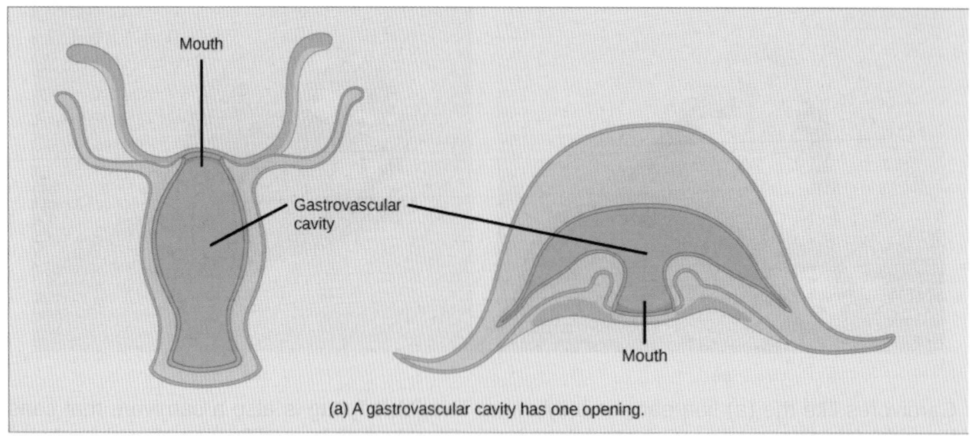

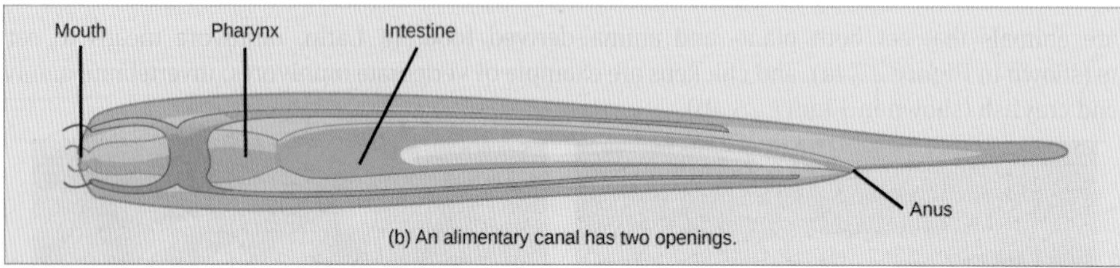

Figure 25.5 (a) A gastrovascular cavity has a single opening through which food is ingested and waste is excreted, as shown in this hydra and in this jellyfish medusa. (b) An alimentary canal has two openings: a mouth for ingesting food, and an anus for eliminating waste, as shown in this nematode.

Vertebrate Digestive Systems

Through evolution, vertebrate digestive systems have adapted to different diets. Some animals have a single stomach, while others have multi-chambered stomachs. Birds have developed a digestive system adapted to eating unmasticated food.

Monogastric: Single-chambered Stomach

As the word **monogastric** suggests, this type of digestive system consists of one ("mono") stomach chamber ("gastric"). Humans and many animals have a monogastric digestive system as illustrated in Figure 25.6**ab**. The process of digestion begins with the mouth and the intake of food. The teeth play an important role in masticating (chewing) or physically breaking down food into smaller particles. The enzymes present in saliva also begin to chemically break down food. The esophagus is a long tube that connects the mouth to the stomach. Using peristalsis, or wave-like smooth muscle contractions, the muscles of the esophagus push the food towards the stomach. In order to speed up the actions of enzymes in the stomach, the stomach is an extremely acidic environment, with a pH between 1.5 and 2.5. The gastric juices, which include enzymes in the stomach, act on the food particles and continue the process of digestion. Further breakdown of food takes place in the small intestine where enzymes produced by the liver, the small intestine, and the pancreas continue the process of digestion. The nutrients are absorbed into the blood stream across the epithelial cells lining the walls of the small intestines. The waste material travels on to the large intestine where water is absorbed and the drier waste material is compacted into feces; it is stored until it is excreted through the rectum.

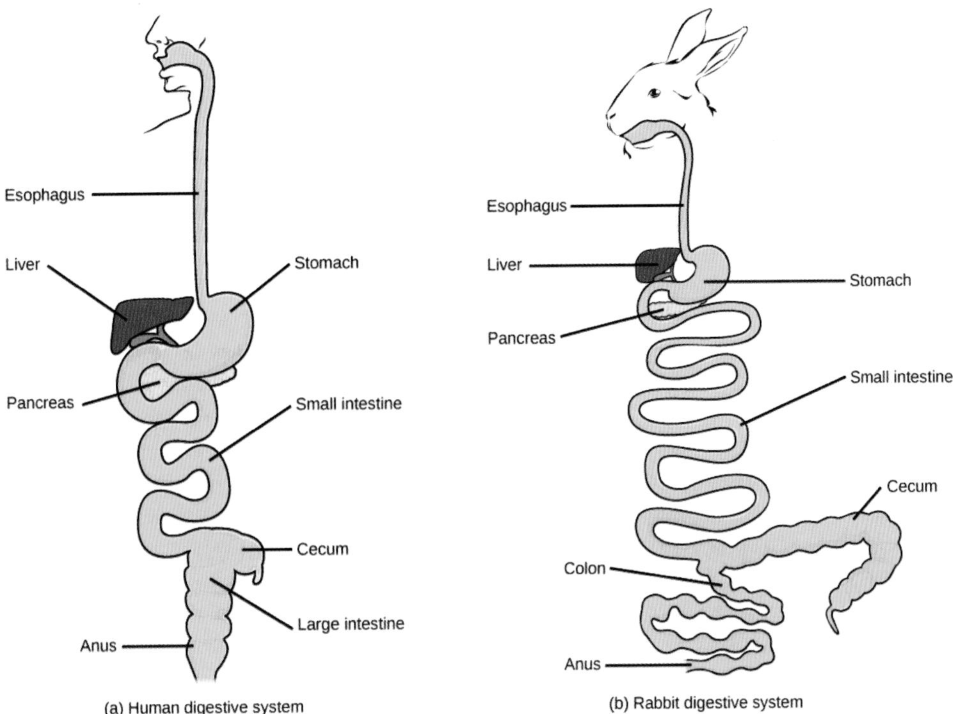

Figure 25.6 (a) Humans and herbivores, such as the (b) rabbit, have a monogastric digestive system. However, in the rabbit the small intestine and cecum are enlarged to allow more time to digest plant material. The enlarged organ provides more surface area for absorption of nutrients. Rabbits digest their food twice: the first time food passes through the digestive system, it collects in the cecum, and then it passes through the anus as soft feces called cecotrophes. The rabbit re-ingests these cecotrophes to further digest them.

Avian

Birds face special challenges when it comes to obtaining nutrition from food. They do not have teeth and so their digestive system, shown in Figure 25.7, must be able to process un-masticated food. Birds have evolved a variety of beak types that reflect the vast variety in their diet, ranging from seeds and insects to fruits and nuts. Because most birds fly, their metabolic rates are high in order to efficiently process food and keep their body weight low. The stomach of birds has two chambers: the **proventriculus**, where gastric juices are produced to digest the food before it enters the stomach, and the **gizzard**, where the food is stored, soaked, and mechanically ground. The undigested material forms food pellets that are sometimes regurgitated. Most of the chemical digestion and absorption happens in the intestine and the waste is excreted through the cloaca.

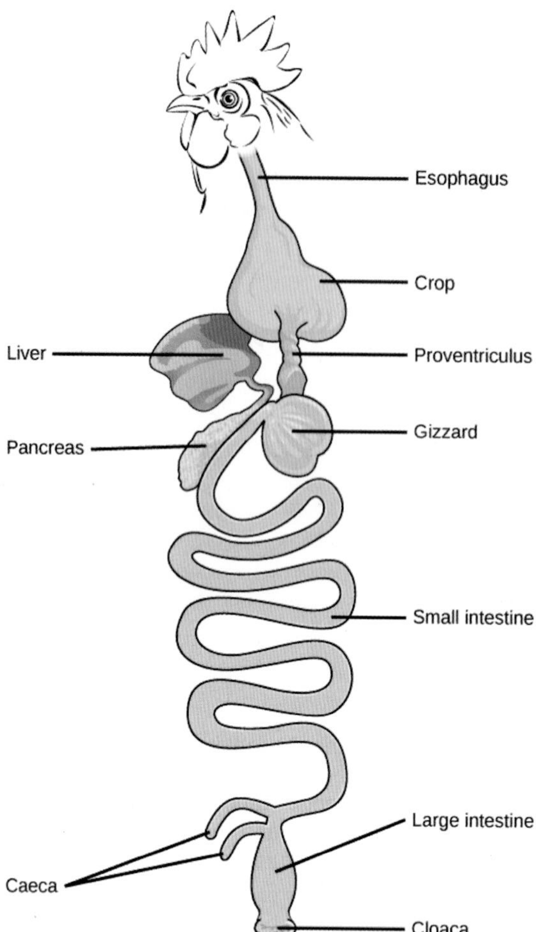

Figure 25.7 The avian esophagus has a pouch, called a crop, which stores food. Food passes from the crop to the first of two stomachs, called the proventriculus, which contains digestive juices that break down food. From the proventriculus, the food enters the second stomach, called the gizzard, which grinds food. Some birds swallow stones or grit, which are stored in the gizzard, to aid the grinding process. Birds do not have separate openings to excrete urine and feces. Instead, uric acid from the kidneys is secreted into the large intestine and combined with waste from the digestive process. This waste is excreted through an opening called the cloaca.

Avian Adaptations

Birds have a highly efficient, simplified digestive system. Recent fossil evidence has shown that the evolutionary divergence of birds from other land animals was characterized by streamlining and simplifying the digestive system. Unlike many other animals, birds do not have teeth to chew their food. In place of lips, they have sharp pointy beaks. The horny beak, lack of jaws, and the smaller tongue of the birds can be traced back to their dinosaur ancestors. The emergence of these changes seems to coincide with the inclusion of seeds in the bird diet. Seed-eating birds have beaks that are shaped for grabbing seeds and the two-compartment stomach allows for delegation of tasks. Since birds need to remain light in order to fly, their metabolic rates are very high, which means they digest their food very quickly and need to eat often. Contrast this with the ruminants, where the digestion of plant matter takes a very long time.

Although both birds and humans are vertebrates, birds have a relatively higher metabolic rate than humans.
a. Why is the metabolic rate of birds relatively higher than that of humans?
b. How do birds compensate for such a high metabolism?

a. a. Birds have smaller surfaces to lose heat than humans, so their metabolic rate must be higher.
b. Birds need to eat greater amounts of food since they digest food quickly.

b. a. Birds need to be light to fly, so they need to digest their food faster than humans.
b. Birds need to eat greater amounts of food since they digest food quickly.

c. a. Birds have smaller surfaces to lose heat than humans, so their metabolic rate must be higher.
b. Birds need to eat often to maintain energy since they digest food quickly.

d. a. Birds need to be light to fly, so they need to digest their food faster than humans.
b. Birds need to eat often to maintain energy since they digest food quickly.

Ruminants

Ruminants are mainly herbivores like cows, sheep, and goats, whose entire diet consists of eating large amounts of **roughage** or fiber. They have evolved digestive systems that help them digest vast amounts of cellulose. An interesting feature of the ruminants' mouth is that they do not have upper incisor teeth. They use their lower teeth, tongue and lips to tear and chew their food. From the mouth, the food travels to the esophagus and on to the stomach.

To help digest the large amount of plant material, the stomach of the ruminants is a multi-chambered organ, as illustrated in Figure 25.8. The four compartments of the stomach are called the rumen, reticulum, omasum, and abomasum. These chambers contain many microbes that break down cellulose and ferment ingested food. The abomasum is the "true" stomach and is the equivalent of the monogastric stomach chamber where gastric juices are secreted. The four-compartment gastric chamber provides larger space and the microbial support necessary to digest plant material in ruminants. The fermentation process produces large amounts of gas in the stomach chamber, which must be eliminated. As in other animals, the small intestine plays an important role in nutrient absorption, and the large intestine helps in the elimination of waste.

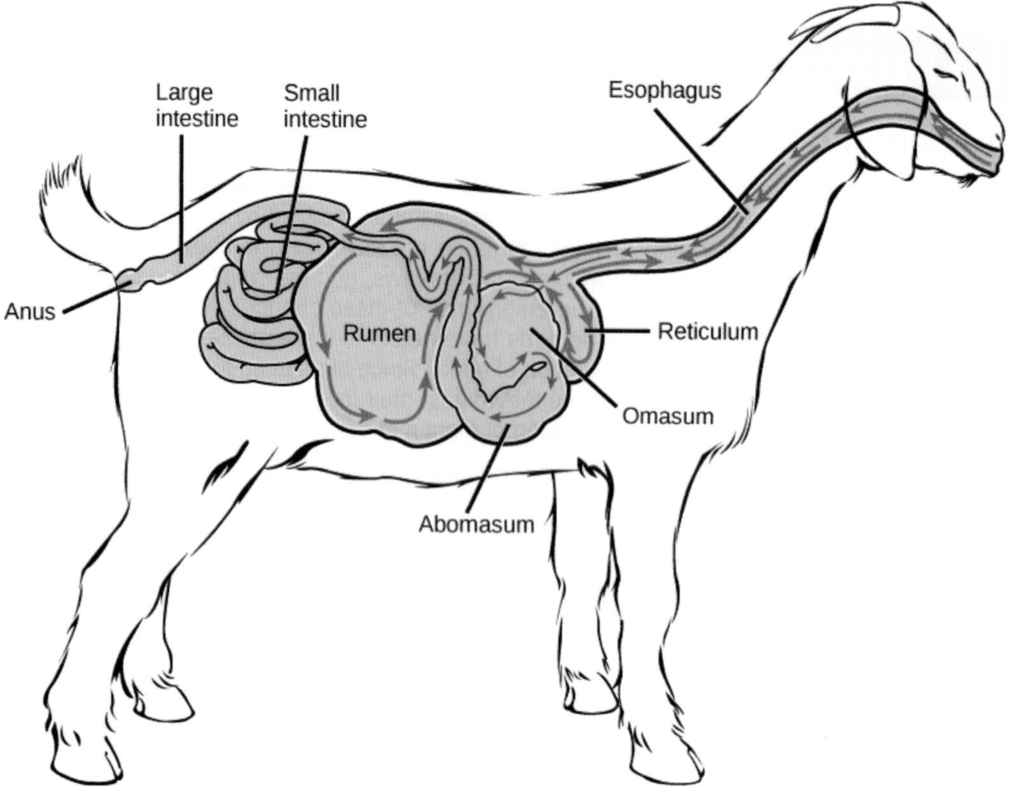

Figure 25.8 Ruminant animals, such as goats and cows, have four stomachs. The first two stomachs, the rumen and the reticulum, contain prokaryotes and protists that are able to digest cellulose fiber. The ruminant regurgitates cud from the reticulum, chews it, and swallows it into a third stomach, the omasum, which removes water. The cud then passes onto the fourth stomach, the abomasum, where it is digested by enzymes produced by the ruminant.

Pseudo-ruminants

Some animals, such as camels and alpacas, are pseudo-ruminants. They eat a lot of plant material and roughage. Digesting plant material is not easy because plant cell walls contain the polymeric sugar molecule cellulose. The digestive enzymes of these animals cannot break down cellulose, but microorganisms present in the digestive system can. Therefore, the digestive system must be able to handle large amounts of roughage and break down the cellulose. Pseudo-ruminants have a three-chamber stomach in the digestive system. However, their cecum—a pouched organ at the beginning of the large intestine containing many microorganisms that are necessary for the digestion of plant materials—is large and is the site where the roughage is fermented and digested. These animals do not have a rumen but have an omasum, abomasum, and reticulum.

Parts of the Digestive System

The vertebrate digestive system is designed to facilitate the transformation of food matter into the nutrient components that sustain organisms.

Oral Cavity

The oral cavity, or mouth, is the point of entry of food into the digestive system, illustrated in Figure 25.9. The food consumed is broken into smaller particles by mastication, the chewing action of the teeth. All mammals have teeth and can chew their food.

The extensive chemical process of digestion begins in the mouth. As food is being chewed, saliva, produced by the salivary glands, mixes with the food. Saliva is a watery substance produced in the mouths of many animals. There are three major glands that secrete saliva—the parotid, the submandibular, and the sublingual. Saliva contains mucus that moistens food and buffers the pH of the food. Saliva also contains immunoglobulins and lysozymes, which have antibacterial action to reduce tooth decay by inhibiting growth of some bacteria. Saliva also contains an enzyme called **salivary amylase** that begins the process of converting starches in the food into a disaccharide called maltose. Another enzyme called **lipase** is produced by the cells in the tongue. Lipases are a class of enzymes that can break down triglycerides. The lingual lipase begins the breakdown of fat components in the food. The chewing and wetting action provided by the teeth and saliva prepare the food into a mass called the **bolus** for swallowing. The tongue helps in swallowing—moving the bolus from the mouth into the pharynx. The pharynx opens to two passageways: the trachea, which leads to the lungs, and the esophagus, which leads to the stomach. The trachea has an opening called the glottis, which is covered by a cartilaginous flap called the epiglottis. When swallowing, the epiglottis closes the glottis and food passes into the esophagus and not the trachea. This arrangement allows food to be kept out of the trachea.

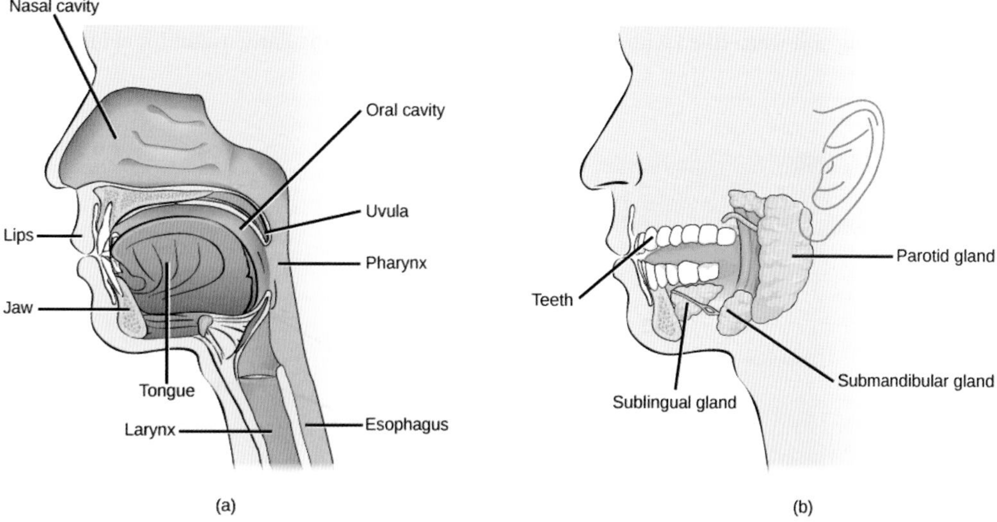

Figure 25.9 Digestion of food begins in the (a) oral cavity. Food is masticated by teeth and moistened by saliva secreted from the (b) salivary glands. Enzymes in the saliva begin to digest starches and fats. With the help of the tongue, the resulting bolus is moved into the esophagus by swallowing. (credit: modification of work by the National Cancer Institute)

Esophagus

The **esophagus** is a tubular organ that connects the mouth to the stomach. The chewed and softened food passes through the esophagus after being swallowed. The smooth muscles of the esophagus undergo a series of wave like movements called **peristalsis** that push the food toward the stomach, as illustrated in Figure 25.10. The peristalsis wave is unidirectional—it moves food from the mouth to the stomach, and reverse movement is not possible. The peristaltic movement of the esophagus is an involuntary reflex; it takes place in response to the act of swallowing.

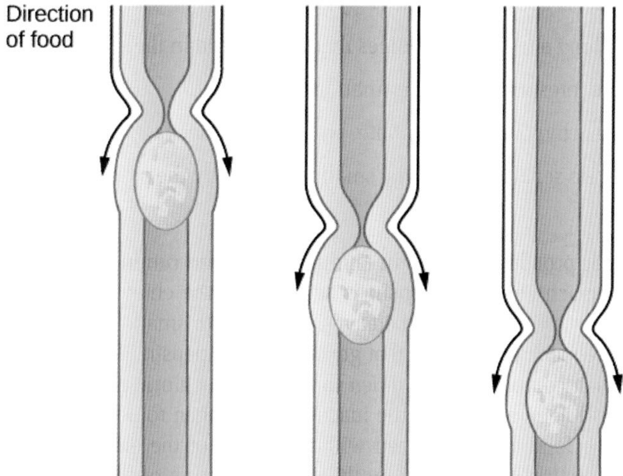

Figure 25.10 The esophagus transfers food from the mouth to the stomach through peristaltic movements.

A ring-like muscle called a **sphincter** forms valves in the digestive system. The gastro-esophageal sphincter is located at the stomach end of the esophagus. In response to swallowing and the pressure exerted by the bolus of food, this sphincter opens, and the bolus enters the stomach. When there is no swallowing action, this sphincter is shut and prevents the contents of the stomach from traveling up the esophagus. Many animals have a true sphincter; however, in humans, there is no true sphincter, but the esophagus remains closed when there is no swallowing action. Acid reflux or "heartburn" occurs when the acidic digestive juices escape into the esophagus.

Stomach

A large part of digestion occurs in the stomach, shown in Figure 25.11. The **stomach** is a saclike organ that secretes gastric digestive juices. The pH in the stomach is between 1.5 and 2.5. This highly acidic environment is required for the chemical breakdown of food and the extraction of nutrients. When empty, the stomach is a rather small organ; however, it can expand to up to 20 times its resting size when filled with food. This characteristic is particularly useful for animals that need to eat when food is available.

visual CONNECTION

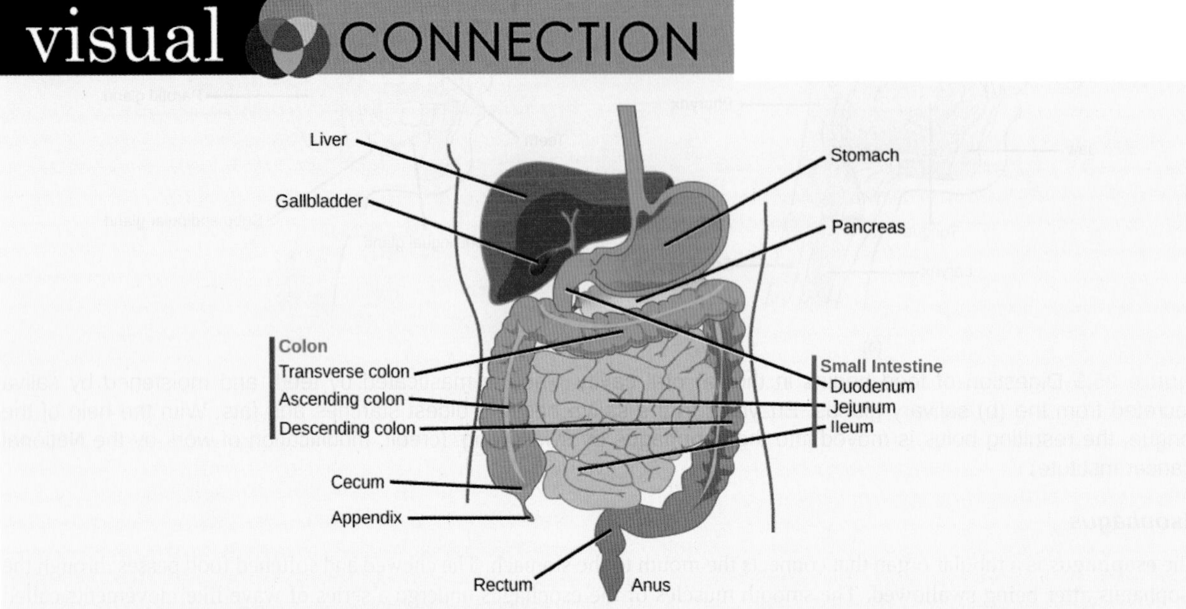

Figure 25.11 The human stomach has an extremely acidic environment where most of the protein gets digested. (credit: modification of work by Mariana Ruiz Villareal)

Which of the following statements about the digestive system is true?

a. Bile is a mixture of food and digestive juices that is produced in the stomach.

b. Food enters the large intestine before the small intestine.

c. In the small intestine, chyme mixes with bile, which emulsifies fats.

d. The large intestines are separated from the small intestines by the pyloric sphincter.

The stomach is the major site for protein digestion in animals other than ruminants. Protein digestion is mediated by an enzyme called pepsin in the stomach chamber. **Pepsin** is secreted by the chief cells in the stomach in an inactive form called **pepsinogen**. Pepsin breaks peptide bonds and cleaves proteins into smaller polypeptides; it also helps activate more pepsinogen, starting a positive feedback mechanism that generates more pepsin. Another cell type—parietal cells—secretes hydrogen and chloride ions, which combine in the lumen to form hydrochloric acid, the primary acidic component of the stomach juices. Hydrochloric acid helps to convert the inactive pepsinogen to pepsin. The highly acidic environment also kills many microorganisms in the food and, combined with the action of the enzyme pepsin, results in the hydrolysis of protein in the food. Chemical digestion is facilitated by the churning action of the stomach. Contraction and relaxation of smooth muscles mixes the stomach contents about every 20 minutes. The partially digested food and gastric juice mixture is called **chyme**. Chyme passes from the stomach to the small intestine. Further protein digestion takes place in the small intestine. Gastric emptying occurs within two to six hours after a meal. Only a small amount of chyme is released into the small intestine at a time. The movement of chyme from the stomach into the small intestine is regulated by the pyloric sphincter.

When digesting protein and some fats, the stomach lining must be protected from getting digested by pepsin. There are two points to consider when describing how the stomach lining is protected. First, as previously mentioned, the enzyme pepsin is synthesized in the inactive form. This protects the chief cells, because pepsinogen does not have the same enzyme functionality of pepsin. Second, the stomach has a thick mucus lining that protects the underlying tissue from the action of the digestive juices. When this mucus lining is ruptured, ulcers can form in the stomach. Ulcers are open wounds in or on an organ caused by bacteria (*Helicobacter pylori*) when the mucus lining is ruptured and fails to reform.

Small Intestine

Chyme moves from the stomach to the small intestine. The **small intestine** is the organ where the digestion of protein, fats, and carbohydrates is completed. The small intestine is a long tube-like organ with a highly folded surface containing finger-like projections called the **villi**. The apical surface of each villus has many microscopic projections called microvilli. These structures, illustrated in Figure 25.12, are lined with epithelial cells on the luminal side and allow for the nutrients to be absorbed from the digested food and absorbed into the blood stream on the other side. The villi and microvilli, with their many folds, increase the surface area of the intestine and increase absorption efficiency of the nutrients. Absorbed nutrients in the blood are carried into the hepatic portal vein, which leads to the liver. There, the liver regulates the distribution of nutrients to the rest of the body and removes toxic substances, including drugs, alcohol, and some pathogens.

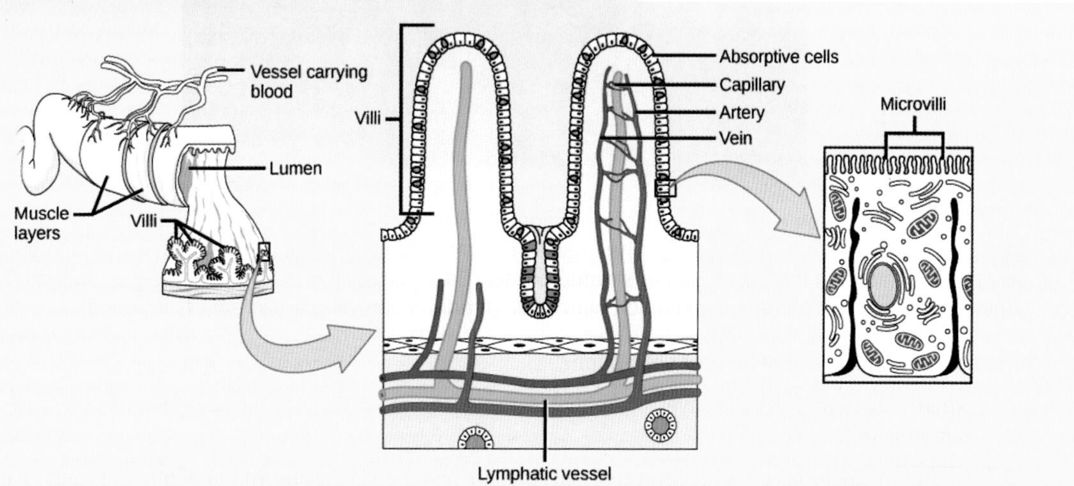

Figure 25.12 Villi are folds on the small intestine lining that increase the surface area to facilitate the absorption of nutrients.

Which of the following statements about the small intestine is true?

a. Absorptive cells that line the small intestine have small projections that increase surface area and aid in the absorption of food.

b. The outside of the small intestine has many folds, called villi.

c. Microvilli are lined with blood vessels as well as lymphatic vessels.

d. The inside of the small intestine is called the lymphatic vessel.

The human small intestine is over 6m long and is divided into three parts: the duodenum, the jejunum, and the ileum. The "C-shaped," fixed part of the small intestine is called the **duodenum** and is shown in Figure 25.11. The duodenum is separated from the stomach by the pyloric sphincter which opens to allow chyme to move from the stomach to the duodenum. In the duodenum, chyme is mixed with pancreatic juices in an alkaline solution rich in bicarbonate that neutralizes the acidity of chyme and acts as a buffer. Pancreatic juices also contain several digestive enzymes. Digestive juices from the pancreas, liver, and gallbladder, as well as from gland cells of the intestinal wall itself, enter the duodenum. **Bile** is produced in the liver and stored and concentrated in the gallbladder. Bile contains bile salts which emulsify lipids while the pancreas produces enzymes that catabolize starches, disaccharides, proteins, and fats. These digestive juices break down the food particles in the chyme into glucose, triglycerides, and amino acids. Some chemical digestion of food takes place in the duodenum. Absorption of fatty acids also takes place in the duodenum.

The second part of the small intestine is called the **jejunum**, shown in Figure 25.11. Here, hydrolysis of nutrients is continued while most of the carbohydrates and amino acids are absorbed through the intestinal lining. The bulk of chemical digestion and nutrient absorption occurs in the jejunum.

The **ileum**, also illustrated in Figure 25.11 is the last part of the small intestine and here the bile salts and vitamins are absorbed into blood stream. The undigested food is sent to the colon from the ileum via peristaltic movements of the muscle. The ileum ends and the large intestine begins at the ileocecal valve. The vermiform, "worm-like," appendix is located at the ileocecal valve. The appendix of humans secretes no enzymes and has an insignificant role in immunity.

everyday CONNECTION for AP® Courses

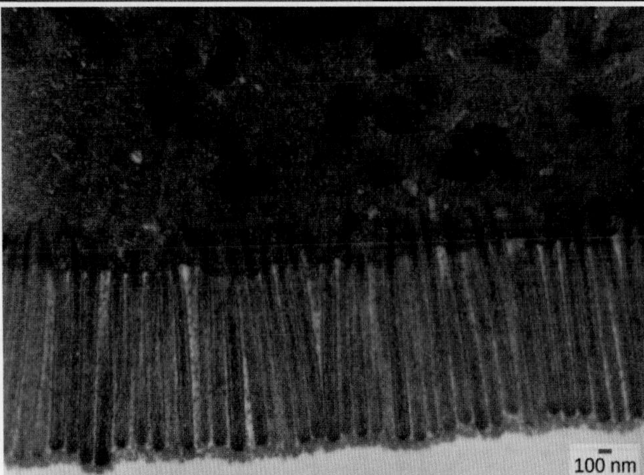

Figure 25.13 Transmission electron microscope image of a thin section cut through an epithelial cell from a human jejunum (segment of the small intestine). The image shows the apical end of an absorptive cell with some of the densely packed microvilli that make up the striated border. Each microvillus is approximately 1 μm long by 0.1 μm in diameter and contains a core of actin microfilaments. (credit: "Microvilli", Wikimedia Commons)

What is the role of microvilli in nutrient absorption?

a. Microvilli form the inner layer of epithelial tissue in the small intestine and increase the absorption of nutrients from chyme.
b. Microvilli are projections of absorptive cells that are involved in the absorption of bile salts and vitamin B12.
c. Microvilli increase the surface area of absorptive cells, and therefore increase the amount of nutrients that can be absorbed.
d. Microvilli use smooth muscle contractions to move the chyme, which contains nutrients, thereby increasing the rate of absorption.

Large Intestine

The **large intestine**, illustrated in Figure 25.14, reabsorbs the water from the undigested food material and processes the waste material. The human large intestine is much smaller in length compared to the small intestine but larger in diameter. It has three parts: the cecum, the colon, and the rectum. The cecum joins the ileum to the colon and is the receiving pouch for the waste matter. The colon is home to many bacteria or "intestinal flora" that aid in the digestive processes. The colon can be divided into four regions, the ascending colon, the transverse colon, the descending colon and the sigmoid colon. The main functions of the colon are to extract the water and mineral salts from undigested food, and to store waste material. Carnivorous mammals have a shorter large intestine compared to herbivorous mammals due to their diet.

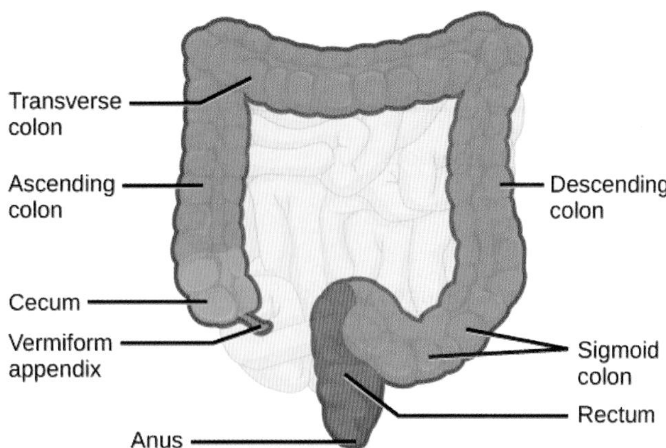

Figure 25.14 The large intestine reabsorbs water from undigested food and stores waste material until it is eliminated.

Rectum and Anus

The **rectum** is the terminal end of the large intestine, as shown in Figure 25.14. The primary role of the rectum is to store the feces until defecation. The feces are propelled using peristaltic movements during elimination. The **anus** is an opening at the far-end of the digestive tract and is the exit point for the waste material. Two sphincters between the rectum and anus control elimination: the inner sphincter is involuntary and the outer sphincter is voluntary.

Accessory Organs

The organs discussed above are the organs of the digestive tract through which food passes. Accessory organs are organs that add secretions (enzymes) that catabolize food into nutrients. Accessory organs include salivary glands, the liver, the pancreas, and the gallbladder. The liver, pancreas, and gallbladder are regulated by hormones in response to the food consumed.

The **liver** is the largest internal organ in humans and it plays a very important role in digestion of fats and detoxifying blood. The liver produces bile, a digestive juice that is required for the breakdown of fatty components of the food in the duodenum. The liver also processes the vitamins and fats and synthesizes many plasma proteins.

The **pancreas** is another important gland that secretes digestive juices. The chyme produced from the stomach is highly acidic in nature; the pancreatic juices contain high levels of bicarbonate, an alkali that neutralizes the acidic chyme. Additionally, the pancreatic juices contain a large variety of enzymes that are required for the digestion of protein and carbohydrates.

The **gallbladder** is a small organ that aids the liver by storing bile and concentrating bile salts. When chyme containing fatty acids enters the duodenum, the bile is secreted from the gallbladder into the duodenum.

science practices CONNECTION for AP® Courses

Activity

Create a mini-poster that shows the procurement, digestion, absorption, and distribution of nutrients through the digestive systems of one invertebrate animal and one vertebrate animal. Explain how the organs of the system promote efficiency in the use of matter and energy.

Think About It

Explain how the villi and microvilli aid in absorption of nutrients from the small intestine into the circulatory system.

25.2 | Nutrition and Energy Production

In this section, you will explore the following questions:

- Why must an animal have a balanced diet?
- What are the primary components of food?
- What are examples of essential nutrients required for cellular function that cannot be synthesized by the animal body?
- How is energy produced through diet and digestion?
- How are excess carbohydrates and energy stored in the body?

Connection for AP® Courses

Much of the content described in this module is not within the scope of AP®. However, as we learn in the chapter on biological macromolecules, in animals the organic molecules required for building cellular materials and tissues come from food. During digestion, complex carbohydrates are broken down into glucose and used to provide energy through metabolic pathways, such as cellular respiration (see the chapter on cellular respiration). Excess sugars in the body are stored as glycogen in the liver and muscles for later use. Another important requirement is nitrogen, and protein catabolism provides a source of nitrogen; amino acids from protein breakdown are building blocks for new proteins. The carbon and nitrogen derived from amino acids also become building blocks for nucleic acids. Excess nitrogen is excreted because it is toxic. Although the animal body can synthesize many of the molecules necessary for function from organic precursors, some essential nutrients must be consumed from food. Vitamins are another class of essential organic molecules that are required in small quantities for many enzymes to function. (No, you do not need to memorize the table of vitamins and their functions!) Deficiencies in nutrients can have detrimental effects on an animal's health. For example, among other things, vitamin D is necessary for calcium absorption for bone development, and vitamin C is critical to multiple biochemical pathways, including immune function.

As we learn in the chapter on cellular respiration, animals need free energy, primarily supplied by carbohydrates, to maintain homeostasis. ATP is the energy currency of the cell and is produced by the oxidative reactions in the cytoplasm and mitochondria, where carbohydrates, proteins, and fats undergo a series of metabolic reactions collectively called cellular respiration. When the amount of ATP available exceeds the body's requirements, the liver uses the excess ATP and glucose to produce molecules of glycogen. The ability to store excess energy is an evolutionary adaptation that helps animals deal with mobility and food shortages.

Information presented and the examples highlighted in the section support concepts outlined in Big Idea 2 of the AP® Biology Curriculum Framework. The AP® Learning Objectives listed in the Curriculum Framework provide a transparent foundation for the AP® Biology course, an inquiry-based laboratory experience, instructional activities, and AP® exam questions. A learning objective merges required content with one or more of the seven science practices.

Big Idea 2	Biological systems utilize free energy and molecular building blocks to grow, to reproduce, and to maintain dynamic homeostasis.
Enduring Understanding 2.A	Growth, reproduction and maintenance of living systems require free energy and matter.
Essential Knowledge	**2.A.2** Organisms capture and store free energy for use in biological processes.
Science Practice	**6.2** The student can construct explanations of phenomena based on evidence produced through scientific practices.
Learning Objective	**2.5** The student is able to construct explanations of the mechanisms and structural features of cells that allow organisms to capture, store or use free energy.

Essential Knowledge	**2.A.3** Organisms must exchange matter with the environment to grow, reproduce and maintain organization.
Science Practice	**4.1** The student can justify the selection of the kind of data needed to answer a particular scientific question.
Learning Objective	**2.8** The student is able to justify the selection of data regarding the types of molecules that an animal will take up as necessary building blocks.

Given the diversity of animal life on our planet, it is not surprising that the animal diet would also vary substantially. The animal diet is the source of materials needed for building DNA and other complex molecules needed for growth, maintenance, and reproduction; collectively these processes are called biosynthesis. The diet is also the source of materials for ATP production in the cells. The diet must be balanced to provide the minerals and vitamins that are required for cellular function.

Food Requirements

What are the fundamental requirements of the animal diet? The animal diet should be well balanced and provide nutrients required for bodily function and the minerals and vitamins required for maintaining structure and regulation necessary for good health and reproductive capability. These requirements for a human are illustrated graphically in **Figure 25.15**

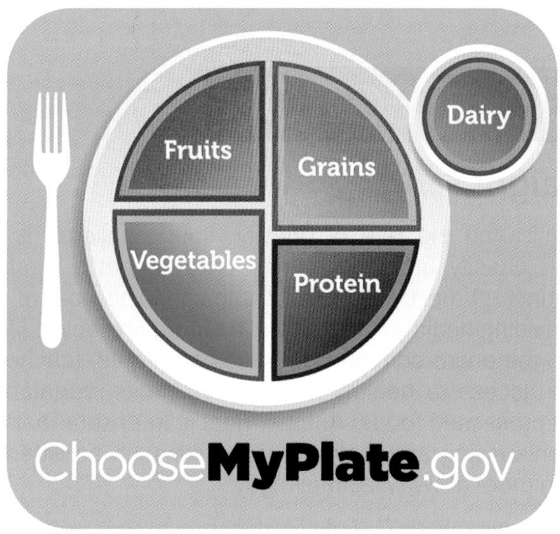

Figure 25.15 For humans, a balanced diet includes fruits, vegetables, grains, and protein. (credit: USDA)

The first step in ensuring that you are meeting the food requirements of your body is an awareness of the food groups and the nutrients they provide. To learn more about each food group and the recommended daily amounts, explore this **interactive site (http://openstaxcollege.org/l/food_groups)** by the United States Department of Agriculture.

How many cups of vegetables per day are recommended for a 61-year-old woman who does not exercise on a regular basis?

a. 1.5 cups

b. 2 cups

c. 2.5 cups

d. 3 cups

everyday CONNECTION

Let's Move! Campaign

Obesity is a growing epidemic and the rate of obesity among children is rapidly rising in the United States. To combat childhood obesity and ensure that children get a healthy start in life, former first lady Michelle Obama has launched the Let's Move! campaign. The goal of this campaign is to educate parents and caregivers on providing healthy nutrition and encouraging active lifestyles to future generations. This program aims to involve the entire community, including parents, teachers, and healthcare providers to ensure that children have access to healthy foods—more fruits, vegetables, and whole grains—and consume fewer calories from processed foods. Another goal is to ensure that children get physical activity. With the increase in television viewing and stationary pursuits such as video games, sedentary lifestyles have become the norm. Learn more at www.letsmove.gov.

How does increased activity help reduce obesity in individuals?

a. A more active individual will burn more calories.

b. A more active individual will consume less fat.

c. A more active individual will consume more calories.

d. The appetite of a more active individual will be less.

Organic Precursors

The organic molecules required for building cellular material and tissues must come from food. Carbohydrates or sugars are the primary source of organic carbons in the animal body. During digestion, digestible carbohydrates are ultimately broken down into glucose and used to provide energy through metabolic pathways. Complex carbohydrates, including polysaccharides, can be broken down into glucose through biochemical modification; however, humans do not produce the enzyme cellulase and lack the ability to derive glucose from the polysaccharide cellulose. In humans, these molecules provide the fiber required for moving waste through the large intestine and a healthy colon. The intestinal flora in the human gut are able to extract some nutrition from these plant fibers. The excess sugars in the body are converted into glycogen and stored in the liver and muscles for later use. Glycogen stores are used to fuel prolonged exertions, such as long-distance running, and to provide energy during food shortage. Excess glycogen can be converted to fats, which are stored in the lower layer of the skin of mammals for insulation and energy storage. Excess digestible carbohydrates are stored by mammals in order to survive famine and aid in mobility.

Another important requirement is that of nitrogen. Protein catabolism provides a source of organic nitrogen. Amino acids are the building blocks of proteins and protein breakdown provides amino acids that are used for cellular function. The carbon and nitrogen derived from these become the building block for nucleotides, nucleic acids, proteins, cells, and tissues. Excess nitrogen must be excreted as it is toxic. Fats add flavor to food and promote a sense of satiety or fullness. Fatty foods are also significant sources of energy because one gram of fat contains nine calories. Fats are required in the diet to aid the absorption of fat-soluble vitamins and the production of fat-soluble hormones.

Essential Nutrients

While the animal body can synthesize many of the molecules required for function from the organic precursors, there are some nutrients that need to be consumed from food. These nutrients are termed **essential nutrients**, meaning they must be eaten, and the body cannot produce them.

The omega-3 alpha-linolenic acid and the omega-6 linoleic acid are essential fatty acids needed to make some membrane phospholipids. **Vitamins** are another class of essential organic molecules that are required in small quantities for many enzymes to function and, for this reason, are considered to be co-enzymes. Absence or low levels of vitamins can have a dramatic effect on health, as outlined in Table 25.1 and Table 25.2. Both fat-soluble and water-soluble vitamins must be obtained from food. **Minerals**, listed in Table 25.3, are inorganic essential nutrients that must be obtained from food. Among their many functions, minerals help in structure and regulation and are considered co-factors. Certain amino acids also must be procured from food and cannot be synthesized by the body. These amino acids are the “essential” amino acids. The human body can synthesize only 11 of the 20 required amino acids; the rest must be obtained from food. The essential amino acids are listed in Table 25.4.

Water-soluble Essential Vitamins

Vitamin	Function	Deficiencies Can Lead To	Sources
Vitamin B_1 (Thiamine)	Needed by the body to process lipids, proteins, and carbohydrates Coenzyme removes CO_2 from organic compounds	Muscle weakness, Beriberi: reduced heart function, CNS problems	Milk, meat, dried beans, whole grains
Vitamin B_2 (Riboflavin)	Takes an active role in metabolism, aiding in the conversion of food to energy (FAD and FMN)	Cracks or sores on the outer surface of the lips (cheliosis); inflammation and redness of the tongue; moist, scaly skin inflammation (seborrheic dermatitis)	Meat, eggs, enriched grains, vegetables
Vitamin B_3 (Niacin)	Used by the body to release energy from carbohydrates and to process alcohol; required for the synthesis of sex hormones; component of coenzyme NAD^+ and $NADP^+$	Pellagra, which can result in dermatitis, diarrhea, dementia, and death	Meat, eggs, grains, nuts, potatoes
Vitamin B_5 (Pantothenic acid)	Assists in producing energy from foods (lipids, in particular); component of coenzyme A	Fatigue, poor coordination, retarded growth, numbness, tingling of hands and feet	Meat, whole grains, milk, fruits, vegetables
Vitamin B_6 (Pyridoxine)	The principal vitamin for processing amino acids and lipids; also helps convert nutrients into energy	Irritability, confusion, mouth sores or ulcers, anemia, muscular twitching	Meat, dairy products, whole grains, orange juice
Vitamin B_7 (Biotin)	Used in energy and amino acid metabolism, fat synthesis, and fat breakdown; helps the body use blood sugar	Hair loss, dermatitis, numbness and tingling in the extremities; neuromuscular disorders	Meat, eggs, legumes and other vegetables

Table 25.1

Water-soluble Essential Vitamins

Vitamin	Function	Deficiencies Can Lead To	Sources
Vitamin B_9 (Folic acid)	Assists the normal development of cells, especially during fetal development; helps metabolize nucleic and amino acids	Deficiency during pregnancy is associated with birth defects, such as neural tube defects and anemia	Leafy green vegetables, whole wheat, fruits, nuts, legumes
Vitamin B_{12} (Cobalamin)	Maintains healthy nervous system and assists with blood cell formation; coenzyme in nucleic acid metabolism	Anemia, neurological disorders, numbness, loss of balance	Meat, eggs, animal products
Vitamin C (Ascorbic acid)	Helps maintain connective tissue: bone, cartilage, and dentin; boosts the immune system	Scurvy, which results in bleeding, hair and tooth loss; joint pain and swelling; delayed wound healing	Citrus fruits, broccoli, tomatoes, red sweet bell peppers

Table 25.1

Fat-soluble Essential Vitamins

Vitamin	Function	Deficiencies Can Lead To	Sources
Vitamin A (Retinol)	Critical to the development of bones, teeth, and skin; helps maintain eyesight, enhances the immune system, fetal development, gene expression	Night-blindness, skin disorders, impaired immunity	Dark green leafy vegetables, yellow-orange vegetables fruits, milk, butter
Vitamin D	Critical for calcium absorption for bone development and strength; maintains a stable nervous system; maintains a normal and strong heartbeat; helps in blood clotting	Rickets, osteomalacia, immunity	Cod liver oil, milk, egg yolk
Vitamin E (Tocopherol)	Lessens oxidative damage of cells,and prevents lung damage from pollutants; vital to the immune system	Deficiency is rare; anemia, nervous system degeneration	Wheat germ oil, unrefined vegetable oils, nuts, seeds, grains
Vitamin K (Phylloquinone)	Essential to blood clotting	Bleeding and easy bruising	Leafy green vegetables, tea

Table 25.2

Figure 25.16 A healthy diet should include a variety of foods to ensure that needs for essential nutrients are met. (credit: Keith Weller, USDA ARS)

Minerals and Their Function in the Human Body

Mineral	Function	Deficiencies Can Lead To	Sources
*Calcium	Needed for muscle and neuron function; heart health; builds bone and supports synthesis and function of blood cells; nerve function	Osteoporosis, rickets, muscle spasms, impaired growth	Milk, yogurt, fish, green leafy vegetables, legumes
*Chlorine	Needed for production of hydrochloric acid (HCl) in the stomach and nerve function; osmotic balance	Muscle cramps, mood disturbances, reduced appetite	Table salt
Copper (trace amounts)	Required component of many redox enzymes, including cytochrome c oxidase; cofactor for hemoglobin synthesis	Copper deficiency is rare	Liver, oysters, cocoa, chocolate, sesame, nuts
Iodine	Required for the synthesis of thyroid hormones	Goiter	Seafood, iodized salt, dairy products
Iron	Required for many proteins and enzymes, notably hemoglobin, to prevent anemia	Anemia, which causes poor concentration, fatigue, and poor immune function	Red meat, leafy green vegetables, fish (tuna, salmon), eggs, dried fruits, beans, whole grains
*Magnesium	Required co-factor for ATP formation; bone formation; normal membrane functions; muscle function	Mood disturbances, muscle spasms	Whole grains, leafy green vegetables
Manganese (trace amounts)	A cofactor in enzyme functions; trace amounts are required	Manganese deficiency is rare	Common in most foods
Molybdenum (trace amounts)	Acts as a cofactor for three essential enzymes in humans: sulfite oxidase, xanthine oxidase, and aldehyde oxidase	Molybdenum deficiency is rare	

Table 25.3

Minerals and Their Function in the Human Body

Mineral	Function	Deficiencies Can Lead To	Sources
*Phosphorus	A component of bones and teeth; helps regulate acid-base balance; nucleotide synthesis	Weakness, bone abnormalities, calcium loss	Milk, hard cheese, whole grains, meats
*Potassium	Vital for muscles, heart, and nerve function	Cardiac rhythm disturbance, muscle weakness	Legumes, potato skin, tomatoes, bananas
Selenium (trace amounts)	A cofactor essential to activity of antioxidant enzymes like glutathione peroxidase; trace amounts are required	Selenium deficiency is rare	Common in most foods
*Sodium	Systemic electrolyte required for many functions; acid-base balance; water balance; nerve function	Muscle cramps, fatigue, reduced appetite	Table salt
Zinc (trace amounts)	Required for several enzymes such as carboxypeptidase, liver alcohol dehydrogenase, and carbonic anhydrase	Anemia, poor wound healing, can lead to short stature	Common in most foods

*Greater than 200mg/day required

Table 25.3

Essential Amino Acids

Amino acids that must be consumed	Amino acids anabolized by the body
isoleucine	alanine
leucine	selenocysteine
lysine	aspartate
methionine	cysteine
phenylalanine	glutamate
tryptophan	glycine
valine	proline
histidine*	serine
threonine	tyrosine
arginine*	asparagine

*The human body can synthesize histidine and arginine, but not in the quantities required, especially for growing children.

Table 25.4

science practices CONNECTION for AP® Courses

Think About It

There are several nations where malnourishment is a common occurrence. What are some of the health challenges posed by malnutrition? What are examples of diseases caused by nutrient deficiencies?

Food Energy and ATP

Animals need food to obtain energy and maintain homeostasis. Homeostasis is the ability of a system to maintain a stable internal environment even in the face of external changes to the environment. For example, the normal body temperature of humans is 37°C (98.6°F). Humans maintain this temperature even when the external temperature is hot or cold. It takes energy to maintain this body temperature, and animals obtain this energy from food.

The primary source of energy for animals is carbohydrates, mainly glucose. Glucose is called the body's fuel. The digestible carbohydrates in an animal's diet are converted to glucose molecules through a series of catabolic chemical reactions.

Adenosine triphosphate, or ATP, is the primary energy currency in cells; ATP stores energy in phosphate ester bonds. ATP releases energy when the phosphodiester bonds are broken and ATP is converted to ADP and a phosphate group. ATP is produced by the oxidative reactions in the cytoplasm and mitochondrion of the cell, where carbohydrates, proteins, and fats undergo a series of metabolic reactions collectively called cellular respiration. For example, glycolysis is a series of reactions in which glucose is converted to pyruvic acid and some of its chemical potential energy is transferred to NADH and ATP.

ATP is required for all cellular functions. It is used to build the organic molecules that are required for cells and tissues; it provides energy for muscle contraction and for the transmission of electrical signals in the nervous system. When the amount of ATP is available in excess of the body's requirements, the liver uses the excess ATP and excess glucose to produce molecules called glycogen. Glycogen is a polymeric form of glucose and is stored in the liver and skeletal muscle cells. When blood sugar drops, the liver releases glucose from stores of glycogen. Skeletal muscle converts glycogen to glucose during intense exercise. The process of converting glucose and excess ATP to glycogen and the storage of excess energy is an evolutionarily important step in helping animals deal with mobility, food shortages, and famine.

everyday CONNECTION

Obesity

Obesity is a major health concern in the United States, and there is a growing focus on reducing obesity and the diseases it may lead to, such as type-2 diabetes, cancers of the colon and breast, and cardiovascular disease. How does the food consumed contribute to obesity?

Fatty foods are calorie-dense, meaning that they have more calories per unit mass than carbohydrates or proteins. One gram of carbohydrates has four calories, one gram of protein has four calories, and one gram of fat has nine calories. Animals tend to seek lipid-rich food for their higher energy content.

The signals of hunger ("time to eat") and satiety ("time to stop eating") are controlled in the hypothalamus region of the brain. Foods that are rich in fatty acids tend to promote satiety more than foods that are rich only in carbohydrates.

Excess carbohydrate and ATP are used by the liver to synthesize glycogen. The pyruvate produced during glycolysis is used to synthesize fatty acids. When there is more glucose in the body than required, the resulting excess pyruvate is converted into molecules that eventually result in the synthesis of fatty acids within the body. These fatty acids are stored in adipose cells—the fat cells in the mammalian body whose primary role is to store fat for later use.

It is important to note that some animals benefit from obesity. Polar bears and seals need body fat for insulation and to keep them from losing body heat during Arctic winters. When food is scarce, stored body fat provides energy for maintaining homeostasis. Fats prevent famine in mammals, allowing them to access energy when food is not available on a daily basis; fats are stored when a large kill is made or lots of food is available.

Which of the following statements about obesity is true?

a. Carbohydrate-rich foods satisfy hunger better than fatty acid–rich food.

b. Obesity is disadvantageous for organisms that live in cold climates.

c. Fat has more calories than protein or carbohydrates.

d. In the presence of excess blood glucose, fatty acids are synthesized and stored in skeletal muscle.

25.3 | Digestive System Processes

In this section, you will explore the following questions:

- What is the process of digestion?
- What steps are involved in digestion and absorption?
- What is elimination?
- What are the roles of the small and large intestines in absorption?

Connection for AP® Courses

Much of the information in this module is not within the scope of AP®. However, when we explored concepts about biological molecules in the chapter on biological macromolecules, we learn how macromolecules—carbohydrates, lipids, proteins, and nucleic acids—are synthesized from monomers. During digestion, these polymers are broken down into monomers, which are then absorbed and transported to all cells of the body. In the Digestive Systems module, we described the fate of the ingredients of a sandwich as they pass through the digestive tract. Food is ingested through the mouth, and digestion and absorption occur in a series of steps, with special enzymes playing important roles in digesting carbohydrates, proteins, and lipids. (You do not need to know the names of the specific enzymes involved in chemical digestion.) While most absorption of nutrients takes place in the small intestine, the remaining water, some vitamins, and any leftover salts are absorbed in the large intestine. Elimination describes the removal of undigested food.

Obtaining nutrition and energy from food is a multi-step process. For true animals, the first step is ingestion, the act of taking in food. This is followed by digestion, absorption, and elimination. In the following sections, each of these steps will be discussed in detail.

Ingestion

The large molecules found in intact food cannot pass through the cell membranes. Food needs to be broken into smaller particles so that animals can harness the nutrients and organic molecules. The first step in this process is **ingestion**. Ingestion is the process of taking in food through the mouth. In vertebrates, the teeth, saliva, and tongue play important roles in mastication (preparing the food into bolus). While the food is being mechanically broken down, the enzymes in saliva begin to chemically process the food as well. The combined action of these processes modifies the food from large particles to a soft mass that can be swallowed and can travel the length of the esophagus.

Digestion and Absorption

Digestion is the mechanical and chemical break down of food into small organic fragments. It is important to break down macromolecules into smaller fragments that are of suitable size for absorption across the digestive epithelium. Large, complex molecules of proteins, polysaccharides, and lipids must be reduced to simpler particles such as simple sugar before they can be absorbed by the digestive epithelial cells. Different organs play specific roles in the digestive process. The animal diet needs carbohydrates, protein, and fat, as well as vitamins and inorganic components for nutritional balance. How each of these components is digested is discussed in the following sections.

Carbohydrates

The digestion of carbohydrates begins in the mouth. The salivary enzyme amylase begins the breakdown of food starches into maltose, a disaccharide. As the bolus of food travels through the esophagus to the stomach, no significant digestion of carbohydrates takes place. The esophagus produces no digestive enzymes but does produce mucous for lubrication. The acidic environment in the stomach stops the action of the amylase enzyme.

The next step of carbohydrate digestion takes place in the duodenum. Recall that the chyme from the stomach enters the duodenum and mixes with the digestive secretion from the pancreas, liver, and gallbladder. Pancreatic juices also contain amylase, which continues the breakdown of starch and glycogen into maltose, a disaccharide. The disaccharides are broken down into monosaccharides by enzymes called **maltases**, **sucrases**, and **lactases**, which are also present in the brush border of the small intestinal wall. Maltase breaks down maltose into glucose. Other disaccharides, such as sucrose and lactose are broken down by sucrase and lactase, respectively. Sucrase breaks down sucrose (or "table sugar") into glucose and fructose, and lactase breaks down lactose (or "milk sugar") into glucose and galactose. The monosaccharides (glucose) thus produced are absorbed and then can be used in metabolic pathways to harness energy. The monosaccharides are transported across the intestinal epithelium into the bloodstream to be transported to the different cells in the body. The steps in carbohydrate digestion are summarized in Figure 25.17 and Table 25.5.

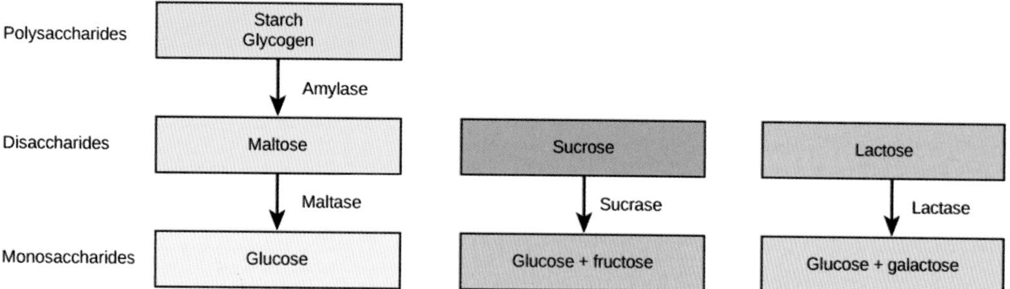

Figure 25.17 Digestion of carbohydrates is performed by several enzymes. Starch and glycogen are broken down into glucose by amylase and maltase. Sucrose (table sugar) and lactose (milk sugar) are broken down by sucrase and lactase, respectively.

Digestion of Carbohydrates

Enzyme	Produced By	Site of Action	Substrate Acting On	End Products
Salivary amylase	Salivary glands	Mouth	Polysaccharides (Starch)	Disaccharides (maltose), oligosaccharides
Pancreatic amylase	Pancreas	Small intestine	Polysaccharides (starch)	Disaccharides (maltose), monosaccharides
Oligosaccharidases	Lining of the intestine; brush border membrane	Small intestine	Disaccharides	Monosaccharides (e.g., glucose, fructose, galactose)

Table 25.5

Protein

A large part of protein digestion takes place in the stomach. The enzyme pepsin plays an important role in the digestion of proteins by breaking down the intact protein to peptides, which are short chains of four to nine amino acids. In the duodenum, other enzymes—**trypsin**, **elastase**, and **chymotrypsin**—act on the peptides reducing them to smaller peptides. Trypsin elastase, carboxypeptidase, and chymotrypsin are produced by the pancreas and released into the duodenum where they act on the chyme. Further breakdown of peptides to single amino acids is aided by enzymes called peptidases (those that break down peptides). Specifically, **carboxypeptidase**, **dipeptidase**, and **aminopeptidase** play important roles in reducing the peptides to free amino acids. The amino acids are absorbed into the bloodstream through the small intestines. The steps in protein digestion are summarized in **Figure 25.18** and **Table 25.6**.

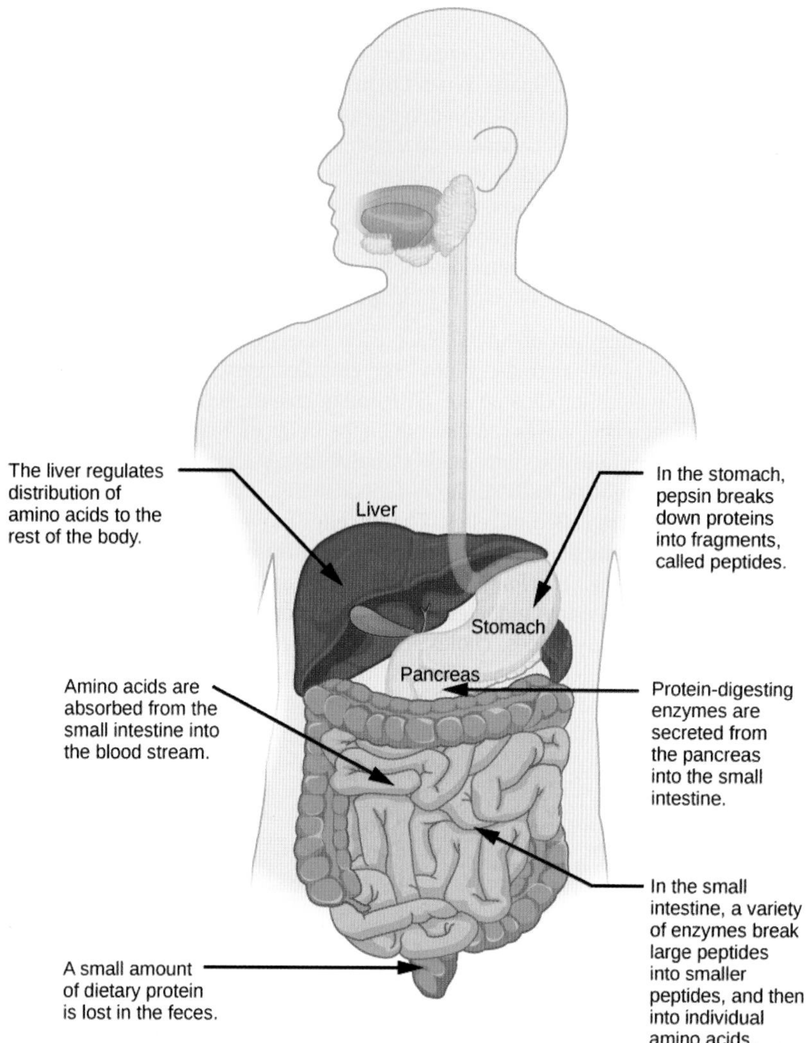
The liver regulates distribution of amino acids to the rest of the body.
Liver
In the stomach, pepsin breaks down proteins into fragments, called peptides.
Stomach
Pancreas
Amino acids are absorbed from the small intestine into the blood stream.
Protein-digesting enzymes are secreted from the pancreas into the small intestine.
In the small intestine, a variety of enzymes break large peptides into smaller peptides, and then into individual amino acids.
A small amount of dietary protein is lost in the feces.

Figure 25.18 Protein digestion is a multistep process that begins in the stomach and continues through the intestines.

Digestion of Protein

Enzyme	Produced By	Site of Action	Substrate Acting On	End Products
Pepsin	Stomach chief cells	Stomach	Proteins	Peptides
Trypsin Elastase Chymotrypsin	Pancreas	Small intestine	Proteins	Peptides
Carboxypeptidase	Pancreas	Small intestine	Peptides	Amino acids and peptides
Aminopeptidase Dipeptidase	Lining of intestine	Small intestine	Peptides	Amino acids

Table 25.6

Lipids

Lipid digestion begins in the stomach with the aid of lingual lipase and gastric lipase. However, the bulk of lipid digestion occurs in the small intestine due to pancreatic lipase. When chyme enters the duodenum, the hormonal responses trigger the release of bile, which is produced in the liver and stored in the gallbladder. Bile aids in the digestion of lipids, primarily triglycerides by emulsification. Emulsification is a process in which large lipid globules are broken down into several small lipid globules. These small globules are more widely distributed in the chyme rather than forming large aggregates. Lipids are hydrophobic substances: in the presence of water, they will aggregate to form globules to minimize exposure to water. Bile contains bile salts, which are amphipathic, meaning they contain hydrophobic and hydrophilic parts. Thus, the bile salts hydrophilic side can interface with water on one side and the hydrophobic side interfaces with lipids on the other. By doing so, bile salts emulsify large lipid globules into small lipid globules.

Why is emulsification important for digestion of lipids? Pancreatic juices contain enzymes called lipases (enzymes that break down lipids). If the lipid in the chyme aggregates into large globules, very little surface area of the lipids is available for the lipases to act on, leaving lipid digestion incomplete. By forming an emulsion, bile salts increase the available surface area of the lipids many fold. The pancreatic lipases can then act on the lipids more efficiently and digest them, as detailed in Figure 25.19. Lipases break down the lipids into fatty acids and glycerides. These molecules can pass through the plasma membrane of the cell and enter the epithelial cells of the intestinal lining. The bile salts surround long-chain fatty acids and monoglycerides forming tiny spheres called micelles. The micelles move into the brush border of the small intestine absorptive cells where the long-chain fatty acids and monoglycerides diffuse out of the micelles into the absorptive cells leaving the micelles behind in the chyme. The long-chain fatty acids and monoglycerides recombine in the absorptive cells to form triglycerides, which aggregate into globules and become coated with proteins. These large spheres are called **chylomicrons**. Chylomicrons contain triglycerides, cholesterol, and other lipids and have proteins on their surface. The surface is also composed of the hydrophilic phosphate "heads" of phospholipids. Together, they enable the chylomicron to move in an aqueous environment without exposing the lipids to water. Chylomicrons leave the absorptive cells via exocytosis. Chylomicrons enter the lymphatic vessels, and then enter the blood in the subclavian vein.

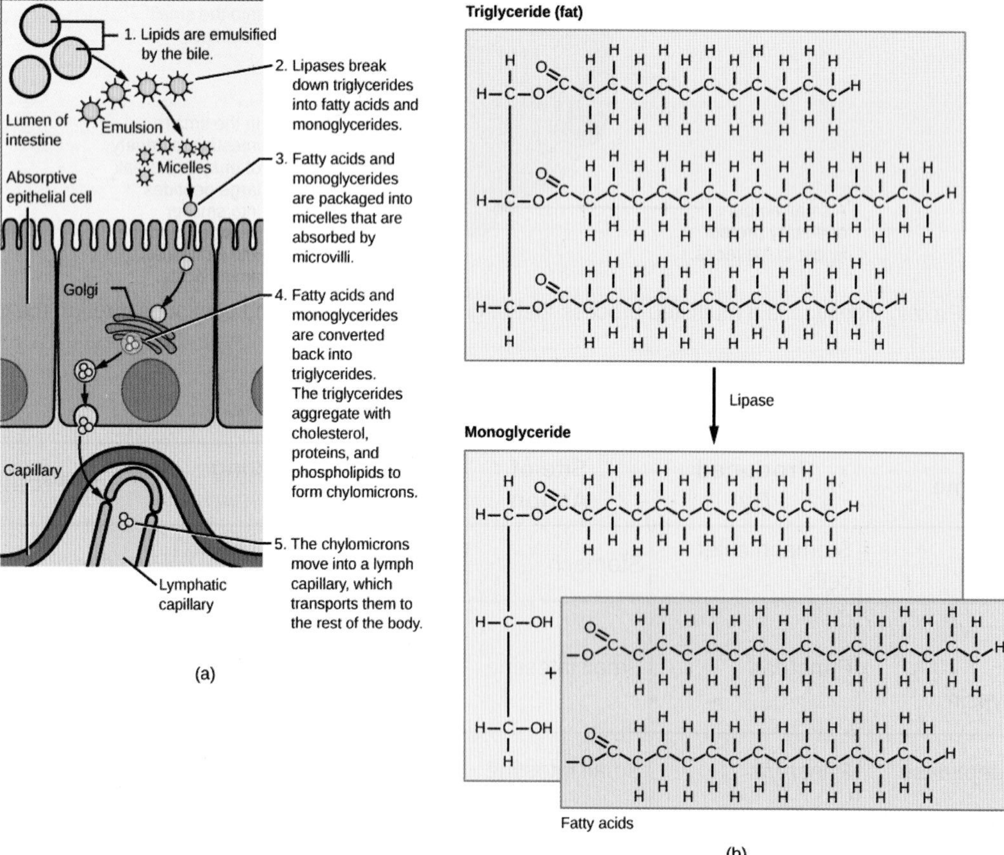

Figure 25.19 Lipids are digested and absorbed in the small intestine.

Vitamins

Vitamins can be either water-soluble or lipid-soluble. Fat soluble vitamins are absorbed in the same manner as lipids. It is important to consume some amount of dietary lipid to aid the absorption of lipid-soluble vitamins. Water-soluble vitamins can be directly absorbed into the bloodstream from the intestine.

This **website (http://openstaxcollege.org/l/digest_enzymes)** has an overview of the digestion of protein, fat, and carbohydrates.

Which of the following events in digestion and absorption is incorrect?

a. Carbohydrate digestion begins in the mouth.

b. Protein is primarily digested in the stomach.

c. Fats are primarily digested in the large intestine.

d. Digested carbohydrate, fat, and protein molecules are absorbed by villi in the small intestine.

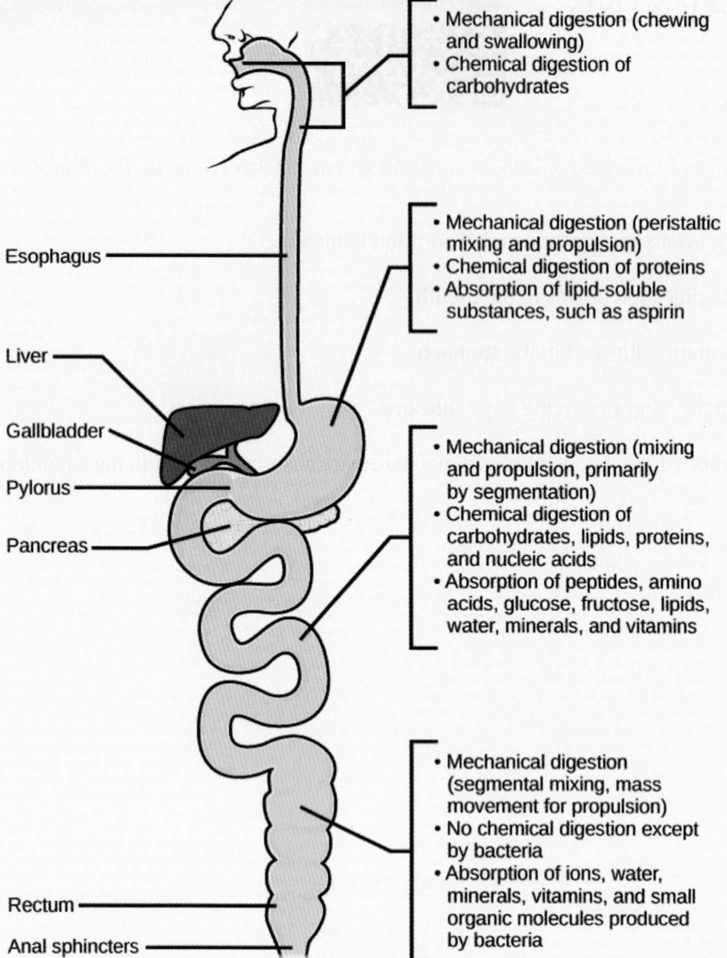

Figure 25.20 Mechanical and chemical digestion of food takes place in many steps, beginning in the mouth and ending in the rectum.

Which of the following statements about digestive processes is true?

a. Bile emulsifies lipids in the small intestine.

b. Trypsin and lipase in the stomach digest protein.

c. Amylase, maltase, and lactase in the mouth digest carbohydrates.

d. Peptides are primarily absorbed in the large intestines.

Elimination

The final step in digestion is the elimination of undigested food content and waste products. The undigested food material enters the colon, where most of the water is reabsorbed. Recall that the colon is also home to the microflora called "intestinal flora" that aid in the digestion process. The semi-solid waste is moved through the colon by peristaltic movements of the muscle and is stored in the rectum. As the rectum expands in response to storage of fecal matter, it triggers the neural signals required to set up the urge to eliminate. The solid waste is eliminated through the anus using peristaltic movements of the rectum.

Common Problems with Elimination

Diarrhea and constipation are some of the most common health concerns that affect digestion. Constipation is a condition where the feces are hardened because of excess water removal in the colon. In contrast, if enough water is not removed from the feces, it results in diarrhea. Many bacteria, including the ones that cause cholera, affect the proteins involved in water reabsorption in the colon and result in excessive diarrhea.

Emesis

Emesis, or vomiting, is elimination of food by forceful expulsion through the mouth. It is often in response to an irritant that affects the digestive tract, including but not limited to viruses, bacteria, emotions, sights, and food poisoning. This forceful expulsion of the food is due to the strong contractions produced by the stomach muscles. The process of emesis is regulated by the medulla.

25.4 | Digestive System Regulation

In this section, you will explore the following questions:

- How is neural regulation involved in the digestive processes?
- How do hormones regulate digestion?

Connection for AP® Courses

The concepts presented in this module are not within the scope for AP® other than to note that the brain houses the control center for the sensation of hunger and satiety (fullness). The functions of the digestive system are regulated through neural and hormonal responses. In the chapter that discusses the endocrine system, we explore in detail the role of the endocrine system in maintaining homeostasis, including the normal functioning of the digestive system.

The brain is the control center for the sensation of hunger and satiety. The functions of the digestive system are regulated through neural and hormonal responses.

Neural Responses to Food

In reaction to the smell, sight, or thought of food, like that shown in **Figure 25.21**, the first response is that of salivation. The salivary glands secrete more saliva in response to stimulation by the autonomic nervous system triggered by the food in preparation for digestion. Simultaneously, the stomach begins to produce hydrochloric acid to digest the food. Recall that the peristaltic movements of the esophagus and other organs of the digestive tract are under the control of the brain. The brain prepares these muscles for movement as well. When the stomach is full, the part of the brain that detects satiety signals fullness. There are three overlapping phases of gastric control—the cephalic phase, the gastric phase, and the intestinal phase—each requires many enzymes and is under neural control as well.

Figure 25.21 Seeing a plate of food triggers the secretion of saliva in the mouth and the production of HCL in the stomach. (credit: Kelly Bailey)

Digestive Phases

The response to food begins even before food enters the mouth. The first phase of ingestion, called the **cephalic phase**, is controlled by the neural response to the stimulus provided by food. All aspects—such as sight, sense, and smell—trigger the neural responses resulting in salivation and secretion of gastric juices. The gastric and salivary secretion in the cephalic phase can also take place due to the thought of food. Right now, if you think about a piece of chocolate or a crispy potato chip, the increase in salivation is a cephalic phase response to the thought. The central nervous system prepares the stomach to receive food.

The **gastric phase** begins once the food arrives in the stomach. It builds on the stimulation provided during the cephalic phase. Gastric acids and enzymes process the ingested materials. The gastric phase is stimulated by (1) distension of the stomach, (2) a decrease in the pH of the gastric contents, and (3) the presence of undigested material. This phase consists of local, hormonal, and neural responses. These responses stimulate secretions and powerful contractions.

The **intestinal phase** begins when chyme enters the small intestine triggering digestive secretions. This phase controls the rate of gastric emptying. In addition to gastric emptying, when chyme enters the small intestine, it triggers other hormonal and neural events that coordinate the activities of the intestinal tract, pancreas, liver, and gallbladder.

Hormonal Responses to Food

The **endocrine system** controls the response of the various glands in the body and the release of hormones at the appropriate times.

One of the important factors under hormonal control is the stomach acid environment. During the gastric phase, the hormone **gastrin** is secreted by G cells in the stomach in response to the presence of proteins. Gastrin stimulates the release of stomach acid, or hydrochloric acid (HCl) which aids in the digestion of the proteins. However, when the stomach is emptied, the acidic environment need not be maintained and a hormone called **somatostatin** stops the release of hydrochloric acid. This is controlled by a negative feedback mechanism.

In the duodenum, digestive secretions from the liver, pancreas, and gallbladder play an important role in digesting chyme during the intestinal phase. In order to neutralize the acidic chyme, a hormone called **secretin** stimulates the pancreas to produce alkaline bicarbonate solution and deliver it to the duodenum. Secretin acts in tandem with another hormone called **cholecystokinin** (CCK). Not only does CCK stimulate the pancreas to produce the requisite pancreatic juices, it also stimulates the gallbladder to release bile into the duodenum.

Visit this website (http://openstaxcollege.org/l/enteric_endo) to learn more about the endocrine system. Review the text and watch the animation of how control is implemented in the endocrine system.

Which of the following statements about the enteric endocrine system is true?

a. Gastrin stimulates pancreatic enzyme and bile secretion.

b. The enteric endocrine system includes all endocrine cells of the gastrointestinal tract.

c. All hormone-secreting cells in the enteric endocrine system are clustered together.

d. Enteric endocrine system cells secrete enzymes in response to specific stimuli.

Another level of hormonal control occurs in response to the composition of food. Foods high in lipids take a long time to digest. A hormone called **gastric inhibitory peptide** is secreted by the small intestine to slow down the peristaltic movements of the intestine to allow fatty foods more time to be digested and absorbed.

Understanding the hormonal control of the digestive system is an important area of ongoing research. Scientists are exploring the role of each hormone in the digestive process and developing ways to target these hormones.

KEY TERMS

alimentary canal tubular digestive system with a mouth and anus

aminopeptidase protease that breaks down peptides to single amino acids; secreted by the brush border of small intestine

anus exit point for waste material

bile digestive juice produced by the liver; important for digestion of lipids

bolus mass of food resulting from chewing action and wetting by saliva

carboxypeptidase protease that breaks down peptides to single amino acids; secreted by the brush border of the small intestine

carnivore animal that consumes animal flesh

cephalic phase first phase of digestion, controlled by the neural response to the stimulus provided by food

cholecystokinin hormone that stimulates the contraction of the gallbladder to release bile

chylomicron small lipid globule

chyme mixture of partially digested food and stomach juices

chymotrypsin pancreatic protease

digestion mechanical and chemical break down of food into small organic fragments

dipeptidase protease that breaks down peptides to single amino acids; secreted by the brush border of small intestine

duodenum first part of the small intestine where a large part of digestion of carbohydrates and fats occurs

elastase pancreatic protease

endocrine system system that controls the response of the various glands in the body and the release of hormones at the appropriate times

esophagus tubular organ that connects the mouth to the stomach

essential nutrient nutrient that cannot be synthesized by the body; it must be obtained from food

gallbladder organ that stores and concentrates bile

gastric inhibitory peptide hormone secreted by the small intestine in the presence of fatty acids and sugars; it also inhibits acid production and peristalsis in order to slow down the rate at which food enters the small intestine

gastric phase digestive phase beginning once food enters the stomach; gastric acids and enzymes process the ingested materials

gastrin hormone which stimulates hydrochloric acid secretion in the stomach

gastrovascular cavity digestive system consisting of a single opening

gizzard muscular organ that grinds food

herbivore animal that consumes strictly plant diet

ileum last part of the small intestine; connects the small intestine to the large intestine; important for absorption of B-12

ingestion act of taking in food

intestinal phase third digestive phase; begins when chyme enters the small intestine triggering digestive secretions and controlling the rate of gastric emptying

jejunum second part of the small intestine

lactase enzyme that breaks down lactose into glucose and galactose

large intestine digestive system organ that reabsorbs water from undigested material and processes waste matter

lipase enzyme that chemically breaks down lipids

liver organ that produces bile for digestion and processes vitamins and lipids

maltase enzyme that breaks down maltose into glucose

mineral inorganic, elemental molecule that carries out important roles in the body

monogastric digestive system that consists of a single-chambered stomach

omnivore animal that consumes both plants and animals

pancreas gland that secretes digestive juices

pepsin enzyme found in the stomach whose main role is protein digestion

pepsinogen inactive form of pepsin

peristalsis wave-like movements of muscle tissue

proventriculus glandular part of a bird's stomach

rectum area of the body where feces is stored until elimination

roughage component of food that is low in energy and high in fiber

ruminant animal with a stomach divided into four compartments

salivary amylase enzyme found in saliva, which converts carbohydrates to maltose

secretin hormone which stimulates sodium bicarbonate secretion in the small intestine

small intestine organ where digestion of protein, fats, and carbohydrates is completed

somatostatin hormone released to stop acid secretion when the stomach is empty

sphincter band of muscle that controls movement of materials throughout the digestive tract

stomach saclike organ containing acidic digestive juices

sucrase enzyme that breaks down sucrose into glucose and fructose

trypsin pancreatic protease that breaks down protein

villi folds on the inner surface of the small intestine whose role is to increase absorption area

vitamin organic substance necessary in small amounts to sustain life

CHAPTER SUMMARY

25.1 Digestive Systems

Different animals have evolved different types of digestive systems specialized to meet their dietary needs. Humans and many other animals have monogastric digestive systems with a single-chambered stomach. Birds have evolved a digestive system that includes a gizzard where the food is crushed into smaller pieces. This compensates for their inability to masticate. Ruminants that consume large amounts of plant material have a multi-chambered stomach that digests roughage. Pseudo-ruminants have similar digestive processes as ruminants but do not have the four-compartment stomach. Processing food involves ingestion (eating), digestion (mechanical and enzymatic breakdown of large molecules), absorption (cellular uptake of nutrients), and elimination (removal of undigested waste as feces).

Many organs work together to digest food and absorb nutrients. The mouth is the point of ingestion and the location where both mechanical and chemical breakdown of food begins. Saliva contains an enzyme called amylase that breaks down carbohydrates. The food bolus travels through the esophagus by peristaltic movements to the stomach. The stomach has an extremely acidic environment. An enzyme called pepsin digests protein in the stomach. Further digestion and absorption take place in the small intestine. The large intestine reabsorbs water from the undigested food and stores waste until elimination.

25.2 Nutrition and Energy Production

Animal diet should be balanced and meet the needs of the body. Carbohydrates, proteins, and fats are the primary components of food. Some essential nutrients are required for cellular function but cannot be produced by the animal body. These include vitamins, minerals, some fatty acids, and some amino acids. Food intake in more than necessary amounts is stored as glycogen in the liver and muscle cells, and in fat cells. Excess adipose storage can lead to obesity and serious health problems. ATP is the energy currency of the cell and is obtained from the metabolic pathways. Excess carbohydrates and energy are stored as glycogen in the body.

25.3 Digestive System Processes

Digestion begins with ingestion, where the food is taken in the mouth. Digestion and absorption take place in a series of steps with special enzymes playing important roles in digesting carbohydrates, proteins, and lipids. Elimination describes removal of undigested food contents and waste products from the body. While most absorption occurs in the small intestines, the large intestine is responsible for the final removal of water that remains after the absorptive process of the small intestines. The cells that line the large intestine absorb some vitamins as well as any leftover salts and water. The large intestine (colon) is also where feces is formed.

25.4 Digestive System Regulation

The brain and the endocrine system control digestive processes. The brain controls the responses of hunger and satiety. The endocrine system controls the release of hormones and enzymes required for digestion of food in the digestive tract.

REVIEW QUESTIONS

1. When you eat an apple, it is first physically broken down into smaller fragments. What is the term for this process?

a. elimination
b. absorption
c. mastication
d. peristalsis

2. Which of the following statements is true?

a. The majority of water is reabsorbed by the small intestines.
b. Elimination is a process that occurs via diffusion.
c. Absorption is the process that chemically breaks down food.
d. The small intestines absorb nutrients.

3. Ruminants and pseudo-ruminants are both able to digest plant materials but have different mechanisms for doing so. Which of the following is a pseudo-ruminant?

a. cow
b. goat
c. crow
d. horse

4. Which of the following statements about animal digestion is true?

a. Roughage is digested very quickly.
b. Birds eat large quantities at one time.
c. Birds have a four-chambered stomach.
d. In pseudo-ruminants, roughage is digested in the cecum.

5. Chemical and mechanical digestion begins in the mouth, and food is prepared into a _____, which is then swallowed.

a. bolus
b. trachea
c. peristalsis
d. sphincter

6. Which of the following statements about digestion is true?

a. Pepsin is converted to pepsinogen with the help of hydrochloric acid.
b. Starch digestion begins in the mouth.
c. Wave-like muscle movements called peristalsis move food from the stomach to the mouth.
d. Amino acids are absorbed through the intestinal lining of the ileum.

7. Chyme is highly acidic. What is secreted by the pancreas to neutralize chyme?

a. hydrochloric acid
b. bicarbonate
c. bile
d. amylase

8. How does the liver assist in fat digestion?

a. produces bicarbonate
b. concentrates bile salts
c. produces bile
d. produces pepsin

9. When you eat food, it is vital that the nutrients be absorbed. How does absorption occur?

a. Food is mechanically and chemically broken down into smaller molecules.
b. Alternating waves of muscular contraction facilitate movement of food.
c. Partially digested food flows into the small intestine and food regurgitation is prevented.
d. Nutrients diffuse across the intestines.

10. Certain organs control the release of hormones that have vital roles in digestion. Which of the following controls hunger and satiety signals?

a. thymus
b. adrenal cortex
c. thyroid
d. hypothalamus

11. One cup of which of the following has the most calories?

a. spaghetti with tomato sauce
b. deep-fried zucchini
c. mixed fruit
d. scrambled eggs

12. Plant materials, such as fruits and vegetables, are difficult to digest because they are difficult to break down. How are humans able to obtain nutrients from fruits and vegetables?

a. Humans produce cellulase, which breaks down cellulose.
b. Intestinal flora have enzymes that break down some of the fiber.
c. Bile is released from the gallbladder to break down fiber.
d. In the stomach, pepsin is produced to break down plant material.

13. Which statement is not an example of how fat is beneficial?

a. Fat helps absorb lipid-soluble vitamins.
b. Fat helps produce lipid-soluble hormones.
c. Fat has low energy density.
d. Fat makes you feel full faster.

14. Certain molecules are required by but not produced by the body. Fat- and water-soluble _______ are organic molecules that cannot be produced by the body but are required for many enzymatic functions.

a. minerals
b. vitamins
c. amino acids
d. sugars

15. What is the result of insufficient amounts of the mineral iodine in the body?

a. muscle weakness
b. poor immune function
c. mood disturbances
d. goiters

16. Adenosine triphosphate, or ATP, is the source of energy for cells. ATP stores energy in _______ bonds.

a. carbohydrate
b. glycolysis
c. glycogen
d. phosphodiester

17. Which of the following statements about glycogen is true?

a. When an individual is sedentary, glycogen is converted to glucose.
b. The liver releases glycogen when blood sugar drops.
c. ATP is produced by excess glycogen and glucose.
d. During glycolysis, glycogen is converted to pyruvic acid.

18. What is produced from excess ATP and glucose?

a. glycogen
b. pyruvate
c. peptides
d. essential nutrients

19. Which of the following is not a reason why ATP is required by animals?

a. ATP is needed to build organic molecules.
b. ATP provides energy for muscle contraction.
c. ATP assists in electrical signal transmission.
d. ATP is the body's fuel source.

20. Different macromolecules have varying amounts of energy density. Which of the following is the least energy dense?

a. protein
b. fat
c. fiber
d. carbohydrates

21. Which of the following does not play a role in masticating food?

a. teeth
b. pharynx
c. saliva
d. tongue

22. Which of the following statements about the process of digestion is true?

a. Organisms absorb large molecules through digestive cells.
b. The last step of digestion is absorption.
c. Food is only mechanically broken down in the mouth.
d. Food is prepared into a bolus before it is swallowed.

23. Which of the following enzymes is involved in carbohydrate digestion?

a. pancreatic amylase
b. elastase
c. trypsin
d. pepsin

24. In protein digestion, what happens in the stomach?

a. Aminopeptidase and dipeptidase break peptides into amino acids.
b. Pepsin breaks proteins into peptides.
c. Trypsin, elastase, and chymotrypsin break proteins into peptides.
d. Carboxypeptidase breaks peptides into amino acids and peptides.

25. Water reabsorption is an essential component of processing food. Where is the majority of water reabsorbed?

a. small intestines
b. rectum
c. colon
d. anus

26. If you come down with the flu, you might experience emesis. What causes emesis?

a. stomach muscle contractions
b. neural signals that urge elimination
c. inadequate water reabsorption
d. excess water reabsorption

27. Not all organs involved in processing food are involved in digestion. Which of the following organs is not involved in digestion?

a. mouth
b. anus
c. stomach
d. small intestine

28. Which of the following statements about digestion of food in the large intestines is true?

a. Mechanical digestion occurs by bacteria.
b. Semi-solid waste is moved by wave-like muscle contractions.
c. Most nutrients are absorbed.
d. Peristaltic mixing occurs.

29. Taking in food, or ____, is the first step of gaining nutrients from food.

a. digestion
b. ingestion
c. elimination
d. absorption

30. What is the correct order of processes by which nutrients and energy are obtained from food?

a. digestion → ingestion → absorption → elimination

b. ingestion → absorption → digestion → elimination

c. ingestion → digestion → absorption → elimination

d. ingestion → digestion → elimination → absorption

31. Gastric control has three phases that assist in digesting food. Which phase is initiated by chyme?

a. intestinal

b. gastric

c. cephalic

d. digestive

32. Which of the following occurs during the cephalic phase of gastric control?

a. Salivation is triggered.

b. Food is processed by gastric acids and enzymes.

c. Gastrin is produced.

d. Digestive secretions are released.

33. Hormones are essential for digesting ingested food items. Which hormone controls the release of bile from the gallbladder?

a. pepsin

b. gastrin

c. amylase

d. cholecystokinin

34. What is the role of gastrin in food digestion and absorption?

a. Gastrin stimulates release of stomach acid.

b. Gastrin stimulates production of bicarbonate.

c. Gastrin stimulates pancreatic juice production.

d. Gastrin stops the release of stomach acid.

35. The gastric phase assists in processing ingested materials. When does the gastric phase begin?

a. when food is smelled

b. when food reaches the stomach

c. when chyme enters the small intestines

d. when food is ingested

CRITICAL THINKING QUESTIONS

36. Explain how villi and microvilli aid in absorption.

a. Villi and microvilli increase the surface area of the small intestines, which aids in the absorption of bile salts and vitamin B12.

b. Villi and microvilli increase the surface area of the small intestine, which increases the absorption of nutrients by diffusion.

c. Villi and microvilli form the inner layer of epithelial tissue in the small intestine and increase the absorption of nutrients from chyme.

d. Villi and microvilli absorb food through the small intestine via smooth muscle contractions called peristalsis.

37. Ruminants, such as this goat, are able to digest large amounts of plant material. How is plant material passed through, digested, and absorbed in the ruminant digestive system?

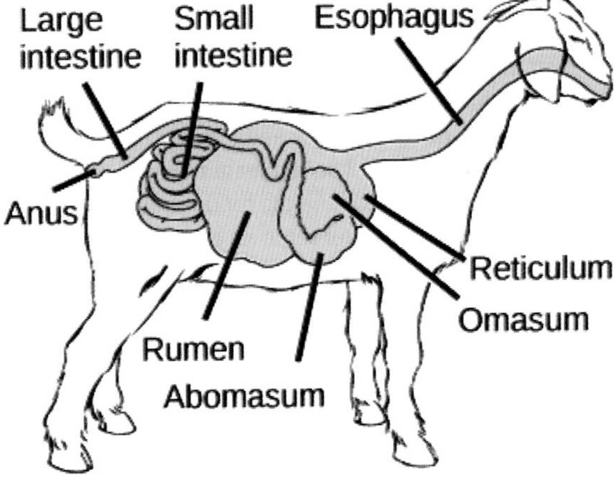

a. Food is chewed in the mouth, then passes through the esophagus into the rumen and then the reticulum, which contain microbes that break down cellulose and ferment the ingested plant material. The ruminant regurgitates cud from the rumen, and the food is passed into the omasum for water removal and then into the small and large intestines for nutrient and further water absorption. Waste is excreted through the anus.

b. Food is chewed in the mouth, then passes through the esophagus into the rumen and then the reticulum, which contain microbes that break down cellulose and ferment the ingested plant material. The ruminant regurgitates cud from the rumen, and the food is passed into the abomasum for water removal and then into the small and large intestines for nutrient and further water absorption. Waste is excreted through the anus.

c. Food is chewed in the mouth, then passes through the esophagus into the rumen and then the reticulum, which contain microbes that break down proteins and ferment the ingested plant material. Ruminants regurgitate cud from the rumen, and the food is passed into the omasum for water removal and then into the small and large intestines for nutrient and further water absorption. Waste is excreted through the anus.

d. Food is chewed in the mouth then passes through the esophagus into the reticulum and then the rumen, which contain microbes that break down cellulose and ferment the ingested plant material. The ruminant regurgitates cud from the rumen, and the food is passed into the omasum for water removal and then into the small and large intestines for nutrient and further water absorption. Waste is excreted through the anus.

38. a. How does a stomach ulcer form?
b. How could you prevent a stomach ulcer from forming in your stomach?

a. a. When the serosa layer of stomach ruptures and does not reform, an open wound is formed. It may be caused by bacteria
b. Ulcers can be prevented by eliminating ingesting items that cause degradation of the mucus lining like foods that irritate the stomach.

b. a. When the mucus lining of the stomach ruptures and does not reform, an open wound is formed. It may be caused by a virus.
b. Ulcers can be prevented by eliminating ingesting items that cause degradation of the mucus lining, like foods that irritate the stomach.

c. a. When the mucus lining of the stomach ruptures and does not reform, an open wound is formed. It may be caused by bacteria.
b. Ulcers can be prevented by ingesting items that will increase the acid content of the stomach.

d. a. When the mucus lining of the stomach ruptures and does not reform, an open wound forms. It may be caused by bacteria.
b. Ulcers can be prevented by eliminating ingesting items that cause degradation of the mucus lining, such as foods that irritate the stomach.

39. How is the gallbladder involved in digestion, even though it is considered an accessory organ?

a. The gallbladder secretes bile to the duodenum, which uses it to break down proteins. It is considered an accessory organ because food does not directly pass through it.

b. The gallbladder secretes bile to the duodenum, which uses it to break down fats. It is considered an accessory organ because food does not directly pass through it.

c. The gallbladder secretes bile to the ileum, which uses it to break down fats. It is considered an accessory organ because food does not directly pass through it.

d. The gallbladder secretes bile to the ileum, which uses it to break down proteins. It is considered an accessory organ because only a very small amount of digestion takes place in the gallbladder.

40. What is the role of saliva in the digestive system?

a. Saliva contains an enzyme called amylase, which starts the chemical digestion in the mouth by breaking down proteins.

b. Saliva contains an enzyme called lipase, which starts chemical digestion in the mouth by breaking down proteins.

c. Saliva contains an enzyme called maltase, which starts chemical digestion in the mouth by breaking down carbohydrates.

d. Saliva contains an enzyme called amylase, which starts chemical digestion in the mouth by breaking down carbohydrates.

41. What are the biological benefits of a balanced diet?

a. A balanced diet provides excess energy to be stored in the body and nutrients to maintain good health and increase reproductive capability.

b. A balanced diet allows excess energy to be stored in the body, thereby increasing the rate of metabolic reactions.

c. A balanced diet provides nutrients needed to maintain proper bodily functions, and vitamins and minerals to maintain good health and reproductive capability.

d. A balanced diet provides nutrients needed to maintain proper bodily functions, and vitamins and minerals to maintain good health and increase reproductive capability.

42. Why is it important to eat carbohydrates, which provide organic carbons?

a. They are needed to provide insulation to mammals.

b. They help to fight infections.

c. They are needed to produce antibodies.

d. They are needed to build cells and tissues.

43. a. Why is it necessary to consume essential nutrients? b. What are two examples of fat-soluble essential vitamins, and what are their functions in the human body?

a. a. Essential nutrients are not synthesized by the body and are not necessary for proper body function.
b. Vitamins B and C are two fat-soluble essential vitamins. Vitamin B helps maintain eyesight, and vitamin C is essential for blood clotting.

b. a. Essential nutrients are not synthesized by the body but are necessary for proper body function.
b. Vitamins A and K are two fat-soluble essential vitamins. Vitamin A helps maintain connective tissue, and vitamin K is essential for blood clotting.

c. a. Essential nutrients are synthesized by the body and are necessary for proper body function.
b. Vitamins D and K are two fat-soluble essential vitamins. Vitamin D helps maintain a stable nervous system, and vitamin K is essential for blood clotting.

d. a. Essential nutrients are not synthesized by the body but are necessary for proper body function.
b. Vitamins A and K are two fat-soluble essential vitamins. Vitamin A helps maintain eyesight, and vitamin K is essential for blood clotting.

44. What happens to glycogen when blood sugar drops?

a. It stimulates the release of insulin, which can regulate the blood sugar level.

b. It is released from the liver and converted to glucose to increase blood sugar levels.

c. It is converted to starch, which breaks down to form glucose and increase blood sugar levels.

d. It is released from the liver and converted to pyruvate, which can then form glucose to increase blood sugar levels.

45. What is the evolutionary significance of glycogen production?

a. Excess ATP and glucose produce glycogen, which can be used at a later point in time to act as co-factor if, for example, a good source is scarce.

b. Excess proteins and glucose produce glycogen, which can be used at a later point in time to produce energy if, for example, food is scarce.

c. Excess ATP and glucose produce glycogen, which can be used at a later point in time to produce energy if, for example, food is scarce.

d. Excess proteins and fats produce glycogen, which can be used at a later point in time to act as source of nitrogen if, for example, a good source is scarce.

46. How can eating too much bread and pasta physiologically promote obesity?

a. Excess blood glucose increases the amount of urea, which is converted into fatty acids. Fatty acids are stored in areolar cells, which increase the amount of body fat.
b. Excess blood glucose increases the amount of pyruvate, which is converted into fatty acids. Fatty acids are stored in adipose cells, which increase the amount of body fat.
c. Bread and pasta are rich in fats. Their digestion produces fatty acids and glycerol. Fatty acids are stored in adipose cells, which increase the amount of body fat.
d. Bread and pasta are rich in fats. Their digestion produces fatty acids and glycerol. Fatty acids are stored in areolar cells, which increase the amount of body fat.

47. How do ingestion and digestion differ?

a. Ingestion is taking food in through mouth, where mechanical digestion begins. Chemical digestion begins in the stomach, where food is further broken down into smaller molecules that can be absorbed and used by the body.
b. Ingestion is the process of taking in food through the mouth, where mechanical and chemical digestion begins to break down the food into smaller molecules that can be absorbed and used by the body.
c. Ingestion is taking food in through the mouth, where mechanical and chemical digestion begins. Digestion in the stomach breaks down proteins and fats present in food into smaller molecules that can be absorbed and used by the body.
d. Ingestion is the transfer of food from the mouth to the esophagus, where mechanical and chemical digestion begin to break down the food into smaller molecules that can be absorbed and used by the body.

48. Why are some dietary lipids a necessary part of a balanced diet?

a. Dietary lipids aid in the absorption of water-soluble vitamins, including B and C, which are needed for various bodily functions.
b. Dietary lipids aid in the absorption of some minerals, including folic acid, iron, and magnesium, which are needed for various bodily functions.
c. Dietary lipids aid in the absorption of vitamins, including A, B, C, D, E, and K, which are needed for various bodily functions
d. Dietary lipids aid in the absorption of fat-soluble vitamins, including A, D, E, and K, which are needed for various bodily functions.

49. What happens to undigested food after the water is reabsorbed?

a. Undigested food is moved through the colon, where intestinal flora aid in digestion by peristalsis, and then stored in the rectum until elimination through the anus.
b. Undigested food is moved through the colon, where intestinal flora aid in digestion by peristalsis; further absorption takes place in the rectum, after which it stores the food until elimination through the anus.
c. Undigested food is moved through the colon, where intestinal flora aid in digestion by segmentation, and then it is stored in the rectum until elimination through the anus.
d. Undigested food is moved through the ileum, where intestinal flora aid in digestion by peristalsis, and then it is stored in the rectum until elimination through the anus.

50. a. What are micelles?
b. Why are micelles integral to lipid absorption?

a. a. Micelles are lipoproteins designed for the transport of lipids that enter lacteals.
b. Micelles facilitate absorption by microvilli, where the fatty acids and proteins diffuse out to form lipoproteins.
b. a. Micelles are lipoproteins designed for the transport of lipids that enter lacteals.
b. Micelles facilitate absorption by microvilli, where the fatty acids and monoglycerides diffuse out to form triglycerides.
c. a. Micelles are bile salt–surrounded fatty acids and phospholipids.
b. Micelles facilitate absorption by microvilli, where the fatty acids and monoglycerides diffuse out to form triglycerides.
d. a. Micelles are bile salt–surrounded fatty acids and monoglycerides.
b. Micelles facilitate absorption by microvilli, where the fatty acids and monoglycerides diffuse out to form triglycerides.

51. On a cellular level, why must food be broken down?

a. Large molecules present in intact food pass through the digestive epithelium and enter the cell through the membrane, thereby damaging the nuclear membrane. Hence it must be broken down.
b. Fats present in intact food contain very large molecules, which cannot pass through cell membranes. Fats need to be passed through the digestive epithelium to be utilized.
c. Large molecules present in intact food cannot pass through cell membranes. Nutrients need to be passed through the digestive epithelium to be utilized.
d. Large molecules, if not broken down, produce toxic substances that pass through the epithelium of the digestive tract and are utilized by the cells. This can be lethal to the cell.

52. What is the importance of neural responses to food stimuli?

a. Neural responses facilitate secretion of fumarase needed for chemical digestion of food as well as other involuntary responses like peristalsis.
b. Neural responses facilitate secretion of enzymes that are needed to digest or break down food as well as other involuntary responses like segmentation in stomach.
c. Neural responses facilitate secretion of enzymes needed to digest or break down food as well as other involuntary responses like peristalsis.
d. Neural responses facilitate secretion of salivary amylase needed to digest or break down food as well as secretion of hormones like secretin and gastrin.

53. How do hormones regulate digestion?

a. Hormones regulate aspects of digestion such as increasing the peristaltic movements in the esophagus when food is sensed.
b. Hormones regulate digestion by signaling when the stomach is full or empty so that an individual will consume food or stop eating.
c. Hormones like gastrin, secretin, adrenocorticotropic are released from the pituitary to regulate which digestive secretions are released.
d. Hormones regulate aspects of digestion such as which digestive secretions are released as well as when they are released.

54. When you are eating a meal, how do you know when you are full?

a. The pituitary gland release hormones when the stomach is full, which therefore reduces hunger.
b. The brain signals when the stomach is full that you are satiated, which therefore reduces hunger.
c. The stomach signals when it is full, which therefore reduces hunger.
d. Low blood sugar levels stimulate a neurotransmitter, which sends a signal to the brain when the stomach is full and therefore reduces hunger.

TEST PREP FOR AP® COURSES

55. Simple cuboidal epithelial cells line the ducts of certain human exocrine glands. Various materials are transported into or out of the cells by diffusion. (The formula for the surface area of a cube is 6 × S2, and the formula for the volume of a cube is S3, where S = the length of a side of a cube.) Which of the following cube-shaped cells would be most efficient in removing waste by diffusion?

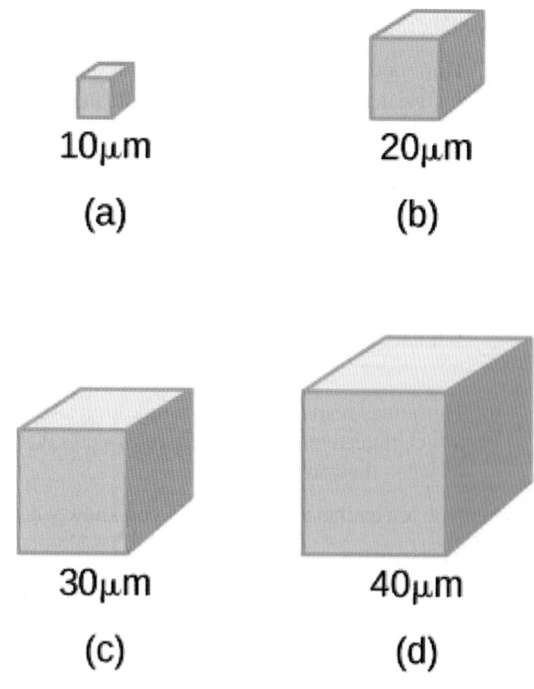

a. 10 µm
b. 20 µm
c. 30 µm
d. 40 µm

56. Celiac disease is dangerous in affected individuals, because ingesting gluten damages the villi of the small intestines. Why is this potentially life threatening?

a. The villi aid in mechanical digestion of food particles. When they are damaged, nutrients cannot be digested properly in the body.
b. Villi increase the surface area of the small intestine, which aids in the absorption of bile salts. This nutrient cannot be absorbed when they are damaged.
c. Villi decrease the surface area of the small intestine available for absorption. Nutrients cannot properly enter the bloodstream when they are damaged.
d. Villi increase the surface area available for nutrient absorption. When villi are damaged, nutrients cannot properly enter the bloodstream.

57. One of the key features of villi and microvilli in the digestive system is their finger-like projection shape. Which of the following is an example of how the shape of microvilli can enhance nutrient absorption?

a. Nutrients can enter the bloodstream through the blood vessels that are located in middle of the microvilli.
b. Larger microvilli have more surface area over which more nutrients are absorbed.
c. The microvilli projections aid in mechanical digestion of food particles.
d. The finger-like projections prevent large particles of food from passing through the digestive system.

58. Microvilli greatly increase the efficiency of nutrient uptake in the small intestines. How do the size and shape of microvilli promote this efficiency?

a. They have a greater surface area-to-volume ratio than larger cells. The finger-like projection shape provides more surface area over the small intestines from which they absorb nutrients and contains blood vessels so nutrients passing through them can enter the bloodstream readily.
b. They have a greater surface area-to-volume ratio than larger cells. The finger-like projection shape is present in the middle of microvilli, which have more surface area over the small intestines from which they absorb nutrients and also contains blood vessels so nutrients can enter the blood easily.
c. They have a greater surface area-to-volume ratio than larger cells. The finger-like projections prevent large particles of food from passing through the digestive system and also contain blood vessels so nutrients passed through them can readily enter the bloodstream.
d. They have a greater surface area-to-volume ratio than larger cells. The finger-like projections aid in mechanical digestion of food particles and contain blood vessels so nutrients passing through them can enter the bloodstream readily.

59. Birds have several unique physical differences from other vertebrates, and several pertain to how birds process food. Some differences are obvious, such as the presence of a beak and no teeth, whereas other differences can be observed in their internal features. For example, birds have a monogastric digestive system like most other vertebrates, but their digestive system structure differs from that of most other monogastric vertebrates. Which of the following is true about how birds process food?

a. Beak emergence coincided with insect inclusion in the bird diet.

b. The gizzard is the primary site of mechanical digestion.

c. Birds excrete nitrogenous waste and feces through separate openings.

d. Birds digest plant material more slowly than ruminants.

60. As shown in this figure, the oral cavity has several components that contribute to ingestion and the initial stages of digestion. How do the components of the oral cavity work together to complete the first step of food processing?

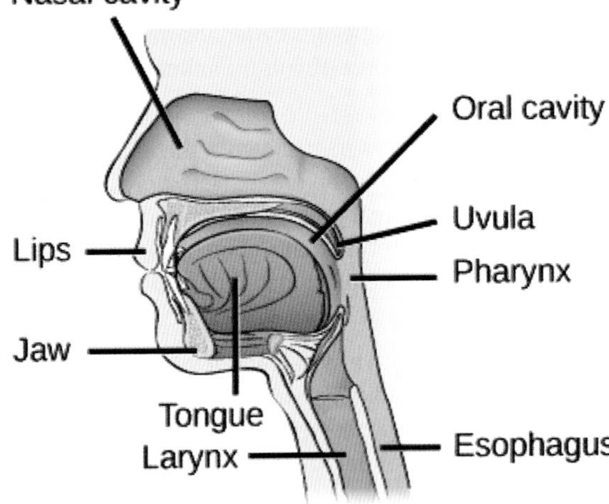

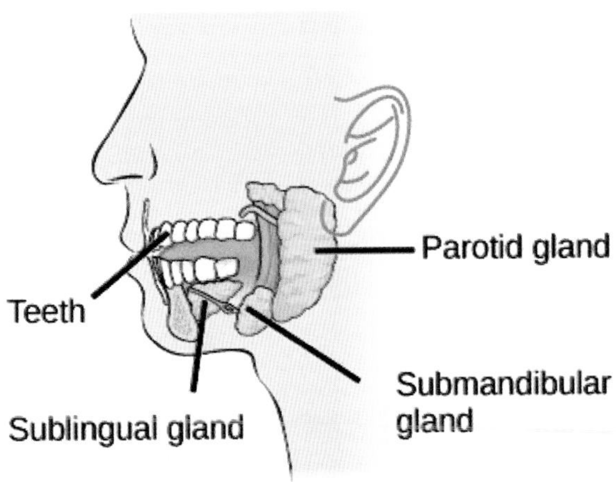

a. The teeth and jaw mechanically chew the food, and saliva from the salivary glands moistens the food and begins chemical digestion. The tongue then physically moves the food to the pharynx, where peristalsis moves the food into the stomach.

b. The teeth and jaw mechanically chew the food, and saliva from the salivary glands moistens the food and initiates mechanical and chemical digestion. The tongue then physically moves the food to the pharynx, where peristalsis moves the food into the stomach.

c. The teeth and jaw mechanically chew the food, and saliva from the salivary glands moistens the food and begins chemical digestion. The tongue then physically moves the food to the larynx, where peristalsis moves the food into the stomach.

d. The teeth and jaw mechanically chew the food, and saliva from the salivary glands moistens the food and initiates mechanical and chemical digestion. The tongue then physically moves the food to the pharynx, where segmentation moves the food into the stomach.

61. Most mammals have a monogastric digestive system, which means they have one stomach chamber. Ruminants and pseudo-ruminants consume a large amount of plant material and have polygastric digestive systems, which means they have more than one stomach chamber. Why is an increased number of stomach chambers beneficial for ruminants and pseudo-ruminants?

a. Microbes in the chambers break down and ferment plant material.

b. Extended exposure to stomach acid breaks down more cellulose.

c. Increased amounts of peristalsis crush more of the plant fibers.

d. Having more stomach chambers increases exposure for nutrients to be absorbed.

62. This figure shows the majority of the digestive tracts of two organisms that consume different food sources. a. Which digestive tract belongs to the herbivore? b. How did you determine this?

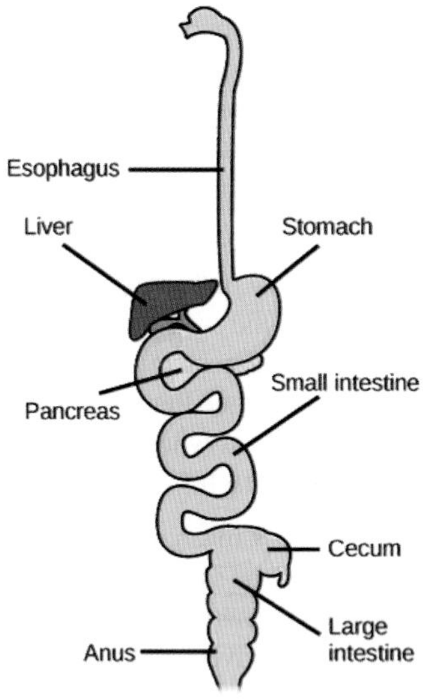

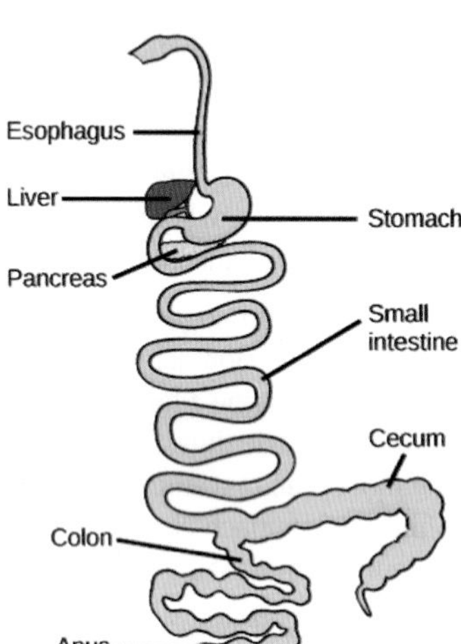

a. a. The digestive tract shown at the bottom belongs to the herbivore. b. Herbivores have a shorter intestinal tract, which allows stronger smooth muscle contractions called peristalsis in a shorter area, providing more opportunity for nutrients to be obtained and absorbed.

b. a. The digestive tract shown at the top belongs to the herbivore. b. Herbivores have a longer intestinal tract, which provides more opportunity for nutrients to be obtained and absorbed, since plant material is difficult for animals to break down.

c. a. The digestive tract shown at the bottom belongs to the herbivore. b. Herbivores have a longer intestinal tract, which provides more opportunity for the nutrients to react with the intestinal enzymes for better absorption, since plant material is difficult for animals to break down.

d. a. The digestive tract shown at the bottom belongs to the herbivore. b. Herbivores have a shorter intestinal tract, which provides more opportunity for nutrients to be obtained and absorbed, since plant material is difficult for animals to break down.

63. The ruminant digestive system has evolved several differences from the traditional mammalian monogastric digestive system because they consume large amounts of plant material. Which of the following is NOT a component of the ruminant digestive system that has evolved to more efficiently digest plant fibers?

a. omasum

b. abomasum

c. reticulum

d. gizzard

64.

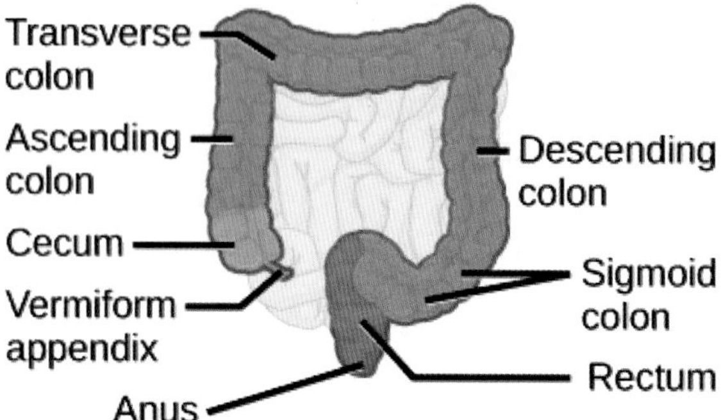

This figure shows the three main components of the large intestine. How do these three parts contribute to processing as food material passes through the large intestine?

a. The cecum receives semi-solid waste from the small intestine and absorbs water, vitamins, and minerals. Then the colon further digests some material. The rectum stores the fecal matter until it is excreted.

b. The cecum receives semi-solid waste from the small intestine. Then the colon digests some materials. The rectum absorbs water and some vitamins and minerals and then stores the fecal matter until it is excreted.

c. The cecum receives semi-solid waste from small intestine. Then, the colon absorbs water and some vitamins and minerals, and further digests some material. The rectum stores the fecal matter until it is excreted.

d. The cecum receives semi-solid waste from the small intestine. The colon is the only region where absorption of vitamins takes place in the digestive system. The rectum stores the fecal matter until it is excreted.

65. This figure shows involuntary muscle movement in part of the digestive system. What stimulates this involuntary response?

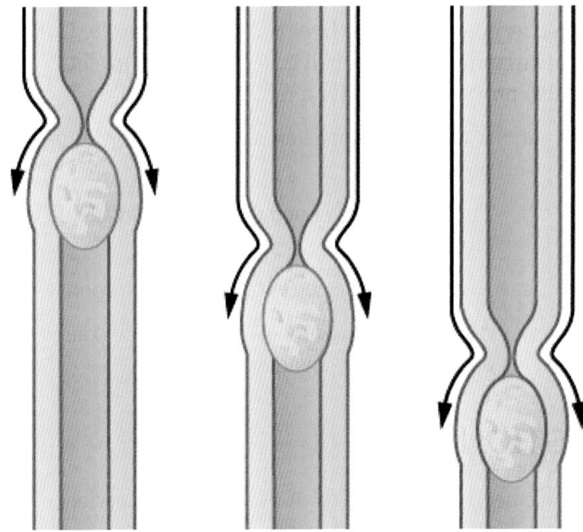

a. smelling food

b. seeing food

c. chewing food

d. swallowing food

66. This image shows the digestive system of a ruminant animal. How does this polygastric digestive system enhance digestion efficiency in ruminants?

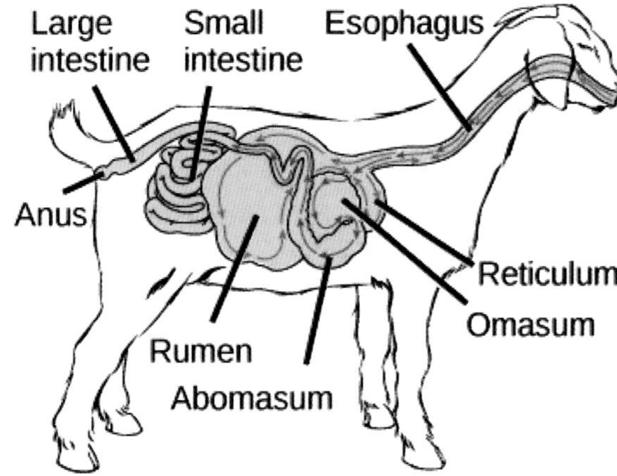

a. Multiple stomach chambers in ruminant animals contain microbes that have cellulase, which breaks down plant material. Plant material is difficult to digest because animals lack cellulase to break down cellulose.

b. Multiple stomach chambers in ruminant animals allow stronger smooth muscle contractions, which break down plant material. Plant material is difficult to digest because animals lack cellulase to break down cellulose.

c. Multiple stomach chambers present in ruminant animals contain cellulase, which break down plant material. Plant material is difficult to digest because animals lack cellulase to break down cellulose.

d. Multiple stomach chambers in ruminant animals allow the food to stay in the stomach for a longer time so that peristaltic movements and the action of enzymes on food particles occurs for a longer time.

67.

An experiment to measure the rate of respiration in mice at 10°C and 25°C was performed using a respirometer, an apparatus that measures changes in gas volume. Respiration was measured in mL of O_2 consumed per gram of organism over several five-minute trials, and the following data were obtained.

Organism	Temperature (°C)	Average respiration (mL 0_2/g/min)
Mouse	10	0.0518
Mouse	25	0.0321

According to these data, mice at 10°C demonstrated

greater oxygen consumption per gram of tissue than mice at 25°C. Which of the following statements best explains the observation?

a. The mice at 10°C had a higher rate of ATP production than the mice at 25°C.
b. The mice at 10°C had a lower metabolic rate than the mice at 25°C.
c. The mice at 25°C weighed less than the mice at 10°C.
d. The mice at 25°C were more active than the mice at 10°C.

68. ATP is essential for organisms because it provides energy to cells. How does ATP provide this energy on a physiological level?

a. When energy is needed, ATP is converted to ADP and a phosphate group. Energy is released from the breaking of the phosphodiester bonds.
b. When energy is needed, ATP is converted to ADP and a phosphate group. Energy is released from the breaking of the glycosidic bonds.
c. When energy is needed, ATP is formed from ADP and a phosphate group. Energy is released from the breaking of the phosphodiester bonds.
d. When energy is needed, ATP is formed from ADP and a phosphate group. Energy is released from the breaking of the phosphoanhydride bonds.

69. An omnivore comes across potatoes, avocados, kale, and eggs and craves only the eggs. In what nutrient is the animal likely deficient?

a. carbohydrates
b. protein
c. fiber
d. fatty acids

70. Carbohydrates often get a bad reputation for their role in promoting weight gain when consumed in excess. However, carbohydrates are necessary for biological functions. Why is it important to consume carbohydrates?

a. Carbohydrates are broken down into glucose, which provides energy as ATP through metabolic pathways. ATP helps to maintain connective tissue.
b. Carbohydrates are broken down into glucose, which is essential for blood clotting.
c. Carbohydrates, along with proteins, help maintain connective tissue and are essential to blood clotting.
d. Carbohydrates are broken down into glucose, which provides energy as ATP through metabolic pathways. ATP is required for proper cellular function.

71. Excess ATP is combined with excess glucose and stored as glycogen in the liver and skeletal muscle. Under what circumstance would glycogen storage in skeletal muscle prove beneficial for a rabbit?

a. A rabbit has not eaten recently and its blood sugar drops.
b. There is an overabundance of food available to a rabbit.
c. A rabbit spots a coyote and flees in response.
d. A young rabbit with an adequate food source is developing into an adult rabbit.

SCIENCE PRACTICE CHALLENGE QUESTIONS

72. *E. coli* colonize the human gastrointestinal tract. The temperature of that environment is tightly regulated. However, the pH ranges from the highly acidic stomach (pH 4.5) to the relatively basic lower intestine (pH 9). Over the entire pH range of the environment the pH of the *E. coli* cytoplasm is maintained in a narrow range between 7.2 and 7.8. Wilks and Slonczewski (*Journal of Bacteriology*, 189, 2007) used a fluorescent dye to follow the recovery of cytoplasmic pH after an acid shock comparable to what occurs in the human stomach. They found that the pH within the cell recovered in approximately 2 minutes.

Rapid restoration of cytoplasmic pH does not occur in the presence of ATPase inhibitors. **Construct an explanation** for the mechanisms that maintain homeostasis with a model of exchange of hydrogen ions (H+) between the cell and its extracellular environment.

73. We need an explanation of the common experience that an "upset stomach" (functional dyspepsia) or constipation can result from stress. Irritable bowel syndrome is a chronic gastrointestinal disease and is treated with the neurotransmitter serotonin. Serotonin receptors are located on the cell membranes of neurons and activate second messenger cascades that regulate gene expression. In humans most serotonin is synthesized in neurons that enervate smooth muscle cells lining the gastrointestinal tract. There is an association of serotonin with a sense of well-being.

A. Based on these data, **justify the claim** that timing of the passage of food in the gastrointestinal tract is regulated by serotonin.

The effect of serotonin on smooth muscle is a clue but it doesn't provide a mechanism connecting stress to the symptoms of functional dyspepsia. Serotonin is synthesized by all Bilateria (animals with bilateral symmetry, including humans) and is released as a response to stress (Puglisi-Allegra and Andolini, *Behavioral Brain Research*, 277, 2015). Serotonin is also synthesized by plants to regulate root growth.

B. **Describe** the role for serotonin that is indicated across domains.

C. **Evaluate** the effect that stress produces in serotonin production, the association of stress with functional dyspepsia, and the role of serotonin in the regulation of expression in smooth muscle cells in terms of evidence of a negative feedback produced by serotonin as a medication.

D. **Justify** your evaluation of the stress and the role of serotonin as a response to the stress in the form of a feedback loop diagrammatically.

Quorum sensing coordinates bacterial expression, stimulating virulence factors, and behavior, inducing the formation of biofilms. Knecht *et al.* (*EBioMedicine*, 9, 2016) have demonstrated that serotonin functions as a quorum sensing messenger among bacteria in the gastrointestinal tract of mice.

E. **Construct an explanation** of the effect of serotonin as a treatment of functional dyspepsia.

26 | THE NERVOUS SYSTEM

Figure 26.1 An athlete's nervous system is hard at work during the planning and execution of a movement as precise as a high jump. Parts of the nervous system are involved in determining how hard to push off and when to turn, as well as controlling the muscles throughout the body that make this complicated movement possible without knocking the bar down—all in just a few seconds. (credit: modification of work by Shane T. McCoy, U.S. Navy)

Chapter Outline

Introduction

While you're reading this book, your nervous system is performing several functions simultaneously. The visual system is processing what is seen on the page, the motor system controls the turn of the pages (or click of the mouse), and the prefrontal cortex maintains attention. Even fundamental functions, like breathing and regulation of body temperature, are controlled by the nervous system. A nervous system is an organism's control center: it processes sensory information from outside (and inside) the body and controls all behaviors—from eating to sleeping to finding a mate.

Scientists have even discovered that certain individual neurons (a type of nerve cell) can multitask. Neuroscientists often use the model organism *C. elegans* (a worm) to study neurons. While studying these worms, it was recently discovered that one type of neuron called AIY regulates both speed and direction of movement. Even though humans have billions of neurons compared to the 302 in *C. elegans*, it is thought that many perform multiple functions.[1] You can read more about this research at the Science Daily website (http://openstaxcollege.org/l/32neurons) .

1. University of Michigan. First peek at how neurons multitask. *Science Daily*, 6 November 2014. www.sciencedaily.com/releases/2014/11/141106131520.htm.

26.1 | Neurons and Glial Cells

In this section, you will explore the following questions:

- What are the functions of the structural components of a neuron?
- What are the four main types of neurons?
- What are the functions of different types of glial cells?

Connection for AP® Courses

Much information about the various organ systems of animals is not within the scope of AP®. The nervous system, however, was selected for in-depth study because an animal's ability to detect, transmit, and respond to information is critical for survival. The nervous system interacts with all other organ systems to coordinate responses. The information in this chapter allows us to apply concepts we explored previously, including structure and function relationships, homeostasis, the movement of substances across cell membranes, cell signaling and communication, and the use of ATP.

Nervous systems in animals range from relatively simple nerve nets in jellyfish to a complex brain, spinal cord, and peripheral nervous in humans. (For the purpose of AP®, you do not need to have detailed information about myriad types of nervous systems in other animals. Instead, just focus on the complex nervous system of humans.) The basic structure of the nervous system that reflects function is the neuron, of which there are three types: sensory, motor, and interneuron. A typical neuron consists of **dendrites**, a cell body, and an **axon** to detect, generate, transmit, and integrate signal information. Many neurons are surrounded by **Schwann cells** (a type of glial cell) that form a **myelin** sheath, which acts as an electrical insulator, like the plastic wrap that surrounds the copper wires in a household appliance cord. The Schwann cells are separated by gaps of unmyelinated fibers called **nodes of Ranvier** over which the nerve impulse travels as the signal passes along the neuron, increasing the speed of transmission. (As we will learn in the Nervous System Disorders section, some diseases of the nervous system result from the loss of myelin.) Glial cells—often thought of as the "supporting cast" of the nervous system—outnumber neurons and play a role in the development of neurons, buffer harmful ions and chemicals, and provide myelin sheaths around neurons. Most brain tumors are caused by mutations in glial cells.

Information presented and the examples highlighted in the section support concepts outlined in Big Idea 3 of the AP® Biology Curriculum Framework. The AP® Learning Objectives listed in the Curriculum Framework provide a transparent foundation for the AP® Biology course, an inquiry-based laboratory experience, instructional activities, and AP® exam questions. A learning objective merges required content with one or more of the seven science practices.

Big Idea 3	Living systems store, retrieve, transmit and respond to information essential to life processes.
Enduring Understanding 3.E	Transmission of information results in changes within and between biological systems.
Essential Knowledge	**3.E.2** Animals have nervous systems that detect external and internal signals, transmit and integrate information, and produce responses.
Science Practice	**1.2** The student can describe representations and models of natural or man-made phenomena and systems in the domain.
Learning Objective	**3.44** The student is able to describe how nervous systems detect external and internal signals.
Essential Knowledge	**3.E.2** Animals have nervous systems that detect external and internal signals, transmit and integrate information, and produce responses.
Science Practice	**1.1** The student can create representations and models of natural or man-made phenomena and systems in the domain.
Learning Objective	**3.48** The student is able to create a visual representation to describe how nervous systems detect external and internal signals.

Nervous systems throughout the animal kingdom vary in structure and complexity, as illustrated by the variety of animals shown in Figure 26.2. Some organisms, like sea sponges, lack a true nervous system. Others, like jellyfish, lack a true brain and instead have a system of separate but connected nerve cells (neurons) called a "nerve net." Echinoderms such as sea stars have nerve cells that are bundled into fibers called nerves. Flatworms of the phylum Platyhelminthes have both a central nervous system (CNS), made up of a small "brain" and two nerve cords, and a peripheral nervous system (PNS) containing a system of nerves that extend throughout the body. The insect nervous system is more complex but also fairly decentralized. It contains a brain, ventral nerve cord, and ganglia (clusters of connected neurons). These ganglia can control movements and behaviors without input from the brain. Octopi may have the most complicated of invertebrate nervous systems—they have neurons that are organized in specialized lobes and eyes that are structurally similar to vertebrate species.

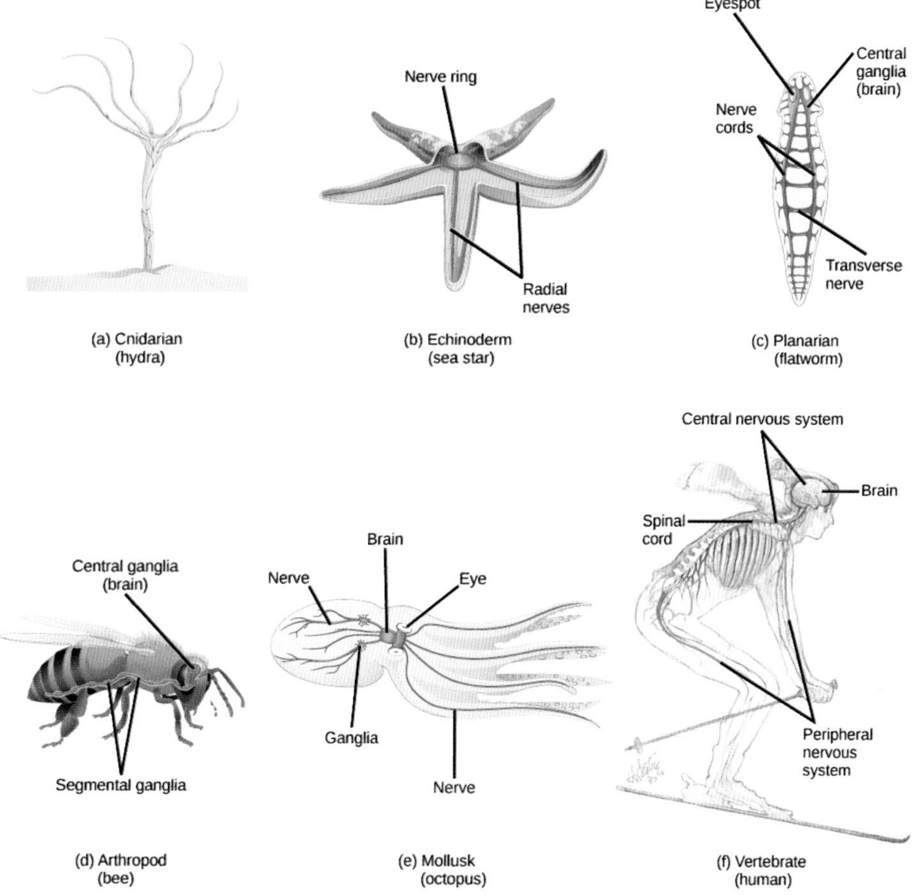

Figure 26.2 Nervous systems vary in structure and complexity. In (a) cnidarians, nerve cells form a decentralized nerve net. In (b) echinoderms, nerve cells are bundled into fibers called nerves. In animals exhibiting bilateral symmetry such as (c) planarians, neurons cluster into an anterior brain that processes information. In addition to a brain, (d) arthropods have clusters of nerve cell bodies, called peripheral ganglia, located along the ventral nerve cord. Mollusks such as squid and (e) octopi, which must hunt to survive, have complex brains containing millions of neurons. In (f) vertebrates, the brain and spinal cord comprise the central nervous system, while neurons extending into the rest of the body comprise the peripheral nervous system. (credit e: modification of work by Michael Vecchione, Clyde F.E. Roper, and Michael J. Sweeney, NOAA; credit f: modification of work by NIH)

Compared to invertebrates, vertebrate nervous systems are more complex, centralized, and specialized. While there is great diversity among different vertebrate nervous systems, they all share a basic structure: a CNS that contains a brain and spinal cord and a PNS made up of peripheral sensory and motor nerves. One interesting difference between the nervous systems of invertebrates and vertebrates is that the nerve cords of many invertebrates are located ventrally whereas the vertebrate spinal cords are located dorsally. There is debate among evolutionary biologists as to whether these different nervous system plans evolved separately or whether the invertebrate body plan arrangement somehow "flipped" during the evolution of vertebrates.

Watch this video (http://openstaxcollege.org/l/vertebrate_evol) of biologist Mark Kirschner discussing the “flipping” phenomenon of vertebrate evolution.

The nervous system is made up of **neurons**, specialized cells that can receive and transmit chemical or electrical signals, and **glia**, cells that provide support functions for the neurons by playing an information processing role that is complementary to neurons. A neuron can be compared to an electrical wire—it transmits a signal from one place to another. Glia can be compared to the workers at the electric company who make sure wires go to the right places, maintain the wires, and take down wires that are broken. Although glia have been compared to workers, recent evidence suggests that also usurp some of the signaling functions of neurons.

There is great diversity in the types of neurons and glia that are present in different parts of the nervous system. There are four major types of neurons, and they share several important cellular components.

Neurons

The nervous system of the common laboratory fly, *Drosophila melanogaster*, contains around 100,000 neurons, the same number as a lobster. This number compares to 75 million in the mouse and 300 million in the octopus. A human brain contains around 86 billion neurons. Despite these very different numbers, the nervous systems of these animals control many of the same behaviors—from basic reflexes to more complicated behaviors like finding food and courting mates. The ability of neurons to communicate with each other as well as with other types of cells underlies all of these behaviors.

Most neurons share the same cellular components. But neurons are also highly specialized—different types of neurons have different sizes and shapes that relate to their functional roles.

Parts of a Neuron

Like other cells, each neuron has a cell body (or soma) that contains a nucleus, smooth and rough endoplasmic reticulum, Golgi apparatus, mitochondria, and other cellular components. Neurons also contain unique structures, illustrated in Figure 26.3 for receiving and sending the electrical signals that make neuronal communication possible. Dendrites are tree-like structures that extend away from the cell body to receive messages from other neurons at specialized junctions called **synapses**. Although some neurons do not have any dendrites, some types of neurons have multiple dendrites. Dendrites can have small protrusions called dendritic spines, which further increase surface area for possible synaptic connections.

Once a signal is received by the dendrite, it then travels passively to the cell body. The cell body contains a specialized structure, the **axon hillock** that integrates signals from multiple synapses and serves as a junction between the cell body and an axon. An axon is a tube-like structure that propagates the integrated signal to specialized endings called **axon terminals**. These terminals in turn synapse on other neurons, muscle, or target organs. Chemicals released at axon terminals allow signals to be communicated to these other cells. Neurons usually have one or two axons, but some neurons, like amacrine cells in the retina, do not contain any axons. Some axons are covered with myelin, which acts as an insulator to minimize dissipation of the electrical signal as it travels down the axon, greatly increasing the speed on conduction. This insulation is important as the axon from a human motor neuron can be as long as a meter—from the base of the spine to the toes. The myelin sheath is not actually part of the neuron. Myelin is produced by glial cells. Along the axon there are periodic gaps in the myelin sheath. These gaps are called nodes of Ranvier and are sites where the signal is “recharged” as it travels along the axon.

It is important to note that a single neuron does not act alone—neuronal communication depends on the connections that neurons make with one another (as well as with other cells, like muscle cells). Dendrites from a single neuron may receive synaptic contact from many other neurons. For example, dendrites from a Purkinje cell in the cerebellum are thought to receive contact from as many as 200,000 other neurons.

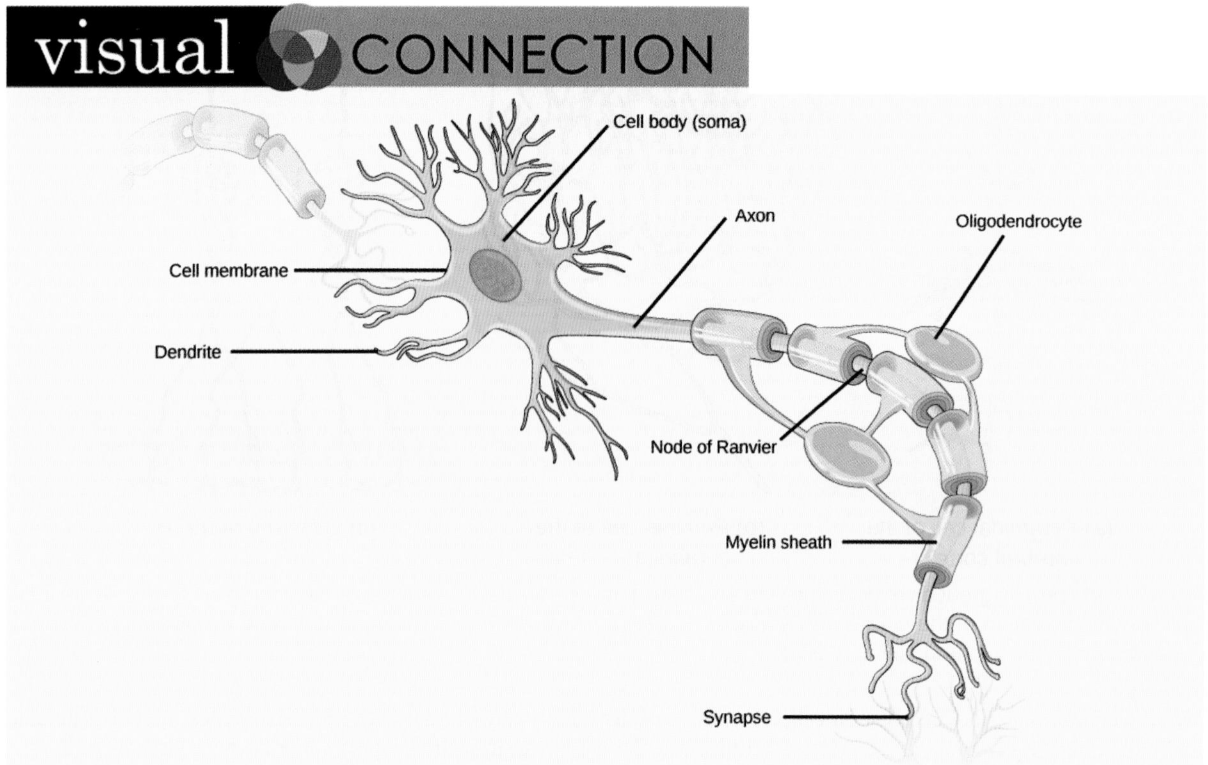

Figure 26.3 Neurons contain organelles common to many other cells, such as a nucleus and mitochondria. They also have more specialized structures, including dendrites and axons.

Types of Neurons

There are different types of neurons, and the functional role of a given neuron is intimately dependent on its structure. There is an amazing diversity of neuron shapes and sizes found in different parts of the nervous system (and across species), as illustrated by the neurons shown in Figure 26.4.

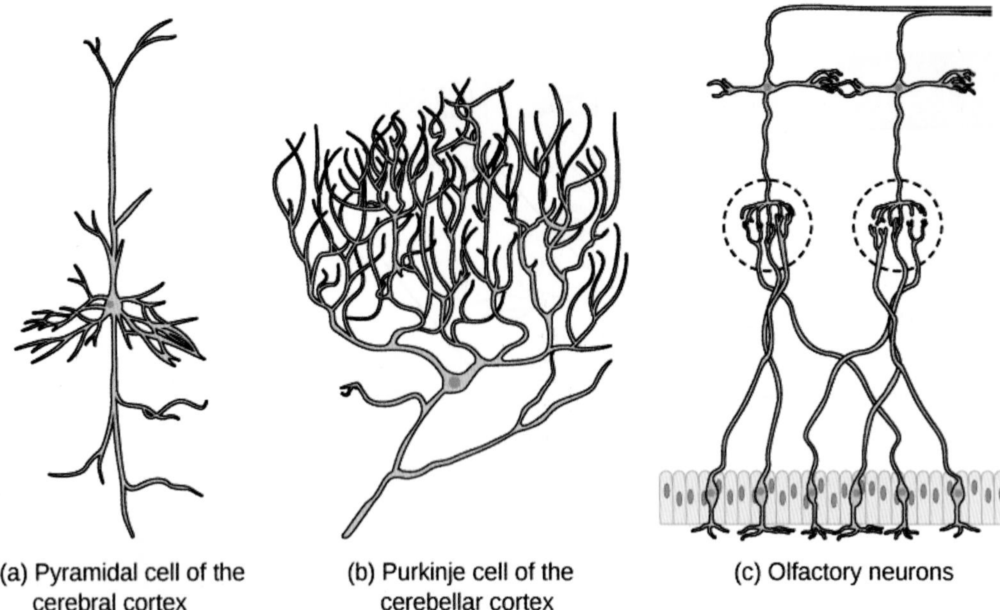

Figure 26.4 There is great diversity in the size and shape of neurons throughout the nervous system. Examples include (a) a pyramidal cell from the cerebral cortex, (b) a Purkinje cell from the cerebellar cortex, and (c) olfactory cells from the olfactory epithelium and olfactory bulb.

While there are many defined neuron cell subtypes, neurons are broadly divided into four basic types: unipolar, bipolar, multipolar, and pseudounipolar. Figure 26.5 illustrates these four basic neuron types. Unipolar neurons have only one structure that extends away from the soma. These neurons are not found in vertebrates but are found in insects where they stimulate muscles or glands. A bipolar neuron has one axon and one dendrite extending from the soma. An example of a bipolar neuron is a retinal bipolar cell, which receives signals from photoreceptor cells that are sensitive to light and transmits these signals to ganglion cells that carry the signal to the brain. Multipolar neurons are the most common type of neuron. Each multipolar neuron contains one axon and multiple dendrites. Multipolar neurons can be found in the central nervous system (brain and spinal cord). An example of a multipolar neuron is a Purkinje cell in the cerebellum, which has many branching dendrites but only one axon. Pseudounipolar cells share characteristics with both unipolar and bipolar cells. A pseudounipolar cell has a single process that extends from the soma, like a unipolar cell, but this process later branches into two distinct structures, like a bipolar cell. Most sensory neurons are pseudounipolar and have an axon that branches into two extensions: one connected to dendrites that receive sensory information and another that transmits this information to the spinal cord.

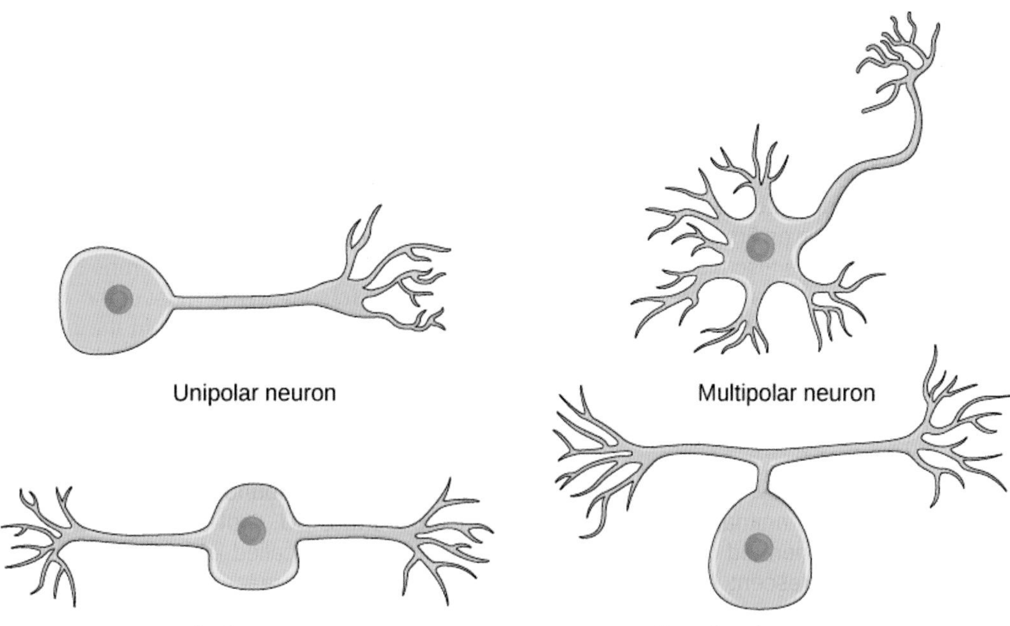

Figure 26.5 Neurons are broadly divided into four main types based on the number and placement of axons: (1) unipolar, (2) bipolar, (3) multipolar, and (4) pseudounipolar.

everyday CONNECTION

Neurogenesis

At one time, scientists believed that people were born with all the neurons they would ever have. Research performed during the last few decades indicates that neurogenesis, the birth of new neurons, continues into adulthood. Neurogenesis was first discovered in songbirds that produce new neurons while learning songs. For mammals, new neurons also play an important role in learning: about 1000 new neurons develop in the hippocampus (a brain structure involved in learning and memory) each day. While most of the new neurons will die, researchers found that an increase in the number of surviving new neurons in the hippocampus correlated with how well rats learned a new task. Interestingly, exercise also promotes neurogenesis in the hippocampus. Stress has the opposite effect. While neurogenesis is quite limited compared to regeneration in other tissues, research in this area may lead to new treatments for disorders such as Alzheimer's, stroke, and epilepsy.

How do scientists identify new neurons? A researcher can inject a compound called bromodeoxyuridine (BrdU) into the brain of an animal. While all cells will be exposed to BrdU, BrdU will only be incorporated into the DNA of newly generated cells that are in S phase. A technique called immunohistochemistry can be used to attach a fluorescent label to the incorporated BrdU, and a researcher can use fluorescent microscopy to visualize the presence of BrdU, and thus new neurons, in brain tissue. Figure 26.6 is a micrograph which shows fluorescently labeled neurons in the hippocampus of a rat.

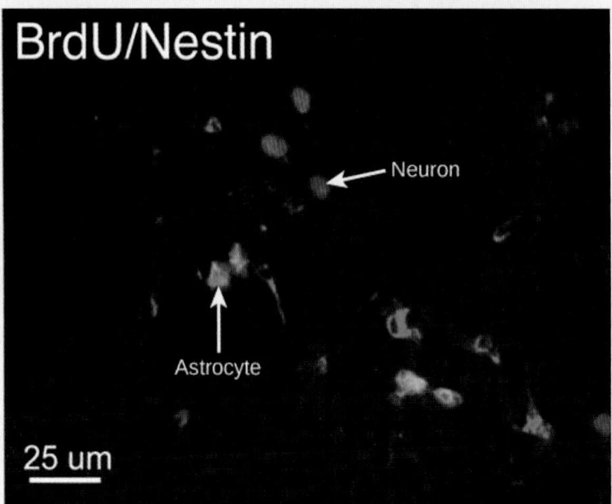

Figure 26.6 This micrograph shows fluorescently labeled new neurons in a rat hippocampus. Cells that are actively dividing have bromodoxyuridine (BrdU) incorporated into their DNA and are labeled in red. Cells that express glial fibrillary acidic protein (GFAP) are labeled in green. Astrocytes, but not neurons, express GFAP. Thus, cells that are labeled both red and green are actively dividing astrocytes, whereas cells labeled red only are actively dividing neurons. (credit: modification of work by Dr. Maryam Faiz, et. al., University of Barcelona; scale-bar data from Matt Russell)

This site (http://openstaxcollege.org/l/neurogenesis) contains more information about neurogenesis, including an interactive laboratory simulation and a video that explains how BrdU labels new cells.

science practices CONNECTION for AP® Courses

Think About It

How does the unique structure of the neuron allow it to detect (and ultimately transmit) incoming signals?

Glia

While glia are often thought of as the supporting cast of the nervous system, the number of glial cells in the brain actually outnumbers the number of neurons by a factor of ten. Neurons would be unable to function without the vital roles that are fulfilled by these glial cells. Glia guide developing neurons to their destinations, buffer ions and chemicals that would otherwise harm neurons, and provide myelin sheaths around axons. Scientists have recently discovered that they also play a role in responding to nerve activity and modulating communication between nerve cells.

Types of Glia

There are several different types of glia with different functions, two of which are shown in Figure 26.7. **Astrocytes**, shown in Figure 26.8**a** make contact with both capillaries and neurons in the CNS. They provide nutrients and other substances to neurons, regulate the concentrations of ions and chemicals in the extracellular fluid, and provide structural support for synapses. Astrocytes also form the blood-brain barrier—a structure that blocks entrance of toxic substances into the brain. Astrocytes, in particular, have been shown through calcium imaging experiments to become active in response to nerve activity, transmit calcium waves between astrocytes, and modulate the activity of surrounding synapses. **Satellite glia** provide nutrients and structural support for neurons in the PNS. **Microglia** scavenge and degrade dead cells and protect the brain from invading microorganisms. **Oligodendrocytes**, shown in Figure 26.8**b** form myelin sheaths around axons in the CNS. One axon can be myelinated by several oligodendrocytes, and one oligodendrocyte can provide myelin for multiple neurons. This is distinctive from the PNS where a single Schwann cell provides myelin for only one axon as the entire Schwann cell surrounds the axon. **Radial glia** serve as scaffolds for developing neurons as they migrate to their end destinations. **Ependymal** cells line fluid-filled ventricles of the brain and the central canal of the spinal cord. They are involved in the production of cerebrospinal fluid, which serves as a cushion for the brain, moves the fluid between the spinal cord and the brain, and is a component for the choroid plexus.

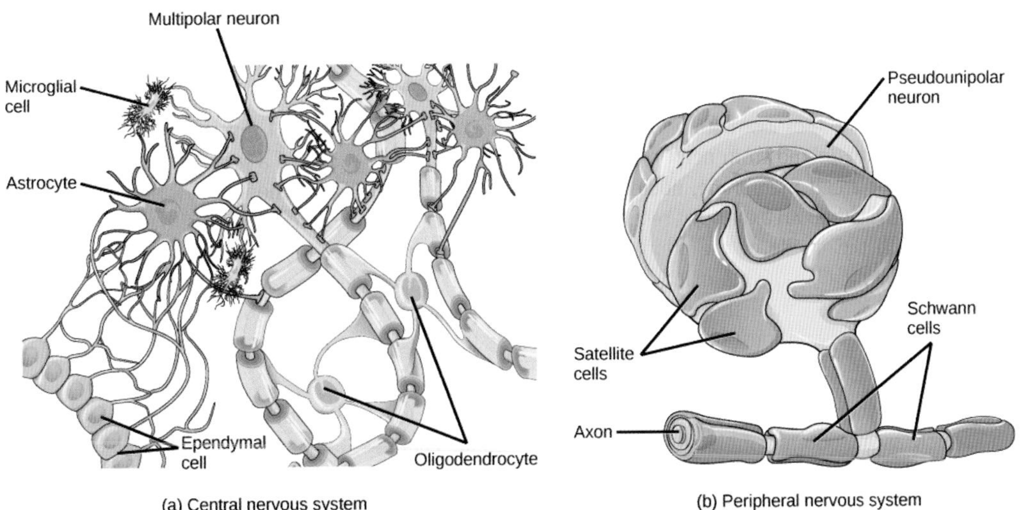

Figure 26.7 Glial cells support neurons and maintain their environment. Glial cells of the (a) central nervous system include oligodendrocytes, astrocytes, ependymal cells, and microglial cells. Oligodendrocytes form the myelin sheath around axons. Astrocytes provide nutrients to neurons, maintain their extracellular environment, and provide structural support. Microglia scavenge pathogens and dead cells. Ependymal cells produce cerebrospinal fluid that cushions the neurons. Glial cells of the (b) peripheral nervous system include Schwann cells, which form the myelin sheath, and satellite cells, which provide nutrients and structural support to neurons.

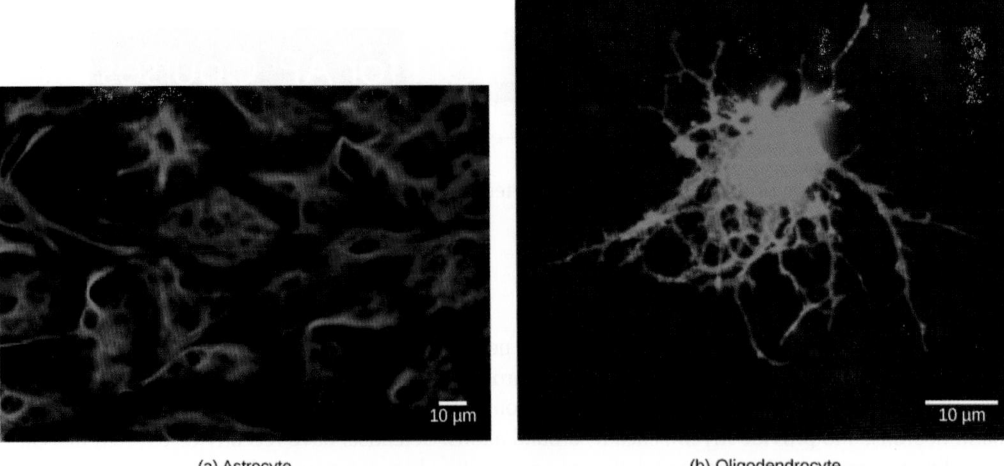

Figure 26.8 (a) Astrocytes and (b) oligodendrocytes are glial cells of the central nervous system. (credit a: modification of work by Uniformed Services University; credit b: modification of work by Jurjen Broeke; scale-bar data from Matt Russell)

26.2 | How Neurons Communicate

In this section, you will explore the following questions:

- What is the basis of the resting membrane potential?
- What are the stages of an action potential, and how are action potentials propagated?
- What are the similarities and differences between chemical and electrical synapses?
- What is long-term potentiation and long-term depression, and how do both relate to transmission of impulses across synapses?

Connection for AP® Courses

The neuron is a great example of a structure-function relationship at the cellular level. Information flow along a neuron is usually from dendrite to axon and from neuron to neuron or from neuron to a cell of a target organ. Like other eukaryotic cells, neurons consist of a cell membrane, nucleus, and organelles, including mitochondria. **Action potentials** propagate impulses along neurons. When an axon is at rest, the membrane is said to be polarized; that is, there is an electrochemical gradient across it, with the inside of the membrane being more negatively charged than the outside. We explored the formation of electrochemical gradients using H^+ when we studied photosynthesis and cellular respiration. The neuron, however, uses Na^+ and K^+ to establish a gradient. It is also important to recall that ions cannot diffuse across the lipid bilayer of the cell membrane and must use transport proteins; in this case, the transport proteins are voltage-gated Na^+ and K^+ channels.

At rest, the Na^+/K^+ pump, powered by ATP, maintains this gradient, known as resting **membrane potential**. In response to a stimulus, such as an odorant molecule, membrane potential changes, and an action potential is generated along the membrane as the voltage-gated Na^+ and K^+ channels open sequentially, causing the membrane to depolarize. In **depolarization**, the inside of the membrane becomes more positive than the outside as Na^+ flows to the inside. Repolarization occurs when K^+ flows across the membrane to the outside. In myelinated neurons, action potentials "jump" between gaps of unmyelinated axons (nodes of Ranvier), a phenomenon called saltatory conduction.

Transmission of a nerve impulse from one neuron to another or to another type of cell such as a muscle cell occurs across a junction called a synapse. **Synaptic vesicles** at the axon terminal of the presynaptic neuron release chemical messengers called neurotransmitters into the junction; neurotransmitters then bind to receptors embedded in the membrane of the postsynaptic neuron. Neurotransmitters may be either excitatory (such as acetylcholine or epinephrine) or inhibitory (such as serotonin or GABA) as they either increase or decrease the change of an action potential in the postsynaptic neuron. Many drugs, including both pharmaceuticals and drugs of abuse, can induce changes in synaptic transmission; for example, tetrahydrocannabinol (more commonly known as THC) in marijuana binds to a naturally occurring neurotransmitter important to short-term memory.

Information presented and the examples highlighted in the section support concepts outlined in Big Idea 3 of the AP® Biology Curriculum Framework. The AP® Learning Objectives listed in the Curriculum Framework provide a transparent foundation for the AP® Biology course, an inquiry-based laboratory experience, instructional activities, and AP® exam questions. A learning objective merges required content with one or more of the seven science practices.

Big Idea 3	Living systems store, retrieve, transmit and respond to information essential to life processes.
Enduring Understanding 3.E	Transmission of information results in changes within and between biological systems.
Essential Knowledge	**3.E.2** Animals have nervous systems that detect external and internal signals, transmit and integrate information, and produce responses.
Science Practice	**6.2** The student can construct explanations of phenomena based on evidence produced through scientific practices.
Learning Objective	**3.43** The student is able to construct an explanation, based on scientific theories and models, about how nervous systems detect external and internal signals, transmit and integrate information, and produce responses.
Essential Knowledge	**3.E.2** Animals have nervous systems that detect external and internal signals, transmit and integrate information, and produce responses.
Science Practice	**1.2** The student can describe representations and models of natural or man-made phenomena and systems in the domain.
Learning Objective	**3.45** The student is able to describe how nervous systems transmit information.
Essential Knowledge	**3.E.2** Animals have nervous systems that detect external and internal signals, transmit and integrate information, and produce responses.
Science Practice	**1.1** The student can create representations and models of natural or man-made phenomena and systems in the domain.
Learning Objective	**3.47** The student is able to create a visual representation of complex nervous systems to describe/explain how these systems detect external and internal signals, transmit and integrate information, and produce responses.

All functions performed by the nervous system—from a simple motor reflex to more advanced functions like making a memory or a decision—require neurons to communicate with one another. While humans use words and body language to communicate, neurons use electrical and chemical signals. Just like a person in a committee, one neuron usually receives and synthesizes messages from multiple other neurons before "making the decision" to send the message on to other neurons.

Nerve Impulse Transmission within a Neuron

For the nervous system to function, neurons must be able to send and receive signals. These signals are possible because each neuron has a charged cellular membrane (a voltage difference between the inside and the outside), and the charge of this membrane can change in response to neurotransmitter molecules released from other neurons and environmental stimuli. To understand how neurons communicate, one must first understand the basis of the baseline or 'resting' membrane charge.

Neuronal Charged Membranes

The lipid bilayer membrane that surrounds a neuron is impermeable to charged molecules or ions. To enter or exit the neuron, ions must pass through special proteins called ion channels that span the membrane. Ion channels have different configurations: open, closed, and inactive, as illustrated in **Figure 26.9**. Some ion channels need to be activated in order to open and allow ions to pass into or out of the cell. These ion channels are sensitive to the environment and can change their shape accordingly. Ion channels that change their structure in response to voltage changes are called voltage-gated ion channels. Voltage-gated ion channels regulate the relative concentrations of different ions inside and outside the cell. The difference in total charge between the inside and outside of the cell is called the **membrane potential**.

Voltage-gated Na^+ Channels

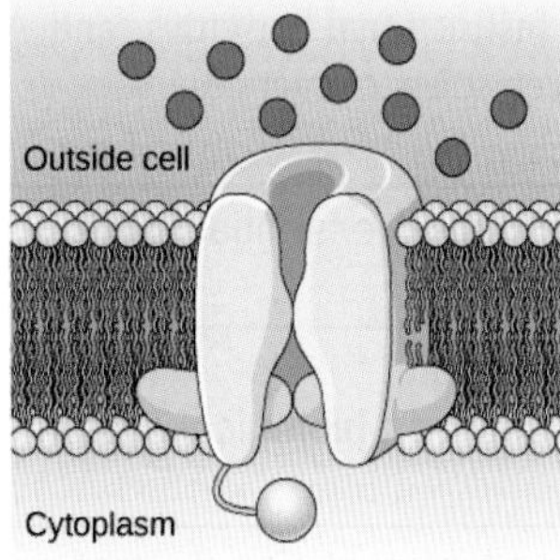

Closed At the resting potential, the channel is closed.

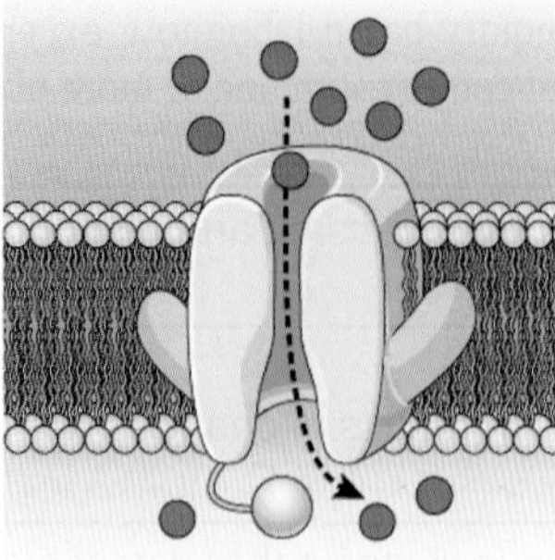

Open In response to a nerve impulse, the gate opens and Na^+ enters the cell.

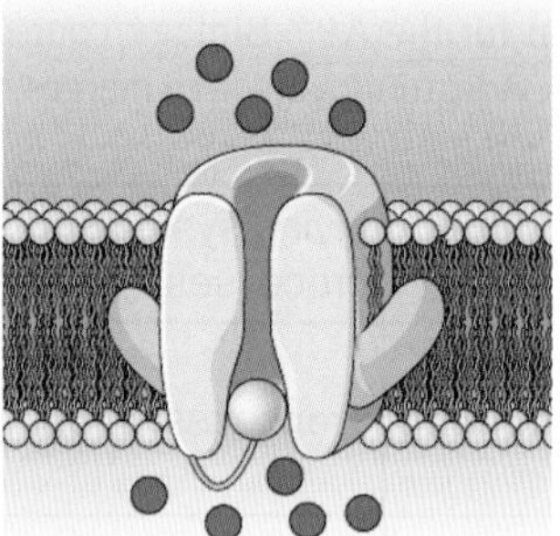

Inactivated For a brief period following activation, the channel does not open in response to a new signal.

Figure 26.9 Voltage-gated ion channels open in response to changes in membrane voltage. After activation, they become inactivated for a brief period and will no longer open in response to a signal.

This video (http://openstaxcollege.org/l/resting_neuron) discusses the basis of the resting membrane potential.

Resting Membrane Potential

A neuron at rest is negatively charged: the inside of a cell is approximately 70 millivolts more negative than the outside (−70 mV, note that this number varies by neuron type and by species). This voltage is called the resting membrane potential; it is caused by differences in the concentrations of ions inside and outside the cell. If the membrane were equally permeable to all ions, each type of ion would flow across the membrane and the system would reach equilibrium. Because ions cannot simply cross the membrane at will, there are different concentrations of several ions inside and outside the cell, as shown in Table 26.1. The difference in the number of positively charged potassium ions (K^+) inside and outside the cell dominates the resting membrane potential (Figure 26.10). When the membrane is at rest, K^+ ions accumulate inside the cell due to a net movement with the concentration gradient. The negative resting membrane potential is created and maintained by increasing the concentration of cations outside the cell (in the extracellular fluid) relative to inside the cell (in the cytoplasm). The negative charge within the cell is created by the cell membrane being more permeable to potassium ion movement than sodium ion movement. In neurons, potassium ions are maintained at high concentrations within the cell while sodium ions are maintained at high concentrations outside of the cell. The cell possesses potassium and sodium leakage channels that allow the two cations to diffuse down their concentration gradient. However, the neurons have far more potassium leakage channels than sodium leakage channels. Therefore, potassium diffuses out of the cell at a much faster rate than sodium leaks in. Because more cations are leaving the cell than are entering, this causes the interior of the cell to be negatively charged relative to the outside of the cell. The actions of the sodium potassium pump help to maintain the resting potential, once established. Recall that sodium potassium pumps brings two K^+ ions into the cell while removing three Na^+ ions per ATP consumed. As more cations are expelled from the cell than taken in, the inside of the cell remains negatively charged relative to the extracellular fluid. It should be noted that chloride ions (Cl^-) tend to accumulate outside of the cell because they are repelled by negatively-charged proteins within the cytoplasm.

Ion Concentration Inside and Outside Neurons

Ion	Extracellular concentration (mM)	Intracellular concentration (mM)	Ratio outside/ inside
Na^+	145	12	12
K+	4	155	0.026
Cl^-	120	4	30
Organic anions (A−)	—	100	

Table 26.1 The resting membrane potential is a result of different concentrations inside and outside the cell.

(a) Resting potential

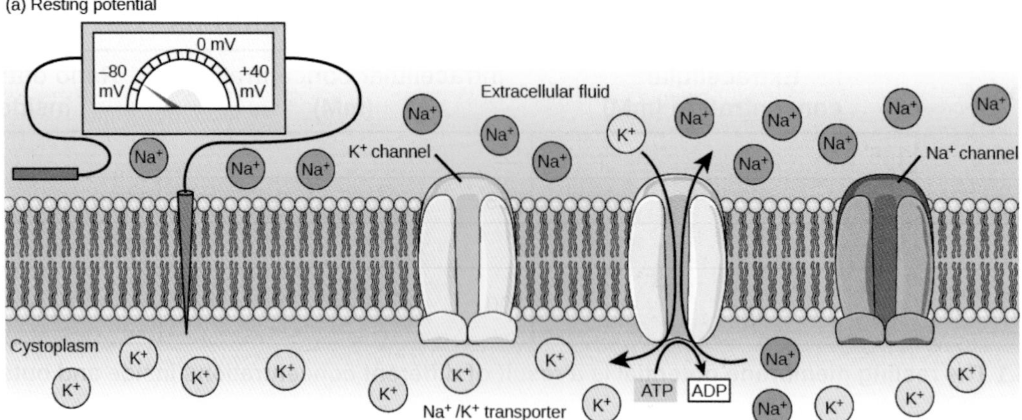

At the resting potential, all voltage-gated Na^+ channels and most voltage-gated K^+ channels are closed. The Na^+/K^+ transporter pumps K^+ ions into the cell and Na^+ ions out.

(b) Depolarization

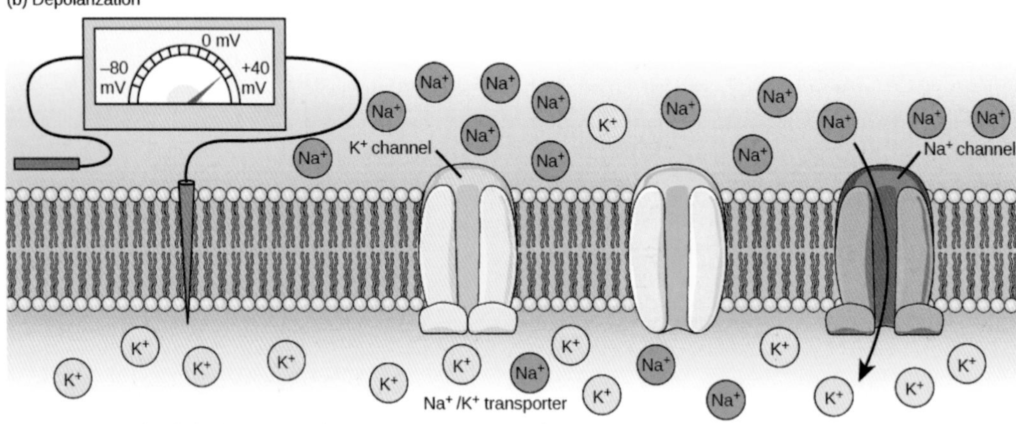

In response to a depolarization, some Na^+ channels open, allowing Na^+ ions to enter the cell. The membrane starts to depolarize (the charge across the membrane lessens). If the threshold of excitation is reached, all the Na^+ channels open.

(c) Hyperpolarization

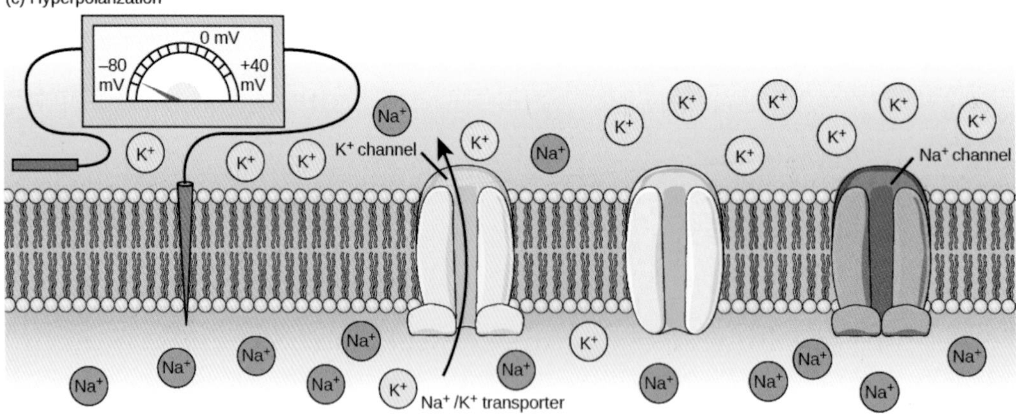

At the peak action potential, Na^+ channels close while K^+ channels open. K^+ leaves the cell, and the membrane eventually becomes hyperpolarized.

Figure 26.10 The (a) resting membrane potential is a result of different concentrations of Na^+ and K^+ ions inside and outside the cell. A nerve impulse causes Na^+ to enter the cell, resulting in (b) depolarization. At the peak action potential, K^+ channels open and the cell becomes (c) hyperpolarized.

Action Potential

A neuron can receive input from other neurons and, if this input is strong enough, send the signal to downstream neurons. Transmission of a signal between neurons is generally carried by a chemical called a neurotransmitter. Transmission of a signal within a neuron (from dendrite to axon terminal) is carried by a brief reversal of the resting membrane potential called an action potential. When neurotransmitter molecules bind to receptors located on a neuron's dendrites, ion channels open. At excitatory synapses, this opening allows positive ions to enter the neuron and results in depolarization of the membrane—a decrease in the difference in voltage between the inside and outside of the neuron. A stimulus from a sensory cell or another neuron depolarizes the target neuron to its threshold potential (-55 mV). Na^+ channels in the axon hillock open, allowing positive ions to enter the cell (Figure 26.10 and Figure 26.11). Once the sodium channels open, the neuron completely depolarizes to a membrane potential of about +40 mV. Action potentials are considered an "all-or nothing" event, in that, once the threshold potential is reached, the neuron always completely depolarizes. Once depolarization is complete, the cell must now "reset" its membrane voltage back to the resting potential. To accomplish this, the Na^+ channels close and cannot be opened. This begins the neuron's **refractory period**, in which it cannot produce another action potential because its sodium channels will not open. At the same time, voltage-gated K^+ channels open, allowing K^+ to leave the cell. As K^+ ions leave the cell, the membrane potential once again becomes negative. The diffusion of K^+ out of the cell actually **hyperpolarizes** the cell, in that the membrane potential becomes more negative than the cell's normal resting potential. At this point, the sodium channels will return to their resting state, meaning they are ready to open again if the membrane potential again exceeds the threshold potential. Eventually the extra K^+ ions diffuse out of the cell through the potassium leakage channels, bringing the cell from its hyperpolarized state, back to its resting membrane potential.

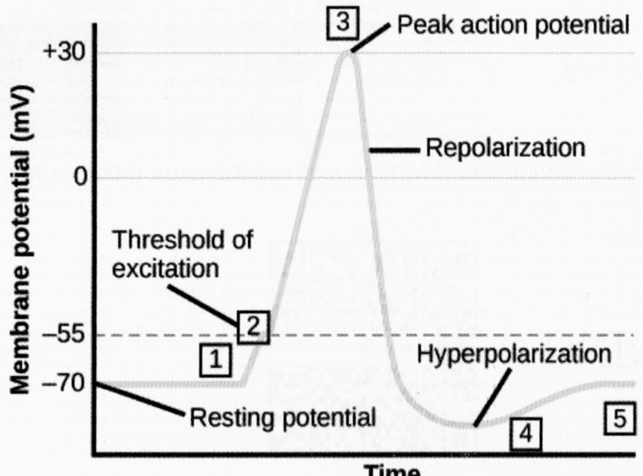

Figure 26.11 The formation of an action potential can be divided into five steps: (1) A stimulus from a sensory cell or another neuron causes the target cell to depolarize toward the threshold potential. (2) If the threshold of excitation is reached, all Na^+ channels open and the membrane depolarizes. (3) At the peak action potential, K^+ channels open and K^+ begins to leave the cell. At the same time, Na^+ channels close. (4) The membrane becomes hyperpolarized as K^+ ions continue to leave the cell. The hyperpolarized membrane is in a refractory period and cannot fire. (5) The K^+ channels close and the Na^+/K^+ transporter restores the resting potential.

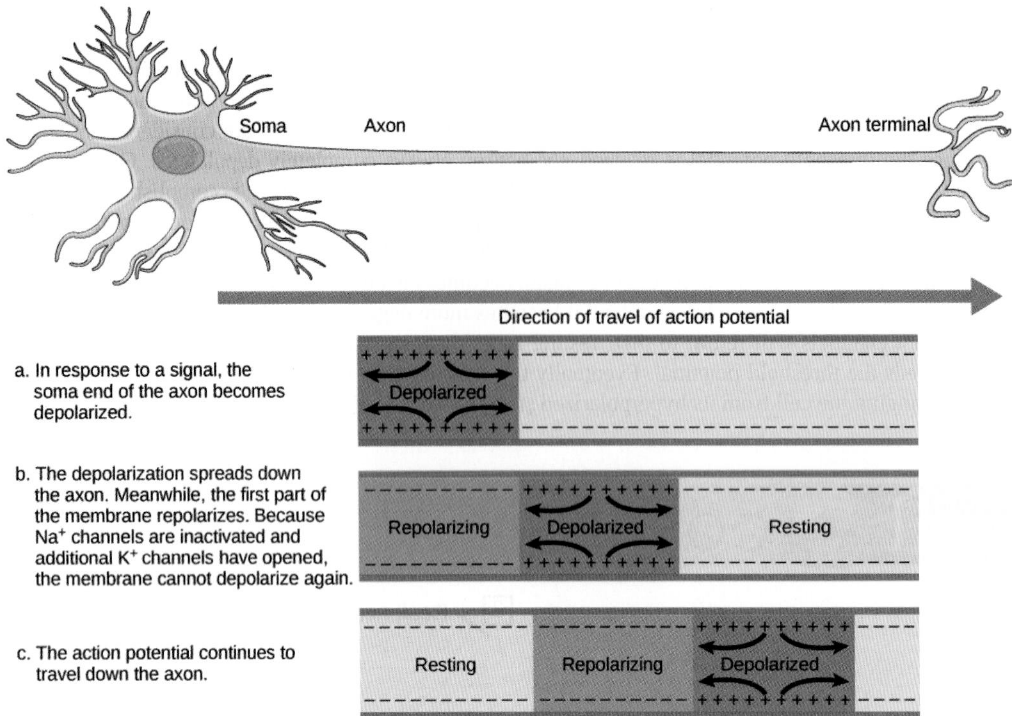

Figure 26.12 The action potential is conducted down the axon as the axon membrane depolarizes, then repolarizes.

This video (http://openstaxcollege.org/l/actionpotential) presents an overview of action potential.

Myelin and the Propagation of the Action Potential

For an action potential to communicate information to another neuron, it must travel along the axon and reach the axon terminals where it can initiate neurotransmitter release. The speed of conduction of an action potential along an axon is influenced by both the diameter of the axon and the axon's resistance to current leak. Myelin acts as an insulator that prevents current from leaving the axon; this increases the speed of action potential conduction. In demyelinating diseases like multiple sclerosis, action potential conduction slows because current leaks from previously insulated axon areas. The nodes of Ranvier, illustrated in Figure 26.13 are gaps in the myelin sheath along the axon. These unmyelinated spaces are about one micrometer long and contain voltage gated Na^+ and K^+ channels. Flow of ions through these channels, particularly the Na^+ channels, regenerates the action potential over and over again along the axon. This 'jumping' of the action potential from one node to the next is called **saltatory conduction**. If nodes of Ranvier were not present along an axon, the action potential would propagate very slowly since Na^+ and K^+ channels would have to continuously regenerate action potentials at every point along the axon instead of at specific points. Nodes of Ranvier also save energy for the neuron since the channels only need to be present at the nodes and not along the entire axon.

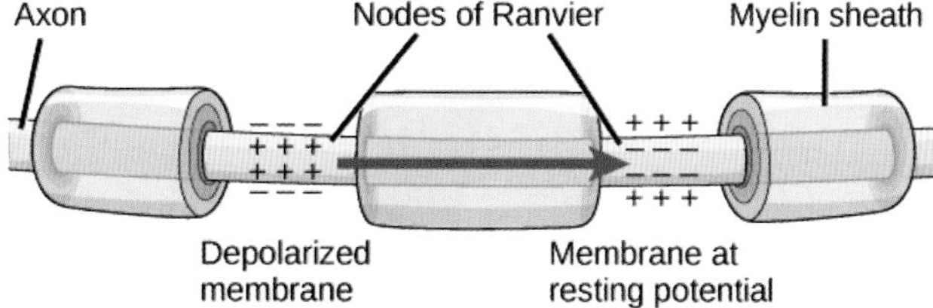

Figure 26.13 Nodes of Ranvier are gaps in myelin coverage along axons. Nodes contain voltage-gated K^+ and Na^+ channels. Action potentials travel down the axon by jumping from one node to the next.

Synaptic Transmission

The synapse or "gap" is the place where information is transmitted from one neuron to another. Synapses usually form between axon terminals and dendritic spines, but this is not universally true. There are also axon-to-axon, dendrite-to-dendrite, and axon-to-cell body synapses. The neuron transmitting the signal is called the presynaptic neuron, and the neuron receiving the signal is called the postsynaptic neuron. Note that these designations are relative to a particular synapse—most neurons are both presynaptic and postsynaptic. There are two types of synapses: chemical and electrical.

Chemical Synapse

When an action potential reaches the axon terminal it depolarizes the membrane and opens voltage-gated Na^+ channels. Na^+ ions enter the cell, further depolarizing the presynaptic membrane. This depolarization causes voltage-gated Ca^{2+} channels to open. Calcium ions entering the cell initiate a signaling cascade that causes small membrane-bound vesicles, called synaptic vesicles, containing neurotransmitter molecules to fuse with the presynaptic membrane. Synaptic vesicles are shown in Figure 26.14, which is an image from a scanning electron microscope.

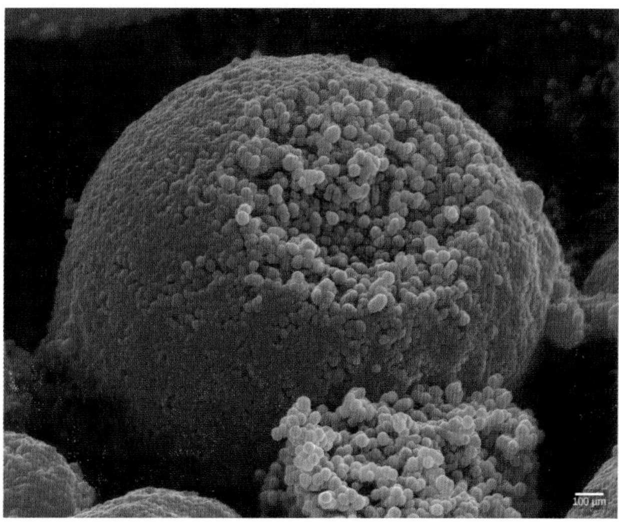

Figure 26.14 This pseudocolored image taken with a scanning electron microscope shows an axon terminal that was broken open to reveal synaptic vesicles (blue and orange) inside the neuron. (credit: modification of work by Tina Carvalho, NIH-NIGMS; scale-bar data from Matt Russell)

Fusion of a vesicle with the presynaptic membrane causes neurotransmitter to be released into the **synaptic cleft**, the extracellular space between the presynaptic and postsynaptic membranes, as illustrated in Figure 26.15. The neurotransmitter diffuses across the synaptic cleft and binds to receptor proteins on the postsynaptic membrane.

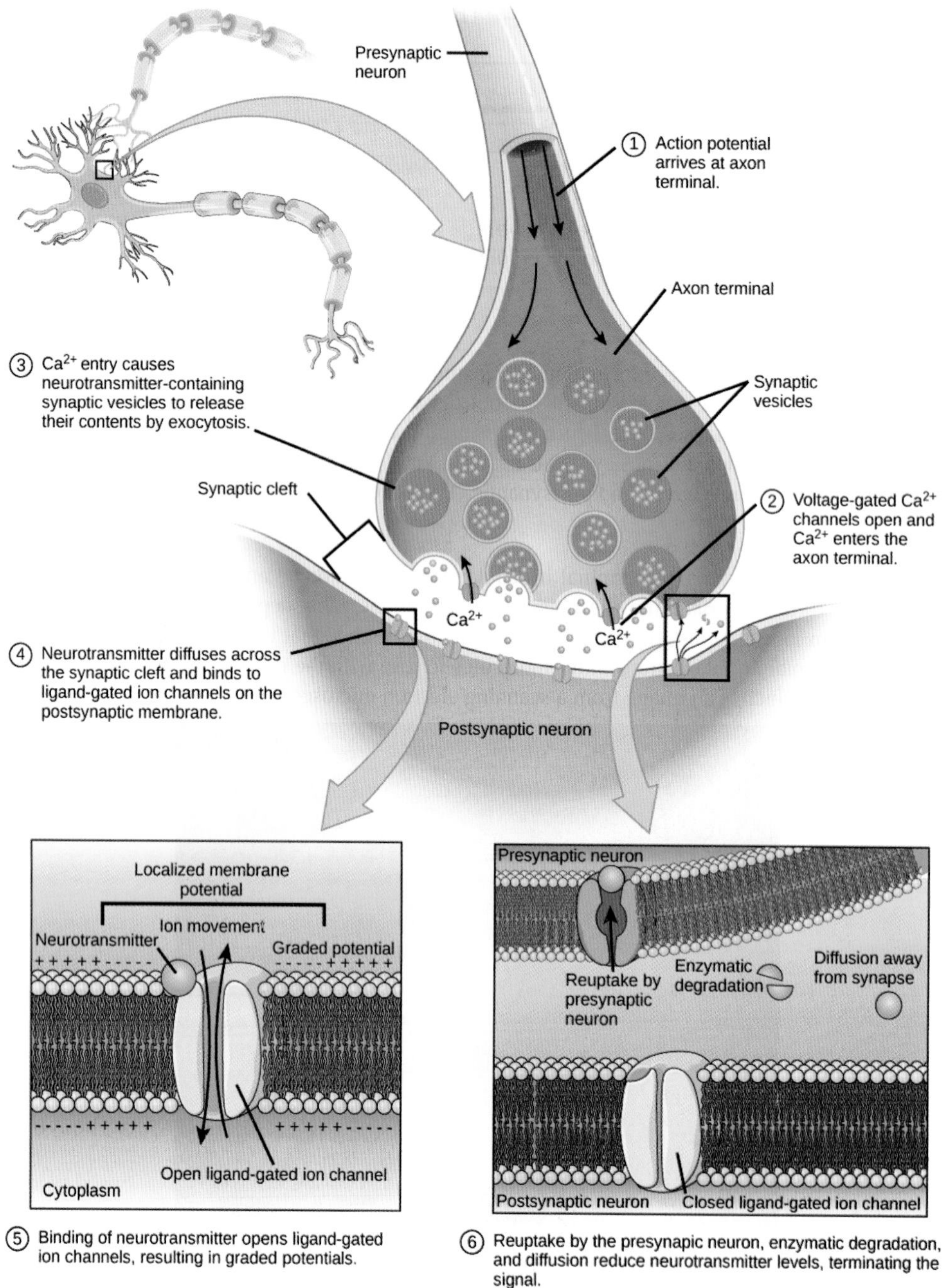

Figure 26.15 Communication at chemical synapses requires release of neurotransmitters. When the presynaptic membrane is depolarized, voltage-gated Ca^{2+} channels open and allow Ca^{2+} to enter the cell. The calcium entry causes synaptic vesicles to fuse with the membrane and release neurotransmitter molecules into the synaptic cleft. The neurotransmitter diffuses across the synaptic cleft and binds to ligand-gated ion channels in the postsynaptic membrane, resulting in a localized depolarization or hyperpolarization of the postsynaptic neuron.

The binding of a specific neurotransmitter causes particular ion channels, in this case ligand-gated channels, on the postsynaptic membrane to open. Neurotransmitters can either have excitatory or inhibitory effects on the postsynaptic membrane, as detailed in Table 26.1. For example, when acetylcholine is released at the synapse between a nerve and muscle (called the neuromuscular junction) by a presynaptic neuron, it causes postsynaptic Na^+ channels to open. Na^+ enters the postsynaptic cell and causes the postsynaptic membrane to depolarize. This depolarization is called an **excitatory postsynaptic potential (EPSP)** and makes the postsynaptic neuron more likely to fire an action potential. Release of neurotransmitter at inhibitory synapses causes **inhibitory postsynaptic potentials (IPSPs)**, a hyperpolarization of the presynaptic membrane. For example, when the neurotransmitter GABA (gamma-aminobutyric acid) is released from a presynaptic neuron, it binds to and opens Cl^- channels. Cl^- ions enter the cell and hyperpolarizes the membrane, making the neuron less likely to fire an action potential.

Once neurotransmission has occurred, the neurotransmitter must be removed from the synaptic cleft so the postsynaptic membrane can "reset" and be ready to receive another signal. This can be accomplished in three ways: the neurotransmitter can diffuse away from the synaptic cleft, it can be degraded by enzymes in the synaptic cleft, or it can be recycled (sometimes called reuptake) by the presynaptic neuron. Several drugs act at this step of neurotransmission. For example, some drugs that are given to Alzheimer's patients work by inhibiting acetylcholinesterase, the enzyme that degrades acetylcholine. This inhibition of the enzyme essentially increases neurotransmission at synapses that release acetylcholine. Once released, the acetylcholine stays in the cleft and can continually bind and unbind to postsynaptic receptors.

Neurotransmitter Examples and Location

Neurotransmitter	Example	Location
Acetylcholine	—	CNS and/or PNS
Biogenic amine	Dopamine, serotonin, norepinephrine	CNS and/or PNS
Amino acid	Glycine, glutamate, aspartate, gamma aminobutyric acid	CNS
Neuropeptide	Substance P, endorphins	CNS and/or PNS

Table 26.2

Electrical Synapse

While electrical synapses are fewer in number than chemical synapses, they are found in all nervous systems and play important and unique roles. The mode of neurotransmission in electrical synapses is quite different from that in chemical synapses. In an electrical synapse, the presynaptic and postsynaptic membranes are very close together and are actually physically connected by channel proteins forming gap junctions. Gap junctions allow current to pass directly from one cell to the next. In addition to the ions that carry this current, other molecules, such as ATP, can diffuse through the large gap junction pores.

There are key differences between chemical and electrical synapses. Because chemical synapses depend on the release of neurotransmitter molecules from synaptic vesicles to pass on their signal, there is an approximately one millisecond delay between when the axon potential reaches the presynaptic terminal and when the neurotransmitter leads to opening of postsynaptic ion channels. Additionally, this signaling is unidirectional. Signaling in electrical synapses, in contrast, is virtually instantaneous (which is important for synapses involved in key reflexes), and some electrical synapses are bidirectional. Electrical synapses are also more reliable as they are less likely to be blocked, and they are important for synchronizing the electrical activity of a group of neurons. For example, electrical synapses in the thalamus are thought to regulate slow-wave sleep, and disruption of these synapses can cause seizures.

Signal Summation

Sometimes a single excitatory postsynaptic potential (EPSP) is strong enough to induce an action potential in the postsynaptic neuron, but often multiple presynaptic inputs must create EPSPs around the same time for the postsynaptic neuron to be sufficiently depolarized to fire an action potential. This process is called **summation** and occurs at the axon hillock, as illustrated in Figure 26.16. Additionally, one neuron often has inputs from many presynaptic neurons—some excitatory and some inhibitory—so IPSPs can cancel out EPSPs and vice versa. It is the net change in postsynaptic membrane voltage that determines whether the postsynaptic cell has reached its threshold of excitation needed to fire an action potential. Together, synaptic summation and the threshold for excitation act as a filter so that random "noise" in the system is not transmitted as important information.

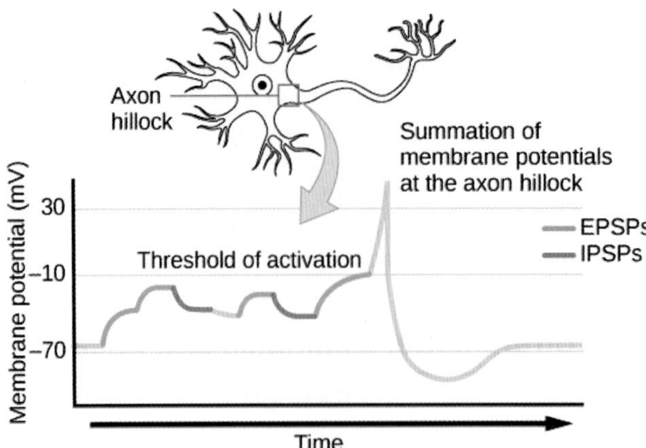

Figure 26.16 A single neuron can receive both excitatory and inhibitory inputs from multiple neurons, resulting in local membrane depolarization (EPSP input) and hyperpolarization (IPSP input). All these inputs are added together at the axon hillock. If the EPSPs are strong enough to overcome the IPSPs and reach the threshold of excitation, the neuron will fire.

everyday CONNECTION

Brain-computer interface

Amyotrophic lateral sclerosis (ALS, also called Lou Gehrig's Disease) is a neurological disease characterized by the degeneration of the motor neurons that control voluntary movements. The disease begins with muscle weakening and lack of coordination and eventually destroys the neurons that control speech, breathing, and swallowing; in the end, the disease can lead to paralysis. At that point, patients require assistance from machines to be able to breathe and to communicate. Several special technologies have been developed to allow "locked-in" patients to communicate with the rest of the world. One technology, for example, allows patients to type out sentences by twitching their cheek. These sentences can then be read aloud by a computer.

A relatively new line of research for helping paralyzed patients, including those with ALS, to communicate and retain a degree of self-sufficiency is called brain-computer interface (BCI) technology and is illustrated in Figure 26.17. This technology sounds like something out of science fiction: it allows paralyzed patients to control a computer using only their thoughts. There are several forms of BCI. Some forms use EEG recordings from electrodes taped onto the skull. These recordings contain information from large populations of neurons that can be decoded by a computer. Other forms of BCI require the implantation of an array of electrodes smaller than a postage stamp in the arm and hand area of the motor cortex. This form of BCI, while more invasive, is very powerful as each electrode can record actual action potentials from one or more neurons. These signals are then sent to a computer, which has been trained to decode the signal and feed it to a tool—such as a cursor on a computer screen. This means that a patient with ALS can use e-mail, read the Internet, and communicate with others by thinking of moving his or her hand or arm (even though the paralyzed patient cannot make that bodily movement). Recent advances have allowed a paralyzed locked-in patient who suffered a stroke 15 years ago to control a robotic arm and even to feed herself coffee using BCI technology.

Despite the amazing advancements in BCI technology, it also has limitations. The technology can require many hours of training and long periods of intense concentration for the patient; it can also require brain surgery to implant the devices.

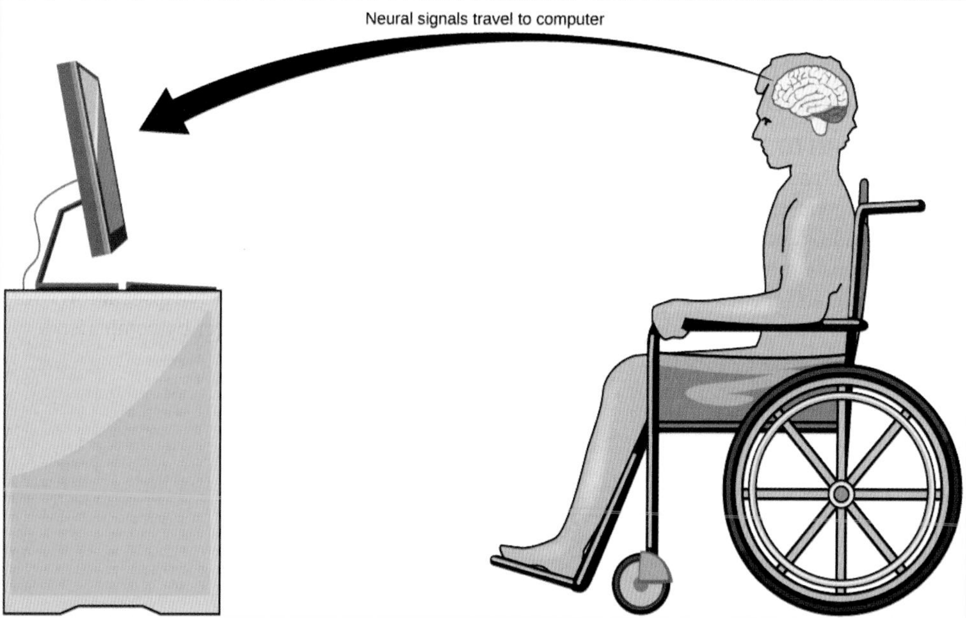

Figure 26.17 With brain-computer interface technology, neural signals from a paralyzed patient are collected, decoded, and then fed to a tool, such as a computer, a wheelchair, or a robotic arm.

Watch this video (http://openstaxcollege.org/l/paralyzation) in which a paralyzed woman use a brain-controlled robotic arm to bring a drink to her mouth, among other images of brain-computer interface technology in action.

Synaptic Plasticity

Synapses are not static structures. They can be weakened or strengthened. They can be broken, and new synapses can be made. Synaptic plasticity allows for these changes, which are all needed for a functioning nervous system. In fact, synaptic plasticity is the basis of learning and memory. Two processes in particular, long-term potentiation (LTP) and long-term depression (LTD) are important forms of synaptic plasticity that occur in synapses in the hippocampus, a brain region that is involved in storing memories.

Long-term Potentiation (LTP)

Long-term potentiation (LTP) is a persistent strengthening of a synaptic connection. LTP is based on the Hebbian principle: cells that fire together wire together. There are various mechanisms, none fully understood, behind the synaptic strengthening seen with LTP. One known mechanism involves a type of postsynaptic glutamate receptor, called NMDA (N-Methyl-D-aspartate) receptors, shown in Figure 26.18. These receptors are normally blocked by magnesium ions; however, when the postsynaptic neuron is depolarized by multiple presynaptic inputs in quick succession (either from one neuron or multiple neurons), the magnesium ions are forced out allowing Ca^{2+} ions to pass into the postsynaptic cell. Next, Ca^{2+} ions entering the cell initiate a signaling cascade that causes a different type of glutamate receptor, called AMPA (α-amino-3-hydroxy-5-methyl-4-isoxazolepropionic acid) receptors, to be inserted into the postsynaptic membrane, since activated AMPA receptors allow positive ions to enter the cell. So, the next time glutamate is released from the presynaptic membrane, it will have a larger excitatory effect (EPSP) on the postsynaptic cell because the binding of glutamate to these AMPA receptors will allow more positive ions into the cell. The insertion of additional AMPA receptors strengthens the synapse and means that the postsynaptic neuron is more likely to fire in response to presynaptic neurotransmitter release.

Long-term Depression (LTD)

Long-term depression (LTD) is essentially the reverse of LTP: it is a long-term weakening of a synaptic connection. One mechanism known to cause LTD also involves AMPA receptors. In this situation, calcium that enters through NMDA receptors initiates a different signaling cascade, which results in the removal of AMPA receptors from the postsynaptic membrane, as illustrated in Figure 26.18. The decrease in AMPA receptors in the membrane makes the postsynaptic neuron less responsive to glutamate released from the presynaptic neuron. While it may seem counterintuitive, LTD may be just as important for learning and memory as LTP. The weakening and pruning of unused synapses allows for unimportant connections to be lost and makes the synapses that have undergone LTP that much stronger by comparison.

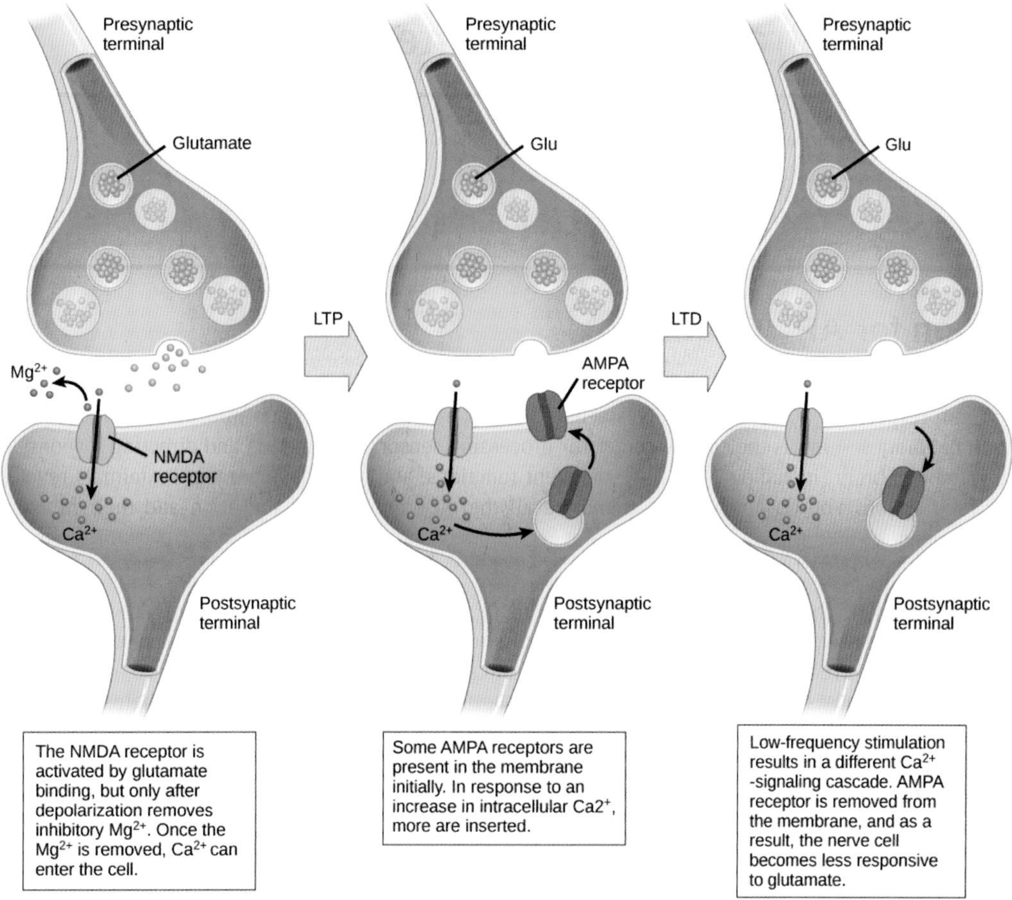
Presynaptic terminal
Glutamate
Mg2+
NMDA receptor
Ca2+
Postsynaptic terminal
LTP
Presynaptic terminal
Glu
AMPA receptor
Ca2+
Postsynaptic terminal
LTD
Presynaptic terminal
Glu
Ca2+
Postsynaptic terminal
The NMDA receptor is activated by glutamate binding, but only after depolarization removes inhibitory Mg2+. Once the Mg2+ is removed, Ca2+ can enter the cell.
Some AMPA receptors are present in the membrane initially. In response to an increase in intracellular Ca2+, more are inserted.
Low-frequency stimulation results in a different Ca2+ -signaling cascade. AMPA receptor is removed from the membrane, and as a result, the nerve cell becomes less responsive to glutamate.

Figure 26.18 Calcium entry through postsynaptic NMDA receptors can initiate two different forms of synaptic plasticity: long-term potentiation (LTP) and long-term depression (LTD). LTP arises when a single synapse is repeatedly stimulated. This stimulation causes a calcium- and CaMKII-dependent cellular cascade, which results in the insertion of more AMPA receptors into the postsynaptic membrane. The next time glutamate is released from the presynaptic cell, it will bind to both NMDA and the newly inserted AMPA receptors, thus depolarizing the membrane more efficiently. LTD occurs when few glutamate molecules bind to NMDA receptors at a synapse (due to a low firing rate of the presynaptic neuron). The calcium that does flow through NMDA receptors initiates a different calcineurin and protein phosphatase 1-dependent cascade, which results in the endocytosis of AMPA receptors. This makes the postsynaptic neuron less responsive to glutamate released from the presynaptic neuron.

science practices CONNECTION for AP® Courses

Activity

Don't Eat the Fugu: Understanding the Neuron. Create a model of a neuron to explain how the vertebrate nervous system detects signals and transmits information. Then use the model to predict how abnormal cell structure, drugs, and toxins (such as tetrodotoxin found in fugu/pufferfish) can affect impulse transmission.

Think About It

Potassium channel blockers, such as procainamide, are often used to treat abnormal activity in the heart. These channel blocks impede the movement of K^+ through voltage-gated K^+ channels. What is the likely effect(s) of these medications on action potentials?

26.3 | The Central Nervous System

In this section, you will explore the following questions:

- What are the major areas of the brain?
- What are the primary functions of the spinal cord, cerebral lobes, cerebellum, and brainstem?

Connection for AP® Courses

The central nervous system (CNS) consists of the brain and **spinal cord**, both of which are protected by the skull and vertebral column, respectively. The CNS receives sensory information, integrates this information, and initiates a motor response, with the brain serving as the control center for processing sensory information and directing responses. Different parts of the vertebrate brain (including ours) have different functions, and brain development in animals reveals a unique evolutionary progression. You do not have to memorize all the different parts of the brain and their functions for AP. However, as a student of biology, you should have a general understanding of the three major parts of the brain and their functions.

In mammals, the parts of the brain include the cerebrum or cortex (which can be broken down into four primary lobes: frontal, temporal, occipital, and parietal), basal ganglia, thalamus, hypothalamus, limbic system, **cerebellum**, and **brainstem**. Information traveling up the spinal cord to the brain is directed to one of the specialized areas of the cerebrum; for example, association areas for hearing are localized in the temporal lobe. The cerebellum helps coordinate skeletal muscle activity, and the medulla oblongata and pons in the brainstem are centers for vital functions, such as breathing and heart rate. Although localization of functions occurs, most complex functions, like language, involve neurons in multiple brain regions. In terms of energy, since the brain consumes about 20 percent of the body's resources (ATP), is it any wonder that you're exhausted after taking an AP® test? Information from the brain travels down the spinal cord, making connections with peripheral nerves; thus, the spinal cord transmits sensory and motor input and controls motor reflexes, like the automatic responses when the pupils of your eye constrict in bright sunlight or when your jerk your hand away from something hot.

Information presented and the examples highlighted in the section support concepts outlined in Big Idea 3 of the AP® Biology Curriculum Framework. The AP® Learning Objectives listed in the Curriculum Framework provide a transparent foundation for the AP® Biology course, an inquiry-based laboratory experience, instructional activities, and AP® exam questions. A learning objective merges required content with one or more of the seven science practices.

Big Idea 3	Living systems store, retrieve, transmit and respond to information essential to life processes.
Enduring Understanding 3.E	Transmission of information results in changes within and between biological systems.
Essential Knowledge	**3.E.2** Animals have nervous systems that detect external and internal signals, transmit and integrate information, and produce responses.
Science Practice	**1.1** The student can create representations and models of natural or man-made phenomena and systems in the domain.
Learning Objective	**3.49** The student is able to create a visual representation to describe how the vertebrate brain integrates information to produce a response.
Essential Knowledge	**3.E.2** Animals have nervous systems that detect external and internal signals, transmit and integrate information, and produce responses.
Science Practice	**1.2** The student can describe representations and models of natural or man-made phenomena and systems in the domain.
Learning Objective	**3.46** The student is able to describe how the vertebrate brain integrates information to produce a response.

Essential Knowledge	**3.E.2** Animals have nervous systems that detect external and internal signals, transmit and integrate information, and produce responses.
Science Practice	**1.1** The student can create representations and models of natural or man-made phenomena and systems in the domain.
Learning Objective	**3.50** The student is able to create a visual representation to describe how the vertebrate brain integrates information to produce a response.

As mentioned above, the central nervous system (CNS) is made up of the brain, a part of which is shown in Figure 26.19 and spinal cord and is covered with three layers of protective coverings called **meninges** (from the Greek word for membrane). The outermost layer is the **dura mater** (Latin for "hard mother"). As the Latin suggests, the primary function for this thick layer is to protect the brain and spinal cord. The dura mater also contains vein-like structures that carry blood from the brain back to the heart. The middle layer is the web-like **arachnoid mater**. The last layer is the **pia mater** (Latin for "soft mother"), which directly contacts and covers the brain and spinal cord like plastic wrap. The space between the arachnoid and pia maters is filled with **cerebrospinal fluid (CSF)**. CSF is produced by a tissue called **choroid plexus** in fluid-filled compartments in the CNS called **ventricles**. The brain floats in CSF, which acts as a cushion and shock absorber and makes the brain neutrally buoyant. CSF also functions to circulate chemical substances throughout the brain and into the spinal cord.

The entire brain contains only about 8.5 tablespoons of CSF, but CSF is constantly produced in the ventricles. This creates a problem when a ventricle is blocked—the CSF builds up and creates swelling and the brain is pushed against the skull. This swelling condition is called hydrocephalus ("water head") and can cause seizures, cognitive problems, and even death if a shunt is not inserted to remove the fluid and pressure.

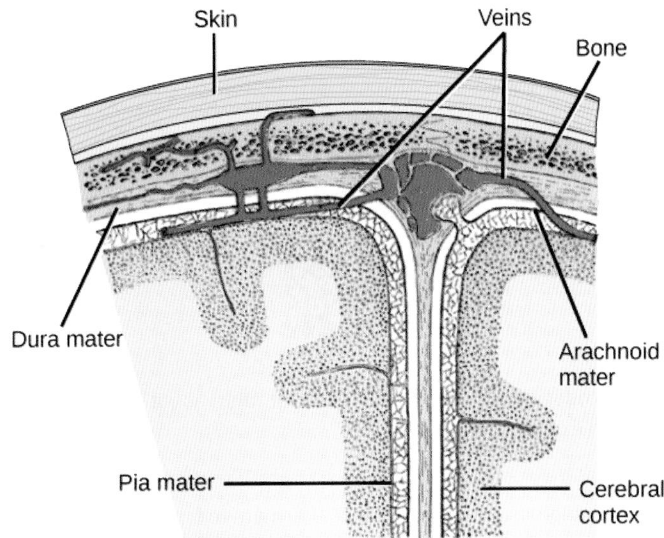

Figure 26.19 The cerebral cortex is covered by three layers of meninges: the dura, arachnoid, and pia maters. (credit: modification of work by Gray's Anatomy)

Brain

The brain is the part of the central nervous system that is contained in the cranial cavity of the skull. It includes the cerebral cortex, limbic system, basal ganglia, thalamus, hypothalamus, and cerebellum. There are three different ways that a brain can be sectioned in order to view internal structures: a sagittal section cuts the brain left to right, as shown in Figure 26.21**b**, a coronal section cuts the brain front to back, as shown in Figure 26.20**a**, and a horizontal section cuts the brain top to bottom.

Cerebral Cortex

The outermost part of the brain is a thick piece of nervous system tissue called the **cerebral cortex**, which is folded into hills called **gyri** (singular: gyrus) and valleys called **sulci** (singular: sulcus). The cortex is made up of two hemispheres—right and left—which are separated by a large sulcus. A thick fiber bundle called the **corpus callosum** (Latin: "tough body") connects the two hemispheres and allows information to be passed from one side to the other. Although there are some brain functions that are localized more to one hemisphere than the other, the functions of the two hemispheres are largely redundant. In fact, sometimes (very rarely) an entire hemisphere is removed to treat severe epilepsy. While patients do suffer some deficits following the surgery, they can have surprisingly few problems, especially when the surgery is performed on children who have very immature nervous systems.

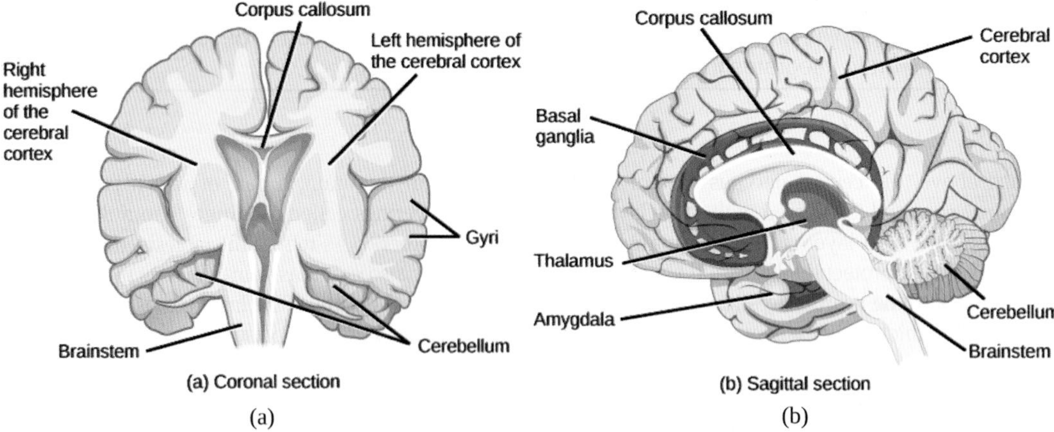

Figure 26.20 These illustrations show the (a) coronal and (b) sagittal sections of the human brain.

In other surgeries to treat severe epilepsy, the corpus callosum is cut instead of removing an entire hemisphere. This causes a condition called split-brain, which gives insights into unique functions of the two hemispheres. For example, when an object is presented to patients' left visual field, they may be unable to verbally name the object (and may claim to not have seen an object at all). This is because the visual input from the left visual field crosses and enters the right hemisphere and cannot then signal to the speech center, which generally is found in the left side of the brain. Remarkably, if a split-brain patient is asked to pick up a specific object out of a group of objects with the left hand, the patient will be able to do so but will still be unable to vocally identify it.

See this website (http://openstaxcollege.org/l/split-brain) to learn more about split-brain patients and to play a game where you can model the split-brain experiments yourself.

Each cortical hemisphere contains regions called lobes that are involved in different functions. Scientists use various techniques to determine what brain areas are involved in different functions: they examine patients who have had injuries or diseases that affect specific areas and see how those areas are related to functional deficits. They also conduct animal studies where they stimulate brain areas and see if there are any behavioral changes. They use a technique called transmagnetic stimulation (TMS) to temporarily deactivate specific parts of the cortex using strong magnets placed outside the head; and they use functional magnetic resonance imaging (fMRI) to look at changes in oxygenated blood flow in particular brain regions that correlate with specific behavioral tasks. These techniques, and others, have given great insight into the functions of different brain regions but have also showed that any given brain area can be involved in more than one behavior or process, and any given behavior or process generally involves neurons in multiple brain areas. That being said, each hemisphere of the mammalian cerebral cortex can be broken down into four functionally and spatially defined lobes: frontal, parietal, temporal, and occipital. Figure 26.21 illustrates these four lobes of the human cerebral cortex.

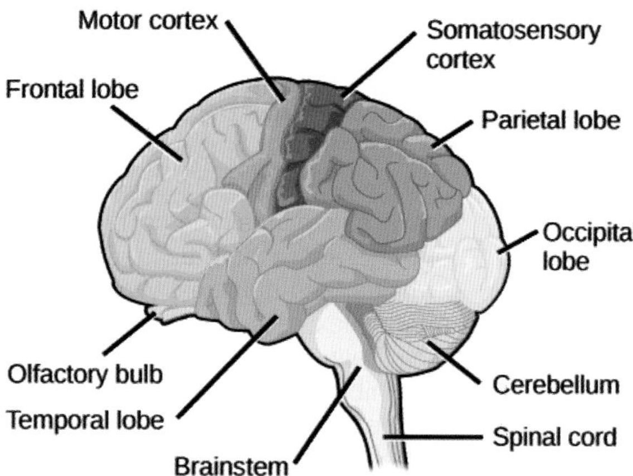

Figure 26.21 The human cerebral cortex includes the frontal, parietal, temporal, and occipital lobes.

The **frontal lobe** is located at the front of the brain, over the eyes. This lobe contains the olfactory bulb, which processes smells. The frontal lobe also contains the motor cortex, which is important for planning and implementing movement. Areas within the motor cortex map to different muscle groups, and there is some organization to this map, as shown in Figure 26.22. For example, the neurons that control movement of the fingers are next to the neurons that control movement of the hand. Neurons in the frontal lobe also control cognitive functions like maintaining attention, speech, and decision-making. Studies of humans who have damaged their frontal lobes show that parts of this area are involved in personality, socialization, and assessing risk.

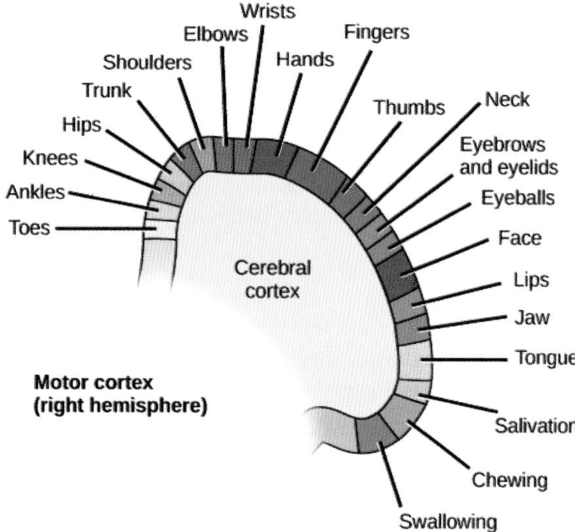

Figure 26.22 Different parts of the motor cortex control different muscle groups. Muscle groups that are neighbors in the body are generally controlled by neighboring regions of the motor cortex as well. For example, the neurons that control finger movement are near the neurons that control hand movement.

The **parietal lobe** is located at the top of the brain. Neurons in the parietal lobe are involved in speech and also reading. Two of the parietal lobe's main functions are processing **somatosensation**—touch sensations like pressure, pain, heat, cold—and processing **proprioception**—the sense of how parts of the body are oriented in space. The parietal lobe contains a somatosensory map of the body similar to the motor cortex.

The **occipital lobe** is located at the back of the brain. It is primarily involved in vision—seeing, recognizing, and identifying the visual world.

The **temporal lobe** is located at the base of the brain by your ears and is primarily involved in processing and interpreting sounds. It also contains the **hippocampus** (Greek for "seahorse")—a structure that processes memory formation. The hippocampus is illustrated in Figure 26.24. The role of the hippocampus in memory was partially determined by studying one famous epileptic patient, HM, who had both sides of his hippocampus removed in an attempt to cure his epilepsy. His seizures went away, but he could no longer form new memories (although he could remember some facts from before his surgery and could learn new motor tasks).

Cerebral Cortex

Compared to other vertebrates, mammals have exceptionally large brains for their body size. An entire alligator's brain, for example, would fill about one and a half teaspoons. This increase in brain to body size ratio is especially pronounced in apes, whales, and dolphins. While this increase in overall brain size doubtlessly played a role in the evolution of complex behaviors unique to mammals, it does not tell the whole story. Scientists have found a relationship between the relatively high surface area of the cortex and the intelligence and complex social behaviors exhibited by some mammals. This increased surface area is due, in part, to increased folding of the cortical sheet (more sulci and gyri). For example, a rat cortex is very smooth with very few sulci and gyri. Cat and sheep cortices have more sulci and gyri. Chimps, humans, and dolphins have even more.

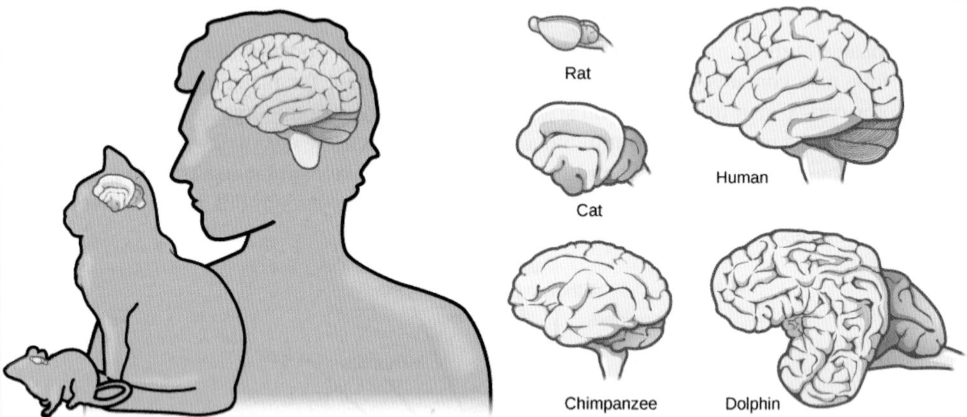

Figure 26.23 Mammals have larger brain-to-body ratios than other vertebrates. Within mammals, increased cortical folding and surface area is correlated with complex behavior.

Basal Ganglia

Interconnected brain areas called the **basal ganglia** (or **basal nuclei**), shown in Figure 26.20**b**, play important roles in movement control and posture. Damage to the basal ganglia, as in Parkinson's disease, leads to motor impairments like a shuffling gait when walking. The basal ganglia also regulate motivation. For example, when a wasp sting led to bilateral basal ganglia damage in a 25-year-old businessman, he began to spend all his days in bed and showed no interest in anything or anybody. But when he was externally stimulated—as when someone asked to play a card game with him—he was able to function normally. Interestingly, he and other similar patients do not report feeling bored or frustrated by their state.

Thalamus

The **thalamus** (Greek for "inner chamber"), illustrated in Figure 26.24, acts as a gateway to and from the cortex. It receives sensory and motor inputs from the body and also receives feedback from the cortex. This feedback mechanism can modulate conscious awareness of sensory and motor inputs depending on the attention and arousal state of the animal. The thalamus helps regulate consciousness, arousal, and sleep states. A rare genetic disorder called fatal familial insomnia causes the degeneration of thalamic neurons and glia. This disorder prevents affected patients from being able to sleep, among other symptoms, and is eventually fatal.

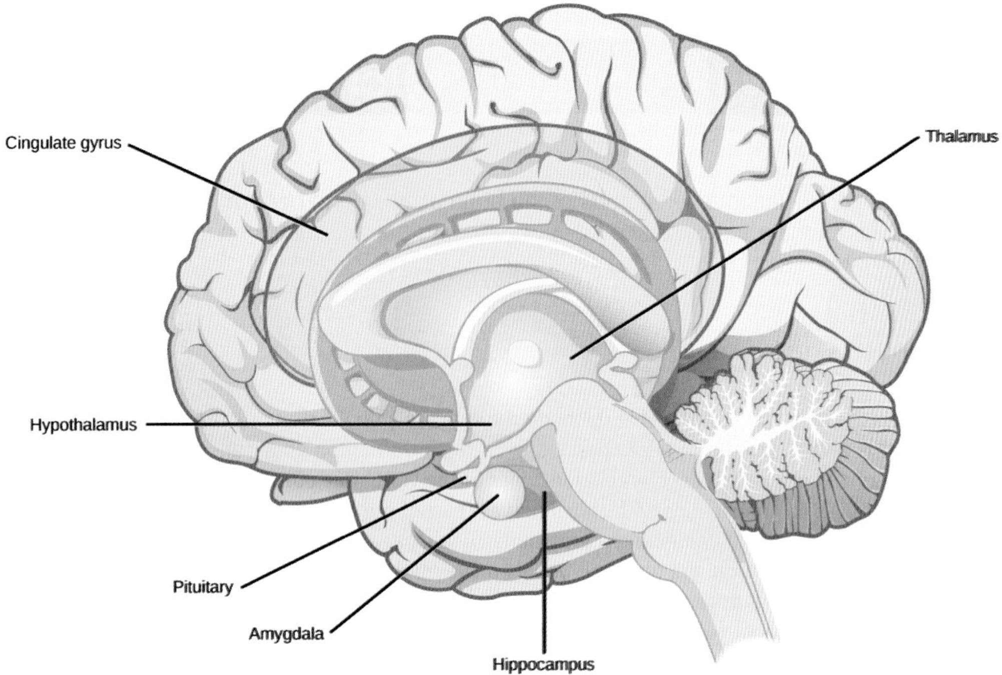

Figure 26.24 The limbic system regulates emotion and other behaviors. It includes parts of the cerebral cortex located near the center of the brain, including the cingulate gyrus and the hippocampus as well as the thalamus, hypothalamus and amygdala.

Hypothalamus

Below the thalamus is the **hypothalamus**, shown in Figure 26.24. The hypothalamus controls the endocrine system by sending signals to the pituitary gland, a pea-sized endocrine gland that releases several different hormones that affect other glands as well as other cells. This relationship means that the hypothalamus regulates important behaviors that are controlled by these hormones. The hypothalamus is the body's thermostat—it makes sure key functions like food and water intake, energy expenditure, and body temperature are kept at appropriate levels. Neurons within the hypothalamus also regulate circadian rhythms, sometimes called sleep cycles.

Limbic System

The **limbic system** is a connected set of structures that regulates emotion, as well as behaviors related to fear and motivation. It plays a role in memory formation and includes parts of the thalamus and hypothalamus as well as the hippocampus. One important structure within the limbic system is a temporal lobe structure called the **amygdala** (Greek for "almond"), illustrated in Figure 26.24. The two amygdala are important both for the sensation of fear and for recognizing fearful faces. The **cingulate gyrus** helps regulate emotions and pain.

Cerebellum

The cerebellum (Latin for "little brain"), shown in Figure 26.21, sits at the base of the brain on top of the brainstem. The cerebellum controls balance and aids in coordinating movement and learning new motor tasks.

Brainstem

The brainstem, illustrated in Figure 26.21, connects the rest of the brain with the spinal cord. It consists of the midbrain, medulla oblongata, and the pons. Motor and sensory neurons extend through the brainstem allowing for the relay of signals between the brain and spinal cord. Ascending neural pathways cross in this section of the brain allowing the left hemisphere of the cerebrum to control the right side of the body and vice versa. The brainstem coordinates motor control signals sent from the brain to the body. The brainstem controls several important functions of the body including alertness, arousal, breathing, blood pressure, digestion, heart rate, swallowing, walking, and sensory and motor information integration.

science practices CONNECTION for AP® Courses

Activity

Create a representation to illustrate what parts of the brain allow you to perform a favorite daily activity, like kicking a soccer ball, learning a new dance move, or reading the information in this section of the text and jotting down a few notes.

Spinal Cord

Connecting to the brainstem and extending down the body through the spinal column is the spinal cord, shown in Figure 26.21. The spinal cord is a thick bundle of nerve tissue that carries information about the body to the brain and from the brain to the body. The spinal cord is contained within the bones of the vertebrate column but is able to communicate signals to and from the body through its connections with spinal nerves (part of the peripheral nervous system). A cross-section of the spinal cord looks like a white oval containing a gray butterfly-shape, as illustrated in Figure 26.25. Myelinated axons make up the "white matter" and neuron and glial cell bodies make up the "gray matter." Gray matter is also composed of interneurons, which connect two neurons each located in different parts of the body. Axons and cell bodies in the dorsal (facing the back of the animal) spinal cord convey mostly sensory information from the body to the brain. Axons and cell bodies in the ventral (facing the front of the animal) spinal cord primarily transmit signals controlling movement from the brain to the body.

The spinal cord also controls motor reflexes. These reflexes are quick, unconscious movements—like automatically removing a hand from a hot object. Reflexes are so fast because they involve local synaptic connections. For example, the knee reflex that a doctor tests during a routine physical is controlled by a single synapse between a sensory neuron and a motor neuron. While a reflex may only require the involvement of one or two synapses, synapses with interneurons in the spinal column transmit information to the brain to convey what happened (the knee jerked, or the hand was hot).

In the United States, there around 10,000 spinal cord injuries each year. Because the spinal cord is the information superhighway connecting the brain with the body, damage to the spinal cord can lead to paralysis. The extent of the paralysis depends on the location of the injury along the spinal cord and whether the spinal cord was completely severed. For example, if the spinal cord is damaged at the level of the neck, it can cause paralysis from the neck down, whereas damage to the spinal column further down may limit paralysis to the legs. Spinal cord injuries are notoriously difficult to treat because spinal nerves do not regenerate, although ongoing research suggests that stem cell transplants may be able to act as a bridge to reconnect severed nerves. Researchers are also looking at ways to prevent the inflammation that worsens nerve damage after injury. One such treatment is to pump the body with cold saline to induce hypothermia. This cooling can prevent swelling and other processes that are thought to worsen spinal cord injuries.

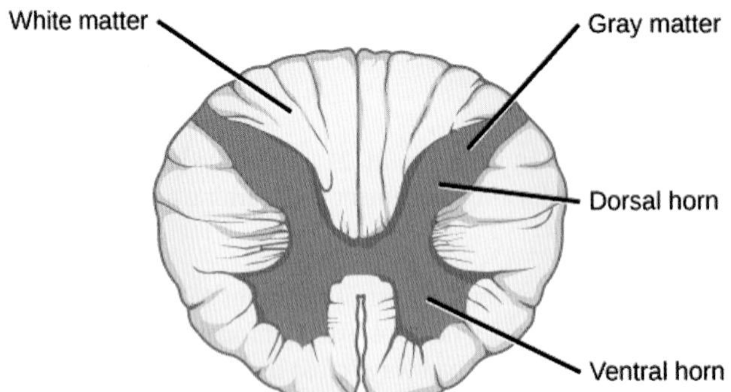

Figure 26.25 A cross-section of the spinal cord shows gray matter (containing cell bodies and interneurons) and white matter (containing axons).

26.4 | The Peripheral Nervous System

In this section, you will explore the following questions:

- What are the organization and functions of the sympathetic and parasympathetic nervous systems?
- What is the organization and function of the sensory-somatic nervous system?

Connection for AP® Courses

The information about the peripheral nervous system is not within the scope of AP®. However, it is important to note that the peripheral nervous system (PNS) is the connection between the central nervous system and the rest of the body. The PNS can be broken down into the autonomic nervous system, which controls bodily functions without conscious control, and the sensory-somatic nervous system, which transmits sensory information from the skin, muscles, and sensory organs to the CNS and motor commands from the CNS to the muscles. The autonomic nervous system can be further divided into the parasympathetic and sympathetic pathways. "Rest and digest" responses are activated by the parasympathetic division, whereas "fight or flight" responses are activated by the sympathetic division. In other words, these two systems often have opposing effects on target organs; for example, activation of the parasympathetic system slows heart rate, whereas activation of the sympathetic system increases heart rate. (If, as you're reading this information, a *Tyrannosaurus rex* barged into the room, which division would be activated?) The sensory-somatic nervous system is made up of cranial and spinal nerves with both sensory and motor neurons.

The peripheral nervous system (PNS) is the connection between the central nervous system and the rest of the body. The CNS is like the power plant of the nervous system. It creates the signals that control the functions of the body. The PNS is like the wires that go to individual houses. Without those "wires," the signals produced by the CNS could not control the body (and the CNS would not be able to receive sensory information from the body either).

The PNS can be broken down into the **autonomic nervous system**, which controls bodily functions without conscious control, and the **sensory-somatic nervous system**, which transmits sensory information from the skin, muscles, and sensory organs to the CNS and sends motor commands from the CNS to the muscles.

Autonomic Nervous System

visual CONNECTION

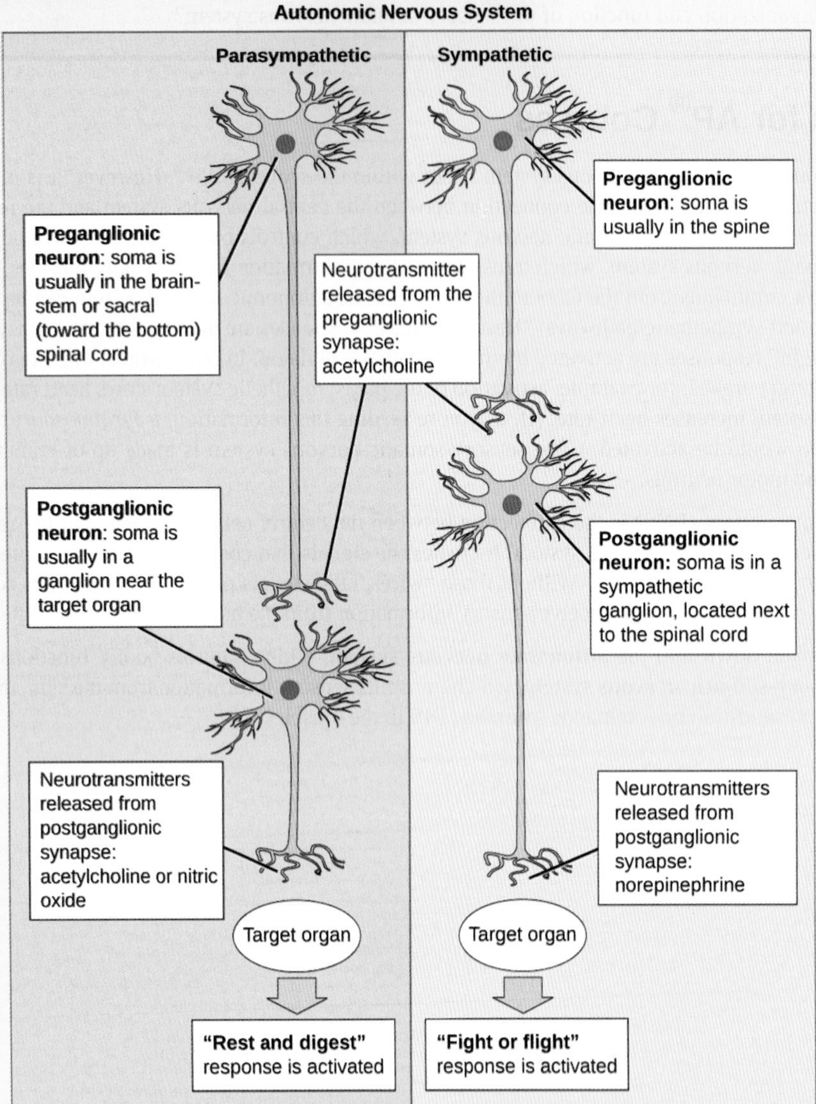

Figure 26.26 In the autonomic nervous system, a preganglionic neuron of the CNS synapses with a postganglionic neuron of the PNS. The postganglionic neuron, in turn, acts on a target organ. Autonomic responses are mediated by the sympathetic and the parasympathetic systems, which are antagonistic to one another. The sympathetic system activates the "fight or flight" response, while the parasympathetic system activates the "rest and digest" response.

Which of the following statements about the autonomic nervous system is true?

a. The sympathetic pathway is responsible for resting the body, whereas the parasympathetic pathway is responsible for preparing for an emergency.
b. Most preganglionic neurons in the sympathetic pathway originate in the spinal cord.
c. Slowing of the heartbeat is a sympathetic response.
d. Parasympathetic neurons are responsible for releasing norepinephrine on the target organ, whereas sympathetic neurons are responsible for releasing acetylcholine.

The autonomic nervous system serves as the relay between the CNS and the internal organs. It controls the lungs, the heart, smooth muscle, and exocrine and endocrine glands. The autonomic nervous system controls these organs largely without conscious control; it can continuously monitor the conditions of these different systems and implement changes as needed. Signaling to the target tissue usually involves two synapses: a preganglionic neuron (originating in the CNS) synapses to a neuron in a ganglion that, in turn, synapses on the target organ, as illustrated in Figure 26.26. There are two divisions of the autonomic nervous system that often have opposing effects: the sympathetic nervous system and the parasympathetic nervous system.

Sympathetic Nervous System

The **sympathetic nervous system** is responsible for the “fight or flight” response that occurs when an animal encounters a dangerous situation. One way to remember this is to think of the surprise a person feels when encountering a snake (“snake” and “sympathetic” both begin with “s”). Examples of functions controlled by the sympathetic nervous system include an accelerated heart rate and inhibited digestion. These functions help prepare an organism’s body for the physical strain required to escape a potentially dangerous situation or to fend off a predator.

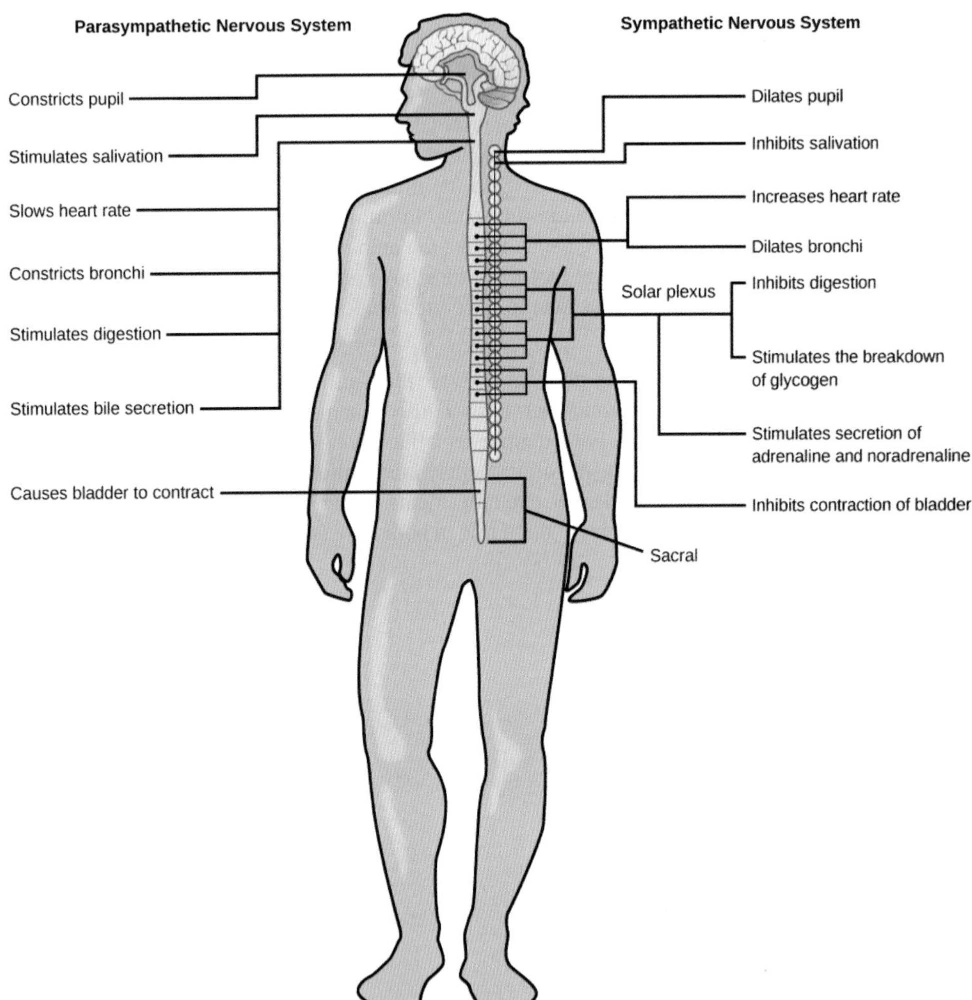

Figure 26.27 The sympathetic and parasympathetic nervous systems often have opposing effects on target organs.

Most preganglionic neurons in the sympathetic nervous system originate in the spinal cord, as illustrated in Figure 26.27. The axons of these neurons release **acetylcholine** on postganglionic neurons within sympathetic ganglia (the sympathetic ganglia form a chain that extends alongside the spinal cord). The acetylcholine activates the postganglionic neurons. Postganglionic neurons then release **norepinephrine** onto target organs. As anyone who has ever felt a rush before a big test, speech, or athletic event can attest, the effects of the sympathetic nervous system are quite pervasive. This is both because one preganglionic neuron synapses on multiple postganglionic neurons, amplifying the effect of the original synapse, and because the adrenal gland also releases norepinephrine (and the closely related hormone epinephrine) into the blood stream. The physiological effects of this norepinephrine release include dilating the trachea and bronchi (making it easier for the animal to breathe), increasing heart rate, and moving blood from the skin to the heart, muscles, and brain (so the animal can think and run). The strength and speed of the sympathetic response helps an organism avoid danger, and scientists have found evidence that it may also increase LTP—allowing the animal to remember the dangerous situation and avoid it in the future.

Parasympathetic Nervous System

While the sympathetic nervous system is activated in stressful situations, the **parasympathetic nervous system** allows an animal to "rest and digest." One way to remember this is to think that during a restful situation like a picnic, the parasympathetic nervous system is in control ("picnic" and "parasympathetic" both start with "p"). Parasympathetic preganglionic neurons have cell bodies located in the brainstem and in the sacral (toward the bottom) spinal cord, as shown in Figure 26.27. The axons of the preganglionic neurons release acetylcholine on the postganglionic neurons, which are generally located very near the target organs. Most postganglionic neurons release acetylcholine onto target organs, although some release nitric oxide.

The parasympathetic nervous system resets organ function after the sympathetic nervous system is activated (the common adrenaline dump you feel after a 'fight-or-flight' event). Effects of acetylcholine release on target organs include slowing of heart rate, lowered blood pressure, and stimulation of digestion.

Sensory-Somatic Nervous System

The sensory-somatic nervous system is made up of cranial and spinal nerves and contains both sensory and motor neurons. Sensory neurons transmit sensory information from the skin, skeletal muscle, and sensory organs to the CNS. Motor neurons transmit messages about desired movement from the CNS to the muscles to make them contract. Without its sensory-somatic nervous system, an animal would be unable to process any information about its environment (what it sees, feels, hears, and so on) and could not control motor movements. Unlike the autonomic nervous system, which has two synapses between the CNS and the target organ, sensory and motor neurons have only one synapse—one ending of the neuron is at the organ and the other directly contacts a CNS neuron. Acetylcholine is the main neurotransmitter released at these synapses.

Humans have 12 **cranial nerves**, nerves that emerge from or enter the skull (cranium), as opposed to the spinal nerves, which emerge from the vertebral column. Each cranial nerve is accorded a name, which are detailed in Figure 26.28. Some cranial nerves transmit only sensory information. For example, the olfactory nerve transmits information about smells from the nose to the brainstem. Other cranial nerves transmit almost solely motor information. For example, the oculomotor nerve controls the opening and closing of the eyelid and some eye movements. Other cranial nerves contain a mix of sensory and motor fibers. For example, the glossopharyngeal nerve has a role in both taste (sensory) and swallowing (motor).

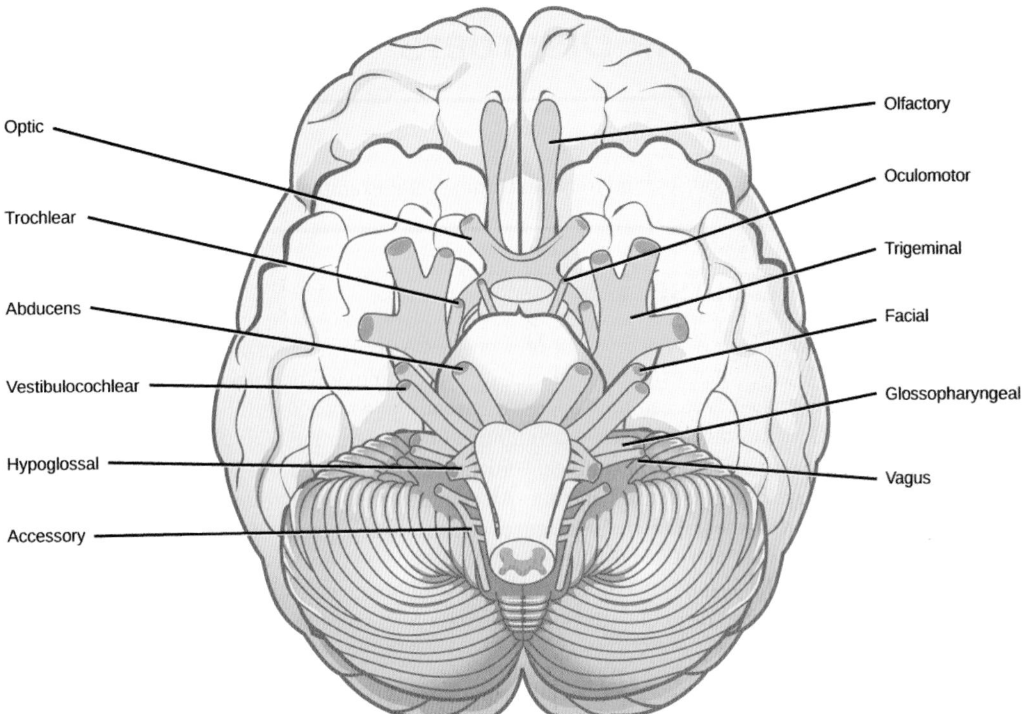

Figure 26.28 The human brain contains 12 cranial nerves that receive sensory input and control motor output for the head and neck.

Spinal nerves transmit sensory and motor information between the spinal cord and the rest of the body. Each of the 31 spinal nerves (in humans) contains both sensory and motor axons. The sensory neuron cell bodies are grouped in structures called dorsal root ganglia and are shown in Figure 26.29. Each sensory neuron has one projection—with a sensory receptor ending in skin, muscle, or sensory organs—and another that synapses with a neuron in the dorsal spinal cord. Motor neurons have cell bodies in the ventral gray matter of the spinal cord that project to muscle through the ventral root. These neurons are usually stimulated by interneurons within the spinal cord but are sometimes directly stimulated by sensory neurons.

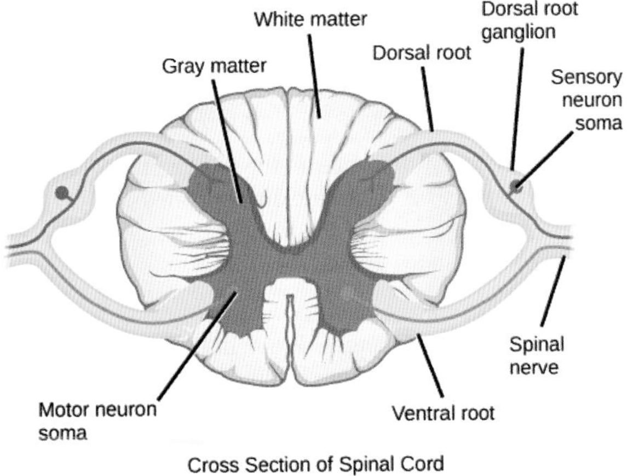

Figure 26.29 Spinal nerves contain both sensory and motor axons. The somas of sensory neurons are located in dorsal root ganglia. The somas of motor neurons are found in the ventral portion of the gray matter of the spinal cord.

26.5 | Nervous System Disorders

In this section, you will explore the following questions:

- What are examples of symptoms, causes, and treatments for several examples of nervous system disorders?

Connection for AP® Courses

Information about disorders of the nervous system is out of scope for AP®. A nervous system that functions correctly is a complex and well-oiled machine—synapses fire appropriately, muscle move when needed, memories are formed and stored, and emotions are well regulated. You can now appreciate what it takes for you to be able to read and comprehend the information in this textbook. Unfortunately, each year millions of people in the United States deal with some sort of disorder involving the nervous system. Neurodegenerative disorders are characterized by loss of nervous system functioning usually caused by the death of neurons; examples include Alzheimer's disease, Parkinson's disease, and amyotrophic lateral sclerosis (ALS). Neurodevelopmental disorders occur when the development of the nervous system is disturbed; examples include autism spectrum disorder (ASD), attention deficit hyperactivity disorder (ADHD), schizophrenia, and major depression. Epilepsy and stroke also have neurological origins. Although scientists have discovered potential causes of many of these diseases, and effective treatments for some, ongoing research into the prevention and treatment of these disorders continues.

A nervous system that functions correctly is a fantastically complex, well-oiled machine—synapses fire appropriately, muscles move when needed, memories are formed and stored, and emotions are well regulated. Unfortunately, each year millions of people in the United States deal with some sort of nervous system disorder. While scientists have discovered potential causes of many of these diseases, and viable treatments for some, ongoing research seeks to find ways to better prevent and treat all of these disorders.

Neurodegenerative Disorders

Neurodegenerative disorders are illnesses characterized by a loss of nervous system functioning that are usually caused by neuronal death. These diseases generally worsen over time as more and more neurons die. The symptoms of a particular neurodegenerative disease are related to where in the nervous system the death of neurons occurs. Spinocerebellar ataxia, for example, leads to neuronal death in the cerebellum. The death of these neurons causes problems in balance and walking. Neurodegenerative disorders include Huntington's disease, amyotrophic lateral sclerosis, Alzheimer's disease and other types of dementia disorders, and Parkinson's disease. Here, Alzheimer's and Parkinson's disease will be discussed in more depth.

Alzheimer's Disease

Alzheimer's disease is the most common cause of dementia in the elderly. In 2012, an estimated 5.4 million Americans suffered from Alzheimer's disease, and payments for their care are estimated at $200 billion. Roughly one in every eight people age 65 or older has the disease. Due to the aging of the baby-boomer generation, there are projected to be as many as 13 million Alzheimer's patients in the United States in the year 2050.

Symptoms of Alzheimer's disease include disruptive memory loss, confusion about time or place, difficulty planning or executing tasks, poor judgment, and personality changes. Problems smelling certain scents can also be indicative of Alzheimer's disease and may serve as an early warning sign. Many of these symptoms are also common in people who are aging normally, so it is the severity and longevity of the symptoms that determine whether a person is suffering from Alzheimer's.

Alzheimer's disease was named for Alois Alzheimer, a German psychiatrist who published a report in 1911 about a woman who showed severe dementia symptoms. Along with his colleagues, he examined the woman's brain following her death and reported the presence of abnormal clumps, which are now called amyloid plaques, along with tangled brain fibers called neurofibrillary tangles. Amyloid plaques, neurofibrillary tangles, and an overall shrinking of brain volume are commonly seen in the brains of Alzheimer's patients. Loss of neurons in the hippocampus is especially severe in advanced Alzheimer's patients. Figure 26.30 compares a normal brain to the brain of an Alzheimer's patient. Many research groups are examining the causes of these hallmarks of the disease.

One form of the disease is usually caused by mutations in one of three known genes. This rare form of early onset Alzheimer's disease affects fewer than five percent of patients with the disease and causes dementia beginning between the ages of 30 and 60. The more prevalent, late-onset form of the disease likely also has a genetic component. One particular gene, apolipoprotein E (APOE) has a variant (E4) that increases a carrier's likelihood of getting the disease. Many other genes have been identified that might be involved in the pathology.

Visit this website (http://openstaxcollege.org/l/alzheimers) for video links discussing genetics and Alzheimer's disease.

What statement about risk genes in Alzheimer's disease is true?

a. Risk genes do not guarantee that a person will get Alzheimer's disease.

b. Risk genes account for <5% of Alzheimer's cases.

c. Risk genes directly cause a disease.

d. Individuals with risk genes have symptoms that develop when an individual is in their 40s or 50s.

Unfortunately, there is no cure for Alzheimer's disease. Current treatments focus on managing the symptoms of the disease. Because decrease in the activity of cholinergic neurons (neurons that use the neurotransmitter acetylcholine) is common in Alzheimer's disease, several drugs used to treat the disease work by increasing acetylcholine neurotransmission, often by inhibiting the enzyme that breaks down acetylcholine in the synaptic cleft. Other clinical interventions focus on behavioral therapies like psychotherapy, sensory therapy, and cognitive exercises. Since Alzheimer's disease appears to hijack the normal aging process, research into prevention is prevalent. Smoking, obesity, and cardiovascular problems may be risk factors for the disease, so treatments for those may also help to prevent Alzheimer's disease. Some studies have shown that people who remain intellectually active by playing games, reading, playing musical instruments, and being socially active in later life have a reduced risk of developing the disease.

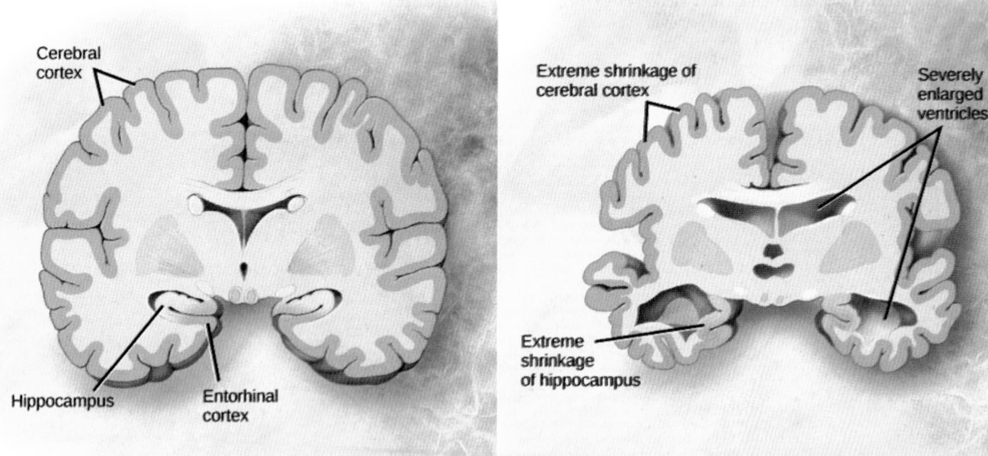

Figure 26.30 Compared to a normal brain (left), the brain from a patient with Alzheimer's disease (right) shows a dramatic neurodegeneration, particularly within the ventricles and hippocampus. (credit: modification of work by "Garrando"/Wikimedia Commons based on original images by ADEAR: "Alzheimer's Disease Education and Referral Center, a service of the National Institute on Aging")

Parkinson's Disease

Like Alzheimer's disease, **Parkinson's disease** is a neurodegenerative disease. It was first characterized by James Parkinson in 1817. Each year, 50,000-60,000 people in the United States are diagnosed with the disease. Parkinson's disease causes the loss of dopamine neurons in the substantia nigra, a midbrain structure that regulates movement. Loss of these neurons causes many symptoms including tremor (shaking of fingers or a limb), slowed movement, speech changes, balance and posture problems, and rigid muscles. The combination of these symptoms often causes a characteristic slow hunched shuffling walk, illustrated in Figure 26.31. Patients with Parkinson's disease can also exhibit psychological symptoms, such as dementia or emotional problems.

Although some patients have a form of the disease known to be caused by a single mutation, for most patients the exact causes of Parkinson's disease remain unknown: the disease likely results from a combination of genetic and environmental factors (similar to Alzheimer's disease). Post-mortem analysis of brains from Parkinson's patients shows the presence of Lewy bodies—abnormal protein clumps—in dopaminergic neurons. The prevalence of these Lewy bodies often correlates with the severity of the disease.

There is no cure for Parkinson's disease, and treatment is focused on easing symptoms. One of the most commonly prescribed drugs for Parkinson's is L-DOPA, which is a chemical that is converted into dopamine by neurons in the brain. This conversion increases the overall level of dopamine neurotransmission and can help compensate for the loss of dopaminergic neurons in the substantia nigra. Other drugs work by inhibiting the enzyme that breaks down dopamine.

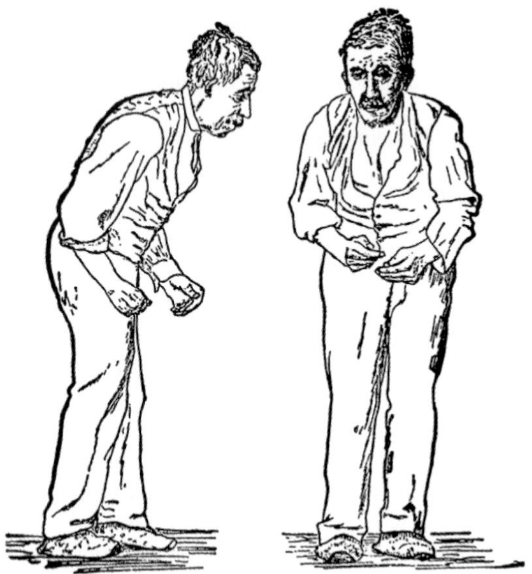

Figure 26.31 Parkinson's patients often have a characteristic hunched walk.

everyday CONNECTION for AP® Courses

Figure 26.32 Amyotrophic lateral sclerosis, also known as ALS or Lou Gehrig's disease, is a rapidly progressing disease that attacks the neurons that control voluntary muscles. Stephen Hawking, one of the greatest scientists in modern times, suffers from ALS. Credit: 2°1°°

The roots of the term amyotrophic lateral sclerosis (ALS) provide clues as to what happens to an individual with this disease. "Amyotrophic" means "no muscle nourishment," "lateral" refers to the part of the spine that tells muscles what to do, and "sclerosis" indicates that the lateral portion of the spine that controls muscle movement hardens. Explain how ALS causes a decline in voluntary muscle control over time.

a. ALS degenerates sensory neurons that control voluntary muscle movement. As the lateral portion of the spine that controls muscle movement hardens, signals are no longer sent to muscles. Initially, muscles weaken but coordination is not effected, and eventually paralysis occurs.

b. ALS degenerates motor neurons that control voluntary muscle movement. As the lateral portion of the spine that controls muscle movement hardens, signals are no longer sent to muscles. Initially, muscles strengthen and coordination is effected, and eventually paralysis occurs.

c. ALS degenerates sensory neurons that control voluntary muscle movement. As the lateral portion of the spine that controls muscle movement hardens, signals are no longer sent to muscles. Initially, muscles weaken and coordination is effected, and eventually paralysis occurs.

d. ALS degenerates motor neurons that control voluntary muscle movement. As the lateral portion of the spine that controls muscle movement hardens, signals are no longer sent to muscles. Initially, muscles weaken and coordination is effected, and eventually paralysis occurs.

Neurodevelopmental Disorders

Neurodevelopmental disorders occur when the development of the nervous system is disturbed. There are several different classes of neurodevelopmental disorders. Some, like Down Syndrome, cause intellectual deficits. Others specifically affect communication, learning, or the motor system. Some disorders like autism spectrum disorder and attention deficit/hyperactivity disorder have complex symptoms.

Autism

Autism spectrum disorder (ASD) is a neurodevelopmental disorder. Its severity differs from person to person. Estimates for the prevalence of the disorder have changed rapidly in the past few decades. Current estimates suggest that one in 88 children will develop the disorder. ASD is four times more prevalent in males than females.

This video (http://openstaxcollege.org/l/autism) discusses possible reasons why there has been a recent increase in the number of people diagnosed with autism.

Which of the following is a partial explanation of the increase in autism spectrum disorder diagnosis between 1992 and 2005?

a. diagnostic criteria changed

b. increased vaccination rates

c. more young parents reproducing

d. decreased ascertainment across classes

A characteristic symptom of ASD is impaired social skills. Children with autism may have difficulty making and maintaining eye contact and reading social cues. They also may have problems feeling empathy for others. Other symptoms of ASD include repetitive motor behaviors (such as rocking back and forth), preoccupation with specific subjects, strict adherence to certain rituals, and unusual language use. Up to 30 percent of patients with ASD develop epilepsy, and patients with some forms of the disorder (like Fragile X) also have intellectual disability. Because it is a spectrum disorder, other ASD patients are very functional and have good-to-excellent language skills. Many of these patients do not feel that they suffer from a disorder and instead think that their brains just process information differently.

Except for some well-characterized, clearly genetic forms of autism (like Fragile X and Rett's Syndrome), the causes of ASD are largely unknown. Variants of several genes correlate with the presence of ASD, but for any given patient, many different mutations in different genes may be required for the disease to develop. At a general level, ASD is thought to be a disease of "incorrect" wiring. Accordingly, brains of some ASD patients lack the same level of synaptic pruning that occurs in non-affected people. In the 1990s, a research paper linked autism to a common vaccine given to children. This paper was retracted when it was discovered that the author falsified data, and follow-up studies showed no connection between vaccines and autism.

Treatment for autism usually combines behavioral therapies and interventions, along with medications to treat other disorders common to people with autism (depression, anxiety, obsessive compulsive disorder). Although early interventions can help mitigate the effects of the disease, there is currently no cure for ASD.

Attention Deficit Hyperactivity Disorder (ADHD)

Approximately three to five percent of children and adults are affected by **attention deficit/hyperactivity disorder (ADHD)**. Like ASD, ADHD is more prevalent in males than females. Symptoms of the disorder include inattention (lack of focus), executive functioning difficulties, impulsivity, and hyperactivity beyond what is characteristic of the normal developmental stage. Some patients do not have the hyperactive component of symptoms and are diagnosed with a subtype of ADHD: attention deficit disorder (ADD). Many people with ADHD also show comorbitity, in that they develop secondary disorders in addition to ADHD. Examples include depression or obsessive compulsive disorder (OCD). Figure 26.33 provides some statistics concerning comorbidity with ADHD.

The cause of ADHD is unknown, although research points to a delay and dysfunction in the development of the prefrontal cortex and disturbances in neurotransmission. According to studies of twins, the disorder has a strong genetic component. There are several candidate genes that may contribute to the disorder, but no definitive links have been discovered. Environmental factors, including exposure to certain pesticides, may also contribute to the development of ADHD in some patients. Treatment for ADHD often involves behavioral therapies and the prescription of stimulant medications, which paradoxically cause a calming effect in these patients.

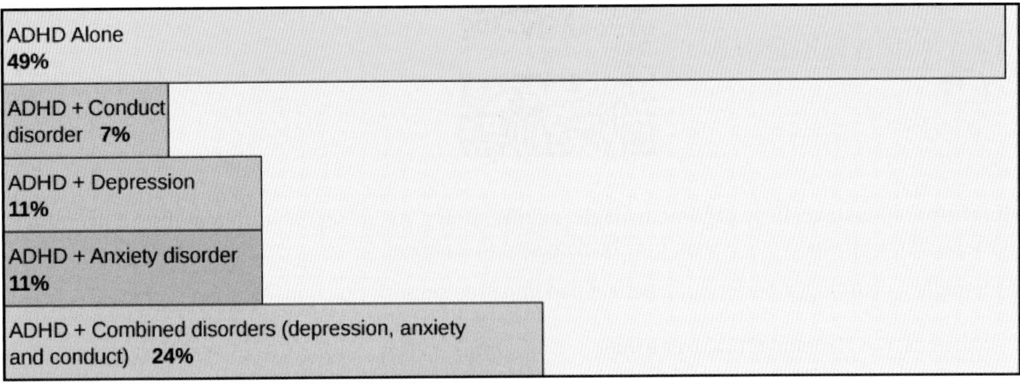

Figure 26.33 Many people with ADHD have one or more other neurological disorders. (credit "chart design and illustration": modification of work by Leigh Coriale; credit "data": Drs. Biederman and Faraone, Massachusetts General Hospital).

Neurologist

Neurologists are physicians who specialize in disorders of the nervous system. They diagnose and treat disorders such as epilepsy, stroke, dementia, nervous system injuries, Parkinson's disease, sleep disorders, and multiple sclerosis. Neurologists are medical doctors who have attended college, medical school, and completed three to four years of neurology residency.

When examining a new patient, a neurologist takes a full medical history and performs a complete physical exam. The physical exam contains specific tasks that are used to determine what areas of the brain, spinal cord, or peripheral nervous system may be damaged. For example, to check whether the hypoglossal nerve is functioning correctly, the neurologist will ask the patient to move his or her tongue in different ways. If the patient does not have full control over tongue movements, then the hypoglossal nerve may be damaged or there may be a lesion in the brainstem where the cell bodies of these neurons reside (or there could be damage to the tongue muscle itself).

Neurologists have other tools besides a physical exam they can use to diagnose particular problems in the nervous system. If the patient has had a seizure, for example, the neurologist can use electroencephalography (EEG), which involves taping electrodes to the scalp to record brain activity, to try to determine which brain regions are involved in the seizure. In suspected stroke patients, a neurologist can use a computerized tomography (CT) scan, which is a type of X-ray, to look for bleeding in the brain or other health conditions. To treat patients with neurological problems, neurologists can prescribe medications or refer the patient to a neurosurgeon for surgery.

This website (http://openstaxcollege.org/l/neurologic_exam) allows you to see the different tests a neurologist might use to see what regions of the nervous system may be damaged in a patient.

What exam might a neurologist perform if a patient had impaired sensory functions?

a. placing a 128 Hz tuning fork over a bone

b. tapping a muscle tendon with a reflex hammer

c. asking a patient to follow commands

d. asking a patient to follow a target through different positions

Mental Illnesses

Mental illnesses are nervous system disorders that result in problems with thinking, mood, or relating with other people. These disorders are severe enough to affect a person's quality of life and often make it difficult for people to perform the routine tasks of daily living. Debilitating mental disorders plague approximately 12.5 million Americans (about 1 in 17 people) at an annual cost of more than $300 billion. There are several types of mental disorders including schizophrenia, major depression, bipolar disorder, anxiety disorders and phobias, post-traumatic stress disorders, and obsessive-compulsive disorder (OCD), among others. The American Psychiatric Association publishes the Diagnostic and Statistical Manual of Mental Disorders (or DSM), which describes the symptoms required for a patient to be diagnosed with a particular mental disorder. Each newly released version of the DSM contains different symptoms and classifications as scientists learn more about these disorders, their causes, and how they relate to each other. A more detailed discussion of two mental illnesses—schizophrenia and major depression—is given below.

Schizophrenia

Schizophrenia is a serious and often debilitating mental illness affecting one percent of people in the United States. Symptoms of the disease include the inability to differentiate between reality and imagination, inappropriate and unregulated emotional responses, difficulty thinking, and problems with social situations. People with schizophrenia can suffer from hallucinations and hear voices; they may also suffer from delusions. Patients also have so-called "negative" symptoms like a flattened emotional state, loss of pleasure, and loss of basic drives. Many schizophrenic patients are diagnosed in their late adolescence or early 20s. The development of schizophrenia is thought to involve malfunctioning dopaminergic neurons and may also involve problems with glutamate signaling. Treatment for the disease usually requires antipsychotic medications that work by blocking dopamine receptors and decreasing dopamine neurotransmission in the brain. This decrease in dopamine can cause Parkinson's disease-like symptoms in some patients. While some classes of antipsychotics can be quite effective at treating the disease, they are not a cure, and most patients must remain medicated for the rest of their lives.

Depression

Major depression affects approximately 6.7 percent of the adults in the United States each year and is one of the most common mental disorders. To be diagnosed with major depressive disorder, a person must have experienced a severely depressed mood lasting longer than two weeks along with other symptoms including a loss of enjoyment in activities that were previously enjoyed, changes in appetite and sleep schedules, difficulty concentrating, feelings of worthlessness, and suicidal thoughts. The exact causes of major depression are unknown and likely include both genetic and environmental risk factors. Some research supports the "classic monoamine hypothesis," which suggests that depression is caused by a decrease in norepinephrine and serotonin neurotransmission. One argument against this hypothesis is the fact that some antidepressant medications cause an increase in norepinephrine and serotonin release within a few hours of beginning treatment—but clinical results of these medications are not seen until weeks later. This has led to alternative hypotheses: for example, dopamine may also be decreased in depressed patients, or it may actually be an increase in norepinephrine and serotonin that causes the disease, and antidepressants force a feedback loop that decreases this release. Treatments for depression include psychotherapy, electroconvulsive therapy, deep-brain stimulation, and prescription medications. There are several classes of antidepressant medications that work through different mechanisms. For example, monoamine oxidase inhibitors (MAO inhibitors) block the enzyme that degrades many neurotransmitters (including dopamine, serotonin, norepinephrine), resulting in increased neurotransmitter in the synaptic cleft. Selective serotonin reuptake inhibitors (SSRIs) block the reuptake of serotonin into the presynaptic neuron. This blockage results in an increase in serotonin in the synaptic cleft. Other types of drugs such as norepinephrine-dopamine reuptake inhibitors and norepinephrine-serotonin reuptake inhibitors are also used to treat depression.

Other Neurological Disorders

There are several other neurological disorders that cannot be easily placed in the above categories. These include chronic pain conditions, cancers of the nervous system, epilepsy disorders, and stroke. Epilepsy and stroke are discussed below.

Epilepsy

Estimates suggest that up to three percent of people in the United States will be diagnosed with **epilepsy** in their lifetime. While there are several different types of epilepsy, all are characterized by recurrent seizures. Epilepsy itself can be a symptom of a brain injury, disease, or other illness. For example, people who have intellectual disability or ASD can experience seizures, presumably because the developmental wiring malfunctions that caused their disorders also put them at risk for epilepsy. For many patients, however, the cause of their epilepsy is never identified and is likely to be a combination of genetic and environmental factors. Often, seizures can be controlled with anticonvulsant medications. However, for very severe cases, patients may undergo brain surgery to remove the brain area where seizures originate.

Stroke

A stroke results when blood fails to reach a portion of the brain for a long enough time to cause damage. Without the oxygen supplied by blood flow, neurons in this brain region die. This neuronal death can cause many different symptoms—depending on the brain area affected— including headache, muscle weakness or paralysis, speech disturbances, sensory problems, memory loss, and confusion. Stroke is often caused by blood clots and can also be caused by the bursting of a weak blood vessel. Strokes are extremely common and are the third most common cause of death in the United States. On average one person experiences a stroke every 40 seconds in the United States. Approximately 75 percent of strokes occur in people older than 65. Risk factors for stroke include high blood pressure, diabetes, high cholesterol, and a family history of stroke. Because a stroke is a medical emergency, patients with symptoms of a stroke should immediately go to the emergency room, where they can receive drugs that will dissolve any clot that may have formed. These drugs will not work if the stroke was caused by a burst blood vessel or if the stroke occurred more than three hours before arriving at the hospital. Treatment following a stroke can include blood pressure medication (to prevent future strokes) and (sometimes intense) physical therapy.

KEY TERMS

acetylcholine neurotransmitter released by neurons in the central nervous system and peripheral nervous system

action potential self-propagating momentary change in the electrical potential of a neuron (or muscle) membrane

Alzheimer's disease neurodegenerative disorder characterized by problems with memory and thinking

amygdala structure within the limbic system that processes fear

arachnoid mater spiderweb-like middle layer of the meninges that cover the central nervous system

astrocyte glial cell in the central nervous system that provide nutrients, extracellular buffering, and structural support for neurons; also makes up the blood-brain barrier

attention deficit hyperactivity disorder (ADHD) neurodevelopmental disorder characterized by difficulty maintaining attention and controlling impulses

autism spectrum disorder (ASD) neurodevelopmental disorder characterized by impaired social interaction and communication abilities

autonomic nervous system part of the peripheral nervous system that controls bodily functions

axon tube-like structure that propagates a signal from a neuron's cell body to axon terminals

axon hillock electrically sensitive structure on the cell body of a neuron that integrates signals from multiple neuronal connections

axon terminal structure on the end of an axon that can form a synapse with another neuron

basal ganglia interconnected collections of cells in the brain that are involved in movement and motivation; also known as basal nuclei

basal nuclei see basal ganglia

brainstem portion of the brain that connects with the spinal cord; controls basic nervous system functions like breathing, heart rate, and swallowing

cerebellum brain structure involved in posture, motor coordination, and learning new motor actions

cerebral cortex outermost sheet of brain tissue; involved in many higher-order functions

cerebrospinal fluid (CSF) clear liquid that surrounds the brain and spinal cord and fills the ventricles and central canal; acts as a shock absorber and circulates material throughout the brain and spinal cord.

choroid plexus spongy tissue within ventricles that produces cerebrospinal fluid

cingulate gyrus helps regulate emotions and pain; thought to directly drive the body's conscious response to unpleasant experiences

corpus callosum thick fiber bundle that connects the cerebral hemispheres

cranial nerve sensory and/or motor nerve that emanates from the brain

dendrite structure that extends away from the cell body to receive messages from other neurons

depolarization change in the membrane potential to a less negative value

dura mater tough outermost layer that covers the central nervous system

ependymal cell that lines fluid-filled ventricles of the brain and the central canal of the spinal cord; involved in production of cerebrospinal fluid

epilepsy neurological disorder characterized by recurrent seizures

excitatory postsynaptic potential (EPSP) depolarization of a postsynaptic membrane caused by neurotransmitter molecules released from a presynaptic cell

frontal lobe part of the cerebral cortex that contains the motor cortex and areas involved in planning, attention, and language

glia (also, glial cells) cells that provide support functions for neurons

gyrus (plural: gyri) ridged protrusions in the cortex

hippocampus brain structure in the temporal lobe involved in processing memories

hyperpolarization change in the membrane potential to a more negative value

hypothalamus brain structure that controls hormone release and body homeostasis

inhibitory postsynaptic potential (IPSP) hyperpolarization of a postsynaptic membrane caused by neurotransmitter molecules released from a presynaptic cell

limbic system connected brain areas that process emotion and motivation

long-term depression (LTD) prolonged decrease in synaptic coupling between a pre- and postsynaptic cell

long-term potentiation (LTP) prolonged increase in synaptic coupling between a pre-and postsynaptic cell

major depression mental illness characterized by prolonged periods of sadness

membrane potential difference in electrical potential between the inside and outside of a cell

meninge membrane that covers and protects the central nervous system

microglia glia that scavenge and degrade dead cells and protect the brain from invading microorganisms

myelin fatty substance produced by glia that insulates axons

neurodegenerative disorder nervous system disorder characterized by the progressive loss of neurological functioning, usually caused by neuron death

neuron specialized cell that can receive and transmit electrical and chemical signals

nodes of Ranvier gaps in the myelin sheath where the signal is recharged

norepinephrine neurotransmitter and hormone released by activation of the sympathetic nervous system

occipital lobe part of the cerebral cortex that contains visual cortex and processes visual stimuli

oligodendrocyte glial cell that myelinates central nervous system neuron axons

parasympathetic nervous system division of autonomic nervous system that regulates visceral functions during rest and digestion

parietal lobe part of the cerebral cortex involved in processing touch and the sense of the body in space

Parkinson's disease neurodegenerative disorder that affects the control of movement

pia mater thin membrane layer directly covering the brain and spinal cord

proprioception sense about how parts of the body are oriented in space

radial glia glia that serve as scaffolds for developing neurons as they migrate to their final destinations

refractory period period after an action potential when it is more difficult or impossible for an action potential to be fired; caused by inactivation of sodium channels and activation of additional potassium channels of the membrane

saltatory conduction “jumping” of an action potential along an axon from one node of Ranvier to the next

satellite glia glial cell that provides nutrients and structural support for neurons in the peripheral nervous system

schizophrenia mental disorder characterized by the inability to accurately perceive reality; patients often have difficulty thinking clearly and can suffer from delusions

Schwann cell glial cell that creates myelin sheath around a peripheral nervous system neuron axon

sensory-somatic nervous system system of sensory and motor nerves

somatosensation sense of touch

spinal cord thick fiber bundle that connects the brain with peripheral nerves; transmits sensory and motor information; contains neurons that control motor reflexes

spinal nerve nerve projecting between skin or muscle and spinal cord

sulcus (plural: sulci) indents or “valleys” in the cortex

summation process of multiple presynaptic inputs creating EPSPs around the same time for the postsynaptic neuron to be sufficiently depolarized to fire an action potential

sympathetic nervous system division of autonomic nervous system activated during stressful “fight or flight” situations

synapse junction between two neurons where neuronal signals are communicated

synaptic cleft space between the presynaptic and postsynaptic membranes

synaptic vesicle spherical structure that contains a neurotransmitter

temporal lobe part of the cerebral cortex that processes auditory input; parts of the temporal lobe are involved in speech, memory, and emotion processing

thalamus brain area that relays sensory information to the cortex

threshold of excitation level of depolarization needed for an action potential to fire

ventricle cavity within brain that contains cerebrospinal fluid

CHAPTER SUMMARY

26.1 Neurons and Glial Cells

The nervous system is made up of neurons and glia. Neurons are specialized cells that are capable of sending electrical as well as chemical signals. Most neurons contain dendrites, which receive these signals, and axons that send signals to other neurons or tissues. There are four main types of neurons: unipolar, bipolar, multipolar, and pseudounipolar neurons. Glia are non-neuronal cells in the nervous system that support neuronal development and signaling. There are several types of glia that serve different functions.

26.2 How Neurons Communicate

Neurons have charged membranes because there are different concentrations of ions inside and outside of the cell. Voltage-gated ion channels control the movement of ions into and out of a neuron. When a neuronal membrane is depolarized to at least the threshold of excitation, an action potential is fired. The action potential is then propagated along a myelinated axon to the axon terminals. In a chemical synapse, the action potential causes release of neurotransmitter molecules into the synaptic cleft. Through binding to postsynaptic receptors, the neurotransmitter can cause excitatory or inhibitory postsynaptic potentials by depolarizing or hyperpolarizing, respectively, the postsynaptic membrane. In electrical synapses, the action potential is directly communicated to the postsynaptic cell through gap junctions—large channel proteins that connect the pre-and postsynaptic membranes. Synapses are not static structures and can be strengthened and weakened. Two mechanisms of synaptic plasticity are long-term potentiation and long-term depression.

26.3 The Central Nervous System

The vertebrate central nervous system contains the brain and the spinal cord, which are covered and protected by three meninges. The brain contains structurally and functionally defined regions. In mammals, these include the cortex (which can be broken down into four primary functional lobes: frontal, temporal, occipital, and parietal), basal ganglia, thalamus, hypothalamus, limbic system, cerebellum, and brainstem—although structures in some of these designations overlap. While functions may be primarily localized to one structure in the brain, most complex functions, like language and sleep, involve neurons in multiple brain regions. The spinal cord is the information superhighway that connects the brain with the rest of the body through its connections with peripheral nerves. It transmits sensory and motor input and also controls motor reflexes.

26.4 The Peripheral Nervous System

The peripheral nervous system contains both the autonomic and sensory-somatic nervous systems. The autonomic nervous system provides unconscious control over visceral functions and has two divisions: the sympathetic and parasympathetic nervous systems. The sympathetic nervous system is activated in stressful situations to prepare the animal for a "fight or flight" response. The parasympathetic nervous system is active during restful periods. The sensory-somatic nervous system is made of cranial and spinal nerves that transmit sensory information from skin and muscle to the CNS and motor commands from the CNS to the muscles.

26.5 Nervous System Disorders

Some general themes emerge from the sampling of nervous system disorders presented above. The causes for most disorders are not fully understood—at least not for all patients—and likely involve a combination of nature (genetic mutations that become risk factors) and nurture (emotional trauma, stress, hazardous chemical exposure). Because the causes have yet to be fully determined, treatment options are often lacking and only address symptoms.

REVIEW QUESTIONS

1. Where are parasympathetic preganglionic cell bodies located?

a. cerebellum
b. brainstem
c. dorsal root ganglia
d. spinal cord

2. Which of the following statements about the parasympathetic nervous system is true?

a. controls "fight or flight" response
b. can reset organ function to the normal range
c. transmits information from the skin to the central nervous system
d. stimulates glycogen breakdown

3. Proper nervous system function involves various types of organic molecules. In particular, what is released by motor nerve endings onto muscle cells or tissue?

a. acetylcholine
b. norepinephrine
c. dopamine
d. serotonin

4. If the sensory-somatic nervous system of an animal is damaged, what might happen?

a. enhanced processing of environmental information
b. decreased digestion ability
c. perpetually low heart rate
d. impaired control of motor movements

5. The nervous system regulates proper processing of information and behavior control. The parasympathetic and sympathetic nervous systems are part of the _____ nervous system.

a. autonomic
b. sensory-somatic
c. central
d. "fight or flight"

6. Medications can be used to treat certain neurodevelopmental disorders. For example, which medications are often used to treat patients with ADHD?

a. tranquilizers
b. blood pressure medications
c. stimulants
d. anti-convulsant medications

7. If a child appears to have impaired social skills, such as difficulty reading social cues or making eye contact, what might they be tested for?

a. major depression
b. attention deficit hyperactivity disorder (ADHD)
c. schizophrenia
d. autism spectrum disorder

8. Parkinson's disease is a neurodegenerative disease that can produce symptoms such as tremors, slowed movement, speech changes, balance and posture problems, and rigid muscles. Parkinson's disease is caused by the degeneration of neurons that release ____.

a. serotonin
b. dopamine
c. glutamate
d. norepinephrine

CRITICAL THINKING QUESTIONS

9. When you stick your hand in a bucket of ice, it grows numb after a while. Based on what you know regarding neuronal signaling, explain how the sensation of touch is blocked from signaling to the brain.

10. Lidocaine is a local anesthetic that works by blocking voltage-gated sodium channels. Explain how blocking voltage-gated sodium channels would cause numbness and pain.

11. What are the main differences between the sympathetic and parasympathetic nervous systems?

a. The sympathetic nervous system is activated by stressful situations, whereas the parasympathetic nervous system resets organ function of sympathetic reactions and allows animals to "rest and digest."
b. The parasympathetic nervous system is activated by stressful situations, whereas the sympathetic nervous system resets organ function of sympathetic reactions and allows animals to "rest and digest."
c. The sympathetic nervous system is involved in unconscious body function control, whereas the parasympathetic nervous system is involved in conscious body function control.
d. The parasympathetic nervous system is involved in unconscious body function control, whereas the sympathetic nervous system is involved in conscious body function control.

12. How is the sensory-somatic nervous system involved in sensing information and motor function?

a. The sensory-somatic nervous system transmits information from the skin, muscles, and sensory organs to the peripheral nervous system. Motor information is sent to and from the central nervous system and the muscles.
b. The sensory-somatic nervous system transmits information from the skin, muscles, and sensory organs to the central nervous system. Motor information is sent to and from the central nervous system and the muscles.
c. The sensory-somatic nervous system transmits information from the skin, muscles, and sensory organs to the central nervous system. Motor information is sent to and from the peripheral nervous system and the muscles.
d. The sensory-somatic nervous system transmits information from the skin, muscles, and sensory organs to the peripheral nervous system. Motor information is sent to and from the peripheral nervous system and the muscles.

13. Public speaking can be very stressful. How can anticipating giving a public speech stimulate the sympathetic nervous system?

a. During stress, multiple preganglionic neurons can synapse on one postganglionic neuron, and the adrenal gland releases adrenaline.
b. During stress, one preganglionic neuron can synapse on multiple postganglionic neurons, and the thymus gland releases norepinephrine.
c. During stress, one postganglionic neuron can synapse on multiple preganglionic neurons, and the adrenal gland releases norepinephrine.
d. During stress, one preganglionic neuron can synapse on multiple postganglionic neurons, and the adrenal gland releases norepinephrine.

14. What might make you suspect that an individual has Alzheimer's disease?

a. disruptive memory loss, confusion about time or place, difficulty with planning and executing tasks, poor judgment, and/or personality changes

b. slowed movements, balance and posture problems, rigid muscles, speech changes, and/or psychological symptoms such as dementia

c. impaired social skills, repetitive motor behaviors, strict adherence to certain rituals, and preoccupation with specific subjects

d. balance and posture problems, repetitive motor behaviors, difficulty with planning and executing tasks, poor judgment, and/or personality changes

15. What treatment options are available for an individual diagnosed with major depression?

a. blood pressure medication, deep-brain stimulation, taking monoamine oxidase inhibitors, psychotherapy, and physical therapy

b. psychotherapy, electroconvulsive therapy, deep-brain stimulation, taking monoamine oxidase inhibitors, and/or taking selective melatonin reuptake inhibitors

c. psychotherapy, electroconvulsive therapy, deep-brain stimulation, taking monoamine oxidase inhibitors, and/or taking selective serotonin reuptake inhibitors

d. blood pressure medication, classes of antipsychotics, psychotherapy, electroconvulsive therapy, deep-brain stimulation, and/or taking selective serotonin reuptake inhibitors

TEST PREP FOR AP® COURSES

16. If a neuron has damaged synapses, what would be impaired?

a. Integration of signals from several synapses

b. Speed of signal transduction

c. Receiving signals from other neurons

d. Ability to recharge electrical signals

17. Signal transmission from one neuron to another requires a series of processes pertaining to different components of each neuron. What happens at the axon terminals to facilitate signal transmission to another neuron?

a. Chemicals released at the axon terminals transmit signals through synapses into other neurons via the second neuron's dendrites.

b. Chemicals released at the axon terminals transmit signals through synapses into other neurons via the second neuron's axons.

c. Chemicals released at the dendrites transmit signals through synapses into other neurons via the second neuron's axon terminal.

d. Chemicals released at the axon terminals transmit signals directly into other neurons via the second neuron's axons.

18. This figure shows a malformed neuron. Why would this neuron be nonfunctional?

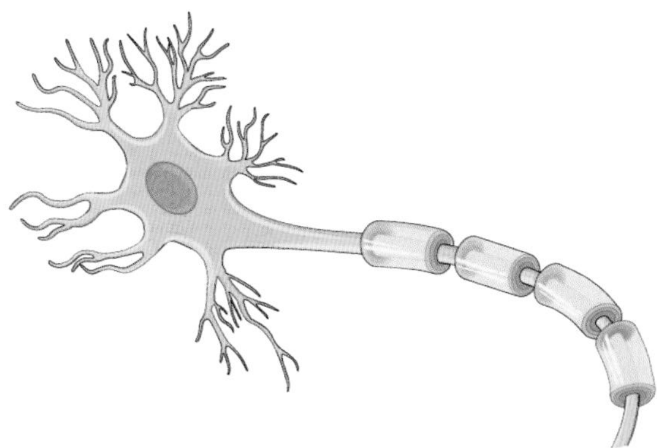

a. This neuron would not be able to receive signals.

b. This neuron would not be able to recharge the signal.

c. This neuron would not be able to integrate information from numerous synapses.

d. This neuron would not be able to send signals.

19.

This figure shows the transmission of a signal among a network of neurons. How is a signal transferred from one neuron to another?

a. A signal is released from an axon, passes through the axon terminal, and synapses with dendrites. Dendrites receive the signal, which passes through the soma. Multiple signals from a single synapse are integrated at the axon hillock, which then passes the signal into the axon, where the signal is transferred to another cell.

b. A signal is released from axon terminal, passes through the axon, and synapse with dendrites. Dendrites receive the signal, which passes through the soma. Multiple signals from multiple synapses are integrated at the axon hillock, which then passes the signal into the axon, where the signal is transferred to another cell.

c. A signal is released from an axon and passes through the axon terminal, which synapses with dendrites. Dendrites receive the signal as it passes through the soma. Multiple signals from multiple synapses are integrated at the axon hillock, which then passes the signal into the axon, where the signal is transferred to another cell.

d. A signal is released from the axon terminal, passes through the axon, and synapse with dendrites. Dendrites receive the signal as it passes through the soma. Multiple signals from a single synapse are integrated at the axon hillock, which then passes the signal into the axon, where the signal is transferred to another cell.

20. Transmission of signals between two neurons requires proper communication between neurons. Dendrites are a component of many neurons that facilitate signal reception. Which of the following is true of dendrites?

a. All neurons have several dendrites for signal reception.

b. Dendritic spines decrease possible synaptic connections.

c. Dendrites carry the signal to the soma.

d. Chemical release at dendrites allows signal communication to other cells.

21.

Ion Concentration Inside and Outside Neurons			
Ion	Extracellular concentration (mM)	Intracellular concentration (mM)	Ratio outside/ inside
1	145	12	12
2	4	155	0.026
3	120	4	30
Organic anions (A−)	—	100	

Resting membrane potential has a negative charge. Which ions correspond to each row of data in the chart?

a. Ion 1: Cl-, Ion 2: Na+, Ion 3: K+
b. Ion 1: Na+, Ion 2: K+, Ion 3: Cl-
c. Ion 1: K+, Ion 2: Na+, Ion 3: Cl-
d. Ion 1:Cl-, Ion 2: K+, Ion 3: Na+

22. Voltage-gated ion channels are essential for producing an action potential and returning a neuron to its resting state. Why would it be impossible to trigger an action potential without voltage-gated ion channels?

a. The cell would not undergo depolarization, which is necessary to fire an action potential and then return the cell to the resting state.
b. The cell would not undergo repolarization, which is necessary to fire an action potential and then return the cell to the resting state.
c. The cell would not undergo depolarization, repolarization, and hyperpolarization, which are necessary to fire an action potential and then return the cell to the resting state.
d. The cell would not undergo depolarization and hyperpolarization, which are necessary to fire an action potential and then return the cell to the resting state.

23.

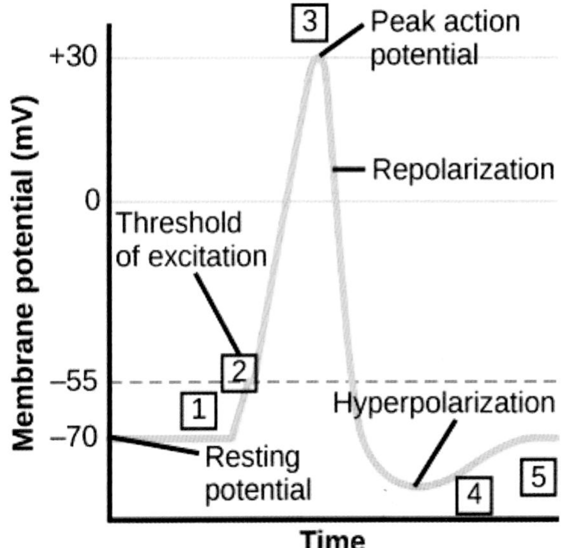

When an action potential is fired, what happens immediately after the peak action potential occurs?

a. Na+ channels open.
b. K+ channels open.
c. K+ channels close.
d. Na+/K+ transporter restores resting potential.

24. Potassium channel blockers, such as amiodarone and procainamide, which are used to treat abnormal electrical activity in the heart, impede the movement of K+through voltage-gated K+channels. Which part of the action potential would potassium channels affect, and why?

a. Depolarization after peak action potential would be affected because that is the point when K+ begins to leave the cell.
b. Repolarization after peak action potential would be affected because that is the point when K+ begins to leave the cell.
c. Repolarization after peak action potential would be affected because that is the point when K+ begins to enter the cell.
d. Polarization after peak action potential would be affected because that is the point when K+ begins to enter the cell.

25.

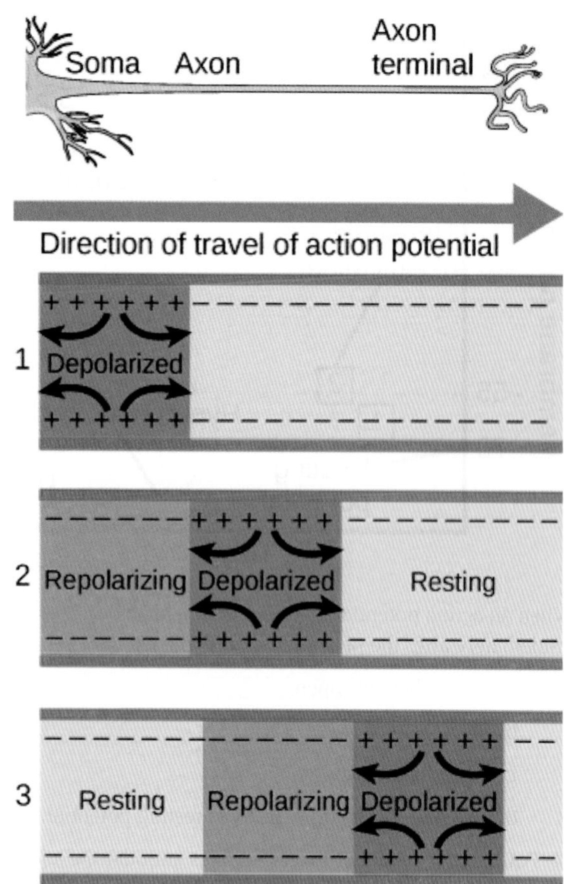

This figure shows the transfer of an action potential through a neuron. What is occurring in panel 3?

a. Depolarization occurs closest to the cell body.

b. The first part of the neuron cannot fire another action potential.

c. The first part of the neuron can fire another action potential.

d. Sodium channels have closed.

26.

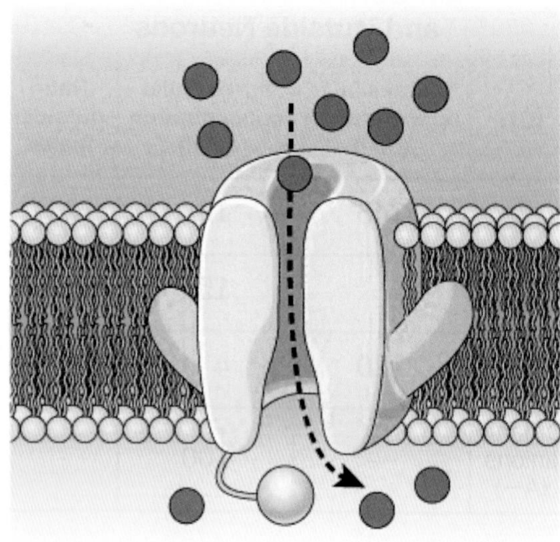

Open In response to a nerve impulse, the gate opens and Na^+ enters the cell.

This figure depicts an essential component of signal formation and transmission in neurons. What is happening in this figure?

a. A nerve impulse opens the Na+ channel, which makes Na+ enter the cell and depolarizes the membrane.

b. A nerve impulse opens the Ca+2 channel, which makes Ca+2 enter the cell and depolarizes the membrane.

c. A nerve impulse opens the Na+ channel, which makes Na+ enter the cell and repolarizes the membrane.

d. A nerve impulse opens the K+ channel, which makes K+ enter the cell and polarizes the membrane.

27. Chemical and electrical synapse are two mechanisms by which signals can be transferred between neurons. Which of the following occurs during chemical synapse?

a. Repolarization at the presynaptic membrane

b. Calcium influx causes synaptic vesicles to fuse to the membrane

c. Neurotransmitters diffuse out of gap junctions

d. Neurotransmitters bind to synaptic vesicles

28. Chemical synapse is a multiple-step process in which neurotransmitters undergo transfer and binding to different parts of the cell. What happens when a neurotransmitter binds to ligand-gated ion channels?

a. The ligand-gated ion channels open.

b. The presynaptic neuron reuptakes the neurotransmitter.

c. The neurotransmitter diffuses away from the synapse.

d. The neurotransmitter is enzymatically degraded.

29. Different components of the brain control different parts of the body. One important part of the brain is the occipital lobe. What might happen if an individual's occipital lobe was damaged?

a. The individual would not feel hot or cold.

b. The individual would be unable to form new memories.

c. The individual would be unable to recognize certain objects.

d. The individual would have no sense of smell.

30. Both cerebral hemispheres are essential for proper body function. However, the left cerebral hemisphere controls the right side of the body, whereas the right cerebral hemisphere controls the left side of the body. Why is this the case?

a. The descending neural connections are not switched in the brainstem, which means that the neural connections of the left hemisphere are transmitted to the right side of the body and vice versa.

b. The ascending neural connections are not switched in the brainstem, which means that the neural connections of the left hemisphere are transmitted to the right side of the body and vice versa.

c. The descending neural connections are switched in the brainstem, which means that the neural connections of the left hemisphere are transmitted to the right side of the body and vice versa.

d. The ascending neural connections are switched in the brainstem, which means that the neural connections of the left hemisphere are transmitted to the right side of the body and vice versa.

31.

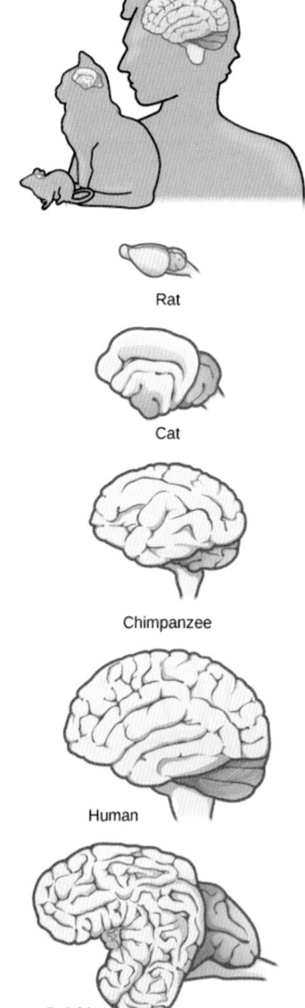

If an increased number of folds in the cortical sheets of the brain is associated with increased social complexity, which of the following animals has the greatest social complexity?

a. Rat

b. Dolphin

c. Chimpanzee

d. Cat

32.

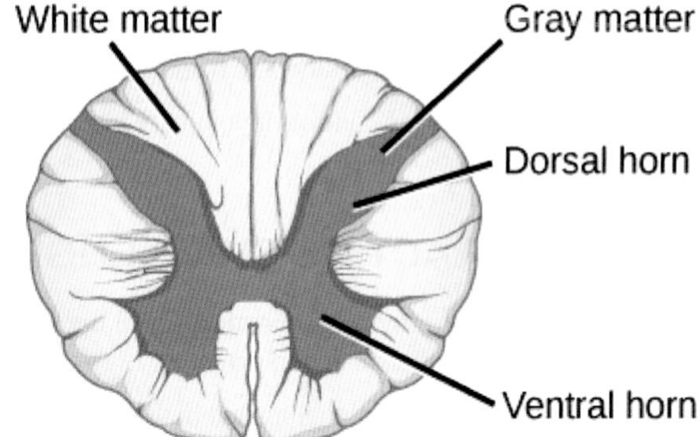

This image shows a cross section of the spinal column. How does gray matter facilitate communication along the spinal column?

a. All myelin sheaths are located in the gray matter, which transmit signals along the brain and spinal cord through the gray matter.
b. All synapses are located in the gray matter, which transmit signals along the brain and spinal cord through the gray matter.
c. All synapses are located in the gray matter, which transmit signals along the spinal cord through the gray matter.
d. All dendrites are located in the gray matter, which transmit signals along the spinal cord through the gray matter.

33.

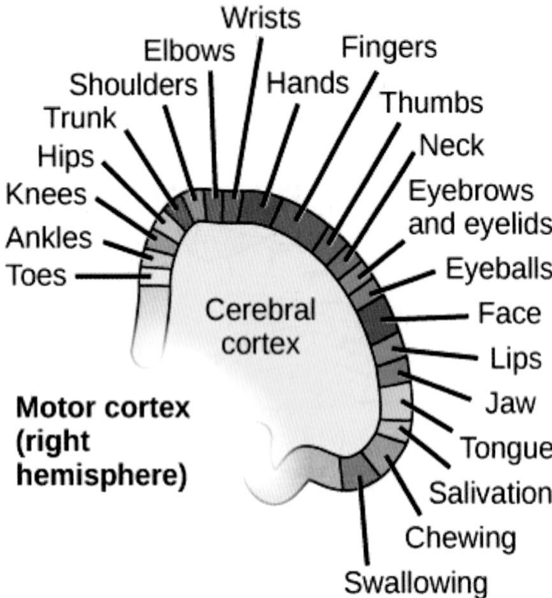

This figure depicts the parts of the body that are controlled by different parts of the motor cortex. What can be inferred about the organization of the motor cortex relative to the organization of muscles in the body?

a. The motor cortex is found throughout the body.
b. Motor cortex neurons are generally located near neurons that control nearby body parts.
c. Motor cortex neurons control speaking and processing what an individual reads.
d. The motor cortex controls involuntary muscle movements.

34.

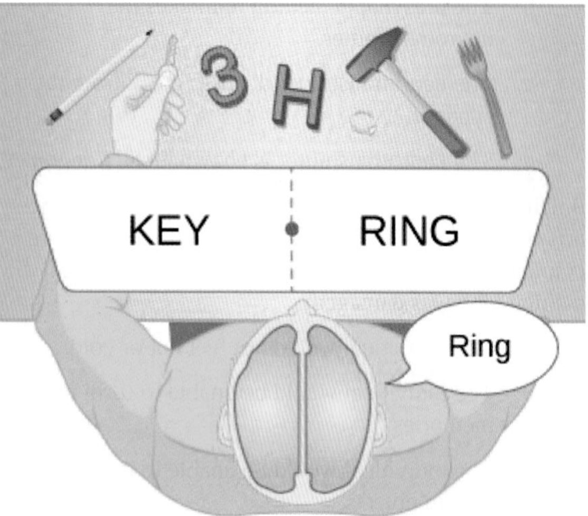

This figure represents a split-brain individual processing information. What has happened to the brain of this individual? Why does the processing of information occur as depicted?

a. The parietal lobe has been cut, which severs the ability of the left hemisphere from communicating but increases the ability of the right hemisphere.
b. The corpus callosum has been cut, which severs the ability of the left hemisphere from communicating but increases the ability of the right hemisphere.
c. The frontal lobe has been cut, which severs the ability of the left and right hemispheres to communicate.
d. The corpus callosum has been cut, which severs the ability of the left and right hemispheres to communicate.

35. The thalamus is part of the brain that is involved in various functions in the human body. What might result from the damage of an individual's thalamus?

a. Insomnia
b. Lack of interest in everything
c. Lack of fear
d. Inability to learn new motor tasks

SCIENCE PRACTICE CHALLENGE QUESTIONS

36. A neurotransmitter provides a chemical signal between neurons to inhibit or excite an action potential.

A. **Describe** a model of this signaling and in this description include the roles played by synapse, receptors, post and pre-synaptic neurons, exocytosis, endocytosis, ligand-gated ion channel and the electric potential of the membrane.

B. **Explain** the stimulatory or inhibitory effect of key ionic elements, Na^+ and Cl^-, on the electric potential of the post-synaptic membrane.

C. Modify the diagram to create a representation of the effect explained above. Select from the following list to fill in the blanks:

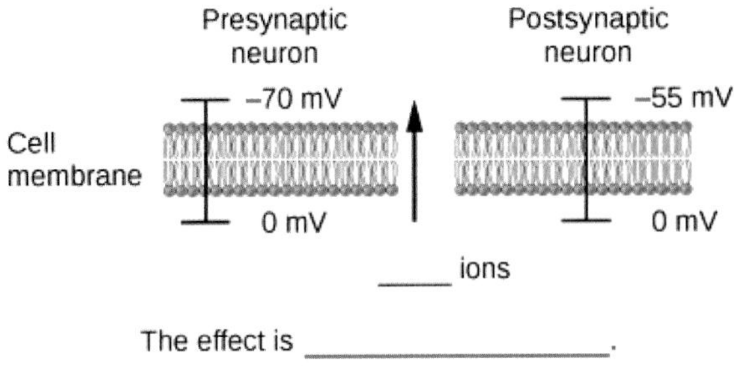

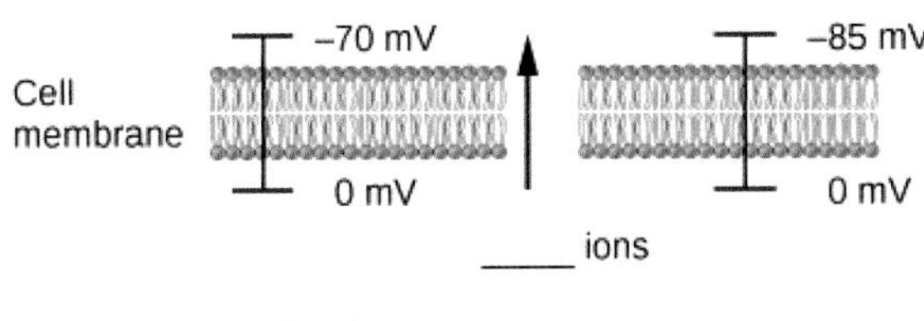

Figure 26.34

- Na^+
- Cl^-
- stimulatory
- inhibitory

D. In the 1960s Burnstock and co-workers provided evidence that ATP is a neurotransmitter. This was received skeptically and largely rejected until 1984 when a modified form of ATP that was known to block the intracellular function of ATP was shown to effect extracellular signal transmission. Based on the central role played by ATP in biological systems **justify** the resistance within the scientific community to accept a role for ATP as a neurotransmitter. Based on the fact that ATP has been conserved throughout evolution of life on Earth **justify** such a role for ATP. Based on these two perspectives **analyze** the role of cooperative interactions in the positive selection of ATP as a neurotransmitter.

37. Neurons and muscle cells maintain a high concentration gradient of potassium ions across the plasma membrane. The extracellular space has a high concentration of sodium ions. At the rest electric potential the cell membrane is polarized.

A. Construct a representation of the cell membrane with annotation of the diagram below that includes the following:

- with a labeled arrow indicate the direction in which the motion of potassium ions is driven by the concentration gradient
- with a labeled arrow indicate the direction in which the motion of sodium ions is driven by the concentration gradient
- give a brief statement of the roles of potassium and sodium ion pumps in maintaining the rest electric potential
- with a labeled arrow indicate the relative sign of the electric potential difference (voltage) between intracellular and extracellular spaces at the rest electric potential

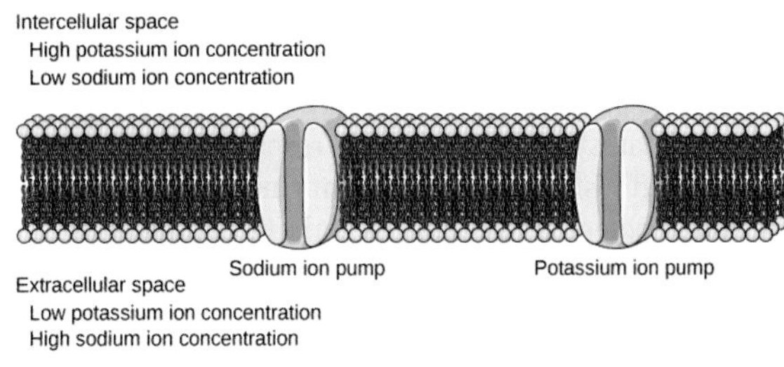

Figure 26.35

When an excitatory neurotransmitter receptor is activated the electric potential difference of membrane of a neuron is lowered inducing a change in the configuration of sodium pump proteins.

B. **Justify** the effect on the flux of sodium ions across the membrane as a positive feedback in a situation in which the electric potential difference falls below a threshold voltage and an action potential is created.

The action potential is transmitted along the neuron as a voltage wave. One cycle of the wave is shown below the diagram at the instant at which the maximum of the electric potential of the membrane has been reached.

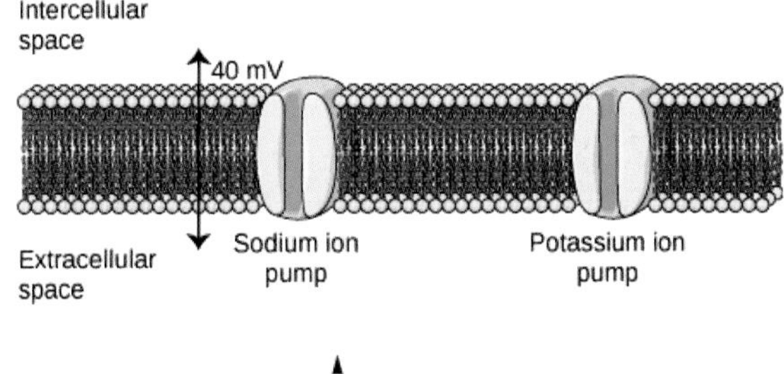

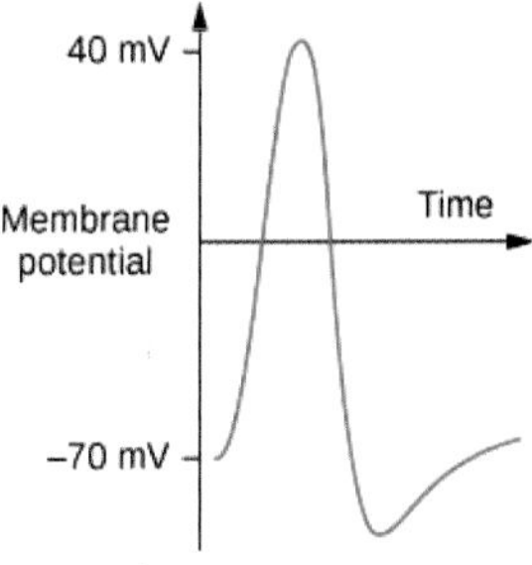

Figure 26.36

C. **Construct** a representation of the key elements of the signal propagation with annotation of the diagram that includes the following:

- a labeled arrow that indicates the direction in which the motion of potassium ions is driven by the concentration gradient
- a labeled arrow that indicates the direction in which the motion of potassium ions is driven by the electric potential difference across the membrane
- give a brief statement of the roles of potassium and sodium ion pumps in terminating the action potential

Most neurons must transmit a signal quickly. The sarcolemmas (muscle cell membranes) of the cardiac muscles receive signals that integrate information from both the sympathetic (quick response with shorter time scale) and parasympathetic (steady response with longer time scale) divisions of the autonomic nervous system. The action potential that induces periodic contractions of the cardiac muscle (see figure below) is broadened at the maximum by the release of Ca^{+2} from the smooth endoplasmic reticulum, referred to as calcium-induced calcium release (CICR).

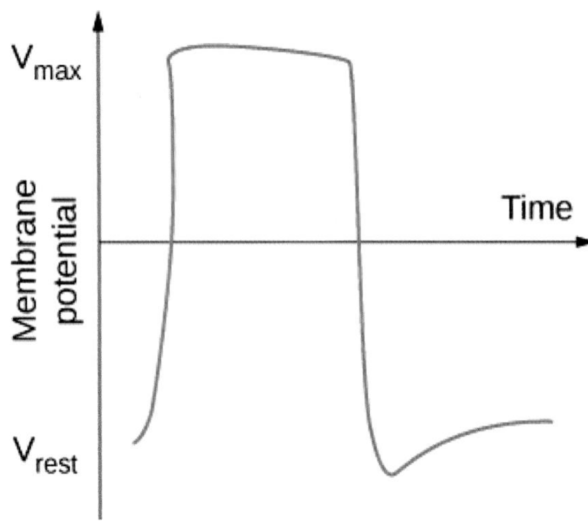

Figure 26.37

D. In terms of the function of the heart in the supply of oxygen and nutrients during "fight or flight" or restful conditions, **justify the claim** that this broadening demonstrates that the coordination of events must be regulated.

E. To stop a beating heart during open-heart surgery a solution of KCl is injected into the cardiac muscle.

Explain the effect of a large dose of extracellular K^+ on the transmission of the action potential in the sarcolemma.

38. The brain integrates new information through the formation of memories and by learning. Alternative explanations of the ability of the brain to remodel in response to experience, called plasticity, are given. This item explores those explanations.

Consider the interaction of these three cell types that integrate information to produce a response to external cues:

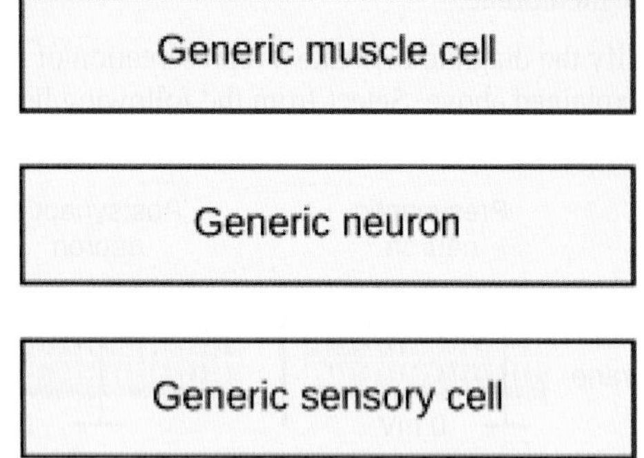

Figure 26.38

A. Use the figure to **construct a representation** of the direction of information flow.

The central body of a neuron is elaborated by tree-like structures called dendrites. These allow the neuron to integrate information from multiple sensory receptors.

B. **Describe** what refinement of the basic stimulus-response system in the diagram is needed to achieve even the simplest response: "move away." Awareness of orientation and motion within a body is called proprioception. **Describe** how multiple neurons are required to acquire proprioception.

The generation of neurons occurs during development. However, adults continue to form memories and learn. Rearrangement of connections between neurons is a possible explanation and in several studies steroid hormones have been shown to produce dendritic plasticity. The hippocampus is active during memory formation and learning and significant variations in the number of dendrites were observed in the hippocampus (Wooley et al., *Journal of Neuroscience*, 10, 1990) were correlated with variations in estrogen during the estrus cycle. More recently variation in these structures is implicated in a collection of behaviors known as chronic unpredictable mild stress (CUMS). In rats CUMS can be induced by environmental factors such as electric shock, immobilization, or isolation (Qiao et al., *Neural Plasticity*, 2016).

C. **Pose** two **scientific questions** that can be investigated to connect the dynamic homeostasis and survival advantage of the individual to dendritic plasticity.

An alternative explanation of the manner in which the brain integrates new information is through synaptic plasticity. This has been demonstrated by Nabavi and co-workers (*Nature*, 511, 2014). An associated memory was created in a rat by pairing two stimuli: an audio tone and a foot shock. The animal had previously been trained to avoid pressing a lever that delivers a reward by associating the lever press with a shock. After conditioning the animal responded to the tone as if it was a shock and avoided reward. The ratio of stimulatory to inhibitory receptors at the synaptic membrane was shown to increase with the experience.

A miniaturized device, optically activated and controlled by flashing light, was inserted in the nuclei of neurons transmitting the tone to the rat's brain. When the experimenters used light with 1 flash per second (1 Hz) the device caused the expression by the cell of one type of protein and when a light with 100 flashes per second (100 Hz) was used the device caused expression of another type of protein. Each of the graphs describe the response of the rat to environmental cues. One day elapsed between each data collection represented by one graph.

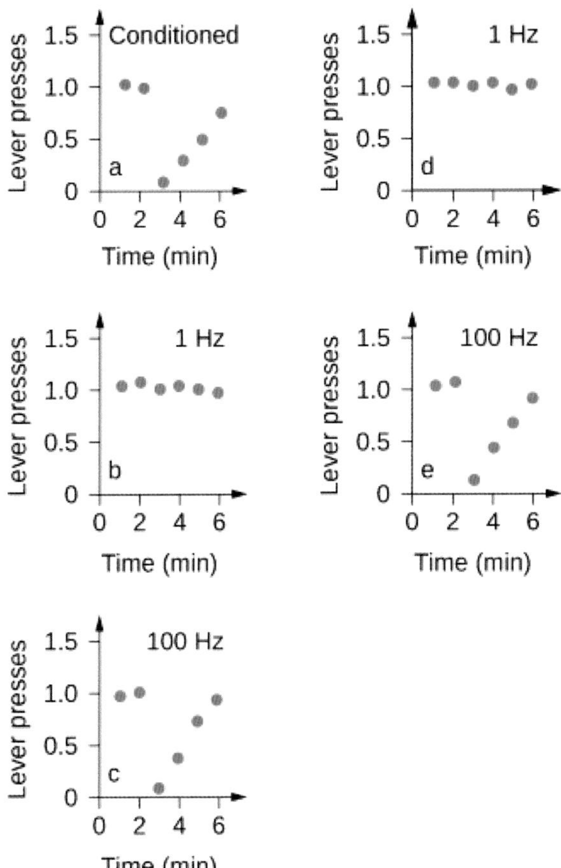

Figure 26.39

D. **Analyze** these data in terms of the evidence provided for synaptic plasticity.

A third explanation for the formation of memory and learning is found in the lab of David Glanzman (*Elife*, 2014). The sea slug (*Aplysia*) can be trained to withdraw its siphon tube. Sensory and motor neurons can be grown in tissue culture. The addition of serotonin to the tissue culture increases the number of synaptic connections and the training can be induced *in vitro*. Cells that had acquired the stimulus-response behavior were treated with an agent that destroys the synaptic receptors. Yet the trained response was retained and there were indications that the information was retrieved from the neuron nucleus.

E. Suppose that this work concerning the location of memory is confirmed. **Create a representation** of information flow in which a fourth box labeled "neuron nucleus" is added to the diagram in part A between the stimulus and the neuron. Annotate the representation to indicate the flow of information.

Explain Pose questions regarding the ethical or social consequences of this technology.

- how this form of plasticity is more dynamic than theories in which memory resides in synaptic or dendritic structures, and
- how it might lead to a treatments for disorders, such as post-traumatic stress syndrome, in which recollection creates a disability.

39. Autism is a collection of communication and socialization behaviors. Evidence of inheritance of genes predisposing the individual during early development is indicated by pedigrees such as the following (after Allen-Brady, Molecular Psychiatry, 14, 2009). Males (squares) and females (circles) are affected when the symbol is filled, are struck through when deceased and the genome cannot be determined, and are dashed when living and the genome was not determined.

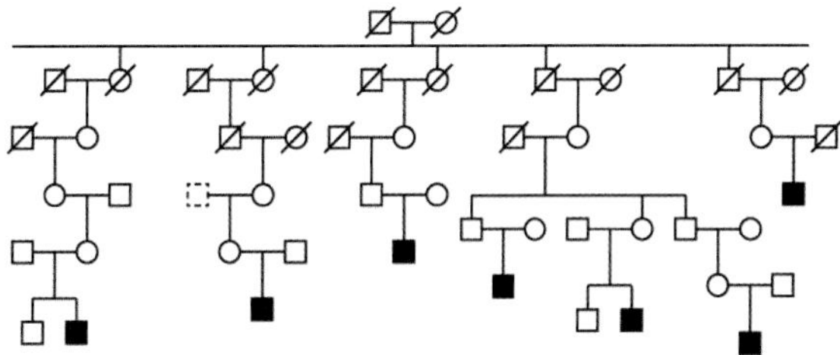

Figure 26.40

A. Other evidence indicates that autism is not x-linked. **Give an alternative explanation** that can account for these data.

B. Stem cells taken from fathers who do not present characteristic of autism and from their sons were induced to form tissue cultures of neurons. Compared to the father those taken from the son showed accelerated growth with a higher number of synapses. **Describe** possible consequences for the integration of information if this *in vitro* growth also occurs *in vivo*.

The variety of phenotypes and large number of genes that have been implicated in this disorder have led researchers to refer to the characteristics as autisms described by a spectrum of disorders, ASD. One of the gene implicated is *bola2*. While humans and other primates have genomes that are reported to have only a 2% deviation the particular form of *bola2* that occurs in 99% of human genomes that have been mapped does not occur in other primates. And *bola2* is not present in the Neanderthal genome. Even more interesting is that single nucleotide variations in human *bola2* are significantly less frequent than genes associated with other brain disorders such as schizophrenia.

C. **Evaluate** the selection pressure and direction (positive or negative) indicated by this observation.

D. Several hundred genes have been implicated in ASD and many others probably will eventually be discovered. Expression in a gene networks can depend on factors that are both genetic and environmental. Given the complexity of ASD **what questions should be researched** by the physician of children or their parents when genetic screening is considered?

40. Describe how neurons transmit information.

41. You are probably acquainted with the effects of local anesthetics. While the injection of lidocaine at the dentist is unpleasant no injection would be more so. Lidocaine is a sodium channel blocker.

A. **Explain** the absence of pain in terms of the effect of lidocaine on signal reception and transduction.

The pain of the dentist's drill is caused by trauma at the cellular level. Chemical messengers such as cytokines, serotonin, and prostaglandins are released by broken cells. The receptors for these messages of trauma are called nociceptors whose activation is transmitted to the central nervous system by specialized cells called the A and C fibres.

B. The nervous system is a network of cells and tissues that is activated by these chemical messengers. **Identify** another system that should be activated by these messengers and **support your claim** by applying the idea that dynamic homeostasis is maintained by timing and coordination of regulated events.

C. Chronic pain often persists after damaged tissue has healed. This pain is often accompanied by sterile inflammation with components of the innate immune system such as macrophages. **Refine the model** of coordinated response identified in part B to describe how chemical messengers associated with the immune response can cause chronic pain.

Unlike local anesthetics general anesthetics block signal transduction of the entire central nervous system and the brain. However, while the patient is unconscious the peripheral nervous system continues to support signaling to other systems such as heart and lungs. An explanation might be that the signal in the central and peripheral nervous systems are segregated and that the latter functions without cognitive integration (thought) as the name "autonomic" implies. The respiratory center that provides autonomic control of breathing is part of the medulla oblongata.

D. **Create a visual representation** of system composed only of the cortex, the medulla oblongata, the heart and the lungs. Using arrows describe the flow of information. Consider "holding your breath" in creating your representation. Consider why you always stop holding your breath eventually. Consider "holding your heart." Experimental data on the voluntary control of heart rate by people who practice yoga have been reported (Raghavendra et al., *International Journal of Yoga*, 6, 2013; Telles et al., *Integrative Physiological and Behavioral Science*, 39, 2004).

E. **Analyze** the data provided in the following sketch of blood flow, a process controlled by the autonomic nervous system, in the two ears of a rabbit (after Blessing, *Trends in Neuroscience*, 20, 1997) in terms of cognitive integration of the response to the stimulus provided by touching the rabbit.

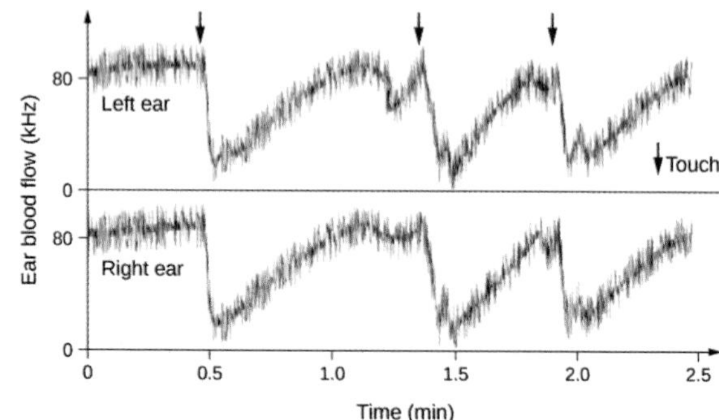

Figure 26.41

27 | SENSORY SYSTEMS

Figure 27.1 This shark uses its senses of sight, vibration (lateral-line system), and smell to hunt, but it also relies on its ability to sense the electric fields of prey, a sense not present in most land animals. (credit: modification of work by Hermanus Backpackers Hostel, South Africa)

Chapter Outline

Introduction

All bilaterally symmetric animals have a sensory system, the development of which has been driven by natural selection. Thus, sensory systems differ among species according to the demands of their environments. Animals' senses are constantly at work, making them aware of stimuli, such as light, or sound, or the presence of a chemical substance in the external environment. They also monitor information about the organism's internal environment. The shark pictured above has the ability to perceive natural electrical stimuli produced by other animals in its environment, a sense called electroreception. This enhanced ability to sense prey gives the shark an evolutionary advantage over other fish. While it is helpful to this underwater predator, electroreception is a sense not found in most land animals. You can read more about electroreception in sharks at the Sharks info website (http://openstax.org/l/32sharks) .

Connection for AP® Courses

The content in this chapter is not within the scope of AP® other than to recognize the link between the sensory organs and the nervous system. The ability to detect and respond to information is critical to an organism's survival and fitness. If time permits, you might explore the evolution of one type of sensory receptor (photoreceptors, chemoreceptor, thermoreceptor, or proprioceptor) in several different animal species, with special consideration of the features that allow it to convert a stimulus to a nerve impulse. (This task is an application of information in Big Idea 1 of the AP® Curriculum Framework—that the evolution of a structure such as a sensory receptor supports the concept that evolution continues to occur.)

27.1 | Sensory Processes

In this section, you will explore the following questions:

- What are the general and special senses in humans?
- What are three important steps in sensory perception?
- What is the concept of just-noticeable difference in sensory perception?

Senses provide information about the body and its environment. Humans have five special senses: olfaction (smell), gustation (taste), equilibrium (balance and body position), vision, and hearing. Additionally, we possess general senses, also called somatosensation, which respond to stimuli like temperature, pain, pressure, and vibration. **Vestibular sensation**, which is an organism's sense of spatial orientation and balance, **proprioception** (position of bones, joints, and muscles), and the sense of limb position that is used to track **kinesthesia** (limb movement) are part of somatosensation. Although the sensory systems associated with these senses are very different, all share a common function: to convert a stimulus (such as light, or sound, or the position of the body) into an electrical signal in the nervous system. This process is called **sensory transduction**.

There are two broad types of cellular systems that perform sensory transduction. In one, a neuron works with a **sensory receptor**, a cell, or cell process that is specialized to engage with and detect a specific stimulus. Stimulation of the sensory receptor activates the associated afferent neuron, which carries information about the stimulus to the central nervous system. In the second type of sensory transduction, a sensory nerve ending responds to a stimulus in the internal or external environment: this neuron constitutes the sensory receptor. Free nerve endings can be stimulated by several different stimuli, thus showing little receptor specificity. For example, pain receptors in your gums and teeth may be stimulated by temperature changes, chemical stimulation, or pressure.

Reception

The first step in sensation is **reception**, which is the activation of sensory receptors by stimuli such as mechanical stimuli (being bent or squished, for example), chemicals, or temperature. The receptor can then respond to the stimuli. The region in space in which a given sensory receptor can respond to a stimulus, be it far away or in contact with the body, is that receptor's **receptive field**. Think for a moment about the differences in receptive fields for the different senses. For the sense of touch, a stimulus must come into contact with body. For the sense of hearing, a stimulus can be a moderate distance away (some baleen whale sounds can propagate for many kilometers). For vision, a stimulus can be very far away; for example, the visual system perceives light from stars at enormous distances.

Transduction

The most fundamental function of a sensory system is the translation of a sensory signal to an electrical signal in the nervous system. This takes place at the sensory receptor, and the change in electrical potential that is produced is called the **receptor potential**. How is sensory input, such as pressure on the skin, changed to a receptor potential? In this example, a type of receptor called a **mechanoreceptor** (as shown in Figure 27.2) possesses specialized membranes that respond to pressure. Disturbance of these dendrites by compressing them or bending them opens gated ion channels in the plasma membrane of the sensory neuron, changing its electrical potential. Recall that in the nervous system, a positive change of a neuron's electrical potential (also called the membrane potential), depolarizes the neuron. Receptor potentials are graded potentials: the magnitude of these graded (receptor) potentials varies with the strength of the stimulus. If the magnitude of depolarization is sufficient (that is, if membrane potential reaches a threshold), the neuron will fire an action potential. In most cases, the correct stimulus impinging on a sensory receptor will drive membrane potential in a positive direction, although for some receptors, such as those in the visual system, this is not always the case.

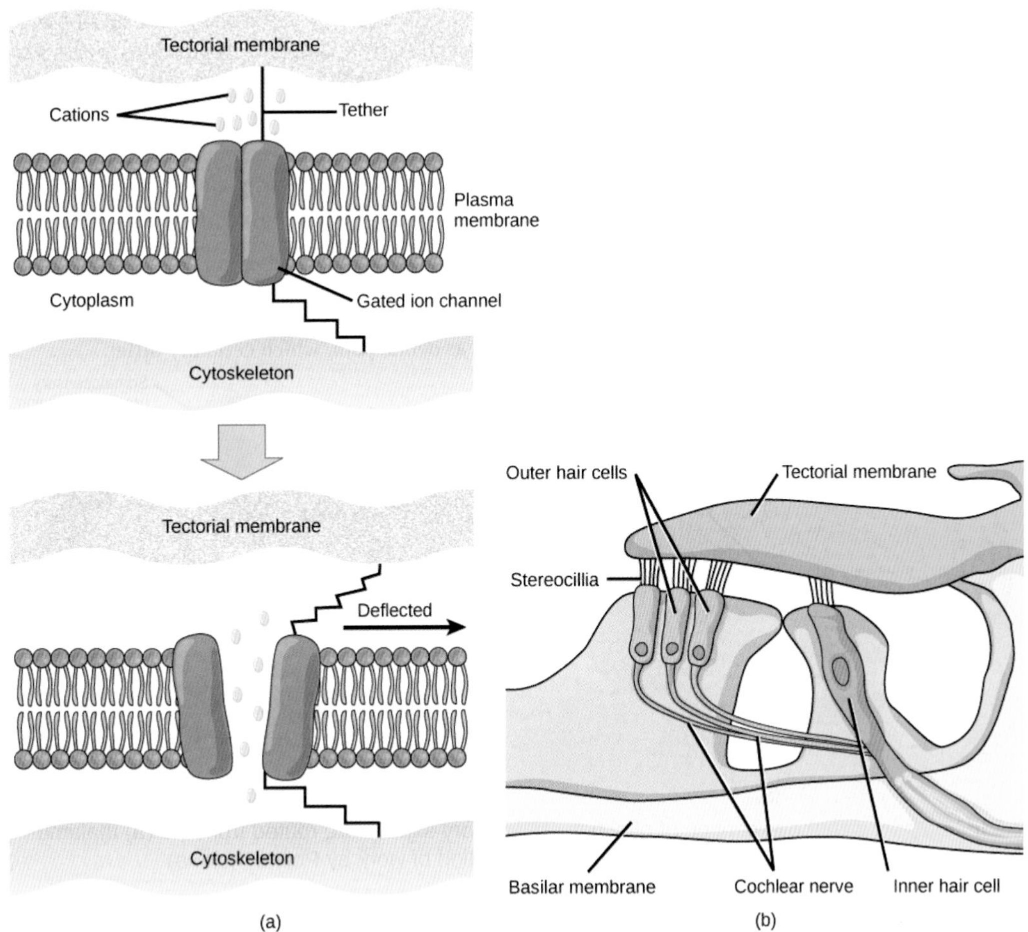

Figure 27.2 (a) Mechanosensitive ion channels are gated ion channels that respond to mechanical deformation of the plasma membrane. A mechanosensitive channel is connected to the plasma membrane and the cytoskeleton by hair-like tethers. When pressure causes the extracellular matrix to move, the channel opens, allowing ions to enter or exit the cell. (b) Stereocilia in the human ear are connected to mechanosensitive ion channels. When a sound causes the stereocilia to move, mechanosensitive ion channels transduce the signal to the cochlear nerve.

Sensory receptors for different senses are very different from each other, and they are specialized according to the type of stimulus they sense: they have receptor specificity. For example, touch receptors, light receptors, and sound receptors are each activated by different stimuli. Touch receptors are not sensitive to light or sound; they are sensitive only to touch or pressure. However, stimuli may be combined at higher levels in the brain, as happens with olfaction, contributing to our sense of taste.

Encoding and Transmission of Sensory Information

Four aspects of sensory information are encoded by sensory systems: the type of stimulus, the location of the stimulus in the receptive field, the duration of the stimulus, and the relative intensity of the stimulus. Thus, action potentials transmitted over a sensory receptor's afferent axons encode one type of stimulus, and this segregation of the senses is preserved in other sensory circuits. For example, auditory receptors transmit signals over their own dedicated system, and electrical activity in the axons of the auditory receptors will be interpreted by the brain as an auditory stimulus—a sound.

The intensity of a stimulus is often encoded in the rate of action potentials produced by the sensory receptor. Thus, an intense stimulus will produce a more rapid train of action potentials, and reducing the stimulus will likewise slow the rate of production of action potentials. A second way in which intensity is encoded is by the number of receptors activated. An intense stimulus might initiate action potentials in a large number of adjacent receptors, while a less intense stimulus might stimulate fewer receptors. Integration of sensory information begins as soon as the information is received in the CNS, and the brain will further process incoming signals.

Perception

Perception is an individual's interpretation of a sensation. Although perception relies on the activation of sensory receptors, perception happens not at the level of the sensory receptor, but at higher levels in the nervous system, in the brain. The brain distinguishes sensory stimuli through a sensory pathway: action potentials from sensory receptors travel along neurons that are dedicated to a particular stimulus. These neurons are dedicated to that particular stimulus and synapse with particular neurons in the brain or spinal cord.

All sensory signals, except those from the olfactory system, are transmitted though the central nervous system and are routed to the thalamus and to the appropriate region of the cortex. Recall that the thalamus is a structure in the forebrain that serves as a clearinghouse and relay station for sensory (as well as motor) signals. When the sensory signal exits the thalamus, it is conducted to the specific area of the cortex (Figure 27.3) dedicated to processing that particular sense.

How are neural signals interpreted? Interpretation of sensory signals between individuals of the same species is largely similar, owing to the inherited similarity of their nervous systems; however, there are some individual differences. A good example of this is individual tolerances to a painful stimulus, such as dental pain, which certainly differ.

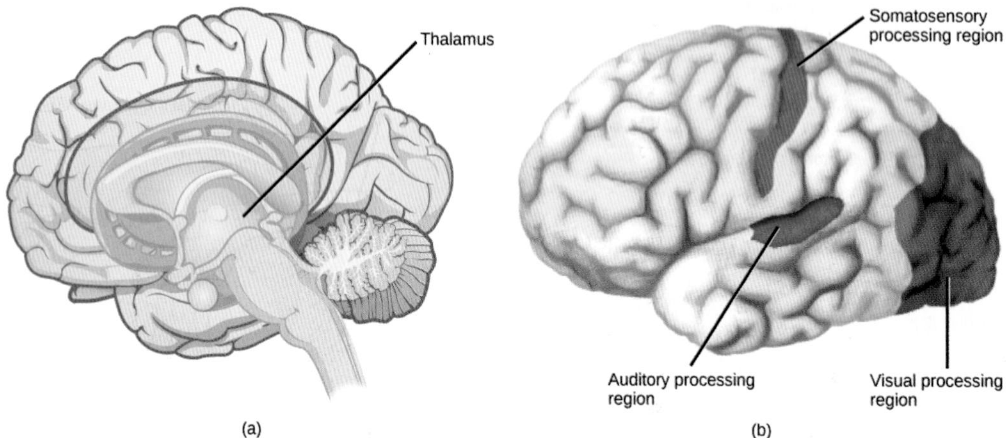

Figure 27.3 In humans, with the exception of olfaction, all sensory signals are routed from the (a) thalamus to (b) final processing regions in the cortex of the brain. (credit b: modification of work by Polina Tishina)

scientific method CONNECTION

Just-Noticeable Difference

It is easy to differentiate between a one-pound bag of rice and a two-pound bag of rice. There is a one-pound difference, and one bag is twice as heavy as the other. However, would it be as easy to differentiate between a 20- and a 21-pound bag?

Question: What is the smallest detectible weight difference between a one-pound bag of rice and a larger bag? What is the smallest detectible difference between a 20-pound bag and a larger bag? In both cases, at what weights are the differences detected? This smallest detectible difference in stimuli is known as the just-noticeable difference (JND).

Background: Research background literature on JND and on Weber's Law, a description of a proposed mathematical relationship between the overall magnitude of the stimulus and the JND. You will be testing JND of different weights of rice in bags. Choose a convenient increment that is to be stepped through while testing. For example, you could choose 10 percent increments between one and two pounds (1.1, 1.2, 1.3, 1.4, and so on) or 20 percent increments (1.2, 1.4, 1.6, and 1.8).

Hypothesis: Develop a hypothesis about JND in terms of percentage of the whole weight being tested (such as "the JND between the two small bags and between the two large bags is proportionally the same," or ". . . is not proportionally the same.") So, for the first hypothesis, if the JND between the one-pound bag and a larger bag is 0.2 pounds (that is, 20 percent; 1.0 pound feels the same as 1.1 pounds, but 1.0 pound feels less than 1.2 pounds), then the JND between the 20-pound bag and a larger bag will also be 20 percent. (So, 20 pounds feels the same as 22 pounds or 23 pounds, but 20 pounds feels less than 24 pounds.)

Test the hypothesis: Enlist 24 participants, and split them into two groups of 12. To set up the demonstration, assuming a 10 percent increment was selected, have the first group be the one-pound group. As a counter-balancing measure against a systematic error, however, six of the first group will compare one pound to two pounds, and step down in weight (1.0 to 2.0, 1.0 to 1.9, and so on.), while the other six will step up (1.0 to 1.1, 1.0 to 1.2, and so on). Apply the same principle to the 20-pound group (20 to 40, 20 to 38, and so on, and 20 to 22, 20 to 24, and so on). Given the large difference between 20 and 40 pounds, you may wish to use 30 pounds as your larger weight. In any case, use two weights that are easily detectable as different.

Record the observations: Record the data in a table similar to the table below. For the one-pound and 20-pound groups (base weights) record a plus sign (+) for each participant that detects a difference between the base weight and the step weight. Record a minus sign (-) for each participant that finds no difference. If one-tenth steps were not used, then replace the steps in the "Step Weight" columns with the step you are using.

Results of JND Testing (+ = difference; – = no difference)

Step Weight	One pound	20 pounds	Step Weight
1.1			22
1.2			24
1.3			26
1.4			28
1.5			30
1.6			32
1.7			34
1.8			36

Results of JND Testing (+ = difference; – = no difference)

Step Weight	One pound	20 pounds	Step Weight
1.9			38
2.0			40

Table 27.1

Analyze the data/report the results: What step weight did all participants find to be equal with one-pound base weight? What about the 20-pound group?

Draw a conclusion: Did the data support the hypothesis? Are the final weights proportionally the same? If not, why not? Do the findings adhere to Weber's Law? Weber's Law states that the concept that a just-noticeable difference in a stimulus is proportional to the magnitude of the original stimulus.

27.2 | Somatosensation

In this section, you will explore the following questions:

- What are four important mechanoreceptors in human skin?
- What is the topographical distribution of somatosensory receptors between glabrous and hairy skin?
- Why is the perception of pain subjective?

Somatosensation is a mixed sensory category and includes all sensation received from the skin and mucous membranes, as well from as the limbs and joints. Somatosensation is also known as tactile sense, or more familiarly, as the sense of touch. Somatosensation occurs all over the exterior of the body and at some interior locations as well. A variety of receptor types—embedded in the skin, mucous membranes, muscles, joints, internal organs, and cardiovascular system—play a role.

Recall that the epidermis is the outermost layer of skin in mammals. It is relatively thin, is composed of keratin-filled cells, and has no blood supply. The epidermis serves as a barrier to water and to invasion by pathogens. Below this, the much thicker dermis contains blood vessels, sweat glands, hair follicles, lymph vessels, and lipid-secreting sebaceous glands (Figure 27.4). Below the epidermis and dermis is the subcutaneous tissue, or hypodermis, the fatty layer that contains blood vessels, connective tissue, and the axons of sensory neurons. The hypodermis, which holds about 50 percent of the body's fat, attaches the dermis to the bone and muscle, and supplies nerves and blood vessels to the dermis.

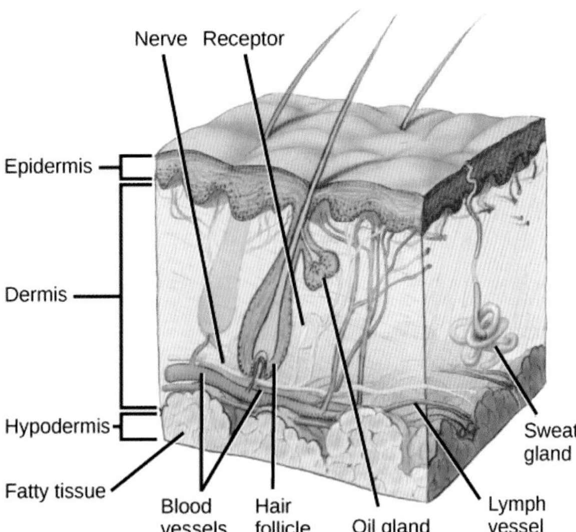

Figure 27.4 Mammalian skin has three layers: an epidermis, a dermis, and a hypodermis. (credit: modification of work by Don Bliss, National Cancer Institute)

Somatosensory Receptors

Sensory receptors are classified into five categories: mechanoreceptors, thermoreceptors, proprioceptors, pain receptors, and chemoreceptors. These categories are based on the nature of stimuli each receptor class transduces. What is commonly referred to as "touch" involves more than one kind of stimulus and more than one kind of receptor. Mechanoreceptors in the skin are described as encapsulated (that is, surrounded by a capsule) or unencapsulated (a group that includes free nerve endings). A **free nerve ending**, as its name implies, is an unencapsulated dendrite of a sensory neuron. Free nerve endings are the most common nerve endings in skin, and they extend into the middle of the epidermis. Free nerve endings are sensitive to painful stimuli, to hot and cold, and to light touch. They are slow to adjust to a stimulus and so are less sensitive to abrupt changes in stimulation.

There are three classes of mechanoreceptors: tactile, proprioceptors, and baroreceptors. Mechanoreceptors sense stimuli due to physical deformation of their plasma membranes. They contain mechanically gated ion channels whose gates open or close in response to pressure, touch, stretching, and sound." There are four primary tactile mechanoreceptors in human skin: Merkel's disks, Meissner's corpuscles, Ruffini endings, and Pacinian corpuscle; two are located toward the surface of the skin and two are located deeper. A fifth type of mechanoreceptor, Krause end bulbs, are found only in specialized regions. **Merkel's disks** (shown in Figure 27.5) are found in the upper layers of skin near the base of the epidermis, both in skin that has hair and on **glabrous** skin, that is, the hairless skin found on the palms and fingers, the soles of the feet, and the lips of humans and other primates. Merkel's disks are densely distributed in the fingertips and lips. They are slow-adapting, encapsulated nerve endings, and they respond to light touch. Light touch, also known as discriminative touch, is a light pressure that allows the location of a stimulus to be pinpointed. The receptive fields of Merkel's disks are small with well-defined borders. That makes them finely sensitive to edges and they come into use in tasks such as typing on a keyboard.

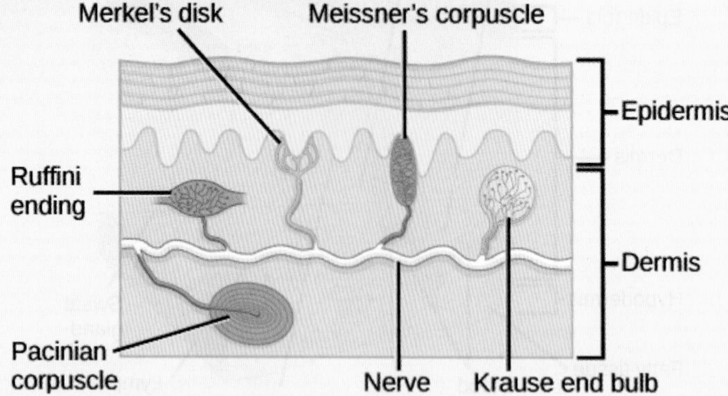

Figure 27.5 Four of the primary mechanoreceptors in human skin are shown. Merkel's disks, which are unencapsulated, respond to light touch. Meissner's corpuscles, Ruffini endings, Pacinian corpuscles, and Krause end bulbs are all encapsulated. Meissner's corpuscles respond to touch and low-frequency vibration. Ruffini endings detect stretch, deformation within joints, and warmth. Pacinian corpuscles detect transient pressure and high-frequency vibration. Krause end bulbs detect cold.

Which of the following statements about mechanoreceptors is true?

a. Meissner's corpuscles extend far into the epidermis.
b. Ruffini endings are the only encapsulated mechanoreceptors.
c. Light touch is detected by Pacini corpuscles.
d. Merkel's disks are abundant on the fingertips and lips.

Meissner's corpuscles, (shown in Figure 27.6) also known as tactile corpuscles, are found in the upper dermis, but they project into the epidermis. They, too, are found primarily in the glabrous skin on the fingertips and eyelids. They respond to fine touch and pressure, but they also respond to low-frequency vibration or flutter. They are rapidly adapting, fluid-filled, encapsulated neurons with small, well-defined borders and are responsive to fine details. Like Merkel's disks, Meissner's corpuscles are not as plentiful in the palms as they are in the fingertips.

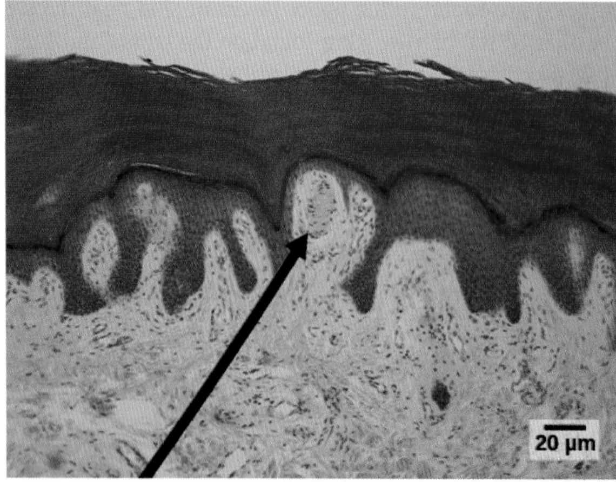

Figure 27.6 Meissner corpuscles in the fingertips, such as the one viewed here using bright field light microscopy, allow for touch discrimination of fine detail. (credit: modification of work by "Wbensmith"/Wikimedia Commons; scale-bar data from Matt Russell)

Deeper in the epidermis, near the base, are **Ruffini endings**, which are also known as bulbous corpuscles. They are found in both glabrous and hairy skin. These are slow-adapting, encapsulated mechanoreceptors that detect skin stretch and deformations within joints, so they provide valuable feedback for gripping objects and controlling finger position and movement. Thus, they also contribute to proprioception and kinesthesia. Ruffini endings also detect warmth. Note that these warmth detectors are situated deeper in the skin than are the cold detectors. It is not surprising, then, that humans detect cold stimuli before they detect warm stimuli.

Pacinian corpuscles (seen in Figure 27.7) are located deep in the dermis of both glabrous and hairy skin and are structurally similar to Meissner's corpuscles; they are found in the bone periosteum, joint capsules, pancreas and other viscera, breast, and genitals. They are rapidly adapting mechanoreceptors that sense deep transient (but not prolonged) pressure and high-frequency vibration. Pacinian receptors detect pressure and vibration by being compressed, stimulating their internal dendrites. There are fewer Pacinian corpuscles and Ruffini endings in skin than there are Merkel's disks and Meissner's corpuscles.

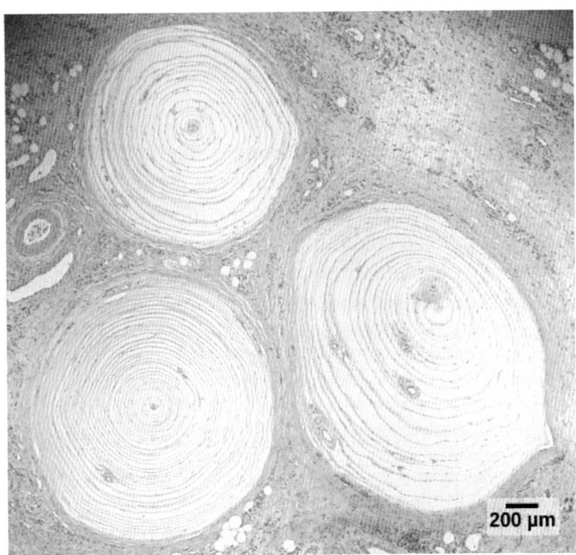

Figure 27.7 Pacinian corpuscles, such as these visualized using bright field light microscopy, detect pressure (touch) and high-frequency vibration. (credit: modification of work by Ed Uthman; scale-bar data from Matt Russell)

In proprioception, proprioceptive and kinesthetic signals travel through myelinated afferent neurons running from the spinal cord to the medulla. Neurons are not physically connected, but communicate via neurotransmitters secreted into synapses or "gaps" between communicating neurons. Once in the medulla, the neurons continue carrying the signals to the thalamus.

Muscle spindles are stretch receptors that detect the amount of stretch, or lengthening of muscles. Related to these are **Golgi tendon organs**, which are tension receptors that detect the force of muscle contraction. Proprioceptive and kinesthetic signals come from limbs. Unconscious proprioceptive signals run from the spinal cord to the cerebellum, the brain region that coordinates muscle contraction, rather than to the thalamus, like most other sensory information.

Baroreceptors detect pressure changes in an organ. They are found in the walls of the carotid artery and the aorta where they monitor blood pressure, and in the lungs where they detect the degree of lung expansion. Stretch receptors are found at various sites in the digestive and urinary systems.

In addition to these two types of deeper receptors, there are also rapidly adapting hair receptors, which are found on nerve endings that wrap around the base of hair follicles. There are a few types of hair receptors that detect slow and rapid hair movement, and they differ in their sensitivity to movement. Some hair receptors also detect skin deflection, and certain rapidly adapting hair receptors allow detection of stimuli that have not yet touched the skin.

Integration of Signals from Mechanoreceptors

The configuration of the different types of receptors working in concert in human skin results in a very refined sense of touch. The nociceptive receptors—those that detect pain—are located near the surface. Small, finely calibrated mechanoreceptors—Merkel's disks and Meissner's corpuscles—are located in the upper layers and can precisely localize even gentle touch. The large mechanoreceptors—Pacinian corpuscles and Ruffini endings—are located in the lower layers and respond to deeper touch. (Consider that the deep pressure that reaches those deeper receptors would not need to be finely localized.) Both the upper and lower layers of the skin hold rapidly and slowly adapting receptors. Both primary somatosensory cortex and secondary cortical areas are responsible for processing the complex picture of stimuli transmitted from the interplay of mechanoreceptors.

Density of Mechanoreceptors

The distribution of touch receptors in human skin is not consistent over the body. In humans, touch receptors are less dense in skin covered with any type of hair, such as the arms, legs, torso, and face. Touch receptors are denser in glabrous skin (the type found on human fingertips and lips, for example), which is typically more sensitive and is thicker than hairy skin (4 to 5 mm versus 2 to 3 mm).

How is receptor density estimated in a human subject? The relative density of pressure receptors in different locations on the body can be demonstrated experimentally using a two-point discrimination test. In this demonstration, two sharp points, such as two thumbtacks, are brought into contact with the subject's skin (though not hard enough to cause pain or break the skin). The subject reports if he or she feels one point or two points. If the two points are felt as one point, it can be inferred that the two points are both in the receptive field of a single sensory receptor. If two points are felt as two separate points, each is in the receptive field of two separate sensory receptors. The points could then be moved closer and re-tested until the subject reports feeling only one point, and the size of the receptive field of a single receptor could be estimated from that distance.

Thermoreception

In addition to Krause end bulbs that detect cold and Ruffini endings that detect warmth, there are different types of cold receptors on some free nerve endings: thermoreceptors, located in the dermis, skeletal muscles, liver, and hypothalamus, that are activated by different temperatures. Their pathways into the brain run from the spinal cord through the thalamus to the primary somatosensory cortex. Warmth and cold information from the face travels through one of the cranial nerves to the brain. You know from experience that a tolerably cold or hot stimulus can quickly progress to a much more intense stimulus that is no longer tolerable. Any stimulus that is too intense can be perceived as pain because temperature sensations are conducted along the same pathways that carry pain sensations

Pain

Pain is the name given to **nociception**, which is the neural processing of injurious stimuli in response to tissue damage. Pain is caused by true sources of injury, such as contact with a heat source that causes a thermal burn or contact with a corrosive chemical. But pain also can be caused by harmless stimuli that mimic the action of damaging stimuli, such as contact with capsaicins, the compounds that cause peppers to taste hot and which are used in self-defense pepper sprays and certain topical medications. Peppers taste "hot" because the protein receptors that bind capsaicin open the same calcium channels that are activated by warm receptors.

Nociception starts at the sensory receptors, but pain, in-as-much as it is the perception of nociception, does not start until it is communicated to the brain. There are several nociceptive pathways to and through the brain. Most axons carrying nociceptive information into the brain from the spinal cord project to the thalamus (as do other sensory neurons) and the neural signal undergoes final processing in the primary somatosensory cortex. Interestingly, one nociceptive pathway projects not to the thalamus but directly to the hypothalamus in the forebrain, which modulates the cardiovascular and neuroendocrine functions of the autonomic nervous system. Recall that threatening—or painful—stimuli stimulate the sympathetic branch of the visceral sensory system, readying a fight-or-flight response.

View this video (http://openstaxcollege.org/l/nociceptive) that animates the five phases of nociceptive pain.

Select the stimulus that can activate the nociceptive system.

a. a pleasant melody on a harp

b. a delicious apple

c. the aroma of freshly baked cookies

d. burning your hand on a stove

27.3 | Taste and Smell

In this section, you will explore the following questions:

- In what way do smell and taste stimuli differ from other sensory stimuli?
- What are the five primary tastes that can be distinguished by humans?
- In anatomical terms why is a dog's sense of smell more acute than a human's?

Taste, also called **gustation**, and smell, also called **olfaction**, are the most interconnected senses in that both involve molecules of the stimulus entering the body and bonding to receptors. Smell lets an animal sense the presence of food or other animals—whether potential mates, predators, or prey—or other chemicals in the environment that can impact their survival. Similarly, the sense of taste allows animals to discriminate between types of foods. While the value of a sense of smell is obvious, what is the value of a sense of taste? Different tasting foods have different attributes, both helpful and harmful. For example, sweet-tasting substances tend to be highly caloric, which could be necessary for survival in lean times. Bitterness is associated with toxicity, and sourness is associated with spoiled food. Salty foods are valuable in maintaining homeostasis by helping the body retain water and by providing ions necessary for cells to function.

Tastes and Odors

Both taste and odor stimuli are molecules taken in from the environment. The primary tastes detected by humans are sweet, sour, bitter, salty and umami. The first four tastes need little explanation. The identification of **umami** as a fundamental taste occurred fairly recently—it was identified in 1908 by Japanese scientist Kikunae Ikeda while he worked with seaweed broth, but it was not widely accepted as a taste that could be physiologically distinguished until many years later. The taste of umami, also known as savoriness, is attributable to the taste of the amino acid L-glutamate. In fact, monosodium glutamate, or MSG, is often used in cooking to enhance the savory taste of certain foods. What is the adaptive value of being able to distinguish umami? Savory substances tend to be high in protein.

All odors that we perceive are molecules in the air we breathe. If a substance does not release molecules into the air from its surface, it has no smell. And if a human or other animal does not have a receptor that recognizes a specific molecule, then that molecule has no smell. Humans have about 350 olfactory receptor subtypes that work in various combinations to allow us to sense about 10,000 different odors. Compare that to mice, for example, which have about 1,300 olfactory receptor types, and therefore probably sense more odors. Both odors and tastes involve molecules that stimulate specific chemoreceptors. Although humans commonly distinguish taste as one sense and smell as another, they work together to create the perception of flavor. A person's perception of flavor is reduced if he or she has congested nasal passages.

Reception and Transduction

Odorants (odor molecules) enter the nose and dissolve in the olfactory epithelium, the mucosa at the back of the nasal cavity (as illustrated in Figure 27.8). The **olfactory epithelium** is a collection of specialized olfactory receptors in the back of the nasal cavity that spans an area about 5 cm^2 in humans. Recall that sensory cells are neurons. An **olfactory receptor**, which is a dendrite of a specialized neuron, responds when it binds certain molecules inhaled from the environment by sending impulses directly to the olfactory bulb of the brain. Humans have about 12 million olfactory receptors, distributed among hundreds of different receptor types that respond to different odors. Twelve million seems like a large number of receptors, but compare that to other animals: rabbits have about 100 million, most dogs have about 1 billion, and bloodhounds—dogs selectively bred for their sense of smell—have about 4 billion. The overall size of the olfactory epithelium also differs between species, with that of bloodhounds, for example, being many times larger than that of humans.

Olfactory neurons are **bipolar neurons** (neurons with two processes from the cell body). Each neuron has a single dendrite buried in the olfactory epithelium, and extending from this dendrite are 5 to 20 receptor-laden, hair-like cilia that trap odorant molecules. The sensory receptors on the cilia are proteins, and it is the variations in their amino acid chains that make the receptors sensitive to different odorants. Each olfactory sensory neuron has only one type of receptor on its cilia, and the receptors are specialized to detect specific odorants, so the bipolar neurons themselves are specialized. When an odorant binds with a receptor that recognizes it, the sensory neuron associated with the receptor is stimulated. Olfactory stimulation is the only sensory information that directly reaches the cerebral cortex, whereas other sensations are relayed through the thalamus.

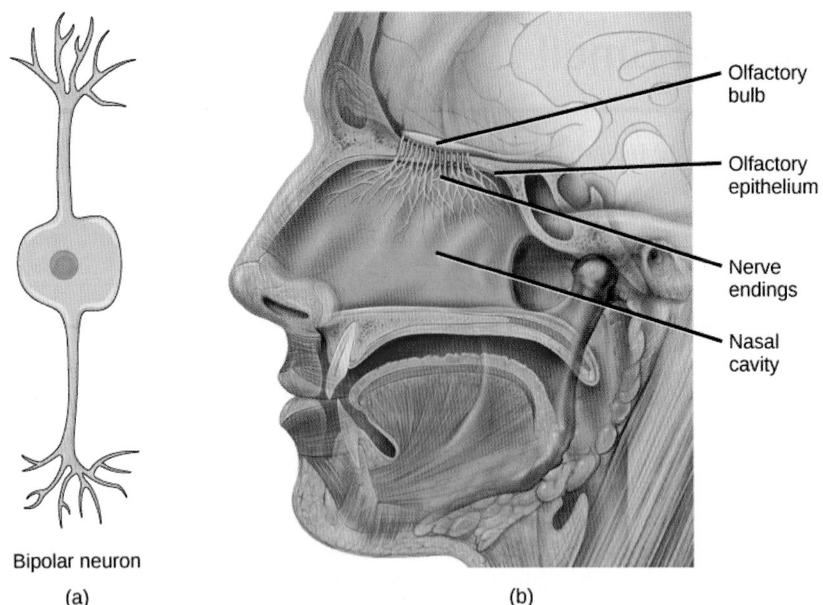

Figure 27.8 In the human olfactory system, (a) bipolar olfactory neurons extend from (b) the olfactory epithelium, where olfactory receptors are located, to the olfactory bulb. (credit: modification of work by Patrick J. Lynch, medical illustrator; C. Carl Jaffe, MD, cardiologist)

evolution CONNECTION

Pheromones

A **pheromone** is a chemical released by an animal that affects the behavior or physiology of animals of the same species. Pheromonal signals can have profound effects on animals that inhale them, but pheromones apparently are not consciously perceived in the same way as other odors. There are several different types of pheromones, which are released in urine or as glandular secretions. Certain pheromones are attractants to potential mates, others are repellants to potential competitors of the same sex, and still others play roles in mother-infant attachment. Some pheromones can also influence the timing of puberty, modify reproductive cycles, and even prevent embryonic implantation. While the roles of pheromones in many nonhuman species are important, pheromones have become less important in human behavior over evolutionary time compared to their importance to organisms with more limited behavioral repertoires.

The vomeronasal organ (VNO, or Jacobson's organ) is a tubular, fluid-filled, olfactory organ present in many vertebrate animals that sits adjacent to the nasal cavity. It is very sensitive to pheromones and is connected to the nasal cavity by a duct. When molecules dissolve in the mucosa of the nasal cavity, they then enter the VNO where the pheromone molecules among them bind with specialized pheromone receptors. Upon exposure to pheromones from their own species or others, many animals, including cats, may display the flehmen response (shown in Figure 27.9), a curling of the upper lip that helps pheromone molecules enter the VNO.

Pheromonal signals are sent, not to the main olfactory bulb, but to a different neural structure that projects directly to the amygdala (recall that the amygdala is a brain center important in emotional reactions, such as fear). The pheromonal signal then continues to areas of the hypothalamus that are key to reproductive physiology and behavior. While some scientists assert that the VNO is apparently functionally vestigial in humans, even though there is a similar structure located near human nasal cavities, others are researching it as a possible functional system that may, for example, contribute to synchronization of menstrual cycles in women living in close proximity.

Figure 27.9 The flehmen response in this tiger results in the curling of the upper lip and helps airborne pheromone molecules enter the vomeronasal organ. (credit: modification of work by "chadh"/Flickr)

Describe how a male snake can physiologically detect the presence of a female that is trying to attract a mate.

a. The pheromones secreted by a female dissolve and enter the vomeronasal organ. The dissolved molecules bind to receptors, which send a signal to the hypothalamus, which in turn sends the signal to the amygdala.

b. The pheromones secreted by a female dissolve and enter the vomeronasal organ. The dissolved molecules bind to receptors, which send a signal to the amygdala, which in turn sends the signal to the hypothalamus.

c. The pheromones secreted by a female dissolve and enter the amygdala. The dissolved molecules bind to receptors, which send a signal to the vomeronasal organ, which in turn sends the signal to the hypothalamus.

d. The pheromones secreted by a female dissolve and enter the amygdala. The dissolved molecules bind to receptors, which send a signal to the hypothalamus, which in turn sends the signal to the vomeronasal organ.

Taste

Detecting a taste (gustation) is fairly similar to detecting an odor (olfaction), given that both taste and smell rely on chemical receptors being stimulated by certain molecules. The primary organ of taste is the taste bud. A **taste bud** is a cluster of gustatory receptors (taste cells) that are located within the bumps on the tongue called **papillae** (singular: papilla) (illustrated in Figure 27.10). There are several structurally distinct papillae. Filiform papillae, which are located across the tongue, are tactile, providing friction that helps the tongue move substances, and contain no taste cells. In contrast, fungiform papillae, which are located mainly on the anterior two-thirds of the tongue, each contain one to eight taste buds and also have receptors for pressure and temperature. The large circumvallate papillae contain up to 100 taste buds and form a V near the posterior margin of the tongue.

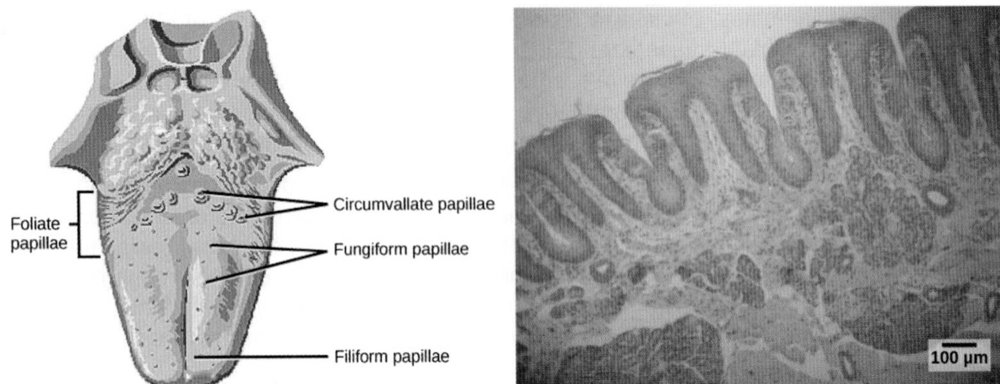

Figure 27.10 (a) Foliate, circumvallate, and fungiform papillae are located on different regions of the tongue. (b) Foliate papillae are prominent protrusions on this light micrograph. (credit a: modification of work by NCI; scale-bar data from Matt Russell)

In addition to those two types of chemically and mechanically sensitive papillae are foliate papillae—leaf-like papillae located in parallel folds along the edges and toward the back of the tongue, as seen in the Figure 27.10 micrograph. Foliate papillae contain about 1,300 taste buds within their folds. Finally, there are circumvallate papillae, which are wall-like papillae in the shape of an inverted "V" at the back of the tongue. Each of these papillae is surrounded by a groove and contains about 250 taste buds.

Each taste bud's taste cells are replaced every 10 to 14 days. These are elongated cells with hair-like processes called microvilli at the tips that extend into the taste bud pore (illustrate in Figure 27.11). Food molecules (**tastants**) are dissolved in saliva, and they bind with and stimulate the receptors on the microvilli. The receptors for tastants are located across the outer portion and front of the tongue, outside of the middle area where the filiform papillae are most prominent.

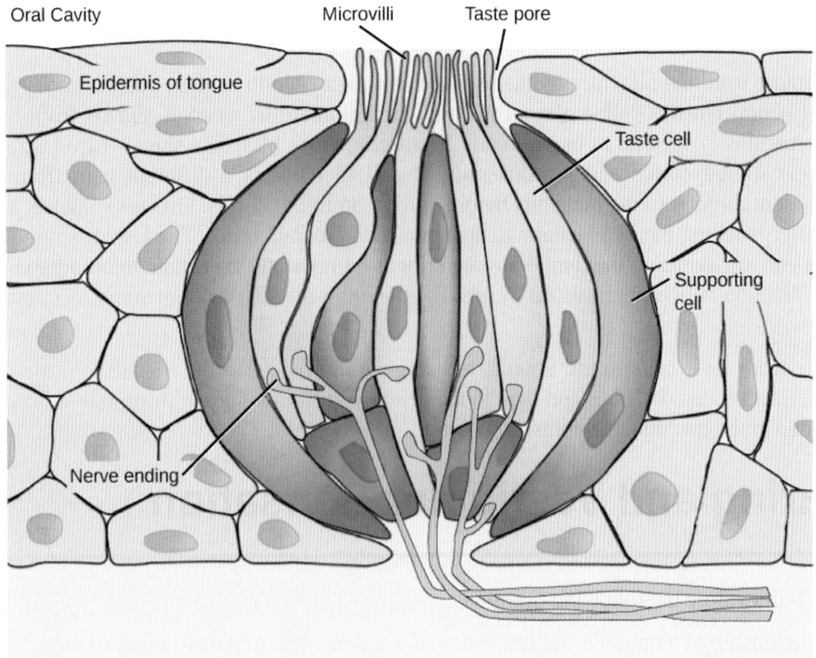

Figure 27.11 Pores in the tongue allow tastants to enter taste pores in the tongue. (credit: modification of work by Vincenzo Rizzo)

In humans, there are five primary tastes, and each taste has only one corresponding type of receptor. Thus, like olfaction, each receptor is specific to its stimulus (tastant). Transduction of the five tastes happens through different mechanisms that reflect the molecular composition of the tastant. A salty tastant (containing NaCl) provides the sodium ions (Na^+) that enter the taste neurons and excite them directly. Sour tastants are acids and belong to the thermoreceptor protein family. Binding of an acid or other sour-tasting molecule triggers a change in the ion channel and these increase hydrogen ion (H^+) concentrations in the taste neurons, thus depolarizing them. Sweet, bitter, and umami tastants require a G-protein coupled receptor. These tastants bind to their respective receptors, thereby exciting the specialized neurons associated with them.

Both tasting abilities and sense of smell change with age. In humans, the senses decline dramatically by age 50 and continue to decline. A child may find a food to be too spicy, whereas an elderly person may find the same food to be bland and unappetizing.

View this **animation (http://openstaxcollege.org/l/taste)** that shows how the sense of taste works.

Which of the following is true about human taste?

a. Taste buds are covered in papillae.

b. Saliva contains taste receptor cells.

c. Papillae stimulate the hair-like endings of taste buds.

d. The hair-like endings of taste buds generate nerve impulses to the brain.

Smell and Taste in the Brain

Olfactory neurons project from the olfactory epithelium to the olfactory bulb as thin, unmyelinated axons. The **olfactory bulb** is composed of neural clusters called **glomeruli**, and each glomerulus receives signals from one type of olfactory receptor, so each glomerulus is specific to one odorant. From glomeruli, olfactory signals travel directly to the olfactory cortex and then to the frontal cortex and the thalamus. Recall that this is a different path from most other sensory information, which is sent directly to the thalamus before ending up in the cortex. Olfactory signals also travel directly to the amygdala, thereafter reaching the hypothalamus, thalamus, and frontal cortex. The last structure that olfactory signals directly travel to is a cortical center in the temporal lobe structure important in spatial, autobiographical, declarative, and episodic memories. Olfaction is finally processed by areas of the brain that deal with memory, emotions, reproduction, and thought.

Taste neurons project from taste cells in the tongue, esophagus, and palate to the medulla, in the brainstem. From the medulla, taste signals travel to the thalamus and then to the primary gustatory cortex. Information from different regions of the tongue is segregated in the medulla, thalamus, and cortex.

27.4 | Hearing and Vestibular Sensation

In this section, you will explore the following questions:

- What is the relationship of amplitude and frequency of a sound wave to the attributes of sound?
- What path does sound travel within the auditory system to the site of transduction of sound?
- What are the structures of the vestibular system that respond to gravity?

Audition, or hearing, is important to humans and to other animals for many different interactions. It enables an organism to detect and receive information about danger, such as an approaching predator, and to participate in communal exchanges like those concerning territories or mating. On the other hand, although it is physically linked to the auditory system, the vestibular system is not involved in hearing. Instead, an animal's vestibular system detects its own movement, both linear and angular acceleration and deceleration, and balance.

Sound

Auditory stimuli are sound waves, which are mechanical, pressure waves that move through a medium, such as air or water. There are no sound waves in a vacuum since there are no air molecules to move in waves. The speed of sound waves differs, based on altitude, temperature, and medium, but at sea level and a temperature of 20° C (68° F), sound waves travel in the air at about 343 meters per second.

As is true for all waves, there are four main characteristics of a sound wave: frequency, wavelength, period, and amplitude. Frequency is the number of waves per unit of time, and in sound is heard as pitch. High-frequency (≥15.000Hz) sounds are higher-pitched (short wavelength) than low-frequency (long wavelengths; ≤100Hz) sounds. Frequency is measured in cycles per second, and for sound, the most commonly used unit is hertz (Hz), or cycles per second. Most humans can perceive sounds with frequencies between 30 and 20,000 Hz. Women are typically better at hearing high frequencies, but everyone's ability to hear high frequencies decreases with age. Dogs detect up to about 40,000 Hz; cats, 60,000 Hz; bats, 100,000 Hz; and dolphins 150,000 Hz, and American shad (*Alosa sapidissima*), a fish, can hear 180,000 Hz. Those frequencies above the human range are called **ultrasound**.

Amplitude, or the dimension of a wave from peak to trough, in sound is heard as volume and is illustrated in Figure 27.12. The sound waves of louder sounds have greater amplitude than those of softer sounds. For sound, volume is measured in decibels (dB). The softest sound that a human can hear is the zero point. Humans speak normally at 60 decibels.

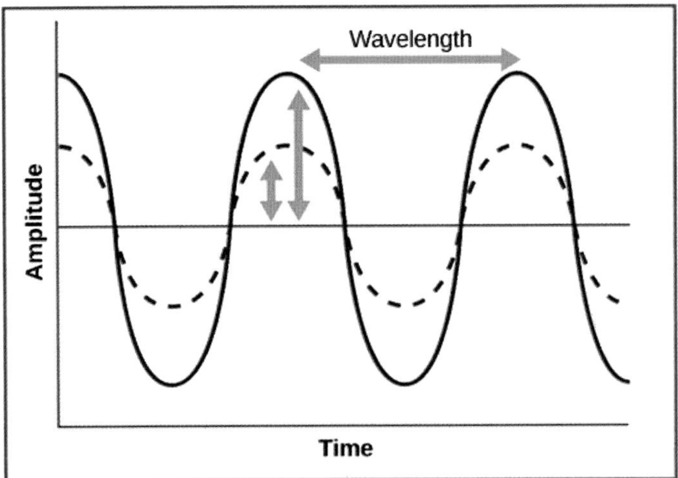

Figure 27.12 For sound waves, wavelength corresponds to pitch. Amplitude of the wave corresponds to volume. The sound wave shown with a dashed line is softer in volume than the sound wave shown with a solid line. (credit: NIH)

Reception of Sound

In mammals, sound waves are collected by the external, cartilaginous part of the ear called the **pinna**, then travel through the auditory canal and cause vibration of the thin diaphragm called the **tympanum** or ear drum, the innermost part of the **outer ear** (illustrated in Figure 27.13). Interior to the tympanum is the **middle ear**. The middle ear holds three small bones called the **ossicles**, which transfer energy from the moving tympanum to the inner ear. The three ossicles are the **malleus** (also known as the hammer), the **incus** (the anvil), and **stapes** (the stirrup). The aptly named stapes looks very much like a stirrup. The three ossicles are unique to mammals, and each plays a role in hearing. The malleus attaches at three points to the interior surface of the tympanic membrane. The incus attaches the malleus to the stapes. In humans, the stapes is not long enough to reach the tympanum. If we did not have the malleus and the incus, then the vibrations of the tympanum would never reach the inner ear. These bones also function to collect force and amplify sounds. The ear ossicles are homologous to bones in a fish mouth: the bones that support gills in fish are thought to be adapted for use in the vertebrate ear over evolutionary time. Many animals (frogs, reptiles, and birds, for example) use the stapes of the middle ear to transmit vibrations to the middle ear.

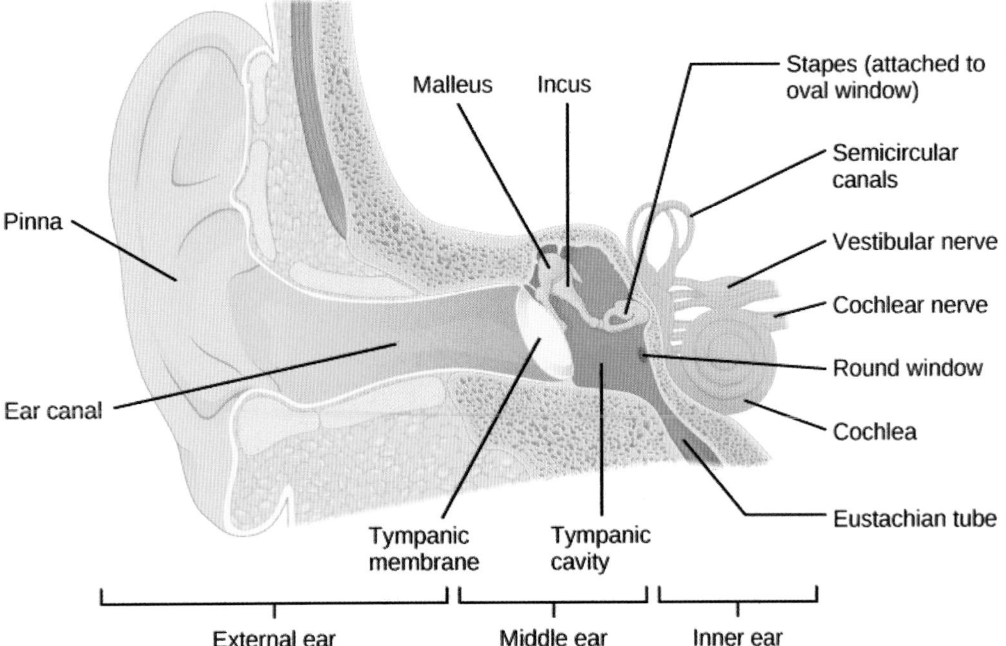

Figure 27.13 Sound travels through the outer ear to the middle ear, which is bounded on its exterior by the tympanic membrane. The middle ear contains three bones called ossicles that transfer the sound wave to the oval window, the exterior boundary of the inner ear. The organ of Corti, which is the organ of sound transduction, lies inside the cochlea.

Transduction of Sound

Vibrating objects, such as vocal cords, create sound waves or pressure waves in the air. When these pressure waves reach the ear, the ear transduces this mechanical stimulus (pressure wave) into a nerve impulse (electrical signal) that the brain perceives as sound. The pressure waves strike the tympanum, causing it to vibrate. The mechanical energy from the moving tympanum transmits the vibrations to the three bones of the middle ear. The stapes transmits the vibrations to a thin diaphragm called the **oval window**, which is the outermost structure of the **inner ear**. The structures of the inner ear are found in the **labyrinth**, a bony, hollow structure that is the most interior portion of the ear. Here, the energy from the sound wave is transferred from the stapes through the flexible oval window and to the fluid of the cochlea. The vibrations of the oval window create pressure waves in the fluid (perilymph) inside the cochlea. The **cochlea** is a whorled structure, like the shell of a snail, and it contains receptors for transduction of the mechanical wave into an electrical signal (as illustrated in Figure 27.14). Inside the cochlea, the **basilar membrane** is a mechanical analyzer that runs the length of the cochlea, curling toward the cochlea's center.

The mechanical properties of the basilar membrane change along its length, such that it is thicker, tauter, and narrower at the outside of the whorl (where the cochlea is largest), and thinner, floppier, and broader toward the apex, or center, of the whorl (where the cochlea is smallest). Different regions of the basilar membrane vibrate according to the frequency of the sound wave conducted through the fluid in the cochlea. For these reasons, the fluid-filled cochlea detects different wave frequencies (pitches) at different regions of the membrane. When the sound waves in the cochlear fluid contact the basilar membrane, it flexes back and forth in a wave-like fashion. Above the basilar membrane is the **tectorial membrane**.

visual CONNECTION

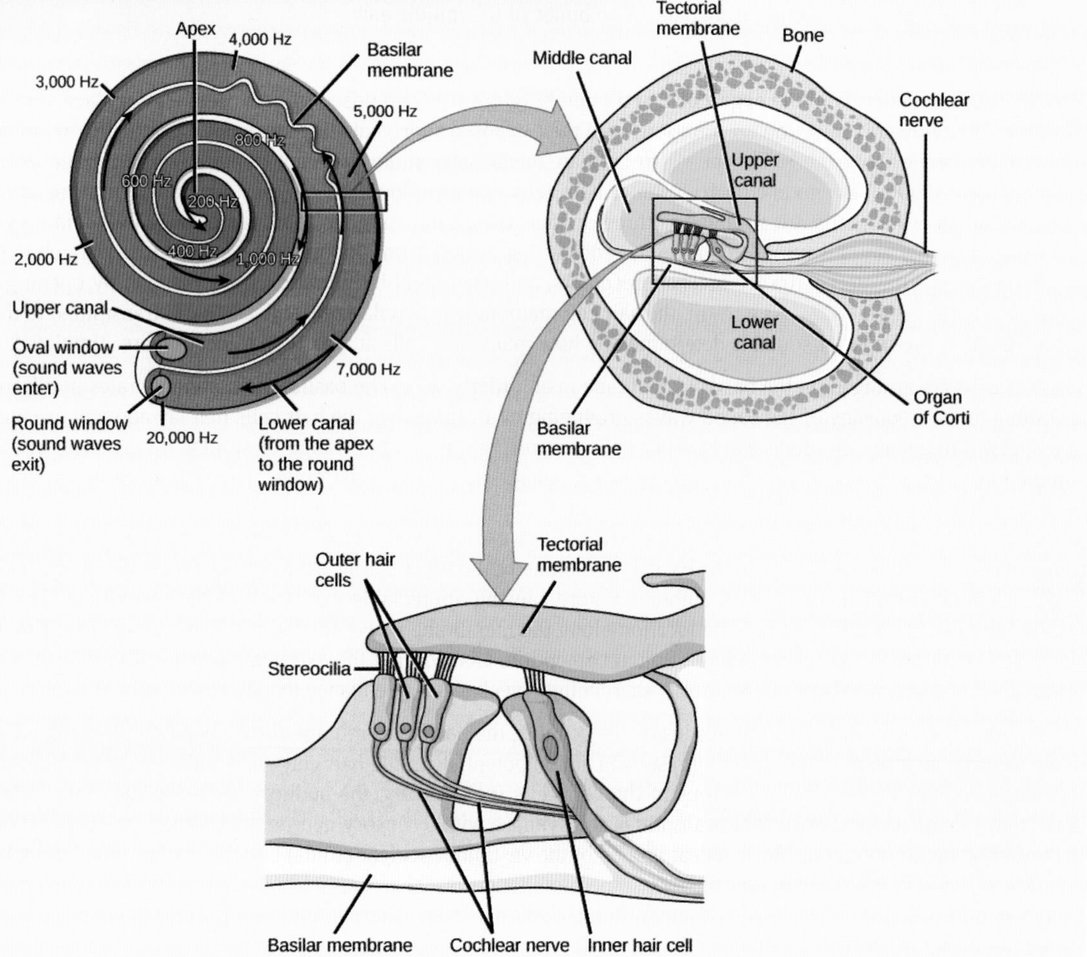

Figure 27.14 In the human ear, sound waves cause the stapes to press against the oval window. Vibrations travel up the fluid-filled interior of the cochlea. The basilar membrane that lines the cochlea gets continuously thinner toward the apex of the cochlea. Different thicknesses of membrane vibrate in response to different frequencies of sound. Sound waves then exit through the round window. In the cross section of the cochlea (top right figure), note that in addition to the upper canal and lower canal, the cochlea also has a middle canal. The organ of Corti (bottom image) is the site of sound transduction. Movement of stereocilia on hair cells results in an action potential that travels along the auditory nerve.

Cochlear implants can restore hearing in people who have a nonfunctional cochlea. The implant consists of a microphone that picks up sound. A speech processor selects sounds in the range of human speech, and a transmitter converts these sounds to electrical impulses, which are then sent to the auditory nerve. Which of the following types of hearing loss would not be restored by a cochlear implant?

1. Hearing loss resulting from absence or loss of hair cells in the organ of Corti.
2. Hearing loss resulting from an abnormal auditory nerve.
3. Hearing loss resulting from fracture of the cochlea.
4. Hearing loss resulting from damage to bones of the middle ear.

Cochlear implants can restore hearing in people who have a nonfunctional cochlea. The implant consists of a microphone that picks up sound. A speech processor selects sounds in the range of human speech, and a transmitter converts these sounds to electrical impulses, which are then sent to the auditory nerve. Which of the following types of hearing loss would not be restored by a cochlear implant?

a. Hearing loss resulting from absence or loss of hair cells in the organ of Corti.
b. Hearing loss resulting from an abnormal auditory nerve.
c. Hearing loss resulting from fracture of the cochlea.
d. Hearing loss resulting from damage to bones of the middle ear.

The site of transduction is in the **organ of Corti** (spiral organ). It is composed of hair cells held in place above the basilar membrane like flowers projecting up from soil, with their exposed short, hair-like **stereocilia** contacting or embedded in the tectorial membrane above them. The inner hair cells are the primary auditory receptors and exist in a single row, numbering approximately 3,500. The stereocilia from inner hair cells extend into small dimples on the tectorial membrane's lower surface. The outer hair cells are arranged in three or four rows. They number approximately 12,000, and they function to fine tune incoming sound waves. The longer stereocilia that project from the outer hair cells actually attach to the tectorial membrane. All of the stereocilia are mechanoreceptors, and when bent by vibrations they respond by opening a gated ion channel (refer to Figure 27.2). As a result, the hair cell membrane is depolarized, and a signal is transmitted to the chochlear nerve. Intensity (volume) of sound is determined by how many hair cells at a particular location are stimulated.

The hair cells are arranged on the basilar membrane in an orderly way. The basilar membrane vibrates in different regions, according to the frequency of the sound waves impinging on it. Likewise, the hair cells that lay above it are most sensitive to a specific frequency of sound waves. Hair cells can respond to a small range of similar frequencies, but they require stimulation of greater intensity to fire at frequencies outside of their optimal range. The difference in response frequency between adjacent inner hair cells is about 0.2 percent. Compare that to adjacent piano strings, which are about six percent different. Place theory, which is the model for how biologists think pitch detection works in the human ear, states that high frequency sounds selectively vibrate the basilar membrane of the inner ear near the entrance port (the oval window). Lower frequencies travel farther along the membrane before causing appreciable excitation of the membrane. The basic pitch-determining mechanism is based on the location along the membrane where the hair cells are stimulated. The place theory is the first step toward an understanding of pitch perception. Considering the extreme pitch sensitivity of the human ear, it is thought that there must be some auditory "sharpening" mechanism to enhance the pitch resolution.

When sound waves produce fluid waves inside the cochlea, the basilar membrane flexes, bending the stereocilia that attach to the tectorial membrane. Their bending results in action potentials in the hair cells, and auditory information travels along the neural endings of the bipolar neurons of the hair cells (collectively, the auditory nerve) to the brain. When the hairs bend, they release an excitatory neurotransmitter at a synapse with a sensory neuron, which then conducts action potentials to the central nervous system. The cochlear branch of the vestibulocochlear cranial nerve sends information on hearing. The auditory system is very refined, and there is some modulation or "sharpening" built in. The brain can send signals back to the cochlea, resulting in a change of length in the outer hair cells, sharpening or dampening the hair cells' response to certain frequencies.

Watch an animation (http://openstaxcollege.org/l/hearing) of sound entering the outer ear, moving through the ear structure, stimulating cochlear nerve impulses, and eventually sending signals to the temporal lobe.

Imagine that your friend's pet dog ran off into the woods while she was hiking. After about 10 minutes while she still hiked, your friend whistled for her dog, who came running back to her. Explain how the dog was able to use your friend's whistling to find her, even though she had moved from the location at which the dog had last seen her.

a. The dog was used to his master's whistling. This enabled the dog to determine where the sound was coming from.

b. The dog was used to the hiking place. This enabled the dog to determine where the sound was coming from.

c. The ears of the dog received the sounds at the same time. This enabled the dog to use the timing of sound reception in each ear to determine where the sound was coming from.

d. The two ears of the dog received the sounds at slightly different times. This enabled the dog to use the timing of sound reception in each ear to determine where the sound was coming from.

Higher Processing

The inner hair cells are most important for conveying auditory information to the brain. About 90 percent of the afferent neurons carry information from inner hair cells, with each hair cell synapsing with 10 or so neurons. Outer hair cells connect to only 10 percent of the afferent neurons, and each afferent neuron innervates many hair cells. The afferent, bipolar neurons that convey auditory information travel from the cochlea to the medulla, through the pons and midbrain in the brainstem, finally reaching the primary auditory cortex in the temporal lobe.

Vestibular Information

The stimuli associated with the vestibular system are linear acceleration (gravity) and angular acceleration and deceleration. Gravity, acceleration, and deceleration are detected by evaluating the inertia on receptive cells in the vestibular system. Gravity is detected through head position. Angular acceleration and deceleration are expressed through turning or tilting of the head.

The vestibular system has some similarities with the auditory system. It utilizes hair cells just like the auditory system, but it excites them in different ways. There are five vestibular receptor organs in the inner ear: the utricle, the saccule, and three semicircular canals. Together, they make up what's known as the vestibular labyrinth that is shown in Figure 27.15. The utricle and saccule respond to acceleration in a straight line, such as gravity. The roughly 30,000 hair cells in the utricle and 16,000 hair cells in the saccule lie below a gelatinous layer, with their stereocilia projecting into the gelatin. Embedded in this gelatin are calcium carbonate crystals—like tiny rocks. When the head is tilted, the crystals continue to be pulled straight down by gravity, but the new angle of the head causes the gelatin to shift, thereby bending the stereocilia. The bending of the stereocilia stimulates the neurons, and they signal to the brain that the head is tilted, allowing the maintenance of balance. It is the vestibular branch of the vestibulocochlear cranial nerve that deals with balance.

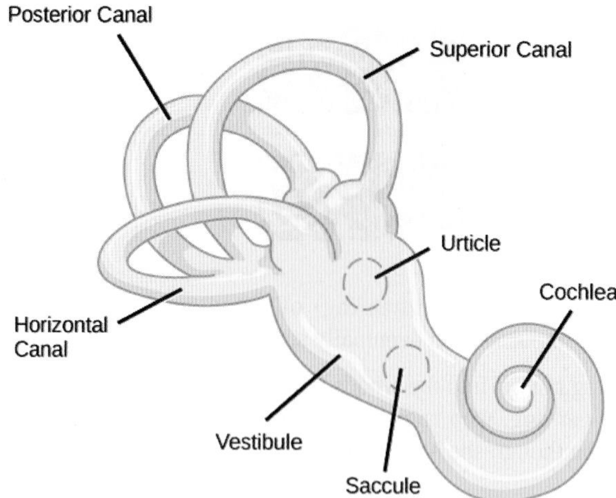

Figure 27.15 The structure of the vestibular labyrinth is shown. (credit: modification of work by NIH)

The fluid-filled **semicircular canals** are tubular loops set at oblique angles. They are arranged in three spatial planes. The base of each canal has a swelling that contains a cluster of hair cells. The hairs project into a gelatinous cap called the cupula and monitor angular acceleration and deceleration from rotation. They would be stimulated by driving your car around a corner, turning your head, or falling forward. One canal lies horizontally, while the other two lie at about 45 degree angles to the horizontal axis, as illustrated in Figure 27.15. When the brain processes input from all three canals together, it can detect angular acceleration or deceleration in three dimensions. When the head turns, the fluid in the canals shifts, thereby bending stereocilia and sending signals to the brain. Upon cessation accelerating or decelerating—or just moving—the movement of the fluid within the canals slows or stops. For example, imagine holding a glass of water. When moving forward, water may splash backwards onto the hand, and when motion has stopped, water may splash forward onto the fingers. While in motion, the water settles in the glass and does not splash. Note that the canals are not sensitive to velocity itself, but to changes in velocity, so moving forward at 60mph with your eyes closed would not give the sensation of movement, but suddenly accelerating or braking would stimulate the receptors.

Higher Processing

Hair cells from the utricle, saccule, and semicircular canals also communicate through bipolar neurons to the cochlear nucleus in the medulla. Cochlear neurons send descending projections to the spinal cord and ascending projections to the pons, thalamus, and cerebellum. Connections to the cerebellum are important for coordinated movements. There are also projections to the temporal cortex, which account for feelings of dizziness; projections to autonomic nervous system areas in the brainstem, which account for motion sickness; and projections to the primary somatosensory cortex, which monitors subjective measurements of the external world and self-movement. People with lesions in the vestibular area of the somatosensory cortex see vertical objects in the world as being tilted. Finally, the vestibular signals project to certain optic muscles to coordinate eye and head movements.

Click through this interactive tutorial (http://openstaxcollege.org/l/ear_anatomy) to review the parts of the ear and how they function to process sound.

You have trouble maintaining balance. Identify the part of your ear that has been damaged.

a. eustachian tube

b. cochlea

c. semicircular canals

d. ear canal

27.5 | Vision

In this section, you will explore the following questions:

- How do electromagnetic waves differ from sound waves?
- What path does light take as it travels through the eye to the point of the optic nerve?
- What is tonic activity as it is manifested in photoreceptors in the retina?

Vision is the ability to detect light patterns from the outside environment and interpret them into images. Animals are bombarded with sensory information, and the sheer volume of visual information can be problematic. Fortunately, the visual systems of species have evolved to attend to the most-important stimuli. The importance of vision to humans is further substantiated by the fact that about one-third of the human cerebral cortex is dedicated to analyzing and perceiving visual information.

Light

As with auditory stimuli, light travels in waves. The compression waves that compose sound must travel in a medium—a gas, a liquid, or a solid. In contrast, light is composed of electromagnetic waves and needs no medium; light can travel in a vacuum (Figure 27.16). The behavior of light can be discussed in terms of the behavior of waves and also in terms of the behavior of the fundamental unit of light—a packet of electromagnetic radiation called a photon. A glance at the electromagnetic spectrum shows that visible light for humans is just a small slice of the entire spectrum, which includes radiation that we cannot see as light because it is below the frequency of visible red light and above the frequency of visible violet light.

Certain variables are important when discussing perception of light. Wavelength (which varies inversely with frequency) manifests itself as hue. Light at the red end of the visible spectrum has longer wavelengths (and is lower frequency), while light at the violet end has shorter wavelengths (and is higher frequency). The wavelength of light is expressed in nanometers (nm); one nanometer is one billionth of a meter. Humans perceive light that ranges between approximately 380 nm and 740 nm. Some other animals, though, can detect wavelengths outside of the human range. For example, bees see near-ultraviolet light in order to locate nectar guides on flowers, and some non-avian reptiles sense infrared light (heat that prey gives off).

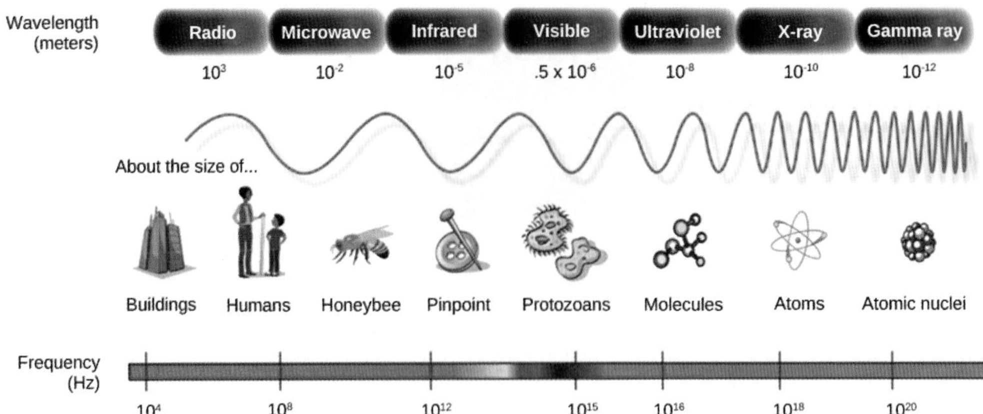

Figure 27.16 In the electromagnetic spectrum, visible light lies between 380 nm and 740 nm. (credit: modification of work by NASA)

Wave amplitude is perceived as luminous intensity, or brightness. The standard unit of intensity of light is the **candela**, which is approximately the luminous intensity of a one common candle.

Light waves travel 299,792 km per second in a vacuum, (and somewhat slower in various media such as air and water), and those waves arrive at the eye as long (red), medium (green), and short (blue) waves. What is termed "white light" is light that is perceived as white by the human eye. This effect is produced by light that stimulates equally the color receptors in the human eye. The apparent color of an object is the color (or colors) that the object reflects. Thus a red object reflects the red wavelengths in mixed (white) light and absorbs all other wavelengths of light.

Anatomy of the Eye

The photoreceptive cells of the eye, where transduction of light to nervous impulses occurs, are located in the **retina** (shown in Figure 27.17) on the inner surface of the back of the eye. But light does not impinge on the retina unaltered. It passes through other layers that process it so that it can be interpreted by the retina (Figure 27.17**b**). The **cornea**, the front transparent layer of the eye, and the crystalline **lens**, a transparent convex structure behind the cornea, both refract (bend) light to focus the image on the retina. The **iris**, which is conspicuous as the colored part of the eye, is a circular muscular ring lying between the lens and cornea that regulates the amount of light entering the eye. In conditions of high ambient light, the iris contracts, reducing the size of the pupil at its center. In conditions of low light, the iris relaxes and the pupil enlarges.

visual CONNECTION

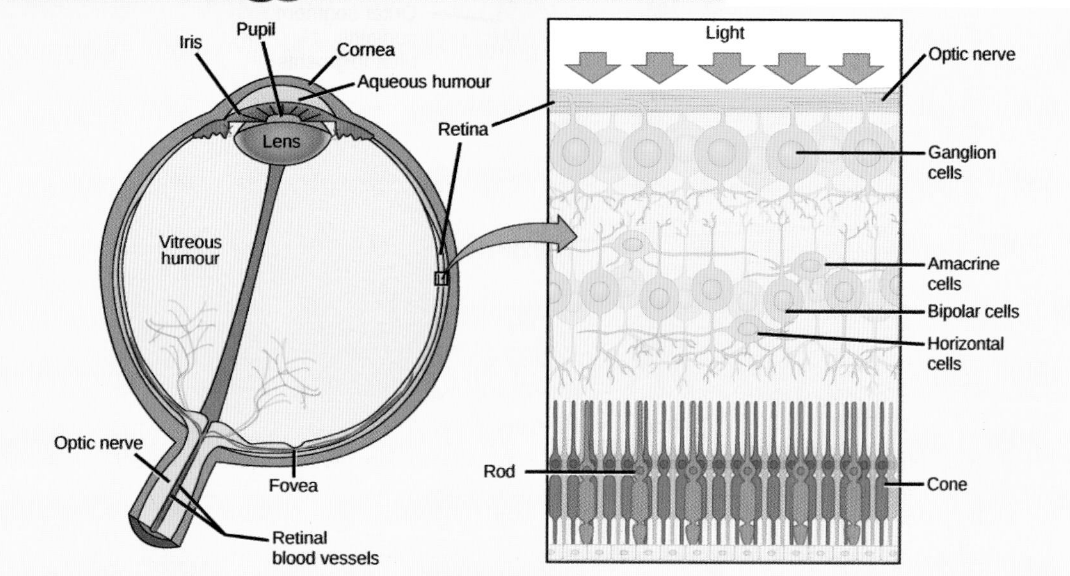

Figure 27.17 (a) The human eye is shown in cross section. (b) A blowup shows the layers of the retina.

Which of the following statements about the human eye is true?

a. Rods detect color, whereas cones detect shades of gray.
b. The pupil is the location of rods and cones.
c. The iris adjusts the amount of light coming into the eye.
d. The fovea is a protective layer on the front of the eye.

The main function of the lens is to focus light on the retina and fovea centralis. The lens is dynamic, focusing and re-focusing light as the eye rests on near and far objects in the visual field. The lens is operated by muscles that stretch it flat or allow it to thicken, changing the focal length of light coming through it to focus it sharply on the retina. With age comes the loss of the flexibility of the lens, and a form of farsightedness called **presbyopia** results. Presbyopia occurs because the image focuses behind the retina. Presbyopia is a deficit similar to a different type of farsightedness called **hyperopia** caused by an eyeball that is too short. For both defects, images in the distance are clear but images nearby are blurry. **Myopia** (nearsightedness) occurs when an eyeball is elongated and the image focus falls in front of the retina. In this case, images in the distance are blurry but images nearby are clear.

There are two types of photoreceptors in the retina: **rods** and **cones**, named for their general appearance as illustrated in Figure 27.18. Rods are strongly photosensitive and are located in the outer edges of the retina. They detect dim light and are used primarily for peripheral and nighttime vision. Cones are weakly photosensitive and are located near the center of the retina. They respond to bright light, and their primary role is in daytime, color vision.

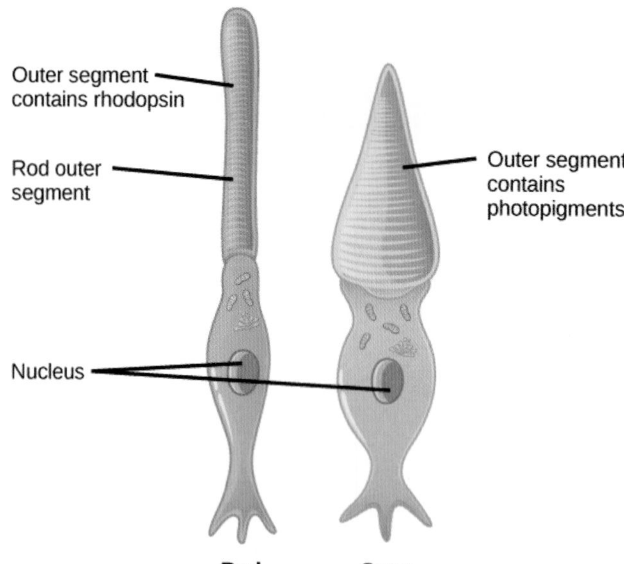

Figure 27.18 Rods and cones are photoreceptors in the retina. Rods respond in low light and can detect only shades of gray. Cones respond in intense light and are responsible for color vision.

The **fovea** is the region in the center back of the eye that is responsible for acute vision. The fovea has a high density of cones. When you bring your gaze to an object to examine it intently in bright light, the eyes orient so that the object's image falls on the fovea. However, when looking at a star in the night sky or other object in dim light, the object can be better viewed by the peripheral vision because it is the rods at the edges of the retina, rather than the cones at the center, that operate better in low light. In humans, cones far outnumber rods in the fovea.

Review the anatomical structure (http://openstaxcollege.org/l/eye_diagram) of the eye, clicking on each part to practice identification.

Identify the part of your eye that could be damaged if your eyes are incapable of focusing an image on the retina.

a. lens

b. iris

c. rods

d. cones

Transduction of Light

The rods and cones are the site of transduction of light to a neural signal. Both rods and cones contain photopigments. In vertebrates, the main photopigment, **rhodopsin**, has two main parts Figure 27.19): an opsin, which is a membrane protein (in the form of a cluster of α-helices that span the membrane), and retinal—a molecule that absorbs light. When light hits a photoreceptor, it causes a shape change in the retinal, altering its structure from a bent (*cis*) form of the molecule to its linear (*trans*) isomer. This isomerization of retinal activates the rhodopsin, starting a cascade of events that ends with the closing of Na^+ channels in the membrane of the photoreceptor. Thus, unlike most other sensory neurons (which become depolarized by exposure to a stimulus) visual receptors become hyperpolarized and thus driven away from threshold (Figure 27.20).

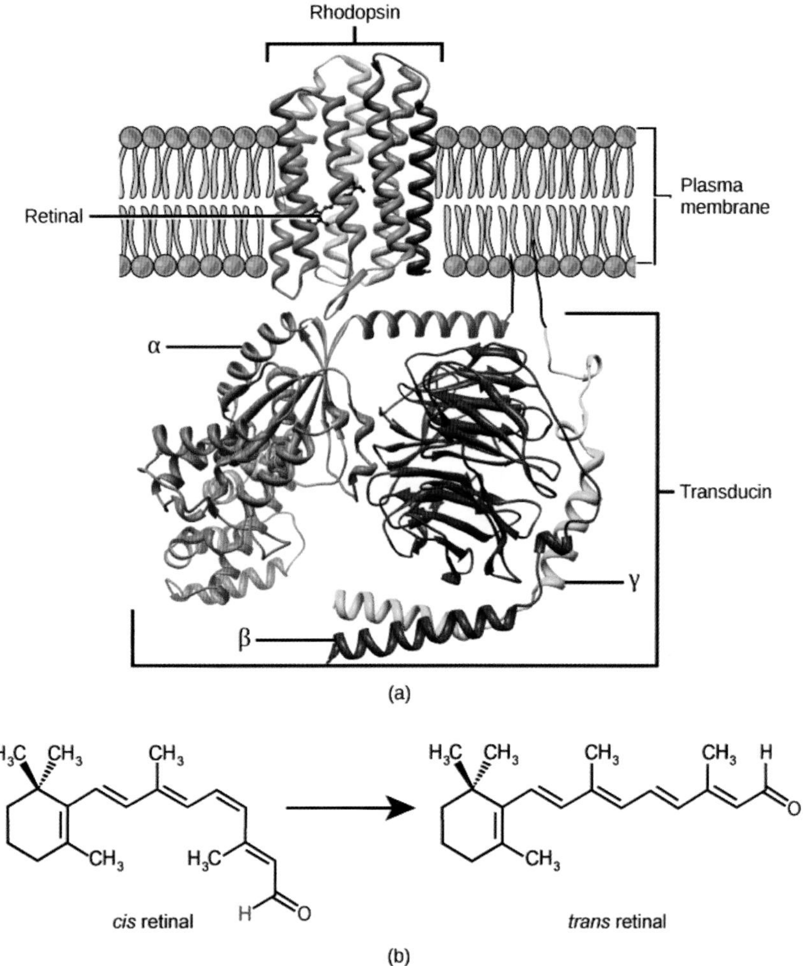

Figure 27.19 (a) Rhodopsin, the photoreceptor in vertebrates, has two parts: the trans-membrane protein opsin, and retinal. When light strikes retinal, it changes shape from (b) a *cis* to a *trans* form. The signal is passed to a G-protein called transducin, triggering a series of downstream events.

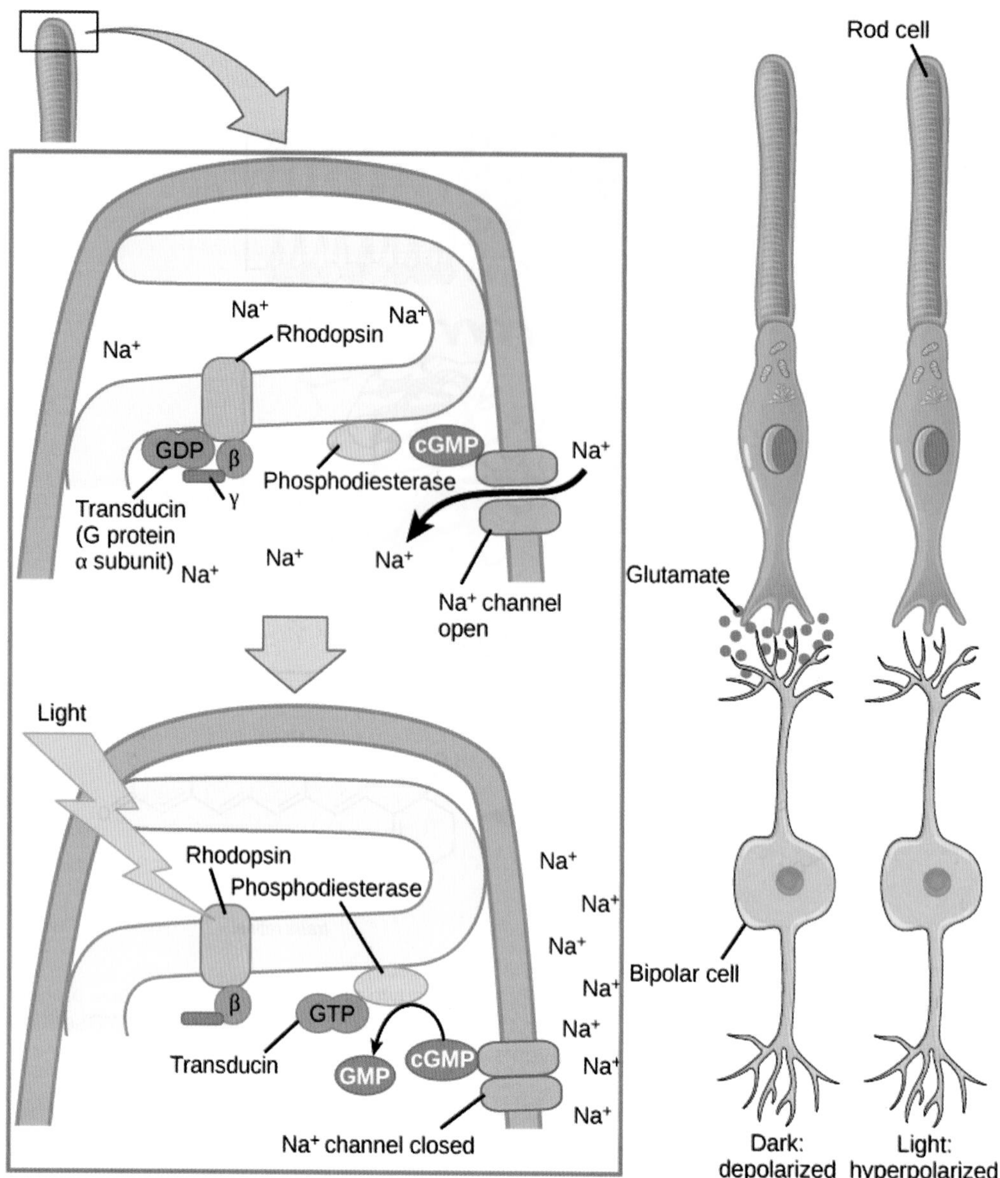

Figure 27.20 When light strikes rhodopsin, the G-protein transducin is activated, which in turn activates phosphodiesterase. Phosphodiesterase converts cGMP to GMP, thereby closing sodium channels. As a result, the membrane becomes hyperpolarized. The hyperpolarized membrane does not release glutamate to the bipolar cell.

Trichromatic Coding

There are three types of cones (with different photopsins), and they differ in the wavelength to which they are most responsive, as shown in Figure 27.21. Some cones are maximally responsive to short light waves of 420 nm, so they are called S cones ("S" for "short"); others respond maximally to waves of 530 nm (M cones, for "medium"); a third group responds maximally to light of longer wavelengths, at 560 nm (L, or "long" cones). With only one type of cone, color vision would not be possible, and a two-cone (dichromatic) system has limitations. Primates use a three-cone (trichromatic) system, resulting in full color vision.

The color we perceive is a result of the ratio of activity of our three types of cones. The colors of the visual spectrum, running from long-wavelength light to short, are red (700 nm), orange (600 nm), yellow (565 nm), green (497 nm), blue (470 nm), indigo (450 nm), and violet (425 nm). Humans have very sensitive perception of color and can distinguish about 500 levels of brightness, 200 different hues, and 20 steps of saturation, or about 2 million distinct colors.

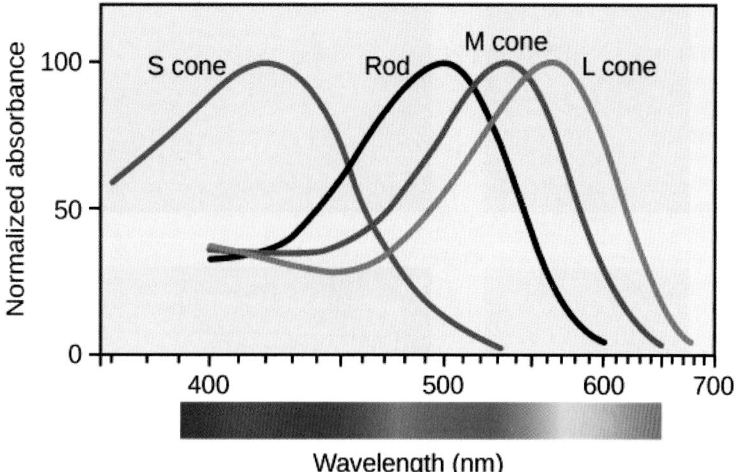

Figure 27.21 Human rod cells and the different types of cone cells each have an optimal wavelength. However, there is considerable overlap in the wavelengths of light detected.

Retinal Processing

Visual signals leave the cones and rods, travel to the bipolar cells, and then to ganglion cells. A large degree of processing of visual information occurs in the retina itself, before visual information is sent to the brain.

Photoreceptors in the retina continuously undergo **tonic activity**. That is, they are always slightly active even when not stimulated by light. In neurons that exhibit tonic activity, the absence of stimuli maintains a firing rate at a baseline; while some stimuli increase firing rate from the baseline, and other stimuli decrease firing rate. In the absence of light, the bipolar neurons that connect rods and cones to ganglion cells are continuously and actively inhibited by the rods and cones. Exposure of the retina to light hyperpolarizes the rods and cones and removes their inhibition of bipolar cells. The now active bipolar cells in turn stimulate the ganglion cells, which send action potentials along their axons (which leave the eye as the optic nerve). Thus, the visual system relies on change in retinal activity, rather than the absence or presence of activity, to encode visual signals for the brain. Sometimes horizontal cells carry signals from one rod or cone to other photoreceptors and to several bipolar cells. When a rod or cone stimulates a horizontal cell, the horizontal cell inhibits more distant photoreceptors and bipolar cells, creating lateral inhibition. This inhibition sharpens edges and enhances contrast in the images by making regions receiving light appear lighter and dark surroundings appear darker. Amacrine cells can distribute information from one bipolar cell to many ganglion cells.

You can demonstrate this using an easy demonstration to “trick” your retina and brain about the colors you are observing in your visual field. Look fixedly at Figure 27.22 for about 45 seconds. Then quickly shift your gaze to a sheet of blank white paper or a white wall. You should see an afterimage of the Norwegian flag in its correct colors. At this point, close your eyes for a moment, then reopen them, looking again at the white paper or wall; the afterimage of the flag should continue to appear as red, white, and blue. What causes this? According to an explanation called opponent process theory, as you gazed fixedly at the green, black, and yellow flag, your retinal ganglion cells that respond positively to green, black, and yellow increased their firing dramatically. When you shifted your gaze to the neutral white ground, these ganglion cells abruptly decreased their activity and the brain interpreted this abrupt downshift as if the ganglion cells were responding now to their “opponent” colors: red, white, and blue, respectively, in the visual field. Once the ganglion cells return to their baseline activity state, the false perception of color will disappear.

Figure 27.22 View this flag to understand how retinal processing works. Stare at the center of the flag (indicated by the white dot) for 45 seconds, and then quickly look at a white background, noticing how colors appear.

Higher Processing

The myelinated axons of ganglion cells make up the optic nerves. Within the nerves, different axons carry different qualities of the visual signal. Some axons constitute the magnocellular (big cell) pathway, which carries information about form, movement, depth, and differences in brightness. Other axons constitute the parvocellular (small cell) pathway, which carries information on color and fine detail. Some visual information projects directly back into the brain, while other information crosses to the opposite side of the brain. This crossing of optical pathways produces the distinctive optic chiasma (Greek, for "crossing") found at the base of the brain and allows us to coordinate information from both eyes.

Once in the brain, visual information is processed in several places, and its routes reflect the complexity and importance of visual information to humans and other animals. One route takes the signals to the thalamus, which serves as the routing station for all incoming sensory impulses except olfaction. In the thalamus, the magnocellular and parvocellular distinctions remain intact, and there are different layers of the thalamus dedicated to each. When visual signals leave the thalamus, they travel to the primary visual cortex at the rear of the brain. From the visual cortex, the visual signals travel in two directions. One stream that projects to the parietal lobe, in the side of the brain, carries magnocellular ("where") information. A second stream projects to the temporal lobe and carries both magnocellular ("where") and parvocellular ("what") information.

Another important visual route is a pathway from the retina to the **superior colliculus** in the midbrain, where eye movements are coordinated and integrated with auditory information. Finally, there is the pathway from the retina to the **suprachiasmatic nucleus** (SCN) of the hypothalamus. The SCN is a cluster of cells that is considered to be the body's internal clock, which controls our **circadian** (day-long) cycle. The SCN sends information to the pineal gland, which is important in sleep/wake patterns and annual cycles.

View this interactive presentation (http://openstaxcollege.org/l/sense_of_sight) to review what you have learned about how vision functions.

Explain how the cornea and sclera are anatomically similar and different.

a. Both are part of the ciliary body. However, the cornea is composed of collagen and elastic fibers, whereas the sclera is composed of connective tissue with epithelia.

b. Both are part of the ciliary body. However, the cornea is composed of connective tissue with epithelia, whereas the sclera is composed of collagen and elastic fibers.

c. Both are part of the outer tunic. However, the cornea is composed of collagen and elastic fibers, whereas the sclera is composed of connective tissue with epithelia.

d. Both are part of outer tunic. However, the cornea is composed of connective tissue with epithelia, whereas the sclera is composed of collagen and elastic fibers.

KEY TERMS

audition sense of hearing

basilar membrane stiff structure in the cochlea that indirectly anchors auditory receptors

bipolar neuron neuron with two processes from the cell body, typically in opposite directions

candela (cd) unit of measurement of luminous intensity (brightness)

circadian describes a time cycle about one day in length

cochlea whorled structure that contains receptors for transduction of the mechanical wave into an electrical signal

cone weakly photosensitive, chromatic, cone-shaped neuron in the fovea of the retina that detects bright light and is used in daytime color vision

cornea transparent layer over the front of the eye that helps focus light waves

fovea region in the center of the retina with a high density of photoreceptors and which is responsible for acute vision

free nerve ending ending of an afferent neuron that lacks a specialized structure for detection of sensory stimuli; some respond to touch, pain, or temperature

glabrous describes the non-hairy skin found on palms and fingers, soles of feet, and lips of humans and other primates

glomerulus in the olfactory bulb, one of the two neural clusters that receives signals from one type of olfactory receptor

Golgi tendon organ muscular proprioceptive tension receptor that provides the sensory component of the Golgi tendon reflex

gustation sense of taste

hyperopia (also, farsightedness) visual defect in which the image focus falls behind the retina, thereby making images in the distance clear, but close-up images blurry

incus (also, anvil) second of the three bones of the middle ear

inner ear innermost part of the ear; consists of the cochlea and the vestibular system

iris pigmented, circular muscle at the front of the eye that regulates the amount of light entering the eye

kinesthesia sense of body movement

labyrinth bony, hollow structure that is the most internal part of the ear; contains the sites of transduction of auditory and vestibular information

lens transparent, convex structure behind the cornea that helps focus light waves on the retina

malleus (also, hammer) first of the three bones of the middle ear

mechanoreceptor sensory receptor modified to respond to mechanical disturbance such as being bent, touch, pressure, motion, and sound

Meissner's corpuscle (also, tactile corpuscle) encapsulated, rapidly-adapting mechanoreceptor in the skin that responds to light touch

Merkel's disc unencapsulated, slowly-adapting mechanoreceptor in the skin that responds to touch

middle ear part of the hearing apparatus that functions to transfer energy from the tympanum to the oval window of the inner ear

muscle spindle proprioceptive stretch receptor that lies within a muscle and that shortens the muscle to an optimal length for efficient contraction

myopia (also, nearsightedness) visual defect in which the image focus falls in front of the retina, thereby making images in the distance blurry, but close-up images clear

nociception neural processing of noxious (such as damaging) stimuli

odorant airborne molecule that stimulates an olfactory receptor

olfaction sense of smell

olfactory bulb neural structure in the vertebrate brain that receives signals from olfactory receptors

olfactory epithelium specialized tissue in the nasal cavity where olfactory receptors are located

olfactory receptor dendrite of a specialized neuron

organ of Corti in the basilar membrane, the site of the transduction of sound, a mechanical wave, to a neural signal

ossicle one of the three bones of the middle ear

outer ear part of the ear that consists of the pinna, ear canal, and tympanum and which conducts sound waves into the middle ear

oval window thin diaphragm between the middle and inner ears that receives sound waves from contact with the stapes bone of the middle ear

Pacinian corpuscle encapsulated mechanoreceptor in the skin that responds to deep pressure and vibration

papilla one of the small bump-like projections from the tongue

perception individual interpretation of a sensation; a brain function

pheromone substance released by an animal that can affect the physiology or behavior of other animals

pinna cartilaginous outer ear

presbyopia visual defect in which the image focus falls behind the retina, thereby making images in the distance clear, but close-up images blurry; caused by age-based changes in the lens

proprioception sense of limb position; used to track kinesthesia

pupil small opening though which light enters

reception receipt of a signal (such as light or sound) by sensory receptors

receptive field region in space in which a stimulus can activate a given sensory receptor

receptor potential membrane potential in a sensory receptor in response to detection of a stimulus

retina layer of photoreceptive and supporting cells on the inner surface of the back of the eye

rhodopsin main photopigment in vertebrates

rod strongly photosensitive, achromatic, cylindrical neuron in the outer edges of the retina that detects dim light and is used in peripheral and nighttime vision

Ruffini ending (also, bulbous corpuscle) slowly-adapting mechanoreceptor in the skin that responds to skin stretch and joint position

semicircular canal one of three half-circular, fluid-filled tubes in the vestibular labyrinth that monitors angular acceleration and deceleration

sensory receptor specialized neuron or other cells associated with a neuron that is modified to receive specific sensory input

sensory transduction conversion of a sensory stimulus into electrical energy in the nervous system by a change in the membrane potential

stapes (also, stirrup) third of the three bones of the middle ear

stereocilia in the auditory system, hair-like projections from hair cells that help detect sound waves

superior colliculus paired structure in the top of the midbrain, which manages eye movements and auditory integration

suprachiasmatic nucleus cluster of cells in the hypothalamus that plays a role in the circadian cycle

tastant food molecule that stimulates gustatory receptors

taste bud clusters of taste cells

tectorial membrane cochlear structure that lies above the hair cells and participates in the transduction of sound at the hair cells

tonic activity in a neuron, slight continuous activity while at rest

tympanum (also, tympanic membrane or ear drum) thin diaphragm between the outer and middle ears

ultrasound sound frequencies above the human detectable ceiling of approximately 20,000 Hz

umami one of the five basic tastes, which is described as "savory" and which may be largely the taste of L-glutamate

vestibular sense sense of spatial orientation and balance

vision sense of sight

CHAPTER SUMMARY

27.1 Sensory Processes

A sensory activation occurs when a physical or chemical stimulus is processed into a neural signal (sensory transduction) by a sensory receptor. Perception is an individual interpretation of a sensation and is a brain function. Humans have special senses: olfaction, gustation, equilibrium, and hearing, plus the general senses of somatosensation.

Sensory receptors are either specialized cells associated with sensory neurons or the specialized ends of sensory neurons that are a part of the peripheral nervous system, and they are used to receive information about the environment (internal or external). Each sensory receptor is modified for the type of stimulus it detects. For example, neither gustatory receptors nor auditory receptors are sensitive to light. Each sensory receptor is responsive to stimuli within a specific region in space, which is known as that receptor's receptive field. The most fundamental function of a sensory system is the translation of a sensory signal to an electrical signal in the nervous system.

All sensory signals, except those from the olfactory system, enter the central nervous system and are routed to the thalamus. When the sensory signal exits the thalamus, it is conducted to the specific area of the cortex dedicated to processing that particular sense.

27.2 Somatosensation

Somatosensation includes all sensation received from the skin and mucous membranes, as well as from the limbs and joints. Somatosensation occurs all over the exterior of the body and at some interior locations as well, and a variety of receptor types, embedded in the skin and mucous membranes, play a role.

There are several types of specialized sensory receptors. Rapidly adapting free nerve endings detect nociception, hot and cold, and light touch. Slowly adapting, encapsulated Merkel's disks are found in fingertips and lips, and respond to light touch. Meissner's corpuscles, found in glabrous skin, are rapidly adapting, encapsulated receptors that detect touch, low-frequency vibration, and flutter. Ruffini endings are slowly adapting, encapsulated receptors that detect skin stretch, joint activity, and warmth. Hair receptors are rapidly adapting nerve endings wrapped around the base of hair follicles that detect hair movement and skin deflection. Finally, Pacinian corpuscles are encapsulated, rapidly adapting receptors that detect transient pressure and high-frequency vibration.

27.3 Taste and Smell

There are five primary tastes in humans: sweet, sour, bitter, salty, and umami. Each taste has its own receptor type that responds only to that taste. Tastants enter the body and are dissolved in saliva. Taste cells are located within taste buds, which are found on three of the four types of papillae in the mouth.

Regarding olfaction, there are many thousands of odorants, but humans detect only about 10,000. Like taste receptors, olfactory receptors are each responsive to only one odorant. Odorants dissolve in nasal mucosa, where they excite their corresponding olfactory sensory cells. When these cells detect an odorant, they send their signals to the main olfactory bulb and then to other locations in the brain, including the olfactory cortex.

27.4 Hearing and Vestibular Sensation

Audition is important for territory defense, predation, predator defense, and communal exchanges. The vestibular system, which is not auditory, detects linear acceleration and angular acceleration and deceleration. Both the auditory system and vestibular system use hair cells as their receptors.

Auditory stimuli are sound waves. The sound wave energy reaches the outer ear (pinna, canal, tympanum), and vibrations of the tympanum send the energy to the middle ear. The middle ear bones shift and the stapes transfers mechanical energy to the oval window of the fluid-filled inner ear cochlea. Once in the cochlea, the energy causes the basilar membrane to flex, thereby bending the stereocilia on receptor hair cells. This activates the receptors, which send their auditory neural signals to the brain.

The vestibular system has five parts that work together to provide the sense of direction, thus helping to maintain balance. The utricle and saccule measure head orientation: their calcium carbonate crystals shift when the head is tilted, thereby activating hair cells. The semicircular canals work similarly, such that when the head is turned, the fluid in the canals bends stereocilia on hair cells. The vestibular hair cells also send signals to the thalamus and to somatosensory cortex, but also to the cerebellum, the structure above the brainstem that plays a large role in timing and coordination of movement.

27.5 Vision

Vision is the only photo responsive sense. Visible light travels in waves and is a very small slice of the electromagnetic radiation spectrum. Light waves differ based on their frequency (wavelength = hue) and amplitude (intensity = brightness).

In the vertebrate retina, there are two types of light receptors (photoreceptors): cones and rods. Cones, which are the source of color vision, exist in three forms—L, M, and S—and they are differentially sensitive to different wavelengths. Cones are located in the retina, along with the dim-light, achromatic receptors (rods). Cones are found in the fovea, the central region of the retina, whereas rods are found in the peripheral regions of the retina.

Visual signals travel from the eye over the axons of retinal ganglion cells, which make up the optic nerves. Ganglion cells come in several versions. Some ganglion cell axons carry information on form, movement, depth, and brightness, while other axons carry information on color and fine detail. Visual information is sent to the superior colliculi in the midbrain, where coordination of eye movements and integration of auditory information takes place. Visual information is also sent to the suprachiasmatic nucleus (SCN) of the hypothalamus, which plays a role in the circadian cycle.

REVIEW QUESTIONS

1. _____ is a type of general sense in humans.

a. gustation
b. olfaction
c. proprioception
d. equilibrium

2. Suppose you burned your tongue and could not taste food for a day. Identify the sense affected.

a. olfaction
b. gustation
c. proprioception
d. kinesthesia

3. State where perception occurs.

a. spinal cord
b. cerebral cortex
c. receptors
d. thalamus

4. If a person's cold receptors no longer convert cold

sensory signals into electrical signals, that person has a problem with _____.

a. reception
b. the receptive field
c. perception
d. transduction

5. What is the smallest difference in stimuli that can be detected?

a. receptor potential
b. sensory transduction
c. just-noticeable difference
d. perception

6. In peppers, spicy heat is rated in SHUs, where 0 is the least amount of spicy heat. If the just-noticeable difference (JND) of the ability to perceive difference in heat detection for an individual is 30%, which of the following represents the JND of two different peppers?

a. 8,500 vs 11,000 SHU
b. 4,050 vs 15,000 SHU
c. 15,000 vs 18,000 SHU
d. 10,500 vs 15,000 SHU

7. What is the role of sensory receptors in sensory perception?

a. detection of specific stimuli
b. sensation interpretation
c. sending electrical signals to the cortex
d. transmitting signals from the brain to the rest of the body

8. Which mechanoreceptors in the skin are unencapsulated?

a. Merkel's disks
b. Meissner's corpuscles
c. Ruffini endings
d. Pacinian corpuscles

9. If an individual is born without the ability to sense high-frequency vibrations, he may have been born with a mutation in a gene that codes for ______.

a. Merkel's disks
b. Meissner's corpuscles
c. Ruffini endings
d. Pacinian corpuscles

10. If you were to burn your epidermis, what receptor type would most likely burn?

a. free nerve endings
b. Ruffini endings
c. Pacinian corpuscles
d. Krause end bulbs

11. _____ are found only in _____ skin, and detect skin deflection.

a. Meissner's corpuscles, hairy
b. Ruffini endings, glabrous
c. Pacinian corpuscles, glabrous
d. hair receptors, hairy

12. To what does nociception respond?

a. injured stimuli
b. deep, fleeting pressure
c. fine touch
d. cold

13. Why do peppers, which contain capsaicin, taste "hot?"

a. Capsaicin is corrosive and damages tissue.
b. Capsaicin contains large quantities of heat that are released upon ingestion.
c. Capsaicin and warm receptors open the same calcium channels.
d. Capsaicin stimulates Krause end bulbs.

14. _____ are mechanoreceptors that facilitate proper gripping of objects.

a. Merkel's disks
b. Meissner's corpuscles
c. Ruffini endings
d. Pacinian corpuscles

15. How many different taste molecules can an individual taste cell detect?

a. one
b. five
c. depends on the type of taste receptor
d. depends on the part of the tongue

16. Describe how gustation and olfaction are similar.

a. Both sense different stimuli in the environment.
b. Both can have hundreds of millions of types of receptors.
c. Both obtain stimuli from within the body.
d. Signals from both are transmitted through the medulla.

17. ____ is the term for savoriness in food.

a. gustation
b. tastants
c. umami
d. pheromone

18. If an individual becomes poisoned from eating excessive amounts of spoiled food, what kind of receptors might they lack?

a. bitter
b. sweet
c. umami
d. sour

19. A typical dog has approximately how many times more olfactory receptors than a typical human?

a. 2
b. 8
c. 83
d. 333

20. Which of the following is true of dog olfaction?

a. Most dogs have 4 billion olfactory receptors.
b. Bloodhounds have more receptors than humans, but humans have more receptors than most dogs.
c. Rabbits and most dogs have the same number of olfactory receptors.
d. Dogs bred for sense of smell can have four times more olfactory cells than most other dogs.

21. Which of the following has the most taste receptors?

a. fungiform papillae
b. circumvallate papillae
c. foliate papillae
d. filiform papillae

22. In sound, pitch is measured in _____, and volume is measured in _____.

a. decibels (dB), hertz (Hz)
b. decibels (dB), nanometers (nm)
c. nanometers (nm), decibels (dB)
d. hertz (Hz), decibels (dB)

23. Identify the animal that would be affected by a 120,000 Hz sound.

a. cat
b. bat
c. dolphin
d. dog

24. Louder sounds have a _____ compared with softer sounds.

a. greater amplitude
b. lower amplitude
c. greater frequency
d. lower frequency

25. Which of the following is true of frequency?

a. Frequency is heard as volume.
b. Louder sounds have a higher frequency.
c. Men hear higher frequencies than women.
d. Frequency is measured in number of sound waves per unit time.

26. The _____ contains receptors for transduction of mechanical waves to produce electrical signals.

a. tympanum
b. cochlea
c. pinna
d. stapes

27. The _____ contains _____, which produces action potentials along the auditory nerve.

a. incus, stapes
b. ear canal, tympanum
c. tympanum, oval window
d. organ of Corti, stereocilia

28. Identify the structure that is found both in the auditory system and the vestibular system.

a. basilar membrane
b. hair cells
c. semicircular canals
d. ossicles

29. You are in a car that suddenly decelerates. Explain what happens inside the ear as the car comes to a stop.

a. Fluid in the semicircular canals moves.
b. Stereocilia are bent.
c. Deceleration signals are sent to the brain.
d. Fluid in the semicircular canals stops moving.

30. Of the following, identify the waves with the highest frequency.

a. microwaves
b. ultraviolet rays
c. x-rays
d. gamma rays

31. Of the following colors, identify the color associated with the shortest wavelength.

a. red
b. yellow
c. green
d. blue

32. Which of the following is true of light detection?

a. Humans see most of the light spectrum.
b. Light signals can pass through a vacuum into the eye.
c. Decibels are used as the unit of wavelength.
d. Violet light has a longer wavelength than red light.

33. The fovea is responsible for _______, because it has a high density of cones.

a. night vision
b. nearsightedness
c. farsightedness
d. acute vision

34. Explain why people over 55 often need reading glasses.

a. Their cornea no longer focuses correctly.
b. Their lens no longer focuses correctly.
c. Their eyeball has elongated with age, causing images to focus in front of their retina.
d. Their retina has thinned with age, making vision more difficult.

35. Where does some visual processing occur before information reaches the brain?

a. cornea
b. lens
c. iris
d. retina

36. A person catching a ball must coordinate her head and eyes. Identify the part of the brain that is helping to do this.

a. hypothalamus
b. superior colliculus
c. thalamus
d. pineal gland

CRITICAL THINKING QUESTIONS

37. Which statement explains how the two types of sensory transduction differ?

a. Receptors can respond to multiple stimuli, whereas free nerve endings are specialized cells that detect a specific stimulus.
b. Receptors are specialized cells that detect a specific stimulus, whereas free nerve endings can respond to multiple stimuli.
c. Receptors are similar for different stimuli, whereas free nerve endings are different for different stimuli.
d. Receptors are specialized cells that detect a specific stimulus, whereas free nerve endings can respond to pressure.

38. Describe how the steps of sensory perception would be affected if a person sustains damage to axons that lead from sensory receptors to the central nervous system.

a. Reception would not be affected. However, signal transduction and perception will be incomplete.
b. Perception would not be affected. However, signal transduction and reception will be incomplete.
c. Signal transduction would not be affected. However, reception and perception will be incomplete.
d. Reception and signal transduction would not be affected. However, perception will be incomplete.

39. Give an example of how Weber's law is applicable to a just-noticeable difference.

a. A difference between 20 and 21 units of weight is more likely detectable than a difference between 1 and 2 units.
b. A difference between 1 and 2 units of weight is more likely detectable than a difference between 20 and 21 units.
c. A difference between 1 and 2 units of weight is more likely detectable than a difference between 2 and 4 units.
d. A difference between 20 and 21 units of weight is more likely detectable than a difference between 2 and 4 units.

40. Humans have both special and general senses. Which

statement explains what both types of senses have in common?

a. All types of senses undergo sensory transduction by converting a stimulus into a chemical signal via the central nervous system.
b. All types of senses undergo sensory transduction by converting a stimulus into an electrical signal via the peripheral nervous system.
c. All types of senses undergo sensory transduction by converting a stimulus into a chemical signal via the nervous system.
d. All types of senses undergo sensory transduction by converting a stimulus into an electrical signal via the nervous system.

41. Explain why there are more Merkel's disks and Meissner's corpuscles in your fingertips than in your palms.

a. These two types of thermoreceptors are used to detect warmth and cold which is necessary to maintain body temperature.
b. These two types of mechanoreceptors are used to detect fine details necessary for many roles of fingertips but not palms such as typing.
c. These two types of proprioceptors are used to detect fine details necessary for many roles of fingertips but not palms, such as typing.
d. These two types of mechanoreceptors are used to detect fine details, which are necessary for many roles of fingertips as well as palms.

42. Explain what can be inferred about the relative sizes of the areas of cortex that process signals from skin not densely innervated with sensory receptors versus skin that is densely innervated with sensory receptors.

a. Areas of the cortex that process signals from skin with fewer sensory receptors are likely to be larger than those having large numbers of sensory receptors.
b. Areas of the cortex that process signals from skin with fewer sensory receptors are likely to be smaller than those having large numbers of sensory receptors.
c. Areas of the cortex that process signals from skin with fewer sensory receptors and large numbers of sensory receptors will likely be the same.
d. There is no relationship between the relative sizes of areas of cortex that process signals from skin and the sensory receptor numbers.

43. Explain why some people think that peppers are painful or hot, while other people do not find peppers painful or hot.

a. Peppers contain capsaicin, which opens the same sodium channels as warm receptors. Excess stimulation gives the perception of pain. Thus people who can tolerate more heat find peppers to be less painful.
b. Peppers contain capsaicin, which opens the same calcium channels as warm receptors. Excess stimulation gives the perception of pain. Thus people who can tolerate more heat find peppers to be less painful.
c. Peppers contain quinine, which opens the same calcium channels as warm receptors. Excess stimulation gives the perception of pain. Thus people who can tolerate more heat find peppers to be less painful.
d. Peppers contain quinine, which opens the same sodium channels as warm receptors. Excess stimulation gives the perception of pain. Thus people who can tolerate more heat find peppers to be less painful.

44. Discuss how the location of mechanoreceptors affect their ability to sense different stimuli.

a. Merkel's disks and Meissner's corpuscles are found in specialized regions and detect the amount of stretch. Pacinian corpuscles and Ruffini endings are able to sense deeper touch, such as deeper pressure.
b. Merkel's disks and Meissner's corpuscles are found deeper in the skin and are able to sense deeper touch, such as deeper pressure. Pacinian corpuscles and Ruffini endings are able to better detect fine touch.
c. Merkel's disks and Meissner's corpuscles are found deeper in the skin and detect fine touch. Pacinian corpuscles and Ruffini endings are able to sense deeper touch, such as deeper pressure.
d. Merkel's disks and Meissner's corpuscles are found in more upper parts of the skin and detect fine touch. Pacinian corpuscles and Ruffini endings are able to sense deeper touch, such as deeper pressure.

45. Explain what happens to the ability to perceive taste and smell as people age.

a. All senses decline with age, most dramatically by age 50 and then continue to decline thereafter.
b. All senses increase with age, most dramatically by age 50 and then continue to increase thereafter.
c. All senses decline with age, most dramatically by age 50 and then increase thereafter.
d. All senses increase with age, most dramatically by age 50 and then decline thereafter.

46. Predict a possible effect on an animal of not being able to perceive taste.

a. The animal might not be able to eat food.
b. The animal might not be able to eat sweet and unspoiled food.
c. The animal might not be able to distinguish food that is bitter and sour.
d. The animal might not be able to distinguish food that is dangerous, bitter, spoiled, sour or sweet.

47. If a young child goes missing, predict why a bloodhound and not a poodle would be used to find the child.

a. Bloodhounds were bred to have a better sense of smell, and thus have fewer olfactory receptors and larger olfactory epithelia.
b. Bloodhounds were bred to have a better sense of smell, and thus have more olfactory receptors and larger olfactory epithelia.
c. Bloodhounds were bred to have a better sense of smell, and thus have more olfactory receptors and smaller olfactory epithelia.
d. Bloodhounds were bred to have a better sense of smell, and thus have more olfactory bulbs and larger olfactory receptors.

48. Explain how pheromones differ from other odorants, from the perspective of the recipient of the signal.

a. Pheromones are sent to the main olfactory bulb instead of the amygdala and are not consciously perceived.
b. Pheromones are sent to the amygdala instead of the main olfactory bulb and are consciously perceived.
c. Pheromones are sent to the amygdala instead of the main olfactory bulb and are not consciously perceived.
d. Pheromones are sent to the main olfactory bulb instead of the amygdala and are consciously perceived.

49. You are sitting with a dog and a cat and decide to test a 50,000 Hz ringtone. Identify which of you is likely to respond to the sound and explain why.

a. The human and dog will respond, because they can hear up to 50,000 Hz.
b. The cat and dog will respond, because they can hear up to 50,000 Hz.
c. Only the dog will respond, because they can hear up to 50,000 Hz.
d. Only the cat will respond, because cats can hear up to 50,000 Hz.

50. You are having a debate with someone in a library. A librarian asks you to "speak softer." What characteristic of sound does the librarian want you to change and how can you change it?

a. wavelength, by lowering the amplitude at which you are speaking
b. amplitude, by lowering the frequency at which you are speaking
c. frequency, by lowering the volume at which you are speaking
d. amplitude, by lowering the volume at which you are speaking.

51. If an individual was born without the malleus in either ear, explain why they might have problems with hearing.

a. Without the malleus and incus, the vibrations of the tympanum would not be able to reach the stapes and then be sent to the cochlea.
b. Without the malleus and incus, the vibrations of the pinna would not be able to reach the stapes and then be sent to the cochlea.
c. Without the malleus and incus, sound waves would not be collected by the tympanum.
d. Without the malleus and incus, sound waves would not be collected by the pinna.

52. Explain how being on the moon, which has less gravity than Earth, might affect vestibular sensation and why.

a. Vestibular sensation relies on gravity's effects on tiny crystals in the inner nostril; therefore, reduced gravity on the moon would likely impair vestibular sensation.
b. Vestibular sensation relies on gravity's effects on huge crystals in the inner ear; therefore, reduced gravity on the moon would likely impair vestibular sensation.
c. Vestibular sensation relies on gravity's effects on tiny crystals in the inner ear; therefore, reduced gravity on the moon would likely impair vestibular sensation.
d. Vestibular sensation relies on gravity's effects on tiny crystals in the outer ear; therefore, reduced gravity on the moon would likely impair vestibular sensation.

53. Explain why you are unable to see the heat emitted by a cricket.

a. Ultraviolet light includes heat emitted by prey organisms of reptiles which is outside the visual spectrum for humans because the wavelength is less than 380 nm.

b. Infrared light includes heat emitted by prey organisms of reptiles which is outside the visual spectrum for humans because the wavelength is less than 380 nm.

c. Infrared light includes heat emitted by prey organisms of reptiles, which is outside the visual spectrum for humans because the wavelength is more than 400 nm.

d. Ultraviolet light includes heat emitted by prey organisms of reptiles, which is outside the visual spectrum for humans because the wavelength is more than 400 nm.

54. Explain what the color receptors in your eyes are perceiving if you see a white building.

a. All of the color receptors in your eyes are equally stimulated when you see the color white.

b. Both L and M cones are equally stimulated in your eyes when you see the color white.

c. Only the S cones are stimulated in your eyes when you see the color white.

d. L cones are stimulated strongly and S cones are weakly stimulated when you see the color white.

55. Discuss how the relationship between photoreceptors and bipolar cells is different from other sensory receptors and adjacent cells.

a. Photoreceptors and bipolar cells are depolarized, whereas other sensory receptors typically remain polarized.

b. Photoreceptors and bipolar cells are hyperpolarized, whereas other sensory receptors typically remain polarized.

c. Photoreceptors and bipolar cells are depolarized, whereas other sensory receptors typically become hyperpolarized.

d. Photoreceptors and bipolar cells are hyperpolarized, whereas other sensory receptors typically become depolarized.

56. Explain what happens once visual signals reach the visual cortex.

a. Some signals go to the temporal lobe, which detects “where” information, and other signals go to the parietal lobe, which detects “where” and “what” signals.

b. Some signals go to the parietal lobe, which detects “where” information, and other signals go to the temporal lobe, which detects “what” signals.

c. Some signals go to the parietal lobe, which detects “where” and “what” information and other signals go to the temporal lobe, which also detects “where” and “what” signals.

d. Some signals go to the parietal lobe, which detects “where” information, and other signals go to the temporal lobe, which detects “where” and “what” signals.

SCIENCE PRACTICE CHALLENGE QUESTIONS

57. Odorants are mixtures of many different molecules. The complexity of the human sense of smell can be represented visually as a grid of 100 cells (10 x 10 grid) with each cell associated with a unique molecule-receptor pair. An odorant is detected when the brain integrates the signals generated by each molecule in the mixture.

Four olfactory sensors, each innervated by a nerve that transmits information to the brain as an action potential, are shown in the diagram at the right. Three of the sensors each respond to one of the three odor molecules in the geometric representation of the odorant mixture.

A. In the diagram the odorant-receptor pairing is imagined geometrically; a round peg fits in a round hold and a square peg does not. The receptors are located in the epidermal cell surface, shown in the drawing as a light gray line. **Create a geometric representation** by drawing receptors on the surfaces of the sensors that are activated by one of the molecules in the mixture. **Draw a geometric representation** of a fourth receptor surface that is not activated by a molecule in the odorant mixture.

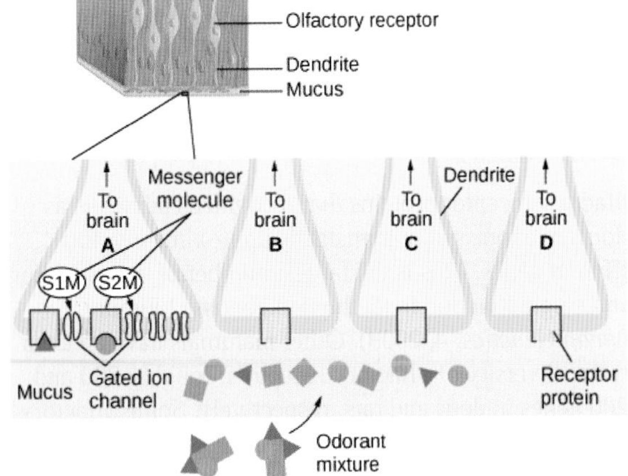

Figure 27.23

In the receptor cell labeled A, two signaling molecules S1M and S2M are shown as are two types of gated ion channels; one that transports Ca^{+2} in response to S1M while generating S2M, and three that transport Na^{+} in response to S2M.

B. **Construct an explanation** of the mechanism for transmission of information when the odorant molecule is detected at receptor A using this signaling cascade. In your explanation include the role of positive feedback and the mechanism of the generation of an action potential.

Signal integration allows the brain to discriminate this particular odorant mixture from others using the time dependence in each signal. The sensitivity of an olfactory system increases as the number of unique receptors increases.

C. Complete the following table to **construct a mathematical representation** of sensitivity to the chemical landscape assuming that there are 100 unique odorant molecules. Use the following mathematic routine to determine the number of odors caused by groups of molecules selected from the 100 odorant molecules:

Number, r, of odor-producing molecules in the odorant	Number of different odorants
3	100•99•98/(3•2)=161,700
4	
5	
6	
7	

Table 27.2

$$\text{number of groups} = \frac{100!}{r!(100-r)!}$$

where $n! = n \cdot (n-1) \cdot (n-2) \cdot (n-3)...\text{and } 0!=1$

Bushdid et al. (*Science*, 343, 2014) extended this model and then used human subjects to experimentally determine the number of unique odorant molecules that they could discriminate to obtain an estimate of 1.72 trillion different detectible smells.

Olfactory receptor proteins that recognize chemicals as odors are expressed in humans by approximately 400 different genes. This is the largest number of genes coding for a single function in the human genome (Nimura, *Human Genetics*, 4, 2009). Other mammals have an even greater diversity of olfactory receptors: roughly 800 and 1200 genes in dogs and rats, respectively. Some olfactory receptors are adapted for odorants in an aqueous environment and some are adapted for an air environment.

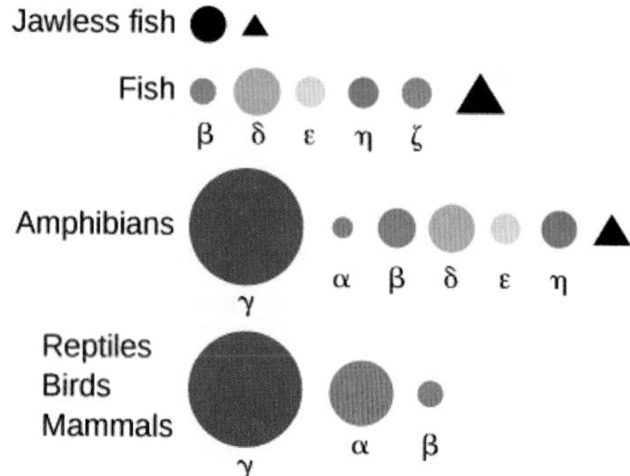

Figure 27.24

D. Use the representation above, showing classes of genes within groups of organisms, to **construct a representation** of the phylogenetic relationships among these groups. Annotate your representation to show gene additions and deletions. To your representation also add annotation that connects the phenotype to the environment.

58. When you get cold you may shiver. The shivering response is a reflex in which the hypothalamus in the brain integrates sensory input, comparing input against a temperature set point. When a threshold signal is detected, nerves of the somatic nervous system that innervate skeletal muscle are stimulated. The extension and contraction of muscle cells releases heat energy that elevates the body temperature.

A. **Construct a representation** of the information flow for the shivering response. Annotate your representation to include

- the sensory input
- signal transmission to the hypothalamus
- signal transmission from the hypothalamus to the somatic nervous system
- transmission to muscle tissue
- and output response.

Include in your annotation the negative feedback loop that is established.

B. Shivering occurs when you have a fever even though your body temperature has not fallen. **Identify** the component of the information flow represented above that can cause this effect and **describe** how the brain has integrated the immune system and nervous system to maintain homeostasis.

Thermogenesis from accelerated metabolism in adipose (fat) tissue is a non-shivering response to a cold stimulus. Using a neurotropic virus, investigators are able to trace the paths of nerves in animals. Neurons infected by virus can then be visualized by exposing the tissue to antibodies that can be stained or using dyes that fluoresce. Ryu and co-workers (*Journal of Neuroscience*, 35, 2015) used this technique to demonstrate communication between nerves of the sympathetic nervous system and nerves of the sensory nervous system innervating thermoreceptors that are sensitive to hot and cold.

C. **Construct a representation** of information flow and annotate the representation with labels for

- signal input caused by low temperature
- signal transmission through nerves of the sensory system
- transmission of signal from the sensory system to the sympathetic system
- transmission to adipose cells
- output response of cells.

Include in your annotation the negative feedback loop that is established.

28 | THE ENDOCRINE SYSTEM

Figure 28.1 The process of amphibian metamorphosis, as seen in the tadpole-to-frog stages shown here, is driven by hormones. (credit "tadpole": modification of work by Brian Gratwicke)

Chapter Outline

Introduction

An animal's endocrine system controls body processes through the production, secretion, and regulation of hormones, which serve as chemical "messengers" functioning in cellular and organ activity and, ultimately, maintaining the body's homeostasis. The endocrine system plays a role in growth, metabolism, and sexual development. In humans, common endocrine system diseases include thyroid disease and diabetes mellitus. In organisms that undergo metamorphosis, the process is controlled by the endocrine system. The transformation from tadpole to frog, for example, is complex and nuanced to adapt to specific environments and ecological circumstances.

The study of the endocrine system has led to many medical advances. Now scientists have discovered a hormone that mimics the effects of exercise by regulating metabolism and fighting insulin resistance.[1] You can read more about this exciting discovery at the Science Daily website (http://openstaxcollege.org/l/32hormoneadv) .

28.1 | Types of Hormones

In this section, you will explore the following questions:

- What are the different types of hormones?
- What is the role of hormones in maintaining homeostasis?

Connection for AP® Courses

Much information about the various organ systems of animals is not within the scope for AP®. The endocrine system, however, was selected for in-depth study because an animal's ability to detect, transmit and respond to information is critical

1. Lee, Changhan, Zeng, Jennifer, Drew, Brian G., Sallam, Tamer, Martin-Montalvo, Alejandro, Wan, Junxiang, Kim, Su-Jeong, Mehta, Hemal, Hevener, Andrea L., de Cabo, Rafael, Cohen, Pinchas. **The Mitochondrial-Derived Peptide MOTS-c Promotes Metabolic Homeostasis and Reduces Obesity and Insulin Resistance**. *Cell Metabolism*, 2015; 21 (3): 443 DOI:10.1016/j.cmet.2015.02.009

to survival. The endocrine and nervous systems work together to maintain homeostasis and adjust physiological activity when external or internal environmental conditions change. The nervous system works by generating action potentials along neurons; the endocrine system uses chemical messengers called hormones that are released from glands, travel to target cells, and elicit a response by the target cell. For AP® you are not expected to memorize a laundry list of the various endocrine glands, their hormones, and the effects of each hormone. You should be able to interpret, however, a diagram that shows the activity of a hormonal signal. We will briefly describe a few of these examples in **How Hormones Work**.

There are three types of hormones classified based on molecular structure and properties. (We explored structure/function relationships at the molecular level in the chapter on Biological Macromolecules.) **Lipid-derived hormones** are lipid-soluble and can diffuse across cell membranes because they are non-polar. Most lipid hormones are derived from cholesterol; examples include steroids such as estrogen and testosterone. Because lipid hormones can diffuse across cell membranes, their receptors are located in the cytoplasm of target cells. The **amino acid-derived hormones** are relatively small molecules derived from the amino acids tyrosine and tryptophan; examples include epinephrine, norepinephrine, thyroxin, and melatonin. **Peptide hormones** such as oxytocin and growth hormone consist of polypeptide chains of amino acids. Because these hormones are water-soluble and insoluble in lipids, they cannot pass through the plasma membrane of cells; their receptors are found on the surface of the target cells.

Information presented and the examples highlighted in the section support concepts outlined in Big Idea 3 and Big Idea 4 of the AP® Biology Curriculum Framework. The AP® Learning Objectives listed in the Curriculum Framework provide a transparent foundation for the AP® Biology course, an inquiry-based laboratory experience, instructional activities, and AP® exam questions. A learning objective merges required content with one or more of the seven science practices.

Big Idea 3	Living systems store, retrieve, transmit and respond to information essential to life processes.
Enduring Understanding 3.D	Cells communicate by generating, transmitting and receiving chemical signals.
Essential Knowledge	**3.D.1** Cell communication processes share common features that reflect a shared evolutionary history.
Science Practice	**6.2** The student can construct explanations of phenomena based on evidence produced through scientific practices.
Learning Objective	**3.33** The student is able to use representations and models to describe features of a cell signaling pathway.
Big Idea 4	Biological systems interact, and these systems and their interactions possess complex properties.
Enduring Understanding 4.A	Interactions within biological systems lead to complex properties.
Essential Knowledge	**4.A.1** The subcomponents of biological molecules and their sequence determine the properties of that molecule.
Science Practice	**7.1** The student can connect phenomena and models across spatial and temporal scales.
Learning Objective	**4.1** The student is able to explain the connection between the sequence and subcomponents of a biological polymer and its properties.

Maintaining homeostasis within the body requires the coordination of many different systems and organs. Communication between neighboring cells, and between cells and tissues in distant parts of the body, occurs through the release of chemicals called hormones. Hormones are released into body fluids (usually blood) that carry these chemicals to their target cells. At the target cells, which are cells that have a receptor for a signal or ligand from a signal cell, the hormones elicit a response. The cells, tissues, and organs that secrete hormones make up the endocrine system. Examples of glands of the endocrine system include the adrenal glands, which produce hormones such as epinephrine and norepinephrine that regulate responses to stress, and the thyroid gland, which produces thyroid hormones that regulate metabolic rates.

Although there are many different hormones in the human body, they can be divided into three classes based on their chemical structure: lipid-derived, amino acid-derived, and peptide (peptide and proteins) hormones. One of the key distinguishing features of lipid-derived hormones is that they can diffuse across plasma membranes whereas the amino acid-derived and peptide hormones cannot.

Lipid-Derived Hormones (or Lipid-soluble Hormones)

Most lipid hormones are derived from cholesterol and thus are structurally similar to it, as illustrated in Figure 28.2. The primary class of lipid hormones in humans is the steroid hormones. Chemically, these hormones are usually ketones or alcohols; their chemical names will end in "-ol" for alcohols or "-one" for ketones. Examples of steroid hormones include estradiol, which is an **estrogen**, or female sex hormone, and testosterone, which is an androgen, or male sex hormone. These two hormones are released by the female and male reproductive organs, respectively. Other steroid hormones include aldosterone and cortisol, which are released by the adrenal glands along with some other types of androgens. Steroid hormones are insoluble in water, and they are transported by transport proteins in blood. As a result, they remain in circulation longer than peptide hormones. For example, cortisol has a half-life of 60 to 90 minutes, while epinephrine, an amino acid derived-hormone, has a half-life of approximately one minute.

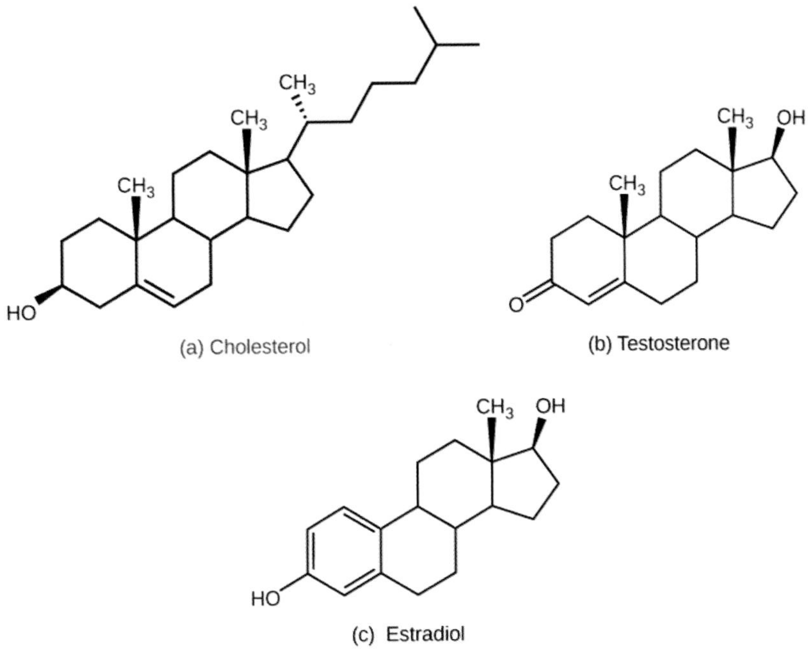

(a) Cholesterol

(b) Testosterone

(c) Estradiol

Figure 28.2 The structures shown here represent (a) cholesterol, plus the steroid hormones (b) testosterone and (c) estradiol.

Amino Acid-Derived Hormones

The amino acid-derived hormones are relatively small molecules that are derived from the amino acids tyrosine and tryptophan, shown in Figure 28.3. If a hormone is amino acid-derived, its chemical name will end in "-ine". Examples of amino acid-derived hormones include epinephrine and norepinephrine, which are synthesized in the medulla of the adrenal glands, and thyroxine, which is produced by the thyroid gland. The pineal gland in the brain makes and secretes melatonin which regulates sleep cycles.

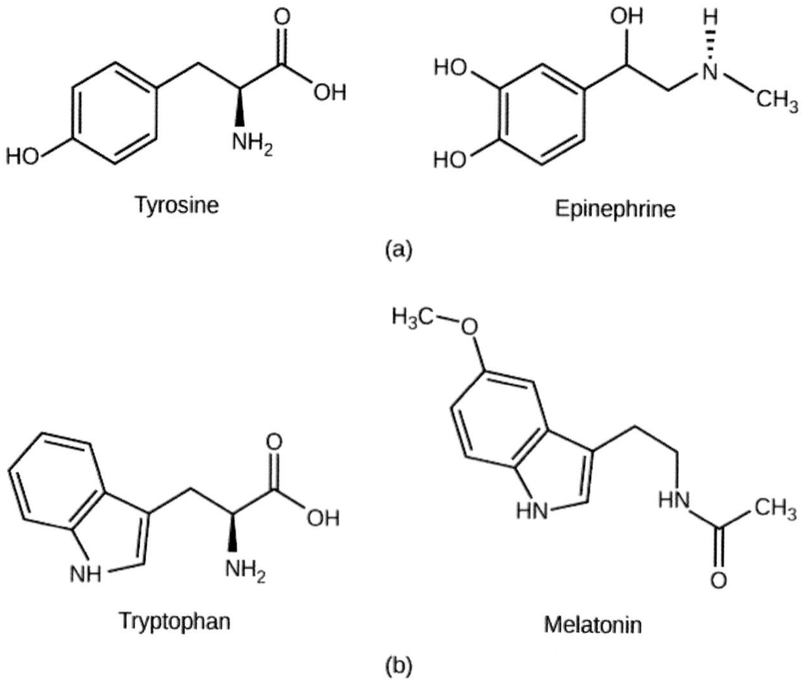

Tyrosine Epinephrine

(a)

Tryptophan Melatonin

(b)

Figure 28.3 (a) The hormone epinephrine, which triggers the fight-or-flight response, is derived from the amino acid tyrosine. (b) The hormone melatonin, which regulates circadian rhythms, is derived from the amino acid tryptophan.

Peptide Hormones

The structure of peptide hormones is that of a polypeptide chain (chain of amino acids). The peptide hormones include molecules that are short polypeptide chains, such as antidiuretic hormone and oxytocin produced in the brain and released into the blood in the posterior pituitary gland. This class also includes small proteins, like growth hormones produced by the pituitary, and large glycoproteins such as follicle-stimulating hormone produced by the pituitary. Figure 28.4 illustrates these peptide hormones.

Secreted peptides like insulin are stored within vesicles in the cells that synthesize them. They are then released in response to stimuli such as high blood glucose levels in the case of insulin. Amino acid-derived and polypeptide hormones are water-soluble and insoluble in lipids. These hormones cannot pass through plasma membranes of cells; therefore, their receptors are found on the surface of the target cells.

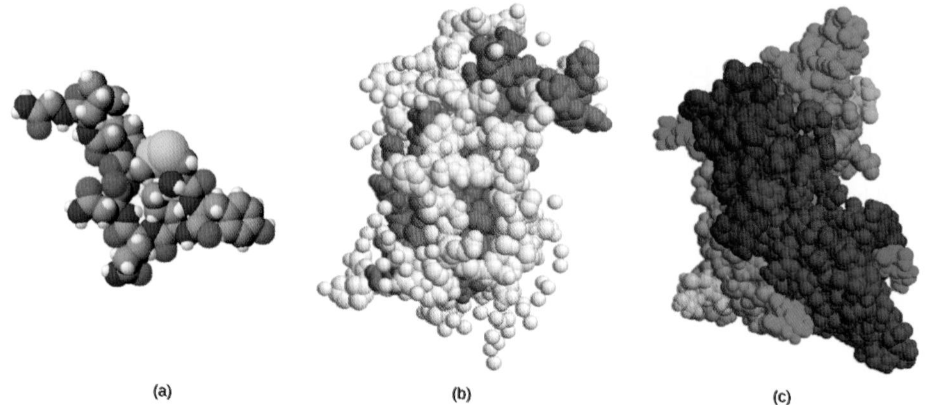

Figure 28.4 The structures of peptide hormones (a) oxytocin, (b) growth hormone, and (c) follicle-stimulating hormone are shown. These peptide hormones are much larger than those derived from cholesterol or amino acids.

Think About It

Although there are many different hormones in the human body, they can be classified based on their chemical structure. What one factor distinguishes them?

Endocrinologist

An endocrinologist is a medical doctor who specializes in treating disorders of the endocrine glands, hormone systems, and glucose and lipid metabolic pathways. An endocrine surgeon specializes in the surgical treatment of endocrine diseases and glands. Some of the diseases that are managed by endocrinologists: disorders of the pancreas (diabetes mellitus), disorders of the pituitary (gigantism, acromegaly, and pituitary dwarfism), disorders of the thyroid gland (goiter and Graves' disease), and disorders of the adrenal glands (Cushing's disease and Addison's disease).

Endocrinologists are required to assess patients and diagnose endocrine disorders through extensive use of laboratory tests. Many endocrine diseases are diagnosed using tests that stimulate or suppress endocrine organ functioning. Blood samples are then drawn to determine the effect of stimulating or suppressing an endocrine organ on the production of hormones. For example, to diagnose diabetes mellitus, patients are required to fast for 12 to 24 hours. They are then given a sugary drink, which stimulates the pancreas to produce insulin to decrease blood glucose levels. A blood sample is taken one to two hours after the sugar drink is consumed. If the pancreas is functioning properly, the blood glucose level will be within a normal range. Another example is the A1C test, which can be performed during blood screening. The A1C test measures average blood glucose levels over the past two to three months by examining how well the blood glucose is being managed over a long time.

Once a disease has been diagnosed, endocrinologists can prescribe lifestyle changes and/or medications to treat the disease. Some cases of diabetes mellitus can be managed by exercise, weight loss, and a healthy diet; in other cases, medications may be required to enhance insulin release. If the disease cannot be controlled by these means, the endocrinologist may prescribe insulin injections.

In addition to clinical practice, endocrinologists may also be involved in primary research and development activities. For example, ongoing islet transplant research is investigating how healthy pancreas islet cells may be transplanted into diabetic patients. Successful islet transplants may allow patients to stop taking insulin injections.

28.2 | How Hormones Work

In this section, you will explore the following questions:

- How do hormones work?
- What is the role of different types of hormone receptors?

Connection for AP® Courses

Much of the information in this section is an application of the material we explored in the Cell Communication chapter about cell communication and signaling pathways. Hormones are chemical signals (ligands) that mediate changes in target cells by binding to specific receptors. Even though hormones released by endocrine glands can travel long distances through the blood and come into contact with many different cell types, they only affect cells that possess the necessary receptors.

Depending on the location of the receptor on the target cell and the chemical structure of the hormone, for example, whether or not it is lipid-soluble, hormones can mediate changes directly by binding to **intracellular hormone receptors** and modulating gene expression (transcription and translation), or indirectly by binding to cell surface receptors and simulating signaling pathways.

The hormone binds to its receptor like a key fits a lock. Because a lipid-derived hormone such as a steroid hormone can diffuse across the membrane of the target cell, they bind to intracellular receptors residing in the cytoplasm or in the nucleus. The cell signaling pathways induced by steroid hormones regulate specific genes by acting as transcription regulators. In turn, this affects the amount of protein produced. Lipid-derived hormones that are not steroids, for example, vitamin D and thyroxin, bind to receptors located in the nucleus of the target cell.

Because amino acid-derived hormones and polypeptide hormones are not lipid-soluble, they bind to **plasma membrane hormone receptors** located on the outer surface of the membrane. Unlike steroid hormones, they cannot act directly on DNA but activate a signaling pathway; this triggers intracellular activity and carries out the specific effects associated with the hormone. The hormone that initiated the signaling pathway is called a **first messenger**. In the case of the epinephrine signaling pathway, binding of the amino acid-derived hormone epinephrine to its receptor activates a G-protein which, in turn, activates cAMP, a second messenger, ultimately resulting in a cellular response such as the conversion of glycogen to glucose.

Information presented and the examples highlighted in the section support concepts outlined in Big Idea 3 of the AP® Biology Curriculum Framework. The AP® Learning Objectives listed in the Curriculum Framework provide a transparent foundation for the AP® Biology course, an inquiry-based laboratory experience, instructional activities, and AP® exam questions. A learning objective merges required content with one or more of the seven science practices.

Big Idea 3	Living systems store, retrieve, transmit and respond to information essential to life processes.
Enduring Understanding 3.D	Cells communicate by generating, transmitting and receiving chemical signals.
Essential Knowledge	**3.D.3** Signal transduction pathways link signal reception with a cellular response.
Science Practice	**1.5** The student can re-express key elements of natural phenomena across multiple representations in the domain.
Learning Objective	**3.36** The student is able to describe a model that expresses the key elements of signal transduction pathways by which a signal is converted to a cellular response.

Hormones mediate changes in target cells by binding to specific **hormone receptors**. In this way, even though hormones circulate throughout the body and come into contact with many different cell types, they only affect cells that possess the necessary receptors. Receptors for a specific hormone may be found on many different cells or may be limited to a small number of specialized cells. For example, thyroid hormones act on many different tissue types, stimulating metabolic activity throughout the body. Cells can have many receptors for the same hormone but often also possess receptors for different types of hormones. The number of receptors that respond to a hormone determines the cell's sensitivity to that hormone, and the resulting cellular response. Additionally, the number of receptors that respond to a hormone can change over time, resulting in increased or decreased cell sensitivity. In **up-regulation**, the number of receptors increases in response to rising hormone levels, making the cell more sensitive to the hormone and allowing for more cellular activity. When the number of receptors decreases in response to rising hormone levels, called **down-regulation**, cellular activity is reduced.

Receptor binding alters cellular activity and results in an increase or decrease in normal body processes. Depending on the location of the protein receptor on the target cell and the chemical structure of the hormone, hormones can mediate changes directly by binding to intracellular hormone receptors and modulating gene transcription, or indirectly by binding to cell surface receptors and stimulating signaling pathways.

Intracellular Hormone Receptors

Lipid-derived (soluble) hormones such as steroid hormones diffuse across the membranes of the endocrine cell. Once outside the cell, they bind to transport proteins that keep them soluble in the bloodstream. At the target cell, the hormones are released from the carrier protein and diffuse across the lipid bilayer of the plasma membrane of cells. The steroid hormones pass through the plasma membrane of a target cell and adhere to intracellular receptors residing in the cytoplasm or in the nucleus. The cell signaling pathways induced by the steroid hormones regulate specific genes on the cell's DNA. The hormones and receptor complex act as transcription regulators by increasing or decreasing the synthesis of mRNA molecules of specific genes. This, in turn, determines the amount of corresponding protein that is synthesized by altering gene expression. This protein can be used either to change the structure of the cell or to produce enzymes that catalyze chemical reactions. In this way, the steroid hormone regulates specific cell processes as illustrated in Figure 28.5.

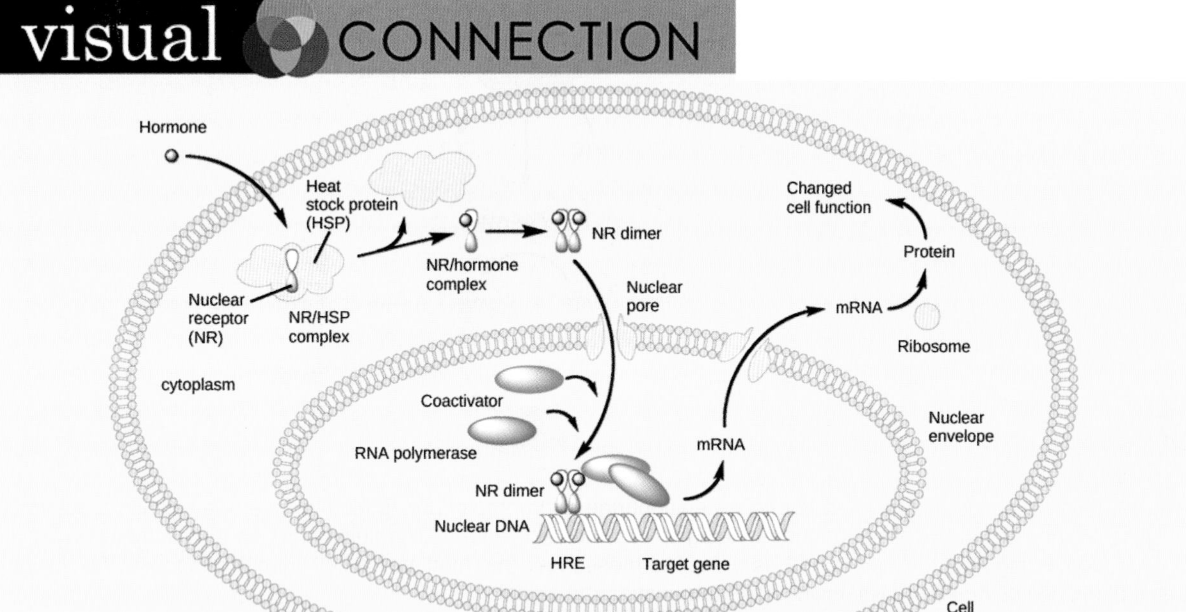

Figure 28.5 An intracellular nuclear receptor (NR) is located in the cytoplasm bound to a heat shock protein (HSP). Upon hormone binding, the receptor dissociates from the heat shock protein and translocates to the nucleus. In the nucleus, the hormone-receptor complex binds to a DNA sequence called a hormone response element (HRE), which triggers gene transcription and translation. The corresponding protein product can then mediate changes in cell function.

Heat shock proteins (HSP) are so named because they help refold misfolded proteins. In response to increased temperature (a "heat shock"), heat shock proteins are activated by release from the nuclear receptor/HSP complex. At the same time, transcription of HSP genes is activated. Explain the role of heat shock in refolding misfolded proteins.

a. Heat is a stimulus that prevents hormone binding.

b. Heat is a stimulus that facilitates hormone binding.

c. Heat is a stimulus that facilitates dissociation of receptor from HSP directly.

d. Heat is a stimulus that facilitates binding of a hormone-receptor complex to a hormone response element.

Other lipid-soluble hormones that are not steroid hormones, such as vitamin D and thyroxine, have receptors located in the nucleus. The hormones diffuse across both the plasma membrane and the nuclear envelope, then bind to receptors in the nucleus. The hormone-receptor complex stimulates transcription of specific genes.

Plasma Membrane Hormone Receptors

Amino acid derived hormones and polypeptide hormones are not lipid-derived (lipid-soluble) and therefore cannot diffuse through the plasma membrane of cells. Lipid insoluble hormones bind to receptors on the outer surface of the plasma membrane, via plasma membrane hormone receptors. Unlike steroid hormones, lipid insoluble hormones do not directly affect the target cell because they cannot enter the cell and act directly on DNA. Binding of these hormones to a cell surface receptor results in activation of a signaling pathway; this triggers intracellular activity and carries out the specific effects associated with the hormone. In this way, nothing passes through the cell membrane; the hormone that binds at the surface remains at the surface of the cell while the intracellular product remains inside the cell. The hormone that initiates the signaling pathway is called a first messenger, which activates a second messenger in the cytoplasm, as illustrated in Figure 28.6.

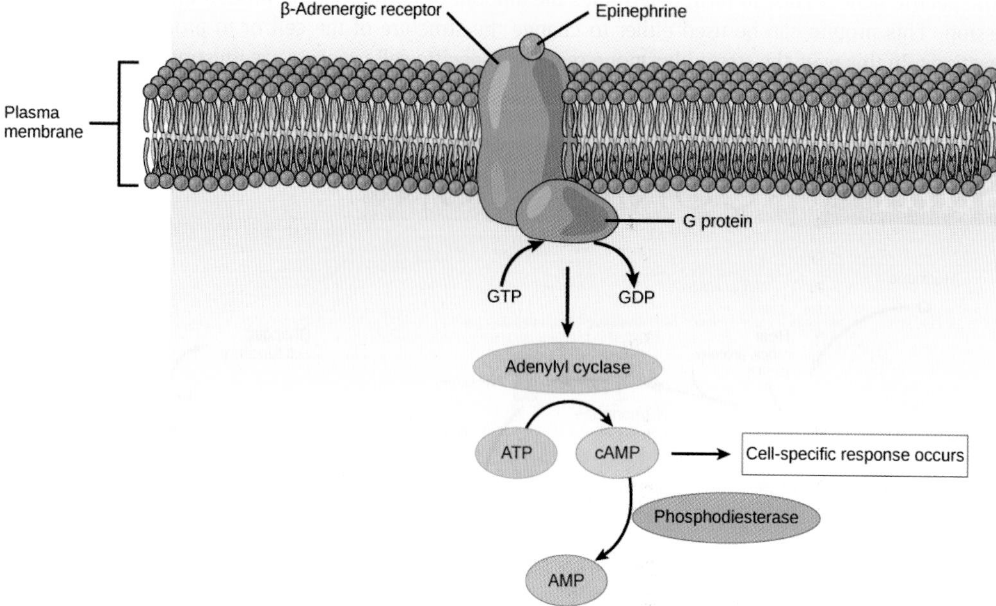

Figure 28.6 The amino acid-derived hormones epinephrine and norepinephrine bind to beta-adrenergic receptors on the plasma membrane of cells. Hormone binding to receptor activates a G-protein, which in turn activates adenylyl cyclase, converting ATP to cAMP. cAMP is a second messenger that mediates a cell-specific response. An enzyme called phosphodiesterase breaks down cAMP, terminating the signal.

One very important second messenger is cyclic AMP (cAMP). When a hormone binds to its membrane receptor, a **G-protein** that is associated with the receptor is activated; G-proteins are proteins separate from receptors that are found in the cell membrane. When a hormone is not bound to the receptor, the G-protein is inactive and is bound to guanosine diphosphate, or GDP. When a hormone binds to the receptor, the G-protein is activated by binding guanosine triphosphate, or GTP, in place of GDP. After binding, GTP is hydrolysed by the G-protein into GDP and becomes inactive.

The activated G-protein in turn activates a membrane-bound enzyme called **adenylyl cyclase**. Adenylyl cyclase catalyzes the conversion of ATP to cAMP. cAMP, in turn, activates a group of proteins called protein kinases, which transfer a phosphate group from ATP to a substrate molecule in a process called phosphorylation. The phosphorylation of a substrate molecule changes its structural orientation, thereby activating it. These activated molecules can then mediate changes in cellular processes.

The effect of a hormone is amplified as the signaling pathway progresses. The binding of a hormone at a single receptor causes the activation of many G-proteins, which activates adenylyl cyclase. Each molecule of adenylyl cyclase then triggers the formation of many molecules of cAMP. Further amplification occurs as protein kinases, once activated by cAMP, can catalyze many reactions. In this way, a small amount of hormone can trigger the formation of a large amount of cellular product. To stop hormone activity, cAMP is deactivated by the cytoplasmic enzyme **phosphodiesterase**, or PDE. PDE is always present in the cell and breaks down cAMP to control hormone activity, preventing overproduction of cellular products.

The specific response of a cell to a lipid insoluble hormone depends on the type of receptors that are present on the cell membrane and the substrate molecules present in the cell cytoplasm. Cellular responses to hormone binding of a receptor include altering membrane permeability and metabolic pathways, stimulating synthesis of proteins and enzymes, and activating hormone release.

Activity

Create a representation to describe how a lipid-soluble hormone and a peptide hormone activate different cellular responses in a target cell.

28.3 | Regulation of Body Processes

In this section, you will explore the following questions:

- How do hormones regulate the excretory system?
- What roles do hormones play in the reproductive system?
- How do hormones regulate metabolism?
- What is the role of hormones in different diseases?

Connection for AP® Courses

The majority of information in this section is illustrative for AP®. You do not need to memorize a list of hormones and their effects on different body processes. However, if provided with a diagram showing the activity of a specific hormone, you should be able to interpret the diagram. This section specifically describes how different hormones affect the excretory system, the reproductive system, metabolism, blood calcium concentrations, growth, and the stress response. Disorders such as diabetes can arise from both the underproduction and overproduction of hormones. It is helpful to take a look at a couple of these examples of hormone activity.

Blood glucose (sugar) levels vary widely over the course of a day as periods of food consumption alternate with periods of fasting. Insulin and glucagon are two primary hormones responsible for maintaining the homeostasis of blood glucose levels. When the blood glucose level is high, beta cells of the pancreas secrete insulin, enhancing the rate of glucose uptake from the blood and utilization by target cells, such as the use of glucose for ATP production. When the blood glucose level is low, alpha cells of the pancreas secrete glucagon, stimulating the breakdown of glycogen to glucose.

A second example is hormonal regulation of the male and female reproductive systems (see the Animal Reproduction and Development chapter). Regulation requires the action of several hormones produced by the pituitary gland, the adrenal cortex, and the gonads. During puberty in both males and females, the hypothalamus produces gonadotropins hormone (GnRH), which stimulates the production and release of follicle-stimulating hormone (FSH) and luteinizing hormone (LH) from the anterior pituitary gland. These hormones regulate the testes in males and ovaries in females. In males, FSH stimulates the maturation of sperm cells; LH stimulates the production of the sex hormones or androgens such as testosterone. (Anabolic steroids, a form of testosterone, have been associated with performance boosting in professional athletes.) In females, FSH stimulates the development of egg cells (ova); LH also plays a role in the development of ova, induction of ovulation, and stimulation of estradiol and progesterone production by the ovaries. Estradiol and progesterone are steroid hormones that regulate the menstrual cycle, among other functions. (Birth control pills designed to prevent ovulation contain fluctuating levels of these hormones.)

Information presented and the examples highlighted in the section support concepts outlined in Big Idea 3 of the AP® Biology Curriculum Framework. The AP® Learning Objectives listed in the Curriculum Framework provide a transparent foundation for the AP® Biology course, an inquiry-based laboratory experience, instructional activities, and AP® exam questions. A learning objective merges required content with one or more of the seven science practices.

Big Idea 3	Living systems store, retrieve, transmit and respond to information essential to life processes.

Enduring Understanding 3.D	Cells communicate by generating, transmitting and receiving chemical signals.
Essential Knowledge	**3.D.2** Cells communicate with each other through direct contact with other cells or from a distance via chemical signaling.
Science Practice	**6.2** The student can construct explanations of phenomena based on evidence produced through scientific practices.
Learning Objective	**3.34** The student is able to construct explanations of cell communication through cell-to-cell direct contact or through chemical signaling.
Essential Knowledge	**3.D.2** Cells communicate with each other through direct contact with other cells or from a distance via chemical signaling.
Science Practice	**6.2** The student can construct explanations of phenomena based on evidence produced through scientific practices.
Learning Objective	**3.39** The student is able to explain how certain drugs affect signal reception and, consequently, signal transduction pathways.
Essential Knowledge	**3.D.2** Cells communicate with each other through direct contact with other cells or from a distance via chemical signaling.
Science Practice	**1.1** The student can create representations and models of natural or man-made phenomena and systems in the domain.
Learning Objective	**3.35** The student is able to create representations that depict how cell-to-cell communication occurs by direct contact or from a distance through chemical signaling.
Big Idea 2	Biological systems utilize free energy and molecular building blocks to grow, to reproduce, and to maintain dynamic homeostasis.
Enduring Understanding 2.C	Organisms use feedback mechanisms to regulate growth and reproduction, and to maintain dynamic homeostasis.
Essential Knowledge	**2.C.1** Organisms use feedback mechanisms to maintain their internal environments and respond to external environmental changes.
Science Practice	**6.1** The student can justify claims with evidence.
Learning Objective	**2.20** The student is able to justify that positive feedback mechanisms amplify responses in organisms.

Hormones have a wide range of effects and modulate many different body processes. The key regulatory processes that will be examined here are those affecting the excretory system, the reproductive system, metabolism, blood calcium concentrations, growth, and the stress response.

Hormonal Regulation of the Excretory System

Maintaining a proper water balance in the body is important to avoid dehydration or over-hydration (hyponatremia). The water concentration of the body is monitored by **osmoreceptors** in the hypothalamus, which detect the concentration of electrolytes in the extracellular fluid. The concentration of electrolytes in the blood rises when there is water loss caused by excessive perspiration, inadequate water intake, or low blood volume due to blood loss. An increase in blood electrolyte levels results in a neuronal signal being sent from the osmoreceptors in hypothalamic nuclei. The pituitary gland has two components: anterior and posterior. The anterior pituitary is composed of glandular cells that secrete protein hormones. The posterior pituitary is an extension of the hypothalamus. It is composed largely of neurons that are continuous with the hypothalamus.

The hypothalamus produces a polypeptide hormone known as **antidiuretic hormone (ADH)**, which is transported to and released from the posterior pituitary gland. The principal action of ADH is to regulate the amount of water excreted by the kidneys. As ADH (which is also known as vasopressin) causes direct water reabsorption from the kidney tubules, salts and wastes are concentrated in what will eventually be excreted as urine. The hypothalamus controls the mechanisms of ADH secretion, either by regulating blood volume or the concentration of water in the blood. Dehydration or physiological stress can cause an increase of osmolarity above 300 mOsm/L, which in turn, raises ADH secretion and water will be retained, causing an increase in blood pressure. ADH travels in the bloodstream to the kidneys. Once at the kidneys, ADH changes the kidneys to become more permeable to water by stimulating the temporary insertion of water channels, aquaporins, into the kidney tubules. Water moves out of the kidney tubules through the aquaporins, reducing urine volume. The water is reabsorbed into the capillaries, lowering blood osmolarity back toward normal. As blood osmolarity decreases, a negative feedback mechanism reduces osmoreceptor activity in the hypothalamus, and ADH secretion is reduced. ADH release can be reduced by certain substances, including alcohol, which can cause increased urine production and dehydration.

Chronic underproduction of ADH or a mutation in the ADH receptor results in **diabetes insipidus**. If the posterior pituitary does not release enough ADH, water cannot be retained by the kidneys and is lost as urine. This causes increased thirst, but water taken in is lost again and must be continually consumed. If the condition is not severe, dehydration may not occur, but severe cases can lead to electrolyte imbalances due to dehydration.

Another hormone responsible for maintaining electrolyte concentrations in extracellular fluids is **aldosterone**, a steroid hormone that is produced by the adrenal cortex. In contrast to ADH, which promotes the reabsorption of water to maintain proper water balance, aldosterone maintains proper water balance by enhancing Na^+ reabsorption and K^+ secretion from extracellular fluid of the cells in kidney tubules. Because it is produced in the cortex of the adrenal gland and affects the concentrations of minerals Na^+ and K^+, aldosterone is referred to as a **mineralocorticoid**, a corticosteroid that affects ion and water balance. Aldosterone release is stimulated by a decrease in blood sodium levels, blood volume, or blood pressure, or an increase in blood potassium levels. It also prevents the loss of Na^+ from sweat, saliva, and gastric juice. The reabsorption of Na^+ also results in the osmotic reabsorption of water, which alters blood volume and blood pressure.

Aldosterone production can be stimulated by low blood pressure, which triggers a sequence of chemical release, as illustrated in Figure 28.7. When blood pressure drops, the renin-angiotensin-aldosterone system (RAAS) is activated. Cells in the juxtaglomerular apparatus, which regulates the functions of the nephrons of the kidney, detect this and release **renin**. Renin, an enzyme, circulates in the blood and reacts with a plasma protein produced by the liver called angiotensinogen. When angiotensinogen is cleaved by renin, it produces angiotensin I, which is then converted into angiotensin II in the lungs. Angiotensin II functions as a hormone and then causes the release of the hormone aldosterone by the adrenal cortex, resulting in increased Na^+ reabsorption, water retention, and an increase in blood pressure. Angiotensin II in addition to being a potent vasoconstrictor also causes an increase in ADH and increased thirst, both of which help to raise blood pressure.

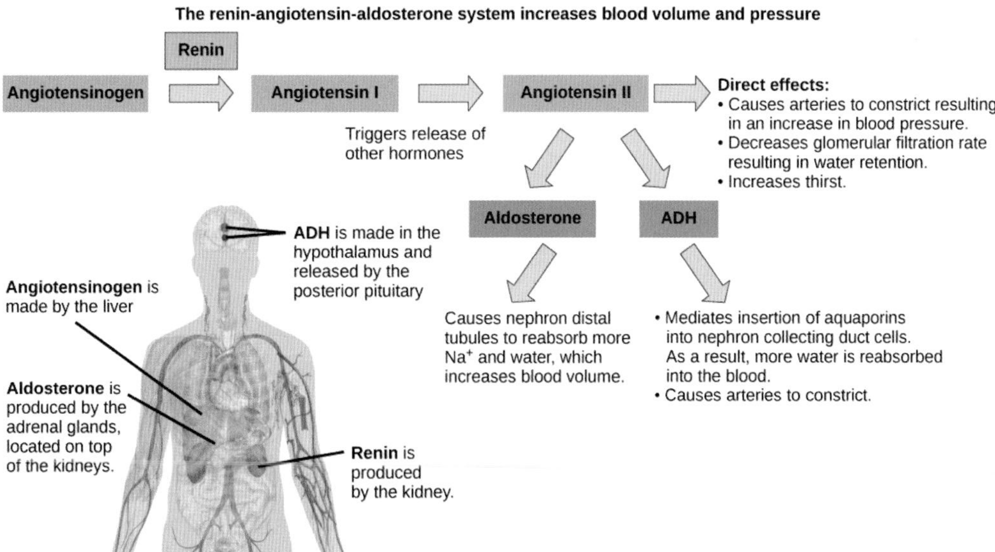

Figure 28.7 ADH and aldosterone increase blood pressure and volume. Angiotensin II stimulates release of these hormones. Angiotensin II, in turn, is formed when renin cleaves angiotensinogen. (credit: modification of work by Mikael Häggström)

Hormonal Regulation of the Reproductive System

Regulation of the reproductive system is a process that requires the action of hormones from the pituitary gland, the adrenal cortex, and the gonads. During puberty in both males and females, the hypothalamus produces gonadotropin-releasing hormone (GnRH), which stimulates the production and release of **follicle-stimulating hormone (FSH)** and luteinizing hormone (LH) from the anterior pituitary gland. These hormones regulate the gonads (testes in males and ovaries in females) and therefore are called **gonadotropins**. In both males and females, FSH stimulates gamete production and LH stimulates production of hormones by the gonads. An increase in gonad hormone levels inhibits GnRH production through a negative feedback loop.

Regulation of the Male Reproductive System

In males, FSH stimulates the maturation of sperm cells. FSH production is inhibited by the hormone inhibin, which is released by the testes. LH stimulates production of the sex hormones (**androgens**) by the interstitial cells of the testes and therefore is also called interstitial cell-stimulating hormone.

The most widely known androgen in males is testosterone. Testosterone promotes the production of sperm and masculine characteristics. The adrenal cortex also produces small amounts of testosterone precursor, although the role of this additional hormone production is not fully understood.

everyday CONNECTION

The Dangers of Synthetic Hormones

Figure 28.8 Professional baseball player Jason Giambi publicly admitted to, and apologized for, his use of anabolic steroids supplied by a trainer. (credit: Bryce Edwards)

Some athletes attempt to boost their performance by using artificial hormones that enhance muscle performance. Anabolic steroids, a form of the male sex hormone testosterone, are one of the most widely known performance-enhancing drugs. Steroids are used to help build muscle mass. Other hormones that are used to enhance athletic performance include erythropoietin, which triggers the production of red blood cells, and human growth hormone, which can help in building muscle mass. Most performance enhancing drugs are illegal for non-medical purposes. They are also banned by many national and international governing bodies, including many amateur and major league sports' associations.

The side effects of synthetic hormones are often significant and non-reversible, and in some cases, fatal. Androgens produce several complications such as liver dysfunctions prostate gland enlargement, difficulty urinating, premature closure of epiphyseal cartilages, testicular atrophy, infertility, and immune system depression. The physiological strain caused by these substances is often greater than what the body can handle, leading to unpredictable and dangerous effects and linking their use to heart attacks, strokes, and impaired cardiac function.

Erythropoietin stimulates red blood cell production and thus increases the amount of oxygen supplied to muscles and, consequently, endurance. Explain why erythropoietin might be potentially dangerous if taken to enhance athletic performance.

a. Erythropoietin increases blood viscosity, which makes it difficult for blood to circulate within the body.
b. Erythropoietin decreases blood viscosity, which makes it difficult for blood to circulate within the body.
c. Erythropoietin increases the activity of anorexigenic neurons, which makes it difficult for blood to circulate within the body.
d. Erythropoietin increases blood viscosity, which reduces hunger and promotes a feeling of satiety.

Regulation of the Female Reproductive System

In females, FSH stimulates development of egg cells, called ova, which develop in structures called follicles. Follicle cells produce the hormone inhibin, which inhibits FSH production. LH also plays a role in the development of ova, induction of ovulation, and stimulation of estradiol and progesterone production by the ovaries, as illustrated in Figure 28.9. Estradiol and progesterone are steroid hormones that prepare the body for pregnancy. Estradiol produces secondary sex characteristics in females, while both estradiol and progesterone regulate the menstrual cycle.

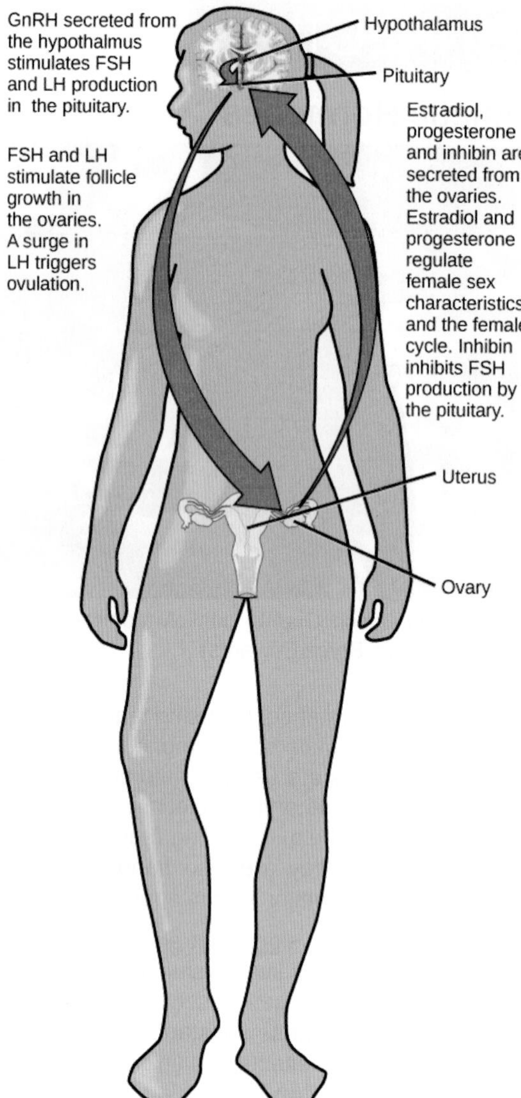
GnRH secreted from the hypothalmus stimulates FSH and LH production in the pituitary.
FSH and LH stimulate follicle growth in the ovaries. A surge in LH triggers ovulation.
Hypothalamus
Pituitary
Estradiol, progesterone and inhibin are secreted from the ovaries. Estradiol and progesterone regulate female sex characteristics and the female cycle. Inhibin inhibits FSH production by the pituitary.
Uterus
Ovary

Figure 28.9 Hormonal regulation of the female reproductive system involves hormones from the hypothalamus, pituitary, and ovaries.

In addition to producing FSH and LH, the anterior portion of the pituitary gland also produces the hormone **prolactin (PRL)** in females. Prolactin stimulates the production of milk by the mammary glands following childbirth. Prolactin levels are regulated by the hypothalamic hormones **prolactin-releasing hormone (PRH)** and **prolactin-inhibiting hormone (PIH)**, which is now known to be dopamine. PRH stimulates the release of prolactin and PIH inhibits it.

The posterior pituitary releases the hormone **oxytocin**, which stimulates uterine contractions during childbirth. The uterine smooth muscles are not very sensitive to oxytocin until late in pregnancy when the number of oxytocin receptors in the uterus peaks. Stretching of tissues in the uterus and cervix stimulates oxytocin release during childbirth. Contractions increase in intensity as blood levels of oxytocin rise via a positive feedback mechanism until the birth is complete. Oxytocin also stimulates the contraction of myoepithelial cells around the milk-producing mammary glands. As these cells contract, milk is forced from the secretory alveoli into milk ducts and is ejected from the breasts in milk ejection ("let-down") reflex. Oxytocin release is stimulated by the suckling of an infant, which triggers the synthesis of oxytocin in the hypothalamus and its release into circulation at the posterior pituitary.

Hormonal Regulation of Metabolism

Blood glucose levels vary widely over the course of a day as periods of food consumption alternate with periods of fasting. Insulin and glucagon are the two hormones primarily responsible for maintaining homeostasis of blood glucose levels. Additional regulation is mediated by the thyroid hormones.

Regulation of Blood Glucose Levels by Insulin and Glucagon

Cells of the body require nutrients in order to function, and these nutrients are obtained through feeding. In order to manage nutrient intake, storing excess intake and utilizing reserves when necessary, the body uses hormones to moderate energy stores. **Insulin** is produced by the beta cells of the pancreas, which are stimulated to release insulin as blood glucose levels rise (for example, after a meal is consumed). Insulin lowers blood glucose levels by enhancing the rate of glucose uptake and utilization by target cells, which use glucose for ATP production. It also stimulates the liver to convert glucose to glycogen, which is then stored by cells for later use. Insulin also increases glucose transport into certain cells, such as muscle cells and the liver. This results from an insulin-mediated increase in the number of glucose transporter proteins in cell membranes, which remove glucose from circulation by facilitated diffusion. As insulin binds to its target cell via insulin receptors and signal transduction, it triggers the cell to incorporate glucose transport proteins into its membrane. This allows glucose to enter the cell, where it can be used as an energy source. However, this does not occur in all cells: some cells, including those in the kidneys and brain, can access glucose without the use of insulin. Insulin also stimulates the conversion of glucose to fat in adipocytes and the synthesis of proteins. These actions mediated by insulin cause blood glucose concentrations to fall, called a hypoglycemic "low sugar" effect, which inhibits further insulin release from beta cells through a negative feedback loop.

This **animation (http://openstaxcollege.org/l/insulin)** describe the role of insulin and the pancreas in diabetes.

Describe why Type 1 diabetes is considered an autoimmune disease.

a. The immune system attacks the hypothalamus, which prevents thyroxine production to regulate blood glucose.

b. The immune system attacks cells of the pituitary gland, which prevents insulin production to regulate blood glucose.

c. The immune system attacks beta cells of the pancreas, which prevents insulin production to regulate blood glucose.

d. The immune system attacks beta cells of the pancreas, which prevents insulin production to regulate growth.

Impaired insulin function can lead to a condition called **diabetes mellitus**, the main symptoms of which are illustrated in **Figure 28.10**. This can be caused by low levels of insulin production by the beta cells of the pancreas, or by reduced sensitivity of tissue cells to insulin. This prevents glucose from being absorbed by cells, causing high levels of blood glucose, or **hyperglycemia** (high sugar). High blood glucose levels make it difficult for the kidneys to recover all the glucose from nascent urine, resulting in glucose being lost in urine. High glucose levels also result in less water being reabsorbed by the kidneys, causing high amounts of urine to be produced; this may result in dehydration. Over time, high blood glucose levels can cause nerve damage to the eyes and peripheral body tissues, as well as damage to the kidneys and cardiovascular system. Oversecretion of insulin can cause **hypoglycemia**, low blood glucose levels. This causes insufficient glucose availability to cells, often leading to muscle weakness, and can sometimes cause unconsciousness or death if left untreated.

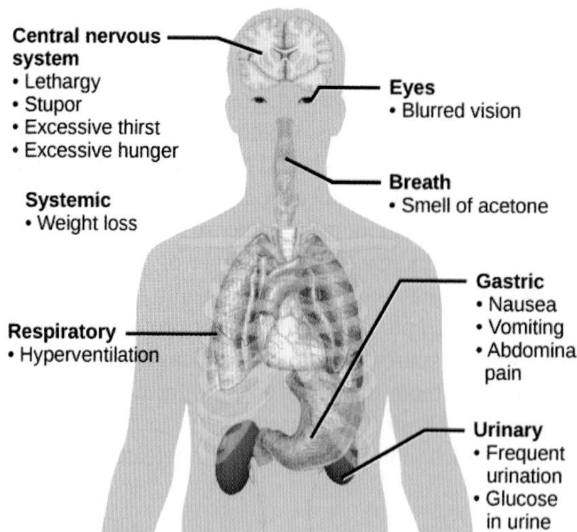

Figure 28.10 The main symptoms of diabetes are shown. (credit: modification of work by Mikael Häggström)

When blood glucose levels decline below normal levels, for example between meals or when glucose is utilized rapidly during exercise, the hormone **glucagon** is released from the alpha cells of the pancreas. Glucagon raises blood glucose levels, eliciting what is called a hyperglycemic effect, by stimulating the breakdown of glycogen to glucose in skeletal muscle cells and liver cells in a process called **glycogenolysis**. Glucose can then be utilized as energy by muscle cells and released into circulation by the liver cells. Glucagon also stimulates absorption of amino acids from the blood by the liver, which then converts them to glucose. This process of glucose synthesis is called **gluconeogenesis**. Glucagon also stimulates adipose cells to release fatty acids into the blood. These actions mediated by glucagon result in an increase in blood glucose levels to normal homeostatic levels. Rising blood glucose levels inhibit further glucagon release by the pancreas via a negative feedback mechanism. In this way, insulin and glucagon work together to maintain homeostatic glucose levels, as shown in Figure 28.11.

visual CONNECTION

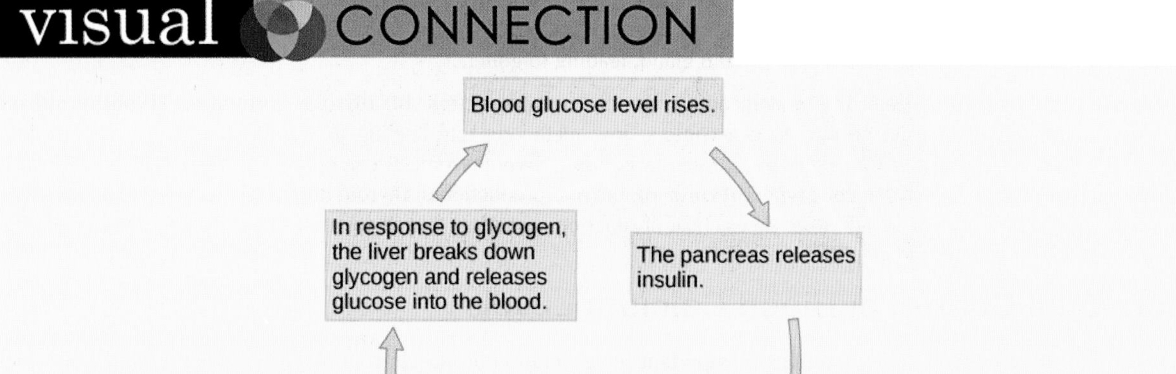

Figure 28.11 Insulin and glucagon regulate blood glucose levels.

Pancreatic tumors may cause excess secretion of glucagon. Type I diabetes results from the failure of the pancreas to produce insulin. Which of the following statement about these two conditions is true?

a. A pancreatic tumor and Type 1 diabetes will have the opposite effects on blood sugar levels.
b. A pancreatic tumor and Type 1 diabetes can both cause hyperglycemia.
c. A pancreatic tumor and Type 1 diabetes can both cause hypoglycemia.
d. Both pancreatic tumors and Type 1 diabetes result in the inability of cells to take up glucose.

Regulation of Blood Glucose Levels by Thyroid Hormones

The basal metabolic rate, which is the amount of calories required by the body at rest, is determined by two hormones produced by the thyroid gland: **thyroxine**, also known as tetraiodothyronine or T_4, and **triiodothyronine**, also known as T_3. These hormones affect nearly every cell in the body except for the adult brain, uterus, testes, blood cells, and spleen. They are transported across the plasma membrane of target cells and bind to receptors on the mitochondria resulting in increased ATP production. In the nucleus, T_3 and T_4 activate genes involved in energy production and glucose oxidation. This results in increased rates of metabolism and body heat production, which is known as the hormone's calorigenic effect.

T_3 and T_4 release from the thyroid gland is stimulated by **thyroid-stimulating hormone (TSH)**, which is produced by the anterior pituitary. TSH binding at the receptors of the follicle of the thyroid triggers the production of T_3 and T_4 from a glycoprotein called **thyroglobulin**. Thyroglobulin is present in the follicles of the thyroid, and is converted into thyroid hormones with the addition of iodine. Iodine is formed from iodide ions that are actively transported into the thyroid follicle from the bloodstream. A peroxidase enzyme then attaches the iodine to the tyrosine amino acid found in thyroglobulin. T_3 has three iodine ions attached, while T_4 has four iodine ions attached. T_3 and T_4 are then released into the bloodstream, with T_4 being released in much greater amounts than T_3. As T_3 is more active than T_4 and is responsible for most of the effects of thyroid hormones, tissues of the body convert T_4 to T_3 by the removal of an iodine ion. Most of the released T_3 and T_4 becomes attached to transport proteins in the bloodstream and is unable to cross the plasma membrane of cells. These protein-bound molecules are only released when blood levels of the unattached hormone begin to decline. In this way, a week's worth of reserve hormone is maintained in the blood. Increased T_3 and T_4 levels in the blood inhibit the release of TSH, which results in lower T_3 and T_4 release from the thyroid.

The follicular cells of the thyroid require iodides (anions of iodine) in order to synthesize T_3 and T_4. Iodides obtained from the diet are actively transported into follicle cells resulting in a concentration that is approximately 30 times higher than in blood. The typical diet in North America provides more iodine than required due to the addition of iodide to table salt. Inadequate iodine intake, which occurs in many developing countries, results in an inability to synthesize T_3 and T_4 hormones. The thyroid gland enlarges in a condition called **goiter**, which is caused by overproduction of TSH without the formation of thyroid hormone. Thyroglobulin is contained in a fluid called colloid, and TSH stimulation results in higher levels of colloid accumulation in the thyroid. In the absence of iodine, this is not converted to thyroid hormone, and colloid begins to accumulate more and more in the thyroid gland, leading to goiter.

Disorders can arise from both the underproduction and overproduction of thyroid hormones. **Hypothyroidism**, underproduction of the thyroid hormones, can cause a low metabolic rate leading to weight gain, sensitivity to cold, and reduced mental activity, among other symptoms. In children, hypothyroidism can cause cretinism, which can lead to mental retardation and growth defects. **Hyperthyroidism**, the overproduction of thyroid hormones, can lead to an increased metabolic rate and its effects: weight loss, excess heat production, sweating, and an increased heart rate. Graves' disease is one example of a hyperthyroid condition.

Hormonal Control of Blood Calcium Levels

Regulation of blood calcium concentrations is important for generation of muscle contractions and nerve impulses, which are electrically stimulated. If calcium levels get too high, membrane permeability to sodium decreases and membranes become less responsive. If calcium levels get too low, membrane permeability to sodium increases and convulsions or muscle spasms can result.

Blood calcium levels are regulated by **parathyroid hormone (PTH)**, which is produced by the parathyroid glands, as illustrated in Figure 28.12. PTH is released in response to low blood Ca^{2+} levels. PTH increases Ca^{2+} levels by targeting the skeleton, the kidneys, and the intestine. In the skeleton, PTH stimulates osteoclasts, which causes bone to be reabsorbed, releasing Ca^{2+} from bone into the blood. PTH also inhibits osteoblasts, reducing Ca^{2+} deposition in bone. In the intestines, PTH increases dietary Ca^{2+} absorption, and in the kidneys, PTH stimulates reabsorption of the CA^{2+}. While PTH acts directly on the kidneys to increase Ca^{2+} reabsorption, its effects on the intestine are indirect. PTH triggers the formation of calcitriol, an active form of vitamin D, which acts on the intestines to increase absorption of dietary calcium. PTH release is inhibited by rising blood calcium levels.

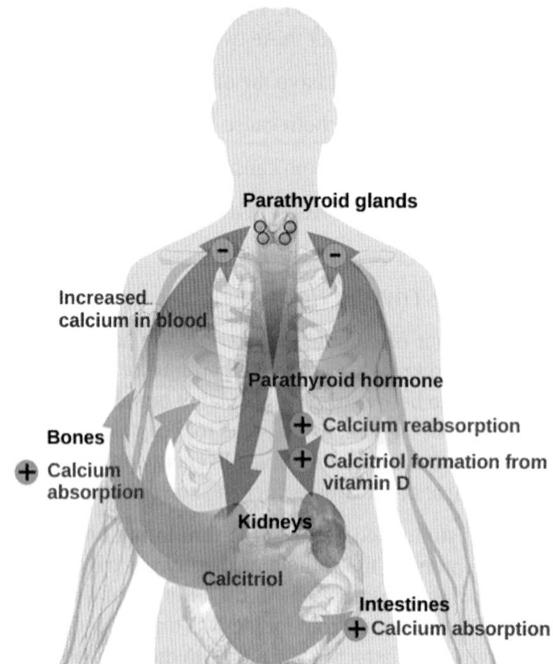

Figure 28.12 Parathyroid hormone (PTH) is released in response to low blood calcium levels. It increases blood calcium levels by targeting the skeleton, the kidneys, and the intestine. (credit: modification of work by Mikael Häggström)

Hyperparathyroidism results from an overproduction of parathyroid hormone. This results in excessive calcium being removed from bones and introduced into blood circulation, producing structural weakness of the bones, which can lead to deformation and fractures, plus nervous system impairment due to high blood calcium levels. Hypoparathyroidism, the underproduction of PTH, results in extremely low levels of blood calcium, which causes impaired muscle function and may result in tetany (severe sustained muscle contraction).

The hormone **calcitonin**, which is produced by the parafollicular or C cells of the thyroid, has the opposite effect on blood calcium levels as does PTH. Calcitonin decreases blood calcium levels by inhibiting osteoclasts, stimulating osteoblasts, and stimulating calcium excretion by the kidneys. This results in calcium being added to the bones to promote structural integrity. Calcitonin is most important in children (when it stimulates bone growth), during pregnancy (when it reduces maternal bone loss), and during prolonged starvation (because it reduces bone mass loss). In healthy nonpregnant, unstarved adults, the role of calcitonin is unclear.

Hormonal Regulation of Growth

Hormonal regulation is required for the growth and replication of most cells in the body. **Growth hormone (GH)**, produced by the anterior portion of the pituitary gland, accelerates the rate of protein synthesis, particularly in skeletal muscle and bones. Growth hormone has direct and indirect mechanisms of action. The first direct action of GH is stimulation of triglyceride breakdown (lipolysis) and release into the blood by adipocytes. This results in a switch by most tissues from utilizing glucose as an energy source to utilizing fatty acids. This process is called a **glucose-sparing effect**. In another direct mechanism, GH stimulates glycogen breakdown in the liver; the glycogen is then released into the blood as glucose. Blood glucose levels increase as most tissues are utilizing fatty acids instead of glucose for their energy needs. The GH mediated increase in blood glucose levels is called a **diabetogenic effect** because it is similar to the high blood glucose levels seen in diabetes mellitus.

The indirect mechanism of GH action is mediated by **insulin-like growth factors (IGFs)** or somatomedins, which are a family of growth-promoting proteins produced by the liver, which stimulates tissue growth. IGFs stimulate the uptake of amino acids from the blood, allowing the formation of new proteins, particularly in skeletal muscle cells, cartilage cells, and other target cells, as shown in Figure 28.13. This is especially important after a meal, when glucose and amino acid concentration levels are high in the blood. GH levels are regulated by two hormones produced by the hypothalamus. GH release is stimulated by **growth hormone-releasing hormone (GHRH)** and is inhibited by **growth hormone-inhibiting hormone (GHIH)**, also called somatostatin.

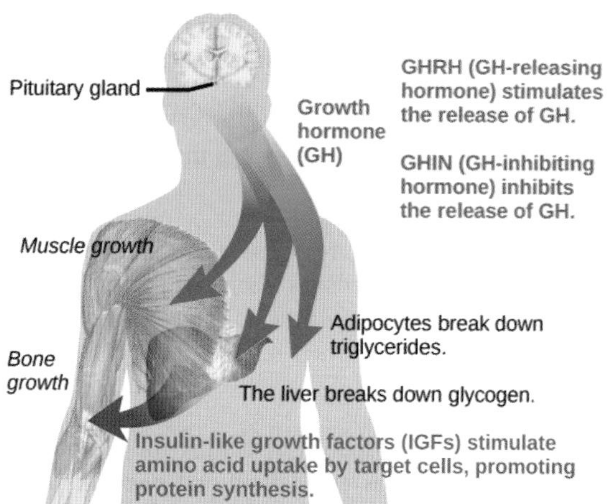

Figure 28.13 Growth hormone directly accelerates the rate of protein synthesis in skeletal muscle and bones. Insulin-like growth factor 1 (IGF-1) is activated by growth hormone and also allows formation of new proteins in muscle cells and bone. (credit: modification of work by Mikael Häggström)

A balanced production of growth hormone is critical for proper development. Underproduction of GH in adults does not appear to cause any abnormalities, but in children it can result in **pituitary dwarfism**, in which growth is reduced. Pituitary dwarfism is characterized by symmetric body formation. In some cases, individuals are under 30 inches in height. Oversecretion of growth hormone can lead to **gigantism** in children, causing excessive growth. In some documented cases, individuals can reach heights of over eight feet. In adults, excessive GH can lead to **acromegaly**, a condition in which there is enlargement of bones in the face, hands, and feet that are still capable of growth.

Hormonal Regulation of Stress

When a threat or danger is perceived, the body responds by releasing hormones that will ready it for the "fight-or-flight" response. The effects of this response are familiar to anyone who has been in a stressful situation: increased heart rate, dry mouth, and hair standing up.

Fight-or-Flight Response

Interactions of the endocrine hormones have evolved to ensure the body's internal environment remains stable. Stressors are stimuli that disrupt homeostasis. The sympathetic division of the vertebrate autonomic nervous system has evolved the fight-or-flight response to counter stress-induced disruptions of homeostasis. In the initial alarm phase, the sympathetic nervous system stimulates an increase in energy levels through increased blood glucose levels. This prepares the body for physical activity that may be required to respond to stress: to either fight for survival or to flee from danger.

However, some stresses, such as illness or injury, can last for a long time. Glycogen reserves, which provide energy in the short-term response to stress, are exhausted after several hours and cannot meet long-term energy needs. If glycogen reserves were the only energy source available, neural functioning could not be maintained once the reserves became depleted due to the nervous system's high requirement for glucose. In this situation, the body has evolved a response to counter long-term stress through the actions of the glucocorticoids, which ensure that long-term energy requirements can be met. The glucocorticoids mobilize lipid and protein reserves, stimulate gluconeogenesis, conserve glucose for use by neural tissue, and stimulate the conservation of salts and water. The mechanisms to maintain homeostasis that are described here are those observed in the human body. However, the fight-or-flight response exists in some form in all vertebrates.

Explain why the fight-or-flight response is advantageous in the short-term but not in the long-term.

a. Fight-or-flight reduces access to glucose reserves and these get depleted fairly quickly.

b. Fight-or-flight reduces access to glycogen reserves and these get depleted fairly quickly.

c. Fight-or-flight stimulates access to glucose reserves, but these get depleted fairly quickly.

d. Fight-or-flight stimulates access to glycogen reserves, but these get depleted fairly quickly.

The sympathetic nervous system regulates the stress response via the hypothalamus. Stressful stimuli cause the hypothalamus to signal the adrenal medulla (which mediates short-term stress responses) via nerve impulses, and the adrenal cortex, which mediates long-term stress responses, via the hormone **adrenocorticotropic hormone (ACTH)**, which is produced by the anterior pituitary.

Short-term Stress Response

When presented with a stressful situation, the body responds by calling for the release of hormones that provide a burst of energy. The hormones **epinephrine** (also known as adrenaline) and **norepinephrine** (also known as noradrenaline) are released by the adrenal medulla. How do these hormones provide a burst of energy? Epinephrine and norepinephrine increase blood glucose levels by stimulating the liver and skeletal muscles to break down glycogen and by stimulating glucose release by liver cells. Additionally, these hormones increase oxygen availability to cells by increasing the heart rate and dilating the bronchioles. The hormones also prioritize body function by increasing blood supply to essential organs such as the heart, brain, and skeletal muscles, while restricting blood flow to organs not in immediate need, such as the skin, digestive system, and kidneys. Epinephrine and norepinephrine are collectively called catecholamines.

Watch this Discovery Channel animation (http://openstaxcollege.org/l/adrenaline) describing the flight-or-flight response.

When would you receive a burst of energy as your body undergoes a fight-or-flight response.

a. increase in blood calcium levels

b. release of carbon monoxide in the atmosphere

c. any threat or life-or-death scenario

d. physical exercise such as running and swimming

Long-term Stress Response

Long-term stress response differs from short-term stress response. The body cannot sustain the bursts of energy mediated by epinephrine and norepinephrine for long times. Instead, other hormones come into play. In a long-term stress response, the hypothalamus triggers the release of ACTH from the anterior pituitary gland. The adrenal cortex is stimulated by ACTH to release steroid hormones called **corticosteroids**. Corticosteroids turn on transcription of certain genes in the nuclei of target cells. They change enzyme concentrations in the cytoplasm and affect cellular metabolism. There are two main corticosteroids: glucocorticoids such as **cortisol**, and mineralocorticoids such as aldosterone. These hormones target the breakdown of fat into fatty acids in the adipose tissue. The fatty acids are released into the bloodstream for other tissues to use for ATP production. The **glucocorticoids** primarily affect glucose metabolism by stimulating glucose synthesis. Glucocorticoids also have anti-inflammatory properties through inhibition of the immune system. For example, cortisone is used as an anti-inflammatory medication; however, it cannot be used long term as it increases susceptibility to disease due to its immune-suppressing effects.

Mineralocorticoids function to regulate ion and water balance of the body. The hormone aldosterone stimulates the reabsorption of water and sodium ions in the kidney, which results in increased blood pressure and volume.

Hypersecretion of glucocorticoids can cause a condition known as **Cushing's disease**, characterized by a shifting of fat storage areas of the body. This can cause the accumulation of adipose tissue in the face and neck, and excessive glucose in the blood. Hyposecretion of the corticosteroids can cause **Addison's disease**, which may result in bronzing of the skin, hypoglycemia, and low electrolyte levels in the blood.

science practices CONNECTION for AP® Courses

Activity

Selecting a hormone of your choice, create a visual representation (e.g., diagram) to describe the effect(s) of the hormone on a body system, for example, reproductive system, or process, for example, maintaining normal blood glucose levels.

28.4 | Regulation of Hormone Production

In this section, you will explore the following questions:

- How is hormone production regulated?
- What are examples of different stimuli that control hormone levels in the body?

Connection for AP® Courses

Hormone production and release are often controlled by **negative feedback** or **positive feedback**, although regulation by negative feedback is more common. In negative feedback, a stimulus elicits the release of a hormone that produces a response, and once the response reaches a certain level, it sends a signal that stops additional release of the hormone. In this way, the concentration of hormones in blood is maintained within a narrow range. For example, the anterior pituitary stimulates the thyroid gland to release thyroid hormones T_3 and T_4. Increased levels of these hormones result in feedback to the hypothalamus and anterior pituitary to inhibit further signaling to the thyroid gland.

Some hormones are regulated by positive feedback in which the response is amplified; an example of hormone regulation by positive feedback is the production of oxytocin during labor and childbirth as uterine contractions cause the production and release of more oxytocin. Disruptions in the mechanisms of feedback often result in deleterious consequences, such as diabetes mellitus resulting in decreased insulin production.

Information presented and the examples highlighted in the section support concepts outlined in Big Idea 2 of the AP® Biology Curriculum Framework. The AP® Learning Objectives listed in the Curriculum Framework provide a transparent foundation for the AP® Biology course, an inquiry-based laboratory experience, instructional activities, and AP® exam questions. A learning objective merges required content with one or more of the seven science practices.

Big Idea 2	Biological systems utilize free energy and molecular building blocks to grow, to reproduce, and to maintain dynamic homeostasis.
Enduring Understanding 2.C	Organisms use feedback mechanisms to regulate growth and reproduction, and to maintain dynamic homeostasis.
Essential Knowledge	**2.C.1** Organisms use feedback mechanisms to maintain their internal environments and respond to external environmental changes.
Science Practice	**6.1** The student can justify claims with evidence.
Learning Objective	**2.15** The student can justify a claim made about the effect(s) on a biological system at the molecular, physiological or organism level when given a scenario in which one or more components within a negative regulatory system is altered.

Hormone production and release are primarily controlled by negative feedback. In negative feedback systems, a stimulus elicits the release of a substance; once the substance reaches a certain level, it sends a signal that stops further release of the substance. In this way, the concentration of hormones in blood is maintained within a narrow range. For example, the anterior pituitary signals the thyroid to release thyroid hormones. Increasing levels of these hormones in the blood then give feedback to the hypothalamus and anterior pituitary to inhibit further signaling to the thyroid gland, as illustrated in Figure 28.14. There are three mechanisms by which endocrine glands are stimulated to synthesize and release hormones: humoral stimuli, hormonal stimuli, and neural stimuli.

visual CONNECTION

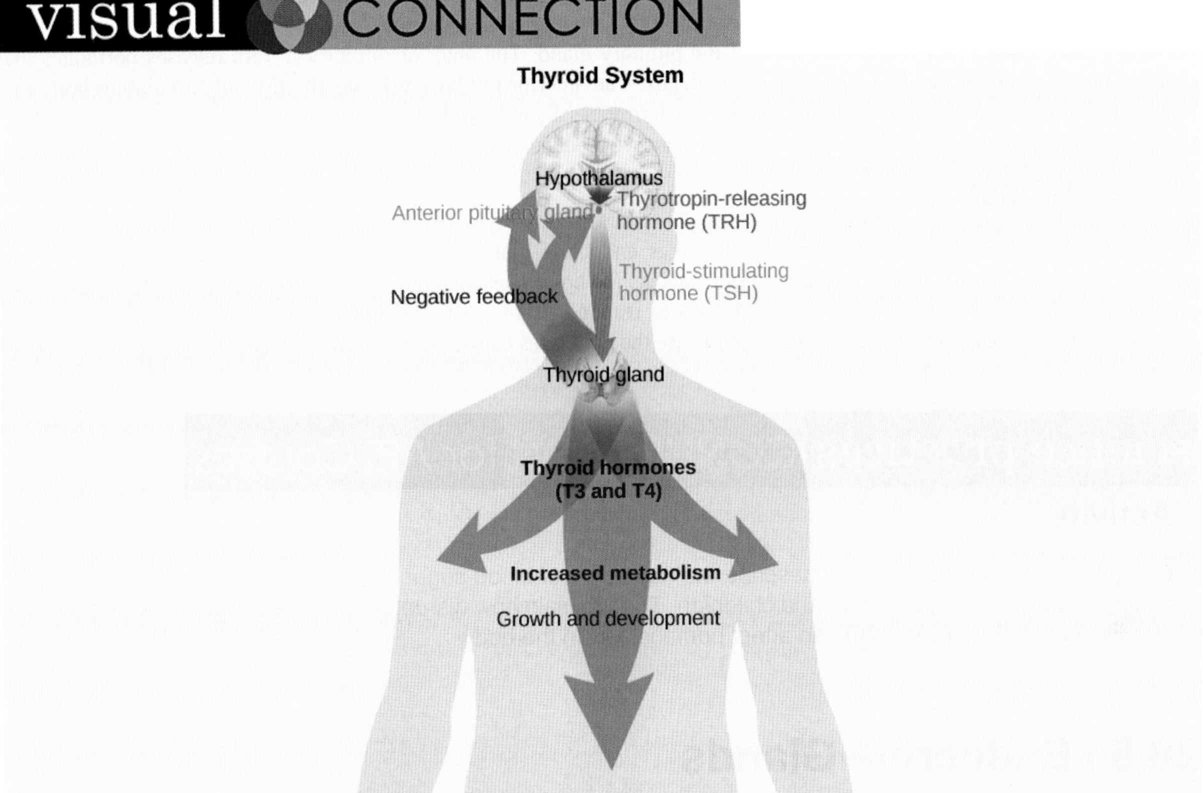

Figure 28.14 The anterior pituitary stimulates the thyroid gland to release thyroid hormones T_3 and T_4. Increasing levels of these hormones in the blood results in feedback to the hypothalamus and anterior pituitary to inhibit further signaling to the thyroid gland. (credit: modification of work by Mikael Häggström)

Hyperthyroidism is a condition in which the thyroid gland is overactive. Hypothyroidism is a condition in which the thyroid gland is underactive. Identify which of the conditions the following two patients would most likely have and explain why.

Patient A has symptoms including weight gain, cold sensitivity, low heart rate and fatigue.

Patient B has symptoms including weight loss, profuse sweating, increased heart rate and difficulty sleeping.

a. Patient A has an underactive thyroid, because less thyroid hormones decreases metabolism. Patient B has an overactive thyroid, because more thyroid hormones increases metabolism.
b. Patient A has an overactive thyroid, because less thyroid hormones decreases metabolism. Patient B has an underactive thyroid, because more thyroid hormones increases metabolism.
c. Patient A has an underactive thyroid, because more thyroid hormones decreases metabolism. Patient B has an overactive thyroid, because less thyroid hormones increases metabolism.
d. Patient A has an overactive thyroid, because less thyroid hormones increases metabolism. Patient B has an underactive thyroid, because more thyroid hormones decreases metabolism.

Humoral Stimuli

The term "humoral" is derived from the term "humor," which refers to bodily fluids such as blood. A **humoral stimulus** refers to the control of hormone release in response to changes in extracellular fluids such as blood or the ion concentration in the blood. For example, a rise in blood glucose levels triggers the pancreatic release of insulin. Insulin causes blood glucose levels to drop, which signals the pancreas to stop producing insulin in a negative feedback loop.

Hormonal Stimuli

Hormonal stimuli refers to the release of a hormone in response to another hormone. A number of endocrine glands release hormones when stimulated by hormones released by other endocrine glands. For example, the hypothalamus produces hormones that stimulate the anterior portion of the pituitary gland. The anterior pituitary in turn releases hormones that regulate hormone production by other endocrine glands. The anterior pituitary releases the thyroid-stimulating hormone, which then stimulates the thyroid gland to produce the hormones T_3 and T_4. As blood concentrations of T_3 and T_4 rise, they inhibit both the pituitary and the hypothalamus in a negative feedback loop.

Neural Stimuli

In some cases, the nervous system directly stimulates endocrine glands to release hormones, which is referred to as **neural stimuli**. Recall that in a short-term stress response, the hormones epinephrine and norepinephrine are important for providing the bursts of energy required for the body to respond. Here, neuronal signaling from the sympathetic nervous system directly stimulates the adrenal medulla to release the hormones epinephrine and norepinephrine in response to stress.

science practices CONNECTION for AP® Courses

Activity

Create a visual representation to describe the regulation of blood sugar levels, growth spurts in teenagers, and events associated with labor and childbirth. Then explain how disruptions to these regulatory processes (e.g., failure to produce insulin) can affect homeostasis in the body.

28.5 | Endocrine Glands

In this section, you will explore the following questions:

- What are the roles of different glands in the endocrine system?
- How do different glands work together to maintain homeostasis?

Connection for AP® Courses

The specific information in this section is outside the scope for AP®. You do not have to memorize a list of endocrine glands, their locations in the body, and the hormones they produce. However, you might want to focus on one or two examples and consider how endocrine glands and their hormone products work together and with the nervous system to communicate and regulate the body's physiology to maintain homeostasis. For example, the hypothalamus in vertebrates integrates the endocrine and nervous systems. The hypothalamus is located in the brain and receives input from the body and other brain areas and initiates endocrine responses to environmental changes. The pituitary gland is attached to the hypothalamus and receives products from the hypothalamus, causing, in turn, the secretion of anterior and posterior pituitary hormones such as growth hormone (GH), follicle-stimulating hormone (FSH), luteinizing hormone (LH), and oxytocin. The thyroid gland, located in the neck just below the larynx, releases T_3 and T_4 in response to thyroid stimulating hormone (TSH) produced by the anterior pituitary. Another example is how frog development is disrupted by estrogen in waste water, which you can read more about at the Science News website (http://openstaxcollege.org/l/32frog) .

Both the endocrine and nervous systems use chemical signals to communicate and regulate the body's physiology. The endocrine system releases hormones that act on target cells to regulate development, growth, energy metabolism, reproduction, and many behaviors. The nervous system releases neurotransmitters or neurohormones that regulate neurons, muscle cells, and endocrine cells. Because the neurons can regulate the release of hormones, the nervous and endocrine systems work in a coordinated manner to regulate the body's physiology.

Hypothalamic-Pituitary Axis

The **hypothalamus** in vertebrates integrates the endocrine and nervous systems. The hypothalamus is an endocrine organ located in the diencephalon of the brain. It receives input from the body and other brain areas and initiates endocrine responses to environmental changes. The hypothalamus acts as an endocrine organ, synthesizing hormones and transporting them along axons to the posterior pituitary gland. It synthesizes and secretes regulatory hormones that control the endocrine cells in the anterior pituitary gland. The hypothalamus contains autonomic centers that control endocrine cells in the adrenal medulla via neuronal control.

The **pituitary gland**, sometimes called the hypophysis or “master gland” is located at the base of the brain in the sella turcica, a groove of the sphenoid bone of the skull, illustrated in Figure 28.15. It is attached to the hypothalamus via a stalk called the **pituitary stalk** (or infundibulum). The anterior portion of the pituitary gland is regulated by releasing or release-inhibiting hormones produced by the hypothalamus, and the posterior pituitary receives signals via neurosecretory cells to release hormones produced by the hypothalamus. The pituitary has two distinct regions—the anterior pituitary and the posterior pituitary—which between them secrete nine different peptide or protein hormones. The posterior lobe of the pituitary gland contains axons of the hypothalamic neurons.

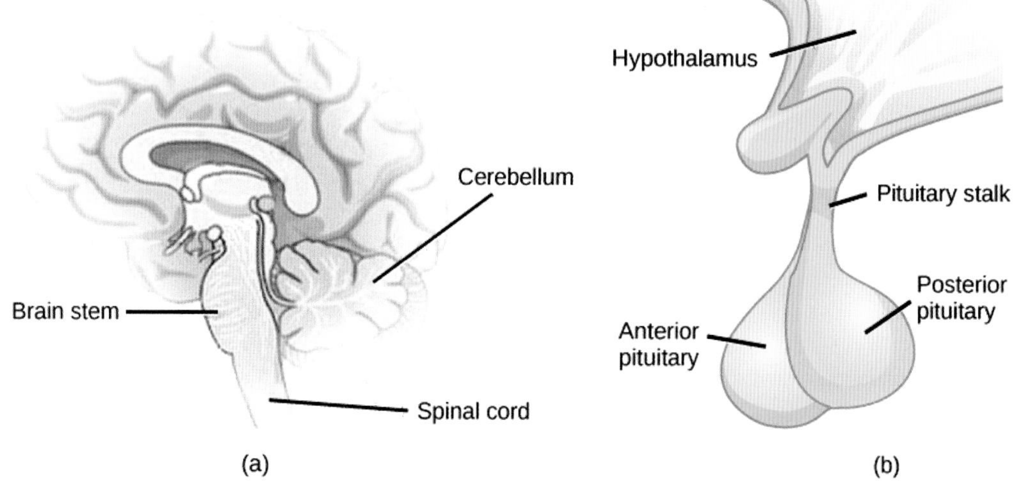

Figure 28.15 The pituitary gland is located at (a) the base of the brain and (b) connected to the hypothalamus by the pituitary stalk. (credit a: modification of work by NCI; credit b: modification of work by Gray’s Anatomy)

Anterior Pituitary

The **anterior pituitary** gland, or adenohypophysis, is surrounded by a capillary network that extends from the hypothalamus, down along the infundibulum, and to the anterior pituitary. This capillary network is a part of the **hypophyseal portal system** that carries substances from the hypothalamus to the anterior pituitary and hormones from the anterior pituitary into the circulatory system. A portal system carries blood from one capillary network to another; therefore, the hypophyseal portal system allows hormones produced by the hypothalamus to be carried directly to the anterior pituitary without first entering the circulatory system.

The anterior pituitary produces seven hormones: growth hormone (GH), prolactin (PRL), thyroid-stimulating hormone (TSH), melanin-stimulating hormone (MSH), adrenocorticotropic hormone (ACTH), follicle-stimulating hormone (FSH), and luteinizing hormone (LH). Anterior pituitary hormones are sometimes referred to as tropic hormones, because they control the functioning of other organs. While these hormones are produced by the anterior pituitary, their production is controlled by regulatory hormones produced by the hypothalamus. These regulatory hormones can be releasing hormones or inhibiting hormones, causing more or less of the anterior pituitary hormones to be secreted. These travel from the hypothalamus through the hypophyseal portal system to the anterior pituitary where they exert their effect. Negative feedback then regulates how much of these regulatory hormones are released and how much anterior pituitary hormone is secreted.

Posterior Pituitary

The **posterior pituitary** is significantly different in structure from the anterior pituitary. It is a part of the brain, extending down from the hypothalamus, and contains mostly nerve fibers and neuroglial cells, which support axons that extend from the hypothalamus to the posterior pituitary. The posterior pituitary and the infundibulum together are referred to as the neurohypophysis.

The hormones antidiuretic hormone (ADH), also known as vasopressin, and oxytocin are produced by neurons in the hypothalamus and transported within these axons along the infundibulum to the posterior pituitary. They are released into the circulatory system via neural signaling from the hypothalamus. These hormones are considered to be posterior pituitary hormones, even though they are produced by the hypothalamus, because that is where they are released into the circulatory system. The posterior pituitary itself does not produce hormones, but instead stores hormones produced by the hypothalamus and releases them into the blood stream.

Thyroid Gland

The **thyroid gland** is located in the neck, just below the larynx and in front of the trachea, as shown in Figure 28.16. It is a butterfly-shaped gland with two lobes that are connected by the **isthmus**. It has a dark red color due to its extensive vascular system. When the thyroid swells due to dysfunction, it can be felt under the skin of the neck.

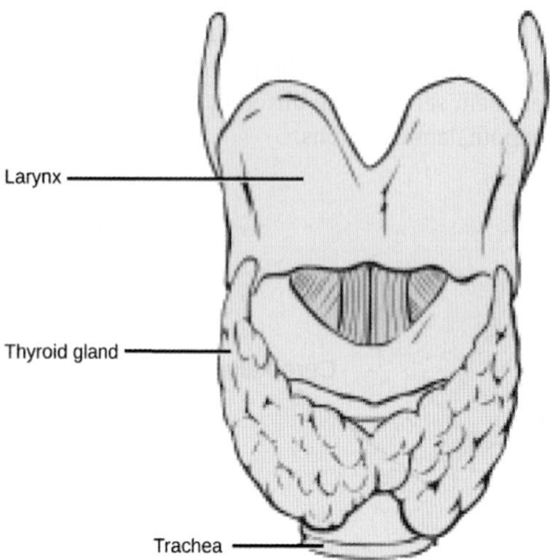

Figure 28.16 This illustration shows the location of the thyroid gland.

The thyroid gland is made up of many spherical thyroid follicles, which are lined with a simple cuboidal epithelium. These follicles contain a viscous fluid, called **colloid**, which stores the glycoprotein thyroglobulin, the precursor to the thyroid hormones. The follicles produce hormones that can be stored in the colloid or released into the surrounding capillary network for transport to the rest of the body via the circulatory system.

Thyroid follicle cells synthesize the hormone thyroxine, which is also known as T_4 because it contains four atoms of iodine, and triiodothyronine, also known as T_3 because it contains three atoms of iodine. Follicle cells are stimulated to release stored T_3 and T_4 by thyroid stimulating hormone (TSH), which is produced by the anterior pituitary. These thyroid hormones increase the rates of mitochondrial ATP production.

A third hormone, calcitonin, is produced by **parafollicular cells** of the thyroid either releasing hormones or inhibiting hormones. Calcitonin release is not controlled by TSH, but instead is released when calcium ion concentrations in the blood rise. Calcitonin functions to help regulate calcium concentrations in body fluids. It acts in the bones to inhibit osteoclast activity and in the kidneys to stimulate excretion of calcium. The combination of these two events lowers body fluid levels of calcium.

Parathyroid Glands

Most people have four **parathyroid glands**; however, the number can vary from two to six. These glands are located on the posterior surface of the thyroid gland, as shown in Figure 28.17. Normally, there is a superior gland and an inferior gland associated with each of the thyroid's two lobes. Each parathyroid gland is covered by connective tissue and contains many secretory cells that are associated with a capillary network.

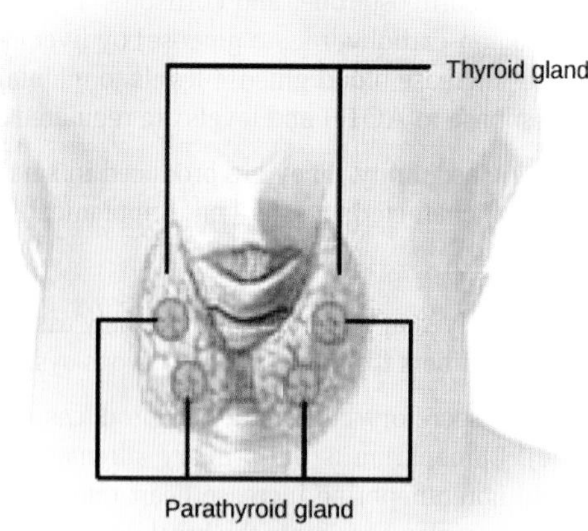

Figure 28.17 The parathyroid glands are located on the posterior of the thyroid gland. (credit: modification of work by NCI)

The parathyroid glands produce parathyroid hormone (PTH). PTH increases blood calcium concentrations when calcium ion levels fall below normal. PTH (1) enhances reabsorption of Ca^{2+} by the kidneys, (2) stimulates osteoclast activity and inhibits osteoblast activity, and (3) it stimulates synthesis and secretion of calcitriol by the kidneys, which enhances Ca^{2+} absorption by the digestive system. PTH is produced by chief cells of the parathyroid. PTH and calcitonin work in opposition to one another to maintain homeostatic Ca^{2+} levels in body fluids. Another type of cells, oxyphil cells, exist in the parathyroid but their function is not known. These hormones encourage bone growth, muscle mass, and blood cell formation in children and women.

Adrenal Glands

The **adrenal glands** are associated with the kidneys; one gland is located on top of each kidney as illustrated in Figure 28.18. The adrenal glands consist of an outer adrenal cortex and an inner adrenal medulla. These regions secrete different hormones.

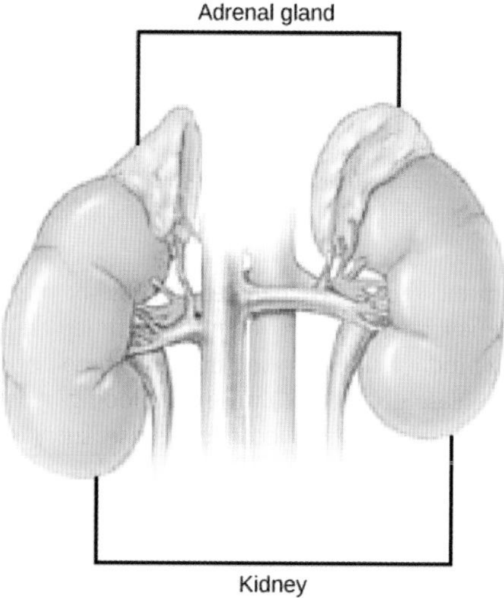

Figure 28.18 The location of the adrenal glands on top of the kidneys is shown. (credit: modification of work by NCI)

Adrenal Cortex

The **adrenal cortex** is made up of layers of epithelial cells and associated capillary networks. These layers form three distinct regions: an outer zona glomerulosa that produces mineralocorticoids, a middle zona fasciculata that produces glucocorticoids, and an inner zona reticularis that produces androgens.

The main mineralocorticoid is aldosterone, which regulates the concentration of Na^{+} ions in urine, sweat, pancreas, and saliva. Aldosterone release from the adrenal cortex is stimulated by a decrease in blood concentrations of sodium ions, blood volume, or blood pressure, or by an increase in blood potassium levels.

The three main glucocorticoids are cortisol, corticosterone, and cortisone. The glucocorticoids stimulate the synthesis of glucose and gluconeogenesis (converting a non-carbohydrate to glucose) by liver cells and they promote the release of fatty acids from adipose tissue. These hormones increase blood glucose levels to maintain levels within a normal range between meals. These hormones are secreted in response to ACTH and levels are regulated by negative feedback.

Androgens are sex hormones that promote masculinity. They are produced in small amounts by the adrenal cortex in both males and females. They do not affect sexual characteristics and may supplement sex hormones released from the gonads.

Adrenal Medulla

The **adrenal medulla** contains large, irregularly shaped cells that are closely associated with blood vessels. These cells are innervated by preganglionic autonomic nerve fibers from the central nervous system.

The adrenal medulla contains two types of secretory cells: one that produces epinephrine (adrenaline) and another that produces norepinephrine (noradrenaline). Epinephrine is the primary adrenal medulla hormone accounting for 75 to 80 percent of its secretions. Epinephrine and norepinephrine increase heart rate, breathing rate, cardiac muscle contractions, blood pressure, and blood glucose levels. They also accelerate the breakdown of glucose in skeletal muscles and stored fats in adipose tissue.

The release of epinephrine and norepinephrine is stimulated by neural impulses from the sympathetic nervous system. Secretion of these hormones is stimulated by acetylcholine release from preganglionic sympathetic fibers innervating the adrenal medulla. These neural impulses originate from the hypothalamus in response to stress to prepare the body for the fight-or-flight response.

Pancreas

The **pancreas**, illustrated in Figure 28.19, is an elongated organ that is located between the stomach and the proximal portion of the small intestine. It contains both exocrine cells that excrete digestive enzymes and endocrine cells that release hormones. It is sometimes referred to as a heterocrine gland because it has both endocrine and exocrine functions.

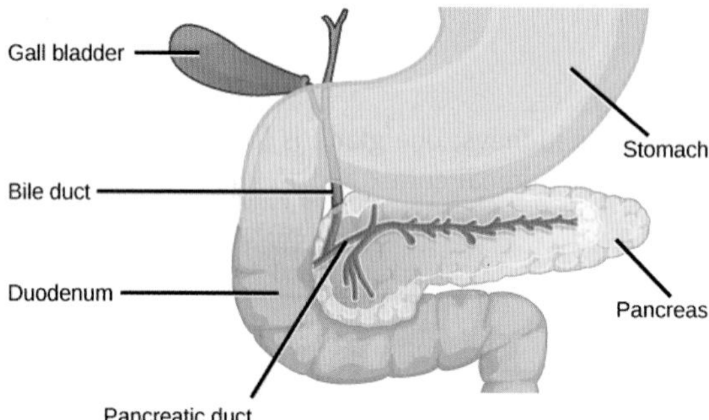

Figure 28.19 The pancreas is found underneath the stomach and points toward the spleen. (credit: modification of work by NCI)

The endocrine cells of the pancreas form clusters called pancreatic islets or the **islets of Langerhans**, as visible in the micrograph shown in Figure 28.20. The pancreatic islets contain two primary cell types: **alpha cells**, which produce the hormone glucagon, and **beta cells**, which produce the hormone insulin. These hormones regulate blood glucose levels. As blood glucose levels decline, alpha cells release glucagon to raise the blood glucose levels by increasing rates of glycogen breakdown and glucose release by the liver. When blood glucose levels rise, such as after a meal, beta cells release insulin to lower blood glucose levels by increasing the rate of glucose uptake in most body cells, and by increasing glycogen synthesis in skeletal muscles and the liver. Together, glucagon and insulin regulate blood glucose levels.

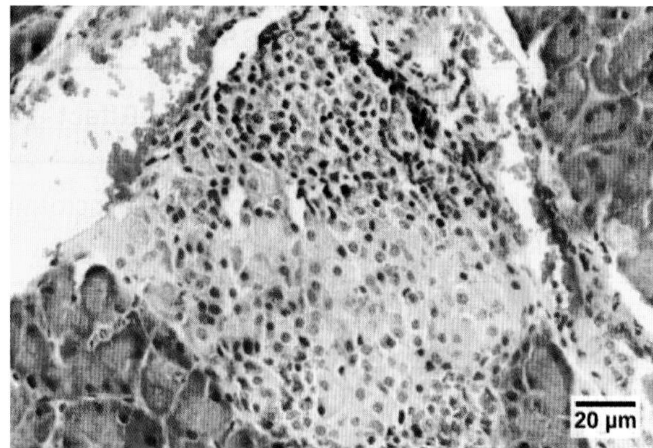

Figure 28.20 The islets of Langerhans are clusters of endocrine cells found in the pancreas; they stain lighter than surrounding cells. (credit: modification of work by Muhammad T. Tabiin, Christopher P. White, Grant Morahan, and Bernard E. Tuch; scale-bar data from Matt Russell)

Pineal Gland

The pineal gland produces melatonin. The rate of melatonin production is affected by the photoperiod. Collaterals from the visual pathways innervate the pineal gland. During the day photoperiod, little melatonin is produced; however, melatonin production increases during the dark photoperiod (night). In some mammals, melatonin has an inhibitory affect on reproductive functions by decreasing production and maturation of sperm, oocytes, and reproductive organs. Melatonin is an effective antioxidant, protecting the CNS from free radicals such as nitric oxide and hydrogen peroxide. Lastly, melatonin is involved in biological rhythms, particularly circadian rhythms such as the sleep-wake cycle and eating habits.

Gonads

The gonads—the male testes and female ovaries—produce steroid hormones. The testes produce androgens, testosterone being the most prominent, which allow for the development of secondary sex characteristics and the production of sperm cells. The ovaries produce estradiol and progesterone, which cause secondary sex characteristics and prepare the body for childbirth.

Endocrine Glands and their Associated Hormones

Endocrine Gland	Associated Hormones	Effect
Hypothalamus	releasing and inhibiting hormones	regulate hormone release from pituitary gland; produce oxytocin; produce uterine contractions and milk secretion in females
	antidiuretic hormone (ADH)	water reabsorption from kidneys; vasoconstriction to increase blood pressure
Pituitary (Anterior)	growth hormone (GH)	promotes growth of body tissues, protein synthesis; metabolic functions
	prolactin (PRL)	promotes milk production
	thyroid stimulating hormone (TSH)	stimulates thyroid hormone release
	adrenocorticotropic hormone (ACTH)	stimulates hormone release by adrenal cortex, glucocorticoids
	follicle-stimulating hormone (FSH)	stimulates gamete production (both ova and sperm); secretion of estradiol
	luteinizing hormone (LH)	stimulates androgen production by gonads; ovulation, secretion of progesterone

Table 28.1

Endocrine Glands and their Associated Hormones

Endocrine Gland	Associated Hormones	Effect
	melanocyte-stimulating hormone (MSH)	stimulates melanocytes of the skin increasing melanin pigment production.
Pituitary (Posterior)	antidiuretic hormone (ADH)	stimulates water reabsorption by kidneys
	oxytocin	stimulates uterine contractions during childbirth; milk ejection; stimulates ductus deferens and prostate gland contraction during emission
Thyroid	thyroxine, triiodothyronine	stimulate and maintain metabolism; growth and development
	calcitonin	reduces blood Ca^{2+} levels
Parathyroid	parathyroid hormone (PTH)	increases blood Ca^{2+} levels
Adrenal (Cortex)	aldosterone	increases blood Na^{+} levels; increase K^{+} secretion
	cortisol, corticosterone, cortisone	increase blood glucose levels; anti-inflammatory effects
Adrenal (Medulla)	epinephrine, norepinephrine	stimulate fight-or-flight response; increase blood gluclose levels; increase metabolic activities
Pancreas	insulin	reduces blood glucose levels
	glucagon	increases blood glucose levels
Pineal gland	melatonin	regulates some biological rhythms and protects CNS from free radicals
Testes	androgens	regulate, promote, increase or maintain sperm production; male secondary sexual characteristics
Ovaries	estrogen	promotes uterine lining growth; female secondary sexual characteristics
	progestins	promote and maintain uterine lining growth

Table 28.1

Organs with Secondary Endocrine Functions

There are several organs whose primary functions are non-endocrine but that also possess endocrine functions. These include the heart, kidneys, intestines, thymus, gonads, and adipose tissue.

The heart possesses endocrine cells in the walls of the atria that are specialized cardiac muscle cells. These cells release the hormone **atrial natriuretic peptide (ANP)** in response to increased blood volume. High blood volume causes the cells to be stretched, resulting in hormone release. ANP acts on the kidneys to reduce the reabsorption of Na^{+}, causing Na^{+} and water to be excreted in the urine. ANP also reduces the amounts of renin released by the kidneys and aldosterone released by the adrenal cortex, further preventing the retention of water. In this way, ANP causes a reduction in blood volume and blood pressure, and reduces the concentration of Na^{+} in the blood.

The gastrointestinal tract produces several hormones that aid in digestion. The endocrine cells are located in the mucosa of the GI tract throughout the stomach and small intestine. Some of the hormones produced include gastrin, secretin, and cholecystokinin, which are secreted in the presence of food, and some of which act on other organs such as the pancreas, gallbladder, and liver. They trigger the release of gastric juices, which help to break down and digest food in the GI tract.

While the adrenal glands associated with the kidneys are major **endocrine glands**, the kidneys themselves also possess endocrine function. Renin is released in response to decreased blood volume or pressure and is part of the renin-angiotensin-aldosterone system that leads to the release of aldosterone. Aldosterone then causes the retention of Na^+ and water, raising blood volume. The kidneys also release calcitriol, which aids in the absorption of Ca^{2+} and phosphate ions. **Erythropoietin (EPO)** is a protein hormone that triggers the formation of red blood cells in the bone marrow. EPO is released in response to low oxygen levels. Because red blood cells are oxygen carriers, increased production results in greater oxygen delivery throughout the body. EPO has been used by athletes to improve performance, as greater oxygen delivery to muscle cells allows for greater endurance. Because red blood cells increase the viscosity of blood, artificially high levels of EPO can cause severe health risks.

The **thymus** is found behind the sternum; it is most prominent in infants, becoming smaller in size through adulthood. The thymus produces hormones referred to as thymosins, which contribute to the development of the immune response.

Adipose tissue is a connective tissue found throughout the body. It produces the hormone **leptin** in response to food intake. Leptin increases the activity of anorexigenic neurons and decreases that of orexigenic neurons, producing a feeling of satiety after eating, thus affecting appetite and reducing the urge for further eating. Leptin is also associated with reproduction. It must be present for GnRH and gonadotropin synthesis to occur. Extremely thin females may enter puberty late; however, if adipose levels increase, more leptin will be produced, improving fertility.

KEY TERMS

acromegaly condition caused by overproduction of GH in adults

Addison's disease disorder caused by the hyposecretion of corticosteroids

adenylate cyclase an enzyme that catalyzes the conversion of ATP to cyclic AMP

adrenal cortex outer portion of adrenal glands that produces corticosteroids

adrenal gland endocrine glands associated with the kidneys

adrenal medulla inner portion of adrenal glands that produces epinephrine and norepinephrine

adrenocorticotropic hormone (ACTH) hormone released by the anterior pituitary, which stimulates the adrenal cortex to release corticosteroids during the long-term stress response

aldosterone steroid hormone produced by the adrenal cortex that stimulates the reabsorption of Na^+ from extracellular fluids and secretion of K^+.

alpha cell endocrine cell of the pancreatic islets that produces the hormone glucagon

amino acid-derived hormone hormone derived from amino acids

androgen male sex hormone such as testosterone

anterior pituitary portion of the pituitary gland that produces six hormones; also called adenohypophysis

antidiuretic hormone (ADH) hormone produced by the hypothalamus and released by the posterior pituitary that increases water reabsorption by the kidneys

atrial natriuretic peptide (ANP) hormone produced by the heart to reduce blood volume, pressure, and Na^+ concentration

beta cell endocrine cell of the pancreatic islets that produces the hormone insulin

calcitonin hormone produced by the parafollicular cells of the thyroid gland that functions to lower blood Ca^{2+} levels and promote bone growth

colloid fluid inside the thyroid gland that contains the glycoprotein thyroglobulin

corticosteroid hormone released by the adrenal cortex in response to long-term stress

cortisol glucocorticoid produced in response to stress

Cushing's disease disorder caused by the hypersecretion of glucocorticoids

diabetes insipidus disorder caused by underproduction of ADH

diabetes mellitus disorder caused by low levels of insulin activity

diabetogenic effect effect of GH that causes blood glucose levels to rise similar to diabetes mellitus

down-regulation a decrease in the number of hormone receptors in response to increased hormone levels

endocrine gland gland that secretes hormones into the surrounding interstitial fluid, which then diffuse into blood and are carried to various organs and tissues within the body

epinephrine hormone released by the adrenal medulla in response to a short term stress

erythropoietin (EPO) hormone produced by the kidneys to stimulate red blood cell production in the bone marrow

estrogens - a group of steroid hormones, including estradiol and several others, that are produced by the ovaries and elicit secondary sex characteristics in females as well as control the maturation of the ova

first messenger the hormone that binds to a plasma membrane hormone receptor to trigger a signal transduction pathway

follicle-stimulating hormone (FSH) hormone produced by the anterior pituitary that stimulates gamete production

G-protein a membrane protein activated by the hormone first messenger to activate formation of cyclic AMP

gigantism condition caused by overproduction of GH in children

glucagon hormone produced by the alpha cells of the pancreas in response to low blood sugar; functions to raise blood sugar levels

glucocorticoid corticosteroid that affects glucose metabolism

gluconeogenesis synthesis of glucose from amino acids

glucose-sparing effect effect of GH that causes tissues to use fatty acids instead of glucose as an energy source

glycogenolysis breakdown of glycogen into glucose

goiter enlargement of the thyroid gland caused by insufficient dietary iodine levels

gonadotropin hormone that regulates the gonads, including FSH and LH

growth hormone (GH) hormone produced by the anterior pituitary that promotes protein synthesis and body growth

growth hormone-inhibiting hormone (GHIH) hormone produced by the hypothalamus that inhibits growth hormone production, also called somatostatin

growth hormone-releasing hormone (GHRH) hormone released by the hypothalamus that triggers the release of GH

hormonal stimuli release of a hormone in response to another hormone

hormone receptor the cellular protein that binds to a hormone

humoral stimuli control of hormone release in response to changes in extracellular fluids such as blood or the ion concentration in the blood

hyperglycemia high blood sugar level

hyperthyroidism overactivity of the thyroid gland

hypoglycemia low blood sugar level

hypophyseal portal system system of blood vessels that carries hormones from the hypothalamus to the anterior pituitary

hypothyroidism underactivity of the thyroid gland

insulin hormone produced by the beta cells of the pancreas in response to high blood glucose levels; functions to lower blood glucose levels

insulin-like growth factor (IGF) growth-promoting protein produced by the liver

intracellular hormone receptor a hormone receptor in the cytoplasm or nucleus of a cell

islets of Langerhans (pancreatic islets) endocrine cells of the pancreas

isthmus tissue mass that connects the two lobes of the thyroid gland

leptin hormone produced by adipose tissue that promotes feelings of satiety and reduces hunger

lipid-derived hormone hormone derived mostly from cholesterol

mineralocorticoid corticosteroid that affects ion and water balance

neural stimuli stimulation of endocrine glands by the nervous system

norepinephrine hormone released by the adrenal medulla in response to a short-term stress hormone production by the gonads

osmoreceptor receptor in the hypothalamus that monitors the concentration of electrolytes in the blood

oxytocin hormone released by the posterior pituitary to stimulate uterine contractions during childbirth and milk let-down in the mammary glands

pancreas organ located between the stomach and the small intestine that contains exocrine and endocrine cells

parafollicular cell thyroid cell that produces the hormone calcitonin

parathyroid gland gland located on the surface of the thyroid that produces parathyroid hormone

parathyroid hormone (PTH) hormone produced by the parathyroid glands in response to low blood Ca^{2+} levels; functions to raise blood Ca^{2+} levels

peptide hormone hormone composed of a polypeptide chain

phosphodiesterase (PDE) enzyme that deactivates cAMP, stopping hormone activity

pituitary dwarfism condition caused by underproduction of GH in children

pituitary gland endocrine gland located at the base of the brain composed of an anterior and posterior region; also called hypophysis

pituitary stalk (also, infundibulum) stalk that connects the pituitary gland to the hypothalamus

plasma membrane hormone receptor a hormone receptor on the surface of the plasma membrane of a cell

posterior pituitary extension of the brain that releases hormones produced by the hypothalamus; along with the infundibulum, it is also referred to as the neurohypophysis

prolactin (PRL) hormone produced by the anterior pituitary that stimulates milk production

prolactin-inhibiting hormone hormone produced by the hypothalamus that inhibits the release of prolactin

prolactin-releasing hormone hormone produced by the hypothalamus that stimulates the release of prolactin

renin enzyme produced by the juxtaglomerular apparatus of the kidneys that reacts with angiotensinogen to cause the release of aldosterone

thymus gland located behind the sternum that produces thymosin hormones that contribute to the development of the immune system

thyroglobulin glycoprotein found in the thyroid that is converted into thyroid hormone

thyroid gland endocrine gland located in the neck that produces thyroid hormones thyroxine and triiodothyronine

thyroid-stimulating hormone (TSH) hormone produced by the anterior pituitary that controls the release of T_3 and T_4 from the thyroid gland

thyroxine (tetraiodothyronine, T_4) thyroid hormone containing 4 iodines that controls the basal metabolic rate

triiodothyronine (T_3) thyroid hormone containing 3 iodines controls the basal metabolic rate

up-regulation an increase in the number of hormone receptors in response to increased hormone levels

CHAPTER SUMMARY

28.1 Types of Hormones

There are three basic types of hormones: lipid-derived, amino acid-derived, and peptide. Lipid-derived hormones are structurally similar to cholesterol and include steroid hormones such as estradiol and testosterone. Amino acid-derived hormones are relatively small molecules and include the adrenal hormones epinephrine and norepinephrine. Peptide hormones are polypeptide chains or proteins and include the pituitary hormones, antidiuretic hormone (vasopressin), and oxytocin.

28.2 How Hormones Work

Hormones cause cellular changes by binding to receptors on target cells. The number of receptors on a target cell can increase or decrease in response to hormone activity. Hormones can affect cells directly through intracellular hormone receptors or indirectly through plasma membrane hormone receptors.

Lipid-derived (soluble) hormones can enter the cell by diffusing across the plasma membrane and binding to DNA to regulate gene transcription and to change the cell's activities by inducing production of proteins that affect, in general, the long-term structure and function of the cell. Lipid insoluble hormones bind to receptors on the plasma membrane surface and trigger a signaling pathway to change the cell's activities by inducing production of various cell products that affect the cell in the short-term. The hormone is called a first messenger and the cellular component is called a second messenger. G-proteins activate the second messenger (cyclic AMP), triggering the cellular response. Response to hormone binding is amplified as the signaling pathway progresses. Cellular responses to hormones include the production of proteins and enzymes and altered membrane permeability.

28.3 Regulation of Body Processes

Water levels in the body are controlled by antidiuretic hormone (ADH), which is produced in the hypothalamus and triggers the reabsorption of water by the kidneys. Underproduction of ADH can cause diabetes insipidus. Aldosterone, a hormone produced by the adrenal cortex of the kidneys, enhances Na^+ reabsorption from the extracellular fluids and subsequent water reabsorption by diffusion. The renin-angiotensin-aldosterone system is one way that aldosterone release is controlled.

The reproductive system is controlled by the gonadotropins follicle-stimulating hormone (FSH) and luteinizing hormone (LH), which are produced by the pituitary gland. Gonadotropin release is controlled by the hypothalamic hormone gonadotropin-releasing hormone (GnRH). FSH stimulates the maturation of sperm cells in males and is inhibited by the hormone inhibin, while LH stimulates the production of the androgen testosterone. FSH stimulates egg maturation in females, while LH stimulates the production of estrogens and progesterone. **Estrogens** are a group of steroid hormones produced by the ovaries that trigger the development of secondary sex characteristics in females as well as control the maturation of the ova. In females, the pituitary also produces prolactin, which stimulates milk production after childbirth, and oxytocin, which stimulates uterine contraction during childbirth and milk let-down during suckling.

Insulin is produced by the pancreas in response to rising blood glucose levels and allows cells to utilize blood glucose and store excess glucose for later use. Diabetes mellitus is caused by reduced insulin activity and causes high blood glucose levels, or hyperglycemia. Glucagon is released by the pancreas in response to low blood glucose levels and stimulates the breakdown of glycogen into glucose, which can be used by the body. The body's basal metabolic rate is controlled by the thyroid hormones thyroxine (T_4) and triiodothyronine (T_3). The anterior pituitary produces thyroid stimulating hormone (TSH), which controls the release of T_3 and T_4 from the thyroid gland. Iodine is necessary in the production of thyroid hormone, and the lack of iodine can lead to a condition called goiter.

Parathyroid hormone (PTH) is produced by the parathyroid glands in response to low blood Ca^{2+} levels. The parafollicular cells of the thyroid produce calcitonin, which reduces blood Ca^{2+} levels. Growth hormone (GH) is produced by the anterior pituitary and controls the growth rate of muscle and bone. GH action is indirectly mediated by insulin-like growth factors (IGFs). Short-term stress causes the hypothalamus to trigger the adrenal medulla to release epinephrine and norepinephrine, which trigger the fight or flight response. Long-term stress causes the hypothalamus to trigger the anterior pituitary to release adrenocorticotropic hormone (ACTH), which causes the release of corticosteroids, glucocorticoids, and mineralocorticoids, from the adrenal cortex.

28.4 Regulation of Hormone Production

Hormone levels are primarily controlled through negative feedback, in which rising levels of a hormone inhibit its further release. The three mechanisms of hormonal release are humoral stimuli, hormonal stimuli, and neural stimuli. Humoral stimuli refers to the control of hormonal release in response to changes in extracellular fluid levels or ion levels. Hormonal stimuli refers to the release of hormones in response to hormones released by other endocrine glands. Neural stimuli refers to the release of hormones in response to neural stimulation.

28.5 Endocrine Glands

The pituitary gland is located at the base of the brain and is attached to the hypothalamus by the infundibulum. The anterior pituitary receives products from the hypothalamus by the hypophyseal portal system and produces six hormones. The posterior pituitary is an extension of the brain and releases hormones (antidiuretic hormone and oxytocin) produced by the hypothalamus.

The thyroid gland is located in the neck and is composed of two lobes connected by the isthmus. The thyroid is made up of follicle cells that produce the hormones thyroxine and triiodothyronine. Parafollicular cells of the thyroid produce calcitonin. The parathyroid glands lie on the posterior surface of the thyroid gland and produce parathyroid hormone.

The adrenal glands are located on top of the kidneys and consist of the renal cortex and renal medulla. The adrenal cortex is the outer part of the adrenal gland and produces the corticosteroids, glucocorticoids, and mineralocorticoids. The adrenal medulla is the inner part of the adrenal gland and produces the catecholamines epinephrine and norepinephrine.

The pancreas lies in the abdomen between the stomach and the small intestine. Clusters of endocrine cells in the pancreas form the islets of Langerhans, which are composed of alpha cells that release glucagon and beta cells that release insulin.

Some organs possess endocrine activity as a secondary function but have another primary function. The heart produces the hormone atrial natriuretic peptide, which functions to reduce blood volume, pressure, and Na^+ concentration. The gastrointestinal tract produces various hormones that aid in digestion. The kidneys produce renin, calcitriol, and erythropoietin. Adipose tissue produces leptin, which promotes satiety signals in the brain.

REVIEW QUESTIONS

1. Although most types of hormones are lipid insoluble, there are some that are lipid soluble and can therefore diffuse through plasma membranes. What class of hormones can diffuse through plasma membranes?

a. lipid-derived hormones
b. amino acid-derived hormones
c. peptide hormones
d. glycoprotein

2. Mary produces relatively low amounts of estradiol and cortisol, but is able to produce proper amounts of other hormones such as thyroxine and insulin. Identify the chemical class of hormones that Mary has difficulty producing.

a. lipid-derived hormones
b. amino acid-derived hormones
c. peptide hormones
d. glycoprotein hormones

3. An endocrinologist is a physician whose specialty is treating endocrine-related disorders. Which of the following diseases would be monitored and treated by an endocrinologist?

a. schizophrenia
b. Alzheimer's disease
c. Parkinson's disease
d. Grave's disease

4. Robert underwent a test to determine if he was diabetic. Within 1.5 hours of eating, his blood glucose was normal. What can be determined from these results?

a. The pancreas is over-producing insulin.
b. The pancreas is under-producing insulin.
c. The pancreas is producing an adequate amount of insulin.
d. The pancreas is not producing any insulin.

5. The hormone that triggers the flight-or-fight response, epinephrine, is derived from tyrosine, and the hormone that regulates circadian rhythms, melatonin, is derived from tryptophan. What class of hormone are these?

a. lipid-derived hormones
b. amino acid-derived hormones
c. peptide hormones
d. glycoprotein hormones

6. A newly discovered hormone contains four amino acids linked together. Identify the chemical class under which this hormone would be classified.

a. lipid-derived hormones
b. amino acid-derived hormones
c. peptide hormones
d. glycoprotein hormones

7. Changes in the body can be mediated by direct or indirect mechanisms. What facilitate(s) direct mediation of change by hormones?

a. intracellular hormone receptors
b. cell surface receptors
c. up-regulation
d. down-regulation

8. How do thyroid hormones stimulate metabolic activity throughout the body?

a. Specialized thyroid-receiving tissues are located throughout the body.
b. Blood circulation stimulates metabolic activity.
c. Different tissues have thyroid hormone receptors.
d. Thyroid tissue is located throughout the body.

9. Different hormones have different roles in cell signaling. Identify the term for a hormone that initiates cell-signaling pathways.

a. intracellular hormone receptor
b. cell surface receptor
c. first messenger
d. second messenger

10. A new antagonist molecule has been discovered that binds to and blocks plasma membrane receptors. Describe the affect this antagonist will have on testosterone, which is a steroid hormone.

a. This molecule will block testosterone from binding to its receptor.
b. This molecule will block testosterone from activating cAMP signaling.
c. This molecule will increase testosterone-mediated signaling.
d. This molecule will not affect testosterone-mediated signaling.

11. Identify what triggers a reduction in the number of receptors if there are elevated hormone levels.

a. intracellular hormone receptors
b. cell surface receptors
c. up-regulation
d. down-regulation

12. Consuming certain products cause a change in urine output. This likely occurs because these products ________.

a. inhibits ADH release
b. stimulates ADH release
c. inhibits TSH release
d. stimulates TSH release

13. FSH and LH release from the anterior pituitary is stimulated by ________.

a. TSH
b. GnRH
c. T_3
d. PTH

14. What hormone is produced by beta cells of the pancreas?

a. T_3
b. glucagon
c. insulin
d. T_4

15. When blood calcium levels are low, PTH stimulates ________.

a. excretion of calcium from the kidneys
b. excretion of calcium from the intestines
c. osteoblasts
d. osteoclasts

16. What enzyme is released when blood pressure drops and stimulates a cascade of events for hormones that promote water reabsorption?

a. aldosterone
b. renin
c. antidiuretic hormone
d. osmoreceptors

17. Drinking alcoholic beverages causes an increase in urine output. This most likely occurs because alcohol ____.

a. inhibits antidiuretic hormone release
b. stimulates antidiuretic hormone release
c. inhibits parathyroid hormone release
d. stimulates parathyroid hormone release

18. The hypothalamus is responsible for a diverse array of metabolic and autonomic nervous system functions. For example, the hypothalamus produces ____ during puberty.

a. follicle-stimulating hormone
b. luteinizing hormone
c. inhibin
d. gonadotropin-releasing hormone

19. Sandra wants to get pregnant but learns that she does not produce a sufficient amount of prolactin. Describe how her reproductive abilities will be affected.

a. Her uterus will not contract during childbirth.
b. She will not ovulate.
c. Her body will not be prepared for pregnancy.
d. She will be unable to produce milk.

20. Different hormones are released as short-term and

long-term stress responses. ____ is/are released as a long-term stress response.

a. Epinephrine
b. Parathyroid hormone
c. Corticosteroids
d. T3 and T4

21. When blood calcium levels are low, parathyroid hormone (PTH) stimulates ________.

a. excretion of calcium from the kidneys
b. excretion of calcium from the intestines
c. osteoblasts
d. osteoclasts

22. If you overproduce insulin after eating a meal, you may experience ___.

a. diabetes mellitus
b. diabetes insipidus
c. hyperglycemia
d. hypoglycemia

23. Charlie has been diagnosed with acromegaly. Identify the symptom(s) that he may have.

a. symmetric body formation
b. excessive body growth
c. enlarged hand, feet, and face bones
d. weak bones and nervous system impairment

24. What hormone is produced by beta cells of the pancreas in response to elevated blood glucose levels?

a. T3
b. glucagon
c. insulin
d. T4

25. There are substantially more hormones that undergo a negative feedback loop than a positive feedback loop. Which of the following hormones is regulated by a positive feedback loop?

a. thyroxine
b. oxytocin
c. triiodothyronine
d. insulin

26. Describe what occurs if a hormone is released by a hormonal stimulus.

a. Hormone release is stimulated by the nervous system.
b. Hormone release is stimulated by change in the blood.
c. Hormone release is stimulated by the external environment.
d. Hormone release is stimulated by another hormone.

27. A rise in blood glucose levels triggers release of insulin from the pancreas. What type of stimulus initiates insulin release?

a. humoral
b. hormonal
c. neural
d. negative

28. Why is the release of thyroid stimulating hormone (TSH) considered a hormonal stimulus?

a. TSH production is triggered by the nervous system.
b. TSH production is triggered by blood ion concentration change.
c. TSH triggers epinephrine production.
d. TSH triggers the production of T3 and T4.

29. What kind of stimulus promotes hormone release in response to ion concentrations in the blood?

a. humoral stimulus
b. hormonal stimulus
c. neural stimulus
d. negative stimulus

30. Which of the following endocrine glands control kidney function?

a. thyroid glands
b. adrenal glands
c. gonads
d. pancreas

31. The islets of Langerhans are clusters of endocrine cells in the pancreas. What is the function of the islets of Langerhans?

a. regulate circadian rhythms
b. regulate secondary sex characteristics
c. regulate blood calcium levels
d. regulate blood glucose

32. What do adipose tissues release after a meal?

a. erythropoietin
b. leptin
c. atrial natriuretic peptide
d. gastrin

33. Describe how the kidneys and adrenal cortex work together to increase blood volume.

a. They adrenal cortex produces renin, which affects aldosterone secretion by the kidneys.
b. The kidneys produce renin, which affects aldosterone secretion by the adrenal cortex.
c. They kidneys produce calcitrol, which affects renin secretion by the adrenal cortex.
d. They kidneys produce calcitrol, which affects aldosterone secretion by the adrenal cortex.

34. The anterior pituitary produces several hormones. Identify which of the following hormones is not produced by the anterior pituitary.

a. oxytocin
b. growth hormone
c. prolactin
d. thyroid-stimulating hormone

CRITICAL THINKING QUESTIONS

35. Although there are many different hormones in the human body, they can be divided into three classes based on their chemical structure. Explain these classes and give one factor that distinguishes each.

a. The classes are peptide hormones, which are water insoluble, and amino acid-derived and lipid-derived hormones, which are water soluble.
b. The classes are lipid-derived hormones, which are water insoluble, and amino acid-derived and peptide hormones, which are water soluble.
c. The classes are lipid-derived hormones, which are water soluble, and amino acid-derived and peptide hormones, which are water insoluble.
d. The classes are amino acid-derived hormones, which are water insoluble, and lipid-derived and peptide hormones, which are water soluble.

36. Explain how hormones promote homeostasis in the body.

a. Hormones increases cell activity by binding to the receptors present in the cell.
b. Hormones facilitate communication between cells present at very distant locations in the body.
c. Hormones facilitate communication between cells at any distance in the body.
d. Hormones mediate changes by directly binding to the intracellular hormone receptors.

37. A new hormone is discovered that binds to receptors on the target cell surface. Describe the chemical class of hormone that this hormone could belong to and explain how you could discern the exact class.

a. It belongs to the class lipid-derived or peptide hormone as it is water insoluble and thus requires a cell surface receptor. The exact class can be determined on the basis of the hormone's size.
b. It belongs to the class amino acid derived hormones as it is lipid insoluble and thus requires a cell surface receptor. This can be discerned by determining the exact structure of the hormone.
c. It belongs to the class lipid-derived or peptide hormone as it is water insoluble and thus requires a cell surface receptor. This can be discerned by determining the exact structure of the hormone.
d. It belongs to the class amino acid derived or peptide hormone as it is lipid insoluble and thus requires a cell surface receptor. The exact class can be determined on the basis of the hormone's size.

38. Explain why hormones are able to travel through the body but only affect certain cells.

a. Hormones only affect cells that have plasma membrane receptors.
b. Hormones only affect cells that have corresponding hormone receptors.
c. Hormones only affect cells that have intracellular receptors.
d. Hormones only affect cells that are infected.

39. Discuss the important functions of hormone receptors.

a. Hormone receptors can induce cell-signaling pathways and mediate changes in target cells in the presence of hormones.

b. Hormone receptors can mediate changes in target cells and act as transcription regulators in the presence of hormones.

c. Hormone receptors can induce cell-signaling pathways and act as transcription regulators in the presence of hormones.

d. Hormone receptors can mediate changes in target cells and can stimulate signaling pathways in the presence of hormones.

40. Describe how cell surface receptors and intracellular receptors are similar and how they differ.

a. Both are types of hormone receptors at target cells. Cell surface receptors facilitate indirect mediation, whereas intracellular receptors facilitate direct mediation.

b. Both are types of hormone receptors at target cells. Cell surface receptors facilitate direct mediation, whereas intracellular receptors facilitate indirect mediation.

c. Both reside in the cytoplasm or in the nucleus. Cell surface receptors facilitate indirect mediation, whereas intracellular receptors facilitate direct mediation.

d. Both reside in the cytoplasm or in the nucleus. Cell surface receptors facilitate direct mediation, whereas intracellular receptors facilitate indirect mediation.

41. Explain why drinking alcohol often results in dehydration.

a. Drinking alcohol reduces antidiuretic hormone production, which is a hormone that helps retain water.

b. Drinking alcohol increases antidiuretic hormone production, which is a hormone that helps with water loss.

c. Drinking alcohol reduces thyroid stimulating hormone production, which is a hormone that helps retain water.

d. Drinking alcohol increases thyroid stimulating hormone production, which is a hormone that helps with water loss.

42. Describe how gonadotropin-releasing hormone production is controlled by a negative feedback loop.

a. Gonadotropin-releasing hormone decreases production of follicle stimulating hormone, which decreases hormone production in the gonads. An increase in gonad hormone production then inhibits gonadotropin-releasing hormone production.

b. Gonadotropin-releasing hormone stimulates production of follicle stimulating hormone, which regulates hormone production in the gonads. An increase in gonad hormone production then inhibits gonadotropin-releasing hormone production.

c. Gonadotropin-releasing hormone decreases production of luteinizing hormone, which decreases hormone production in the gonads. an increase in gonad hormone production then inhibits gonadotropin-releasing hormone production.

d. Gonadotropin-releasing hormone stimulates production of luteinizing hormone, which regulates hormone production in the gonads. an increase in gonad hormone production then inhibits gonadotropin-releasing hormone production.

43. Explain where insulin is stored and under what circumstances it is released.

a. It is stored in the pancreas and is released as glucose increases in the blood to enhance the rate of glucose uptake.

b. It is stored in the liver and is released as glucose increases in the blood to enhance the rate of glucose uptake.

c. It is stored in the pancreas and is released as glucose levels decrease in blood to decrease the rate of glucose uptake.

d. It is stored in the liver and is released as glucose levels decrease in the blood to decrease the rate of glucose uptake.

44. Ralph is always thirsty and recently learned that he synthesizes mutated antidiuretic hormone (ADH). Discuss why Ralph would be at higher risk for diabetes insipidus.

a. ADH helps in the loss of water. Overproduction of ADH would cause improper functioning of kidneys.

b. Underproduction of ADH inhibits the release of aldosterone that would cause improper functioning of kidneys.

c. ADH helps retain water. Underproduction of ADH would cause improper functioning of kidneys.

d. ADH helps in retaining electrolytes. Underproduction of ADH causes improper functioning of kidneys.

45. Describe how stress promotes water retention, which can lead to weight gain.

a. Stress decreases osmolality, which increases antidiuretic hormone secretion. Antidiuretic hormone helps retain water.

b. Stress increases osmolality, which increases antidiuretic hormone secretion. Antidiuretic hormone helps retain water.

c. Stress increases osmolality, which decreases antidiuretic hormone secretion. Antidiuretic hormone helps with water loss.

d. Stress decreases osmolality, which decreases antidiuretic hormone secretion. Antidiuretic hormone helps with water loss.

46. Identify which type of feedback mechanism primarily controls hormone production and release and explain why this occurs.

a. Positive feedback loop to help maintain the water concentration in the body.

b. Negative feedback loop to help maintain the water concentration in the body.

c. Negative feedback loop to help maintain proper bodily functions within a specific range.

d. Positive feedback loop to help maintain proper bodily functions within a specific range.

47. Compare and contrast humoral and hormonal stimuli.

a. Both humoral and hormonal stimuli release proteins. Humoral stimuli are hormones that stimulate other hormones, whereas hormonal stimuli are extracellular fluid-related stimuli.

b. Both humoral and hormonal stimuli release proteins. Humoral stimuli are extracellular fluid-related stimuli, whereas hormonal stimuli are hormones that stimulate other hormones.

c. Both humoral and hormonal stimuli release hormones. Humoral stimuli are extracellular fluid-related stimuli, whereas hormonal stimuli are hormones that stimulate other hormones.

d. Both humoral and hormonal stimuli release hormones. Humoral stimuli are hormones that stimulate other hormones, whereas hormonal stimuli are extracellular fluid-related stimuli.

48. Explain why it would be problematic if most hormones were regulated by a positive feedback loop.

a. Excessive production of actions would be stimulated by hormones such as growth and blood glucose levels.

b. Production of actions would be reduced by hormones such as growth and blood glucose levels.

c. Inhibition of GnRH production by increase in gonad hormone levels.

d. Inhibition of release of insulin by decrease in blood glucose concentrations.

49. Identify what aldosterone regulates, and explain how it is stimulated.

a. Aldosterone regulates the amount of water excreted by the kidneys and causes direct water reabsorption from the kidney tubules. It is stimulated by decreased water concentration in blood, or increased amounts of blood potassium.

b. Aldosterone regulates sodium concentrations in urine, sweat, the pancreas, and saliva. It is stimulated by decreased blood sodium ion concentrations, blood volume, or blood pressure, or increased amounts of blood potassium.

c. Aldosterone regulates calcium concentrations in urine, saliva and the pancreas. It is stimulated by decreased blood calcium ion concentrations, blood pressure, blood volume, or increased amounts of blood potassium.

d. Aldosterone regulates blood glucose levels by stimulating the breakdown of glycogen to glucose. It is stimulated by decreased concentrations of glucose levels in blood, blood volume, or blood pressure.

50. Discuss which aspect of the endocrine system often renders extremely thin females less fertile. Explain why this occurs.

a. Adipose tissue releases leptin, which is needed to produce gonadotropin-releasing hormone and gonadotropin. Leptin cannot be released without sufficient body fat.

b. Adipose tissue releases thymosins needed to produce gonadotropin-releasing hormone and gonadotropin. Thymosins cannot be produced without sufficient body fat.

c. Adipose tissue releases leptin needed to produce gonadotropin-releasing hormone and gonadotropin. Leptins cannot be produced in the absence of body fat.

d. Adipose tissue releases leptin needed to produce estrogens and progesterone. Leptin cannot be released without sufficient body fat.

51. The adrenal medulla secretes two types of hormones. Identify what is secreted and describe their functions.

a. They secrete cortisol and aldosterone, which increase heart rate, breathing rate, muscle contractions, blood pressure, and blood glucose as short-term stress response.
b. They secrete epinephrine and norepinephrine, which increase heart rate, breathing rate, muscle contractions, blood pressure, and blood glucose as long-term stress response.
c. They secrete cortisol and aldosterone, which increase heart rate, breathing rate, muscle contractions, blood pressure, and blood glucose as long-term stress response.
d. They secrete epinephrine and norepinephrine, which increase heart rate, breathing rate, muscle contractions, blood pressure, and blood glucose as short-term stress response.

TEST PREP FOR AP® COURSES

52. There are three types of hormones based on chemical structure: lipid-derived, amino acid-derived, and peptide hormones. Identify the hormone that is lipid-derived.

a. 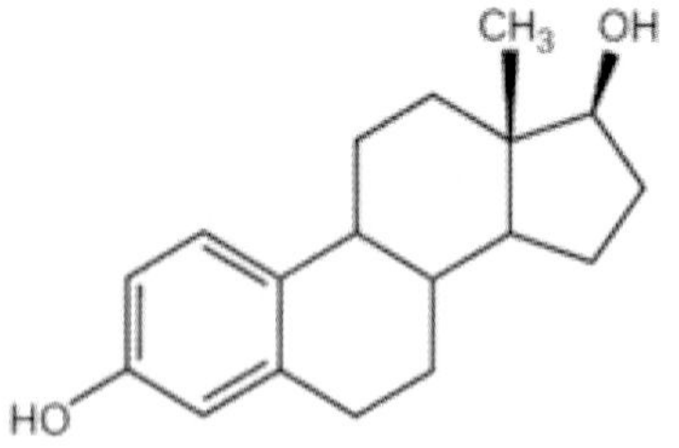
b. 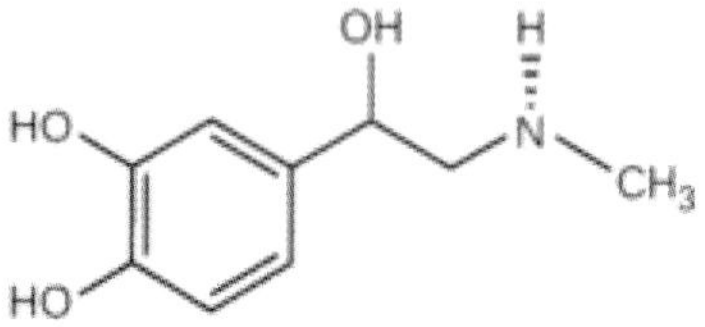
c. 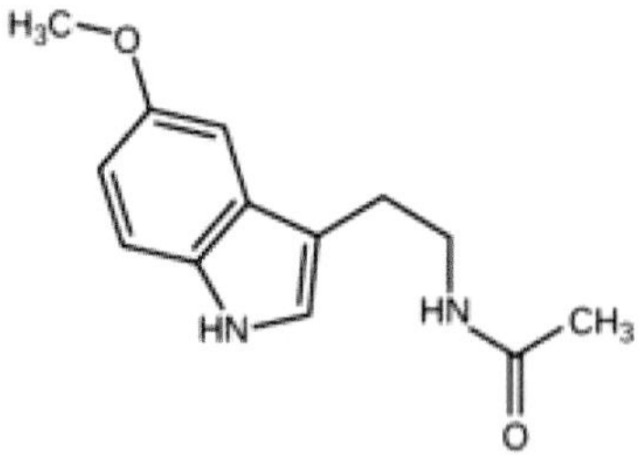
d.

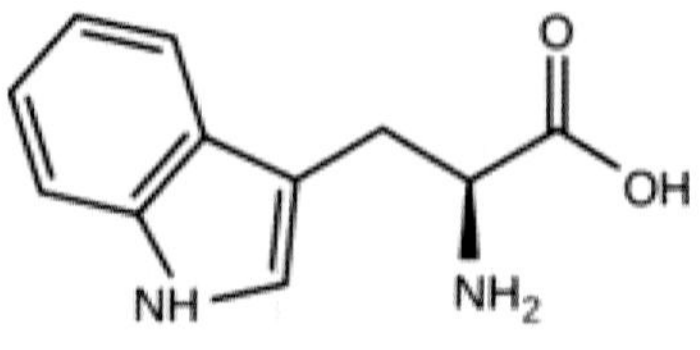

53. Hormones are essential for facilitating communication between cells, which can help maintain homeostasis within the body. Explain how hormones facilitate communication on a molecular level.

a. A hormone is released in response to a stimulus, travels through the body, and then binds to receptors of the target cell to illicit a response.
b. A hormone is released from the pituitary gland in response to a stimulus, travels through the body, and then binds to a receptor of a target cell to illicit response.
c. A hormone is released in response to a stimulus, travels through the body, and then binds to receptors to stimulate the signaling pathway.
d. A hormone is released in response to a stimulus, travels through the body and then binds to the intracellular receptors of target cells to illicit a response.

54. Steroid hormones are known to circulate in the blood longer than peptide hormones. Describe why this occurs.

a. Peptide hormones cannot pass through cell membranes.
b. Steroid hormones are water insoluble.
c. Peptide hormones are water insoluble.
d. Steroid hormones cannot pass through cell membranes.

55. Lipid-derived hormones, such as steroid hormones, utilize intracellular receptors, whereas peptide and amino acid-derived hormones utilize cell surface receptors. Discuss why these hormones utilize different types of receptors.

a. Lipid-derived hormones have receptors located in the nucleus, and thus utilize intracellular receptors, whereas peptide and amino acid-derived hormones have receptors only on the surface of the cell.

b. Lipid-derived hormones can permeate the plasma membrane and thus utilize intracellular receptors. Peptide and amino acid- derived hormones are lipid insoluble and thus require cell surface receptors.

c. Lipid-derived hormones can permeate plasma membranes as they need to remain in circulation for a longer duration. Peptide and amino acid-derived hormones are lipid insoluble and need surface receptors.

d. Lipid-derived hormones can permeate plasma membranes and thus utilize intracellular receptors. Some peptide and amino acid-derived hormones can cross the membrane but most are lipid insoluble and thus require cell surface receptors.

56. There are three types of hormones based on chemical structure: lipid-derived, amino acid-derived, and peptide hormones. Identify the peptide hormone.

a.

b.

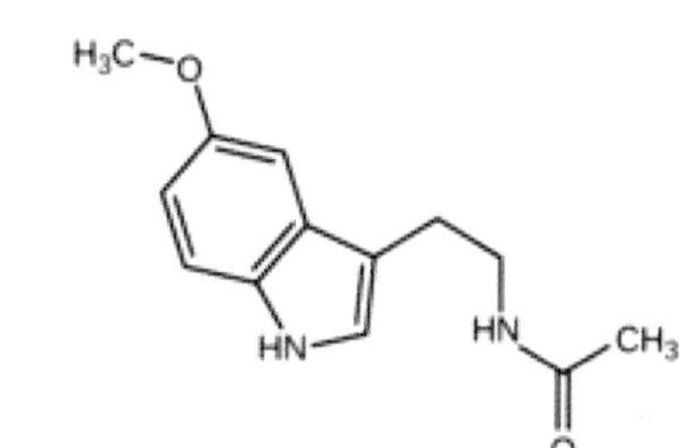

c.

d.

57. Cellular activity can vary based on sensitivity to hormones, and cellular activity can therefore either be up-regulated or down-regulated by those hormones. What would likely cause a greater response from cells that are controlled by a hormone?

a. hormone levels increase and the number of target cell receptors increase

b. hormone levels decrease and the number of target cell receptors increase

c. hormone levels increase and the number of target cell receptors decrease

d. hormone levels decrease and the number of target cell receptors decrease

58. Determine what kind of hormone is undergoing binding in this figure and explain how you know.

a. A lipid-derived hormone because it is fat insoluble and therefore able to bind to receptors on the outer surface of the plasma membrane.

b. A lipid-derived hormone because it is fat soluble and therefore able to pass through the cell membrane to reach intracellular receptors.

c. A polypeptide-derived hormone because it is fat soluble and therefore able to pass through the cell membrane to reach intracellular receptors.

d. A polypeptide-derived hormone because it is fat insoluble and therefore binds to receptors on the outer surface of the plasma membrane.

59. In this figure, what kind of hormone is bound to the target cell receptor?

a. steroid

b. lipid-derived

c. estradiol

d. amino acid-derived

60. Blood pressure and blood volume are increased by the production of the hormones antidiuretic hormone (ADH) and aldosterone. Describe how renin promotes release of ADH and aldosterone.

a. Renin cleaves angiotensinogen.

b. Renin directly simulates ADH and aldosterone production.

c. Renin produces angiotensin II.

d. Angiotensin I is converted to angiotensin II.

61. Antidiuretic hormone (ADH) is essential for water regulation in the kidneys. Once released from the pituitary, ADH travels through to the kidneys. Explain how ADH promotes water reabsorption.

a. ADH initiates a series of events that lead to release of more vasopressin hormone in the kidney, leading to the movement of water out of kidneys

b. ADH initiates a series of events that lead to temporary insertion of aquaporins in the kidney, through which water moves in the kidney.

c. ADH initiates a series of events leading to temporary insertion of aquaporins in the kidney, through which water moves out of the kidneys.

d. ADH initiates a series of events that leads to the movement of water out of the kidneys through simple diffusion.

62. David, an athlete, wants to enhance his baseball performance by taking erythropoietin. Identify what David is trying to change.

a. build more muscle

b. improve endurance

c. reduce fertility

d. decrease need to urinate

63. Some athletes may want to take synthetic hormones to improve their performance in their given sport. However, the use of certain synthetic hormones is banned in many professional sports. Explain why synthetic hormones are often banned.

a. There can be severe side effects such as insomnia, depression and prostate enlargement. These side effects are often severe and irreversible.

b. There can be severe side effects such as impaired heart function, testicular atrophy, and prostate enlargement. These side effects can be cured through surgeries.

c. There can be severe side effects such as impaired heart function, testicular atrophy, and prostate enlargement. These are often severe and irreversible.

d. There can be severe side effects such as insomnia, depression and prostate enlargement. These side effects can be cured through surgeries.

64.

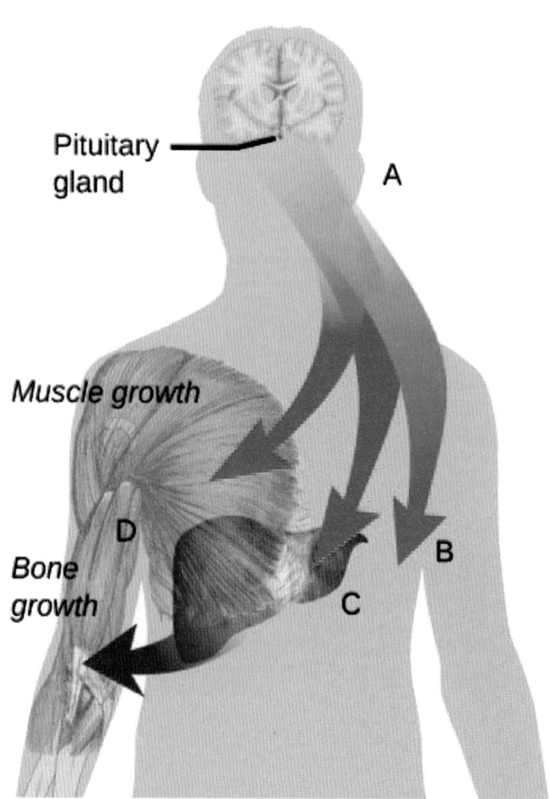

This figure shows how growth hormone communicates with cells to promote muscle and bone growth. Identify growth hormone's exact role.

a. inhibits growth hormone-inhibiting hormone release
b. stimulates growth hormone-releasing hormone release
c. breaks down glycogen
d. activates insulin-like growth factors

65. Growth hormone helps promote growth by accelerating the rate of protein synthesis. Describe how growth hormone switches the energy source of most cells.

a. Growth hormone is able to break down triglycerides through lipogenesis. When triglycerides are released, most tissues switch to fatty acids as energy sources.
b. Growth hormone is able to break down triglycerides through lipolysis. When triglycerides are released, most tissues switch to fatty acids as an energy source.
c. Growth hormone is able to break down triglycerides through lipolysis. When triglycerides are released, most tissues switch to glucose as an energy source.
d. Growth hormone is able to break down triglycerides through lipogenesis. When triglycerides are released, most tissues switch to glucose as an energy source.

66. Positive feedback loops are rare in the endocrine system but some do exist. Identify an example of a positive feedback loop.

a. Insulin facilitates decrease of blood sugar levels.
b. Oxytocin release stimulates milk release.
c. Increased blood calcium levels halt PTH production.
d. Increased amounts of T3 and T4 inhibit further production.

67. Although positive feedback loops are rare in the endocrine system, they are present in childbirth. Explain how childbirth is controlled by a positive feedback loop.

a. When a child pushes on the cervix, a signal is sent to stimulate oxytocin release, which stimulates more contractions. This promotes more oxytocin release that allows the child to be pushed through the birth canal.
b. When a child pushes on the cervix, a signal is sent to stimulate oxytocin release, which stimulates contractions. This promotes release of progesterone that allows the child to be pushed through the birth canal.
c. When a child pushes on the cervix, a signal is sent to stimulate prolactin release, which stimulates more contractions. This promotes release of more prolactin that allows the child to be pushed through the birth canal.
d. When a child pushes on the cervix, a signal is sent to stimulate progesterone release, which stimulates contractions. This promotes release of oxytocin that allows the child to be pushed through the birth canal.

68. Osmoreceptors are essential for monitoring water concentrations within the body. Describe how osmoreceptors complete this task.

a. Osmoreceptors insert aquaporins in the kidneys.
b. Osmoreceptors signal increase sodium reabsorption.
c. Osmoreceptors detect when blood electrolyte levels change.
d. Osmoreceptors signal increased sodium reabsorption.

69. Laura has Type 1 diabetes and her body cannot properly produce insulin in response to elevated blood glucose levels. Identify which type of stimulus Laura is unable to respond to.

a. humoral
b. hormonal
c. neural
d. negative

70. Terry recently gained weight and has been more tired than usual. Terry's doctor suggested that he might not produce enough thyroid-stimulating hormone (TSH). Explain why a TSH deficiency could cause Terry's weight gain and fatigue.

a. Without TSH, there would be excessive production of T3 and T4 leading to a high metabolic rate, causing weight gain and fatigue.

b. Without TSH, there would be excessive production of T3 and T4 leading to a low metabolic rate, causing weight gain and fatigue.

c. Without TSH, T3 and T4 cannot be properly produced, leading to a high metabolic rate, causing weight gain and fatigue.

d. Without TSH, T3 and T4 cannot be properly produced, leading to a low metabolic rate, causing weight gain and fatigue.

71. Marcus experienced nervous system damage in a car accident. Identify which of the following endocrine-related body functions will be most likely impaired as a result.

a. ability to lower blood glucose levels

b. fight-or-flight response

c. urine production

d. body heat regulation

SCIENCE PRACTICE CHALLENGE QUESTIONS

72. Many hormones repress or enhance protein expression by binding to transcription factors called nuclear receptors. Other hormones regulate processes by binding to cell surface receptors that induce cell signaling cascades.

A. **Represent** these two different processes for cell-cell communication by creating a flow chart showing the direction of information in a process regulating homeostasis such as the control of blood sugar or water loss. Annotate your diagram to **describe** the key elements of each step in the particular example that you choose.

B. **Justify the claim** that a developmental process is more likely to involve nuclear receptors, while regulation of metabolism is more likely to involve cell surface receptors.

The lancelet is a chordate, fish-like filter feeder that buries itself in marine sands. Their ancestors and vertebrates diverged approximately 500 million years ago. Lancelet and human are members of a superphylum of animals with bilateral symmetry, *Deuterostomia*. In one model of animal evolution, the other superphylum, *Protostomia*, includes fruit fly and nematode. In an alternative model, insects are included with lancelet and human in a superphylum called the *Coelomata*, and the nematode is separate. Molecular studies of fruit fly, lancelet, human, and nematode show that homologous genes, when present, are strongly conserved. For example, the genes for the receptors of germ cell nuclear factor (GCNF) and retinoids, hormones that regulate cellular differentiation during development, are present in each species. Homologous genes for nuclear receptor estrogen and thyroid hormone are present in lancelet and human but missing in nematode and fruit fly. Genes for the vitamin D receptor are absent in fruit fly but are present in the other species.

Many neuropeptide hormones found in human, fruit fly and nematode such as GnRH (gonadotropin-releasing hormone) and the gonadotropins luteinizing and follicle stimulating hormones (LH and FSH) have not been found in lancelet. However, genes for the cell surface receptors activated by these hormones are expressed. The same is true for many different hormones and their corresponding receptors. A large number of such "orphan" nuclear receptors have been reported in animals where there is no evidence of the presence of the hormone to which they bind.

C. **Analyze** these data (a table to organize the data is suggested) for supporting evidence of the alternative superphylum, *Coelomata*. Consider:

- separate selection of signaling molecules and the proteins that detect them
- constitutive (always transcribed) expression
- the possible effect of gene deletion

D. **Evaluate** the legitimacy of a claim that a hormone is not present although the receptor for that hormone has been found.

Genes for receptors and the hormones to which they bind are often found on different chromosomes and have co-evolved. Other ligands may have an affinity for orphaned receptors. By understanding the three-dimensional shape of the ligand binding site of a nuclear receptor, new drugs can be developed to match the site and regulate expression when the endocrine system fails. Even greater flexibility in drug design is allowed when small molecules, called positive (PAM) and negative (NAM) allosteric modulators, change the shape of the ligand binding site. The receptors for follicle stimulating hormone (FSH) and luteinizing hormone (LH) were subjects in a drug discovery program using PAMs and NAMs (Nataraja et al., *Frontiers in Endocrinology*, 6, 2015).

E. **Explain** how the refinement of nuclear receptor by attachment of a molecule other than the ligand of the receptor can increase the level of expression of genes targeted by the transcription factor.

73. Gonadotrophin-releasing hormone (GnRH) stimulates the production of follicle-stimulating hormone (FSH) and luteinizing hormone (LH). The concentration of these hormones over time in females regulates the menstrual cycle. GnRH expressing neurons (GEN) are scattered throughout the forebrain and hypothalamus and secrete into ducts leading to the pituitary gland, causing the secretion of FSH and LH into the bloodstream. Ca^{+2} concentrations oscillate in time, changing the electric membrane potential of the GnRH neurons, GEN. The period of the oscillation is only a few seconds in duration. The mechanism controlling the oscillating membrane potential is unknown, but during maturation the frequency of the oscillations of the Ca^{+2} concentration in the GEN increases.

A. **Explain** how the absence of direct contact among the GnRH neurons and the coordinated release of FSH and LH suggest another timing mechanism.

An association of high concentrations of anti-Mullerian hormone (AMH) and elevated LH levels among women with a common reproductive disorder called polycystic ovary syndrome (PCOS) caused investigators to study the effects of AMH on membrane potentials of GnRH expressing neurons. The researchers (Cimino et al., *Nature Communications*, 7, 2016) found that very small concentrations of AMH initiated oscillations.

B. The graph illustrates the time dependence of LH and estrogen in the blood of a female. A goal of research in human reproductive physiology is to construct a model that accounts for the spike in luteinizing hormone at approximately 14 days. **Predict** how a positive feedback loop involving the release of a hormone such as AMH could be used to account for this response. **Explain** why estrogen is probably not a good candidate for use in this model.

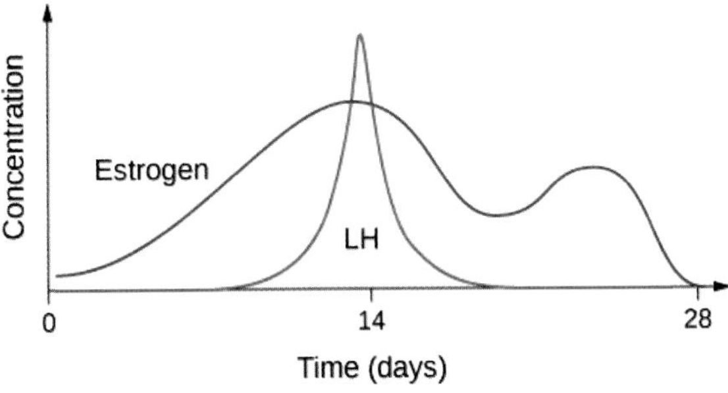

Figure 28.21

FSH and LH inhibit production of GnRH. Exposure of ovarian follicles to high levels of FSH and LH causes the follicle to rupture, releasing an oocyte to the oviduct. Birth control drugs suppress the LH surge by maintaining a constant blood concentration of progesterone (PG). After 40 years of use, the mechanism of suppression is still unknown. However, we do know that during pregnancy progesterone levels remain elevated and that cells in both the pituitary gland and GnRH expressing neurons (GEN) have progesterone nuclear receptors (PGR) that act as transcription factors to either i) inhibit production of GnRH possibly by blocking transcription of *GNRH1*, the gene coding for GnRH, or ii) inhibit production of LH by blocking transcription in the GnRH neurons of the gene, *LH1*, coding for LH.

C. **Construct two alternative explanations** of the role of progesterone as a birth control drug. Your explanation can be in the form of descriptions or in terms of diagrams involving the key molecular components PG, PGR, LH, *LH1*, GEN, GnRH, and *GnRH1*.

An endocrine disruptor is a molecule with a structure that mimics a hormone and can interfere with regulation. The chemical bis-phenol A (BPA) has been used for many years in the production of plastics and is now widespread. BPA mimics estrogen. BPA is present in most humans at the concentration of 5 micrograms per kilogram of body weight. Whether or not that concentration is harmful is uncertain.

In a study of Ca^{+2} oscillations in GnRH expressing neurons, Klenke and co-workers (*Endocrinology*, 157, 2016) presented evidence that BPA switches off oscillations even at these very low concentrations. This suggests a mechanism for the results from an earlier investigation in which female rats were fed low and high levels of estrogen (EE) and BPA during pregnancy. Measurements were made of the levels of expression of an estrogen nuclear receptor in the hypothalamus of the pups just after birth (Cao et al., *Toxicological Sciences*, 133, 2013). Their data are shown in the graph below.

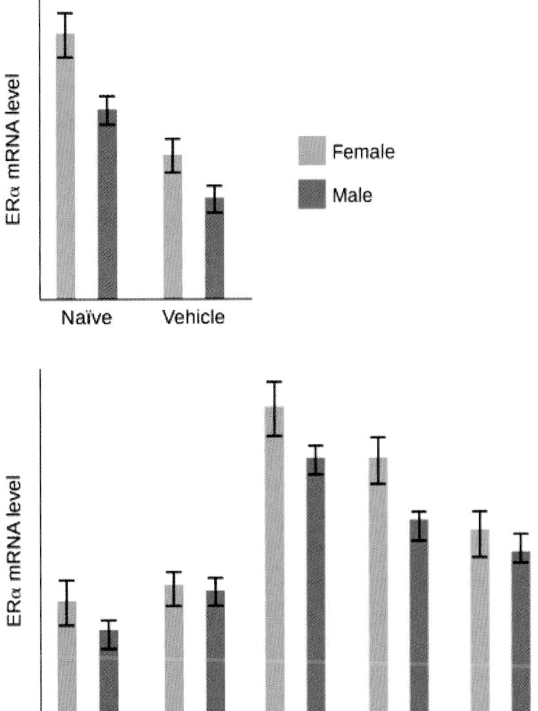

Figure 28.22

Using the data, the graph at the top compares expression in a “do-nothing” control (Naïve) and a control (Vehicle) in which a feeding tube is used to deliver nutrients during pregnancy. The graph at the bottom shows expression levels in pups born to female rats with four different treatments of estrogen (EE) and bis-phenol A (BPA).

D. Compared to the naïve control where homeostasis is not disrupted, qualitatively **analyze** these data for the disruption of the endocrine system in offspring of a female rat exposed to both physical and chemical stresses.

E. In female sheep, the estrus cycle is coordinated by the length of the day and does not begin until day length shortens. The gestation period of sheep is roughly 150 days.

- **Predict** the effect on fitness of this control of gene expression by an external stimulus.
- The "ram effect" is a livestock management practice in Australia to induce ovulation by exposing an anestrus (when the estrus cycle is inactive) ewe to a ram. Compare this phenomenon with the results of delivering nutrients and hormones using a feeding tube to **construct** a possible **explanation** for the ram effect.

29 | THE MUSCULOSKELETAL SYSTEM

Figure 29.1 Improvements in the design of prostheses have allowed for a wider range of activities in recipients. (credit: modification of work by Stuart Grout)

Chapter Outline

Introduction

The muscular and skeletal systems provide support to the body and allow for a wide range of movement. The bones of the skeletal system protect the body's internal organs and support the weight of the body. The muscles of the muscular system contract and pull on the bones, allowing for movements as diverse as standing, walking, running, and grasping items.

Injury or disease affecting the musculoskeletal system can be very debilitating. In humans, the most common musculoskeletal diseases worldwide are caused by malnutrition. Ailments that affect the joints are also widespread, such as arthritis, which can make movement difficult and—in advanced cases—completely impair mobility. In severe cases in which the joint has suffered extensive damage, joint replacement surgery may be needed.

Progress in the science of prosthesis design has resulted in the development of artificial joints, with joint replacement surgery in the hips and knees being the most common. Replacement joints for shoulders, elbows, and fingers are also available. Even with this progress, there is still room for improvement in the design of prostheses. The state-of-the-art prostheses have limited durability and therefore wear out quickly, particularly in young or active individuals.

The field of robotic prosthesis focuses on prosthetics that are attached directly to the skeleton and can be controlled by the mind by using implanted neuromuscular interfaces. You can read more about this exciting research at the **Science Daily website (http://openstaxcollege.org/l/32prosthesis)** .

29.1 | Types of Skeletal Systems

In this section, you will explore the following questions:

- What are the characteristics of the different types of animal skeletal systems?
- What are the roles of the various components of the human skeletal system?

Connection for AP® Courses

Much of the information in this section is not in scope for AP®. However, as a student of biology you should have a fundamental understanding of how the muscular and skeletal systems work together to provide support and protection while allowing for a range of movement. Bones provide a storage area for calcium and phosphorus salts and also are the site of blood cell formation. In a later section, knowledge of the nervous system will be used to understand the musculoskeletal system because muscle contraction depends on neural input. Events occurring at the neuromuscular junction are similar to events occurring at synapses between neurons as discussed in the chapter on the nervous system. Humans, and most animals depend on movement for daily activities. From an evolutionary perspective, the transition of animals onto land required changes in body design as locomotion on land presented a number of new challenges for animals that were adapted to movement in the water, such as the effect of gravity and lack of buoyancy. Literally step-by-step, these adaptations accumulated. Exploring the evolution of the musculoskeletal system in animals would provide information on this history.

Information presented and examples highlighted in this section are not within the scope for AP® and do not align to the Curriculum Framework.

Hydrostatic Skeleton

A **hydrostatic skeleton** is a skeleton formed by a fluid-filled compartment within the body, called the coelom. The organs of the coelom are supported by the aqueous fluid, which also resists external compression. This compartment is under hydrostatic pressure because of the fluid and supports the other organs of the organism. This type of skeletal system is found in soft-bodied animals such as sea anemones, earthworms, Cnidaria, and other invertebrates (**Figure 29.2**).

Figure 29.2 The skeleton of the red-knobbed sea star (*Protoreaster linckii*) is an example of a hydrostatic skeleton. (credit: “Amada44”/Wikimedia Commons)

Movement in a hydrostatic skeleton is provided by muscles that surround the coelom. The muscles in a hydrostatic skeleton contract to change the shape of the coelom; the pressure of the fluid in the coelom produces movement. For example, earthworms move by waves of muscular contractions of the skeletal muscle of the body wall hydrostatic skeleton, called peristalsis, which alternately shorten and lengthen the body. Lengthening the body extends the anterior end of the organism. Most organisms have a mechanism to fix themselves in the substrate. Shortening the muscles then draws the posterior portion of the body forward. Although a hydrostatic skeleton is well-suited to invertebrate organisms such as earthworms and some aquatic organisms, it is not an efficient skeleton for terrestrial animals.

Exoskeleton

An **exoskeleton** is an external skeleton that consists of a hard encasement on the surface of an organism. For example, the shells of crabs and insects are exoskeletons (Figure 29.3). This skeleton type provides defence against predators, supports the body, and allows for movement through the contraction of attached muscles. As with vertebrates, muscles must cross a joint inside the exoskeleton. Shortening of the muscle changes the relationship of the two segments of the exoskeleton. Arthropods such as crabs and lobsters have exoskeletons that consist of 30–50 percent chitin, a polysaccharide derivative of glucose that is a strong but flexible material. Chitin is secreted by the epidermal cells. The exoskeleton is further strengthened by the addition of calcium carbonate in organisms such as the lobster. Because the exoskeleton is acellular, arthropods must periodically shed their exoskeletons because the exoskeleton does not grow as the organism grows.

Figure 29.3 Muscles attached to the exoskeleton of the Halloween crab (*Gecarcinus quadratus*) allow it to move.

Endoskeleton

An **endoskeleton** is a skeleton that consists of hard, mineralized structures located within the soft tissue of organisms. An example of a primitive endoskeletal structure is the spicules of sponges. The bones of vertebrates are composed of tissues, whereas sponges have no true tissues (Figure 29.4). Endoskeletons provide support for the body, protect internal organs, and allow for movement through contraction of muscles attached to the skeleton.

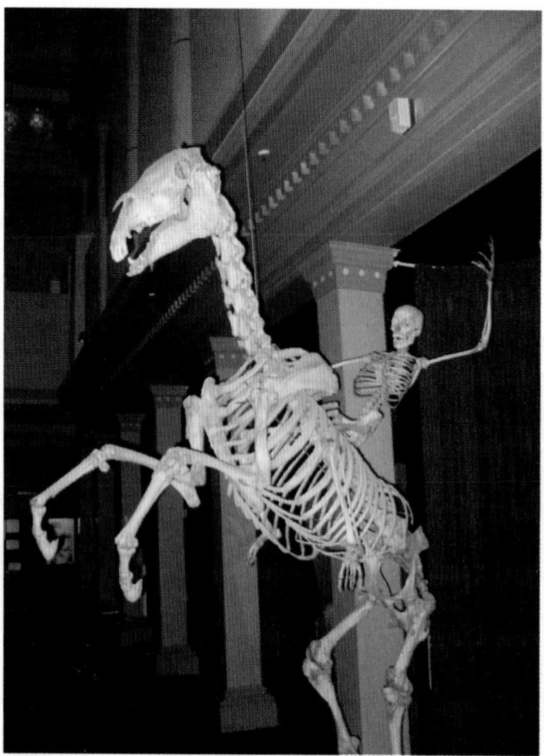

Figure 29.4 The skeletons of humans and horses are examples of endoskeletons. (credit: Ross Murphy)

The human skeleton is an endoskeleton that consists of 206 bones in the adult. It has five main functions: providing support to the body, storing minerals and lipids, producing blood cells, protecting internal organs, and allowing for movement. The skeletal system in vertebrates is divided into the axial skeleton (which consists of the skull, vertebral column, and rib cage), and the appendicular skeleton (which consists of the shoulders, limb bones, the pectoral girdle, and the pelvic girdle).

Visit the interactive body (http://openstaxcollege.org/l/virt_skeleton) site to build a virtual skeleton: select "skeleton" and click through the activity to place each bone.

List at least three bones that you positioned in the virtual body (in this simulation (http://www.bbc.co.uk/science/humanbody/body/interactives/3djigsaw_02/index.shtml?skeleton)).

a. ribs, fibula, sacrum

b. fibula, patella, sternum

c. gliding joint, sacrum, sternum

d. ribs, mandible, fibula

Human Axial Skeleton

The **axial skeleton** forms the central axis of the body and includes the bones of the skull, ossicles of the middle ear, hyoid bone of the throat, vertebral column, and the thoracic cage (ribcage) (Figure 29.5). The function of the axial skeleton is to provide support and protection for the brain, the spinal cord, and the organs in the ventral body cavity. It provides a surface for the attachment of muscles that move the head, neck, and trunk, performs respiratory movements, and stabilizes parts of the appendicular skeleton.

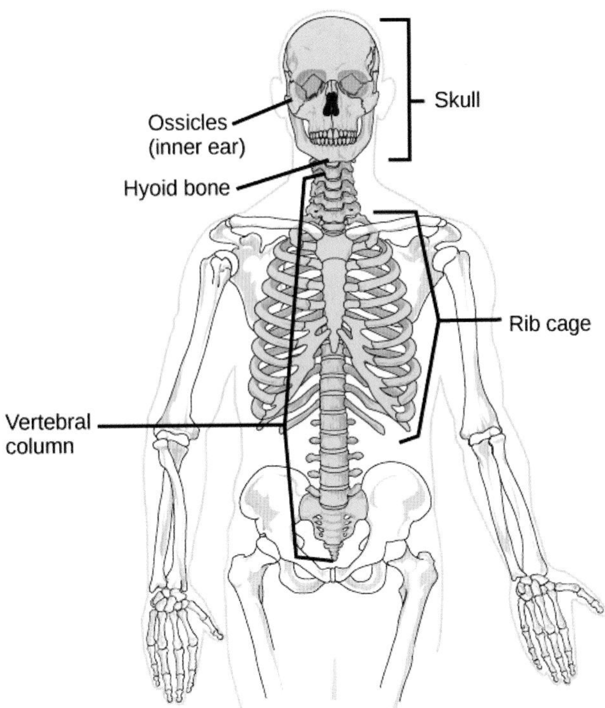

Figure 29.5 The axial skeleton consists of the bones of the skull, ossicles of the middle ear, hyoid bone, vertebral column, and rib cage. (credit: modification of work by Mariana Ruiz Villareal)

The Skull

The bones of the **skull** support the structures of the face and protect the brain. The skull consists of 22 bones, which are divided into two categories: cranial bones and facial bones. The **cranial bones** are eight bones that form the cranial cavity, which encloses the brain and serves as an attachment site for the muscles of the head and neck. The eight cranial bones are the frontal bone, two parietal bones, two temporal bones, occipital bone, sphenoid bone, and the ethmoid bone. Although the bones developed separately in the embryo and fetus, in the adult, they are tightly fused with connective tissue and adjoining bones do not move (Figure 29.6).

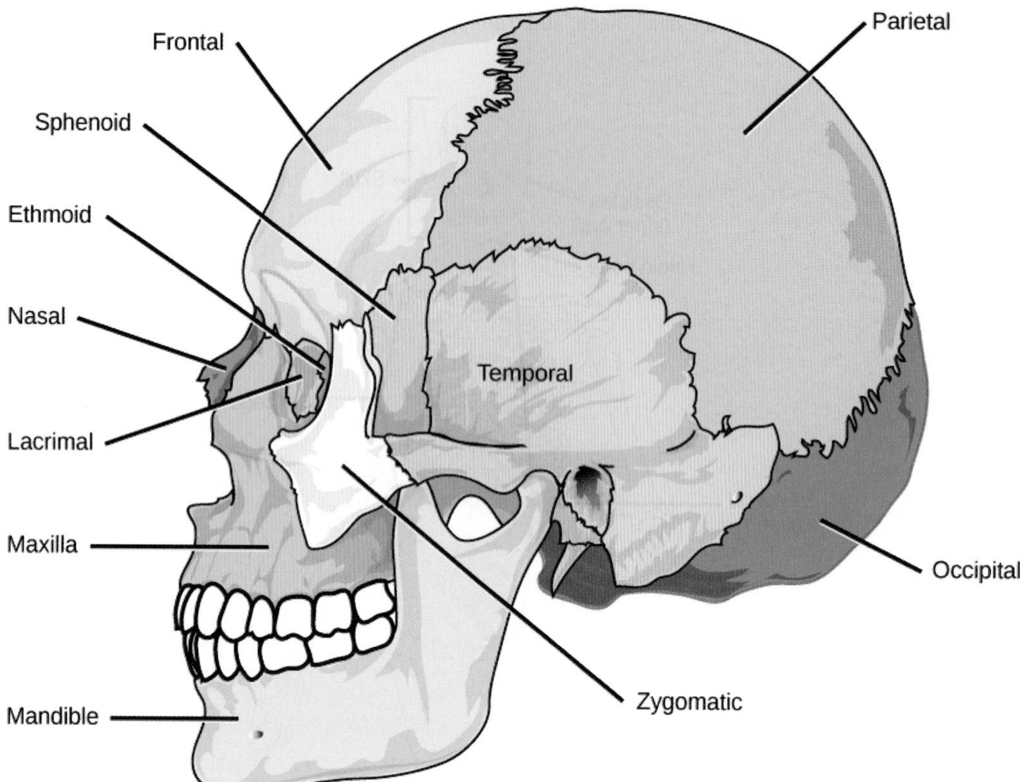

Figure 29.6 The bones of the skull support the structures of the face and protect the brain. (credit: modification of work by Mariana Ruiz Villareal)

The **auditory ossicles** of the middle ear transmit sounds from the air as vibrations to the fluid-filled cochlea. The auditory ossicles consist of three bones each: the malleus, incus, and stapes. These are the smallest bones in the body and are unique to mammals.

Fourteen **facial bones** form the face, provide cavities for the sense organs (eyes, mouth, and nose), protect the entrances to the digestive and respiratory tracts, and serve as attachment points for facial muscles. The 14 facial bones are the nasal bones, the maxillary bones, zygomatic bones, palatine, vomer, lacrimal bones, the inferior nasal conchae, and the mandible. All of these bones occur in pairs except for the mandible and the vomer (Figure 29.7).

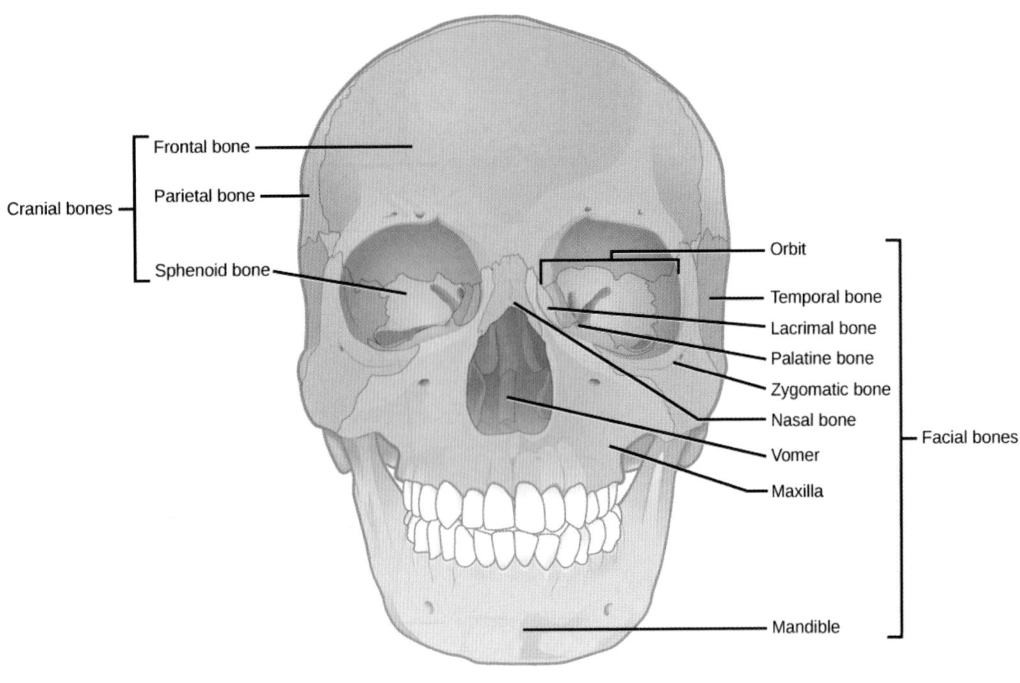

Figure 29.7 The cranial bones, including the frontal, parietal, and sphenoid bones, cover the top of the head. The facial bones of the skull form the face and provide cavities for the eyes, nose, and mouth.

Although it is not found in the skull, the hyoid bone is considered a component of the axial skeleton. The **hyoid bone** lies below the mandible in the front of the neck. It acts as a movable base for the tongue and is connected to muscles of the jaw, larynx, and tongue. The mandible articulates with the base of the skull. The mandible controls the opening to the airway and gut. In animals with teeth, the mandible brings the surfaces of the teeth in contact with the maxillary teeth.

The Vertebral Column

The **vertebral column**, or spinal column, surrounds and protects the spinal cord, supports the head, and acts as an attachment point for the ribs and muscles of the back and neck. The adult vertebral column comprises 26 bones: the 24 vertebrae, the sacrum, and the coccyx bones. In the adult, the sacrum is typically composed of five vertebrae that fuse into one. The coccyx is typically 3–4 vertebrae that fuse into one. Around the age of 70, the sacrum and the coccyx may fuse together. We begin life with approximately 33 vertebrae, but as we grow, several vertebrae fuse together. The adult vertebrae are further divided into the 7 cervical vertebrae, 12 thoracic vertebrae, and 5 lumbar vertebrae (Figure 29.8).

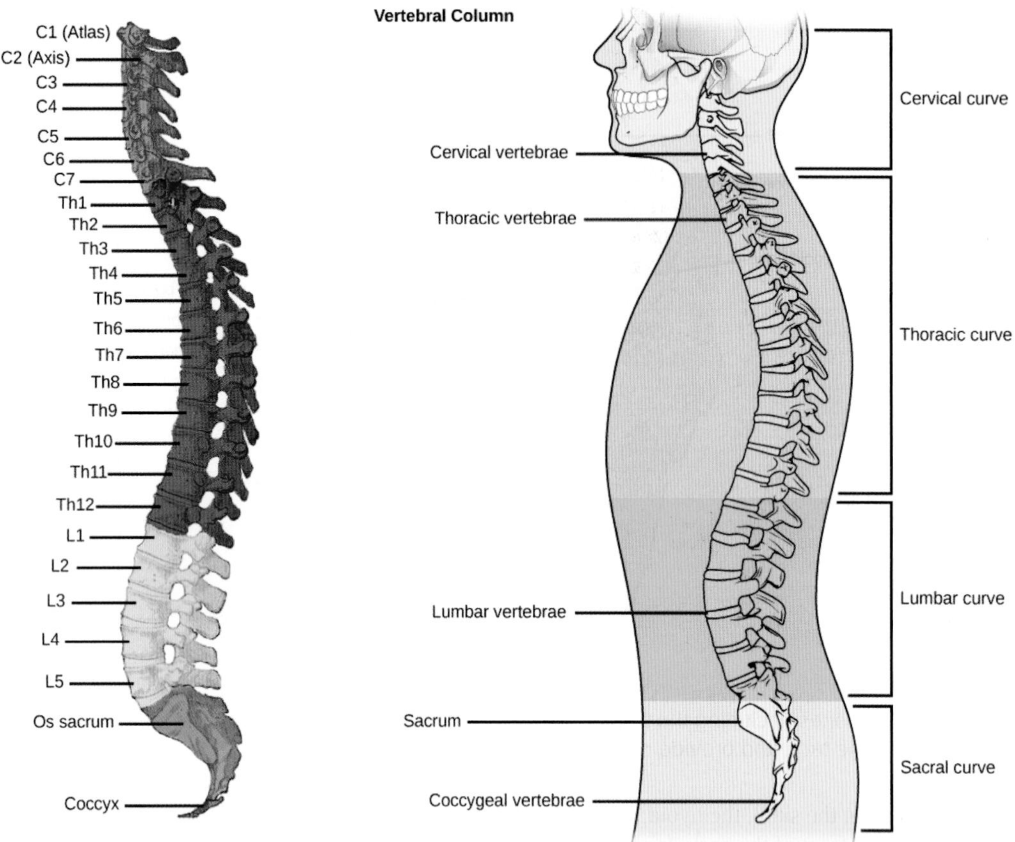

Figure 29.8 (a) The vertebral column consists of seven cervical vertebrae (C1–7) twelve thoracic vertebrae (Th1–12), five lumbar vertebrae (L1–5), the os sacrum, and the coccyx. (b) Spinal curves increase the strength and flexibility of the spine. (credit a: modification of work by Uwe Gille based on original work by Gray's Anatomy; credit b: modification of work by NCI, NIH)

Each vertebral body has a large hole in the center through which the nerves of the spinal cord pass. There is also a notch on each side through which the spinal nerves, which serve the body at that level, can exit from the spinal cord. The vertebral column is approximately 71 cm (28 inches) in adult male humans and is curved, which can be seen from a side view. The names of the spinal curves correspond to the region of the spine in which they occur. The thoracic and sacral curves are concave (curve inwards relative to the front of the body) and the cervical and lumbar curves are convex (curve outwards relative to the front of the body). The arched curvature of the vertebral column increases its strength and flexibility, allowing it to absorb shocks like a spring (Figure 29.8).

Intervertebral discs composed of fibrous cartilage lie between adjacent vertebral bodies from the second cervical vertebra to the sacrum. Each disc is part of a joint that allows for some movement of the spine and acts as a cushion to absorb shocks from movements such as walking and running. Intervertebral discs also act as ligaments to bind vertebrae together. The inner part of discs, the nucleus pulposus, hardens as people age and becomes less elastic. This loss of elasticity diminishes its ability to absorb shocks.

The Thoracic Cage

The **thoracic cage**, also known as the ribcage, is the skeleton of the chest, and consists of the ribs, sternum, thoracic vertebrae, and costal cartilages (Figure 29.9). The thoracic cage encloses and protects the organs of the thoracic cavity, including the heart and lungs. It also provides support for the shoulder girdles and upper limbs, and serves as the attachment point for the diaphragm, muscles of the back, chest, neck, and shoulders. Changes in the volume of the thorax enable breathing.

The **sternum**, or breastbone, is a long, flat bone located at the anterior of the chest. It is formed from three bones that fuse in the adult. The **ribs** are 12 pairs of long, curved bones that attach to the thoracic vertebrae and curve toward the front of the body, forming the ribcage. Costal cartilages connect the anterior ends of the ribs to the sternum, with the exception of rib pairs 11 and 12, which are free-floating ribs.

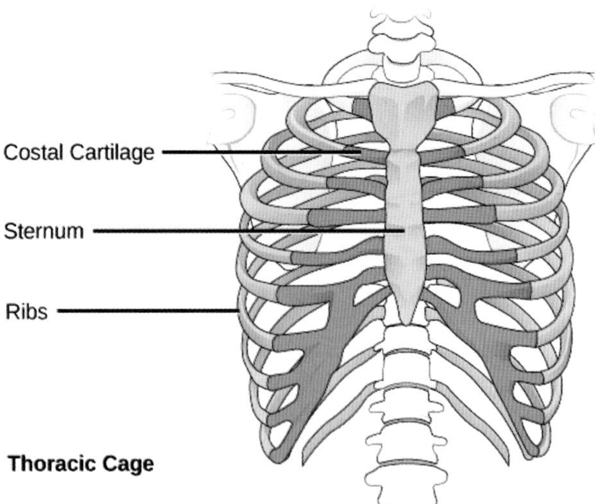

Figure 29.9 The thoracic cage, or rib cage, protects the heart and the lungs. (credit: modification of work by NCI, NIH)

Human Appendicular Skeleton

The **appendicular skeleton** is composed of the bones of the upper limbs (which function to grasp and manipulate objects) and the lower limbs (which permit locomotion). It also includes the pectoral girdle, or shoulder girdle, that attaches the upper limbs to the body, and the pelvic girdle that attaches the lower limbs to the body (Figure 29.10).

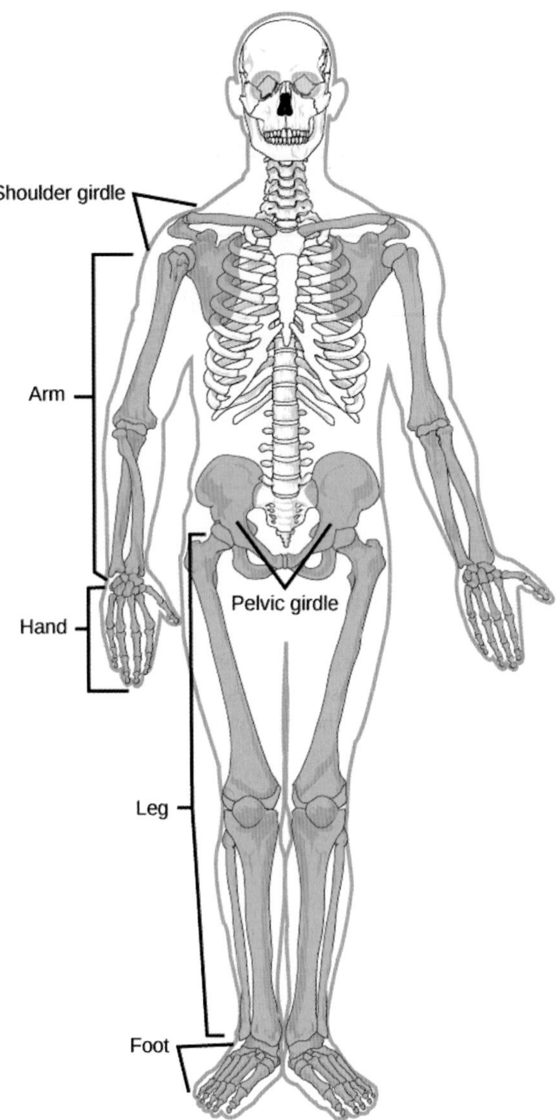

Figure 29.10 The appendicular skeleton is composed of the bones of the pectoral limbs (arm, forearm, hand), the pelvic limbs (thigh, leg, foot), the pectoral girdle, and the pelvic girdle. (credit: modification of work by Mariana Ruiz Villareal)

The Pectoral Girdle

The **pectoral girdle** bones provide the points of attachment of the upper limbs to the axial skeleton. The human pectoral girdle consists of the clavicle (or collarbone) in the anterior, and the scapula (or shoulder blades) in the posterior (Figure 29.11).

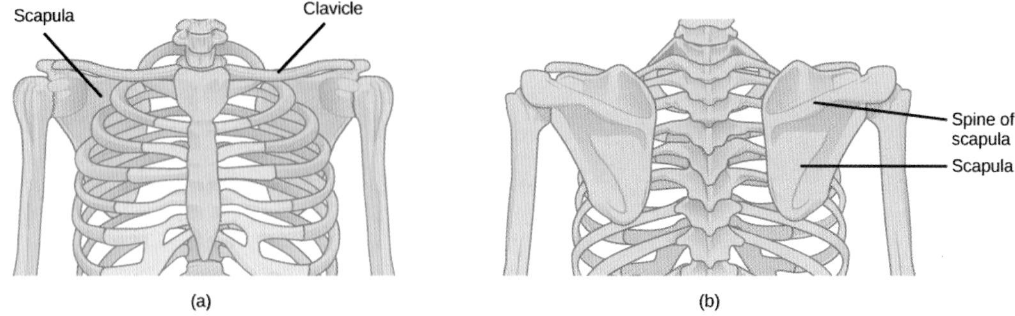

Figure 29.11 (a) The pectoral girdle in primates consists of the clavicles and scapulae. (b) The posterior view reveals the spine of the scapula to which muscle attaches.

The **clavicles** are S-shaped bones that position the arms on the body. The clavicles lie horizontally across the front of the thorax (chest) just above the first rib. These bones are fairly fragile and are susceptible to fractures. For example, a fall with the arms outstretched causes the force to be transmitted to the clavicles, which can break if the force is excessive. The clavicle articulates with the sternum and the scapula.

The **scapulae** are flat, triangular bones that are located at the back of the pectoral girdle. They support the muscles crossing the shoulder joint. A ridge, called the spine, runs across the back of the scapula and can easily be felt through the skin (Figure 29.11). The spine of the scapula is a good example of a bony protrusion that facilitates a broad area of attachment for muscles to bone.

The Upper Limb

The upper limb contains 30 bones in three regions: the arm (shoulder to elbow), the forearm (ulna and radius), and the wrist and hand (Figure 29.12).

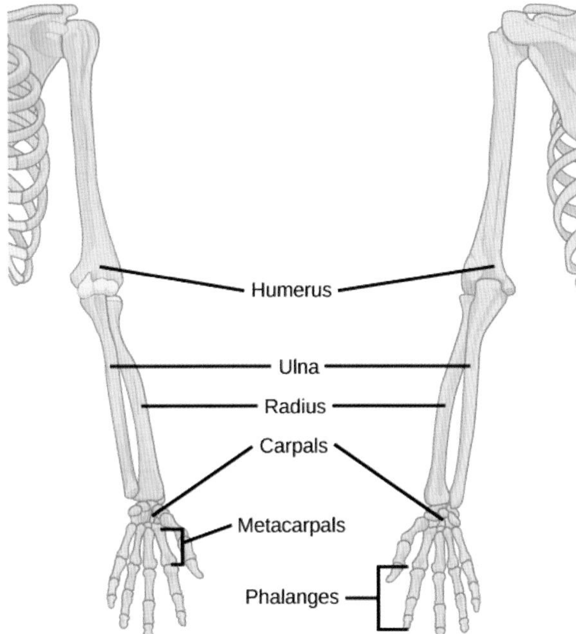

Figure 29.12 The upper limb consists of the humerus of the upper arm, the radius and ulna of the forearm, eight bones of the carpus, five bones of the metacarpus, and 14 bones of the phalanges.

An **articulation** is any place at which two bones are joined. The **humerus** is the largest and longest bone of the upper limb and the only bone of the arm. It articulates with the scapula at the shoulder and with the forearm at the elbow. The **forearm** extends from the elbow to the wrist and consists of two bones: the ulna and the radius. The **radius** is located along the lateral (thumb) side of the forearm and articulates with the humerus at the elbow. The **ulna** is located on the medial aspect (pinky-finger side) of the forearm. It is longer than the radius. The ulna articulates with the humerus at the elbow. The radius and ulna also articulate with the carpal bones and with each other, which in vertebrates enables a variable degree of rotation of the carpus with respect to the long axis of the limb. The hand includes the eight bones of the **carpus** (wrist), the five bones of the **metacarpus** (palm), and the 14 bones of the **phalanges** (digits). Each digit consists of three phalanges, except for the thumb, when present, which has only two.

The Pelvic Girdle

The **pelvic girdle** attaches to the lower limbs of the axial skeleton. Because it is responsible for bearing the weight of the body and for locomotion, the pelvic girdle is securely attached to the axial skeleton by strong ligaments. It also has deep sockets with robust ligaments to securely attach the femur to the body. The pelvic girdle is further strengthened by two large hip bones. In adults, the hip bones, or **coxal bones**, are formed by the fusion of three pairs of bones: the ilium, ischium, and pubis. The pelvis joins together in the anterior of the body at a joint called the pubic symphysis and with the bones of the sacrum at the posterior of the body.

The female pelvis is slightly different from the male pelvis. Over generations of evolution, females with a wider pubic angle and larger diameter pelvic canal reproduced more successfully. Therefore, their offspring also had pelvic anatomy that enabled successful childbirth (Figure 29.13).

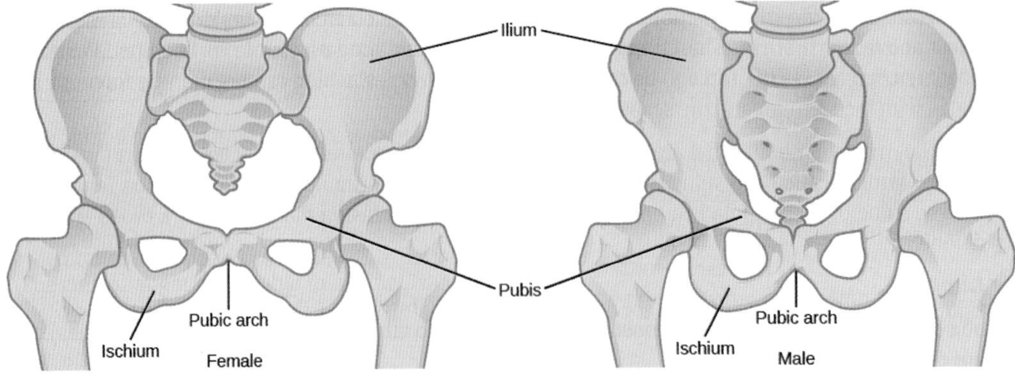

Figure 29.13 To adapt to reproductive fitness, the (a) female pelvis is lighter, wider, shallower, and has a broader angle between the pubic bones than (b) the male pelvis.

The Lower Limb

The **lower limb** consists of the thigh, the leg, and the foot. The bones of the lower limb are the femur (thigh bone), patella (kneecap), tibia and fibula (bones of the leg), tarsals (bones of the ankle), and metatarsals and phalanges (bones of the foot) (Figure 29.14). The bones of the lower limbs are thicker and stronger than the bones of the upper limbs because of the need to support the entire weight of the body and the resulting forces from locomotion. In addition to evolutionary fitness, the bones of an individual will respond to forces exerted upon them.

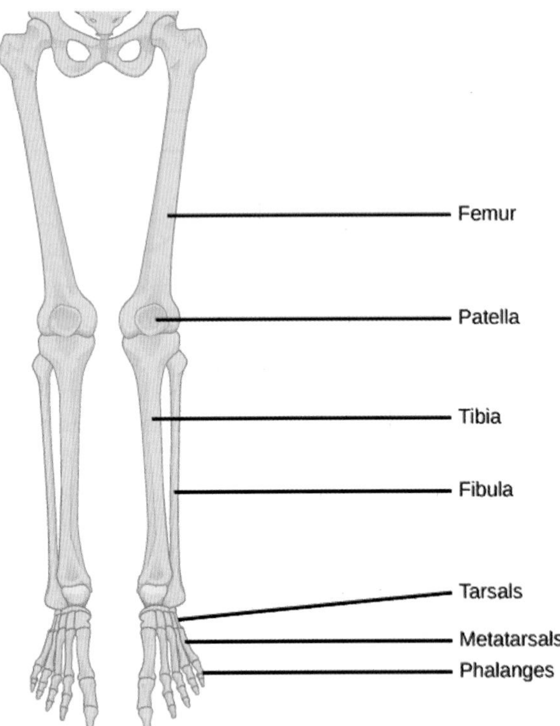

Figure 29.14 The lower limb consists of the thigh (femur), kneecap (patella), leg (tibia and fibula), ankle (tarsals), and foot (metatarsals and phalanges) bones.

The **femur**, or thighbone, is the longest, heaviest, and strongest bone in the body. The femur and pelvis form the hip joint at the proximal end. At the distal end, the femur, tibia, and patella form the knee joint. The **patella**, or kneecap, is a triangular bone that lies anterior to the knee joint. The patella is embedded in the tendon of the femoral extensors (quadriceps). It improves knee extension by reducing friction. The **tibia**, or shinbone, is a large bone of the leg that is located directly below the knee. The tibia articulates with the femur at its proximal end, with the fibula and the tarsal bones at its distal end. It is the second largest bone in the human body and is responsible for transmitting the weight of the body from the femur to the foot. The **fibula**, or calf bone, parallels and articulates with the tibia. It does not articulate with the femur and does not bear weight. The fibula acts as a site for muscle attachment and forms the lateral part of the ankle joint.

The **tarsals** are the seven bones of the ankle. The ankle transmits the weight of the body from the tibia and the fibula to the foot. The **metatarsals** are the five bones of the foot. The phalanges are the 14 bones of the toes. Each toe consists of three phalanges, except for the big toe that has only two (Figure 29.15). Variations exist in other species; for example, the horse's metacarpals and metatarsals are oriented vertically and do not make contact with the substrate.

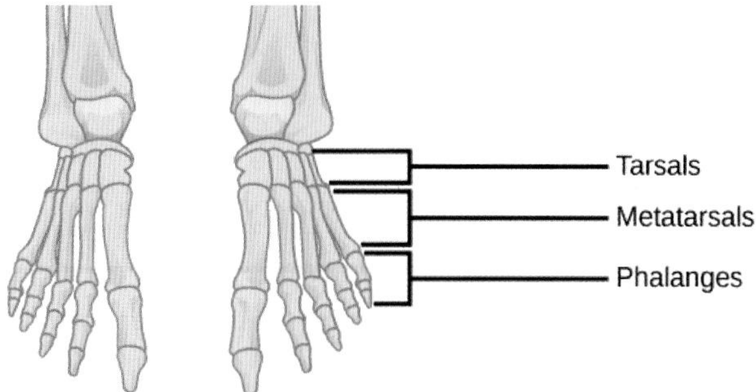

Figure 29.15 This drawing shows the bones of the human foot and ankle, including the metatarsals and the phalanges.

Evolution of Body Design for Locomotion on Land

The transition of vertebrates onto land required a number of changes in body design, as movement on land presents a number of challenges for animals that are adapted to movement in water. The buoyancy of water provides a certain amount of lift, and a common form of movement by fish is lateral undulations of the entire body. This back and forth movement pushes the body against the water, creating forward movement. In most fish, the muscles of paired fins attach to girdles within the body, allowing for some control of locomotion. As certain fish began moving onto land, they retained their lateral undulation form of locomotion (anguilliform). However, instead of pushing against water, their fins or flippers became points of contact with the ground, around which they rotated their bodies.

The effect of gravity and the lack of buoyancy on land meant that body weight was suspended on the limbs, leading to increased strengthening and ossification of the limbs. The effect of gravity also required changes to the axial skeleton. Lateral undulations of land animal vertebral columns cause torsional strain. A firmer, more ossified vertebral column became common in terrestrial tetrapods because it reduces strain while providing the strength needed to support the body's weight. In later tetrapods, the vertebrae began allowing for vertical motion rather than lateral flexion. Another change in the axial skeleton was the loss of a direct attachment between the pectoral girdle and the head. This reduced the jarring to the head caused by the impact of the limbs on the ground. The vertebrae of the neck also evolved to allow movement of the head independently of the body.

The appendicular skeleton of land animals is also different from aquatic animals. The shoulders attach to the pectoral girdle through muscles and connective tissue, thus reducing the jarring of the skull. Because of a lateral undulating vertebral column, in early tetrapods, the limbs were splayed out to the side and movement occurred by performing "push-ups." The vertebrae of these animals had to move side-to-side in a similar manner to fish and reptiles. This type of motion requires large muscles to move the limbs toward the midline; it was almost like walking while doing push-ups, and it is not an efficient use of energy. Later tetrapods have their limbs placed under their bodies, so that each stride requires less force to move forward. This resulted in decreased adductor muscle size and an increased range of motion of the scapulae. This also restricts movement primarily to one plane, creating forward motion rather than moving the limbs upward as well as forward. The femur and humerus were also rotated, so that the ends of the limbs and digits were pointed forward, in the direction of motion, rather than out to the side. By placement underneath the body, limbs can swing forward like a pendulum to produce a stride that is more efficient for moving over land.

Which of the following changes evolved in the animal skeletal system as animals moved from water to land?

a. decreased ossification of bones
b. increased attachment between pectoral girdle and head
c. rotation of femur and humerus to point to the side
d. placement of limbs under the body

29.2 | Bone

In this section, you will explore the following questions:

- What are examples of the different types of bones and their functions in the human skeleton?
- What are the roles of the different cell types and tissue types in bone?
- How do bones develop, grow, and undergo remodeling and repair?

Connection for AP® Courses

The information in this section is not within the scope for AP® and does not align with the curriculum framework. However, as a student of biology it is important to understand the types of bones and bone tissues as well as their functions because this basic part of anatomy is an excellent example of form follows function. For example, spongy bone tissue is found in the inner layer of bones and contains blood vessels to deliver nutrients and remove waster from bone cells.

Bone, or **osseous tissue**, is a connective tissue that constitutes the endoskeleton. It contains specialized cells and a matrix of mineral salts and collagen fibers.

The mineral salts primarily include hydroxyapatite, a mineral formed from calcium phosphate. **Calcification** is the process of deposition of mineral salts on the collagen fiber matrix that crystallizes and hardens the tissue. The process of calcification only occurs in the presence of collagen fibers.

The bones of the human skeleton are classified by their shape: long bones, short bones, flat bones, sutural bones, sesamoid bones, and irregular bones (Figure 29.16).

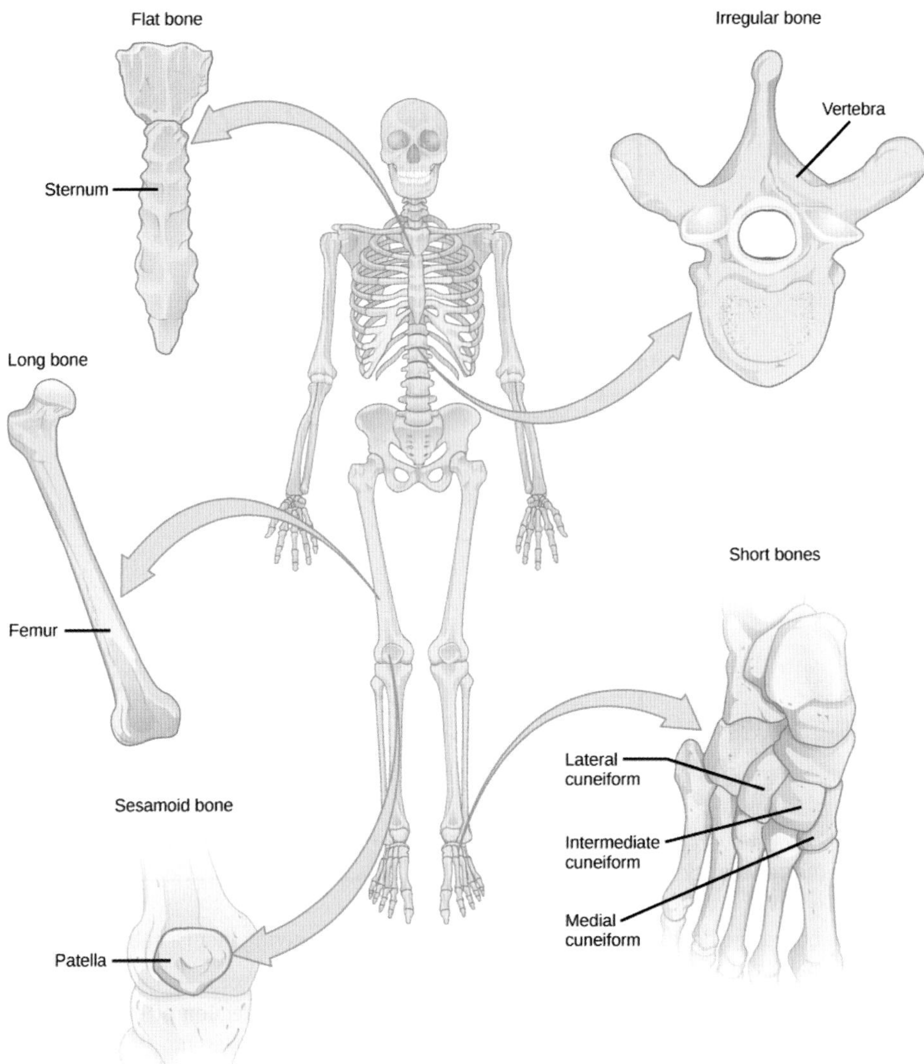

Figure 29.16 Shown are different types of bones: flat, irregular, long, short, and sesamoid.

Long bones are longer than they are wide and have a shaft and two ends. The **diaphysis**, or central shaft, contains bone marrow in a marrow cavity. The rounded ends, the **epiphyses**, are covered with articular cartilage and are filled with red bone marrow, which produces blood cells (Figure 29.17). Most of the limb bones are long bones—for example, the femur, tibia, ulna, and radius. Exceptions to this include the patella and the bones of the wrist and ankle.

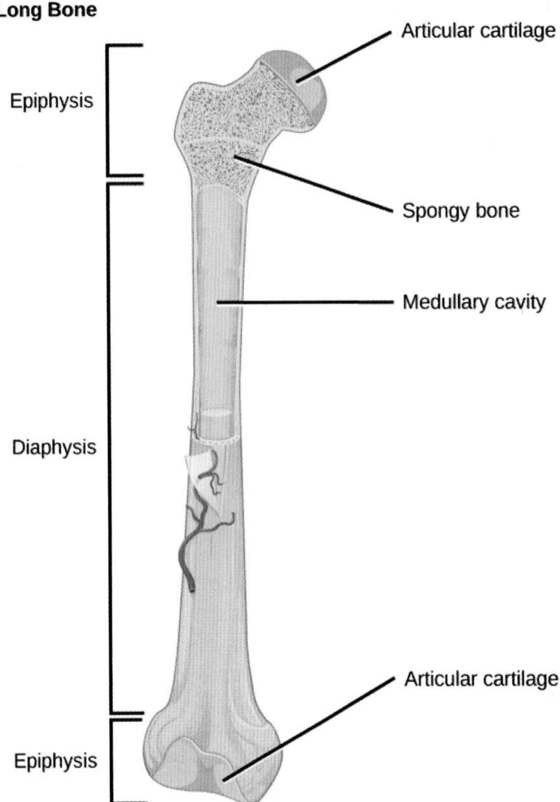

Figure 29.17 The long bone is covered by articular cartilage at either end and contains bone marrow (shown in yellow in this illustration) in the marrow cavity.

Short bones, or cuboidal bones, are bones that are the same width and length, giving them a cube-like shape. For example, the bones of the wrist (carpals) and ankle (tarsals) are short bones (Figure 29.16).

Flat bones are thin and relatively broad bones that are found where extensive protection of organs is required or where broad surfaces of muscle attachment are required. Examples of flat bones are the sternum (breast bone), ribs, scapulae (shoulder blades), and the roof of the skull (Figure 29.16).

Irregular bones are bones with complex shapes. These bones may have short, flat, notched, or ridged surfaces. Examples of irregular bones are the vertebrae, hip bones, and several skull bones.

Sesamoid bones are small, flat bones and are shaped similarly to a sesame seed. The patellae are sesamoid bones (Figure 29.18). Sesamoid bones develop inside tendons and may be found near joints at the knees, hands, and feet.

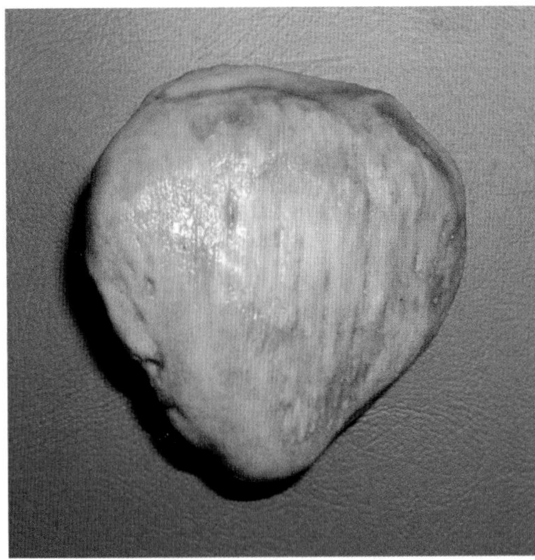

Figure 29.18 The patella of the knee is an example of a sesamoid bone.

Sutural bones are small, flat, irregularly shaped bones. They may be found between the flat bones of the skull. They vary in number, shape, size, and position.

Bone Tissue

Bones are considered organs because they contain various types of tissue, such as blood, connective tissue, nerves, and bone tissue. Osteocytes, the living cells of bone tissue, form the mineral matrix of bones. There are two types of bone tissue: compact and spongy.

Compact Bone Tissue

Compact bone (or cortical bone) forms the hard external layer of all bones and surrounds the medullary cavity, or bone marrow. It provides protection and strength to bones. Compact bone tissue consists of units called osteons or Haversian systems. **Osteons** are cylindrical structures that contain a mineral matrix and living osteocytes connected by canaliculi, which transport blood. They are aligned parallel to the long axis of the bone. Each osteon consists of **lamellae**, which are layers of compact matrix that surround a central canal called the Haversian canal. The **Haversian canal** (osteonic canal) contains the bone's blood vessels and nerve fibers (Figure 29.19). Osteons in compact bone tissue are aligned in the same direction along lines of stress and help the bone resist bending or fracturing. Therefore, compact bone tissue is prominent in areas of bone at which stresses are applied in only a few directions.

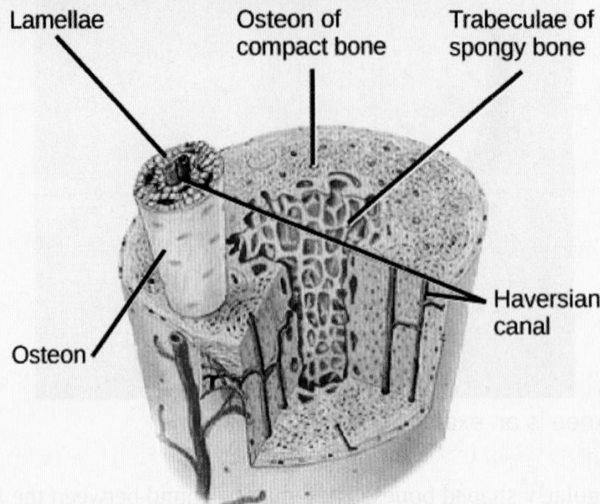

Figure 29.19 Compact bone tissue consists of osteons that are aligned parallel to the long axis of the bone, and the Haversian canal that contains the bone's blood vessels and nerve fibers. The inner layer of bones consists of spongy bone tissue. The small dark ovals in the osteon represent the living osteocytes. (credit: modification of work by NCI, NIH)

Spongy Bone Tissue

Whereas compact bone tissue forms the outer layer of all bones, **spongy bone** or cancellous bone forms the inner layer of all bones. Spongy bone tissue does not contain osteons that constitute compact bone tissue. Instead, it consists of **trabeculae**, which are lamellae that are arranged as rods or plates. Red bone marrow is found between the trabuculae. Blood vessels within this tissue deliver nutrients to osteocytes and remove waste. The red bone marrow of the femur and the interior of other large bones, such as the ileum, forms blood cells.

Spongy bone reduces the density of bone and allows the ends of long bones to compress as the result of stresses applied to the bone. Spongy bone is prominent in areas of bones that are not heavily stressed or where stresses arrive from many directions. The epiphyses of bones, such as the neck of the femur, are subject to stress from many directions. Imagine laying a heavy framed picture flat on the floor. You could hold up one side of the picture with a toothpick if the toothpick was perpendicular to the floor and the picture. Now drill a hole and stick the toothpick into the wall to hang up the picture. In this case, the function of the toothpick is to transmit the downward pressure of the picture to the wall. The force on the picture is straight down to the floor, but the force on the toothpick is both the picture wire pulling down and the bottom of the hole in the wall pushing up. The toothpick will break off right at the wall.

The neck of the femur is horizontal like the toothpick in the wall. The weight of the body pushes it down near the joint, but the vertical diaphysis of the femur pushes it up at the other end. The neck of the femur must be strong enough to transfer the downward force of the body weight horizontally to the vertical shaft of the femur (**Figure 29.20**).

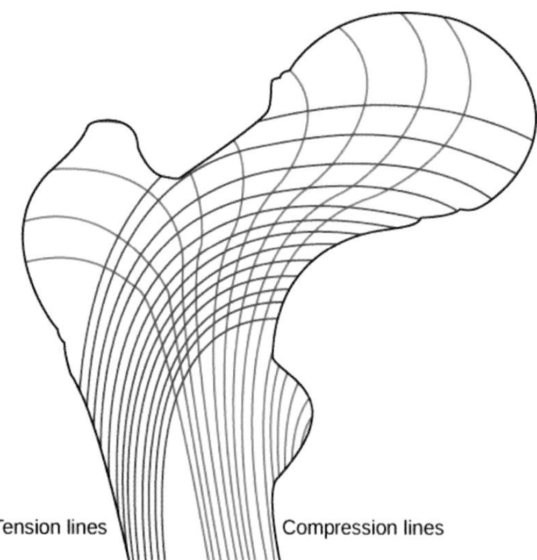

Figure 29.20 Trabeculae in spongy bone are arranged such that one side of the bone bears tension and the other withstands compression.

View micrographs (http://openstaxcollege.org/l/muscle_tissue) of musculoskeletal tissues as you review the anatomy.

Which type of connective tissue lacks collagen fibers?

a. blood

b. loose connective tissue

c. cartilage

d. bone

Cell Types in Bones

Bone consists of four types of cells: osteoblasts, osteoclasts, osteocytes, and osteoprogenitor cells. **Osteoblasts** are bone cells that are responsible for bone formation. Osteoblasts synthesize and secrete the organic part and inorganic part of the extracellular matrix of bone tissue, and collagen fibers. Osteoblasts become trapped in these secretions and differentiate into less active osteocytes. **Osteoclasts** are large bone cells with up to 50 nuclei. They remove bone structure by releasing lysosomal enzymes and acids that dissolve the bony matrix. These minerals, released from bones into the blood, help regulate calcium concentrations in body fluids. Bone may also be resorbed for remodeling, if the applied stresses have changed. **Osteocytes** are mature bone cells and are the main cells in bony connective tissue; these cells cannot divide. Osteocytes maintain normal bone structure by recycling the mineral salts in the bony matrix. **Osteoprogenitor cells** are squamous stem cells that divide to produce daughter cells that differentiate into osteoblasts. Osteoprogenitor cells are important in the repair of fractures.

Development of Bone

Ossification, or osteogenesis, is the process of bone formation by osteoblasts. Ossification is distinct from the process of calcification; whereas calcification takes place during the ossification of bones, it can also occur in other tissues. Ossification begins approximately six weeks after fertilization in an embryo. Before this time, the embryonic skeleton consists entirely of fibrous membranes and hyaline cartilage. The development of bone from fibrous membranes is called intramembranous ossification; development from hyaline cartilage is called endochondral ossification. Bone growth continues until approximately age 25. Bones can grow in thickness throughout life, but after age 25, ossification functions primarily in bone remodeling and repair.

Intramembranous Ossification

Intramembranous ossification is the process of bone development from fibrous membranes. It is involved in the formation of the flat bones of the skull, the mandible, and the clavicles. Ossification begins as mesenchymal cells form a template of the future bone. They then differentiate into osteoblasts at the ossification center. Osteoblasts secrete the extracellular matrix and deposit calcium, which hardens the matrix. The non-mineralized portion of the bone or osteoid continues to form around blood vessels, forming spongy bone. Connective tissue in the matrix differentiates into red bone marrow in the fetus. The spongy bone is remodeled into a thin layer of compact bone on the surface of the spongy bone.

Endochondral Ossification

Endochondral ossification is the process of bone development from hyaline cartilage. All of the bones of the body, except for the flat bones of the skull, mandible, and clavicles, are formed through endochondral ossification.

In long bones, chondrocytes form a template of the hyaline cartilage diaphysis. Responding to complex developmental signals, the matrix begins to calcify. This calcification prevents diffusion of nutrients into the matrix, resulting in chondrocytes dying and the opening up of cavities in the diaphysis cartilage. Blood vessels invade the cavities, and osteoblasts and osteoclasts modify the calcified cartilage matrix into spongy bone. Osteoclasts then break down some of the spongy bone to create a marrow, or medullary, cavity in the center of the diaphysis. Dense, irregular connective tissue forms a sheath (periosteum) around the bones. The periosteum assists in attaching the bone to surrounding tissues, tendons, and ligaments. The bone continues to grow and elongate as the cartilage cells at the epiphyses divide.

In the last stage of prenatal bone development, the centers of the epiphyses begin to calcify. Secondary ossification centers form in the epiphyses as blood vessels and osteoblasts enter these areas and convert hyaline cartilage into spongy bone. Until adolescence, hyaline cartilage persists at the **epiphyseal plate** (growth plate), which is the region between the diaphysis and epiphysis that is responsible for the lengthwise growth of long bones (Figure 29.21).

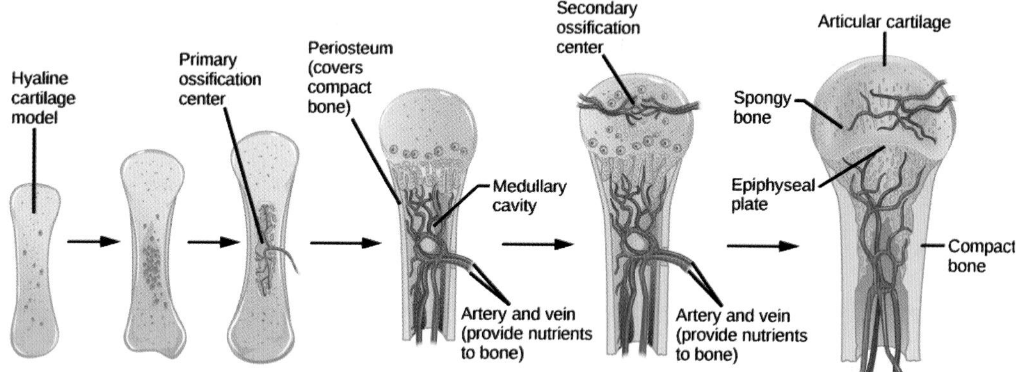

Figure 29.21 Endochondral ossification is the process of bone development from hyaline cartilage. The periosteum is the connective tissue on the outside of bone that acts as the interface between bone, blood vessels, tendons, and ligaments.

Growth of Bone

Long bones continue to lengthen, potentially until adolescence, through the addition of bone tissue at the epiphyseal plate. They also increase in width through appositional growth.

Lengthening of Long Bones

Chondrocytes on the epiphyseal side of the epiphyseal plate divide; one cell remains undifferentiated near the epiphysis, and one cell moves toward the diaphysis. The cells, which are pushed from the epiphysis, mature and are destroyed by calcification. This process replaces cartilage with bone on the diaphyseal side of the plate, resulting in a lengthening of the bone.

Long bones stop growing at around the age of 18 in females and the age of 21 in males in a process called epiphyseal plate closure. During this process, cartilage cells stop dividing and all of the cartilage is replaced by bone. The epiphyseal plate fades, leaving a structure called the epiphyseal line or epiphyseal remnant, and the epiphysis and diaphysis fuse.

Thickening of Long Bones

Appositional growth is the increase in the diameter of bones by the addition of bony tissue at the surface of bones. Osteoblasts at the bone surface secrete bone matrix, and osteoclasts on the inner surface break down bone. The osteoblasts differentiate into osteocytes. A balance between these two processes allows the bone to thicken without becoming too heavy.

Bone Remodeling and Repair

Bone renewal continues after birth into adulthood. **Bone remodeling** is the replacement of old bone tissue by new bone tissue. It involves the processes of bone deposition by osteoblasts and bone resorption by osteoclasts. Normal bone growth requires vitamins D, C, and A, plus minerals such as calcium, phosphorous, and magnesium. Hormones such as parathyroid hormone, growth hormone, and calcitonin are also required for proper bone growth and maintenance.

Bone turnover rates are quite high, with five to seven percent of bone mass being recycled every week. Differences in turnover rate exist in different areas of the skeleton and in different areas of a bone. For example, the bone in the head of the femur may be fully replaced every six months, whereas the bone along the shaft is altered much more slowly.

Bone remodeling allows bones to adapt to stresses by becoming thicker and stronger when subjected to stress. Bones that are not subject to normal stress, for example when a limb is in a cast, will begin to lose mass. A fractured or broken bone undergoes repair through four stages:

1. Blood vessels in the broken bone tear and hemorrhage, resulting in the formation of clotted blood, or a hematoma, at the site of the break. The severed blood vessels at the broken ends of the bone are sealed by the clotting process, and bone cells that are deprived of nutrients begin to die.
2. Within days of the fracture, capillaries grow into the hematoma, and phagocytic cells begin to clear away the dead cells. Though fragments of the blood clot may remain, fibroblasts and osteoblasts enter the area and begin to reform bone. Fibroblasts produce collagen fibers that connect the broken bone ends, and osteoblasts start to form spongy bone. The repair tissue between the broken bone ends is called the fibrocartilaginous callus, as it is composed of both hyaline and fibrocartilage (Figure 29.22). Some bone spicules may also appear at this point.
3. The fibrocartilaginous callus is converted into a bony callus of spongy bone. It takes about two months for the broken bone ends to be firmly joined together after the fracture. This is similar to the endochondral formation of bone, as cartilage becomes ossified; osteoblasts, osteoclasts, and bone matrix are present.
4. The bony callus is then remodelled by osteoclasts and osteoblasts, with excess material on the exterior of the bone and within the medullary cavity being removed. Compact bone is added to create bone tissue that is similar to the original, unbroken bone. This remodeling can take many months, and the bone may remain uneven for years.

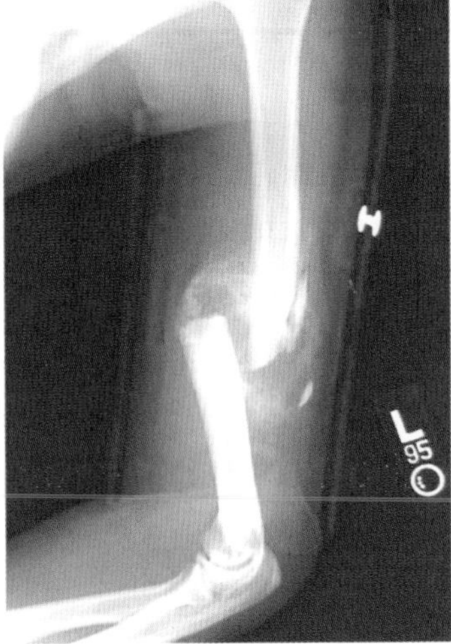

Figure 29.22 After this bone is set, a callus will knit the two ends together. (credit: Bill Rhodes)

scientific method CONNECTION

Decalcification of Bones

Question: What effect does the removal of calcium and collagen have on bone structure?

Background: Conduct a literature search on the role of calcium and collagen in maintaining bone structure. Conduct a literature search on diseases in which bone structure is compromised.

Hypothesis: Develop a hypothesis that states predictions of the flexibility, strength, and mass of bones that have had the calcium and collagen components removed. Develop a hypothesis regarding the attempt to add calcium back to decalcified bones.

Test the hypothesis: Test the prediction by removing calcium from chicken bones by placing them in a jar of vinegar for seven days. Test the hypothesis regarding adding calcium back to decalcified bone by placing the decalcified chicken bones into a jar of water with calcium supplements added. Test the prediction by denaturing the collagen from the bones by baking them at 250°C for three hours.

Analyze the data: Create a table showing the changes in bone flexibility, strength, and mass in the three different environments.

Report the results: Under which conditions was the bone most flexible? Under which conditions was the bone the strongest?

Draw a conclusion: Did the results support or refute the hypothesis? How do the results observed in this experiment correspond to diseases that destroy bone tissue?

29.3 | Joints and Skeletal Movement

In this section, you will explore the following questions:

- What are the different types of joints on the basis of structure?
- What is the role of joints in skeletal movement?

Connection for AP® Courses

The information in this section is not within the scope for AP® and does not align with the curriculum framework. However, the material in this section is important to understanding how joints provide stability to the skeletal system. Furthermore, understanding the different types of joints will help one understand how the muscles are able to move bones in specific ways.

The point at which two or more bones meet is called a **joint**, or **articulation**. Joints are responsible for movement, such as the movement of limbs, and stability, such as the stability found in the bones of the skull.

Classification of Joints on the Basis of Structure

There are two ways to classify joints: on the basis of their structure or on the basis of their function. The structural classification divides joints into bony, fibrous, cartilaginous, and synovial joints depending on the material composing the joint and the presence or absence of a cavity in the joint.

Fibrous Joints

The bones of **fibrous joints** are held together by fibrous connective tissue. There is no cavity, or space, present between the bones and so most fibrous joints do not move at all, or are only capable of minor movements. There are three types of fibrous joints: sutures, syndesmoses, and gomphoses. **Sutures** are found only in the skull and possess short fibers of connective tissue that hold the skull bones tightly in place (Figure 29.23).

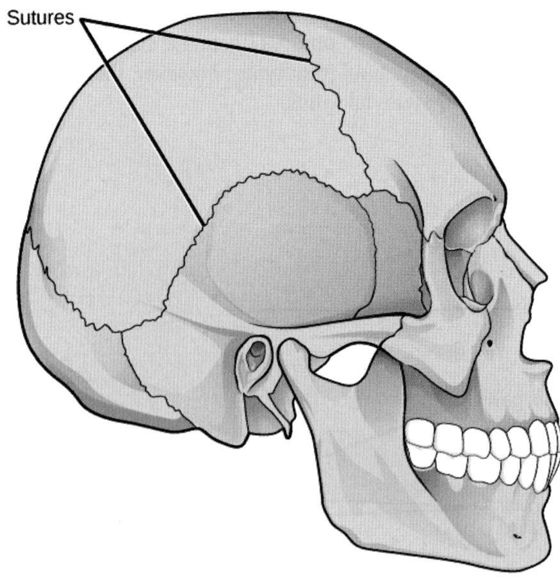

Figure 29.23 Sutures are fibrous joints found only in the skull.

Syndesmoses are joints in which the bones are connected by a band of connective tissue, allowing for more movement than in a suture. An example of a syndesmosis is the joint of the tibia and fibula in the ankle. The amount of movement in these types of joints is determined by the length of the connective tissue fibers. **Gomphoses** occur between teeth and their sockets; the term refers to the way the tooth fits into the socket like a peg (Figure 29.24). The tooth is connected to the socket by a connective tissue referred to as the periodontal ligament.

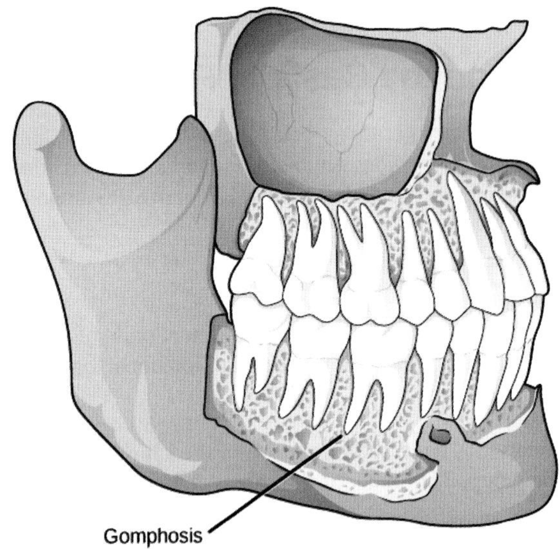

Figure 29.24 Gomphoses are fibrous joints between the teeth and their sockets. (credit: modification of work by Gray's Anatomy)

Cartilaginous Joints

Cartilaginous joints are joints in which the bones are connected by cartilage. There are two types of cartilaginous joints: synchondroses and symphyses. In a **synchondrosis**, the bones are joined by hyaline cartilage. Synchondroses are found in the epiphyseal plates of growing bones in children. In **symphyses**, hyaline cartilage covers the end of the bone but the connection between bones occurs through fibrocartilage. Symphyses are found at the joints between vertebrae. Either type of cartilaginous joint allows for very little movement.

Synovial Joints

Synovial joints are the only joints that have a space between the adjoining bones (Figure 29.25). This space is referred to as the synovial (or joint) cavity and is filled with synovial fluid. Synovial fluid lubricates the joint, reducing friction between the bones and allowing for greater movement. The ends of the bones are covered with articular cartilage, a hyaline cartilage, and the entire joint is surrounded by an articular capsule composed of connective tissue that allows movement of the joint while resisting dislocation. Articular capsules may also possess ligaments that hold the bones together. Synovial joints are capable of the greatest movement of the three structural joint types; however, the more mobile a joint, the weaker the joint. Knees, elbows, and shoulders are examples of synovial joints.

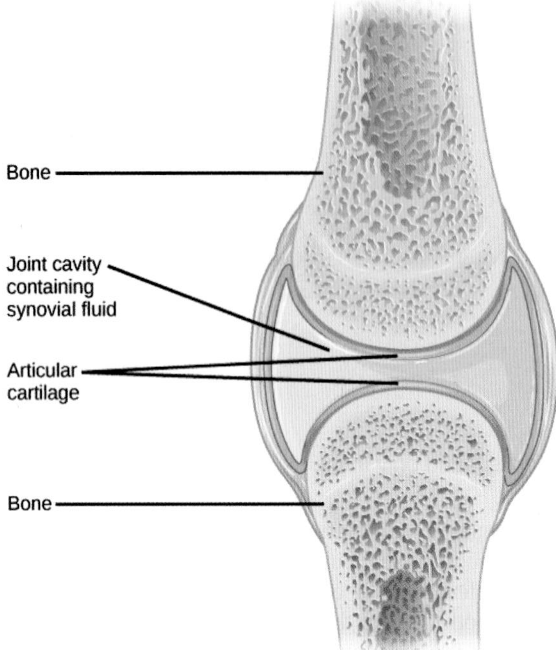

Figure 29.25 Synovial joints are the only joints that have a space or "synovial cavity" in the joint.

Classification of Joints on the Basis of Function

The functional classification divides joints into three categories: synarthroses, amphiarthroses, and diarthroses. A **synarthrosis** is a joint that is immovable. This includes sutures, gomphoses, and synchondroses. **Amphiarthroses** are joints that allow slight movement, including syndesmoses and symphyses. **Diarthroses** are joints that allow for free movement of the joint, as in synovial joints.

Movement at Synovial Joints

The wide range of movement allowed by synovial joints produces different types of movements. The movement of synovial joints can be classified as one of four different types: gliding, angular, rotational, or special movement.

Gliding Movement

Gliding movements occur as relatively flat bone surfaces move past each other. Gliding movements produce very little rotation or angular movement of the bones. The joints of the carpal and tarsal bones are examples of joints that produce gliding movements.

Angular Movement

Angular movements are produced when the angle between the bones of a joint changes. There are several different types of angular movements, including flexion, extension, hyperextension, abduction, adduction, and circumduction. **Flexion**, or bending, occurs when the angle between the bones decreases. Moving the forearm upward at the elbow or moving the wrist to move the hand toward the forearm are examples of flexion. **Extension** is the opposite of flexion in that the angle between the bones of a joint increases. Straightening a limb after flexion is an example of extension. Extension past the regular anatomical position is referred to as **hyperextension**. This includes moving the neck back to look upward, or bending the wrist so that the hand moves away from the forearm.

Abduction occurs when a bone moves away from the midline of the body. Examples of abduction are moving the arms or legs laterally to lift them straight out to the side. **Adduction** is the movement of a bone toward the midline of the body. Movement of the limbs inward after abduction is an example of adduction. **Circumduction** is the movement of a limb in a circular motion, as in moving the arm in a circular motion.

Rotational Movement

Rotational movement is the movement of a bone as it rotates around its longitudinal axis. Rotation can be toward the midline of the body, which is referred to as **medial rotation**, or away from the midline of the body, which is referred to as **lateral rotation**. Movement of the head from side to side is an example of rotation.

Special Movements

Some movements that cannot be classified as gliding, angular, or rotational are called special movements. **Inversion** involves the soles of the feet moving inward, toward the midline of the body. **Eversion** is the opposite of inversion, movement of the sole of the foot outward, away from the midline of the body. **Protraction** is the anterior movement of a bone in the horizontal plane. **Retraction** occurs as a joint moves back into position after protraction. Protraction and retraction can be seen in the movement of the mandible as the jaw is thrust outwards and then back inwards. **Elevation** is the movement of a bone upward, such as when the shoulders are shrugged, lifting the scapulae. **Depression** is the opposite of elevation—movement downward of a bone, such as after the shoulders are shrugged and the scapulae return to their normal position from an elevated position. **Dorsiflexion** is a bending at the ankle such that the toes are lifted toward the knee. **Plantar flexion** is a bending at the ankle when the heel is lifted, such as when standing on the toes. **Supination** is the movement of the radius and ulna bones of the forearm so that the palm faces forward. **Pronation** is the opposite movement, in which the palm faces backward. **Opposition** is the movement of the thumb toward the fingers of the same hand, making it possible to grasp and hold objects.

Types of Synovial Joints

Synovial joints are further classified into six different categories on the basis of the shape and structure of the joint. The shape of the joint affects the type of movement permitted by the joint (Figure 29.26). These joints can be described as planar, hinge, pivot, condyloid, saddle, or ball-and-socket joints.

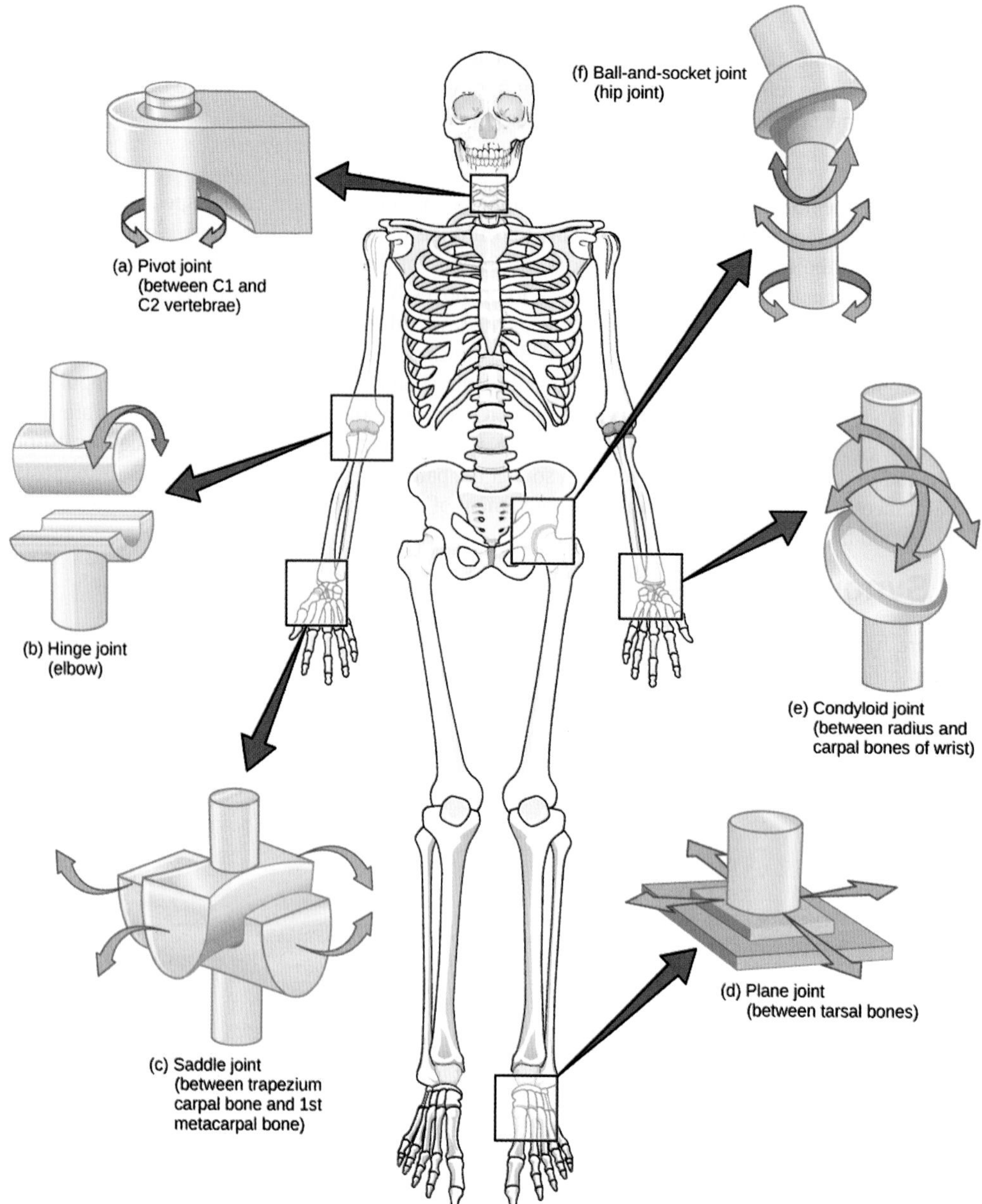

Figure 29.26 Different types of joints allow different types of movement. Planar, hinge, pivot, condyloid, saddle, and ball-and-socket are all types of synovial joints.

Planar Joints

Planar joints have bones with articulating surfaces that are flat or slightly curved faces. These joints allow for gliding movements, and so the joints are sometimes referred to as gliding joints. The range of motion is limited in these joints and does not involve rotation. Planar joints are found in the carpal bones in the hand and the tarsal bones of the foot, as well as between vertebrae (Figure 29.27).

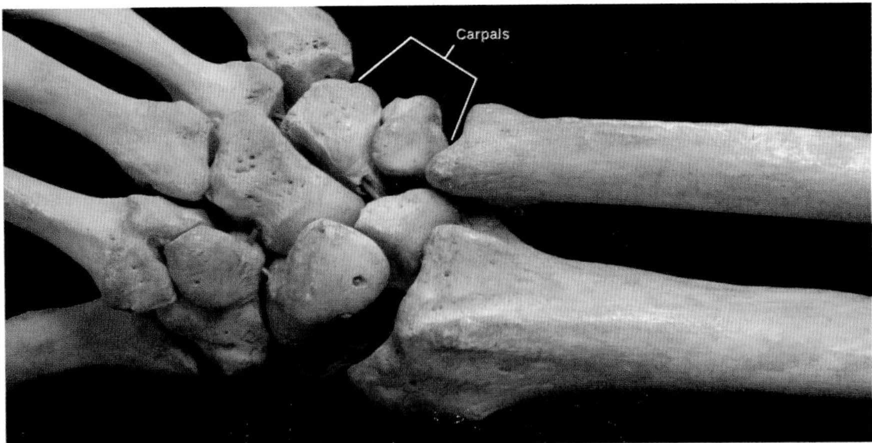

Figure 29.27 The joints of the carpal bones in the wrist are examples of planar joints. (credit: modification of work by Brian C. Goss)

Hinge Joints

In **hinge joints**, the slightly rounded end of one bone fits into the slightly hollow end of the other bone. In this way, one bone moves while the other remains stationary, like the hinge of a door. The elbow is an example of a hinge joint. The knee is sometimes classified as a modified hinge joint (Figure 29.28).

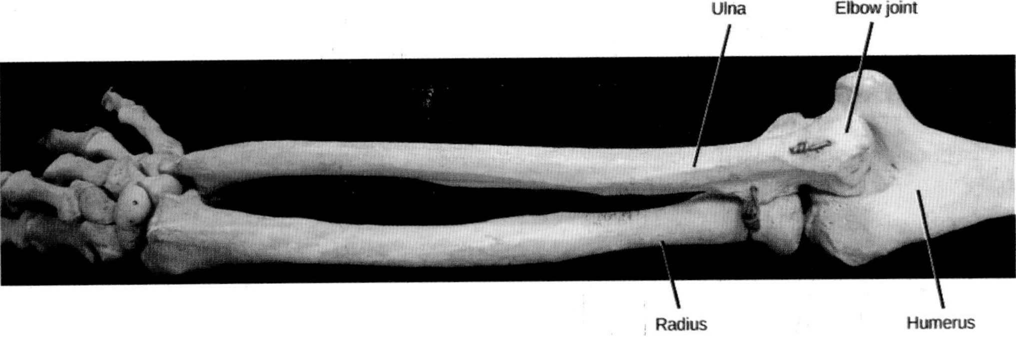

Figure 29.28 The elbow joint, where the radius articulates with the humerus, is an example of a hinge joint. (credit: modification of work by Brian C. Goss)

Pivot Joints

Pivot joints consist of the rounded end of one bone fitting into a ring formed by the other bone. This structure allows rotational movement, as the rounded bone moves around its own axis. An example of a pivot joint is the joint of the first and second vertebrae of the neck that allows the head to move back and forth (Figure 29.29). The joint of the wrist that allows the palm of the hand to be turned up and down is also a pivot joint.

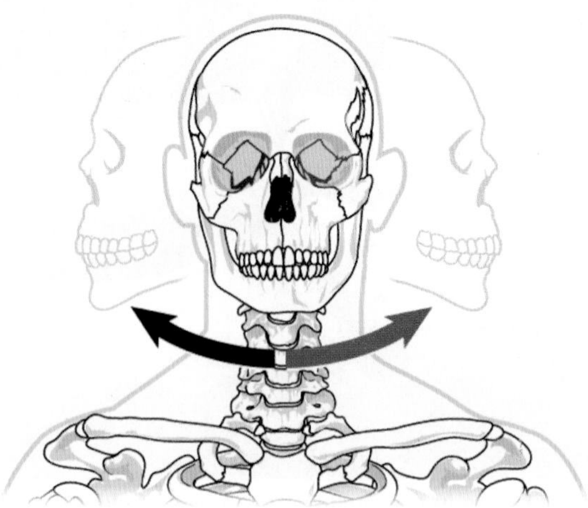

Figure 29.29 The joint in the neck that allows the head to move back and forth is an example of a pivot joint.

Condyloid Joints

Condyloid joints consist of an oval-shaped end of one bone fitting into a similarly oval-shaped hollow of another bone (Figure 29.30). This is also sometimes called an ellipsoidal joint. This type of joint allows angular movement along two axes, as seen in the joints of the wrist and fingers, which can move both side to side and up and down.

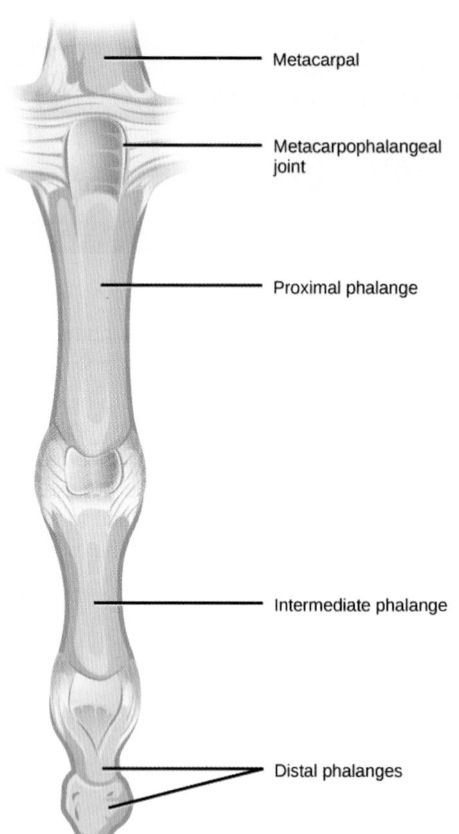

Figure 29.30 The metacarpophalangeal joints in the finger are examples of condyloid joints. (credit: modification of work by Gray's Anatomy)

Saddle Joints

Saddle joints are so named because the ends of each bone resemble a saddle, with concave and convex portions that fit together. Saddle joints allow angular movements similar to condyloid joints but with a greater range of motion. An example of a saddle joint is the thumb joint, which can move back and forth and up and down, but more freely than the wrist or fingers (Figure 29.31).

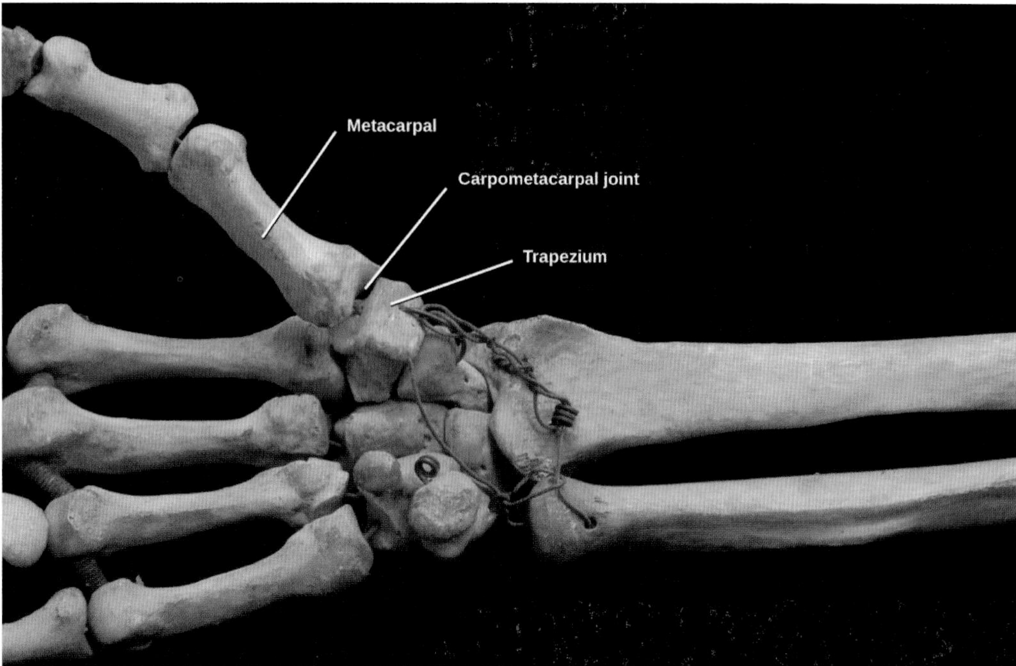

Figure 29.31 The carpometacarpal joints in the thumb are examples of saddle joints. (credit: modification of work by Brian C. Goss)

Ball-and-Socket Joints

Ball-and-socket joints possess a rounded, ball-like end of one bone fitting into a cuplike socket of another bone. This organization allows the greatest range of motion, as all movement types are possible in all directions. Examples of ball-and-socket joints are the shoulder and hip joints (Figure 29.32).

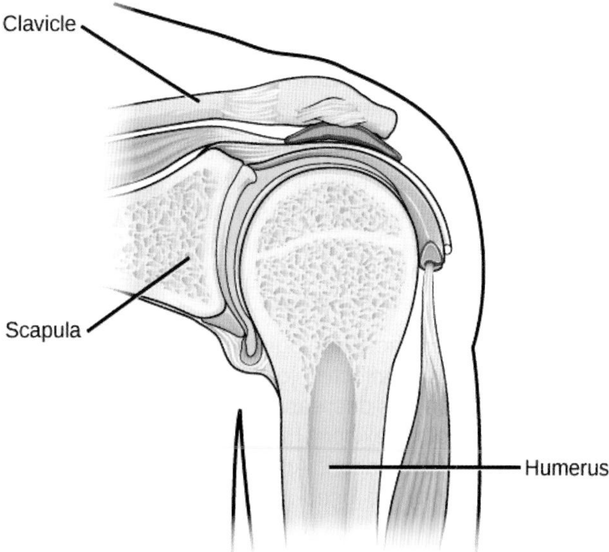

Figure 29.32 The shoulder joint is an example of a ball-and-socket joint.

Watch this animation (http://openstaxcollege.org/l/synovial_joints) showing the six types of synovial joints.

The shoulder and hip joints are an example of a ball-and-socket joint which _____.

a. permits extension

b. allows only gliding movement

c. allows abduction or adduction

d. allows rotation

career CONNECTION

Rheumatologist

Rheumatologists are medical doctors who specialize in the diagnosis and treatment of disorders of the joints, muscles, and bones. They diagnose and treat diseases such as arthritis, musculoskeletal disorders, osteoporosis, and autoimmune diseases such as ankylosing spondylitis and rheumatoid arthritis.

Rheumatoid arthritis (RA) is an inflammatory disorder that primarily affects the synovial joints of the hands, feet, and cervical spine. Affected joints become swollen, stiff, and painful. Although it is known that RA is an autoimmune disease in which the body's immune system mistakenly attacks healthy tissue, the cause of RA remains unknown. Immune cells from the blood enter joints and the synovium causing cartilage breakdown, swelling, and inflammation of the joint lining. Breakdown of cartilage causes bones to rub against each other causing pain. RA is more common in women than men and the age of onset is usually 40–50 years of age.

Rheumatologists can diagnose RA on the basis of symptoms such as joint inflammation and pain, X-ray and MRI imaging, and blood tests. Arthrography is a type of medical imaging of joints that uses a contrast agent, such as a dye, that is opaque to X-rays. This allows the soft tissue structures of joints—such as cartilage, tendons, and ligaments—to be visualized. An arthrogram differs from a regular X-ray by showing the surface of soft tissues lining the joint in addition to joint bones. An arthrogram allows early degenerative changes in joint cartilage to be detected before bones become affected.

There is currently no cure for RA; however, rheumatologists have a number of treatment options available. Early stages can be treated with rest of the affected joints by using a cane or by using joint splints that minimize inflammation. When inflammation has decreased, exercise can be used to strengthen the muscles that surround the joint and to maintain joint flexibility. If joint damage is more extensive, medications can be used to relieve pain and decrease inflammation. Anti-inflammatory drugs such as aspirin, topical pain relievers, and corticosteroid injections may be used. Surgery may be required in cases in which joint damage is severe.

29.4 | Muscle Contraction and Locomotion

In this section, you will explore the following questions:

- What are the different types of muscle tissue?
- What is the role of muscle contraction in locomotion?

Connection for AP® Courses

Muscles move bones, and, in turn, muscle contraction is dependent upon input from the nervous systems. The activities at the neuromuscular junction are similar to the activities occurring at the synapses between neurons.

There are approximately 650 skeletal muscles in the human body, each of which is composed of muscle fibers. (The body also contains specialized smooth and cardiac muscle tissue.) In addition to the collection of organelles typical of eukaryotic cells, each muscle fiber contains myofibrils, which, in turn, consist of arrangements of protein filaments called actin and myosin. In the sliding filament model of muscle contraction, the thicker myosin filaments have cross-bridges that attach and detach to thinner actin filaments. The binding of myosin to actin causes the actin filaments to slide, shortening the muscle fiber. ATP produced in cellular respiration provides the energy needed for contraction. However, contraction requires a signal from the nervous system (excitation-contraction coupling).

Nerve impulses traveling down motor neurons cause the release of the acetylcholine from vesicles in the axon terminus into the synapse between the neuron and the muscle fiber. Acetylcholine binds to receptors on the plasma membrane (sarcolemma) of the muscle fiber, allowing an action potential to move to the endoplasmic reticulum where calcium ions are stored. When Ca^{2+} is released in response to the change in voltage, it binds to actin, causing actin filaments to shift position and revealing myosin binding sites for the cross-bridges. The muscle contracts until the nerve impulse stops and Ca^{2+} returns to its storage sites. The enzyme acetylcholinesterase removes lingering acetylcholine from the synaptic cleft.

Information presented and the examples highlighted in the section support concepts outlined in Big Idea 4 of the AP® Biology Curriculum Framework. The AP® Learning Objectives listed in the Curriculum Framework provide a transparent foundation for the AP® Biology course, an inquiry-based laboratory experience, instructional activities, and AP® exam questions. A learning objective merges required content with one or more of the seven science practices.

Big Idea 4	Biological systems interact, and these systems and their interactions possess complex properties.
Enduring Understanding 4.A	Interactions within biological systems lead to complex properties.
Essential Knowledge	**4.A.4** Organisms exhibit complex properties due to interactions between their constituent parts.
Science Practice	**3.3** The student can evaluate scientific questions.
Learning Objective	**4.8** The student is able to evaluate scientific questions concerning organisms that exhibit complex properties due to the interaction of their constituent parts.
Essential Knowledge	**4.A.4** Organisms exhibit complex properties due to interactions between their constituent parts.
Science Practice	**6.4** The student can make claims and predictions about natural phenomena based on scientific theories and models.
Learning Objective	**4.9** The student is able to predict the effects of a change in a component(s) of a biological system on the functionality of an organism(s).
Essential Knowledge	**4.A.4** Organisms exhibit complex properties due to interactions between their constituent parts.

Science Practice	**1.3** The student can refine representations and models of natural or man-made phenomena and systems in the domain.
Learning Objective	**4.10** The student is able to refine representations and models to illustrate biocomplexity due to interactions of the constituent parts.

Muscle cells are specialized for contraction. Muscles allow for motions such as walking, and they also facilitate bodily processes such as respiration and digestion. The body contains three types of muscle tissue: skeletal muscle, cardiac muscle, and smooth muscle (Figure 29.33).

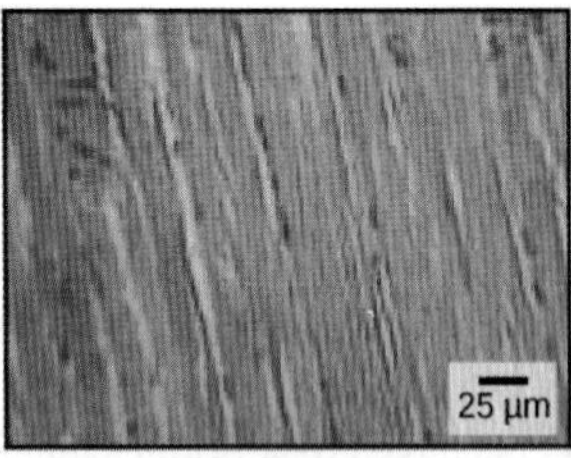

Skeletal muscle

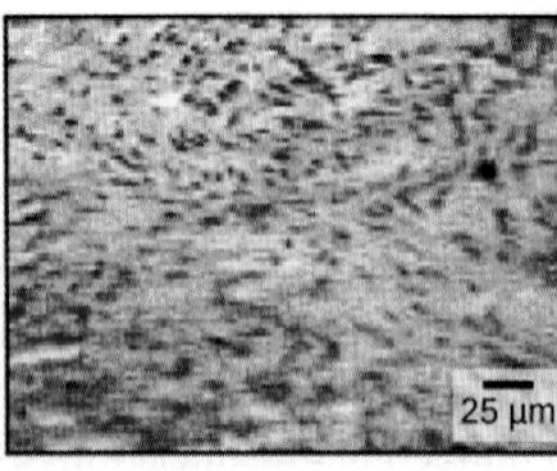

Smooth muscle

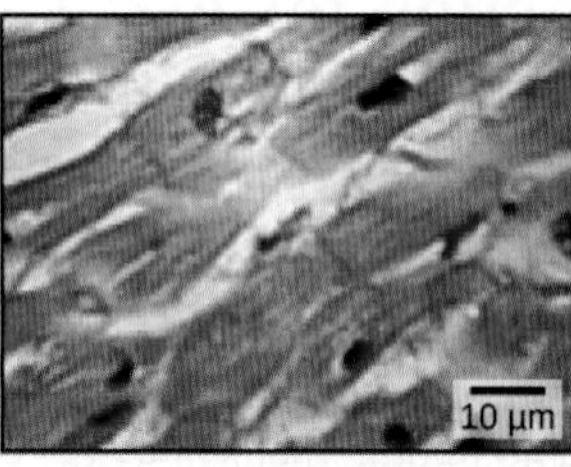

Cardiac muscle

Figure 29.33 The body contains three types of muscle tissue: skeletal muscle, smooth muscle, and cardiac muscle, visualized here using light microscopy. Smooth muscle cells are short, tapered at each end, and have only one plump nucleus in each. Cardiac muscle cells are branched and striated, but short. The cytoplasm may branch, and they have one nucleus in the center of the cell. (credit: modification of work by NCI, NIH; scale-bar data from Matt Russell)

Skeletal muscle tissue forms skeletal muscles, which attach to bones or skin and control locomotion and any movement that can be consciously controlled. Because it can be controlled by thought, skeletal muscle is also called voluntary muscle. Skeletal muscles are long and cylindrical in appearance; when viewed under a microscope, skeletal muscle tissue has a striped or striated appearance. The striations are caused by the regular arrangement of contractile proteins (actin and myosin). **Actin** is a globular contractile protein that interacts with **myosin** for muscle contraction. Skeletal muscle also has multiple nuclei present in a single cell.

Smooth muscle tissue occurs in the walls of hollow organs such as the intestines, stomach, and urinary bladder, and around passages such as the respiratory tract and blood vessels. Smooth muscle has no striations, is not under voluntary control, has only one nucleus per cell, is tapered at both ends, and is called involuntary muscle.

Cardiac muscle tissue is only found in the heart, and cardiac contractions pump blood throughout the body and maintain blood pressure. Like skeletal muscle, cardiac muscle is striated, but unlike skeletal muscle, cardiac muscle cannot be consciously controlled and is called involuntary muscle. It has one nucleus per cell, is branched, and is distinguished by the presence of intercalated disks.

Skeletal Muscle Fiber Structure

Each skeletal muscle fiber is a skeletal muscle cell. These cells are incredibly large, with diameters of up to 100 µm and lengths of up to 30 cm. The plasma membrane of a skeletal muscle fiber is called the **sarcolemma**. The sarcolemma is the site of action potential conduction, which triggers muscle contraction. Within each muscle fiber are **myofibrils**—long cylindrical structures that lie parallel to the muscle fiber. Myofibrils run the entire length of the muscle fiber, and because they are only approximately 1.2 µm in diameter, hundreds to thousands can be found inside one muscle fiber. They attach to the sarcolemma at their ends, so that as myofibrils shorten, the entire muscle cell contracts (Figure 29.34).

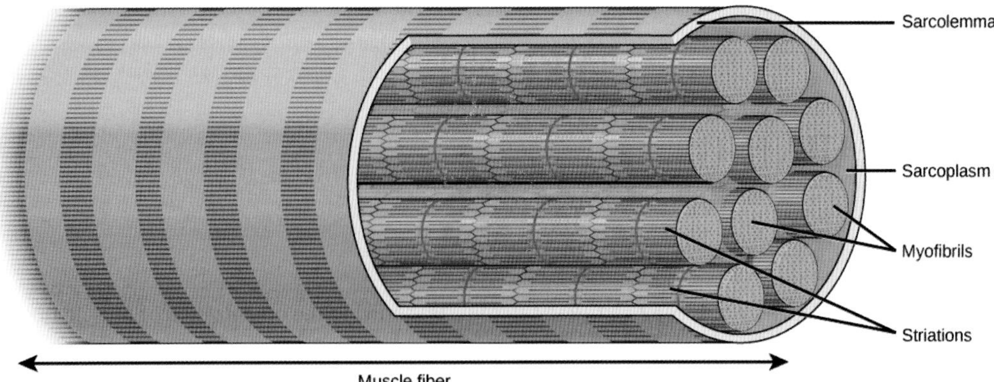

Figure 29.34 A skeletal muscle cell is surrounded by a plasma membrane called the sarcolemma with a cytoplasm called the sarcoplasm. A muscle fiber is composed of many fibrils, packaged into orderly units.

The striated appearance of skeletal muscle tissue is a result of repeating bands of the proteins actin and myosin that are present along the length of myofibrils. Dark A bands and light I bands repeat along myofibrils, and the alignment of myofibrils in the cell causes the entire cell to appear striated or banded.

Each I band has a dense line running vertically through the middle called a Z disc or Z line. The Z discs mark the border of units called **sarcomeres**, which are the functional units of skeletal muscle. One sarcomere is the space between two consecutive Z discs and contains one entire A band and two halves of an I band, one on either side of the A band. A myofibril is composed of many sarcomeres running along its length, and as the sarcomeres individually contract, the myofibrils and muscle cells shorten (Figure 29.35).

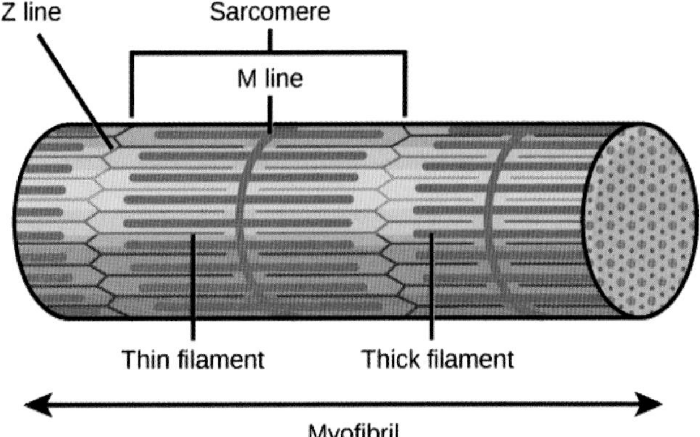

Figure 29.35 A sarcomere is the region from one Z line to the next Z line. Many sarcomeres are present in a myofibril, resulting in the striation pattern characteristic of skeletal muscle.

Myofibrils are composed of smaller structures called **myofilaments**. There are two main types of filaments: thick filaments and thin filaments; each has different compositions and locations. **Thick filaments** occur only in the A band of a myofibril. **Thin filaments** attach to a protein in the Z disc called alpha-actinin and occur across the entire length of the I band and partway into the A band. The region at which thick and thin filaments overlap has a dense appearance, as there is little space between the filaments. Thin filaments do not extend all the way into the A bands, leaving a central region of the A band that only contains thick filaments. This central region of the A band looks slightly lighter than the rest of the A band and is called the H zone. The middle of the H zone has a vertical line called the M line, at which accessory proteins hold together thick filaments. Both the Z disc and the M line hold myofilaments in place to maintain the structural arrangement and layering of the myofibril. Myofibrils are connected to each other by intermediate, or desmin, filaments that attach to the Z disc.

Thick and thin filaments are themselves composed of proteins. Thick filaments are composed of the protein myosin. The tail of a myosin molecule connects with other myosin molecules to form the central region of a thick filament near the M line, whereas the heads align on either side of the thick filament where the thin filaments overlap. The primary component of thin filaments is the actin protein. Two other components of the thin filament are tropomyosin and troponin. Actin has binding sites for myosin attachment. Strands of tropomyosin block the binding sites and prevent actin–myosin interactions when the muscles are at rest. Troponin consists of three globular subunits. One subunit binds to tropomyosin, one subunit binds to actin, and one subunit binds Ca^{2+} ions.

View this animation (http://openstaxcollege.org/l/skeletal_muscle) showing the organization of muscle fibers.

____ are among the largest cells in the human body.

a. myofibrils

b. T-Tubules

c. muscle fibers

d. sarcomeres

Sliding Filament Model of Contraction

For a muscle cell to contract, the sarcomere must shorten. However, thick and thin filaments—the components of sarcomeres—do not shorten. Instead, they slide by one another, causing the sarcomere to shorten while the filaments remain the same length. The sliding filament theory of muscle contraction was developed to fit the differences observed in the named bands on the sarcomere at different degrees of muscle contraction and relaxation. The mechanism of contraction is the binding of myosin to actin, forming cross-bridges that generate filament movement (Figure 29.36).

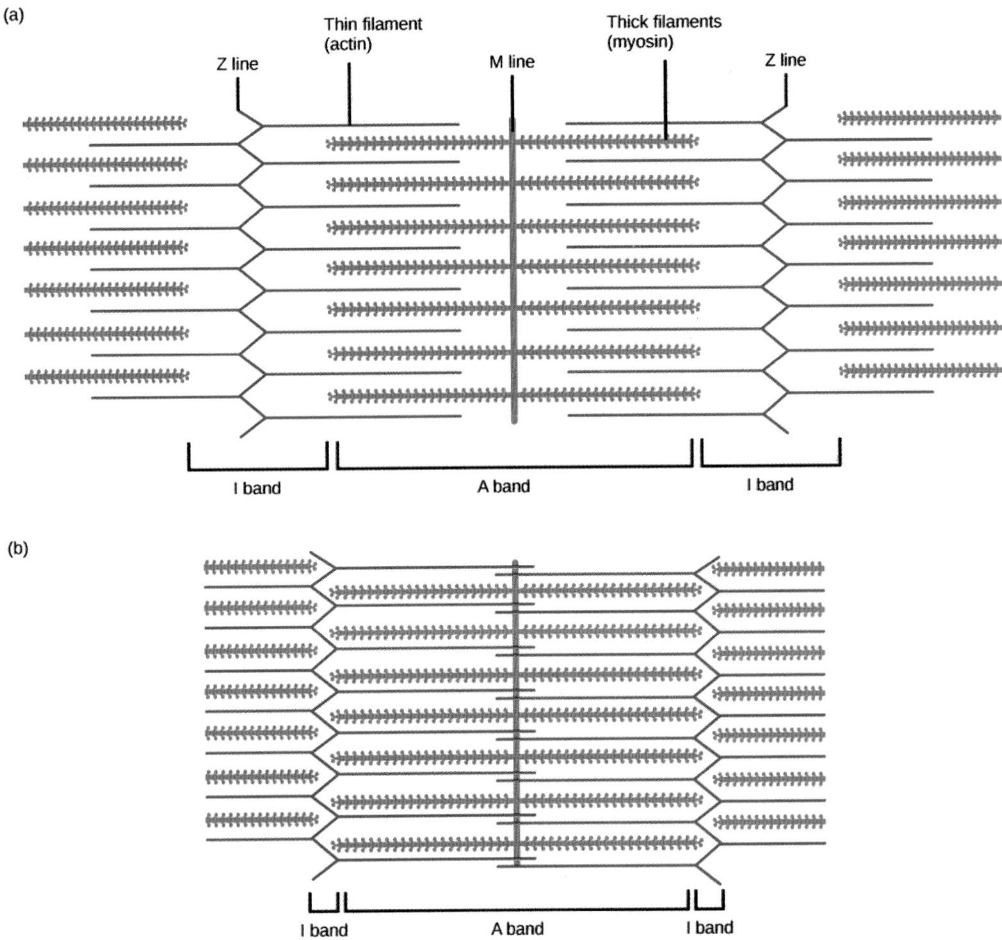

Figure 29.36 When (a) a sarcomere (b) contracts, the Z lines move closer together and the I band gets smaller. The A band stays the same width and, at full contraction, the thin filaments overlap.

When a sarcomere shortens, some regions shorten whereas others stay the same length. A sarcomere is defined as the distance between two consecutive Z discs or Z lines; when a muscle contracts, the distance between the Z discs is reduced. The H zone—the central region of the A zone—contains only thick filaments and is shortened during contraction. The I band contains only thin filaments and also shortens. The A band does not shorten—it remains the same length—but A bands of different sarcomeres move closer together during contraction, eventually disappearing. Thin filaments are pulled by the thick filaments toward the center of the sarcomere until the Z discs approach the thick filaments. The zone of overlap, in which thin filaments and thick filaments occupy the same area, increases as the thin filaments move inward.

ATP and Muscle Contraction

The motion of muscle shortening occurs as myosin heads bind to actin and pull the actin inwards. This action requires energy, which is provided by ATP. Myosin binds to actin at a binding site on the globular actin protein. Myosin has another binding site for ATP at which enzymatic activity hydrolyzes ATP to ADP, releasing an inorganic phosphate molecule and energy.

ATP binding causes myosin to release actin, allowing actin and myosin to detach from each other. After this happens, the newly bound ATP is converted to ADP and inorganic phosphate, P_i. The enzyme at the binding site on myosin is called ATPase. The energy released during ATP hydrolysis changes the angle of the myosin head into a "cocked" position. The myosin head is then in a position for further movement, possessing potential energy, but ADP and P_i are still attached. If actin binding sites are covered and unavailable, the myosin will remain in the high energy configuration with ATP hydrolyzed, but still attached.

If the actin binding sites are uncovered, a cross-bridge will form; that is, the myosin head spans the distance between the actin and myosin molecules. P_i is then released, allowing myosin to expend the stored energy as a conformational change. The myosin head moves toward the M line, pulling the actin along with it. As the actin is pulled, the filaments move approximately 10 nm toward the M line. This movement is called the power stroke, as it is the step at which force is produced. As the actin is pulled toward the M line, the sarcomere shortens and the muscle contracts.

When the myosin head is "cocked," it contains energy and is in a high-energy configuration. This energy is expended as the myosin head moves through the power stroke; at the end of the power stroke, the myosin head is in a low-energy position. After the power stroke, ADP is released; however, the cross-bridge formed is still in place, and actin and myosin are bound together. ATP can then attach to myosin, which allows the cross-bridge cycle to start again and further muscle contraction can occur (Figure 29.37).

Watch this video (http://openstaxcollege.org/l/contract_muscle) explaining how a muscle contraction is signaled.

Why can't actin and myosin interact in the absence of calcium?

a. Actin binding sites are covered by acetylcholine to which the troponin complex is attached. This complex is calcium sensitive. Troponin binds to the calcium and moves the tropomyosin binding site.

b. Myosin binding sites are covered by the troponin complex to which is attached tropomyosin. Tropomyosin is calcium sensitive. It binds to the calcium and moves the troponin binding site.

c. Actin binding sites are covered by tropomyosin to which the troponin complex is attached. This complex is calcium sensitive. Troponin binds to the calcium and moves the tropomyosin binding site.

d. Myosin binding sites are covered by tropomyosin to which the troponin complex is attached. This complex is calcium sensitive. Troponin binds to the calcium and moves the tropomyosin binding site.

visual CONNECTION

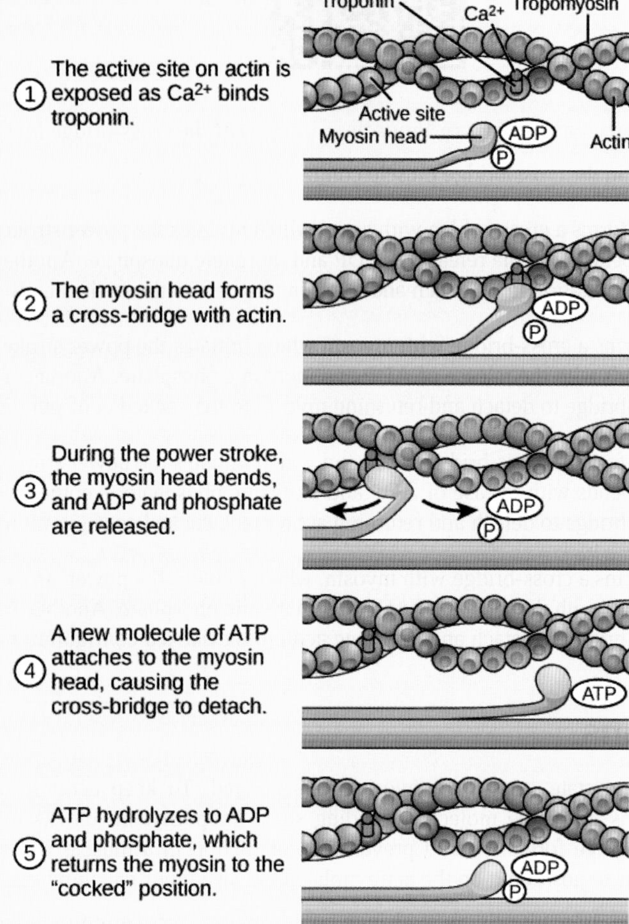
Troponin
Ca^{2+}
Tropomyosin
The active site on actin is exposed as Ca^{2+} binds troponin.
Active site
Myosin head
ADP
P
Actin
The myosin head forms a cross-bridge with actin.
ADP
P
During the power stroke, the myosin head bends, and ADP and phosphate are released.
ADP
P
A new molecule of ATP attaches to the myosin head, causing the cross-bridge to detach.
ATP
ATP hydrolyzes to ADP and phosphate, which returns the myosin to the "cocked" position.
ADP
P

Figure 29.37 The cross-bridge muscle contraction cycle, which is triggered by Ca^{2+} binding to the actin active site, is shown. With each contraction cycle, actin moves relative to myosin.

Which of the following statements about the "power stroke" of muscle contraction is true?

a. It occurs when ATP is hydrolyzed to ADP and phosphate.
b. It occurs a new molecule of ATP attaches to the myosin head.
c. It occurs when ADP and phosphate separate from the myosin head.
d. It occurs when ADP and phosphate separate from the actin active site.

View this animation (http://openstaxcollege.org/l/muscle_contract) of the cross-bridge muscle contraction.

Describe the steps involved in the cross-bridge muscle contraction process.

a. The myosin head forms a cross-bridge with actin, which initiates the power stroke. During the power stroke, the myosin head bends with the release of ADP and inorganic phosphate. Another ATP binds to the myosin head, causing the cross-bridge to detach and returning myosin to the cocked configuration.

b. The actin head forms a cross-bridge with myosin which initiates the power stroke. During the power stroke, the actin head bends with the release of ADP and inorganic phosphate. Another ATP binds the myosin head, causing the cross-bridge to detach and returning myosin to the cocked configuration.

c. The myosin head forms a cross-bridge with actin which initiates the power stroke. During the power stroke, the myosin head bends with release of ADP and inorganic phosphate. Another ATP binds to the actin head, causing the cross-bridge to detach and returning actin to the cocked configuration.

d. The actin head forms a cross-bridge with myosin, which initiates the power stroke. During the power stroke, the actin head bends with the release of ADP and inorganic phosphate. Another ATP binds to the actin head, causing the cross-bridge to detach and returning actin to the cocked configuration.

Regulatory Proteins

When a muscle is in a resting state, actin and myosin are separated. To keep actin from binding to the active site on myosin, regulatory proteins block the molecular binding sites. **Tropomyosin** blocks myosin binding sites on actin molecules, preventing cross-bridge formation and preventing contraction in a muscle without nervous input. **Troponin** binds to tropomyosin and helps to position it on the actin molecule; it also binds calcium ions.

To enable a muscle contraction, tropomyosin must change conformation, uncovering the myosin-binding site on an actin molecule and allowing cross-bridge formation. This can only happen in the presence of calcium, which is kept at extremely low concentrations in the sarcoplasm. If present, calcium ions bind to troponin, causing conformational changes in troponin that allow tropomyosin to move away from the myosin binding sites on actin. Once the tropomyosin is removed, a cross-bridge can form between actin and myosin, triggering contraction. Cross-bridge cycling continues until Ca^{2+} ions and ATP are no longer available and tropomyosin again covers the binding sites on actin.

Excitation–Contraction Coupling

Excitation–contraction coupling is the link (transduction) between the action potential generated in the sarcolemma and the start of a muscle contraction. The trigger for calcium release from the sarcoplasmic reticulum into the sarcoplasm is a neural signal. Each skeletal muscle fiber is controlled by a motor neuron, which conducts signals from the brain or spinal cord to the muscle. The area of the sarcolemma on the muscle fiber that interacts with the neuron is called the **motor end plate**. The end of the neuron's axon is called the synaptic terminal, and it does not actually contact the motor end plate. A small space called the synaptic cleft separates the synaptic terminal from the motor end plate. Electrical signals travel along the neuron's axon, which branches through the muscle and connects to individual muscle fibers at a neuromuscular junction.

The ability of cells to communicate electrically requires that the cells expend energy to create an electrical gradient across their cell membranes. This charge gradient is carried by ions, which are differentially distributed across the membrane. Each ion exerts an electrical influence and a concentration influence. Just as milk will eventually mix with coffee without the need to stir, ions also distribute themselves evenly, if they are permitted to do so. In this case, they are not permitted to return to an evenly mixed state.

The sodium–potassium ATPase uses cellular energy to move K^+ ions inside the cell and Na^+ ions outside. This alone accumulates a small electrical charge, but a big concentration gradient. There is lots of K^+ in the cell and lots of Na^+ outside the cell. Potassium is able to leave the cell through K^+ channels that are open 90% of the time, and it does. However, Na^+

channels are rarely open, so Na^+ remains outside the cell. When K^+ leaves the cell, obeying its concentration gradient, that effectively leaves a negative charge behind. So at rest, there is a large concentration gradient for Na^+ to enter the cell, and there is an accumulation of negative charges left behind in the cell. This is the resting membrane potential. Potential in this context means a separation of electrical charge that is capable of doing work. It is measured in volts, just like a battery. However, the transmembrane potential is considerably smaller (0.07 V); therefore, the small value is expressed as millivolts (mV) or 70 mV. Because the inside of a cell is negative compared with the outside, a minus sign signifies the excess of negative charges inside the cell, −70 mV.

If an event changes the permeability of the membrane to Na^+ ions, they will enter the cell. That will change the voltage. This is an electrical event, called an action potential, that can be used as a cellular signal. Communication occurs between nerves and muscles through neurotransmitters. Neuron action potentials cause the release of neurotransmitters from the synaptic terminal into the synaptic cleft, where they can then diffuse across the synaptic cleft and bind to a receptor molecule on the motor end plate. The motor end plate possesses junctional folds—folds in the sarcolemma that create a large surface area for the neurotransmitter to bind to receptors. The receptors are actually sodium channels that open to allow the passage of Na^+ into the cell when they receive neurotransmitter signal.

Acetylcholine (ACh) is a neurotransmitter released by motor neurons that binds to receptors in the motor end plate. Neurotransmitter release occurs when an action potential travels down the motor neuron's axon, resulting in altered permeability of the synaptic terminal membrane and an influx of calcium. The Ca^{2+} ions allow synaptic vesicles to move to and bind with the presynaptic membrane (on the neuron), and release neurotransmitter from the vesicles into the synaptic cleft. Once released by the synaptic terminal, ACh diffuses across the synaptic cleft to the motor end plate, where it binds with ACh receptors. As a neurotransmitter binds, these ion channels open, and Na^+ ions cross the membrane into the muscle cell. This reduces the voltage difference between the inside and outside of the cell, which is called depolarization. As ACh binds at the motor end plate, this depolarization is called an end-plate potential. The depolarization then spreads along the sarcolemma, creating an action potential as sodium channels adjacent to the initial depolarization site sense the change in voltage and open. The action potential moves across the entire cell, creating a wave of depolarization.

ACh is broken down by the enzyme **acetylcholinesterase** (AChE) into acetyl and choline. AChE resides in the synaptic cleft, breaking down ACh so that it does not remain bound to ACh receptors, which would cause unwanted extended muscle contraction (**Figure 29.38**).

visual CONNECTION

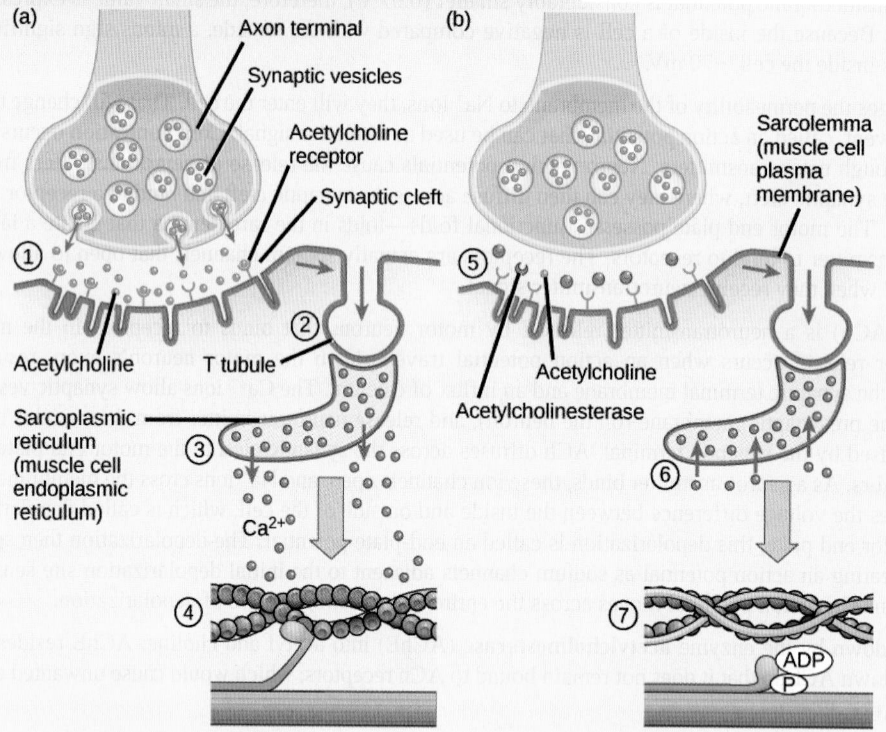

1. Acetylcholine released from the axon terminal binds to receptors on the sarcolemma.
2. An action potential is generated and travels down the T tubule.
3. Ca^{2+} is released from the sarcoplasmic reticulum in response to the change in voltage.
4. Ca^{2+} binds troponin; Cross-bridges form between actin and myosin.
5. Acetylcholinesterase removes acetylcholine from the synaptic cleft.
6. Ca^{2+} is transported back into the sarcoplasmic reticulum.
7. Tropomyosin binds active sites on actin causing the cross-bridge to detach.

Figure 29.38 This diagram shows excitation-contraction coupling in a skeletal muscle contraction. The sarcoplasmic reticulum is a specialized endoplasmic reticulum found in muscle cells.

Where are the Ca^{2+} ions stored?

a. Sarcomere
b. sarcoplasm
c. sarcolemma
d. sarcoplasmic reticulum

After depolarization, the membrane returns to its resting state. This is called repolarization, during which voltage-gated sodium channels close. Potassium channels continue at 90% conductance. Because the plasma membrane sodium–potassium ATPase always transports ions, the resting state (negatively charged inside relative to the outside) is restored. The period immediately following the transmission of an impulse in a nerve or muscle, in which a neuron or muscle cell regains its ability to transmit another impulse, is called the refractory period. During the refractory period, the membrane cannot generate another action potential. . The refractory period allows the voltage-sensitive ion channels to return to their resting configurations. The sodium potassium ATPase continually moves Na^+ back out of the cell and K^+ back into the cell, and the K^+ leaks out leaving negative charge behind. Very quickly, the membrane repolarizes, so that it can again be depolarized.

Control of Muscle Tension

Neural control initiates the formation of actin–myosin cross-bridges, leading to the sarcomere shortening involved in muscle contraction. These contractions extend from the muscle fiber through connective tissue to pull on bones, causing skeletal movement. The pull exerted by a muscle is called tension, and the amount of force created by this tension can vary. This enables the same muscles to move very light objects and very heavy objects. In individual muscle fibers, the amount of tension produced depends on the cross-sectional area of the muscle fiber and the frequency of neural stimulation.

The number of cross-bridges formed between actin and myosin determine the amount of tension that a muscle fiber can produce. Cross-bridges can only form where thick and thin filaments overlap, allowing myosin to bind to actin. If more cross-bridges are formed, more myosin will pull on actin, and more tension will be produced.

The ideal length of a sarcomere during production of maximal tension occurs when thick and thin filaments overlap to the greatest degree. If a sarcomere at rest is stretched past an ideal resting length, thick and thin filaments do not overlap to the greatest degree, and fewer cross-bridges can form. This results in fewer myosin heads pulling on actin, and less tension is produced. As a sarcomere is shortened, the zone of overlap is reduced as the thin filaments reach the H zone, which is composed of myosin tails. Because it is myosin heads that form cross-bridges, actin will not bind to myosin in this zone, reducing the tension produced by this myofiber. If the sarcomere is shortened even more, thin filaments begin to overlap with each other—reducing cross-bridge formation even further, and producing even less tension. Conversely, if the sarcomere is stretched to the point at which thick and thin filaments do not overlap at all, no cross-bridges are formed and no tension is produced. This amount of stretching does not usually occur because accessory proteins, internal sensory nerves, and connective tissue oppose extreme stretching.

The primary variable determining force production is the number of myofibers within the muscle that receive an action potential from the neuron that controls that fiber. When using the biceps to pick up a pencil, the motor cortex of the brain only signals a few neurons of the biceps, and only a few myofibers respond. In vertebrates, each myofiber responds fully if stimulated. When picking up a piano, the motor cortex signals all of the neurons in the biceps and every myofiber participates. This is close to the maximum force the muscle can produce. As mentioned above, increasing the frequency of action potentials (the number of signals per second) can increase the force a bit more, because the tropomyosin is flooded with calcium.

science practices CONNECTION for AP® Courses

Think About It

- The deadly nerve gas Sarin irreversibly inhibits the enzyme, acetylcholinesterase. What effect would Sarin have on muscle contraction?
- How are the activities at the neuromuscular junction similar to the activities occurring at the synapses between neurons?

KEY TERMS

abduction when a bone moves away from the midline of the body

acetylcholinesterase (AChE) enzyme that breaks down ACh into acetyl and choline

actin globular contractile protein that interacts with myosin for muscle contraction

adduction movement of the limbs inward after abduction

amphiarthrosis joint that allows slight movement; includes syndesmoses and symphyses

angular movement produced when the angle between the bones of a joint changes

appendicular skeleton composed of the bones of the upper limbs, which function to grasp and manipulate objects, and the lower limbs, which permit locomotion

appositional growth increase in the diameter of bones by the addition of bone tissue at the surface of bones

articulation any place where two bones are joined

auditory ossicle (also, middle ear) transduces sounds from the air into vibrations in the fluid-filled cochlea

axial skeleton forms the central axis of the body and includes the bones of the skull, the ossicles of the middle ear, the hyoid bone of the throat, the vertebral column, and the thoracic cage (ribcage)

ball-and-socket joint joint with a rounded, ball-like end of one bone fitting into a cuplike socket of another bone

bone (also, osseous tissue) connective tissue that constitutes the endoskeleton

bone remodeling replacement of old bone tissue by new bone tissue

calcification process of deposition of mineral salts in the collagen fiber matrix that crystallizes and hardens the tissue

cardiac muscle tissue muscle tissue found only in the heart; cardiac contractions pump blood throughout the body and maintain blood pressure

carpus eight bones that comprise the wrist

cartilaginous joint joint in which the bones are connected by cartilage

circumduction movement of a limb in a circular motion.

clavicle S-shaped bone that positions the arms laterally

compact bone forms the hard external layer of all bones

condyloid joint oval-shaped end of one bone fitting into a similarly oval-shaped hollow of another bone

coxal bone hip bone

cranial bone one of eight bones that form the cranial cavity that encloses the brain and serves as an attachment site for the muscles of the head and neck

depression movement downward of a bone, such as after the shoulders are shrugged and the scapulae return to their normal position from an elevated position; opposite of elevation

diaphysis central shaft of bone, contains bone marrow in a marrow cavity

diarthrosis joint that allows for free movement of the joint; found in synovial joints

dorsiflexion bending at the ankle such that the toes are lifted toward the knee

elevation movement of a bone upward, such as when the shoulders are shrugged, lifting the scapulae

endochondral ossification process of bone development from hyaline cartilage

endoskeleton skeleton of living cells that produce a hard, mineralized tissue located within the soft tissue of organisms

epiphyseal plate region between the diaphysis and epiphysis that is responsible for the lengthwise growth of long bones

epiphysis rounded end of bone, covered with articular cartilage and filled with red bone marrow, which produces blood cells

eversion movement of the sole of the foot outward, away from the midline of the body; opposite of inversion

exoskeleton a secreted cellular product external skeleton that consists of a hard encasement on the surface of an organism

extension movement in which the angle between the bones of a joint increases; opposite of flexion

facial bone one of the 14 bones that form the face; provides cavities for the sense organs (eyes, mouth, and nose) and attachment points for facial muscles

femur (also, thighbone) longest, heaviest, and strongest bone in the body

fibrous joint joint held together by fibrous connective tissue

fibula (also, calf bone) parallels and articulates with the tibia

flat bone thin and relatively broad bone found where extensive protection of organs is required or where broad surfaces of muscle attachment are required

flexion movement in which the angle between the bones decreases; opposite of extension

forearm extends from the elbow to the wrist and consists of two bones: the ulna and the radius

gliding movement when relatively flat bone surfaces move past each other

gomphosis the joint in which the tooth fits into the socket like a peg

Haversian canal contains the bone's blood vessels and nerve fibers

hinge joint slightly rounded end of one bone fits into the slightly hollow end of the other bone

humerus only bone of the arm

hydrostatic skeleton skeleton that consists of aqueous fluid held under pressure in a closed body compartment

hyoid bone lies below the mandible in the front of the neck

hyperextension extension past the regular anatomical position

intervertebral disc composed of fibrous cartilage; lies between adjacent vertebrae from the second cervical vertebra to the sacrum

intramembranous ossification process of bone development from fibrous membranes

inversion soles of the feet moving inward, toward the midline of the body

irregular bone bone with complex shapes; examples include vertebrae and hip bones

joint point at which two or more bones meet

lamella layer of compact tissue that surrounds a central canal called the Haversian canal

lateral rotation rotation away from the midline of the body

long bone bone that is longer than wide, and has a shaft and two ends

lower limb consists of the thigh, the leg, and the foot

medial rotation rotation toward the midline of the body

metacarpus five bones that comprise the palm

metatarsal one of the five bones of the foot

motor end plate sarcolemma of the muscle fiber that interacts with the neuron

myofibril long cylindrical structures that lie parallel to the muscle fiber

myofilament small structures that make up myofibrils

myosin contractile protein that interacts with actin for muscle contraction

opposition movement of the thumb toward the fingers of the same hand, making it possible to grasp and hold objects

osseous tissue connective tissue that constitutes the endoskeleton

ossification (also, osteogenesis) process of bone formation by osteoblasts

osteoblast bone cell responsible for bone formation

osteoclast large bone cells with up to 50 nuclei, responsible for bone remodeling

osteocyte mature bone cells and the main cell in bone tissue

osteon cylindrical structure aligned parallel to the long axis of the bone

patella (also, kneecap) triangular bone that lies anterior to the knee joint

pectoral girdle bones that transmit the force generated by the upper limbs to the axial skeleton

pelvic girdle bones that transmit the force generated by the lower limbs to the axial skeleton

phalange one of the bones of the fingers or toes

pivot joint joint with the rounded end of one bone fitting into a ring formed by the other bone

planar joint joint with bones whose articulating surfaces are flat

plantar flexion bending at the ankle such that the heel is lifted, such as when standing on the toes

pronation movement in which the palm faces backward

protraction anterior movement of a bone in the horizontal plane

radius bone located along the lateral (thumb) side of the forearm; articulates with the humerus at the elbow

resorption process by which osteoclasts release minerals stored in bones

retraction movement in which a joint moves back into position after protraction

rib one of 12 pairs of long, curved bones that attach to the thoracic vertebrae and curve toward the front of the body to form the ribcage

rotational movement movement of a bone as it rotates around its own longitudinal axis

saddle joint joint with concave and convex portions that fit together; named because the ends of each bone resemble a saddle

sarcolemma plasma membrane of a skeletal muscle fiber

sarcomere functional unit of skeletal muscle

scapula flat, triangular bone located at the posterior pectoral girdle

sesamoid bone small, flat bone shaped like a sesame seed; develops inside tendons

short bone bone that has the same width and length, giving it a cube-like shape

skeletal muscle tissue forms skeletal muscles, which attach to bones and control locomotion and any movement that can be consciously controlled

skull bone that supports the structures of the face and protects the brain

smooth muscle tissue occurs in the walls of hollow organs such as the intestines, stomach, and urinary bladder, and around passages such as the respiratory tract and blood vessels

spongy bone tissue forms the inner layer of all bones

sternum (also, breastbone) long, flat bone located at the front of the chest

supination movement of the radius and ulna bones of the forearm so that the palm faces forward

suture short fiber of connective tissue that holds the skull bones tightly in place; found only in the skull

suture bone small, flat, irregularly shaped bone that forms between the flat bones of the cranium

symphysis hyaline cartilage covers the end of the bone, but the connection between bones occurs through fibrocartilage; symphyses are found at the joints between vertebrae

synarthrosis joint that is immovable

synchondrosis bones joined by hyaline cartilage; synchondroses are found in the epiphyseal plates of growing bones in children

syndesmosis joint in which the bones are connected by a band of connective tissue, allowing for more movement than in a suture

synovial joint only joint that has a space between the adjoining bones

tarsal one of the seven bones of the ankle

thick filament a group of myosin molecules

thin filament two polymers of actin wound together along with tropomyosin and troponin

thoracic cage (also, ribcage) skeleton of the chest, which consists of the ribs, thoracic vertebrae, sternum, and costal cartilages

tibia (also, shinbone) large bone of the leg that is located directly below the knee

trabeculae lamellae that are arranged as rods or plates

tropomyosin acts to block myosin binding sites on actin molecules, preventing cross-bridge formation and preventing contraction until a muscle receives a neuron signal

troponin binds to tropomyosin and helps to position it on the actin molecule, and also binds calcium ions

ulna bone located on the medial aspect (pinky-finger side) of the forearm

vertebral column (also, spine) surrounds and protects the spinal cord, supports the head, and acts as an attachment point for ribs and muscles of the back and neck

CHAPTER SUMMARY

29.1 Types of Skeletal Systems

The three types of skeleton designs are hydrostatic skeletons, exoskeletons, and endoskeletons. A hydrostatic skeleton is formed by a fluid-filled compartment held under hydrostatic pressure; movement is created by the muscles producing pressure on the fluid. An exoskeleton is a hard external skeleton that protects the outer surface of an organism and enables movement through muscles attached on the inside. An endoskeleton is an internal skeleton composed of hard, mineralized tissue that also enables movement by attachment to muscles. The human skeleton is an endoskeleton that is composed of the axial and appendicular skeleton. The axial skeleton is composed of the bones of the skull, ossicles of the ear, hyoid bone, vertebral column, and ribcage. The skull consists of eight cranial bones and 14 facial bones. Six bones make up the ossicles of the middle ear, while the hyoid bone is located in the neck under the mandible. The vertebral column contains 26 bones, and it surrounds and protects the spinal cord. The thoracic cage consists of the sternum, ribs, thoracic vertebrae, and costal cartilages. The appendicular skeleton is made up of the limbs of the upper and lower limbs. The pectoral girdle is composed of the clavicles and the scapulae. The upper limb contains 30 bones in the arm, the forearm, and the hand. The pelvic girdle attaches the lower limbs to the axial skeleton. The lower limb includes the bones of the thigh, the leg, and the foot.

29.2 Bone

Bone, or osseous tissue, is connective tissue that includes specialized cells, mineral salts, and collagen fibers. The human skeleton can be divided into long bones, short bones, flat bones, and irregular bones. Compact bone tissue is composed of osteons and forms the external layer of all bones. Spongy bone tissue is composed of trabeculae and forms the inner part of all bones. Four types of cells compose bony tissue: osteocytes, osteoclasts, osteoprogenitor cells, and osteoblasts. Ossification is the process of bone formation by osteoblasts. Intramembranous ossification is the process of bone development from fibrous membranes. Endochondral ossification is the process of bone development from hyaline cartilage. Long bones lengthen as chondrocytes divide and secrete hyaline cartilage. Osteoblasts replace cartilage with bone. Appositional growth is the increase in the diameter of bones by the addition of bone tissue at the surface of bones. Bone remodeling involves the processes of bone deposition by osteoblasts and bone resorption by osteoclasts. Bone repair occurs in four stages and can take several months.

29.3 Joints and Skeletal Movement

The structural classification of joints divides them into bony, fibrous, cartilaginous, and synovial joints. The bones of fibrous joints are held together by fibrous connective tissue; the three types of fibrous joints are sutures, syndesomes, and gomphoses. Cartilaginous joints are joints in which the bones are connected by cartilage; the two types of cartilaginous joints are synchondroses and symphyses. Synovial joints are joints that have a space between the adjoining bones. The functional classification divides joints into three categories: synarthroses, amphiarthroses, and diarthroses. The movement of synovial joints can be classified as one of four different types: gliding, angular, rotational, or special movement. Gliding movements occur as relatively flat bone surfaces move past each other. Angular movements are produced when the angle between the bones of a joint changes. Rotational movement is the movement of a bone as it rotates around its own longitudinal axis. Special movements include inversion, eversion, protraction, retraction, elevation, depression, dorsiflexion, plantar flexion, supination, pronation, and opposition. Synovial joints are also classified into six different categories on the basis of the shape and structure of the joint: planar, hinge, pivot, condyloid, saddle, and ball-and-socket.

29.4 Muscle Contraction and Locomotion

The body contains three types of muscle tissue: skeletal muscle, cardiac muscle, and smooth muscle. Skeleton muscle tissue is composed of sarcomeres, the functional units of muscle tissue. Muscle contraction occurs when sarcomeres shorten, as thick and thin filaments slide past each other, which is called the sliding filament model of muscle contraction. ATP provides the energy for cross-bridge formation and filament sliding. Regulatory proteins, such as troponin and tropomyosin, control cross-bridge formation. Excitation–contraction coupling transduces the electrical signal of the neuron, via acetylcholine, to an electrical signal on the muscle membrane, which initiates force production. The number of muscle fibers contracting determines how much force the whole muscle produces.

REVIEW QUESTIONS

1. Which type of skeletal system of animals is formed by the pressure exerted by the aqueous contents of the coelom on surrounding organs?

a. hydrostatic skeleton

b. exoskeleton

c. axial skeleton

d. appendicular skeleton

2. The skeletal system is necessary to support the body, protect internal organs, and allow movement. Which of the following organisms must shed and then regenerate its skeletal system as it grows?

a. earthworm

b. lobster

c. snake

d. sea anemone

3. Which of the following is a role of the human vertebral column?

a. to protect the heart and lungs

b. to support the head

c. to attach the upper limbs to the axial skeleton

d. to permit locomotion

4. Abnormalities of the thoracic cage are relatively rare, but when they exist they can cause disorders. Which of the following would most be at risk if someone had a defective thoracic cage?

a. middle ear

b. brain

c. spinal cord

d. heart

5. Which type of skeletal system of animals is composed of a hard skeletal layer found on the exterior of the organism?

a. hydrostatic skeleton

b. exoskeleton

c. axial skeleton

d. appendicular skeleton

6. Which type of organism moves by peristaltic muscle contraction, extending its body in one direction, then shortening and pulling itself along a surface?

a. ants

b. lizards

c. sea stars

d. sponges

7. Which type of bone is cuboidal in shape and may be found in the wrist and ankle?

a. sesamoid bones

b. sutural bones

c. short bones

d. flat bones

8. The bones of human skeletons are classified by their shape. How does the structure of sesamoid bones differ from that of short bones?

a. Sesamoid bones are small and flat, whereas short bones are approximately equal in height and width.

b. Sesamoid bones are thin and broad, whereas short bones have a central shaft and two ends.

c. Sesamoid bones are small, flat, and irregularly shaped, whereas short bones are cuboidal in shape.

d. Sesamoid bones are thin and broad, whereas short bones are small and flat.

9. The cells responsible for bone resorption are_____.

a. osteoclasts

b. osteoblasts

c. fibroblasts

d. osteocytes

10. A patient was diagnosed with low calcium levels in the blood, which affected nervous system and muscle functions. You decide to examine the functioning of various cells composing the patient's bone tissue. Which type of bone cell is most likely dysfunctional?

a. osteoclasts

b. osteoblasts

c. osteoprogenitor cells

d. osteocytes

11. Which of the following bones or bone structures forms primarily due to endochondral ossification?

a. skull

b. clavicle

c. mandible

d. femur

12. What outcome might you expect in an individual with premature epiphyseal plate closure?

a. overly thick bones

b. short stature

c. tall stature

d. overly thin bones

13. Which type of bone has a central shaft and two rounded ends?

a. flat bones
b. irregular bones
c. sutural bones
d. long bones

14. Synchondroses and symphyses are connected by _____.

a. fibers
b. synovial fluid
c. cartilage
d. condyloid

15. _____ is a characteristic of the synovial fluid.

a. Stability
b. Lubrication
c. Minor movement
d. Increase of friction

16. Which of the following is an example of a pivot joint?

a. elbow
b. thumb
c. hip
d. the joint of the wrist

17. Synovial joints allow different types of movement. Turning your head to look over your shoulder is an example of _____.

a. abduction
b. medial rotation
c. lateral rotation
d. adduction

18. Which of the following is a fibrous joint?

a. suture
b. planar joint
c. hinge joint
d. pivot joint

19. Joints are classified based on the material composing the joint and the presence or absence of a cavity in the joint. Which of the following are the weakest joints?

a. synchondrosis
b. fibrous
c. synovial
d. symphyses

20. _____ muscles are also called voluntary muscles.

a. Cardiac
b. Smooth
c. Striated
d. Skeletal

21. Which of the following best describes a function of smooth muscle tissue?

a. It affects the flow of blood and blood pressure
b. It stimulates contraction of the heart
c. It changes your facial expression.
d. It maintains your posture.

22. In relaxed muscle, the myosin binding site on actin is blocked by _____.

a. ATP
b. tropomyosin
c. the cross-bridge
d. troponin

23. Which of the following statements does not accurately describe muscle contraction?

a. During muscle contraction, the sarcomere shortens.
b. During muscle contraction, the thick and thin filaments shorten.
c. During muscle contraction, the H zone shortens.
d. During muscle contraction, the A band does not shorten.

24. The small structures that make up myofibrils are called _____.

a. sarcolemma
b. myosins
c. myofilaments
d. sarcomeres

CRITICAL THINKING QUESTIONS

25. You discover an unusual new organism in the deep sea and are studying its skeletal system in a laboratory aquarium. The organism appears to have a radial body plan with a center fluid-filled cavity. If you remove fluid from its interior using a syringe, it seems to collapse somewhat. What kind of skeletal system does this organism likely have?

a. exoskeleton
b. hydrostatic skeleton or exoskeleton
c. hydrostatic skeleton
d. endoskeleton

26. You discover the carcass of an unusual new organism on the beach while on vacation. As a scientist, you decide to chemically analyze the carcass in order to characterize it. The chemical analysis reveals significant amounts of chitin. What other molecule might you also find associated with the skeletal system of this organism?

a. calcium carbonate
b. calcium phosphate
c. hydroxyapatite
d. magnesium carbonate

27. What types of issues related to bone function would you predict for an individual suffering from a genetic lysosomal storage disease?

a. Individuals may have deformities in the appendicular skeleton and possible phosphate homeostasis issues.
b. Individual may have skeletal deformities and possible calcium homeostasis issues.
c. Individuals may have axial skeleton deformities and possible calcium homeostasis issues.
d. Individual's brain would be more prone to injury and a possible calcium homeostasis issues.

28. A world-class pianist gets into a serious car accident. Injuries to which types of bones will most directly interfere with her career as a pianist?

a. Injuries to carpals, humerus, radius, ulna, clavicle, metacarpals, metatarsals, tarsals and various flat bones like scapulae would cause issues.
b. Injuries to carpals, humerus, radius, ulna, clavicle, metacarpals, phalanges and various flat bones like scapulae would cause issues.
c. Injuries to carpals, humerus, radius, ulna, clavicle, metacarpals, femur, tibia and various flat bones like scapulae would cause issues.
d. Injuries to carpals, humerus, femur, tibia, metatarsals, tarsals, phalanges and various flat bones like scapulae would cause issues.

29. What types of issues related to bone development and repair would you expect associated with someone suffering from osteogenesis imperfecta, a genetic disorder most commonly resulting from defects in collagen production and processing?

a. Bones are abnormally weak, brittle and highly flexible. In severe cases, individuals may have abnormal bone formation as manifested by thicker and longer bones resulting in a taller stature.
b. Abnormally weak bones prone to breakage and fracturing upon mild trauma would be expected. In severe cases, individuals may have abnormal bone formation as manifested by thicker and longer bones resulting in a taller stature.
c. Bones are abnormally weak and highly flexible. In severe cases, individuals may have abnormal bone formation as manifested by thinner and/or shorter bones, perhaps resulting in a shorter stature.
d. Abnormally weak bones prone to breakage and fracturing upon mild trauma would be expected. In severe cases, individuals may have abnormal bone formation as manifested by thinner and/or shorter bones, perhaps resulting in a shorter stature.

30. Osteoporosis is a clinical manifestation of an imbalance between bone resorption and bone formation, resulting in weakened bones that easily fracture. How may one design a therapeutic drug targeting specific bone cell type(s) for the treatment of osteoporosis?

a. A therapeutic drug that inhibits osteoblast activity would be useful. A drug that enhances the bone formation activity of osteoclasts may also be a good strategy.
b. A therapeutic drug that inhibits osteoclast activity would be useful. One that reduces the activity of osteoblasts may also be a good strategy.
c. A therapeutic drug that inhibits osteoblast activity would be useful. One that enhances the bone formation activity of osteoblasts may also be a good strategy.
d. A therapeutic drug that inhibits osteoclast activity would be useful. One that enhances the bone formation activity of osteoblasts may also be a good strategy.

31. Why are shoulder dislocations more common than dislocations of the carpal bones in the hand?

a. The less mobile a joint, the weaker the joint. The shoulder joint allows the greatest range of motion, while carpal bones are more stable.

b. The less mobile a joint, the weaker the joint. Carpal bones allow the greatest range of motion, while shoulder joints are more stable.

c. The more mobile a joint, the weaker the joint. Carpal bones allow the greatest range of motion while shoulder joints are more stable.

d. The more mobile a joint, the weaker the joint. The shoulder joint allows the greatest range of motion while carpal bones are more stable.

32. What angular movements occur at the hip joint and knees as you bend down to touch your toes?

a. Both the hip joint and knees are flexed.

b. Both the hip joint and knees are extended.

c. The hip joint is extended and the knees are flexed.

d. The hip joint is flexed and the knees are extended.

33. What is the main structural difference between synovial joints and cartilaginous and fibrous joints?

a. Synovial joints allow movement while fibrous and cartilaginous joints do not move at all.

b. Synovial joints do not move at all while fibrous and cartilaginous joints allow movement.

c. Synovial joints do not have a space between the adjoining bones while fibrous and cartilaginous joints have a joint cavity.

d. Synovial joints have a space between the adjoining bones while fibrous and cartilaginous joints do not have a joint cavity.

34. What do all types of muscle tissue have in common?

a. Voluntary muscles cannot be consciously controlled, as is the case with cardiac muscles. Involuntary muscles can be controlled by an individual's will, as is the case with skeletal muscles.

b. Voluntary muscles can be controlled by an individual's will, as is the case with cardiac muscles. Involuntary muscles cannot be consciously controlled, as is the case with skeletal muscles.

c. Voluntary muscles cannot be consciously controlled, as is the case with the movement of legs while walking. Involuntary muscles can be controlled by an individual's will, as is the case with muscles in the digestive system.

d. Voluntary muscles can be controlled by an individual's will, as is the case with skeletal muscles. Involuntary muscles cannot be consciously controlled, as is the case with cardiac muscles.

35. How would muscle contractions be affected if ATP was completely depleted in a muscle fiber?

a. Myosin heads will detach rapidly from the actin-binding sites, resulting in muscle relaxation. In a live person this causes rigor mortis, while in a recently dead person it results in "writer's cramp".

b. Myosin heads will not detach from the actin-binding sites, resulting in muscle stiffness. In a live person this causes rigor mortis, while in a recently dead person it results in "writer's cramp".

c. Myosin heads will detach rapidly from the actin-binding sites, resulting in muscle relaxation. In a live person this causes "writer's cramp", while in a recently dead person it results in rigor mortis.

d. Myosin heads will not detach from the actin-binding sites, resulting in muscle stiffness. In a live person this causes "writer's cramp", while in a recently dead person it results in rigor mortis.

36. What is the difference between voluntary and involuntary muscles? Give an example of each.

a. Voluntary muscles cannot be consciously controlled, such as cardiac muscles. Involuntary muscles can be controlled by an individual's will, such as skeletal muscles.

b. Voluntary muscles can be controlled by an individual's will, such as cardiac muscles. Involuntary muscles cannot be consciously controlled, such as skeletal muscles.

c. Voluntary muscles cannot be consciously controlled, such as the movement of legs while walking. Involuntary muscles can be controlled by an individual's will, such as muscles in the digestive system.

d. Voluntary muscles can be controlled by an individual's will, such as skeletal muscles. Involuntary muscles cannot be consciously controlled, such as cardiac muscles.

SCIENCE PRACTICE CHALLENGE QUESTIONS

37. Biomimetics is the design of engineering solutions guided by biological solutions to similar problems. Support materials in biological systems must be tough, flexible, and light. Engineers define a tough material as one that can absorb energy without fracturing. Flexibility is the ability to deform elastically but able to return to the original shape. Size of in both biological and designed system is often determined by many factors. Density of a material becomes important when size cannot be adjusted but lightness is needed. An analysis of several biological materials in terms of these parameters (Wegst and Ashby, *Philosophical Magazine*, 84, 2004) shows that selection has conserved a bounding value in the product of these parameters; the square root of all of the ratios of toughness and elasticity lie above the dashed line. Patterns like this lead to new science but, in applications to biomimetics, they can also lead to improved technologies.

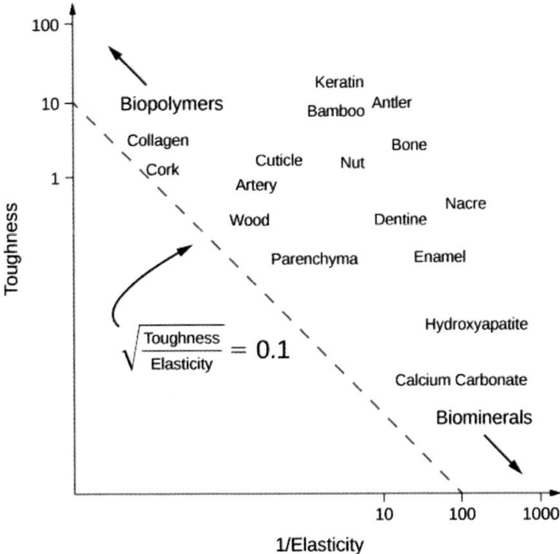

Figure 29.39

Biopolymers like collagen have higher toughness and higher elasticity. Biominerals like enamel have lower toughness but provide rigidity. Some organisms support soft tissue by combining biopolymers and biomaterials. Some rely more on biopolymers. Note that this is a logarithm scale not a linear scale. So that the difference in toughness of keratin and bone is roughly 100 and the difference in rigidity of these to materials is nearly that large.

A. Use this graph to **pose questions** about the fitness of various biological solutions to the problem of capturing, storing, and using free energy. (Remember that engineers define "toughness" as the ability to absorb energy without fracturing.)

B. **Refine** this representation by identifying an important property of a biomaterial that is missing and explain its importance in terms of free energy acquisition and use.

C. **Explain** how these data indicates that the properties of biopolymers will lead to a better biomimetic design of the humanoid robot than is imagined in C3PO of Star Wars fame

38. An investigation of the evolution of muscle was made by Steinmetz et al. (*Nature*, 487, 2012), and a sample of data is presented in the following diagram. Below the accepted phylogeny of major groups are rows with families of genes that code for different muscle proteins, including actin and myosin. Shared genes are shown where the cell is darkened. Samples of genes associated with striated and smooth muscle and the Z-disc that terminates the actin-myosin pair are clustered. These are shown in the diagram below, where groups in which muscle cells occur lie within the box whose edges are dashed lines.

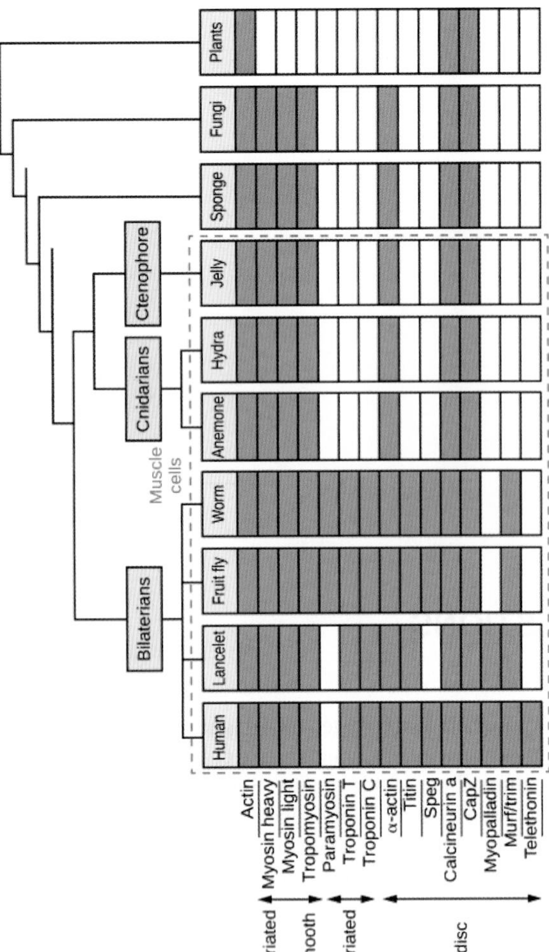

Figure 29.40

A. **Analyze** these data in terms of evidence of common ancestry and evidence of the convergent evolution of the muscle cell.

Molecular phylogenetics has provided many insights into the evolution of genes. Because this work is framed by the central organizing principle of evolution it is possible to forget that there are people living today who need evidence that speciation and extinction have occurred throughout Earth's history.

B. Describe in broad outline a plan using molecular databases for either protein or DNA sequences that you could help those who are in need of evidence construct it.

30 | THE RESPIRATORY SYSTEM

Figure 30.1 Lungs, which appear as nearly transparent tissue surrounding the heart in this X-ray of a dog (left), are the central organs of the respiratory system. The left lung is smaller than the right lung to accommodate space for the heart. A dog's nose (right) has a slit on the side of each nostril. When tracking a scent, the slits open, blocking the front of the nostrils. This allows the dog to exhale though the now-open area on the side of the nostrils without losing the scent that is being followed. (credit a: modification of work by Geoff Stearns; credit b: modification of work by Cory Zanker)

Chapter Outline

Introduction

Breathing is an involuntary event. How often a breath is taken and how much air is inhaled or exhaled are tightly regulated by the respiratory center in the brain. Humans, when they aren't exerting themselves, breathe approximately 15 times per minute on average. Canines, like the dog in Figure 30.1, have a respiratory rate of about 15–30 breaths per minute. In addition to exhaling carbon dioxide when we breathe, scientists believe people with cancerous lung cells also exhale tiny amounts of volatile organic compounds. Researchers used specially trained dogs to see if they could tell the difference between people with and without lung cancer. The dogs correctly identified 71 out of 100 lung cancer patients and 372 out of 400 who did not. You can read more about this exciting research here (http://openstaxcollege.org/l/32lungcancer) .

30.1 | Systems of Gas Exchange

In this section, you will explore the following questions:

- How does air pass from the outside environment to the lungs?
- How are lungs protected from particulate matter?

Connection for AP® Courses

Much of the information in this chapter is not within the scope for AP®. However, studying the respiratory system provides an opportunity to apply concepts we have previously explored, including chemistry and pH, cell membrane structure, and diffusion of molecules across membranes. The respiratory systems of both invertebrate and vertebrate animals—from the tracheal system of insects and gills of fish to lungs in reptiles, birds, and mammals—reflect a distinct pattern of evolution as animals transitioned from aquatic to terrestrial environments. The function of all respiratory systems is to facilitate the exchange of oxygen (O_2) and carbon dioxide (CO_2) with the environment. Energy production in cellular respiration requires O_2, and CO_2 is produced as a toxic by-product. Some animals, such as worms and amphibians, use their entire body surface for respiration. Terrestrial animals, including humans, needed a more efficient system for gas exchange. So, take a deep breath (pun intended!) as we take a dive into the activities and functions of the respiratory system.

Do not confuse the respiratory system with cellular respiration although both involve the movement of O_2 and CO_2 (gas exchange) between organism and environment.

Information presented and the examples highlighted in the section support concepts outlined in Big Idea 2 and Big Idea 4 of the AP® Biology Curriculum Framework. The AP® Learning Objectives listed in the Curriculum Framework provide a transparent foundation for the AP® Biology course, an inquiry-based laboratory experience, instructional activities, and AP® exam questions. A learning objective merges required content with one or more of the seven science practices.

Big Idea 2	Biological systems utilize free energy and molecular building blocks to grow, to reproduce, and to maintain dynamic homeostasis.
Enduring Understanding 2.A	Growth, reproduction and maintenance of living systems require free energy and matter.
Essential Knowledge	**2.A.3** Organisms must exchange matter with the environment to grow, reproduce and maintain organization.
Science Practice	**6.2** The student can construct explanations of phenomena based on evidence produced through scientific practices.
Learning Objective	**2.7** The student is able to explain how cell size and shape effect the overall rate of nutrient intake and the rate of waste elimination.
Big Idea 4	Biological systems interact, and these systems and their interactions possess complex properties.
Enduring Understanding 4.A	Interactions within biological systems lead to complex properties.
Essential Knowledge	**4.A.6** Interactions among living systems and with their environment result in the movement of matter and energy.
Science Practice	**1.3** The student can refine representations and models of natural or man-made phenomena and systems in the domain.
Learning Objective	**4.15** The student is able to use visual representations to analyze situation or solve problems quantitatively to illustrate how interactions among living systems and within their environment result in the movement of matter and energy.

The primary function of the respiratory system is to deliver oxygen to the cells of the body's tissues and remove carbon dioxide, a cell waste product. The main structures of the human respiratory system are the nasal cavity, the trachea, and lungs.

All aerobic organisms require oxygen to carry out their metabolic functions. Along the evolutionary tree, different organisms have devised different means of obtaining oxygen from the surrounding atmosphere. The environment in which the animal lives greatly determines how an animal respires. The complexity of the respiratory system is correlated with the size of the organism. As animal size increases, diffusion distances increase and the ratio of surface area to volume drops. In unicellular organisms, diffusion across the cell membrane is sufficient for supplying oxygen to the cell (**Figure 30.2**).

Diffusion is a slow, passive transport process. In order for diffusion to be a feasible means of providing oxygen to the cell, the rate of oxygen uptake must match the rate of diffusion across the membrane. In other words, if the cell were very large or thick, diffusion would not be able to provide oxygen quickly enough to the inside of the cell. Therefore, dependence on diffusion as a means of obtaining oxygen and removing carbon dioxide remains feasible only for small organisms or those with highly-flattened bodies, such as many flatworms (Platyhelminthes). Larger organisms had to evolve specialized respiratory tissues, such as gills, lungs, and respiratory passages accompanied by complex circulatory systems, to transport oxygen throughout their entire body.

Figure 30.2 The cell of the unicellular algae *Ventricaria ventricosa* is one of the largest known, reaching one to five centimeters in diameter. Like all single-celled organisms, *V. ventricosa* exchanges gases across the cell membrane.

Direct Diffusion

For small multicellular organisms, diffusion across the outer membrane is sufficient to meet their oxygen needs. Gas exchange by direct diffusion across surface membranes is efficient for organisms less than 1 mm in diameter. In simple organisms, such as cnidarians and flatworms, every cell in the body is close to the external environment. Their cells are kept moist and gases diffuse quickly via direct diffusion. Flatworms are small, literally flat worms, which 'breathe' through diffusion across the outer membrane (Figure 30.3). The flat shape of these organisms increases the surface area for diffusion, ensuring that each cell within the body is close to the outer membrane surface and has access to oxygen. If the flatworm had a cylindrical body, then the cells in the center would not be able to get oxygen.

Figure 30.3 This flatworm's process of respiration works by diffusion across the outer membrane. (credit: Stephen Childs)

Skin and Gills

Earthworms and amphibians use their skin (integument) as a respiratory organ. A dense network of capillaries lies just below the skin and facilitates gas exchange between the external environment and the circulatory system. The respiratory surface must be kept moist in order for the gases to dissolve and diffuse across cell membranes.

Organisms that live in water need to obtain oxygen from the water. Oxygen dissolves in water but at a lower concentration than in the atmosphere. The atmosphere has roughly 21 percent oxygen. In water, the oxygen concentration is much smaller than that. Fish and many other aquatic organisms have evolved gills to take up the dissolved oxygen from water (Figure 30.4). Gills are thin tissue filaments that are highly branched and folded. When water passes over the gills, the dissolved oxygen in water rapidly diffuses across the gills into the bloodstream. The circulatory system can then carry the oxygenated blood to the other parts of the body. In animals that contain coelomic fluid instead of blood, oxygen diffuses across the gill surfaces into the coelomic fluid. Gills are found in mollusks, annelids, and crustaceans.

Figure 30.4 This common carp, like many other aquatic organisms, has gills that allow it to obtain oxygen from water. (credit: "Guitardude012"/Wikimedia Commons)

The folded surfaces of the gills provide a large surface area to ensure that the fish gets sufficient oxygen. Diffusion is a process in which material travels from regions of high concentration to low concentration until equilibrium is reached. In this case, blood with a low concentration of oxygen molecules circulates through the gills. The concentration of oxygen molecules in water is higher than the concentration of oxygen molecules in gills. As a result, oxygen molecules diffuse from water (high concentration) to blood (low concentration), as shown in Figure 30.5. Similarly, carbon dioxide molecules in the blood diffuse from the blood (high concentration) to water (low concentration).

The illustration shows a fish, with a box indicating the location of the gills, behind the head. A close-up image shows the gills, each of which resembles a feathery worm. Two stacks of gills attach to a structure called a columnar gill arch, forming a tall V. Water travels in from the outside of the V, between each gill, then travels out of the top of the V. Veins travel into the gill from the base of the gill arch, and arteries travel back out on the opposite side. A close-up image of a single gill shows that water travels over the gill, passing over deoxygenated veins first, then over oxygenated arteries.

Figure 30.5 As water flows over the gills, oxygen is transferred to blood via the veins. (credit "fish": modification of work by Duane Raver, NOAA)

Tracheal Systems

Insect respiration is independent of its circulatory system; therefore, the blood does not play a direct role in oxygen transport. Insects have a highly specialized type of respiratory system called the tracheal system, which consists of a network of small tubes that carries oxygen to the entire body. The tracheal system is the most direct and efficient respiratory system in active animals. The tubes in the tracheal system are made of a polymeric material called chitin.

Insect bodies have openings, called spiracles, along the thorax and abdomen. These openings connect to the tubular network, allowing oxygen to pass into the body (Figure 30.6) and regulating the diffusion of CO_2 and water vapor. Air enters and leaves the tracheal system through the spiracles. Some insects can ventilate the tracheal system with body movements.

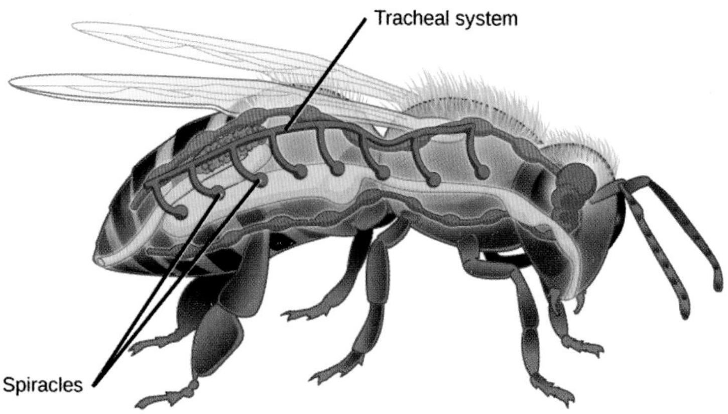

Figure 30.6 Insects perform respiration via a tracheal system.

Mammalian Systems

In mammals, pulmonary ventilation occurs via inhalation (breathing). During inhalation, air enters the body through the **nasal cavity** located just inside the nose (Figure 30.7). As air passes through the nasal cavity, the air is warmed to body temperature and humidified. The respiratory tract is coated with mucus to seal the tissues from direct contact with air. Mucus is high in water. As air crosses these surfaces of the mucous membranes, it picks up water. These processes help equilibrate the air to the body conditions, reducing any damage that cold, dry air can cause. Particulate matter that is floating in the air is removed in the nasal passages via mucus and cilia. The processes of warming, humidifying, and removing particles are important protective mechanisms that prevent damage to the trachea and lungs. Thus, inhalation serves several purposes in addition to bringing oxygen into the respiratory system.

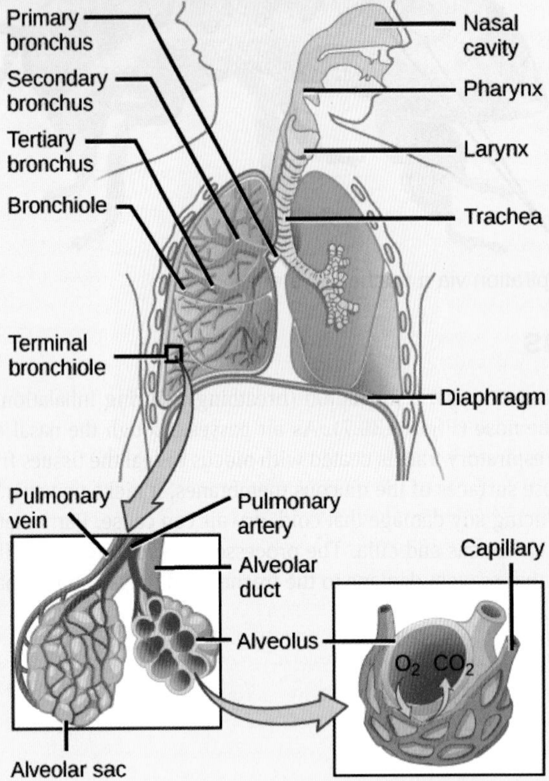

Figure 30.7 Air enters the respiratory system through the nasal cavity and pharynx, and then passes through the trachea and into the bronchi, which bring air into the lungs. (credit: modification of work by NCI)

In which order does inhaled air travel from the pharynx to the bronchioles?

a. pharynx → trachea → larynx → bronchi → bronchioles.
b. pharynx → larynx → trachea → bronchi → bronchioles
c. pharynx → larynx → trachea → bronchioles → bronchi
d. pharynx → trachea → larynx → bronchioles → bronchi

From the nasal cavity, air passes through the **pharynx** (throat) and the **larynx** (voice box), as it makes its way to the **trachea** (Figure 30.7). The main function of the trachea is to funnel the inhaled air to the lungs and the exhaled air back out of the body. The human trachea is a cylinder about 10 to 12 cm long and 2 cm in diameter that sits in front of the esophagus and extends from the larynx into the chest cavity where it divides into the two primary bronchi at the midthorax. It is made of incomplete rings of hyaline cartilage and smooth muscle (Figure 30.8). The trachea is lined with mucus-producing goblet cells and ciliated epithelia. The cilia propel foreign particles trapped in the mucus toward the pharynx. The cartilage provides strength and support to the trachea to keep the passage open. The smooth muscle can contract, decreasing the trachea's diameter, which causes expired air to rush upwards from the lungs at a great force. The forced exhalation helps expel mucus when we cough. Smooth muscle can contract or relax, depending on stimuli from the external environment or the body's nervous system.

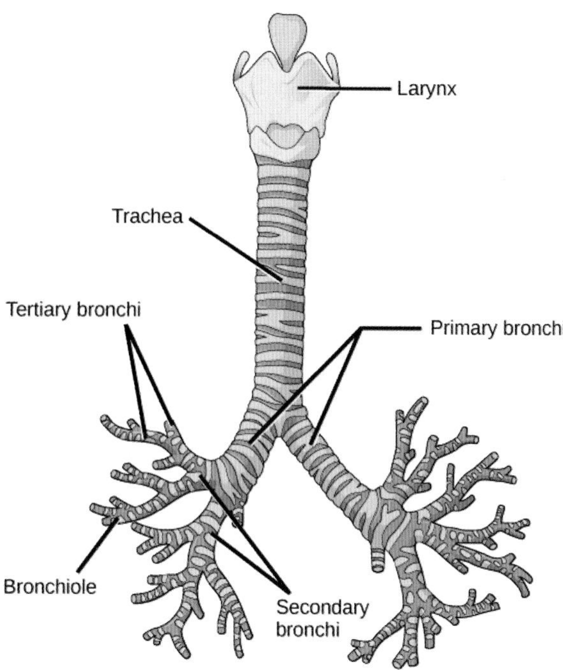

Figure 30.8 The trachea and bronchi are made of incomplete rings of cartilage. (credit: modification of work by Gray's Anatomy)

Lungs: Bronchi and Alveoli

The end of the trachea bifurcates (divides) to the right and left lungs. The lungs are not identical. The right lung is larger and contains three lobes, whereas the smaller left lung contains two lobes (Figure 30.9). The muscular **diaphragm**, which facilitates breathing, is inferior to (below) the lungs and marks the end of the thoracic cavity.

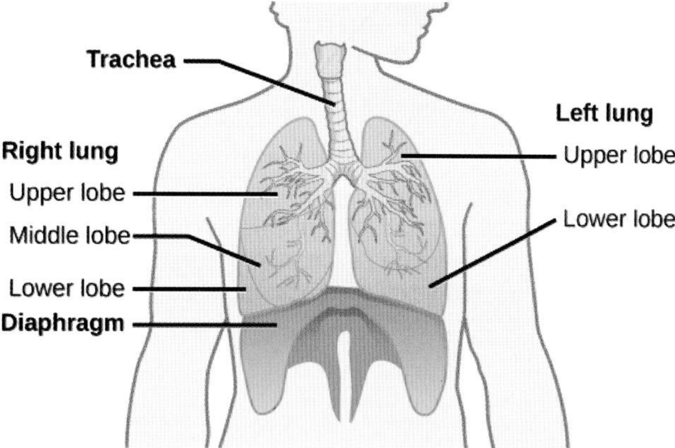

Figure 30.9 The trachea bifurcates into the right and left bronchi in the lungs. The right lung is made of three lobes and is larger. To accommodate the heart, the left lung is smaller and has only two lobes.

In the lungs, air is diverted into smaller and smaller passages, or **bronchi**. Air enters the lungs through the two **primary (main) bronchi** (singular: bronchus). Each bronchus divides into secondary bronchi, then into tertiary bronchi, which in turn divide, creating smaller and smaller diameter **bronchioles** as they split and spread through the lung. Like the trachea, the bronchi are made of cartilage and smooth muscle. At the bronchioles, the cartilage is replaced with elastic fibers. Bronchi are innervated by nerves of both the parasympathetic and sympathetic nervous systems that control muscle contraction (parasympathetic) or relaxation (sympathetic) in the bronchi and bronchioles, depending on the nervous system's cues. In humans, bronchioles with a diameter smaller than 0.5 mm are the **respiratory bronchioles**. They lack cartilage and therefore rely on inhaled air to support their shape. As the passageways decrease in diameter, the relative amount of smooth muscle increases.

The **terminal bronchioles** subdivide into microscopic branches called respiratory bronchioles. The respiratory bronchioles subdivide into several alveolar ducts. Numerous alveoli and alveolar sacs surround the alveolar ducts. The alveolar sacs resemble bunches of grapes tethered to the end of the bronchioles (Figure 30.10). In the acinar region, the **alveolar ducts** are attached to the end of each bronchiole. At the end of each duct are approximately 100 **alveolar sacs**, each containing 20 to 30 **alveoli** that are 200 to 300 microns in diameter. Gas exchange occurs only in alveoli. Alveoli are made of thin-walled parenchymal cells, typically one-cell thick, that look like tiny bubbles within the sacs. Alveoli are in direct contact with capillaries (one-cell thick) of the circulatory system. Such intimate contact ensures that oxygen will diffuse from alveoli into the blood and be distributed to the cells of the body. In addition, the carbon dioxide that was produced by cells as a waste product will diffuse from the blood into alveoli to be exhaled. The anatomical arrangement of capillaries and alveoli emphasizes the structural and functional relationship of the respiratory and circulatory systems. Because there are so many alveoli (~300 million per lung) within each alveolar sac and so many sacs at the end of each alveolar duct, the lungs have a sponge-like consistency. This organization produces a very large surface area that is available for gas exchange. The surface area of alveoli in the lungs is approximately 75 m^2. This large surface area, combined with the thin-walled nature of the alveolar parenchymal cells, allows gases to easily diffuse across the cells.

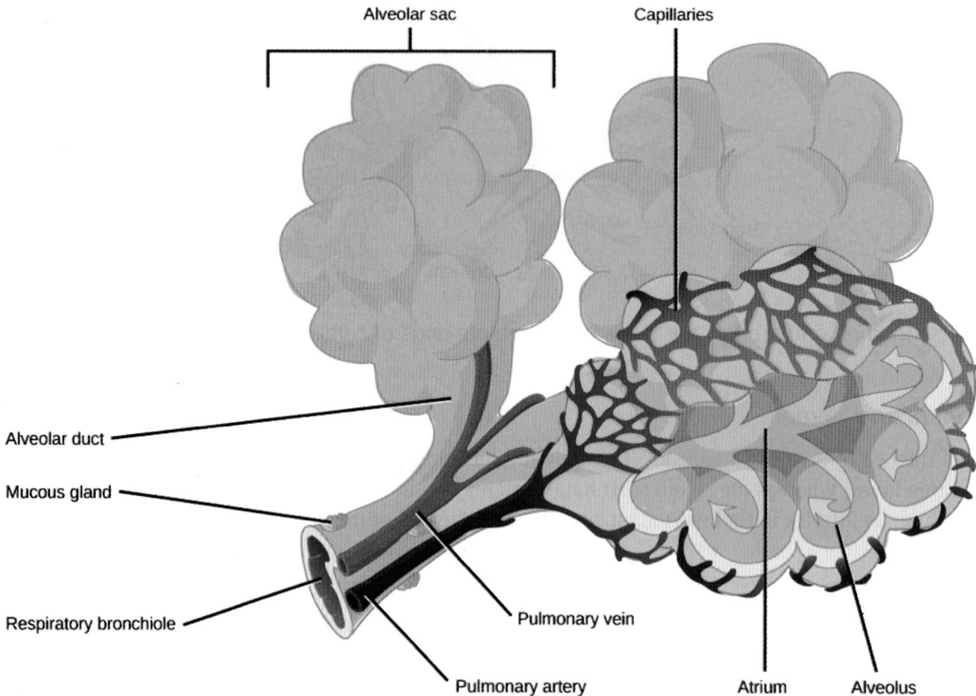

Figure 30.10 Terminal bronchioles are connected by respiratory bronchioles to alveolar ducts and alveolar sacs. Each alveolar sac contains 20 to 30 spherical alveoli and has the appearance of a bunch of grapes. Air flows into the atrium of the alveolar sac, then circulates into alveoli where gas exchange occurs with the capillaries. Mucous glands secrete mucous into the airways, keeping them moist and flexible. (credit: modification of work by Mariana Ruiz Villareal)

Watch the following video (http://openstaxcollege.org/l/lungs_pulmonary) to review the respiratory system.

Explain how the structures of the nasal cavity, oral cavity, and pharynx allow one to breathe even when their nostrils are congested due to a cold.

a. The trachea extends into the nose and mouth.

b. The pharynx connects the nasal cavity to the lungs, while the larynx connects the oral cavity to the lungs.

c. The oral and nasal cavities connect to separate lungs.

d. The nasal and oral cavities combine above the pharynx.

Protective Mechanisms

The air that organisms breathe contains **particulate matter** such as dust, dirt, viral particles, and bacteria that can damage the lungs or trigger allergic immune responses. The respiratory system contains several protective mechanisms to avoid problems or tissue damage. In the nasal cavity, hairs and mucus trap small particles, viruses, bacteria, dust, and dirt to prevent their entry.

If particulates do make it beyond the nose, or enter through the mouth, the bronchi and bronchioles of the lungs also contain several protective devices. The lungs produce **mucus**—a sticky substance made of **mucin**, a complex glycoprotein, as well as salts and water—that traps particulates. The bronchi and bronchioles contain cilia, small hair-like projections that line the walls of the bronchi and bronchioles (Figure 30.11). These cilia beat in unison and move mucus and particles out of the bronchi and bronchioles back up to the throat where it is swallowed and eliminated via the esophagus.

In humans, for example, tar and other substances in cigarette smoke destroy or paralyze the cilia, making the removal of particles more difficult. In addition, smoking causes the lungs to produce more mucus, which the damaged cilia are not able to move. This causes a persistent cough, as the lungs try to rid themselves of particulate matter, and makes smokers more susceptible to respiratory ailments.

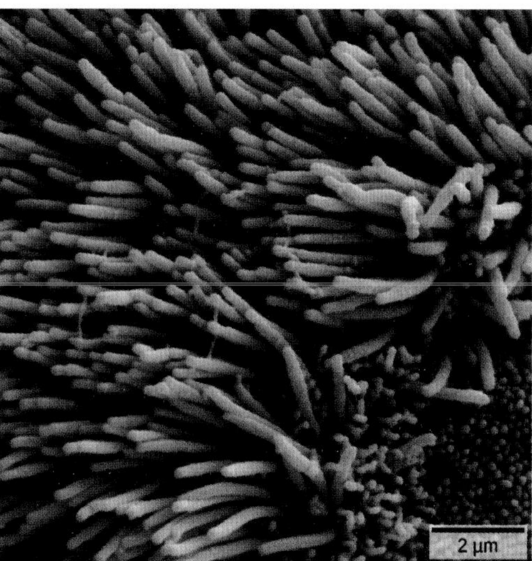

Figure 30.11 The bronchi and bronchioles contain cilia that help move mucus and other particles out of the lungs. (credit: Louisa Howard, modification of work by Dartmouth Electron Microscope Facility)

Think About It

How does the structure of alveoli maximize gas exchange?

30.2 | Gas Exchange across Respiratory Surfaces

In this section, you will explore the following questions:

- What are the names and descriptions of lung volumes and capacities?
- How does gas pressure influence the movement of gases into and out of the body?

Connection for AP® Courses

The information in this section about lung volumes and capacities is outside the scope for AP®. However, the content about the movement of gases across the membranes of alveoli is an important application of the principles of diffusion that we explored in the chapter on passive transport. In addition, gas exchange provides the oxygen needed for aerobic cellular respiration and for the removal of carbon dioxide produced as a metabolic waste product.

Gas movement into or out of the lungs is dependent on the pressure of the gas. Because the air we breathe is a mixture of several gases, including N, O_2 and CO_2, the amount of each gas is measured by its partial pressure. As you remember from our earlier exploration of diffusion, molecules move from an area of higher concentration to lower concentration, or, in the case of gases, from higher partial pressure (measured in mmHg) to lower partial pressure. In other words, O_2 and CO_2 move with their concentration gradients. Because both gases are small, nonpolar molecules, they freely travel across the phospholipid bilayer of the plasma cell membrane.

Information presented and the examples highlighted in the section support concepts outlined in Big Idea 2 of the AP® Biology Curriculum Framework. The AP® Learning Objectives listed in the Curriculum Framework provide a transparent foundation for the AP® Biology course, an inquiry-based laboratory experience, instructional activities, and AP® exam questions. A learning objective merges required content with one or more of the seven science practices.

Big Idea 2	Biological systems utilize free energy and molecular building blocks to grow, to reproduce, and to maintain dynamic homeostasis.
Enduring Understanding 2.B	Growth, reproduction and dynamic homeostasis require that cell create and maintain internal environments that are different form their external environment.
Essential Knowledge	**2.B.2** Growth and dynamic homeostasis are maintained by the constant movement of molecules across membranes.
Science Practice	**1.4** The student can use representations and models to analyze situations or solve problems qualitatively and quantitatively.
Science Practice	**1.1** The student can create representations and models of natural or man-made phenomena and systems in the domain.
Science Practice	**7.2** The student can connect concepts in and across domain(s) to generalize or extrapolate in and/or across enduring understandings and/or big ideas.
Learning Objective	**2.12** The student is able to use representations and models to analyze situations or solve problems qualitatively and quantitatively to investigate whether dynamic homeostasis is maintained by the movement of molecules across membranes.

The structure of the lung maximizes its surface area to increase gas diffusion. Because of the enormous number of alveoli (approximately 300 million in each human lung), the surface area of the lung is very large (75 m^2). Having such a large surface area increases the amount of gas that can diffuse into and out of the lungs.

Basic Principles of Gas Exchange

Gas exchange during respiration occurs primarily through diffusion. Diffusion is a process in which transport is driven by a concentration gradient. Gas molecules move from a region of high concentration to a region of low concentration. Blood that is low in oxygen concentration and high in carbon dioxide concentration undergoes gas exchange with air in the lungs. The air in the lungs has a higher concentration of oxygen than that of oxygen-depleted blood and a lower concentration of carbon dioxide. This concentration gradient allows for gas exchange during respiration.

Partial pressure is a measure of the concentration of the individual components in a mixture of gases. The total pressure exerted by the mixture is the sum of the partial pressures of the components in the mixture. The rate of diffusion of a gas is proportional to its partial pressure within the total gas mixture. This concept is discussed further in detail below.

Lung Volumes and Capacities

Different animals have different lung capacities based on their activities. Cheetahs have evolved a much higher lung capacity than humans; it helps provide oxygen to all the muscles in the body and allows them to run very fast. Elephants also have a high lung capacity. In this case, it is not because they run fast but because they have a large body and must be able to take up oxygen in accordance with their body size.

Human lung size is determined by genetics, sex, and height. At maximal capacity, an average lung can hold almost six liters of air, but lungs do not usually operate at maximal capacity. Air in the lungs is measured in terms of **lung volumes** and **lung capacities** (Figure 30.12 and Table 30.1). Volume measures the amount of air for one function (such as inhalation or exhalation). Capacity is any two or more volumes (for example, how much can be inhaled from the end of a maximal exhalation).

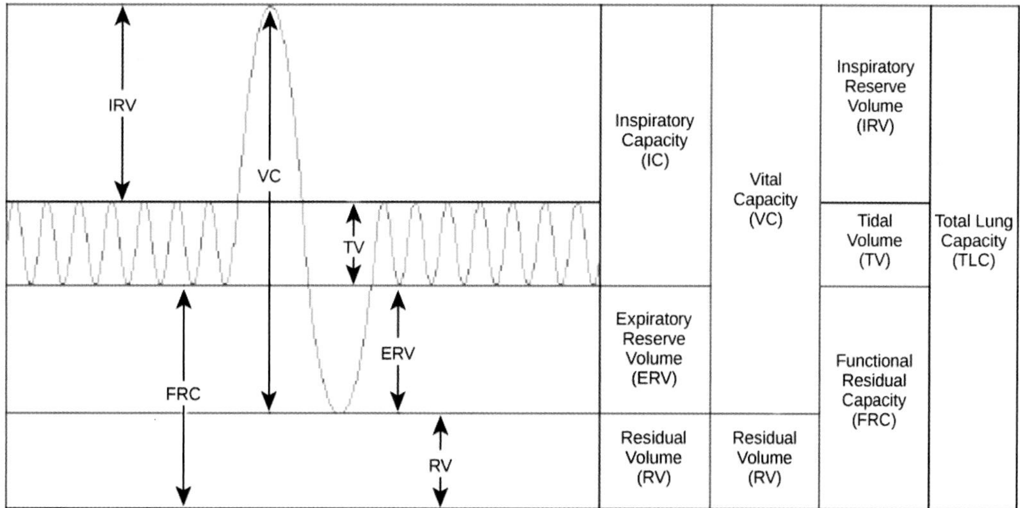

Figure 30.12 Human lung volumes and capacities are shown. The total lung capacity of the adult male is six liters. Tidal volume is the volume of air inhaled in a single, normal breath. Inspiratory capacity is the amount of air taken in during a deep breath, and residual volume is the amount of air left in the lungs after forceful respiration.

Lung Volumes and Capacities (Avg Adult Male)

Volume/ Capacity	Definition	Volume (liters)	Equations
Tidal volume (TV)	Amount of air inhaled during a normal breath	0.5	-
Expiratory reserve volume (ERV)	Amount of air that can be exhaled after a normal exhalation	1.2	-

Table 30.1

Lung Volumes and Capacities (Avg Adult Male)

Volume/ Capacity	Definition	Volume (liters)	Equations
Inspiratory reserve volume (IRV)	Amount of air that can be further inhaled after a normal inhalation	3.1	-
Residual volume (RV)	Air left in the lungs after a forced exhalation	1.2	-
Vital capacity (VC)	Maximum amount of air that can be moved in or out of the lungs in a single respiratory cycle	4.8	ERV+TV+IRV
Inspiratory capacity (IC)	Volume of air that can be inhaled in addition to a normal exhalation	3.6	TV+IRV
Functional residual capacity (FRC)	Volume of air remaining after a normal exhalation	2.4	ERV+RV
Total lung capacity (TLC)	Total volume of air in the lungs after a maximal inspiration	6.0	RV+ERV+TV+IRV
Forced expiratory volume (FEV1)	How much air can be forced out of the lungs over a specific time period, usually one second	~4.1 to 5.5	-

Table 30.1

The volume in the lung can be divided into four units: tidal volume, expiratory reserve volume, inspiratory reserve volume, and residual volume. **Tidal volume (TV)** measures the amount of air that is inspired and expired during a normal breath. On average, this volume is around one-half liter, which is a little less than the capacity of a 20-ounce drink bottle. The **expiratory reserve volume (ERV)** is the additional amount of air that can be exhaled after a normal exhalation. It is the reserve amount that can be exhaled beyond what is normal. Conversely, the **inspiratory reserve volume (IRV)** is the additional amount of air that can be inhaled after a normal inhalation. The **residual volume (RV)** is the amount of air that is left after expiratory reserve volume is exhaled. The lungs are never completely empty: There is always some air left in the lungs after a maximal exhalation. If this residual volume did not exist and the lungs emptied completely, the lung tissues would stick together and the energy necessary to re-inflate the lung could be too great to overcome. Therefore, there is always some air remaining in the lungs. Residual volume is also important for preventing large fluctuations in respiratory gases (O_2 and CO_2). The residual volume is the only lung volume that cannot be measured directly because it is impossible to completely empty the lung of air. This volume can only be calculated rather than measured.

Capacities are measurements of two or more volumes. The **vital capacity (VC)** measures the maximum amount of air that can be inhaled or exhaled during a respiratory cycle. It is the sum of the expiratory reserve volume, tidal volume, and inspiratory reserve volume. The **inspiratory capacity (IC)** is the amount of air that can be inhaled after the end of a normal expiration. It is, therefore, the sum of the tidal volume and inspiratory reserve volume. The **functional residual capacity (FRC)** includes the expiratory reserve volume and the residual volume. The FRC measures the amount of additional air that can be exhaled after a normal exhalation. Lastly, the **total lung capacity (TLC)** is a measurement of the total amount of air that the lung can hold. It is the sum of the residual volume, expiratory reserve volume, tidal volume, and inspiratory reserve volume.

Lung volumes are measured by a technique called **spirometry**. An important measurement taken during spirometry is the **forced expiratory volume (FEV)**, which measures how much air can be forced out of the lung over a specific period, usually one second (FEV1). In addition, the forced vital capacity (FVC), which is the total amount of air that can be forcibly exhaled, is measured. The ratio of these values (**FEV1/FVC ratio**) is used to diagnose lung diseases including asthma, emphysema, and fibrosis. If the FEV1/FVC ratio is high, the lungs are not compliant (meaning they are stiff and unable to bend properly), and the patient most likely has lung fibrosis. Patients exhale most of the lung volume very quickly. Conversely, when the FEV1/FVC ratio is low, there is resistance in the lung that is characteristic of asthma. In this instance, it is hard for the patient to get the air out of his or her lungs, and it takes a long time to reach the maximal exhalation volume. In either case, breathing is difficult and complications arise.

Respiratory Therapist

Respiratory therapists or respiratory practitioners evaluate and treat patients with lung and cardiovascular diseases. They work as part of a medical team to develop treatment plans for patients. Respiratory therapists may treat premature babies with underdeveloped lungs, patients with chronic conditions such as asthma, or older patients suffering from lung disease such as emphysema and chronic obstructive pulmonary disease (COPD). They may operate advanced equipment such as compressed gas delivery systems, ventilators, blood gas analyzers, and resuscitators. Specialized programs to become a respiratory therapist generally lead to a bachelor's degree with a respiratory therapist specialty. Because of a growing aging population, career opportunities as a respiratory therapist are expected to remain strong.

Gas Pressure and Respiration

The respiratory process can be better understood by examining the properties of gases. Gases move freely, but gas particles are constantly hitting the walls of their vessel, thereby producing gas pressure.

Air is a mixture of gases, primarily nitrogen (N_2; 78.6 percent), oxygen (O_2; 20.9 percent), water vapor (H_2O; 0.5 percent), and carbon dioxide (CO_2; 0.04 percent). Each gas component of that mixture exerts a pressure. The pressure for an individual gas in the mixture is the partial pressure of that gas. Approximately 21 percent of atmospheric gas is oxygen. Carbon dioxide, however, is found in relatively small amounts, 0.04 percent. The partial pressure for oxygen is much greater than that of carbon dioxide. The partial pressure of any gas can be calculated by:

$$P = (P_{atm}) \times (\text{percent content in mixture}).$$

P_{atm}, the atmospheric pressure, is the sum of all of the partial pressures of the atmospheric gases added together,

$$P_{atm} = P_{N_2} + P_{O_2} + P_{H_2O} + P_{CO_2} = 760 \text{ mm Hg}$$

× (percent content in mixture).

The pressure of the atmosphere at sea level is 760 mm Hg. Therefore, the partial pressure of oxygen is:

$$P_{O_2} = (760 \text{ mm Hg})\ (0.21) = 160 \text{ mm Hg}$$

and for carbon dioxide:

$$P_{CO_2} = (760 \text{ mm Hg})\ (0.0004) = 0.3 \text{ mm Hg}.$$

At high altitudes, P_{atm} decreases but concentration does not change; the partial pressure decrease is due to the reduction in P_{atm}.

When the air mixture reaches the lung, it has been humidified. The pressure of the water vapor in the lung does not change the pressure of the air, but it must be included in the partial pressure equation. For this calculation, the water pressure (47 mm Hg) is subtracted from the atmospheric pressure:

$$760 \text{ mm Hg} - 47 \text{ mm Hg} = 713 \text{ mm Hg}$$

and the partial pressure of oxygen is:

$$(760 \text{ mm Hg} - 47 \text{ mm Hg}) \times 0.21 = 150 \text{ mm Hg}.$$

These pressures determine the gas exchange, or the flow of gas, in the system. Oxygen and carbon dioxide will flow according to their pressure gradient from high to low. Therefore, understanding the partial pressure of each gas will aid in understanding how gases move in the respiratory system.

Gas Exchange across the Alveoli

In the body, oxygen is used by cells of the body's tissues and carbon dioxide is produced as a waste product. The ratio of carbon dioxide production to oxygen consumption is the **respiratory quotient (RQ)**. RQ varies between 0.7 and 1.0. If just glucose were used to fuel the body, the RQ would equal one. One mole of carbon dioxide would be produced for every mole of oxygen consumed. Glucose, however, is not the only fuel for the body. Protein and fat are also used as fuels for the body.

Because of this, less carbon dioxide is produced than oxygen is consumed and the RQ is, on average, about 0.7 for fat and about 0.8 for protein.

The RQ is used to calculate the partial pressure of oxygen in the alveolar spaces within the lung, the **alveolar P_{O_2}** Above, the partial pressure of oxygen in the lungs was calculated to be 150 mm Hg. However, lungs never fully deflate with an exhalation; therefore, the inspired air mixes with this residual air and lowers the partial pressure of oxygen within the alveoli. This means that there is a lower concentration of oxygen in the lungs than is found in the air outside the body. Knowing the RQ, the partial pressure of oxygen in the alveoli can be calculated:

$$\text{alveolar } P_{O_2} = \text{inspired } P_{O_2} - \left(\frac{\text{alveolar } P_{O_2}}{RQ}\right)$$

With an RQ of 0.8 and a P_{CO_2} in the alveoli of 40 mm Hg, the alveolar P_{O_2} is equal to:

$$\text{alveolar } P_{O_2} = 150 \text{ mm Hg} - \left(\frac{40 \text{ mm Hg}}{0.8}\right) = \text{mm Hg.}$$

Notice that this pressure is less than the external air. Therefore, the oxygen will flow from the inspired air in the lung (P_{O_2} = 150 mm Hg) into the bloodstream (P_{O_2} = 100 mm Hg) (**Figure 30.13**).

In the lungs, oxygen diffuses out of the alveoli and into the capillaries surrounding the alveoli. Oxygen (about 98 percent) binds reversibly to the respiratory pigment hemoglobin found in red blood cells (RBCs). RBCs carry oxygen to the tissues where oxygen dissociates from the hemoglobin and diffuses into the cells of the tissues. More specifically, alveolar P_{O_2} is higher in the alveoli (P_{ALVO_2} = 100 mm Hg) than blood P_{O_2} (40 mm Hg) in the capillaries. Because this pressure gradient exists, oxygen diffuses down its pressure gradient, moving out of the alveoli and entering the blood of the capillaries where O_2 binds to hemoglobin. At the same time, alveolar P_{CO_2} is lower P_{ALVO_2} = 40 mm Hg than blood P_{CO_2} = (45 mm Hg). CO_2 diffuses down its pressure gradient, moving out of the capillaries and entering the alveoli.

Oxygen and carbon dioxide move independently of each other; they diffuse down their own pressure gradients. As blood leaves the lungs through the pulmonary veins, the **venous P_{O_2}** = 100 mm Hg, whereas the **venous P_{CO_2}** = 40 mm Hg. As blood enters the systemic capillaries, the blood will lose oxygen and gain carbon dioxide because of the pressure difference of the tissues and blood. In systemic capillaries, P_{O_2} = 100 mm Hg, but in the tissue cells, P_{O_2} = 40 mm Hg. This pressure gradient drives the diffusion of oxygen out of the capillaries and into the tissue cells. At the same time, blood P_{CO_2} = 40 mm Hg and systemic tissue P_{CO_2} = 45 mm Hg. The pressure gradient drives CO_2 out of tissue cells and into the capillaries. The blood returning to the lungs through the pulmonary arteries has a venous P_{O_2} = 40 mm Hg and a P_{CO_2} = 45 mm Hg. The blood enters the lung capillaries where the process of exchanging gases between the capillaries and alveoli begins again (**Figure 30.13**).

visual CONNECTION

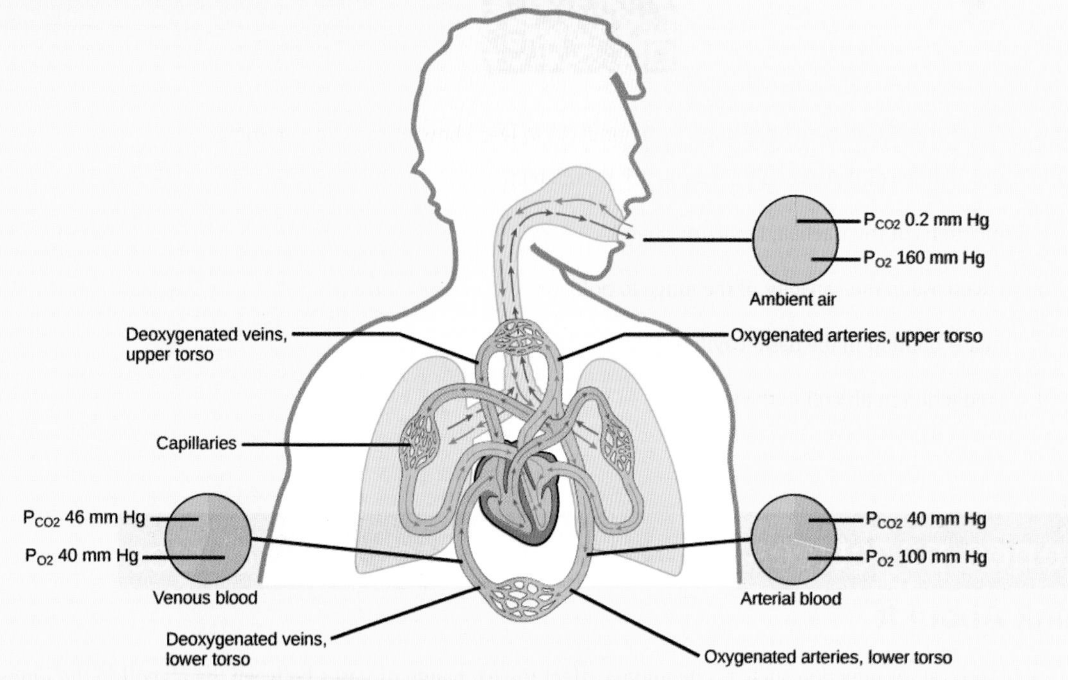

Figure 30.13 The partial pressures of oxygen and carbon dioxide change as blood moves through the body.

How do PO_2 and PCO_2 change as blood passes from the arteries to the veins within body tissues?

a. PO_2 drops and PCO_2 drops.

b. PO_2 increases and PCO_2 decreases.

c. PO_2 increases and PCO_2 increases.

d. PO_2 drops and PCO_2 increases.

In short, the change in partial pressure from the alveoli to the capillaries drives the oxygen into the tissues and the carbon dioxide into the blood from the tissues. The blood is then transported to the lungs where differences in pressure in the alveoli result in the movement of carbon dioxide out of the blood into the lungs, and oxygen into the blood.

Watch this video (http://openstaxcollege.org/l/spirometry) to learn how to carry out spirometry.

What kinds of injuries or disease could spirometry best detect?

a. infections of the trachea, larynx or pharynx

b. a decrease in the capacity of the lungs to hold air

c. mucus buildup in the nasal cavities

d. a reduction in alveoli in the lungs

science practices CONNECTION for AP® Courses

Think About It

How can a respiratory infection such as pneumonia affect the exchange of gases between the alveoli in the lungs and the capillaries surrounding them?

30.3 | Breathing

In this section, you will explore the following questions:

- How do the structure of the lungs and thoracic cavity control the mechanics of breathing?
- What is the importance of compliance and resistance in the lungs?

Connection for AP® Courses

The information in this section is not within the scope for AP® and does not align to the Curriculum Framework. However, understanding how breathing occurs enhances ones understanding of the structure and function of the respiratory system.

Mammalian lungs are located in the thoracic cavity where they are surrounded and protected by the rib cage, intercostal muscles, and bound by the chest wall. The bottom of the lungs is contained by the diaphragm, a skeletal muscle that facilitates breathing. Breathing requires the coordination of the lungs, the chest wall, and most importantly, the diaphragm.

Types of Breathing

Amphibians have evolved multiple ways of breathing. Young amphibians, like tadpoles, use gills to breathe, and they don't leave the water. Some amphibians retain gills for life. As the tadpole grows, the gills disappear and lungs grow. These lungs are primitive and not as evolved as mammalian lungs. Adult amphibians are lacking or have a reduced diaphragm, so breathing via lungs is forced. The other means of breathing for amphibians is diffusion across the skin. To aid this diffusion, amphibian skin must remain moist.

Birds face a unique challenge with respect to breathing: They fly. Flying consumes a great amount of energy; therefore, birds require a lot of oxygen to aid their metabolic processes. Birds have evolved a respiratory system that supplies them with the oxygen needed to enable flying. Similar to mammals, birds have lungs, which are organs specialized for gas exchange. Oxygenated air, taken in during inhalation, diffuses across the surface of the lungs into the bloodstream, and carbon dioxide diffuses from the blood into the lungs and expelled during exhalation. The details of breathing between birds and mammals differ substantially.

In addition to lungs, birds have air sacs inside their body. Air flows in one direction from the posterior air sacs to the lungs and out of the anterior air sacs. The flow of air is in the opposite direction from blood flow, and gas exchange takes place much more efficiently. This type of breathing enables birds to obtain the requisite oxygen, even at higher altitudes where the oxygen concentration is low. This directionality of airflow requires two cycles of air intake and exhalation to completely get the air out of the lungs.

evolution CONNECTION

Avian Respiration

Birds have evolved a respiratory system that enables them to fly. Flying is a high-energy process and requires a lot of oxygen. Furthermore, many birds fly in high altitudes where the concentration of oxygen in low. How did birds evolve a respiratory system that is so unique?

Decades of research by paleontologists have shown that birds evolved from therapods, meat-eating dinosaurs (Figure 30.14). In fact, fossil evidence shows that meat-eating dinosaurs that lived more than 100 million years ago had a similar flow-through respiratory system with lungs and air sacs. *Archaeopteryx* and *Xiaotingia*, for example, were flying dinosaurs and are believed to be early precursors of birds.

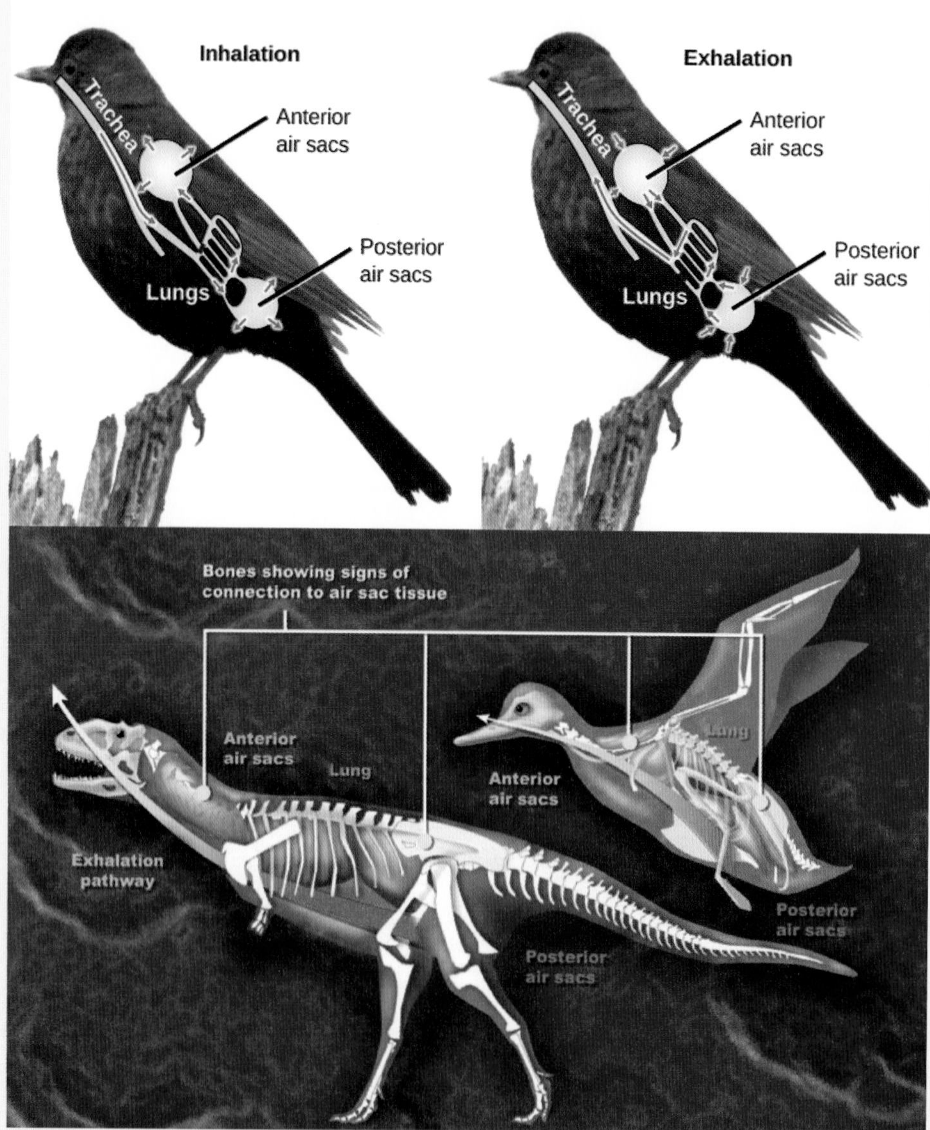

Figure 30.14 (a) Birds have a flow-through respiratory system in which air flows unidirectionally from the posterior sacs into the lungs, then into the anterior air sacs. The air sacs connect to openings in hollow bones. (b) Dinosaurs, from which birds descended, have similar hollow bones and are believed to have had a similar respiratory system. (credit b: modification of work by Zina Deretsky, National Science Foundation)

Most of us consider that dinosaurs are extinct. However, modern birds are descendants of avian dinosaurs. The respiratory system of modern birds has been evolving for hundreds of millions of years.

Recall the exhalation pathway of birds. What is meant by the statement, "these animals have a 'flow-through respiratory system,'" and how does this aid in flight?

a. The "flow-through respiratory system" allows air to only entirely in one direction, without retracing its pathway at all, allowing the animal to breathe faster while in flight

b. The "flow-through respiratory system" contains several air sacs that make the animal lighter compared to similar-sized animals with no air sacs.

c. The "flow-through respiratory system" contains many lungs, which allow the animals to take in the large quantities of oxygen needed for flight.

d. The "flow-through respiratory system" allows air to move in an almost unidirectional pathway to reach a series of air sacs that provide air to hollow bones, making the animals lighter and providing efficient respiration.

All mammals have lungs that are the main organs for breathing. Lung capacity has evolved to support the animal's activities. During inhalation, the lungs expand with air, and oxygen diffuses across the lung's surface and enters the bloodstream. During exhalation, the lungs expel air and lung volume decreases. In the next few sections, the process of human breathing will be explained.

The Mechanics of Human Breathing

Boyle's Law is the gas law that states that in a closed space, pressure and volume are inversely related. As volume decreases, pressure increases and vice versa (Figure 30.15). The relationship between gas pressure and volume helps to explain the mechanics of breathing.

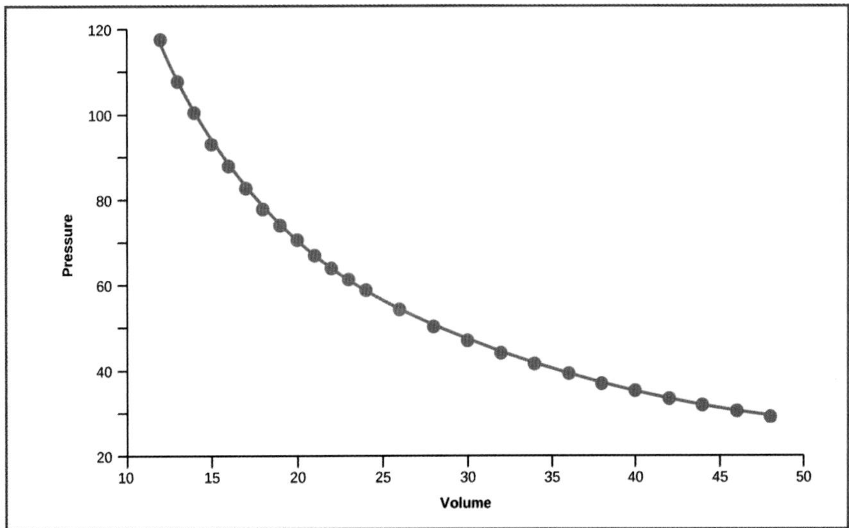

Figure 30.15 This graph shows data from Boyle's original 1662 experiment, which shows that pressure and volume are inversely related. No units are given as Boyle used arbitrary units in his experiments.

There is always a slightly negative pressure within the thoracic cavity, which aids in keeping the airways of the lungs open. During inhalation, volume increases as a result of contraction of the diaphragm, and pressure decreases (according to Boyle's Law). This decrease of pressure in the thoracic cavity relative to the environment makes the cavity less than the atmosphere (Figure 30.16**a**). Because of this drop in pressure, air rushes into the respiratory passages. To increase the volume of the lungs, the chest wall expands. This results from the contraction of the **intercostal muscles**, the muscles that are connected to the rib cage. Lung volume expands because the diaphragm contracts and the intercostals muscles contract, thus expanding the thoracic cavity. This increase in the volume of the thoracic cavity lowers pressure compared to the atmosphere, so air rushes into the lungs, thus increasing its volume. The resulting increase in volume is largely attributed to an increase in alveolar space, because the bronchioles and bronchi are stiff structures that do not change in size.

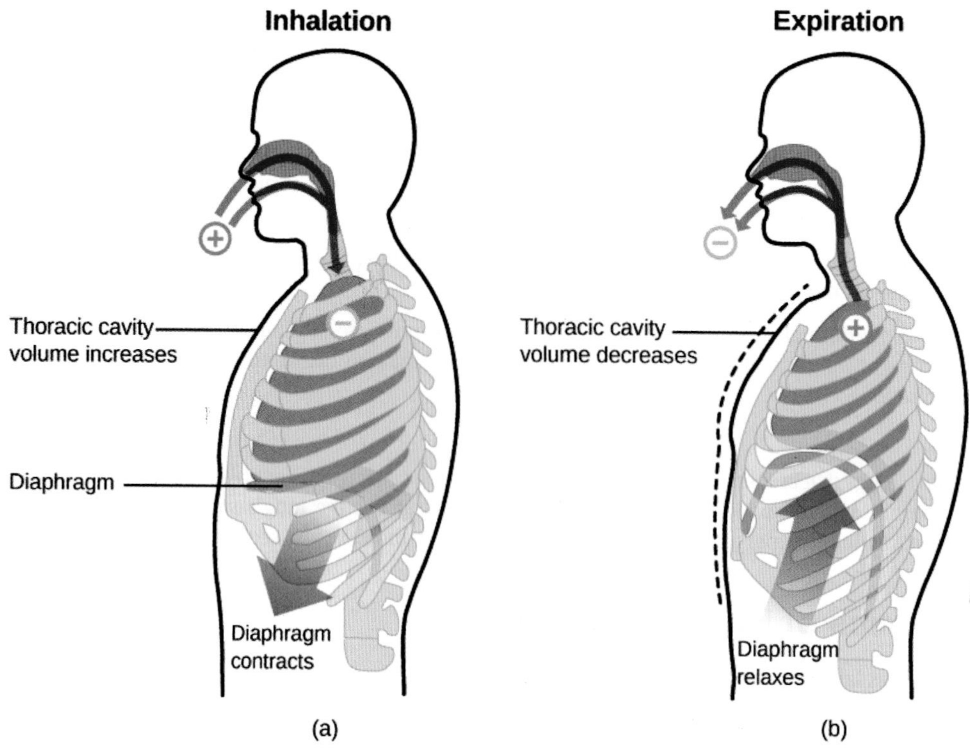

Figure 30.16 The lungs, chest wall, and diaphragm are all involved in respiration, both (a) inhalation and (b) expiration.

The chest wall expands out and away from the lungs. The lungs are elastic; therefore, when air fills the lungs, the **elastic recoil** within the tissues of the lung exerts pressure back toward the interior of the lungs. These outward and inward forces compete to inflate and deflate the lung with every breath. Upon exhalation, the lungs recoil to force the air out of the lungs, and the intercostal muscles relax, returning the chest wall back to its original position (Figure 30.16**b**). The diaphragm also relaxes and moves higher into the thoracic cavity. This increases the pressure within the thoracic cavity relative to the environment, and air rushes out of the lungs. The movement of air out of the lungs is a passive event. No muscles are contracting to expel the air.

Each lung is surrounded by an invaginated sac. The layer of tissue that covers the lung and dips into spaces is called the visceral **pleura**. A second layer of parietal pleura lines the interior of the thorax (Figure 30.17). The space between these layers, the **intrapleural space**, contains a small amount of fluid that protects the tissue and reduces the friction generated from rubbing the tissue layers together as the lungs contract and relax. **Pleurisy** results when these layers of tissue become inflamed; it is painful because the inflammation increases the pressure within the thoracic cavity and reduces the volume of the lung.

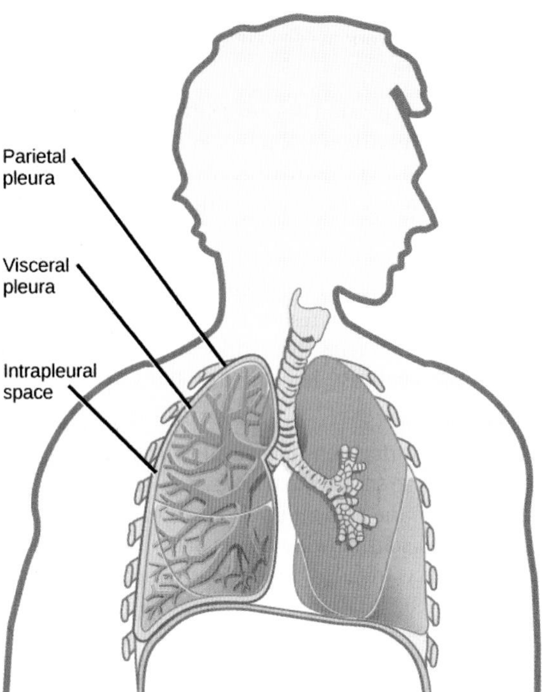

Figure 30.17 A tissue layer called pleura surrounds the lung and interior of the thoracic cavity. (credit: modification of work by NCI)

View (http://openstaxcollege.org/l/boyle_breathing) how Boyle's Law is related to breathing and watch this video (http://openstaxcollege.org/l/boyles_law) on Boyle's Law.

How does the relationship between the pressure and volume of a gas, as described by Boyle's law, relate to the changes in lung pressure during inhalation and exhalation?

a. Boyle's law states the pressure of a gas is directly proportional to its volume. Therefore, the lungs control the volume of air by altering the air pressure of the thoracic cavity.

b. Boyle's law states the pressure of a gas is inversely proportional to its volume. Therefore, the lungs control air pressure by altering the volume of the thoracic cavity.

c. Boyle's law states the pressure of a gas is inversely proportional to its volume. Therefore, the lungs control air pressure by expanding and pushing out the muscles of the thoracic cavity.

d. Boyle's law states the pressure of a gas is directly proportional to its volume. Therefore, the lungs control air pressure by controlling the volume of the thoracic cavity, not vice versa.

The Work of Breathing

The number of breaths per minute is the **respiratory rate**. On average, under non-exertion conditions, the human respiratory rate is 12–15 breaths/minute. The respiratory rate contributes to the **alveolar ventilation**, or how much air moves into and out of the alveoli. Alveolar ventilation prevents carbon dioxide buildup in the alveoli. There are two ways to keep the alveolar ventilation constant: increase the respiratory rate while decreasing the tidal volume of air per breath (shallow breathing), or decrease the respiratory rate while increasing the tidal volume per breath. In either case, the ventilation remains the same, but the work done and type of work needed are quite different. Both tidal volume and respiratory rate are closely regulated when oxygen demand increases.

There are two types of work conducted during respiration, flow-resistive and elastic work. **Flow-resistive** refers to the work of the alveoli and tissues in the lung, whereas **elastic work** refers to the work of the intercostal muscles, chest wall, and diaphragm. Increasing the respiration rate increases the flow-resistive work of the airways and decreases the elastic work of the muscles. Decreasing the respiratory rate reverses the type of work required.

Surfactant

The air-tissue/water interface of the alveoli has a high surface tension. This surface tension is similar to the surface tension of water at the liquid-air interface of a water droplet that results in the bonding of the water molecules together. **Surfactant** is a complex mixture of phospholipids and lipoproteins that works to reduce the surface tension that exists between the alveoli tissue and the air found within the alveoli. By lowering the surface tension of the alveolar fluid, it reduces the tendency of alveoli to collapse.

Surfactant works like a detergent to reduce the surface tension and allows for easier inflation of the airways. When a balloon is first inflated, it takes a large amount of effort to stretch the plastic and start to inflate the balloon. If a little bit of detergent was applied to the interior of the balloon, then the amount of effort or work needed to begin to inflate the balloon would decrease, and it would become much easier to start blowing up the balloon. This same principle applies to the airways. A small amount of surfactant to the airway tissues reduces the effort or work needed to inflate those airways. Babies born prematurely sometimes do not produce enough surfactant. As a result, they suffer from **respiratory distress syndrome**, because it requires more effort to inflate their lungs. Surfactant is also important for preventing collapse of small alveoli relative to large alveoli.

Lung Resistance and Compliance

Pulmonary diseases reduce the rate of gas exchange into and out of the lungs. Two main causes of decreased gas exchange are **compliance** (how elastic the lung is) and **resistance** (how much obstruction exists in the airways). A change in either can dramatically alter breathing and the ability to take in oxygen and release carbon dioxide.

Examples of **restrictive diseases** are respiratory distress syndrome and pulmonary fibrosis. In both diseases, the airways are less compliant and they are stiff or fibrotic. There is a decrease in compliance because the lung tissue cannot bend and move. In these types of restrictive diseases, the intrapleural pressure is more positive and the airways collapse upon exhalation, which traps air in the lungs. Forced or **functional vital capacity (FVC)**, which is the amount of air that can be forcibly exhaled after taking the deepest breath possible, is much lower than in normal patients, and the time it takes to exhale most of the air is greatly prolonged (Figure 30.18). A patient suffering from these diseases cannot exhale the normal amount of air.

Obstructive diseases and conditions include emphysema, asthma, and pulmonary edema. In emphysema, which mostly arises from smoking tobacco, the walls of the alveoli are destroyed, decreasing the surface area for gas exchange. The overall compliance of the lungs is increased, because as the alveolar walls are damaged, lung elastic recoil decreases due to a loss of elastic fibers, and more air is trapped in the lungs at the end of exhalation. Asthma is a disease in which inflammation is triggered by environmental factors. Inflammation obstructs the airways. The obstruction may be due to edema (fluid accumulation), smooth muscle spasms in the walls of the bronchioles, increased mucus secretion, damage to the epithelia of the airways, or a combination of these events. Those with asthma or edema experience increased occlusion from increased inflammation of the airways. This tends to block the airways, preventing the proper movement of gases (Figure 30.18). Those with obstructive diseases have large volumes of air trapped after exhalation and breathe at a very high lung volume to compensate for the lack of airway recruitment.

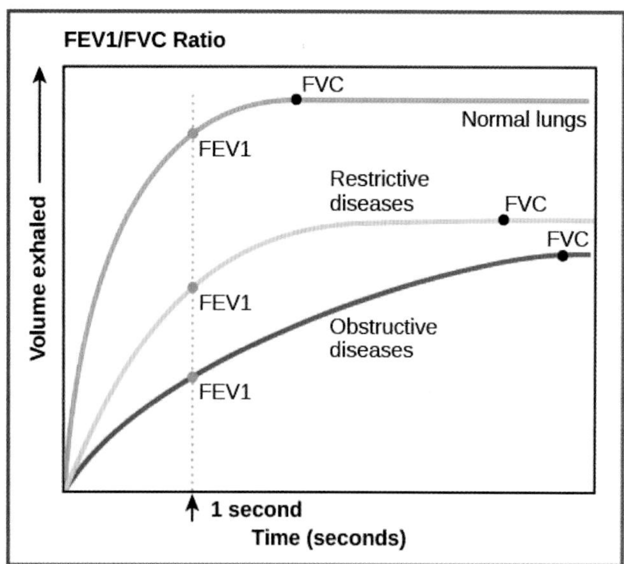

Figure 30.18 The ratio of FEV1 (the amount of air that can be forcibly exhaled in one second after taking a deep breath) to FVC (the total amount of air that can be forcibly exhaled) can be used to diagnose whether a person has restrictive or obstructive lung disease. In restrictive lung disease, FVC is reduced but airways are not obstructed, so the person is able to expel air reasonably fast. In obstructive lung disease, airway obstruction results in slow exhalation as well as reduced FVC. Thus, the FEV1/FVC ratio is lower in persons with obstructive lung disease (less than 69 percent) than in persons with restrictive disease (88 to 90 percent).

Dead Space: V/Q Mismatch

Pulmonary circulation pressure is very low compared to that of the systemic circulation. It is also independent of cardiac output. This is because of a phenomenon called **recruitment**, which is the process of opening airways that normally remain closed when cardiac output increases. As cardiac output increases, the number of capillaries and arteries that are perfused (filled with blood) increases. These capillaries and arteries are not always in use but are ready if needed. At times, however, there is a mismatch between the amount of air (ventilation, V) and the amount of blood (perfusion, Q) in the lungs. This is referred to as **ventilation/perfusion (V/Q) mismatch**.

There are two types of V/Q mismatch. Both produce **dead space**, regions of broken down or blocked lung tissue. Dead spaces can severely impact breathing, because they reduce the surface area available for gas diffusion. As a result, the amount of oxygen in the blood decreases, whereas the carbon dioxide level increases. Dead space is created when no ventilation and/or perfusion takes place. **Anatomical dead space** or anatomical shunt, arises from an anatomical failure, while **physiological dead space** or physiological shunt, arises from a functional impairment of the lung or arteries.

An example of an anatomical shunt is the effect of gravity on the lungs. The lung is particularly susceptible to changes in the magnitude and direction of gravitational forces. When someone is standing or sitting upright, the pleural pressure gradient leads to increased ventilation further down in the lung. As a result, the intrapleural pressure is more negative at the base of the lung than at the top, and more air fills the bottom of the lung than the top. Likewise, it takes less energy to pump blood to the bottom of the lung than to the top when in a prone position. Perfusion of the lung is not uniform while standing or sitting. This is a result of hydrostatic forces combined with the effect of airway pressure. An anatomical shunt develops because the ventilation of the airways does not match the perfusion of the arteries surrounding those airways. As a result, the rate of gas exchange is reduced. Note that this does not occur when lying down, because in this position, gravity does not preferentially pull the bottom of the lung down.

A physiological shunt can develop if there is infection or edema in the lung that obstructs an area. This will decrease ventilation but not affect perfusion; therefore, the V/Q ratio changes and gas exchange is affected.

The lung can compensate for these mismatches in ventilation and perfusion. If ventilation is greater than perfusion, the arterioles dilate and the bronchioles constrict. This increases perfusion and reduces ventilation. Likewise, if ventilation is less than perfusion, the arterioles constrict and the bronchioles dilate to correct the imbalance.

Visit this site (http://openstaxcollege.org/l/breathing) to view the mechanics of breathing.

How does the downward movement of the diaphragm allow us to breathe?

a. It reduces the volume of the thoracic cavity, increasing the air pressure in the lungs and triggering inhalation.

b. It reduces the volume of the thoracic cavity, increasing the air pressure in the lungs and triggering exhalation.

c. It creates a partial vacuum in the thoracic cavity into which outside air flows during exhalation.

d. It creates a partial vacuum in the thoracic cavity into which outside air flows during inhalation.

30.4 | Transport of Gases in Human Bodily Fluids

In this section, you will explore the following questions:

- How is oxygen bound to hemoglobin and transported to body tissues?
- How is carbon dioxide transported from body tissues to the lungs?

Connection for AP® Courses

Gas exchange at the tissue level also occurs by diffusion. The majority of oxygen transported from the lungs to body tissue is bound to a protein called hemoglobin. Hemoglobin is a quaternary protein comprise of four iron-containing heme groups; iron has a great affinity for oxygen. (We know this because iron rusts when exposed to air.)

Information presented and the examples highlighted in the section support concepts outlined in Big Idea 4 of the AP® Biology Curriculum Framework. The AP® Learning Objectives listed in the Curriculum Framework provide a transparent foundation for the AP® Biology course, an inquiry-based laboratory experience, instructional activities, and AP® exam questions. A learning objective merges required content with one or more of the seven science practices.

Big Idea 4	Biological systems interact, and these systems and their interactions possess complex properties.
Enduring Understanding 4.A	Interactions within biological systems lead to complex properties.
Essential Knowledge	**4.A.1** The subcomponents of biological molecules and their sequence determine the properties of that molecule.
Science Practice	**6.1** The student can justify claims with evidence.
Science Practice	**6.4** The student can make claims and predictions about natural phenomena based on scientific theories and models.
Learning Objective	**4.3** The student is able to use models to predict and justify that changes in the subcomponents of a biological polymer affect the functionality of the molecule.

Once the oxygen diffuses across the alveoli, it enters the bloodstream and is transported to the tissues where it is unloaded, and carbon dioxide diffuses out of the blood and into the alveoli to be expelled from the body. Although gas exchange is a continuous process, the oxygen and carbon dioxide are transported by different mechanisms.

Transport of Oxygen in the Blood

Although oxygen dissolves in blood, only a small amount of oxygen is transported this way. Only 1.5 percent of oxygen in the blood is dissolved directly into the blood itself. Most oxygen—98.5 percent—is bound to a protein called hemoglobin and carried to the tissues.

Hemoglobin

Hemoglobin, or Hb, is a protein molecule found in red blood cells (erythrocytes) made of four subunits: two alpha subunits and two beta subunits (Figure 30.19). Each subunit surrounds a central **heme group** that contains iron and binds one oxygen molecule, allowing each hemoglobin molecule to bind four oxygen molecules. Molecules with more oxygen bound to the heme groups are brighter red. As a result, oxygenated arterial blood where the Hb is carrying four oxygen molecules is bright red, while venous blood that is deoxygenated is darker red.

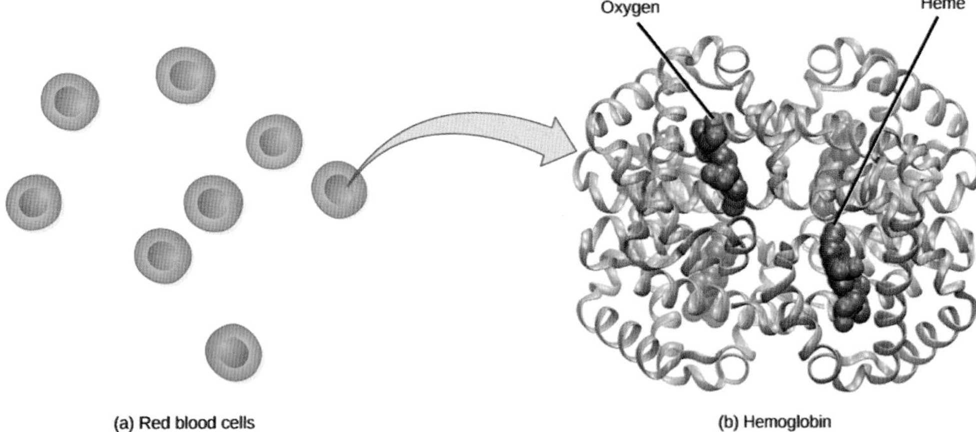

Figure 30.19 The protein inside (a) red blood cells that carries oxygen to cells and carbon dioxide to the lungs is (b) hemoglobin. Hemoglobin is made up of four symmetrical subunits and four heme groups. Iron associated with the heme binds oxygen. It is the iron in hemoglobin that gives blood its red color.

It is easier to bind a second and third oxygen molecule to Hb than the first molecule. This is because the hemoglobin molecule changes its shape, or conformation, as oxygen binds. The fourth oxygen is then more difficult to bind. The binding of oxygen to hemoglobin can be plotted as a function of the partial pressure of oxygen in the blood (x-axis) versus the relative Hb-oxygen saturation (y-axis). The resulting graph—an **oxygen dissociation curve**—is sigmoidal, or S-shaped (Figure 30.20). As the partial pressure of oxygen increases, the hemoglobin becomes increasingly saturated with oxygen.

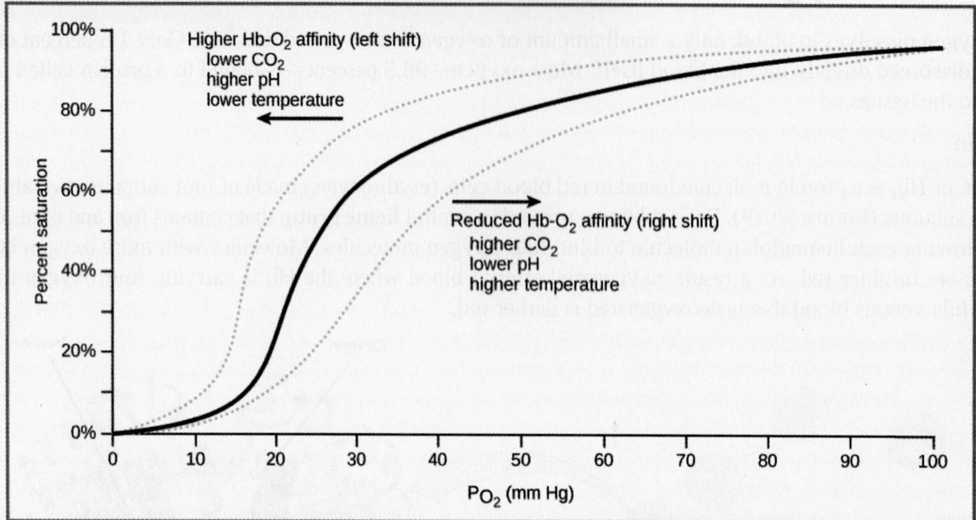

Figure 30.20 The oxygen dissociation curve demonstrates that, as the partial pressure of oxygen increases, more oxygen binds hemoglobin. However, the affinity of hemoglobin for oxygen may shift to the left or the right depending on environmental conditions.

The kidneys are responsible for removing excess hydrogen ions from the blood. If the kidneys fail, what would happen to blood pH and hemoglobin affinity for oxygen?

a. The blood pH will drop and hemoglobin affinity for oxygen will increase.
b. The blood pH will increase and hemoglobin affinity for oxygen will drop.
c. The blood pH will drop and hemoglobin affinity for oxygen will decrease.
d. The blood pH will increase and hemoglobin affinity for oxygen will also increase.

Factors That Affect Oxygen Binding

The **oxygen-carrying capacity** of hemoglobin determines how much oxygen is carried in the blood. In addition to P_{O_2}, other environmental factors and diseases can affect oxygen carrying capacity and delivery.

Carbon dioxide levels, blood pH, and body temperature affect oxygen-carrying capacity (Figure 30.20). When carbon dioxide is in the blood, it reacts with water to form bicarbonate (HCO_3^-) and hydrogen ions (H^+). As the level of carbon dioxide in the blood increases, more H^+ is produced and the pH decreases. This increase in carbon dioxide and subsequent decrease in pH reduce the affinity of hemoglobin for oxygen. The oxygen dissociates from the Hb molecule, shifting the oxygen dissociation curve to the right. Therefore, more oxygen is needed to reach the same hemoglobin saturation level as when the pH was higher. A similar shift in the curve also results from an increase in body temperature. Increased temperature, such as from increased activity of skeletal muscle, causes the affinity of hemoglobin for oxygen to be reduced.

Diseases like sickle cell anemia and thalassemia decrease the blood's ability to deliver oxygen to tissues and its oxygen-carrying capacity. In **sickle cell anemia**, the shape of the red blood cell is crescent-shaped, elongated, and stiffened, reducing its ability to deliver oxygen (Figure 30.21). In this form, red blood cells cannot pass through the capillaries. This is painful when it occurs. **Thalassemia** is a rare genetic disease caused by a defect in either the alpha or the beta subunit of Hb. Patients with thalassemia produce a high number of red blood cells, but these cells have lower-than-normal levels of hemoglobin. Therefore, the oxygen-carrying capacity is diminished.

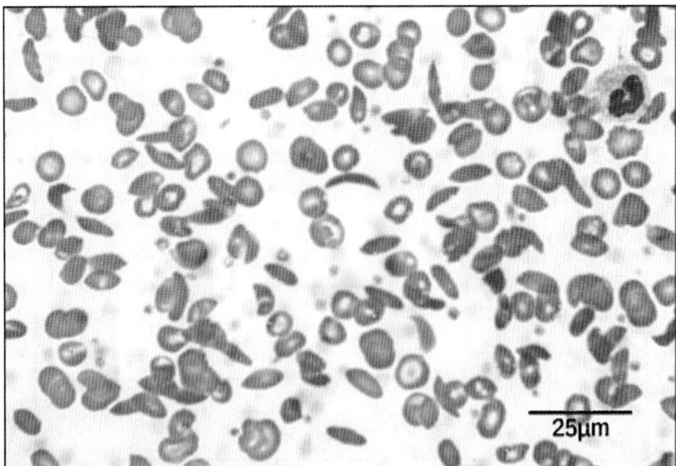

Figure 30.21 Individuals with sickle cell anemia have crescent-shaped red blood cells. (credit: modification of work by Ed Uthman; scale-bar data from Matt Russell)

Transport of Carbon Dioxide in the Blood

Carbon dioxide molecules are transported in the blood from body tissues to the lungs by one of three methods: dissolution directly into the blood, binding to hemoglobin, or carried as a bicarbonate ion. Several properties of carbon dioxide in the blood affect its transport. First, carbon dioxide is more soluble in blood than oxygen. About 5 to 7 percent of all carbon dioxide is dissolved in the plasma. Second, carbon dioxide can bind to plasma proteins or can enter red blood cells and bind to hemoglobin. This form transports about 10 percent of the carbon dioxide. When carbon dioxide binds to hemoglobin, a molecule called **carbaminohemoglobin** is formed. Binding of carbon dioxide to hemoglobin is reversible. Therefore, when it reaches the lungs, the carbon dioxide can freely dissociate from the hemoglobin and be expelled from the body.

Third, the majority of carbon dioxide molecules (85 percent) are carried as part of the **bicarbonate buffer system**. In this system, carbon dioxide diffuses into the red blood cells. **Carbonic anhydrase (CA)** within the red blood cells quickly converts the carbon dioxide into carbonic acid (H_2CO_3). Carbonic acid is an unstable intermediate molecule that immediately dissociates into **bicarbonate ions** ($\mathbf{HCO_3^-}$) and hydrogen (H^+) ions. Since carbon dioxide is quickly converted into bicarbonate ions, this reaction allows for the continued uptake of carbon dioxide into the blood down its concentration gradient. It also results in the production of H^+ ions. If too much H^+ is produced, it can alter blood pH. However, hemoglobin binds to the free H^+ ions and thus limits shifts in pH. The newly synthesized bicarbonate ion is transported out of the red blood cell into the liquid component of the blood in exchange for a chloride ion (Cl^-); this is called the **chloride shift**. When the blood reaches the lungs, the bicarbonate ion is transported back into the red blood cell in exchange for the chloride ion. The H^+ ion dissociates from the hemoglobin and binds to the bicarbonate ion. This produces the carbonic acid intermediate, which is converted back into carbon dioxide through the enzymatic action of CA. The carbon dioxide produced is expelled through the lungs during exhalation.

$$CO_2 + H_2O \leftrightarrow \underset{\text{(carbonic acid)}}{H_2CO_3} \leftrightarrow \underset{\text{(bicarbonate)}}{HCO_3 + H^+}$$

The benefit of the bicarbonate buffer system is that carbon dioxide is "soaked up" into the blood with little change to the pH of the system. This is important because it takes only a small change in the overall pH of the body for severe injury or death to result. The presence of this bicarbonate buffer system also allows for people to travel and live at high altitudes: When the partial pressure of oxygen and carbon dioxide change at high altitudes, the bicarbonate buffer system adjusts to regulate carbon dioxide while maintaining the correct pH in the body.

Carbon Monoxide Poisoning

While carbon dioxide can readily associate and dissociate from hemoglobin, other molecules such as carbon monoxide (CO) cannot. Carbon monoxide has a greater affinity for hemoglobin than oxygen. Therefore, when carbon monoxide is present, it binds to hemoglobin preferentially over oxygen. As a result, oxygen cannot bind to hemoglobin, so very little oxygen is transported through the body (Figure 30.22). Carbon monoxide is a colorless, odorless gas and is therefore difficult to detect. It is produced by gas-powered vehicles and tools. Carbon monoxide can cause headaches, confusion, and nausea; long-term exposure can cause brain damage or death. Administering 100 percent (pure) oxygen is the usual treatment for carbon monoxide poisoning. Administration of pure oxygen speeds up the separation of carbon monoxide from hemoglobin.

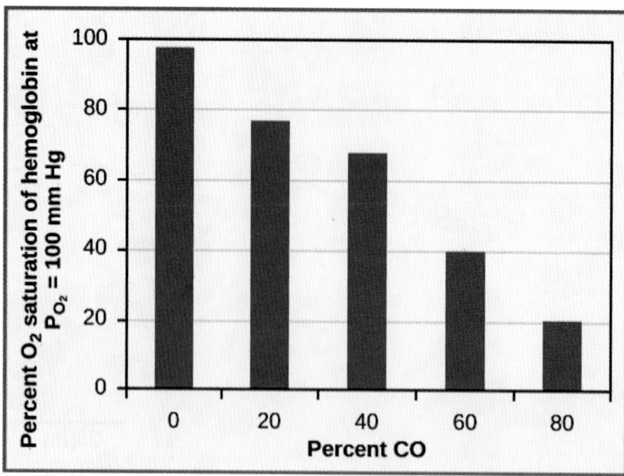

Figure 30.22 As percent CO increases, the oxygen saturation of hemoglobin decreases.

science practices CONNECTION for AP® Courses

Think About It

How does the administration of 100 percent oxygen save a patient from carbon monoxide poisoning? Why wouldn't giving carbon dioxide work?

everyday CONNECTION for AP® Courses

Fuel burning items around the home can leak carbon monoxide gas. Because it is tasteless and odorless, people might not be aware of the leak, putting them at great risk for carbon monoxide poisoning. Carbon monoxide detectors, such as the one pictured here, have saved countless lives by alerting people to a dangerous build-up of carbon monoxide.

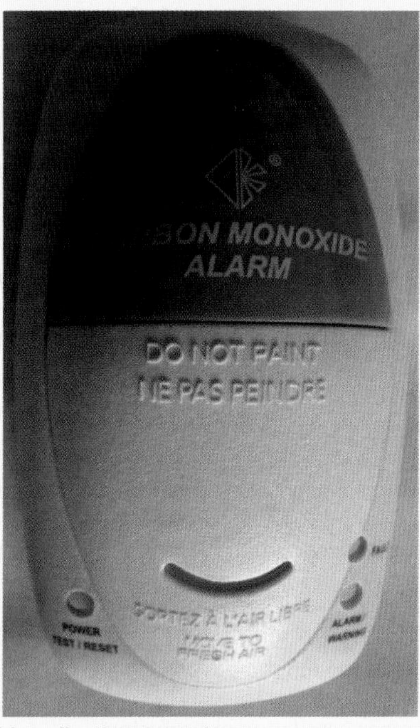

Figure 30.23 (credit: Sideroxylon, Wikimedia Commons)

Why is it more important to have a detector for carbon monoxide than other household gases, such as ammonia or natural gas?

a. Because carbon monoxide is tasteless and has a light odor, which is detected very late in exposure.

b. Because carbon monoxide has a stronger odor, making it more unpleasant and dangerous.

c. Because carbon monoxide is odorless and tasteless, unlike ammonia and household natural gas which have distinct smells.

d. Because carbon monoxide should not be present in the environment at all.

KEY TERMS

alveolar P_{O_2} partial pressure of oxygen in the alveoli (usually around 100 mmHg)

alveolar duct duct that extends from the terminal bronchiole to the alveolar sac

alveolar sac structure consisting of two or more alveoli that share a common opening

alveolar ventilation how much air is in the alveoli

alveolus (plural: alveoli) (also, air sac) terminal region of the lung where gas exchange occurs

anatomical dead space (also, anatomical shunt) region of the lung that lacks proper ventilation/perfusion due to an anatomical block

bicarbonate (HCO_3^-) ion ion created when carbonic acid dissociates into H^+ and (HCO_3^-)

bicarbonate buffer system system in the blood that absorbs carbon dioxide and regulates pH levels

bronchiole airway that extends from the main tertiary bronchi to the alveolar sac

bronchus (plural: bronchi) smaller branch of cartilaginous tissue that stems off of the trachea; air is funneled through the bronchi to the region where gas exchange occurs in alveoli

carbaminohemoglobin molecule that forms when carbon dioxide binds to hemoglobin

carbonic anhydrase (CA) enzyme that catalyzes carbon dioxide and water into carbonic acid

chloride shift chloride shift exchange of chloride for bicarbonate into or out of the red blood cell

compliance measurement of the elasticity of the lung

dead space area in the lung that lacks proper ventilation or perfusion

diaphragm domed-shaped skeletal muscle located under lungs that separates the thoracic cavity from the abdominal cavity

elastic recoil property of the lung that drives the lung tissue inward

elastic work work conducted by the intercostal muscles, chest wall, and diaphragm

expiratory reserve volume (ERV) amount of additional air that can be exhaled after a normal exhalation

FEV1/FVC ratio ratio of how much air can be forced out of the lung in one second to the total amount that is forced out of the lung; a measurement of lung function that can be used to detect disease states

flow-resistive work of breathing performed by the alveoli and tissues in the lung

forced expiratory volume (FEV) (also, forced vital capacity) measure of how much air can be forced out of the lung from maximal inspiration over a specific amount of time

functional residual capacity (FRC) expiratory reserve volume plus residual volume

functional vital capacity (FVC) amount of air that can be forcibly exhaled after taking the deepest breath possible

heme group centralized iron-containing group that is surrounded by the alpha and beta subunits of hemoglobin

hemoglobin molecule in red blood cells that can bind oxygen, carbon dioxide, and carbon monoxide

inspiratory capacity (IC) tidal volume plus inspiratory reserve volume

inspiratory reserve volume (IRV) amount of additional air that can be inspired after a normal inhalation

intercostal muscle muscle connected to the rib cage that contracts upon inspiration

intrapleural space space between the layers of pleura

larynx voice box, a short passageway connecting the pharynx and the trachea

lung capacity measurement of two or more lung volumes (how much air can be inhaled from the end of an expiration to maximal capacity)

lung volume measurement of air for one lung function (normal inhalation or exhalation)

mucin complex glycoprotein found in mucus

mucus sticky protein-containing fluid secretion in the lung that traps particulate matter to be expelled from the body

nasal cavity opening of the respiratory system to the outside environment

obstructive disease disease (such as emphysema and asthma) that arises from obstruction of the airways; compliance increases in these diseases

oxygen dissociation curve curve depicting the affinity of oxygen for hemoglobin

oxygen-carrying capacity amount of oxygen that can be transported in the blood

partial pressure amount of pressure exerted by one gas within a mixture of gases

particulate matter small particle such as dust, dirt, viral particles, and bacteria that are in the air

pharynx throat; a tube that starts in the internal nares and runs partway down the neck, where it opens into the esophagus and the larynx

physiological dead space (also, physiological shunt) region of the lung that lacks proper ventilation/perfusion due to a physiological change in the lung (like inflammation or edema)

pleura tissue layer that surrounds the lungs and lines the interior of the thoracic cavity

pleurisy painful inflammation of the pleural tissue layers

primary bronchus (also, main bronchus) region of the airway within the lung that attaches to the trachea and bifurcates to each lung where it branches into secondary bronchi

recruitment process of opening airways that normally remain closed when the cardiac output increases

residual volume (RV) amount of air remaining in the lung after a maximal expiration

resistance measurement of lung obstruction

respiratory bronchiole terminal portion of the bronchiole tree that is attached to the terminal bronchioles and alveoli ducts, alveolar sacs, and alveoli

respiratory distress syndrome disease that arises from a deficient amount of surfactant

respiratory quotient (RQ) ratio of carbon dioxide production to each oxygen molecule consumed

respiratory rate number of breaths per minute

restrictive disease disease that results from a restriction and decreased compliance of the alveoli; respiratory distress syndrome and pulmonary fibrosis are examples

sickle cell anemia genetic disorder that affects the shape of red blood cells, and their ability to transport oxygen and move through capillaries

spirometry method to measure lung volumes and to diagnose lung diseases

surfactant detergent-like liquid in the airways that lowers the surface tension of the alveoli to allow for expansion

terminal bronchiole region of bronchiole that attaches to the respiratory bronchioles

thalassemia rare genetic disorder that results in mutation of the alpha or beta subunits of hemoglobin, creating smaller red blood cells with less hemoglobin

tidal volume (TV) amount of air that is inspired and expired during normal breathing

total lung capacity (TLC) sum of the residual volume, expiratory reserve volume, tidal volume, and inspiratory reserve volume

trachea cartilaginous tube that transports air from the larynx to the primary bronchi

venous P_{CO_2} partial pressure of carbon dioxide in the veins (40 mm Hg in the pulmonary veins)

venous P_{O_2} partial pressure of oxygen in the veins (100 mm Hg in the pulmonary veins)

ventilation/perfusion (V/Q) mismatch region of the lung that lacks proper alveolar ventilation (V) and/or arterial perfusion (Q)

vital capacity (VC) sum of the expiratory reserve volume, tidal volume, and inspiratory reserve volume

CHAPTER SUMMARY

30.1 Systems of Gas Exchange

Animal respiratory systems are designed to facilitate gas exchange. In mammals, air is warmed and humidified in the nasal cavity. Air then travels down the pharynx, through the trachea, and into the lungs. In the lungs, air passes through the branching bronchi, reaching the respiratory bronchioles, which house the first site of gas exchange. The respiratory bronchioles open into the alveolar ducts, alveolar sacs, and alveoli. Because there are so many alveoli and alveolar sacs in the lung, the surface area for gas exchange is very large. Several protective mechanisms are in place to prevent damage or infection. These include the hair and mucus in the nasal cavity that trap dust, dirt, and other particulate matter before they can enter the system. In the lungs, particles are trapped in a mucus layer and transported via cilia up to the esophageal opening at the top of the trachea to be swallowed.

30.2 Gas Exchange across Respiratory Surfaces

The lungs can hold a large volume of air, but they are not usually filled to maximal capacity. Lung volume measurements include tidal volume, expiratory reserve volume, inspiratory reserve volume, and residual volume. The sum of these equals the total lung capacity. Gas movement into or out of the lungs is dependent on the pressure of the gas. Air is a mixture of gases; therefore, the partial pressure of each gas can be calculated to determine how the gas will flow in the lung. The difference between the partial pressure of the gas in the air drives oxygen into the tissues and carbon dioxide out of the body.

30.3 Breathing

The structure of the lungs and thoracic cavity control the mechanics of breathing. Upon inspiration, the diaphragm contracts and lowers. The intercostal muscles contract and expand the chest wall outward. The intrapleural pressure drops, the lungs expand, and air is drawn into the airways. When exhaling, the intercostal muscles and diaphragm relax, returning the intrapleural pressure back to the resting state. The lungs recoil and airways close. The air passively exits the lung. There is high surface tension at the air-airway interface in the lung. Surfactant, a mixture of phospholipids and lipoproteins, acts like a detergent in the airways to reduce surface tension and allow for opening of the alveoli.

Breathing and gas exchange are both altered by changes in the compliance and resistance of the lung. If the compliance of the lung decreases, as occurs in restrictive diseases like fibrosis, the airways stiffen and collapse upon exhalation. Air becomes trapped in the lungs, making breathing more difficult. If resistance increases, as happens with asthma or emphysema, the airways become obstructed, trapping air in the lungs and causing breathing to become difficult. Alterations in the ventilation of the airways or perfusion of the arteries can affect gas exchange. These changes in ventilation and perfusion, called V/Q mismatch, can arise from anatomical or physiological changes.

30.4 Transport of Gases in Human Bodily Fluids

Hemoglobin is a protein found in red blood cells that is comprised of two alpha and two beta subunits that surround an iron-containing heme group. Oxygen readily binds this heme group. The ability of oxygen to bind increases as more oxygen molecules are bound to heme. Disease states and altered conditions in the body can affect the binding ability of oxygen, and increase or decrease its ability to dissociate from hemoglobin.

Carbon dioxide can be transported through the blood via three methods. It is dissolved directly in the blood, bound to plasma proteins or hemoglobin, or converted into bicarbonate. The majority of carbon dioxide is transported as part of the bicarbonate system. Carbon dioxide diffuses into red blood cells. Inside, carbonic anhydrase converts carbon dioxide into carbonic acid (H_2CO_3), which is subsequently hydrolyzed into bicarbonate (HCO_3^-) and H^+. The H^+ ion binds to hemoglobin in red blood cells, and bicarbonate is transported out of the red blood cells in exchange for a chloride ion. This is called the chloride shift. Bicarbonate leaves the red blood cells and enters the blood plasma. In the lungs, bicarbonate is transported back into the red blood cells in exchange for chloride. The H^+ dissociates from hemoglobin and combines with bicarbonate to form carbonic acid with the help of carbonic anhydrase, which further catalyzes the reaction to convert carbonic acid back into carbon dioxide and water. The carbon dioxide is then expelled from the lungs.

REVIEW QUESTIONS

1. What is the primary function of the respiratory system?

a. provides body tissues with oxygen
b. provides body tissues with oxygen and carbon dioxide
c. establishes how many breaths are taken per minute
d. provides the body with carbon dioxide

2. What is the order of airflow during inhalation?

a. nasal cavity, larynx, trachea, bronchi, bronchioles, alveoli
b. nasal cavity, larynx, trachea, bronchioles, bronchi, alveoli
c. nasal cavity, trachea, larynx, bronchi, bronchioles, alveoli
d. nasal cavity, trachea, larynx, bronchi, bronchioles, alveoli

3. What advantages does warming air within the nasal passages provide?

a. reduces rates of lung infection
b. prevents foreign objects from entering the lungs
c. prevents cell damage caused by cold air
d. reduces fluid accumulation from cold, wet air

4. Emphysema is a disease characterized by a great reduction in the number of functioning alveoli in the lungs. What effect would emphysema likely have on the respiratory system?

a. Less gas exchange would occur with the blood.
b. Less air could travel through the trachea.
c. Air could no longer pass through the nasal cavity.
d. Air could no longer vibrate the vocal cords of the larynx.

5. The inspiratory reserve volume measures the____.

a. amount of air remaining in the lung after a maximal exhalation
b. amount of air the lung holds
c. amount of air that can be further exhaled after a normal breath
d. amount of air that can be further inhaled after a normal breath

6. The total lung capacity is calculated using which formula?

a. residual volume + tidal volume + inspiratory reserve volume
b. residual volume + expiratory reserve volume + inspiratory reserve volume
c. expiratory reserve volume + tidal volume + inspiratory reserve volume
d. residual volume + expiratory reserve volume + tidal volume + inspiratory reserve volume

7. Why is the partial pressure of oxygen lower in the lung than in the external air?

a. Oxygen is constantly being removed by air in the lungs through the blood.
b. Carbon dioxide does not mix with oxygen in the lung.
c. The lungs exert pressure on the air to reduce the oxygen pressure.
d. Changes in water vapor pressure cause less oxygen to enter the air in the lungs.

8. How can a decrease in the percent of oxygen in the air affect the movement of oxygen in the body?

a. It would not affect the rate of diffusion into the blood because there would be no difference between the partial pressures of the air and blood.

b. It would decrease the rate of diffusion into the blood because it increases the difference between the partial pressures of the air and blood.

c. It would increase the rate of diffusion into the blood because it reduces the difference between the partial pressures of the air and blood.

d. It would decrease the rate of diffusion into the blood because it reduces the difference between the partial pressures of the air and blood.

9. What role do the intercostal muscles play in inspiration and expiration?

a. They move down, causing inspiration, and move up, causing expiration.

b. They move up, causing inspiration, and move down, causing expiration.

c. They relax, causing inspiration, and contract, causing expiration.

d. They contract, causing inspiration, and relax, causing expiration.

10. How would paralysis of the diaphragm alter inspiration?

a. It would prevent contraction of the intercostal muscles.

b. It would prevent inhalation because the intrapleural pressure would not change.

c. It would decrease the intrapleural pressure and allow more air to enter the lungs.

d. It would slow expiration because the lung would not relax.

11. Restrictive airway diseases _____.

a. increase the compliance of the lung

b. decrease the compliance of the lung

c. increase the lung volume

d. decrease the work of breathing

12. A patient is suffering from an allergic reaction that causes his airways to swell up. How would this most likely affect resistance of the respiratory system, and why?

a. Resistance decreases because it will be harder for air to flow through the airways.

b. Resistance decreases because the airways are more compliant.

c. Resistance increases because it will be harder for air to flow through the airways.

d. Resistance increases because the airways are more compliant.

13. What is a physiological dead space and what could be its cause?

a. A physiological dead space is a region of lung tissue that is leaking air. It could be caused by a puncture wound.

b. A physiological dead space is a region of lung tissue that is not receiving electrical stimulation from the nervous system. It could be caused by a reduction in neurotransmitters.

c. A physiological dead space is a region of lung tissue that is not involved in gas exchange because the tissue is not functioning properly. It could be caused by the alveoli capillaries are not receiving blood flow.

d. A physiological dead space is a region of lung tissue that is not involved in gas exchange because the tissue has a defect in its structure. It could be caused by a genetic condition.

14. How will the respiratory rate and volume of air per breath change if alveolar ventilation is too high or too low?

a. If ventilation is low, the respiratory rate will decrease while the volume of air per breath is decreased. If ventilation is high, the respiratory rate will increase while the volume of air per breath decreases.

b. If ventilation is low, the respiratory rate will decrease while the volume of air per breath is increased. If ventilation is high, the respiratory rate will increase while the volume of air per breath decreases.

c. If ventilation is low, the respiratory rate will increase while the volume of air per breath is decreased. If ventilation is high, the respiratory rate will increase while the volume of air per breath increases.

d. If ventilation is low, the respiratory rate will increase while the volume of air per breath is decreased. If ventilation is high, the respiratory rate will increase while the volume of air per breath decreases.

15. What does elastic recoil in the lungs refer to and does it aid inspiration or expiration?

a. the ability of the diaphragm to contract and relax to change the volume of the lung, inspiration
b. the reserve air in the lungs that is present even after maximum exhalation, expiration
c. the ability of the bronchioles to expand and retract as air enters and exits, inspiration
d. the ability of lung tissue to exert pressure back towards the lung's interior, expiration

16. Low pH in the blood will _____ hemoglobin's affinity for _____.

a. increase, carbon dioxide
b. increase, oxygen
c. decrease, carbon dioxide
d. decrease, oxygen

17. Which of the following will not facilitate the transfer of oxygen to tissues?

a. decreased body temperature
b. decreased pH of the blood
c. increased carbon dioxide
d. increased exercise

18. How is the majority of carbon dioxide in the blood transported?

a. binding to hemoglobin
b. dissolution in the blood
c. as bicarbonate
d. binding to plasma proteins

19. How is the chloride shift related to the transport of carbon dioxide in the blood?

a. It allows carbon dioxide, in the form of bicarbonate ions, to enter the blood plasma.
b. It creates carbaminohemoglobin within the red blood cells.
c. It allows the conversion of carbon dioxide into carbonic acid within red blood cells.
d. It prevents the formation of bicarbonate ions in the blood.

CRITICAL THINKING QUESTIONS

20. How does the structure of alveoli maximize gas exchange?

a. Their sac-like structure increases their surface area.
b. Their direct connection to the bronchi maximizes their access to air.
c. They actively transport the gases between the air and blood.
d. They are spheres that fully fill with blood, which will come in contact with air.

21. What structures of the respiratory system warm and remove impurities from inhaled air?

a. The epiglottis deflects impurities out of the trachea and into the esophagus, while the nasal cavity warms the air.
b. Hair and mucus in the nose and trachea catch impurities, while the nasal cavity warms the air.
c. Saliva in the mouth and hair in the trachea catch impurities, while the pharynx warms the air.
d. The closed-off compartments of the larynx trap impurities in the air and warm the air.

22. If you were travelling in a miniaturized ship through the respiratory system, from the pharynx to an alveolus, which structures would you pass along the way, and in what order?

a. trachea, larynx, bronchi, and bronchioles
b. larynx, trachea, bronchi, and bronchioles
c. bronchioles, bronchi, trachea, and larynx
d. bronchioles, trachea, bronchi, and larynx

23. What does FEV1/FVC measure and why will the ratio increase with lung fibrosis?

a. the forced expiratory volume in one second in relation to the total forced vital capacity; lung fibrosis causes the lungs to decrease in size
b. the functional expiratory volume in one second in relation to the total functional vital capacity; lung fibrosis causes the lungs to decrease in size
c. the functional expiratory volume in one second in relation to the total functional vital capacity; lung fibrosis causes the lungs to become less pliable
d. the forced expiratory volume in one second in relation to the total forced vital capacity; lung fibrosis causes the lungs to become less pliable

24. Compare the partial pressure of oxygen between venous blood in an alveolus and air and between arterial blood and body tissues?

a. higher in the blood than in the air and higher in the blood than in the body tissues
b. lower in the blood than in the air and higher in the blood than in the body tissues
c. higher in the blood than in the air and lower in the blood than in the body tissues
d. lower in the blood than in the air and lower in the blood than in the body tissues

25. What conditions of the lungs would cause a an increase in FEV1/FVC? What about a decrease FEV1/FVC?

a. This ratio increases as the lungs become stiff and less pliable, increasing further when there is increased resistance in the lung.
b. This ratio decreases as the lungs become stiff and less pliable, increasing when there is increased resistance in the lung.
c. This ratio increases as the lungs become stiff and less pliable, decreasing when there is increased resistance in the lung.
d. This ratio decreases as the lungs become stiff and less pliable, decreasing further when there is increased resistance in the lung.

26. Amphibians, such as frogs, breathe by collecting air in a pouch below their throat. Muscles then contract the pouch and force air into their lungs. How does this differ from inhalation in humans and other mammals?

a. Inhalation in humans and other mammals involves the openings called spiracles, which connect to the tubular network to allow the oxygen to pass into the body.
b. Inhalation in humans and other mammals involve direct diffusion across the outer membrane to meet oxygen requirements. Gases can diffuse quickly through direct diffusion.
c. Inhalation in humans and other mammals involve contracting the thoracic cavity by creating negative pressure in the lungs, which causes air to diffuse into the lungs.
d. Inhalation in humans and other mammals involves expanding the thoracic cavity by creating negative pressure in the lungs, which causes air to diffuse into the lungs.

27. If a patient has increased resistance in his or her lungs, how can this be detected by a doctor? What does this mean?

a. This can be detected using a nebulizer. By detecting the rate at which air can be taken into the lung, a diagnosis of a restrictive disease can be made.
b. This can be detected using spirometry. By detecting the rate at which air can be taken into the lung, a diagnosis of a restrictive disease can be made.
c. This can be detected using a nebulizer. By detecting the rate at which air can be expelled from the lung, a diagnosis of a restrictive disease can be made.
d. This can be detected using spirometry. By detecting the rate at which air can be expelled from the lung, a diagnosis of a restrictive disease can be made.

28. When someone is standing, gravity stretches the bottom of the lung down toward the floor to a greater extent than the top of the lung. What implication could this have on ventilation in the lungs?

a. Concentration gradient leads to increased ventilation further down in the lung.
b. Pleural pressure gradient leads to increased ventilation further down in the lung.
c. Pleural pressure gradient leads to decreased ventilation further down in the lung.
d. Concentration gradient leads to decreased ventilation further down in the lung.

29. How does the administration of 100 percent oxygen save a patient from carbon monoxide poisoning? Why wouldn't giving carbon dioxide work?

a. At that concentration, oxygen will be transported in the body at a high rate by dissolving in blood. Oxygen has more affinity for hemoglobin than carbon dioxide.
b. At that concentration, oxygen will displace the carbon monoxide from the hemoglobin. Oxygen has more affinity for hemoglobin than carbon dioxide.
c. At that concentration, oxygen will displace the carbon monoxide from the hemoglobin. Carbon dioxide has more affinity for hemoglobin than oxygen.
d. At that concentration, oxygen will be transported in the body at a high rate by dissolving in blood. Carbon dioxide has more affinity for hemoglobin than oxygen.

30. What would happen if no carbonic anhydrase was present in red blood cells?

a. Carbon dioxide would be hydrolyzed into carbonic acid or bicarbonate. The maximum amount of carbon dioxide would be transported in the blood away from the tissues.
b. Carbon dioxide would not be hydrolyzed into carbonic acid or bicarbonate. The maximum amount of carbon dioxide would be transported in the blood away from the tissues.
c. Oxygen would not be hydrolyzed into carbonic acid or bicarbonate. Only 15 percent of carbon dioxide would be transported in the blood away from the tissues.
d. Carbon dioxide would not be hydrolyzed into carbonic acid or bicarbonate. Only 15 percent of carbon dioxide would be transported in the blood away from the tissues.

31. What is sickle cell anemia and how does it affect the perfusion of oxygen in the blood?

a. It is a genetic disease in which red blood cells are sickle-shaped, reducing oxygen perfusion into the blood.
b. It is a genetic disease in which red blood cells are sickle-shaped, increasing oxygen perfusion into the blood.
c. It is a deficiency disease in which red blood cells are sickle-shaped, reducing oxygen perfusion into the blood.
d. It is a deficiency disease in which red blood cells are sickle-shaped, increasing oxygen perfusion into the blood.

TEST PREP FOR AP® COURSES

32.

The cell of the unicellular algae *Ventricaria ventricosa* is one of the largest known, reaching one to five centimeters in diameter. Like all single-celled organisms, *V. ventricosa* exchanges gases across the cell membrane. What adaptations would *V. ventricosa* likely have evolved related to its large size and ability to exchange materials with the outside environment?

a. adaptations that would decrease cell metabolism to meet the needs of the large cell
b. adaptations that would make the cell thicker, to reduce the loss of nutrients
c. adaptations that make diffusion or nutrient passage across their cell membrane more efficient due to the large size of the cell
d. adaptations that allow the cell to take in larger food objects using the components of its cell membrane

33. In the past, the Earth has experienced environmental changes, which have changed the amount of available oxygen and carbon dioxide in the water and air. For example, there is evidence of less oxygen available in the air during the time of the dinosaurs, a result of high volcanic activity creating a large amount of carbon dioxide. How might red blood cells in the dinosaurs have evolved, in terms of size and shape, to adapt to the lower-oxygen atmosphere?

a. evolve smaller size and flatter shape.
b. evolve larger size and a pointy shape.
c. evolve smaller size and a thicker shape.
d. evolve larger size and a shorter shape.

34. Figure 30.10 shows a human alveolus, which is part of the respiratory system. What do arrows A and B represent in the diagram?

a. A: inhaled air; B: blood travelling from the heart
b. A: exhaled air; B: blood travelling from the heart
c. A: inhaled air; B: blood travelling to the heart
d. A: exhaled air; B: blood traveling from the heart

35. Intubation is a procedure used by ambulance crews that allows a person to breathe if part of the respiratory system is blocked by a foreign object (or otherwise injured). During intubation, a long, plastic tube is placed in the respiratory system so that air can bypass the obstructed area and reach the lungs. Typically, air is supplied artificially using a squeezable bag that connects to the top of the tube.The illustration shows the human respiratory system. The nasal cavity is a wide cavity above and behind the nostrils, and the pharynx is the passageway behind the mouth. The nasal cavity and pharynx join and enter the trachea through the larynx. The larynx is somewhat wider than the trachea and flat. The trachea has concentric, ring-like grooves, giving it a bumpy appearance. The trachea bifurcates into two primary bronchi, which are also grooved. The primary bronchi enter the lungs, and branch into secondary bronchi. The secondary bronchi in turn branch into many tertiary bronchi. The tertiary bronchi branch into bronchioles, which branch into terminal bronchioles. The diaphragm pushes up against the lungs. There is an intubation site indicated at the beginning of the pharynx. A patient has been surgically intubated in the location shown in the diagram. Based on this information, explain where the injury likely occurred in the patient's respiratory system. Justify your answer.

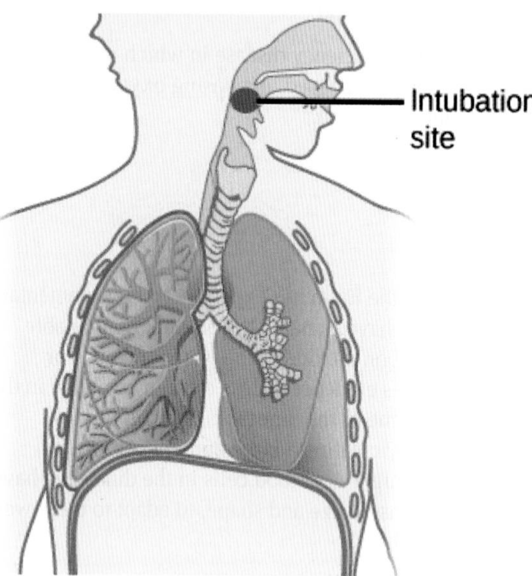

a. in the oral cavity, because it is above the injury
b. in the oral cavity, because it is below the injury
c. in the larynx, because it is above the injury
d. in the larynx, because it is below the injury

36.

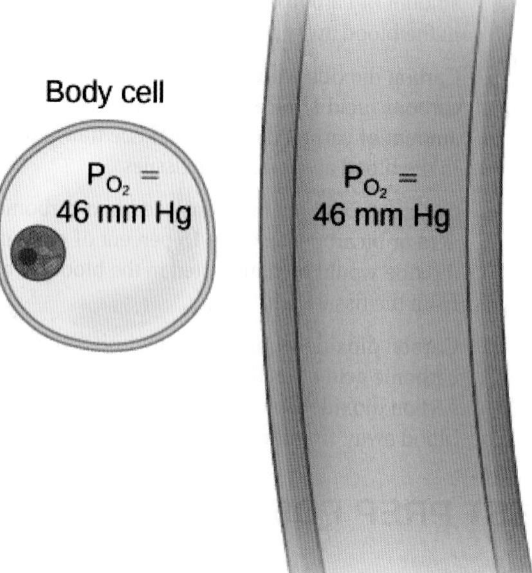

Our body systems work to maintain homeostasis by adjusting when body cells need more oxygen or are experiencing a buildup of carbon dioxide. How would the body likely respond if some of its cells were experiencing the situation pictured?

a. Generating neural signals that stimulate the heart to beat at a faster rate.
b. Releasing hormones that stimulate body cells to undergo more active transport.
c. Releasing red blood cells that can accept oxygen using diffusion as opposed to facilitated passive transport.
d. Adjust blood pH to decrease the partial pressure of CO_2 in the body cells.

37.

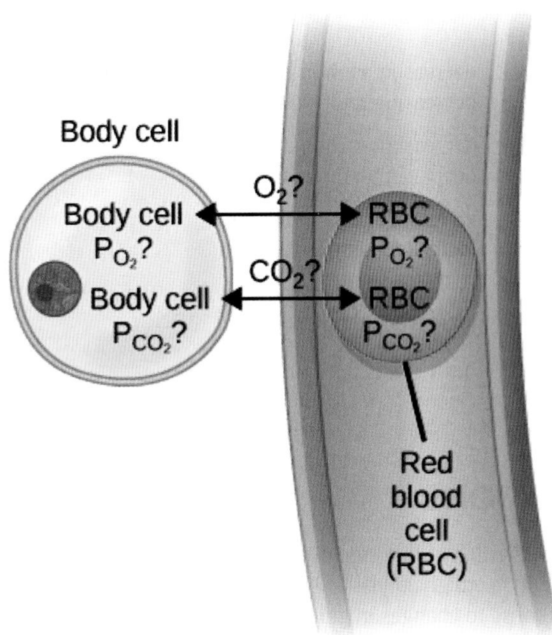

The diagram shows a red blood cell in an alveolus and then in a body tissue. In which direction should the arrows point for the diffusion of oxygen and CO_2? How should each partial pressure (body cell and RBC) be labeled as "high" or "low" to accomplish this diffusion?

a. $O_2 \rightarrow$ $CO_2 \leftarrow$; Body cell PO_2= low; RBC PO_2= high; Body cell PCO_2= high, RBC PCO_2= low
b. $O_2 \leftarrow$ $CO_2 \rightarrow$; Body cell PO_2= high; RBC PO_2= low; Body cell PCO_2= low, RBC PCO_2= high
c. $O_2 \leftarrow$ $CO_2 \rightarrow$; Body cell PO_2= low; RBC PO_2= high; Body cell PCO_2= high, RBC PCO_2= low
d. $O_2 \rightarrow$ $CO_2 \leftarrow$; Body cell PO_2= high; RBC PO_2= low; Body cell PCO_2= low, RBC PCO_2= high

38.

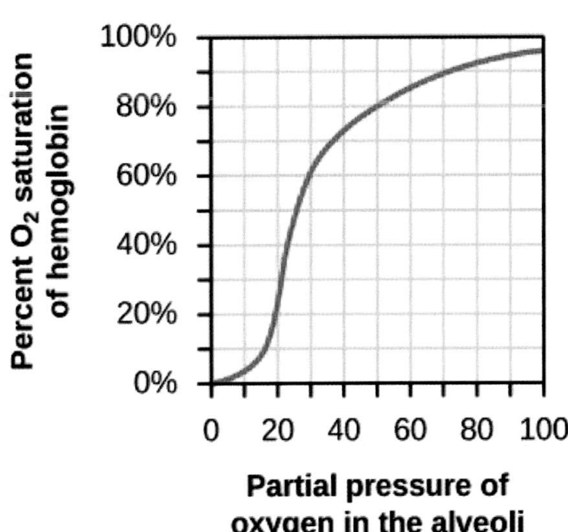

The graph plots percent oxygen saturation of hemoglobin as a function of oxygen partial pressure in the alveoli. Oxygen saturation increases in an S-shaped curve, from 0 to 100 percent as the partial pressure of oxygen increases from 0 to 100. What happens as the curve levels off around a partial pressure of 60 mmHg?

a. As the percent saturation of hemoglobin increases to its maximum, hemoglobin's affinity for oxygen increases as the availability of oxygen increases.
b. As the percent saturation of hemoglobin decreases (without all of the oxygen dissociating), hemoglobin's affinity for oxygen decreases as the availability of oxygen decreases.
c. As the percent saturation of hemoglobin increases to very high levels, hemoglobin's affinity for oxygen decreases due to its decreasing ability to bind oxygen.
d. As the percent saturation of hemoglobin decreases, hemoglobin's affinity for oxygen increases as the availability of oxygen decreases.

39.

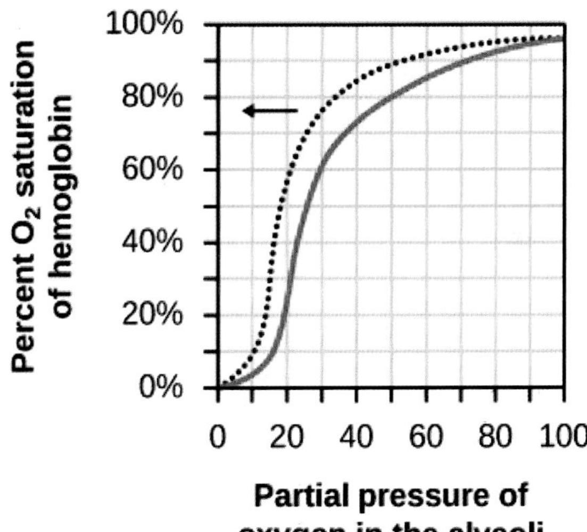

The graph shows an oxygen dissociation curve for hemoglobin. Based on the graph, what would likely cause the curve to shift to the left, as shown by the dotted plot line?

a. a decrease in carbon dioxide, increase in pH, or a decrease in temperature
b. an increase in carbon dioxide, increase in pH, or a decrease in temperature
c. a decrease in carbon dioxide, decrease in pH, or a decrease in temperature
d. a decrease in carbon dioxide, increase in pH, or an increase in temperature

40.

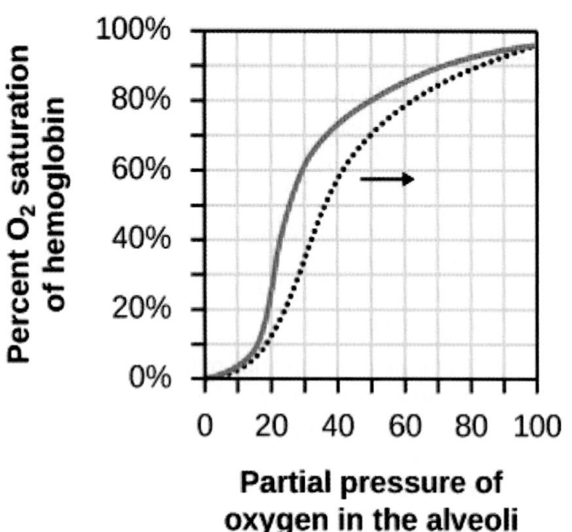

The graph shows an oxygen dissociation curve for hemoglobin. Based on the graph, what would likely cause the curve to shift to the right, as shown by the dotted plot line?

a. decreasing carbon dioxide, increasing pH, or decreasing temperature
b. decreasing carbon dioxide, decreasing pH, or decreasing temperature
c. increasing carbon dioxide, increasing pH or increasing temperature.
d. increasing carbon dioxide, decreasing pH, or increasing temperature.

SCIENCE PRACTICE CHALLENGE QUESTIONS

41. Oxygen deprivation produces symptoms such as fatigue, headaches, and confusion that are collectively referred to as hypoxia. A vacation in the Rocky Mountains of the US, where the partial pressure of oxygen is just 15% lower than you are accustomed to on the coast, can induce these symptoms. The body has a very narrow range of environment oxygen tolerance. It essentially has no capacity for storage of oxygen that is continuously consumed to maintain energy homeostasis.

The response to oxygen deprivation is to increase breathing rate and increase the volume of each breath. The input for a negative feedback loop that maintains homeostasis by detecting oxygen concentrations is a sensor (the carotid body) located on the interior of carotid artery. The output is at the diaphragm. The signal is processed in the respiratory centers (RCs) of the medulla in the brainstem.

A. **Describe** how the nervous system integrates information about oxygen concentration in the blood to maintain homeostasis. In your description include the concepts of negative feedback and a set point.

An alternative model (Evens et al., *Biochemical Journal*, 473, 2016) of the response to oxygen deprivation is suggested by the observation that high-altitude Andean populations have a gene for a protein kinase (AMPK encoded by *PRKAA1*) that has a fixed single nucleotide variation. This AMP-activated kinase is coupled with mitochondrial oxidative phosphorylation to detect reduced oxygen and signal the RCs of the medulla directly—a distributed network for detection and response. The authors of this work note that a homologous gene in yeast allows colony-wide signaling to switch individuals in the colony from glycolysis to oxidative phosphorylation in response to changes in glucose resources.

B. **Describe** the connection of a changing environment to changing genomes in both species in terms of the adaptive advantage provided and the likelihood that an AMPK signaling process has been conserved across domains.

Studies of a genetic adaptation in Tibetan population have shown that other mutations have been selected. One mutation *EPAS1* was shown to be correlated with increased lactic acid concentrations in the blood. Another mutation, PPARA, was found to be correlated with fatty acid production, which is typically seen during hibernation (Ge et al., *Molecular Genetics and Metabolism*, 106, 2012; Lorenzo et al., *Nature Genetics*, 46, 2014)

C. **Analyze** these observations in terms of the regulation of metabolism due to changes in genetic makeup and construct an explanation for the divergence of the homeostatic mechanisms as an adaptation to the environment.

The Tibetan population is not isolated. However, these investigations show the near dominance of the mutated form of these two genes has arisen in just 8000 years. Neanderthal, Denisovans and ancestors of modern humans were contemporaries.

D. **Describe** conditions that lead to speciation in terms of the accumulation of many small genetic changes where very sharp differences in oxygen availability were geographically imposed.

31 | THE CIRCULATORY SYSTEM

Figure 31.1 Just as highway systems transport people and goods through a complex network, the circulatory system transports nutrients, gases, and wastes throughout the animal body. (credit: modification of work by Andrey Belenko)

Chapter Outline

Introduction

Most animals are complex multicellular organisms that require a mechanism for transporting nutrients throughout their bodies and removing waste products. The circulatory system has evolved over time from simple diffusion through cells in the early evolution of animals to a complex network of blood vessels that reach all parts of the human body. This extensive network supplies the cells, tissues, and organs with oxygen and nutrients, and removes carbon dioxide and waste, which are byproducts of respiration.

At the core of the human circulatory system is the heart. The size of a clenched fist, the human heart is protected beneath the rib cage. Made of specialized and unique cardiac muscle, it pumps blood throughout the body and to the heart itself. Heart contractions are driven by intrinsic electrical impulses that the brain and endocrine hormones help to regulate.

Understanding the heart's basic anatomy and function is important to understanding the body's circulatory and respiratory systems. Because one in four deaths in the United States is due to heart disease, billions of dollars are spent each year researching ways to prevent and treat it. For example, researchers have been trying to find a way to get damaged cardiac muscle to repair itself. A team of researchers at the Weizmann Institute of Science recently discovered that activating a protein called ERBB2 causes heart cells in adult mice to regenerate. The research team is continuing their research to determine how this knowledge might be applied to human medicine. You can read more about this exciting research on the Science Daily website (http://openstaxcollege.org/l/32ERBB2) .

31.1 | Overview of the Circulatory System

In this section, you will explore the following questions:

- What is the difference between an open circulatory system and a closed circulatory system?
- What are the components of interstitial fluid and hemolymph?
- What are the differences and similarities among the organization and evolution of different vertebrate circulatory systems?

Connection for AP® Courses

Much of the information in this chapter is not in scope for AP®. However, the chapter is filled with examples that are applicable to concepts we have previously explored. The circulatory system links to all other organ systems. For example, nutrients pass from the digestive system into the blood, and the excretory system rids the blood of wastes. In addition, because heart disease is a leading cause of death in humans, the information is relevant.

Circulatory systems in animals show a distinct pattern of evolution—from none in sponges and jellyfish to open circulatory systems characteristic of insects to closed circulatory systems with hearts, valves, and vessels in vertebrates. Circulatory systems provide body cells with oxygen and nutrients, remove wastes, transports hormones, protect against invaders, and aids in temperature regulation. Although some animals such as the sponge have had no adaptive need to develop a complex circulatory system (they exchange nutrients and wastes directly with the environment), as demands for oxygen increased with terrestrial living, natural selection favored a closed circulatory system in which blood is transported in vessels. To increase efficiency, within closed systems the heart evolved from two chambers in fish (one atrium and one ventricle) to the four-chambered heart (two atria and two ventricles) seen in crocodiles, birds, and mammals.

Information presented and the examples highlighted in the section support concepts outlined in Big Idea 1 of the AP® Biology Curriculum Framework. The AP® Learning Objectives listed in the Curriculum Framework provide a transparent foundation for the AP® Biology course, an inquiry-based laboratory experience, instructional activities, and AP® exam questions. A learning objective merges required content with one or more of the seven science practices.

Big Idea 1	The process of evolution drives the diversity and unity of life.
Enduring Understanding 1.A	Change in the genetic makeup of a population over time is evolution.
Essential Knowledge	**1.A.1** An adaptation, such as the number of heart chambers, is a genetic variation that is favored by natural selection and provides an advantage to an organism in a particular environment.
Science Practice	**2.2** The student can apply mathematical routines to quantities that describe natural phenomena.
Science Practice	**5.3** The student can evaluate the evidence provided by data sets in relation to a particular scientific question.
Learning Objective	**1.2** The student is able to evaluate evidence provided by data to qualitatively and quantitatively investigate the role of natural selection in evolution.
Enduring Understanding 1.B	Organisms are linked by lines of descent from common ancestry.
Essential Knowledge	**1.B.2** Phylogenetic trees and cladogram can represent traits, such as the number of heart chambers in animals, which are derived or lost due to evolution.
Science Practice	**3.1** The student can pose scientific questions.

Learning Objective	**1.17** The student is able to pose scientific questions about a group of organisms whose relatedness is described by a phylogenetic tree or cladogram in order to (1) identify shared characteristics, (2) make inferences about the evolutionary history of the group, and (3) identify character data that could extend or improve the phylogenetic tree.
Essential Knowledge	**1.B.2** Phylogenetic trees and cladogram can represent traits, such as the number of heart chambers in animals, which are derived or lost due to evolution.
Science Practice	**1.1** The student can create representations and models of natural or man-made phenomena and systems in the domain.
Learning Objective	**1.19** The student is able to create a phylogenetic tree or simple cladogram that correctly represents evolutionary history and speciation from a provided data set.

Circulatory System Architecture

The circulatory system is effectively a network of cylindrical vessels: the arteries, veins, and capillaries that emanate from a pump, the heart. In all vertebrate organisms, as well as some invertebrates, this is a closed-loop system, in which the blood is not free in a cavity. In a **closed circulatory system**, blood is contained inside blood vessels and circulates **unidirectionally** from the heart around the systemic circulatory route, then returns to the heart again, as illustrated in Figure 31.2**a**. As opposed to a closed system, arthropods—including insects, crustaceans, and most mollusks—have an open circulatory system, as illustrated in Figure 31.2**b**. In an **open circulatory system**, the blood is not enclosed in the blood vessels but is pumped into a cavity called a **hemocoel** and is called **hemolymph** because the blood mixes with the **interstitial fluid**. As the heart beats and the animal moves, the hemolymph circulates around the organs within the body cavity and then reenters the hearts through openings called **ostia**. This movement allows for gas and nutrient exchange. An open circulatory system does not use as much energy as a closed system to operate or to maintain; however, there is a trade-off with the amount of blood that can be moved to metabolically active organs and tissues that require high levels of oxygen. In fact, one reason that insects with wing spans of up to two feet wide (70 cm) are not around today is probably because they were outcompeted by the arrival of birds 150 million years ago. Birds, having a closed circulatory system, are thought to have moved more agilely, allowing them to get food faster and possibly to prey on the insects.

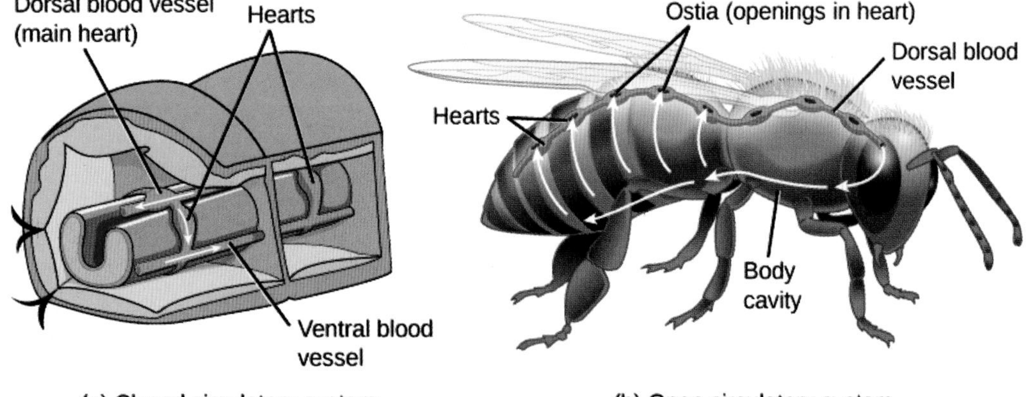

Figure 31.2 In (a) closed circulatory systems, the heart pumps blood through vessels that are separate from the interstitial fluid of the body. Most vertebrates and some invertebrates, like this annelid earthworm, have a closed circulatory system. In (b) open circulatory systems, a fluid called hemolymph is pumped through a blood vessel that empties into the body cavity. Hemolymph returns to the blood vessel through openings called ostia. Arthropods like this bee and most mollusks have open circulatory systems.

Circulatory System Variation in Animals

The circulatory system varies from simple systems in invertebrates to more complex systems in vertebrates. The simplest animals, such as the sponges (Porifera) and rotifers (Rotifera), do not need a circulatory system because diffusion allows adequate exchange of water, nutrients, and waste, as well as dissolved gases, as shown in Figure 31.3**a**. Organisms that are more complex but still only have two layers of cells in their body plan, such as jellies (Cnidaria) and comb jellies (Ctenophora) also use diffusion through their epidermis and internally through the gastrovascular compartment. Both their internal and external tissues are bathed in an aqueous environment and exchange fluids by diffusion on both sides, as illustrated in Figure 31.3**b**. Exchange of fluids is assisted by the pulsing of the jellyfish body.

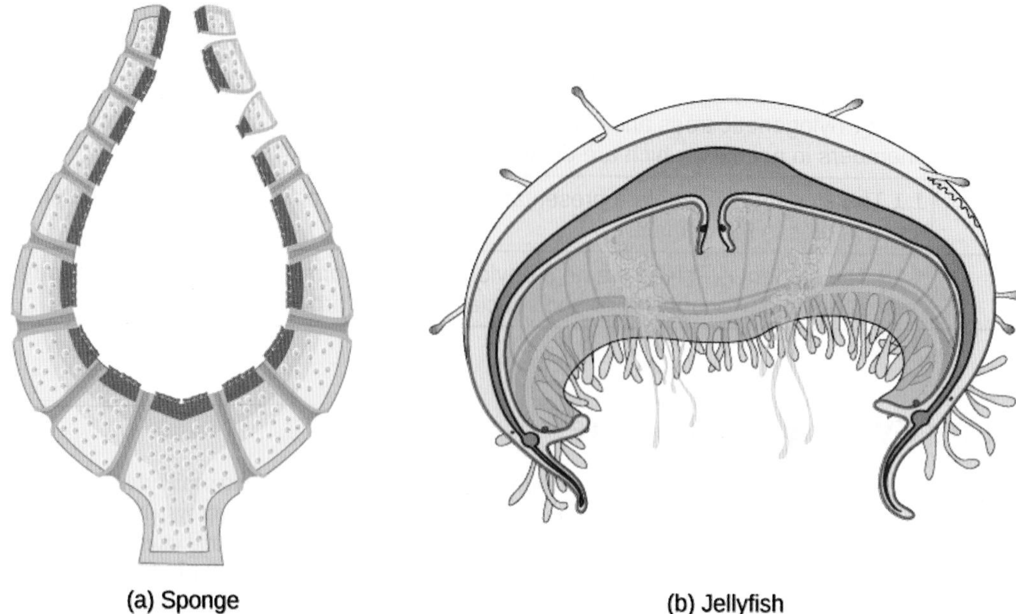

Figure 31.3 Simple animals consisting of a single cell layer such as the (a) sponge or only a few cell layers such as the (b) jellyfish do not have a circulatory system. Instead, gases, nutrients, and wastes are exchanged by diffusion.

For more complex organisms, diffusion is not efficient for cycling gases, nutrients, and waste effectively through the body; therefore, more complex circulatory systems evolved. Most arthropods and many mollusks have open circulatory systems. In an open system, an elongated beating heart pushes the hemolymph through the body and muscle contractions help to move fluids. The larger more complex crustaceans, including lobsters, have developed arterial-like vessels to push blood through their bodies, and the most active mollusks, such as squids, have evolved a closed circulatory system and are able to move rapidly to catch prey. Closed circulatory systems are a characteristic of vertebrates; however, there are significant differences in the structure of the heart and the circulation of blood between the different vertebrate groups due to adaptation during evolution and associated differences in anatomy. Figure 31.4 illustrates the basic circulatory systems of some vertebrates: fish, amphibians, reptiles, and mammals.

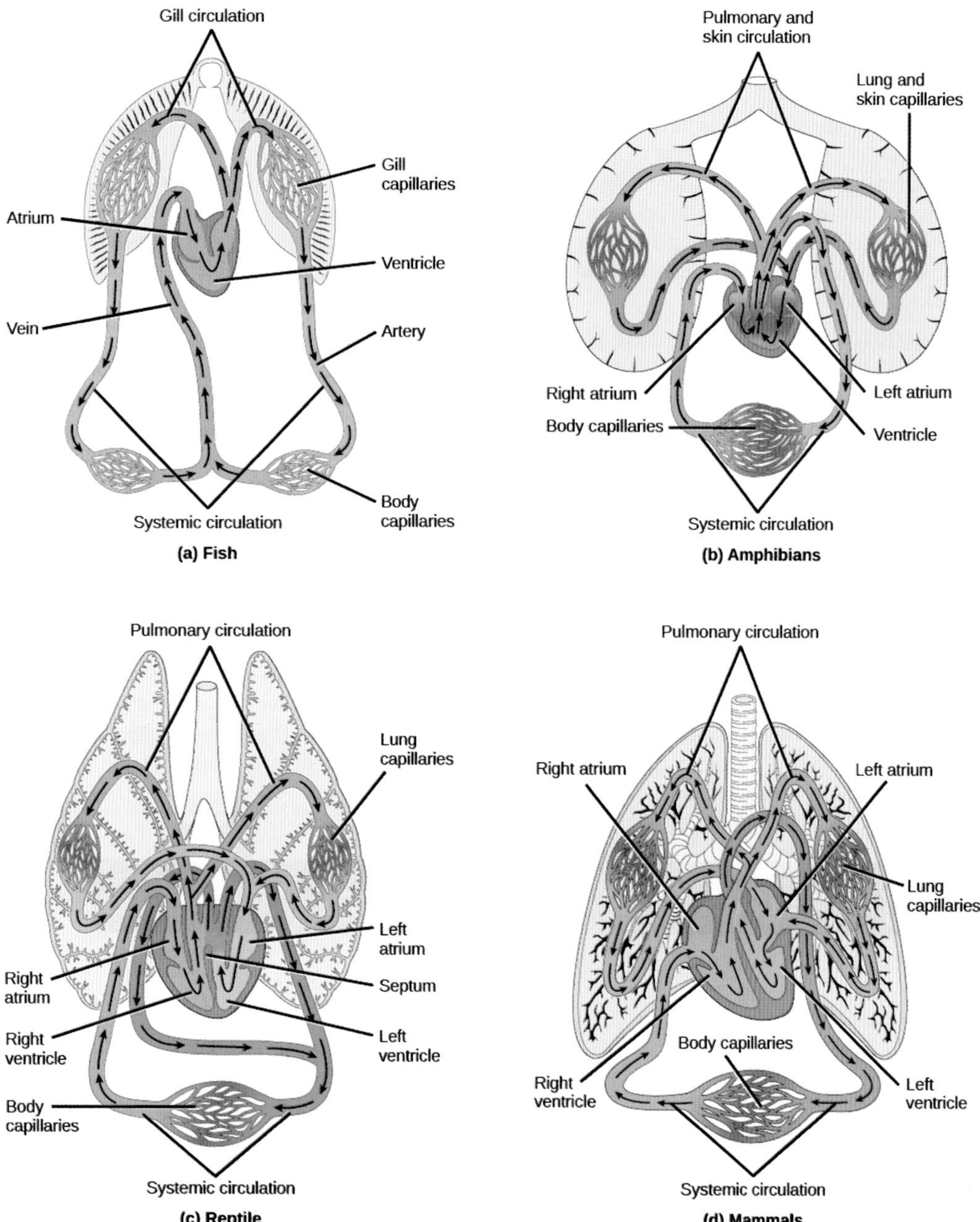

Figure 31.4 (a) Fish have the simplest circulatory systems of the vertebrates: blood flows unidirectionally from the two-chambered heart through the gills and then the rest of the body. (b) Amphibians have two circulatory routes: one for oxygenation of the blood through the lungs and skin, and the other to take oxygen to the rest of the body. The blood is pumped from a three-chambered heart with two atria and a single ventricle. (c) Reptiles also have two circulatory routes; however, blood is only oxygenated through the lungs. The heart is three chambered, but the ventricles are partially separated so some mixing of oxygenated and deoxygenated blood occurs except in crocodilians and birds. (d) Mammals and birds have the most efficient heart with four chambers that completely separate the oxygenated and deoxygenated blood; it pumps only oxygenated blood through the body and deoxygenated blood to the lungs.

As illustrated in Figure 31.4**a** Fish have a single circuit for blood flow and a two-chambered heart that has only a single atrium and a single ventricle. The atrium collects blood that has returned from the body and the ventricle pumps the blood to the gills where gas exchange occurs and the blood is re-oxygenated; this is called **gill circulation**. The blood then continues through the rest of the body before arriving back at the atrium; this is called **systemic circulation**. This unidirectional flow of blood produces a gradient of oxygenated to deoxygenated blood around the fish's systemic circuit. The result is a limit in the amount of oxygen that can reach some of the organs and tissues of the body, reducing the overall metabolic capacity of fish.

In amphibians, reptiles, birds, and mammals, blood flow is directed in two circuits: one through the lungs and back to the heart, which is called **pulmonary circulation**, and the other throughout the rest of the body and its organs including the brain (systemic circulation). In amphibians, gas exchange also occurs through the skin during pulmonary circulation and is referred to as **pulmocutaneous circulation**.

As shown in Figure 31.4**b**, amphibians have a three-chambered heart that has two atria and one ventricle rather than the two-chambered heart of fish. The two **atria** (superior heart chambers) receive blood from the two different circuits (the lungs and the systems), and then there is some mixing of the blood in the heart's **ventricle** (inferior heart chamber), which reduces the efficiency of oxygenation. The advantage to this arrangement is that high pressure in the vessels pushes blood to the lungs and body. The mixing is mitigated by a ridge within the ventricle that diverts oxygen-rich blood through the systemic circulatory system and deoxygenated blood to the pulmocutaneous circuit. For this reason, amphibians are often described as having **double circulation**.

Most reptiles also have a three-chambered heart similar to the amphibian heart that directs blood to the pulmonary and systemic circuits, as shown in Figure 31.4**c**. The ventricle is divided more effectively by a partial septum, which results in less mixing of oxygenated and deoxygenated blood. Some reptiles (alligators and crocodiles) are the most primitive animals to exhibit a four-chambered heart. Crocodilians have a unique circulatory mechanism where the heart shunts blood from the lungs toward the stomach and other organs during long periods of submergence, for instance, while the animal waits for prey or stays underwater waiting for prey to rot. One adaptation includes two main arteries that leave the same part of the heart: one takes blood to the lungs and the other provides an alternate route to the stomach and other parts of the body. Two other adaptations include a hole in the heart between the two ventricles, called the foramen of Panizza, which allows blood to move from one side of the heart to the other, and specialized connective tissue that slows the blood flow to the lungs. Together these adaptations have made crocodiles and alligators one of the most evolutionarily successful animal groups on earth.

In mammals and birds, the heart is also divided into four chambers: two atria and two ventricles, as illustrated in Figure 31.4**d**. The oxygenated blood is separated from the deoxygenated blood, which improves the efficiency of double circulation and is probably required for the warm-blooded lifestyle of mammals and birds. The four-chambered heart of birds and mammals evolved independently from a three-chambered heart. The independent evolution of the same or a similar biological trait is referred to as convergent evolution.

science practices CONNECTION for AP® Courses

Think About It

What advantages are supplied by closed circulatory systems with chambered hearts in terrestrial vertebrates?

31.2 | Components of the Blood

In this section, you will explore the following questions:

- What are the basic components of blood?
- What are the differences between red blood cells and white blood cells?
- What is the difference between blood plasma and blood serum?

Connection for AP® Courses

Most of us have suffered a cut or a scraped knee and have seen our own blood. Blood consists of different types of cells bathed in a water-based liquid called plasma. Red blood cells are specialized to carry hemoglobin (Hgb), a quaternary protein that transports oxygen and some carbon dioxide around the body, to and from the heart and lungs. Hemoglobin also has an affinity for carbon monoxide, a toxic and deadly gas. Variants of hemoglobin help animals adapt to different environments. For example, Hgb-S causes sickle-cell anemia; although this variant of hemoglobin is not as efficient at transporting O^2, it does provide some protection against malaria, thus providing an advantage to heterozygous individuals. Another variant is Hgb-F or fetal hemoglobin, which transports O^2 efficiently in low oxygen conditions. Red blood cells develop and mature in the bone marrow and when released into circulation lack nuclei and mitochondria. Blood types such as A, B, AB, and O are related to proteins on the surface of red blood cells. For example, persons with type A blood have A glycoproteins on the surface of their red blood cells. We will take a deeper dive into blood typing, antigens, and antibodies when we explore the immune system in a later chapter, and we also will learn in that the five types of white blood cells play important roles in immunity. Platelets and plasma proteins function in normal blood clotting; alterations in the feedback mechanism(s) that result in normal clotting can have deleterious effects, including hemophilia and stroke.

Information presented and the examples highlighted in the section support concepts outlined in Big Idea 2 and Big Idea 4 of the AP® Biology Curriculum Framework. The AP® Learning Objectives listed in the Curriculum Framework provide a transparent foundation for the AP® Biology course, an inquiry-based laboratory experience, instructional activities, and AP® exam questions. A learning objective merges required content with one or more of the seven science practices.

Big Idea 2	Biological systems utilize free energy and molecular building blocks to grow, to reproduce, and to maintain dynamic homeostasis.
Enduring Understanding 2.C	Organisms use feedback mechanisms to regulate growth and reproduction, and to maintain dynamic homeostasis.
Essential Knowledge	**2.C.1** Alterations in the mechanisms of negative and positive feedback mechanisms can have deleterious consequences to the body.
Science Practice	**6.4** The student can make claims and predictions about natural phenomena based on scientific theories and models.
Learning Objective	**2.19** The student is able to make predictions about how positive feedback mechanisms amplify activities and processes in organisms based on scientific theories and models.
Big Idea 4	Biological systems interact, and these systems and their interactions possess complex properties.
Enduring Understanding 4.A	Interactions within biological systems lead to complex properties.
Essential Knowledge	**4.A.4** Organisms exhibit complex properties due to interactions between and among organs and organ systems.
Science Practice	**1.3** The student can refine representations and models of natural or man-made phenomena and systems in the domain
Learning Objective	**4.10** The student is able to refine representations and models to illustrate biocomplexity due to interactions of constituent parts.
Enduring Understanding 4.C	Naturally occurring diversity among and between components within biological systems affects interactions with the environment.
Essential Knowledge	**4.C.1** Variations that produce different varieties of molecules help organisms adapt to different environmental conditions.
Science Practice	**6.2** The student can construct explanations of phenomena based on evidence produced through scientific practices.
Learning Objective	**4.22** The student is able to construct explanations based on evidence of how variation in molecular units provides cells with a wide range of functions.

Hemoglobin is responsible for distributing oxygen, and to a lesser extent, carbon dioxide, throughout the circulatory systems of humans, vertebrates, and many invertebrates. The blood is more than the proteins, though. Blood is actually a term used to describe the liquid that moves through the vessels and includes **plasma** (the liquid portion, which contains water, proteins, salts, lipids, and glucose) and the cells (red and white cells) and cell fragments called **platelets**. Blood plasma is actually the dominant component of blood and contains the water, proteins, electrolytes, lipids, and glucose. The cells are responsible for carrying the gases (red cells) and immune the response (white). The platelets are responsible for blood clotting. Interstitial fluid that surrounds cells is separate from the blood, but in hemolymph, they are combined. In humans, cellular components make up approximately 45 percent of the blood and the liquid plasma 55 percent. Blood is 20 percent of a person's extracellular fluid and eight percent of weight.

The Role of Blood in the Body

Blood, like the human blood illustrated in Figure 31.5 is important for regulation of the body's systems and homeostasis. Blood helps maintain homeostasis by stabilizing pH, temperature, osmotic pressure, and by eliminating excess heat. Blood supports growth by distributing nutrients and hormones, and by removing waste. Blood plays a protective role by transporting clotting factors and platelets to prevent blood loss and transporting the disease-fighting agents or **white blood cells** to sites of infection.

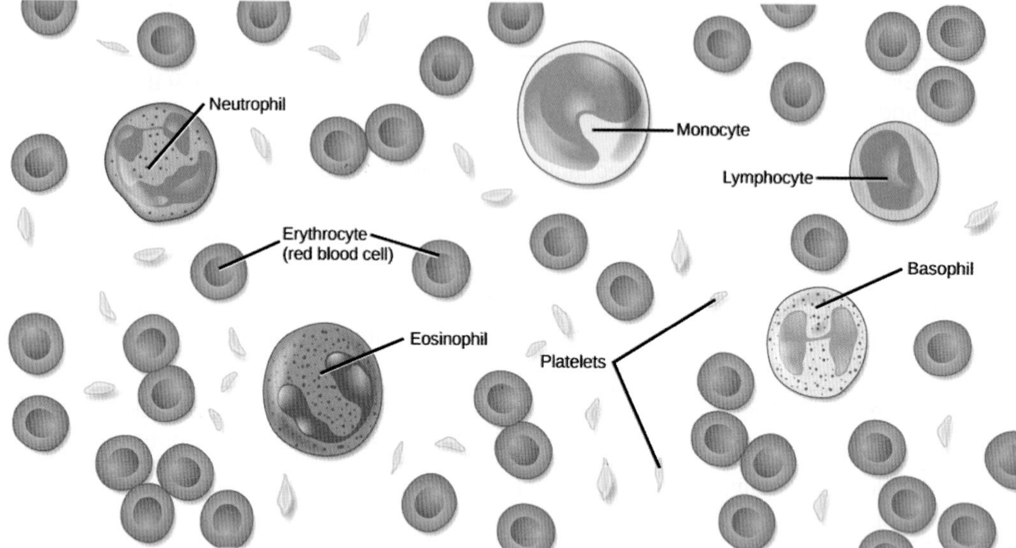

Figure 31.5 The cells and cellular components of human blood are shown. Red blood cells deliver oxygen to the cells and remove carbon dioxide. White blood cells—including neutrophils, monocytes, lymphocytes, eosinophils, and basophils—are involved in the immune response. Platelets form clots that prevent blood loss after injury.

Red Blood Cells

Red blood cells, or erythrocytes (erythro- = "red"; -cyte = "cell"), are specialized cells that circulate through the body delivering oxygen to cells; they are formed from stem cells in the bone marrow. In mammals, red blood cells are small biconcave cells that at maturity do not contain a nucleus or mitochondria and are only 7–8 µm in size. In birds and non-avian reptiles, a nucleus is still maintained in red blood cells.

The red coloring of blood comes from the iron-containing protein hemoglobin, illustrated in Figure 31.6**a**. The principal job of this protein is to carry oxygen, but it also transports carbon dioxide as well. Hemoglobin is packed into red blood cells at a rate of about 250 million molecules of hemoglobin per cell. Each hemoglobin molecule binds four oxygen molecules so that each red blood cell carries one billion molecules of oxygen. There are approximately 25 trillion red blood cells in the five liters of blood in the human body, which could carry up to 25 sextillion (25×10^{21}) molecules of oxygen in the body at any time. In mammals, the lack of organelles in erythrocytes leaves more room for the hemoglobin molecules, and the lack of mitochondria also prevents use of the oxygen for metabolic respiration. Only mammals have anucleated red blood cells, and some mammals (camels, for instance) even have nucleated red blood cells. The advantage of nucleated red blood cells is that these cells can undergo mitosis. Anucleated red blood cells metabolize anaerobically (without oxygen), making use of a primitive metabolic pathway to produce ATP and increase the efficiency of oxygen transport.

Not all organisms use hemoglobin as the method of oxygen transport. Invertebrates that utilize hemolymph rather than blood use different pigments to bind to the oxygen. These pigments use copper or iron to bind the oxygen. Invertebrates have a variety of other respiratory pigments. Hemocyanin, a blue-green, copper-containing protein, illustrated in Figure 31.6**b** is found in mollusks, crustaceans, and some of the arthropods. Chlorocruorin, a green-colored, iron-containing pigment is found in four families of polychaete tubeworms. Hemerythrin, a red, iron-containing protein is found in some polychaete worms and annelids and is illustrated in Figure 31.6**c**. Despite the name, hemerythrin does not contain a heme group and its oxygen-carrying capacity is poor compared to hemoglobin.

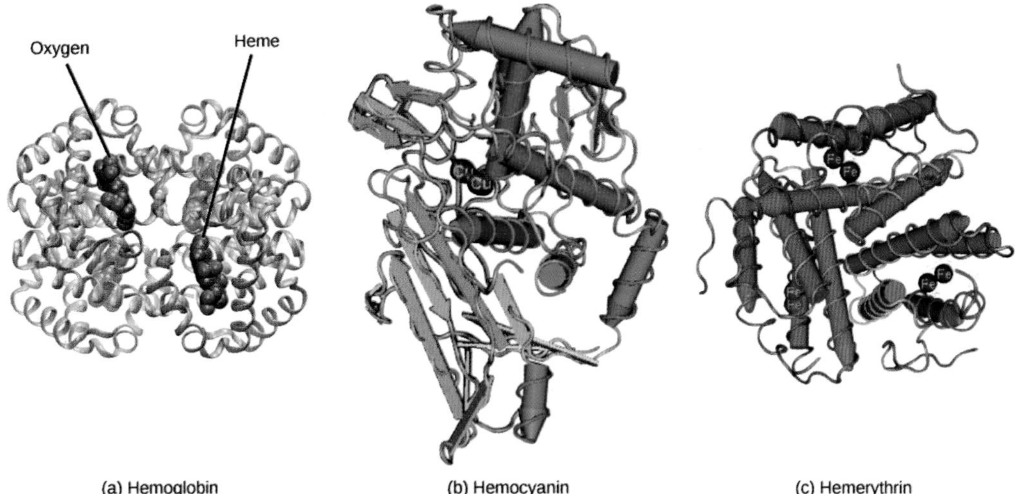

Figure 31.6 In most vertebrates, (a) hemoglobin delivers oxygen to the body and removes some carbon dioxide. Hemoglobin is composed of four protein subunits, two alpha chains and two beta chains, and a heme group that has iron associated with it. The iron reversibly associates with oxygen, and in so doing is oxidized from Fe^{2+} to Fe^{3+}. In most mollusks and some arthropods, (b) hemocyanin delivers oxygen. Unlike hemoglobin, hemolymph is not carried in blood cells, but floats free in the hemolymph. Copper instead of iron binds the oxygen, giving the hemolymph a blue-green color. In annelids, such as the earthworm, and some other invertebrates, (c) hemerythrin carries oxygen. Like hemoglobin, hemerythrin is carried in blood cells and has iron associated with it, but despite its name, hemerythrin does not contain heme.

The small size and large surface area of red blood cells allows for rapid diffusion of oxygen and carbon dioxide across the plasma membrane. In the lungs, carbon dioxide is released and oxygen is taken in by the blood. In the tissues, oxygen is released from the blood and carbon dioxide is bound for transport back to the lungs. Studies have found that hemoglobin also binds nitrous oxide (NO). NO is a vasodilator that relaxes the blood vessels and capillaries and may help with gas exchange and the passage of red blood cells through narrow vessels. Nitroglycerin, a heart medication for angina and heart attacks, is converted to NO to help relax the blood vessels and increase oxygen flow through the body.

A characteristic of red blood cells is their glycolipid and glycoprotein coating; these are lipids and proteins that have carbohydrate molecules attached. In humans, the surface glycoproteins and glycolipids on red blood cells vary between individuals, producing the different blood types, such as A, B, and O. Red blood cells have an average life span of 120 days, at which time they are broken down and recycled in the liver and spleen by phagocytic macrophages, a type of white blood cell.

White Blood Cells

White blood cells, also called leukocytes (leuko = white), make up approximately one percent by volume of the cells in blood. The role of white blood cells is very different than that of red blood cells: they are primarily involved in the immune response to identify and target pathogens, such as invading bacteria, viruses, and other foreign organisms. White blood cells are formed continually; some only live for hours or days, but some live for years.

The morphology of white blood cells differs significantly from red blood cells. They have nuclei and do not contain hemoglobin. The different types of white blood cells are identified by their microscopic appearance after histologic staining, and each has a different specialized function. The two main groups, both illustrated in Figure 31.7 are the granulocytes, which include the neutrophils, eosinophils, and basophils, and the agranulocytes, which include the monocytes and lymphocytes.

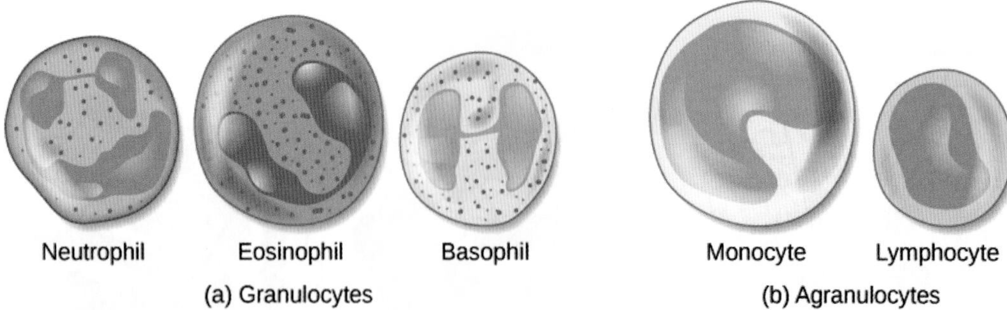

Figure 31.7 (a) Granulocytes—including neutrophils, eosinophils and basophils—are characterized by a lobed nucleus and granular inclusions in the cytoplasm. Granulocytes are typically first-responders during injury or infection. (b) Agranulocytes include lymphocytes and monocytes. Lymphocytes, including B and T cells, are responsible for adaptive immune response. Monocytes differentiate into macrophages and dendritic cells, which in turn respond to infection or injury.

Granulocytes contain granules in their cytoplasm; the agranulocytes are so named because of the lack of granules in their cytoplasm. Some leukocytes become macrophages that either stay at the same site or move through the blood stream and gather at sites of infection or inflammation where they are attracted by chemical signals from foreign particles and damaged cells. Lymphocytes are the primary cells of the immune system and include B cells, T cells, and natural killer cells. B cells destroy bacteria and inactivate their toxins. They also produce antibodies. T cells attack viruses, fungi, some bacteria, transplanted cells, and cancer cells. T cells attack viruses by releasing toxins that kill the viruses. Natural killer cells attack a variety of infectious microbes and certain tumor cells.

One reason that HIV poses significant management challenges is because the virus directly targets T cells by gaining entry through a receptor. Once inside the cell, HIV then multiplies using the T cell's own genetic machinery. After the HIV virus replicates, it is transmitted directly from the infected T cell to macrophages. The presence of HIV can remain unrecognized for an extensive period of time before full disease symptoms develop.

Platelets and Coagulation Factors

Blood must clot to heal wounds and prevent excess blood loss. Small cell fragments called platelets (thrombocytes) are attracted to the wound site where they adhere by extending many projections and releasing their contents. These contents activate other platelets and also interact with other coagulation factors, which convert fibrinogen, a water-soluble protein present in blood serum into fibrin (a non-water soluble protein), causing the blood to clot. Many of the clotting factors require vitamin K to work, and vitamin K deficiency can lead to problems with blood clotting. Many platelets converge and stick together at the wound site forming a platelet plug (also called a fibrin clot), as illustrated in Figure 31.8**b**. The plug or clot lasts for a number of days and stops the loss of blood. Platelets are formed from the disintegration of larger cells called megakaryocytes, like that shown in Figure 31.8**a**. For each megakaryocyte, 2000–3000 platelets are formed with 150,000 to 400,000 platelets present in each cubic millimeter of blood. Each platelet is disc shaped and 2–4 μm in diameter. They contain many small vesicles but do not contain a nucleus.

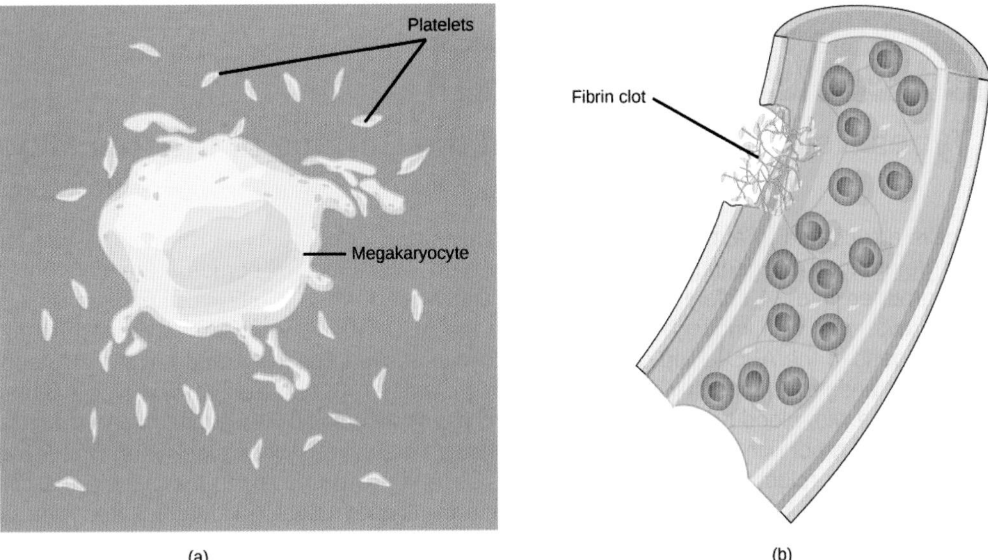

Figure 31.8 (a) Platelets are formed from large cells called megakaryocytes. The megakaryocyte breaks up into thousands of fragments that become platelets. (b) Platelets are required for clotting of the blood. The platelets collect at a wound site in conjunction with other clotting factors, such as fibrinogen, to form a fibrin clot that prevents blood loss and allows the wound to heal.

Plasma and Serum

The liquid component of blood is called plasma, and it is separated by spinning or centrifuging the blood at high rotations (3000 rpm or higher). The blood cells and platelets are separated by centrifugal forces to the bottom of a specimen tube. The upper liquid layer, the plasma, consists of 90 percent water along with various substances required for maintaining the body's pH, osmotic load, and for protecting the body. The plasma also contains the coagulation factors and antibodies.

The plasma component of blood without the coagulation factors is called the **serum**. Serum is similar to interstitial fluid in which the correct composition of key ions acting as electrolytes is essential for normal functioning of muscles and nerves. Other components in the serum include proteins that assist with maintaining pH and osmotic balance while giving viscosity to the blood. The serum also contains antibodies, specialized proteins that are important for defense against viruses and bacteria. Lipids, including cholesterol, are also transported in the serum, along with various other substances including nutrients, hormones, metabolic waste, plus external substances, such as, drugs, viruses, and bacteria.

Human serum albumin is the most abundant protein in human blood plasma and is synthesized in the liver. Albumin, which constitutes about half of the blood serum protein, transports hormones and fatty acids, buffers pH, and maintains osmotic pressures. Immunoglobin is a protein antibody produced in the mucosal lining and plays an important role in antibody mediated immunity.

evolution CONNECTION

Blood Types Related to Proteins on the Surface of the Red Blood Cells

Red blood cells are coated in antigens made of glycolipids and glycoproteins. The composition of these molecules is determined by genetics, which have evolved over time. In humans, the different surface antigens are grouped into 24 different blood groups with more than 100 different antigens on each red blood cell. The two most well known blood groups are the ABO, shown in Figure 31.9, and Rh systems. The surface antigens in the ABO blood group are glycolipids, called antigen A and antigen B. People with blood type A have antigen A, those with blood type B have antigen B, those with blood type AB have both antigens, and people with blood type O have neither antigen. Antibodies called agglutinougens are found in the blood plasma and react with the A or B antigens, if the two are mixed. When type A and type B blood are combined, agglutination (clumping) of the blood occurs because of antibodies in the plasma that bind with the opposing antigen; this causes clots that coagulate in the kidney causing kidney failure. Type O blood has neither A or B antigens, and therefore, type O blood can be given to all blood types. Type O negative blood is the universal donor. Type AB positive blood is the universal acceptor because it has both A and B antigen. The ABO blood groups were discovered in 1900 and 1901 by Karl Landsteiner at the University of Vienna.

The Rh blood group was first discovered in Rhesus monkeys. Most people have the Rh antigen (Rh+) and do not have anti-Rh antibodies in their blood. The few people who do not have the Rh antigen and are Rh– can develop anti-Rh antibodies if exposed to Rh+ blood. This can happen after a blood transfusion or after an Rh– woman has an Rh+ baby. The first exposure does not usually cause a reaction; however, at the second exposure, enough antibodies have built up in the blood to produce a reaction that causes agglutination and breakdown of red blood cells. An injection can prevent this reaction.

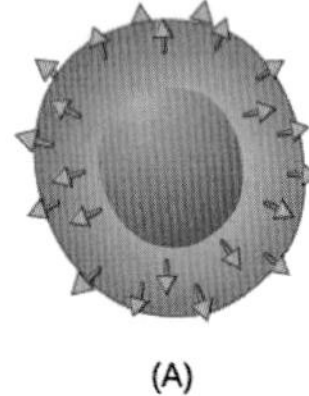

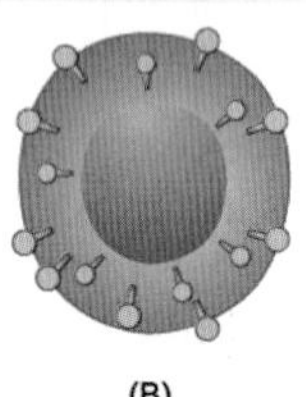

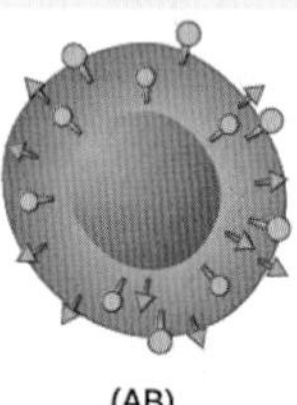

Figure 31.9 Human red blood cells may have either type A or B glycoproteins on their surface, both glycoproteins combined (AB), or neither (O). The glycoproteins serve as antigens and can elicit an immune response in a person who receives a transfusion containing unfamiliar antigens. Type O blood, which has no A or B antigens, does not elicit an immune response when injected into a person of any blood type. Thus, O is considered the universal donor. Persons with type AB blood can accept blood from any blood type, and type AB is considered the universal acceptor.

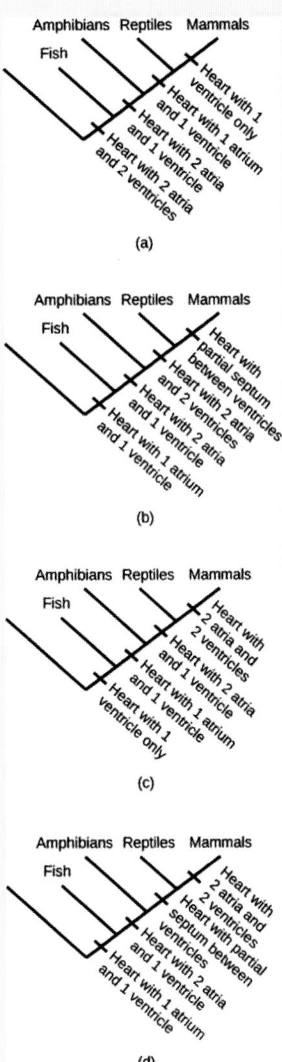

Which of the following phylogenies, created based on features of the circulatory system of vertebrates, is most accurate?

a. A
b. B
c. C
d. D

Play a blood typing game on the Nobel Prize website (http://openstaxcollege.org/l/blood_typing) to solidify your understanding of blood types.

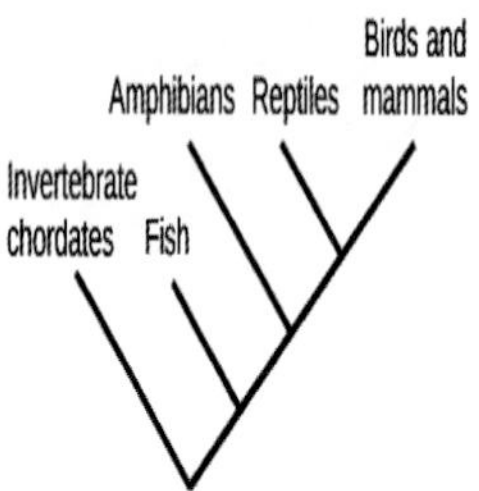

This simplified phylogeny shows the currently accepted evolutionary history of vertebrates, which are part of the phylum Chordata. How do differences in heart anatomy among these groups support this phylogeny?

a. The anatomy of the heart among these groups shows a gradually increasing number of heart chambers across the phylogeny. Fish have a two-chambered heart, amphibians and reptiles have a three-chambered heart, where latter has a partial separation of ventricles. Birds and mammals both have four-chambered hearts.

b. The anatomy of the heart among these groups shows a gradually increasing number of heart chambers across the phylogeny. Fish have a two-chambered heart. Amphibians and reptiles have a three-chambered heart where the former has a partial separation of ventricles. Birds and mammals both have four-chambered hearts.

c. The anatomy of the heart among these groups shows a gradually increasing number of heart chambers across the phylogeny. Fish and amphibians have a two-chambered heart. Reptiles have a three-chambered heart with a partial separation of ventricles. Birds and mammals both have four-chambered hearts.

d. The anatomy of the heart among these groups shows a gradually increasing number of heart chambers across the phylogeny. Fish and amphibians have two-chambered hearts. Reptiles and birds have three-chambered hearts, where the former has a partial separation of ventricles. Mammals have a four-chambered heart.

31.3 | Mammalian Heart and Blood Vessels

In this section, you will explore the following questions:

- What is the structure of the heart and how does cardiac muscle differ from other muscles?
- What are the events in the cardiac cycle?
- What is the structure of arteries, veins, and capillaries, and how does blood flow through the body?

Connection for AP® Courses

Much of the information in this section is not within the scope for AP®. You likely have studied the pathway of blood through the heart in a previous course, and as a student of biology, you should have some knowledge of this pathway. (No, you do not need to memorize the names of all arteries and veins or the names of the specific valves of the heart.)

The heart is a perfect example of the relationship between structure and function. The four-chambered heart of mammals with its unique cardiac muscle, one-way valves, and vessels is designed to transport vital oxygen (O^2) to the body cells and remove carbon dioxide (CO^2) from tissues. The intricate design of the heart separates blood that is low in O^2 from blood that is high in O^2. This ensures that oxygen-rich blood is delivered to all tissues and cells of the body where it will be used for cellular respiration. Blood returning from the tissues is high in CO^2 and low in O^2 will return to the heart and be pumped to the lungs, where gases are exchanged by diffusion at capillary beds.

Information presented and the examples highlighted in the section support concepts outlined in Big Idea 4 of the AP® Biology Curriculum Framework. The AP® Learning Objectives listed in the Curriculum Framework provide a transparent foundation for the AP® Biology course, an inquiry-based laboratory experience, instructional activities, and AP® exam questions. A learning objective merges required content with one or more of the seven science practices.

Big Idea 4	Biological systems interact, and these systems and their interactions possess complex properties.
Enduring Understanding 4.A	Interactions within biological systems lead to complex properties.
Essential Knowledge	**4.A.4** Interactions and coordination between organ systems provide essential biological activities for the organism as a whole.
Science Practice	**6.4** The student can make claims and predictions about natural phenomena based on scientific theories and models.
Learning Objective	**4.9** The student is able to predict the effects of a change in a component(s) of a biological system on the functionality of an organism(s).
Essential Knowledge	**4.A.4** Interactions and coordination between organ systems provide essential biological activities for the organism as a whole.
Science Practice	**1.3** The student can refine representations and models of natural or man-made phenomena and systems in the domain.
Learning Objective	**4.10** The student is able to refine representations and models to illustrate biocomplexity due to interactions of the constituent parts.
Enduring Understanding 4.B	Competition and cooperation are important aspects of biological systems.
Essential Knowledge	**4.B.2** Specialization of the heart and blood vessels contributes to the overall function of the body.
Science Practice	**1.4** The student can use representations and models to analyze situations or solve problems qualitatively and quantitatively.
Learning Objective	**4.18** The student is able to use representations and models to analyze how cooperative interactions within organisms promote efficiency in the use of energy and matter.

The heart is a complex muscle that pumps blood through the three divisions of the circulatory system: the coronary (vessels that serve the heart), pulmonary (heart and lungs), and systemic (systems of the body), as shown in Figure 31.10. Coronary circulation intrinsic to the heart takes blood directly from the main artery (aorta) coming from the heart. For pulmonary and systemic circulation, the heart has to pump blood to the lungs or the rest of the body, respectively. In vertebrates, the lungs are relatively close to the heart in the thoracic cavity. The shorter distance to pump means that the muscle wall on the right side of the heart is not as thick as the left side which must have enough pressure to pump blood all the way to your big toe.

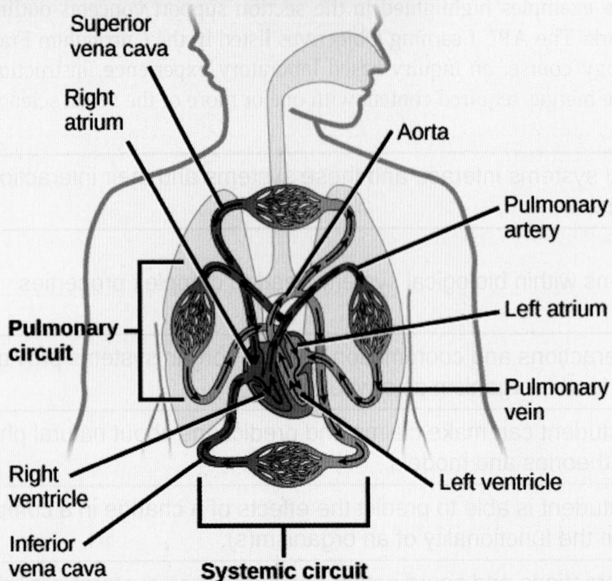

Figure 31.10 The mammalian circulatory system is divided into three circuits: the systemic circuit, the pulmonary circuit, and the coronary circuit. Blood is pumped from veins of the systemic circuit into the right atrium of the heart, then into the right ventricle. Blood then enters the pulmonary circuit, and is oxygenated by the lungs. From the pulmonary circuit, blood re-enters the heart through the left atrium. From the left ventricle, blood re-enters the systemic circuit through the aorta and is distributed to the rest of the body. The coronary circuit, which provides blood to the heart, is not shown.

Compare the functions and structures of red and white blood cells.

a. Red blood cells lack nuclei at maturity and contain hemoglobin, which distributes oxygen throughout the body. White blood cells are primarily involved in the immune response to identify and target pathogens. They have nuclei and lack hemoglobin

b. Red blood cells lack nuclei at maturity and contain hemoglobin, which distributes oxygen throughout the body. White blood cells are primarily involved in the immune response to identify and target pathogens. They lack both nuclei and hemoglobin.

c. Red blood cells contain nuclei and hemoglobin, which distributes oxygen throughout the body. White blood cells are primarily involved in the immune response to identify and target pathogens. They lack both nuclei and hemoglobin.

d. Red blood cells lack nuclei at maturity and contain hemoglobin, which is involved in the immune response, assisting in identification and targeting of pathogens. White blood cells distribute oxygen throughout the body. They have nuclei and lack hemoglobin.

Structure of the Heart

The heart muscle is asymmetrical as a result of the distance blood must travel in the pulmonary and systemic circuits. Since the right side of the heart sends blood to the pulmonary circuit it is smaller than the left side which must send blood out to the whole body in the systemic circuit, as shown in Figure 31.11. In humans, the heart is about the size of a clenched fist; it is divided into four chambers: two atria and two ventricles. There is one atrium and one ventricle on the right side and one atrium and one ventricle on the left side. The atria are the chambers that receive blood, and the ventricles are the chambers that pump blood. The right atrium receives deoxygenated blood from the **superior vena cava**, which drains blood from the jugular vein that comes from the brain and from the veins that come from the arms, as well as from the **inferior vena cava** which drains blood from the veins that come from the lower organs and the legs. In addition, the right atrium receives blood from the coronary sinus which drains deoxygenated blood from the heart itself. This deoxygenated blood then passes to the right ventricle through the **atrioventricular valve** or the **tricuspid valve**, a flap of connective tissue that opens in only one direction to prevent the backflow of blood. The valve separating the chambers on the left side of the heart valve is called the biscuspid or mitral valve. After it is filled, the right ventricle pumps the blood through the pulmonary arteries, by-passing the **semilunar valve** (or pulmonic valve) to the lungs for re-oxygenation. After blood passes through the pulmonary arteries, the right semilunar valves close preventing the blood from flowing backwards into the right ventricle. The left atrium then receives the oxygen-rich blood from the lungs via the pulmonary veins. This blood passes through the **bicuspid valve** or mitral valve (the atrioventricular valve on the left side of the heart) to the left ventricle where the blood is pumped out through **aorta**, the major artery of the body, taking oxygenated blood to the organs and muscles of the body. Once blood is pumped out of the left ventricle and into the aorta, the aortic semilunar valve (or aortic valve) closes preventing blood from flowing backward into the left ventricle. This pattern of pumping is referred to as double circulation and is found in all mammals.

visual CONNECTION

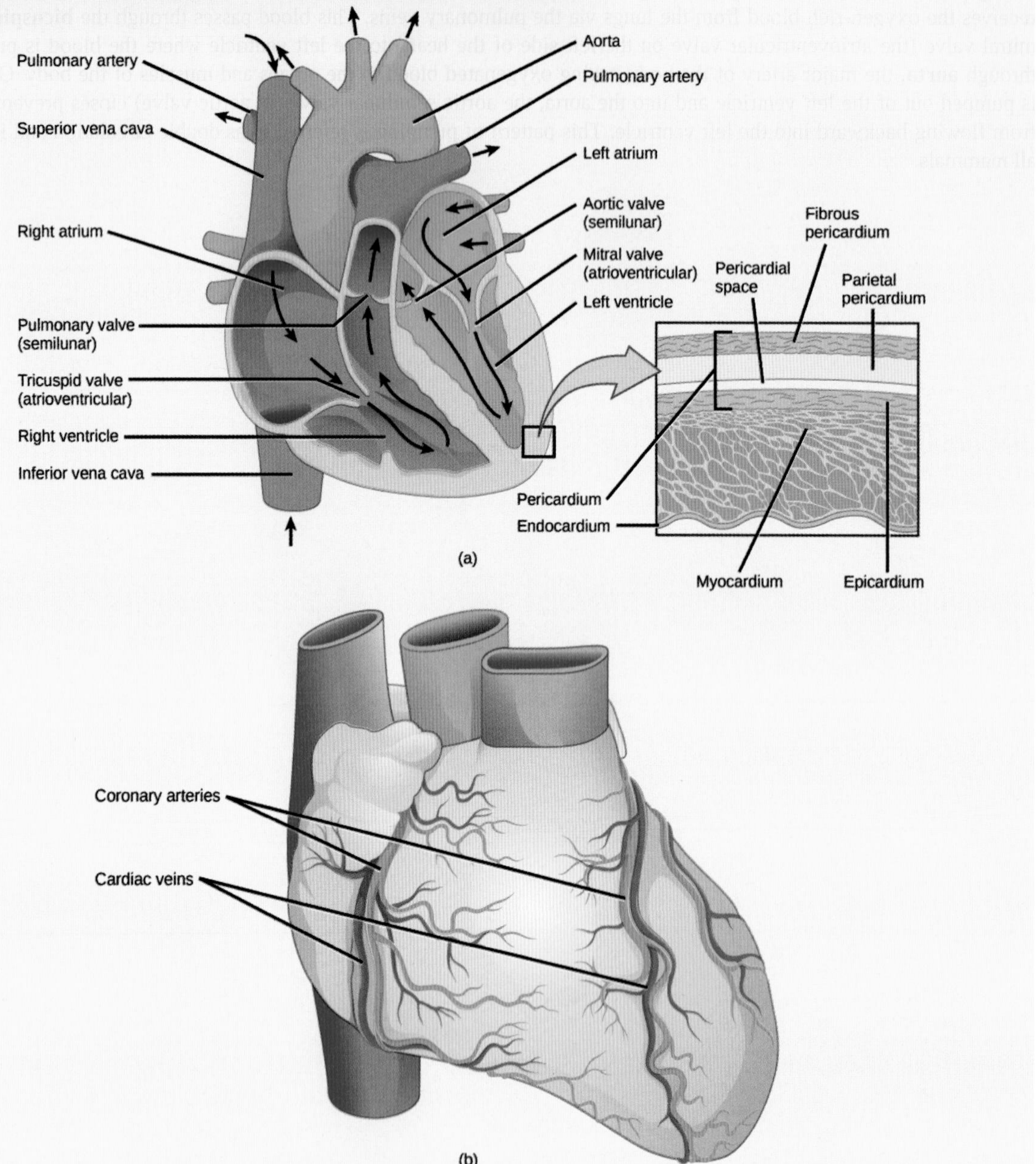

Figure 31.11 (a) The heart is primarily made of a thick muscle layer, called the myocardium, surrounded by membranes. One-way valves separate the four chambers. (b) Blood vessels of the coronary system, including the coronary arteries and veins, keep the heart musculature oxygenated.

Plasma and serum are common terms. Both are important parts of blood. What is the difference between blood plasma and blood serum?

a. Blood plasma is made up of blood serum and other components. Serum is the component of plasma containing blood coagulation factors.

b. Blood serum is made up of blood plasma and other components. Plasma is the component of serum containing blood coagulation factors.

c. Blood plasma is made of blood serum and other components. Serum is the component of plasma without the blood coagulation factors.

d. Blood plasma is made up of blood serum and other components. Serum is the component of plasma, which lacks antibodies and hormones.

The heart is composed of three layers; the epicardium, the myocardium, and the endocardium, illustrated in Figure 31.11. The inner wall of the heart has a lining called the **endocardium**. The **myocardium** consists of the heart muscle cells that make up the middle layer and the bulk of the heart wall. The outer layer of cells is called the **epicardium**, of which the second layer is a membranous layered structure called the **pericardium** that surrounds and protects the heart; it allows enough room for vigorous pumping but also keeps the heart in place to reduce friction between the heart and other structures.

The heart has its own blood vessels that supply the heart muscle with blood. The **coronary arteries** branch from the aorta and surround the outer surface of the heart like a crown. They diverge into capillaries where the heart muscle is supplied with oxygen before converging again into the **coronary veins** to take the deoxygenated blood back to the right atrium where the blood will be re-oxygenated through the pulmonary circuit. The heart muscle will die without a steady supply of blood. **Atherosclerosis** is the blockage of an artery by the buildup of fatty plaques. Because of the size (narrow) of the coronary arteries and their function in serving the heart itself, atherosclerosis can be deadly in these arteries. The slowdown of blood flow and subsequent oxygen deprivation that results from atherosclerosis causes severe pain, known as **angina**, and complete blockage of the arteries will cause **myocardial infarction**: the death of cardiac muscle tissue, commonly known as a heart attack.

The Cardiac Cycle

The main purpose of the heart is to pump blood through the body; it does so in a repeating sequence called the cardiac cycle. The **cardiac cycle** is the coordination of the filling and emptying of the heart of blood by electrical signals that cause the heart muscles to contract and relax. The human heart beats over 100,000 times per day. In each cardiac cycle, the heart contracts (**systole**), pushing out the blood and pumping it through the body; this is followed by a relaxation phase (**diastole**), where the heart fills with blood, as illustrated in Figure 31.12. The atria contract at the same time, forcing blood through the atrioventricular valves into the ventricles. Closing of the atrioventricular valves produces a monosyllabic "lup" sound. Following a brief delay, the ventricles contract at the same time forcing blood through the semilunar valves into the aorta and the artery transporting blood to the lungs (via the pulmonary artery). Closing of the semilunar valves produces a monosyllabic "dup" sound.

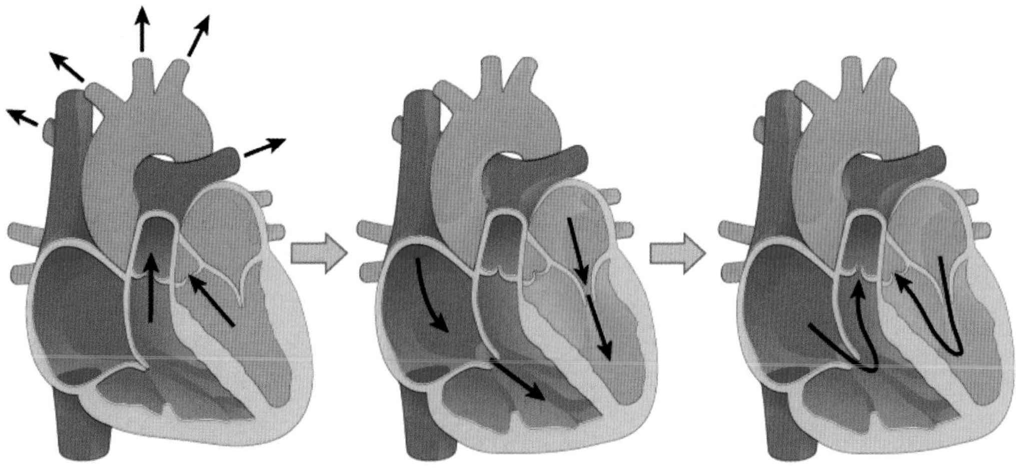

(a) **Atrial diastole, ventricular systole**: after the atria relax, the ventricles contract, pushing blood out of the heart.
(b) **Cardiac diastole**: all chambers are relaxed, and blood flows into the heart.
(c) **Atrial systole, ventricular diastole**: atria contract, pushing blood into the ventricles.

Figure 31.12 During (a) atrial diastole, the ventricles contract, forcing blood out of the heart. During (b) cardiac diastole, the heart muscle is relaxed and blood flows into the heart. During (c) atrial systole, the atria contract, pushing blood into the ventricles.

The pumping of the heart is a function of the cardiac muscle cells, or cardiomyocytes, that make up the heart muscle. **Cardiomyocytes**, shown in Figure 31.13, are distinctive muscle cells that are striated like skeletal muscle but pump rhythmically and involuntarily like smooth muscle; they are connected by intercalated disks exclusive to cardiac muscle. They are self-stimulated for a period of time and isolated cardiomyocytes will beat if given the correct balance of nutrients and electrolytes.

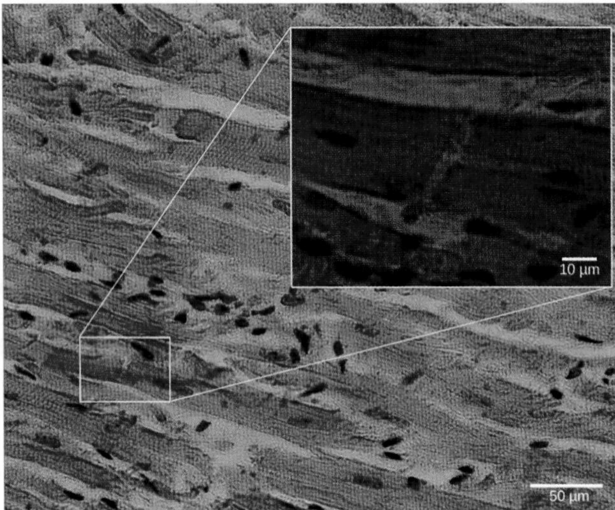

Figure 31.13 Cardiomyocytes are striated muscle cells found in cardiac tissue. (credit: modification of work by Dr. S. Girod, Anton Becker; scale-bar data from Matt Russell)

The autonomous beating of cardiac muscle cells is regulated by the heart's internal pacemaker that uses electrical signals to time the beating of the heart. The electrical signals and mechanical actions, illustrated in Figure 31.14, are intimately intertwined. The internal pacemaker starts at the **sinoatrial (SA) node**, which is located near the wall of the right atrium. Electrical charges spontaneously pulse from the SA node causing the two atria to contract in unison. The pulse reaches a second node, called the atrioventricular (AV) node, between the right atrium and right ventricle where it pauses for approximately 0.1 second before spreading to the walls of the ventricles. From the AV node, the electrical impulse enters the bundle of His, then to the left and right bundle branches extending through the interventricular septum. Finally, the Purkinje fibers conduct the impulse from the apex of the heart up the ventricular myocardium, and then the ventricles contract. This pause allows the atria to empty completely into the ventricles before the ventricles pump out the blood. The electrical impulses in the heart produce electrical currents that flow through the body and can be measured on the skin using electrodes. This information can be observed as an **electrocardiogram (ECG)**—a recording of the electrical impulses of the cardiac muscle.

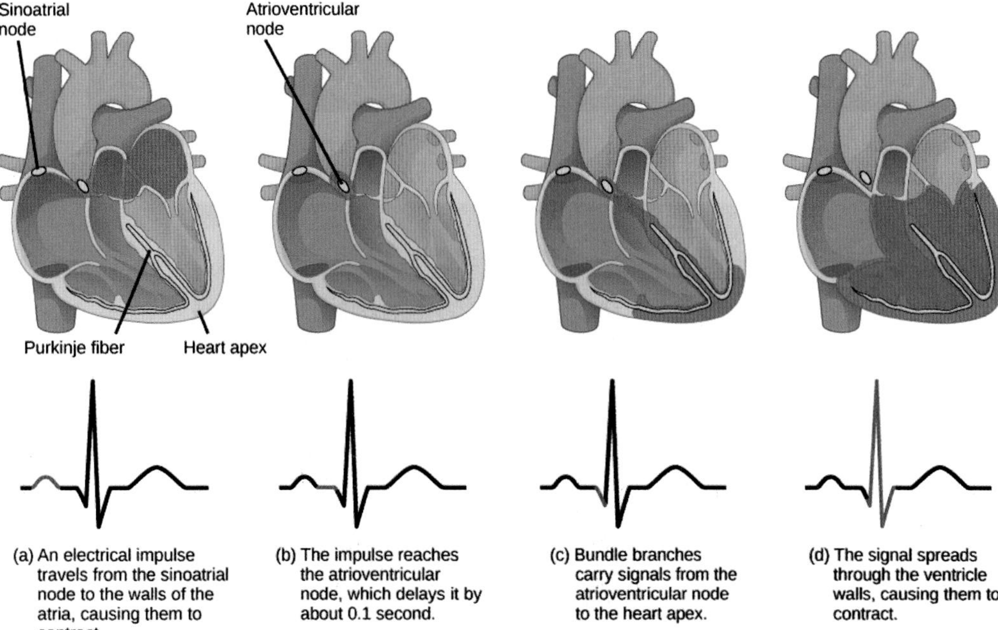

Figure 31.14 The beating of the heart is regulated by an electrical impulse that causes the characteristic reading of an ECG. The signal is initiated at the sinoatrial valve. The signal then (a) spreads to the atria, causing them to contract. The signal is (b) delayed at the atrioventricular node before it is passed on to the (c) heart apex. The delay allows the atria to relax before the (d) ventricles contract. The final part of the ECG cycle prepares the heart for the next beat.

Visit this site (http://openstaxcollege.org/l/electric_heart) to see the heart's "pacemaker" in action.

Some white blood cells release chemicals upon encountering a pathogen. These chemicals attract other white blood cells to the point of infection. Which of the following statements explains the feedback loop that occurs and predicts what would likely happen if the number of pathogens entering the body increases?

a. This is positive feedback. Fewer white blood cells will be attracted to the site as the number of pathogens in the body increases.

b. This is negative feedback. Fewer white blood cells will be attracted to the site as the number of pathogens in the body increases

c. This is positive feedback. More white blood cells will be attracted to the site as the number of pathogens in the body increases.

d. This is negative feedback. More white blood cells will be attracted to the site as the number of pathogens in the body increases.

everyday CONNECTION for AP® Courses

An echocardiogram (ECG) is an ultrasound of the heart that is used to determine if the heart valves and muscles are working correctly. In this photo, all four chambers of the heart can be seen.

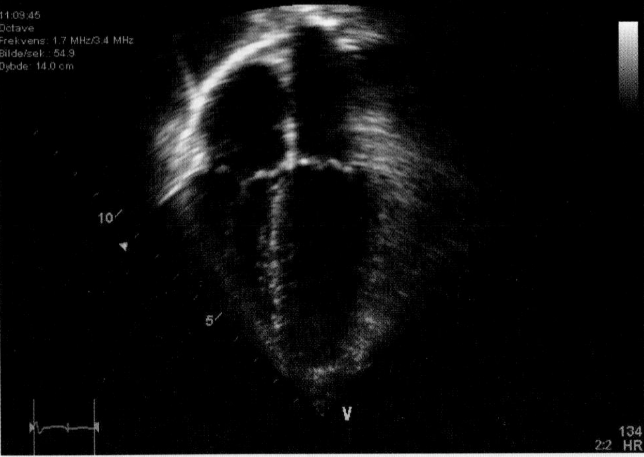

Figure 31.15 (credit: Kjetil Lenes, Wikimedia Commons)

Arteries, Veins, and Capillaries

The blood from the heart is carried through the body by a complex network of blood vessels (Figure 31.16). **Arteries** take blood away from the heart. The main artery is the aorta that branches into major arteries that take blood to different limbs and organs. These major arteries include the carotid artery that takes blood to the brain, the brachial arteries that take blood to the arms, and the thoracic artery that takes blood to the thorax and then into the hepatic, renal, and gastric arteries for the liver, kidney, and stomach, respectively. The iliac artery takes blood to the lower limbs. The major arteries diverge into minor arteries, and then smaller vessels called **arterioles**, to reach more deeply into the muscles and organs of the body.

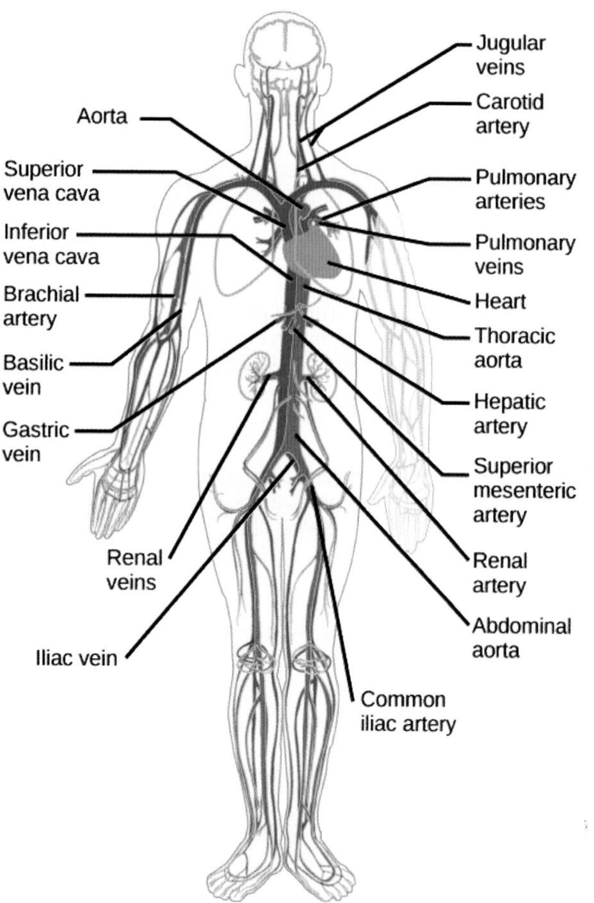

Figure 31.16 The major human arteries and veins are shown. (credit: modification of work by Mariana Ruiz Villareal)

Arterioles diverge into capillary beds. **Capillary beds** contain a large number (10 to 100) of **capillaries** that branch among the cells and tissues of the body. Capillaries are narrow-diameter tubes that can fit red blood cells through in single file and are the sites for the exchange of nutrients, waste, and oxygen with tissues at the cellular level. Fluid also crosses into the interstitial space from the capillaries. The capillaries converge again into **venules** that connect to minor veins that finally connect to major veins that take blood high in carbon dioxide back to the heart. **Veins** are blood vessels that bring blood back to the heart. The major veins drain blood from the same organs and limbs that the major arteries supply. Fluid is also brought back to the heart via the lymphatic system.

The structure of the different types of blood vessels reflects their function or layers. There are three distinct layers, or tunics, that form the walls of blood vessels (Figure 31.17). The first tunic is a smooth, inner lining of endothelial cells that are in contact with the red blood cells. The endothelial tunic is continuous with the endocardium of the heart. In capillaries, this single layer of cells is the location of diffusion of oxygen and carbon dioxide between the endothelial cells and red blood cells, as well as the exchange site via endocytosis and exocytosis. The movement of materials at the site of capillaries is regulated by **vasoconstriction**, narrowing of the blood vessels, and **vasodilation**, widening of the blood vessels; this is important in the overall regulation of blood pressure.

Veins and arteries both have two further tunics that surround the endothelium: the middle tunic is composed of smooth muscle and the outermost layer is connective tissue (collagen and elastic fibers). The elastic connective tissue stretches and supports the blood vessels, and the smooth muscle layer helps regulate blood flow by altering vascular resistance through vasoconstriction and vasodilation. The arteries have thicker smooth muscle and connective tissue than the veins to accommodate the higher pressure and speed of freshly pumped blood. The veins are thinner walled as the pressure and rate of flow are much lower. In addition, veins are structurally different than arteries in that veins have valves to prevent the backflow of blood. Because veins have to work against gravity to get blood back to the heart, contraction of skeletal muscle assists with the flow of blood back to the heart.

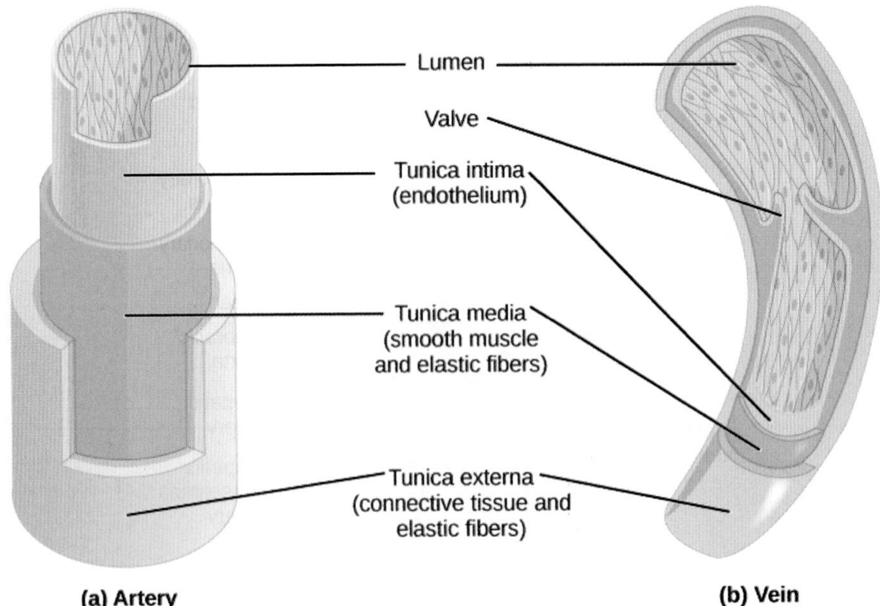

Figure 31.17 Arteries and veins consist of three layers: an outer tunica externa, a middle tunica media, and an inner tunica intima. Capillaries consist of a single layer of epithelial cells, the tunica intima. (credit: modification of work by NCI, NIH)

science practices CONNECTION for AP® Courses

Activity

Create a representation to track the pathway of a single red blood cell as it travels from a vein in your lower leg to the lung where it delivers carbon dioxide and picks up oxygen. Then describe the pathway it takes through the heart and vessels to return to your lower leg.

Think About It

How do the events in the cardiac cycle link the circulatory system with the nervous system?

31.4 | Blood Flow and Blood Pressure Regulation

In this section, you will explore the following questions:

- How does blood flow through the body?
- How is blood pressure regulated?

Connection for AP® Courses

The information in this section is not within the scope for AP®. However, the exchange of oxygen and carbon dioxide at capillary beds is an application of diffusion, a phenomenon we explored in detail in an earlier chapter. In addition, because many persons suffer from high blood pressure, often called the "silent killer," you might find it informative to know how blood pressure is regulated and why lack of appropriate regulation is detrimental.

Blood pressure (BP) is the pressure exerted by blood on the walls of a blood vessel that helps to push blood through the body. Systolic blood pressure measures the amount of pressure that blood exerts on vessels while the heart is beating. The optimal systolic blood pressure is 120 mmHg. Diastolic blood pressure measures the pressure in the vessels between heartbeats. The optimal diastolic blood pressure is 80 mmHg. Many factors can affect blood pressure, such as hormones, stress, exercise, eating, sitting, and standing. Blood flow through the body is regulated by the size of blood vessels, by the action of smooth muscle, by one-way valves, and by the fluid pressure of the blood itself.

How Blood Flows Through the Body

Blood is pushed through the body by the action of the pumping heart. With each rhythmic pump, blood is pushed under high pressure and velocity away from the heart, initially along the main artery, the aorta. In the aorta, the blood travels at 30 cm/sec. As blood moves into the arteries, arterioles, and ultimately to the capillary beds, the rate of movement slows dramatically to about 0.026 cm/sec, one-thousand times slower than the rate of movement in the aorta. While the diameter of each individual arteriole and capillary is far narrower than the diameter of the aorta, and according to the law of continuity, fluid should travel faster through a narrower diameter tube, the rate is actually slower due to the overall diameter of all the combined capillaries being far greater than the diameter of the individual aorta.

The slow rate of travel through the capillary beds, which reach almost every cell in the body, assists with gas and nutrient exchange and also promotes the diffusion of fluid into the interstitial space. After the blood has passed through the capillary beds to the venules, veins, and finally to the main venae cavae, the rate of flow increases again but is still much slower than the initial rate in the aorta. Blood primarily moves in the veins by the rhythmic movement of smooth muscle in the vessel wall and by the action of the skeletal muscle as the body moves. Because most veins must move blood against the pull of gravity, blood is prevented from flowing backward in the veins by one-way valves. Because skeletal muscle contraction aids in venous blood flow, it is important to get up and move frequently after long periods of sitting so that blood will not pool in the extremities.

Blood flow through the capillary beds is regulated depending on the body's needs and is directed by nerve and hormone signals. For example, after a large meal, most of the blood is diverted to the stomach by vasodilation of vessels of the digestive system and vasoconstriction of other vessels. During exercise, blood is diverted to the skeletal muscles through vasodilation while blood to the digestive system would be lessened through vasoconstriction. The blood entering some capillary beds is controlled by small muscles, called precapillary sphincters, illustrated in Figure 31.18. If the sphincters are open, the blood will flow into the associated branches of the capillary blood. If all of the sphincters are closed, then the blood will flow directly from the arteriole to the venule through the thoroughfare channel (see Figure 31.18). These muscles allow the body to precisely control when capillary beds receive blood flow. At any given moment only about 5-10% of our capillary beds actually have blood flowing through them.

visual CONNECTION

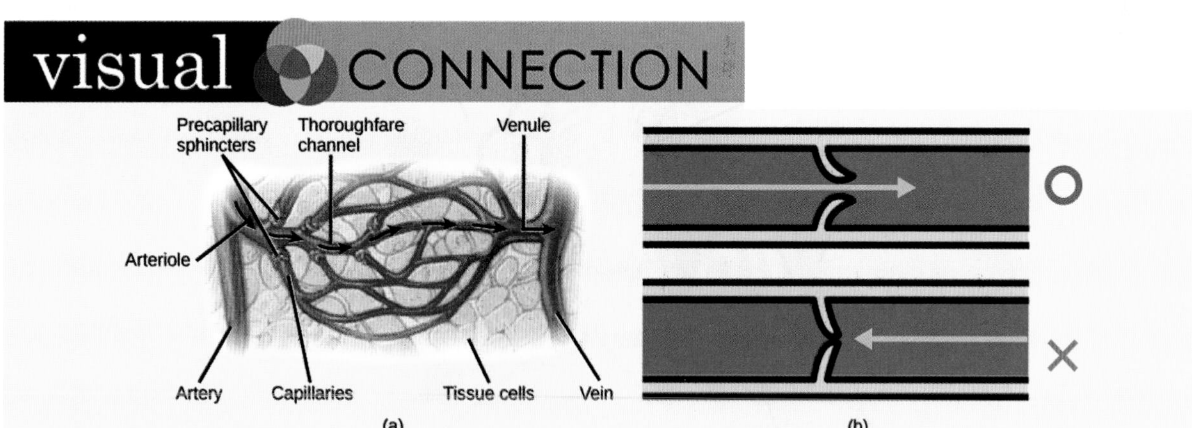

Figure 31.18 (a) Precapillary sphincters are rings of smooth muscle that regulate the flow of blood through capillaries; they help control the location of blood flow to where it is needed. (b) Valves in the veins prevent blood from moving backward. (credit a: modification of work by NCI)

How do arteries differ from veins?

a. Arteries have thicker smooth muscle layers to accommodate the changes in pressure from the heart.
b. Arteries carry plasma.
c. Arteries have thinner smooth muscle layers and valves and move blood by the action of skeletal muscle.
d. Arteries are thin walled.

Visit this site (http://openstaxcollege.org/l/circulation) to see the circulatory system's blood flow.

Capillaries are the smallest of blood vessels. They consist of a _____ layer of endothelial cells where diffusion and exchange of materials take place.

a. single

b. double

c. triple

d. bilateral

Proteins and other large solutes cannot leave the capillaries. The loss of the watery plasma creates a hyperosmotic solution within the capillaries, especially near the venules. This causes about 85% of the plasma that leaves the capillaries to eventually diffuses back into the capillaries near the venules. The remaining 15% of blood plasma drains out from the interstitial fluid into nearby lymphatic vessels (Figure 31.19). The fluid in the lymph is similar in composition to the interstitial fluid. The lymph fluid passes through lymph nodes before it returns to the heart via the vena cava. **Lymph nodes** are specialized organs that filter the lymph by percolation through a maze of connective tissue filled with white blood cells. The white blood cells remove infectious agents, such as bacteria and viruses, to clean the lymph before it returns to the bloodstream. After it is cleaned, the lymph returns to the heart by the action of smooth muscle pumping, skeletal muscle action, and one-way valves joining the returning blood near the junction of the venae cavae entering the right atrium of the heart.

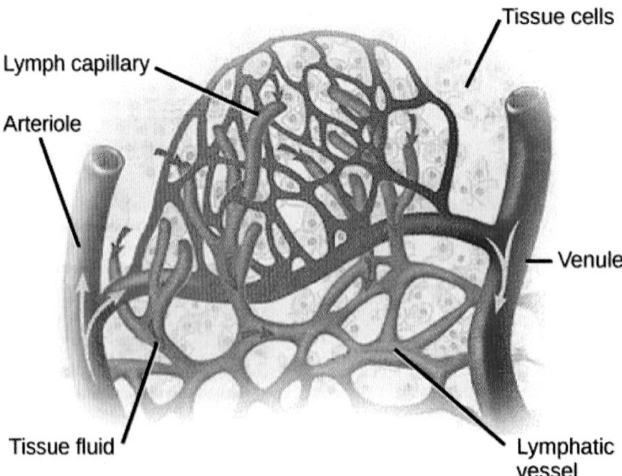

Figure 31.19 Fluid from the capillaries moves into the interstitial space and lymph capillaries by diffusion down a pressure gradient and also by osmosis. Out of 7,200 liters of fluid pumped by the average heart in a day, over 1,500 liters is filtered. (credit: modification of work by NCI, NIH)

Vertebrate Diversity in Blood Circulation

Blood circulation has evolved differently in vertebrates and may show variation in different animals for the required amount of pressure, organ and vessel location, and organ size. Animals with longs necks and those that live in cold environments have distinct blood pressure adaptations.

Long necked animals, such as giraffes, need to pump blood upward from the heart against gravity. The blood pressure required from the pumping of the left ventricle would be equivalent to 250 mm Hg (mm Hg = millimeters of mercury, a unit of pressure) to reach the height of a giraffe's head, which is 2.5 meters higher than the heart. However, if checks and balances were not in place, this blood pressure would damage the giraffe's brain, particularly if it was bending down to drink. These checks and balances include valves and feedback mechanisms that reduce the rate of cardiac output. Long-necked dinosaurs such as the sauropods had to pump blood even higher, up to ten meters above the heart. This would have required a blood pressure of more than 600 mm Hg, which could only have been achieved by an enormous heart. Evidence for such an enormous heart does not exist and mechanisms to reduce the blood pressure required include the slowing of metabolism as these animals grew larger. It is likely that they did not routinely feed on tree tops but grazed on the ground.

Living in cold water, whales need to maintain the temperature in their blood. This is achieved by the veins and arteries being close together so that heat exchange can occur. This mechanism is called a countercurrent heat exchanger. The blood vessels and the whole body are also protected by thick layers of blubber to prevent heat loss. In land animals that live in cold environments, thick fur and hibernation are used to retain heat and slow metabolism.

The heart is asymmetrical in shape. How does the way that the heart functions determine this feature of the heart's structure?

a. The right and left sides of the heart are responsible for pumping blood to separate regions of the body covering same distances.

b. The right side of heart sends blood to the lungs to be deoxygenated in the pulmonary circuit, while the left side sends oxygenated blood to the rest of the body in the systemic circuit.

c. The left side of heart sends blood to the lungs to be oxygenated in the pulmonary circuit, while the right side sends blood to the rest of the body in the systemic circuit.

d. The right side of heart sends blood to the lungs to be oxygenated in the pulmonary circuit, while the left side sends blood to the rest of the body in the systemic circuit.

Blood Pressure

The pressure of the blood flow in the body is produced by the hydrostatic pressure of the fluid (blood) against the walls of the blood vessels. Fluid will move from areas of high to low hydrostatic pressures. In the arteries, the hydrostatic pressure near the heart is very high and blood flows to the arterioles where the rate of flow is slowed by the narrow openings of the arterioles. During systole, when new blood is entering the arteries, the artery walls stretch to accommodate the increase of pressure of the extra blood; during diastole, the walls return to normal because of their elastic properties. The blood pressure of the systole phase and the diastole phase, graphed in **Figure 31.20**, gives the two pressure readings for blood pressure. For example, 120/80 indicates a reading of 120 mm Hg during the systole and 80 mm Hg during diastole. Throughout the cardiac cycle, the blood continues to empty into the arterioles at a relatively even rate. This resistance to blood flow is called **peripheral resistance**.

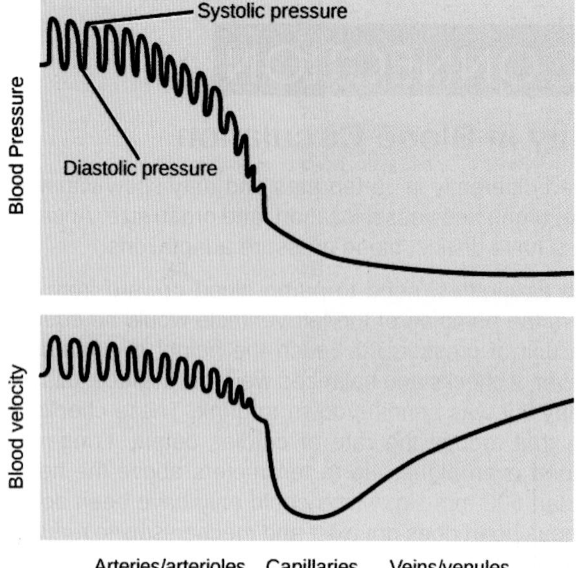

Figure 31.20 Blood pressure is related to the blood velocity in the arteries and arterioles. In the capillaries and veins, the blood pressure continues to decease but velocity increases.

Blood Pressure Regulation

Cardiac output is the volume of blood pumped by the heart in one minute. It is calculated by multiplying the number of heart contractions that occur per minute (heart rate) times the **stroke volume** (the volume of blood pumped into the aorta per contraction of the left ventricle). Therefore, cardiac output can be increased by increasing heart rate, as when exercising. However, cardiac output can also be increased by increasing stroke volume, such as if the heart contracts with greater strength. Stroke volume can also be increased by speeding blood circulation through the body so that more blood enters the heart between contractions. During heavy exertion, the blood vessels relax and increase in diameter, offsetting the increased heart rate and ensuring adequate oxygenated blood gets to the muscles. Stress triggers a decrease in the diameter of the blood vessels, consequently increasing blood pressure. These changes can also be caused by nerve signals or hormones, and even standing up or lying down can have a great effect on blood pressure.

KEY TERMS

angina pain caused by partial blockage of the coronary arteries by the buildup of plaque and lack of oxygen to the heart muscle

aorta major artery of the body that takes blood away from the heart

arteriole small vessel that connects an artery to a capillary bed

artery blood vessel that takes blood away from the heart

atherosclerosis buildup of fatty plaques in the coronary arteries in the heart

atrioventricular valve one-way membranous flap of connective tissue between the atrium and the ventricle in the right side of the heart; also known as tricuspid valve

atrium (plural: atria) chamber of the heart that receives blood from the veins and sends blood to the ventricles

bicuspid valve (also, mitral valve; left atrioventricular valve) one-way membranous flap between the atrium and the ventricle in the left side of the heart

blood pressure (BP) pressure of blood in the arteries that helps to push blood through the body

capillary smallest blood vessel that allows the passage of individual blood cells and the site of diffusion of oxygen and nutrient exchange

capillary bed large number of capillaries that converge to take blood to a particular organ or tissue

cardiac cycle filling and emptying the heart of blood by electrical signals that cause the heart muscles to contract and relax

cardiac output the volume of blood pumped by the heart in one minute as a product of heart rate multiplied by stroke volume

cardiomyocyte specialized heart muscle cell that is striated but contracts involuntarily like smooth muscle

closed circulatory system system in which the blood is separated from the bodily interstitial fluid and contained in blood vessels

coronary artery vessel that supplies the heart tissue with blood

coronary vein vessel that takes blood away from the heart tissue back to the chambers in the heart

diastole relaxation phase of the cardiac cycle when the heart is relaxed and the ventricles are filling with blood

double circulation flow of blood in two circuits: the pulmonary circuit through the lungs and the systemic circuit through the organs and body

electrocardiogram (ECG) recording of the electrical impulses of the cardiac muscle

endocardium innermost layer of tissue in the heart

epicardium outermost tissue layer of the heart

gill circulation circulatory system that is specific to animals with gills for gas exchange; the blood flows through the gills for oxygenation

hemocoel cavity into which blood is pumped in an open circulatory system

hemolymph mixture of blood and interstitial fluid that is found in insects and other arthropods as well as most mollusks

inferior vena cava drains blood from the veins that come from the lower organs and the legs

interstitial fluid fluid between cells

lymph node specialized organ that contains a large number of macrophages that clean the lymph before the fluid is returned to the heart

myocardial infarction (also, heart attack) complete blockage of the coronary arteries and death of the cardiac muscle tissue

myocardium heart muscle cells that make up the middle layer and the bulk of the heart wall

open circulatory system system in which the blood is mixed with interstitial fluid and directly covers the organs

ostium (plural: ostia) holes between blood vessels that allow the movement of hemolymph through the body of insects, arthropods, and mollusks with open circulatory systems

pericardium membrane layer protecting the heart; also part of the epicardium

peripheral resistance resistance of the artery and blood vessel walls to the pressure placed on them by the force of the heart pumping

plasma liquid component of blood that is left after the cells are removed

platelet (also, thrombocyte) small cellular fragment that collects at wounds, cross-reacts with clotting factors, and forms a plug to prevent blood loss

precapillary sphincter small muscle that controls blood circulation in the capillary beds

pulmocutaneous circulation circulatory system in amphibians; the flow of blood to the lungs and the moist skin for gas exchange

pulmonary circulation flow of blood away from the heart through the lungs where oxygenation occurs and then returns to the heart again

red blood cell small (7–8 μm) biconcave cell without mitochondria (and in mammals without nuclei) that is packed with hemoglobin, giving the cell its red color; transports oxygen through the body

semilunar valve membranous flap of connective tissue between the aorta and a ventricle of the heart (the aortic or pulmonary semilunar valves)

serum plasma without the coagulation factors

sinoatrial (SA) node the heart's internal pacemaker; located near the wall of the right atrium

stroke volume the volume of blood pumped into the aorta per contraction of the left ventricle

superior vena cava drains blood from the jugular vein that comes from the brain and from the veins that come from the arms

systemic circulation flow of blood away from the heart to the brain, liver, kidneys, stomach, and other organs, the limbs, and the muscles of the body, and then the return of this blood to the heart

systole contraction phase of cardiac cycle when the ventricles are pumping blood into the arteries

tricuspid valve one-way membranous flap of connective tissue between the atrium and the ventricle in the right side of the heart; also known as atrioventricular valve

unidirectional circulation flow of blood in a single circuit; occurs in fish where the blood flows through the gills, then past the organs and the rest of the body, before returning to the heart

vasoconstriction narrowing of a blood vessel

vasodilation widening of a blood vessel

vein blood vessel that brings blood back to the heart

vena cava major vein of the body returning blood from the upper and lower parts of the body; see the superior vena cava and inferior vena cava

ventricle (heart) large inferior chamber of the heart that pumps blood into arteries

venule blood vessel that connects a capillary bed to a vein

white blood cell large (30 μm) cell with nuclei of which there are many types with different roles including the protection of the body from viruses and bacteria, and cleaning up dead cells and other waste

CHAPTER SUMMARY

31.1 Overview of the Circulatory System

In most animals, the circulatory system is used to transport blood through the body. Some primitive animals use diffusion for the exchange of water, nutrients, and gases. However, complex organisms use the circulatory system to carry gases, nutrients, and waste through the body. Circulatory systems may be open (mixed with the interstitial fluid) or closed (separated from the interstitial fluid). Closed circulatory systems are a characteristic of vertebrates; however, there are significant differences in the structure of the heart and the circulation of blood between the different vertebrate groups due to adaptions during evolution and associated differences in anatomy. Fish have a two-chambered heart with unidirectional circulation. Amphibians have a three-chambered heart, which has some mixing of the blood, and they have double circulation. Most non-avian reptiles have a three-chambered heart, but have little mixing of the blood; they have double circulation. Mammals and birds have a four-chambered heart with no mixing of the blood and double circulation.

31.2 Components of the Blood

Specific components of the blood include red blood cells, white blood cells, platelets, and the plasma, which contains coagulation factors and serum. Blood is important for regulation of the body's pH, temperature, osmotic pressure, the circulation of nutrients and removal of waste, the distribution of hormones from endocrine glands, and the elimination of excess heat; it also contains components for blood clotting. Red blood cells are specialized cells that contain hemoglobin and circulate through the body delivering oxygen to cells. White blood cells are involved in the immune response to identify and target invading bacteria, viruses, and other foreign organisms; they also recycle waste components, such as old red blood cells. Platelets and blood clotting factors cause the change of the soluble protein fibrinogen to the insoluble protein fibrin at a wound site forming a plug. Plasma consists of 90 percent water along with various substances, such as coagulation factors and antibodies. The serum is the plasma component of the blood without the coagulation factors.

31.3 Mammalian Heart and Blood Vessels

The heart muscle pumps blood through three divisions of the circulatory system: coronary, pulmonary, and systemic. There is one atrium and one ventricle on the right side and one atrium and one ventricle on the left side. The pumping of the heart is a function of cardiomyocytes, distinctive muscle cells that are striated like skeletal muscle but pump rhythmically and involuntarily like smooth muscle. The internal pacemaker starts at the sinoatrial node, which is located near the wall of the right atrium. Electrical charges pulse from the SA node causing the two atria to contract in unison; then the pulse reaches the atrioventricular node between the right atrium and right ventricle. A pause in the electric signal allows the atria to empty completely into the ventricles before the ventricles pump out the blood. The blood from the heart is carried through the body by a complex network of blood vessels; arteries take blood away from the heart, and veins bring blood back to the heart.

31.4 Blood Flow and Blood Pressure Regulation

Blood primarily moves through the body by the rhythmic movement of smooth muscle in the vessel wall and by the action of the skeletal muscle as the body moves. Blood is prevented from flowing backward in the veins by one-way valves. Blood flow through the capillary beds is controlled by precapillary sphincters to increase and decrease flow depending on the body's needs and is directed by nerve and hormone signals. Lymph vessels take fluid that has leaked out of the blood to the lymph nodes where it is cleaned before returning to the heart. During systole, blood enters the arteries, and the artery walls stretch to accommodate the extra blood. During diastole, the artery walls return to normal. The blood pressure of the systole phase and the diastole phase gives the two pressure readings for blood pressure.

REVIEW QUESTIONS

1. Which of the following organisms has an open circulatory system?

a. a cat
b. a bee
c. a human
d. a bird

2. What is an advantage of an open circulatory system?

a. It uses less metabolic energy.
b. It enables an organism to move faster.
c. It is a more efficient way to move gases, nutrients, and waste around an organism's body.
d. It allows organisms to grow larger.

3. Which of the following statements about circulatory systems is false?

a. In closed circulatory systems, blood flows through vessels that are separate from the interstitial fluid of the body.
b. The earthworm has a closed circulatory system.
c. In an open circulatory system, hemolymph empties into the body cavity.
d. Lobsters are organisms that have closed circulatory systems.

4. Which of the following statements best defines the open circulatory system?

a. In an open circulatory system, blood mixes with interstitial fluid in the hemocoel.
b. In an open circulatory system, the blood is separated from the bodily interstitial fluid and contained blood vessels.
c. Blood circulates unidirectionally from the heart around systemic circulatory root.
d. An open circulatory system uses more energy than a closed circulatory system.

5. A simple organism such as a jellyfish uses _____ to exchange gases and nutrients with their surrounding environment.

a. blood
b. diffusion
c. atria
d. blood vessels

6. Fish and birds have closed circulation. They both have a systemic circulatory system, which delivers blood from the heart and out to the organs of the body. Birds differ from fish in that they have a circuit that leads through the lungs and back to the heart. What is this called?

a. pulmonary circulatory circuit
b. gill circulatory circuit
c. pulmocutaneous circulatory circuit
d. lymph circulatory circuit

7.

Organism	Method of circulation
A	Closed 2-chambered heart
B	Closed within 4-chambered heart
C	Open with some closed arterial vessels
D	Closed within 3-chambered heart
E	Open within hemocoel
F	Diffusion

A student is attempting to reorganize some preserved animals in the biology lab that have lost their labels. The student notices there are some notes on each jar, providing information on each animal's classification. The student labels the unknown animals A-F and enters each animal's circulatory system characteristics in a table. If the student wished to create a phylogeny of organisms A through F, which organism would likely be on the extreme right of the phylogenetic tree?

a. organism A
b. organism B
c. organism E
d. organism F

8.

Organism	Method of circulation
A	Closed 2-chambered heart
B	Closed within 4-chambered heart
C	Open with some closed arterial vessels
D	Closed within 3-chambered heart
E	Open within hemocoel
F	Diffusion

A student is attempting to reorganize some preserved animals in the biology lab that have lost their labels. The student notices there are some notes on each jar, providing information on each animal's classification. The student labels the unknown animals A-F and enters each animal's circulatory system characteristics in a table. If the student wished to create a phylogeny of organisms A through F, in what order would the organisms most likely appear on the tree, from left to right, and why?

a. The order would be F, E, C, A, B, D as the general trend in circulatory system evolution is toward increasingly closed systems.
b. The order would be B, D, A, C, E, F as the general trend in circulatory system evolution is toward increasingly open systems.
c. The order would be F, E, C, A, D, B as the general trend in circulatory system evolution is toward increasingly closed systems.
d. The order would be F, E, C, D, B, A as the general trend in circulatory system evolution is toward increasingly open systems.

9. Differences in human blood types show how genetic differences have evolved over time, affecting red blood cell structure. What is the basis for blood type classifications?

a. It is based on antigens made of carbohydrates, specifically glycoside and N-acetylglucosamine, found on the surface of red blood cells.
b. It is based on antigens made of proteins, specifically glycolipids and glycoproteins, found on the surface of red blood cells.
c. It is based on antigens made of proteins, specifically peripheral and integral proteins, found on the surface of the red blood cell.
d. It is based on antigens made of lipids, specifically glycerophospholipids, found on the surface of red blood cells.

10. If a person has blood type AB/Rh-, what antibodies will be found in the blood?

a. A antibodies
b. A antibodies and B antibodies
c. Rh antibodies
d. B antibodies

11. Components found in human blood include white blood cells, red blood cells, and _______.

a. platelets
b. ostia
c. hemolymph
d. cardiomyocytes

12. Up to four components can be derived from donated blood. One of those components is plasma. Which of the following is not a basic component of plasma?

a. water
b. proteins
c. salts
d. red blood cells

13. Many platelets converge and stick together at a wound site, eventually forming a platelet plug, also called a fibrin clot. Platelets continue to arrive at the wound site until the plug is completely formed. Describe the feedback mechanisms taking place and predict what would likely happen if part of the platelet plug broke away before the wound was healed.

a. A positive feedback loop, which would restart if part of the platelet plug broke away, calling more platelets to the site to repair the broken plug.
b. A negative feedback loop, which would restart if part of the platelet plug broke away, calling more platelets to the site to repair the broken plug.
c. A positive feedback loop, which would not restart if part of the platelet plug broke away.
d. A negative feedback loop, which would not restart if part of the platelet plug broke away.

14.

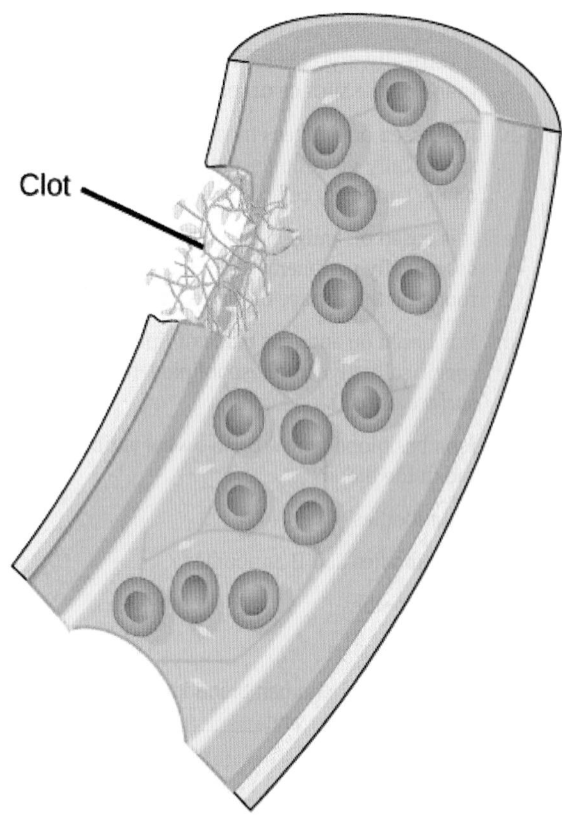

The diagram shows a fibrin clot forming within a blood vessel. What constituents of the blood interact to form the clot?

a. red blood cells, serum, and vitamin K
b. ribrin, megakaryocytes and blood proteins
c. granulocytes, platelets and red blood cells
d. platelets, fibrinogen, and clotting factors

15.

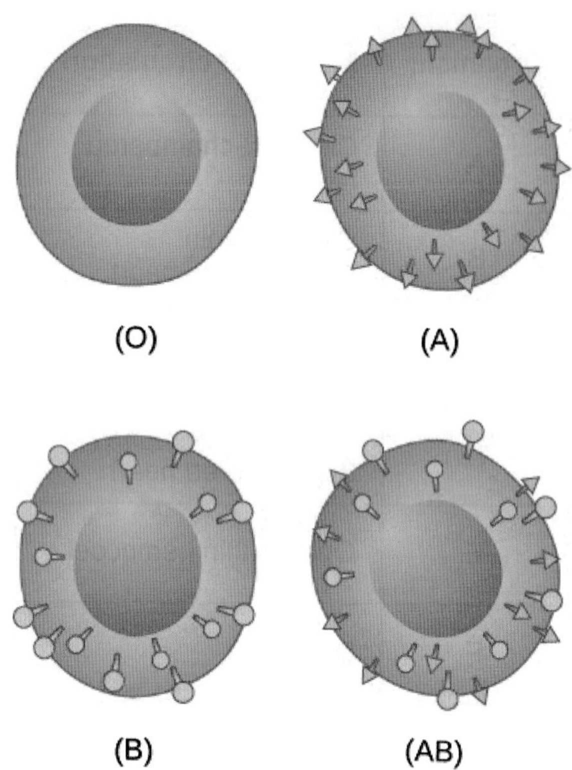

The diagram models the four different types of red blood cells in humans. Describe what is represented by the colored shapes on the surface of the cells and explain their function.

a. Antigens, which identify the red blood cells as part of the body, as opposed to foreign red blood cells, which may be attacked by antibodies within the blood.
b. Glycoproteins, which identify the red blood cells as part of the body, as opposed to foreign red blood cells, which may be attacked by antigens within the blood.
c. Glycoproteins which identify the red blood cells as part of the body, as opposed to foreign red blood cells, which may be attacked by antibodies within the blood.
d. Antibodies which identify the red blood cells as part of the body, as opposed to foreign red blood cells, causing neutralization of the foreign cells.

16. Your heart is a pump that circulates blood and oxygen around your body. Which of the following statements about the circulatory system is false?

a. Blood in the pulmonary veins is deoxygenated.
b. Blood in the inferior vena cava is deoxygenated.
c. Blood in the pulmonary artery is deoxygenated.
d. Blood in the aorta is oxygenated.

17. Which of the following statements about the heart is false?

a. The mitral valve separates the left ventricle from the left atrium.
b. Blood travels through the bicuspid valve to the left atrium.
c. Both the aortic and the pulmonary valves are semilunar valves.
d. The mitral valve is an atrioventricular valve.

18. In a healthy heart, a heartbeat begins within an electrical signal from which part of the heart?

a. bundle of His
b. atrioventricular (AV) node
c. sinoatrial (SA) node
d. atrial diastole

19. Describe the cardiac cycle and explain what drives it.

a. The heart contracts to pump blood through the body during systole and is filled with blood during diastole. An electrical charge spontaneously pulses from SA node causing two atria to contract. The pulse reaches AV node where it pauses before spreading to the walls of the ventricles. It enters the bundle of His, then to left and right bundle branches extending through the interventricular septum. Purkinje fibers conduct impulse from the apex up the ventricular myocardium, causing the ventricles to contract. This pause allows the atria to empty their contents into the ventricles before the ventricles pump out the blood.
b. The heart contracts to pump blood through the body during diastole and is filled with blood during systole. An electrical charge spontaneously pulses from SA node causing two atria to contract. The pulse reaches AV node where it pauses before spreading to the walls of the ventricles. It enters the bundle of His, then to left and right bundle branches extending through the interventricular septum. Purkinje fibers conduct the impulse from the apex up the ventricular myocardium, causing the ventricles to contract. This pause allows the atria to empty their contents into the ventricles before the ventricles pump out the blood.
c. The heart contracts to pump blood through the body during systole and is filled with blood during diastole. An electrical charge spontaneously pulses from AV node causing two atria to contract. The pulse reaches SA node where it pauses before spreading to the walls of the ventricles. It enters the bundle of His, then to left and right bundle branches extending through the interventricular septum. Purkinje fibers conduct impulse from the apex up the ventricular myocardium, causing the ventricles to contract. This pause allows the atria to empty their contents into the ventricles before the ventricles pump out the blood.
d. The heart contracts to pump blood through the body during systole and is filled with blood during diastole. An electrical charge spontaneously pulses from SA node causing two atria to contract. The pulse reaches AV node where it pauses before spreading to the walls of the ventricles. It enters the Purkinje fibers, then to left and right bundle branches extending through the interventricular septum. The bundle of His conduct impulse from the apex up the ventricular myocardium, causing the ventricles to contract. This pause allows the atria to empty their contents into the ventricles before the ventricles pump out the blood.

20. Compare and contrast veins and arteries.

a. Both veins and arteries have three distinct layers. Veins take blood away from the heart and arteries bring blood back to the heart.

b. Both veins and arteries have three distinct layers. Arteries take blood away from the heart and veins bring blood back to the heart.

c. Both veins and arteries have valves to prevent the backflow of blood. Arteries take blood away from the heart and veins bring blood back to the heart.

d. Both veins and arteries have valves to prevent the backflow of blood. Veins take blood away from the heart and arteries bring blood back to the heart.

21.

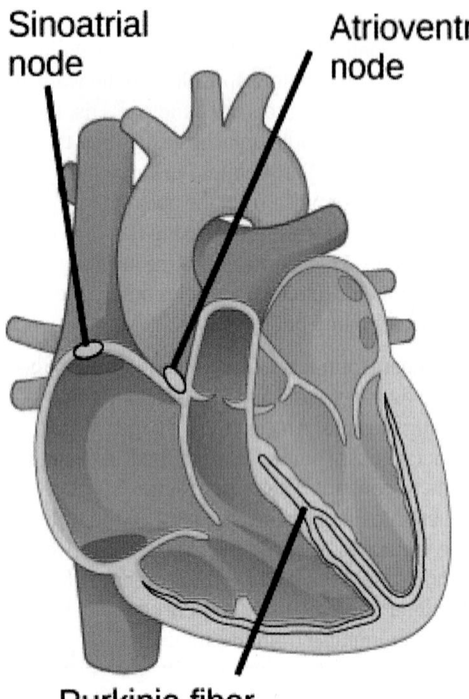

The diagram below shows the neural structures that control and coordinate the beating of the heart. How would the cardiac cycle be affected if neural signals were blocked within the Purkinje fiber?

a. The atria and ventricles would contract at the same time.

b. The ventricles would not contract.

c. The atria would contract first, followed by the ventricles.

d. Only the left atrium would contract.

22.

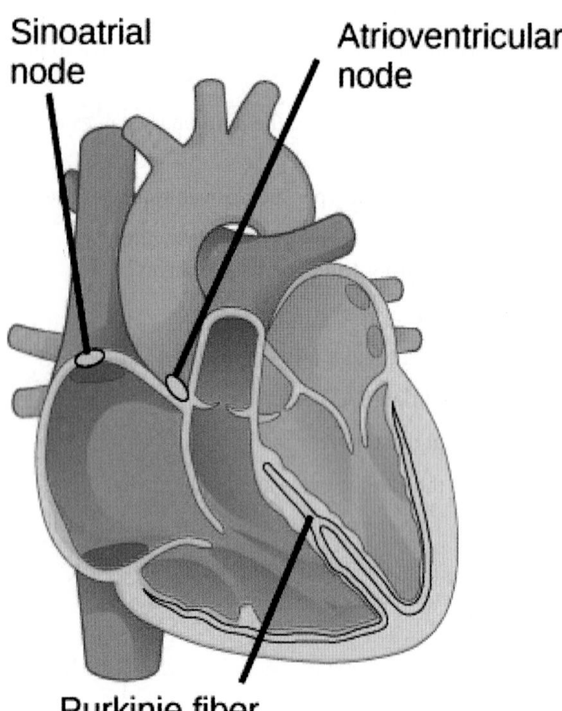

The diagram shows the neural structures that control and coordinate the beating of the heart. Explain fully how the cardiac cycle would be affected if the signal was blocked at the atrioventricular node and why.

a. The atria would contract, but the ventricles would not, because the atrioventricular node passes signals to the Purkinje fibers, which allow the ventricles to contract.

b. The ventricles would contract, but the atria would not, because the atrioventricular node passes the signal to the Purkinje fibers, which allow the ventricles to contract.

c. The atria would contract, but the ventricles would not, because the atrioventricular node passes the signal to the Purkinje fibers, which allow the atria to contract.

d. The ventricles would contract, but the atria would not, because the atrioventricular node passes the signal to the Purkinje fibers, which causes the atria to contract.

CRITICAL THINKING QUESTIONS

23. Define a closed circulatory system and compare the differences in heart structure for animals with closed circulatory systems.

a. A closed circulatory system is a system in which the blood mixes with the interstitial fluid. Fish have a two-chambered heart. Amphibians and reptiles have a three-chambered heart, but the latter has little mixing of blood. Mammals and birds have a four-chambered heart and double circulation.

b. A closed circulatory system is a system in which blood is separate from the interstitial fluid. Fish have a two-chambered heart. Amphibians and reptiles have a three-chambered heart, but the latter has little mixing of blood. Mammals and birds have a four-chambered heart and double circulation.

c. A closed circulatory system is a system in which blood is separate from the interstitial fluid. Amphibians have a two-chambered heart. Fishes and reptiles have a three-chambered heart, but the latter has little mixing of blood. Mammals and birds have a four-chambered heart and double circulation.

d. A closed circulatory system is a system in which blood mixes with the interstitial fluid. Amphibians have a two-chambered heart. Fishes and reptiles have a three-chambered heart, but the latter has little mixing of blood. Mammals and birds have a four-chambered heart and double circulation.

24. A circulatory system is the main method for transporting gases and nutrients throughout the body. Explain what happens in a closed circulatory system and compare a closed circulatory system to an open closed circulatory system.

a. Blood in closed circulatory system is present inside blood vessels and circulates unidirectional from the heart, around the systemic circulatory route, then returns to the heart. It is less controlled and structured than an open circulatory system, but nutrients and waste products are transported more efficiently.

b. Blood in closed circulatory system is not enclosed in blood vessels, but is pumped into a hemocoel, which circulates around the organs, then reenters the heart through ostia. It is more structured, controlled, and nutrients and waste products are transported more efficiently.

c. Blood in closed circulatory system is not enclosed in blood vessels, but is pumped into a hemocoel, which circulates around the organs, then reenters the heart through ostia. It is less controlled and structured than an open circulatory system, but nutrients and waste products are transported more efficiently.

d. Blood in a closed circulatory system is present inside blood vessels, circulates unidirectional from heart around the systemic circulatory route, and then returns to the heart. It is more structured, controlled, and nutrients and waste products are transported more efficiently than in open circulatory system.

25. What is one advantage of a four chambered heart over a three chambered heart?

a. Oxygenated blood carried by the right side of the heart is completely separated from the left side carrying deoxygenated blood, which assists in more efficient movement of oxygen around the body and aids in allowing the body to quickly move when needed.

b. A four-chambered heart keeps oxygenated and deoxygenated blood separated and has double circulation whereas a three-chambered heart has a single circulation. This assists in more efficient movement of oxygen around the body.

c. Oxygenated and deoxygenated blood are kept separate in a four-chambered heart, which assists in more efficient movement of carbon dioxide around the body.

d. Oxygenated and deoxygenated blood are kept separate in a four-chambered heart, which assists in more efficient movement of oxygen around the body and aids in allowing the body to move quickly when needed.

26. What are red blood cells also known as?

a. lymphocytes
b. monocytes
c. erythrocytes
d. basophils

27. How does the structure of red blood cells allow them to deliver oxygen to the cells of the body?

a. Their size and shape allow them to carry and transfer oxygen.
b. Their disc shape contains many small vesicles that allow them to carry and transfer oxygen.
c. They have nuclei and do not contain hemoglobin.
d. They contain coagulation factors and antibodies.

28. Which of the following best describes plasma?

a. It is a protein synthesized in the liver.
b. It is a liquid that contains only lipids and antibodies.
c. It is a blood component that is separated by spinning blood.
d. It is an antibody produced in the mucosal lining.

29. What is the heart's internal pacemaker?

a. An internal implant sends an electrical impulse through the heart.
b. It is an electrical impulse that starts in cardiac muscle cells at the sinoatrial node.
c. It is the excitation of cardiac muscle cells at the atrioventricular node followed by the sinoatrial node.
d. It starts in the aorta.

30. Cardiomyocytes are similar to skeletal muscle because _______.

a. they beat involuntarily
b. they are attached to bones
c. they pulse rhythmically
d. they are striated

31.

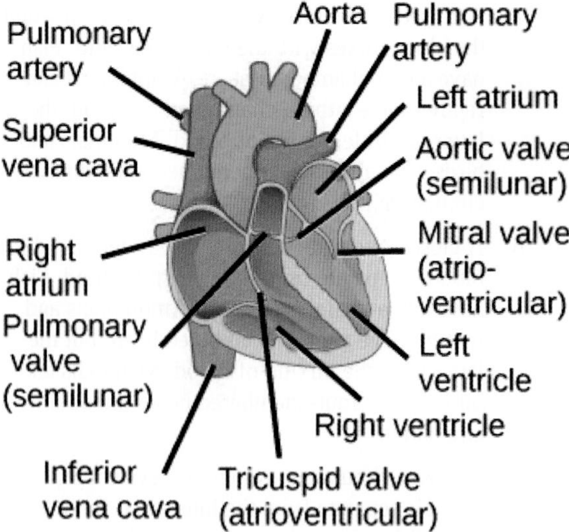

The diagram shows the internal anatomy of the heart. How would blood circulation beyond the heart be affected if the pulmonary valve could not open?

a. Blood could not reach the rest of the body.
b. Blood could not reach the lungs.
c. Blood could not return from the lungs.
d. Blood could not return from the rest of the body.

32.

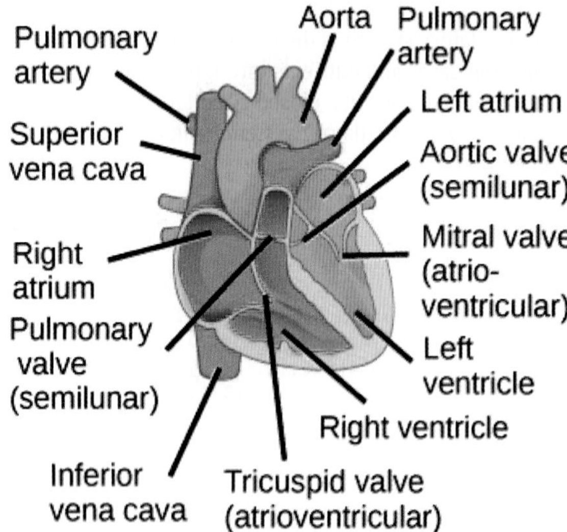

The diagram below shows the internal anatomy of the heart. How would blood circulation beyond the heart be affected if the tricuspid valve could not open?

a. Blood could not enter the pulmonary veins; therefore, it could not reach the lungs.

b. Blood could not enter the pulmonary artery; therefore, it could not reach the heart.

c. Blood could not enter the pulmonary artery; therefore, it could not reach the lungs.

d. Blood could not enter the pulmonary veins; therefore, it could not reach the heart.

33. Why is it useful for blood to travel slowly through capillary beds?

a. To allow antibodies to enter infected cells and to promote the diffusion of fluid into the interstitial space.

b. To assist with gas and nutrient exchange and to prevent the diffusion of fluid into the interstitial space.

c. To assist with gas and nutrient exchange and to promote the diffusion of fluid into the interstitial space.

d. To allow antibodies to enter infected cells and to prevent the diffusion of fluid into the interstitial space.

TEST PREP FOR AP® COURSES

34. Insects have open circulatory systems in which blood, or hemolymph, circulates through the body cavity rather than through closed blood vessels. Birds, like other vertebrates, have closed circulatory systems in which blood remains within arteries, veins, and capillaries as it circulates. Based on their difference in circulatory system, which of the following statements best describes an organism that would be favored by selection during a food shortage?

a. Insects would be favored because an open circulatory system requires less energy.

b. Insects would be favored because an open circulatory system stores energy.

c. Birds would be favored because a closed circulatory system loses less energy to heat.

d. Birds would be favored because a closed circulatory system is more efficient at delivering nutrients.

35.

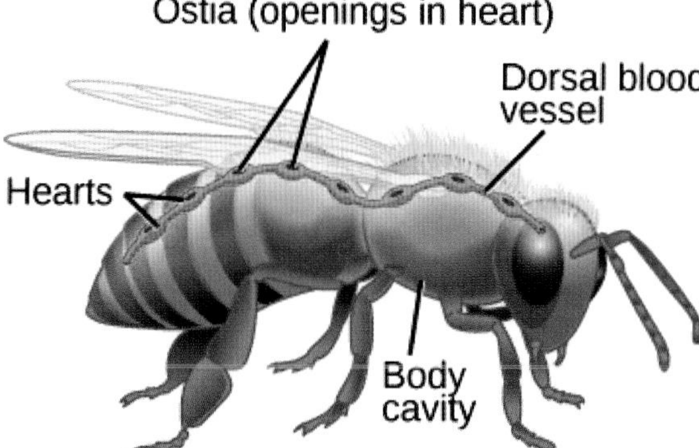

This diagram shows how insects have a heart that is elongated throughout much of their body. This is opposed to the heart of vertebrates, such as humans, which does not spread throughout the length of the body. Why was it likely advantageous for insects to evolve an elongated heart as opposed to the centrally located heart of vertebrates?

a. Because an elongated heart allows blood to easily reach all the parts of the body from the heart.

b. Because the elongated heart allows more blood to reach all the parts of the body, it allows for more nutrient exchange.

c. Because an elongated heart allows blood to easily return to the heart from a few points within the body cavity.

d. Because an elongated heart allows blood to easily return to the heart from most points within the body cavity.

36. Insects have open circulatory systems in which blood, or hemolymph, circulates through the body cavity rather than through closed blood vessels. Birds, like other vertebrates, have closed circulatory systems in which blood remains within arteries, veins, and capillaries as it circulates. How has this difference most likely influenced the evolution of birds and insects?

a. The open circulatory system of birds warms their entire body quicker, allowing them to live in colder climates more successfully than insects.

b. The closed circulatory system allows blood flow to increase to the flight muscles during flight, allowing insects to be better fliers than birds.

c. The greater efficiency of a closed circulatory system allowed birds to become larger than insects.

d. The simplicity of the open circulatory system allows insects to have a higher metabolism than birds.

37. Serum is used to diagnose and monitor diseases, and it is also used to classify blood types. Which of the following statements best describes serum?

a. It is a liquid consisting of 90% water and has coagulation factors.

b. It is plasma without the coagulation factors.

c. Serum is only made of albumin.

d. Serum is the same substance as interstitial fluid.

38. Explain how blood types are distinguished from one another.

a. Blood types are distinguished on the basis of the presence or absence of different carbohydrates found on the surface of red blood cells.

b. Blood types are distinguished on the basis of the presence or absence of different proteins found inside the red blood cells.

c. Blood types are distinguished on the basis of the presence or absence of different lipids found on the surface of red blood cells.

d. Blood types are distinguished based on the presence or absence of different antigens found on the surface of the red blood cells.

39. The inflammatory response involves increasing blood flow to areas of the body that contain immune system cells fighting a pathogen or foreign object. The inflammatory response is an example of a positive feedback loop. Based on this, what would cause the inflammatory response to stop in a certain area of the body?

a. The white blood cells destroy all of the pathogens/foreign objects.

b. The white blood cells disperse away from the site.

c. More white blood cells arrive to fight the pathogens/foreign objects.

d. Fewer white blood cells are needed to finish fighting the infection

40. ________ is the phase of the cardiac cycle where the heart contracts, which pushes out the blood and pumps it around the body.

a. diastole

b. cardiac output

c. myocardial infarction

d. systole

41. In routine physicals, doctors often test for problems with the electrical activity of your heart. A(n) _____ can measure the electrical impulses in the heart.

a. endocardium

b. electrocardiogram (ECG)

c. peripheral resistance

d. cardiac output

42.

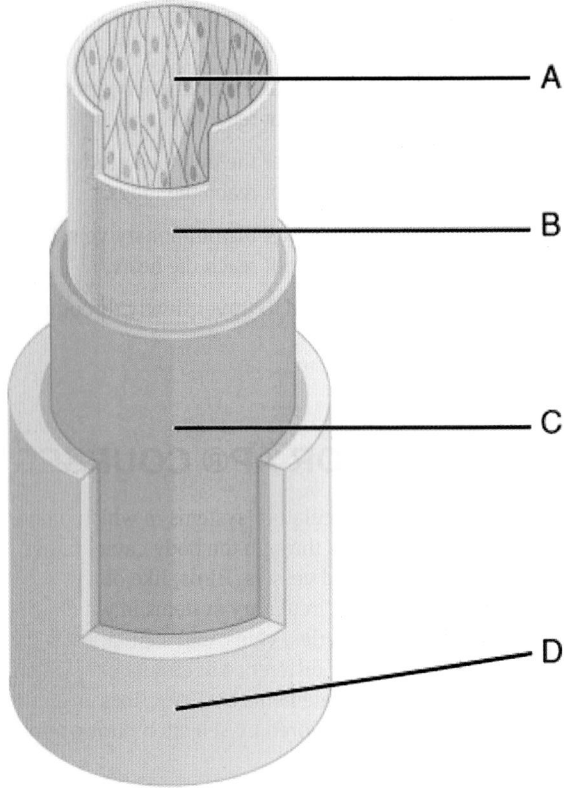

The diagram shows a cross section of a blood vessel. Which part of the labeled structure would allow vasodilation in the blood vessel and under what conditions would vasodilation occur?

a. Part B would allow vasodilation in the blood vessel if the blood vessel brings blood to relatively inactive cells, such as fat cells.

b. Part C would allow vasodilation in the blood vessel if the heart and body's metabolism slow.

c. Part B would allow vasodilation in the blood vessel if the blood vessel takes blood away from an active organ system.

d. Part C would allow vasodilation in the blood vessel if the blood vessel takes blood to a muscle cell that is contracting quickly.

43.

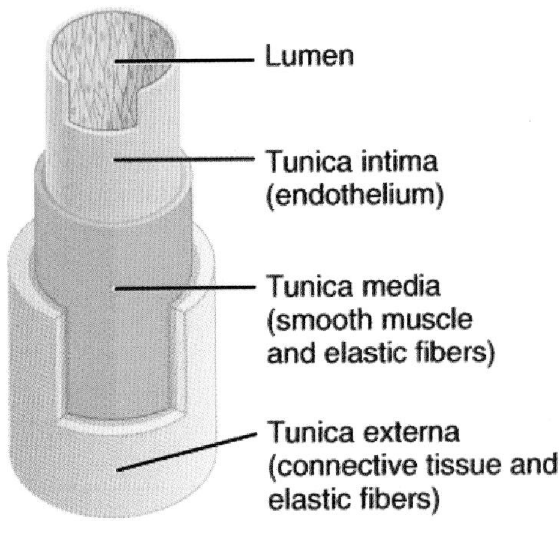

(a) Artery

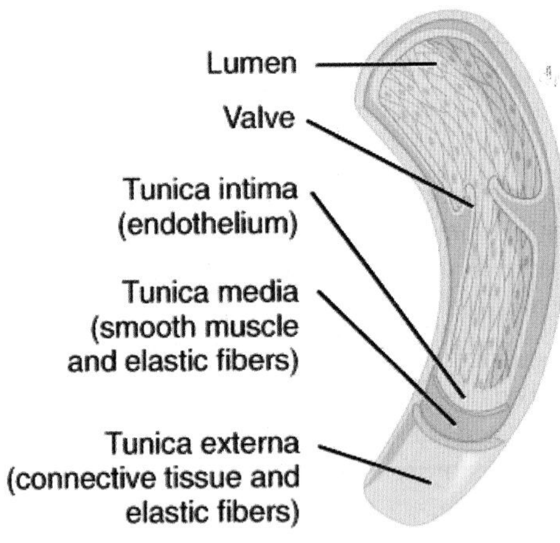

(b) Vein

The diagram shows a cross section of an artery and vein. What is the function of the tunica externa and why is it thicker in the artery than in the vein?

a. The tunica externa prevents blood cell adhesion to the wall of the vessel. It is thicker in the artery to protect against the higher blood pressure found in arteries.

b. The tunica externa protects the vessel from wear and tear and also provides support for the vessel. It is thicker in the artery to protect against the higher blood pressure found in arteries.

c. The tunica externa protects the vessel from wear and tear and provides support for the vessel. It is thicker in the artery to protect against the lower blood pressure found in arteries.

d. The tunica externa prevents blood cell adhesion to the wall of the vessel. It is thicker in the artery to protect against the lower blood pressure found in arteries.

SCIENCE PRACTICE CHALLENGE QUESTIONS

44. Like Gram-positive bacteria, red blood cells have carbohydrates on the cell surface. The A, B, A/B, and O blood types are designations of the phenotypes expressed by the alleles that code for these cell surface carbohydrates.

A. **Describe** the relationship between regulation of expression and the differences among the A, B, A/B, and O types of blood cells.

B. **Explain** how the blood group phenotype does not display non-Mendelian inheritance and the simplest alternative model that explains this deviation.

Immune system T-cells recognize cell surface carbohydrates of bacterial and red blood cells. That these similarities have consequences for survival is indicated by the observation that individuals with blood type O are more susceptible to infection by *Vibrio*, the Gram-negative bacteria that causes cholera, and individuals with type A/B are more susceptible to infections from a broad range of *E. coli* variants, all of which are also Gram-negative.

C. **Describe** the likely reason for the increased susceptibility of individuals with type A/B blood in terms of the antigen-antibody model of specific immune response. **Justify** the selection of data that would allow a test of your reasoning.

D. The distribution of blood types was determined in a population. The results are displayed in the table.

Type	Observed	Frequency
A	501	
B	794	
A/B	236	
O	601	
Total, N	2132	

Table 31.1

Recall that the frequency of an allele can be determined if the genotype is known. For example, for a gene with two possible alleles the frequency of the dominant allele in a homozygous dominant population is just twice the number of individuals 2N divided by the number of alleles which is 2N also since each individual has 2 alleles at each gene. The frequency would be 1. For a population composed entirely of heterozygous individuals the frequency would be 0.5.

- Using the usual mathematical relationship and the three-allele system calculate the frequency of each type and add that value to the table.

  From these frequencies the probabilities of the A, B, and O alleles in the population were determined as shown in the table below.

Allele	probability
A	0.201
B	0.265
O	0.542

Table 31.2

- Using these probabilities **calculate** the expected frequencies, E, of each blood type using

$$E(A) = (p_A^2 + 2p_A + 2p_A p_O)N$$
$$E(B) = (p_B^2 + 2p_B + 2p_B p_O)N$$
$$E(A/\ B) = 2 \cdot p_a \cdot p_B \cdot N$$
$$E(O) = p_O^2 \cdot N$$

  Add these expected frequencies to the table.

Type	Observed, O	Expected Frequency, E
A	501	
B	794	
A/B	236	
O	601	

Table 31.3

- **Apply your understanding** of the conceptual foundation of these equations by restating in words the relationship represented by E(A).

- Apply a χ^2 test at the 95% confidence level and 3 degrees of freedom (number of traits minus one) to **evaluate the claim** that these data indicate Hardy-Weinberg equilibrium of the ABO system for this population. The definition of the statistic

$$\chi^2 = \sum \frac{(O-E)^2}{E}$$

  and this table are provided on the AP Biology Exam.

	Degrees of Freedom							
p	1	2	3	4	5	6	7	8
0.05	3.84	5.99	7.82	9.49	11.07	12.59	14.07	15.51
0.01	6.64	9.32	11.34	13.28	15.09	16.81	18.48	20.09

Table 31.4

- Hardy-Weinberg equilibrium is consistent with the assumption of no change in the distribution of alleles over time. **Justify the selection of data** that should be obtained to further test this assumption.

Homologous genes coding for the carbohydrates that are presented on the surfaces of red blood cells are found in amphibians and mammals but not in fish, implying a last common ancestor for the ABO gene system at least 20 million years ago.

E. The difference between genes coding for A and B is a single nucleotide replacement. **Evaluate** the likelihood that negative selection pressures have been active in the evolution of this system.

45. The immune system rejection of transplanted organs and the availability of organ donors are key factors in determining survival. Blood ABO compatibility is always a criterion in matching donors and recipients in adult patients and was once a consideration for infant patients. Period of time on the waitlist for a suitable donor is critical because the health of the patient degrades while waiting. Dipchand *et al.* (*American Journal of Transplantation*, 10, 2010) made a comparison of survival rates for infants where the donor heart was ABO compatible and incompatible as shown in the graph.

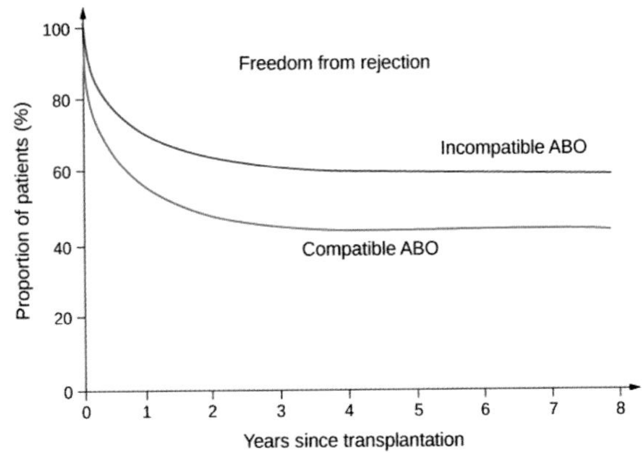

Figure 31.21

Based on these data justify the claim that expression of blood group immune response develops over time and that this provides a window of opportunity for transplantation.

32 | OSMOTIC REGULATION AND EXCRETION

Figure 32.1 Just as humans recycle what we can and dump the remains into landfills, our bodies use and recycle what they can and excrete the remaining waste products. Our bodies' complex systems have developed ways to treat waste and maintain a balanced internal environment. (credit: modification of work by Redwin Law)

Chapter Outline

Introduction

The daily intake recommendation for human water consumption is eight to ten glasses of water. In order to achieve a healthy balance, the human body should excrete the eight to ten glasses of water every day. This occurs via the processes of urination, defecation, sweating and, to a small extent, respiration. The organs and tissues of the human body are soaked in fluids that are maintained at constant temperature, pH, and solute concentration, all crucial elements of homeostasis. The solutes in body fluids are mainly mineral salts and sugars, and osmotic regulation is the process by which the mineral salts and water are kept in balance. Osmotic homeostasis is maintained despite the influence of external factors like temperature, diet, and weather conditions.

Osmotic balance is especially important in the brain. The brain is 80% water, and osmotic balance between water and spinal fluid is critical to proper brain function. Too much or too little water can cause severe medical conditions. Researchers have recently discovered the mechanism that controls water flow between brain cells. The speed of water flow is controlled by water channels called aquaporin channels, which are controlled by a neurotransmitter called gamma-aminobutyric acid. You can read more about this interesting research at the Science Daily website (http://openstaxcollege.org/l/32brain) .

32.1 | Osmoregulation and Osmotic Balance

In this section, you will explore the following questions:

- Why are osmoregulation and osmotic balance important to body functions?
- What is osmolarity and how is it measured?
- What are osmoregulators or osmoconformers, and how do these tools allow animals to adapt to different environments?

Connection for AP® Courses

Much of the information in this chapter is not within the scope for AP®. However, the chapter is filled with illustrative examples that are applicable to concepts we've explored previously, including chemistry, structure of the plasma cell membrane, and movement of molecules across membranes. With this in mind, it is helpful to have a general understanding how the human body, specifically the excretory system, maintains osmotic homeostasis despite the influence of external factors like temperature, diet, and varying environmental conditions. For example, if we drink eight to ten glasses of water per day, the human body excretes that water via urination, defecation, sweating, and, to a small extent, respiration.

Information presented and the examples highlighted in the section support concepts outlined in Big Idea 2 of the AP® Biology Curriculum Framework. The AP® Learning Objectives listed in the Curriculum Framework provide a transparent foundation for the AP® Biology course, an inquiry-based laboratory experience, instructional activities, and AP® exam questions. A learning objective merges required content with one or more of the seven science practices.

Big Idea 2	Biological systems utilize free energy and molecular building blocks to grow, to reproduce, and to maintain dynamic homeostasis.
Enduring Understanding 2.B	Growth, reproduction and dynamic homeostasis require that cell create and maintain internal environments that are different form their external environment.
Essential Knowledge	**2.B.1** Cell membranes are selectively permeable due to their structure.
Science Practice	**1.1** The student can create representations and models of natural or man-made phenomena and systems in the domain.
Science Practice	**7.1** The student can connect phenomena and models across spatial and temporal scales.
Science Practice	**7.2** The student can connect concepts in and across domain(s) to generalize or extrapolate in and/or across enduring understandings and/or big ideas.
Learning Objective	**2.11** The student is able to construct models that connect the movement of molecules across membranes with membrane structure and function.
Essential Knowledge	**2.B.2** Growth and dynamic homeostasis are maintained by the constant movement of molecules across membranes.
Science Practice	**1.4** The student can use representations and models to analyze situations or solve problems qualitatively and quantitatively.
Learning Objective	**2.12** The student is able to use representations and models to analyze situations or solve problems qualitatively and quantitatively to investigate whether dynamic homeostasis is maintained by the active movement of molecules across membranes.

Osmosis is the diffusion of water across a membrane in response to **osmotic pressure** caused by an imbalance of molecules on either side of the membrane. **Osmoregulation** is the process of maintenance of salt and water balance (**osmotic balance**) across membranes within the body's fluids, which are composed of water, plus electrolytes and non-electrolytes. An

electrolyte is a solute that dissociates into ions when dissolved in water. A **non-electrolyte**, in contrast, doesn't dissociate into ions during water dissolution. Both electrolytes and non-electrolytes contribute to the osmotic balance. The body's fluids include blood plasma, the cytosol within cells, and interstitial fluid, the fluid that exists in the spaces between cells and tissues of the body. The membranes of the body (such as the pleural, serous, and cell membranes) are **semi-permeable membranes**. Semi-permeable membranes are permeable (or permissive) to certain types of solutes and water. Solutions on two sides of a semi-permeable membrane tend to equalize in solute concentration by movement of solutes and/or water across the membrane. As seen in Figure 32.2, a cell placed in water tends to swell due to gain of water from the hypotonic or "low salt" environment. A cell placed in a solution with higher salt concentration, on the other hand, tends to make the membrane shrivel up due to loss of water into the hypertonic or "high salt" environment. Isotonic cells have an equal concentration of solutes inside and outside the cell; this equalizes the osmotic pressure on either side of the cell membrane which is a semi-permeable membrane.

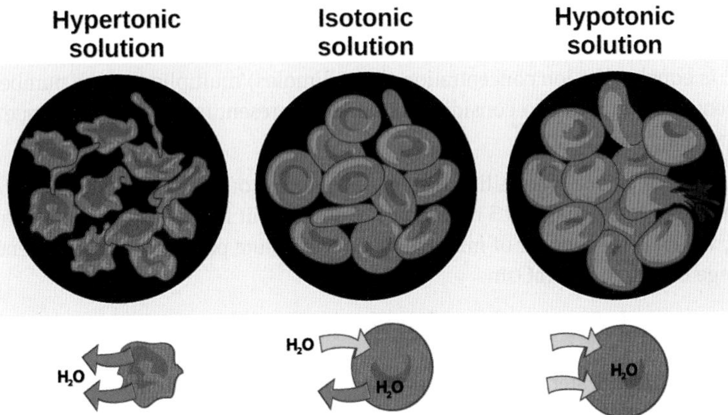

Figure 32.2 Cells placed in a hypertonic environment tend to shrink due to loss of water. In a hypotonic environment, cells tend to swell due to intake of water. The blood maintains an isotonic environment so that cells neither shrink nor swell. (credit: Mariana Ruiz Villareal)

The body does not exist in isolation. There is a constant input of water and electrolytes into the system. While osmoregulation is achieved across membranes within the body, excess electrolytes and wastes are transported to the kidneys and excreted, helping to maintain osmotic balance.

Need for Osmoregulation

Biological systems constantly interact and exchange water and nutrients with the environment by way of consumption of food and water and through excretion in the form of sweat, urine, and feces. Without a mechanism to regulate osmotic pressure, or when a disease damages this mechanism, there is a tendency to accumulate toxic waste and water, which can have dire consequences.

Mammalian systems have evolved to regulate not only the overall osmotic pressure across membranes, but also specific concentrations of important electrolytes in the three major fluid compartments: blood plasma, extracellular fluid, and intracellular fluid. Since osmotic pressure is regulated by the movement of water across membranes, the volume of the fluid compartments can also change temporarily. Because blood plasma is one of the fluid components, osmotic pressures have a direct bearing on blood pressure.

Transport of Electrolytes across Cell Membranes

Electrolytes, such as sodium chloride, ionize in water, meaning that they dissociate into their component ions. In water, sodium chloride (NaCl), dissociates into the sodium ion (Na^+) and the chloride ion (Cl^-). The most important ions, whose concentrations are very closely regulated in body fluids, are the cations sodium (Na^+), potassium (K^+), calcium (Ca^{+2}), magnesium (Mg^{+2}), and the anions chloride (Cl^-), carbonate (CO_3^{-2}), bicarbonate (HCO_3^-), and phosphate(PO_3^-). Electrolytes are lost from the body during urination and perspiration. For this reason, athletes are encouraged to replace electrolytes and fluids during periods of increased activity and perspiration.

Osmotic pressure is influenced by the concentration of solutes in a solution. It is directly proportional to the number of solute atoms or molecules and not dependent on the size of the solute molecules. Because electrolytes dissociate into their component ions, they, in essence, add more solute particles into the solution and have a greater effect on osmotic pressure, per mass than compounds that do not dissociate in water, such as glucose.

Water can pass through membranes by passive diffusion. If electrolyte ions could passively diffuse across membranes, it would be impossible to maintain specific concentrations of ions in each fluid compartment therefore they require special mechanisms to cross the semi-permeable membranes in the body. This movement can be accomplished by facilitated diffusion and active transport. Facilitated diffusion requires protein-based channels for moving the solute. Active transport requires energy in the form of ATP conversion, carrier proteins, or pumps in order to move ions against the concentration gradient.

Concept of Osmolality and Milliequivalent

In order to calculate osmotic pressure, it is necessary to understand how solute concentrations are measured. The unit for measuring solutes is the **mole**. One mole is defined as the gram molecular weight of the solute. For example, the molecular weight of sodium chloride is 58.44. Thus, one mole of sodium chloride weighs 58.44 grams. The **molarity** of a solution is the number of moles of solute per liter of solution. The **molality** of a solution is the number of moles of solute per kilogram of solvent. If the solvent is water, one kilogram of water is equal to one liter of water. While molarity and molality are used to express the concentration of solutions, electrolyte concentrations are usually expressed in terms of milliequivalents per liter (mEq/L): the mEq/L is equal to the ion concentration (in millimoles) multiplied by the number of electrical charges on the ion. The unit of milliequivalent takes into consideration the ions present in the solution (since electrolytes form ions in aqueous solutions) and the charge on the ions.

Thus, for ions that have a charge of one, one milliequivalent is equal to one millimole. For ions that have a charge of two (like calcium), one milliequivalent is equal to 0.5 millimoles. Another unit for the expression of electrolyte concentration is the milliosmole (mOsm), which is the number of milliequivalents of solute per kilogram of solvent. Body fluids are usually maintained within the range of 280 to 300 mOsm.

Osmoregulators and Osmoconformers

Persons lost at sea without any fresh water to drink are at risk of severe dehydration because the human body cannot adapt to drinking seawater, which is hypertonic in comparison to body fluids. Organisms such as goldfish that can tolerate only a relatively narrow range of salinity are referred to as stenohaline. About 90 percent of all bony fish are restricted to either freshwater or seawater. They are incapable of osmotic regulation in the opposite environment. It is possible, however, for a few fishes like salmon to spend part of their life in fresh water and part in sea water. Organisms like the salmon and molly that can tolerate a relatively wide range of salinity are referred to as euryhaline organisms. This is possible because some fish have evolved **osmoregulatory** mechanisms to survive in all kinds of aquatic environments. When they live in fresh water, their bodies tend to take up water because the environment is relatively hypotonic, as illustrated in Figure 32.3**a**. In such hypotonic environments, these fish do not drink much water. Instead, they pass a lot of very dilute urine, and they achieve electrolyte balance by active transport of salts through the gills. When they move to a hypertonic marine environment, these fish start drinking sea water; they excrete the excess salts through their gills and their urine, as illustrated in Figure 32.3**b**. Most marine invertebrates, on the other hand, may be isotonic with sea water (**osmoconformers**). Their body fluid concentrations conform to changes in seawater concentration. Cartilaginous fishes' salt composition of the blood is similar to bony fishes; however, the blood of sharks contains the organic compounds urea and trimethylamine oxide (TMAO). This does not mean that their electrolyte composition is similar to that of sea water. They achieve isotonicity with the sea by storing large concentrations of urea. These animals that secrete urea are called ureotelic animals. TMAO stabilizes proteins in the presence of high urea levels, preventing the disruption of peptide bonds that would occur in other animals exposed to similar levels of urea. Sharks are cartilaginous fish with a rectal gland to secrete salt and assist in osmoregulation.

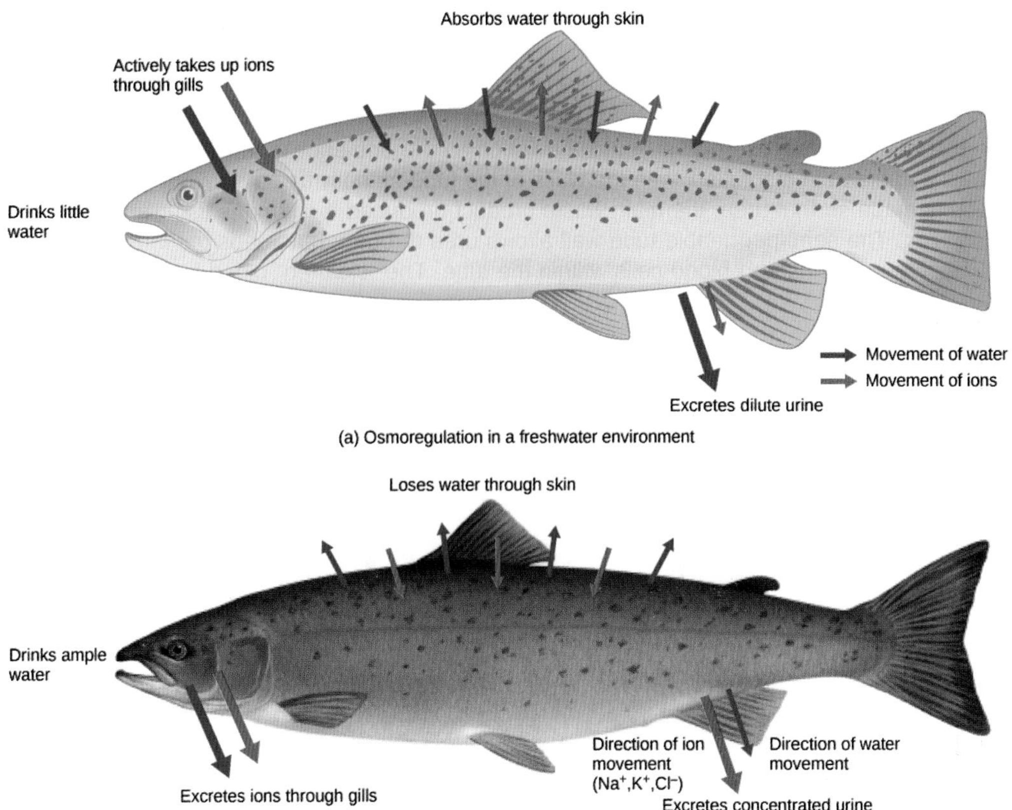

Figure 32.3 Fish are osmoregulators, but must use different mechanisms to survive in (a) freshwater or (b) saltwater environments. (credit: modification of work by Duane Raver, NOAA)

career CONNECTION

Dialysis Technician

Dialysis is a medical process of removing wastes and excess water from the blood by diffusion and ultrafiltration. When kidney function fails, dialysis must be done to artificially rid the body of wastes. This is a vital process to keep patients alive. In some cases, the patients undergo artificial dialysis until they are eligible for a kidney transplant. In others who are not candidates for kidney transplants, dialysis is a life-long necessity.

Dialysis technicians typically work in hospitals and clinics. While some roles in this field include equipment development and maintenance, most dialysis technicians work in direct patient care. Their on-the-job duties, which typically occur under the direct supervision of a registered nurse, focus on providing dialysis treatments. This can include reviewing patient history and current condition, assessing and responding to patient needs before and during treatment, and monitoring the dialysis process. Treatment may include taking and reporting a patient's vital signs and preparing solutions and equipment to ensure accurate and sterile procedures.

everyday CONNECTION for AP® Courses

Patients undergoing dialysis use dialysis machines such as the one shown here. Their blood runs through a tube that is immersed in a solution, with the walls of the tube actually being semipermeable membranes. The solution is made so that urea, the main waste product produced by humans, is pulled out of the blood through diffusion. The semi-permeable tube wall allows urea through, but keeps the larger components of the blood, such as proteins and blood cells, within the tube. The "cleaned" blood is eventually returned to the body.

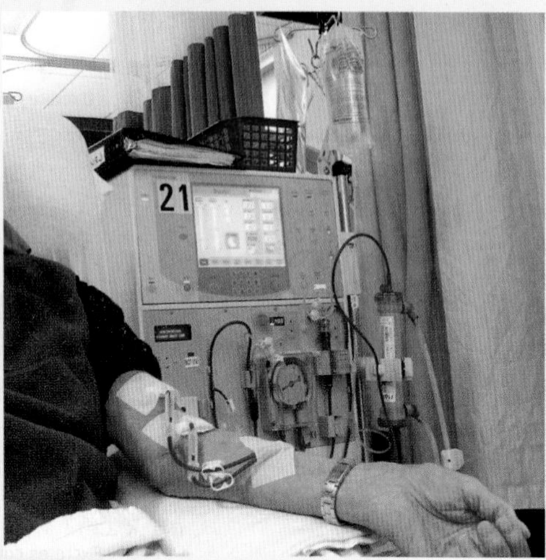

Figure 32.4

How do dialysis machines remove harmful urea from the blood?

a. by facilitated diffusion that allows urea to diffuse out of the blood
b. by active transport, which allows urea to diffuse out of the blood
c. by creating an osmotic gradient that allows urea to diffuse out of the blood across a permeable membrane
d. by creating an osmotic gradient that allows urea to diffuse out of the blood

science practices CONNECTION for AP® Courses

Think About It

Why is excretion important in order to achieve osmotic balance?

32.2 | The Kidneys and Osmoregulatory Organs

In this section, you will explore the following questions:

- How does the structure of the kidneys relate to its function as the main osmoregulatory organs in mammalian systems?
- How is the nephron the functional unit of the kidney and how does it actively filter blood and generate urine?
- What are the roles of glomerular filtration, tubular reabsorption, and tubular secretion in the formation of urine?

Connection for AP® Courses

Much of the information in this section is outside the scope for AP®. Although the curriculum does not require you to have detailed knowledge about the structure and physiology of the kidneys, learning how we filter blood to eliminate wastes—while also retaining vital water and other substances—provides an opportunity to apply concepts we've explored previously. Lack of kidney function can have detrimental effects on our health.

In coordination with the circulatory and endocrine systems, the human excretory system serves several functions: excretion of metabolic wastes, maintenance of water-salt balance (osmoregulation), maintenance of pH balance, and production of hormones. The organs of the system are the kidneys, ureters, urinary bladder, and urethra. Specialized cells of the kidney called nephrons (not to be confused with neurons of the nervous system) are closely associated with capillaries. Urine formation by nephrons involves three steps: filtration, in which water, nutrients, and wastes pass from the blood into the nephron; reabsorption, in which nutrients such as glucose and most water are reabsorbed back into the blood; and secretion, in which additional wastes and H^+ are added to urine to maintain homeostatic pH. The processes of diffusion, osmosis, and active transport ensure that the urine excreted from the body is hypertonic, thus preventing dehydration. For example, water is reabsorbed throughout nephron tubules back into capillaries via osmosis, and in another part of the tubule (ascending loop of Henle), Na^+ and Cl^- are actively transported into the interstitial fluid.

Information presented and the examples highlighted in the section support concepts outlined in Big Idea 4 of the AP® Biology Curriculum Framework. The AP® Learning Objectives listed in the Curriculum Framework provide a transparent foundation for the AP® Biology course, an inquiry-based laboratory experience, instructional activities, and AP® exam questions. A learning objective merges required content with one or more of the seven science practices.

Big Idea 4	Biological systems interact, and these systems and their interactions possess complex properties.
Enduring Understanding 4.A	Interactions within biological systems lead to complex properties.
Essential Knowledge	**4.A.4** Organisms exhibit complex properties due to interactions between their constituent parts.
Science Practice	**6.4** The student can make claims and predictions about natural phenomena based on scientific theories and models.
Learning Objective	**4.9** The student is able to predict the effects of a change in the component(s) of a biological system on the functionality of an organism(s).
Essential Knowledge	**4.A.4** Organisms exhibit complex properties due to interactions between their constituent parts.
Science Practice	**1.3** The student can refine representations and models of natural or man-made phenomena and systems in the domain.
Learning Objective	**4.10** The student is able to refine representations and models to illustrate biocomplexity due to interactions of the constituent parts.
Enduring Understanding 4.B	Competition and cooperation are important aspects of biological systems.
Essential Knowledge	**4.B.2** Cooperative interactions within organisms promote efficiency in the use of energy and matter.
Science Practice	**1.4** The student can use representations and models to analyze situations or solve problems qualitatively and quantitatively.
Learning Objective	**4.18** The student is able to use representations and models to analyze how cooperation interactions within organisms promote efficiency in the use of energy and matter.

Although the kidneys are the major osmoregulatory organ, the skin and lungs also play a role in the process. Water and electrolytes are lost through sweat glands in the skin, which helps moisturize and cool the skin surface, while the lungs expel a small amount of water in the form of mucous secretions and via evaporation of water vapor.

Kidneys: The Main Osmoregulatory Organ

The **kidneys**, illustrated in Figure 32.5, are a pair of bean-shaped structures that are located just below and posterior to the liver in the peritoneal cavity. The adrenal glands sit on top of each kidney and are also called the suprarenal glands. Kidneys filter blood and purify it. All the blood in the human body is filtered many times a day by the kidneys; these organs use up almost 25 percent of the oxygen absorbed through the lungs to perform this function. Oxygen allows the kidney cells to efficiently manufacture chemical energy in the form of ATP through aerobic respiration. The filtrate coming out of the kidneys is called **urine**.

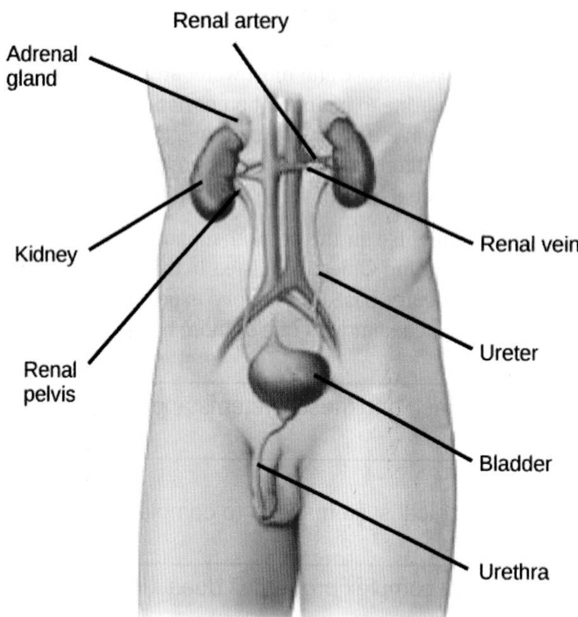

Figure 32.5 Kidneys filter the blood, producing urine that is stored in the bladder prior to elimination through the urethra. (credit: modification of work by NCI)

Kidney Structure

Externally, the kidneys are surrounded by three layers, illustrated in Figure 32.6. The outermost layer is a tough connective tissue layer called the **renal fascia**. The second layer is called the **perirenal fat capsule**, which helps anchor the kidneys in place. The third and innermost layer is the **renal capsule**. Internally, the kidney has three regions—an outer **cortex**, a **medulla** in the middle, and the **renal pelvis** in the region called the **hilum** of the kidney. The hilum is the concave part of the bean-shape where blood vessels and nerves enter and exit the kidney; it is also the point of exit for the ureters. The renal cortex is granular due to the presence of **nephrons**—the functional unit of the kidney. The medulla consists of multiple pyramidal tissue masses, called the **renal pyramids**. In between the pyramids are spaces called **renal columns** through which the blood vessels pass. The tips of the pyramids, called renal papillae, point toward the renal pelvis. There are, on average, eight renal pyramids in each kidney. The renal pyramids along with the adjoining cortical region are called the **lobes of the kidney**. The renal pelvis leads to the **ureter** on the outside of the kidney. On the inside of the kidney, the renal pelvis branches out into two or three extensions called the major **calyces**, which further branch into the minor calyces. The ureters are urine-bearing tubes that exit the kidney and empty into the **urinary bladder**.

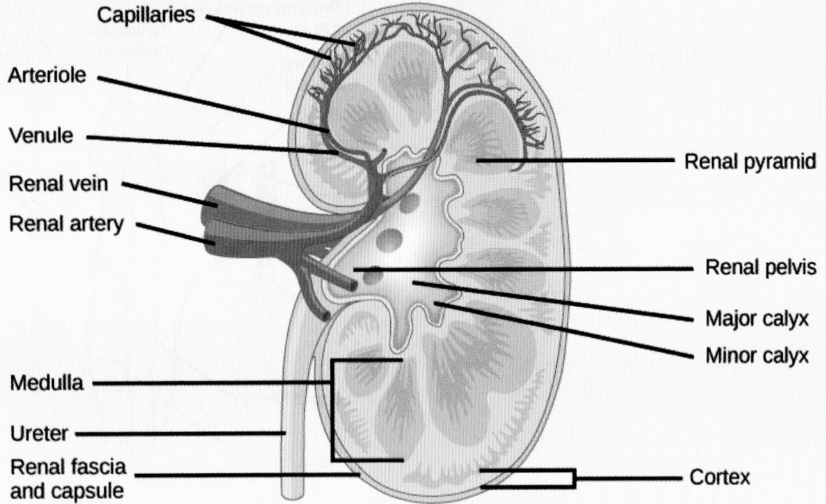

Figure 32.6 The internal structure of the kidney is shown. (credit: modification of work by NCI)

A surgeon is performing surgery on the minor calyces of the kidney. What layers of the kidney would she have to cut through, and in what order?

a. medulla and renal capsule
b. renal fascia, renal capsule, medulla, and cortex
c. renal fascia, renal capsule, cortex, and medulla
d. cortex and medulla

Because the kidney filters blood, its network of blood vessels is an important component of its structure and function. The arteries, veins, and nerves that supply the kidney enter and exit at the renal hilum. Renal blood supply starts with the branching of the aorta into the **renal arteries** (which are each named based on the region of the kidney they pass through) and ends with the exiting of the **renal veins** to join the **inferior vena cava**. The renal arteries split into several **segmental arteries** upon entering the kidneys. Each segmental artery splits further into several **interlobar arteries** and enters the renal columns, which supply the renal lobes. The interlobar arteries split at the junction of the renal cortex and medulla to form the **arcuate arteries**. The arcuate "bow shaped" arteries form arcs along the base of the medullary pyramids. **Cortical radiate arteries**, as the name suggests, radiate out from the arcuate arteries. The cortical radiate arteries branch into numerous afferent arterioles, and then enter the capillaries supplying the nephrons. Veins trace the path of the arteries and have similar names, except there are no segmental veins.

As mentioned previously, the functional unit of the kidney is the nephron, illustrated in Figure 32.7. Each kidney is made up of over one million nephrons that dot the renal cortex, giving it a granular appearance when sectioned sagittally. There are two types of nephrons—**cortical nephrons** (85 percent), which are deep in the renal cortex, and **juxtamedullary nephrons** (15 percent), which lie in the renal cortex close to the renal medulla. A nephron consists of three parts—a **renal corpuscle**, a **renal tubule**, and the associated capillary network, which originates from the cortical radiate arteries.

visual CONNECTION

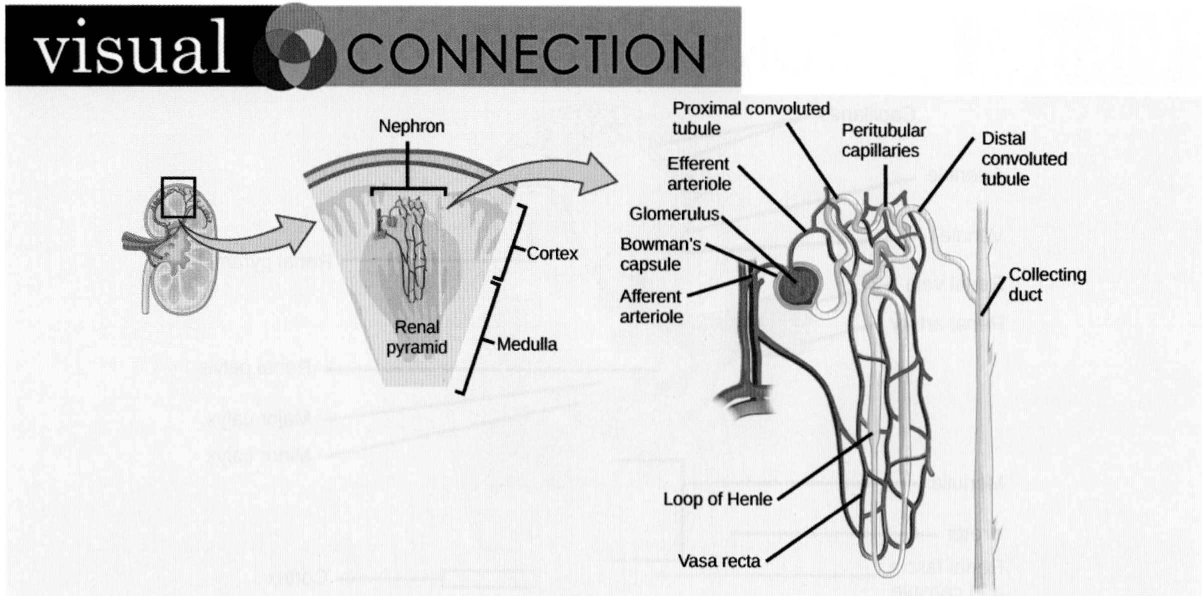

Figure 32.7 The nephron is the functional unit of the kidney. The glomerulus and convoluted tubules are located in the kidney cortex, while collecting ducts are located in the pyramids of the medulla. (credit: modification of work by NIDDK)

Which of the following statements about the nephron is false?

a. The collecting duct empties into the distal convoluted tubule.
b. The Bowman's capsule surrounds the glomerulus.
c. The loop of Henle is between the proximal and distal convoluted tubules.
d. The loop of Henle empties into the distal convoluted tubule.

Renal Corpuscle

The renal corpuscle, located in the renal cortex, is made up of a network of capillaries known as the **glomerulus** and the capsule, a cup-shaped chamber that surrounds it, called the glomerular or **Bowman's capsule**.

Renal Tubule

The renal tubule is a long and convoluted structure that emerges from the glomerulus and can be divided into three parts based on function. The first part is called the **proximal convoluted tubule (PCT)** due to its proximity to the glomerulus; it stays in the renal cortex. The second part is called the **loop of Henle**, or nephritic loop, because it forms a loop (with **descending** and **ascending limbs**) that goes through the renal medulla. The third part of the renal tubule is called the **distal convoluted tubule (DCT)** and this part is also restricted to the renal cortex. The DCT, which is the last part of the nephron, connects and empties its contents into collecting ducts that line the medullary pyramids. The collecting ducts amass contents from multiple nephrons and fuse together as they enter the papillae of the renal medulla.

Capillary Network within the Nephron

The capillary network that originates from the renal arteries supplies the nephron with blood that needs to be filtered. The branch that enters the glomerulus is called the **afferent arteriole**. The branch that exits the glomerulus is called the **efferent arteriole**. Within the glomerulus, the network of capillaries is called the glomerular capillary bed. Once the efferent arteriole exits the glomerulus, it forms the **peritubular capillary network**, which surrounds and interacts with parts of the renal tubule. In cortical nephrons, the peritubular capillary network surrounds the PCT and DCT. In juxtamedullary nephrons, the peritubular capillary network forms a network around the loop of Henle and is called the **vasa recta**.

Go to this website (http://openstaxcollege.org/l/kidney_section) to see another coronal section of the kidney and to explore an animation of the workings of nephrons.

Describe the structure of the kidneys.

a. Externally, the kidneys are surrounded by three layers. The outermost layer is the renal fascia, the second layer is the perineal fat capsule, and the third layer is the renal capsule. Internally, the kidney has three layers: an outer cortex, the middle medulla, and the inner renal pelvis.

b. Externally, the kidneys are surrounded by three layers. The outermost layer is the renal fascia, the second layer is the perineal fat capsule, and the third layer is the renal capsule. Internally, the kidney has three layers: an outer medulla, the middle cortex, and the inner renal pelvis.

c. Externally, the kidneys are surrounded by three layers. The outermost layer is the renal capsule, the second layer is the perineal fat capsule, and the third layer is the renal fascia. Internally, the kidney has three layers: an outer cortex, the middle medulla, and the inner renal pelvis.

d. Externally, the kidneys are surrounded by three layers. The outermost layer is the renal fascia, the second layer is the perineal fat capsule, and the third layer is the renal capsule. Internally, the kidney has three layers: an outer cortex, the middle hilum, and the inner renal pelvis.

Kidney Function and Physiology

Kidneys filter blood in a three-step process. First, the nephrons filter blood that runs through the capillary network in the glomerulus. Almost all solutes, except for proteins, are filtered out into the glomerulus by a process called **glomerular filtration**. Second, the filtrate is collected in the renal tubules. Most of the solutes get reabsorbed in the PCT by a process called **tubular reabsorption**. In the loop of Henle, the filtrate continues to exchange solutes and water with the renal medulla and the peritubular capillary network. Water is also reabsorbed during this step. Then, additional solutes and wastes are secreted into the kidney tubules during **tubular secretion**, which is, in essence, the opposite process to tubular reabsorption. The collecting ducts collect filtrate coming from the nephrons and fuse in the medullary papillae. From here, the papillae deliver the filtrate, now called urine, into the minor calyces that eventually connect to the ureters through the renal pelvis. This entire process is illustrated in Figure 32.8.

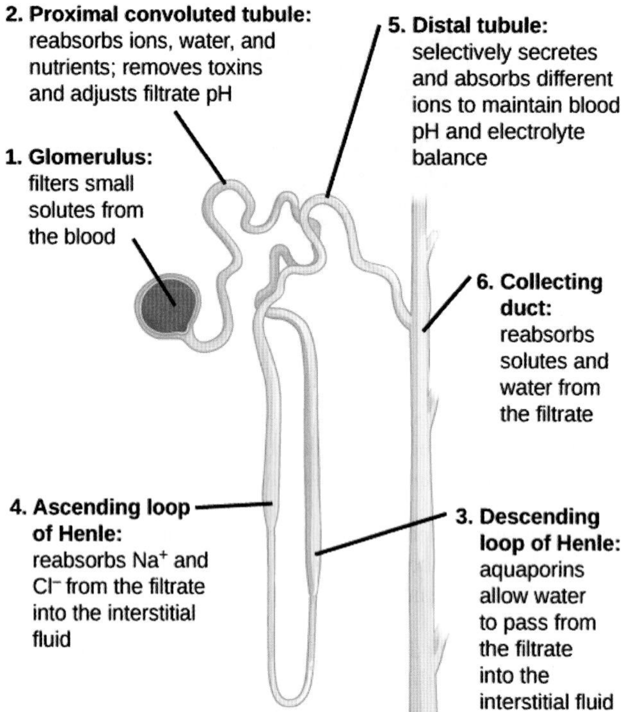

Figure 32.8 Each part of the nephron performs a different function in filtering waste and maintaining homeostatic balance. (1) The glomerulus forces small solutes out of the blood by pressure. (2) The proximal convoluted tubule reabsorbs ions, water, and nutrients from the filtrate into the interstitial fluid, and actively transports toxins and drugs from the interstitial fluid into the filtrate. The proximal convoluted tubule also adjusts blood pH by selectively secreting ammonia (NH_3) into the filtrate, where it reacts with H^+ to form NH_4^+. The more acidic the filtrate, the more ammonia is secreted. (3) The descending loop of Henle is lined with cells containing aquaporins that allow water to pass from the filtrate into the interstitial fluid. (4) In the thin part of the ascending loop of Henle, Na^+ and Cl^- ions diffuse into the interstitial fluid. In the thick part, these same ions are actively transported into the interstitial fluid. Because salt but not water is lost, the filtrate becomes more dilute as it travels up the limb. (5) In the distal convoluted tubule, K^+ and H^+ ions are selectively secreted into the filtrate, while Na^+, Cl^-, and HCO_3^- ions are reabsorbed to maintain pH and electrolyte balance in the blood. (6) The collecting duct reabsorbs solutes and water from the filtrate, forming dilute urine. (credit: modification of work by NIDDK)

Glomerular Filtration

Glomerular filtration filters out most of the solutes due to high blood pressure and specialized membranes in the afferent arteriole. The blood pressure in the glomerulus is maintained independent of factors that affect systemic blood pressure. The "leaky" connections between the endothelial cells of the glomerular capillary network allow solutes to pass through easily. All solutes in the glomerular capillaries, except for macromolecules like proteins, pass through by passive diffusion. There is no energy requirement at this stage of the filtration process. **Glomerular filtration rate (GFR)** is the volume of glomerular filtrate formed per minute by the kidneys. GFR is regulated by multiple mechanisms and is an important indicator of kidney function.

To learn more about the vascular system of kidneys, click through this review (http://openstaxcollege.org/l/kidneys) and the steps of blood flow.

Explain the three-step process by which the kidneys filter blood.

a. First, the nephrons filter blood that runs through the capillary network in the glomerulus, which filters out almost all solutes, except for proteins, by glomerular filtration. Second, the filtrate is collected in the renal tubules. Most of the solutes get reabsorbed in the proximal convoluted tubule by tubular secretion. Third, additional solutes and wastes are secreted into the tubules of the kidney during tubular reabsorption.

b. First, the nephrons filter blood that runs through the capillary network in the glomerulus, which filters out almost all solutes, except for proteins, by glomerular filtration. Second, the filtrate is collected in the renal tubules. Most of the solutes get reabsorbed in the proximal convoluted tubule by tubular reabsorption. Third, additional solutes and wastes are secreted into the tubules of the kidney during tubular secretion.

c. First, the nephrons filter blood that runs through the capillary network in the glomerulus, which filters out almost all solutes, except for uric acid, by glomerular filtration. Second, the filtrate is collected in the renal tubules. Most of the solutes get reabsorbed in the proximal convoluted tubule by tubular reabsorption. Third, additional solutes and wastes are secreted into the tubules of the kidney during tubular secretion.

d. First, the nephrons filter blood that runs through the capillary network in the glomerulus, which filters out almost all solutes, except for proteins, by glomerular filtration. Second, the filtrate is collected in the renal tubules. Most of the solutes get reabsorbed in the distal convoluted tubule by tubular reabsorption. Third, additional solutes and wastes are secreted into the tubules of the kidney during tubular secretion.

Tubular Reabsorption and Secretion

Tubular reabsorption occurs in the PCT part of the renal tubule. Almost all nutrients are reabsorbed, and this occurs either by passive or active transport. Reabsorption of water and some key electrolytes are regulated and can be influenced by hormones. Sodium (Na^+) is the most abundant ion and most of it is reabsorbed by active transport and then transported to the peritubular capillaries. Because Na^+ is actively transported out of the tubule, water follows it to even out the osmotic pressure. Water is also independently reabsorbed into the peritubular capillaries due to the presence of aquaporins, or water channels, in the PCT. This occurs due to the low blood pressure and high osmotic pressure in the peritubular capillaries. However, every solute has a **transport maximum** and the excess is not reabsorbed.

In the loop of Henle, the permeability of the membrane changes. The descending limb is permeable to water, not solutes; the opposite is true for the ascending limb. Additionally, the loop of Henle invades the renal medulla, which is naturally high in salt concentration and tends to absorb water from the renal tubule and concentrate the filtrate. The osmotic gradient increases as it moves deeper into the medulla. Because two sides of the loop of Henle perform opposing functions, as illustrated in Figure 32.9, it acts as a **countercurrent multiplier**. The vasa recta around it acts as the **countercurrent exchanger**.

visual CONNECTION

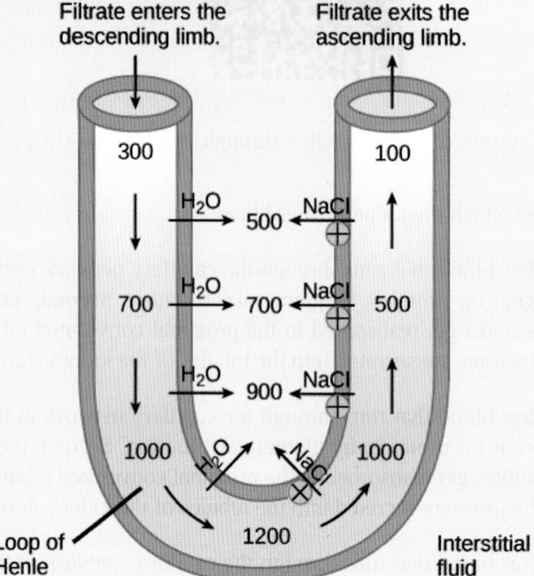

Figure 32.9 The loop of Henle acts as a countercurrent multiplier that uses energy to create concentration gradients. The descending limb is water permeable. Water flows from the filtrate to the interstitial fluid, so osmolality inside the limb increases as it descends into the renal medulla. At the bottom, the osmolality is higher inside the loop than in the interstitial fluid. Thus, as filtrate enters the ascending limb, Na^+ and Cl^- ions exit through ion channels present in the cell membrane. Further up, Na^+ is actively transported out of the filtrate and Cl^- follows. Osmolarity is given in units of milliosmoles per liter (mOsm/L).

A drug has a side effect that increases the frequency of urination. What might cause this?

a. The drug is most likely an oliguric used to treat hypertension. The oliguric is probably working on the loop of Henle and is inhibiting the reabsorption of Na^+ and Cl^- .
b. The drug is most likely a diuretic used to treat hypotension. The diuretic is probably working on the loop of Henle and is inhibiting the reabsorption of Na^+ and Cl^-.
c. The drug is most likely an oliguric used to treat hypotension. The oliguric is probably working on the loop of Henle and is inhibiting the reabsorption of Na^+ and Cl^-.
d. The drug is most likely a diuretic used to treat hypertension. The diuretic is probably working on the loop of Henle and is inhibiting the reabsorption of Na^+ and Cl^-.

By the time the filtrate reaches the DCT, most of the urine and solutes have been reabsorbed. If the body requires additional water, all of it can be reabsorbed at this point. Further reabsorption is controlled by hormones, which will be discussed in a later section. Excretion of wastes occurs due to lack of reabsorption combined with tubular secretion. Undesirable products like metabolic wastes, urea, uric acid, and certain drugs, are excreted by tubular secretion. Most of the tubular secretion happens in the DCT, but some occurs in the early part of the collecting duct. Kidneys also maintain an acid-base balance by secreting excess H^+ ions.

Although parts of the renal tubules are named proximal and distal, in a cross-section of the kidney, the tubules are placed close together and in contact with each other and the glomerulus. This allows for exchange of chemical messengers between the different cell types. For example, the DCT ascending limb of the loop of Henle has masses of cells called **macula densa**, which are in contact with cells of the afferent arterioles called **juxtaglomerular cells**. Together, the macula densa and juxtaglomerular cells form the juxtaglomerular complex (JGC). The JGC is an endocrine structure that secretes the enzyme renin and the hormone erythropoietin. When hormones trigger the macula densa cells in the DCT due to variations in blood volume, blood pressure, or electrolyte balance, these cells can immediately communicate the problem to the capillaries in the afferent and efferent arterioles, which can constrict or relax to change the glomerular filtration rate of the kidneys.

Nephrologist

A nephrologist studies and deals with diseases of the kidneys—both those that cause kidney failure (such as diabetes) and the conditions that are produced by kidney disease (such as hypertension). Blood pressure, blood volume, and changes in electrolyte balance come under the purview of a nephrologist.

Nephrologists usually work with other physicians who refer patients to them or consult with them about specific diagnoses and treatment plans. Patients are usually referred to a nephrologist for symptoms such as blood or protein in the urine, very high blood pressure, kidney stones, or renal failure.

Nephrology is a subspecialty of internal medicine. To become a nephrologist, medical school is followed by additional training to become certified in internal medicine. An additional two or more years is spent specifically studying kidney disorders and their accompanying effects on the body.

science practices CONNECTION for AP® Courses

Think About It

What special adaptations do organs of the excretory system have for the excretion of wastes? Loop diuretics are drugs sometimes used to treat hypertension (high blood pressure).These drugs inhibit the reabsorption of Na^+ and Cl^- ions by the ascending limb of the loop of Henle in the nephron. A side effect is that they increase urination. Why do you think this is the case?

32.3 | Excretion Systems

In this section, you will explore the following questions:

- How do vacuoles, present in microorganisms, work to excrete waste?
- How do flame cells and nephridia in worms perform excretory functions and maintain osmotic balance?
- How do insects use Malpighian tubules to excrete wastes and maintain osmotic balance?

Connection for AP® Courses

The information in this section is not within the scope for AP® other than to appreciate that other organisms, including microorganisms and invertebrate animals, use more primitive and simple mechanisms to get rid of metabolic waste and maintain osmotic balance. For example, contractile vacuoles are common in microorganisms; flame cells and nephridia in certain species and worms, and Malpighian tubules in insects are other examples of excretory systems. Osmoregulation is vital for all organisms to maintain homeostasis.

Information presented and examples highlighted in this section are not within the scope for AP® and do not align to the Curriculum Framework.

Contractile Vacuoles in Microorganisms

The most fundamental feature of life is the presence of a cell. In other words, a cell is the simplest functional unit of a life. Bacteria are unicellular, prokaryotic organisms that have some of the least complex life processes in place; however, prokaryotes such as bacteria do not contain membrane-bound vacuoles. The cells of microorganisms like bacteria, protozoa, and fungi are bound by cell membranes and use them to interact with the environment. Some cells, including some leucocytes in humans, are able to engulf food by endocytosis—the formation of vesicles by involution of the cell membrane within the cells. The same vesicles are able to interact and exchange metabolites with the intracellular environment. In some unicellular eukaryotic organisms such as the amoeba, shown in Figure 32.10, cellular wastes and excess water are excreted by exocytosis, when the contractile vacuoles merge with the cell membrane and expel wastes into the environment. Contractile vacuoles (CV) should not be confused with vacuoles, which store food or water.

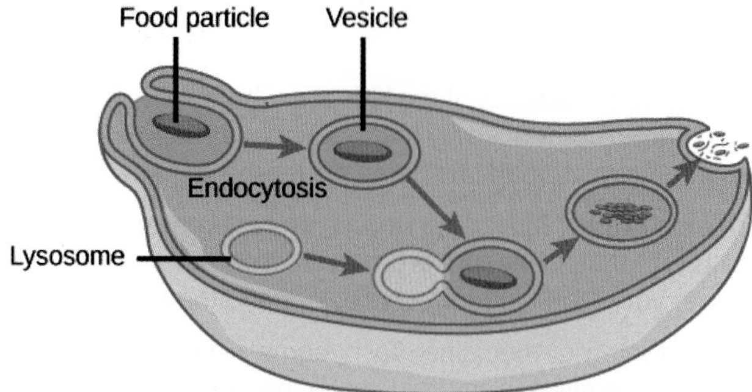

Figure 32.10 Some unicellular organisms, such as the amoeba, ingest food by endocytosis. The food vesicle fuses with a lysosome, which digests the food. Waste is excreted by exocytosis.

Flame Cells of Planaria and Nephridia of Worms

As multi-cellular systems evolved to have organ systems that divided the metabolic needs of the body, individual organs evolved to perform the excretory function. Planaria are flatworms that live in fresh water. Their excretory system consists of two tubules connected to a highly branched duct system. The cells in the tubules are called **flame cells** (or **protonephridia**) because they have a cluster of cilia that looks like a flickering flame when viewed under the microscope, as illustrated in Figure 32.11**a**. The cilia propel waste matter down the tubules and out of the body through excretory pores that open on the body surface; cilia also draw water from the interstitial fluid, allowing for filtration. Any valuable metabolites are recovered by reabsorption. Flame cells are found in flatworms, including parasitic tapeworms and free-living planaria. They also maintain the organism's osmotic balance.

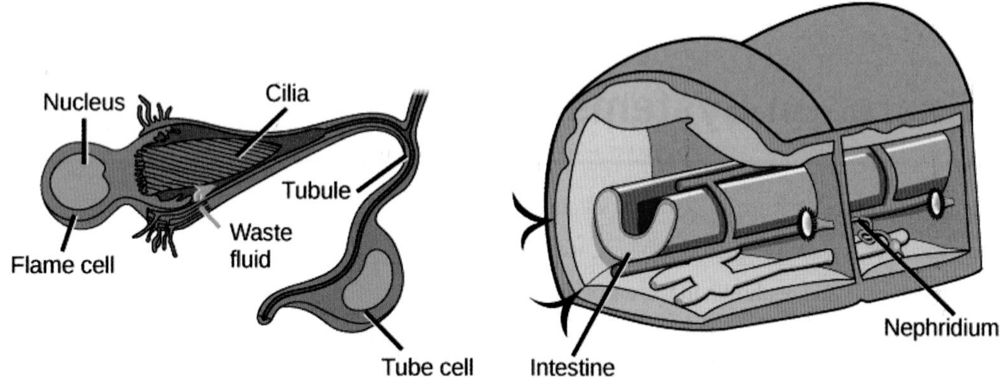

Figure 32.11 In the excretory system of the (a) planaria, cilia of flame cells propel waste through a tubule formed by a tube cell. Tubules are connected into branched structures that lead to pores located all along the sides of the body. The filtrate is secreted through these pores. In (b) annelids such as earthworms, nephridia filter fluid from the coelom, or body cavity. Beating cilia at the opening of the nephridium draw water from the coelom into a tubule. As the filtrate passes down the tubules, nutrients and other solutes are reabsorbed by capillaries. Filtered fluid containing nitrogenous and other wastes is stored in a bladder and then secreted through a pore in the side of the body.

Earthworms (annelids) have slightly more evolved excretory structures called **nephridia**, illustrated in Figure 32.11**b**. A pair of nephridia is present on each segment of the earthworm. They are similar to flame cells in that they have a tubule with cilia. Excretion occurs through a pore called the **nephridiopore**. They are more evolved than the flame cells in that they have a system for tubular reabsorption by a capillary network before excretion.

Malpighian Tubules of Insects

Malpighian tubules are found lining the gut of some species of arthropods, such as the bee illustrated in Figure 32.12. They are usually found in pairs and the number of tubules varies with the species of insect. Malpighian tubules are convoluted, which increases their surface area, and they are lined with **microvilli** for reabsorption and maintenance of osmotic balance. Malpighian tubules work cooperatively with specialized glands in the wall of the rectum. Body fluids are not filtered as in the case of nephridia; urine is produced by tubular secretion mechanisms by the cells lining the Malpighian tubules that are bathed in hemolymph (a mixture of blood and interstitial fluid that is found in insects and other arthropods as well as most mollusks). Metabolic wastes like uric acid freely diffuse into the tubules. There are exchange pumps lining the tubules, which actively transport H^+ ions into the cell and K^+ or Na^+ ions out; water passively follows to form urine. The secretion of ions alters the osmotic pressure which draws water, electrolytes, and nitrogenous waste (uric acid) into the tubules. Water and electrolytes are reabsorbed when these organisms are faced with low-water environments, and uric acid is excreted as a thick paste or powder. Not dissolving wastes in water helps these organisms to conserve water; this is especially important for life in dry environments.

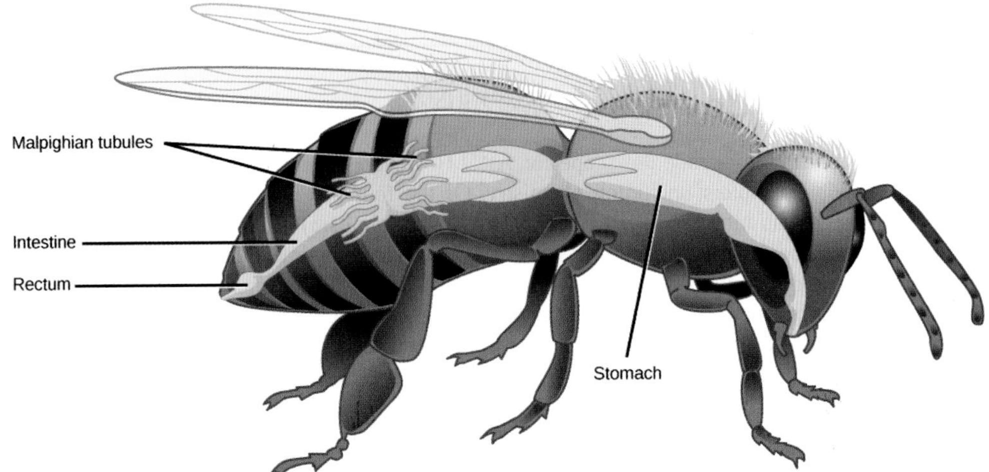

Figure 32.12 Malpighian tubules of insects and other terrestrial arthropods remove nitrogenous wastes and other solutes from the hemolymph. Na^+ and/or K^+ ions are actively transported into the lumen of the tubules. Water then enters the tubules via osmosis, forming urine. The urine passes through the intestine, and into the rectum. There, nutrients diffuse back into the hemolymph. Na^+ and/or K^+ ions are pumped into the hemolymph, and water follows. The concentrated waste is then excreted.

Visit this site (http://openstaxcollege.org/l/malpighian) to see a dissected cockroach, including a close-up look at its Malpighian tubules.

What are Malpighian tubules and which organism possesses them?

a. Malpighian tubules are the tubules within a nephron in humans.

b. Malpighian tubules are the opening of the digestive sac in box jellyfish.

c. Malpighian tubules are organs that filter waste from hemolymph in cockroaches.

d. Malpighian tubules are tiny, bulb-shaped organs that open to an excretory pore in leeches.

32.4 | Nitrogenous Wastes

In this section, you will explore the following questions:

- What are the differences in the ways aquatic animals and terrestrial animals can eliminate toxic ammonia from their systems?
- What are the major byproducts of ammonia metabolism in mammals compared to fish, reptiles, birds, and insects?

Connection for AP® Courses

Much information in this section is outside the scope for AP®. However, the concepts provide an opportunity to apply concepts explored in previous chapters, including chemistry. Of the four macromolecules in biological systems, both proteins and nucleic acids contain nitrogen. During the breakdown (catabolism) of nitrogen-containing macromolecules, carbon, hydrogen, and oxygen are extracted and stored in the form of carbohydrates and fats. However, excess nitrogen must be excreted from the body because nitrogenous wastes tend to form toxic **ammonia**, which raises the pH of body fluids and disrupts homeostasis. The formation of toxic ammonia requires energy in the form of ATP and large quantities of water to dilute it out of a biological system. Aquatic animals, such as fishes, can release ammonia directly into the environment. Animals that excrete ammonia are said to be **ammonotelic**. Terrestrial animals, including mammals, must detoxify ammonia by converting it into relatively nontoxic forms such as uric acid or urea. Animals that secrete urea as the primary nitrogenous waste material are called **ureotelic** animals. Birds and reptiles excrete uric acid, a water-insoluble form of nitrogenous waste, thus reducing water loss. From an evolutionary standpoint, life likely started in an aquatic environment, so it not surprising that biochemical pathways like the conversion of ammonia to urea typical in mammals evolved to adapt to terrestrial conditions; more arid conditions probably led to the evolution of the uric acid pathway as a means of conserving water.

Information presented and the examples highlighted in the section support concepts outlined in Big Idea 2 of the AP® Biology Curriculum Framework. The AP® Learning Objectives listed in the Curriculum Framework provide a transparent foundation for the AP® Biology course, an inquiry-based laboratory experience, instructional activities, and AP® exam questions. A learning objective merges required content with one or more of the seven science practices.

Big Idea 2	Biological systems utilize free energy and molecular building blocks to grow, to reproduce, and to maintain dynamic homeostasis.
Enduring Understanding 2.D	Growth and dynamic homeostasis of a biological system are influenced by changes in the system's environment.
Essential Knowledge	**2.D.2** Homeostatic mechanisms reflect both common ancestry and divergence due to adaptation in different environments.
Science Practice	**6.2** The student can construct explanations of phenomena based on evidence produced through scientific practices.
Learning Objective	**2.25** The student can construct explanations based on scientific evidence that homeostatic mechanisms reflect continuity due to common ancestry and/or divergence due to adaptation in different environments.
Essential Knowledge	**2.D.2** Homeostatic mechanisms reflect both common ancestry and divergence due to adaptation in different environments.
Science Practice	**5.1** The student can analyze data to identify patterns or relationships.
Learning Objective	**2.26** The student is able to analyze data to identify phylogenetic patterns or relationships showing that homeostatic mechanisms reflect both continuity due to common ancestry and change due to evolution in different environments.

Essential Knowledge	**2.D.2** Homeostatic mechanisms reflect both common ancestry and divergence due to adaptation in different environments.
Science Practice	**7.1** The student can connect phenomena and models across spatial and temporal scales.
Learning Objective	**2.27** The student is able to connect differences in the environment with the evolution of homeostatic mechanisms.

Nitrogenous Waste in Terrestrial Animals: The Urea Cycle

The **urea cycle** is the primary mechanism by which mammals convert ammonia to urea. Urea is made in the liver and excreted in urine. The overall chemical reaction by which ammonia is converted to urea is 2 NH_3 (ammonia) + CO_2 + 3 ATP + H_2O → $H_2N\text{-}CO\text{-}NH_2$ (urea) + 2 ADP + 4 P_i + AMP.

The urea cycle utilizes five intermediate steps, catalyzed by five different enzymes, to convert ammonia to urea, as shown in Figure 32.13. The amino acid L-ornithine gets converted into different intermediates before being regenerated at the end of the urea cycle. Hence, the urea cycle is also referred to as the ornithine cycle. The enzyme ornithine transcarbamylase catalyzes a key step in the urea cycle and its deficiency can lead to accumulation of toxic levels of ammonia in the body. The first two reactions occur in the mitochondria and the last three reactions occur in the cytosol. Urea concentration in the blood, called **blood urea nitrogen** or BUN, is used as an indicator of kidney function.

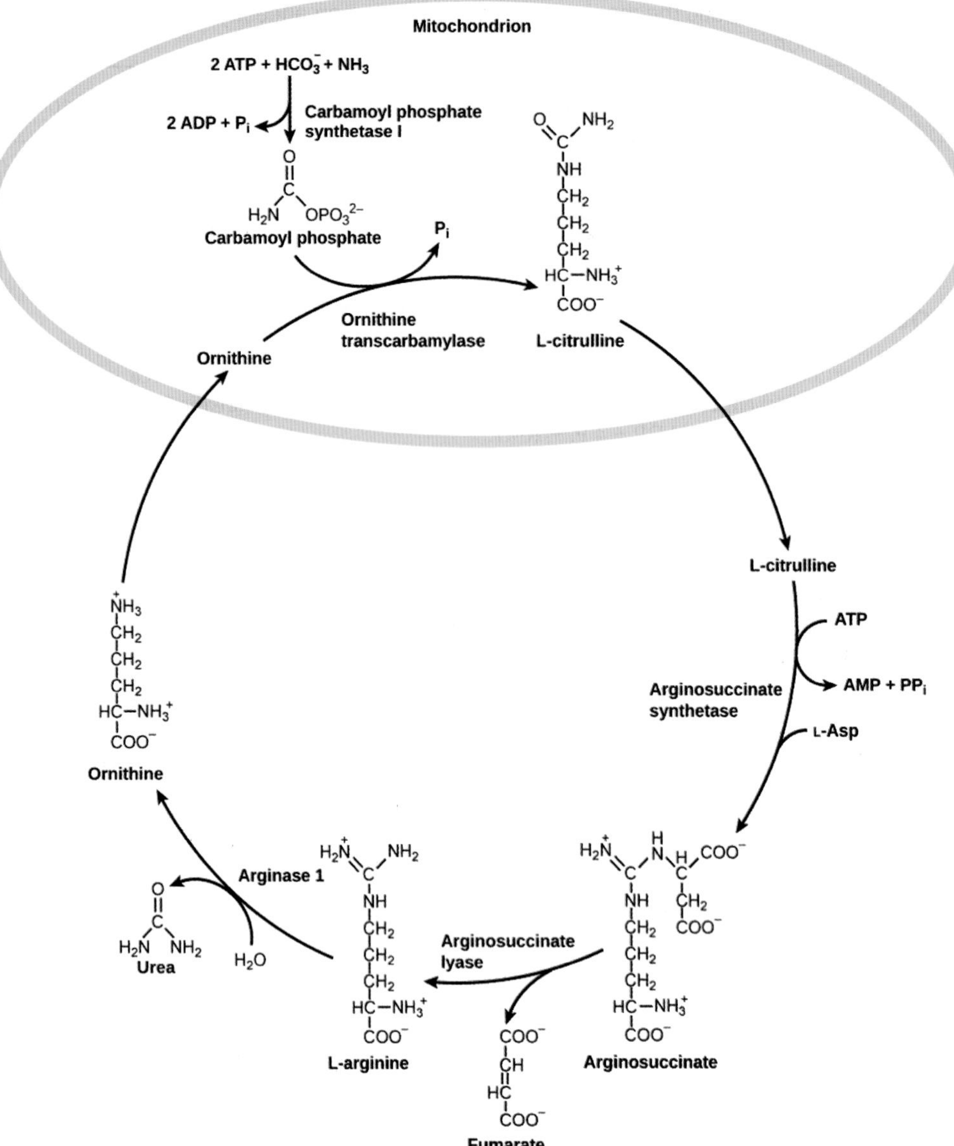

Figure 32.13 The urea cycle converts ammonia to urea.

evolution CONNECTION

Excretion of Nitrogenous Waste

The theory of evolution proposes that life started in an aquatic environment. It is not surprising to see that biochemical pathways like the urea cycle evolved to adapt to a changing environment when terrestrial life forms evolved. Arid conditions probably led to the evolution of the uric acid pathway as a means of conserving water.

Nitrogenous waste is eliminated in which forms?

a. ammonia and K^+ only

b. uric acid and urea only

c. urea, uric acid, and K^+

d. urea, uric acid, and ammonia

Nitrogenous Waste in Birds and Reptiles: Uric Acid

Birds, reptiles, and most terrestrial arthropods convert toxic ammonia to **uric acid** or the closely related compound guanine (guano) instead of urea. Mammals also form some uric acid during breakdown of nucleic acids. Uric acid is a compound similar to purines found in nucleic acids. It is water insoluble and tends to form a white paste or powder; it is excreted by birds, insects, and reptiles. Conversion of ammonia to uric acid requires more energy and is much more complex than conversion of ammonia to urea Figure 32.14.

NH3
Ammonia
H2N NH2
Urea
Uric acid
(a) Many invertebrates and aquatic species excrete ammonia.
(b) Mammals, many adult amphibians, and some marine species excrete urea.
(c) Insects, land snails, birds, and many reptiles excrete uric acid.

Figure 32.14 Nitrogenous waste is excreted in different forms by different species. These include (a) ammonia, (b) urea, and (c) uric acid. (credit a: modification of work by Eric Engbretson, USFWS; credit b: modification of work by B. "Moose" Peterson, USFWS; credit c: modification of work by Dave Menke, USFWS)

everyday CONNECTION

Gout

Mammals use uric acid crystals as an **antioxidant** in their cells. However, too much uric acid tends to form kidney stones and may also cause a painful condition called gout, where uric acid crystals accumulate in the joints, as illustrated in Figure 32.15. Food choices that reduce the amount of nitrogenous bases in the diet help reduce the risk of gout. For example, tea, coffee, and chocolate have purine-like compounds, called xanthines, and should be avoided by people with gout and kidney stones.

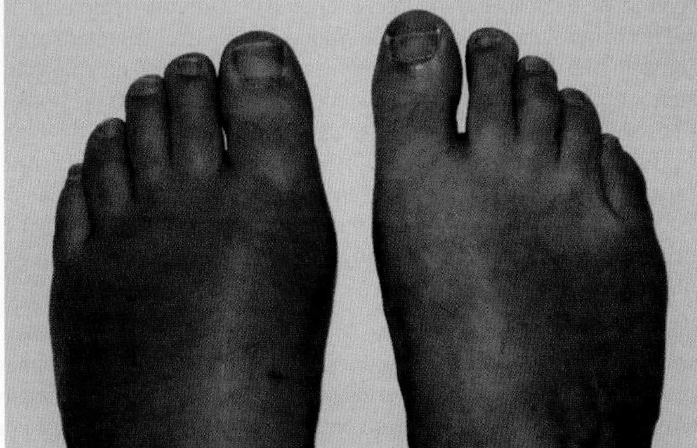

Figure 32.15 Gout causes the inflammation visible in this person's left big toe joint. (credit: "Gonzosft"/Wikimedia Commons)

Why does gout often result in pain?

a. The urethra swells, making urination slower and more painful.
b. Uric acid crystals build up in the joints, resulting in painful body movements.
c. Ammonia begins to degrade the linking of the bladder, causing constant pain.
d. Urea is always highly concentrated, resulting in kidney stones that make urination painful.

science practices CONNECTION for AP® Courses

Think About It

In terms of evolution, why is the urea cycle advantageous in terrestrial organisms? Why is it reasonable to conclude that the uric acid cycle of reptiles was an adaptation to arid environments?

32.5 | Hormonal Control of Osmoregulatory Functions

In this section, you will explore the following questions:

- How do hormonal cures help the kidneys synchronize the osmotic needs of the body?
- How do hormones and other chemical messengers including epinephrine, norepinephrine, rennin-angiotensin, aldosterone, antidiuretic hormone, and atrial natriuretic peptide help regulate waste elimination, maintain correct osmolarity, and perform other osmoregulatory functions?

Connection for AP® Courses

As we learned in an earlier section, the excretory system works with the circulatory and endocrine systems to maintain osmotic balance, eliminate wastes, and maintain blood pressure. For AP®, you do not need to memorize the list of hormones that control osmoregulatory functions or their specific function(s). However, information in this section applies to concepts previously explored.

The kidneys synchronize with hormonal cues. As you recall from our study of the endocrine system, hormones are small messenger molecules that travel in the bloodstream to affect a target cell. Different regions of the nephron have specialized cells with receptors to respond to chemical messengers and hormones. Table 32.1 summarizes the hormones that control the osmoregulatory functions. For example, the flight/flight hormones epinephrine and norepinephrine, released by the adrenal medulla and nervous subsystem, respectively, halt kidney function temporarily when the body is under extreme stress and much of the body's energy is used to combat imminent danger. Another example is the rennin-angiotensin-aldosterone system that increases blood pressure and volume primarily by constricting blood vessels. Another hormone, antidiuretic hormone (ADH) increases membrane permeability to water in the collecting ducts of the nephron by adding aquaporins, causing more water to be reabsorbed. You've experienced the effects of ADH when it's hot outside and you're running around the athletic field; since you're losing water by sweating and breathing hard, ADH prevents you from losing more water in urine and risking dehydration.

Information presented and the examples highlighted in the section support concepts outlined in Big Idea 3 of the AP® Biology Curriculum Framework. The AP® Learning Objectives listed in the Curriculum Framework provide a transparent foundation for the AP® Biology course, an inquiry-based laboratory experience, instructional activities, and AP® exam questions. A learning objective merges required content with one or more of the seven science practices.

Big Idea 3	Living systems store, retrieve, transmit and respond to information essential to life processes.
Enduring Understanding 3.D	Cells communicate by generating, transmitting and receiving chemical signals.
Essential Knowledge	**3.D.2** Cells communicate with each other through direct contact with other cells or from a distance via chemical signaling.
Science Practice	**6.2** The student can construct explanations of phenomena based on evidence produced through scientific practices.

Learning Objective	**3.34** The student is able to construct explanations of cell communication through cell-to-cell direct contact or through chemical signaling.
Essential Knowledge	**3.D.2** Cells communicate with each other through direct contact with other cells or from a distance via chemical signaling.
Science Practice	**1.1** The student can create representations and models of natural or man-made phenomena and systems in the domain.
Learning Objective	**3.35** The student is able to create representation(s) that depict how cell-to-cell communication occurs by direct contact or from a distance through chemical signaling.

Hormones That Affect Osmoregulation

Hormone	Where produced	Function
Epinephrine and Norepinephrine	Adrenal medulla	Can decrease kidney function temporarily by vasoconstriction
Renin	Kidney nephrons	Increases blood pressure by acting on angiotensinogen
Angiotensin	Liver	Angiotensin II affects multiple processes and increases blood pressure
Aldosterone	Adrenal cortex	Prevents loss of sodium and water
Anti-diuretic hormone (vasopressin)	Hypothalamus (stored in the posterior pituitary)	Prevents water loss
Atrial natriuretic peptide	Heart atrium	Decreases blood pressure by acting as a vasodilator and increasing glomerular filtration rate; decreases sodium reabsorption in kidneys

Table 32.1

Epinephrine and Norepinephrine

Epinephrine and norepinephrine are released by the adrenal medulla and nervous system respectively. They are the flight/fight hormones that are released when the body is under extreme stress. During stress, much of the body's energy is used to combat imminent danger. Kidney function is halted temporarily by epinephrine and norepinephrine. These hormones function by acting directly on the smooth muscles of blood vessels to constrict them. Once the afferent arterioles are constricted, blood flow into the nephrons stops. These hormones go one step further and trigger the **renin-angiotensin-aldosterone** system.

Renin-Angiotensin-Aldosterone

The renin-angiotensin-aldosterone system, illustrated in Figure 32.16 proceeds through several steps to produce **angiotensin II**, which acts to stabilize blood pressure and volume. Renin (secreted by a part of the juxtaglomerular complex) is produced by the granular cells of the afferent and efferent arterioles. Thus, the kidneys control blood pressure and volume directly. Renin acts on angiotensinogen, which is made in the liver and converts it to **angiotensin I**. **Angiotensin converting enzyme (ACE)** converts angiotensin I to angiotensin II. Angiotensin II raises blood pressure by constricting blood vessels. It also triggers the release of the mineralocorticoid aldosterone from the adrenal cortex, which in turn stimulates the renal tubules to reabsorb more sodium. Angiotensin II also triggers the release of **anti-diuretic hormone (ADH)** from the hypothalamus, leading to water retention in the kidneys. It acts directly on the nephrons and decreases glomerular filtration rate. Medically, blood pressure can be controlled by drugs that inhibit ACE (called ACE inhibitors).

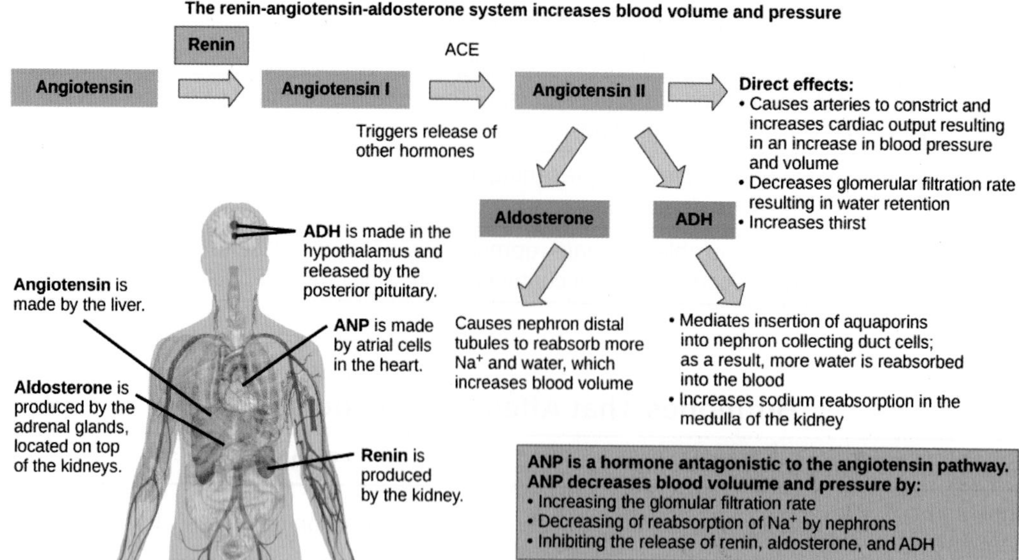

Figure 32.16 The renin-angiotensin-aldosterone system increases blood pressure and volume. The hormone ANP has antagonistic effects. (credit: modification of work by Mikael Häggström)

Mineralocorticoids

Mineralocorticoids are hormones synthesized by the adrenal cortex that affect osmotic balance. Aldosterone is a mineralocorticoid that regulates sodium levels in the blood. Almost all of the sodium in the blood is reclaimed by the renal tubules under the influence of aldosterone. Because sodium is always reabsorbed by active transport and water follows sodium to maintain osmotic balance, aldosterone manages not only sodium levels but also the water levels in body fluids. In contrast, the aldosterone also stimulates potassium secretion concurrently with sodium reabsorption. In contrast, absence of aldosterone means that no sodium gets reabsorbed in the renal tubules and all of it gets excreted in the urine. In addition, the daily dietary potassium load is not secreted and the retention of K^+ can cause a dangerous increase in plasma K^+ concentration. Patients who have Addison's disease have a failing adrenal cortex and cannot produce aldosterone. They lose sodium in their urine constantly, and if the supply is not replenished, the consequences can be fatal.

Antidiurectic Hormone

As previously discussed, antidiuretic hormone or ADH (also called **vasopressin**), as the name suggests, helps the body conserve water when body fluid volume, especially that of blood, is low. It is formed by the hypothalamus and is stored and released from the posterior pituitary. It acts by inserting aquaporins in the collecting ducts and promotes reabsorption of water. ADH also acts as a vasoconstrictor and increases blood pressure during hemorrhaging.

Atrial Natriuretic Peptide Hormone

The atrial natriuretic peptide (ANP) lowers blood pressure by acting as a **vasodilator**. It is released by cells in the atrium of the heart in response to high blood pressure and in patients with sleep apnea. ANP affects salt release, and because water passively follows salt to maintain osmotic balance, it also has a diuretic effect. ANP also prevents sodium reabsorption by the renal tubules, decreasing water reabsorption (thus acting as a diuretic) and lowering blood pressure. Its actions suppress the actions of aldosterone, ADH, and renin.

science practices CONNECTION for AP® Courses

Think About It

Create a diagram to show an example of a hormone and how the hormone works in regulating an osmoregulatory process such as maintaining blood pressure and blood volume and altering kidney function to reduce the amount of water eliminated in urine.

KEY TERMS

afferent arteriole arteriole that branches from the cortical radiate artery and enters the glomerulus

ammonia compound made of one nitrogen atom and three hydrogen atoms

ammonotelic describes an animal that excretes ammonia as the primary waste material

angiotensin converting enzyme (ACE) enzyme that converts angiotensin I to angiotensin II

angiotensin I product in the renin-angiotensin-aldosterone pathway

angiotensin II molecule that affects different organs to increase blood pressure

anti-diuretic hormone (ADH) hormone that prevents the loss of water

antioxidant agent that prevents cell destruction by reactive oxygen species

arcuate artery artery that branches from the interlobar artery and arches over the base of the renal pyramids

ascending limb part of the loop of Henle that ascends from the renal medulla to the renal cortex

blood urea nitrogen (BUN) estimate of urea in the blood and an indicator of kidney function

Bowman's capsule structure that encloses the glomerulus

calyx structure that connects the renal pelvis to the renal medulla

cortex (animal) outer layer of an organ like the kidney or adrenal gland

cortical nephron nephron that lies in the renal cortex

cortical radiate artery artery that radiates from the arcuate arteries into the renal cortex

countercurrent exchanger peritubular capillary network that allows exchange of solutes and water from the renal tubules

countercurrent multiplier osmotic gradient in the renal medulla that is responsible for concentration of urine

descending limb part of the loop of Henle that descends from the renal cortex into the renal medulla

distal convoluted tubule (DCT) part of the renal tubule that is the most distant from the glomerulus

efferent arteriole arteriole that exits from the glomerulus

electrolyte solute that breaks down into ions when dissolved in water

flame cell (also, protonephridia) excretory cell found in flatworms

glomerular filtration filtration of blood in the glomerular capillary network into the glomerulus

glomerular filtration rate (GFR) amount of filtrate formed by the glomerulus per minute

glomerulus (renal) part of the renal corpuscle that contains the capillary network

hilum region in the renal pelvis where blood vessels, nerves, and ureters bunch before entering or exiting the kidney

inferior vena cava one of the main veins in the human body

interlobar artery artery that branches from the segmental artery and travels in between the renal lobes

juxtaglomerular cell cell in the afferent and efferent arterioles that responds to stimuli from the macula densa

juxtamedullary nephron nephron that lies in the cortex but close to the renal medulla

kidney organ that performs excretory and osmoregulatory functions

lobes of the kidney renal pyramid along with the adjoining cortical region

loop of Henle part of the renal tubule that loops into the renal medulla

macula densa group of cells that senses changes in sodium ion concentration; present in parts of the renal tubule and collecting ducts

Malpighian tubule excretory tubules found in arthropods

medulla middle layer of an organ like the kidney or adrenal gland

microvilli cellular processes that increase the surface area of cells

molality number of moles of solute per kilogram of solvent

molarity number of moles of solute per liter of solution

mole gram equivalent of the molecular weight of a substance

nephridia excretory structures found in annelids

nephridiopore pore found at the end of nephridia

nephron functional unit of the kidney

non-electrolyte solute that does not break down into ions when dissolved in water

osmoconformer organism that changes its tonicity based on its environment

osmoregulation mechanism by which water and solute concentrations are maintained at desired levels

osmoregulator organism that maintains its tonicity irrespective of its environment

osmotic balance balance of the amount of water and salt input and output to and from a biological system without disturbing the desired osmotic pressure and solute concentration in every compartment

osmotic pressure pressure exerted on a membrane to equalize solute concentration on either side

perirenal fat capsule fat layer that suspends the kidneys

peritubular capillary network capillary network that surrounds the renal tubule after the efferent artery exits the glomerulus

proximal convoluted tubule (PCT) part of the renal tubule that lies close to the glomerulus

renal artery branch of the artery that enters the kidney

renal capsule layer that encapsulates the kidneys

renal column area of the kidney through which the interlobar arteries travel in the process of supplying blood to the renal lobes

renal corpuscle glomerulus and the Bowman's capsule together

renal fascia connective tissue that supports the kidneys

renal pelvis region in the kidney where the calyces join the ureters

renal pyramid conical structure in the renal medulla

renal tubule tubule of the nephron that arises from the glomerulus

renal vein branch of a vein that exits the kidney and joins the inferior vena cava

renin-angiotensin-aldosterone biochemical pathway that activates angiotensin II, which increases blood pressure

segmental artery artery that branches from the renal artery

semi-permeable membrane membrane that allows only certain solutes to pass through

transport maximum maximum amount of solute that can be transported out of the renal tubules during reabsorption

tubular reabsorption reclamation of water and solutes that got filtered out in the glomerulus

tubular secretion process of secretion of wastes that do not get reabsorbed

urea cycle pathway by which ammonia is converted to urea

ureotelic describes animals that secrete urea as the primary nitrogenous waste material

ureter urine-bearing tube coming out of the kidney; carries urine to the bladder

uric acid byproduct of ammonia metabolism in birds, insects, and reptiles

urinary bladder structure that the ureters empty the urine into; stores urine

urine filtrate produced by kidneys that gets excreted out of the body

vasa recta peritubular network that surrounds the loop of Henle of the juxtamedullary nephrons

vasodilator compound that increases the diameter of blood vessels

vasopressin another name for anti-diuretic hormone

CHAPTER SUMMARY

32.1 Osmoregulation and Osmotic Balance

Solute concentrations across a semi-permeable membranes influence the movement of water and solutes across the membrane. It is the number of solute molecules and not the molecular size that is important in osmosis. Osmoregulation and osmotic balance are important bodily functions, resulting in water and salt balance. Not all solutes can pass through a semi-permeable membrane. Osmosis is the movement of water across the membrane. Osmosis occurs to equalize the number of solute molecules across a semi-permeable membrane by the movement of water to the side of higher solute concentration. Facilitated diffusion utilizes protein channels to move solute molecules from areas of higher to lower concentration while active transport mechanisms are required to move solutes against concentration gradients. Osmolarity is measured in units of milliequivalents or milliosmoles, both of which take into consideration the number of solute particles and the charge on them. Fish that live in fresh water or saltwater adapt by being osmoregulators or osmoconformers.

32.2 The Kidneys and Osmoregulatory Organs

The kidneys are the main osmoregulatory organs in mammalian systems; they function to filter blood and maintain the osmolarity of body fluids at 300 mOsm. They are surrounded by three layers and are made up internally of three distinct regions—the cortex, medulla, and pelvis.

The blood vessels that transport blood into and out of the kidneys arise from and merge with the aorta and inferior vena cava, respectively. The renal arteries branch out from the aorta and enter the kidney where they further divide into segmental, interlobar, arcuate, and cortical radiate arteries.

The nephron is the functional unit of the kidney, which actively filters blood and generates urine. The nephron is made up of the renal corpuscle and renal tubule. Cortical nephrons are found in the renal cortex, while juxtamedullary nephrons are found in the renal cortex close to the renal medulla. The nephron filters and exchanges water and solutes with two sets of blood vessels and the tissue fluid in the kidneys.

There are three steps in the formation of urine: glomerular filtration, which occurs in the glomerulus; tubular reabsorption, which occurs in the renal tubules; and tubular secretion, which also occurs in the renal tubules.

32.3 Excretion Systems

Many systems have evolved for excreting wastes that are simpler than the kidney and urinary systems of vertebrate animals. The simplest system is that of contractile vacuoles present in microorganisms. Flame cells and nephridia in worms perform excretory functions and maintain osmotic balance. Some insects have evolved Malpighian tubules to excrete wastes and maintain osmotic balance.

32.4 Nitrogenous Wastes

Ammonia is the waste produced by metabolism of nitrogen-containing compounds like proteins and nucleic acids. While aquatic animals can easily excrete ammonia into their watery surroundings, terrestrial animals have evolved special mechanisms to eliminate the toxic ammonia from their systems. Urea is the major byproduct of ammonia metabolism in vertebrate animals. Uric acid is the major byproduct of ammonia metabolism in birds, terrestrial arthropods, and reptiles.

32.5 Hormonal Control of Osmoregulatory Functions

Hormonal cues help the kidneys synchronize the osmotic needs of the body. Hormones like epinephrine, norepinephrine, renin-angiotensin, aldosterone, anti-diuretic hormone, and atrial natriuretic peptide help regulate the needs of the body as well as the communication between the different organ systems.

REVIEW QUESTIONS

1. Why is the sodium ion at the highest concentration in extracellular fluid?

a. Sodium diffuses freely through the cell membrane.
b. The sodium/potassium pump removes sodium ions from the cell.
c. The blood contains a high concentration of sodium.
d. Sodium is actively taken up by the cells for use in the cytoplasm.

2. What is given to a dehydrated human patient when he or she needs to be given fluids intravenously?

a. Water, which is hypotonic with respect to body fluids.
b. Saline at a concentration that is isotonic with respect to body fluids.
c. Glucose because it is a non-electrolyte.
d. blood

3. What is the approximate osmolarity of body fluids?

a. 100 mOsm
b. 300 mOsm
c. 1000 mOsm
d. It is not constantly maintained.

4. One milliequivalent of a ferric (III) ion (Fe^{+3}) is equal to how many millimoles?

a. 0.13
b. 0.75
c. 0.5
d. 0.25

5. What is the difference between an osmoregulator and an osmoconformer?

a. Osmoregulators can change the osmotic pressure of their body fluids, while osmoconformers cannot.
b. Osmoconformers can change the osmotic pressure of their body fluids, while osmoregulators cannot.
c. Osmoregulators match the osmotic pressure of their cells with that of the environment, while osmoconformers do not.
d. Osmoconformers match the osmotic pressure of their cells with that of the environment, while osmoregulators do not.

6. Why does a salmon have to be an osmoregulator?

a. They need to remove excess salt from ocean water.
b. They move between areas of fresh and salt water.
c. They travel for short stretches across the land between streams.
d. Freshwater is osmotically neutral compared with their body fluids.

7. What tends to happen to cells in a hypotonic environment?

a. They remain the same size.
b. They shrink due to water loss.
c. They allow water to flow in and out at the same rate.
d. They swell due to water gain.

8. Which of the following is a function of the kidney?

a. osmoregulation
b. excretion of solid waste
c. production of oxygen
d. reabsorption of all nutrients

9. The kidney is made up of over a million nephrons that give it a granular appearance. What is a nephron?

a. a network of capillaries
b. the cup-shaped chamber surrounding the glomerulus
c. the functional unit of the kidney
d. the bow-shaped artery at the base of medullary pyramids

10. How do juxtamedullary nephrons differ from cortical nephrons?

a. Juxtamedullary nephrons have a longer loop of Henle, allowing them to regulate urine concentration better than cortical nephrons.
b. Juxtamedullary nephrons have a shorter loop of Henle, allowing them to regulate urine concentration better than cortical nephrons.
c. Juxtamedullary nephrons have a larger glomerulus, allowing them to filter blood at a greater rate than cortical nephrons.
d. Juxtamedullary nephrons have a smaller glomerulus, allowing them to filter blood at a greater rate than cortical nephrons.

11. What is the casing around the glomerulus called?

a. distal tubule
b. loop of Henle
c. Bowman's capsule
d. renal pyramid

12. In the loop of Henle, the permeability of the membrane changes. The descending limb and ascending limb are permeable to which of the following, respectively?

a. solutes and water
b. proteins and solutes
c. water and proteins
d. water and solutes

13. What do humans excrete, and how soluble is it compared to uric acid?

a. urea, which is less soluble than uric acid
b. urea, which is more soluble than uric acid
c. ammonia, which is more soluble than uric acid
d. ammonia, which is less soluble than uric acid

14. Describe the network of blood vessels of the kidney.

a. Blood enters and exits the kidney at the renal hilum, and the renal blood supply starts with the branching of the aorta into the renal arteries. They end with the exiting of the renal veins to join the superior vena cava. Each segmental renal artery formed by the splitting of the renal arteries splits again into interlobar arteries and enters the renal columns. These again split to form arcuate arteries, from which cortical radiate arteries radiate out and branch into many afferent arterioles that enter the capillaries supplying the nephrons. Veins trace the path of arteries and have similar names, except there are no segmental veins.
b. Blood enters and exits the kidney at the renal hilum, and the renal blood supply starts with the branching of the aorta into the renal arteries. They end with the exiting of the renal veins to join the inferior vena cava. Each segmental renal artery formed by the splitting of the renal arteries splits again into interlobar arteries and enters the renal columns. These again split to form arcuate arteries, from which cortical radiate arteries radiate out and branch into many afferent arterioles that enter the capillaries supplying the nephrons. Veins trace the path of arteries and have similar names, except there are no segmental veins.
c. Blood enters and exits the kidney at the renal hilum, and the renal blood supply starts with the branching of the aorta into the renal arteries. They end with the exiting of the renal veins to join the inferior vena cava. Each segmental renal artery formed by the splitting of the renal arteries splits again into interlobar arteries and enters the renal columns. These again split to form cortical radiate arteries that radiate out and branch into many afferent arterioles that enter the capillaries supplying the nephrons. Veins trace the path of arteries and have similar names, except there are no segmental veins.
d. Blood enters and exits the kidney at the renal hilum, and the renal blood supply starts with the branching of the aorta into the renal arteries. They end with the exiting of the renal veins to join the inferior vena cava. Each segmental renal artery formed by the splitting of the renal arteries splits again into interlobar arteries and enters the renal columns. These again split to form arcuate arteries, from which cortical radiate arteries radiate out and branch into many afferent arterioles that enter the capillaries supplying the nephrons. Veins trace the path of arteries and have all the same names as the arteries following the same path.

15. Which statement about contractile vacuoles in microorganisms is true?

a. They exclusively perform an excretory function.
b. They contain digestive enzymes.
c. They originate from the cell membrane.
d. They are only used for fluid storage.

16. Some unicellular organisms, such as the amoeba, ingest food by endocytosis. The food vesicle fuses with a lysosome, which digests the food. Waste is excreted by which process?

a. exocytosis
b. filtration
c. osmoregulation
d. dilatation

17. What does active transport of K^+ in the Malpighian tubules ensure?

a. Water leaves the Malpighian tubules.
b. Water moves into the Malpighian tubules.
c. K^+ moves into the Malpighian tubules.
d. K^+ leaves the Malpighian tubules.

18. Flame cells are primitive excretory organs found in which organisms?

a. arthropods
b. annelids
c. mammals
d. flatworms

19. A cell has a malfunction in its contractile vacuoles. How would this affect the cell?

a. The cell's nephrons would no longer be able to reabsorb water.
b. The cell's cytoplasm would become very concentrated.
c. The cell could no longer excrete waste products.
d. The cell would uncontrollably take on water until it burst.

20. Which toxic substance is formed by nitrogenous waste?

a. chlorine
b. potassium
c. ammonia
d. sodium

21. What substance is secreted by most aquatic animals, and why?

a. ammonia, because it can be easily diluted in an aquatic environment
b. uric acid, because aquatic animals must preserve water
c. urea, because ammonia needs to be converted before it can safely be stored in the body.
d. chlorine, because it can easily be converted to a gas

22. Which water-insoluble compound is similar to purines found in nucleic acids and tends to form a white paste or powder?

a. urea
b. guanine
c. ammonia
d. uric acid

23. The urea cycle is also referred to as the _____ cycle.

a. Krebs
b. ornithine
c. citric acid
d. uric acid

24. Renin is produced in the kidney nephrons and performs what function?

a. increases vasoconstriction
b. prevents loss of sodium
c. increases blood pressure
d. prevents water loss

25. Which hormone elicits the "fight or flight" response, and under which circumstance is it released?

a. anti-diuretic hormone, presence of alcohol in the blood
b. atrial natriuretic peptide, high blood pressure
c. aldosterone, low water content in the blood
d. epinephrine, extreme stress

26. What are the cause and treatment of Addison's disease?

a. an excess of uric acid in the blood, uric acid-dissolving drugs
b. an inability to produce adh, drink excess water
c. an excess of K^+ secretion into the urine, take in excess potassium
d. an inability to produce aldosterone, take in excess sodium

27. How does atrial natriuretic peptide hormone act to lower blood pressure?

a. vasoconstrictor
b. vasodilator
c. inhibitor
d. vasopressin

28. Which cells or organs secrete renin?

a. granular cells of the juxtaglomerular apparatus
b. the kidneys
c. the nephrons
d. water-reabsorbing cells of the collecting duct

CRITICAL THINKING QUESTIONS

29. An organism is excreting ions in its urine. What is likely the current tonicity of the organism's cells, and why?

a. hypotonicity due to too much solute in its body fluids
b. hypertonicity due to less solute in its body fluids
c. hypertonicity due to too much solute in its body fluids
d. hypotonicity due to less solute in its body fluids

30. A student measures the osmolality of two aqueous solutions, A and B. The student finds that the osmolality of solution B is much higher than solution A. Based on this result, how do solutions A and B likely differ in the concentration of solutes in their solution, and why?

a. Solution A likely is the more concentrated solution because osmolality measures the moles of solute per kilogram of solute.
b. Solution B likely is the more concentrated solution because osmolality measures the moles of solute per kilogram of solvent.
c. Solution A likely is the more concentrated solution because osmolality measures the moles of solute per kilogram of solvent.
d. Solution B likely is the more concentrated solution because osmolality measures the moles of solute per kilogram of solute.

31. Would an organism that is constantly in a hypertonic environment likely be an osmoregulator or an osmoconformer? Why?

a. osmoconformer, because it would need to prevent water from leaving its body to remain alive
b. osmoregulator, because it would need to prevent solutes from leaving its body to remain alive
c. osmoconformer, because it would need to prevent solutes from leaving its body to remain alive
d. osmoregulator, because it would need to prevent water from leaving its body to remain alive.

32. Why is excretion important in order to achieve osmotic balance?

a. The body accumulates water within itself when excretion does not occur, which can have dire consequences.
b. Excretion regulates the movement of water within the membranes, which ultimately maintains osmotic balance.
c. In the absence of excretion, there is a shift in the concentrations, which disrupts osmotic balance.
d. The body builds up many chemical compounds that need to be excreted to maintain homeostasis and osmotic balance.

33. What is the structure of the nephron?

a. The nephron consists of three parts: the glomerulus, the renal tubule, and the associated capillary network originating from the cortical radiate arteries.
b. The nephron consists of three parts: the renal corpuscle, the Bowman's capsule, and the associated capillary network originating from the cortical radiate arteries.
c. The nephron consists of three parts: the renal corpuscle, the renal tubule, and the associated capillary network originating from the segmental renal artery.
d. The nephron consists of three parts: the renal corpuscle, the renal tubule, and the associated capillary network originating from the cortical radiate arteries.

34. How does the loop of Henle act as a countercurrent multiplier?

a. The descending limb of the loop of Henle is water permeable, so the water flows from the filtrate to the interstitial fluid. Osmolality in the limb decreases, and it is lower inside the loop than in the interstitial fluid. As the filtrate enters the ascending limb, Na^+ and Cl^- ions exit through ion channels present in the cell membrane. Further up, only sodium is passively transported out of the filtrate.

b. The descending limb of the loop of Henle is water impermeable, so the water flows from the filtrate to the interstitial fluid. Osmolality in the limb increases, and it is higher inside the loop than in the interstitial fluid. As the filtrate enters the ascending limb, Na^+ and Cl^- ions exit through ion channels present in the cell membrane. Further up, only sodium is passively transported out of the filtrate.

c. The descending limb of the loop of Henle is water impermeable, so the water flows from the filtrate to the interstitial fluid. Osmolality in the limb increases, and it is higher inside the loop than in the interstitial fluid. As the filtrate enters the ascending limb, Na^+ and Cl^- ions exit through ion channels present in the cell membrane. Further up, sodium is actively transported out of the filtrate, and chlorine ions follow.

d. The descending limb of the loop of Henle is water permeable, so the water flows from the filtrate to the interstitial fluid. Osmolality in the limb increases, and it is higher inside the loop than in the interstitial fluid. As the filtrate enters the ascending limb, Na^+ and Cl^- ions exit through ion channels present in the cell membrane. Further up, sodium is actively transported out of the filtrate, and chlorine ions follows.

35. Why might specialized organs have evolved for excretion of wastes?

a. Specialized organs have evolved to provide a measure of safety for organisms.

b. Specialized organs have evolved to distinguish different types of organisms.

c. Specialized organs have evolved for excretion of wastes to conserve metabolic energy.

d. Specialized organs have evolved for excretion of wastes so that organisms can survive in adverse conditions.

36. Explain two different excretory systems other than the kidneys.

a. (1) An excretory mechanism occurs in annelids through the Malpighian tubules. Metabolic wastes like uric acid freely diffuse into the tubules. Uric acid is excreted as a thick paste or powder. (2) An excretory mechanism occurs in the flatworm, which contains two tubules with cells called flame cells. They have cilia that propel waste matter down the tubules and out of the body.

b. (1) An excretory mechanism occurs in arthropods through a pore called the nephridiopore. These organisms have a system for tubular reabsorption. (2) An excretory mechanism occurs in annelids through the Malpighian tubules. Metabolic wastes like uric acid freely diffuse into the tubules. Uric acid is excreted as a thick paste or powder.

c. (1) An excretory mechanism is endocytosis, which occurs when vacuoles merge with the cell membrane and excrete cellular wastes in the environment. (2) An excretory mechanism occurs in annelids through a pore called the nephridiopore. These organisms have a system for tubular reabsorption.

d. (1) An excretory mechanism is exocytosis, which occurs when vacuoles merge with the cell membrane and excrete cellular wastes in the environment. (2) An excretory mechanism occurs in flatworms which consists of two tubules containing cells called flame cells. They have a cluster of cilia that propel waste matter down the tubules and out of the body.

37. How do contractile vacuoles work as excretory systems in microorganisms?

a. Contractile vacuoles excrete excess water and waste by the process of endocytosis, in which these vacuoles merge with cell membrane and expel wastes into the environment.

b. Contractile vacuoles excrete uric acid by the process of exocytosis, in which water as well as uric acid is excreted by contraction of a cell when the vacuole merges with the cell membrane.

c. Contractile vacuoles excrete excess water and uric acid by the process of endocytosis when the vacuole merges with the cell membrane.

d. Contractile vacuoles excrete excess water and waste by the process of exocytosis, in which the vacuoles merge with the cell membrane and expel wastes into the environment.

38. Describe the urea cycle.

a. The urea cycle is the mechanism of conversion of urea to ammonia involving five intermediate steps catalyzed by five different enzymes. Of the five steps, the first two occur in the mitochondria and the last three in the cytosol.

b. The urea cycle is the mechanism of conversion of ammonia to urea involving five intermediate steps catalyzed by five different enzymes. Of the five steps, the first two occur in the mitochondria and the last three in the cytosol.

c. The urea cycle is the mechanism of conversion of ammonia to urea involving five intermediate steps catalyzed by five different enzymes. Of the five steps, the first two occur in the cytosol and the last three in the mitochondria.

d. The urea cycle is the mechanism of conversion of ammonia to urea involving five intermediate steps all catalyzed by one enzyme. Of the five steps, the first two occur in the mitochondria and the last three in the cytosol.

39. How are the formation of urea and uric acid similar and different?

a. In birds, reptiles, and insects, the urea cycle converts ammonia to urea. In mammals, the uric acid cycle converts ammonia to uric acid. Formation of urea from ammonia requires less energy and is less complex than uric acid formation.

b. In mammals, the urea cycle converts ammonia to urea. In birds, reptiles, and insects, the uric acid cycle converts ammonia to uric acid. Formation of urea from ammonia requires more energy and is less complex than uric acid formation.

c. In mammals, the urea cycle converts ammonia to urea. In birds, reptiles, and insects, the uric acid cycle converts ammonia to uric acid. Formation of urea from ammonia requires less energy and is more complex than uric acid formation.

d. In mammals, the urea cycle converts ammonia to urea. In birds, reptiles, and insects, the uric acid cycle converts ammonia to uric acid. Formation of urea from ammonia requires less energy and is less complex than uric acid formation.

40. In terms of evolution, why might the urea cycle have evolved in organisms?

a. so organisms could adapt to the changing environment when terrestrial life forms evolved

b. so organisms could evolve the ability to switch between direct ammonia excretion and urea

c. so organisms could reduce their excretion of ammonia in the form of urea

d. so organisms could adapt to the changing environment and excrete higher concentrations of uric acid

41. How do hormones regulate blood pressure, blood volume, and kidney function?

a. Different regions of the liver have specialized cells that respond to chemical messengers and hormones like epinephrine, renin, aldosterone, ADH, and ANP. These regulate the needs of the body and communication between different organ systems.

b. Different regions of the nephrons have specialized cells that respond to chemical messengers and hormones like epinephrine, renin, aldosterone, ADH, and ANP. These regulate the rate of respiration and communication between the different organ systems.

c. Different regions of the kidneys have specialized cells that respond to chemical messengers and hormones like epinephrine, renin, aldosterone, ADH, and ANP. These regulate the rate of respiration and communication between the different organ systems.

d. Different regions of the nephrons have specialized cells that respond to chemical messengers and hormones like epinephrine, renin, aldosterone, ADH, and ANP. These regulate the needs of the body and communication between the different organ systems.

42. How does the renin-angiotensin-aldosterone mechanism function?

a. Renin, which is secreted by part of the juxtaglomerular complex, acts on angiotensin to form angiotensin I, which is then converted to angiotensin II by ACE. Angiotensin II then stimulates the release of aldosterone and ADH. Angiotensin II acts to destabilize blood pressure and volume.
b. Renin, which is secreted by part of the juxtaglomerular complex, acts on angiotensin to form angiotensin II, which is then converted to angiotensin I by ACE. Angiotensin II then stimulates the release of aldosterone and ADH. Angiotensin II acts to stabilize blood pressure and volume.
c. Renin, which is secreted by part of the juxtaglomerular complex, acts on angiotensin to form angiotensin I, which is then converted to angiotensin II and ADH by ACE. ADH then stimulates the release of aldosterone. Angiotensin II acts to stabilize blood pressure and volume.
d. Renin, which is secreted by part of the juxtaglomerular complex, acts on angiotensin to form angiotensin I, which is then converted to angiotensin II by ACE. Angiotensin II then stimulates the release of aldosterone and ADH. Angiotensin II acts to stabilize blood pressure and volume.

43. What is the “fight or flight” response, and what is its effect on the excretory system?

a. Aldosterone is the “fight or flight” that is released by the adrenal medulla under extreme stress. This hormone constricts the smooth muscles of the blood vessels. It constricts the afferent arterioles, causing the flow of blood into the nephrons to stop.
b. Epinephrine and norepinephrine are the “fight or flight” hormones that are released by the adrenal medulla and the nervous system, respectively, under extreme stress. These hormones constrict the smooth muscles of the blood vessels. They constrict the afferent arterioles, causing the flow of blood into the nephrons to stop.
c. ADH is the “fight or flight” hormone that is released by the adrenal medulla under extreme stress. This hormone constricts the smooth muscles of the blood vessels. It constricts the efferent arterioles, causing the flow of blood into the nephrons to stop.
d. Epinephrine and norepinephrine are the “fight or flight” hormones that are released by the adrenal medulla and the nervous system, respectively, under extreme stress. These hormones constrict the smooth muscles of the blood vessels. They constrict the efferent arterioles, causing the flow of blood into the nephrons to stop.

TEST PREP FOR AP® COURSES

44.

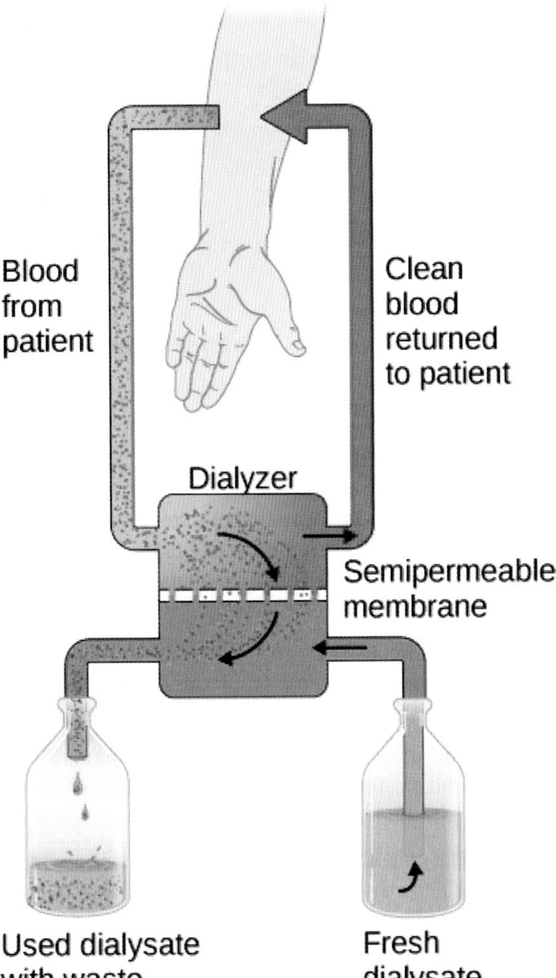

Patients with kidney illnesses use dialysis machines to remove harmful urea from their blood. The blood is separated from a solution, called the dialysate, that is designed to remove wastes by diffusion through a semipermeable membrane. How does the concentration of solutes likely differ between the upper component of the dialyzer and the lower compartment, containing the fresh dialysate, for the dialysis to successfully remove wastes from the blood?

a. In the upper component, the dialysate has a higher solute concentration than the blood, which allows the urea to diffuse to the lower dialysate down its concentration gradient.

b. In the upper component, the dialysate has a lower solute concentration than the blood, which allows the urea to be separated via active transport down the concentration gradient.

c. In the upper component, the dialysate has a higher solute concentration than the blood, which allows the urea to utilize facilitated diffusion in order to diffuse to the lower dialysate.

d. In the upper component, the dialysate has a lower solute concentration than the blood, which allows the urea to diffuse to the lower dialysate down its concentration gradient.

45.

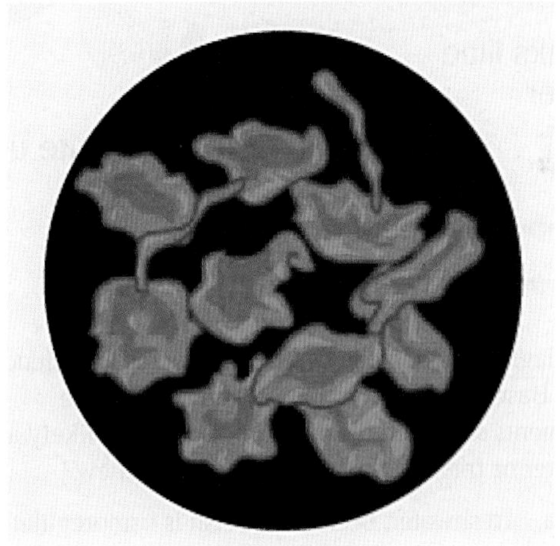
Solution A

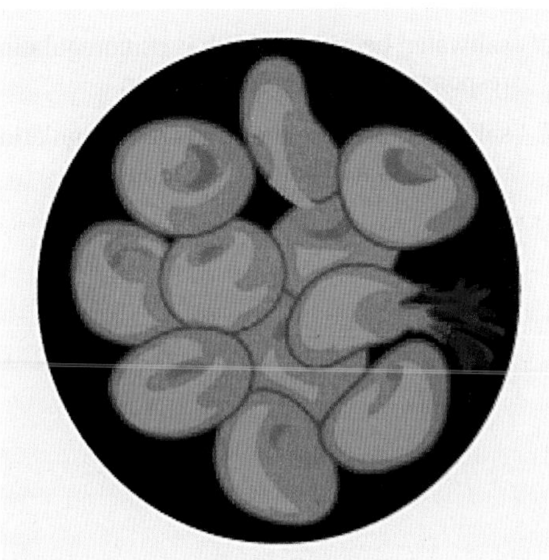
Solution B

The diagram shows red blood cells in two different NaCl solutions. What is likely causing the cells to differ in shape in the two solutions?

a. Solution A has high osmolarity. Solution B has low osmolarity.
b. Solution A has low osmolarity. Solution B high osmolarity.
c. The cells in solution A are osmoregulators. The cells in solution B are osmoconformers.
d. The cells in solution A are osmoconformers. The cells in solution B are osmoregulators.

46.

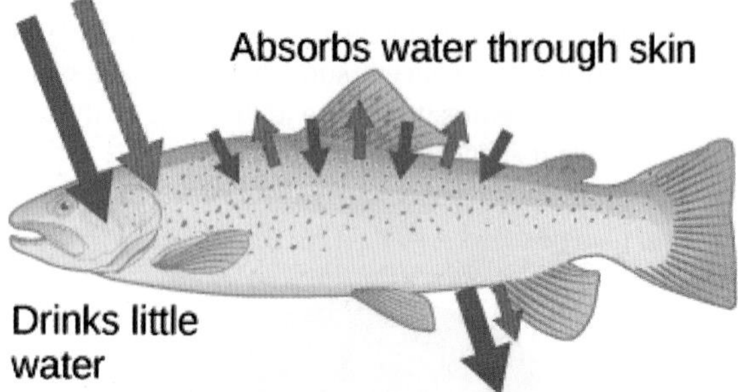

This diagram models the osmotic pressures experienced by a fish. Based on the direction of water and solute movements shown in the diagram, is this fish likely a saltwater or freshwater fish? How do you know?

a. freshwater, because the fish is osmoregulating in response to a hypertonic solution
b. freshwater, because the fish is osmoregulating in response to a hypotonic solution
c. saltwater, because the fish is osmoregulating in response to a hypertonic solution
d. saltwater, because the fish is osmoregulating in response to a hypotonic solution

47.

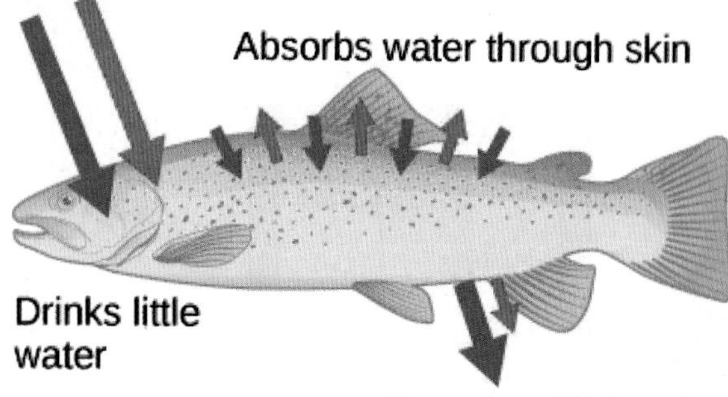

The diagram models the osmotic pressures experienced by a fish. Why would this fish most likely drink little water but excrete dilute urine? Explain your answer in terms of the osmolarity of the water it lives in.

a. The high osmolarity of the water would cause accumulation of too many salts in the body of the fish.
b. The water it lives in has very low osmolarity, which causes water to constantly diffuse into the fish's body.
c. The water it lives in has very high osmolarity, which causes water to constantly diffuse out of the fish's body.
d. The water it lives in has very high osmolarity, which causes water to constantly diffuse into the fish's body.

48.

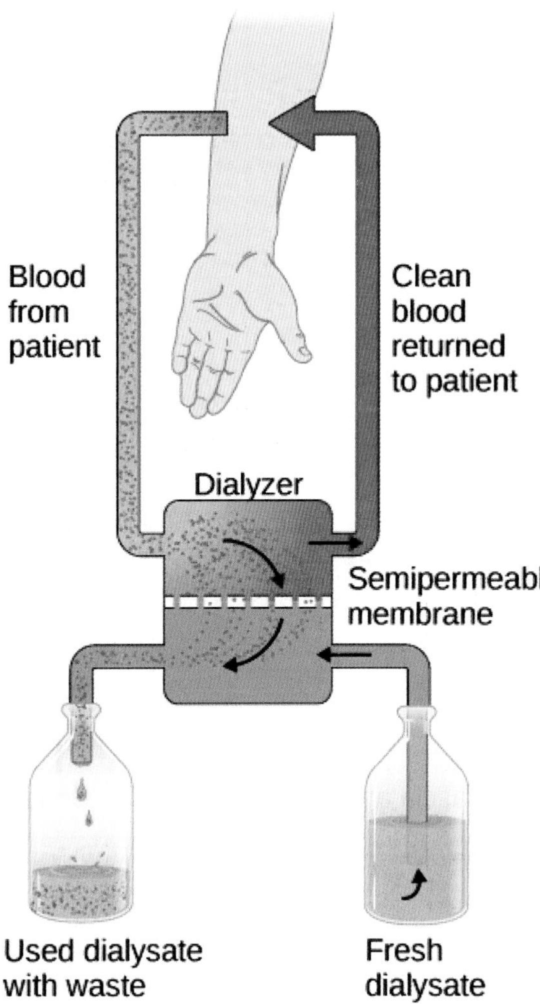

Patients with kidney illnesses use dialysis machines to remove harmful urea from their blood. The blood is separated from a solution, called the dialysate, that is designed to remove wastes by diffusion through a semipermeable membrane. The semipermeable membrane is likely permeable to _____ and impermeable to _____.

a. red blood cells, urea
b. dialysate, blood plasma
c. blood plasma, urea
d. urea, red blood cells

49.

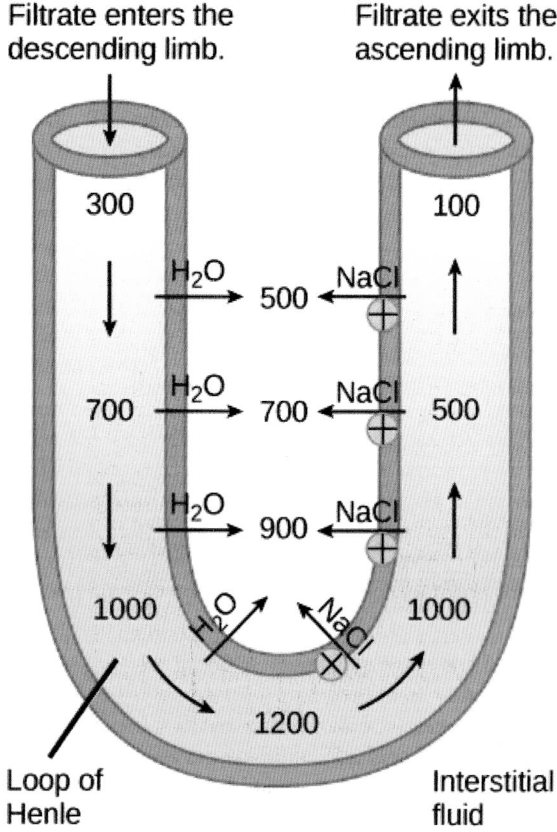

The diagram models the countercurrent exchange mechanism within the loop of Henle. The numbers within the loop show the osmolarity of the filtrate, while the numbers between the two loops indicate the osmolarity of the interstitial fluid within the kidney tissue. What would likely occur to the osmolarity of the filtrate in the ascending limb if the active transport of NaCl stopped?

a. Filtrate osmolarity would increase, then decrease.
b. Filtrate osmolarity would stay the same.
c. Filtrate osmolarity would decrease.
d. Filtrate osmolarity would increase.

50.

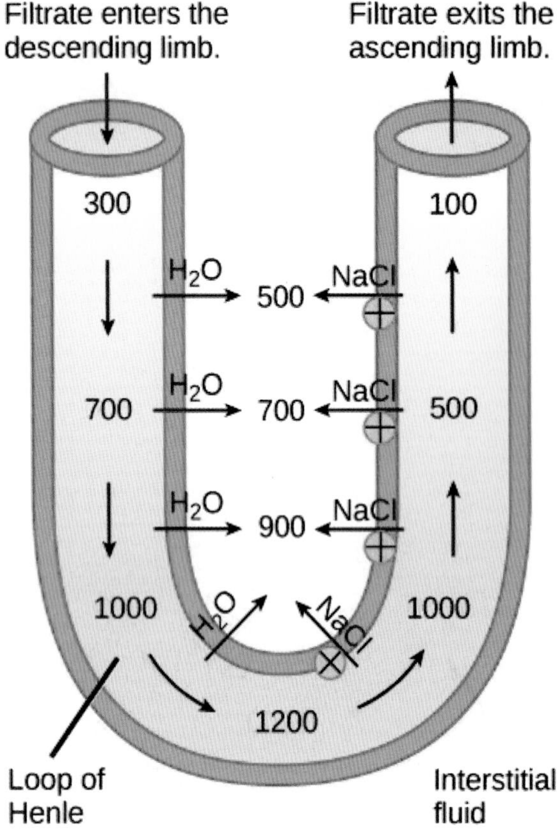

The diagram models the countercurrent exchange mechanism within the loop of Henle. The numbers within the loop show the osmolarity of the filtrate, while the numbers between the two loops indicate the osmolarity of the interstitial fluid within the kidney tissue. What would happen to the osmolarity of the interstitial fluid if water could not exit the descending limb?

a. Osmolarity of the interstitial fluid would increase.
b. Osmolarity of the interstitial fluid would decrease.
c. There would be no change in the osmolarity.
d. Osmolarity would increase or decrease depending upon the amount of water.

51.

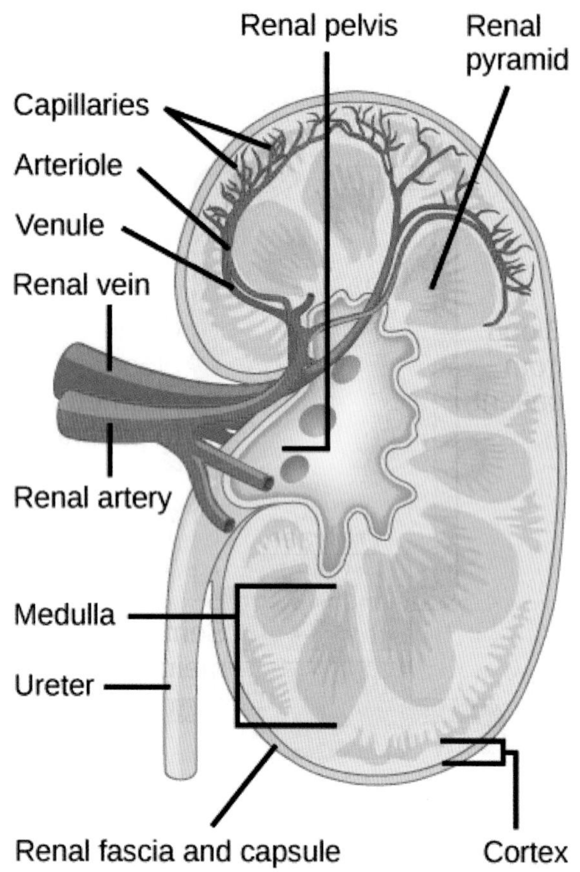

The diagram shows a cross-section of a kidney. What would likely occur if there was a blood clot in the renal artery?

a. Filtration in the glomerulus would decrease.
b. Fluid levels in the renal pelvis would increase.
c. Blood would not drain into the convoluted tubule.
d. Urea production would increase.

52.

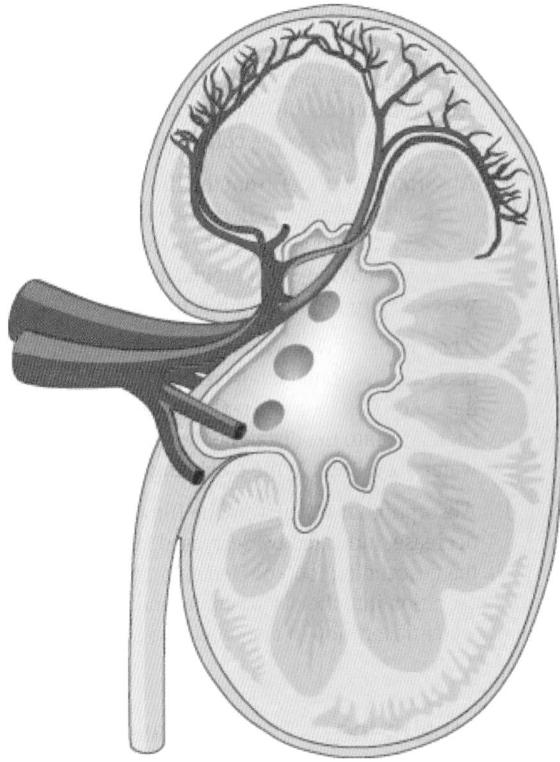

The diagram shows the left kidney. Why do the capillaries carrying blood from the renal artery run over the top of the renal pyramids?

a. The capillaries deliver blood to the glomerulus and run parallel to the proximal convoluted tubule. Both are located in the medulla.

b. The capillaries deliver blood to the glomerulus and run perpendicular to the proximal convoluted tubule. Both are located in the cortex.

c. The capillaries deliver blood to the glomerulus and run perpendicular to the distal convoluted tubule. Both are located in the cortex.

d. The capillaries deliver blood to the glomerulus and run parallel to the distal convoluted tubule. Both are located in the cortex.

53.

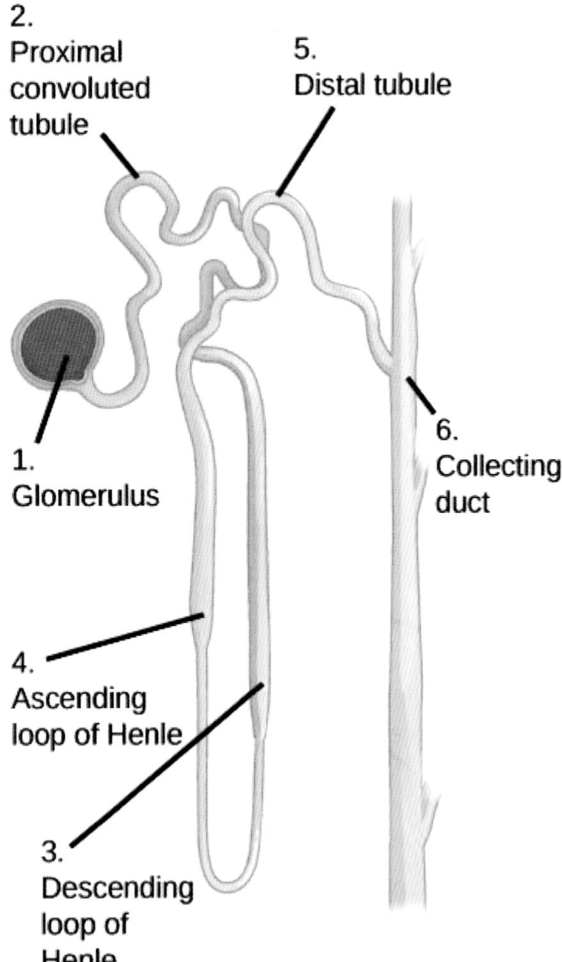

The figure shows the components of a nephron located within the kidneys. What would likely occur in the collecting duct if there was increased blood flow to the glomerulus?

a. More water would enter the collecting duct.

b. More urea would enter the collecting duct.

c. Less NaCl would leave the collecting duct.

d. Less urea would leave the collecting duct.

54.

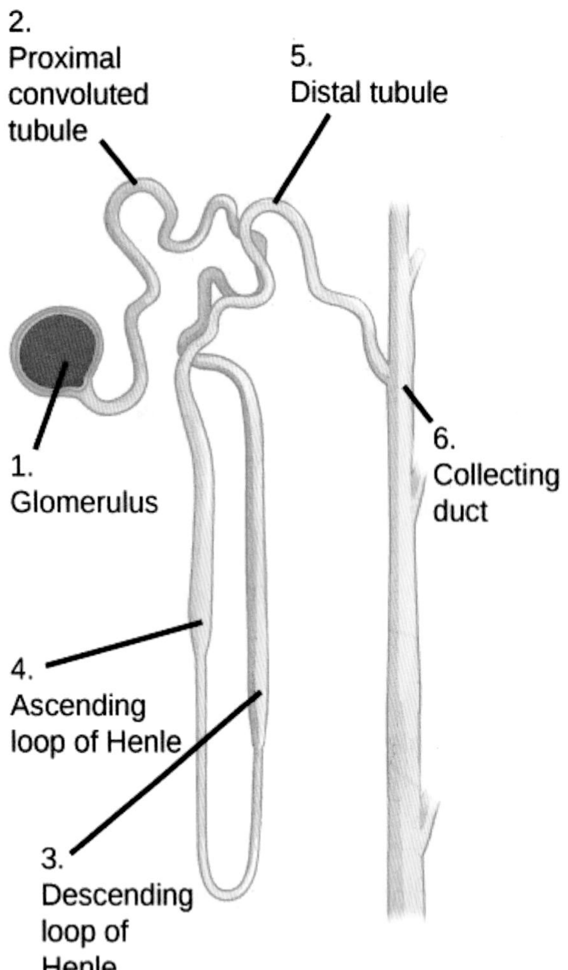

The figure below shows the components of a nephron located within the kidneys. Alcohol impairs the pituitary gland, which controls how much water is reabsorbed by the nephrons. The hormone produced by the pituitary gland, anti-diuretic hormone, increases water reabsorption by the kidney. How would impairment of this hormone likely affect the various components of the nephron pictured below?

a. Absorption of water from the filtrate would decrease, indicated by decreased loss of water in the descending loop of Henle, increased solute secretion into the distal tubule, and decreased water absorbtion in the collecting duct.
b. Absorption of water from the filtrate would decrease, indicated by decreased loss of water in the ascending loop of Henle, increased solute secretion into the distal tubule, and increased water absorption in the collecting duct.
c. Absorption of water from the filtrate would decrease, indicated by decreased loss of water in the ascending loop of Henle, increased solute secretion into the distal tubule, and decreased water absorbtion in the collecting duct.
d. Absorption of water from the filtrate would decrease, indicated by decreased loss of water in the descending loop of Henle, increased solute secretion into the distal tubule, and increased water absorption in the collecting duct.

55.

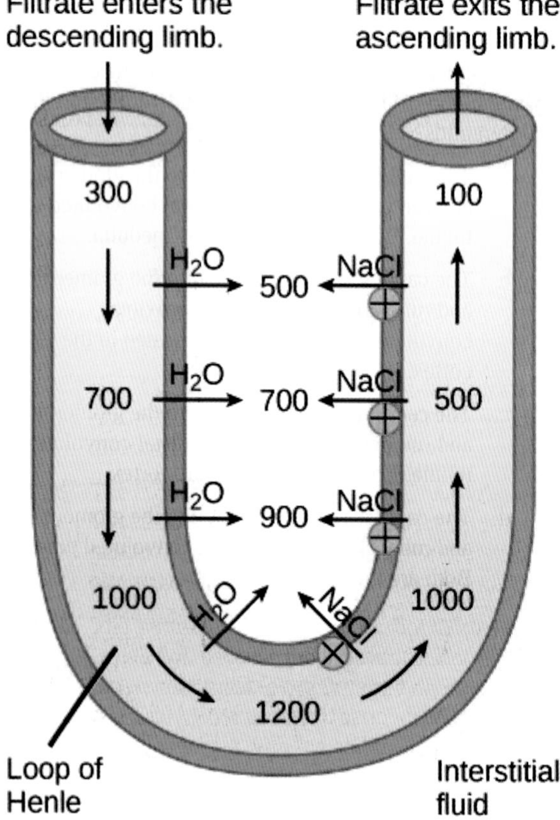

The diagram models the countercurrent exchange mechanism within the loop of Henle. The numbers within the loop show the osmolarity of the filtrate, while the numbers between the two loops indicate the osmolarity of the interstitial fluid within the kidney tissue. What would likely happen to the osmolarity of the filtrate in the ascending limb if the body released urea into the interstitial fluid?

a. The osmolarity would decrease, allowing the interstitial fluid to reabsorb solutes.
b. The osmolarity would decrease, allowing the interstitial fluid to reabsorb water.
c. The osmolarity would increase, allowing the interstitial fluid to reabsorb solutes.
d. The osmolarity would increase, allowing the interstitial fluid to reabsorb water.

56. Planaria are flatworms that live in fresh water. Their excretory system, or protonephridia, consists of two tubules connected to a highly branched tube system. The intake end of the tubes contain cilia that propel waste matter down the tubules and out of the body through excretory pores that open on the body surface. Cilia also draw water from the interstitial fluid, allowing for filtration. Any valuable metabolites are recovered by reabsorption. What structure in the human kidneys most closely resembles the cilia of the protonephridia, and why?

a. The renal artery, because it facilitates the exchange of nutrients with the blood
b. The convoluted tubule, because it facilitates the exchange of nutrients with the blood
c. The glomerulus, because it facilitates filtering of the blood
d. The ureter, because it facilitates filtering of the blood

57. Planaria are flatworms that live in fresh water. Their excretory system, or protonephridia, consists of two tubules connected to a highly branched tube system. The intake end of the tubes contain cilia that propel waste matter down the tubules and out of the body through excretory pores that open on the body surface. Cilia also draw water from the interstitial fluid, allowing for filtration. Any valuable metabolites are recovered by reabsorption. What structure in the human kidneys most closely resembles the highly branched tube system of the protonephridia, and why?

a. The renal artery, because it facilitates the exchange of nutrients with the blood
b. The convoluted tubule, because it facilitates the exchange of nutrients with the blood
c. The glomerulus, because it facilitates filtering of the blood
d. The ureter, because it facilitates filtering of the blood

58. Planaria are flatworms that live in fresh water. Their excretory system, or protonephridia, consists of two tubules connected to a highly branched tube system. The intake end of the tubes contain cilia that propel waste matter down the tubules and out of the body through excretory pores that open on the body surface. Cilia also draw water from the interstitial fluid, allowing for filtration. Any valuable metabolites are recovered by reabsorption. What structure in the human kidneys most closely resembles the excretory pores of the protonephridia, and why?

a. The urethral opening, because this is where wastes leave the body
b. The convoluted tubule, because this is where reabsorption and secretion occur
c. The glomerulus, because this is where reabsorption and secretion occur
d. The ureter, because this is where wastes leave the body.

59. The Malpighian tubules filter waste materials out of the blood, or hemolymph, of insects. There are cells lining the tubules that pump solutes (mainly ions) into the space surrounding the Malpighian tubules. If you observed a gradual increase in the solute concentration outside of the Malpighian tubules, what would you expect to happen?

a. Water would be drawn out of the hemolymph within the tubule.
b. Water would be drawn into the tubule.
c. Ions would be drawn out of the hemolymph within the tubule.
d. Ions would be drawn into the tubule.

60. The flame cells of a protonephridia filter waste materials out of the blood, or hemolymph, of invertebrates. What would this be most similar to, in function, in the human excretory system?

a. the ascending loop of henle
b. the descending loop of henle
c. the distal convoluted tubule
d. Bowman's capsule

61. Terrestrial arthropods, birds, and reptiles convert toxic ammonia to uric acid or the closely related compound guanine (guano). However, the conversion of ammonia to uric acid requires more energy and is much more complex than the conversion of ammonia to urea, or the excretion of ammonia as performed by fish. Based on these findings, how may the excretory system of one of the terrestrial organisms listed above change if it evolved to spend most of its time in water?

a. They may evolve the ability to switch between uric acid and direct ammonia excretion.
b. They would further reduce their excretion of ammonia.
c. They may evolve the ability to excrete uric acid without having to dissolve it in any water.
d. They would excrete higher concentrations of uric acid.

62. Birds and reptiles convert toxic ammonia to uric acid or the closely related compound guanine (guano), reflecting the close evolutionary ancestry of these groups. However, terrestrial arthropods also convert ammonia to uric acid. This is as opposed to fish, which excrete ammonia directly, without converting it to another substance. However, the conversion of ammonia to uric acid requires more energy and is much more complex than the conversion of ammonia to urea. What do these findings suggest about why these organisms evolved the conversion of ammonia to uric acid?

a. To evolve the ability to switch between uric acid and ammonia excretion
b. To conserve water to allow them to persist on land
c. For reduction in excretion of ammonia
d. For excretion of higher concentrations of ammonia

63. The kidneys are controlled by hormones from the brain, liver, and other locations. However, the kidneys also produce the hormone renin in their juxtaglomerular complex. How would damage to the juxtaglomerular complex affect the renin-angiotensin-aldosterone system?

a. Aldosterone will not be produced, decreasing blood volume
b. Angiotensin I will not be produced, decreasing blood pressure
c. Angiotensin-converting enzyme will not be produced, increasing sodium reabsorption.
d. Angiotensin II will not be produced, increasing the glomerular filtration rate.

64. The atrial natriuretic peptide (ANP) lowers blood pressure by acting as a vasodilator. It is released by cells in the atrium of the heart in response to high blood pressure and in patients with sleep apnea. ANP prevents sodium reabsorption by the renal tubules. Therefore, what excretory system symptom might someone with sleep apnea also experience and why?

a. reduction in urination due to reduction of water reabsorption in the kidneys
b. excessive sodium reabsorption by renal tubes due to increase in water reabsorption in the kidneys
c. excessive sodium reabsorption by renal tubes due to reduction of water reabsorption in the kidneys
d. excessive urination due to reduction of water reabsorption in the kidneys

65.

This diagram was made by a student to illustrate the angiotensin-aldosterone system. What part of this diagram contains an error?

a. ADH is not produced in this system.
b. The diagram is missing ANP.
c. ACE and renin should be switched.
d. ACE and angiotensin should be switched.

66.

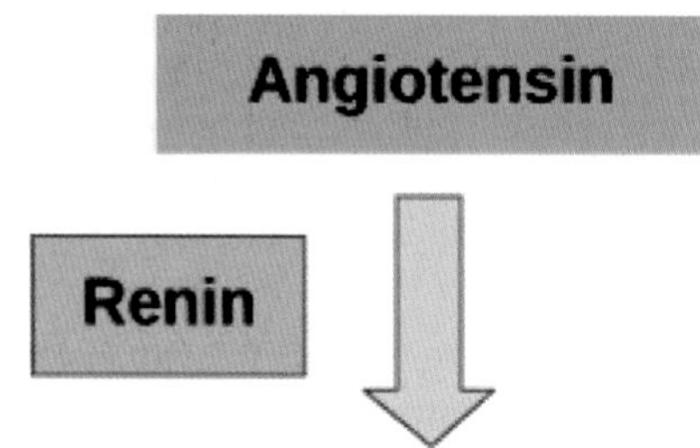

This diagram was made by a student to illustrate the angiotensin-aldosterone system. How would you complete this diagram to make it an accurate model of the renin-angiotensin system?

a. Renin acts on angiotensin to directly stimulate the release of aldosterone and ADH.

b. Renin acts on angiotensin to form ACE and angiotensin II, which then stimulates the release of aldosterone and ADH.

c. Angiotensin II is formed from angiotensin, which is then converted to angiotensin I by ACE. Aldosterone and ADH are then stimulated to be released from angiotensin I.

d. Angiotensin I is formed from angiotensin, which is then converted to angiotensin II by ACE. Aldosterone and ADH are then stimulated to be released from angiotensin II.

33 | THE IMMUNE SYSTEM

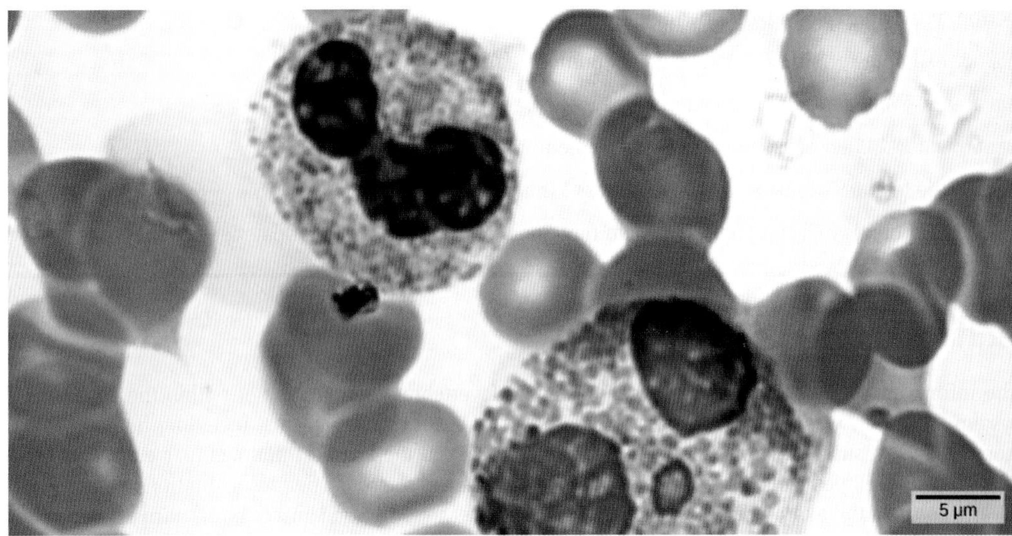

Figure 33.1 In this compound light micrograph purple-stained neutrophil (upper left) and eosinophil (lower right) are white blood cells that float among red blood cells in this blood smear. Neutrophils provide an early, rapid, and nonspecific defense against invading pathogens. Eosinophils play a variety of roles in the immune response. Red blood cells are about 7–8 µm in diameter, and a neutrophil is about 10–12µm. (credit: modification of work by Dr. David Csaba)

Chapter Outline

Introduction

The environment consists of numerous **pathogens**, which are agents, usually microorganisms, that cause diseases in their hosts. A **host** is the organism that is invaded and often harmed by a pathogen. Pathogens include bacteria, protists, fungi and other infectious organisms. We are constantly exposed to pathogens in food and water, on surfaces, and in the air. Mammalian immune systems evolved for protection from such pathogens; they are composed of an extremely diverse array of specialized cells and soluble molecules that coordinate a rapid and flexible defense system capable of providing protection from a majority of these disease agents.

Vaccines were developed to reduce the chance of infection of a particular disease, such as measles, mumps, polio, or chicken pox, by assisting the body to develop immunity. However, many diseases still do not have a vaccine, such as the deadly disease caused by the Ebola virus. Data from the World Health Organization indicates that more than 11,000 people died out of over 27,000 cases reported during the 2014–2015 outbreak. Though the majority of the cases were in Africa, Ebola did spread to other countries and prompted researchers to try to find a treatment. You can read more about this research at the Science Daily website (http://openstaxcollege.org/l/32ebolavirus) .

33.1 | Innate Immune Response

In this section, you will explore the following questions:

- What are examples of physical and chemical immune barriers?
- What are the immediate and induced immune responses?
- What are natural killer cells, and what is their role in immunity?
- What are the features of histocompatibility class I molecules?
- How do the proteins in a complement system function to destroy extracellular pathogens?

Connection for AP® Courses

Much of the information about the different organ systems of vertebrate animals is not within the scope for AP®. The immune system, however, was chosen for in-depth exploration because all organisms, including humans, must maintain dynamic homeostasis to survive within changing environments. Even the simplest multicellular eukaryotes like sponges and cnidarians have developed cells that specialize in immune defenses to protect against disruptions to homeostasis. News headlines warn us of outbreaks of diseases, including Ebola, measles, flu, and insect-borne viruses such as West Nile and chikungunya, that spread rapidly through populations, often with devastating consequences. We also hear about the emergence of new infections, especially ones caused by bacteria that have evolved resistance to antibiotics.

Immune systems in animals range from a loose cluster of phagocytic cells in sponges to complex interactions of molecules, cells, tissues, and organs that provide immunity in mammals. Components of the immune system constantly search the body for signs of disease-causing microorganisms called pathogens. Immune factors mobilize, identify the nature of the pathogen, strengthen the corresponding cells and molecules to combat the infection, and then halt the immune response after the infection is cleared to avoid unnecessary host cell damage. Because of its programmable memory system, the immune system can remember pathogens and initiate a more rapid response upon re-exposure. The immune response can be either innate or adaptive. The adaptive immune response stores information about past infections and mounts pathogen-specific defense. The innate immune response is always present and defends against all pathogens.

Despite the barriers of skin, tears, and mucus, pathogens may still enter the body. The innate immune system responds with inflammation, pathogen engulfment, and secretion of immune factors and proteins. Several types of cells are involved in the innate immune system, including mast cells that release histamines (causing those annoying symptoms associated with allergies and colds), macrophages that consume pathogens and cancer cells, natural killer (NK) cells that destroy tumor cells and virus-infected cells, several types of white blood cells, and even protective proteins like complement and interferon. We know from experience, however, that these barriers can fail. Fortunately, adaptive immune responses provide another, more specific line of defense.

Information presented and the examples highlighted in the section support concepts outlined in Big Idea 2 of the AP® Biology Curriculum Framework. The AP® Learning Objectives listed in the Curriculum Framework provide a transparent foundation for the AP® Biology course, an inquiry-based laboratory experience, instructional activities, and AP® exam questions. A learning objective merges required content with one or more of the seven science practices.

Big Idea 2	Biological systems utilize free energy and molecular building blocks to grow, to reproduce, and to maintain dynamic homeostasis.
Enduring Understanding 2.D	Growth and dynamic homeostasis of a biological system are influenced by changes in the system's environment.
Essential Knowledge	**2.D.4** Plants and animals have a variety of chemical defenses against infections that affect dynamic homeostasis.
Science Practice	**1.1** The student can create representations and models of natural or man-made phenomena and systems in the domain.
Science Practice	**1.2** The student can describe representations and models of natural or man-made phenomena and systems in the domain.

Learning Objective	**2.30** The student can create representations or models to describe nonspecific immune defenses in animals.

The immune system comprises both innate and adaptive immune responses. **Innate immunity** occurs naturally because of genetic factors or physiology; it is not induced by infection or vaccination but works to reduce the workload for the adaptive immune response. Both the innate and adaptive levels of the immune response involve secreted proteins, receptor-mediated signaling, and intricate cell-to-cell communication. The innate immune system developed early in animal evolution, roughly a billion years ago, as an essential response to infection. Innate immunity has a limited number of specific targets: any pathogenic threat triggers a consistent sequence of events that can identify the type of pathogen and either clear the infection independently or mobilize a highly specialized adaptive immune response. For example, tears and mucus secretions contain microbicidal factors.

Physical and Chemical Barriers

Before any immune factors are triggered, the skin functions as a continuous, impassable barrier to potentially infectious pathogens. Pathogens are killed or inactivated on the skin by desiccation (drying out) and by the skin's acidity. In addition, beneficial microorganisms that coexist on the skin compete with invading pathogens, preventing infection. Regions of the body that are not protected by skin (such as the eyes and mucus membranes) have alternative methods of defense, such as tears and mucus secretions that trap and rinse away pathogens, and cilia in the nasal passages and respiratory tract that push the mucus with the pathogens out of the body. Throughout the body are other defenses, such as the low pH of the stomach (which inhibits the growth of pathogens), blood proteins that bind and disrupt bacterial cell membranes, and the process of urination (which flushes pathogens from the urinary tract).

Despite these barriers, pathogens may enter the body through skin abrasions or punctures, or by collecting on mucosal surfaces in large numbers that overcome the mucus or cilia. Some pathogens have evolved specific mechanisms that allow them to overcome physical and chemical barriers. When pathogens do enter the body, the innate immune system responds with inflammation, pathogen engulfment, and secretion of immune factors and proteins.

Pathogen Recognition

An infection may be intracellular or extracellular, depending on the pathogen. All viruses infect cells and replicate within those cells (intracellularly), whereas bacteria and other parasites may replicate intracellularly or extracellularly, depending on the species. The innate immune system must respond accordingly: by identifying the extracellular pathogen and/or by identifying host cells that have already been infected. When a pathogen enters the body, cells in the blood and lymph detect the specific **pathogen-associated molecular patterns (PAMPs)** on the pathogen's surface. PAMPs are carbohydrate, polypeptide, and nucleic acid "signatures" that are expressed by viruses, bacteria, and parasites but which differ from molecules on host cells. The immune system has specific cells, described in Figure 33.2 and shown in Figure 33.3, with receptors that recognize these PAMPs. A **macrophage** is a large phagocytic cell that engulfs foreign particles and pathogens. Macrophages recognize PAMPs via complementary **pattern recognition receptors (PRRs)**. PRRs are molecules on macrophages and dendritic cells which are in contact with the external environment. A **monocyte** is a type of white blood cell that circulates in the blood and lymph and differentiates into macrophages after it moves into infected tissue. Dendritic cells bind molecular signatures of pathogens and promote pathogen engulfment and destruction. Toll-like receptors (TLRs) are a type of PRR that recognizes molecules that are shared by pathogens but distinguishable from host molecules). TLRs are present in invertebrates as well as vertebrates, and appear to be one of the most ancient components of the immune system. TLRs have also been identified in the mammalian nervous system.

Cell type	Characteristics	Location	Image
Mast cell	Dilates blood vessels and induces inflammation through release of histamines and heparin. Recruits macrophages and neutrophils. Involved in wound healing and defense against pathogens but can also be responsible for allergic reactions.	Connective tissues, mucous membranes	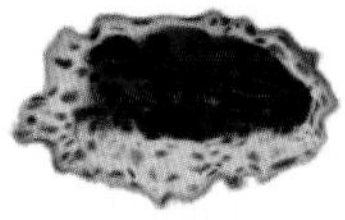
Macrophage	Phagocytic cell that consumes foreign pathogens and cancer cells. Stimulates response of other immune cells.	Migrates from blood vessels into tissues.	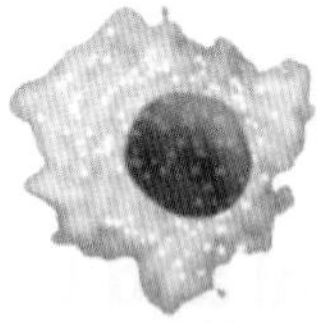
Natural killer cell	Kills tumor cells and virus-infected cells.	Circulates in blood and migrates into tissues.	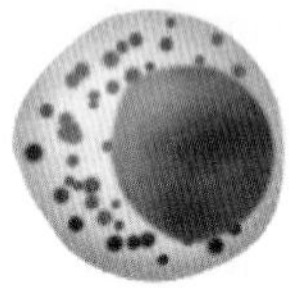
Dendritic cell	Presents antigens on its surface, thereby triggering adaptive immunity.	Present in epithelial tissue, including skin, lung and tissues of the digestive tract. Migrates to lymph nodes upon activation.	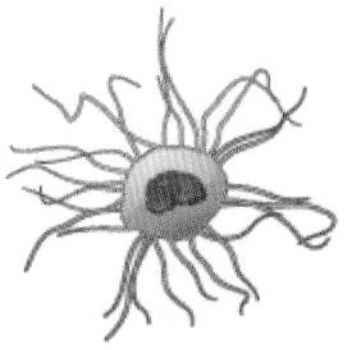
Monocyte	Differentiates into macrophages and dendritic cells in response to inflammation.	Stored in spleen, moves through blood vessels to infected tissues.	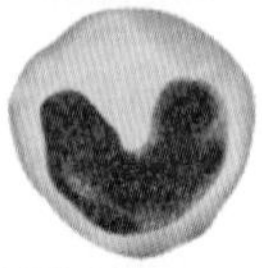
Neutrophil	First responders at the site of infection or trauma, this abundant phagocytic cell represents 50-60 percent of all leukocytes. Releases toxins that kill or inhibit bacteria and fungi and recruits other immune cells to the site of infection.	Migrates from blood vessels into tissues.	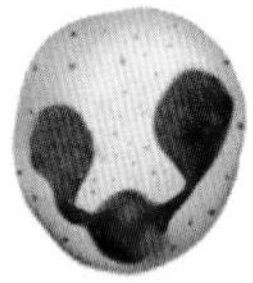
Basophil	Responsible for defense against parasites. Releases histamines that cause inflammation and may be responsible for allergic reactions.	Circulates in blood and migrates to tissues.	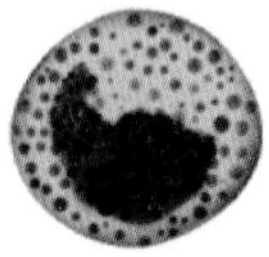
Eosinophil	Releases toxins that kill bacteria and parasites but also causes tissue damage.	Circulates in blood and migrates to tissues.	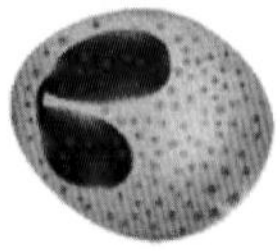

Figure 33.2 The characteristics and location of cells involved in the innate immune system are described. (credit: modification of work by NIH)

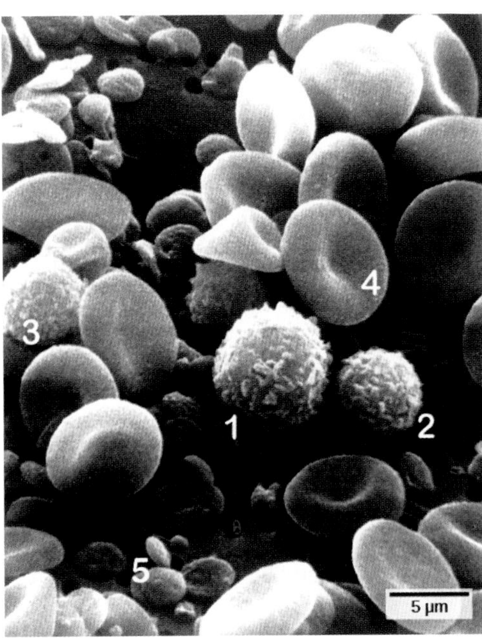

Figure 33.3 Cells of the blood include (1) monocytes, (2) lymphocytes, (3) neutrophils, (4) red blood cells, and (5) platelets. Note the very similar morphologies of the leukocytes (1, 2, 3). (credit: modification of work by Bruce Wetzel, Harry Schaefer, NCI; scale-bar data from Matt Russell)

Effects of Cytokine Release

The binding of PRRs with PAMPs triggers the release of cytokines, which signal that a pathogen is present and needs to be destroyed along with any infected cells. A **cytokine** is a chemical messenger that regulates cell differentiation (form and function), proliferation (production), and gene expression to affect immune responses. At least 40 types of cytokines exist in humans that differ in terms of the cell type that produces them, the cell type that responds to them, and the changes they produce. One type cytokine, interferon, is illustrated in Figure 33.4.

One subclass of cytokines is the interleukin (IL), so named because they mediate interactions between leukocytes (white blood cells). Interleukins are involved in bridging the innate and adaptive immune responses. In addition to being released from cells after PAMP recognition, cytokines are released by the infected cells which bind to nearby uninfected cells and induce those cells to release cytokines, which results in a cytokine burst.

A second class of early-acting cytokines is interferons, which are released by infected cells as a warning to nearby uninfected cells. One of the functions of an **interferon** is to inhibit viral replication. They also have other important functions, such as tumor surveillance. Interferons work by signaling neighboring uninfected cells to destroy RNA and reduce protein synthesis, signaling neighboring infected cells to undergo apoptosis (programmed cell death), and activating immune cells.

In response to interferons, uninfected cells alter their gene expression, which increases the cells' resistance to infection. One effect of interferon-induced gene expression is a sharply reduced cellular protein synthesis. Virally infected cells produce more viruses by synthesizing large quantities of viral proteins. Thus, by reducing protein synthesis, a cell becomes resistant to viral infection.

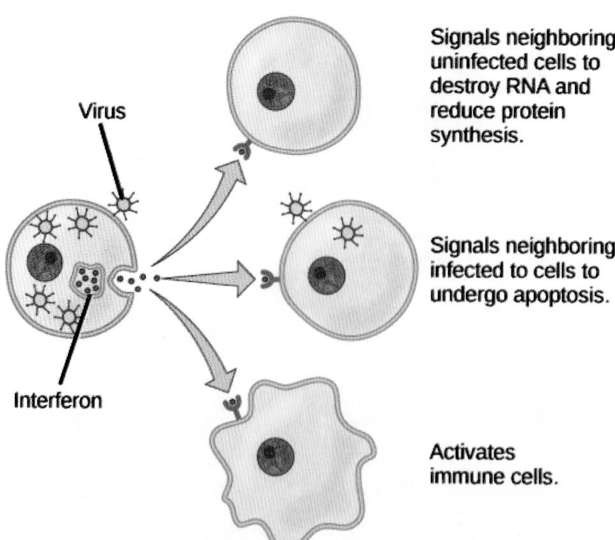

Figure 33.4 Interferons are cytokines that are released by a cell infected with a virus. Response of neighboring cells to interferon helps stem the infection.

Phagocytosis and Inflammation

The first cytokines to be produced are pro-inflammatory; that is, they encourage **inflammation**, the localized redness, swelling, heat, and pain that result from the movement of leukocytes and fluid through increasingly permeable capillaries to a site of infection. The population of leukocytes that arrives at an infection site depends on the nature of the infecting pathogen. Both macrophages and dendritic cells engulf pathogens and cellular debris through phagocytosis. A **neutrophil** is also a phagocytic leukocyte that engulfs and digests pathogens. Neutrophils, shown in Figure 33.3, are the most abundant leukocytes of the immune system. Neutrophils have a nucleus with two to five lobes, and they contain organelles, called lysosomes, that digest engulfed pathogens. An **eosinophil** is a leukocyte that works with other eosinophils to surround a parasite; it is involved in the allergic response and in protection against helminthes (parasitic worms).

Neutrophils and eosinophils are particularly important leukocytes that engulf large pathogens, such as bacteria and fungi. A **mast cell** is a leukocyte that produces inflammatory molecules, such as histamine, in response to large pathogens. A **basophil** is a leukocyte that, like a neutrophil, releases chemicals to stimulate the inflammatory response as illustrated in Figure 33.5. Basophils are also involved in allergy and hypersensitivity responses and induce specific types of inflammatory responses. Eosinophils and basophils produce additional inflammatory mediators to recruit more leukocytes. A hypersensitive immune response to harmless antigens, such as in pollen, often involves the release of histamine by basophils and mast cells.

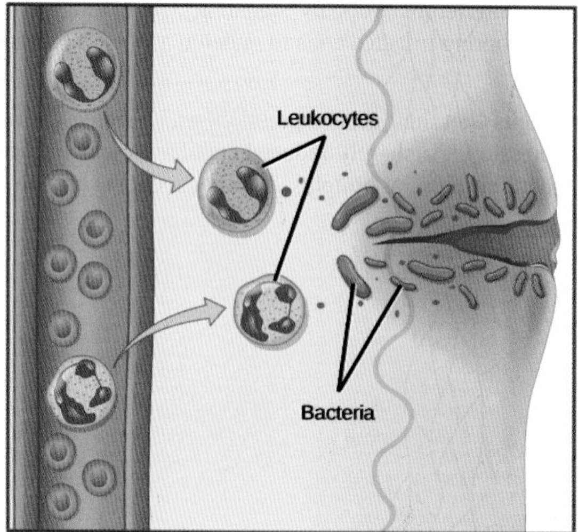

Figure 33.5 In response to a cut, mast cells secrete histamines that cause nearby capillaries to dilate. Neutrophils and monocytes leave the capillaries. Monocytes mature into macrophages. Neutrophils, dendritic cells and macrophages release chemicals to stimulate the inflammatory response. Neutrophils and macrophages also consume invading bacteria by phagocytosis.

Cytokines also send feedback to cells of the nervous system to bring about the overall symptoms of feeling sick, which include lethargy, muscle pain, and nausea. These effects may have evolved because the symptoms encourage the individual to rest and prevent them from spreading the infection to others. Cytokines also increase the core body temperature, causing a fever, which causes the liver to withhold iron from the blood. Without iron, certain pathogens, such as some bacteria, are unable to replicate; this is called nutritional immunity.

Watch this 23-second stop-motion video (http://openstaxcollege.org/l/conidia) showing a neutrophil that searches for and engulfs fungus spores during an elapsed time of about 79 minutes.

How does the action shown in the video clip (http://openstaxcollege.org/l/conidia (http://openstaxcollege.org/l/conidia)) demonstrate an immune response?

a. Neutrophils phagocytize pathogens invading the body and release chemical histamines that cause pathogen destruction and removal from the body. This prevents pathogens from producing toxic compounds that harm cells.

b. Neutrophils phagocytize pathogens invading the body, resulting in their death and removal from the body. This prevents pathogens from multiplying or producing toxic compounds that harm human cells.

c. Neutrophils are phagocytic and are the first responders to infection. They produce large quantities of cytokines, which cause pathogen destruction and removal from the body.

d. Neutrophils produce cytokines that help phagocytes to recognize foreign material that will destroy and remove pathogens from the body.

Natural Killer Cells

Lymphocytes are leukocytes that are histologically identifiable by their large, darkly staining nuclei; they are small cells with very little cytoplasm, as shown in Figure 33.6. Infected cells are identified and destroyed by **natural killer (NK) cells**, lymphocytes that can kill cells infected with viruses or tumor cells (abnormal cells that uncontrollably divide and invade other tissue). T cells and B cells of the adaptive immune system also are classified as lymphocytes. **T cells** are lymphocytes that mature in the thymus gland, and **B cells** are lymphocytes that mature in the bone marrow. NK cells identify intracellular infections, especially from viruses, by the altered expression of **major histocompatibility class (MHC) I molecules** on the surface of infected cells. MHC I molecules are proteins on the surfaces of all nucleated cells, thus they are scarce on red blood cells and platelets which are non-nucleated. The function of MHC I molecules is to display fragments of proteins from the infectious agents within the cell to T-cells; healthy cells will be ignored, while "non-self" or foreign proteins will be attacked by the immune system. MHC II molecules are found mainly on cells containing antigens ("non-self proteins") and on lymphocytes. **MHC II molecules** interact with helper T-cells to trigger the appropriate immune response, which may include the inflammatory response.

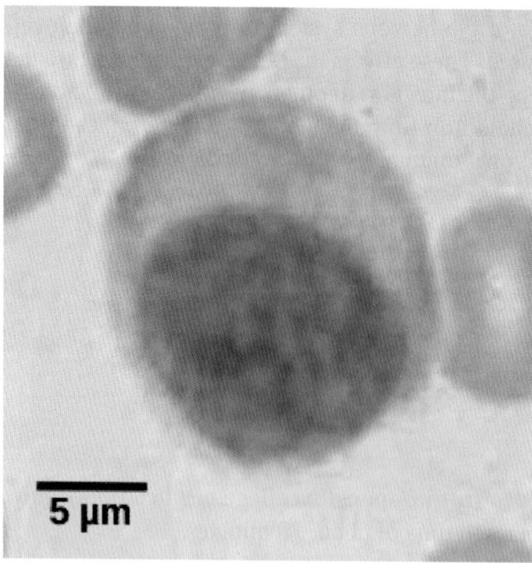

Figure 33.6 Lymphocytes, such as NK cells, are characterized by their large nuclei that actively absorb Wright stain and therefore appear dark colored under a microscope.

An infected cell (or a tumor cell) is usually incapable of synthesizing and displaying MHC I molecules appropriately. The metabolic resources of cells infected by some viruses produce proteins that interfere with MHC I processing and/or trafficking to the cell surface. The reduced MHC I on host cells varies from virus to virus and results from active inhibitors being produced by the viruses. This process can deplete host MHC I molecules on the cell surface, which NK cells detect as "unhealthy" or "abnormal" while searching for cellular MHC I molecules. Similarly, the dramatically altered gene expression of tumor cells leads to expression of extremely deformed or absent MHC I molecules that also signal "unhealthy" or "abnormal."

NK cells are always active; an interaction with normal, intact MHC I molecules on a healthy cell disables the killing sequence, and the NK cell moves on. After the NK cell detects an infected or tumor cell, its cytoplasm secretes granules comprised of **perforin**, a destructive protein that creates a pore in the target cell. Granzymes are released along with the perforin in the immunological synapse. A **granzyme** is a protease that digests cellular proteins and induces the target cell to undergo programmed cell death, or apoptosis. Phagocytic cells then digest the cell debris left behind. NK cells are constantly patrolling the body and are an effective mechanism for controlling potential infections and preventing cancer progression.

Complement

An array of approximately 20 types of soluble proteins, called a **complement system**, functions to destroy extracellular pathogens. Cells of the liver and macrophages synthesize complement proteins continuously; these proteins are abundant in the blood serum and are capable of responding immediately to infecting microorganisms. The complement system is so named because it is complementary to the antibody response of the adaptive immune system. Complement proteins bind to the surfaces of microorganisms and are particularly attracted to pathogens that are already bound by antibodies. Binding of complement proteins occurs in a specific and highly regulated sequence, with each successive protein being activated by cleavage and/or structural changes induced upon binding of the preceding protein(s). After the first few complement proteins bind, a cascade of sequential binding events follows in which the pathogen rapidly becomes coated in complement proteins.

Complement proteins perform several functions. The proteins serve as a marker to indicate the presence of a pathogen to phagocytic cells, such as macrophages and B cells, and enhance engulfment; this process is called **opsonization**. Certain complement proteins can combine to form attack complexes that open pores in microbial cell membranes. These structures destroy pathogens by causing their contents to leak, as illustrated in Figure 33.7.

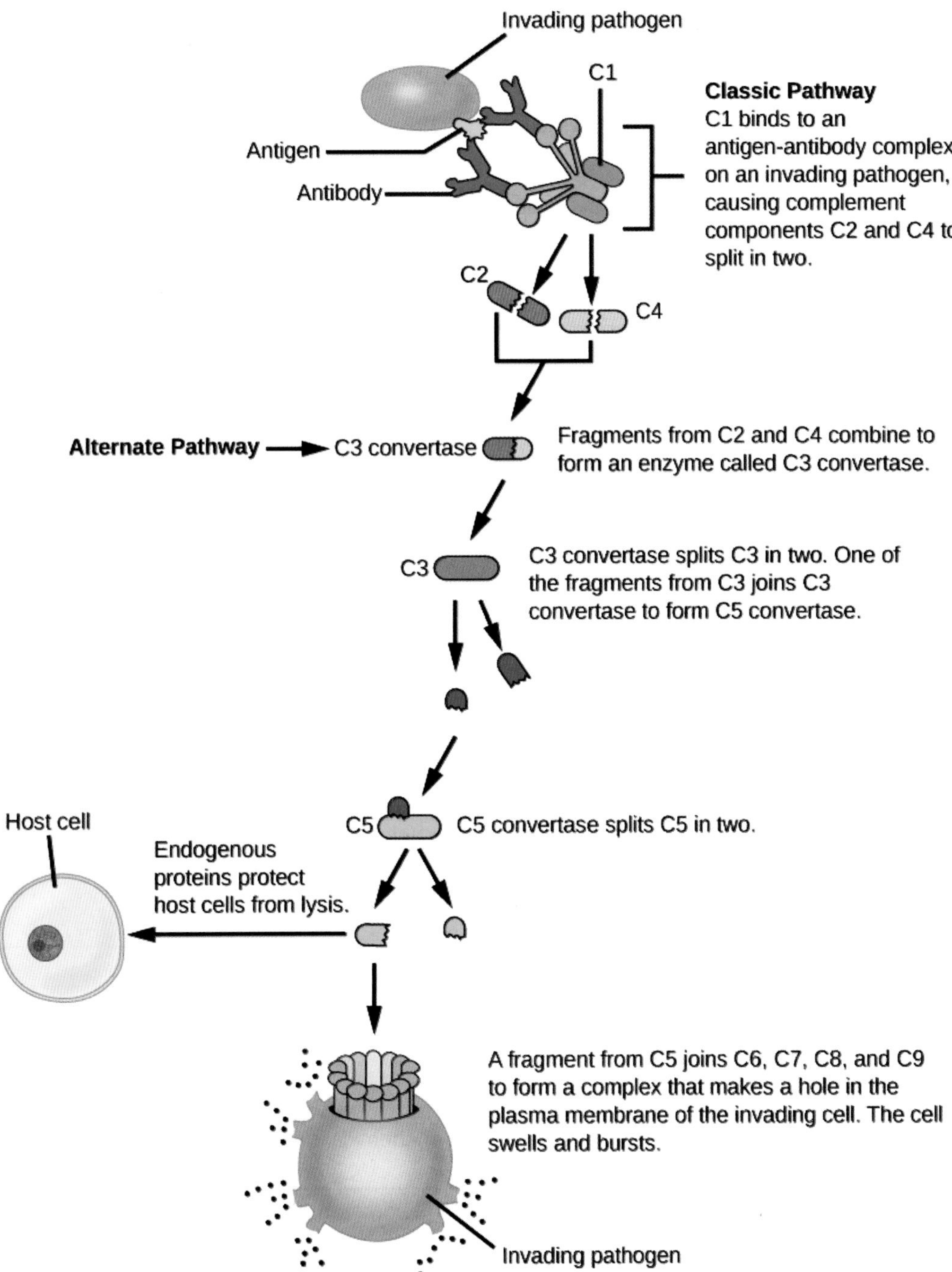

Figure 33.7 The classic pathway for the complement cascade involves the attachment of several initial complement proteins to an antibody-bound pathogen followed by rapid activation and binding of many more complement proteins and the creation of destructive pores in the microbial cell envelope and cell wall. The alternate pathway does not involve antibody activation. Rather, C3 convertase spontaneously breaks down C3. Endogenous regulatory proteins prevent the complement complex from binding to host cells. Pathogens lacking these regulatory proteins are lysed. (credit: modification of work by NIH)

33.2 | Adaptive Immune Response

In this section, you will explore the following questions:

- What is adaptive immunity?
- What is the difference between adaptive and innate immunity?
- What are the cell-mediated immune response and the humoral immune response?
- What is immune tolerance?

Connection for AP® Courses

Adaptive immune response takes days or even weeks to become established—much longer than the innate response—and is more specific to pathogens and involves molecular memory. This type of immunity occurs after we've been exposed to an antigen either from a pathogen or through vaccination and is activated when the innate immune response is insufficient to control the infection. There are two types of adaptive responses: **cell-mediated immune response**, carried out by T cells, and the **humoral immune response**, controlled by activated B cells and their production of antibodies. **Adaptive immunity** involves memory so that re-exposure to the same pathogen will elicit an efficient and quick response. This gives long-term protection from reinfection.

The information in this section will seem overwhelmingly complex with its discussion of antigens, antigen-presenting cells, major histocompatibility (MHC) molecules, different types of T cells, antibody-secreting B cells, and the programming of memory cells. One suggestion is to read the information slowly, study the figures and their captions carefully, and make your own series of diagrams. Despite the difficulty of the information, many concepts will seem familiar, such as the role of proteins embedded in plasma cell membranes and interactions among different types of cells and molecules.

Information presented and the examples highlighted in the section support concepts outlined in Big Idea 2 and Big Idea 3 of the AP® Biology Curriculum Framework. The AP® Learning Objectives listed in the Curriculum Framework provide a transparent foundation for the AP® Biology course, an inquiry-based laboratory experience, instructional activities, and AP® exam questions. A learning objective merges required content with one or more of the seven science practices.

Big Idea 2	Biological systems utilize free energy and molecular building blocks to grow, to reproduce, and to maintain dynamic homeostasis.
Enduring Understanding 2.D	Growth and dynamic homeostasis of a biological system are influenced by changes in the system's environment.
Essential Knowledge	**2.D.4** Plants and animals have a variety of chemical defenses against infections that affect dynamic homeostasis.
Science Practice	**1.1** The student can create representations and models of natural or man-made phenomena and systems in the domain.
Science Practice	**1.2** The student can describe representations and models of natural or man-made phenomena and systems in the domain.
Learning Objective	**2.29** The student can create representations and models to describe immune responses.
Big Idea 3	Living systems store, retrieve, transmit and respond to information essential to life processes.
Enduring Understanding 3.D	Cells communicate by generating, transmitting and receiving chemical signals.
Essential Knowledge	**3.D.2** Cells communicate with each other through direct contact with other cells or from a distance via chemical signaling.

Science Practice	**6.2** The student can construct explanations of phenomena based on evidence produced through scientific practices.
Learning Objective	**3.34** The student is able to construct explanations of cell communication through cell-to-cell direct contact or through chemical signaling.
Essential Knowledge	**3.D.2** Cells communicate with each other through direct contact with other cells or from a distance via chemical signaling.
Science Practice	**1.1** The student can create representations and models of natural or man-made phenomena and systems in the domain.
Learning Objective	**3.35** The student is able to create representations that depict how cell-to-cell communication occurs by direct contact or from a distance through chemical signaling.

Antigen-presenting Cells

Unlike NK cells of the innate immune system, B cells (B lymphocytes) are a type of white blood cell that gives rise to antibodies, whereas T cells (T lymphocytes) are a type of white blood cell that plays an important role in the immune response. T cells are a key component in the cell-mediated response—the specific immune response that utilizes T cells to neutralize cells that have been infected with viruses and certain bacteria. There are three types of T cells: cytotoxic, helper, and suppressor T cells. Cytotoxic T cells destroy virus-infected cells in the cell-mediated immune response, and helper T cells play a part in activating both the antibody and the cell-mediated immune responses. Suppressor T cells deactivate T cells and B cells when needed, and thus prevent the immune response from becoming too intense.

An **antigen** is a foreign or "non-self" macromolecule that reacts with cells of the immune system. Not all antigens will provoke a response. For instance, individuals produce innumerable "self" antigens and are constantly exposed to harmless foreign antigens, such as food proteins, pollen, or dust components. The suppression of immune responses to harmless macromolecules is highly regulated and typically prevents processes that could be damaging to the host, known as tolerance.

The innate immune system contains cells that detect potentially harmful antigens, and then inform the adaptive immune response about the presence of these antigens. An **antigen-presenting cell (APC)** is an immune cell that detects, engulfs, and informs the adaptive immune response about an infection. When a pathogen is detected, these APCs will phagocytose the pathogen and digest it to form many different fragments of the antigen. Antigen fragments will then be transported to the surface of the APC, where they will serve as an indicator to other immune cells. **Dendritic cells** are immune cells that process antigen material; they are present in the skin (Langerhans cells) and the lining of the nose, lungs, stomach, and intestines. Sometimes a dendritic cell presents on the surface of other cells to induce an immune response, thus functioning as an antigen-presenting cell. Macrophages also function as APCs. Before activation and differentiation, B cells can also function as APCs.

After phagocytosis by APCs, the phagocytic vesicle fuses with an intracellular lysosome forming phagolysosome. Within the phagolysosome, the components are broken down into fragments; the fragments are then loaded onto MHC class I or MHC class II molecules and are transported to the cell surface for antigen presentation, as illustrated in Figure 33.8. Note that T lymphocytes cannot properly respond to the antigen unless it is processed and embedded in an MHC II molecule. APCs express MHC on their surfaces, and when combined with a foreign antigen, these complexes signal a "non-self" invader. Once the fragment of antigen is embedded in the MHC II molecule, the immune cell can respond. Helper T- cells are one of the main lymphocytes that respond to antigen-presenting cells. Recall that all other nucleated cells of the body expressed MHC I molecules, which signal "healthy" or "normal."

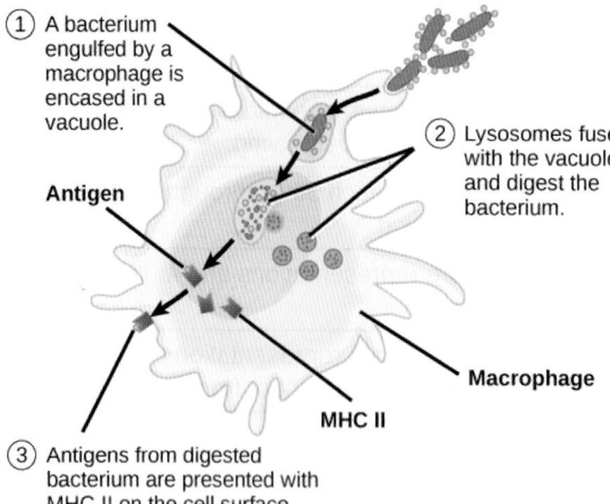
① A bacterium engulfed by a macrophage is encased in a vacuole.
② Lysosomes fuse with the vacuole and digest the bacterium.
Antigen
Macrophage
MHC II
③ Antigens from digested bacterium are presented with MHC II on the cell surface.

Figure 33.8 An APC, such as a macrophage, engulfs and digests a foreign bacterium. An antigen from the bacterium is presented on the cell surface in conjunction with an MHC II molecule Lymphocytes of the adaptive immune response interact with antigen-embedded MHC II molecules to mature into functional immune cells.

LINK TO LEARNING

openstax COLLEGE

This animation (http://openstaxcollege.org/l/immune_system) from Rockefeller University shows how dendritic cells act as sentinels in the body's immune system.

What key role do dendritic cells play in the human immune response?

a. Dendritic cells directly kill infected cells and emit cytokines, which amplify the immune response.

b. Dendritic cells recognize foreign proteins and prepare them to be displayed to immune cells in the lymph. This activates an immune response.

c. Dendritic cells identify tumor cells or cells infected with viruses and destroy them.

d. Dendritic cells act as phagocytes. They engulf and digest pathogens.

T and B Lymphocytes

Lymphocytes in human circulating blood are approximately 80 to 90 percent T cells, shown in Figure 33.9, and 10 to 20 percent B cells. Recall that the T cells are involved in the cell-mediated immune response, whereas B cells are part of the humoral immune response.

T cells encompass a heterogeneous population of cells with extremely diverse functions. Some T cells respond to APCs of the innate immune system, and indirectly induce immune responses by releasing cytokines. Other T cells stimulate B cells to prepare their own response. Another population of T cells detects APC signals and directly kills the infected cells. Other T cells are involved in suppressing inappropriate immune reactions to harmless or "self" antigens.

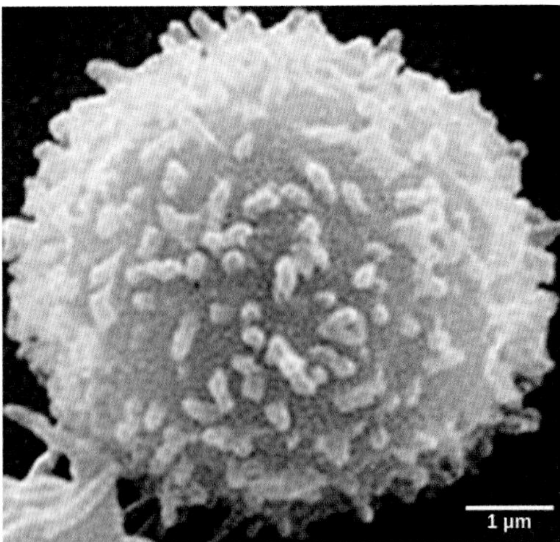

Figure 33.9 This scanning electron micrograph shows a T lymphocyte, which is responsible for the cell-mediated immune response. T cells are able to recognize antigens. (credit: modification of work by NCI; scale-bar data from Matt Russell)

T and B cells exhibit a common theme of recognition/binding of specific antigens via a complementary receptor, followed by activation and self-amplification/maturation to specifically bind to the particular antigen of the infecting pathogen. T and B lymphocytes are also similar in that each cell only expresses one type of antigen receptor. Any individual may possess a population of T and B cells that together express a near limitless variety of antigen receptors that are capable of recognizing virtually any infecting pathogen. T and B cells are activated when they recognize small components of antigens, called **epitopes**, presented by APCs, illustrated in Figure 33.10. Note that recognition occurs at a specific epitope rather than on the entire antigen; for this reason, epitopes are known as "antigenic determinants." In the absence of information from APCs, T and B cells remain inactive, or naïve, and are unable to prepare an immune response. The requirement for information from the APCs of innate immunity to trigger B cell or T cell activation illustrates the essential nature of the innate immune response to the functioning of the entire immune system.

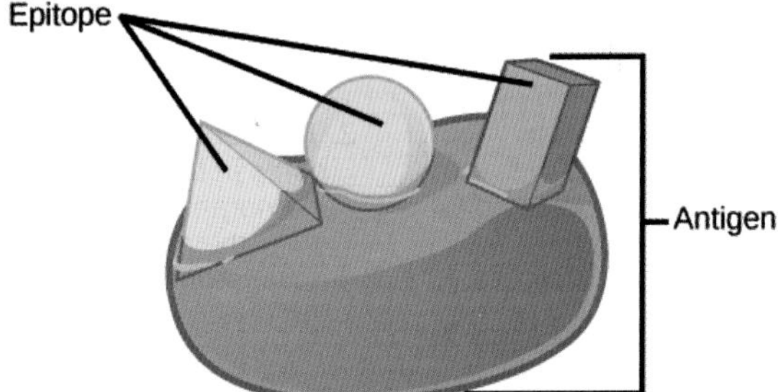

Figure 33.10 An antigen is a macromolecule that reacts with components of the immune system. A given antigen may contain several motifs that are recognized by immune cells. Each motif is an epitope. In this figure, the entire structure is an antigen, and the orange, salmon and green components projecting from it represent potential epitopes.

Naïve T cells can express one of two different molecules, CD4 or CD8, on their surface, as shown in Figure 33.11, and are accordingly classified as $CD4^+$ or $CD8^+$ cells. These molecules are important because they regulate how a T cell will interact with and respond to an APC. Naïve $CD4^+$ cells bind APCs via their antigen-embedded MHC II molecules and are stimulated to become **helper T (T_H) lymphocytes**, cells that go on to stimulate B cells (or cytotoxic T cells) directly or secrete cytokines to inform more and various target cells about the pathogenic threat. In contrast, $CD8^+$ cells engage antigen-embedded MHC I molecules on APCs and are stimulated to become **cytotoxic T lymphocytes (CTLs)**, which directly kill infected cells by apoptosis and emit cytokines to amplify the immune response. The two populations of T cells have different mechanisms of immune protection, but both bind MHC molecules via their antigen receptors called T cell receptors (TCRs). The CD4 or CD8 surface molecules differentiate whether the TCR will engage an MHC II or an MHC I molecule. Because they assist in binding specificity, the CD4 and CD8 molecules are described as coreceptors.

visual CONNECTION

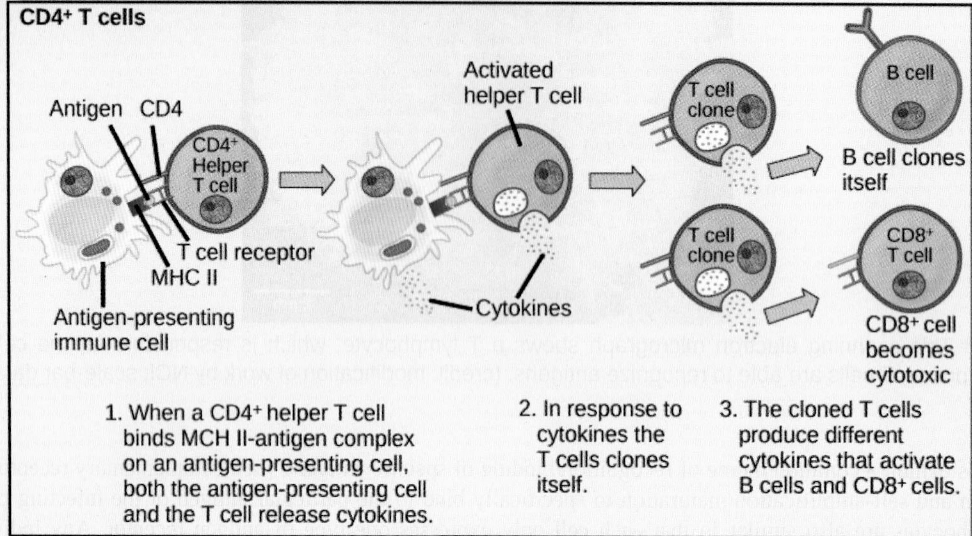

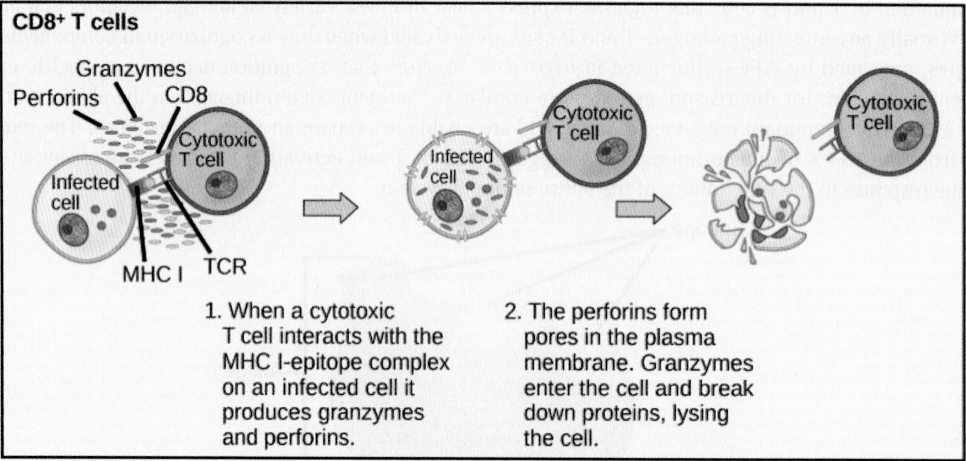

Figure 33.11 Naïve CD4$^+$ T cells engage MHC II molecules on antigen-presenting cells (APCs) and become activated. Clones of the activated helper T cell, in turn, activate B cells and CD8$^+$ T cells, which become cytotoxic T cells. Cytotoxic T cells kill infected cells.

Which of the following statements about T cells is false?

a. The T cell receptor is found on both CD4+ and CD8+T cells.

b. Helper T cells are CD4+, while cytotoxic T cells are CD8+.

c. Helper T cells release cytokines, while cytotoxic T cells kill the infected cell.

d. MHC II is a receptor found on most body cells, while MHC I is a receptor found only on immune cells.

Consider the innumerable possible antigens that an individual will be exposed to during a lifetime. The mammalian adaptive immune system is adept in responding appropriately to each antigen. Mammals have an enormous diversity of T cell populations, resulting from the diversity of TCRs. Each TCR consists of two polypeptide chains that span the T cell membrane, as illustrated in **Figure 33.12**; the chains are linked by a disulfide bridge. Each polypeptide chain is comprised of a constant domain and a variable domain: a domain, in this sense, is a specific region of a protein that may be regulatory or structural. The intracellular domain is involved in intracellular signaling. A single T cell will express thousands of identical copies of one specific TCR variant on its cell surface. The specificity of the adaptive immune system occurs because it synthesizes millions of different T cell populations, each expressing a TCR that differs in its variable domain. This TCR diversity is achieved by the mutation and recombination of genes that encode these receptors in stem cell precursors of T cells. The binding between an antigen-displaying MHC molecule and a complementary TCR "match" indicates that the adaptive immune system needs to activate and produce that specific T cell because its structure is appropriate to recognize and destroy the invading pathogen.

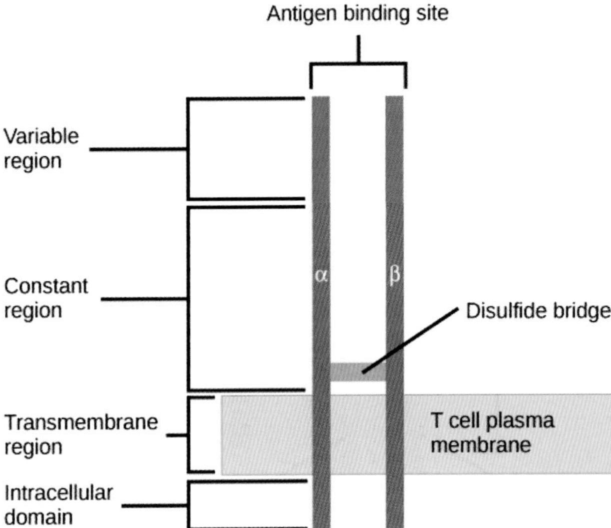

Figure 33.12 A T cell receptor spans the membrane and projects variable binding regions into the extracellular space to bind processed antigens via MHC molecules on APCs.

Helper T Lymphocytes

The T_H lymphocytes function indirectly to identify potential pathogens for other cells of the immune system. These cells are important for extracellular infections, such as those caused by certain bacteria, helminths, and protozoa. T_H lymphocytes recognize specific antigens displayed in the MHC II complexes of APCs. There are two major populations of T_H cells: T_H1 and T_H2. T_H1 cells secrete cytokines to enhance the activities of macrophages and other T cells. T_H1 cells activate the action of cyotoxic T cells, as well as macrophages. T_H2 cells stimulate naïve B cells to destroy foreign invaders via antibody secretion. Whether a T_H1 or a T_H2 immune response develops depends on the specific types of cytokines secreted by cells of the innate immune system, which in turn depends on the nature of the invading pathogen.

The T_H1-mediated response involves macrophages and is associated with inflammation. Recall the frontline defenses of macrophages involved in the innate immune response. Some intracellular bacteria, such as *Mycobacterium tuberculosis*, have evolved to multiply in macrophages after they have been engulfed. These pathogens evade attempts by macrophages to destroy and digest the pathogen. When *M. tuberculosis* infection occurs, macrophages can stimulate naïve T cells to become T_H1 cells. These stimulated T cells secrete specific cytokines that send feedback to the macrophage to stimulate its digestive capabilities and allow it to destroy the colonizing *M. tuberculosis*. In the same manner, T_H1-activated macrophages also become better suited to ingest and kill tumor cells. In summary; T_H1 responses are directed toward intracellular invaders while T_H2 responses are aimed at those that are extracellular.

B Lymphocytes

When stimulated by the T_H2 pathway, naïve B cells differentiate into antibody-secreting plasma cells. A **plasma cell** is an immune cell that secrets antibodies; these cells arise from B cells that were stimulated by antigens. Similar to T cells, naïve B cells initially are coated in thousands of B cell receptors (BCRs), which are membrane-bound forms of Ig (immunoglobulin, or an antibody). The B cell receptor has two heavy chains and two light chains connected by disulfide linkages. Each chain has a constant and a variable region; the latter is involved in antigen binding. Two other membrane proteins, Ig alpha and Ig beta, are involved in signaling. The receptors of any particular B cell, as shown in Figure 33.13 are all the same, but the hundreds of millions of different B cells in an individual have distinct recognition domains that contribute to extensive diversity in the types of molecular structures to which they can bind. In this state, B cells function as APCs. They bind and engulf foreign antigens via their BCRs and then display processed antigens in the context of MHC II molecules to T_H2 cells. When a T_H2 cell detects that a B cell is bound to a relevant antigen, it secretes specific cytokines that induce the B cell to proliferate rapidly, which makes thousands of identical (clonal) copies of it, and then it synthesizes and secretes antibodies with the same antigen recognition pattern as the BCRs. The activation of B cells corresponding to one specific BCR variant and the dramatic proliferation of that variant is known as **clonal selection**. This phenomenon drastically, but briefly, changes the proportions of BCR variants expressed by the immune system, and shifts the balance toward BCRs specific to the infecting pathogen.

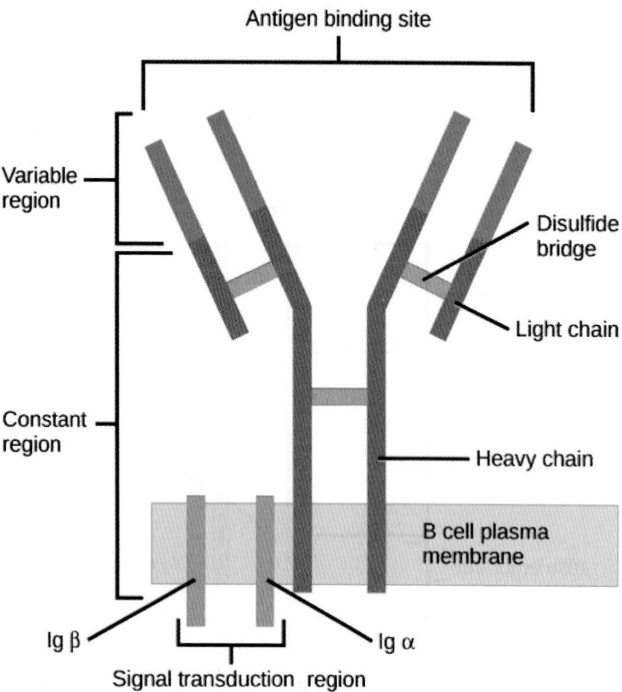

Figure 33.13 B cell receptors are embedded in the membranes of B cells and bind a variety of antigens through their variable regions. The signal transduction region transfers the signal into the cell.

T and B cells differ in one fundamental way: whereas T cells bind antigens that have been digested and embedded in MHC molecules by APCs, B cells function as APCs that bind intact antigens that have not been processed. Although T and B cells both react with molecules that are termed "antigens," these lymphocytes actually respond to very different types of molecules. B cells must be able to bind intact antigens because they secrete antibodies that must recognize the pathogen directly, rather than digested remnants of the pathogen. Bacterial carbohydrate and lipid molecules can activate B cells independently from the T cells.

Cytotoxic T Lymphocytes

CTLs, a subclass of T cells, function to clear infections directly. The cell-mediated part of the adaptive immune system consists of CTLs that attack and destroy infected cells. CTLs are particularly important in protecting against viral infections; this is because viruses replicate within cells where they are shielded from extracellular contact with circulating antibodies. When APCs phagocytize pathogens and present MHC I-embedded antigens to naïve $CD8^+$ T cells that express complementary TCRs, the $CD8^+$ T cells become activated to proliferate according to clonal selection. These resulting CTLs then identify non-APCs displaying the same MHC I-embedded antigens (for example, viral proteins)—for example, the CTLs identify infected host cells.

Intracellularly, infected cells typically die after the infecting pathogen replicates to a sufficient concentration and lyses the cell, as many viruses do. CTLs attempt to identify and destroy infected cells before the pathogen can replicate and escape, thereby halting the progression of intracellular infections. CTLs also support NK lymphocytes to destroy early cancers. Cytokines secreted by the T_H1 response that stimulates macrophages also stimulate CTLs and enhance their ability to identify and destroy infected cells and tumors.

CTLs sense MHC I-embedded antigens by directly interacting with infected cells via their TCRs. Binding of TCRs with antigens activates CTLs to release perforin and granzyme, degradative enzymes that will induce apoptosis of the infected cell. Recall that this is a similar destruction mechanism to that used by NK cells. In this process, the CTL does not become infected and is not harmed by the secretion of perforin and granzymes. In fact, the functions of NK cells and CTLs are complementary and maximize the removal of infected cells, as illustrated in Figure 33.14. If the NK cell cannot identify the "missing self" pattern of down-regulated MHC I molecules, then the CTL can identify it by the complex of MHC I with foreign antigens, which signals "altered self." Similarly, if the CTL cannot detect antigen-embedded MHC I because the receptors are depleted from the cell surface, NK cells will destroy the cell instead. CTLs also emit cytokines, such as interferons, that alter surface protein expression in other infected cells, such that the infected cells can be easily identified and destroyed. Moreover, these interferons can also prevent virally infected cells from releasing virus particles.

visual CONNECTION

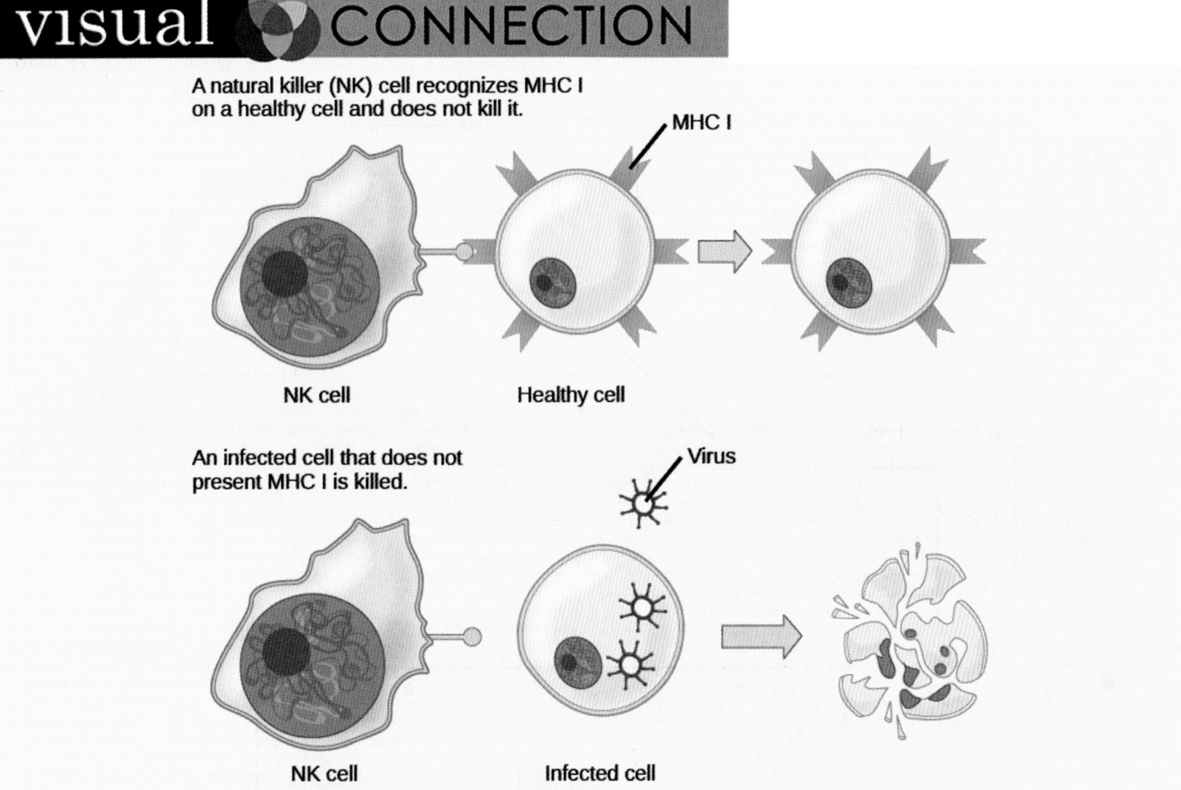

Figure 33.14 Natural killer (NK) cells recognize the MHC I receptor on healthy cells. If MHC I is absent, the cell is lysed.

Based on what you know about MHC receptors, why do you think an organ transplanted from an incompatible donor to a recipient will be rejected?

a. The natural killer cells of the recipient will recognize the MHC II proteins present on the cell surface of incompatible organ as foreign and activate macrophages, which will phagocytose foreign cells. The attack will cause the organ to be rejected.
b. Neutrophils will recognize the proteins on incompatible organ as foreign and will phagocytose the foreign cells of the incompatible organ.
c. The natural killer cells of the recipient will recognize the MHC II proteins present on the cell surface of incompatible organ as foreign and will attack these foreign proteins. The attack will cause the organ to be rejected.
d. The recipient's immune system will recognize the proteins on the incompatible organ as foreign and will attack these foreign proteins. The attack will cause the organ to be rejected.

Plasma cells and CTLs are collectively called **effector cells**: they represent differentiated versions of their naïve counterparts, and they are involved in bringing about the immune defense of killing pathogens and infected host cells.

Mucosal Surfaces and Immune Tolerance

The innate and adaptive immune responses discussed thus far comprise the systemic immune system (affecting the whole body), which is distinct from the mucosal immune system. Mucosal immunity is formed by mucosa-associated lymphoid tissue, which functions independently of the systemic immune system, and which has its own innate and adaptive components. **Mucosa-associated lymphoid tissue (MALT)**, illustrated in Figure 33.15, is a collection of lymphatic tissue that combines with epithelial tissue lining the mucosa throughout the body. This tissue functions as the immune barrier and response in areas of the body with direct contact to the external environment. The systemic and mucosal immune systems use many of the same cell types. Foreign particles that make their way to MALT are taken up by absorptive epithelial cells called M cells and delivered to APCs located directly below the mucosal tissue. M cells function in the transport described, and are located in the Peyer's patch, a lymphoid nodule. APCs of the mucosal immune system are primarily dendritic cells, with B cells and macrophages having minor roles. Processed antigens displayed on APCs are detected by T cells in the MALT and at various mucosal induction sites, such as the tonsils, adenoids, appendix, or the mesenteric lymph nodes of the intestine. Activated T cells then migrate through the lymphatic system and into the circulatory system to mucosal sites of infection.

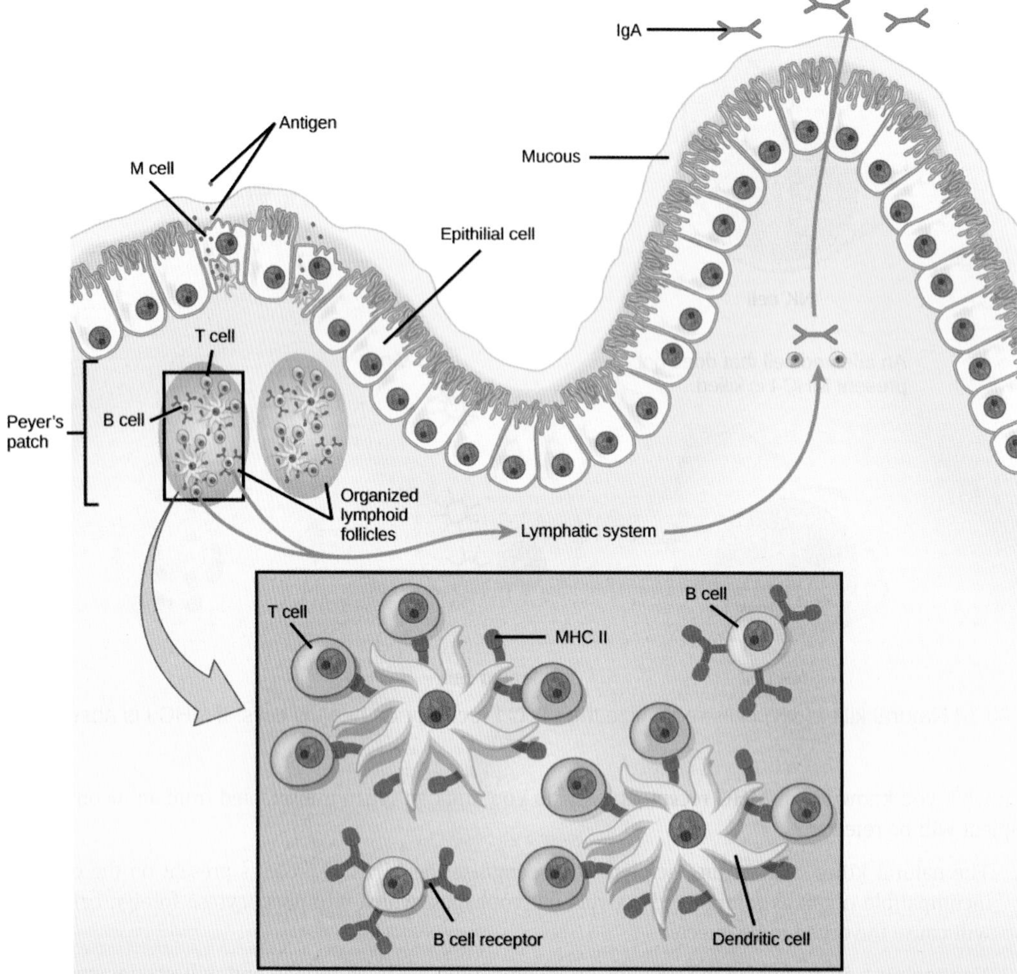

Figure 33.15 The topology and function of intestinal MALT is shown. Pathogens are taken up by M cells in the intestinal epithelium and excreted into a pocket formed by the inner surface of the cell. The pocket contains antigen-presenting cells such as dendritic cells, which engulf the antigens, then present them with MHC II molecules on the cell surface. The dendritic cells migrate to an underlying tissue called a Peyer's patch. Antigen-presenting cells, T cells, and B cells aggregate within the Peyer's patch, forming organized lymphoid follicles. There, some T cells and B cells are activated. Other antigen-loaded dendritic cells migrate through the lymphatic system where they activate B cells, T cells, and plasma cells in the lymph nodes. The activated cells then return to MALT tissue effector sites. IgA and other antibodies are secreted into the intestinal lumen.

MALT is a crucial component of a functional immune system because mucosal surfaces, such as the nasal passages, are the first tissues onto which inhaled or ingested pathogens are deposited. The mucosal tissue includes the mouth, pharynx, and esophagus, and the gastrointestinal, respiratory, and urogenital tracts.

The immune system has to be regulated to prevent wasteful, unnecessary responses to harmless substances, and more importantly so that it does not attack "self." The acquired ability to prevent an unnecessary or harmful immune response to a detected foreign substance known not to cause disease is described as **immune tolerance**. Immune tolerance is crucial for maintaining mucosal homeostasis given the tremendous number of foreign substances (such as food proteins) that APCs of the oral cavity, pharynx, and gastrointestinal mucosa encounter. Immune tolerance is brought about by specialized APCs in the liver, lymph nodes, small intestine, and lung that present harmless antigens to an exceptionally diverse population of **regulatory T (T_{reg}) cells**, specialized lymphocytes that suppress local inflammation and inhibit the secretion of stimulatory immune factors. The combined result of T_{reg} cells is to prevent immunologic activation and inflammation in undesired tissue on climate change?

a. Red List

b. Montreal Protocol

c. International Union for the Conservation of Nature (IUCN)

d. Kyoto Protocol

CRITICAL THINKING QUESTIONS

28. Which factor explains that in general, temperate and polar regions have less biodiversity than tropical regions?

a. The tropical regions are subjected to extreme changes of season.

b. The polar regions were populated earliest in the history of Earth.

c. The polar regions receive more intense solar energy.

d. The tropical regions contain more micro-ecosystems.

29. One method used to calculate contemporary extinction rates is based on the recorded extinction of species in the last 500 years. A second method is a calculation based on the rate of habitat destruction. The construction of a new dam is being projected. A team of conservation biologists is preparing a report on the environmental impact of the dam. Decide which of the two methods should be adopted to estimate the effect of the construction of the extinction rate in the area and analyze the advantages and disadvantages of each method.

a. The extinction rates calculation method should be adopted. It is based on a large number of observations and measurements but overestimates rates of extinction. The rate of habitat destruction calculation method uses species-area curves, but underestimates the rate of extinction.

b. The extinction rates calculation method should be adopted. It is based on a large number of observations and measurements, but overestimates rates of extinction. The rate of habitat destruction calculation method uses species-area curves, but underestimates the rate of extinction.

c. The rate of habitat destruction calculation method should be adopted. The extinction rates calculation method is based on a large number of observations and measurements but overestimates rates of extinction. The rate of habitat destruction calculation method uses species-area curves, but underestimates the rate of extinction.

d. Extinction rates are calculated based on the recorded extinction of species in the past 500 years using data from a large number of observations and measurements. They do not take into account unobserved extinctions and undiscovered species. In this way, the method underestimates rates of extinction. The second method based on the amount of habitat destruction and on species-area curves is more adapted to this situation, although it is not based on existing data and is likely to overestimate the rate of extinction.

30. Analyze the evidence scientists provide for the cause of the Cretaceous–Paleogene mass extinction.

a. the unusual abundance of iridium in the Cretaceous-Paleogene layers, the disappearance of so many species at its transition, volcanic activity that led to global warming, and the crater found in the Yucatan peninsula

b. the unusual abundance of iridium in the Cretaceous-Paleogene layers, gamma-ray burst caused by a nearby supernova, rocks found in the clay layer at its boundary, and the crater found in the Yucatan peninsula

c. the unusual abundance of iridium in the Cretaceous-Paleogene layers, the disappearance of so many species at its transition, rocks found in the clay layer at its boundary, asteroid impact, and volcanic eruptions at large

d. the unusual abundance of iridium in the Cretaceous-Paleogene layers, the disappearance of so many species at its transition, rocks found in the clay layer at its boundary, and the crater found in the Yucatan peninsula

31. The island of Madagascar is located in the tropics 300 miles east of the coast of Africa, from which it separated 165 million years ago. It is characterized by a large number of endemic species. What are the main reasons that Madagascar is a hotspot of endemic biodiversity?

a. Madagascar has a climate that is more conducive to evolution than the larger African continent.

b. Madagascar is close to the tropics of Africa and consequently has a large number of species.

c. Madagascar shows species diversity of both temperate and tropical regions.

d. Madagascar has been isolated geographically and species evolved there without interaction with outside influences.

32. Consider the following examples. The toxicity in the venom from a Brazilian viper (Bothropsjararaca) is due to a sudden, massive drop in blood pressure, which slows down the reaction of a bitten prey. Solutions made from the opium poppy have been used in the past to dull the sensation of pain and induces a sense of wellbeing. How can the effects of these natural compounds be applied to the development of medical treatments?

a. Compounds similar to the snake's active toxin are used routinely as antivirals. Opioids are used as immunomodulators, which modifies an immune response.

b. Compounds similar to the snake's active toxin are used routinely as painkillers. Opioids help in the lowering of blood pressure.

c. Compounds similar to the snake's active toxin are used to treat inflammations. Opioids are used to prevent muscle spasms.

d. Compounds similar to the snake's active toxin are used to lower blood pressure. Opioids are used routinely as painkillers.

33. Phylloxera, a pest related to aphids, destroyed many vineyards in France at the end of the 19th century. The vineyards were restored by grafting old vines on American root stocks, which were resistant to the pest. Using this situation, explain how biodiversity loss can impact crop diversity.

a. Loss of wild species would result in inbreeding depression, as crop varieties must be bred with wild species to remain viable.

b. Loss of biodiversity reduces large-scale monocultures but reinforces genetic homogeneity contributing in the loss of crop diversity.

c. Loss of wild species would result in an increase of intraspecific diversity within the different crop varieties, but decrease in interspecific crop diversity.

d. Loss of wild species would reduce the genetic variations as genes from wild relatives are brought into crop varieties to add valued characteristics to crops.

34. Predict the consequences of the bee colony collapse disorder in a state such as California, which is a large supplier of produce.

a. Only pharmaceutical manufacturing and industries involved in honey production are going to be affected due to this disorder.

b. Other pollinators would replace the bees in the ecosystem and there would probably not be a major impact on the production of produce.

c. Lack of pollinators would affect the honey industry, but not the fruit harvest industry, because other pollinators are present to carry out pollination.

d. The lack of pollinators will affect the fruit harvest directly, and indirectly affect industries linked to it like the honey and jam preparation industries.

35. Many chemical pesticides can be found in the bark and leaves of tropical plants. What is a difference in tropical plants that makes it especially beneficial to produce compounds that kill insects throughout the year?

a. Because plants have to protect themselves year-round, as cold spells in winter do not kill pests as they do in temperate areas.

b. Because the plants must protect themselves from insects as repellants and toxins sprayed by humans do not work in tropical areas.

c. Because the compounds produced to kill insects also enhances the ability of the plant to recover from damage caused by various phenomena.

d. Because compounds produced to kill insects also influence the behavior and growth of tropical plants.

36. Explain how the increase in human population and resource use causes increased extinction rates by altering ecosystems.

a. Human population growth leads to unsustainable resource use, habitat destruction, and the unsustainable fishing and hunting of wild animal populations. All these incidences results in a slow evolutionary rate of formation of new species.

b. Human population growth leads to unsustainable resource use, habitat destruction, and the unsustainable fishing and hunting of wild animal populations. Climate change also occurs due to excessive use of fossil fuels.

c. Human population growth leads to unsustainable resource use, habitat destruction, and unsustainable fishing and hunting of wild animal populations. Excessive use of fossil fuels is leading to reduced populations of fish species.

d. Human population growth leads to unsustainable resource use, habitat destruction, and unsustainable fishing and hunting of wild animal populations. Larger human populations are also leading to decreased value of products obtained from species.

37. As a conservationist, you are preparing a report on a frog population living on a mountainside in Costa Rica. In your report, which potential threats to the survival of the species will you predict taking into account environmental abiotic conditions and human activities?

a. The frog is at risk from climate change, habitat destruction, and aggressive predators.

b. The frog is at risk from climate change, exotic species, and possible habitat destruction.

c. The frog is at risk from climate change, habitat destruction, and sparse availability of food.

d. The frog is at risk from climate change, exotic species, and over-hunting in its habitat.

38. Epidemiologists are predicting that diseases such as West Nile virus infection, dengue fever, and even malaria may expand their range. If the pathogens are viruses or protists, how could they most rapidly expand their range over a large geographic area?

a. through the air

b. through contaminated food and water

c. through direct human contact from increased presence in wilderness areas

d. through vectors such as mosquitoes

39. Explain why the hunting of large, top predators such as sharks or wolves, endanger the entire ecosystems in which they live.

a. The disappearance of top predators results in unrestricted multiplication of producers. Producers will overgraze primary consumers.

b. If a top predator disappears, the primary consumers will multiply without restriction, but producers will not be affected.

c. If a top predator disappears, producers will multiply without restriction.

d. The disappearance of top predators results in unrestricted multiplication of primary consumers. Primary consumers will overgraze producers.

40. The Convention on International Trade in Endangered Species (CITES) passed a resolution to protect rhinoceroses in the wild. Rhinoceroses have been hunted to the brink of extinction because their horns, which are made of simple keratin, are considered an aphrodisiac and a powerful drug in some cultures. Why does the protection of rhinoceroses require an international agreement?

a. The rhinoceroses are hunted in their native countries, but the trade crosses borders.

b. The use of rhinoceros' horns as an aphrodisiac has showed various negative effects internationally.

c. The hunters from different countries travel to the native country to hunt for rhinoceroses.

d. Their demand is greater in foreign countries as compared to their native countries.

41. A preserve design is proposed for a densely populated suburban area. Which overall design plan would be best for preservation of local ecosystems?

a. Set up many, small, protected areas.

b. Select one, small area that is isolated from residences.

c. Plan buffer zones around all backyard spaces.

d. Set up several, larger areas to be set aside for natural ecosystems.

42. Wolves are a keystone species in the Yellowstone National Park. Predict what would happen if they were hunted to extinction.

a. Many species would increase and the elk population would disappear.

b. Many species would disappear and the elk population would increase.

c. Many species along with elk population would increase.

d. Many species, along with the elk population, would disappear.

43. Why have international treaties been rarely enforced so far?

a. Signatory nations follow through with their good intentions. No governing body enforces international environmental protection.

b. Signatory nations do not follow through with their good intentions. A governing body enforces international environmental protection.

c. Signatory nations do not follow through with their good intentions. No governing body enforces international environmental protection.

d. Signatory nations follow through with their good intentions. A governing body enforces international environmental protection, but neither is effective.

TEST PREP FOR AP® COURSES

44.

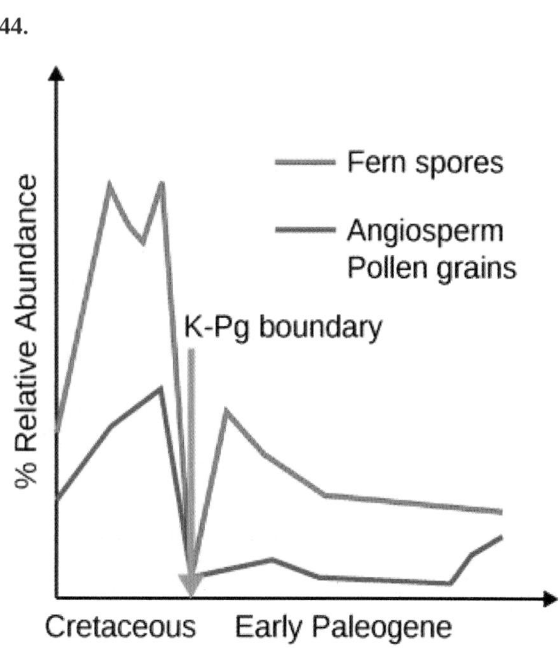

Students analyze pollen grains and fern spores recovered from sediments taken below and above the Cretaceous-Paleogene boundary. Their results are summarized in the graph. Which of the following conclusions can be drawn from the graph regarding the impact of the mass extinction that took place at the K-Pg boundary on plants?

a. The mass extinction event reduced the number of ferns and angiosperms.

b. Based on their reduced pollen counts found in the samples, the mass extinction event clearly reduced the number of ferns and angiosperms.

c. The mass extinction affected only the ferns.

d. Ferns were more abundant after the Cretaceous-Paleogene (K-Pg) mass extinction than before.

45.

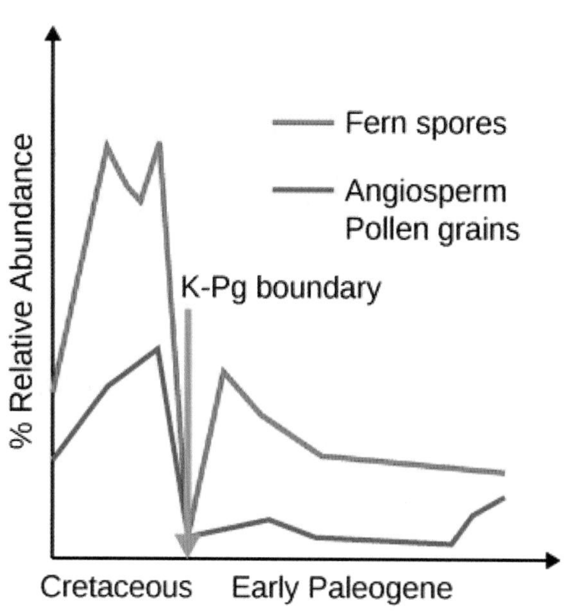

Analyze the graph and discuss the reasons for the fern spike seen in the early Paleogene, considering ferns were the first plants seen on the ground after the volcanic eruption of Krakatoa and Mt. St. Helens. Propose reasons for the observed increase in fern spores following the mass extinction.

a. Ferns are considered early colonizers as they grow fast on poor soil and reproduce rapidly. Also, mass extinction gave an opportunity for the surviving species to expand and radiate to occupy vacated niches.

b. Ferns, having a selective advantage of being early colonizers, grew fast on poor soil and reproduced rapidly, thus replaced angiosperms in the landscape.

c. Ferns are considered early colonizers as they grow fast on poor soil and reproduce rapidly. Also, mass extinction gave an opportunity for new species to radiate and thereby occupy vacated niches.

d. Most of the fern varieties became extinct, only a single species survived; therefore, the remaining fern spores had many vacated niches to occupy which lead to an increase in fern numbers.

46.

Mass Extinction	Time of Extinction (millions of years ago)	Organisms Greatly Reduced or Made Extinct
End of the Ordovician period	443	Trilobites Brachiopods Echinoderms Corals
End of the Devonian period	354	Marine families on tropical reefs Corals Brachiopods Bivalves
End of the Permian period	248	Trilobites Mollusks Brachiopods Many vertebrates
End of the Triassic period	206	Mollusks Sponges Marine vertebrates Large amphibians
End of the Cretaceous period	65	Ammonites Dinosaurs Brachiopods Bivalves Echinoderms

A group of students summarized information on five great extinction events.The students are sampling a site in search of fossils from the Devonian period. Based on the chart, which of the following would be the most reasonable plan for the students to follow?

a. Searching horizontally rock layers in any class of rock and trying to find those that contain the greatest number of fossils.

b. Collecting fossils from rock layers deposited prior to the Permian period that contain some early vertebrate bones.

c. Looking in sedimentary layers next to bodies of water in order to find marine fossils of bivalves and trilobites

d. Using relative dating techniques to determine the geological ages of the fossils so they can calculate the rate of speciation of early organisms.

47.

	Average Number of Grains/m^2	Morphology
Below Cretaceous-Paleogene	102	Many different shapes
Above Cretaceous-Paleogene	30	A few common shapes

Students are sorting fossils of angiosperm pollen grains, some recovered from layers below the Cretaceous-Paleogene boundary and some from layers above the Cretaceous-Paleogene boundaries. The pollen grains are sorted by morphology.

The results are summarized in a table.

Can you explain the results?

a. The mass extinction that took place at the Cretaceous-Paleogene boundaries reduced the total number of organisms, seen by fewer shapes of pollen grains, and led to a loss of diversity, seen by the less number.

b. The mass extinction that took place at the Cretaceous-Paleogene boundaries reduced the total number of organisms, seen by less number of pollen grains, and led to a loss of diversity, seen by fewer shapes.

c. The mass extinction that took place at the Cretaceous-Paleogene boundaries reduced the total number of organisms, seen by less number of pollen grains.

d. The mass extinction that took place at the Cretaceous-Paleogene boundaries led to a loss of diversity, seen by fewer shapes of pollen grains.

48.

Mass Extinction	Time of Extinction (millions of years ago)	Organisms Greatly Reduced or Made Extinct
End of the Ordovician period	443	Trilobites Brachiopods Echinoderms Corals
End of the Devonian period	354	Marine families on tropical reefs Corals Brachiopods Bivalves
End of the Permian period	248	Trilobites Mollusks Brachiopods Many vertebrates
End of the Triassic period	206	Mollusks Sponges Marine vertebrates Large amphibians
End of the Cretaceous period	65	Ammonites Dinosaurs Brachiopods Bivalves Echinoderms

A dig in a farmland soil rich in calcium carbonate reveals the following findings: 1. Numerous shells of bivalves 2. Chips of corals 3. The partial imprint of a trilobite 4. A few vertebrae dated to 250 million years ago. The table of extinction summarizes information on the five major extinction events.

According to the table of extinction, which conclusion about the fossils is most reasonable?

a. The trilobites were the first animals to conquer land.

b. The rocks can be dated to the Cretaceous Cretaceous-Paleogene boundary.

c. The farmland was probably part of the seafloor in the Permian period

d. The fossils can be dated to the Ordovician period.

49.

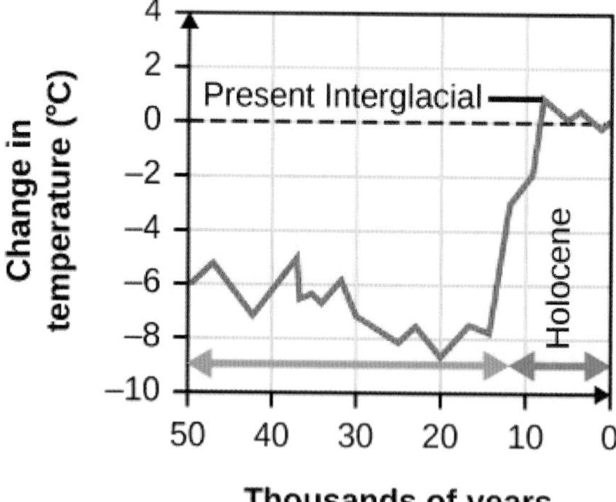

The average temperatures varied during the Pleistocene as glaciation periods were followed by warm intervals. Using the graph above and your existing knowledge, discuss what happened to woolly mammoths and other cold-adapted megafauna 10,000 years ago.

a. Habitat destruction due to varying temperatures and over-hunting by humans leading to their extinction.

b. Sudden increase in temperature and over-hunting by humans leading to their extinction.

c. Gradual increase in temperature and over-hunting by humans leading to their extinction.

d. Sudden increase in temperature and in predation by larger mammals leading to their extinction.

50.

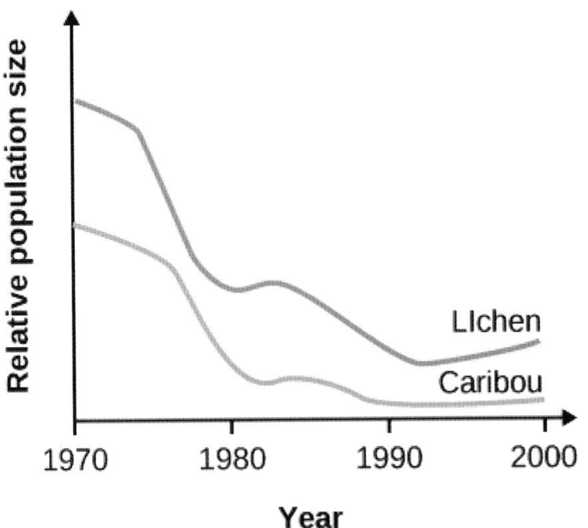

In winter, lichens are the only food for the caribou herds that roam the tundra. As the average temperatures increase with climate change, the lichen are gradually being replaced by shrubs and trees in the southern parts of the tundra. The graph illustrates the changes in abundance of lichens and caribou over time in a regional forest of Canada.Which statement best explains the changes in the caribou population between 1975 and 1980?

a. The caribou population expanded after the population of lichens dropped.
b. The decline of the caribou population and the lichen population are not related.
c. The population of caribou decreased following the drop in lichen availability.
d. The caribou population was eliminated once the lichens decreased.

51. A chain within the food web in the arctic ocean is shown below:

Phytoplankton —> zooplankton —> arctic char/cod —> ringed seal—> polar bear. A chain within the arctic food web on land is shown below: Lichen/shrub —> Caribou/hare/small rodent —> fox/lynx/bird of prey

If polar bears move to land to hunt due to loss of sea ice, what will happen to the balance of the food web?

a. Polar bears, being top predators, will edge out the other consumers without gaining enough calories themselves.
b. Polar bears, being secondary consumers, will edge out the other consumers without gaining enough calories themselves.
c. Polar bears, being top predators, will edge out the producers without gaining enough calories themselves.
d. Polar bears, being secondary consumers, will edge out the producers without gaining enough calories themselves.

52.

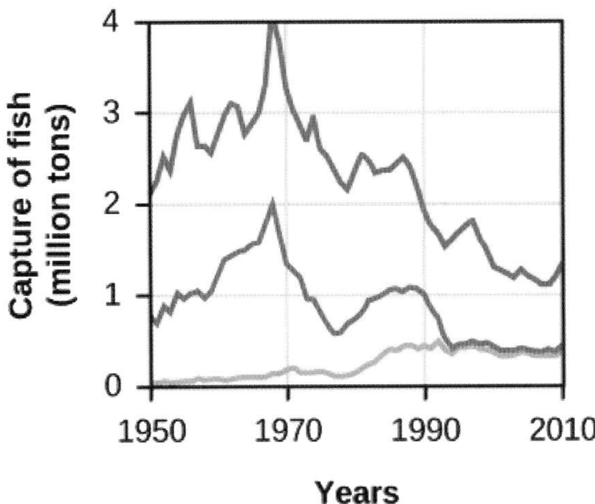

Historically, the Atlantic Ocean off Canada and the Northeast of the US has been some of the richest and most popular fishing grounds. Huge factory ships developed in the 1960's converged on the region from all over the world attracted by the rich catches. The graph shown represents the population of cod in recent years. Based on the graph, what is the likely explanation for the collapse of the northwest cod?

a. A tropical disease decimated the populations of cod.
b. Overfishing led to the collapse of the cod population.
c. The cod population migrated somewhere else.
d. The cod population is going through its cycle of rise and fall.

53.

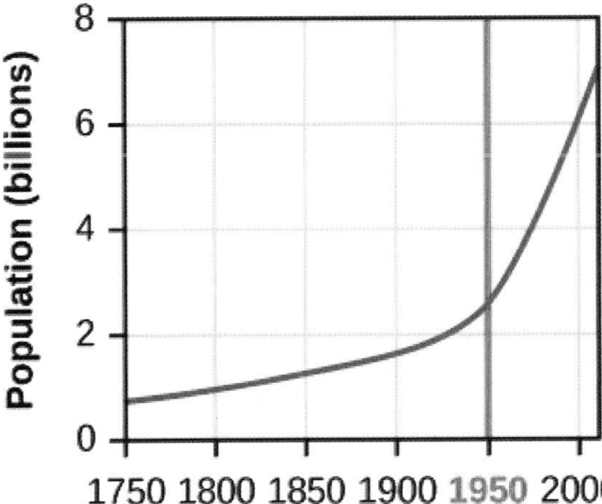

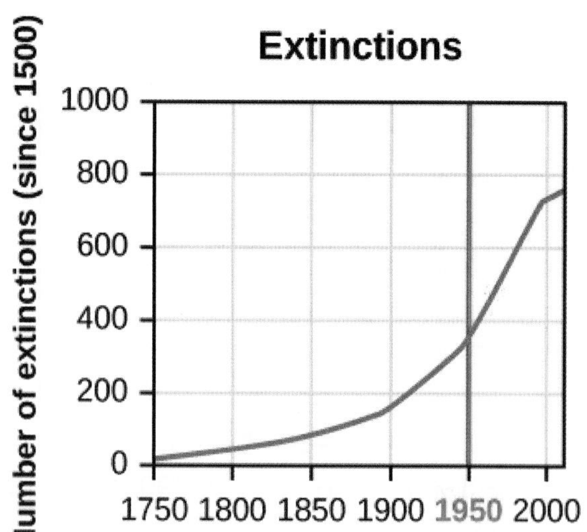

The following graphs show the changes in the human population and the rate of extinction:Which statement most likely explains how the increase in human population could lead to a decrease in biodiversity?

a. Every human added to the planet replaces a different species of organism.
b. The more people inhabiting the planet, the more the average temperature increases, causing loss of other species.
c. With the increase in population the demands for land, water, food, and energy increase, leading to the destruction of habitat.
d. Increases in human population reduce the amount of land available for use by all species.

APPENDIX A | THE PERIODIC TABLE OF ELEMENTS

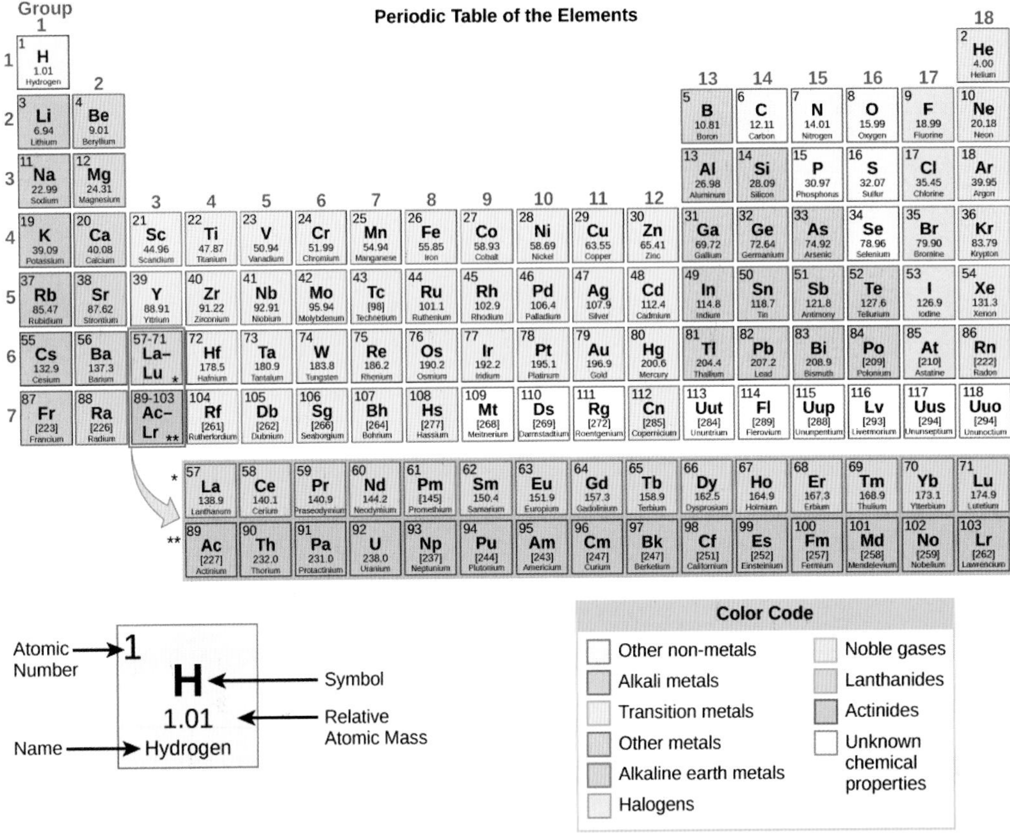

Figure A1

APPENDIX B | GEOLOGICAL TIME

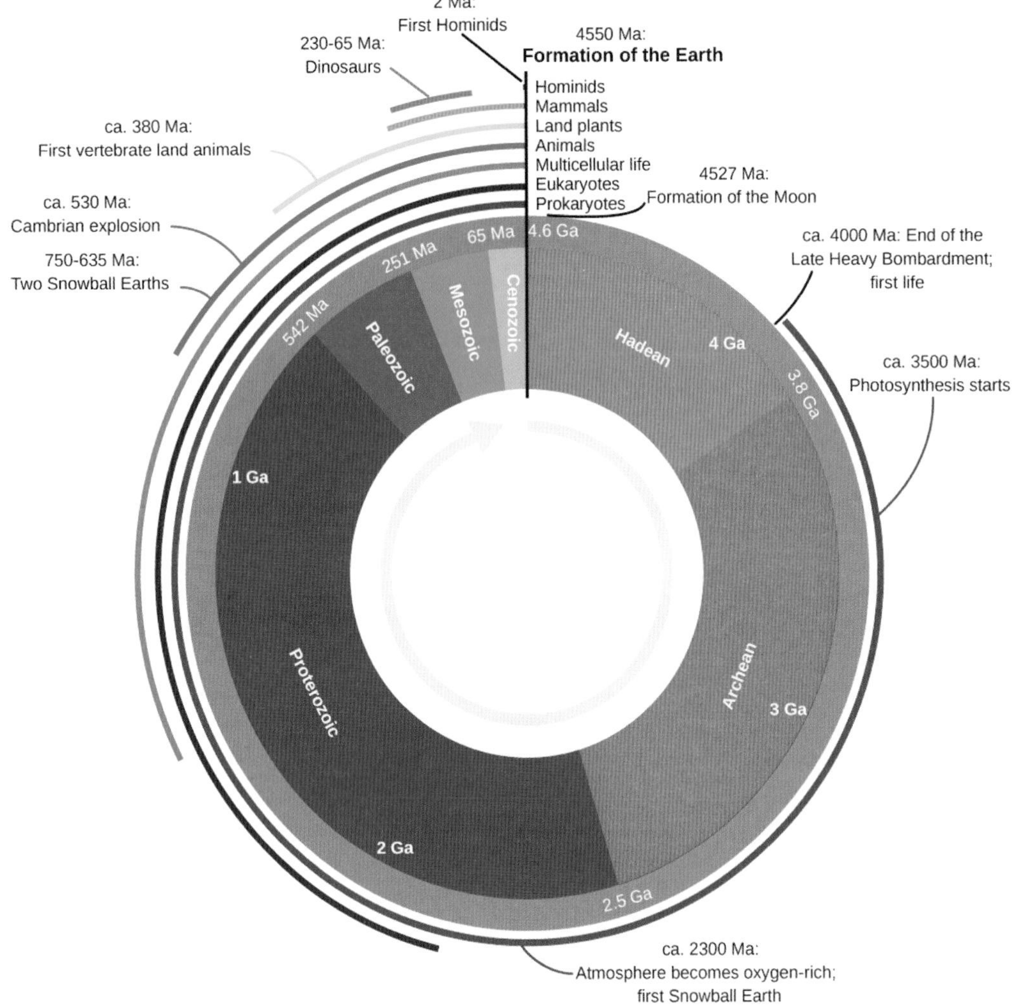

Figure B1 Geological Time Clock

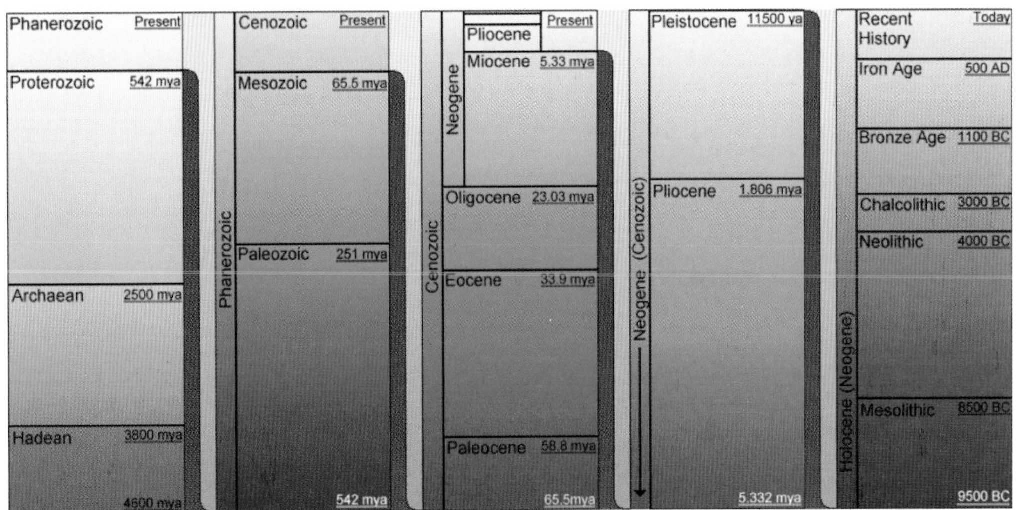

Figure B2 Geological Time Chart
(credit: Richard S. Murphy, Jr.)

APPENDIX C | MEASUREMENTS AND THE METRIC SYSTEM

Measurements and the Metric System

<table>
<tr><th>Measurement</th><th>Unit</th><th>Abbreviation</th><th>Metric Equivalent</th><th>Approximate Standard Equivalent</th></tr>
<tr><td rowspan="6">Length</td><td>nanometer</td><td>nm</td><td>1 nm = 10^{-9} m</td><td rowspan="6">1 mm = 0.039 inch
1 cm = 0.394 inch
1 m = 39.37 inches
1 m = 3.28 feet
1 m = 1.093 yards
1 km = 0.621 miles</td></tr>
<tr><td>micrometer</td><td>µm</td><td>1 µm = 10^{-6} m</td></tr>
<tr><td>millimeter</td><td>mm</td><td>1 mm = 0.001 m</td></tr>
<tr><td>centimeter</td><td>cm</td><td>1 cm = 0.01 m</td></tr>
<tr><td>meter</td><td>m</td><td>1 m = 100 cm
1 m = 1000 mm</td></tr>
<tr><td>kilometer</td><td>km</td><td>1 km = 1000 m</td></tr>
<tr><td rowspan="4">Mass</td><td>microgram</td><td>µg</td><td>1 µg = 10^{-6} g</td><td rowspan="4">1 g = 0.035 ounce
1 kg = 2.205 pounds</td></tr>
<tr><td>milligram</td><td>mg</td><td>1 mg = 10^{-3} g</td></tr>
<tr><td>gram</td><td>g</td><td>1 g = 1000 mg</td></tr>
<tr><td>kilogram</td><td>kg</td><td>1 kg = 1000 g</td></tr>
<tr><td rowspan="4">Volume</td><td>microliter</td><td>µl</td><td>1 µl = 10^{-6} l</td><td rowspan="4">1 ml = 0.034 fluid ounce
1 l = 1.057 quarts
1 kl = 264.172 gallons</td></tr>
<tr><td>milliliter</td><td>ml</td><td>1 ml = 10^{-3} l</td></tr>
<tr><td>liter</td><td>l</td><td>1 l = 1000 ml</td></tr>
<tr><td>kiloliter</td><td>kl</td><td>1 kl = 1000 l</td></tr>
<tr><td rowspan="3">Area</td><td>square centimeter</td><td>cm^2</td><td>1 cm^2 = 100 mm^2</td><td rowspan="3">1 cm^2 = 0.155 square inch
1 m^2 = 10.764 square feet
1 m^2 = 1.196 square yards
1 ha = 2.471 acres</td></tr>
<tr><td>square meter</td><td>m^2</td><td>1 m^2 = 10,000 cm^2</td></tr>
<tr><td>hectare</td><td>ha</td><td>1 ha = 10,000 m^2</td></tr>
<tr><td>Temperature</td><td>Celsius</td><td>°C</td><td>—</td><td>1 °C = 5/9 × (°F − 32)</td></tr>
</table>

Table C1

INDEX

Symbols

A

B

C

D

E

F

G

H

I

J

K

L

M

N

O

P

T

U

V

W

X

Z

compartments and to allow the immune system to focus on pathogens instead. In addition to promoting immune tolerance of harmless antigens, other subsets of T_{reg} cells are involved in the prevention of the **autoimmune response**, which is an inappropriate immune response to host cells or self-antigens. Another T_{reg} class suppresses immune responses to harmful pathogens after the infection has cleared to minimize host cell damage induced by inflammation and cell lysis.

Immunological Memory

The adaptive immune system possesses a memory component that allows for an efficient and dramatic response upon reinvasion of the same pathogen. Memory is handled by the adaptive immune system with little reliance on cues from the innate response. During the adaptive immune response to a pathogen that has not been encountered before, called a primary response, plasma cells secreting antibodies and differentiated T cells increase, then plateau over time. As B and T cells mature into effector cells, a subset of the naïve populations differentiates into B and T memory cells with the same antigen specificities, as illustrated in Figure 33.16.

A **memory cell** is an antigen-specific B or T lymphocyte that does not differentiate into effector cells during the primary immune response, but that can immediately become effector cells upon re-exposure to the same pathogen. During the primary immune response, memory cells do not respond to antigens and do not contribute to host defenses. As the infection is cleared and pathogenic stimuli subside, the effectors are no longer needed, and they undergo apoptosis. In contrast, the memory cells persist in the circulation.

visual CONNECTION

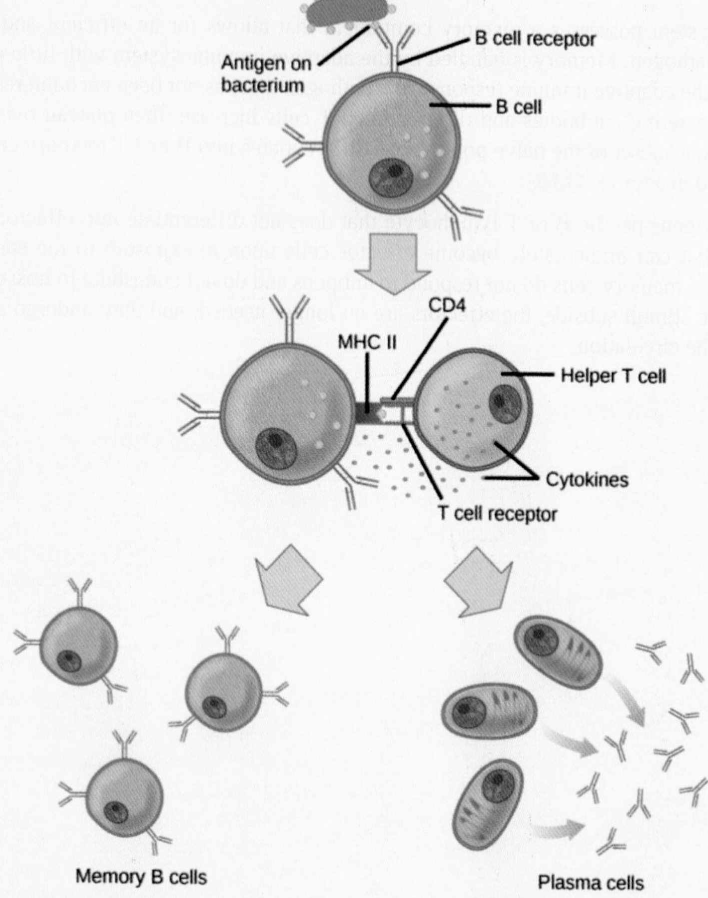

Figure 33.16 After initially binding an antigen to the B cell receptor (BCR), a B cell internalizes the antigen and presents it on MHC II. A helper T cell recognizes the MHC II–antigen complex and activates the B cell. As a result, memory B cells and plasma cells are made.

Why are both plasma B cells and memory B cells made when helper T cells activate B cells?

a. Plasma B cells produce antibodies to fight against pathogen. Memory B cells retain the information about this particular pathogen so that during the subsequent exposure to the same pathogen, a stronger response can be generated.

b. Plasma B cells phagocytose the pathogen. Memory B cells retain the information about this particular pathogen so that during the subsequent exposure to the same pathogen, a stronger response can be generated.

c. Plasma B cells produce antibodies to fight against a pathogen. Memory B cells retain the information about this particular pathogen so that during the subsequent exposure to the same pathogen, a stronger response can be generated, but antibodies are not produced.

d. Plasma B cells produces some cytokines that allows memory B cells to recognize the pathogen and produce antibodies to fight against the pathogen.

If the pathogen is never encountered again during the individual's lifetime, B and T memory cells will circulate for a few years or even several decades and will gradually die off, having never functioned as effector cells. However, if the host is re-exposed to the same pathogen type, circulating memory cells will immediately differentiate into plasma cells and CTLs without input from APCs or T_H cells. One reason the adaptive immune response is delayed is because it takes time for naïve

B and T cells with the appropriate antigen specificities to be identified and activated. Upon reinfection, this step is skipped, and the result is a more rapid production of immune defenses. Memory B cells that differentiate into plasma cells output tens to hundreds-fold greater antibody amounts than were secreted during the primary response, as the graph in **Figure 33.17** illustrates. This rapid and dramatic antibody response may stop the infection before it can even become established, and the individual may not realize they had been exposed.

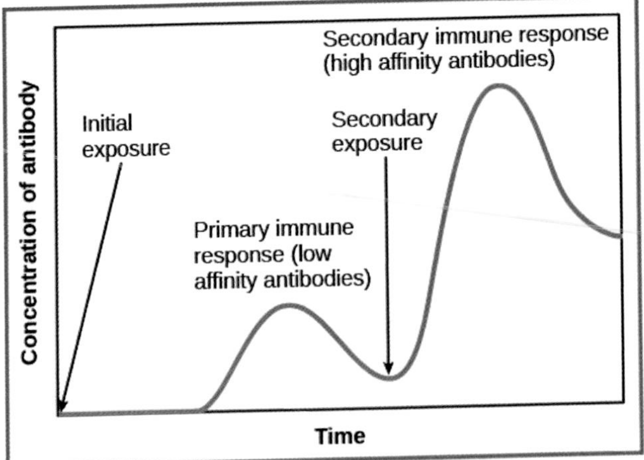

Figure 33.17 In the primary response to infection, antibodies are secreted first from plasma cells. Upon re-exposure to the same pathogen, memory cells differentiate into antibody-secreting plasma cells that output a greater amount of antibody for a longer period of time.

Vaccination is based on the knowledge that exposure to noninfectious antigens, derived from known pathogens, generates a mild primary immune response. The immune response to vaccination may not be perceived by the host as illness but still confers immune memory. When exposed to the corresponding pathogen to which an individual was vaccinated, the reaction is similar to a secondary exposure. Because each reinfection generates more memory cells and increased resistance to the pathogen, and because some memory cells die, certain vaccine courses involve one or more booster vaccinations to mimic repeat exposures: for instance, tetanus boosters are necessary every ten years because the memory cells only live that long.

Mucosal Immune Memory

A subset of T and B cells of the mucosal immune system differentiates into memory cells just as in the systemic immune system. Upon reinvasion of the same pathogen type, a pronounced immune response occurs at the mucosal site where the original pathogen deposited, but a collective defense is also organized within interconnected or adjacent mucosal tissue. For instance, the immune memory of an infection in the oral cavity would also elicit a response in the pharynx if the oral cavity was exposed to the same pathogen.

career CONNECTION

Vaccinologist

Vaccination (or immunization) involves the delivery, usually by injection as shown in **Figure 33.18**, of noninfectious antigen(s) derived from known pathogens. Other components, called adjuvants, are delivered in parallel to help stimulate the immune response. Immunological memory is the reason vaccines work. Ideally, the effect of vaccination is to elicit immunological memory, and thus resistance to specific pathogens without the individual having to experience an infection.

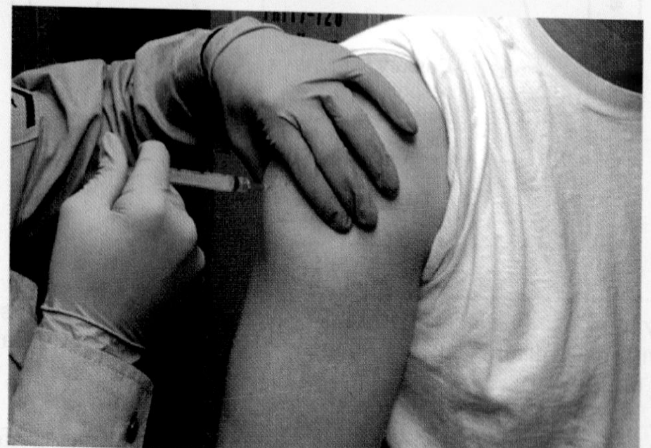

Figure 33.18 Vaccines are often delivered by injection into the arm. (credit: U.S. Navy Photographer's Mate Airman Apprentice Christopher D. Blachly)

Vaccinologists are involved in the process of vaccine development from the initial idea to the availability of the completed vaccine. This process can take decades, can cost millions of dollars, and can involve many obstacles along the way. For instance, injected vaccines stimulate the systemic immune system, eliciting humoral and cell-mediated immunity, but have little effect on the mucosal response, which presents a challenge because many pathogens are deposited and replicate in mucosal compartments, and the injection does not provide the most efficient immune memory for these disease agents. For this reason, vaccinologists are actively involved in developing new vaccines that are applied via intranasal, aerosol, oral, or transcutaneous (absorbed through the skin) delivery methods. Importantly, mucosal-administered vaccines elicit both mucosal and systemic immunity and produce the same level of disease resistance as injected vaccines.

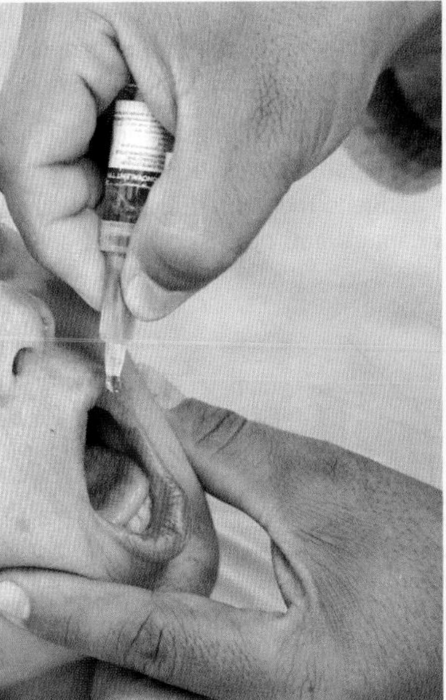

Figure 33.19 The polio vaccine can be administered orally. (credit: modification of work by UNICEF Sverige)

Currently, a version of intranasal influenza vaccine is available, and the polio and typhoid vaccines can be administered orally, as shown in Figure 33.19. Similarly, the measles and rubella vaccines are being adapted to aerosol delivery using inhalation devices. Eventually, transgenic plants may be engineered to produce vaccine antigens that can be eaten to confer disease resistance. Other vaccines may be adapted to rectal or vaginal application to elicit immune responses in rectal, genitourinary, or reproductive mucosa. Finally, vaccine antigens may be adapted to transdermal application in which the skin is lightly scraped and microneedles are used to pierce the outermost layer. In addition to mobilizing the mucosal immune response, this new generation of vaccines may end the anxiety associated with injections and, in turn, improve patient participation.

science practices CONNECTION for AP® Courses

Activity

Construct a diagram to illustrate how T cells and B cells differ from each other with respect to the antigens that they bind.

Think About It

Why is it advantageous to be able to mount a faster immune response upon re-exposure to the same pathogen? How does the immune system accomplish this response?

Primary Centers of the Immune System

Although the immune system is characterized by circulating cells throughout the body, the regulation, maturation, and intercommunication of immune factors occur at specific sites. The blood circulates immune cells, proteins, and other factors through the body. Approximately 0.1 percent of all cells in the blood are leukocytes, which encompass monocytes (the precursor of macrophages) and lymphocytes. The majority of cells in the blood are erythrocytes (red blood cells). **Lymph** is a watery fluid that bathes tissues and organs with protective white blood cells and does not contain erythrocytes. Cells of the immune system can travel between the distinct lymphatic and blood circulatory systems, which are separated by interstitial space, by a process called extravasation (passing through to surrounding tissue).

The cells of the immune system originate from hematopoietic stem cells in the bone marrow. Cytokines stimulate these stem cells to differentiate into immune cells. B cell maturation occurs in the bone marrow, whereas naïve T cells transit from the bone marrow to the thymus for maturation. In the thymus, immature T cells that express TCRs complementary to self-antigens are destroyed. This process helps prevent autoimmune responses.

On maturation, T and B lymphocytes circulate to various destinations. Lymph nodes scattered throughout the body, as illustrated in Figure 33.20, house large populations of T and B cells, dendritic cells, and macrophages. Lymph gathers antigens as it drains from tissues. These antigens then are filtered through lymph nodes before the lymph is returned to circulation. APCs in the lymph nodes capture and process antigens and inform nearby lymphocytes about potential pathogens.

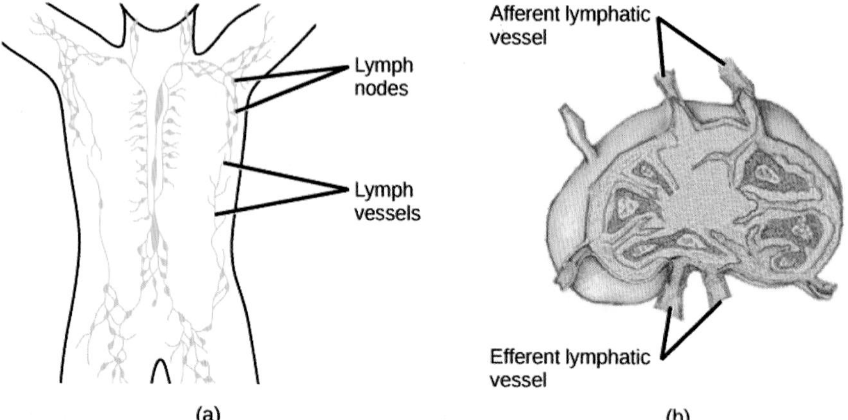

Figure 33.20 (a) Lymphatic vessels carry a clear fluid called lymph throughout the body. The liquid enters (b) lymph nodes through afferent vessels. Lymph nodes are filled with lymphocytes that purge infecting cells. The lymph then exits through efferent vessels. (credit: modification of work by NIH, NCI)

The spleen houses B and T cells, macrophages, dendritic cells, and NK cells. The spleen, shown in Figure 33.21, is the site where APCs that have trapped foreign particles in the blood can communicate with lymphocytes. Antibodies are synthesized and secreted by activated plasma cells in the spleen, and the spleen filters foreign substances and antibody-complexed pathogens from the blood. Functionally, the spleen is to the blood as lymph nodes are to the lymph.

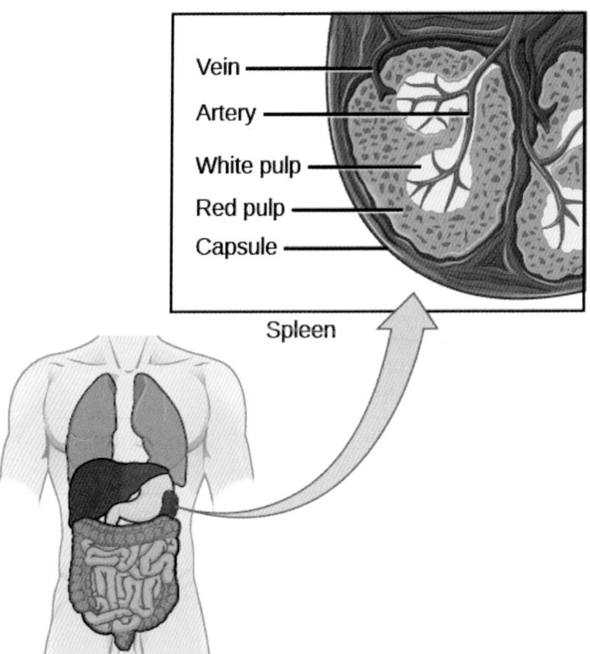

Figure 33.21 The spleen is similar to a lymph node but is much larger and filters blood instead of lymph. Blood enters the spleen through arteries and exits through veins. The spleen contains two types of tissue: red pulp and white pulp. Red pulp consists of cavities that store blood. Within the red pulp, damaged red blood cells are removed and replaced by new ones. White pulp is rich in lymphocytes that remove antigen-coated bacteria from the blood. (credit: modification of work by NCI)

33.3 | Antibodies

In this section, you will explore the following questions:

- What is cross-reactivity?
- What is the basic structure of an antibody, and what are the functions of antibodies?
- How are antibodies produced?

Connection for AP® Courses

Much of the information in this section is not within the scope for AP®. **Antibodies**, also known as immunoglobulins, are proteins produced and secreted by plasma cells (differentiated B lymphocytes) that mediate the humoral immune response. Antibodies are Y-shaped proteins consisting of four polypeptides with at least two binding sites for a specific antigen. The areas where the antigen is recognized on the antibody are variable domains. For AP®, you do not need to know the different classes of antibodies or the molecular structure of a specific antibody. What is important to understand is that antibodies are antigen-specific. When antibodies bind antigens, they can neutralize pathogens, mark them for phagocytosis, or activate the complement cascade. Because secreted antibodies can remain in the circulation for many years, secondary exposure to a pathogen results in a faster immune response. Antibodies occur in the blood, in gastric and mucus secretions, and in breast milk, thus providing passive immunity to the infant.

Information presented and the examples highlighted in the section support concepts outlined in Big Idea 2 and Big Idea 4 of the AP® Biology Curriculum Framework. The AP® Learning Objectives listed in the Curriculum Framework provide a transparent foundation for the AP® Biology course, an inquiry-based laboratory experience, instructional activities, and AP® exam questions. A learning objective merges required content with one or more of the seven science practices.

Big Idea 2	Biological systems utilize free energy and molecular building blocks to grow, to reproduce, and to maintain dynamic homeostasis.
Enduring Understanding 2.D	Growth and dynamic homeostasis of a biological system are influenced by changes in the system's environment.
Essential Knowledge	**2.D.4** Plants and animals have a variety of chemical defenses against infections that affect dynamic homeostasis.
Science Practice	**1.1** The student can create representations and models of natural or man-made phenomena and systems in the domain.
Science Practice	**1.2** The student can describe representations and models of natural or man-made phenomena and systems in the domain.
Learning Objective	**2.30** The student can create representations or models to describe nonspecific immune defenses in animals.
Big Idea 4	Biological systems interact, and these systems and their interactions possess complex properties.
Enduring Understanding 4.C	Naturally occurring diversity among and between components within biological systems affects interactions with the environment.
Essential Knowledge	**4.C.1** Variation in molecular units provides cells with a wider range of functions.
Science Practice	**6.2** The student can construct explanations of phenomena based on evidence produced through scientific practices.
Learning Objective	**4.22** The student is able to construct explanations based on evidence of how variation in molecular units provides cells with a wider range of functions.

Antibody Structure

An antibody molecule is comprised of four polypeptides: two identical heavy chains (large peptide units) that are partially bound to each other in a "Y" formation, which are flanked by two identical light chains (small peptide units), as illustrated in Figure 33.22. Bonds between the cysteine amino acids in the antibody molecule attach the polypeptides to each other. The areas where the antigen is recognized on the antibody are variable domains and the antibody base is composed of constant domains.

In germ-line B cells, the variable region of the light chain gene has 40 variable (V) and five joining (J) segments. An enzyme called DNA recombinase randomly excises most of these segments out of the gene, and splices one V segment to one J segment. During RNA processing, all but one V and J segment are spliced out. Recombination and splicing may result in over 10^6 possible VJ combinations. As a result, each differentiated B cell in the human body typically has a unique variable chain. The constant domain, which does not bind antibody, is the same for all antibodies.

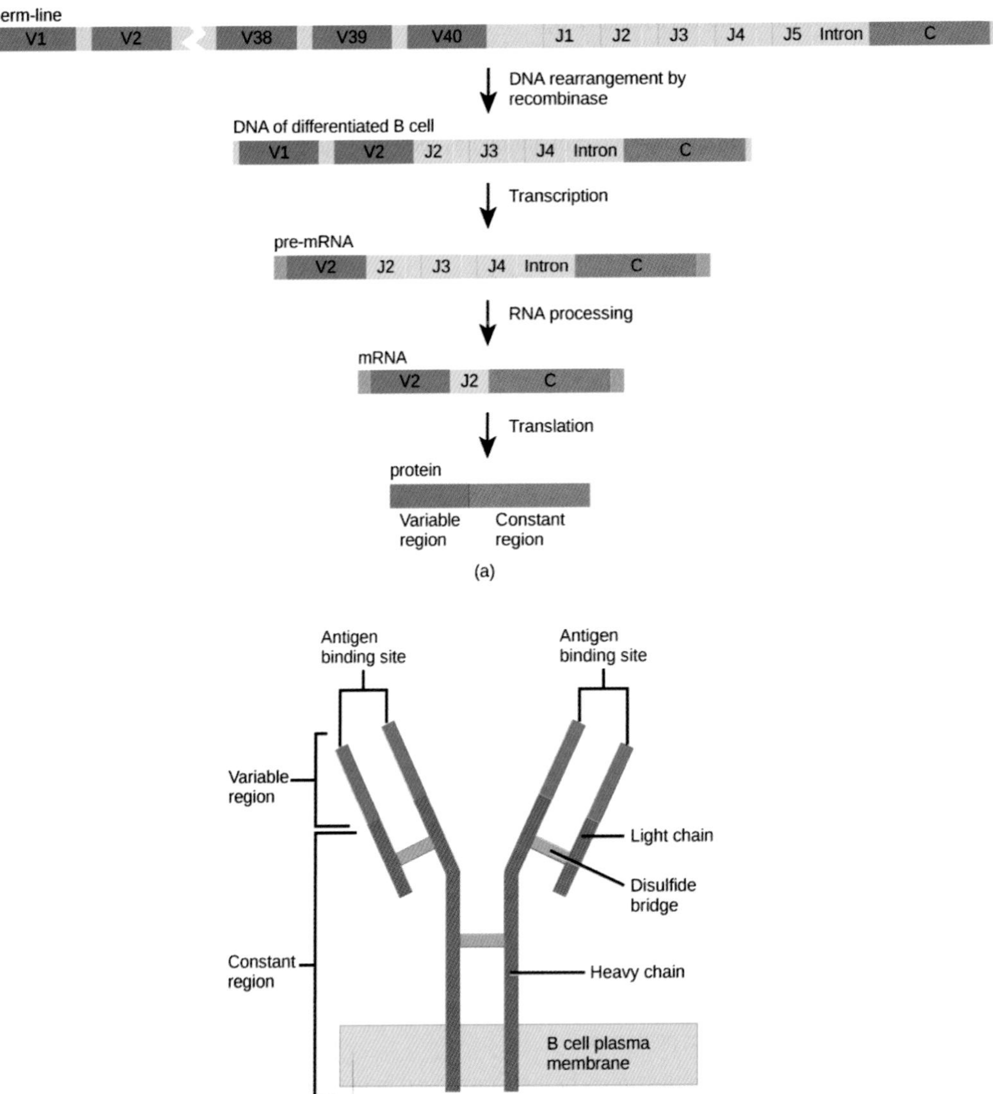

Figure 33.22 (a) As a germ-line B cell matures, an enzyme called DNA recombinase randomly excises V and J segments from the light chain gene. Splicing at the mRNA level results in further gene rearrangement. As a result, (b) each antibody has a unique variable region capable of binding a different antigen.

Similar to TCRs and BCRs, antibody diversity is produced by the mutation and recombination of approximately 300 different gene segments encoding the light and heavy chain variable domains in precursor cells that are destined to become B cells. The variable domains from the heavy and light chains interact to form the binding site through which an antibody can bind a specific epitope on an antigen. The numbers of repeated constant domains in Ig classes are the same for all antibodies corresponding to a specific class. Antibodies are structurally similar to the extracellular component of the BCRs, and B cell maturation to plasma cells can be visualized in simple terms as the cell acquires the ability to secrete the extracellular portion of its BCR in large quantities.

Antibody Classes

Antibodies can be divided into five classes—IgM, IgG, IgA, IgD, IgE—based on their physiochemical, structural, and immunological properties. IgGs, which make up about 80 percent of all antibodies, have heavy chains that consist of one variable domain and three identical constant domains. IgA and IgD also have three constant domains per heavy chain, whereas IgM and IgE each have four constant domains per heavy chain. The variable domain determines binding specificity and the constant domain of the heavy chain determines the immunological mechanism of action of the corresponding antibody class. It is possible for two antibodies to have the same binding specificities but be in different classes and, therefore, to be involved in different functions.

After an adaptive defense is produced against a pathogen, typically plasma cells first secrete IgM into the blood. BCRs on naïve B cells are of the IgM class and occasionally IgD class. IgM molecules make up approximately ten percent of all antibodies. Prior to antibody secretion, plasma cells assemble IgM molecules into pentamers (five individual antibodies) linked by a joining (J) chain, as shown in Figure 33.23. The pentamer arrangement means that these macromolecules can bind ten identical antigens. However, IgM molecules released early in the adaptive immune response do not bind to antigens as stably as IgGs, which are one of the possible types of antibodies secreted in large quantities upon re-exposure to the same pathogen. Figure 33.23 summarizes the properties of immunoglobulins and illustrates their basic structures.

Name	Properties	Structure
IgA	Found in mucous, saliva, tears, and breast milk. Protects against pathogens.	
IgD	Part of the B cell receptor. Activates basophils and mast cells.	
IgE	Protects against parasitic worms. Responsible for allergic reactions.	
IgG	Secreted by plasma cells in the blood. Able to cross the placenta into the fetus.	
IgM	May be attached to the surface of a B cell or secreted into the blood. Responsible for early stages of immunity.	

Figure 33.23 Immunoglobulins have different functions, but all are composed of light and heavy chains that form a Y-shaped structure.

IgAs populate the saliva, tears, breast milk, and mucus secretions of the gastrointestinal, respiratory, and genitourinary tracts. Collectively, these bodily fluids coat and protect the extensive mucosa (4000 square feet in humans). The total number of IgA molecules in these bodily secretions is greater than the number of IgG molecules in the blood serum. A small amount of IgA is also secreted into the serum in monomeric form. Conversely, some IgM is secreted into bodily fluids of the mucosa. Similar to IgM, IgA molecules are secreted as polymeric structures linked with a J chain. However, IgAs are secreted mostly as dimeric molecules, not pentamers.

IgE is present in the serum in small quantities and is best characterized in its role as an allergy mediator. IgD is also present in small quantities. Similar to IgM, BCRs of the IgD class are found on the surface of naïve B cells. This class supports antigen recognition and maturation of B cells to plasma cells.

Antibody Functions

Differentiated plasma cells are crucial players in the humoral response, and the antibodies they secrete are particularly significant against extracellular pathogens and toxins. Antibodies circulate freely and act independently of plasma cells. Antibodies can be transferred from one individual to another to temporarily protect against infectious disease. For instance, a person who has recently produced a successful immune response against a particular disease agent can donate blood to a nonimmune recipient and confer temporary immunity through antibodies in the donor's blood serum. This phenomenon is called **passive immunity**; it also occurs naturally during breastfeeding, which makes breastfed infants highly resistant to infections during the first few months of life.

Antibodies coat extracellular pathogens and neutralize them, as illustrated in Figure 33.24, by blocking key sites on the pathogen that enhance their infectivity (such as receptors that "dock" pathogens on host cells). Antibody neutralization can prevent pathogens from entering and infecting host cells, as opposed to the CTL-mediated approach of killing cells that are already infected to prevent progression of an established infection. The neutralized antibody-coated pathogens can then be filtered by the spleen and eliminated in urine or feces.

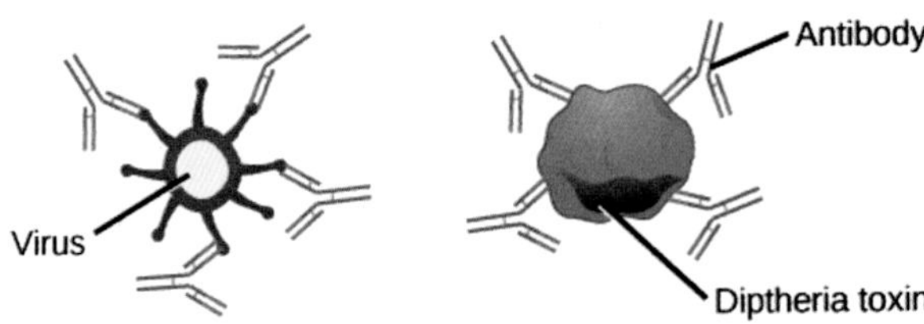
(a) Neutralization Antibodies prevent a virus or toxic protein from binding their target.
Antibody
Virus
Diptheria toxin

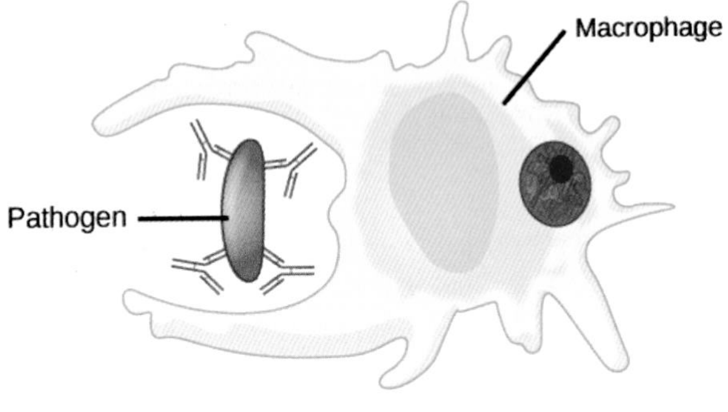
(b) Opsonization A pathogen tagged by antibodies is consumed by a macrophage or neutrophil.
Macrophage
Pathogen

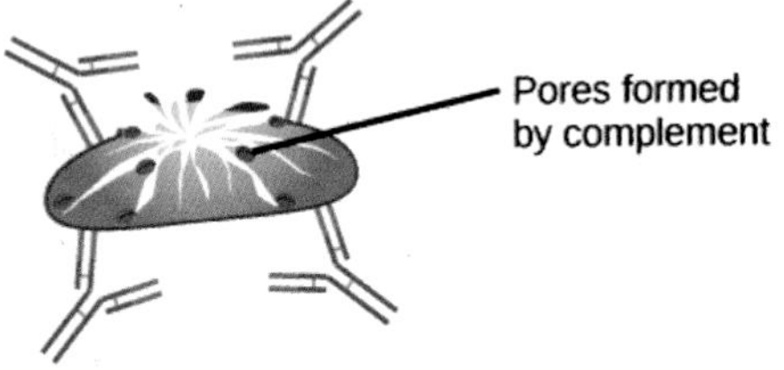
(c) Complement activation Antibodies attached to the surface of a pathogen cell activate the complement system.
Pores formed by complement

Figure 33.24 Antibodies may inhibit infection by (a) preventing the antigen from binding its target, (b) tagging a pathogen for destruction by macrophages or neutrophils, or (c) activating the complement cascade.

Antibodies also mark pathogens for destruction by phagocytic cells, such as macrophages or neutrophils, because phagocytic cells are highly attracted to macromolecules complexed with antibodies. Phagocytic enhancement by antibodies is called opsonization. In a process called complement fixation, IgM and IgG in serum bind to antigens and provide docking sites onto which sequential complement proteins can bind. The combination of antibodies and complement enhances opsonization even further and promotes rapid clearing of pathogens.

Affinity, Avidity, and Cross Reactivity

Not all antibodies bind with the same strength, specificity, and stability. In fact, antibodies exhibit different **affinities** (attraction) depending on the molecular complementarity between antigen and antibody molecules, as illustrated in Figure 33.25. An antibody with a higher affinity for a particular antigen would bind more strongly and stably, and thus would be expected to present a more challenging defense against the pathogen corresponding to the specific antigen.

(a) Affinity versus avidity

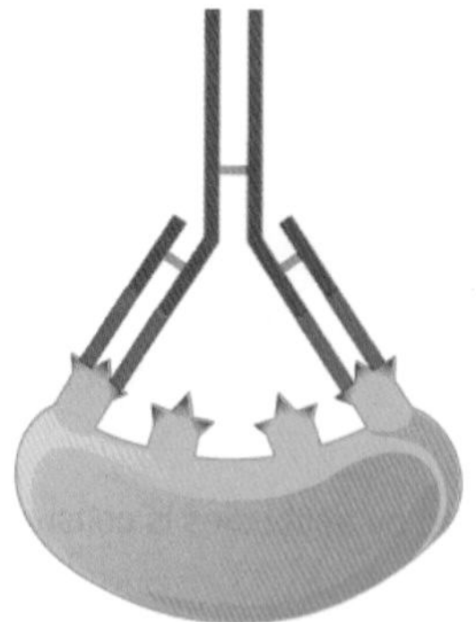

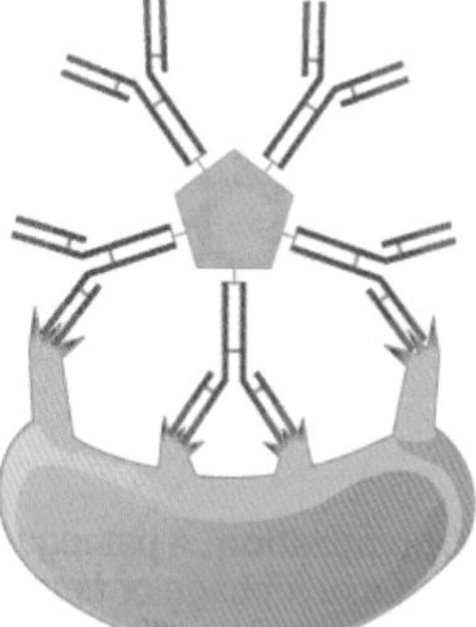

Affinity refers to the strength of a single antibody–antigen interaction. Each IgG antigen binding site typically has high affinity for its target.

Avidity refers to the strength of all interactions combined. IgM typically has low affinity antigen binding sites, but there are ten of them, so avidity is high.

(b) Cross reactivity

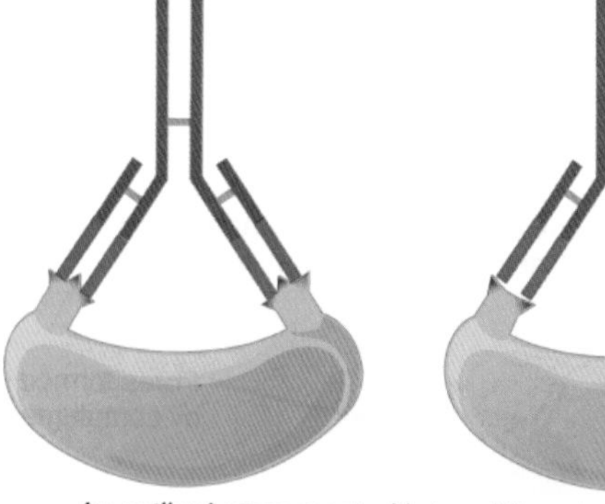

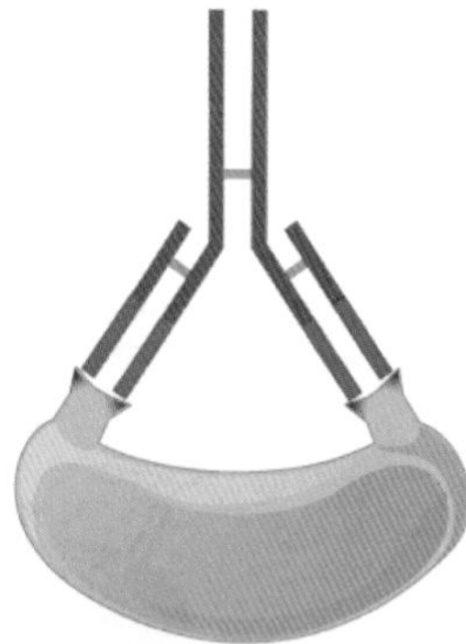

An antibody may react with two different epitopes.

Figure 33.25 (a) Affinity refers to the strength of single interaction between antigen and antibody, while avidity refers to the strength of all interactions combined. (b) An antibody may cross react with different epitopes.

The term **avidity** describes binding by antibody classes that are secreted as joined, multivalent structures (such as IgM and IgA). Although avidity measures the strength of binding, just as affinity does, the avidity is not simply the sum of the affinities of the antibodies in a multimeric structure. The avidity depends on the number of identical binding sites on the antigen being detected, as well as other physical and chemical factors. Typically, multimeric antibodies, such as pentameric IgM, are classified as having lower affinity than monomeric antibodies, but high avidity. Essentially, the fact that multimeric antibodies can bind many antigens simultaneously balances their slightly lower binding strength for each antibody/antigen interaction.

Antibodies secreted after binding to one epitope on an antigen may exhibit cross reactivity for the same or similar epitopes on different antigens. Because an epitope corresponds to such a small region (the surface area of about four to six amino acids), it is possible for different macromolecules to exhibit the same molecular identities and orientations over short regions. **Cross reactivity** describes when an antibody binds not to the antigen that elicited its synthesis and secretion, but to a different antigen.

Cross reactivity can be beneficial if an individual develops immunity to several related pathogens despite having only been exposed to or vaccinated against one of them. For instance, antibody cross reactivity may occur against the similar surface structures of various Gram-negative bacteria. Conversely, antibodies raised against pathogenic molecular components that resemble self molecules may incorrectly mark host cells for destruction and cause autoimmune damage. Patients who develop systemic lupus erythematosus (SLE) commonly exhibit antibodies that react with their own DNA. These antibodies may have been initially raised against the nucleic acid of microorganisms but later cross-reacted with self-antigens. This phenomenon is also called molecular mimicry.

Antibodies of the Mucosal Immune System

Antibodies synthesized by the mucosal immune system include IgA and IgM. Activated B cells differentiate into mucosal plasma cells that synthesize and secrete dimeric IgA, and to a lesser extent, pentameric IgM. Secreted IgA is abundant in tears, saliva, breast milk, and in secretions of the gastrointestinal and respiratory tracts. Antibody secretion results in a local humoral response at epithelial surfaces and prevents infection of the mucosa by binding and neutralizing pathogens.

33.4 | Disruptions in the Immune System

In this section, you will explore the following questions:

- What is hypersensitivity?
- What is autoimmunity, and what is an example of an autoimmune disease?

Connection for AP® Courses

Much of the information in this section is not within the scope for AP®. Immune systems can, at times, be defeated by pathogens. For example, some bacteria, including *Streptococcus pneumoniae*, surround themselves with a capsule that inhibits phagocytes from engulfing them and displaying antigens to the adaptive immune system. Human immunodeficiency virus (HIV), the virus that causes AIDS, infects helper T-cells via their CD4 surface molecules, gradually depleting the number of T_H cells in the body; this inhibits the adaptive immune system's capacity to sufficiently respond to infection or tumors that persons with healthy immune systems can defend against. Allergies to pollen or pet dander occur when the immune system attacks the body's own cells or tissues. Other example of autoimmune diseases include type I diabetes and ALS. In the rejection of transplanted organs, the immune system is responding to unmatched MHC proteins on the cells of the donated ("non-self") organ. However, the immune system usually responds as it should, defending you against infection and getting you back to your AP® Biology class as soon as possible.

Information presented and the examples highlighted in the section support concepts outlined in Big Idea 2 of the AP® Biology Curriculum Framework. The AP® Learning Objectives listed in the Curriculum Framework provide a transparent foundation for the AP® Biology course, an inquiry-based laboratory experience, instructional activities, and AP® exam questions. A learning objective merges required content with one or more of the seven science practices.

Big Idea 2	Biological systems utilize free energy and molecular building blocks to grow, to reproduce, and to maintain dynamic homeostasis.
Enduring Understanding 2.D	Growth and dynamic homeostasis of a biological system are influenced by changes in the system's environment.
Essential Knowledge	**2.D.3** Biological systems are affected by disruptions to their dynamic homeostasis.
Science Practice	**1.4** The student can use representations and models to analyze situations or solve problems qualitatively and quantitatively.
Learning Objective	**2.28** The student is able to use representations or models to analyze quantitatively and qualitatively the effects of disruptions to dynamic homeostasis in biological systems.

Immunodeficiency

Failures, insufficiencies, or delays at any level of the immune response can allow pathogens or tumor cells to gain a foothold and replicate or proliferate to high enough levels that the immune system becomes overwhelmed. **Immunodeficiency** is the failure, insufficiency, or delay in the response of the immune system, which may be acquired or inherited. Immunodeficiency can be acquired as a result of infection with certain pathogens (such as HIV), chemical exposure (including certain medical treatments), malnutrition, or possibly by extreme stress. For instance, radiation exposure can destroy populations of lymphocytes and elevate an individual's susceptibility to infections and cancer. Dozens of genetic disorders result in immunodeficiencies, including Severe Combined Immunodeficiency (SCID), Bare lymphocyte syndrome, and MHC II deficiencies. Rarely, primary immunodeficiencies that are present from birth may occur. Neutropenia is one form in which the immune system produces a below-average number of neutrophils, the body's most abundant phagocytes. As a result, bacterial infections may go unrestricted in the blood, causing serious complications.

everyday CONNECTION for AP® Courses

This is a white severe combined immunodeficiency (SCID) mouse. SCID mice are used to study the immune system.

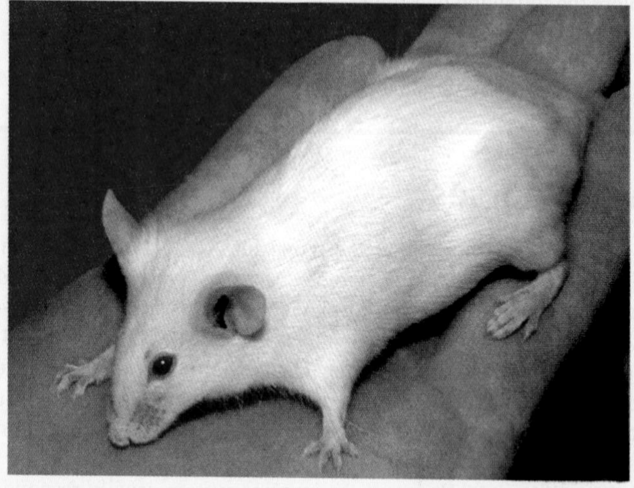

Figure 33.26

Hypersensitivities

Maladaptive immune responses toward harmless foreign substances or self antigens that occur after tissue sensitization are termed **hypersensitivities**. The types of hypersensitivities include immediate, delayed, and autoimmunity. A large proportion of the population is affected by one or more types of hypersensitivity.

Allergies

The immune reaction that results from immediate hypersensitivities in which an antibody-mediated immune response occurs within minutes of exposure to a harmless antigen is called an **allergy**. In the United States, 20 percent of the population exhibits symptoms of allergy or asthma, whereas 55 percent test positive against one or more allergens. Upon initial exposure to a potential allergen, an allergic individual synthesizes antibodies of the IgE class via the typical process of APCs presenting processed antigen to T_H cells that stimulate B cells to produce IgE. This class of antibodies also mediates the immune response to parasitic worms. The constant domain of the IgE molecules interact with mast cells embedded in connective tissues. This process primes, or sensitizes, the tissue. Upon subsequent exposure to the same allergen, IgE molecules on mast cells bind the antigen via their variable domains and stimulate the mast cell to release the modified amino acids histamine and serotonin; these chemical mediators then recruit eosinophils which mediate allergic responses. Figure 33.27 shows an example of an allergic response to ragweed pollen. The effects of an allergic reaction range from mild symptoms like sneezing and itchy, watery eyes to more severe or even life-threatening reactions involving intensely itchy welts or hives, airway contraction with severe respiratory distress, and plummeting blood pressure. This extreme reaction is known as anaphylactic shock. If not treated with epinephrine to counter the blood pressure and breathing effects, this condition can be fatal.

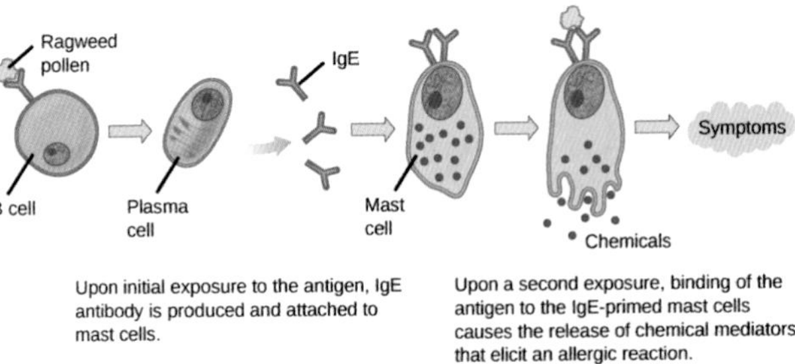
Ragweed pollen
IgE
Symptoms
B cell
Plasma cell
Mast cell
Chemicals
Upon initial exposure to the antigen, IgE antibody is produced and attached to mast cells.
Upon a second exposure, binding of the antigen to the IgE-primed mast cells causes the release of chemical mediators that elicit an allergic reaction.

Figure 33.27 On first exposure to an allergen, an IgE antibody is synthesized by plasma cells in response to a harmless antigen. The IgE molecules bind to mast cells, and on secondary exposure, the mast cells release histamines and other modulators that affect the symptoms of allergy. (credit: modification of work by NIH)

Delayed hypersensitivity is a cell-mediated immune response that takes approximately one to two days after secondary exposure for a maximal reaction to be observed. This type of hypersensitivity involves the T_H1 cytokine-mediated inflammatory response and may manifest as local tissue lesions or contact dermatitis (rash or skin irritation). Delayed hypersensitivity occurs in some individuals in response to contact with certain types of jewelry or cosmetics. Delayed hypersensitivity facilitates the immune response to poison ivy and is also the reason why the skin test for tuberculosis results in a small region of inflammation on individuals who were previously exposed to *Mycobacterium tuberculosis*. That is also why cortisone is used to treat such responses: it will inhibit cytokine production.

Autoimmunity

Autoimmunity is a type of hypersensitivity to self antigens that affects approximately five percent of the population. Most types of autoimmunity involve the humoral immune response. Antibodies that inappropriately mark self components as foreign are termed **autoantibodies**. In patients with the autoimmune disease myasthenia gravis, muscle cell receptors that induce contraction in response to acetylcholine are targeted by antibodies. The result is muscle weakness that may include marked difficultly with fine and/or gross motor functions. In systemic lupus erythematosus, a diffuse autoantibody response to the individual's own DNA and proteins results in various systemic diseases. As illustrated in Figure 33.28, systemic lupus erythematosus may affect the heart, joints, lungs, skin, kidneys, central nervous system, or other tissues, causing tissue damage via antibody binding, complement recruitment, lysis, and inflammation.

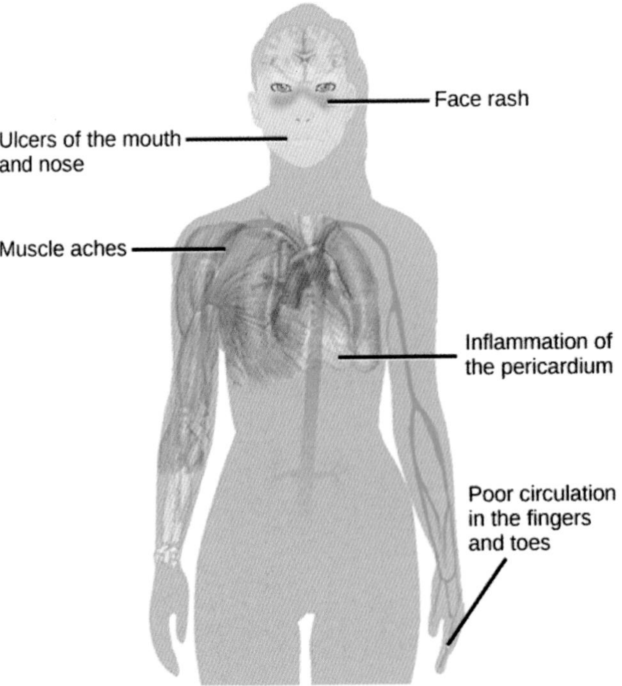
Face rash
Ulcers of the mouth and nose
Muscle aches
Inflammation of the pericardium
Poor circulation in the fingers and toes

Figure 33.28 Systemic lupus erythematosus is characterized by autoimmunity to the individual's own DNA and/or proteins, which leads to varied dysfunction of the organs. (credit: modification of work by Mikael Häggström)

Autoimmunity can develop with time, and its causes may be rooted in molecular mimicry. Antibodies and TCRs may bind self antigens that are structurally similar to pathogen antigens, which the immune receptors first raised. As an example, infection with *Streptococcus pyogenes* (bacterium that causes strep throat) may generate antibodies or T cells that react with heart muscle, which has a similar structure to the surface of *S. pyogenes*. These antibodies can damage heart muscle with autoimmune attacks, leading to rheumatic fever. Insulin-dependent (Type 1) diabetes mellitus arises from a destructive inflammatory T_H1 response against insulin-producing cells of the pancreas. Patients with this autoimmunity must be injected with insulin that originates from other sources.

KEY TERMS

adaptive immunity immunity that has memory and occurs after exposure to an antigen either from a pathogen or a vaccination

affinity attraction of molecular complementarity between antigen and antibody molecules

allergy immune reaction that results from immediate hypersensitivities in which an antibody-mediated immune response occurs within minutes of exposure to a harmless antigen

antibody protein that is produced by plasma cells after stimulation by an antigen; also known as an immunoglobulin

antigen foreign or "non-self" protein that triggers the immune response

antigen-presenting cell (APC) immune cell that detects, engulfs, and informs the adaptive immune response about an infection by presenting the processed antigen on the cell surface

autoantibody antibody that incorrectly marks "self" components as foreign and stimulates the immune response

autoimmune response inappropriate immune response to host cells or self-antigens

autoimmunity type of hypersensitivity to self antigens

avidity total binding strength of a multivalent antibody with antigen

B cell lymphocyte that matures in the bone marrow and differentiates into antibody-secreting plasma cells

basophil leukocyte that releases chemicals usually involved in the inflammatory response

cell-mediated immune response adaptive immune response that is carried out by T cells

clonal selection activation of B cells corresponding to one specific BCR variant and the dramatic proliferation of that variant

complement system array of approximately 20 soluble proteins of the innate immune system that enhance phagocytosis, bore holes in pathogens, and recruit lymphocytes; enhances the adaptive response when antibodies are produced

cross reactivity binding of an antibody to an epitope corresponding to an antigen that is different from the one the antibody was raised against

cytokine chemical messenger that regulates cell differentiation, proliferation, gene expression, and cell trafficking to effect immune responses

cytotoxic T lymphocyte (CTL) adaptive immune cell that directly kills infected cells via perforin and granzymes, and releases cytokines to enhance the immune response

dendritic cell immune cell that processes antigen material and presents it on the surface of other cells to induce an immune response

effector cell lymphocyte that has differentiated, such as a B cell, plasma cell, or cytotoxic T lymphocyte

eosinophil leukocyte that responds to parasites and is involved in the allergic response

epitope small component of an antigen that is specifically recognized by antibodies, B cells, and T cells; the antigenic determinant

granzyme protease that enters target cells through perforin and induces apoptosis in the target cells; used by NK cells and killer T cells

helper T lymphocyte (T_H) cell of the adaptive immune system that binds APCs via MHC II molecules and stimulates B cells or secretes cytokines to initiate the immune response

host an organism that is invaded by a pathogen or parasite

humoral immune response adaptive immune response that is controlled by activated B cells and antibodies

hypersensitivities spectrum of maladaptive immune responses toward harmless foreign particles or self antigens; occurs after tissue sensitization and includes immediate-type (allergy), delayed-type, and autoimmunity

immune tolerance acquired ability to prevent an unnecessary or harmful immune response to a detected foreign body known not to cause disease or to self-antigens

immunodeficiency failure, insufficiency, or delay at any level of the immune system, which may be acquired or inherited

inflammation localized redness, swelling, heat, and pain that results from the movement of leukocytes and fluid through opened capillaries to a site of infection

innate immunity immunity that occurs naturally because of genetic factors or physiology, and is not induced by infection or vaccination

interferon cytokine that inhibits viral replication and modulates the immune response

lymph watery fluid that bathes tissues and organs with protective white blood cells and does not contain erythrocytes

lymphocyte leukocyte that is histologically identifiable by its large nuclei; it is a small cell with very little cytoplasm

macrophage large phagocytic cell that engulfs foreign particles and pathogens

major histocompatibility class (MHC) I/II molecule protein found on the surface of all nucleated cells (I) or specifically on antigen-presenting cells (II) that signals to immune cells whether the cell is healthy/normal or is infected/cancerous; it provides the appropriate template into which antigens can be loaded for recognition by lymphocytes

mast cell leukocyte that produces inflammatory molecules, such as histamine, in response to large pathogens and allergens

memory cell antigen-specific B or T lymphocyte that does not differentiate into effector cells during the primary immune response but that can immediately become an effector cell upon re-exposure to the same pathogen

monocyte type of white blood cell that circulates in the blood and lymph and differentiates into macrophages after it moves into infected tissue

mucosa-associated lymphoid tissue (MALT) collection of lymphatic tissue that combines with epithelial tissue lining the mucosa throughout the body

natural killer (NK) cell lymphocyte that can kill cells infected with viruses or tumor cells

neutrophil phagocytic leukocyte that engulfs and digests pathogens

opsonization process that enhances phagocytosis using proteins to indicate the presence of a pathogen to phagocytic cells

passive immunity transfer of antibodies from one individual to another to provide temporary protection against pathogens

pathogen an agent, usually a microorganism, that causes disease in the organisms that they invade

pathogen-associated molecular pattern (PAMP) carbohydrate, polypeptide, and nucleic acid "signature" that is expressed by viruses, bacteria, and parasites but differs from molecules on host cells

pattern recognition receptor (PRR) molecule on macrophages and dendritic cells that binds molecular signatures of pathogens and promotes pathogen engulfment and destruction

perforin destructive protein that creates a pore in the target cell; used by NK cells and killer T cells

plasma cell immune cell that secrets antibodies; these cells arise from B cells that were stimulated by antigens

regulatory T (T_{reg}) cell specialized lymphocyte that suppresses local inflammation and inhibits the secretion of cytokines, antibodies, and other stimulatory immune factors; involved in immune tolerance

T cell lymphocyte that matures in the thymus gland; one of the main cells involved in the adaptive immune system

CHAPTER SUMMARY

33.1 Innate Immune Response

The innate immune system serves as a first responder to pathogenic threats that bypass natural physical and chemical barriers of the body. Using a combination of cellular and molecular attacks, the innate immune system identifies the nature of a pathogen and responds with inflammation, phagocytosis, cytokine release, destruction by NK cells, and/or a complement system. When innate mechanisms are insufficient to clear an infection, the adaptive immune response is informed and mobilized.

33.2 Adaptive Immune Response

The adaptive immune response is a slower-acting, longer-lasting, and more specific response than the innate response. However, the adaptive response requires information from the innate immune system to function. APCs display antigens via MHC molecules to complementary naïve T cells. In response, the T cells differentiate and proliferate, becoming T_H cells or CTLs. T_H cells stimulate B cells that have engulfed and presented pathogen-derived antigens. B cells differentiate into plasma cells that secrete antibodies, whereas CTLs induce apoptosis in intracellularly infected or cancerous cells. Memory cells persist after a primary exposure to a pathogen. If re-exposure occurs, memory cells differentiate into effector cells without input from the innate immune system. The mucosal immune system is largely independent from the systemic immune system but functions in a parallel fashion to protect the extensive mucosal surfaces of the body.

33.3 Antibodies

Antibodies (immunoglobulins) are the molecules secreted from plasma cells that mediate the humoral immune response. There are five antibody classes; an antibody's class determines its mechanism of action and production site but does not control its binding specificity. Antibodies bind antigens via variable domains and can either neutralize pathogens or mark them for phagocytosis or activate the complement cascade.

33.4 Disruptions in the Immune System

Immune disruptions may involve insufficient immune responses or inappropriate immune targets. Immunodeficiency increases an individual's susceptibility to infections and cancers. Hypersensitivities are misdirected responses either to harmless foreign particles, as in the case of allergies, or to host factors, as in the case of autoimmunity. Reactions to self components may be the result of molecular mimicry.

REVIEW QUESTIONS

1. What is the mechanism that skin uses to protect against diseases caused by organisms?

a. high pH
b. mucus
c. tears
d. desiccation

2. How does the human body use a chemical barrier as part of the innate immune response?

a. Mucus secretions trap and rinse pathogens out of the body.
b. Urination carries pathogens out of the urinary tract.
c. Low pH conditions in the stomach kill some pathogens and prevent other pathogens from growing.
d. Cilia in the nasal passages and respiratory tract push mucus containing trapped pathogens out of the body.

3. Which of the following produces an immediate innate immune response by recognizing an invading pathogen and engulfing it?

a. macrophage
b. cytokine
c. inflammation
d. antibody

4. How does inflammation develop?

a. Inflammation is induced by molecules such as cytokines and histamine that are produced by various host cells in response to pathogens at the site of injury or infection.
b. During inflammation, all blood cells retreat from the site of infection in order to protect the circulatory system from pathogen infection.
c. Inflammation is an ongoing condition in the human body, part of the way that the innate immune system can respond immediately to an infection.
d. When an infection occurs, an immediate inflammatory response occurs as soon as pathogens enter the body.

5. Which innate immune system component uses major histocompatibility class (MHC) I molecules directly in its defense strategy?

a. macrophages
b. neutrophils
c. natural killer cells
d. interferon

6. What is the difference between natural killer cells and macrophages?

a. Natural killer cells are not always present in the body and must be induced, whereas macrophages are constantly present.
b. Natural killer cells actually kill foreign cells, whereas macrophages serve only a signaling function.
c. Only macrophages can invade host tissues to fight foreign cells that make their way into those tissues.
d. Natural killer cells kill foreign cells through the processes of lysis and proteolysis, whereas macrophages kill foreign cells by phagocytosis.

7. What is the composition of major histocompatibility class (MHC) I molecules?

a. lipids
b. nucleic acids
c. carbohydrates
d. proteins

8. What is the function of major histocompatibility class (MHC) I molecules?

a. MHC I molecules assist with strengthening the cell membrane.
b. MHC I molecules present antigens on the surface of a cell.
c. MHC I molecules allow movement of materials across the cell membrane.
d. MHC I molecules provide signals for processes involved in cell division.

9. What is the complement system?

a. The complement system contains macrophages that phagocytize foreign pathogens.
b. The complement system monitors MHC I molecules on cells and destroys any cell that displays an antigen belonging to a pathogen.
c. The complement system contains a group of about 20 proteins in the blood that attack pathogens in a cascading fashion to mark and destroy them.
d. The complement system is made up of antibodies specific to each pathogen that are synthesized when a pathogen enters the body.

10. Which of the following occurs more rapidly as the result of activation of the complement system?

a. pathogen invasion
b. pathogen detection
c. pathogen reproduction
d. pathogen engulfment

11. What is another term for adaptive immunity?

a. acquired immunity
b. innate immunity
c. passive immunity
d. humoral immunity

12. How does adaptive immunity work?

a. A person is born having a specific immune responses against any pathogen that the body is exposed to.
b. A person is born with the ability to develop a specific immune response against any pathogen within minutes of being exposed to that pathogen.
c. A person does not have any immune response against a pathogen, but develops a temporary specific response to that pathogen that is then forgotten.
d. A person does not have specific immune response against a pathogen, but develops a specific response to that pathogen that is rapidly recalled later if infection by the same pathogen occurs again.

13. What component of the innate immune system is not part of the adaptive immune system?

a. T cells
b. antibodies
c. mast cells
d. B cells

14. What is the difference between innate and adaptive immune responses?

a. The adaptive immune system is faster-acting than the innate immune system.
b. The adaptive immune system produces a longer-lasting defense than the innate immune system.
c. The innate immune system produces a more specific defense than the adaptive immune system.
d. The innate immune system has a more sophisticated memory than the adaptive immune system.

15. Which cells are unique to the humoral immune response?

a. cytotoxic T cells
b. antigen-presenting cells
c. helper T cells
d. B cells

16. How does the humoral immune response operate?

a. The humoral immune response primarily targets infected host cells to destroy them before the infecting pathogen can reproduce.
b. The humoral immune response produces antibodies that are specifically targeted against each pathogen.
c. The humoral immune response produces cytotoxic T cells that induce apoptosis in pathogen-infected cells.
d. The humoral immune response is the only system that involves memory cells that are able to respond later to a pathogen that has invaded the body at an earlier time.

17. An antibody sometimes binds to an antigen other than the antigen that elicited its synthesis. What term refers to this behavior?

a. avidity
b. cross reactivity
c. hypersensitivity
d. affinity

18. A biologist runs some tests and observes that the same antibody binds to several different proteins. Why might this occur?

a. The antibody is showing that it has high affinity for antigens.
b. The antibody is showing that it has high avidity for antigens.
c. The antibody is showing cross reactivity to the antigens.
d. The antibody is showing hypersensitivity to the antigens.

19. How many and what types of polypeptides make up an antibody molecule?

a. One heavy polypeptide chain and one light polypeptide chain
b. Two heavy polypeptide chains and one light polypeptide chain
c. Two heavy polypeptide chains and two light polypeptide chains
d. One heavy polypeptide chain and two light polypeptide chains

20. Why do antibodies isolated from the same individual show a variety of constant domains?

a. The antibodies were synthesized in response to infections by different pathogens.
b. The antibodies were transmitted as the result of passive immunity.
c. The antibodies have different specificities of antigen binding.
d. The antibodies belong to different classes of immunoglobulin molecules.

21. What enzyme is responsible for the random excision of variable gene segments making up an antibody light chain in DNA?

a. DNA polymerase
b. DNA recombinase
c. DNA ligase
d. DNA helicase

22. How are antibodies produced in a B cell?

a. RNA processing → DNA rearrangement → transcription → translation → mature antibody
b. Transcription → RNA processing → DNA rearrangement → translation → mature antibody
c. DNA rearrangement → RNA processing → transcription → translation → mature antibody
d. DNA rearrangement → transcription → RNA processing → translation → mature antibody

23. What is a definition of hypersensitivity?

a. maladaptive immune responses to otherwise harmless proteins
b. measure of the attraction between an antigen and an antibody
c. total binding strength of a multivalent antibody with an antigen
d. binding of an antibody to an antigen different from the one that elicited its synthesis

24. An allergy has been described as a non-protective immune response. Which statement provides information supporting this description?

a. An allergic response occurs when B cells produce IgE molecules in response to a foreign protein, which causes histamine to be released.
b. An allergy results from an immune response to a protein that does not cause harm and that the body needs no defense against.
c. People with allergies develop unpleasant symptoms such as watery, itchy eyes, swollen tissues, and sneezing.
d. When their blood is tested, people with allergies show that they have antibodies that bind to one or more foreign proteins.

25. What is the term for antibodies that inappropriately mark self components as foreign?

a. cross reactive
b. epitopes
c. allergens
d. autoantibodies

26. Why do some people with type 1 diabetes develop the disease as the result of an immune response?

a. Their B cells produced IgE molecules in response to a harmless protein, which caused histamine to be released.
b. Their B cells responded to a self protein to produce autoantibodies, which elicited inflammation that caused organ damage.
c. They had a delayed response to a harmful protein that entered the body and activated both the innate and adaptive immune systems.
d. They acquired antibodies to insulin through passive immunity, and these antibodies bind to insulin whenever it is produced in the body.

27. What are the three types of hypersensitivity?

a. innate, acquired, and immunodeficiency
b. variable, constant, and recombinant
c. immediate, delayed, and autoimmunity
d. active, passive, and adaptive

28. What is the definition of autoimmunity?

a. binding of an antibody to a viral antigen
b. immune response to self antigens
c. maladaptive immune response to harmless foreign proteins
d. failure to mount an immune response

CRITICAL THINKING QUESTIONS

29. Why does the human body need more than its skin to function as a barrier to infecting pathogens?

a. Skin works only against some types of bacteria. To prevent the entry of other pathogens, other physical or chemical barriers are needed.
b. Skin does not provide a broad coverage against invasion of the body by any foreign particle, so it is not a very effective barrier.
c. Pathogens could enter the body through several places that are not covered by skin that need to have a barrier to prevent infection.
d. Skin acts only as a chemical barrier against pathogens. The body also needs physical barriers to prevent various types of infection.

30. Cell surface recognition occurs during many types of immune responses, including immediate and induced immune responses. How do natural killer cells and interferons represent one of each type of immune response (immediate and induced), and how does cell surface recognition play a role?

a. Natural killer cells are an example of induced immune response as they attack host cells that have lost normal cell surface markers. Interferons are an example of immediate immune response as they are induced after cell surface markers on invading pathogens are recognized by host cells.

b. Natural killer cells are an example of immediate immune response as they attack host cells that have lost normal cell surface markers. Interferons are an example of induced immune response as they are induced after cell surface markers on invading pathogens are recognized by host cells.

c. Natural killer cells are an example of immediate immune response as they are induced after cell surface markers on invading pathogens are recognized by host cells. Interferons are an example of induced immune response as they attack host cells that have lost normal cell surface markers.

d. Natural killer cells are an example of induced immune response as they are induced after cell surface markers on invading pathogens are recognized by host cells. Interferons are an example of immediate immune response as they attack host cells that have lost normal cell surface markers.

31. Why might different MHC I molecules between donor and recipient cells lead to rejection of a transplanted organ or tissue?

a. The natural killer cells in the recipient will identify the MHC I molecules on transplanted organ as non-self proteins, causing lysis of transplanted cells. Other host cells will join to phagocytize the foreign cells.

b. The neutrophils in the recipient will identify the MHC I molecules on transplanted organ as non-self proteins, causing lysis of transplanted cells. Other host cells will join to phagocytize the foreign cells.

c. B lymphocytes in the recipient will identify the MHC I molecules on transplanted organ as non-self proteins. The foreign cells will then be engulfed and destroyed by B lymphocytes.

d. The macrophages in the recipient will identify the MHC I molecules on transplanted organ as non-self proteins, causing lysis of transplanted cells. Other host cells will join to phagocytize the foreign cells.

32. Suppose a person was born without the ability to produce MHC I molecules. What problem would that create?

a. A person without the ability to produce MHC I molecules would die immediately.

b. A person without the ability to produce MHC I molecules would recognize self as non-self, resulting in autoimmune disease.

c. The person's immune system would not be able to distinguish self and non-self. This would make the person very vulnerable to infection.

d. The person's immune system would not be able to destroy foreign pathogen due to lack of hydrolytic enzymes. This would make the person very vulnerable to infection.

33. Suppose a series of genetic mutations prevented some, but not all, of the complement proteins from binding antibodies or pathogens. Would the entire complement system be compromised? Why or why not?

a. No, because the complement system functions as a cascade, with each protein triggering the activity of the next protein in the cascade.

b. Yes, because the complement system functions as a cascade, with each protein triggering the activity of the next protein in the cascade.

c. Yes, because all the proteins of the complement system function independently.

d. No, because all the proteins of the complement system function independently.

34. What is a likely reason to explain why vertebrate animals evolved an adaptive immune system rather than an innate system involving specific responses to specific pathogens?

a. An adaptive immune system requires an immense amount of information to be stored, which allows vertebrate cells to be able to mount specific responses to every pathogen.

b. As new pathogens evolve all the time, it is more conservative of energy and information storage to have an adaptive immune system that can respond to same pathogens in different ways.

c. As new pathogens evolve all the time, it is more conservative of energy and information storage to have an adaptive immune system that can respond to different pathogens in a specific way.

d. As new pathogens evolve all the time, it is more conservative of energy and information storage to have an adaptive immune system that can respond to different pathogens in a non-specific way.

35. Invertebrate animals have innate immune systems but lack adaptive immune systems. Vertebrates, including fish, amphibians, reptiles, birds, and mammals have both systems. What does this suggest about the evolution of these two immune systems?

a. This suggests that the innate immune system evolved first. Invertebrates and vertebrates had a common ancestor, which had an innate immune system. After the two lineages diverged, the vertebrate line developed adaptive immunity, which continued to evolve in all vertebrates.
b. This suggests that the adaptive immune system evolved first. Invertebrates and vertebrates had a common ancestor, which had an innate immune system. After the two lineages diverged, the vertebrate line developed adaptive immunity, which continued to evolve in all vertebrates.
c. This suggests that the innate immune system evolved first. Invertebrates and vertebrates had a common ancestor, which had an adaptive immune system. After the two lineages diverged, the vertebrate line developed innate immunity, which continued to evolve in all vertebrates.
d. This suggests that the adaptive immune system evolved first. Invertebrates and vertebrates had a common ancestor, which had an adaptive immune system. After the two lineages diverged, the vertebrate line developed innate immunity, which continued to evolve in all vertebrates.

36. What are naïve B or T cells and how do they function in cell-mediated and humoral immune responses?

a. Naïve B and T cells are lymphocytes of the B and T types that have come into contact with pathogenic antigens. Naïve T cells produce antibodies in the humoral immune response, while naïve B cells stimulate the cell-mediated immune response.
b. Naïve B and T cells are lymphocytes of the B and T types that normally circulate in the body at all times and have not come into contact with any pathogenic antigens. Activated T cells produce antibodies in the humoral immune response, while activated B cells stimulate the cell-mediated immune response.
c. Naïve B and T cells are lymphocytes of the B and T types that normally circulate in the body at all times and have not come into contact with any pathogenic antigens. Activated B cells produce antibodies in the humoral immune response, while activated T cells stimulate the cell-mediated immune response.
d. Naïve B and T cells are lymphocytes of the B and T types that have come into contact with pathogenic antigens. Naïve B cells produce antibodies in the humoral immune response, while naïve T cells stimulate the cell-mediated immune response.

37. A person given a flu vaccine in November comes down with a severe case of influenza in January. What can you conclude about the flu vaccine and cross reactivity?

a. The flu vaccine elicited antibodies in the person's body that were specific to a particular flu virus. Unfortunately, the flu virus that infected the person later in January was different enough for cross reactivity to occur between the virus antigens causing the infection.
b. The flu vaccine suppresses antibodies in the person's body that were specific to a particular flu virus. Unfortunately, the flu virus that infected the person later in January was different enough for cross reactivity to occur between the virus antigens causing the infection.
c. The flu vaccine suppresses antibodies in the person's body that were specific to a particular flu virus. Unfortunately, the flu virus that infected the person later in January was similar enough for cross reactivity to occur between the virus antigens causing the infection.
d. The flu vaccine suppresses antibodies in the person's body that were specific to a particular flu virus. Unfortunately, the flu virus that infected the person later in January was similar enough for cross reactivity to occur between the virus antigens causing the infection.

38. What function does the diversity of the variable region of an antibody help it perform?

a. It helps in communication of antibodies with other components of immune system.
b. It helps the antibodies to function with very low affinity and specificity.
c. It enables many different antibodies to be made that all have different specificities of binding.
d. It enables many different antibodies to be made that all have same specificities of binding.

39. How can you explain that the same antibodies found in an infant's body are also present in the infant's mother?

a. Antibodies produced in the mother's body are passed to the infant via passive immunity through breast milk.
b. Antibodies produced in the mother's body are passed to the infant via active immunity through breast milk.
c. Antibodies produced in the mother's body are passed to the infant via passive immunity through the placenta.
d. Antibodies produced in the infant's body are passed to the mother through the placenta.

40. Researchers have been working on developing methods for stimulating the human immune system to recognize foreign proteins as self proteins. Why would this research be applicable to treating allergies?

a. In an allergy, a person’s immune system has been compromised, which causes unpleasant symptoms.
b. In an allergy, a person’s immune system reacts to its own proteins, which causes unpleasant symptoms.
c. In an allergy, a person’s immune system reacts to a harmless protein from the environment, which causes unpleasant symptoms.
d. In an allergy, a person’s immune system reacts to a harmless protein from the environment, which causes pleasant symptoms.

41. A patient has just been informed that they have an autoimmune disease that attacks the salivary glands. How would you explain to the patient what is happening inside their body?

a. The immune system is producing antibodies against their own proteins present in their salivary glands, causing the salivary glands to break down and become non-functional.
b. The ability of the immune system to fight the antigen present in the salivary glands might have been compromised, causing the salivary glands to break down and become non-functional.
c. The immune system might have reacted in an abnormal way to an antigen that may have entered salivary glands, causing the salivary glands to break down and become non-functional.
d. Some pathogen might have entered the salivary glands, causing the salivary glands to break down and become non-functional.

42. An allergic response sometimes leads to a person’s death. How can you explain this?

a. The allergen may bind to the hemoglobin, decreasing the affinity of hemoglobin for oxygen, leading to death.
b. If a person has a very strong and fast response to an allergen, the tissues in the throat can swell so much in a very short time that the person cannot breathe and blood pressure may increase very quickly. Oxygen will not be carried to the brain and the person may die.
c. If a person has a very strong and fast response to an allergen, the tissues in the throat can swell so much in a very short time that the person cannot breathe and blood pressure may drop very quickly. Oxygen will reach the cells at a faster rate and the person may die.
d. If a person has a very strong and fast response to an allergen, the tissues in the throat can swell so much in a very short time that the person cannot breathe and blood pressure may drop very quickly. Oxygen will not be carried to the brain and the person may die.

TEST PREP FOR AP® COURSES

43. A pathogenic bacterium has been engulfed by a phagocytic cell as part of the innate immune response. Which of the following illustrations best represents the response? [source: AP Biology Course and Exam Description Fall 2012, p. 132]

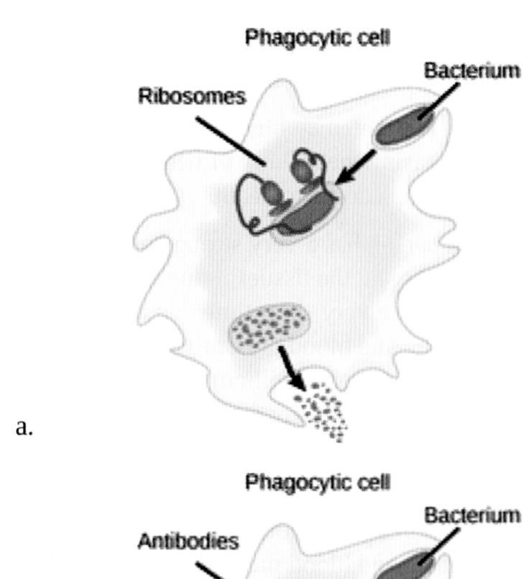

a.

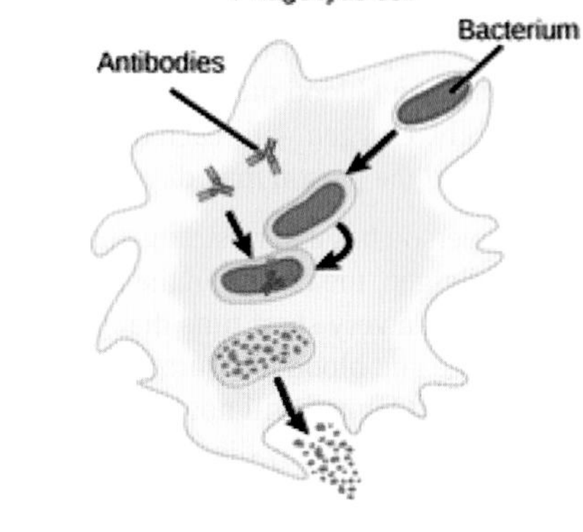

b.

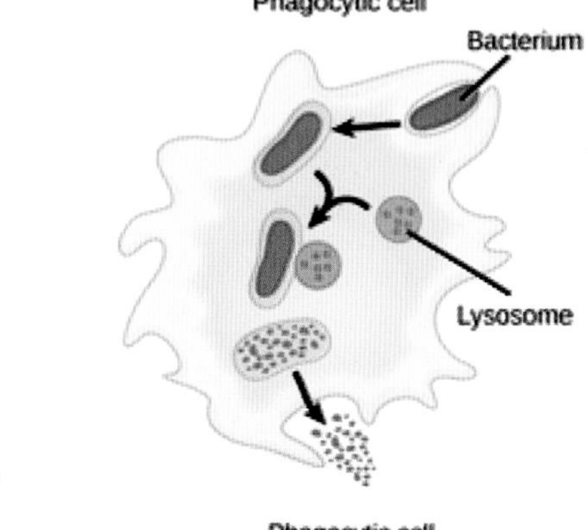

c.

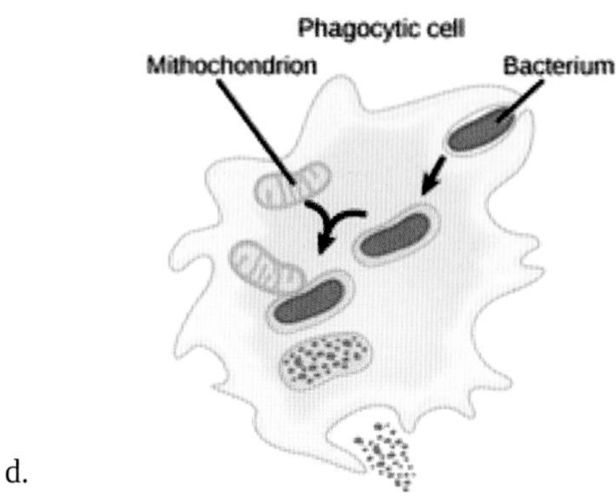

d.

44. How do natural killer cells react to healthy cells compared to cells infected with a pathogen?

a. Natural killer cells recognize MHC I on a healthy cell and do not kill it, while the infected cells that do not present MHC I are killed.

b. Natural killer cells recognize MHC I on an infected cell and kill it, while the healthy cells that do not present MHC I are not killed.

c. Natural killer cells recognize MHC II on a healthy cell and do not kill it, while the infected cells that do not present MHC II are killed.

d. Natural killer cells recognize MHC II on an infected cell and kill it, while the healthy cells that do not present MHC II are not killed.

45.

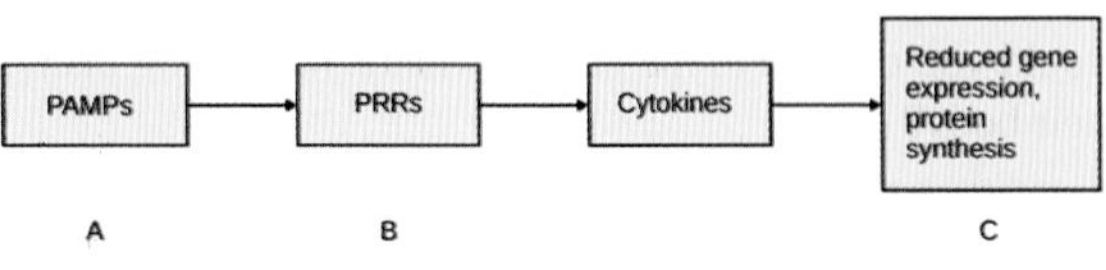

The following incomplete diagram represents a series of events during an innate immune response. The labels A, B, and C need to be replaced with the names of the cells involved. Which set of cells correctly completes this diagram?

a. A = infected host cell, B = pathogen, C = healthy host cell

b. A = healthy host cell, B = pathogen, C = dendritic cell

c. A = dendritic cell, B = infected host cell, C = pathogen

d. A = pathogen, B = dendritic cell, C = healthy host cell

46. A healthy person produces antibodies to pathogens that invade the body. However, if this person becomes infected with HIV, the body loses the ability to produce antibodies. Research has shown that the virus attacks and destroys CD4+T cells. Why does destruction of CD4+T cells lead to a loss of antibody synthesis in HIV-infected patients?

a. CD4+T cells are a required intermediate in a series of cell-to-cell signaling events that must be completed before B cells can mature.

b. CD4+T cells have CD4 molecules covalently bound to their cell surfaces and do not induce apoptosis in other cells during an immune response.

c. CD4+T cell counts are about 1,000 per microliter in a healthy person, but drop below 400 per microliter in a person who cannot mount an immune response.

d. CD4+T cell precursors are formed in the bone marrow and then migrate to the thymus, where they develop their T cell receptors.

47. Which of the following diagrams best illustrates how a macrophage activates a helper T cell (THcell)?

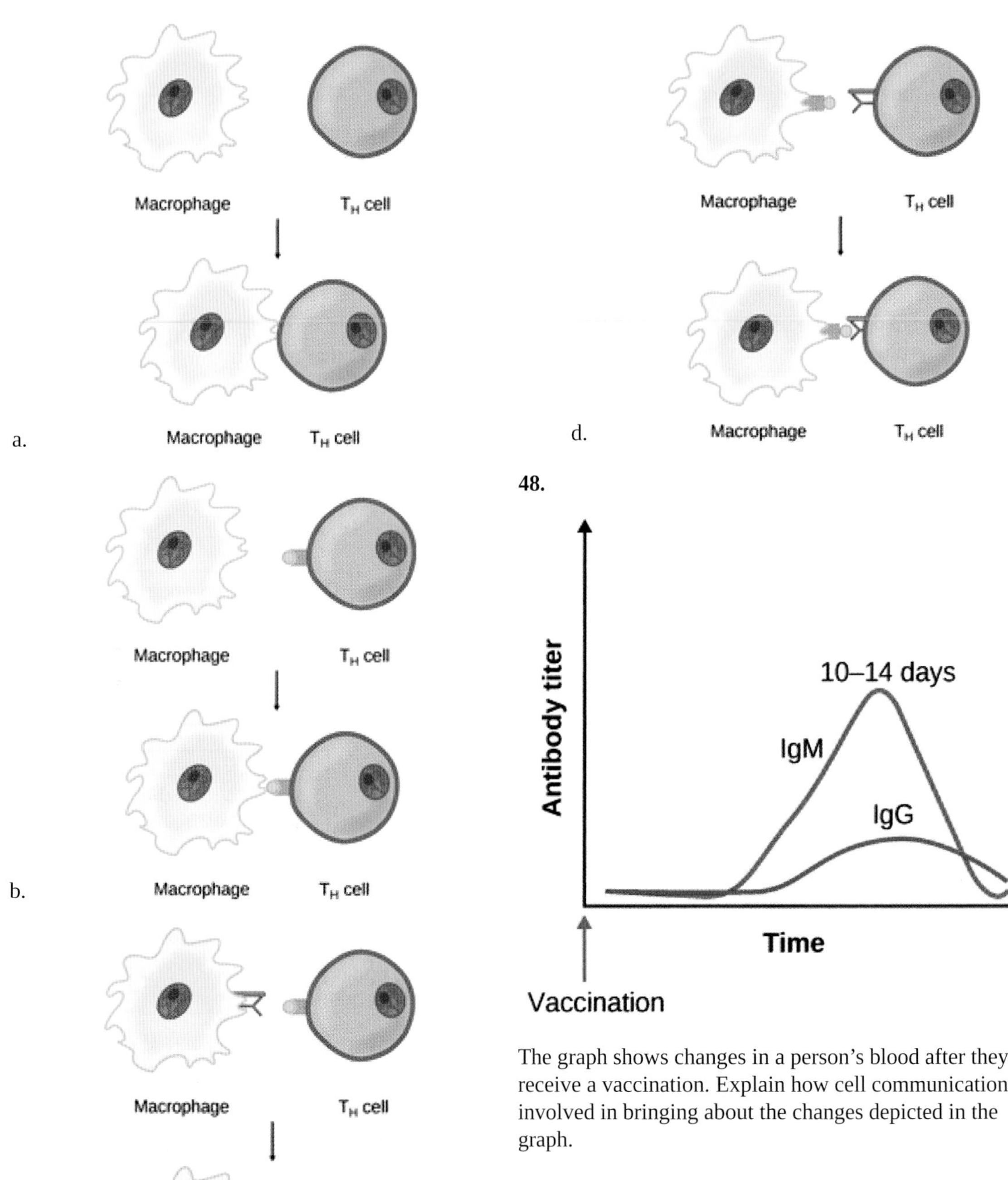

48.

The graph shows changes in a person’s blood after they receive a vaccination. Explain how cell communication is involved in bringing about the changes depicted in the graph.

a. The vaccine introduces antigens specific to a pathogen into the person's blood. These antigens are moved to the cell surface of antigen-presenting cells present in the blood. Receptors on helper T cells bind to the antigens present on the antigen-presenting cell. This direct cell-to-cell contact initiates a series of events that leads to production of antibodies by B lymphocytes.

b. The vaccine introduces antigens specific to a pathogen into the person's blood. These antigens bind to the receptors on the surface of T cells. This direct cell-to-cell contact initiates a series of events that leads to production of antibodies by B lymphocytes.

c. The vaccine introduces antigens specific to a pathogen into the person's blood. These antigens are moved to the cell surface of antigen-presenting cells present in the blood. This direct cell-to-cell contact initiates a series of events that leads to production of antibodies by B lymphocytes.

d. The vaccine introduces antigens specific to a pathogen into the person's blood. These antigens are moved to the cell surface of antigen-presenting cells present in the blood. Receptors on helper T cells bind to the antigens present on the antigen-presenting cell. This direct cell-to-cell contact initiates a series of events that activates the complement system.

49. B cells are important immune cells that fight infections. How is a naïve B cell stimulated to mature into a plasma cell that secretes antibodies?

a. T cells secrete cytokines, which help the B cell to multiply and mature into an antibody-producing plasma cell.

b. Natural killer cells secrete cytokines, which help the B cell to multiply and mature into an antibody-producing plasma cell.

c. T cells secrete interferons, which help the B cell to multiply and mature into an antibody-producing plasma cell.

d. Natural killer cells secrete interferons, which help the B cell to multiply and mature into an antibody-producing plasma cell.

50.

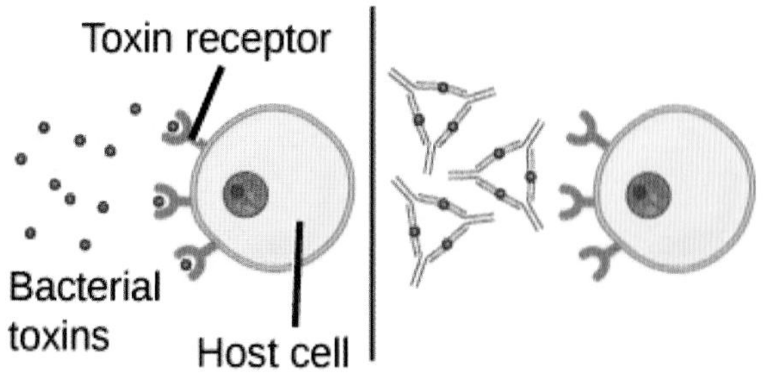

The diagram illustrates a process taking place during an immune response. What process is represented by this diagram?

a. opsonization

b. apoptosis

c. neutralization

d. complement activation

51.

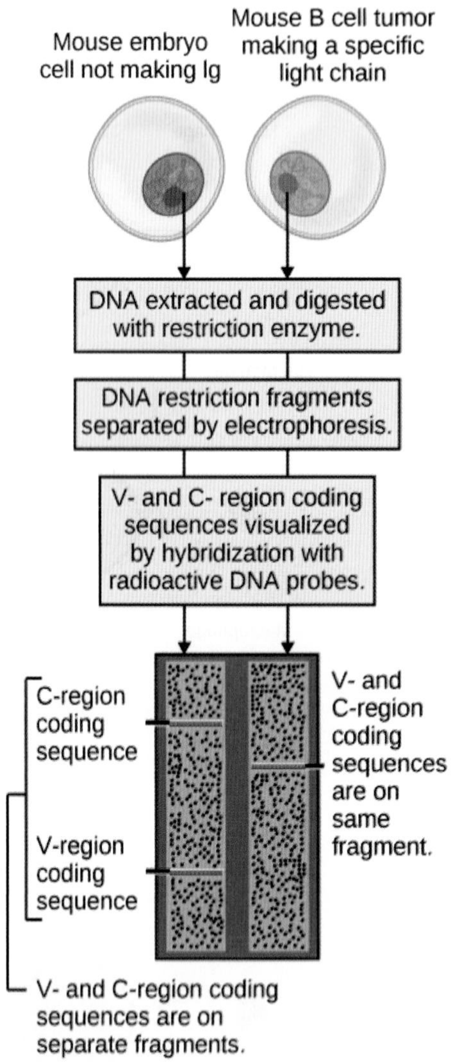

Scientists performed an experiment using a cell from a mouse embryo and a B cell from an adult mouse. The mouse embryo cell does not make antibodies, yet its DNA contains nucleotide sequences encoding antibody polypeptides. The adult mouse B cell makes and secretes a single type of antibody. In the experiment, radiolabeled DNA probes were synthesized to be complementary to the DNA encoding the light chains of antibody produced by the adult mouse B cells. Then, DNA from the mouse embryo cell and from the adult B cell were isolated and tested to see if either hybridized with the synthesized radiolabeled DNA probes. The results are shown in the diagram. Which claim is best supported by the data?

a. The mouse genome contains an enormous number of antibody genes, which accounts for the huge diversity of antibody molecules that can be made.

b. Rearrangement of gene segments encoding antibody polypeptides occurs at the level of DNA to produce an enormous diversity of antibody molecules.

c. The tremendous diversity of antibody molecules that can be made results from post-translational modifications of antibody polypeptide chains.

d. Each antibody is encoded by its own unique gene in the DNA, which explains how antibodies can have different antigen binding properties.

52. How does an antibody molecule bind specifically to one antigen but not to others?

a. due to the presence of a specific antigen binding site

b. due to the constant region

c. due to diversity of variable region

d. due to the complete antibody structure

53. The human genome contains less than 50,000 genes, yet a human has the capability of producing more than 1012different antibody molecules. How can this evidence be used to support the claim that the human body has an immune system that is both effective and efficient?

a. There are so many different antibody molecules that can be made, each of which can specifically target a particular pathogen to destroy it. This specificity makes the immune system more effective. The immune system is also efficient because each antibody need to have its own gene.

b. There are so many different antibody molecules that can be made, each of which can non-specifically target a particular pathogen to destroy it. This non-specificity makes the immune system more effective. The immune system is also efficient because each antibody does not need to have its own gene.

c. There are so many different antibody molecules that can be made, each of which can specifically target a particular pathogen to destroy it. This specificity makes the immune system more efficient. The immune system is also effective because each antibody does not need to have its own gene.

d. There are so many different antibody molecules that can be made, each of which can specifically target a particular pathogen to destroy it. This specificity makes the immune system more effective. The immune system is also efficient because each antibody does not need to have its own gene.

54.

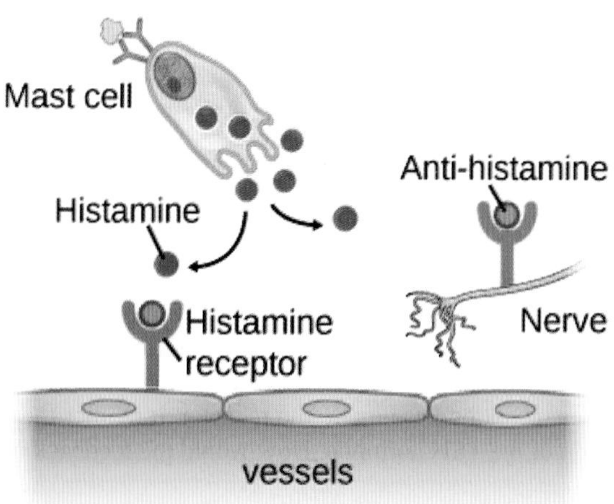

An allergy is caused by the immune system reacting to a foreign protein to produce IgE molecules that recognize the protein. These IgE molecules become associated with mast cells that respond to future exposures to the protein by releasing histamines into the body. The diagram shows this release and also shows how a drug called an antihistamine can help an allergy sufferer reduce their allergy symptoms. Which of the following statements explains how an antihistamine helps restore homeostasis during an allergic reaction?

a. Antihistamines prevent mast cells from becoming associated with IgE molecules that recognize the foreign protein allergen.

b. Antihistamines prevent mast cells from releasing histamines and causing the unpleasant allergy symptoms.

c. Antihistamines prevent histamines that have been released by mast cells from stimulating the itching and swelling of body tissues.

d. Antihistamines prevent mast cells from producing histamines, which halts their effect on the body.

55.

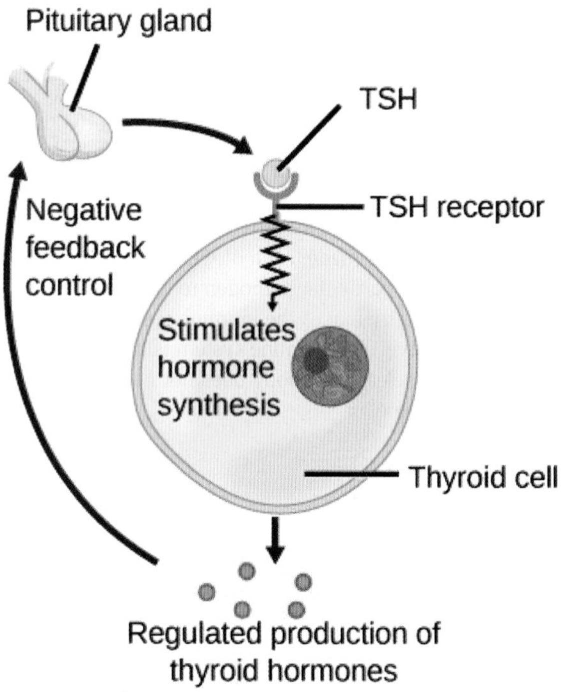

The diagram shows the normal feedback loop that controls the production of thyroid hormones in the human body. Graves' disease is an autoimmune disease in which the body produces autoantibodies to the TSH receptor. When these autoantibodies bind to the receptor, it mimics the action of the TSH hormone. How would the feedback loop and the regulated production of thyroid hormones shown in the diagram be affected in a person with Graves' disease?

a. The feedback loop would be disrupted. Autoantibodies would bind to the TSH receptors, allowing them to continue to produce thyroid hormones. As a result, there would be an overproduction of thyroid hormones because the negative feedback system would be unable to function.

b. The feedback loop would be not be disrupted. Autoantibodies would bind to the TSH receptors, allowing them to continue to produce thyroid hormones. As a result, there would be an overproduction of thyroid hormones because the negative feedback system would be unable to function.

c. The feedback loop would be disrupted. Autoantibodies would not bind to the TSH receptors, allowing them to continue to produce thyroid hormones. As a result, there would be an overproduction of thyroid hormones because the negative feedback system would be unable to function.

d. The feedback loop would be disrupted. Autoantibodies would bind to the TSH receptors, allowing them to continue to produce thyroid hormones. As a result, there would be an overproduction of thyroid hormones because the negative feedback system was functional.

56.

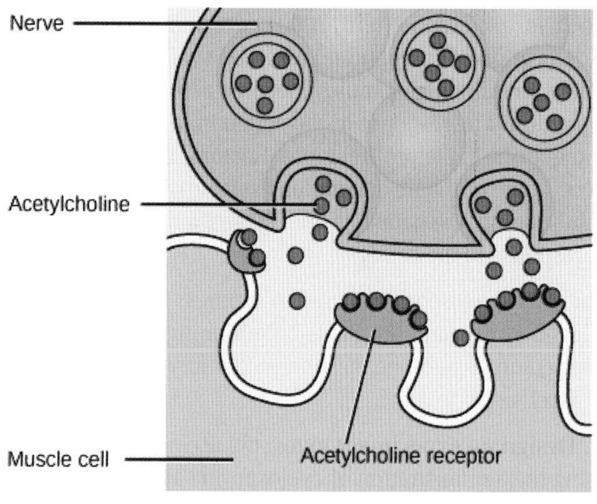

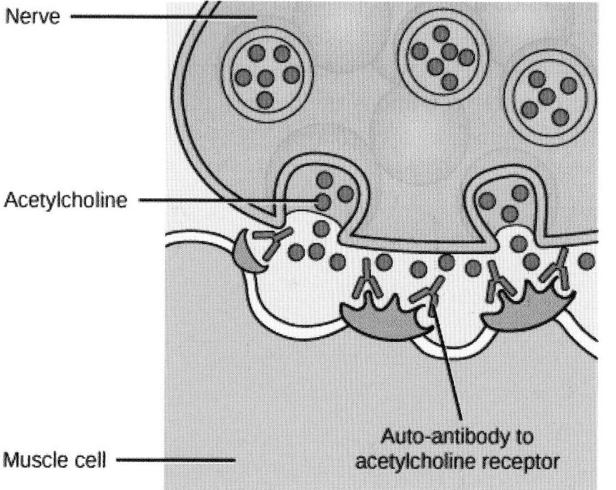

Myasthenia gravis is an autoimmune disease that initially presents with muscle weakness and can progress to complete impairment of muscle movement. The diagram compares a healthy individual with an individual suffering from this disease. Which statement best explains what happens to bring about this disease?

a. The body produces antibodies against nerve cells, which prevents the nerve cells from releasing acetylcholine during signal transmissions to muscle.

b. The body produces antibodies against acetylcholine, which prevents acetylcholine from transmitting signals from nerves to muscle.

c. The body produces antibodies against receptors in muscle, which prevents acetylcholine from binding and completing nerve signal transmission.

d. The body produces antibodies against acetylcholine, which prevents acetylcholine from breaking down after signal transmission is complete.

SCIENCE PRACTICE CHALLENGE QUESTIONS

57. Describe the difference between the mammalian cell-mediated and humoral responses to a pathogen. Include in your description the roles of antigens and antibodies, T-cells, B-cells, inoculation with vaccines, and the relative response times.

58. Immune response must recognize threat by distinguishing wellness from un-wellness. Recognition of pathogen-generated antigens is an adaptive response. Generic pathogen identifiers such as bacterial surface polysaccharides or viral capsid proteins are recognized by cells of the innate immune system. However, cellular debris and dysfunctional whole cells such as tumor cells or cells marked for apoptosis must also be recognized for autophagy (“self-devouring”) by the innate immune system.

A. **Describe** the characteristics of a model of innate immunity that distinguishes wellness from un-wellness without the specificity of antigen receptors.

Autoimmunity is the breakdown in the immune system’s ability to distinguish self from non-self. The list of diseases categorized as autoimmune diseases grows, as does the intensity of research into the causes. One criterion for classification as an autoimmune disease is the presence of high antibody concentrations in the blood. An auto-inflammatory disease is defined by chronic inflammation, unprovoked by an infection, when antibody concentrations are not high. Consider the following:

- Macrophages and phagocytes share information with the adaptive immune system by displaying protein fragments of their targets on their surfaces to communicate with T cells.
- The onset of autoimmune disease often follows an infection.
- After an infection has passed, tissue must be repaired, and macrophages and phagocytes remain active in the affected tissue, often leading to chronic inflammation.
- Type 2 diabetes, traditionally categorized as a metabolic disease, begins as chronic inflammation and is now classified as an autoimmune disease by many scientists.
- Autophagy is induced by stresses such as starvation.

B. **Evaluate** the strength of the **question**, do cell fragments produced by the innate immune response during inflammation communicate self as non-self to T cells leading to autoimmunity?

In the “fight or flight” response, neural signals are sent to the adrenal gland activating the release of epinephrine. Epinephrine increases metabolic activity, heart rate and alertness. The activation of the endocrine system by the nervous system has been positively selected by survival in response to threat.

C. **Describe** a model for the evolution of the activation of immune system by the nervous system in an environment in which wounds are frequent and potentially lethal. Include the selection process in your description.

In the famous experiment of Pavlov, a reward (unconditioned stimulus) received synchronously with a bell (conditioned stimulus) became associated in the mind of the dog. After a few repetitions, the response of the dog to the bell was to drool. The digestive system had been activated by the nervous system through a conditioned stimulus.

An emerging area of research is psychoneuroimmunology, the study of the relationship between the immune system and the nervous system. Exton and co-workers (*Brain Behavioral Research*, 110, 2000) have shown that a reward (an injection of epinephrine) received synchronously with candy (conditioned stimulus) become associated through repetition. The response of the patient to a shot of epinephrine is the proliferation of natural killer, NK, cells (a cell type of the innate immune system). After conditioning, the patient displayed an increase in NK cells in response to the candy.

The drug cyclosporine is used to suppress immune rejection of organ transplants by inhibiting production of interleukin, a cytokine messenger that increases expression in T cells.

D. **Design an experiment** to test the use of conditioning using the administration of cyclosporine as the unconditioned stimulus and sugar water as the conditioned stimulus by measuring the blood concentration of interleukin. Assume that interleukin is flushed from the blood in a single day. In your design include a vehicle control where conditions are identical to the treatment and a “do-nothing” or naïve control.

34 | ANIMAL REPRODUCTION AND DEVELOPMENT

Figure 34.1 Female seahorses produce eggs for reproduction that are then fertilized by the male. Unlike almost all other animals, the male seahorse then gestates the young until birth. (credit: modification of work by "cliff1066"/Flickr)

Chapter Outline

Introduction

Animal reproduction is necessary for the survival of a species. In the animal kingdom, there are innumerable ways that species reproduce. Asexual reproduction produces genetically identical organisms (clones), whereas in sexual reproduction, the genetic material of two individuals combines to produce offspring that are genetically different from their parents. During sexual reproduction the male gamete (sperm) may be placed inside the female's body for internal fertilization, or the sperm and eggs may be released into the environment for external fertilization. Seahorses, like the one shown in Figure

34.1, provide an example of the latter. Following a mating dance, the female lays eggs in the male seahorse's abdominal brood pouch where they are fertilized. The eggs hatch and the offspring develop in the pouch for several weeks.

Some animals are able to reproduce asexually by a process called parthenogenesis. While this process is common in invertebrate animals, it is rare in vertebrates. At first scientists thought that vertebrate parthenogenesis happened only with captive animals, such as birds, snakes, and sharks; however, it was recently discovered that about one in five smalltooth sawfish in Florida is the result of parthenogenesis. This species of fish is endangered, and researchers suspect that this form of reproduction may be an adaptation to help keep the species from going extinct. You can read more about this exciting research **here (http://openstaxcollege.org/l/32ocgiant)** .

34.1 | Reproduction Methods

In this section, you will explore the following questions:

- What are advantages and disadvantages of asexual and sexual reproduction?
- What are examples of methods of asexual reproduction among animals?
- What are examples of methods of sexual reproduction among animals?

Connection for AP® Courses

Much of the information about the different reproductive systems of animals is not within the scope for AP®. You likely studied human reproduction in a health course or previous biology course. Reproduction is necessary for the survival of a species, and animals have evolved various reproductive strategies. In a previous chapter we learned that asexual reproduction via mitosis produces genetically identical organisms (clones). We also previously explored how meiosis followed by **sexual reproduction** produces offspring that are genetically different from their parents. Whether or not the material in this chapter is required or illustrative as part of your AP® course, you should find the concepts interesting and relevant to your lives outside the classroom.

Both asexual and sexual reproductive strategies have their advantages and disadvantages. Organisms that reproduce asexually—for example, bacteria and some eukaryotes—may be at a disadvantage in an unstable or unpredictable environment because, barring mutation, the identical offspring may not have sufficient genetic variation to survive in new or different conditions. On the other hand, the rapid rates of **asexual reproduction** may allow a speedy response to changing environmental conditions. Although sexual reproduction allows for greater genetic variation in offspring, organisms that reproduce sexually must maintain males and females in the population, which can limit the ability to colonize new habitats.

Information presented and the examples highlighted in the section support concepts outlined in Big Idea 3 of the AP® Biology Curriculum Framework. The AP® Learning Objectives listed in the Curriculum Framework provide a transparent foundation for the AP® Biology course, an inquiry-based laboratory experience, instructional activities, and AP® exam questions. A learning objective merges required content with one or more of the seven science practices.

Big Idea 3	Living systems store, retrieve, transmit and respond to information essential to life processes.
Enduring Understanding 3.A	Heritable information provides for continuity of life.
Essential Knowledge	**3.A.2** In eukaryotes, heritable information is passed to the next generation via processes that include the cell cycle and mitosis or meiosis plus fertilization.
Science Practice	**6.2** The student can construct explanations of phenomena based on evidence produced through scientific practices.
Learning Objective	**3.9** The student is able to construct an explanation, using visual representations or narratives, as to how DNA in chromosomes is transmitted to the next generation via mitosis, or meiosis followed by fertilization.

Essential Knowledge	**3.A.2** In eukaryotes, heritable information is passed to the next generation via processes that include the cell cycle and mitosis or meiosis plus fertilization.
Science Practice	**7.1** The student can connect phenomena and models across spatial and temporal scales.
Learning Objective	**3.10** The student is able to represent the connection between meiosis and increased genetic diversity necessary for evolution.

Asexual Reproduction

Asexual reproduction occurs in prokaryotic microorganisms (bacteria) and in some eukaryotic single-celled and multi-celled organisms. There are a number of ways that animals reproduce asexually.

Fission

Fission, also called binary fission, occurs in prokaryotic microorganisms and in some invertebrate, multi-celled organisms. After a period of growth, an organism splits into two separate organisms. Some unicellular eukaryotic organisms undergo binary fission by mitosis. In other organisms, part of the individual separates and forms a second individual. This process occurs, for example, in many asteroid echinoderms through splitting of the central disk. Some sea anemones and some coral polyps (Figure 34.2) also reproduce through fission.

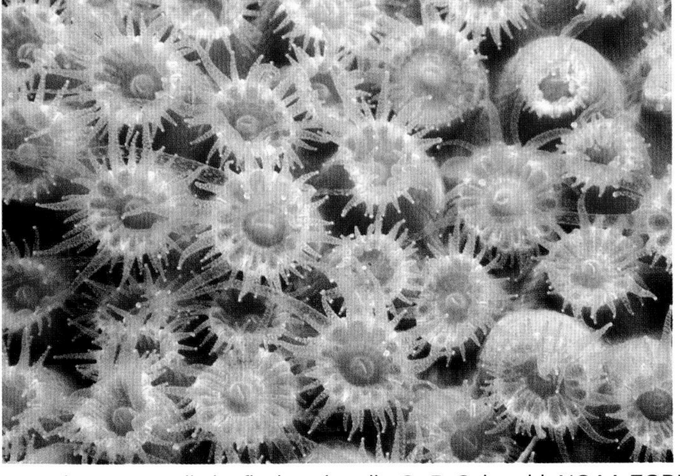

Figure 34.2 Coral polyps reproduce asexually by fission. (credit: G. P. Schmahl, NOAA FGBNMS Manager)

Budding

Budding is a form of asexual reproduction that results from the outgrowth of a part of a cell or body region leading to a separation from the original organism into two individuals. Budding occurs commonly in some invertebrate animals such as corals and hydras. In hydras, a bud forms that develops into an adult and breaks away from the main body, as illustrated in Figure 34.3, whereas in coral budding, the bud does not detach and multiplies as part of a new colony.

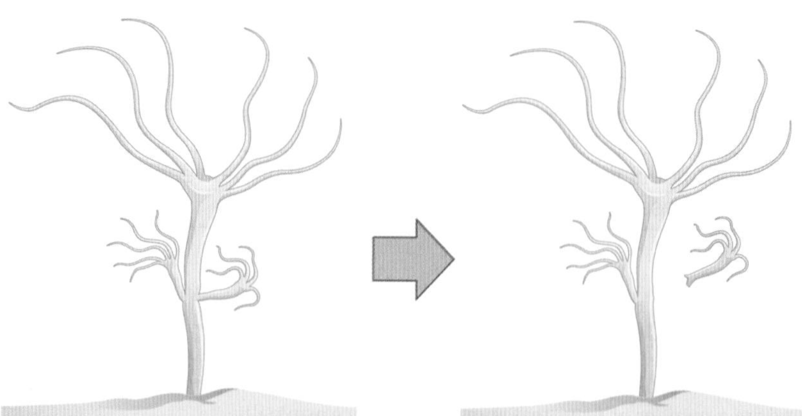

Figure 34.3 Hydra reproduce asexually through budding.

Watch a video (http://openstaxcollege.org/l/budding_hydra) of a hydra budding.

Hydras can reproduce through budding. How will the daughter hydra appear?

a. genetically identical to the mother

b. not genetically identical to the mother

c. genetically unique

d. smaller in size

Fragmentation

Fragmentation is the breaking of the body into two parts with subsequent regeneration. If the animal is capable of fragmentation, and the part is big enough, a separate individual will regrow.

For example, in many sea stars, asexual reproduction is accomplished by fragmentation. Figure 34.4 illustrates a sea star for which an arm of the individual is broken off and regenerates a new sea star. Fisheries workers have been known to try to kill the sea stars eating their clam or oyster beds by cutting them in half and throwing them back into the ocean. Unfortunately for the workers, the two parts can each regenerate a new half, resulting in twice as many sea stars to prey upon the oysters and clams. Fragmentation also occurs in annelid worms, turbellarians, and poriferans.

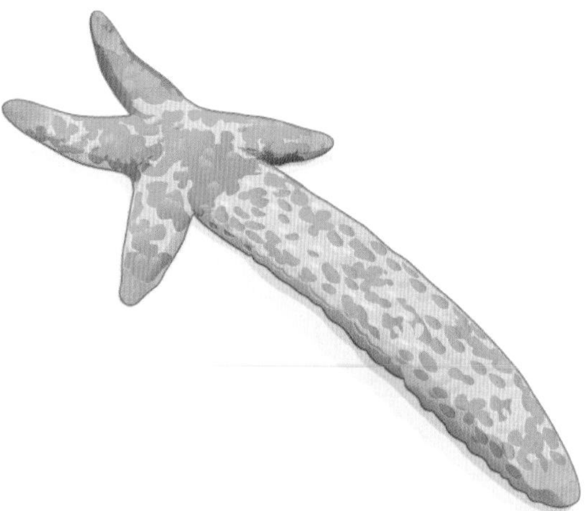

Figure 34.4 Sea stars can reproduce through fragmentation. The large arm, a fragment from another sea star, is developing into a new individual.

Note that in fragmentation, there is generally a noticeable difference in the size of the individuals, whereas in fission, two individuals of approximate size are formed.

Parthenogenesis

Parthenogenesis is a form of asexual reproduction where an egg develops into a complete individual without being fertilized. The resulting offspring can be either haploid or diploid, depending on the process and the species. Parthenogenesis occurs in invertebrates such as water flees, rotifers, aphids, stick insects, some ants, wasps, and bees. Bees and wasps use parthenogenesis to produce haploid males (called drones). If an egg is fertilized, it develops as a diploid female.

Some vertebrate animals—such as certain reptiles, amphibians, and fish—also reproduce through parthenogenesis. Although more common in plants, parthenogenesis has been observed in animal species that were segregated by sex in terrestrial or marine zoos. Two female Komodo dragons, a hammerhead shark, and a blacktop shark have produced parthenogenic young when the females have been isolated from males.

Sexual Reproduction

Sexual reproduction is the combination of (usually haploid) reproductive cells from two individuals to form a third (usually diploid) unique offspring. Sexual reproduction produces offspring with novel combinations of genes. This can be an adaptive advantage in unstable or unpredictable environments. As humans, we are used to thinking of animals as having two separate sexes—male and female—determined at conception. However, in the animal kingdom, there are many variations on this theme.

Lab Investigation

AP® Biology Investigative Labs: Inquiry-Based, Investigation 7: Cell Division: Mitosis and Meiosis. Design and conduct a series of experiments to investigate how eukaryotic cells divide to produce genetically identical cells or to produce gametes with half the normal DNA.

Think About It

Why is sexual reproduction useful if two separate cells must be combined to form a third?

Hermaphroditism

Hermaphroditism occurs in animals where one individual has both male and female reproductive parts. Invertebrates such as earthworms, slugs, tapeworms and snails, shown in Figure 34.5, are often hermaphroditic. Hermaphrodites may self-fertilize or may mate with another of their species, fertilizing each other and both producing offspring. Self fertilization is common in animals that have limited mobility or are not motile, such as barnacles and clams.

Figure 34.5 Many snails are hermaphrodites. When two individuals mate, they can produce up to one hundred eggs each. (credit: Assaf Shtilman)

Sex Determination

Mammalian sex determination is determined genetically by the presence of X and Y chromosomes. Individuals homozygous for X (XX) are female and heterozygous individuals (XY) are male. The presence of a Y chromosome causes the development of male characteristics and its absence results in female characteristics. The XY system is also found in some insects and plants.

Avian sex determination is dependent on the presence of Z and W chromosomes. Homozygous for Z (ZZ) results in a male and heterozygous (ZW) results in a female. The W appears to be essential in determining the sex of the individual, similar to the Y chromosome in mammals. Some fish, crustaceans, insects (such as butterflies and moths), and reptiles use this system.

The sex of some species is not determined by genetics but by some aspect of the environment. Sex determination in some crocodiles and turtles, for example, is often dependent on the temperature during critical periods of egg development. This is referred to as environmental sex determination, or more specifically as temperature-dependent sex determination. In many turtles, cooler temperatures during egg incubation produce males and warm temperatures produce females. In some crocodiles, moderate temperatures produce males and both warm and cool temperatures produce females. In some species, sex is both genetic- and temperature-dependent.

Individuals of some species change their sex during their lives, alternating between male and female. If the individual is female first, it is termed protogyny or “first female,” if it is male first, its termed protandry or “first male.” Oysters, for example, are born male, grow, and become female and lay eggs; some oyster species change sex multiple times.

everyday CONNECTION for AP® Courses

The temperature during incubation determines the sex of loggerhead sea turtles while developing in their eggs. If the temperature is warm enough, all will be females. If the temperature is cooler, all will be males. If the temperature is just right, called the pivotal temperature, then there will be about half females and half males.

Figure 34.6 (credit: Hillebrand Steve, U.S. Fish and Wildlife Service)

Many species of plants, including the sunflower pictured here, are capable of self-fertilization. If pollination does not occur with the help of pollinating insects, the stigma of the flower will wrap itself around the pollen of the same flower. Although self-fertilization forms seeds by meiosis, all of the resulting plants will be identical. In other words, self-fertilization decreases genetic diversity.

Figure 34.7 (credit: Wikipedia Commons, Helianthus annuus)

The sex of some crocodiles and turtles is dependent on the temperature during critical points in egg development. How is sex determined in mammalian species?

a. genetics
b. nutrition
c. temperature
d. genetics and temperature

34.2 | Fertilization

In this section, you will explore the following questions:

- What are the differences between internal and external methods of fertilization?
- What are examples of methods animals use for development of offspring during gestation?
- What are examples of anatomical adaptations that evolved in animals to facilitate reproduction?

Connection for AP® Courses

Sexual reproduction starts with the combination of a sperm and an egg in a process called fertilization. The methods of fertilization described in this section are not within the scope for AP®. However, from an evolutionary perspective, it is important to note that animals exhibit means of both **external fertilization** and **internal fertilization**, likely determined by their environment. In aquatic environments, water conveys sperm to egg (as in fish and amphibians), but in most terrestrial animals (such as reptiles, birds, and mammals), fertilization occurs internally. The adaptation of the shelled (**amniote**) egg with extraembryonic membranes in reptiles and birds allowed offspring to develop in the conditions associated with land, particularly the lack of water. Placental mammals, including humans, retain the embryo in the female's body until birth.

Information presented and examples highlighted in this section are not within the scope for AP® and do not align to the Curriculum Framework.

External Fertilization

External fertilization usually occurs in aquatic environments where both eggs and sperm are released into the water. After the sperm reaches the egg, fertilization takes place. Most external fertilization happens during the process of spawning where one or several females release their eggs and the male(s) release sperm in the same area, at the same time. The release of the reproductive material may be triggered by water temperature or the length of daylight. Nearly all fish spawn, as do crustaceans (such as crabs and shrimp), mollusks (such as oysters), squid, and echinoderms (such as sea urchins and sea cucumbers). Figure 34.8 shows salmon spawning in a shallow stream. Frogs, like those shown in Figure 34.9, corals, squid, and octopuses also spawn.

Figure 34.8 Salmon reproduce through spawning. (credit: Dan Bennett)

Figure 34.9 During sexual reproduction in toads, the male grasps the female from behind and externally fertilizes the eggs as they are deposited. (credit: "OakleyOriginals"/Flickr)

Pairs of fish that are not broadcast spawners may exhibit courtship behavior. This allows the female to select a particular male. The trigger for egg and sperm release (spawning) causes the egg and sperm to be placed in a small area, enhancing the possibility of fertilization.

External fertilization in an aquatic environment protects the eggs from drying out. Broadcast spawning can result in a greater mixture of the genes within a group, leading to higher genetic diversity and a greater chance of species survival in a hostile environment. For sessile aquatic organisms like sponges, broadcast spawning is the only mechanism for fertilization and colonization of new environments. The presence of the fertilized eggs and developing young in the water provides opportunities for predation resulting in a loss of offspring. Therefore, millions of eggs must be produced by individuals, and the offspring produced through this method must mature rapidly. The survival rate of eggs produced through broadcast spawning is low.

Internal Fertilization

Internal fertilization occurs most often in land-based animals, although some aquatic animals also use this method. There are three ways that offspring are produced following internal fertilization. In **oviparity**, fertilized eggs are laid outside the female's body and develop there, receiving nourishment from the yolk that is a part of the egg. This occurs in most bony fish, many reptiles, some cartilaginous fish, most amphibians, two mammals, and all birds. Reptiles and insects produce leathery eggs, while birds and turtles produce eggs with high concentrations of calcium carbonate in the shell, making them hard. Chicken eggs are an example of this second type.

In **ovoviparity**, fertilized eggs are retained in the female, but the embryo obtains its nourishment from the egg's yolk and the young are fully developed when they are hatched. This occurs in some bony fish (like the guppy *Lebistes reticulatus*), some sharks, some lizards, some snakes (such as the garter snake *Thamnophis sirtalis*), some vipers, and some invertebrate animals (like the Madagascar hissing cockroach *Gromphadorhina portentosa*).

In **viviparity** the young develop within the female, receiving nourishment from the mother's blood through a placenta. The offspring develops in the female and is born alive. This occurs in most mammals, some cartilaginous fish, and a few reptiles.

Internal fertilization has the advantage of protecting the fertilized egg from dehydration on land. The embryo is isolated within the female, which limits predation on the young. Internal fertilization enhances the fertilization of eggs by a specific male. Fewer offspring are produced through this method, but their survival rate is higher than that for external fertilization.

The Evolution of Reproduction

Once multicellular organisms evolved and developed specialized cells, some also developed tissues and organs with specialized functions. An early development in reproduction occurred in the Annelids. These organisms produce sperm and eggs from undifferentiated cells in their coelom and store them in that cavity. When the coelom becomes filled, the cells are released through an excretory opening or by the body splitting open. Reproductive organs evolved with the development of gonads that produce sperm and eggs. These cells went through meiosis, an adaption of mitosis, which reduced the number of chromosomes in each reproductive cell by half, while increasing the number of cells through cell division.

Complete reproductive systems were developed in insects, with separate sexes. Sperm are made in testes and then travel through coiled tubes to the epididymis for storage. Eggs mature in the ovary. When they are released from the ovary, they travel to the uterine tubes for fertilization. Some insects have a specialized sac, called a **spermatheca**, which stores sperm for later use, sometimes up to a year. Fertilization can be timed with environmental or food conditions that are optimal for offspring survival.

Vertebrates have similar structures, with a few differences. Non-mammals, such as birds and reptiles, have a common body opening, called a **cloaca**, for the digestive, excretory and reproductive systems. Coupling between birds usually involves positioning the cloaca openings opposite each other for transfer of sperm. Mammals have separate openings for the systems in the female and a uterus for support of developing offspring. The uterus has two chambers in species that produce large numbers of offspring at a time, while species that produce one offspring, such as primates, have a single uterus.

Sperm transfer from the male to the female during reproduction ranges from releasing the sperm into the watery environment for external fertilization, to the joining of cloaca in birds, to the development of a penis for direct delivery into the female's vagina in mammals.

science practices CONNECTION for AP® Courses

Think About It

The measure of an individual's reproductive success is based on its ability to produce offspring. What adaptations would a male have to have to be reproductively successful if his species utilizes external fertilization? Internal fertilization?

34.3 | Human Reproductive Anatomy and Gametogenesis

In this section, you will explore the following questions:

- What are the features of the human male and female reproductive anatomies?
- What are the events associated with the human sexual response?
- What are the differences and similarities between spermatogenesis and oogenesis?

Connection for AP® Courses

Much of the information in this section is not within the scope for AP®. You do not need to match a list of the different anatomical features of the male and female reproductive systems with their functions, but you likely will find the material informative and relevant. The reproductive structures that evolved in land animals, including humans, allow males and females to mate, fertilize internally, and support the growth and development of offspring. The section provides an opportunity to review the process of meiosis that we first explored in a previous chapter.

Information presented and the examples highlighted in the section support concepts outlined in Big Idea 3 of the AP® Biology Curriculum Framework. The AP® Learning Objectives listed in the Curriculum Framework provide a transparent foundation for the AP® Biology course, an inquiry-based laboratory experience, instructional activities, and AP® exam questions. A learning objective merges required content with one or more of the seven science practices.

Big Idea 3	Living systems store, retrieve, transmit and respond to information essential to life processes.

Enduring Understanding 3.A	Heritable information provides for continuity of life.
Essential Knowledge	**3.A.2** In eukaryotes, heritable information is passed to the next generation via processes that include the cell cycle and mitosis or meiosis plus fertilization.
Science Practice	**6.2** The student can construct explanations of phenomena based on evidence produced through scientific practices.
Learning Objective	**3.9** The student is able to construct an explanation, using visual representations or narratives, as to how DNA in chromosomes is transmitted to the next generation via mitosis, or meiosis followed by fertilization.
Essential Knowledge	**3.A.2** In eukaryotes, heritable information is passed to the next generation via processes that include the cell cycle and mitosis or meiosis plus fertilization.
Science Practice	**7.1** The student can connect phenomena and models across spatial and temporal scales.
Learning Objective	**3.10** The student is able to represent the connection between meiosis and increased genetic diversity necessary for evolution.

Human Reproductive Anatomy

The reproductive tissues of male and female humans develop similarly *in utero* until a low level of the hormone testosterone is released from male gonads. Testosterone causes the undeveloped tissues to differentiate into male sexual organs. When testosterone is absent, the tissues develop into female sexual tissues. Primitive gonads become testes or ovaries. Tissues that produce a penis in males produce a clitoris in females. The tissue that will become the scrotum in a male becomes the labia in a female; that is, they are homologous structures.

Male Reproductive Anatomy

In the male reproductive system, the **scrotum** houses the testicles or testes (singular: testis), including providing passage for blood vessels, nerves, and muscles related to testicular function. The **testes** are a pair of male reproductive organs that produce sperm and some reproductive hormones. Each testis is approximately 2.5 by 3.8 cm (1.5 by 1 in) in size and divided into wedge-shaped lobules by connective tissue called septa. Coiled in each wedge are seminiferous tubules that produce sperm.

Sperm are immobile at body temperature; therefore, the scrotum and penis are external to the body, as illustrated in **Figure 34.10** so that a proper temperature is maintained for motility. In land mammals, the pair of testes must be suspended outside the body at about 2° C lower than body temperature to produce viable sperm. Infertility can occur in land mammals when the testes do not descend through the abdominal cavity during fetal development.

visual CONNECTION

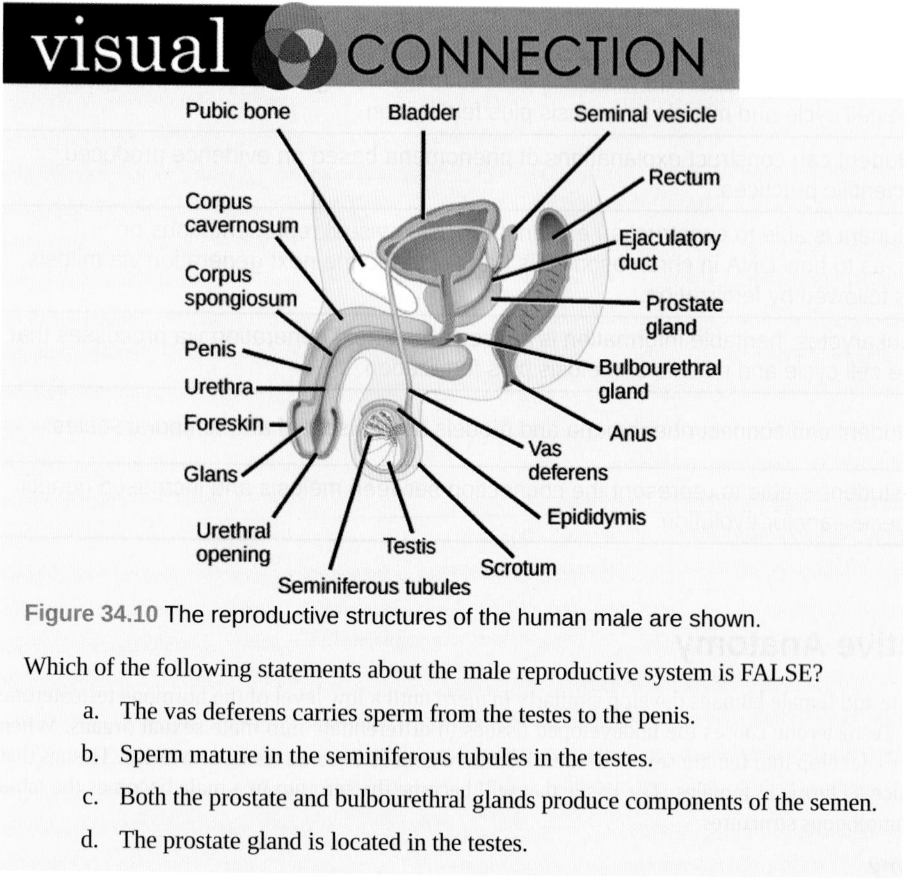

Figure 34.10 The reproductive structures of the human male are shown.

Which of the following statements about the male reproductive system is FALSE?

a. The vas deferens carries sperm from the testes to the penis.
b. Sperm mature in the seminiferous tubules in the testes.
c. Both the prostate and bulbourethral glands produce components of the semen.
d. The prostate gland is located in the testes.

Sperm mature in **seminiferous tubules** that are coiled inside the testes, as illustrated in Figure 34.10. The walls of the seminiferous tubules are made up of the developing sperm cells, with the least developed sperm at the periphery of the tubule and the fully developed sperm in the lumen. The sperm cells are mixed with "nursemaid" cells called Sertoli cells which protect the germ cells and promote their development. Other cells mixed in the wall of the tubules are the interstitial cells of Leydig. These cells produce high levels of testosterone once the male reaches adolescence.

When the sperm have developed flagella and are nearly mature, they leave the testicles and enter the epididymis, shown in Figure 34.10. This structure resembles a comma and lies along the top and posterior portion of the testes; it is the site of sperm maturation. The sperm leave the epididymis and enter the vas deferens (or ductus deferens), which carries the sperm, behind the bladder, and forms the ejaculatory duct with the duct from the seminal vesicles. During a vasectomy, a section of the vas deferens is removed, preventing sperm from being passed out of the body during ejaculation and preventing fertilization.

Semen is a mixture of sperm and spermatic duct secretions (about 10 percent of the total) and fluids from accessory glands that contribute most of the semen's volume. Sperm are haploid cells, consisting of a flagellum as a tail, a neck that contains the cell's energy-producing mitochondria, and a head that contains the genetic material. Figure 34.11 shows a micrograph of human sperm as well as a diagram of the parts of the sperm. An acrosome is found at the top of the head of the sperm. This structure contains lysosomal enzymes that can digest the protective coverings that surround the egg to help the sperm penetrate and fertilize the egg. An ejaculate will contain from two to five milliliters of fluid with from 50–120 million sperm per milliliter.

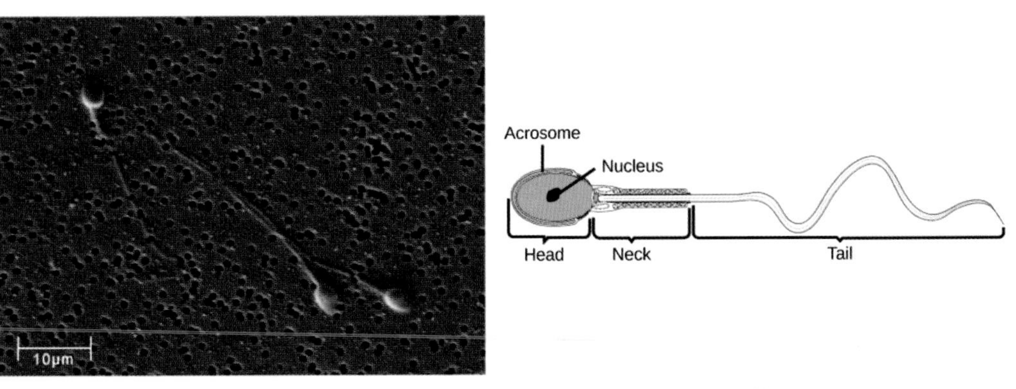

Figure 34.11 Human sperm, visualized using scanning electron microscopy, have a flagellum, neck, and head. (credit b: modification of work by Mariana Ruiz Villareal; scale-bar data from Matt Russell)

The bulk of the semen comes from the accessory glands associated with the male reproductive system. These are the seminal vesicles, the prostate gland, and the bulbourethral gland, all of which are illustrated in Figure 34.10. The **seminal vesicles** are a pair of glands that lie along the posterior border of the urinary bladder. The glands make a solution that is thick, yellowish, and alkaline. As sperm are only motile in an alkaline environment, a basic pH is important to reverse the acidity of the vaginal environment. The solution also contains mucus, fructose (a sperm mitochondrial nutrient), a coagulating enzyme, ascorbic acid, and local-acting hormones called prostaglandins. The seminal vesicle glands account for 60 percent of the bulk of semen.

The **penis**, illustrated in Figure 34.10, is an organ that drains urine from the renal bladder and functions as a copulatory organ during intercourse. The penis contains three tubes of erectile tissue running through the length of the organ. These consist of a pair of tubes on the dorsal side, called the corpus cavernosum, and a single tube of tissue on the ventral side, called the corpus spongiosum. This tissue will become engorged with blood, becoming erect and hard, in preparation for intercourse. The organ is inserted into the vagina culminating with an ejaculation. During intercourse, the smooth muscle sphincters at the opening to the renal bladder close and prevent urine from entering the penis. An orgasm is a two-stage process: first, glands and accessory organs connected to the testes contract, then semen (containing sperm) is expelled through the urethra during ejaculation. After intercourse, the blood drains from the erectile tissue and the penis becomes flaccid.

The walnut-shaped **prostate gland** surrounds the urethra, the connection to the urinary bladder. It has a series of short ducts that directly connect to the urethra. The gland is a mixture of smooth muscle and glandular tissue. The muscle provides much of the force needed for ejaculation to occur. The glandular tissue makes a thin, milky fluid that contains citrate (a nutrient), enzymes, and prostate specific antigen (PSA). PSA is a proteolytic enzyme that helps to liquefy the ejaculate several minutes after release from the male. Prostate gland secretions account for about 30 percent of the bulk of semen.

The **bulbourethral gland**, or Cowper's gland, releases its secretion prior to the release of the bulk of the semen. It neutralizes any acid residue in the urethra left over from urine. This usually accounts for a couple of drops of fluid in the total ejaculate and may contain a few sperm. Withdrawal of the penis from the vagina before ejaculation to prevent pregnancy may not work if sperm are present in the bulbourethral gland secretions. The location and functions of the male reproductive organs are summarized in Table 34.1.

Male Reproductive Anatomy

Organ	Location	Function
Scrotum	External	Carry and support testes
Penis	External	Deliver urine, copulating organ
Testes	Internal	Produce sperm and male hormones
Seminal Vesicles	Internal	Contribute to semen production
Prostate Gland	Internal	Contribute to semen production

Table 34.1

Male Reproductive Anatomy

Organ	Location	Function
Bulbourethral Glands	Internal	Clean urethra at ejaculation

Table 34.1

Female Reproductive Anatomy

A number of reproductive structures are exterior to the female's body. These include the breasts and the vulva, which consists of the mons pubis, clitoris, labia majora, labia minora, and the vestibular glands, all illustrated in Figure 34.12. The location and functions of the female reproductive organs are summarized in Table 34.2. The vulva is an area associated with the vestibule which includes the structures found in the inguinal (groin) area of women. The mons pubis is a round, fatty area that overlies the pubic symphysis. The **clitoris** is a structure with erectile tissue that contains a large number of sensory nerves and serves as a source of stimulation during intercourse. The **labia majora** are a pair of elongated folds of tissue that run posterior from the mons pubis and enclose the other components of the vulva. The labia majora derive from the same tissue that produces the scrotum in a male. The **labia minora** are thin folds of tissue centrally located within the labia majora. These labia protect the openings to the vagina and urethra. The mons pubis and the anterior portion of the labia majora become covered with hair during adolescence; the labia minora is hairless. The greater vestibular glands are found at the sides of the vaginal opening and provide lubrication during intercourse.

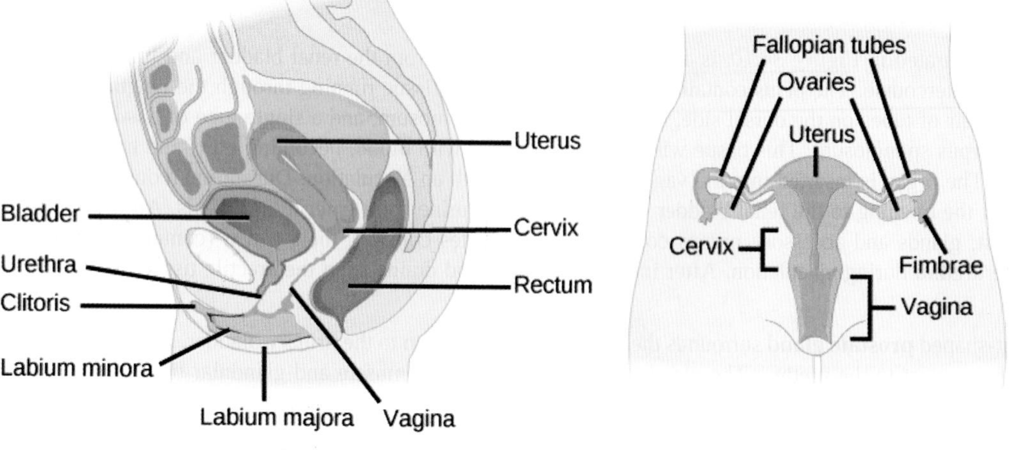

Figure 34.12 The reproductive structures of the human female are shown. (credit a: modification of work by Gray's Anatomy; credit b: modification of work by CDC)

Female Reproductive Anatomy

Organ	Location	Function
Clitoris	External	Sensory organ
Mons pubis	External	Fatty area overlying pubic bone
Labia majora	External	Covers labia minora
Labia minora	External	Covers vestibule
Greater vestibular glands	External	Secrete mucus; lubricate vagina
Breast	External	Produce and deliver milk
Ovaries	Internal	Carry and develop eggs

Table 34.2

Female Reproductive Anatomy

Organ	Location	Function
Oviducts (Fallopian tubes)	Internal	Transport egg to uterus
Uterus	Internal	Support developing embryo
Vagina	Internal	Common tube for intercourse, birth canal, passing menstrual flow

Table 34.2

The breasts consist of mammary glands and fat. The size of the breast is determined by the amount of fat deposited behind the gland. Each gland consists of 15 to 25 lobes that have ducts that empty at the nipple and that supply the nursing child with nutrient- and antibody-rich milk to aid development and protect the child.

Internal female reproductive structures include ovaries, oviducts, the **uterus**, and the vagina, shown in Figure 34.12. The pair of ovaries is held in place in the abdominal cavity by a system of ligaments. Ovaries consist of a medulla and cortex: the medulla contains nerves and blood vessels to supply the cortex with nutrients and remove waste. The outer layers of cells of the cortex are the functional parts of the ovaries. The cortex is made up of follicular cells that surround eggs that develop during fetal development *in utero*. During the menstrual period, a batch of follicular cells develops and prepares the eggs for release. At ovulation, one follicle ruptures and one egg is released, as illustrated in Figure 34.13**a**.

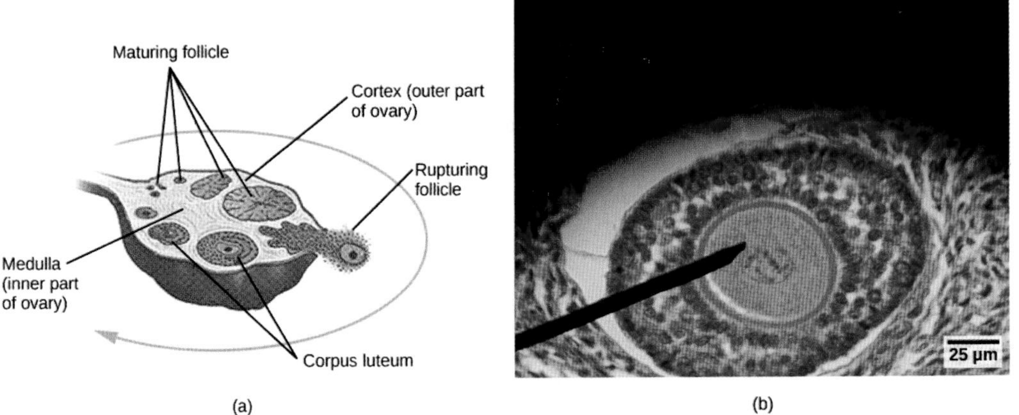

Figure 34.13 Oocytes develop in (a) follicles, located in the ovary. At the beginning of the menstrual cycle, the follicle matures. At ovulation, the follicle ruptures, releasing the egg. The follicle becomes a corpus luteum, which eventually degenerates. The (b) follicle in this light micrograph has an oocyte at its center. (credit a: modification of work by NIH; scale-bar data from Matt Russell)

The **oviducts**, or fallopian tubes, extend from the uterus in the lower abdominal cavity to the ovaries, but they are not in contact with the ovaries. The lateral ends of the oviducts flare out into a trumpet-like structure and have a fringe of finger-like projections called fimbriae, illustrated in Figure 34.12**b**. When an egg is released at ovulation, the fimbrae help the non-motile egg enter into the tube and passage to the uterus. The walls of the oviducts are ciliated and are made up mostly of smooth muscle. The cilia beat toward the middle, and the smooth muscle contracts in the same direction, moving the egg toward the uterus. Fertilization usually takes place within the oviducts and the developing embryo is moved toward the uterus for development. It usually takes the egg or embryo a week to travel through the oviduct. Sterilization in women is called a tubal ligation; it is analogous to a vasectomy in males in that the oviducts are severed and sealed.

The uterus is a structure about the size of a woman's fist. This is lined with an endometrium rich in blood vessels and mucus glands. The uterus supports the developing embryo and fetus during gestation. The thickest portion of the wall of the uterus is made of smooth muscle. Contractions of the smooth muscle in the uterus aid in passing the baby through the vagina during labor. A portion of the lining of the uterus sloughs off during each menstrual period, and then builds up again in preparation for an implantation. Part of the uterus, called the cervix, protrudes into the top of the vagina. The cervix functions as the birth canal.

The **vagina** is a muscular tube that serves several purposes. It allows menstrual flow to leave the body. It is the receptacle for the penis during intercourse and the vessel for the delivery of offspring. It is lined by stratified squamous epithelial cells to protect the underlying tissue.

Sexual Response during Intercourse

The sexual response in humans is both psychological and physiological. Both sexes experience sexual arousal through psychological and physical stimulation. There are four phases of the sexual response. During phase one, called excitement, vasodilation leads to vasocongestion in erectile tissues in both men and women. The nipples, clitoris, labia, and penis engorge with blood and become enlarged. Vaginal secretions are released to lubricate the vagina to facilitate intercourse. During the second phase, called the plateau, stimulation continues, the outer third of the vaginal wall enlarges with blood, and breathing and heart rate increase.

During phase three, or orgasm, rhythmic, involuntary contractions of muscles occur in both sexes. In the male, the reproductive accessory glands and tubules constrict placing semen in the urethra, then the urethra contracts expelling the semen through the penis. In women, the uterus and vaginal muscles contract in waves that may last slightly less than a second each. During phase four, or resolution, the processes described in the first three phases reverse themselves and return to their normal state. Men experience a refractory period in which they cannot maintain an erection or ejaculate for a period of time ranging from minutes to hours.

Gametogenesis (Spermatogenesis and Oogenesis)

Gametogenesis, the production of sperm and eggs, takes place through the process of meiosis. During meiosis, two cell divisions separate the paired chromosomes in the nucleus and then separate the chromatids that were made during an earlier stage of the cell's life cycle. Meiosis produces haploid cells with half of each pair of chromosomes normally found in diploid cells. The production of sperm is called **spermatogenesis** and the production of eggs is called **oogenesis**.

Spermatogenesis

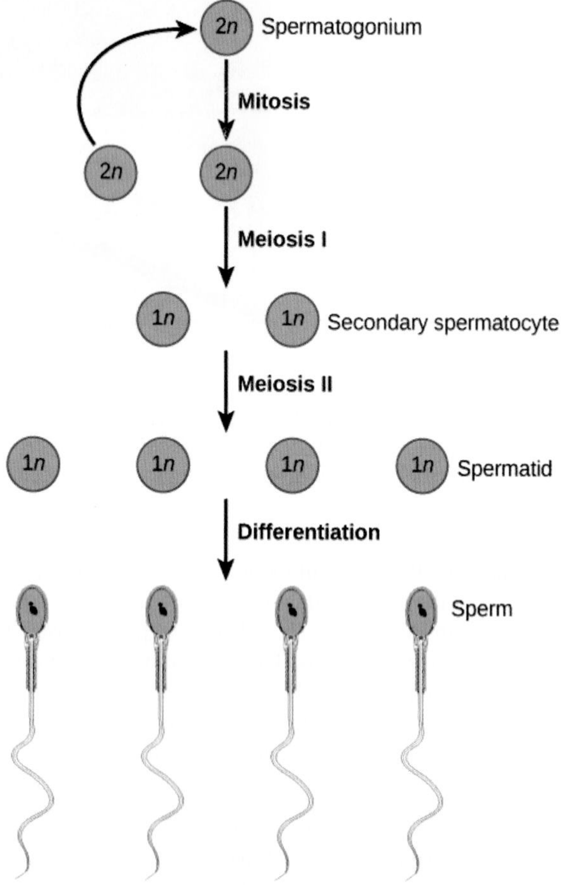

Figure 34.14 During spermatogenesis, four sperm result from each primary spermatocyte.

Spermatogenesis, illustrated in Figure 34.14, occurs in the wall of the seminiferous tubules (Figure 34.10), with stem cells at the periphery of the tube and the spermatozoa at the lumen of the tube. Immediately under the capsule of the tubule are diploid, undifferentiated cells. These stem cells, called spermatogonia (singular: spermatagonium), go through mitosis with one offspring going on to differentiate into a sperm cell and the other giving rise to the next generation of sperm.

Meiosis starts with a cell called a primary spermatocyte. At the end of the first meiotic division, a haploid cell is produced called a secondary spermatocyte. This cell is haploid and must go through another meiotic cell division. The cell produced at the end of meiosis is called a spermatid and when it reaches the lumen of the tubule and grows a flagellum, it is called a sperm cell. Four sperm result from each primary spermatocyte that goes through meiosis.

Stem cells are deposited during gestation and are present at birth through the beginning of adolescence, but in an inactive state. During adolescence, gonadotropic hormones from the anterior pituitary cause the activation of these cells and the production of viable sperm. This continues into old age.

Visit this site (http://openstaxcollege.org/l/spermatogenesis) to see the process of spermatogenesis.

During spermatogenesis, which cells undergo meiosis to ultimately produce haploid gametes?

a. spermatogonia

b. primary spermatocytes

c. secondary spermatocytes

d. spermatids

Oogenesis

Oogenesis, illustrated in Figure 34.15, occurs in the outermost layers of the ovaries. As with sperm production, oogenesis starts with a germ cell, called an oogonium (plural: oogonia), but this cell undergoes mitosis to increase in number, eventually resulting in up to about one to two million cells in the embryo.

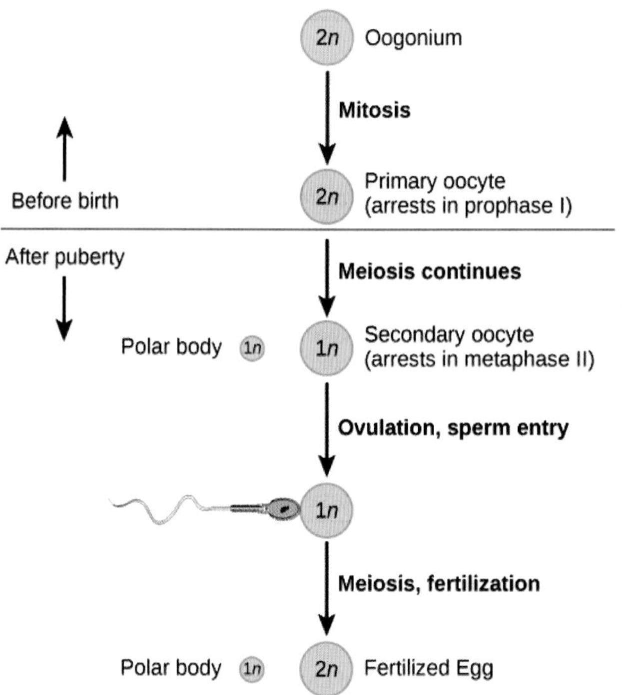

Figure 34.15 The process of oogenesis occurs in the ovary's outermost layer.

The cell starting meiosis is called a primary oocyte, as shown in **Figure 34.15**. This cell will start the first meiotic division and be arrested in its progress in the first prophase stage. At the time of birth, all future eggs are in the prophase stage. At adolescence, anterior pituitary hormones cause the development of a number of follicles in an ovary. This results in the primary oocyte finishing the first meiotic division. The cell divides unequally, with most of the cellular material and organelles going to one cell, called a secondary oocyte, and only one set of chromosomes and a small amount of cytoplasm going to the other cell. This second cell is called a polar body and usually dies. A secondary meiotic arrest occurs, this time at the metaphase II stage. At ovulation, this secondary oocyte will be released and travel toward the uterus through the oviduct. If the secondary oocyte is fertilized, the cell continues through the meiosis II, producing a second polar body and a fertilized egg containing all 46 chromosomes of a human being, half of them coming from the sperm.

Egg production begins before birth, is arrested during meiosis until puberty, and then individual cells continue through at each menstrual cycle. One egg is produced from each meiotic process, with the extra chromosomes and chromatids going into polar bodies that degenerate and are reabsorbed by the body.

science practices CONNECTION for AP® Courses

Think About It

Compare spermatogenesis and oogenesis as to the timing of the processes and the number and type of cells finally produced.

34.4 | Hormonal Control of Human Reproduction

In this section, you will explore the following questions:

- What are the roles of male and female reproductive hormones?
- What is the link between the ovarian and menstrual cycles?
- What events are associated with menopause?

Connection for AP® Courses

The information in this section is an application of concepts we learned when exploring the endocrine system in a previous chapter. The human male and female reproductive cycles are regulated by the interaction of hormones from the hypothalamus and anterior pituitary with hormones from reproductive tissues and organs. Detailed knowledge about sperm production and the ovarian and menstrual cycles is not within the scope for AP®, and you likely studied this information in a health class. Since the material in this section is practical and relevant, a brief review is helpful.

Information presented and the examples highlighted in the section support concepts outlined in Big Idea 2 and Big Idea 3 of the AP® Biology Curriculum Framework. The AP® Learning Objectives listed in the Curriculum Framework provide a transparent foundation for the AP® Biology course, an inquiry-based laboratory experience, instructional activities, and AP® exam questions. A learning objective merges required content with one or more of the seven science practices.

Big Idea 2	Biological systems utilize free energy and molecular building blocks to grow, to reproduce, and to maintain dynamic homeostasis.
Enduring Understanding 2.C	Organisms use feedback mechanisms to regulate growth and reproduction, and to maintain dynamic homeostasis.
Essential Knowledge	**2.C.1** Organisms use feedback mechanisms to maintain their internal environments and respond to external environmental changes.

Science Practice	**7.2** The student can connect concepts in and across domain(s) to generalize or extrapolate in and/or across enduring understandings and/or big ideas.
Learning Objective	**2.16** The student is able to connect how organisms use negative feedback to maintain their internal environments.
Essential Knowledge	**2.C.1** Organisms use feedback mechanisms to maintain their internal environments and respond to external environmental changes.
Science Practice	**5.3** The student can evaluate the evidence provided by data sets in relation to a particular scientific question.
Learning Objective	**2.17** The student is able to evaluate data that show the effect(s) of changes in concentration of key molecules on negative feedback mechanisms.
Big Idea 3	Living systems store, retrieve, transmit and respond to information essential to life processes.
Enduring Understanding 3.D	Cells communicate by generating, transmitting and receiving chemical signals.
Essential Knowledge	**3.D.2** Cells communicate with each other through direct contact with other cells or from a distance via chemical signaling.
Science Practice	**6.2** The student can construct explanations of phenomena based on evidence produced through scientific practices.
Learning Objective	**3.34** The student is able to construct explanations of cell communication through cell-to-cell direct contact or through chemical signaling.
Essential Knowledge	**3.D.2** Cells communicate with each other through direct contact with other cells or from a distance via chemical signaling.
Science Practice	**1.1** The student can create representations and models of natural or man-made phenomena and systems in the domain.
Learning Objective	**3.35** The student is able to create representation(s) that depict how cell-to-cell communication occurs by direct contact or from a distance through chemical signaling.

Male Hormones

At the onset of puberty, the hypothalamus causes the release of **follicle stimulating hormone (FSH)** and **luteinizing hormone (LH)** into the male system for the first time. FSH enters the testes and stimulates the **Sertoli cells** to begin facilitating spermatogenesis using negative feedback, as illustrated in **Figure 34.16**. LH also enters the testes and stimulates the **interstitial cells of Leydig** to make and release testosterone into the testes and the blood.

Testosterone, the hormone responsible for the secondary sexual characteristics that develop in the male during adolescence, stimulates spermatogenesis. These secondary sex characteristics include a deepening of the voice, the growth of facial, axillary, and pubic hair, and the beginnings of the sex drive.

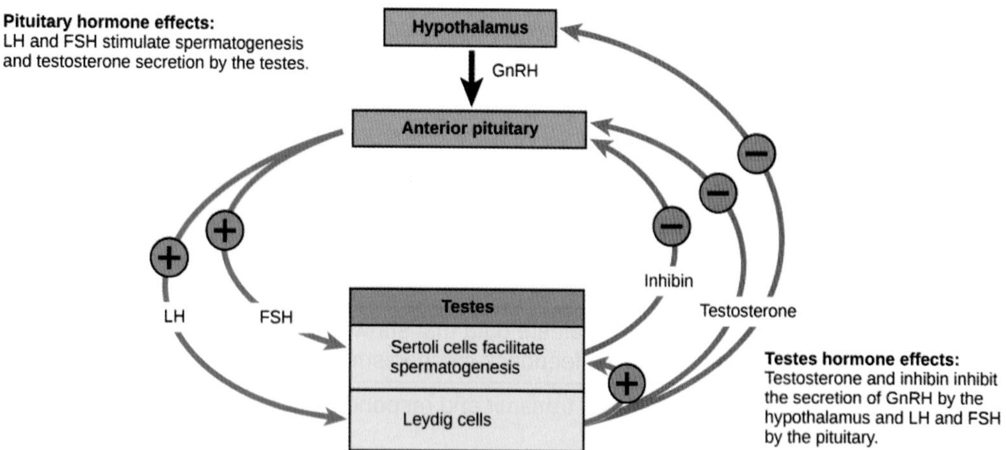

Figure 34.16 Hormones control sperm production in a negative feedback system.

A negative feedback system occurs in the male with rising levels of testosterone acting on the hypothalamus and anterior pituitary to inhibit the release of **gonadotropin-releasing hormone (GnRH)** , FSH, and LH. The Sertoli cells produce the hormone **inhibin**, which is released into the blood when the sperm count is too high. This inhibits the release of GnRH and FSH, which will cause spermatogenesis to slow down. If the sperm count reaches 20 million/ml, the Sertoli cells cease the release of inhibin, and the sperm count increases.

Female Hormones

The control of reproduction in females is more complex. As with the male, the anterior pituitary hormones cause the release of the hormones FSH and LH. In addition, estrogens and progesterone are released from the developing follicles. **Estrogen** is the reproductive hormone in females that assists in endometrial regrowth, ovulation, and calcium absorption; it is also responsible for the secondary sexual characteristics of females. These include breast development, flaring of the hips, and a shorter period necessary for bone maturation. **Progesterone** assists in endometrial re-growth and inhibition of FSH and LH release.

In females, FSH stimulates development of egg cells, called ova, which develop in structures called follicles. Follicle cells produce the hormone inhibin, which inhibits FSH production. LH also plays a role in the development of ova, induction of ovulation, and stimulation of estradiol and progesterone production by the ovaries. Estradiol and progesterone are steroid hormones that prepare the body for pregnancy. Estradiol produces secondary sex characteristics in females, while both estradiol and progesterone regulate the menstrual cycle.

The Ovarian Cycle and the Menstrual Cycle

The **ovarian cycle** governs the preparation of endocrine tissues and release of eggs, while the **menstrual cycle** governs the preparation and maintenance of the uterine lining. These cycles occur concurrently and are coordinated over a 22–32 day cycle, with an average length of 28 days.

The first half of the ovarian cycle is the follicular phase shown in Figure 34.17. Slowly rising levels of FSH and LH cause the growth of follicles on the surface of the ovary. This process prepares the egg for ovulation. As the follicles grow, they begin releasing estrogens and a low level of progesterone. Progesterone maintains the endometrium to help ensure pregnancy. The trip through the fallopian tube takes about seven days. At this stage of development, called the morula, there are 30-60 cells. If pregnancy implantation does not occur, the lining is sloughed off. After about five days, estrogen levels rise and the menstrual cycle enters the proliferative phase. The endometrium begins to regrow, replacing the blood vessels and glands that deteriorated during the end of the last cycle.

visual CONNECTION

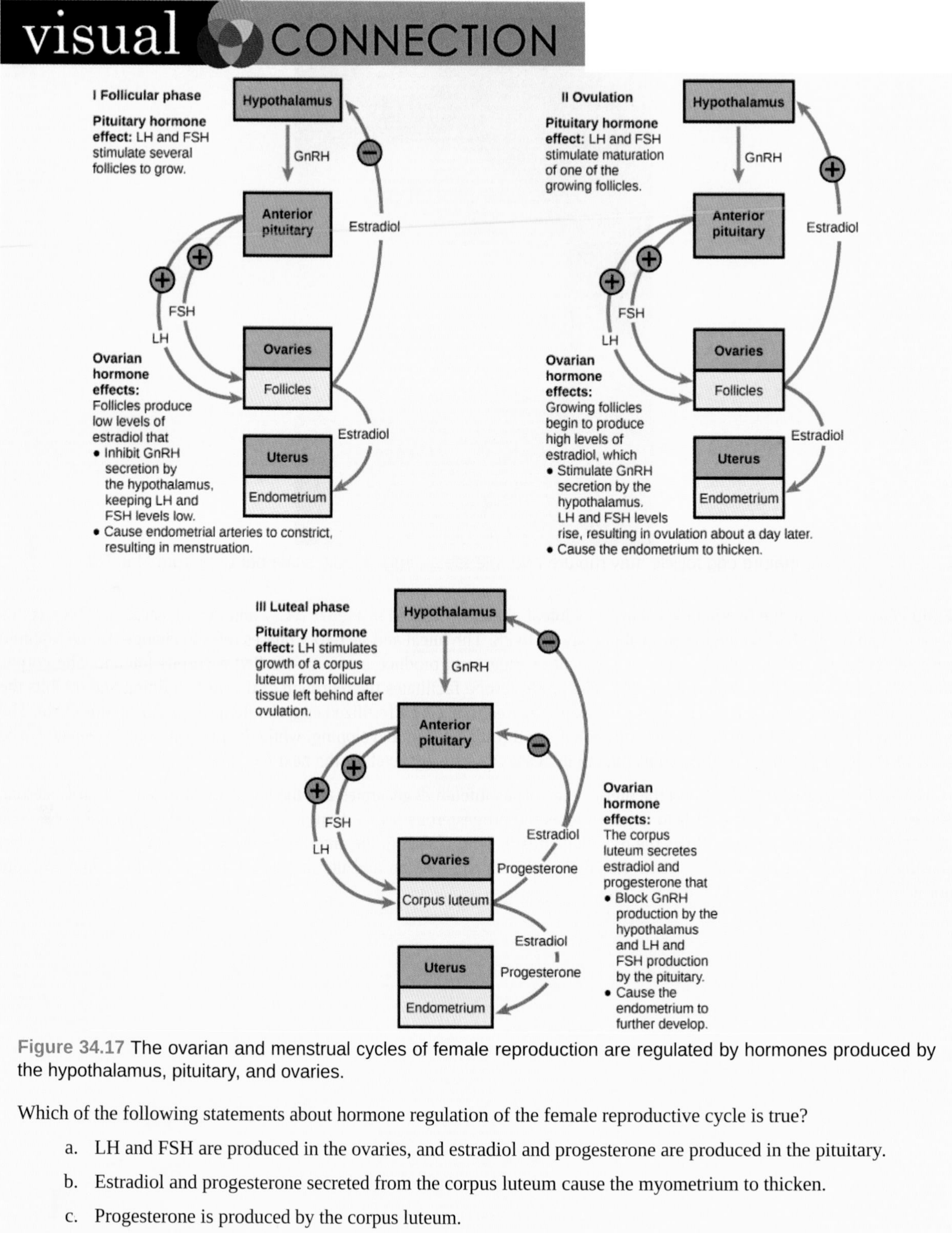

Figure 34.17 The ovarian and menstrual cycles of female reproduction are regulated by hormones produced by the hypothalamus, pituitary, and ovaries.

Which of the following statements about hormone regulation of the female reproductive cycle is true?

a. LH and FSH are produced in the ovaries, and estradiol and progesterone are produced in the pituitary.

b. Estradiol and progesterone secreted from the corpus luteum cause the myometrium to thicken.

c. Progesterone is produced by the corpus luteum.

d. Secretion of GnRH by the hypothalamus is inhibited by high levels of estradiol, but stimulated by low levels of estradiol.

Just prior to the middle of the cycle (approximately day 14), the high level of estrogen causes FSH and especially LH to rise rapidly, then fall. The spike in LH causes **ovulation**: the most mature follicle, like that shown in Figure 34.18, ruptures and releases its egg. The follicles that did not rupture degenerate and their eggs are lost. The level of estrogen decreases when the extra follicles degenerate.

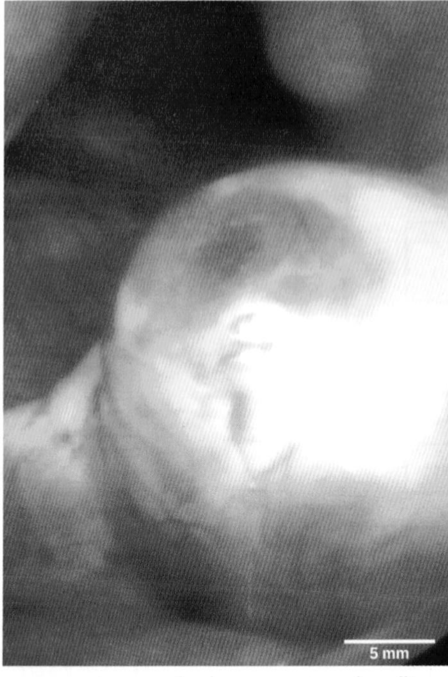

Figure 34.18 This mature egg follicle may rupture and release an egg. (credit: scale-bar data from Matt Russell)

Following ovulation, the ovarian cycle enters its luteal phase, illustrated in Figure 34.17 and the menstrual cycle enters its secretory phase, both of which run from about day 15 to 28. The luteal and secretory phases refer to changes in the ruptured follicle. The cells in the follicle undergo physical changes and produce a structure called a corpus luteum. The corpus luteum produces estrogen and progesterone. The progesterone facilitates the regrowth of the uterine lining and inhibits the release of further FSH and LH. The uterus is being prepared to accept a fertilized egg, should it occur during this cycle. The inhibition of FSH and LH prevents any further eggs and follicles from developing, while the progesterone is elevated. The level of estrogen produced by the corpus luteum increases to a steady level for the next few days.

If no fertilized egg is implanted into the uterus, the corpus luteum degenerates and the levels of estrogen and progesterone decrease. The endometrium begins to degenerate as the progesterone levels drop, initiating the next menstrual cycle. The decrease in progesterone also allows the hypothalamus to send GnRH to the anterior pituitary, releasing FSH and LH and starting the cycles again. Figure 34.19 visually compares the ovarian and uterine cycles as well as the commensurate hormone levels.

visual CONNECTION

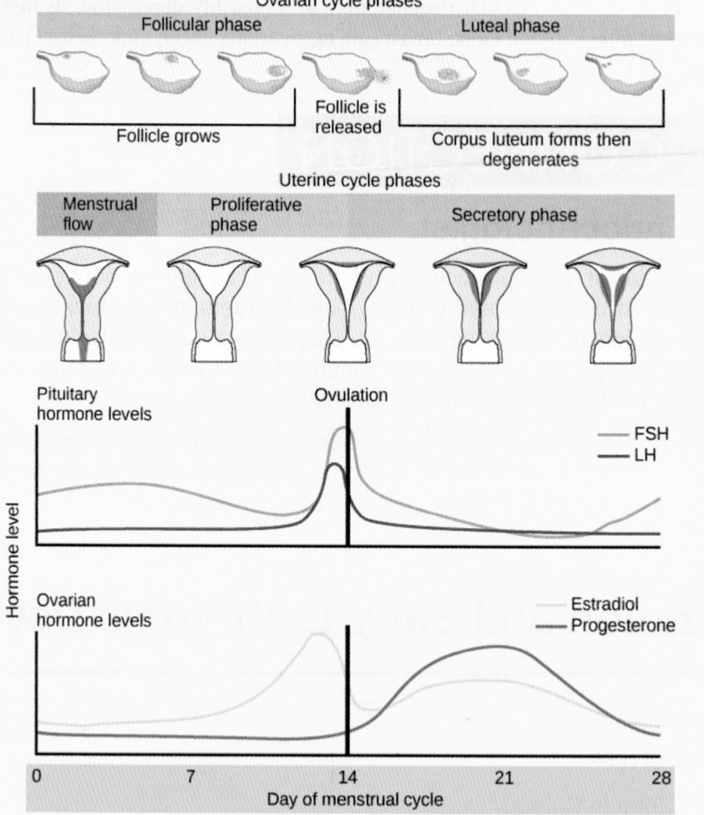

Figure 34.19 Rising and falling hormone levels result in progression of the ovarian and menstrual cycles. (credit: modification of work by Mikael Häggström)

Which of the following statements about the menstrual cycle is TRUE?

a. Estrogen levels rise during the luteal phase of the ovarian cycle and the secretory phase of the uterine cycle.
b. Menstruation occurs much before LH and FSH levels peak.
c. Menstruation occurs after progesterone levels rise.
d. Progesterone levels rise before ovulation, while estrogen levels rise after.

science practices CONNECTION for AP® Courses

Think About It

What are the major events in the ovarian cycle leading up to ovulation, and how are these events regulated by negative feedback mechanisms?

Menopause

As women approach their mid-40s to mid-50s, their ovaries begin to lose their sensitivity to FSH and LH. Menstrual periods become less frequent and finally cease; this is **menopause**. There are still eggs and potential follicles on the ovaries, but without the stimulation of FSH and LH, they will not produce a viable egg to be released. The outcome of this is the inability to have children.

The side effects of menopause include hot flashes, heavy sweating (especially at night), headaches, some hair loss, muscle pain, vaginal dryness, insomnia, depression, weight gain, and mood swings. Estrogen is involved in calcium metabolism and, without it, blood levels of calcium decrease. To replenish the blood, calcium is lost from bone which may decrease the bone density and lead to osteoporosis. Supplementation of estrogen in the form of hormone replacement therapy (HRT) can prevent bone loss, but the therapy can have negative side effects. While HRT is thought to give some protection from colon cancer, osteoporosis, heart disease, macular degeneration, and possibly depression, its negative side effects include increased risk of: stroke or heart attack, blood clots, breast cancer, ovarian cancer, endometrial cancer, gall bladder disease, and possibly dementia.

career CONNECTION

Reproductive Endocrinologist

A reproductive endocrinologist is a physician who treats a variety of hormonal disorders related to reproduction and infertility in both men and women. The disorders include menstrual problems, infertility, pregnancy loss, sexual dysfunction, and menopause. Doctors may use fertility drugs, surgery, or assisted reproductive techniques (ART) in their therapy. ART involves the use of procedures to manipulate the egg or sperm to facilitate reproduction, such as *in vitro* fertilization.

Reproductive endocrinologists undergo extensive medical training, first in a four-year residency in obstetrics and gynecology, then in a three-year fellowship in reproductive endocrinology. To be board certified in this area, the physician must pass written and oral exams in both areas.

34.5 | Fertilization and Early Embryonic Development

In this section, you will explore the following questions:

- How does fertilization occur?
- How does the embryo form from the zygote?
- What are the roles of cleavage and fertilization in animal development?

Connection for AP® Courses

The information in this section is not within the scope for AP® other than to note that the process by which an organism develops from a single-celled zygote to a multi-cellular organism with specialized cells, tissues, and organs is complex and well regulated. The organization into a multi-cellular organism is regulated by an organism's genes. Cell differentiation is a result of specific gene expression, and homeotic (*HOX*) genes and morphogens control the pattern and timing of developmental stages.

Information presented and examples highlighted in this section are not within the scope for AP® and do not align to the Curriculum Framework.

Fertilization

Fertilization, pictured in Figure 34.20**a** is the process in which gametes (an egg and sperm) fuse to form a zygote. The egg and sperm each contain one set of chromosomes. To ensure that the offspring has only one complete diploid set of chromosomes, only one sperm must fuse with one egg. In mammals, the egg is protected by a layer of extracellular matrix consisting mainly of glycoproteins called the **zona pellucida**. When a sperm binds to the zona pellucida, a series of biochemical events, called the **acrosomal reactions**, take place. In placental mammals, the acrosome contains digestive enzymes that initiate the degradation of the glycoprotein matrix protecting the egg and allowing the sperm plasma membrane to fuse with the egg plasma membrane, as illustrated in Figure 34.20**b**. The fusion of these two membranes creates an opening through which the sperm nucleus is transferred into the ovum. The nuclear membranes of the egg and sperm break down and the two haploid genomes condense to form a diploid genome.

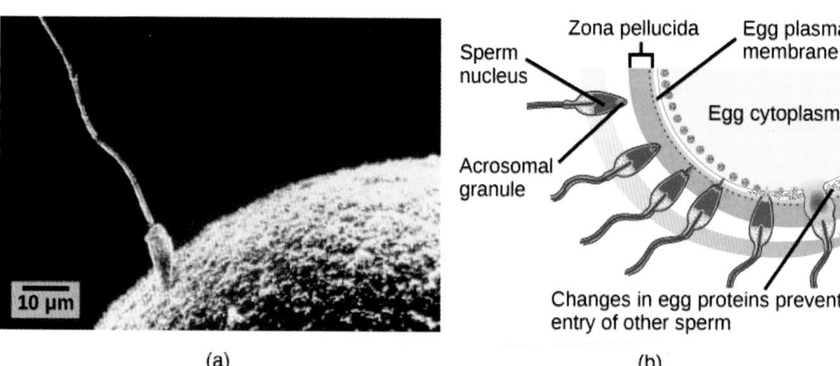

Figure 34.20 (a) Fertilization is the process in which sperm and egg fuse to form a zygote. (b) Acrosomal reactions help the sperm degrade the glycoprotein matrix protecting the egg and allow the sperm to transfer its nucleus. (credit: (b) modification of work by Mariana Ruiz Villareal; scale-bar data from Matt Russell)

To ensure that no more than one sperm fertilizes the egg, once the acrosomal reactions take place at one location of the egg membrane, the egg releases proteins in other locations to prevent other sperm from fusing with the egg. If this mechanism fails, multiple sperm can fuse with the egg, resulting in **polyspermy**. The resulting embryo is not genetically viable and dies within a few days.

Cleavage and Blastula Stage

The development of multi-cellular organisms begins from a single-celled zygote, which undergoes rapid cell division to form the blastula. The rapid, multiple rounds of cell division are termed cleavage. Cleavage is illustrated in (Figure 34.21**a**). After the cleavage has produced over 100 cells, the embryo is called a blastula. The blastula is usually a spherical layer of cells (the blastoderm) surrounding a fluid-filled or yolk-filled cavity (the blastocoel). Mammals at this stage form a structure called the blastocyst, characterized by an inner cell mass that is distinct from the surrounding blastula, shown in Figure 34.21**b**. During cleavage, the cells divide without an increase in mass; that is, one large single-celled zygote divides into multiple smaller cells. Each cell within the blastula is called a blastomere.

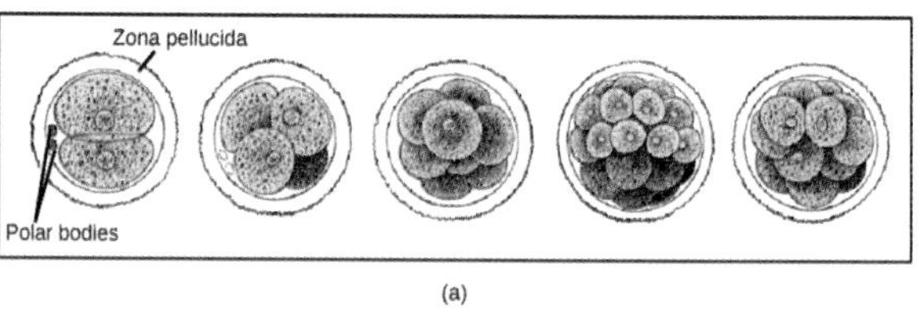

(a)

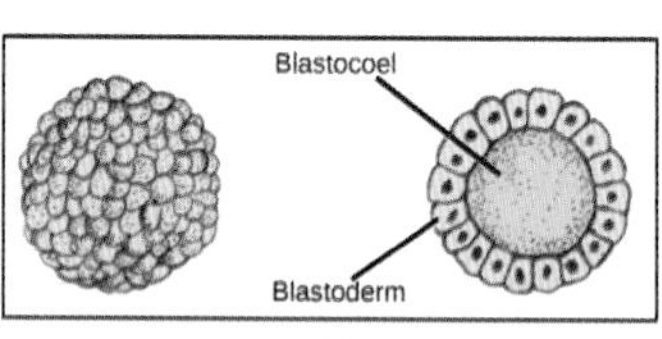

(b)

Figure 34.21 (a) During cleavage, the zygote rapidly divides into multiple cells without increasing in size. (b) The cells rearrange themselves to form a hollow ball with a fluid-filled or yolk-filled cavity called the blastula. (credit a: modification of work by Gray's Anatomy; credit b: modification of work by Pearson Scott Foresman, donated to the Wikimedia Foundation)

Cleavage can take place in two ways: **holoblastic** (total) cleavage or **meroblastic** (partial) cleavage. The type of cleavage depends on the amount of yolk in the eggs. In placental mammals (including humans) where nourishment is provided by the mother's body, the eggs have a very small amount of yolk and undergo holoblastic cleavage. Other species, such as birds, with a lot of yolk in the egg to nourish the embryo during development, undergo meroblastic cleavage.

In mammals, the blastula forms the **blastocyst** in the next stage of development. Here the cells in the blastula arrange themselves in two layers: the **inner cell mass**, and an outer layer called the **trophoblast**. The inner cell mass is also known as the embryoblast and this mass of cells will go on to form the embryo. At this stage of development, illustrated in Figure 34.22 the inner cell mass consists of embryonic stem cells that will differentiate into the different cell types needed by the organism. The trophoblast will contribute to the placenta and nourish the embryo.

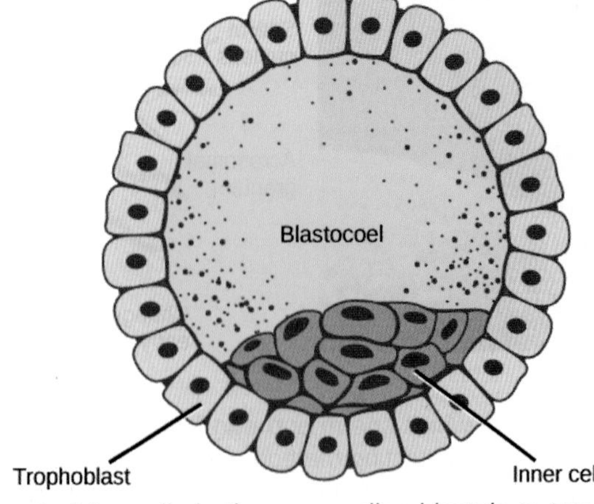

Figure 34.22 The rearrangement of the cells in the mammalian blastula to two layers—the inner cell mass and the trophoblast—results in the formation of the blastocyst.

Visit the **Virtual Human Embryo project (http://openstaxcollege.org/l/human_embryo)** at the Endowment for Human Development site to step through an interactive that shows the stages of embryo development, including micrographs and rotating 3-D images.

Which early embryonic stage is characterized by a fluid-filled cavity with an inner cell mass surrounded by a layer of cells?

a. blastocyst

b. blastula

c. blastocoel

d. gastrula

Gastrulation

The typical blastula is a ball of cells. The next stage in embryonic development is the formation of the body plan. The cells in the blastula rearrange themselves spatially to form three layers of cells. This process is called **gastrulation**. During gastrulation, the blastula folds upon itself to form the three layers of cells. Each of these layers is called a germ layer and each germ layer differentiates into different organ systems.

The three germs layers, shown in Figure 34.23, are the endoderm, the ectoderm, and the mesoderm. The ectoderm gives rise to the nervous system and the epidermis. The mesoderm gives rise to the muscle cells and connective tissue in the body. The endoderm gives rise to columnar cells found in the digestive system and many internal organs.

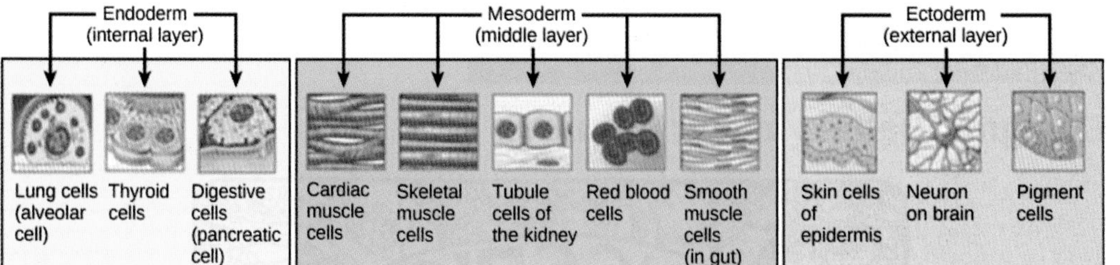

Figure 34.23 The three germ layers give rise to different cell types in the animal body. (credit: modification of work by NIH, NCBI)

everyday CONNECTION

Are Designer Babies in Our Future?

Figure 34.24 This logo from the Second International Eugenics Conference in New York City in September of 1921 shows how eugenics attempted to merge several fields of study with the goal of producing a genetically superior human race.

If you could prevent your child from getting a devastating genetic disease, would you do it? Would you select the sex of your child or select for their attractiveness, strength, or intelligence? How far would you go to maximize the possibility of resistance to disease? The genetic engineering of a human child, the production of "designer babies" with desirable phenotypic characteristics, was once a topic restricted to science fiction. This is the case no longer: science fiction is now overlapping into science fact. Many phenotypic choices for offspring are already available, with many more likely to be possible in the not too distant future. Which traits should be selected and how they should be selected are topics of much debate within the worldwide medical community. The ethical and moral line is not always clear or agreed upon, and some fear that modern reproductive technologies could lead to a new form of eugenics.

Eugenics is the use of information and technology from a variety of sources to improve the genetic makeup of the human race. The goal of creating genetically superior humans was quite prevalent (although controversial) in several countries during the early 20th century, but fell into disrepute when Nazi Germany developed an extensive eugenics program in the 1930's and 40's. As part of their program, the Nazis forcibly sterilized hundreds of thousands of the so-called "unfit" and killed tens of thousands of institutionally disabled people as part of a systematic program to develop a genetically superior race of Germans known as Aryans. Ever since, eugenic ideas have not been as publicly expressed, but there are still those who promote them.

Efforts have been made in the past to control traits in human children using donated sperm from men with desired traits. In fact, eugenicist Robert Klark Graham established a sperm bank in 1980 that included samples exclusively from donors with high IQs. The "genius" sperm bank failed to capture the public's imagination and the operation closed in 1999.

In more recent times, the procedure known as prenatal genetic diagnosis (PGD) has been developed. PGD involves the screening of human embryos as part of the process of *in vitro* fertilization, during which embryos are conceived and grown outside the mother's body for some period of time before they are implanted. The term PGD usually refers to both the diagnosis, selection, and the implantation of the selected embryos.

In the least controversial use of PGD, embryos are tested for the presence of alleles which cause genetic diseases such as sickle cell disease, muscular dystrophy, and hemophilia, in which a single disease-causing allele or pair of alleles has been identified. By excluding embryos containing these alleles from implantation into the mother, the disease is prevented, and the unused embryos are either donated to science or discarded. There are relatively few in the worldwide medical community that question the ethics of this type of procedure, which allows individuals scared to have children because of the alleles they carry to do so successfully. The major limitation to this procedure is its expense. Not usually covered by medical insurance and thus out of reach financially for most couples, only a very small percentage of all live births use such complicated methodologies. Yet, even in cases like these where the ethical issues may seem to be clear-cut, not everyone agrees with the morality of these types of procedures. For example, to those who take the position that human life begins at conception, the discarding of unused embryos, a necessary result of PGD, is unacceptable under any circumstances.

A murkier ethical situation is found in the selection of a child's sex, which is easily performed by PGD. Currently, countries such as Great Britain have banned the selection of a child's sex for reasons other than preventing sex-linked diseases. Other countries allow the procedure for "family balancing", based on the desire of some parents to have at least one child of each sex. Still others, including the United States, have taken a scattershot approach to regulating these practices, essentially leaving it to the individual practicing physician to decide which practices are acceptable and which are not.

Even murkier are rare instances of disabled parents, such as those with deafness or dwarfism, who select embryos via PGD to ensure that they share their disability. These parents usually cite many positive aspects of their disabilities and associated culture as reasons for their choice, which they see as their moral right. To others, to purposely cause a disability in a child violates the basic medical principle of *Primum non nocere,* "first, do no harm." This procedure, although not illegal in most countries, demonstrates the complexity of ethical issues associated with choosing genetic traits in offspring.

Where could this process lead? Will this technology become more affordable and how should it be used? With the ability of technology to progress rapidly and unpredictably, a lack of definitive guidelines for the use of reproductive technologies before they arise might make it difficult for legislators to keep pace once they are in fact realized, assuming the process needs any government regulation at all. Other bioethicists argue that we should only deal with technologies that exist now, and not in some uncertain future. They argue that these types of procedures will always be expensive and rare, so the fears of eugenics and "master" races are unfounded and overstated. The debate continues.

Prenatal genetic diagnosis (PGD) is often sought by parents before an embryo is implanted in the mother. Which of the following CANNOT be diagnosed by PGD?

a. inheritance of sickle cell anemia

b. Down's syndrome

c. determination of sex

d. inheritance of sexually transmitted diseases

34.6 | Organogenesis and Vertebrate Formation

In this section, you will explore the following questions:

- What are the stages in the process of organogenesis in vertebrate animals?
- What are the anatomical axes in vertebrates and their significance in development?

Connection for AP® Courses

The information in this section is not within the scope of AP®. The formation of organs from embryonic germ layers results from the expression of specific sets of genes that determine cell type. **Organogenesis** has been studied in the laboratory using the fruit fly (*Drosophila*) and the nematode *Caenorhabditis elegans*. In vertebrates, one of the primary steps during organogenesis is the formation of the neural system from embryonic ectoderm. Formation of body axes (lateral-medial, dorsal-ventral, and anterior-posterior) is another important developmental stage under genetic control.

Information presented and examples highlighted in this section are not within the scope for AP® and do not align to the Curriculum Framework.

Gastrulation leads to the formation of the three germ layers that give rise, during further development, to the different organs in the animal body. This process is called organogenesis. Organogenesis is characterized by rapid and precise movements of the cells within the embryo.

Organogenesis

Organs form from the germ layers through the process of differentiation. During differentiation, the embryonic stem cells express specific sets of genes which will determine their ultimate cell type. For example, some cells in the ectoderm will express the genes specific to skin cells. As a result, these cells will differentiate into epidermal cells. The process of differentiation is regulated by cellular signaling cascades.

Scientists study organogenesis extensively in the lab in fruit flies (*Drosophila*) and the nematode *Caenorhabditis elegans*. *Drosophila* have segments along their bodies, and the patterning associated with the segment formation has allowed scientists to study which genes play important roles in organogenesis along the length of the embryo at different time points. The nematode *C.elegans* has roughly 1000 somatic cells and scientists have studied the fate of each of these cells during their development in the nematode life cycle. There is little variation in patterns of cell lineage between individuals, unlike in mammals where cell development from the embryo is dependent on cellular cues.

In vertebrates, one of the primary steps during organogenesis is the formation of the neural system. The ectoderm forms epithelial cells and tissues, and neuronal tissues. During the formation of the neural system, special signaling molecules called growth factors signal some cells at the edge of the ectoderm to become epidermis cells. The remaining cells in the center form the neural plate. If the signaling by growth factors were disrupted, then the entire ectoderm would differentiate into neural tissue.

The neural plate undergoes a series of cell movements where it rolls up and forms a tube called the **neural tube**, as illustrated in Figure 34.25. In further development, the neural tube will give rise to the brain and the spinal cord.

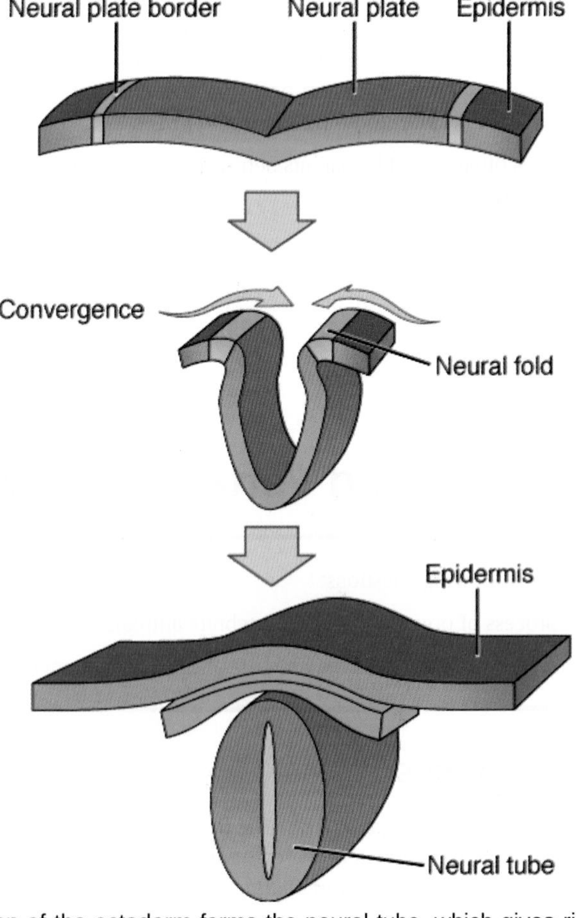

Figure 34.25 The central region of the ectoderm forms the neural tube, which gives rise to the brain and the spinal cord.

The mesoderm that lies on either side of the vertebrate neural tube will develop into the various connective tissues of the animal body. A spatial pattern of gene expression reorganizes the mesoderm into groups of cells called **somites** with spaces between them. The somites, illustrated in Figure 34.26 will further develop into the ribs, lungs, and segmental (spine) muscle. The mesoderm also forms a structure called the notochord, which is rod-shaped and forms the central axis of the animal body.

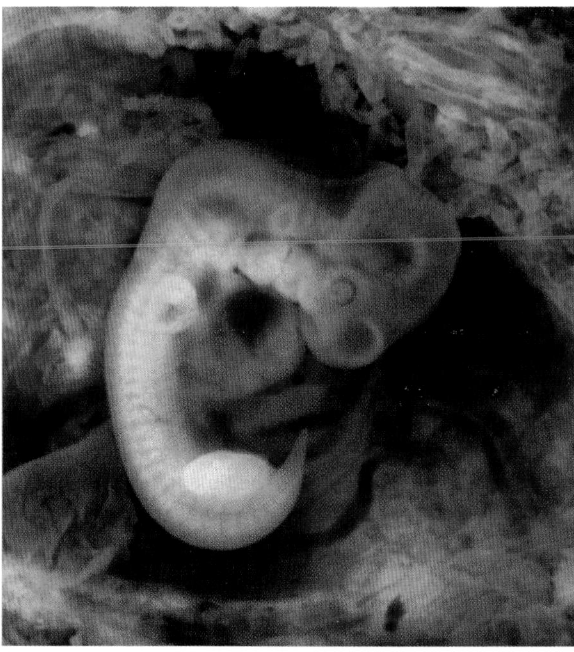

Figure 34.26 In this five-week old human embryo, somites are segments along the length of the body. (credit: modification of work by Ed Uthman)

Vertebrate Axis Formation

Even as the germ layers form, the ball of cells still retains its spherical shape. However, animal bodies have lateral-medial (left-right), dorsal-ventral (back-belly), and anterior-posterior (head-feet) axes, illustrated in Figure 34.27.

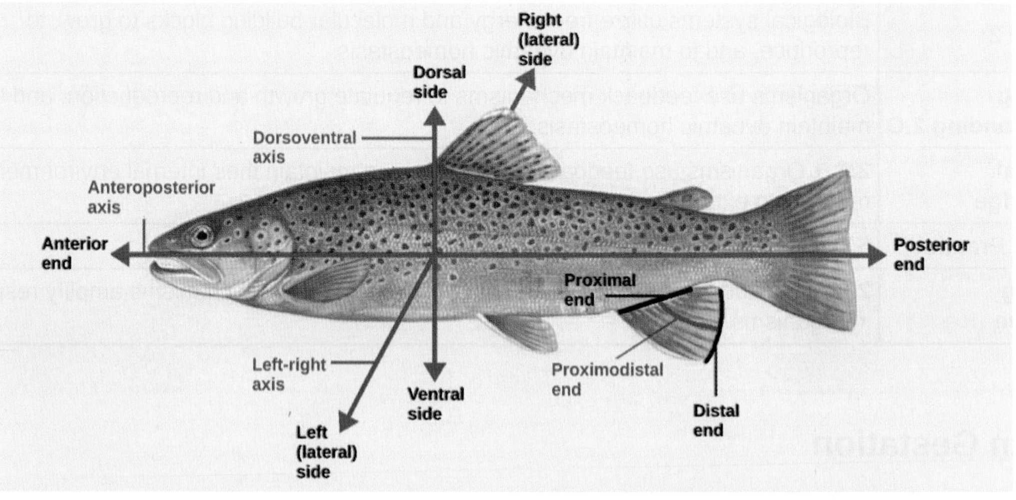

Figure 34.27 Animal bodies have three axes for symmetry. (credit: modification of work by NOAA)

How are these established? In one of the most seminal experiments ever to be carried out in developmental biology, Spemann and Mangold took dorsal cells from one embryo and transplanted them into the belly region of another embryo. They found that the transplanted embryo now had two notochords: one at the dorsal site from the original cells and another at the transplanted site. This suggested that the dorsal cells were genetically programmed to form the notochord and define the axis. Since then, researchers have identified many genes that are responsible for axis formation. Mutations in these genes leads to the loss of symmetry required for organism development.

Animal bodies have externally visible symmetry. However, the internal organs are not symmetric. For example, the heart is on the left side and the liver on the right. The formation of the central left-right axis is an important process during development. This internal asymmetry is established very early during development and involves many genes. Research is still ongoing to fully understand the developmental implications of these genes.

34.7 | Human Pregnancy and Birth

In this section, you will explore the following questions:

- What are the stages of fetal development during the first three trimesters of gestation?
- What the events in labor and delivery?
- What are the efficacy and duration of various types of contraception?
- What are causes of infertility and the therapeutic options available?

Connection for AP® Courses

The information in this section is not within the scope for AP®, and you likely studied this information in a prior health class. However, if you are unfamiliar with the material, now is the time to learn it. Not only is the material interesting and informative, it is practical and relevant to any person of reproductive age, including high school students in an AP® course.

Pregnancy begins with the fertilization of an egg and continues through the birth of the individual. The length of time of **gestation** in animals varies, from 60 days in dogs and cats to 266 days in humans. The prevention of pregnancy occurs under the terms of contraception or birth control. Because knowledge of the endocrine systems and how hormones work is required for AP®, the information in the section about hormonal methods of contraception, such as birth control, is especially applicable.

Information presented and the examples highlighted in the section support concepts outlined in Big Idea 2 of the AP® Biology Curriculum Framework. The AP® Learning Objectives listed in the Curriculum Framework provide a transparent foundation for the AP® Biology course, an inquiry-based laboratory experience, instructional activities, and AP® exam questions. A learning objective merges required content with one or more of the seven science practices.

Big Idea 2	Biological systems utilize free energy and molecular building blocks to grow, to reproduce, and to maintain dynamic homeostasis.
Enduring Understanding 2.C	Organisms use feedback mechanisms to regulate growth and reproduction, and to maintain dynamic homeostasis.
Essential Knowledge	**2.C.1** Organisms use feedback mechanisms to maintain their internal environments and respond to external environmental changes.
Science Practice	**6.1** The student can justify claims with evidence.
Learning Objective	**2.20** The student is able to justify that positive feedback mechanisms amplify responses in organisms.

Human Gestation

Twenty-four hours before fertilization, the egg has finished meiosis and becomes a mature oocyte. When fertilized (at conception) the egg becomes known as a zygote. The zygote travels through the oviduct to the uterus (Figure 34.28). The developing embryo must implant into the wall of the uterus within seven days, or it will deteriorate and die. The outer layers of the zygote (blastocyst) grow into the endometrium by digesting the endometrial cells, and wound healing of the endometrium closes up the blastocyst into the tissue. Another layer of the blastocyst, the chorion, begins releasing a hormone called **human beta chorionic gonadotropin (β-HCG)** which makes its way to the corpus luteum and keeps that structure active. This ensures adequate levels of progesterone that will maintain the endometrium of the uterus for the support of the developing embryo. Pregnancy tests determine the level of β-HCG in urine or serum. If the hormone is present, the test is positive.

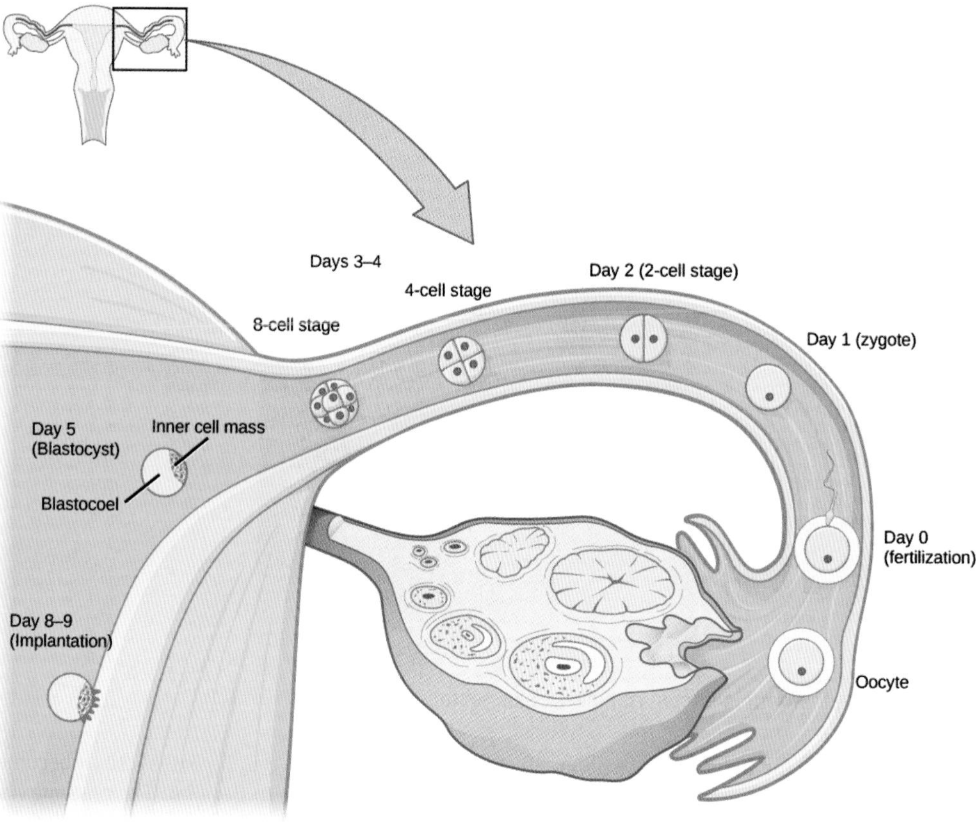

Figure 34.28 In humans, fertilization occurs soon after the oocyte leaves the ovary. Implantation occurs eight or nine days later.(credit: Ed Uthman)

The gestation period is divided into three equal periods or trimesters. During the first two to four weeks of the first trimester, nutrition and waste are handled by the endometrial lining through diffusion. As the trimester progresses, the outer layer of the embryo begins to merge with the endometrium, and the **placenta** forms. This organ takes over the nutrient and waste requirements of the embryo and fetus, with the mother's blood passing nutrients to the placenta and removing waste from it. Chemicals from the fetus, such as bilirubin, are processed by the mother's liver for elimination. Some of the mother's immunoglobulins will pass through the placenta, providing passive immunity against some potential infections.

Internal organs and body structures begin to develop during the first trimester. By five weeks, limb buds, eyes, the heart, and liver have been basically formed. By eight weeks, the term fetus applies, and the body is essentially formed, as shown in Figure 34.29. The individual is about five centimeters (two inches) in length and many of the organs, such as the lungs and liver, are not yet functioning. Exposure to any toxins is especially dangerous during the first trimester, as all of the body's organs and structures are going through initial development. Anything that affects that development can have a severe effect on the fetus' survival.

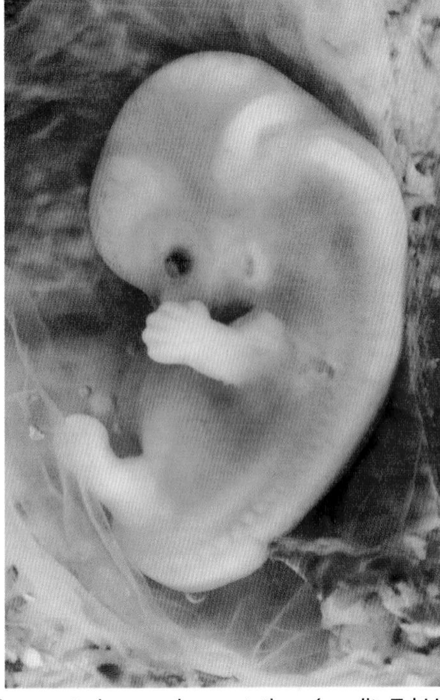

Figure 34.29 Fetal development is shown at nine weeks gestation. (credit: Ed Uthman)

During the second trimester, the fetus grows to about 30 cm (12 inches), as shown in Figure 34.30. It becomes active and the mother usually feels the first movements. All organs and structures continue to develop. The placenta has taken over the functions of nutrition and waste and the production of estrogen and progesterone from the corpus luteum, which has degenerated. The placenta will continue functioning up through the delivery of the baby.

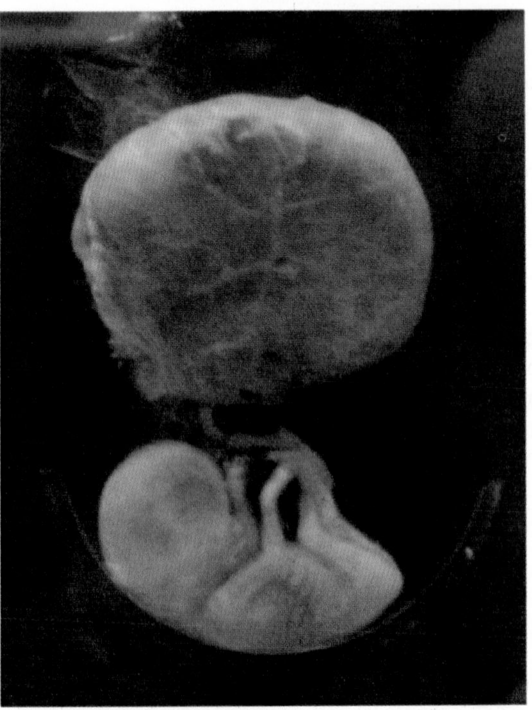

Figure 34.30 This fetus is just entering the second trimester, when the placenta takes over more of the functions performed as the baby develops. (credit: National Museum of Health and Medicine)

During the third trimester, the fetus grows to 3 to 4 kg (6 ½ -8 ½ lbs.) and about 50 cm (19-20 inches) long, as illustrated in Figure 34.31. This is the period of the most rapid growth during the pregnancy. Organ development continues to birth (and some systems, such as the nervous system and liver, continue to develop after birth). The mother will be at her most uncomfortable during this trimester. She may urinate frequently due to pressure on the bladder from the fetus. There may also be intestinal blockage and circulatory problems, especially in her legs. Clots may form in her legs due to pressure from the fetus on returning veins as they enter the abdominal cavity.

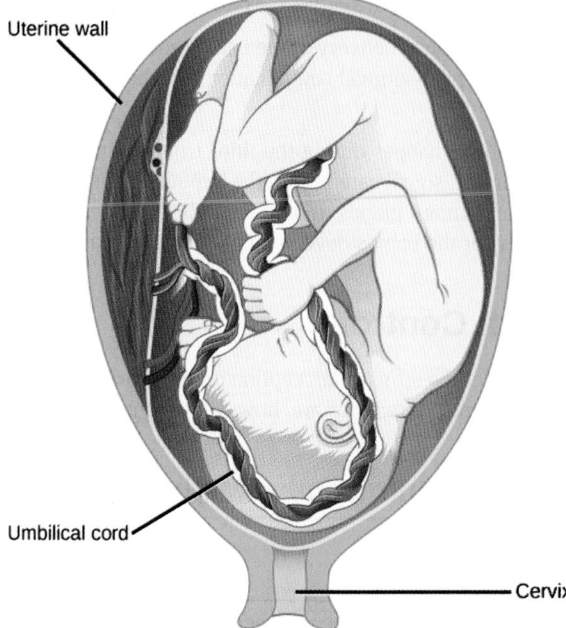

Figure 34.31 There is rapid fetal growth during the third trimester. (credit: modification of work by Gray's Anatomy)

Visit this site (http://openstaxcollege.org/l/embryo_fetus) to see the stages of human fetal development.

In humans, by which week of gestation are all limbs and essential organs formed?

a. 5

b. 6

c. 7

d. 8

Labor and Birth

Labor is the physical efforts of expulsion of the fetus and the placenta from the uterus during birth (parturition). Toward the end of the third trimester, estrogen causes receptors on the uterine wall to develop and bind the hormone oxytocin. At this time, the baby reorients, facing forward and down with the back or crown of the head engaging the cervix (uterine opening). This causes the cervix to stretch and nerve impulses are sent to the hypothalamus, which signals for the release of oxytocin from the posterior pituitary. The oxytocin causes the smooth muscle in the uterine wall to contract. At the same time, the placenta releases prostaglandins into the uterus, increasing the contractions. A positive feedback relay occurs between the uterus, hypothalamus, and the posterior pituitary to assure an adequate supply of oxytocin. As more smooth muscle cells are recruited, the contractions increase in intensity and force.

There are three stages to labor. During stage one, the cervix thins and dilates. This is necessary for the baby and placenta to be expelled during birth. The cervix will eventually dilate to about 10 cm. During stage two, the baby is expelled from the uterus. The uterus contracts and the mother pushes as she compresses her abdominal muscles to aid the delivery. The last stage is the passage of the placenta after the baby has been born and the organ has completely disengaged from the uterine wall. If labor should stop before stage two is reached, synthetic oxytocin can be administered to restart and maintain labor.

An alternative to labor and delivery is the surgical delivery of the baby through a procedure called a Caesarian section. This is major abdominal surgery and can lead to post-surgical complications for the mother, but in some cases it may be the only way to safely deliver the baby.

The mother's mammary glands go through changes during the third trimester to prepare for lactation and breastfeeding. When the baby begins suckling at the breast, signals are sent to the hypothalamus causing the release of prolactin from the anterior pituitary. Prolactin causes the mammary glands to produce milk. Oxytocin is also released, promoting the release of the milk. The milk contains nutrients for the baby's development and growth as well as immunoglobulins to protect the child from bacterial and viral infections.

Contraception and Birth Control

The prevention of a pregnancy comes under the terms contraception or birth control. Strictly speaking, **contraception** refers to preventing the sperm and egg from joining. Both terms are, however, frequently used interchangeably.

Contraceptive Methods

Method	Examples	Failure Rate in Typical Use Over 12 Months
Barrier	male condom, female condom, sponge, cervical cap, diaphragm, spermicides	15 to 24%
Hormonal	oral, patch, vaginal ring	8%
	injection	3%
	implant	less than 1%
Other	natural family planning	12 to 25%
	withdrawal	27%
	sterilization	less than 1%

Table 34.3

Table 34.3 lists common methods of contraception. The failure rates listed are not the ideal rates that could be realized, but the typical rates that occur. A failure rate is the number of pregnancies resulting from the method's use over a twelve-month period. Barrier methods, such as condoms, cervical caps, and diaphragms, block sperm from entering the uterus, preventing fertilization. Spermicides are chemicals that are placed in the vagina that kill sperm. Sponges, which are saturated with spermicides, are placed in the vagina at the cervical opening. Combinations of spermicidal chemicals and barrier methods achieve lower failure rates than do the methods when used separately.

Nearly a quarter of the couples using barrier methods, natural family planning, or withdrawal can expect a failure of the method. Natural family planning is based on the monitoring of the menstrual cycle and having intercourse only during times when the egg is not available. A woman's body temperature may rise a degree Celsius at ovulation and the cervical mucus may increase in volume and become more pliable. These changes give a general indication of when intercourse is more or less likely to result in fertilization. Withdrawal involves the removal of the penis from the vagina during intercourse, before ejaculation occurs. This is a risky method with a high failure rate due to the possible presence of sperm in the bulbourethral gland's secretion, which may enter the vagina prior to removing the penis.

Hormonal methods use synthetic progesterone (sometimes in combination with estrogen), to inhibit the hypothalamus from releasing FSH or LH, and thus prevent an egg from being available for fertilization. The method of administering the hormone affects failure rate. The most reliable method, with a failure rate of less than 1 percent, is the implantation of the hormone under the skin. The same rate can be achieved through the sterilization procedures of vasectomy in the man or of tubal ligation in the woman, or by using an intrauterine device (IUD). IUDs are inserted into the uterus and establish an inflammatory condition that prevents fertilized eggs from implanting into the uterine wall.

Compliance with the contraceptive method is a strong contributor to the success or failure rate of any particular method. The only method that is completely effective at preventing conception is abstinence. The choice of contraceptive method depends on the goals of the woman or couple. Tubal ligation and vasectomy are considered permanent prevention, while other methods are reversible and provide short-term contraception.

Termination of an existing pregnancy can be spontaneous or voluntary. Spontaneous termination is a miscarriage and usually occurs very early in the pregnancy, usually within the first few weeks. This occurs when the fetus cannot develop properly and the gestation is naturally terminated. Voluntary termination of a pregnancy is an abortion. Laws regulating abortion vary between states and tend to view fetal viability as the criteria for allowing or preventing the procedure.

Infertility

Infertility is the inability to conceive a child or carry a child to birth. About 75 percent of causes of infertility can be identified; these include diseases, such as sexually transmitted diseases that can cause scarring of the reproductive tubes in either men or women, or developmental problems frequently related to abnormal hormone levels in one of the individuals. Inadequate nutrition, especially starvation, can delay menstruation. Stress can also lead to infertility. Short-term stress can affect hormone levels, while long-term stress can delay puberty and cause less frequent menstrual cycles. Other factors that affect fertility include toxins (such as cadmium), tobacco smoking, marijuana use, gonadal injuries, and aging.

If infertility is identified, several assisted reproductive technologies (ART) are available to aid conception. A common type of ART is *in vitro* fertilization (IVF) where an egg and sperm are combined outside the body and then placed in the uterus. Eggs are obtained from the woman after extensive hormonal treatments that prepare mature eggs for fertilization and prepare the uterus for implantation of the fertilized egg. Sperm are obtained from the man and they are combined with the eggs and supported through several cell divisions to ensure viability of the zygotes. When the embryos have reached the eight-cell stage, one or more is implanted into the woman's uterus. If fertilization is not accomplished by simple IVF, a procedure that injects the sperm into an egg can be used. This is called intracytoplasmic sperm injection (ICSI) and is shown in Figure 34.32. IVF procedures produce a surplus of fertilized eggs and embryos that can be frozen and stored for future use. The procedures can also result in multiple births.

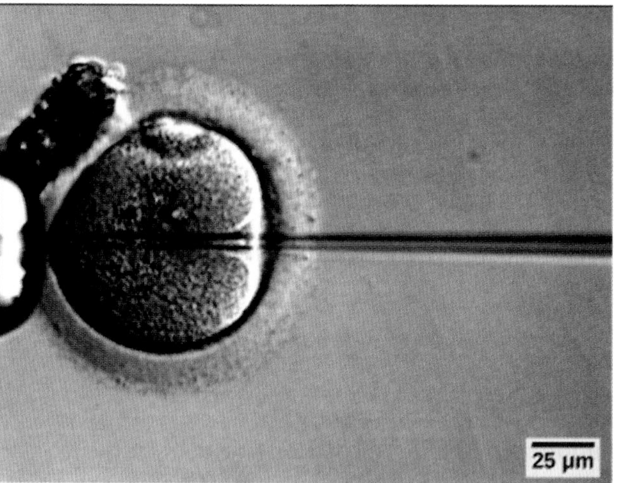

Figure 34.32 A sperm is inserted into an egg for fertilization during intracytoplasmic sperm injection (ICSI). (credit: scale-bar data from Matt Russell)

KEY TERMS

acrosomal reaction series of biochemical reactions that the sperm uses to break through the zona pellucida

amniote an organism whose embryo develops within a shelled egg with extraembryonic membranes

asexual reproduction form of reproduction that produces offspring that are genetically identical to the parent

blastocyst structure formed when cells in the mammalian blastula separate into an inner and outer layer

budding form of asexual reproduction that results from the outgrowth of a part of a cell leading to a separation from the original animal into two individuals

bulbourethral gland secretion that cleanses the urethra prior to ejaculation

clitoris sensory structure in females; stimulated during sexual arousal

cloaca common body opening for the digestive, excretory, and reproductive systems found in non-mammals, such as birds

contraception (also, birth control) various means used to prevent pregnancy

estrogen reproductive hormone in females that assists in endometrial regrowth, ovulation, and calcium absorption

external fertilization fertilization of egg by sperm outside animal body, often during spawning

fission (also, binary fission) method by which multicellular organisms increase in size or asexual reproduction in which a unicellular organism splits into two separate organisms by mitosis

follicle stimulating hormone (FSH) reproductive hormone that causes sperm production in men and follicle development in women

fragmentation cutting or fragmenting of the original animal into parts and the growth of a separate animal from each part

gastrulation process in which the blastula folds over itself to form the three germ layers

gestation length of time for fetal development to birth

gonadotropin-releasing hormone (GnRH) hormone from the hypothalamus that causes the release of FSH and LH from the anterior pituitary

hermaphroditism state of having both male and female reproductive parts within the same individual

holoblastic complete cleavage; takes place in cells with a small amount of yolk

human beta chorionic gonadotropin (β-HCG) hormone produced by the chorion of the zygote that helps to maintain the corpus luteum and elevated levels of progesterone

infertility inability to conceive, carry, and deliver children

inhibin hormone made by Sertoli cells; provides negative feedback to hypothalamus in control of FSH and GnRH release

inner cell mass inner layer of cells in the blastocyst

internal fertilization fertilization of egg by sperm inside the body of the female

interstitial cell of Leydig cell in seminiferous tubules that makes testosterone

labia majora large folds of tissue covering the inguinal area

labia minora smaller folds of tissue within the labia majora

luteinizing hormone (LH) reproductive hormone in both men and women, causes testosterone production in men and ovulation and lactation in women

menopause loss of reproductive capacity in women due to decreased sensitivity of the ovaries to FSH and LH

menstrual cycle cycle of the degradation and re-growth of the endometrium

meroblastic partial cleavage; takes place in cells with a large amount of yolk

morning sickness condition in the mother during the first trimester; includes feelings of nausea

neural tube tube-like structure that forms from the ectoderm and gives rise to the brain and spinal cord

oogenesis process of producing haploid eggs

organogenesis process of organ formation

ovarian cycle cycle of preparation of egg for ovulation and the conversion of the follicle to the corpus luteum

oviduct (also, fallopian tube) muscular tube connecting the uterus with the ovary area

oviparity process by which fertilized eggs are laid outside the female's body and develop there, receiving nourishment from the yolk that is a part of the egg

ovoviparity process by which fertilized eggs are retained within the female; the embryo obtains its nourishment from the egg's yolk and the young are fully developed when they are hatched

ovulation release of the egg by the most mature follicle

parthenogenesis form of asexual reproduction where an egg develops into a complete individual without being fertilized

penis male reproductive structure for urine elimination and copulation

placenta organ that supports the diffusion of nutrients and waste between the mother's and fetus' blood

polyspermy condition in which one egg is fertilized by multiple sperm

progesterone reproductive hormone in women; assists in endometrial re-growth and inhibition of FSH and LH release

prostate gland structure that is a mixture of smooth muscle and glandular material and that contributes to semen

scrotum sac containing testes; exterior to the body

semen fluid mixture of sperm and supporting materials

seminal vesicle secretory accessory gland in males; contributes to semen

seminiferous tubule site of sperm production in testes

Sertoli cell cell in seminiferous tubules that assists developing sperm and makes inhibin

sexual reproduction mixing of genetic material from two individuals to produce genetically unique offspring

somite group of cells separated by small spaces that form from the mesoderm and give rise to connective tissue

spermatheca specialized sac that stores sperm for later use

spermatogenesis process of producing haploid sperm

testes pair of reproductive organs in males

testosterone reproductive hormone in men that assists in sperm production and promoting secondary sexual characteristics

trophoblast outer layer of cells in the blastocyst

uterus environment for developing embryo and fetus

vagina muscular tube for the passage of menstrual flow, copulation, and birth of offspring

viviparity process in which the young develop within the female, receiving nourishment from the mother's blood through a placenta

zona pellucida protective layer of glycoproteins on the mammalian egg

CHAPTER SUMMARY

34.1 Reproduction Methods

Reproduction may be asexual when one individual produces genetically identical offspring, or sexual when the genetic material from two individuals is combined to produce genetically diverse offspring. Asexual reproduction occurs through fission, budding, and fragmentation. Sexual reproduction may mean the joining of sperm and eggs within animalsâ€™ bodies or it may mean the release of sperm and eggs into the environment. An individual may be one sex, or both; it may start out as one sex and switch during its life, or it may stay male or female.

34.2 Fertilization

Sexual reproduction starts with the combination of a sperm and an egg in a process called fertilization. This can occur either outside the bodies or inside the female. Both methods have advantages and disadvantages. Once fertilized, the eggs can develop inside the female or outside. If the egg develops outside the body, it usually has a protective covering over it. Animal anatomy evolved various ways to fertilize, hold, or expel the egg. The method of fertilization varies among animals. Some species release the egg and sperm into the environment, some species retain the egg and receive the sperm into the female body and then expel the developing embryo covered with shell, while still other species retain the developing offspring through the gestation period.

34.3 Human Reproductive Anatomy and Gametogenesis

As animals became more complex, specific organs and organ systems developed to support specific functions for the organism. The reproductive structures that evolved in land animals allow males and females to mate, fertilize internally, and support the growth and development of offspring. Processes developed to produce reproductive cells that had exactly half the number of chromosomes of each parent so that new combinations would have the appropriate amount of genetic material. Gametogenesis, the production of sperm (spermatogenesis) and eggs (oogenesis), takes place through the process of meiosis.

34.4 Hormonal Control of Human Reproduction

The male and female reproductive cycles are controlled by hormones released from the hypothalamus and anterior pituitary as well as hormones from reproductive tissues and organs. The hypothalamus monitors the need for the FSH and LH hormones made and released from the anterior pituitary. FSH and LH affect reproductive structures to cause the formation of sperm and the preparation of eggs for release and possible fertilization. In the male, FSH and LH stimulate Sertoli cells and interstitial cells of Leydig in the testes to facilitate sperm production. The Leydig cells produce testosterone, which also is responsible for the secondary sexual characteristics of males. In females, FSH and LH cause estrogen and progesterone to be produced. They regulate the female reproductive system which is divided into the ovarian cycle and the menstrual cycle. Menopause occurs when the ovaries lose their sensitivity to FSH and LH and the female reproductive cycles slow to a stop.

34.5 Fertilization and Early Embryonic Development

The early stages of embryonic development begin with fertilization. The process of fertilization is tightly controlled to ensure that only one sperm fuses with one egg. After fertilization, the zygote undergoes cleavage to form the blastula. The blastula, which in some species is a hollow ball of cells, undergoes a process called gastrulation, in which the three germ layers form. The ectoderm gives rise to the nervous system and the epidermal skin cells, the mesoderm gives rise to the muscle cells and connective tissue in the body, and the endoderm gives rise to columnar cells and internal organs.

34.6 Organogenesis and Vertebrate Formation

Organogenesis is the formation of organs from the germ layers. Each germ layer gives rise to specific tissue types. The first stage is the formation of the neural system in the ectoderm. The mesoderm gives rise to somites and the notochord. Formation of vertebrate axis is another important developmental stage.

34.7 Human Pregnancy and Birth

Human pregnancy begins with fertilization of an egg and proceeds through the three trimesters of gestation. The labor process has three stages (contractions, delivery of the fetus, expulsion of the placenta), each propelled by hormones. The first trimester lays down the basic structures of the body, including the limb buds, heart, eyes, and the liver. The second trimester continues the development of all of the organs and systems. The third trimester exhibits the greatest growth of the fetus and culminates in labor and delivery. Prevention of a pregnancy can be accomplished through a variety of methods including barriers, hormones, or other means. Assisted reproductive technologies may help individuals who have infertility problems.

REVIEW QUESTIONS

1. Which method of reproduction produces identical offspring and is most successful in a stable environment?

a. asexual reproduction
b. sexual
c. conjugation
d. inbreeding

2. Which method produces genetically-unique offspring?

a. parthenogenesis
b. budding
c. fragmentation
d. sexual reproduction

3. Which of the following statements is false?

a. Budding is a method of asexual reproduction.
b. Fragmentation is a method of asexual reproduction.
c. Parthenogenesis is a type of sexual reproduction that produces diverse offspring.
d. Binary fission is a method of asexual reproduction.

4. Sea stars are broken apart by workers to save the clams they feed on, and then thrown back into the ocean. Often the numbers of sea stars are seen to double after this. Give the reason why this happens.

a. regeneration
b. fragmentation
c. budding
d. the presence of suitable conditions

5. Which form of reproduction might be utilized by a sexually reproducing animal that has limited mobility?

a. fragmentation
b. budding
c. hermaphroditism
d. parthenogenesis

6. In sexual reproduction, gametes with either an X or Y chromosome are formed in males, whereas gametes in females contain a single X chromosome. What is the nature of both male and female gametes?

a. diploid
b. haploid
c. homozygous
d. heterozygous

7. External fertilization most commonly occurs in which type of environment?

a. aquatic
b. forests
c. savanna
d. steppe

8. Why is broadcast spawning considered advantageous?

a. Production of many eggs increases the chance of fertilization.
b. Production of many sperm increases the chance of fertilization.
c. It results in mixing of genes and greater genetic diversity.
d. Animals that are motile carry out this process.

9. Which term applies to egg development outside the female with nourishment derived from a yolk?

a. oviparity
b. viviparity
c. ovoviparity
d. ovovoparity

10. How are the offspring of viviparous animals different from the offspring of oviparous animals?

a. They are protected from the external environment.
b. They are produced in higher numbers.
c. They can live longer.
d. They can utilize nutrients better.

11. Which of the following structures is involved in mating in birds?

a. cloaca
b. spermatheca
c. uterus
d. coelom

12. The spermatheca, which is found in many insects, worms, and mollusks, is useful for _____.

a. spermatogenesis
b. sperm motility
c. growth of embryos
d. storing sperm and as a site for fertilization

13. Which part of the male reproductive system produces most of the semen?

a. scrotum
b. seminal vesicles
c. seminiferous tubules
d. prostate gland

14. How is an oocyte released from a human ovary so it can enter the oviduct?

a. the beating action of the flagellum on the oocyte
b. the force of the follicular ejection directing the oocyte into the oviduct
c. the wavelike beating of cilia lining the oviduct
d. muscular contraction of the ovaries

15. Which female organ has the same embryonic origin as the penis?

a. clitoris
b. labia majora
c. greater vestibular glands
d. vagina

16. Which structure is only related to the male urinary system, as opposed to the male reproductive system?

a. urinary bladder
b. cowper's gland
c. bulbourethral gland
d. urethra

17. How many eggs are produced as a result of one meiotic series of cell divisions?

a. 1
b. 2
c. 3
d. 4

18. Which of the following events activate the germ cells at puberty to produce spermatozoa?

a. activation by gonadotropin-releasing hormone
b. activation by increased hair growth
c. increase in blood volume
d. increase of secretion of testosterone

19. What stimulates Leydig cells in the testes to produce testosterone?

a. FSH
b. LH
c. inhibin
d. estrogen

20. In both males and females, the hormones FSH and LH play a critical role in the reproductive phase. What regulates the secretion of these hormones?

a. GnRH
b. estrogen
c. progesterone
d. inhibin

21. Which hormone prepares the endometrial lining of the uterus for potential implantation?

a. testosterone
b. estrogen
c. GnRH
d. progesterone

22. With the onset of menopause, the follicles stop responding to which of the following hormones?

a. estradiol and progesterone
b. progesterone and estrogen
c. FSH and LH
d. FSH and GnRH

23. After ovulation, increasing amounts of _____ cause the endometrium to start to thicken.

a. fluid
b. LH
c. progesterone
d. GnRH

24. What characterizes the acrosomal reactions?

a. The sperm degrades the outermost layer of the egg to penetrate it.
b. motility of the sperm
c. fusion of the egg and sperm
d. breakdown of the envelope covering the sperm head

25. What occurs as a result of fertilization of an egg and sperm?

a. Fertilization restores diploidy.
b. Fertilization always results in a viable embryo.
c. Fertilization merges two diploid cells into a haploid cell.
d. Fertilization precedes ovulation.

26. Which of the following statements regarding early embryonic stages is false?

a. The endoderm, mesoderm, and ectoderm are germ layers.
b. The trophoblast is a germ layer.
c. The inner cell mass is a source of embryonic stem cells.
d. The blastula is often a hollow ball of cells.

27. Gastrulation is the process in which the cells in the blastula rearrange themselves and form three layers of cells. Each layer will differentiate into a different organ system. At what point of development do the major organs begin to develop?

a. fertilization
b. first trimester
c. second trimester
d. third trimester

28. What happens to the number of cells during cleavage?

a. increases
b. decreases
c. doubles with every cell division
d. does not change significantly

29. The blastula stage is a mass of specialized cells. Of the following, which forms the liver cells?

a. inner cell mass
b. trophoblast
c. blastula
d. blastomere

30. Which germ layer forms the skin cells?

a. endoderm
b. ectoderm
c. mesoderm
d. trophoblast

31. What are the three phases of embryonic development in chronological order?

a. blastula → gastrula → cleavage
b. blastula → cleavage → gastrula
c. cleavage → gastrula → blastula
d. cleavage → blastula → gastrula

32. Which of the following does not describe axes of symmetry in animals?

a. anterior-posterior
b. dorsal-ventral
c. upper-lower
d. lateral-median

33. Which of the following statements best summarizes the factors controlling symmetry?

a. Axis formation is genetically determined.
b. Body symmetry is independent of genes.
c. Body symmetry is determined at the blastula stage.
d. Body symmetry is determined as the embryo grows in length.

34. The neural plate undergoes folding and movement of cells to form which structure?

a. neural tube
b. epidermis
c. mesoderm
d. neural cord

35. What is necessary for normal human fertilization to occur?

a. Many eggs must be released.
b. The uterus must be enlarged.
c. One sperm needs to penetrate one egg.
d. Secretion of pituitary FSH and LH must decrease.

36. Before pregnancy, progesterone is produced by the ovaries to thicken the endometrial lining and ensure pregnancy. During the third trimester of pregnancy, which organ produces progesterone?

a. placenta
b. endometrial lining
c. chorion
d. corpus luteum

37. Which hormone is primarily responsible for the contractions during labor?

a. oxytocin
b. estrogen
c. β-HCG
d. progesterone

38. What happens before the baby and placenta are expelled?

a. Thinning and dilation of the cervix take place.
b. There is increased blood flow to the baby.
c. Enlargement of the uterus takes place.
d. Increased production of estrogen occurs.

39. Which type of short-term contraceptive method is generally more effective than others?

a. barrier
b. hormonal implants
c. natural family planning
d. withdrawal

40. Which of the following best indicates that a female is ovulating?

a. slight decrease in body temperature
b. decrease in cervical volume
c. more pliable cervical secretions
d. change in breast size

41. Fertility is generally unaffected by_____.

a. sexually transmitted diseases
b. obstruction of reproductive tubes
c. drug use
d. genetic factors

42. What occurs in the procedure known as in vitro fertilization (IVF)?

a. A sperm is injected into the egg externally.
b. An egg is fertilized by the sperm internally in the oviduct.
c. Eggs and sperm are combined externally and then implanted.
d. Egg and sperm are combined externally and the resulting embryo is implanted.

CRITICAL THINKING QUESTIONS

43. Due to global climate change and pollution, a lake experiences changes in temperature and pH. The lake has many species, including sexually reproducing frogs, water fleas that multiply by parthenogenesis, hydra that multiply by budding, and sponges that multiply by fragmentation. Which of these species will most likely survive the changing conditions of the lake?

a. hydra
b. sponges
c. water fleas
d. sexually-reproducing frogs

44. Why is sexual reproduction useful when only half the individuals reproduce and two cells must combine to form a new cell?

a. It completes in a very short period of time.
b. It results in the rapid production of many offspring.
c. It increases genetic diversity, allowing organisms to survive in an unpredictable environment.
d. It requires less energy and leads to genetic variation in the offspring.

45. Sex determination in humans and other mammals is dictated by the presence of sex chromosomes. Are there different factors that determine the sex of other types of animals?

a. No, the sex of an individual is only determined by the presence of sex chromosomes.
b. Yes, temperature also determines the sex of an individual.
c. Yes, humidity and temperature determine the sex of an individual.
d. Yes, pH and humidity determine the sex of an individual.

46. What are some advantages of internal compared with external fertilization?

a. Internal fertilization leads to more genetic variations and increases the survival rates of offsprings.
b. Internal fertilization increases the survival rates of offspring, and large numbers of offspring are produced.
c. Internal fertilization increases the survival rates of offspring, and the chance of fertilization with a specific partner also increases.
d. Internal fertilization increases the survival rates of offspring and decreases the chance of fertilization with a specific partner.

47. What are the mechanisms that protect and nurture the embryo in oviparous animals?

a. The hard leathery exterior of bird eggs and the hard calcium covering of reptile eggs provides protection to the growing embryo. Nourishment is provided by yolk in the eggs.
b. The hard leathery exterior of reptile eggs and the hard calcium covering of bird eggs provide protection to the growing embryo. Nourishment is provided by endosperm in the eggs.
c. The hard leathery exterior of reptile eggs and the hard calcium covering of bird eggs provide protection to the growing embryo. Nourishment is provided by placenta in the eggs.
d. The hard leathery exterior of reptile eggs and the hard calcium covering of bird eggs provide protection to the growing embryo. Nourishment is provided by yolk in the eggs.

48. Compare the specialization of reproductive structures found in different types of land animals.

a. In birds, an opening called the cloaca is used to transfer sperm, whereas in mammals, the presence of the penis and vagina allows direct delivery. Complete reproductive systems are formed in insects, with eggs maturing in the testes and sperm maturing in the ovaries.
b. In birds, an opening called the cloaca is used to transfer sperm, whereas in mammals, the presence of the penis and vagina allows direct delivery. Complete reproductive systems are formed in insects, with eggs maturing in the ovaries and sperm maturing in the testes.
c. In birds, sperm are transferred via the spermatheca, whereas in mammals, the presence of the penis and vagina allows direct delivery. Complete reproductive systems are formed in insects, with eggs maturing in the ovaries and sperm maturing in the testes.
d. In birds, an opening called the cloaca is used to transfer sperm, whereas in mammals, the presence of the penis and vagina allows direct delivery. Insects always use parthenogenesis.

49. Explain the fate of the newly released secondary oocyte after ovulation.

a. If it fuses with a sperm, the resulting zygote enters the cervix for implantation. If it is not fertilized, it will return to the oviduct.
b. If it fuses with a sperm, the resulting zygote enters the uterus for implantation. If it is not fertilized, it will return to oviduct.
c. If it fuses with a sperm, the resulting zygote enters the uterus for implantation. If it is not fertilized, it will degrade and exit the body.
d. If it fuses with a sperm, the resulting zygote enters the cervix for implantation. If it is not fertilized, it will degrade and exit the body.

50. Explain the similarities and differences in sexual response in males and females.

a. Both males and females show specific arousal, but the sexual response differs in intensity and duration.
b. Both males and females show specific arousal. In males, breathing rate and heart rate are increased. In females, there is a decrease in breathing rate and heart rate.
c. Vasodilation occurs in both males and females, allowing blood to engorge erectile tissue in the nipples, clitoris, labia, vagina, and penis. In males, breathing rate and heart rate are increased. In females, there is a decrease in breathing rate and heart rate.
d. Both males and females show an increase in heart rate, breathing rate, and blood pressure during phase one and phase two. However, sexual response differs in intensity and duration in males and females. Also, males show specific arousal, while females show non-specific arousal.

51. Compare and contrast spermatogenesis and oogenesis.

a. Both are the form of gametogenesis that takes place through mitosis. Spermatogenesis is the process of formation of four sperm in the testes in males. The process of formation of one ovum in the ovaries in females is called oogenesis.
b. Both are the form of gametogenesis that takes place through meiosis. Spermatogenesis is the process of formation of four sperm in the testes in males. The process of formation of four ova in the ovaries in females is called oogenesis.
c. Bothare the form of gametogenesis that takes place through meiosis. Spermatogenesis is the process of formation of four sperm in the testes in males. The process of formation of one ovum in the ovaries in females is called oogenesis.
d. Both are the form of gametogenesis that takes place through meiosis. Spermatogenesis is the process of formation of one sperm in the testes in males, while the process of formation of one ovum in the ovaries in females is called oogenesis.

52. How does the hypothalamus regulate the secretion of reproductive hormones in males?

a. The hypothalamus releases FSH and LH at puberty by secreting of GnRH. FSH stimulates the Leydig cells in the testes and LH stimulates the Sertoli cells to synthesize and secrete testosterone.
b. The hypothalamus releases FSH and LH at puberty by the secretion of GHRH. FSH stimulates the Sertoli cells in the testes and LH stimulates the Leydig cells to synthesize and secrete testosterone.
c. The hypothalamus stimulates the release of FSH and LH at puberty by secreting of GnRH. FSH stimulates the Sertoli cells in the testes and LH stimulates the Leydig cells to synthesize and secrete testosterone.
d. The hypothalamus releases TSH and LH at puberty by the secretion of GnRH. TSH stimulates the Sertoli cells in the testes and LH stimulates the Leydig cells to synthesize and secrete testosterone.

53. What are the events that take place in a non-pregnant woman after ovulation?

a. Because a fertilized egg is not implanted into the uterus in a non-pregnant woman, the corpus luteum degenerates, and the levels of estrogen and progesterone decrease. The endometrium begins to degenerate as the progesterone level drops, initiating the next menstrual cycle.
b. Because a fertilized egg is not implanted into the uterus in a non-pregnant woman, the corpus luteum degenerates, and the levels of estrogen and progesterone increase. The endometrium begins to degenerate as the estrogen level increases, initiating the next menstrual cycle.
c. Because a fertilized egg is not implanted into the uterus in a non-pregnant woman, the corpus luteum degenerates and the levels of estrogen and progesterone increase. The endometrium begins to degenerate as the progesterone level rises, initiating the next menstrual cycle.
d. Because a fertilized egg is not implanted into the uterus in a non-pregnant woman, the corpus luteum degenerates and the levels of estrogen and progesterone decrease. The myometrium begins to degenerate as the progesterone level drops, initiating the next menstrual cycle.

54. The side effects of menopause can be diminished by hormone replacement therapy (HRT). However, many doctors are hesitant to recommend it. What are the possible reasons for this?

a. Its negative side effects, which include increased risk of colon cancer, osteoporosis, heart disease, macular degeneration, and possibly depression
b. Its negative side effects, which include increased risk of stroke or heart attack, blood clots, breast cancer, ovarian cancer, endometrial cancer, gall bladder disease, and possibly depression.
c. Its negative side effects, which include increased risk of stroke or heart attack, blood clots, breast cancer, colon cancer, endometrial cancer, gall bladder disease, and possibly dementia.
d. Its negative side effects, which include increased risk of stroke or heart attack, blood clots, breast cancer, ovarian cancer, endometrial cancer, gall bladder disease and possibly dementia.

55. If multiple sperm were to combine with an egg, what would be the outcome?

a. A cortical reaction would occur if multiple sperm combine with an egg, resulting in a genetically inviable embryo.
b. The embryo would be genetically inviable and would die in a few days. The zygote might have multiple sets of chromosomes.
c. The zygote might possess multiple sets of chromosomes, which will result in a neural tube defect in the developing fetus.
d. The zygote would be viable, but the resulting embryo would be genetically inviable.

56. After the blastula is formed, where do the embryonic stem cells and germ layers originate?

a. The inner cell mass contains embryonic stem cells, which arrange themselves into the three germ layers.
b. The trophoblast in the blastula contains embryonic stem cells, which arrange themselves into three germ layers.
c. The inner cell mass contains embryonic stem cells, whereas the germ cells originate from the trophoblast.
d. The embryonic stem cells and germ layers originate from the blastocoel present inside the blastula.

57. What determines whether a zygote will undergo total or partial cleavage?

a. Total cleavage takes place in eggs having a large amount of yolk, whereas partial cleavage occurs in eggs having very little or no yolk.
b. Total cleavage occurs when eggs possess equal concentration of yolk at both poles, whereas partial cleavage occurs when the yolk is not equally distributed.
c. Total cleavage takes place in eggs having little or no yolk, whereas partial cleavage occurs in eggs having a large amount of yolk.
d. Total cleavage occurs when divisions of the blastomeres are separate, whereas partial cleavage occurs when blastomeres stay partially connected.

58. During organogenesis, the ectoderm forms the neural cells and the epidermal cells. How do the ectoderm cells determine which type of cells to form?

a. Growth factors signal some of the ectodermal cells to form epidermal cells, and the remaining cells form the neural plate.
b. The notochord cells of the mesoderm signal the ectodermal cells to form epidermal cells as well as the neural plate.
c. Growth factors signal some of the ectodermal cells to form epidermal cells, and the remaining cells form neural crest cells.
d. Proteins involved in the Wnt signaling pathway signal the ectodermal cells to form the epidermal cells and the neural plate.

59. What will be the outcome if the axis is not formed during the developmental stages?

a. The animal will possess two notochords and may not have a dorsal-ventral or anterior-posterior side.
b. The animal will lack an anterior-posterior or dorsal-ventral side and may not have complete differentiation of cell layers.
c. The animal will lack an anterior-posterior or lateral-medial side and may not have complete differentiation of cell layers.
d. The animal will have incorrect positioning of the dorsal-ventral and lateral-medial sides and differentiation of cell layers will be incomplete.

60. Explain what the mesoderm is and what it eventually differentiates into.

a. The mesoderm, located on either side of the vertebrate neural tube, develops into various connective tissues. It is reorganized into groups of cells called somites, which develop into facial cartilage, ribs, and lungs.
b. The mesoderm, located at the border of the neural plate and the non-neural ectoderm, develops into various connective tissues such as the ribs, lungs, segmental muscle, and the notochord, which forms the central axis of the animal body.
c. The mesoderm, located on either side of the vertebrate neural tube, develops into various connective tissues. It is reorganized into groups of cells called somites, which develop into ribs, lungs, segmental muscle, and the notochord.
d. The mesoderm, located at the border of the neural plate and the non-neural ectoderm, develops into various connective tissues such as the facial cartilage, ribs, and lungs.

61. Which best describes the three stages of labor?

a. During stage one, the cervix thins. During stage two, the cervix is dilated to about 10 cm and the baby is expelled from the uterus. The last stage is the passage of the placenta after the baby has been born.

b. During stage one, the cervix thins and is dilated to about 10 cm. During stage two, the baby is expelled from the uterus. The last stage is the passage of the placenta after the baby has been born.

c. During stage one, the cervix thins. During stage two, the cervix is dilated to about 10 cm. During the last stage, the baby is expelled from the uterus, followed by the placenta.

d. During stage one, the cervix thins and may or may not be dilated. During stage two, the baby is expelled from the uterus. The last stage is the passage of the placenta after the baby has been born.

TEST PREP FOR AP® COURSES

62. If a plant species with a diploid number of 32 is crossed with another plant species with a diploid number of 24, what will be the diploid number of the resulting first generation of offspring? After the zygote multiplies to form a mass of cells, what is the chromosome number of each cell?

a. 32, 28

b. 24, 24

c. 28, 28

d. 28, 32

63. Compare and contrast sex determination in birds and mammals.

a. In mammals, sex is determined by the presence of XX (homozygous) in males and XY (heterozygous) in females, while in birds, sex is determined by the presence of ZZ (homozygous) in females and ZW (heterozygous) in males.

b. In mammals, sex is determined by the presence of XX (homozygous) in males and XY (heterozygous) in females, while in birds, sex is determined by the presence of ZW (heterozygous) in females and ZZ (homozygous) in males.

c. In mammals, sex is determined by the presence of XX (homozygous) in females and XY (heterozygous) in males, while in birds, sex is determined by the presence of ZZ (homozygous) in females and ZW (heterozygous) in males.

d. In mammals, sex is determined by the presence of XX (homozygous) in females and XY (heterozygous) in males, while in birds, sex is determined by the presence of ZW (heterozygous) in females and ZZ (homozygous) in males.

64. What is the advantage of sexual reproduction?

a. Sexual reproduction allows animals to conserve resources and reproduce only during optimal conditions.
b. Sexual reproduction results in offspring with diverse phenotypes, which may enhance survival of a population in a changing environment.
c. Sexual reproduction guarantees that both parents will provide parental care.
d. Sexual reproduction yields more numerous offspring more rapidly than is possible with asexual reproduction.

65. In sexual reproduction, two cells of a species combine to form another cell. Why is this useful?

a. It produces new combination of genes, which enables offspring to survive during environmental changes.
b. It results in the production of many offspring in a short period of time.
c. It does not involve gamete formation and requires less energy.
d. It allows immobile organisms to reproduce in the absence of a mate.

66. Spawning is often triggered by a signal such as water temperature or day length. What is an advantage of using this type of signal versus using individual courtship behaviors?

a. It allows many individuals to spawn simultaneously without males and females having to choose individual mates.
b. It is the only way that males and females can time gamete release simultaneously.
c. These are the only types of signals that can be used.
d. It increases the distance that gametes can travel.

67. Which of the following statements about hormone regulation of the female reproductive cycle is true?

a. LH and FSH are produced in the ovaries, and estradiol and progesterone are produced in the pituitary.
b. Estradiol and progesterone secreted from the corpus luteum cause the myometrium to thicken.
c. Progesterone is produced by the corpus luteum.
d. Secretion of GnRH by the hypothalamus is inhibited by high levels of estradiol, but stimulated by low levels of estradiol.

68. Which of the following statements about the menstrual cycle is TRUE?

a. Estrogen levels rise during the luteal phase of the ovarian cycle and the secretory phase of the uterine cycle.
b. Menstruation occurs much before LH and FSH levels peak.
c. Menstruation occurs after progesterone levels rise.
d. Progesterone levels rise before ovulation, while estrogen levels rise after.

69. What stimulates Leydig cells in the testes to produce testosterone?

a. FSH
b. LH
c. inhibin
d. estrogen

70. What is the nature of the oogonium and the secondary oocyte? Which process results in the formation of the secondary oocyte?

a. A diploid oogonium forms a haploid oocyte by the process of mitosis.
b. A haploid oogonium forms a diploid oocyte by the process of meiosis.
c. A diploid oogonium forms a haploid oocyte by the process of meiosis.
d. A haploid oogonium forms a haploid haploid oocyte by the process of meiosis.

71. Why are the diploid zygotes produced after fertilization of sperm cells produced by spermatogenesis not similar?

a. Their chromosome numbers are not the same.
b. The size of the sperm produced are different.
c. Some sperm may have a tail, whereas others may not.
d. Crossing over occurs during spermatogenesis.

72. The endocrine system incorporates feedback mechanisms that maintain homeostasis. Which of the following mechanisms demonstrates negative feedback by the reproductive system in mammals?

a. Increasing levels of testosterone inhibit the production of GnRH, LH, and FSH by the hypothalamus and pituitary.
b. LH and FSH stimulate the interstitial cells of Leydig to release testosterone.
c. The growing follicle starts releasing estrogen in increasing amounts.
d. The corpus luteum releases progesterone after ovulation.

73. Discuss the positive feedback mechanisms by LH and FSH during the follicular and ovulation phase of the ovarian cycle.

a. The stimulation of the anterior pituitary by GHRH secretes the hormones LH and FSH. The increasing amounts of these hormones stimulate several follicles in the ovary to start growing, but only one of these matures to release the egg.
b. The stimulation of the anterior pituitary by GnRH secretes the hormones LH and TSH. The increasing amounts of these hormones stimulate several follicles in the ovary to start growing, but only one of these matures to release the egg.
c. The stimulation of the anterior pituitary by GnRH triggers the secretion of the hormones LH and FSH. The increasing amounts of these hormones stimulate several follicles in the ovary to start growing, but only one of these matures to release the egg.
d. The stimulation of the anterior pituitary by GHRH secretes the hormones LH and TSH. The increasing amounts of these hormones stimulate several follicles in the ovary to start growing, but only one of these matures to release the egg.

74. Describe the possible event that would occur if the corpus luteum did not produce increasing amounts of progesterone.

a. The implanted zygote will not be able to derive sufficient nutrition from the endometrium.
b. Even if fertilization is successful, the zygote may not be able to implant successfully. If it does manage to implant, it will not be able to derive sufficient nutrition from the myometrium.
c. Even if fertilization is successful, the zygote may not be able to implant successfully. If it does manage to implant, it will not be able to derive sufficient nutrition from the endometrium.
d. The contraction of the uterus during childbirth and lactation will not take place, causing problems and complications in the mother.

75. What does a female contraceptive pill that inhibits the release of GnRH from the hypothalamus do?

a. reduce the secretion of FSH and LH from the anterior pituitary gland
b. initiate ovulation
c. increase the flow phase of the menstrual cycle
d. increase the production of estrogen and progesterone by the ovaries

76. What do the rising levels of FSH and LH in the follicular phase cause?

a. The follicles on the surface of the ovary start growing in preparation for ovulation.
b. The endometrium starts to thicken.
c. The corpus luteum starts secreting progesterone.
d. One of the mature follicles bursts, releasing the egg.

77. A couple has been trying to conceive for some time and goes to an endocrinologist for advice. If the endocrinologist diagnoses an obstruction in the oviducts of the female, what type of treatment can she recommend?

a. opting for in vivo fertilization or ligation of the fallopian tubes surgically so that the tubes are sealed
b. opting for in vivofertilization or removal of the obstruction surgically and then re-ligation of the ends of the fallopian tubes
c. opting for in vitro fertilization or ligation of the fallopian tubes surgically so that the tubes are sealed
d. opting for in vitro fertilization or removal of the obstruction surgically and then re-ligation of the ends of the fallopian tubes

78. How does a reproductive hormone that is secreted directly from the anterior pituitary stimulate the reproductive organs to produce hormones?

a. by traveling through the blood to reach the target organs
b. by binding with proteins to reach the reproductive organs
c. by sending a chemical messenger to activate the reproductive organs
d. by converting into an active form before targeting the reproductive organs

79. Explain the mechanisms by which hormones from the brain and ovaries interact, eventually leading to menstruation.

a. After the release of the egg from the follicle, the corpus luteum is formed, which inhibits FSH and LH production, which then inhibits GnRH production, causing no other follicle to develop. When no fertilization takes place, the corpus luteum degenerates and the progesterone level declines, initiating the breakdown of the myometrium and the start of the menstrual cycle.
b. After the release of the egg from the follicle, the corpus luteum is formed, which inhibits FSH and LH production, which then inhibits GnRH production, causing no other follicle to develop. When no fertilization takes place, the corpus luteum degenerates and the progesterone level declines, initiating the breakdown of the endometrium and the start of the menstrual cycle.
c. After the release of the egg from the follicle, the corpus luteum is formed, which inhibits FSH and LH production, which then facilitates GnRH production, causing no other follicle to develop. When no fertilization takes place, the corpus luteum degenerates and the progesterone level declines, initiating the breakdown of the endometrium and the start of the menstrual cycle.
d. After the release of the egg from the follicle, the corpus luteum is formed, which inhibits FSH and LH production, which then inhibits GnRH production, causing no other follicle to develop. When no fertilization takes place, the corpus luteum degenerates and the progesterone level rises, initiating the breakdown of the endometrium and the start of the menstrual cycle.

80. Multiple hormones work together to coordinate the female reproductive cycle. Which of these hormones is also responsible for the development of female secondary sexual characteristics, including breast development and hip widening?

a. estrogen
b. progesterone
c. follicle stimulating hormone
d. luteinizing hormone

81. Which hormone is released by the anterior pituitary as a part of the positive feedback loop between it and the ovary?

a. Progesterone
b. GnRH
c. LH
d. Estradiol

82. How does the feedback mechanism of hormones lead to muscular contractions during labor?

a. A feedback relay occurs between the uterus, hypothalamus, and posterior pituitary to assure an adequate supply of oxytocin, which causes the contraction of smooth muscles of the uterus, leading to the birth of the baby.
b. The posterior pituitary continuously produces oxytocin, which is sufficient for muscular contraction in the uterus, thereby causing the birth of the baby.
c. A feedback relay occurs between the uterus, hypothalamus, and posterior pituitary to assure an adequate supply of prolactin, which causes the contraction of the smooth muscles of the uterus, leading to the birth of the baby.
d. A feedback relay occurs between the uterus, hypothalamus, and posterior pituitary to assure an adequate supply of progesterone, which causes the contraction of the smooth muscles of the uterus, leading to the birth of the baby.

83. During childbirth, the hormone oxytocin causes contraction of the uterine wall muscles. As muscular contractions increase, more oxytocin is released from the pituitary, leading to more contractions. This is an example of which mechanism?

a. end product inhibition
b. negative feedback mechanism
c. positive feedback mechanism
d. feedback inhibition

SCIENCE PRACTICE CHALLENGE QUESTIONS

84. Humans are bilateral and have biaxial symmetry. However, small variations in body symmetry occur. One foot may be slightly larger than another and we might never know. Because the eyes are so important in communication the condition called heterochromia iridium is very noticeable. Body plans are very noticeable aspects of the phenotype.

In guppy courtship the male displays himself to the female. Some males are more orange than others and some males have asymmetry with one side being more brightly colored orange than the other side. A pattern in the courtship display is shown in the graphs (Gross et al., *Proceedings of the Royal Society B:Biological Sciences*, 274, 2007).

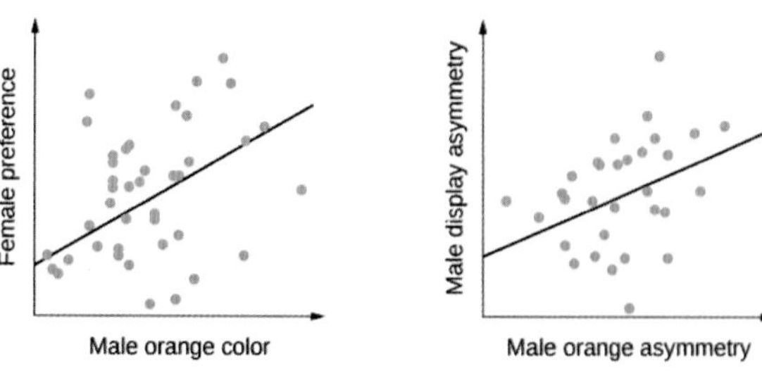

Figure 34.33

A. **Analyze** the data to support the claim that the female guppy is responding to information, that the male guppy is aware of this response, and that this communication affects natural selection.

If there were no process that maintained variation in the gene controlling the orange coloration then perhaps all male guppies would symmetrically bright orange. Yet variation remains.

B. A guppy is a small fish and small fish are eaten by bigger fish. **Make and justify** a claim regarding the effect of allelic variation on the stability of the guppy population.

Phenotype is an expression of the genotype and within a population genotypic variation occurs. For a population to maintain stability in a changing environment genetic variation within the population provides selective advantage at the population level.

C. **Make and justify** a claim regarding the effect of genetic variation in guppies on the stability of an ecosystem of which the guppy is a member.

The fluctuation of symmetry in body plan of an organism, such as the asymmetry of guppy coloration, is unusual. Large scale fluctuations where the fully developed organism is viable, such as the emergence of an appendage from the eye of the *Drosophila*, are very rare. The overall body plan is controlled in *Drosophila* by a cluster of genes called the Hox genes. In the fruit fly there is a single cluster and the arrangement of genes in the genome is a map of the anterior to posterior body plan. In all vertebrate multiple Hox clusters control the development of the body plan and they too show the sequential anterior to posterior arrangement in the genome.

D. During development the transcription factors expressed by the Hox genes initiate and terminate the expression of specialized cells and tissues. **Describe** the evidence for shared ancestry in this conserved strategy for communication between cells through regulation of transcription factors.

E. **Describe** one other example of conserved core shared by all domains or within one domain.

35 | ECOLOGY AND THE BIOSPHERE

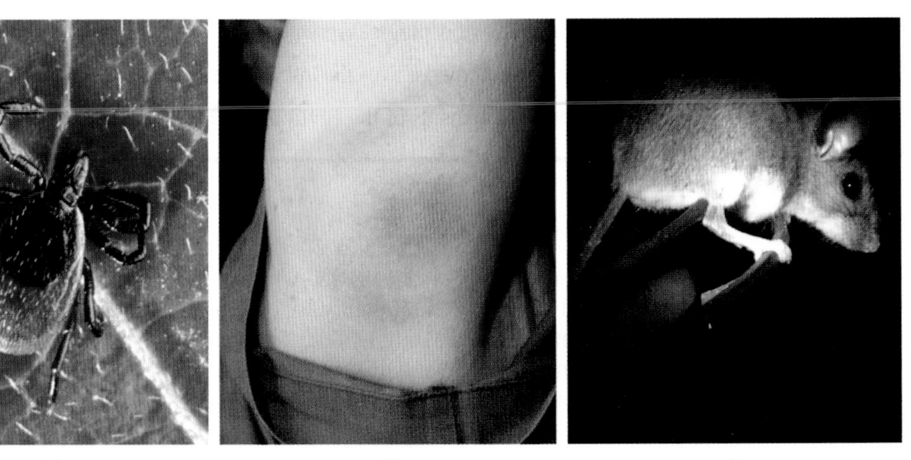

Figure 35.1 The (a) deer tick carries the bacterium that produces Lyme disease in humans, often evident in (b) a symptomatic bull's eye rash. The (c) white-footed mouse is one well-known host to deer ticks carrying the Lyme disease bacterium. (credit a: modification of work by Scott Bauer, USDA ARS; credit b: modification of work by James Gathany, CDC; credit c: modification of work by Rob Ireton)

Chapter Outline

Introduction

Why study ecology? Perhaps you are interested in learning about the natural world and how living things have adapted to the physical conditions of their environment. Or, perhaps you're a future physician seeking to understand the connection between human health and ecology.

Humans are a part of the ecological landscape, and human health is one important part of human interaction with our physical and living environment. Lyme disease, for instance, serves as one modern-day example of the connection between our health and the natural world (Figure 35.1). More formally known as Lyme borreliosis, Lyme disease is a bacterial infection that can be transmitted to humans when they are bitten by the deer tick (*Ixodes scapularis*), which is the primary vector for this disease. However, not all deer ticks carry the bacteria that will cause Lyme disease in humans, and *I. scapularis* can have other hosts besides deer. In fact, it turns out that the probability of infection depends on the type of host upon which the tick develops: a higher proportion of ticks that live on white-footed mice carry the bacterium than do ticks that live on deer. Knowledge about the environments and population densities in which the host species is abundant would help a physician or an epidemiologist better understand how Lyme disease is transmitted and how its incidence could be reduced.

For example, the mild winter in the northeast during 2010–2011 caused a boom in acorns, which in turn caused an increase in the white-footed mice population. However, the following winter was cooler, leading to fewer acorns, and the subsequent decrease in the mice population means that the ticks will be more likely to seek out humans for their blood meals. You can read more about the relationship between acorns, mice, and Lyme disease at the Science Daily

website (http://openstaxcollege.org/l/32lyme) and you can read more about Lyme disease from the **CDC website (http://openstaxcollege.org/l/32lymecdc)** .

35.1 | The Scope of Ecology

In this section, you will explore the following questions:

- What is ecology, and what are the four levels of ecological research?
- What are examples of the ways in which ecology requires the integration of different scientific disciplines?
- What are examples of biotic and abiotic components of the environment?

Connection for AP® Courses

Ecology is the study of the interactions among living organisms and with their environment. This includes relationships between organisms of the same species and also between different species. One core goal of ecology is to understand the distribution and abundance of organisms that inhabit the Earth. Ecology integrates multiple scientific disciplines in addition to biology, including molecular biology, physiology, evolution, biodiversity, geology, and climatology. Some ecological research also applies aspects of chemistry and physics, and it frequently uses mathematical models.

Information presented and the examples highlighted in the section support concepts outlined in Big Idea 4 of the AP® Biology Curriculum Framework. The AP® Learning Objectives listed in the Curriculum Framework provide a transparent foundation for the AP® Biology course, an inquiry-based laboratory experience, instructional activities, and AP® exam questions. A learning objective merges required content with one or more of the seven science practices.

Big Idea 4	Biological systems interact, and these systems and their interactions possess complex properties.
Enduring Understanding 4.A	Interactions within biological systems lead to complex properties.
Essential Knowledge	**4.A.6** Interactions among living organisms and with their environment results in the movement of matter and energy.
Science Practice	**1.4** The student can use representations and models to analyze situations or solve problems qualitatively and quantitatively.
Learning Objective	**4.15** The student is able to use visual representations to analyze situations or solve problems qualitatively to illustrate how interactions among living systems and with their environment result in the movement of matter and energy.

Climate change can alter where organisms live, which can sometimes directly affect human health. Watch the PBS video **"Feeling the Effects of Climate Change" (http://openstaxcollege.org/l/climate_health)** in which researchers discover a pathogenic organism living far outside of its normal range.

The fungus *Cryptococcus gattii* has been known to cause a fatal illness. This fungus originally found in the tropics is now growing in parts of North America. What have scientists found out about this fungus?

a. The fungus was inadvertently introduced in North America by travelers

b. This fungus acquired pathogenic characteristics over time.

c. The disease was caused by contact with infected people

d. The fungus started growing more in colder climates as temperatures have risen due to global warming.

Levels of Ecological Study

When a discipline such as biology is studied, it is often helpful to subdivide it into smaller, related areas. For instance, cell biologists interested in cell signaling need to understand the chemistry of the signal molecules (which are usually proteins) as well as the result of cell signaling. Ecologists interested in the factors that influence the survival of an endangered species might use mathematical models to predict how current conservation efforts affect endangered organisms. To produce a sound set of management options, a conservation biologist needs to collect accurate data, including current population size, factors affecting reproduction (like physiology and behavior), habitat requirements (such as plants and soils), and potential human influences on the endangered population and its habitat (which might be derived through studies in sociology and urban ecology). Within the discipline of ecology, researchers work at four specific levels, sometimes discretely and sometimes with overlap: organism, population, community, and ecosystem (**Figure 35.2**).

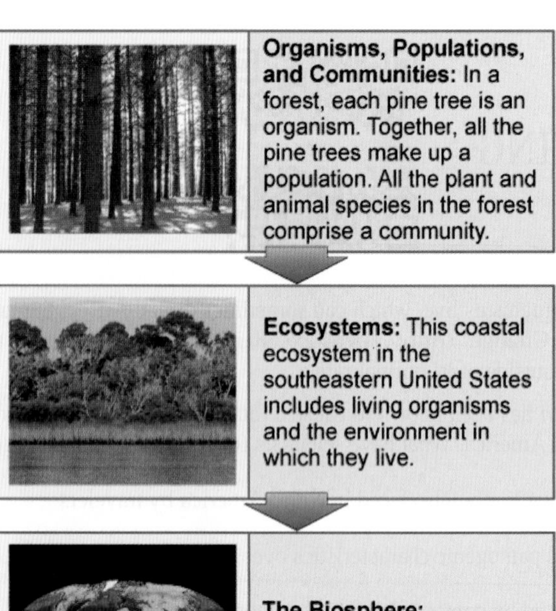
Organisms, Populations, and Communities: In a forest, each pine tree is an organism. Together, all the pine trees make up a population. All the plant and animal species in the forest comprise a community.
Ecosystems: This coastal ecosystem in the southeastern United States includes living organisms and the environment in which they live.
The Biosphere: Encompasses all the ecosystems on Earth.

Figure 35.2 Ecologists study within several biological levels of organization. (credit "organisms": modification of work by "Crystl"/Flickr; credit "ecosystems": modification of work by Tom Carlisle, US Fish and Wildlife Service Headquarters; credit "biosphere": NASA)

Organismal Ecology

Researchers studying ecology at the organismal level are interested in the adaptations that enable individuals to live in specific habitats. These adaptations can be morphological, physiological, and behavioral. For instance, the Karner blue butterfly (*Lycaeides melissa samuelis*) (Figure 35.3) is considered a specialist because the females preferentially oviposit (that is, lay eggs) on wild lupine. This preferential adaptation means that the Karner blue butterfly is highly dependent on the presence of wild lupine plants for its continued survival.

Figure 35.3 The Karner blue butterfly (*Lycaeides melissa samuelis*) is a rare butterfly that lives only in open areas with few trees or shrubs, such as pine barrens and oak savannas. It can only lay its eggs on lupine plants. (credit: modification of work by J & K Hollingsworth, USFWS)

After hatching, the larval caterpillars emerge and spend four to six weeks feeding solely on wild lupine (Figure 35.4). The caterpillars pupate (undergo metamorphosis) and emerge as butterflies after about four weeks. The adult butterflies feed on the nectar of flowers of wild lupine and other plant species. A researcher interested in studying Karner blue butterflies at the organismal level might, in addition to asking questions about egg laying, ask questions about the butterflies' preferred temperature (a physiological question) or the behavior of the caterpillars when they are at different larval stages (a behavioral question).

Figure 35.4 The wild lupine (*Lupinus perennis*) is the host plant for the Karner blue butterfly.

Population Ecology

A population is a group of interbreeding organisms that are members of the same species living in the same area at the same time. (Organisms that are all members of the same species are called **conspecifics**.) A population is identified, in part, by where it lives, and its area of population may have natural or artificial boundaries: natural boundaries might be rivers, mountains, or deserts, while examples of artificial boundaries include mowed grass, manmade structures, or roads. The study of population ecology focuses on the number of individuals in an area and how and why population size changes over time. Population ecologists are particularly interested in counting the Karner blue butterfly, for example, because it is classified as federally endangered. However, the distribution and density of this species is highly influenced by the distribution and abundance of wild lupine. Researchers might ask questions about the factors leading to the decline of wild lupine and how these affect Karner blue butterflies. For example, ecologists know that wild lupine thrives in open areas where trees and shrubs are largely absent. In natural settings, intermittent wildfires regularly remove trees and shrubs, helping to maintain the open areas that wild lupine requires. Mathematical models can be used to understand how wildfire suppression by humans has led to the decline of this important plant for the Karner blue butterfly.

Community Ecology

A biological community consists of the different species within an area, typically a three-dimensional space, and the interactions within and among these species. Community ecologists are interested in the processes driving these interactions and their consequences. Questions about conspecific interactions often focus on competition among members of the same species for a limited resource. Ecologists also study interactions among various species; members of different species are called **heterospecifics**. Examples of heterospecific interactions include predation, parasitism, herbivory, competition, and pollination. These interactions can have regulating effects on population sizes and can impact ecological and evolutionary processes affecting diversity.

For example, Karner blue butterfly larvae form mutualistic relationships with ants. Mutualism is a form of a long-term relationship that has coevolved between two species and from which each species benefits. For mutualism to exist between individual organisms, each species must receive some benefit from the other as a consequence of the relationship. Researchers have shown that there is an increase in the probability of survival when Karner blue butterfly larvae (caterpillars) are tended by ants. This might be because the larvae spend less time in each life stage when tended by ants, which provides an advantage for the larvae. Meanwhile, the Karner blue butterfly larvae secrete a carbohydrate-rich substance that is an important energy source for the ants. Both the Karner blue larvae and the ants benefit from their interaction.

Ecosystem Ecology

Ecosystem ecology is an extension of organismal, population, and community ecology. The ecosystem is composed of all the **biotic** components (living things) in an area along with the **abiotic** components (non-living things) of that area. Some of the abiotic components include air, water, and soil. Ecosystem biologists ask questions about how nutrients and energy are stored and how they move among organisms and the surrounding atmosphere, soil, and water.

The Karner blue butterflies and the wild lupine live in an oak-pine barren habitat. This habitat is characterized by natural disturbance and nutrient-poor soils that are low in nitrogen. The availability of nutrients is an important factor in the distribution of the plants that live in this habitat. Researchers interested in ecosystem ecology could ask questions about the importance of limited resources and the movement of resources, such as nutrients, though the biotic and abiotic portions of the ecosystem.

career CONNECTION

Ecologist

A career in ecology contributes to many facets of human society. Understanding ecological issues can help society meet the basic human needs of food, shelter, and health care. Ecologists can conduct their research in the laboratory and outside in natural environments (Figure 35.5). These natural environments can be as close to home as the stream running through your campus or as far away as the hydrothermal vents at the bottom of the Pacific Ocean. Ecologists manage natural resources such as white-tailed deer populations (*Odocoileus virginianus*) for hunting or aspen (*Populus* spp.) timber stands for paper production. Ecologists also work as educators who teach children and adults at various institutions including universities, high schools, museums, and nature centers. Ecologists may also work in advisory positions assisting local, state, and federal policymakers to develop laws that are ecologically sound, or they may develop those policies and legislation themselves. To become an ecologist requires an undergraduate degree, usually in a natural science. The undergraduate degree is often followed by specialized training or an advanced degree, depending on the area of ecology selected. Ecologists should also have a broad background in the physical sciences, as well as a sound foundation in mathematics and statistics.

Figure 35.5 This landscape ecologist is releasing a black-footed ferret into its native habitat as part of a study. (credit: USFWS Mountain Prairie Region, NPS)

Visit this site (http://openstaxcollege.org/l/ecologist_role) to see Stephen Wing, a marine ecologist from the University of Otago, discuss the role of an ecologist and the types of issues ecologists explore.

A marine ecologist studies interactions in the ocean. Which of the following subjects would a marine ecologist include in his studies?

a. chemistry

b. philosophy

c. political science

d. epidemiology

35.2 | Biogeography

In this section, you will explore the following questions:

- What is biogeography?
- What are examples of abiotic factors that affect the global distribution of plant and animal species?
- What are examples of how abiotic factors can impact aquatic and terrestrial environments?
- What are the effects of abiotic factors on net primary productivity?

Connection for AP® Courses

Many forces influence the communities of living organisms present in different parts of the biosphere (all of the parts of Earth inhabited by life). The biosphere extends into the atmosphere (several kilometers above Earth) and into the depths of the oceans. Despite its apparent vastness to an individual human, the biosphere occupies only a minute space when compared to the known universe. Many abiotic forces influence where life can exist and the types of organisms found in different parts of the biosphere. The abiotic factors influence the distribution of **biomes**: large areas of land with similar climate, flora, and fauna.

Information presented and the examples highlighted in the section support concepts outlined in Big Idea 2 of the AP® Biology Curriculum Framework. The AP® Learning Objectives listed in the Curriculum Framework provide a transparent foundation for the AP® Biology course, an inquiry-based laboratory experience, instructional activities, and AP® exam questions. A learning objective merges required content with one or more of the seven science practices.

Big Idea 2	Biological systems utilize free energy and molecular building blocks to grow, to reproduce, and to maintain dynamic homeostasis.
Enduring Understanding 2.D	Growth and dynamic homeostasis of a biological system are influenced by changes in the system's environment.
Essential Knowledge	**2.D.1** Populations, communities, and ecosystems are affected by interactions with abiotic factors in the environment.

Science Practice	**1.3** The student can refine representations and models of natural or man-made phenomena and systems in the domain.
Science Practice	**3.2** The student can refine scientific questions.
Learning Objective	**2.22** The student is able to refine scientific models and questions about the effect of complex biotic and abiotic interactions on all biological systems, from cells and organisms to populations, communities, and ecosystems.
Essential Knowledge	**2.D.1** Populations, communities, and ecosystems are affected by interactions with abiotic factors in the environment.
Science Practice	**4.2** The student can design a plan for collecting data to answer a particular scientific question.
Science Practice	**7.2** The student can connect concepts in and across domain(s) to generalize or extrapolate in and/or across enduring understandings and/or big ideas.
Learning Objective	**2.23** The student is able to design a plan for collecting data to show that all biological systems are affected by complex biotic and abiotic interactions.
Essential Knowledge	**2.D.1** Populations, communities, and ecosystems are affected by interactions with abiotic factors in the environment.
Science Practice	**5.1** The student can analyze data to identify patterns or relationships.
Learning Objective	**2.24** The student is able to analyze data to identify possible patterns and relationships between a biotic or abiotic factor and a biological system.

Biogeography

Biogeography is the study of the geographic distribution of living things and the abiotic factors that affect their distribution. Abiotic factors such as temperature and rainfall vary based mainly on latitude and elevation. As these abiotic factors change, the composition of plant and animal communities also changes. For example, if you were to begin a journey at the equator and walk north, you would notice gradual changes in plant communities. At the beginning of your journey, you would see tropical wet forests with broad-leaved evergreen trees, which are characteristic of plant communities found near the equator. As you continued to travel north, you would see these broad-leaved evergreen plants eventually give rise to seasonally dry forests with scattered trees. You would also begin to notice changes in temperature and moisture. At about 30 degrees north, these forests would give way to deserts, which are characterized by low precipitation.

Moving farther north, you would see that deserts are replaced by grasslands or prairies. Eventually, grasslands are replaced by deciduous temperate forests. These deciduous forests give way to the boreal forests found in the subarctic, the area south of the Arctic Circle. Finally, you would reach the Arctic tundra, which is found at the most northern latitudes. This trek north reveals gradual changes in both climate and the types of organisms that have adapted to environmental factors associated with ecosystems found at different latitudes. However, different ecosystems exist at the same latitude due in part to abiotic factors such as jet streams, the Gulf Stream, and ocean currents. If you were to hike up a mountain, the changes you would see in the vegetation would parallel those as you move to higher latitudes.

Ecologists who study biogeography examine patterns of species distribution. No species exists everywhere; for example, the Venus flytrap is endemic to a small area in North and South Carolina. An **endemic** species is one which is naturally found only in a specific geographic area that is usually restricted in size. Other species are generalists: species which live in a wide variety of geographic areas; the raccoon, for example, is native to most of North and Central America.

Species distribution patterns are based on biotic and abiotic factors and their influences during the very long periods of time required for species evolution; therefore, early studies of biogeography were closely linked to the emergence of evolutionary thinking in the eighteenth century. Some of the most distinctive assemblages of plants and animals occur in regions that have been physically separated for millions of years by geographic barriers. Biologists estimate that Australia, for example, has between 600,000 and 700,000 species of plants and animals. Approximately 3/4 of living plant and mammal species are endemic species found solely in Australia (**Figure 35.6ab**).

(a) (b)

Figure 35.6 Australia is home to many endemic species. The (a) wallaby (*Wallabia bicolor*), a medium-sized member of the kangaroo family, is a pouched mammal, or marsupial. The (b) echidna (*Tachyglossus aculeatus*) is an egg-laying mammal. (credit a: modification of work by Derrick Coetzee; credit b: modification of work by Allan Whittome)

Sometimes ecologists discover unique patterns of species distribution by determining where species are *not* found. Hawaii, for example, has no native land species of reptiles or amphibians, and has only one native terrestrial mammal, the hoary bat. Most of New Guinea, as another example, lacks placental mammals.

Check out this video (http://openstaxcollege.org/l/platypus) to observe a platypus swimming in its natural habitat in New South Wales, Australia.

Marsupials such as such as wallabies, platypuses, and kangaroos are found exclusively in Australia. Species found in a limited area are most specifically called _____.

a. endemic species

b. generalist species

c. native species

d. common species

Plants can be endemic or generalists: endemic plants are found only on specific regions of the Earth, while generalists are found on many regions. Isolated land masses—such as Australia, Hawaii, and Madagascar—often have large numbers of endemic plant species. Some of these plants are endangered due to human activity. The forest gardenia (*Gardenia brighamii*), for instance, is endemic to Hawaii; only an estimated 15–20 trees are thought to exist (Figure 35.7).

science practices CONNECTION for AP® Courses

Think About It

Many endemic species are found in areas that are geographically isolated. What is a possible scientific explanation for this observation? Justify your answer.

Lab Investigation

Use *The College Board Advanced Placement Program: Measuring Primary Productivity—Grass Plants: Student Lab Template*, found here (http://openstaxcollege.org/l/32grass) to explore the concept of primary productivity versus gross productivity. You will calculate primary productivity, be introduced to the benefits of measuring dry mass versus wet mass, and make predictions about the changes in net primary productivity based on the variables you decide to focus on.

To learn more about calculating net primary productivity, watch this video (https://openstaxcollege.org/l/32nppcalc) .

Figure 35.7 Listed as federally endangered, the forest gardenia is a small tree with distinctive flowers. It is found only in five of the Hawaiian Islands in small populations consisting of a few individual specimens. (credit: Forest & Kim Starr)

Energy Sources

Energy from the sun is captured by green plants, algae, cyanobacteria, and photosynthetic protists. These organisms convert solar energy into the chemical energy needed by all living things. Light availability can be an important force directly affecting the evolution of adaptations in photosynthesizers. For instance, plants in the understory of a temperate forest are shaded when the trees above them in the canopy completely leaf out in the late spring. Not surprisingly, understory plants have adaptations to successfully capture available light. One such adaptation is the rapid growth of spring ephemeral plants such as the spring beauty (Figure 35.8). These spring flowers achieve much of their growth and finish their life cycle (reproduce) early in the season before the trees in the canopy develop leaves.

Figure 35.8 The spring beauty is an ephemeral spring plant that flowers early in the spring to avoid competing with larger forest trees for sunlight. (credit: John Beetham)

In aquatic ecosystems, the availability of light may be limited because sunlight is absorbed by water, plants, suspended particles, and resident microorganisms. Toward the bottom of a lake, pond, or ocean, there is a zone that light cannot reach. Photosynthesis cannot take place there and, as a result, a number of adaptations have evolved that enable living things to survive without light. For instance, aquatic plants have photosynthetic tissue near the surface of the water; for example, think of the broad, floating leaves of a water lily—water lilies cannot survive without light. In environments such as hydrothermal vents, some bacteria extract energy from inorganic chemicals because there is no light for photosynthesis.

The availability of nutrients in aquatic systems is also an important aspect of energy or photosynthesis. Many organisms sink to the bottom of the ocean when they die in the open water; when this occurs, the energy found in that living organism is sequestered for some time unless ocean upwelling occurs. **Ocean upwelling** is the rising of deep ocean waters that occurs when prevailing winds blow along surface waters near a coastline (Figure 35.9). As the wind pushes ocean waters offshore, water from the bottom of the ocean moves up to replace this water. As a result, the nutrients once contained in dead organisms become available for reuse by other living organisms.

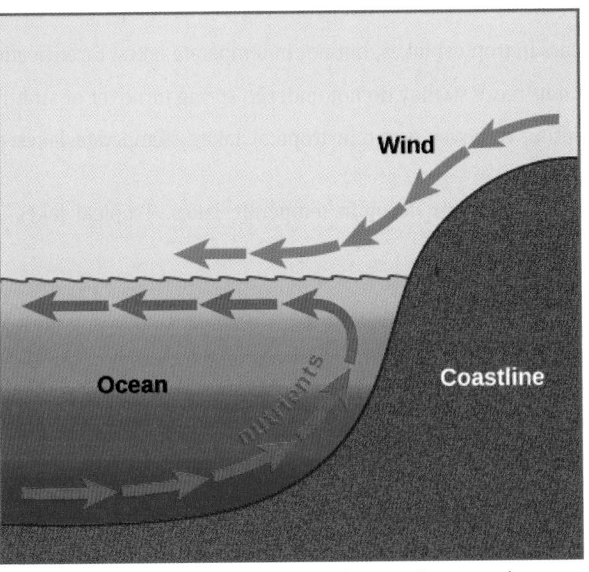

Figure 35.9 Ocean upwelling is an important process that recycles nutrients and energy in the ocean. As wind (green arrows) pushes offshore, it causes water from the ocean bottom (red arrows) to move to the surface, bringing up nutrients from the ocean depths.

In freshwater systems, the recycling of nutrients occurs in response to air temperature changes. The nutrients at the bottom of lakes are recycled twice each year: in the spring and fall turnover. The **spring and fall turnover** is a seasonal process that recycles nutrients and oxygen from the bottom of a freshwater ecosystem to the top of a body of water (Figure 35.10). These turnovers are caused by the formation of a **thermocline**: a layer of water with a temperature that is significantly different from that of the surrounding layers. In wintertime, the surface of lakes found in many northern regions is frozen. However, the water under the ice is slightly warmer, and the water at the bottom of the lake is warmer yet at 4 °C to 5 °C (39.2 °F to 41 °F). Water is densest at 4 °C; therefore, the deepest water is also the densest. The deepest water is oxygen poor because the decomposition of organic material at the bottom of the lake uses up available oxygen that cannot be replaced by means of oxygen diffusion into the water due to the surface ice layer.

visual CONNECTION

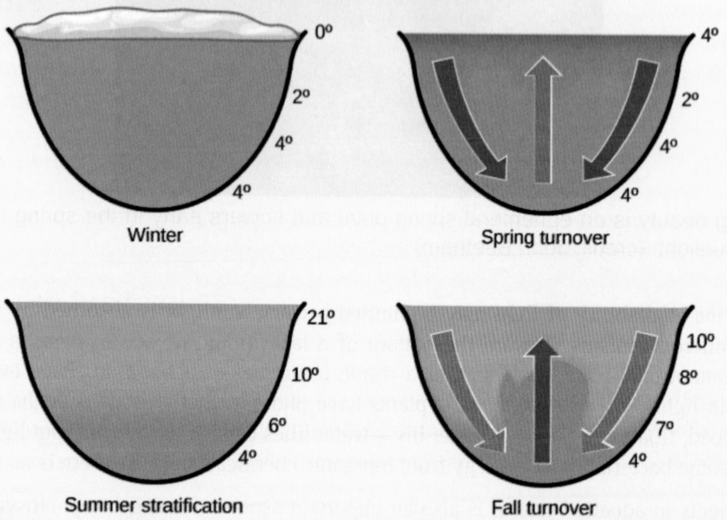

Figure 35.10 The spring and fall turnovers are important processes in freshwater lakes that act to move the nutrients and oxygen at the bottom of deep lakes to the top. Turnover occurs because water has a maximum density at 4 °C. Surface water temperature changes as the seasons progress, and denser water sinks.

The spring and fall turnovers are important processes in freshwater lakes that act to move nutrients and water from the bottom to the top. Explain how this is different in temperate regions as compared to the tropics.

a. Spring turnover occurs in tropical lakes, but not in temperate lakes. Stratification occurs in temperate lakes.
b. Temperate lakes do not freeze so they do not undergo spring turnover or stratification.
c. Stratification and spring turnover occur in tropical lakes. Temperate lakes do not freeze so they do not undergo spring turnover.
d. Stratification and spring turnover occur in temperate lakes. Tropical lakes do not freeze so they do not undergo spring turnover.

In springtime, air temperatures increase and surface ice melts. When the temperature of the surface water begins to reach 4 °C, the water becomes heavier and sinks to the bottom. The water at the bottom of the lake is then displaced by the heavier surface water and, thus, rises to the top. As that water rises to the top, the sediments and nutrients from the lake bottom are brought along with it. During the summer months, the lake water stratifies, or forms layers, with the warmest water at the lake surface.

As air temperatures drop in the fall, the temperature of the lake water cools to 4 °C; therefore, this causes fall turnover as the heavy cold water sinks and displaces the water at the bottom. The oxygen-rich water at the surface of the lake then moves to the bottom of the lake, while the nutrients at the bottom of the lake rise to the surface (Figure 35.10). During the winter, the oxygen at the bottom of the lake is used by decomposers and other organisms requiring oxygen, such as fish.

Temperature

Temperature affects the physiology of living things as well as the density and state of water. Temperature exerts an important influence on living things because few living things can survive at temperatures below 0 °C (32 °F) due to metabolic constraints. It is also rare for living things to survive at temperatures exceeding 45 °C (113 °F); this is a reflection of evolutionary response to typical temperatures. Enzymes are most efficient within a narrow and specific range of temperatures; enzyme degradation can occur at higher temperatures. Therefore, organisms either must maintain an internal temperature or they must inhabit an environment that will keep the body within a temperature range that supports metabolism. Some animals have adapted to enable their bodies to survive significant temperature fluctuations, such as seen in hibernation or reptilian torpor. Similarly, some bacteria are adapted to surviving in extremely hot temperatures such as geysers. Such bacteria are examples of extremophiles: organisms that thrive in extreme environments.

Temperature can limit the distribution of living things. Animals faced with temperature fluctuations may respond with adaptations, such as migration, in order to survive. Migration, the movement from one place to another, is an adaptation found in many animals, including many that inhabit seasonally cold climates. Migration solves problems related to temperature, locating food, and finding a mate. In migration, for instance, the Arctic Tern (*Sterna paradisaea*) makes a 40,000 km (24,000 mi) round trip flight each year between its feeding grounds in the southern hemisphere and its breeding grounds in the Arctic Ocean. Monarch butterflies (*Danaus plexippus*) live in the eastern United States in the warmer months and migrate to Mexico and the southern United States in the wintertime. Some species of mammals also make migratory forays. Reindeer (*Rangifer tarandus*) travel about 5,000 km (3,100 mi) each year to find food. Amphibians and reptiles are more limited in their distribution because they lack migratory ability. Not all animals that can migrate do so: migration carries risk and comes at a high energy cost.

Some animals hibernate or estivate to survive hostile temperatures. Hibernation enables animals to survive cold conditions, and estivation allows animals to survive the hostile conditions of a hot, dry climate. Animals that hibernate or estivate enter a state known as torpor: a condition in which their metabolic rate is significantly lowered. This enables the animal to wait until its environment better supports its survival. Some amphibians, such as the wood frog (*Rana sylvatica*), have an antifreeze-like chemical in their cells, which retains the cells' integrity and prevents them from bursting.

Water

Water is required by all living things because it is critical for cellular processes. Since terrestrial organisms lose water to the environment by simple diffusion, they have evolved many adaptations to retain water.

- Plants have a number of interesting features on their leaves, such as leaf hairs and a waxy cuticle, that serve to decrease the rate of water loss via transpiration.
- Freshwater organisms are surrounded by water and are constantly in danger of having water rush into their cells because of osmosis. Many adaptations of organisms living in freshwater environments have evolved to ensure that solute concentrations in their bodies remain within appropriate levels. One such adaptation is the excretion of dilute urine.
- Marine organisms are surrounded by water with a higher solute concentration than the organism and, thus, are in danger of losing water to the environment because of osmosis. These organisms have morphological and physiological adaptations to retain water and release solutes into the environment. For example, Marine iguanas (*Amblyrhynchus cristatus*), sneeze out water vapor that is high in salt in order to maintain solute concentrations within an acceptable range while swimming in the ocean and eating marine plants.

Inorganic Nutrients and Soil

Inorganic nutrients, such as nitrogen and phosphorus, are important in the distribution and the abundance of living things. Plants obtain these inorganic nutrients from the soil when water moves into the plant through the roots. Therefore, soil structure (particle size of soil components), soil pH, and soil nutrient content play an important role in the distribution of plants. Animals obtain inorganic nutrients from the food they consume. Therefore, animal distributions are related to the distribution of what they eat. In some cases, animals will follow their food resource as it moves through the environment.

Other Aquatic Factors

Some abiotic factors, such as oxygen, are important in aquatic ecosystems as well as terrestrial environments. Terrestrial animals obtain oxygen from the air they breathe. Oxygen availability can be an issue for organisms living at very high elevations, however, where there are fewer molecules of oxygen in the air. In aquatic systems, the concentration of dissolved oxygen is related to water temperature and the speed at which the water moves. Cold water has more dissolved oxygen than warmer water. In addition, salinity, current, and tide can be important abiotic factors in aquatic ecosystems.

Other Terrestrial Factors

Wind can be an important abiotic factor because it influences the rate of evaporation and transpiration. The physical force of wind is also important because it can move soil, water, or other abiotic factors, as well as an ecosystem's organisms.

Fire is another terrestrial factor that can be an important agent of disturbance in terrestrial ecosystems. Some organisms are adapted to fire and, thus, require the high heat associated with fire to complete a part of their life cycle. For example, the jack pine—a coniferous tree—requires heat from fire for its seed cones to open (**Figure 35.11**). Through the burning of pine needles, fire adds nitrogen to the soil and limits competition by destroying undergrowth.

Figure 35.11 The mature cones of the jack pine *(Pinus banksiana)* open only when exposed to high temperatures, such as during a forest fire. A fire is likely to kill most vegetation, so a seedling that germinates after a fire is more likely to receive ample sunlight than one that germinates under normal conditions. (credit: USDA)

Abiotic Factors Influencing Plant Growth

Temperature and moisture are important influences on plant production (primary productivity) and the amount of organic matter available as food (net primary productivity). **Net primary productivity** is an estimation of all of the organic matter available as food; it is calculated as the total amount of carbon fixed per year minus the amount that is oxidized during cellular respiration. In terrestrial environments, net primary productivity is estimated by measuring the **aboveground biomass** per unit area, which is the total mass of living plants, excluding roots. This means that a large percentage of plant biomass which exists underground is not included in this measurement. Net primary productivity is an important variable when considering differences in biomes. Very productive biomes have a high level of aboveground biomass.

Annual biomass production is directly related to the abiotic components of the environment. Environments with the greatest amount of biomass have conditions in which photosynthesis, plant growth, and the resulting net primary productivity are optimized. The climate of these areas is warm and wet. Photosynthesis can proceed at a high rate, enzymes can work most efficiently, and stomata can remain open without the risk of excessive transpiration; together, these factors lead to the maximal amount of carbon dioxide (CO_2) moving into the plant, resulting in high biomass production. The aboveground biomass produces several important resources for other living things, including habitat and food. Conversely, dry and cold environments have lower photosynthetic rates and therefore less biomass. The animal communities living there will also be affected by the decrease in available food.

35.3 | Terrestrial Biomes

In this section, you will explore the following questions:

- What are the two major abiotic factors that determine terrestrial biomes?
- What are distinguishing characteristics of each of the major terrestrial biomes?

Connection for AP® Courses

Much of the information in this section is outside the scope of AP®. You do not need to memorize a list of Earth's major terrestrial biomes and their descriptive features. However, we learned previously that organisms interact with each other and with their environments to move matter and energy. Biomes are ripe with examples of these interactions. A biome refers to a major type of terrestrial (or aquatic) community distributed according to climate, which determines the predominant vegetation. In turn, the vegetation influences what types of animals can inhabit the area. Comparing the annual totals of precipitation and fluctuations in precipitation from one biome to another provides clues as to the importance of abiotic factors in the distribution of biomes. The same type of biome can occur in different areas of the world (Figure 35.12).

Information presented and the examples highlighted in the section support concepts outlined in Big Idea 2 of the AP® Biology Curriculum Framework. The AP® Learning Objectives listed in the Curriculum Framework provide a transparent foundation for the AP® Biology course, an inquiry-based laboratory experience, instructional activities, and AP® exam questions. A learning objective merges required content with one or more of the seven science practices.

Big Idea 2	Biological systems utilize free energy and molecular building blocks to grow, to reproduce, and to maintain dynamic homeostasis.
Enduring Understanding 2.D	Growth and dynamic homeostasis of a biological system are influenced by changes in the system's environment.
Essential Knowledge	**2.D.1** Abiotic factors in an environment determine the characteristics of the environment (biome).
Science Practice	**1.3** The student can refine representations and models of natural or man-made phenomena and systems in the domain.
Science Practice	**3.2** The student can refine scientific questions.
Learning Objective	**2.22** The student is able to refine scientific models and questions about the effect of complex biotic and abiotic interactions on biological systems, from cells and organisms to populations, communities, and ecosystems.
Essential Knowledge	**2.D.1** Abiotic factors in an environment determine the characteristics of the environment (biome).
Science Practice	**5.1** The student can analyze data to identify patterns or relationships.
Learning Objective	**2.24** The student is able to analyze data to identify possible patterns and relationships between a biotic or abiotic factor and a biological system (cells, organisms, populations, communities, or ecosystems).

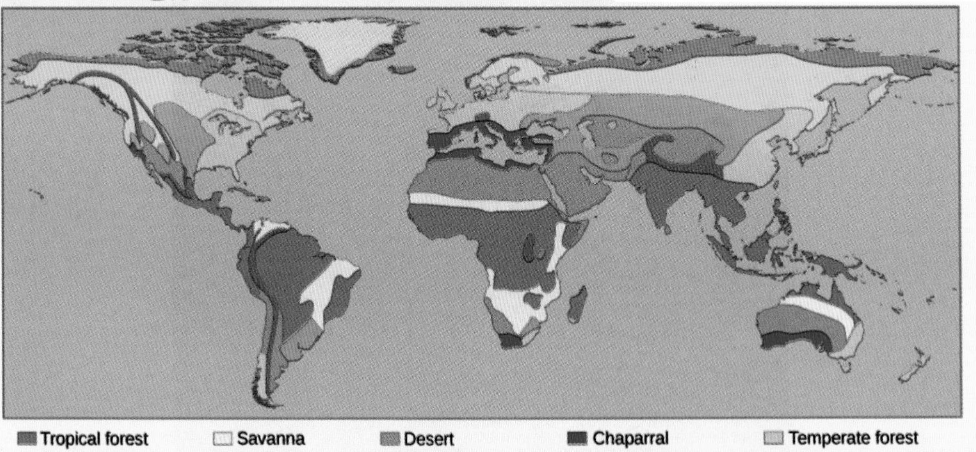

Figure 35.12 Each of the world's major biomes is distinguished by characteristic temperatures and amounts of precipitation. Polar ice and mountains are also shown.

Which of the following statements about biomes is false?

a. Chapparal is dominated by shrubs.

b. Grasses dominate savannas and temperate grasslands.

c. Boreal forests are dominated by deciduous trees.

d. Lichens are common in the arctic tundra.

Tropical Wet Forest

Tropical wet forests are also referred to as tropical rainforests. This biome is found in equatorial regions (**Figure 35.12**). The vegetation is characterized by plants with broad leaves that fall off throughout the year. Unlike the trees of deciduous forests, the trees in this biome do not have a seasonal loss of leaves associated with variations in temperature and sunlight; these forests are "evergreen" year-round.

The temperature and sunlight profiles of tropical wet forests are very stable in comparison to that of other terrestrial biomes, with the temperatures ranging from 20 °C to 34 °C (68 °F to 93 °F). When one compares the annual temperature variation of tropical wet forests with that of other forest biomes, the lack of seasonal temperature variation in the tropical wet forest becomes apparent. This lack of seasonality leads to year-round plant growth, rather than the seasonal (spring, summer, and fall) growth seen in other biomes. In contrast to other ecosystems, tropical ecosystems do not have long days and short days during the yearly cycle. Instead, a constant daily amount of sunlight (11–12 hrs per day) provides more solar radiation, thereby, a longer period of time for plant growth.

The annual rainfall in tropical wet forests ranges from 125 to 660 cm (50–200 in) with some monthly variation. While sunlight and temperature remain fairly consistent, annual rainfall is highly variable. Tropical wet forests have wet months in which there can be more than 30 cm (11–12 in) of precipitation, as well as dry months in which there are fewer than 10 cm (3.5 in) of rainfall. However, the driest month of a tropical wet forest still exceeds the *annual* rainfall of some other biomes, such as deserts.

Tropical wet forests have high net primary productivity because the annual temperatures and precipitation values in these areas are ideal for plant growth. Therefore, the extensive biomass present in the tropical wet forest leads to plant communities with very high species diversities (**Figure 35.13**). Tropical wet forests have more species of trees than any other biome; on average between 100 and 300 species of trees are present in a single hectare (2.5 acres) of South America. One way to visualize this is to compare the distinctive horizontal layers within the tropical wet forest biome. On the forest floor is a sparse layer of plants and decaying plant matter. Above that is an understory of short shrubby foliage. A layer of trees rises above this understory and is topped by a closed upper **canopy**—the uppermost overhead layer of branches and leaves. Some additional trees emerge through this closed upper canopy. These layers provide diverse and complex habitats for the variety of plants, fungi, animals, and other organisms within the tropical wet forests. For instance, epiphytes are plants that grow on other plants, which typically are not harmed. Epiphytes are found throughout tropical wet forest biomes. Many species of animals use the variety of plants and the complex structure of the tropical wet forests for food and shelter. Some organisms live several meters above ground and have adapted to this arboreal lifestyle.

Figure 35.13 Tropical wet forests, such as these forests of Madre de Dios, Peru, near the Amazon River, have high species diversity. (credit: Roosevelt Garcia)

Savannas

Savannas are grasslands with scattered trees, and they are located in Africa, South America, and northern Australia (**Figure 35.12**). Savannas are hot, tropical areas with temperatures averaging from 24 °C to 29 °C (75 °F to 84 °F) and an annual rainfall of 10–40 cm (3.9–15.7 in). Savannas have an extensive dry season; for this reason, forest trees do not grow as well as they do in the tropical wet forest (or other forest biomes). As a result, within the grasses and forbs (herbaceous flowering plants) that dominate the savanna, there are relatively few trees (**Figure 35.14**). Since fire is an important source of disturbance in this biome, plants have evolved well-developed root systems that allow them to quickly re-sprout after a fire.

Figure 35.14 Savannas, like this one in Taita Hills Wildlife Sanctuary in Kenya, are dominated by grasses. (credit: Christopher T. Cooper)

Subtropical Deserts

Subtropical deserts exist between 15 ° and 30 ° north and south latitude and are centered on the Tropics of Cancer and Capricorn (Figure 35.12). This biome is very dry; in some years, evaporation exceeds precipitation. Subtropical hot deserts can have daytime soil surface temperatures above 60 °C (140 °F) and nighttime temperatures approaching 0 °C (32 °F). In cold deserts, temperatures can be as high as 25 °C and can drop below -30 °C (-22 °F). Subtropical deserts are characterized by low annual precipitation of fewer than 30 cm (12 in) with little monthly variation and lack of predictability in rainfall. In some cases, the annual rainfall can be as low as 2 cm (0.8 in) in subtropical deserts located in central Australia ("the Outback") and northern Africa.

The vegetation and low animal diversity of this biome is closely related to this low and unpredictable precipitation. Very dry deserts lack perennial vegetation that lives from one year to the next; instead, many plants are annuals that grow quickly and reproduce when rainfall does occur, then they die. Many other plants in these areas are characterized by having a number of adaptations that conserve water, such as deep roots, reduced foliage, and water-storing stems (Figure 35.15). Seed plants in the desert produce seeds that can be in dormancy for extended periods between rains. Adaptations in desert animals include nocturnal behavior and burrowing.

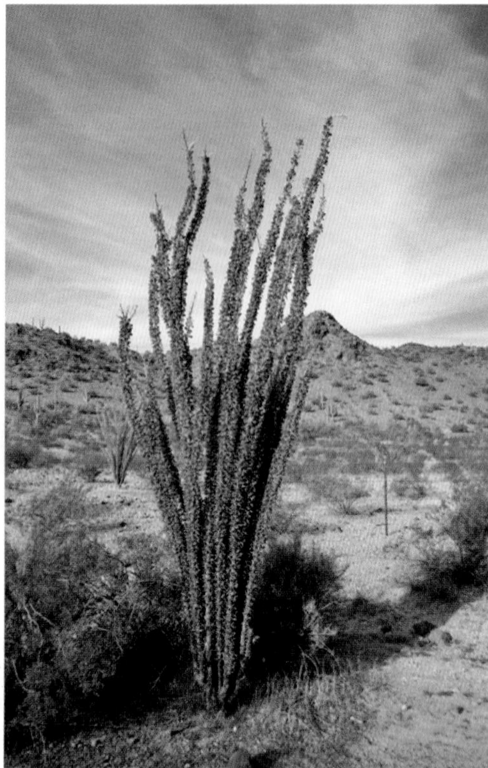

Figure 35.15 To reduce water loss, many desert plants have tiny leaves or no leaves at all. The leaves of ocotillo (*Fouquieria splendens*), shown here in the Sonora Desert near Gila Bend, Arizona, appear only after rainfall, and then are shed.

Chaparral

The chaparral is also called the scrub forest and is found in California, along the Mediterranean Sea, and along the southern coast of Australia (Figure 35.12). The annual rainfall in this biome ranges from 65 cm to 75 cm (25.6–29.5 in), and the majority of the rain falls in the winter. Summers are very dry and many chaparral plants are dormant during the summertime. The chaparral vegetation, shown in Figure 35.16, is dominated by shrubs and is adapted to periodic fires, with some plants producing seeds that only germinate after a hot fire. The ashes left behind after a fire are rich in nutrients like nitrogen that fertilize the soil and promote plant regrowth.

Figure 35.16 The chaparral is dominated by shrubs. (credit: Miguel Vieira)

Temperate Grasslands

Temperate grasslands are found throughout central North America, where they are also known as prairies; they are also in Eurasia, where they are known as steppes (Figure 35.12). Temperate grasslands have pronounced annual fluctuations in temperature with hot summers and cold winters. The annual temperature variation produces specific growing seasons for plants. Plant growth is possible when temperatures are warm enough to sustain plant growth and when ample water is available, which occurs in the spring, summer, and fall. During much of the winter, temperatures are low, and water, which is stored in the form of ice, is not available for plant growth.

Annual precipitation ranges from 25 cm to 75 cm (9.8–29.5 in). Because of relatively lower annual precipitation in temperate grasslands, there are few trees except for those found growing along rivers or streams. The dominant vegetation tends to consist of grasses and some prairies sustain populations of grazing animals Figure 35.17. The vegetation is very dense and the soils are fertile because the subsurface of the soil is packed with the roots and rhizomes (underground stems) of these grasses. The roots and rhizomes act to anchor plants into the ground and replenish the organic material (humus) in the soil when they die and decay.

Figure 35.17 The American bison (*Bison bison*), more commonly called the buffalo, is a grazing mammal that once populated American prairies in huge numbers. (credit: Jack Dykinga, USDA Agricultural Research Service)

Fires, mainly caused by lightning, are a natural disturbance in temperate grasslands. When fire is suppressed in temperate grasslands, the vegetation eventually converts to scrub and dense forests. Often, the restoration or management of temperate grasslands requires the use of controlled burns to suppress the growth of trees and maintain the grasses.

Temperate Forests

Temperate forests are the most common biome in eastern North America, Western Europe, Eastern Asia, Chile, and New Zealand (Figure 35.12). This biome is found throughout mid-latitude regions. Temperatures range between -30 °C and 30 °C (-22 °F to 86 °F) and drop to below freezing on an annual basis. These temperatures mean that temperate forests have defined growing seasons during the spring, summer, and early fall. Precipitation is relatively constant throughout the year and ranges between 75 cm and 150 cm (29.5–59 in).

Because of the moderate annual rainfall and temperatures, deciduous trees are the dominant plant in this biome (Figure 35.18). Deciduous trees lose their leaves each fall and remain leafless in the winter. Thus, no photosynthesis occurs in the deciduous trees during the dormant winter period. Each spring, new leaves appear as the temperature increases. Because of the dormant period, the net primary productivity of temperate forests is less than that of tropical wet forests. In addition, temperate forests show less diversity of tree species than tropical wet forest biomes.

Figure 35.18 Deciduous trees are the dominant plant in the temperate forest. (credit: Oliver Herold)

The trees of the temperate forests leaf out and shade much of the ground; however, this biome is more open than tropical wet forests because trees in the temperate forests do not grow as tall as the trees in tropical wet forests. The soils of the temperate forests are rich in inorganic and organic nutrients. This is due to the thick layer of leaf litter on forest floors. As this leaf litter decays, nutrients are returned to the soil. The leaf litter also protects soil from erosion, insulates the ground, and provides habitats for invertebrates (such as the pill bug or roly-poly, *Armadillidium vulgare*) and their predators, such as the red-backed salamander (*Plethodon cinereus*).

Boreal Forests

The boreal forest, also known as taiga or coniferous forest, is found south of the Arctic Circle and across most of Canada, Alaska, Russia, and northern Europe (Figure 35.12). This biome has cold, dry winters and short, cool, wet summers. The annual precipitation is from 40 cm to 100 cm (15.7–39 in) and usually takes the form of snow. Little evaporation occurs because of the cold temperatures.

The long and cold winters in the boreal forest have led to the predominance of cold-tolerant cone-bearing plants. These are evergreen coniferous trees like pines, spruce, and fir, which retain their needle-shaped leaves year-round. Evergreen trees can photosynthesize earlier in the spring than deciduous trees because less energy from the sun is required to warm a needle-like leaf than a broad leaf. This benefits evergreen trees, which grow faster than deciduous trees in the boreal forest. In addition, soils in boreal forest regions tend to be acidic with little available nitrogen. Leaves are a nitrogen-rich structure and deciduous trees must produce a new set of these nitrogen-rich structures each year. Therefore, coniferous trees that retain nitrogen-rich needles may have a competitive advantage over the broad-leafed deciduous trees.

The net primary productivity of boreal forests is lower than that of temperate forests and tropical wet forests. The aboveground biomass of boreal forests is high because these slow-growing tree species are long lived and accumulate standing biomass over time. Plant species diversity is less than that seen in temperate forests and tropical wet forests. Boreal forests lack the pronounced elements of the layered forest structure seen in tropical wet forests. The structure of a boreal forest is often only a tree layer and a ground layer (Figure 35.19). When conifer needles are dropped, they decompose more slowly than broad leaves; therefore, fewer nutrients are returned to the soil to fuel plant growth.

Figure 35.19 The boreal forest (taiga) has low lying plants and conifer trees. (credit: L.B. Brubaker)

Arctic Tundra

The Arctic tundra lies north of the subarctic boreal forest and is located throughout the Arctic regions of the northern hemisphere (Figure 35.12). The average winter temperature is -34 °C (-34 °F) and the average summer temperature is from 3 °C to 12 °C (37 °F–52 °F). Plants in the arctic tundra have a very short growing season of approximately 10–12 weeks. However, during this time, there are almost 24 hours of daylight and plant growth is rapid. The annual precipitation of the Arctic tundra is very low with little annual variation in precipitation. And, as in the boreal forests, there is little evaporation due to the cold temperatures.

Plants in the Arctic tundra are generally low to the ground (Figure 35.20). There is little species diversity, low net primary productivity, and low aboveground biomass. The soils of the Arctic tundra may remain in a perennially frozen state referred to as **permafrost**. The permafrost makes it impossible for roots to penetrate deep into the soil and slows the decay of organic matter, which inhibits the release of nutrients from organic matter. During the growing season, the ground of the Arctic tundra can be completely covered with plants or lichens.

Figure 35.20 Low-growing plants such as shrub willow dominate the tundra landscape, shown here in the Arctic National Wildlife Refuge. (credit: USFWS Arctic National Wildlife Refuge)

Watch this **Assignment Discovery: Biomes video (http://openstaxcollege.org/l/biomes)** for an overview of biomes. To explore further, select one of the biomes on the extended playlist: desert, savanna, temperate forest, temperate grassland, tropic, tundra.

Which of the following biomes is characterized by low precipitation, cactus, hardy shrubs, and high temperatures?

a. tundra

b. chapparal

c. desert

d. boreal forest

science practices CONNECTION for AP® Courses

Activity

For five different terrestrial biomes, create a visual representation to describe each biome and factors that affect its climate. What unique adaptations help plants and animals survive in each biome?

Think About It

In what ways are the subtropical desert and the Arctic tundra similar?

35.4 | Aquatic Biomes

In this section, you will explore the following questions:

- What are the effects of abiotic factors on the composition of plant and animal communities in aquatic biomes?
- What are the similarities and differences among the ocean zones?
- What are characteristics of standing water and flowing water freshwater biomes?

Connection for AP® Courses

Much of the information in this section is outside the scope for AP®. You do not need to memorize a list of Earth's different aquatic biomes and their descriptive features. However, we learned previously that organisms interact with each other and with their environments to move matter and energy. Aquatic biomes are ripe with these interactions. Coral reefs, for example, exhibit rich biodiversity.

Information presented and the examples highlighted in the section support concepts outlined in Big Idea 2 of the AP® Biology Curriculum Framework. The AP® Learning Objectives listed in the Curriculum Framework provide a transparent foundation for the AP® Biology course, an inquiry-based laboratory experience, instructional activities, and AP® exam questions. A learning objective merges required content with one or more of the seven science practices.

Big Idea 2	Biological systems utilize free energy and molecular building blocks to grow, to reproduce, and to maintain dynamic homeostasis.
Enduring Understanding 2.D	Growth and dynamic homeostasis of a biological system are influenced by changes in the system's environment.
Essential Knowledge	**2.D.1** Abiotic factors in an environment determine the characteristics of the environment (biome).
Science Practice	**5.1** The student can analyze data to identify patterns or relationships.
Learning Objective	**2.24** The student is able to analyze data to identify possible patterns and relationships between a biotic or abiotic factor and a biological system.

Abiotic Factors Influencing Aquatic Biomes

Like terrestrial biomes, aquatic biomes are influenced by a series of abiotic factors. The aquatic medium—water— has different physical and chemical properties than air, however. Even if the water in a pond or other body of water is perfectly clear (there are no suspended particles), water, on its own, absorbs light. As one descends into a deep body of water, there will eventually be a depth which the sunlight cannot reach. While there are some abiotic and biotic factors in a terrestrial ecosystem that might obscure light (like fog, dust, or insect swarms), usually these are not permanent features of the environment. The importance of light in aquatic biomes is central to the communities of organisms found in both freshwater and marine ecosystems. In freshwater systems, stratification due to differences in density is perhaps the most critical abiotic factor and is related to the energy aspects of light. The thermal properties of water (rates of heating and cooling) are significant to the function of marine systems and have major impacts on global climate and weather patterns. Marine systems are also influenced by large-scale physical water movements, such as currents; these are less important in most freshwater lakes.

The ocean is categorized by several areas or zones (Figure 35.21). All of the ocean's open water is referred to as the **pelagic realm** (or zone). The **benthic realm** (or zone) extends along the ocean bottom from the shoreline to the deepest parts of the ocean floor. Within the pelagic realm is the **photic zone**, which is the portion of the ocean that light can penetrate (approximately 200 m or 650 ft). At depths greater than 200 m, light cannot penetrate; thus, this is referred to as the **aphotic zone**. The majority of the ocean is aphotic and lacks sufficient light for photosynthesis. The deepest part of the ocean, the Challenger Deep (in the Mariana Trench, located in the western Pacific Ocean), is about 11,000 m (about 6.8 mi) deep. To give some perspective on the depth of this trench, the ocean is, on average, 4267 m or 14,000 ft deep. These realms and zones are relevant to freshwater lakes as well.

visual CONNECTION

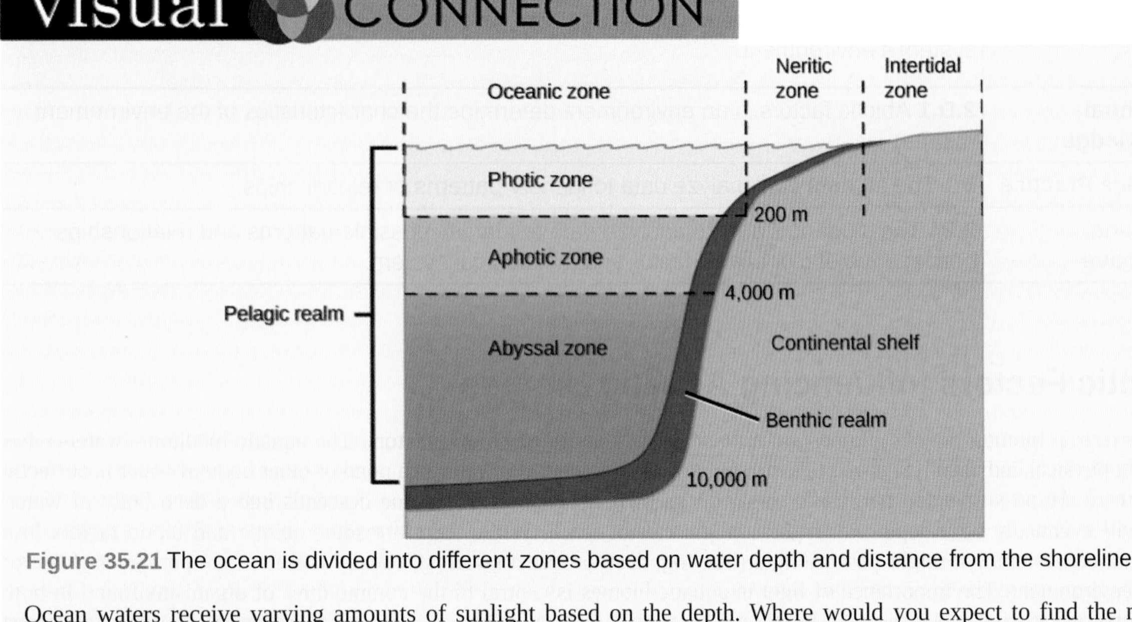

Figure 35.21 The ocean is divided into different zones based on water depth and distance from the shoreline.

Ocean waters receive varying amounts of sunlight based on the depth. Where would you expect to find the most photosynthesis in an ocean biome?

a. aphotic zone
b. abyssal zone
c. benthic realm
d. intertidal zone

Marine Biomes

The ocean is the largest marine biome. It is a continuous body of salt water that is relatively uniform in chemical composition; it is a weak solution of mineral salts and decayed biological matter. Within the ocean, coral reefs are a second kind of marine biome. Estuaries, coastal areas where salt water and fresh water mix, form a third unique marine biome.

Ocean

The physical diversity of the ocean is a significant influence on plants, animals, and other organisms. The ocean is categorized into different zones based on how far light reaches into the water. Each zone has a distinct group of species adapted to the biotic and abiotic conditions particular to that zone.

The **intertidal zone**, which is the zone between high and low tide, is the oceanic region that is closest to land (Figure 35.21). Generally, most people think of this portion of the ocean as a sandy beach. In some cases, the intertidal zone is indeed a sandy beach, but it can also be rocky or muddy. The intertidal zone is an extremely variable environment because of tides. Organisms are exposed to air and sunlight at low tide and are underwater most of the time, especially during high tide. Therefore, living things that thrive in the intertidal zone are adapted to being dry for long periods of time. The shore of the intertidal zone is also repeatedly struck by waves, and the organisms found there are adapted to withstand damage from the pounding action of the waves (Figure 35.22). The exoskeletons of shoreline crustaceans (such as the shore crab, *Carcinus maenas*) are tough and protect them from desiccation (drying out) and wave damage. Another consequence of the pounding waves is that few algae and plants establish themselves in the constantly moving rocks, sand, or mud.

Figure 35.22 Sea urchins, mussel shells, and starfish are often found in the intertidal zone, shown here in Kachemak Bay, Alaska. (credit: NOAA)

The **neritic zone** (Figure 35.21) extends from the intertidal zone to depths of about 200 m (or 650 ft) at the edge of the continental shelf. Since light can penetrate this depth, photosynthesis can occur in the neritic zone. The water here contains silt and is well-oxygenated, low in pressure, and stable in temperature. Phytoplankton and floating ***Sargassum*** (a type of free-floating marine seaweed) provide a habitat for some sea life found in the neritic zone. Zooplankton, protists, small fishes, and shrimp are found in the neritic zone and are the base of the food chain for most of the world's fisheries.

Beyond the neritic zone is the open ocean area known as the **oceanic zone** (Figure 35.21). Within the oceanic zone there is thermal stratification where warm and cold waters mix because of ocean currents. Abundant plankton serve as the base of the food chain for larger animals such as whales and dolphins. Nutrients are scarce and this is a relatively less productive part of the marine biome. When photosynthetic organisms and the protists and animals that feed on them die, their bodies fall to the bottom of the ocean where they remain; unlike freshwater lakes, the open ocean lacks a process for bringing the organic nutrients back up to the surface. The majority of organisms in the aphotic zone include sea cucumbers (phylum Echinodermata) and other organisms that survive on the nutrients contained in the dead bodies of organisms in the photic zone.

Beneath the pelagic zone is the benthic realm, the deepwater region beyond the continental shelf (Figure 35.21). The bottom of the benthic realm is comprised of sand, silt, and dead organisms. Temperature decreases, remaining above freezing, as water depth increases. This is a nutrient-rich portion of the ocean because of the dead organisms that fall from the upper layers of the ocean. Because of this high level of nutrients, a diversity of fungi, sponges, sea anemones, marine worms, sea stars, fishes, and bacteria exist.

The deepest part of the ocean is the **abyssal zone**, which is at depths of 4000 m or greater. The abyssal zone (Figure 35.21) is very cold and has very high pressure, high oxygen content, and low nutrient content. There are a variety of invertebrates and fishes found in this zone, but the abyssal zone does not have plants because of the lack of light. Hydrothermal vents are found primarily in the abyssal zone; chemosynthetic bacteria utilize the hydrogen sulfide and other minerals emitted from the vents. These chemosynthetic bacteria use the hydrogen sulfide as an energy source and serve as the base of the food chain found in the abyssal zone.

Coral Reefs

Coral reefs are ocean ridges formed by marine invertebrates living in warm shallow waters within the photic zone of the ocean. They are found within 30° north and south of the equator. The Great Barrier Reef is a well-known reef system located several miles off the northeastern coast of Australia. Other coral reef systems are fringing islands, which are directly adjacent to land, or atolls, which are circular reef systems surrounding a former landmass that is now underwater. The coral organisms (members of phylum Cnidaria) are colonies of saltwater polyps that secrete a calcium carbonate skeleton. These calcium-rich skeletons slowly accumulate, forming the underwater reef (Figure 35.23). Corals found in shallower waters (at a depth of approximately 60 m or about 200 ft) have a mutualistic relationship with photosynthetic unicellular algae. The relationship provides corals with the majority of the nutrition and the energy they require. The waters in which these corals live are nutritionally poor and, without this mutualism, it would not be possible for large corals to grow. Some corals living in deeper and colder water do not have a mutualistic relationship with algae; these corals attain energy and nutrients using stinging cells on their tentacles to capture prey.

Watch this National Oceanic and Atmospheric Administration (NOAA) video (http://openstaxcollege.org/l/marine_biology) to see marine ecologist Dr. Peter Etnoyer discusses his research on coral organisms.

Corals are found in deep seas. How do marine ecologists study deep sea corals without having to destroy their habitat?

a. deep sea diving

b. multibeam echo sounder

c. sonar

d. laser

It is estimated that more than 4,000 fish species inhabit coral reefs. These fishes can feed on coral, the **cryptofauna** (invertebrates found within the calcium carbonate substrate of the coral reefs), or the seaweed and algae that are associated with the coral. In addition, some fish species inhabit the boundaries of a coral reef; these species include **predators**, herbivores, or **planktivores**. Predators are animal species that hunt and are carnivores or "flesh eaters." Herbivores eat plant material, and planktivores eat plankton.

Figure 35.23 Coral reefs are formed by the calcium carbonate skeletons of coral organisms, which are marine invertebrates in the phylum Cnidaria. (credit: Terry Hughes)

Global Decline of Coral Reefs

It takes a long time to build a coral reef. The animals that create coral reefs have evolved over millions of years, continuing to slowly deposit the calcium carbonate that forms their characteristic ocean homes. Bathed in warm tropical waters, the coral animals and their symbiotic algal partners evolved to survive at the upper limit of ocean water temperature.

Together, climate change and human activity pose dual threats to the long-term survival of the world's coral reefs. As global warming due to fossil fuel emissions raises ocean temperatures, coral reefs are suffering. The excessive warmth causes the reefs to expel their symbiotic, food-producing algae, resulting in a phenomenon known as bleaching. When bleaching occurs, the reefs lose much of their characteristic color as the algae and the coral animals die if loss of the symbiotic zooxanthellae is prolonged.

Rising levels of atmospheric carbon dioxide further threaten the corals in other ways; as CO_2 dissolves in ocean waters, it lowers the pH and increases ocean acidity. As acidity increases, it interferes with the calcification that normally occurs as coral animals build their calcium carbonate homes.

When a coral reef begins to die, species diversity plummets as animals lose food and shelter. Coral reefs are also economically important tourist destinations, so the decline of coral reefs poses a serious threat to coastal economies.

Human population growth has damaged corals in other ways, too. As human coastal populations increase, the runoff of sediment and agricultural chemicals has increased, too, causing some of the once-clear tropical waters to become cloudy. At the same time, overfishing of popular fish species has allowed the predator species that eat corals to go unchecked.

Although a rise in global temperatures of 1–2°C (a conservative scientific projection) in the coming decades may not seem large, it is very significant to this biome. When change occurs rapidly, species can become extinct before evolution leads to new adaptations. Many scientists believe that global warming, with its rapid (in terms of evolutionary time) and inexorable increases in temperature, is tipping the balance beyond the point at which many of the world's coral reefs can recover.

What are the effects of global climate change and increasing levels of carbon dioxide on the coral reefs? How does it affect the local ecosystem?

a. Due to rising temperature, coral reefs lose their symbiotic partner, the algae, in the process called bleaching. Rising CO_2 changes the pH of water, which interferes with calcification. Animals whose source of food is coral reefs also decline in numbers.

b. Due to rising temperature the hard calcium carbonate skeleton of coral reefs is destroyed due to a process called bleaching. Rising CO_2 changes pH of water which interferes with calcification. Animals whose source of food is coral reefs also decline in numbers.

c. Due to rising temperature, coral reefs lose their symbiotic partner, the algae, in the process called ocean acidification. Rising CO_2 changes the pH of water, which interferes with calcification. Animals whose source of food is coral reefs also decline in numbers.

d. Due to rising temperature, coral reefs lose their symbiotic partner, the algae. Rising CO_2 changes the pH of water through the process called bleaching. Animals whose source of food is coral reefs also decline in numbers.

Estuaries: Where the Ocean Meets Fresh Water

Estuaries are biomes that occur where a source of fresh water, such as a river, meets the ocean. Therefore, both fresh water and salt water are found in the same vicinity; mixing results in a diluted (brackish) saltwater. Estuaries form protected areas where many of the young offspring of crustaceans, mollusks, and fish begin their lives. Salinity is a very important factor that influences the organisms and the adaptations of the organisms found in estuaries. The salinity of estuaries varies and is based on the rate of flow of its freshwater sources. Once or twice a day, high tides bring salt water into the estuary. Low tides occurring at the same frequency reverse the current of salt water.

The short-term and rapid variation in salinity due to the mixing of fresh water and salt water is a difficult physiological challenge for the plants and animals that inhabit estuaries. Many estuarine plant species are halophytes: plants that can tolerate salty conditions. Halophytic plants are adapted to deal with the salinity resulting from saltwater on their roots or from sea spray. In some halophytes, filters in the roots remove the salt from the water that the plant absorbs. Other plants are able to pump oxygen into their roots. Animals, such as mussels and clams (phylum Mollusca), have developed behavioral adaptations that expend a lot of energy to function in this rapidly changing environment. When these animals are exposed to low salinity, they stop feeding, close their shells, and switch from aerobic respiration (in which they use gills) to anaerobic respiration (a process that does not require oxygen). When high tide returns to the estuary, the salinity and oxygen content of the water increases, and these animals open their shells, begin feeding, and return to aerobic respiration.

everyday CONNECTION for AP® Courses

Figure 35.24 Estuaries are formed when marine water and fresh water meet. As a result, the water in estuaries vary widely in salinity. Organisms living in estuaries, such as the mangroves pictured here, must be able to tolerate a wide variation of salinity. (credit: Moni3, Wikimedia Commons)

The spring and fall turnovers are important processes in freshwater lakes that act to move nutrients and water from the bottom to the top. Explain how this is different in temperate regions as compared to the tropics.

a. Spring turnover occurs in tropical lakes, but not in temperate lakes. Stratification occurs in temperate lakes.
b. Temperate lakes do not freeze so they do not undergo spring turnover or stratification.
c. Stratification and spring turnover occur in tropical lakes. Temperate lakes do not freeze so they do not undergo spring turnover.
d. Stratification and spring turnover occur in temperate lakes. Tropical lakes do not freeze so they do not undergo spring turnover.

Freshwater Biomes

Freshwater biomes include lakes and ponds (standing water) as well as rivers and streams (flowing water). They also include wetlands, which will be discussed later. Humans rely on freshwater biomes to provide aquatic resources for drinking water, crop irrigation, sanitation, and industry. These various roles and human benefits are referred to as **ecosystem services**. Lakes and ponds are found in terrestrial landscapes and are, therefore, connected with abiotic and biotic factors influencing these terrestrial biomes.

Lakes and Ponds

Lakes and ponds can range in area from a few square meters to thousands of square kilometers. Temperature is an important abiotic factor affecting living things found in lakes and ponds. In the summer, thermal stratification of lakes and ponds occurs when the upper layer of water is warmed by the sun and does not mix with deeper, cooler water. Light can penetrate within the photic zone of the lake or pond. Phytoplankton (algae and cyanobacteria) are found here and carry out photosynthesis, providing the base of the food web of lakes and ponds. Zooplankton, such as rotifers and small crustaceans, consume these phytoplankton. At the bottom of lakes and ponds, bacteria in the aphotic zone break down dead organisms that sink to the bottom.

Nitrogen and phosphorus are important limiting nutrients in lakes and ponds. Because of this, they are determining factors in the amount of phytoplankton growth in lakes and ponds. When there is a large input of nitrogen and phosphorus (from sewage and runoff from fertilized lawns and farms, for example), the growth of algae skyrockets, resulting in a large accumulation of algae called an **algal bloom**. Algal blooms (Figure 35.25) can become so extensive that they reduce light penetration in water. As a result, the lake or pond becomes aphotic and photosynthetic plants cannot survive. When the algae die and decompose, severe oxygen depletion of the water occurs. Fishes and other organisms that require oxygen are then more likely to die, and resulting dead zones are found across the globe. Lake Erie and the Gulf of Mexico represent freshwater and marine habitats where phosphorus control and storm water runoff pose significant environmental challenges.

Figure 35.25 The uncontrolled growth of algae in this lake has resulted in an algal bloom. (credit: Jeremy Nettleton)

Rivers and Streams

Rivers and streams are continuously moving bodies of water that carry large amounts of water from the source, or headwater, to a lake or ocean. The largest rivers include the Nile River in Africa, the Amazon River in South America, and the Mississippi River in North America.

Abiotic features of rivers and streams vary along the length of the river or stream. Streams begin at a point of origin referred to as **source water**. The source water is usually cold, low in nutrients, and clear. The **channel** (the width of the river or stream) is narrower than at any other place along the length of the river or stream. Because of this, the current is often faster here than at any other point of the river or stream.

The fast-moving water results in minimal silt accumulation at the bottom of the river or stream; therefore, the water is clear. Photosynthesis here is mostly attributed to algae that are growing on rocks; the swift current inhibits the growth of phytoplankton. An additional input of energy can come from leaves or other organic material that falls into the river or stream from trees and other plants that border the water. When the leaves decompose, the organic material and nutrients in the leaves are returned to the water. Plants and animals have adapted to this fast-moving water. For instance, leeches (phylum Annelida) have elongated bodies and suckers on both ends. These suckers attach to the substrate, keeping the leech anchored in place. Freshwater trout species (phylum Chordata) are an important predator in these fast-moving rivers and streams.

As the river or stream flows away from the source, the width of the channel gradually widens and the current slows. This slow-moving water, caused by the gradient decrease and the volume increase as tributaries unite, has more sedimentation. Phytoplankton can also be suspended in slow-moving water. Therefore, the water will not be as clear as it is near the source. The water is also warmer. Worms (phylum Annelida) and insects (phylum Arthropoda) can be found burrowing into the mud. The higher order predator vertebrates (phylum Chordata) include waterfowl, frogs, and fishes. These predators must find food in these slow moving, sometimes murky, waters and, unlike the trout in the waters at the source, these vertebrates may not be able to use vision as their primary sense to find food. Instead, they are more likely to use taste or chemical cues to find prey.

Wetlands

Wetlands are environments in which the soil is either permanently or periodically saturated with water. Wetlands are different from lakes because wetlands are shallow bodies of water whereas lakes vary in depth. **Emergent vegetation** consists of wetland plants that are rooted in the soil but have portions of leaves, stems, and flowers extending above the water's surface. There are several types of wetlands including marshes, swamps, bogs, mudflats, and salt marshes (Figure 35.26). The three shared characteristics among these types—what makes them wetlands—are their hydrology, hydrophytic vegetation, and hydric soils.

Figure 35.26 Located in southern Florida, Everglades National Park is vast array of wetland environments, including sawgrass marshes, cypress swamps, and estuarine mangrove forests. Here, a great egret walks among cypress trees. (credit: NPS)

Freshwater marshes and swamps are characterized by slow and steady water flow. Bogs develop in depressions where water flow is low or nonexistent. Bogs usually occur in areas where there is a clay bottom with poor percolation. Percolation is the movement of water through the pores in the soil or rocks. The water found in a bog is stagnant and oxygen depleted because the oxygen that is used during the decomposition of organic matter is not replaced. As the oxygen in the water is depleted, decomposition slows. This leads to organic acids and other acids building up and lowering the pH of the water. At a lower pH, nitrogen becomes unavailable to plants. This creates a challenge for plants because nitrogen is an important limiting resource. Some types of bog plants (such as sundews, pitcher plants, and Venus flytraps) capture insects and extract the nitrogen from their bodies. Bogs have low net primary productivity because the water found in bogs has low levels of nitrogen and oxygen.

35.5 | Climate and the Effects of Global Climate Change

In this section, you will explore the following questions:

- What is global climate change?
- What are the effects of the Industrial Revolution on global atmospheric carbon dioxide concentration?
- What are examples of natural factors that affect long-term global climate?
- What are examples of greenhouse gases and their role(s) in the greenhouse effect?

Connection for AP® Courses

Both terrestrial and aquatic biomes are affected by global conditions, such as climate. Scientists have noted marked changes that have altered global weather patterns. Collectively, these changes are called **global climate change** and include a worldwide increase in temperature due primarily to rising levels of atmospheric carbon dioxide. There are several causes of global climate change, including human activity. The effects of human activity on other aspects of ecosystems will be explored in the Conservation Biology and Biodiversity chapter.

Information presented and the examples highlighted in the section support concepts outlined in Big Idea 4 of the AP® Biology Curriculum Framework. The AP® Learning Objectives listed in the Curriculum Framework provide a transparent foundation for the AP® Biology course, an inquiry-based laboratory experience, instructional activities, and AP® exam questions. A learning objective merges required content with one or more of the seven science practices.

Big Idea 4	Biological systems interact, and these systems and their interactions possess complex properties.

Enduring Understanding 4.A	Interactions within biological systems lead to complex properties.
Essential Knowledge	**4.A.6** Interactions among living systems and with their environment results in the movement of matter and energy.
Science Practice	**6.4** The student can make claims and predictions about natural phenomena based on scientific theories and models.
Learning Objective	**4.16** The student is able to predict the effects of a change of matter or energy availability on communities.

Climate and Weather

A common misconception about global climate change is that a specific weather event occurring in a particular region (for example, a very cool week in June in central Indiana) is evidence of global climate change. However, a cold week in June is a weather-related event and not a climate-related one. These misconceptions often arise because of confusion over the terms climate and weather.

Climate refers to the long-term, predictable atmospheric conditions of a specific area. The climate of a biome is characterized by having consistent temperature and annual rainfall ranges. Climate does not address the amount of rain that fell on one particular day in a biome or the colder-than-average temperatures that occurred on one day. In contrast, **weather** refers to the conditions of the atmosphere during a short period of time. Weather forecasts are usually made for 48-hour cycles. Long-range weather forecasts are available but can be unreliable.

To better understand the difference between climate and weather, imagine that you are planning an outdoor event in northern Wisconsin. You would be thinking about *climate* when you plan the event in the summer rather than the winter because you have long-term knowledge that any given Saturday in the months of May to August would be a better choice for an outdoor event in Wisconsin than any given Saturday in January. However, you cannot determine the specific day that the event should be held on because it is difficult to accurately predict the weather on a specific day. Climate can be considered "average" weather.

Global Climate Change

Climate change can be understood by approaching three areas of study:

- current and past global climate change
- causes of past and present-day global climate change
- ancient and current results of climate change

It is helpful to keep these three different aspects of climate change clearly separated when consuming media reports about global climate change. It is common for reports and discussions about global climate change to confuse the data showing that Earth's climate is changing with the factors that drive this climate change.

Evidence for Global Climate Change

Since scientists cannot go back in time to directly measure climatic variables, such as average temperature and precipitation, they must instead indirectly measure temperature. To do this, scientists rely on historical evidence of Earth's past climate.

Antarctic ice cores are a key example of such evidence. These ice cores are samples of polar ice obtained by means of drills that reach thousands of meters into ice sheets or high mountain glaciers. Viewing the ice cores is like traveling backwards through time; the deeper the sample, the earlier the time period. Trapped within the ice are bubbles of air and other biological evidence that can reveal temperature and carbon dioxide data. Antarctic ice cores have been collected and analyzed to indirectly estimate the temperature of the Earth over the past 400,000 years (Figure 35.27**a**). The 0 °C on this graph refers to the long-term average. Temperatures that are greater than 0 °C exceed Earth's long-term average temperature. Conversely, temperatures that are less than 0 °C are less than Earth's average temperature. This figure shows that there have been periodic cycles of increasing and decreasing temperature.

Before the late 1800s, the Earth has been as much as 9 °C cooler and about 3 °C warmer. Note that the graph in Figure 35.27**b** shows that the atmospheric concentration of carbon dioxide has also risen and fallen in periodic cycles; note the relationship between carbon dioxide concentration and temperature. Figure 35.27**b** shows that carbon dioxide levels in the atmosphere have historically cycled between 180 and 300 parts per million (ppm) by volume.

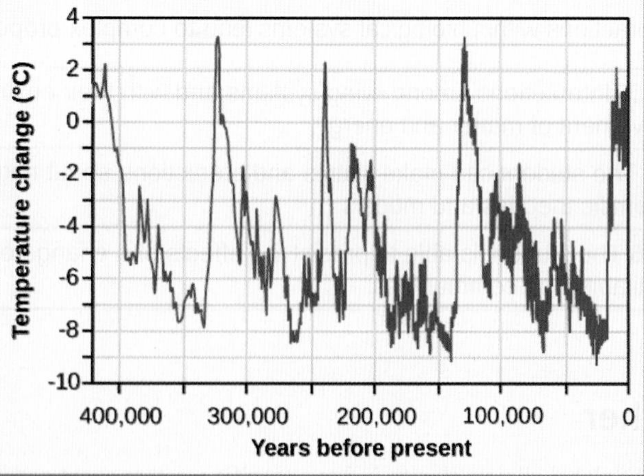

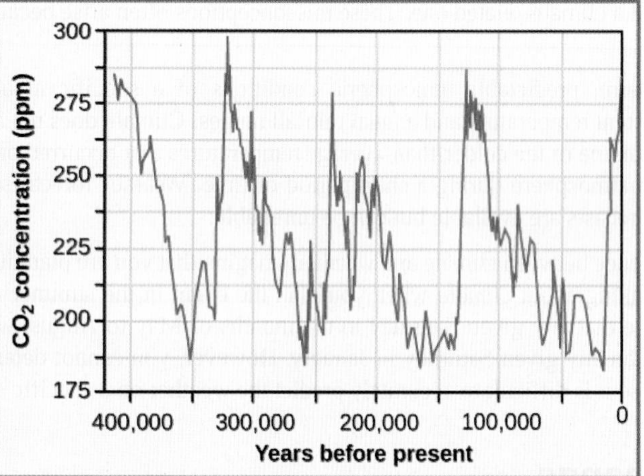

Figure 35.27 Ice at the Russian Vostok station in East Antarctica was laid down over the course 420,000 years and reached a depth of over 3,000 m. By measuring the amount of CO_2 trapped in the ice, scientists have determined past atmospheric CO_2 concentrations. Temperatures relative to modern day were determined from the amount of deuterium (an isotope of hydrogen) present.

Figure 35.27a does not show the last 2,000 years with enough detail to compare the changes of Earth's temperature during the last 400,000 years with the temperature change that has occurred in the more recent past. Two significant temperature anomalies, or irregularities, have occurred in the last 2000 years. These are the Medieval Climate Anomaly (or the Medieval Warm Period) and the Little Ice Age. A third temperature anomaly aligns with the Industrial Era. The Medieval Climate Anomaly occurred between 900 and 1300 AD. During this time period, many climate scientists think that slightly warmer weather conditions prevailed in many parts of the world; the higher-than-average temperature changes varied between 0.10 °C and 0.20 °C above the norm. Although 0.10 °C does not seem large enough to produce any noticeable change, it did free seas of ice. Because of this warming, the Vikings were able to colonize Greenland.

The Little Ice Age was a cold period that occurred between 1550 AD and 1850 AD. During this time, a slight cooling of a little less than 1 °C was observed in North America, Europe, and possibly other areas of the Earth. This 1 °C change in global temperature is a seemingly small deviation in temperature (as was observed during the Medieval Climate Anomaly); however, it also resulted in noticeable changes. Historical accounts reveal a time of exceptionally harsh winters with much snow and frost.

The Industrial Revolution, which began around 1750, was characterized by changes in much of human society. Advances in agriculture increased the food supply, which improved the standard of living for people in Europe and the United States. New technologies were invented and provided jobs and cheaper goods. These new technologies were powered using fossil fuels, especially coal. The Industrial Revolution starting in the early nineteenth century ushered in the beginning of the Industrial Era. When a fossil fuel is burned, carbon dioxide is released. With the beginning of the Industrial Era, atmospheric carbon dioxide began to rise (**Figure 35.28**).

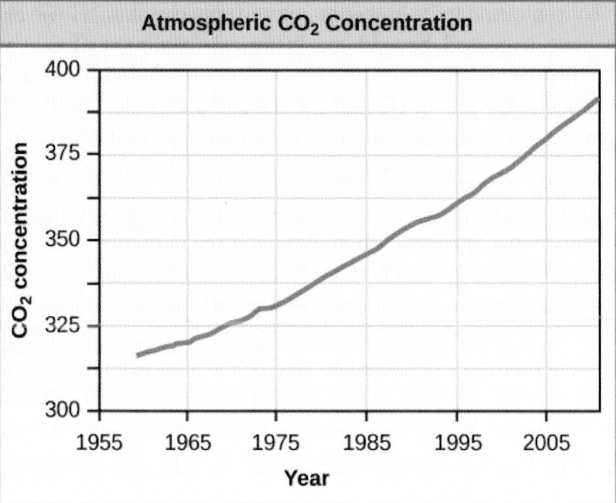

Figure 35.28 The atmospheric concentration of CO_2 has risen steadily since the beginning of industrialization.

Current and Past Drivers of Global Climate Change

Since it is not possible to go back in time to directly observe and measure climate, scientists use indirect evidence to determine the drivers, or factors, that may be responsible for climate change. The indirect evidence includes data collected using ice cores, boreholes (a narrow shaft bored into the ground), tree rings, glacier lengths, pollen remains, and ocean sediments. The data shows a correlation between the timing of temperature changes and drivers of climate change: before the Industrial Era (pre-1780), there were three drivers of climate change that were not related to human activity or atmospheric gases. The first of these is the Milankovitch cycles. The **Milankovitch cycles** describe the effects of slight changes in the Earth's orbit on Earth's climate. The length of the Milankovitch cycles ranges between 19,000 and 100,000 years. In other words, one could expect to see some predictable changes in the Earth's climate associated with changes in the Earth's orbit at a minimum of every 19,000 years.

The variation in the sun's intensity is the second natural factor responsible for climate change. **Solar intensity** is the amount of solar power or energy the sun emits in a given amount of time. There is a direct relationship between solar intensity and temperature. As solar intensity increases (or decreases), the Earth's temperature correspondingly increases (or decreases). Changes in solar intensity have been proposed as one of several possible explanations for the Little Ice Age.

Finally, volcanic eruptions are a third natural driver of climate change. Volcanic eruptions can last a few days, but the solids and gases released during an eruption can influence the climate over a period of a few years, causing short-term climate changes. The gases and solids released by volcanic eruptions can include carbon dioxide, water vapor, sulfur dioxide, hydrogen sulfide, hydrogen, and carbon monoxide. Generally, volcanic eruptions cool the climate. This occurred in 1783 when volcanos in Iceland erupted and caused the release of large volumes of sulfuric oxide. This led to **haze-effect cooling**, a global phenomenon that occurs when dust, ash, or other suspended particles block out sunlight and trigger lower global temperatures as a result; haze-effect cooling usually extends for one or more years. In Europe and North America, haze-effect cooling produced some of the lowest average winter temperatures on record in 1783 and 1784.

Greenhouse gases are probably the most significant drivers of the climate. When heat energy from the sun strikes the Earth, gases known as **greenhouse gases** trap the heat in the atmosphere, as do the glass panes of a greenhouse keep heat from escaping. The greenhouse gases that affect Earth include carbon dioxide, methane, water vapor, nitrous oxide, and ozone. Approximately half of the radiation from the sun passes through these gases in the atmosphere and strikes the Earth. This radiation is converted into thermal radiation on the Earth's surface, and then a portion of that energy is re-radiated back into the atmosphere. Greenhouse gases, however, reflect much of the thermal energy back to the Earth's surface. The more greenhouse gases there are in the atmosphere, the more thermal energy is reflected back to the Earth's surface. Greenhouse gases absorb and emit radiation and are an important factor in the **greenhouse effect**: the warming of Earth due to carbon dioxide and other greenhouse gases in the atmosphere.

Evidence supports the relationship between atmospheric concentrations of carbon dioxide and temperature: as carbon dioxide rises, global temperature rises. Since 1950, the concentration of atmospheric carbon dioxide has increased from about 280 ppm to 382 ppm in 2006. In 2011, the atmospheric carbon dioxide concentration was 392 ppm. However, the planet would not be inhabitable by current life forms if water vapor did not produce its drastic greenhouse warming effect.

Scientists look at patterns in data and try to explain differences or deviations from these patterns. The atmospheric carbon dioxide data reveal a historical pattern of carbon dioxide increasing and decreasing, cycling between a low of 180 ppm and a high of 300 ppm. Scientists have concluded that it took around 50,000 years for the atmospheric carbon dioxide level to increase from its low minimum concentration to its higher maximum concentration. However, starting recently, atmospheric carbon dioxide concentrations have increased beyond the historical maximum of 300 ppm. The current increases in atmospheric carbon dioxide have happened very quickly—in a matter of hundreds of years rather than thousands of years. What is the reason for this difference in the rate of change and the amount of increase in carbon dioxide? A key factor that must be recognized when comparing the historical data and the current data is the presence of modern human society; no other driver of climate change has yielded changes in atmospheric carbon dioxide levels at this rate or to this magnitude.

Human activity releases carbon dioxide and methane, two of the most important greenhouse gases, into the atmosphere in several ways. The primary mechanism that releases carbon dioxide is the burning of fossil fuels, such as gasoline, coal, and natural gas (**Figure 35.29**). Deforestation, cement manufacture, animal agriculture, the clearing of land, and the burning of forests are other human activities that release carbon dioxide. Methane (CH_4) is produced when bacteria break down organic matter under anaerobic conditions. Anaerobic conditions can happen when organic matter is trapped underwater (such as in rice paddies) or in the intestines of herbivores. Methane can also be released from natural gas fields and the decomposition that occurs in landfills. Another source of methane is the melting of clathrates. **Clathrates** are frozen chunks of ice and methane found at the bottom of the ocean. When water warms, these chunks of ice melt and methane is released. As the ocean's water temperature increases, the rate at which clathrates melt is increasing, releasing even more methane. This leads to increased levels of methane in the atmosphere, which further accelerates the rate of global warming. This is an example of the positive feedback loop that is leading to the rapid rate of increase of global temperatures.

Figure 35.29 The burning of fossil fuels in industry and by vehicles releases carbon dioxide and other greenhouse gases into the atmosphere. (credit: "Pöllö"/Wikimedia Commons)

Documented Results of Climate Change: Past and Present

Scientists have geological evidence of the consequences of long-ago climate change. Modern-day phenomena such as retreating glaciers and melting polar ice cause a continual rise in sea level. Meanwhile, changes in climate can negatively affect organisms.

Geological Climate Change

Global warming has been associated with at least one planet-wide extinction event during the geological past. The Permian extinction event occurred about 251 million years ago toward the end of the roughly 50-million-year-long geological time span known as the Permian period. This geologic time period was one of the three warmest periods in Earth's geologic history. Scientists estimate that approximately 70 percent of the terrestrial plant and animal species and 84 percent of marine species became extinct, vanishing forever near the end of the Permian period. Organisms that had adapted to wet and warm climatic conditions, such as annual rainfall of 300–400 cm (118–157 in) and 20 °C–30 °C (68 °F–86 °F) in the tropical wet forest, may not have been able to survive the Permian climate change.

Watch this NASA video (http://openstaxcollege.org/l/climate_plants) to discover the mixed effects of global warming on plant growth. While scientists found that warmer temperatures in the 1980s and 1990s caused an increase in plant productivity, this advantage has since been counteracted by more frequent droughts.

What impact does climate change have on plants?

a. Warmer temperatures extend the growing season of plants, which increases their water requirement throughout the season. Once the growing season ends, shorter, milder winters fail to kill pests increasing the risk of large, damaging infestations in subsequent seasons.

b. Warmer temperatures extend growing season of plants, which increases their nutrient requirements throughout the season. The nutrient requirements are not met once the growing season ends, increasing the risk of low productivity.

c. Warmer temperatures reduce the growing season of plants, which increase the risk of low productivity. Once the growing season ends, shorter, milder winters fail to kill pests increasing the risk of damaging infestations in subsequent seasons, which also leads to low productivity.

d. Warmer temperatures reduce the growing season of plants, which increase the risk of low productivity. Once the growing season ends, milder and shorter winters fail to provide sufficient nutrients to plants increasing the risk of plant death.

Present Climate Change

A number of global events have occurred that may be attributed to climate change during our lifetimes. Glacier National Park in Montana is undergoing the retreat of many of its glaciers, a phenomenon known as glacier recession. In 1850, the area contained approximately 150 glaciers. By 2010, however, the park contained only about 24 glaciers greater than 25 acres in size. One of these glaciers is the Grinnell Glacier (**Figure 35.30**) at Mount Gould. Between 1966 and 2005, the size of Grinnell Glacier shrank by 40 percent. Similarly, the mass of the ice sheets in Greenland and the Antarctic is decreasing: Greenland lost 150–250 km^3 of ice per year between 2002 and 2006. In addition, the size and thickness of the Arctic sea ice is decreasing.

Figure 35.30 The effect of global warming can be seen in the continuing retreat of Grinnel Glacier. The mean annual temperature in the park has increased 1.33 °C since 1900. The loss of a glacier results in the loss of summer meltwaters, sharply reducing seasonal water supplies and severely affecting local ecosystems. (credit: modification of work by USGS)

This loss of ice is leading to increases in the global sea level. On average, the sea is rising at a rate of 1.8 mm per year.

However, between 1993 and 2010 the rate of sea level increase ranged between 2.9 and 3.4 mm per year. A variety of factors affect the volume of water in the ocean, including the temperature of the water (the density of water is related to its temperature) and the amount of water found in rivers, lakes, glaciers, polar ice caps, and sea ice. As glaciers and polar ice caps melt, there is a significant contribution of liquid water that was previously frozen.

In addition to some abiotic conditions changing in response to climate change, many organisms are also being affected by the changes in temperature. Temperature and precipitation play key roles in determining the geographic distribution and phenology of plants and animals. (Phenology is the study of the effects of climatic conditions on the timing of periodic lifecycle events, such as flowering in plants or migration in birds.) Researchers have shown that 385 plant species in Great Britain are flowering 4.5 days sooner than was recorded earlier during the previous 40 years. In addition, insect-pollinated species were more likely to flower earlier than wind-pollinated species. The impact of changes in flowering date would be mitigated if the insect pollinators emerged earlier. This mismatched timing of plants and pollinators could result in injurious ecosystem effects because, for continued survival, insect-pollinated plants must flower when their pollinators are present.

science practices CONNECTION for AP® Courses

Think About It

What are possible short-term and long-term effects of natural and human-induced processes on global climate change and, consequently, ecosystems?

KEY TERMS

abiotic nonliving components of the environment

aboveground biomass total mass of aboveground living plants per area

abyssal zone deepest part of the ocean at depths of 4000 m or greater

algal bloom rapid increase of algae in an aquatic system

aphotic zone part of the ocean where no light penetrates

benthic realm (also, benthic zone) part of the ocean that extends along the ocean bottom from the shoreline to the deepest parts of the ocean floor

biogeography study of the geographic distribution of living things and the abiotic factors that affect their distribution

biome ecological community of plants, animals, and other organisms that is adapted to a characteristic set of environmental conditions

biotic living components of the environment

canopy branches and foliage of trees that form a layer of overhead coverage in a forest

channel width of a river or stream from one bank to the other bank

clathrates frozen chunks of ice and methane found at the bottom of the ocean

climate long-term, predictable atmospheric conditions present in a specific area

conspecifics individuals that are members of the same species

coral reef ocean ridges formed by marine invertebrates living in warm, shallow waters within the photic zone

cryptofauna invertebrates found within the calcium carbonate substrate of coral reefs

ecology study of interaction between living things and their environment

ecosystem services human benefits and services provided by natural ecosystems

emergent vegetation wetland plants that are rooted in the soil but have portions of leaves, stems, and flowers extending above the water's surface

endemic species found only in a specific geographic area that is usually restricted in size

estuary biomes where a source of fresh water, such as a river, meets the ocean

fall and spring turnover seasonal process that recycles nutrients and oxygen from the bottom of a freshwater ecosystem to the top

global climate change altered global weather patterns, including a worldwide increase in temperature, due largely to rising levels of atmospheric carbon dioxide

greenhouse effect warming of Earth due to carbon dioxide and other greenhouse gases in the atmosphere

greenhouse gases atmospheric gases such as carbon dioxide and methane that absorb and emit radiation, thus trapping heat in Earth's atmosphere

haze-effect cooling effect of the gases and solids from a volcanic eruption on global climate

heterospecifics individuals that are members of different species

intertidal zone part of the ocean that is closest to land; parts extend above the water at low tide

Milankovitch cycles cyclic changes in the Earth's orbit that may affect climate

neritic zone part of the ocean that extends from low tide to the edge of the continental shelf

net primary productivity measurement of the energy accumulation within an ecosystem, calculated as the total amount of carbon fixed per year minus the amount that is oxidized during cellular respiration

ocean upwelling rising of deep ocean waters that occurs when prevailing winds blow along surface waters near a coastline

oceanic zone part of the ocean that begins offshore where the water measures 200 m deep or deeper

pelagic realm (also, pelagic zone) open ocean waters that are not close to the bottom or near the shore

permafrost perennially frozen portion of the Arctic tundra soil

photic zone portion of the ocean that light can penetrate

planktivore animal species that eats plankton

predator animal species that hunt and are carnivores or “flesh eaters”

Sargassum type of free-floating marine seaweed

solar intensity amount of solar power energy the sun emits in a given amount of time

source water point of origin of a river or stream

thermocline layer of water with a temperature that is significantly different from that of the surrounding layers

weather conditions of the atmosphere during a short period of time

CHAPTER SUMMARY

35.1 The Scope of Ecology

Ecology is the study of the interactions of living things with their environment. Ecologists ask questions across four levels of biological organization—organismal, population, community, and ecosystem. At the organismal level, ecologists study individual organisms and how they interact with their environments. At the population and community levels, ecologists explore, respectively, how a population of organisms changes over time and the ways in which that population interacts with other species in the community. Ecologists studying an ecosystem examine the living species (the biotic components) of the ecosystem as well as the nonliving portions (the abiotic components), such as air, water, and soil, of the environment.

35.2 Biogeography

Biogeography is the study of the geographic distribution of living things and the abiotic factors that affect their distribution. Endemic species are species that are naturally found only in a specific geographic area. The distribution of living things is influenced by several environmental factors that are, in part, controlled by the latitude or elevation at which an organism is found. Ocean upwelling and spring and fall turnovers are important processes regulating the distribution of nutrients and other abiotic factors important in aquatic ecosystems. Energy sources, temperature, water, inorganic nutrients, and soil are factors limiting the distribution of living things in terrestrial systems. Net primary productivity is a measure of the amount of biomass produced by a biome.

35.3 Terrestrial Biomes

The Earth has terrestrial biomes and aquatic biomes. Aquatic biomes include both freshwater and marine environments. There are eight major terrestrial biomes: tropical wet forests, savannas, subtropical deserts, chaparral, temperate grasslands, temperate forests, boreal forests, and Arctic tundra. The same biome can occur in different geographic locations with similar climates. Temperature and precipitation, and variations in both, are key abiotic factors that shape the composition of animal and plant communities in terrestrial biomes. Some biomes, such as temperate grasslands and temperate forests, have distinct seasons, with cold weather and hot weather alternating throughout the year. In warm, moist biomes, such as the tropical wet forest, net primary productivity is high, as warm temperatures, abundant water, and a year-round growing season fuel plant growth. Other biomes, such as deserts and tundra, have low primary productivity due to extreme temperatures and a shortage of available water.

35.4 Aquatic Biomes

Aquatic ecosystems include both saltwater and freshwater biomes. The abiotic factors important for the structuring of aquatic ecosystems can be different than those seen in terrestrial systems. Sunlight is a driving force behind the structure of forests and also is an important factor in bodies of water, especially those that are very deep, because of the role of photosynthesis in sustaining certain organisms. Density and temperature shape the structure of aquatic systems. Oceans may be thought of as consisting of different zones based on water depth and distance from the shoreline and light penetrance. Different kinds of organisms are adapted to the conditions found in each zone. Coral reefs are unique marine ecosystems that are home to a wide variety of species. Estuaries are found where rivers meet the ocean; their shallow waters provide nourishment and shelter for young crustaceans, mollusks, fishes, and many other species. Freshwater biomes include lakes, ponds, rivers, streams, and wetlands. Bogs are an interesting type of wetland characterized by standing water, lower pH, and a lack of nitrogen.

35.5 Climate and the Effects of Global Climate Change

The Earth has gone through periodic cycles of increases and decreases in temperature. During the past 2000 years, the Medieval Climate Anomaly was a warmer period, while the Little Ice Age was unusually cool. Both of these irregularities can be explained by natural causes of changes in climate, and, although the temperature changes were small, they had significant effects. Natural drivers of climate change include Milankovitch cycles, changes in solar activity, and volcanic eruptions. None of these factors, however, leads to rapid increases in global temperature or sustained increases in carbon dioxide. The burning of fossil fuels is an important source of greenhouse gases, which plays a major role in the greenhouse effect. Long ago, global warming resulted in the Permian extinction: a large-scale extinction event that is documented in the fossil record. Currently, modern-day climate change is associated with the increased melting of glaciers and polar ice sheets, resulting in a gradual increase in sea level. Plants and animals can also be affected by global climate change when the timing of seasonal events, such as flowering or pollination, is affected by global warming.

REVIEW QUESTIONS

1. C, H, O and N are nutrients that are cycled through the Earth in different forms. Which of the following levels of ecology will include the study of nutrient cycling though the environment?

a. organismal ecology
b. population ecology
c. community ecology
d. ecosystem ecology

2. Which of the following are arranged from least inclusive to most inclusive?

a. population>ecosystem>community>biosphere
b. ecosystem < population < biosphere < community
c. biosphere < ecosystem < community < population
d. population < community < ecosystem < biosphere

3. An ecologist is studying the patterns on the wings of an endangered butterfly species that allow it to escape predators such as birds. This is an example of __.

a. mimicry
b. organismal ecology
c. mutualism
d. community ecology

4. Each year, Lake Michigan beach visitors are warned of possible E.coli, which can cause illness. In order to understand how environmental conditions, both biotic and abiotic, affect E. coli risk, which type of individual should an infectious disease specialist collaborate with?

a. an ecosystem ecologist
b. a podiatrist
c. a community ecologist
d. a population ecologist

5. Some bacterial species can use nitrogen directly from the atmosphere. In this situation, the bacteria are a _____.

a. biotic factor
b. abiotic factor
c. predator
d. symbiotic partner

6. Photosynthetic organisms are important to most ecosystems because they_____.

a. synthesize organic compounds they obtain from decaying heterotrophs.
b. can use carbon dioxide and sunlight and synthesize their own food.
c. use wind energy to synthesize organic compounds.
d. synthesize inorganic compounds from organic compounds.

7. The study of population ecology focuses on ___.

a. The number of individuals of one species in an area and how and why that number changes over time.
b. The processes driving interactions within and among different species within an area.
c. The adaptations that enable individuals to live in specific habitats.
d. Plants and animals living in an enclosed area

8. The study of the effect of abiotic factors such as rain and temperature on the distribution of living organisms is known as ___.

a. community ecology
b. biogeography
c. ecosystem
d. geography

9. Many species of pine trees are found in different geographical locations in North America and Canada. This is because _____.

a. they were not separated geographically over millions of years and did not evolve to be different species.
b. plant breeders carried seeds to different areas.
c. pollen from pollen tree was able to travel far.
d. pine was present widely and in some areas they dried out.

10. An ecologist hiking up a mountain may notice different biomes along the way due to changes in all of the following except ____.

a. elevation
b. rainfall
c. latitude
d. temperature

11. Temperate forests have plants of varying sizes. Understory plants in a temperate forest have adaptations to capture limited ____.

a. water
b. nutrients
c. heat
d. sunlight

12. In which of the following bodies of water does temperature stratification not take place?

a. estuaries
b. lakes
c. seas
d. oceans

13. Plants living in deserts have adaptations such as hair on leaves and a thick cuticle. What purpose do these adaptations serve?

a. to conserve water
b. to prevent exposure to sunlight
c. to increase oxygen intake
d. to decrease carbon dioxide intake

14. Which of the following biomes would have maximum net primary production?

a. deciduous forests
b. deserts
c. arctic tundra
d. savannas

15. When the Net Primary Productivity was measured in the presented graph, what was included in those measurements?

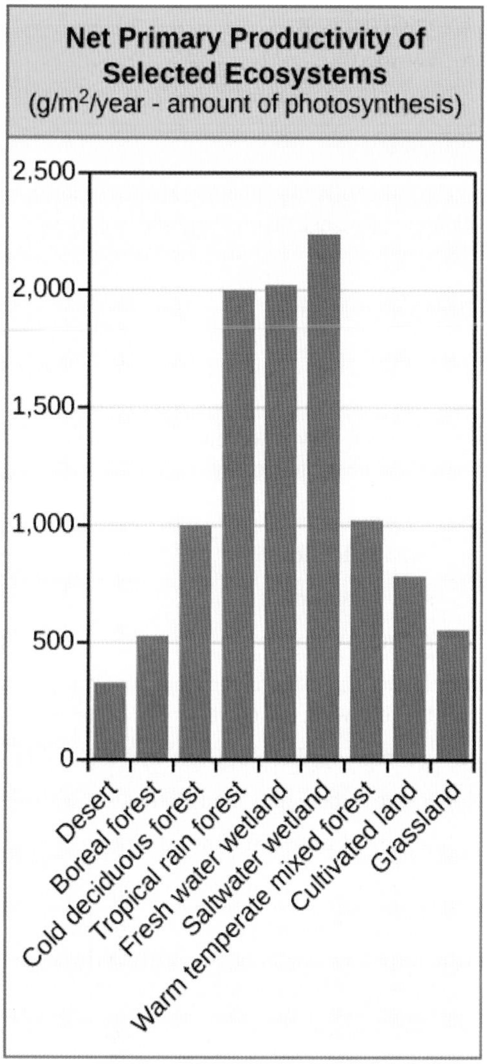

Net Primary Productivity of Selected Ecosystems
(g/m^2/year - amount of photosynthesis)

2,500
2,000
1,500
1,000
500
0
Desert
Boreal forest
Cold deciduous forest
Tropical rain forest
Fresh water wetland
Saltwater wetland
Warm temperate mixed forest
Cultivated land
Grassland

a. Above and underground biomass are included in net primary productivity.
b. Net primary productivity is the total amount of carbon fixed.
c. Net primary productivity is the amount of carbon fixed minus the amount used during cellular respiration and includes only the aboveground biomass in terrestrial biomes.
d. Net primary productivity refers to the amount of total amount of carbon fixed.

16. Biogeography is the study of the geographic distribution of living things and the ______ that affect their distribution.

a. Abiotic factors
b. Biotic factors
c. Biomes
d. Conspecifics

17. In which of the biomes are plants unable to grow because the soil is frozen most of the year?

a. arctic tundra
b. boreal forests
c. grasslands
d. chapparals

18. In grasslands, forest fires are a common occurrence. Which of the following statements regarding grasslands is true?

a. They have the ability to withstand fires.
b. They have a well-developed root system, which allows them to regrow after a fire.
c. Grasses are tall and only their top portions are destroyed.
d. Trees shield some of the grass thus protecting it from fire.

19. Savannas are grasslands with scattered trees. Which statement is correct about savannas?

a. They receive abundant rainfall.
b. The temperatures are cold throughout the year.
c. They have relatively long dry seasons.
d. Savannas are dominated by fluctuations in temperature.

20. The boreal forest, also known as taiga or coniferous forest, is found south of the Arctic Circle and across most of Canada, Alaska, Russia, and northern Europe. What are the characteristics of the boreal forest?

a. high temperature
b. deciduous trees
c. high humidity
d. acidic soil

21. The amount of sunlight and rainfall affects the growing season of plants in different biomes Which of the following biomes is characterized by short growing seasons?

a. savanna
b. temperate grasslands
c. arctic tundra
d. tropical wet forest

22. The figure shows different zones present in the ocean. Which of the following statements about marine biomes is true?

a. The benthic zone includes the ocean's open water and shore.
b. The pelagic realm includes all of the ocean's open water.
c. The majority of the ocean includes the photic zone.
d. The deepest zone of the ocean is known as the aphotic zone.

23. Corals have a mutualistic relationship with photosynthetic algae in the photic zones of water. What purpose does this serve?

a. Corals are able to derive their nutrition from the algae and thus survive in the nutritionally poor water.
b. Corals are able to accumulate calcium carbonate from the algae.
c. They can form coral reefs because of this association.
d. The corals provide protection to the algae.

24. Which of the following abiotic factors is most important for sustaining life in marine biomes?

a. wind
b. soil
c. salt
d. warmth

25. There are several different marine zones. In which zone are organisms exposed to air and sunlight at low tide and are underwater most of the time, especially during high tide?

a. intertidal zone
b. neritic
c. oceanic
d. abyssal

26. Which of the following photosynthetic organisms are more likely to grow in a lake as opposed to a river?

a. fungi
b. phytoplankton
c. moss
d. lichens

27. Water flow can vary in wetlands. Freshwater marshes and swamps are characterized by _____.

a. dry soil
b. rapid water flow
c. slow water flow
d. irregular water flow

28. Water bodies can differ in the amount of salt present. Which of the following is a characteristic of an estuary?

a. a continuous body of water with high salinity
b. an area where the salinity varies
c. a body of water with low salinity
d. a body of water with low salt entering land

29. The earth's geological past has witnessed many important events. Which of the following periods was associated with global warming?

a. Permian period
b. Cambrian period
c. 2nd and 3rd century BC
d. 20th century

30. One of the indirect consequences of global warming has been ___.

a. loss of biodiversity
b. increase in temperature
c. change in water quality
d. increase in temperature tolerance of plants

31. Which one of the following fuels was used extensively during the Industrial Revolution, leading to increases in levels of carbon dioxide?

a. coal
b. petroleum
c. natural gas
d. solar energy

32. Global warming is due to many factors. Which of the following is known to change with CO_2 concentration?

a. solar intensity
b. wind intensity
c. temperature
d. humidity

33. All of the following are natural factors have led to slow increases in global temperatures except____.

a. volcanic eruptions
b. change in solar intensity
c. earthquakes
d. changes in the earth's orbit

34. Global temperatures have been steadily increasing since the Industrial Revolution largely as a result of ___.

a. agricultural production
b. burning of fossil fuels
c. increase in movement of people
d. use of pesticides

35. Which of the following gases is not considered a significant contributor to global warming?

a. carbon dioxide
b. methane
c. nitric oxide
d. oxygen

36. Carbon dioxide, methane, and nitrous oxide are considered greenhouse gases because___.

a. They trap solar radiation released from the sun as it reaches the Earth's surface, similar to the glass in a greenhouse.
b. They are found mostly in green houses.
c. These gases are essential for plant growth in a green house.
d. They trap solar radiation, which is converted into thermal radiation on the Earth's surface of which some is reradiated back into the atmosphere.

37. The Medieval Climate Anomaly occurred between 900 and 1300 AD. Temperatures during this time were between 0.10 and 0.20 higher. This allowed _____.

a. the Vikings to colonize Greenland
b. large amounts of new technologies to be invented
c. advances in agriculture
d. harsh winters

CRITICAL THINKING QUESTIONS

38. Define and describe community ecology. Give an example.

a. It is the study of the number of individuals of one species in an area as well as how and why the number changes over time. An example would be counting the number of individuals of the Karner blue butterfly, a federally endangered species whose population density is highly influenced by the abundance of wild lupine.

b. It is the study of the processes and consequences of interactions within and among different species within an area. An example would be the work of scientists who work in a marsh studying the various interactions of several populations of birds, crabs, and grasses without studying the water or air quality.

c. It is the study of the physiological, morphological, and behavioral adaptations that enable individuals to live in specific habitats. An example would be the work of scientists who work in a marsh studying the various interactions of several populations of birds, crabs, and grasses without studying the water or air quality.

d. It is the study of the processes and consequences of interactions within and among different species within an area. An example would be counting the number of individuals of the Karner blue butterfly, a federally endangered species whose population density is highly influenced by the abundance of wild lupine.

39. Ecologists often collaborate with other researchers interested in ecological questions. Describe the levels of ecology that would be easier for collaboration because of the similarities of questions asked. What levels of ecology might be more difficult for collaboration?

a. It is easier to study community and ecosystem ecology as the effect of biotic and abiotic factors can be studied in a community or ecosystem more easily. Organismal and population ecology might be more difficult for collaboration.

b. It is easier to study organismal and population ecology as the effect of biotic and abiotic factors can be studied in an organism or population more easily. Community and ecosystem ecology might be more difficult for collaboration.

c. It is easier to study community and population ecology as the effect of biotic and abiotic factors can be studied in easily in a community or population more easily. Organismal and ecosystem ecology might be more difficult for collaboration.

d. It is easier to study organismal and ecosystem ecology as the effect of biotic and abiotic factors can be studied in an organism or ecosystem more easily. Community and population ecology might be more difficult for collaboration.

40. How do organisms return nutrients and water to the environment?

a. By cycling between the abiotic and biotic environment.

b. By cycling between evaporation and transpiration.

c. By cycling between the flora and fauna of the Earth.

d. By cycling between temperature and moisture.

41. Define and give an example of organismal, population and community ecology.

a. Organismal ecology includes the study of the number of individuals in an area as well as how and why population size changes over time, such as a study of the drop in antelope population. Population ecology includes the study of adaptations that enable individuals to live in specific habitats, such as a study of the use of opposable thumbs. Community ecology includes the study of the processes and consequences of interactions within and among different species in an area, such as a study of interactions between wolves and deer.

b. Organismal ecology includes the study of the processes and consequences of interactions within and among different species in an area, such as a study of the interactions between wolves and deer. Population ecology includes the study of the number of individuals in an area as well as how and why population size changes over time, such as a study of the drop in antelope population. Community ecology includes the study of adaptations that enable individuals to live in specific habitats, such as a study of the use of opposable thumbs.

c. Organismal ecology includes the study of adaptations that enable individuals to live in specific habitats, such as a study of the use of opposable thumbs. Population ecology includes the study of the number of individuals in an area as well as how and why population size changes over time, such as a study of the drop in antelope population. Community ecology includes studies of the processes and consequences of interactions within and among different species in an area, such as a study of the interactions between wolves and deer.

d. Organismal ecology includes studies of the adaptations that enable individuals to live in specific habitats, such as a study of the use of opposable thumbs. Population ecology includes studies of the processes and consequences of interactions within and among different species in an area, such as a study of the interactions between wolves and deer. Community ecology includes studies of the number of individuals in an area as well as how and why population size changes over time, such as a study of the drop in antelope population.

42. Many endemic species are found in areas that are geographically isolated. Suggest a plausible scientific explanation why this is so.

a. Geographically isolated areas have provided high temperature conditions for certain species to evolve. Over time, these species retained their unique characteristics because they remained separated from other species.

b. Geographically isolated areas have provided a unique environment for certain species to evolve. Over time, these species retained their unique characteristics because they remained separated from other species.

c. Certain species are introduced into some geographically isolated areas, which provide them unique environments. Over time, these species retained their unique characteristics because they remained separated from other species.

d. A unique environment is provided for certain species to evolve in vitro and these species are introduced into geographically isolated areas. Over time, these species retained their unique characteristics because they remained separated from other species.

43. The American white pelican migrates from North America to Central America in the winter months. Give three reasons why these birds follow an annual migration pattern.

a. The American white pelican follows an annual migration pattern in search of suitable mates, warmer climates, and suitable habitat. Warmer climates help them in maintaining a constant body temperature.

b. The American white pelican follows an annual migration pattern in search of food, salt water, and cooler climates. Cooler climates help these birds in reproduction.

c. The American white pelican follows an annual migration pattern in search of food, warmer climates, and suitable habitat. Warmer climates help them in maintaining a constant body temperature.

d. The American white pelican follows an annual migration pattern in search of warmer climates only. Warmer climates help them in maintaining a constant body temperature.

44. Why is it essential for organisms to maintain a constant body temperature? Describe adaptations that help the organisms cope with changes in environmental temperature.

a. The rate of metabolic processes increases at very high or low temperatures. So, organisms have to maintain a constant body temperature. This can be achieved only by migration to avoid seasonal temperature changes.
b. Enzymes that carry out metabolic processes are denatured at very high temperatures. So, organisms have to maintain a constant body temperature. This can be achieved by hibernation, aestivation, or migration.
c. The rate of metabolic processes increases at very high or low temperatures. So, organisms have to maintain a constant body temperature. This can be achieved by hibernation, aestivation, or migration.
d. Enzymes that carry out metabolic processes are denatured at very high temperatures. So, organisms have to maintain a constant body temperature. This can be achieved only by migration to avoid seasonal temperature changes.

45. The extremely low precipitation of subtropical desert biomes might lead one to expect fire to be a major disturbance factor. However, fire is more common in the temperate grassland biome than in the sub tropic desert biome. Why is this?

a. Due to higher net primary productivity, biomass in deserts is significantly more than in temperate grassland biomes. However, it is easier for fire to spread in grasslands as they are found in abundance.
b. Due to lower net primary productivity, biomass in deserts is significantly less than in temperate grassland biomes. It is easier for fire to spread in grasslands as they are found in abundance.
c. Due to lower net primary productivity, biomass in deserts is significantly less than in temperate grassland biomes. It is easier for fire to spread in grasslands as they have very low precipitation and high temperatures.
d. Due to higher net primary productivity, biomass in deserts is significantly more than in temperate grassland biomes. However, it is easier for fire to spread in grasslands as they have very low precipitation and high temperatures.

46. What are endemic species? Give an example and explain how endemic species differ from generalist species.

a. Endemic species are found naturally in specific geographic areas that are usually restricted in size. For example, the raccoon is found only in Australia. Generalist species are found in a wide range of geographical locations. For example, the koala is native to most of North and Central America.
b. Endemic species are those which are likely to be extinct. For example, the koala (a marsupial) is found only in Australia. Generalist species are found in a wide range of geographical locations. For example, the raccoon is native to most of North and Central America.
c. Endemic species are found in a wide range of geographical locations. For example, the koala (a marsupial) is found only in Australia. Generalist species are found naturally in specific geographic areas that are usually restricted in size. For example, the raccoon is native to most of North and Central America.
d. Endemic species are found naturally in specific geographic areas that are usually restricted in size. For example, the koala (a marsupial) is found only in Australia. Generalist species are found in a wide range of geographical locations. For example, the raccoon is native to most of North and Central America.

47. Deserts and subtropical deserts experience low precipitation and extremes in temperature. For a plant to survive and reproduce, what adaptations should it have? Why?

a. To survive, they need prop roots, reduced foliage and fleshy leaves with sunken stomata to reduce transpiration. Also, they should have seeds that can remain dormant over long periods.
b. To survive, they need deep roots, reduced foliage and fleshy leaves with sunken stomata to reduce transpiration. Also, they should have seeds that can remain dormant over long periods.
c. To survive, they need deep roots, reduced foliage and fleshy leaves with sunken stomata to reduce transpiration. Also, these plants need to grow in clumps.
d. To survive, they need deep roots, increased foliage, and fleshy leaves with sunken stomata to reduce transpiration. Also, the plants need seeds that can remain dormant over long periods.

48. In what ways are the subtropical desert and the arctic tundra similar?

a. Both are characterized by animals, which are adapted to burrowing.
b. Both are characterized by plants, which prefer to grow in clumps.
c. Both are characterized by low water availability and, as a result, low net primary productivity.
d. Both are characterized by plants, which are mostly perennials.

49. Describe the chaparral biome. How does it does it differ from subtropical deserts?

a. Shrubs dominate chaparral vegetation and are well adapted to the periodic fires in the area. Ashes left behind after fires are rich in nutrients, which promote regrowth. Subtropical deserts are characterized by their high precipitation and water-retaining plants.
b. Shrubs dominate chaparral vegetation and are well adapted to the periodic fires in the area. Ashes left behind after fires are rich in nutrients, which promote regrowth. Subtropical deserts are characterized by their low precipitation and water-retaining plants.
c. Lichens dominate chaparral vegetation and are well adapted to the periodic fires in the area. Ashes left behind after fires are rich in nutrients, which promote regrowth. Subtropical deserts are characterized by their low precipitation and water-retaining plants.
d. Shrubs dominate chaparral vegetation but are not well adapted to the periodic fires in the area. Ashes left behind after fires are rich in nutrients, which promote regrowth. Subtropical deserts are characterized by their low precipitation and water-retaining plants.

50. What happens to aquatic life in deep lakes when water freezes during the winter months?

a. During winters, layer of ice falls on water surface as it is less dense than water. Water is densest at 7° C and retains its liquid form below the water surface. The aquatic life can exist in liquid water.
b. During winters, the aquatic life exists in liquid water, which is present below the surface layer, by consuming more resources so they can survive during the harsh winter season.
c. During winters, a layer of ice forms on the water surface, as ice is less dense than water. Water is densest at 4°C and retains its liquid form below the water surface, where the ice layer is. In liquid water, the aquatic life can survive using the resources available.
d. During winters, ice forms only on the surface and a few meters below the surface of water. Water is densest at 4°C and retains its liquid form below the water surface, where the ice layer is. In liquid water, the aquatic life can exist using the resources available.

51. Explain the challenges facing organisms living in the intertidal zone and their adaptations to meet these challenges.

a. They are subject to constant exposure to air, sunlight, periods of dryness, and pounding waves. For this reason, some species have an exoskeleton.
b. They are subject to periodic exposures to air, sunlight, periods of dryness, and pounding waves. For this reason, some species have an exoskeleton.
c. They are subject to periodic exposures to air, sunlight, periods of dryness, and pounding waves. For this reason, all species have an exoskeleton.
d. They are subject to periodic exposures to air, sunlight, periods of dryness, and pounding waves. For this reason, most species have an endoskeleton.

52. If algae grows out of proportion as seen during algal blooms, how does it affect the ecosystem?

a. Photosynthetic organisms will not be able to grow. The animals and birds that live on those organisms will be affected. As the algae die, oxygen will be depleted, affecting fish and other aquatic animals. The pH of water will change, affecting metabolic processes as well.
b. Non-photosynthetic organisms will not be able to grow due to lack of light. The photosynthetic organisms that require them to live will be affected. As the algae die, oxygen will be depleted, affecting fish and other aquatic animals. The pH of water will change, affecting metabolic processes as well.
c. Photosynthetic organisms will not be able to grow. The animals and birds that live on those organisms will be affected. As the algae die, carbon dioxide will be depleted, affecting fish and other aquatic animals. The pH of water will change, affecting metabolic processes as well.
d. Non-photosynthetic organisms will not be able to grow. The animals and birds that live on those organisms will be affected. As the algae die, carbon dioxide will be depleted, affecting fish and other aquatic animals. The pH of water will change, affecting metabolic processes as well.

53. What are some abiotic factors that affect freshwater biomes? Explain.

a. Salinity and sunlight are both abiotic factors that influence life in freshwater biomes. As organisms living in freshwater biomes require high salt density for survival, its depletion would kill the organisms. Many organisms that serve as food for others are photosynthetic and would die if algae blooms obscured the light. Their decomposition as well as the depletion of oxygen by algae would cause organisms that require oxygen to die out as well.
b. Salinity and sunlight are both abiotic factors that influence life in freshwater biomes. As organisms living in freshwater biomes cannot tolerate high salt levels, these organisms would not survive if it increased. Many organisms that serve as food for others are photosynthetic would die if algal blooms obscured the light. Their decomposition and the depletion of carbon dioxide by algae would cause organisms that require carbon dioxide to die out as well.
c. Salinity and sunlight are both abiotic factors that influence life in freshwater biomes. As organisms living in freshwater biomes cannot tolerate high salt levels, these organisms would not survive if it were to increase significantly. Many organisms that serve as food for others are photosynthetic and would die if algal blooms obscure light. Their decomposition and depletion of oxygen by algae would cause organisms that require oxygen to die out as well.
d. Salinity and temperature are both abiotic factors that influence life in freshwater biomes. As organisms living in freshwater biomes cannot tolerate high salt concentrations, those organisms would not survive if salt concentrations increased significantly. Many organisms that serve as food for others are photosynthetic and would die if algal blooms obscured the light. Their decomposition and the depletion of oxygen by algae would cause organisms that require oxygen to die out as well.

54. Is it possible to reverse global warming? What measures may help in reducing global climate change?

a. It is possible to reverse global warming by reducing the usage of fossil fuels, using alternative fuels, using alternatives to CFC's and using natural sources of energy.

b. It is not possible to reverse global warming, as major climate changes have already been occurred and settled in the environment. Reducing fossil fuel usage, using natural sources of energy and alternative fuels may slow down global climate change.

c. It is not possible to reverse global warming, as we are already witnessing changes in the environment, plants and animal behavior. Reducing fossil fuel usage and using natural sources of energy may slow down global climate change.

d. It is possible to reverse global warming by working on new technologies that will help in preventing temperature changes worldwide. Using wind power and high efficiency natural gas generation will help in achieving this goal.

55. As global temperatures change, many flowering plants are flowering earlier. What change would most likely occur if the insect pollinators are not around at the same time?

a. Insects will be deprived of their nectar, leading to decrease in numbers; but flowering plants will not be affected, as other animals will pollinate them.

b. Flowering plants will not be pollinated resulting in their less population; but insects will not be affected, as insects will feed on other organisms.

c. Neither plants nor pollinators will be affected, as new or different species of insects are going to pollinate the flowering plants.

d. Both plant and pollinator numbers would decrease, as insects will be deprived of nectar and plants will not be pollinated.

56. If scientists had to predict the rise in Earth's temperature in the next one hundred years, what would they take into consideration?

a. Scientists can predict the change in earth's temperature only by analyzing previous and current data such as dimensions and locations of glaciers as well as the water levels in lakes, rivers, and oceans.

b. Scientists could predict rise in temperature by analyzing previous and current data like dimensions and locations of glaciers, water levels in lakes, rivers and oceans and by counting and examining number of annual rings in trees.

c. Scientists could predict rise in earth's temperature by measuring the greenhouse gases present in the current atmosphere. Counting and examining the number of annual rings in trees would also point to the climactic changes over the years.

d. Scientists can predict the change in earth's atmosphere by counting and analyzing the number of annual rings in trees. Also, analyzing ice cores for over a year would predict the rise in Earth's temperature in the next one hundred years.

57. Many people cannot imagine a world without fossil fuels, but fossil fuels are finite resources and will eventually run out. This is why drilling had begun in Arctic in an effort to find a new source of fossil fuels, though it is currently stopped. What are the dangers of drilling in the Arctic? What are the alternatives?

a. Drilling as well as melting of ice in the Arctic results in the release of large amounts of methane, accelerating global warming. Investing in clean energy like wind, water, and solar power, which do not release harmful gases, could be the alternative.

b. Drilling as well as melting of ice in the Arctic results in the release of large amounts of carbon monoxide, accelerating global warming. Investing in clean energy like wind, water, and solar power, which do not release harmful gases, could be the alternative.

c. Drilling as well as melting of ice in the Arctic results in the release of large amounts of carbon monoxide, which is lethal and can cause death. Investing in clean energy like wind, water, and solar power, which do not release harmful gases, could be the alternative.

d. Drilling as well as melting of ice in the Arctic results in the release of large amounts of methane, accelerating global warming. Investing in mining of earth minerals and metal ores could be the alternative.

TEST PREP FOR AP® COURSES

58. The Karner blue butterfly has been declared an endangered species. It is dependent on wild lupine for larval development. The butterfly species, which was found abundantly in Indiana Dunes National Park, is now found further North in Wisconsin and Michigan. Wild lupine has been destroyed in areas where it grew abundantly because of development and construction in the open grasslands where it prefers to grow. Which of the following biotic factors are present in the community?

a. Karner blue butterfly
b. Karner blue butterfly and wild lupine
c. Karner blue butterfly, wild lupine, and fire
d. Karner blue butterfly, wild lupine, and grasslands

59. In a temperate grassland system area of North America, vegetation has been destroyed by fire. What will happen to the net primary productivity and the local ecosystem when rains return in the next season?

a. The grasses will grow back, but the herbivores that lived there will not return, as they would have found new land to live on. Therefore, the net primary productivity would decrease.
b. The grasses will not grow back, therefore the herbivores that lived there will not return. Thus, the net primary productivity would decrease.
c. The grasses will grow back and the herbivores that lived there will return. The net primary productivity should also be similar to the previous season.
d. The grasses will grow back and the herbivores that lived there will return. The net primary productivity would be less than the previous season.

60. The Karner blue butterfly larva secretes a carbohydrate, which is a source of energy for ants. In turn, ants tend to the larva, increasing its likelihood to grow into an adult butterfly. This is an example of _____.

a. predation
b. competition
c. mutualism
d. parasitism

61. A lake in the Midwest witnesses a sudden increase in the algae population (algae bloom) that covers the lake. The factors that affect net primary productivity are __.

a. Light and nutrient availability
b. predation by primary consumers
c. pollution
d. carbon d oxide

62. Paleontologists have discovered bodies of humans and animals in bogs that have been there for hundreds of years in a perfectly preserved state. Explain the reason for this.

a. Bogs have high oxygen content and organic acids, which lowers the pH. Low pH and high oxygen content prevents oxidation thus, slowing down decomposition.
b. Bogs have low oxygen content and organic acids, which increases the pH. High pH and low oxygen content prevents oxidation thus, slowing down decomposition.
c. Bogs have low oxygen content and organic acids, which lowers the pH. Low pH and low oxygen content prevent oxidation, thus slowing down decomposition.
d. Bogs have low oxygen content and organic acids, which lowers the pH. Low pH and low oxygen content prevents reduction, thus slowing down decomposition.

63. You are asked to estimate the nutrient content of a lake and its possible effect on net primary productivity. What data will you collect to determine the effect?

a. Sample water from different parts of the lake and determine nutrient composition
b. Sample the carbon content of the phytoplankton growing
c. Take sample of lake water and artificially enrich it, then see the effect of the enrichment on phytoplankton growth compared with growth in unenriched lake water
d. Wait for spring turnover to check for nutrients found in the ocean floor

64. The population of a certain species of deer has been reduced drastically because of indiscriminate hunting. How will you determine its impact on the local ecosystem?

a. To determine the effect of indiscriminate hunting on local ecosystem, environmental conditions should be determined. If a drastic change in environmental conditions is observed then, indiscriminate hunting of deer should be discouraged.

b. The number of predators, their effect on plants they feed on, availability of nutrients in soil, and number of pests should be determined. If there is a drastic change in numbers, then indiscriminate hunting of deer should be discouraged.

c. Determining the number of predators alone is sufficient to determine the impact of indiscriminate hunting on local ecosystem. If there is a drastic change in numbers, then indiscriminate hunting of deer should be discouraged.

d. Determination of the availability of nutrients in soil helps in determining the impact of indiscriminate hunting on local ecosystem. If there is a drastic change in the availability, then indiscriminate hunting of deer should be discouraged.

65. In a forest fire, many oak trees were destroyed. After the fire, numerous taller trees replaced the oak trees. What is the best explanation of this event?

a. The tall trees grow faster and create a canopy, which did not allow oak trees to grow.

b. The burning of the trees changed the pH of the soil, which did not allow oak to grow.

c. Roots of shrubs and trees proliferate, taking over the place of the oak trees.

d. Oak trees succumb to pests, thus other pest resistant trees are able to proliferate.

66. What are possible consequences if there is a big oil spill in the middle of the ocean? How will it affect the biodiversity and the net primary productivity? What are some strategies to clean up this oil spill?

a. Oil spills increase the amount of light and oxygen entering the ocean. The phytoplanktons may perish. Presence of oil would limit mobility of marine animals and may result in death. Some chemicals and bioremediation can help oil clean up.

b. Oil spills increase the amount of light and oxygen entering the ocean. The phytoplanktons may increase. The mobility of marine animals increases. Biodiversity and, therefore, net primary productivity increases. Some chemicals and bioremediation can help oil clean up.

c. Oil spills cover the surface of the ocean, reducing the amount of light entering the ocean. The marine organisms that can survive independent of light will not be affected. Some chemicals and bioremediation can help oil clean up.

d. Oil spills cover the surface of the ocean, reducing the amount of light and oxygen entering the ocean. The phytoplankton may perish. Presence of oil would limit mobility of marine animals and may result in death. Some chemicals and bioremediation can help oil clean up.

67. Global climate change has led to butterflies emerging earlier and amphibians mating earlier in the United Kingdom. What impact is it most likely to have on their populations in the next few years?

a. There will be no impact on butterfly and amphibian population.

b. Their numbers will definitely decline with rising temperatures.

c. Their numbers will decline as their plant hosts of butterflies may not flower earlier and young amphibians may not be viable as there might be a lack of water.

d. It is hard to predict what will happen to their populations as there are no similar studies.

68. What are possible short-term and long-term effects of natural and human-induced processes on global climate change and, consequently, ecosystems?

a. Short term changes include melting of glaciers, rise in levels of water bodies which may cover islands close to sea level, destroying the local ecosystem and animals, and so on. Long-term changes experienced could include changes in seasonal patterns, unseasonal rainfall, and changes in the life cycle of insects.

b. Short term changes include changes in seasonal patterns, unseasonal rainfall, changes in the life cycle of insects and animals, and so on. Long-term changes could be change in flowering times of flowers, and the rise in levels of water bodies, which may cover islands close to sea level, destroying the local ecosystem.

c. Short-term changes include changes in seasonal patterns,unseasonal rainfall, changes in the life cycle of insects and animals, and so on. Long-term changes could be melting of glaciers, and a rise in levels of water bodies which may cover islands close to sea level, destroying the local ecosystem.

d. Short term changes include melting of glaciers, unseasonal rainfall, changes in the life cycle of insects and animals, etc. Long-term changes could be rise in levels of water bodies which may cover islands close to sea level, destroying the local ecosystem.

SCIENCE PRACTICE CHALLENGE QUESTIONS

69. Twenty targets for the protection of biodiversity by 2020 were established by the 2010 Convention on Biological Diversity. Midway to the target date it is widely agreed that the goals will not be met. The *2016 Living Planet Report* from the World Wildlife Federation claims global populations of animals fell by 58 percent between 1970 and 2012 and extrapolates the loss by 2020 to 67%. E.O. Wilson's estimate of the current extinction rate is three species per hour. Geologic periods are defined by mass extinctions. The proposed name for the current geological period is the Anthropocene (Waters et al., *Science*, 2016).

During the current period of mass extinction, human activities are driving loss of habitat and climate change. Climate change during the last 500,000 years is a direct consequence of rising atmospheric CO_2 levels, as the graph shows. The relative abundance of O^{16} and O^{18} isotopes can be used to infer temperature because as temperature increases the lower mass isotope is enriched in the atmosphere (objects with a smaller mass have a higher velocity at equal molecular kinetic energy that is proportional to temperature).

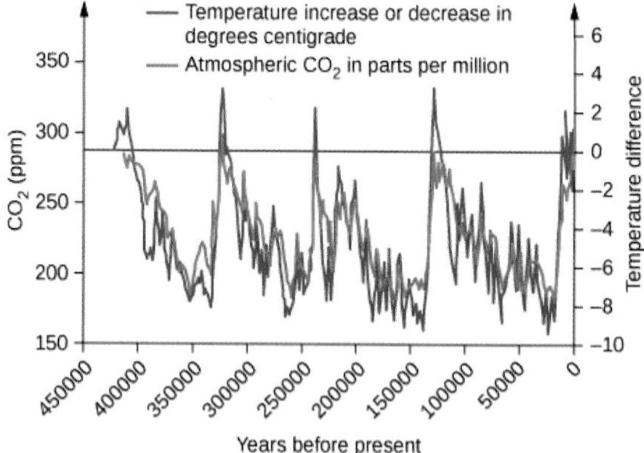

Figure 35.31

The role of humans in the last great extinction, the Holocene Extinction, during which the megafauna such as the wooly mammoth, the wooly rhinoceros and the giant deer disappeared, has long been debated. Did we hunt these creatures to extinction? By examining all available DNA evidence, Cooper et al. (*Science*, 349, 2015) have compared time extinction intervals with these oscillations of climate as shown in the table.

Animal	Label	Loc-ation	Begin extinct event (TYA)	End extinct event (TYA)
Bear	a	Ber-ingia	24	21
Bison	b	Europe	35	32
Rhino-ceros	c	Britain	36	32
Rhino-ceros	d	Russia	14	13
Horse	e	North America	15	13
Horse	f	Ber-ingia	43	38
Mast-odon	g	North America	12	11
Mam-moth	h	Europe	13	12
Mam-moth	i	Eurasia	11	10
Musk Ox	j	Eurasia	48	44
Deer	k	Europe	13	12
Cave Lion	l	Ber-ingia	14	12
Cave Bear	m	Europe	29	27

Table 35.1 TYA = thousand years ago

Additionally, the data shown in the graph below are obtained from ice cores. The deeper the sample, the older the sample. The percent departure from the current O^{18} percentage that is graphed above is a measure of temperature relative to the present temperature. The higher the isotope concentration, the higher the average temperature of the ocean.

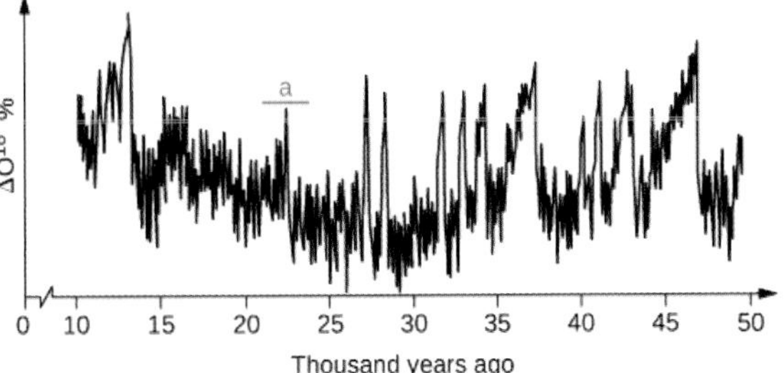

Figure 35.32

A. **Refine** the graph by adding the interval of time of extinction with a label drawn from the table as shown by "a".

B. **Analyze** these data in terms of the clustering of extinction events.

C. Based on your analysis, **explain** how ecosystems have changed during the last 40,000 years, changed and **identify** the factor that caused these changes.

D. Based on the correlation between Earth's temperature and the concentration of CO_2 in the atmosphere, **predict** what will happen to animal populations in the future.

36 | POPULATION AND COMMUNITY ECOLOGY

Figure 36.1 Asian carp jump out of the water in response to electrofishing. The Asian carp in the inset photograph were harvested from the Little Calumet River in Illinois in May, 2010, using rotenone, a toxin often used as an insecticide, in an effort to learn more about the population of the species. (credit main image: modification of work by USGS; credit inset: modification of work by Lt. David French, USCG)

Chapter Outline

Introduction

Imagine sailing down a river in a small motorboat on a weekend afternoon; the water is smooth and you are enjoying the warm sunshine and cool breeze when suddenly you are hit in the head by a 20-pound silver carp. This is a risk now on many rivers and canal systems in Illinois and Missouri because of the presence of Asian carp.

This fish—actually a group of species including the silver, black, grass, and big head carp—has been farmed and eaten in China for over 1000 years. It is one of the most important aquaculture food resources worldwide. In the United States, however, Asian carp is considered a dangerous invasive species that disrupts community structure and composition to the point of threatening native species.

The Asian carp is now threatening to invade the Great Lakes. You can read more about this invasion **here (http://openstaxcollege.org/l/32asiancarp)** .

36.1 | Population Demography

In this section, you will explore the following questions:

- How do ecologists measure population size and density?
- What are three different patterns of population distribution?
- How can life tables be used to calculate mortality rates?
- What are the three types of survivorship curves and how do they relate to specific populations?

Connection for AP® Courses

By using mathematics, ecologists can study how interactions among living organisms and with their environment affect the distribution, abundance, density, and life strategies of species. A population consists of individuals of the same species living within a specific area. Populations fluctuate based on both biotic and abiotic factors. When studying a population, characteristics of that population are quantified and their change is monitored. This statistical study of these changes, **demography**, investigates how populations respond to these fluctuations. A shift in populations can affect community structure and the ecosystem as a whole.

Information presented and the examples highlighted in the section support concepts outlined in Big Idea 2 and Big Idea 4 of the AP® Biology Curriculum Framework. The AP® Learning Objectives listed in the Curriculum Framework provide a transparent foundation for the AP® Biology course, an inquiry-based laboratory experience, instructional activities, and AP® exam questions. A learning objective merges required content with one or more of the seven science practices.

Big Idea 2	Biological systems utilize free energy and molecular building blocks to grow, to reproduce, and to maintain dynamic homeostasis.
Enduring Understanding 2.D	Growth and dynamic homeostasis of a biological system are influenced by changes in the system's environment.
Essential Knowledge	**2.D.1** All biological systems from cells and organisms to populations, communities and ecosystems are affected by complex biotic and abiotic interactions involving exchange of matter and free energy.
Science Practice	**6.4** The student can make claims and predictions about natural phenomena based on scientific theories and models.
Learning Objective	**2.3** The student is able to predict how changes in free energy availability affect organisms, populations, and ecosystems.
Essential Knowledge	**2.D.1** All biological systems from cells and organisms to populations, communities and ecosystems are affected by complex biotic and abiotic interactions involving exchange of matter and free energy.
Science Practice	**1.3** The student can refine representations and models of natural or man-made phenomena and systems in the domain.
Science Practice	**3.2** The student can refine scientific questions.
Learning Objective	**2.22** The student is able to refine scientific models and questions about the effect of complex biotic and abiotic interactions on all biological systems, from cells and organisms to populations, communities and ecosystems.
Essential Knowledge	**2.D.1** All biological systems from cells and organisms to populations, communities and ecosystems are affected by complex biotic and abiotic interactions involving exchange of matter and free energy.

Science Practice	**4.2** The student can design a plan for collecting data to answer a particular scientific question.
Science Practice	**7.2** The student can connect concepts in and across domain(s) to generalize or extrapolate in and/or across enduring understandings and/or big ideas.
Learning Objective	**2.23** The student is able to design a plan for collecting data to show that all biological systems, including populations, are affected by complex biotic and abiotic interactions.
Essential Knowledge	**2.D.1** All biological systems from cells and organisms to populations, communities and ecosystems are affected by complex biotic and abiotic interactions involving exchange of matter and free energy.
Science Practice	**5.1** The student can analyze data to identify patterns or relationships.
Learning Objective	**2.24** The student is able to analyze data to identify possible patterns and relationships between a biotic or abiotic factors and a biological system, including populations.
Big Idea 4	Biological systems interact, and these systems and their interactions possess complex properties.
Enduring Understanding 4.A	Interactions within biological systems lead to complex properties.
Essential Knowledge	**4.A.5** Communities are composed of populations of organisms that interact in complex ways.
Science Practice	**1.4** The student can use representations and models to analyze situations or solve problems qualitatively and quantitatively.
Science Practice	**4.2** The student can design a plan for collecting data to answer a particular scientific question.
Learning Objective	**4.11** The student is able to justify the selection of the kind of data needed to answer scientific questions about the interaction of populations within communities.
Essential Knowledge	**4.A.5** Communities are composed of populations of organisms that interact in complex ways.
Science Practice	**2.2** The student can apply mathematical routines to quantities that describe natural phenomena.
Learning Objective	**4.12** The student is able to apply mathematical routines to quantities that describe communities composed of populations of organisms that interact in complex ways.
Essential Knowledge	**4.A.5** Communities are composed of populations of organisms that interact in complex ways.
Science Practice	**6.4** The student can make claims and predictions about natural phenomena based on scientific theories and models.
Learning Objective	**4.13** The student is able to predict the effects of a change in the community's populations on the community.

Populations are dynamic entities. Populations consist all of the species living within a specific area, and populations fluctuate based on a number of factors: seasonal and yearly changes in the environment, natural disasters such as forest fires and volcanic eruptions, and competition for resources between and within species. The statistical study of population dynamics, demography, uses a series of mathematical tools to investigate how populations respond to changes in their biotic and abiotic environments. Many of these tools were originally designed to study human populations. For example, **life tables**, which detail the life expectancy of individuals within a population, were initially developed by life insurance companies to set insurance rates. In fact, while the term "demographics" is commonly used when discussing humans, all living populations can be studied using this approach.

Population Size and Density

The study of any population usually begins by determining how many individuals of a particular species exist, and how closely associated they are with each other. Within a particular habitat, a population can be characterized by its **population size (*N*)**, the total number of individuals, and its **population density**, the number of individuals within a specific area or volume. Population size and density are the two main characteristics used to describe and understand populations. For example, populations with more individuals may be more stable than smaller populations based on their genetic variability, and thus their potential to adapt to the environment. Alternatively, a member of a population with low population density (more spread out in the habitat), might have more difficulty finding a mate to reproduce compared to a population of higher density. As is shown in Figure 36.2, smaller organisms tend to be more densely distributed than larger organisms.

visual CONNECTION

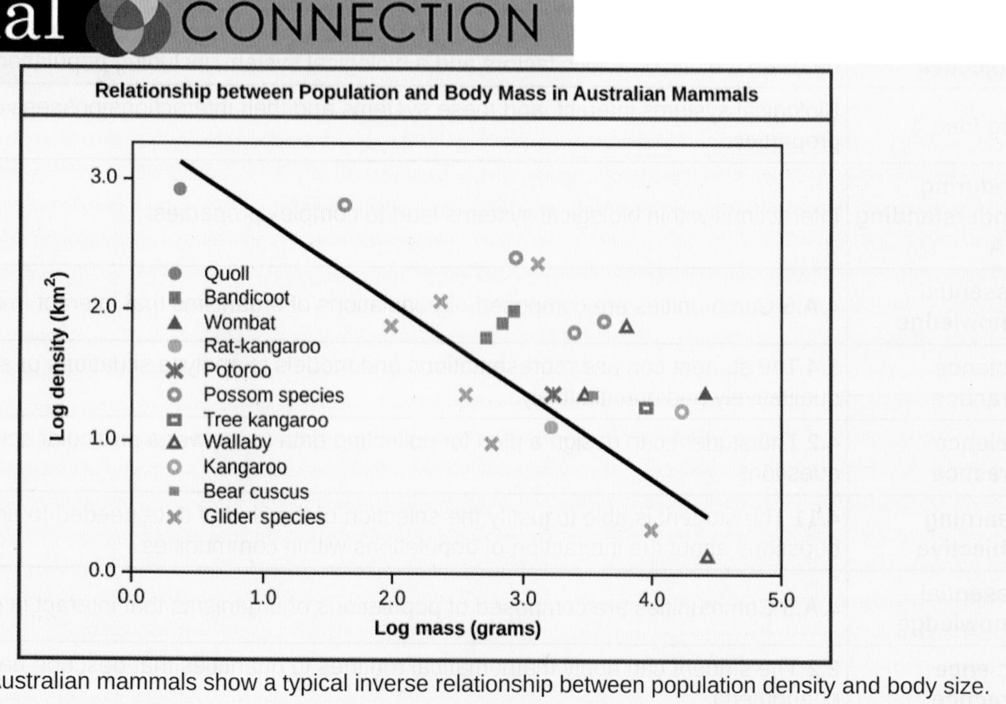

Figure 36.2 Australian mammals show a typical inverse relationship between population density and body size.

Population Research Methods

The most accurate way to determine population size is to simply count all of the individuals within the habitat. However, this method is often not logistically or economically feasible, especially when studying large habitats. Thus, scientists usually study populations by sampling a representative portion of each habitat and using this data to make inferences about the habitat as a whole. A variety of methods can be used to sample populations to determine their size and density. For immobile organisms such as plants, or for very small and slow-moving organisms, a **quadrat** may be used (Figure 36.3). A quadrat is a way of marking off square areas within a habitat, either by staking out an area with sticks and string, or by the use of a wood, plastic, or metal square placed on the ground. After setting the quadrats, researchers then count the number of individuals that lie within their boundaries. Multiple quadrat samples are performed throughout the habitat at several random locations. All of this data can then be used to estimate the population size and population density within the entire habitat. The number and size of quadrat samples depends on the type of organisms under study and other factors, including the density of the organism. For example, if sampling daffodils, a 1 m^2 quadrat might be used whereas with giant redwoods, which are larger and live much further apart from each other, a larger quadrat of 100 m^2 might be employed. This ensures that enough individuals of the species are counted to get an accurate sample that correlates with the habitat, including areas not sampled.

Figure 36.3 A scientist uses a quadrat to measure population size and density. (credit: NPS Sonoran Desert Network)

For mobile organisms, such as mammals, birds, or fish, a technique called **mark and recapture** is often used. This method involves marking a sample of captured animals in some way (such as tags, bands, paint, or other body markings), and then releasing them back into the environment to allow them to mix with the rest of the population; later, a new sample is collected, including some individuals that are marked (recaptures) and some individuals that are unmarked (**Figure 36.4**).

Figure 36.4 Mark and recapture is used to measure the population size of mobile animals such as (a) bighorn sheep, (b) the California condor, and (c) salmon. (credit a: modification of work by Neal Herbert, NPS; credit b: modification of work by Pacific Southwest Region USFWS; credit c: modification of work by Ingrid Taylar)

Using the ratio of marked and unmarked individuals, scientists determine how many individuals are in the sample. From this, calculations are used to estimate the total population size. This method assumes that the larger the population, the lower the percentage of tagged organisms that will be recaptured since they will have mixed with more untagged individuals. For example, if 80 deer are captured, tagged, and released into the forest, and later 100 deer are captured and 20 of them are already marked, we can determine the population size (*N*) using the following equation:

$$\frac{\text{(number marked first catch x total number of second catch)}}{\text{number marked second catch}} = N$$

Using our example, the population size would be estimated at 400.

$$\frac{(80 \text{ x } 100)}{20} = 400$$

Therefore, there are an estimated 400 total individuals in the original population.

There are some limitations to the mark and recapture method. Some animals from the first catch may learn to avoid capture in the second round, thus inflating population estimates. Alternatively, animals may preferentially be retrapped (especially if a food reward is offered), resulting in an underestimate of population size. Also, some species may be harmed by the marking technique, reducing their survival. A variety of other techniques have been developed, including the electronic tracking of animals tagged with radio transmitters and the use of data from commercial fishing and trapping operations to estimate the size and health of populations and communities.

Species Distribution

In addition to measuring simple density, further information about a population can be obtained by looking at the distribution of the individuals. **Species dispersion patterns** (or distribution patterns) show the spatial relationship between members of a population within a habitat at a particular point in time. In other words, they show whether members of the species live close together or far apart, and what patterns are evident when they are spaced apart.

Individuals in a population can be more or less equally spaced apart, dispersed randomly with no predictable pattern, or clustered in groups. These are known as uniform, random, and clumped dispersion patterns, respectively (Figure 36.5). Uniform dispersion is observed in plants that secrete substances inhibiting the growth of nearby individuals (such as the release of toxic chemicals by the sage plant *Salvia leucophylla,* a phenomenon called allelopathy) and in animals like the penguin that maintain a defined territory. An example of random dispersion occurs with dandelion and other plants that have wind-dispersed seeds that germinate wherever they happen to fall in a favorable environment. A clumped dispersion may be seen in plants that drop their seeds straight to the ground, such as oak trees, or animals that live in groups (schools of fish or herds of elephants). Clumped dispersions may also be a function of habitat heterogeneity. Thus, the dispersion of the individuals within a population provides more information about how they interact with each other than does a simple density measurement. Just as lower density species might have more difficulty finding a mate, solitary species with a random distribution might have a similar difficulty when compared to social species clumped together in groups.

Figure 36.5 Species may have uniform, random, or clumped distribution. Territorial birds such as penguins tend to have uniform distribution. Plants such as dandelions with wind-dispersed seeds tend to be randomly distributed. Animals such as elephants that travel in groups exhibit clumped distribution. (credit a: modification of work by Ben Tubby; credit b: modification of work by Rosendahl; credit c: modification of work by Rebecca Wood)

Demography

While population size and density describe a population at one particular point in time, scientists must use demography to study the dynamics of a population. Demography is the statistical study of population changes over time: birth rates, death rates, and life expectancies. Each of these measures, especially birth rates, may be affected by the population characteristics described above. For example, a large population size results in a higher birth rate because more potentially reproductive individuals are present. In contrast, a large population size can also result in a higher death rate because of competition, disease, and the accumulation of waste. Similarly, a higher population density or a clumped dispersion pattern results in more potential reproductive encounters between individuals, which can increase birth rate. Lastly, a female-biased sex ratio (the ratio of males to females) or age structure (the proportion of population members at specific age ranges) composed of many individuals of reproductive age can increase birth rates.

In addition, the demographic characteristics of a population can influence how the population grows or declines over time. If birth and death rates are equal, the population remains stable. However, the population size will increase if birth rates exceed death rates; the population will decrease if birth rates are less than death rates. Life expectancy is another important factor; the length of time individuals remain in the population impacts local resources, reproduction, and the overall health of the population. These demographic characteristics are often displayed in the form of a life table.

Life Tables

Life tables provide important information about the life history of an organism. Life tables divide the population into age groups and often sexes, and show how long a member of that group is likely to live. They are modeled after actuarial tables used by the insurance industry for estimating human life expectancy. Life tables may include the probability of individuals dying before their next birthday (i.e., their **mortality rate**), the percentage of surviving individuals dying at a particular age interval, and their life expectancy at each interval. An example of a life table is shown in Table 36.1 from a study of Dall mountain sheep, a species native to northwestern North America. Notice that the population is divided into age intervals (column A). The mortality rate (per 1000), shown in column D, is based on the number of individuals dying during the age interval (column B) divided by the number of individuals surviving at the beginning of the interval (Column C), multiplied by 1000.

$$\text{mortality rate} = \frac{\text{number of individuals dying}}{\text{number of individuals surviving}} \times 1000$$

For example, between ages three and four, 12 individuals die out of the 776 that were remaining from the original 1000 sheep. This number is then multiplied by 1000 to get the mortality rate per thousand.

$$\text{mortality rate} = \frac{12}{776} \times 1000 \approx 15.5$$

As can be seen from the mortality rate data (column D), a high death rate occurred when the sheep were between 6 and 12 months old, and then increased even more from 8 to 12 years old, after which there were few survivors. The data indicate that if a sheep in this population were to survive to age one, it could be expected to live another 7.7 years on average, as shown by the life expectancy numbers in column E.

Life Table of Dall Mountain Sheep[1]

Age interval (years)	Number dying in age interval out of 1000 born	Number surviving at beginning of age interval out of 1000 born	Mortality rate per 1000 alive at beginning of age interval	Life expectancy or mean lifetime remaining to those attaining age interval
0-0.5	54	1000	54.0	7.06
0.5-1	145	946	153.3	--
1-2	12	801	15.0	7.7
2-3	13	789	16.5	6.8
3-4	12	776	15.5	5.9
4-5	30	764	39.3	5.0
5-6	46	734	62.7	4.2
6-7	48	688	69.8	3.4
7-8	69	640	107.8	2.6
8-9	132	571	231.2	1.9
9-10	187	439	426.0	1.3
10-11	156	252	619.0	0.9
11-12	90	96	937.5	0.6
12-13	3	6	500.0	1.2
13-14	3	3	1000	0.7

Table 36.1 This life table of *Ovis dalli* shows the number of deaths, number of survivors, mortality rate, and life expectancy at each age interval for the Dall mountain sheep.

Survivorship Curves

Another tool used by population ecologists is a **survivorship curve**, which is a graph of the number of individuals surviving at each age interval plotted versus time (usually with data compiled from a life table). These curves allow us to compare the life histories of different populations (Figure 36.6). Humans and most primates exhibit a Type I survivorship curve because a high percentage of offspring survive their early and middle years—death occurs predominantly in older individuals. These types of species usually have small numbers of offspring at one time, and they give a high amount of parental care to them to ensure their survival. Birds are an example of an intermediate or Type II survivorship curve because birds die more or

1. Data Adapted from Edward S. Deevey, Jr., "Life Tables for Natural Populations of Animals," *The Quarterly Review of Biology* 22, no. 4 (December 1947): 283-314.

less equally at each age interval. These organisms also may have relatively few offspring and provide significant parental care. Trees, marine invertebrates, and most fishes exhibit a Type III survivorship curve because very few of these organisms survive their younger years; however, those that make it to an old age are more likely to survive for a relatively long period of time. Organisms in this category usually have a very large number of offspring, but once they are born, little parental care is provided. Thus these offspring are "on their own" and vulnerable to predation, but their sheer numbers assure the survival of enough individuals to perpetuate the species.

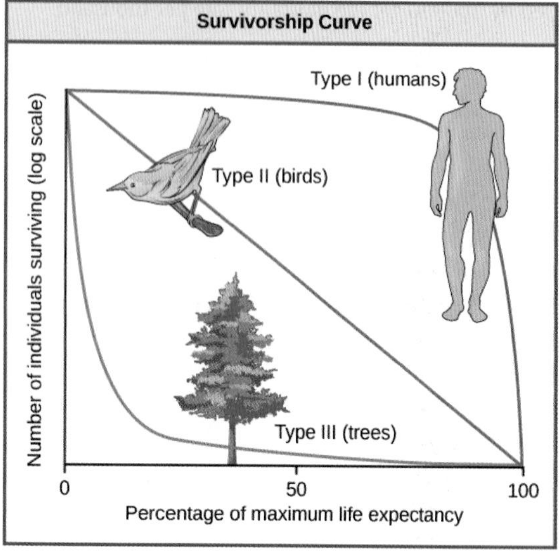

Figure 36.6 Survivorship curves show the distribution of individuals in a population according to age. Humans and most mammals have a Type I survivorship curve because death primarily occurs in the older years. Birds have a Type II survivorship curve, as death at any age is equally probable. Trees have a Type III survivorship curve because very few survive the younger years, but after a certain age, individuals are much more likely to survive.

science practices CONNECTION for AP® Courses

Activity

Design an investigation that a researcher might use to determine the size of a penguin population in the Antarctic using the mark and release method. What biotic or abiotic factors might influence the size of the penguin population in a given area?

Section Summary

Populations are individuals of a species that live in a particular habitat. Ecologists measure characteristics of populations: size, density, dispersion pattern, age structure, and sex ratio. Life tables are useful to calculate life expectancies of individual population members. Survivorship curves show the number of individuals surviving at each age interval plotted versus time.

36.2 | Life Histories and Natural Selection

In this section, you will explore the following questions:

- How are life history patterns influenced by natural selection?
- What are different life history patterns, and how do different reproductive strategies affect species survival?

Connection for AP® Courses

All living systems, including populations, require free energy to maintain order, to grow and to reproduce. As we learned in earlier chapters, changes in free energy availability can cause fluctuations in population. All species have an **energy budget** and must balance energy intake with their use of energy for metabolism, parental care, and energy storage.

It's amazing how much free energy is required for reproduction and the subsequent care of offspring. Fecundity describes how many offspring could be produced if an individual has as many offspring as possible. In animals, fecundity is inversely proportional to the amount of care given to an individual offspring.

Information presented and the examples highlighted in the section support concepts outlined in Big Idea 1 and Big Idea 2 of the AP® Biology Curriculum Framework. The AP® Learning Objectives listed in the Curriculum Framework provide a transparent foundation for the AP® Biology course, an inquiry-based laboratory experience, instructional activities, and AP® exam questions. A learning objective merges required content with one or more of the seven science practices.

Big Idea 1	The process of evolution drives the diversity and unity of life.
Enduring Understanding 1.A	Change in the genetic makeup of a population over time is evolution.
Essential Knowledge	**1.A.2** Natural selection acts on phenotypic variations in populations.
Science Practice	**2.2** The student can apply mathematical routines to quantities that describe natural phenomena.
Science Practice	**5.3** The student can evaluate the evidence provided by data sets in relation to a particular scientific question.
Learning Objective	**1.2** The student is able to evaluate evidence provided by data to qualitatively and quantitatively investigate the role of natural selection in evolution.
Big Idea 2	Biological systems utilize free energy and molecular building blocks to grow, to reproduce, and to maintain dynamic homeostasis.
Enduring Understanding 2.A	Growth, reproduction and maintenance of living systems require free energy and matter.
Essential Knowledge	**2.A.1** All living systems require constant input of free energy.
Science Practice	**6.2** The student can construct explanations of phenomena based on evidence produced through scientific practices.
Learning Objective	**2.1** The student is able to explain how biological systems use free energy based on empirical data that all organisms require constant energy input to maintain organization, to grow and to reproduce.

A species' **life history** describes the series of events over its lifetime, such as how resources are allocated for growth, maintenance, and reproduction. Life history traits affect the life table of an organism. A species' life history is genetically determined and shaped by the environment and natural selection.

Life History Patterns and Energy Budgets

Energy is required by all living organisms for their growth, maintenance, and reproduction; at the same time, energy is often a major limiting factor in determining an organism's survival. Plants, for example, acquire energy from the sun via photosynthesis, but must expend this energy to grow, maintain health, and produce energy-rich seeds to produce the next generation. Animals have the additional burden of using some of their energy reserves to acquire food. Furthermore, some animals must expend energy caring for their offspring. Thus, all species have an energy budget: they must balance energy intake with their use of energy for metabolism, reproduction, parental care, and energy storage (such as bears building up body fat for winter hibernation).

Parental Care and Fecundity

Fecundity is the potential reproductive capacity of an individual within a population. In other words, fecundity describes how many offspring could ideally be produced if an individual has as many offspring as possible, repeating the reproductive cycle as soon as possible after the birth of the offspring. In animals, fecundity is inversely related to the amount of parental care given to an individual offspring. Species, such as many marine invertebrates, that produce many offspring usually provide little if any care for the offspring (they would not have the energy or the ability to do so anyway). Most of their energy budget is used to produce many tiny offspring. Animals with this strategy are often self-sufficient at a very early age. This is because of the energy tradeoff these organisms have made to maximize their evolutionary fitness. Because their energy is used for producing offspring instead of parental care, it makes sense that these offspring have some ability to be able to move within their environment and find food and perhaps shelter. Even with these abilities, their small size makes them extremely vulnerable to predation, so the production of many offspring allows enough of them to survive to maintain the species.

Animal species that have few offspring during a reproductive event usually give extensive parental care, devoting much of their energy budget to these activities, sometimes at the expense of their own health. This is the case with many mammals, such as humans, kangaroos, and pandas. The offspring of these species are relatively helpless at birth and need to develop before they achieve self-sufficiency.

Plants with low fecundity produce few energy-rich seeds (such as coconuts and chestnuts) with each having a good chance to germinate into a new organism; plants with high fecundity usually have many small, energy-poor seeds (like orchids) that have a relatively poor chance of surviving. Although it may seem that coconuts and chestnuts have a better chance of surviving, the energy tradeoff of the orchid is also very effective. It is a matter of where the energy is used, for large numbers of seeds or for fewer seeds with more energy.

Early versus Late Reproduction

The timing of reproduction in a life history also affects species survival. Organisms that reproduce at an early age have a greater chance of producing offspring, but this is usually at the expense of their growth and the maintenance of their health. Conversely, organisms that start reproducing later in life often have greater fecundity or are better able to provide parental care, but they risk that they will not survive to reproductive age. Examples of this can be seen in fishes. Small fish like guppies use their energy to reproduce rapidly, but never attain the size that would give them defense against some predators. Larger fish, like the bluegill or shark, use their energy to attain a large size, but do so with the risk that they will die before they can reproduce or at least reproduce to their maximum. These different energy strategies and tradeoffs are key to understanding the evolution of each species as it maximizes its fitness and fills its niche. In terms of energy budgeting, some species "blow it all" and use up most of their energy reserves to reproduce early before they die. Other species delay having reproduction to become stronger, more experienced individuals and to make sure that they are strong enough to provide parental care if necessary.

Single versus Multiple Reproductive Events

Some life history traits, such as fecundity, timing of reproduction, and parental care, can be grouped together into general strategies that are used by multiple species. **Semelparity** occurs when a species reproduces only once during its lifetime and then dies. Such species use most of their resource budget during a single reproductive event, sacrificing their health to the point that they do not survive. Examples of semelparity are bamboo, which flowers once and then dies, and the Chinook salmon (**Figure 36.7a**), which uses most of its energy reserves to migrate from the ocean to its freshwater nesting area, where it reproduces and then dies. Scientists have posited alternate explanations for the evolutionary advantage of the Chinook's post-reproduction death: a programmed suicide caused by a massive release of corticosteroid hormones, presumably so the parents can become food for the offspring, or simple exhaustion caused by the energy demands of reproduction; these are still being debated.

Iteroparity describes species that reproduce repeatedly during their lives. Some animals are able to mate only once per year, but survive multiple mating seasons. The pronghorn antelope is an example of an animal that goes into a seasonal estrus cycle ("heat"): a hormonally induced physiological condition preparing the body for successful mating (**Figure 36.7b**). Females of these species mate only during the estrus phase of the cycle. A different pattern is observed in primates, including humans and chimpanzees, which may attempt reproduction at any time during their reproductive years, even though their menstrual cycles make pregnancy likely only a few days per month during ovulation (**Figure 36.7c**).

(a) (b) (c)

Figure 36.7 The (a) Chinook salmon mates once and dies. The (b) pronghorn antelope mates during specific times of the year during its reproductive life. Primates, such as humans and (c) chimpanzees, may mate on any day, independent of ovulation. (credit a: modification of work by Roger Tabor, USFWS; credit b: modification of work by Mark Gocke, USDA; credit c: modification of work by "Shiny Things"/Flickr)

Play this interactive PBS evolution-based mating game (http://openstaxcollege.org/l/mating_game) to learn more about reproductive strategies.

Explain why it is possible to make good guesses about the best mate selections in this game.

a. Organisms have reproductive strategies that are fairly easy to predict once the type of organism and the type of habitat they live in is known.

b. Organisms have nutritional strategies that are fairly easy to predict once the type of organism and the type of habitat they live in is known.

c. Organisms have reproductive strategies that are fairly easy to predict once the nutritional requirements and the type of habitat they live in is known.

d. Organisms have nutritional strategies that are fairly easy to predict once the nutritional requirements and the type of habitat they live in is known.

Energy Budgets, Reproductive Costs, and Sexual Selection in *Drosophila*

Research into how animals allocate their energy resources for growth, maintenance, and reproduction has used a variety of experimental animal models. Some of this work has been done using the common fruit fly, *Drosophila melanogaster*. Studies have shown that not only does reproduction have a cost as far as how long male fruit flies live, but also fruit flies that have already mated several times have limited sperm remaining for reproduction. Fruit flies maximize their last chances at reproduction by selecting optimal mates.

In a 1981 study, male fruit flies were placed in enclosures with either virgin or inseminated females. The males that mated with virgin females had shorter life spans than those in contact with the same number of inseminated females with which they were unable to mate. This effect occurred regardless of how large (indicative of their age) the males were. Thus, males that did not mate lived longer, allowing them more opportunities to find mates in the future.

More recent studies, performed in 2006, show how males select the female with which they will mate and how this is affected by previous matings (Figure 36.8).[2] Males were allowed to select between smaller and larger females. Findings showed that larger females had greater fecundity, producing twice as many offspring per mating as the smaller females did. Males that had previously mated, and thus had lower supplies of sperm, were termed "resource-depleted," while males that had not mated were termed "non-resource-depleted." The study showed that although non-resource-depleted males preferentially mated with larger females, this selection of partners was more pronounced in the resource-depleted males. Thus, males with depleted sperm supplies, which were limited in the number of times that they could mate before they replenished their sperm supply, selected larger, more fecund females, thus maximizing their chances for offspring. This study was one of the first to show that the physiological state of the male affected its mating behavior in a way that clearly maximizes its use of limited reproductive resources.

	Ratio large/small females mated
Non sperm-depleted	8 ± 5
Sperm-depleted	15 ± 5

Figure 36.8 Male fruit flies that had previously mated (sperm-depleted) picked larger, more fecund females more often than those that had not mated (non-sperm-depleted). This change in behavior causes an increase in the efficiency of a limited reproductive resource: sperm.

These studies demonstrate two ways in which the energy budget is a factor in reproduction. First, energy expended on mating may reduce an animal's lifespan, but by this time they have already reproduced, so in the context of natural selection this early death is not of much evolutionary importance. Second, when resources such as sperm (and the energy needed to replenish it) are low, an organism's behavior can change to give them the best chance of passing their genes on to the next generation. These changes in behavior, so important to evolution, are studied in a discipline known as behavioral biology, or ethology, at the interface between population biology and psychology.

Discuss how natural selection might influence the phenomenon revealed by this study.

a. Sperm-depleted males were successful in producing offspring when mated with small females. So, the genes that influenced the behavior of sperm-depleted males to choose larger, more fecund females were selected.
b. Sperm-depleted males were successful in producing offspring when mated with large females. So, the genes that influenced the behavior of sperm-depleted males to choose smaller, more fecund females were selected.
c. Sperm-depleted males were successful in producing offspring when mated with large females. So, the genes that influenced the behavior of sperm-depleted males to choose larger, more fecund females were selected.
d. Sperm-depleted males were successful in producing offspring when mated with smaller females. So, the genes that influenced the behavior of sperm-depleted males to choose smaller, less fecund females were

selected.

science practices CONNECTION for AP® Courses

Think About It

Why is long-term parental care not associated with having many offspring during a reproductive episode?

Section Summary

All species have evolved a pattern of living, called a life history strategy, in which they partition energy for growth, maintenance, and reproduction. These patterns evolve through natural selection; they allow species to adapt to their environment to obtain the resources they need to successfully reproduce. There is an inverse relationship between fecundity and parental care. A species may reproduce early in life to ensure surviving to a reproductive age or reproduce later in life to become larger and healthier and better able to give parental care. A species may reproduce once (semelparity) or many times (iteroparity) in its life.

36.3 | Environmental Limits to Population Growth

In this section, you will explore the following questions:

- What are the characteristics of and differences between exponential and logistic growth patterns?
- What are examples of exponential and logistic growth in natural populations?

Connection for AP® Courses

Population ecologists use mathematical methods to model population dynamics. These models can be used to describe changes occurring in a population and to better predict future changes. Applying mathematics to these models (and being able to manipulate the equations) is in scope for AP®. (Remember that for the AP® Exam you will have access to a formula sheet with these equations.)

Information presented and the examples highlighted in the section support concepts outlined in Big Idea 4 of the AP® Biology Curriculum Framework. The AP® Learning Objectives listed in the Curriculum Framework provide a transparent foundation for the AP® Biology course, an inquiry-based laboratory experience, instructional activities, and AP® exam questions. A learning objective merges required content with one or more of the seven science practices.

Big Idea 4	Biological systems interact, and these systems and their interactions possess complex properties.
Enduring Understanding 4.A	Interactions within biological systems lead to complex properties.
Essential Knowledge	**4.A.5** Communities are composed of populations of organisms that interact in complex ways.
Science Practice	**2.2** The student can apply mathematical routines to quantities that describe natural phenomena.

2. Adapted from Phillip G. Byrne and William R. Rice, "Evidence for adaptive male mate choice in the fruit fly *Drosophila melanogaster*," Proc Biol Sci. 273, no. 1589 (2006): 917-922, doi: 10.1098/rspb.2005.3372.

Learning Objective	**4.12** The student is able to apply mathematical routines to quantities that describe communities composed of populations of organisms that interact in complex ways.
Essential Knowledge	**4.A.5** Communities are composed of populations of organisms that interact in complex ways.
Science Practice	**6.4** The student can make claims and predictions about natural phenomena based on scientific theories and models.
Learning Objective	**4.13** The student is able to predict the effects of a change in the community's populations on the community.

Although life histories describe the way many characteristics of a population (such as their age structure) change over time in a general way, population ecologists make use of a variety of methods to model population dynamics mathematically. These more precise models can then be used to accurately describe changes occurring in a population and better predict future changes. Certain models that have been accepted for decades are now being modified or even abandoned due to their lack of predictive ability, and scholars strive to create effective new models.

Exponential Growth

Charles Darwin, in his theory of natural selection, was greatly influenced by the English clergyman Thomas Malthus. Malthus published a book in 1798 stating that populations with unlimited natural resources grow very rapidly, and then population growth decreases as resources become depleted. This accelerating pattern of increasing population size is called **exponential growth**.

The best example of exponential growth is seen in bacteria. Bacteria are prokaryotes that reproduce by prokaryotic fission. This division takes about an hour for many bacterial species. If 1000 bacteria are placed in a large flask with an unlimited supply of nutrients (so the nutrients will not become depleted), after an hour, there is one round of division and each organism divides, resulting in 2000 organisms—an increase of 1000. In another hour, each of the 2000 organisms will double, producing 4000, an increase of 2000 organisms. After the third hour, there should be 8000 bacteria in the flask, an increase of 4000 organisms. The important concept of exponential growth is that the **population growth rate**—the number of organisms added in each reproductive generation—is accelerating; that is, it is increasing at a greater and greater rate. After 1 day and 24 of these cycles, the population would have increased from 1000 to more than 16 billion. When the population size, *N*, is plotted over time, a **J-shaped growth curve** is produced (Figure 36.9).

The bacteria example is not representative of the real world where resources are limited. Furthermore, some bacteria will die during the experiment and thus not reproduce, lowering the growth rate. Therefore, when calculating the growth rate of a population, the **death rate (*D*)** (number organisms that die during a particular time interval) is subtracted from the **birth rate (*B*)** (number organisms that are born during that interval). This is shown in the following formula:

$$\frac{\Delta N \text{ (change in number)}}{\Delta T \text{ (change in time)}} = B \text{ (birth rate)} - D \text{ (death rate)}$$

The birth rate is usually expressed on a per capita (for each individual) basis. Thus, *B* (birth rate) = *bN* (the per capita birth rate "*b*" multiplied by the number of individuals "*N*") and *D* (death rate) =*dN* (the per capita death rate "d" multiplied by the number of individuals "*N*"). Additionally, ecologists are interested in the population at a particular point in time, an infinitely small time interval. For this reason, the terminology of differential calculus is used to obtain the "instantaneous" growth rate, replacing the *change* in number and time with an instant-specific measurement of number and time.

$$\frac{dN}{dT} = bN - dN = (b - d)N$$

Notice that the "*d*" associated with the first term refers to the derivative (as the term is used in calculus) and is different from the death rate, also called "*d*." The difference between birth and death rates is further simplified by substituting the term "*r*" (intrinsic rate of increase) for the relationship between birth and death rates:

$$\frac{dN}{dT} = rN$$

The value "*r*" can be positive, meaning the population is increasing in size; or negative, meaning the population is decreasing in size; or zero, where the population's size is unchanging, a condition known as **zero population growth**. A further refinement of the formula recognizes that different species have inherent differences in their intrinsic rate of increase (often thought of as the potential for reproduction), even under ideal conditions. Obviously, a bacterium can reproduce more rapidly and have a higher intrinsic rate of growth than a human. The maximal growth rate for a species is its **biotic potential, or r_{max}**, thus changing the equation to:

$$\frac{dN}{dT} = r_{\max} N$$

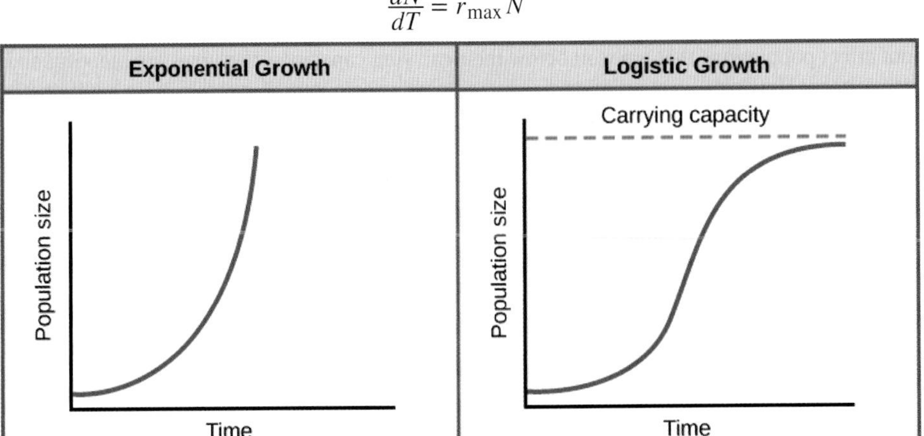

Figure 36.9 When resources are unlimited, populations exhibit exponential growth, resulting in a J-shaped curve. When resources are limited, populations exhibit logistic growth. In logistic growth, population expansion decreases as resources become scarce, and it levels off when the carrying capacity of the environment is reached, resulting in an S-shaped curve.

Logistic Growth

Exponential growth is possible only when infinite natural resources are available; this is not the case in the real world. Charles Darwin recognized this fact in his description of the "struggle for existence," which states that individuals will compete (with members of their own or other species) for limited resources. The successful ones will survive to pass on their own characteristics and traits (which we know now are transferred by genes) to the next generation at a greater rate (natural selection). To model the reality of limited resources, population ecologists developed the **logistic growth** model.

Carrying Capacity and the Logistic Model

In the real world, with its limited resources, exponential growth cannot continue indefinitely. Exponential growth may occur in environments where there are few individuals and plentiful resources, but when the number of individuals gets large enough, resources will be depleted, slowing the growth rate. Eventually, the growth rate will plateau or level off (Figure 36.9). This population size, which represents the maximum population size that a particular environment can support, is called the **carrying capacity, or *K*.**

The formula we use to calculate logistic growth adds the carrying capacity as a moderating force in the growth rate. The expression "$K – N$" is indicative of how many individuals may be added to a population at a given stage, and "$K – N$" divided by "K" is the fraction of the carrying capacity available for further growth. Thus, the exponential growth model is restricted by this factor to generate the logistic growth equation:

$$\frac{dN}{dT} = r_{\max}\frac{dN}{dT} = r_{\max}N\frac{(K\ -\ N)}{K}$$

Notice that when N is very small, $(K\text{-}N)/K$ becomes close to K/K or 1, and the right side of the equation reduces to $r_{max}N$, which means the population is growing exponentially and is not influenced by carrying capacity. On the other hand, when N is large, $(K\text{-}N)/K$ come close to zero, which means that population growth will be slowed greatly or even stopped. Thus, population growth is greatly slowed in large populations by the carrying capacity K. This model also allows for the population of a negative population growth, or a population decline. This occurs when the number of individuals in the population exceeds the carrying capacity (because the value of (K-N)/K is negative).

A graph of this equation yields an **S-shaped curve** (Figure 36.9), and it is a more realistic model of population growth than exponential growth. There are three different sections to an S-shaped curve. Initially, growth is exponential because there are few individuals and ample resources available. Then, as resources begin to become limited, the growth rate decreases. Finally, growth levels off at the carrying capacity of the environment, with little change in population size over time.

Role of Intraspecific Competition

The logistic model assumes that every individual within a population will have equal access to resources and, thus, an equal chance for survival. For plants, the amount of water, sunlight, nutrients, and the space to grow are the important resources, whereas in animals, important resources include food, water, shelter, nesting space, and mates.

In the real world, phenotypic variation among individuals within a population means that some individuals will be better adapted to their environment than others. The resulting competition between population members of the same species for resources is termed **intraspecific competition** (intra- = "within"; -specific = "species"). Intraspecific competition for resources may not affect populations that are well below their carrying capacity—resources are plentiful and all individuals can obtain what they need. However, as population size increases, this competition intensifies. In addition, the accumulation of waste products can reduce an environment's carrying capacity.

Examples of Logistic Growth

Yeast, a microscopic fungus used to make bread, exhibits the classical S-shaped curve when grown in a test tube (**Figure 36.10a**). Its growth levels off as the population depletes the nutrients that are necessary for its growth. In the real world, however, there are variations to this idealized curve. Examples in wild populations include sheep and harbor seals (**Figure 36.10b**). In both examples, the population size exceeds the carrying capacity for short periods of time and then falls below the carrying capacity afterwards. This fluctuation in population size continues to occur as the population oscillates around its carrying capacity. Still, even with this oscillation, the logistic model is confirmed.

science practices CONNECTION for AP® Courses

Think About It

Describe the rate of population growth that would be expected at various parts of the S-shaped curve of logistic growth.

visual CONNECTION

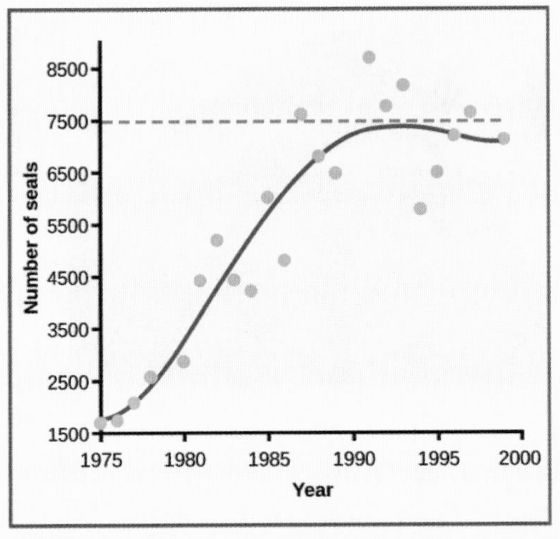

(a)

(b)

Figure 36.10 (a) Yeast grown in ideal conditions in a test tube show a classical S-shaped logistic growth curve, whereas (b) a natural population of seals shows real-world fluctuation.

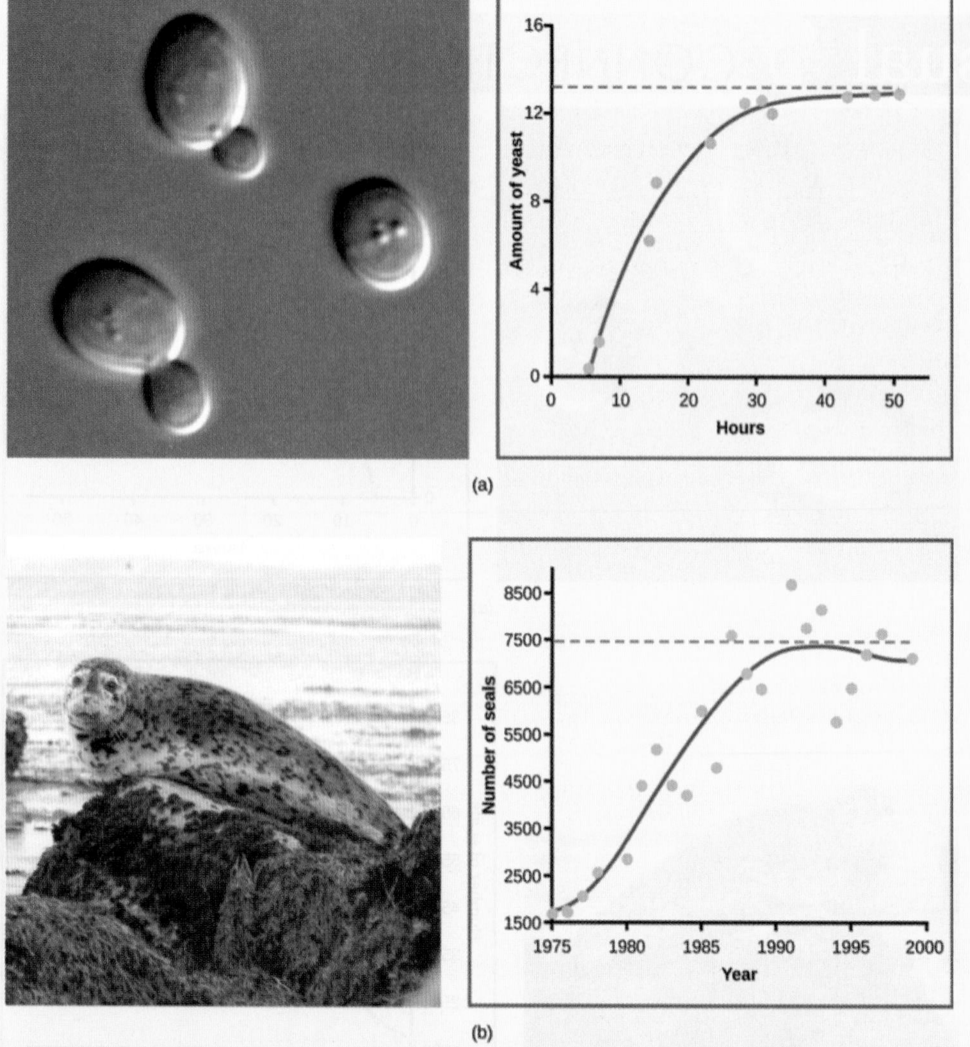

Explain the underlying reasons for the differences in the two curves shown in these examples.

a. Yeast is grown under ideal conditions, so the curve reflects limitations of resources in the controlled environment. Seals live in a natural habitat where the same types of resources are limited; but, they face other pressures like migration and changing weather.
b. Yeast is grown under natural conditions, so the curve reflects limitations of resources due to the environment. Seals were also observed in natural conditions; but, there were more pressures in addition to the limitation of resources like migration and changing weather.
c. Yeast is grown under ideal conditions, so the curve reflects limitations of resources in the uncontrolled environment. Seals live in a natural environment where same types of resources are limited; but they face other pressures like migration and changing weather.
d. Yeast is grown under ideal conditions, so the curve reflects limitations of resources in the controlled environment. Seals live in a natural environment where the same types of resources are limited; but, they face another pressure of migration of seals out of the population.

Section Summary

Populations with unlimited resources grow exponentially, with an accelerating growth rate. When resources become limiting, populations follow a logistic growth curve. The population of a species will level off at the carrying capacity of its environment.

36.4 | Population Dynamics and Regulation

In this section, you will investigate the following questions:

- How can the carrying capacity of a habitat change?
- What are the similarities and differences between density-dependent growth regulation and density-independent growth regulation, and what are some examples of both?
- How do natural selection and environmental adaptation lead to the evolution of particular life-history patterns?

Connection for AP® Courses

While looking at the logistic model is very useful when studying population dynamics, additional methods are used when considering more complex situations, such as changes in the carrying capacity of the environment. Abiotic and biotic factors can affect the growth and death rates of a population, so these fluctuations also require consideration when modeling a population's change over time. Sometimes, scientists need to consider how reproductive strategies play a part into the dynamics of a population over time. To consider how these different factors interact, populations are looked at from a variety of perspectives.

Information presented and the examples highlighted in the section support concepts outlined in Big Idea 4 of the AP® Biology Curriculum Framework. The AP® Learning Objectives listed in the Curriculum Framework provide a transparent foundation for the AP® Biology course, an inquiry-based laboratory experience, instructional activities, and AP® exam questions. A learning objective merges required content with one or more of the seven science practices.

Big Idea 4	Biological systems interact, and these systems and their interactions possess complex properties.
Enduring Understanding 4.A	Interactions within biological systems lead to complex properties.
Essential Knowledge	**4.A.5** Communities are composed of populations of organisms that interact in complex ways.
Science Practice	**1.4** The student can use representations and models to analyze situations or solve problems qualitatively and quantitatively.
Science Practice	**4.1** The student can justify the selection of the kind of data needed to answer a particular scientific question.
Learning Objective	**4.11** The student is able to justify the selection of the kind of data needed to answer scientific questions about the interactions of populations within communities.

The logistic model of population growth, while valid in many natural populations and a useful model, is a simplification of real-world population dynamics. Implicit in the model is that the carrying capacity of the environment does not change, which is not the case. The carrying capacity varies annually: for example, some summers are hot and dry whereas others are cold and wet. In many areas, the carrying capacity during the winter is much lower than it is during the summer. Also, natural events such as earthquakes, volcanoes, and fires can alter an environment and hence its carrying capacity. Additionally, populations do not usually exist in isolation. They engage in **interspecific competition**: that is, they share the environment with other species, competing with them for the same resources. These factors are also important to understanding how a specific population will grow.

Nature regulates population growth in a variety of ways. These are grouped into **density-dependent** factors, in which the density of the population at a given time affects growth rate and mortality, and **density-independent** factors, which influence mortality in a population regardless of population density. Note that in the former, the effect of the factor on the population depends on the density of the population at onset. Conservation biologists want to understand both types because this helps them manage populations and prevent extinction or overpopulation.

Density-dependent Regulation

Most density-dependent factors are biological in nature (biotic), and include predation, inter- and intraspecific competition, accumulation of waste, and diseases such as those caused by parasites. Usually, the denser a population is, the greater its mortality rate. For example, during intra- and interspecific competition, the reproductive rates of the individuals will usually be lower, reducing their population's rate of growth. In addition, low prey density increases the mortality of its predator because it has more difficulty locating its food source.

An example of density-dependent regulation is shown in **Figure 36.11** with results from a study focusing on the giant intestinal roundworm (*Ascaris lumbricoides*), a parasite of humans and other mammals.[3] Denser populations of the parasite exhibited lower fecundity: they contained fewer eggs. One possible explanation for this is that females would be smaller in more dense populations (due to limited resources) and that smaller females would have fewer eggs. This hypothesis was tested and disproved in a 2009 study which showed that female weight had no influence.[4] The actual cause of the density-dependence of fecundity in this organism is still unclear and awaiting further investigation.

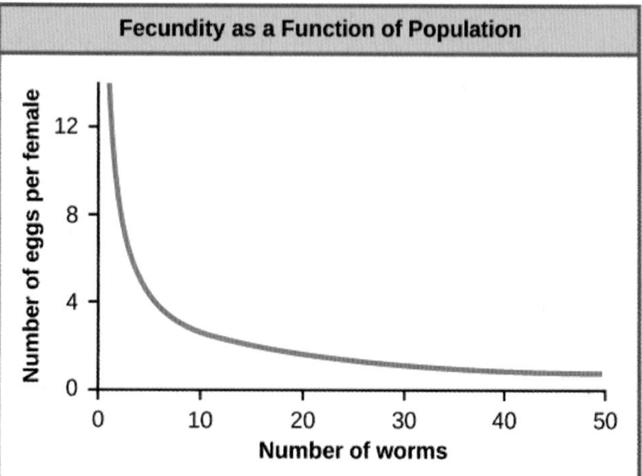

Figure 36.11 In this population of roundworms, fecundity (number of eggs) decreases with population density.[5]

3. N.A. Croll et al., "The Population Biology and Control of *Ascaris lumbricoides* in a Rural Community in Iran." *Transactions of the Royal Society of Tropical Medicine and Hygiene* 76, no. 2 (1982): 187-197, doi:10.1016/0035-9203(82)90272-3.
4. Martin Walker et al., "Density-Dependent Effects on the Weight of Female *Ascaris lumbricoides* Infections of Humans and its Impact on Patterns of Egg Production." *Parasites & Vectors* 2, no. 11 (February 2009), doi:10.1186/1756-3305-2-11.
5. N.A. Croll et al., "The Population Biology and Control of *Ascaris lumbricoides* in a Rural Community in Iran." *Transactions of the Royal Society of Tropical Medicine and Hygiene* 76, no. 2 (1982): 187-197, doi:10.1016/0035-9203(82)90272-3.

everyday CONNECTION for AP® Courses

One of the consequences of an overly dense population is the spread of disease. The brown bat pictured below has a contagious fungal infection called white nose syndrome.

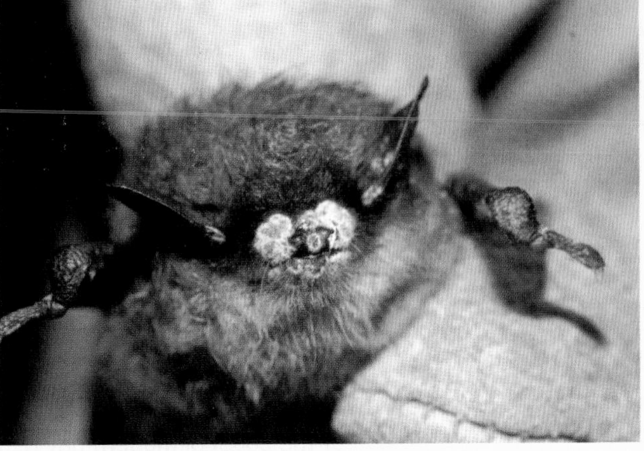

Figure 36.12 (credit: U.S. Fish and Wildlife Service Headquarters)

How would infection of zebras by *Bacillus anthracis* be described—as a density-dependent or density-independent factor that regulates population growth?

a. This is an example of a density-independent factor because it becomes worse as the population density increases.
b. This is an example of a density-dependent factor because it becomes better as the population density increases.
c. This is an example of a density-dependent factor because it becomes worse as the population density increases.
d. This is an example of a density-independent factor since it becomes better as the population density increases.

Density-independent Regulation and Interaction with Density-dependent Factors

Many factors, typically physical or chemical in nature (abiotic), influence the mortality of a population regardless of its density, including weather, natural disasters, and pollution. An individual deer may be killed in a forest fire regardless of how many deer happen to be in that area. Its chances of survival are the same whether the population density is high or low. The same holds true for cold winter weather.

In real-life situations, population regulation is very complicated and density-dependent and independent factors can interact. A dense population that is reduced in a density-independent manner by some environmental factor(s) will be able to recover differently than a sparse population. For example, a population of deer affected by a harsh winter will recover faster if there are more deer remaining to reproduce.

science practices CONNECTION for AP® Courses

Think About It

Describe an example of how density-dependent and density-independent factors might interact.

evolution CONNECTION

Why Did the Woolly Mammoth Go Extinct?

(a) (b) (c)

Figure 36.13 The three photos include: (a) 1916 mural of a mammoth herd from the American Museum of Natural History, (b) the only stuffed mammoth in the world, from the Museum of Zoology located in St. Petersburg, Russia, and (c) a one-month-old baby mammoth, named Lyuba, discovered in Siberia in 2007. (credit a: modification of work by Charles R. Knight; credit b: modification of work by "Tanapon"/Flickr; credit c: modification of work by Matt Howry)

It's easy to get lost in the discussion of dinosaurs and theories about why they went extinct 65 million years ago. Was it due to a meteor slamming into Earth near the coast of modern-day Mexico, or was it from some long-term weather cycle that is not yet understood? One hypothesis that will never be proposed is that humans had something to do with it. Mammals were small, insignificant creatures of the forest 65 million years ago, and no humans existed.

Woolly mammoths, however, began to go extinct about 10,000 years ago, when they shared the Earth with humans who were no different anatomically than humans today (Figure 36.13). Mammoths survived in isolated island populations as recently as 1700 BC. We know a lot about these animals from carcasses found frozen in the ice of Siberia and other regions of the north. Scientists have sequenced at least 50 percent of its genome and believe mammoths are between 98 and 99 percent identical to modern elephants.

It is commonly thought that climate change and human hunting led to their extinction. A 2008 study estimated that climate change reduced the mammoth's range from 3,000,000 square miles 42,000 years ago to 310,000 square miles 6,000 years ago.[6] It is also well documented that humans hunted these animals. A 2012 study showed that no single factor was exclusively responsible for the extinction of these magnificent creatures.[7] In addition to human hunting, climate change, and reduction of habitat, these scientists demonstrated another important factor in the mammoth's extinction was the migration of humans across the Bering Strait to North America during the last ice age 20,000 years ago.

The maintenance of stable populations was and is very complex, with many interacting factors determining the outcome. It is important to remember that humans are also part of nature. Once we contributed to a species' decline using primitive hunting technology only.

Explain the factors that may have contributed to the extinction of the woolly mammoth, and caused it to occur over a long period of time.

a. Deforestation affected the ability of the woolly mammoth to find adequate habitat and food, and humans contributed to declines in their population by hunting them.
b. Climate change affected the ability of the woolly mammoth to find adequate habitat and food, and humans contributed to the decline in their population by hunting them.
c. Climate change affected the ability of the woolly mammoth to find adequate food even though they had plenty of habitat, and humans contributed to declines in their population by hunting them.
d. Climate change affected the ability of the woolly mammoth to find adequate habitat and food, and a plague affected Earth during that time causing their extinction.

6. David Nogués-Bravo et al., "Climate Change, Humans, and the Extinction of the Woolly Mammoth." *PLoS Biol* 6 (April 2008): e79, doi:10.1371/journal.pbio.0060079.
7. G.M. MacDonald et al., "Pattern of Extinction of the Woolly Mammoth in Beringia." *Nature Communications* 3, no. 893 (June 2012), doi:10.1038/ncomms1881.

Life Histories of *K*-selected and *r*-selected Species

While reproductive strategies play a key role in life histories, they do not account for important factors like limited resources and competition. The regulation of population growth by these factors can be used to introduce a classical concept in population biology, that of *K*-selected versus *r*-selected species.

Early Theories about Life History: K-selected and r-selected Species

By the second half of the twentieth century, the concept of K- and r-selected species was used extensively and successfully to study populations. The concept relates not only reproductive strategies, but also to a species' habitat and behavior, especially in the way that they obtain resources and care for their young. It includes length of life and survivorship factors as well. For this analysis, population biologists have grouped species into the two large categories—*K*-selected and *r*-selected—although they are really two ends of a continuum.

***K*-selected species** are species selected by stable, predictable environments. Populations of *K*-selected species tend to exist close to their carrying capacity (hence the term *K*-selected) where intraspecific competition is high. These species have few, large offspring, a long gestation period, and often give long-term care to their offspring (Table B45_04_01). While larger in size when born, the offspring are relatively helpless and immature at birth. By the time they reach adulthood, they must develop skills to compete for natural resources. In plants, scientists think of parental care more broadly: how long fruit takes to develop or how long it remains on the plant are determining factors in the time to the next reproductive event. Examples of *K*-selected species are primates (including humans), elephants, and plants such as oak trees (**Figure 36.14a**).

Oak trees grow very slowly and take, on average, 20 years to produce their first seeds, known as acorns. As many as 50,000 acorns can be produced by an individual tree, but the germination rate is low as many of these rot or are eaten by animals such as squirrels. In some years, oaks may produce an exceptionally large number of acorns, and these years may be on a two- or three-year cycle depending on the species of oak (*r*-selection).

As oak trees grow to a large size and for many years before they begin to produce acorns, they devote a large percentage of their energy budget to growth and maintenance. The tree's height and size allow it to dominate other plants in the competition for sunlight, the oak's primary energy resource. Furthermore, when it does reproduce, the oak produces large, energy-rich seeds that use their energy reserve to become quickly established (*K*-selection).

In contrast, ***r*-selected species** have a large number of small offspring (hence their *r* designation (**Table 36.2**). This strategy is often employed in unpredictable or changing environments. Animals that are *r*-selected do not give long-term parental care and the offspring are relatively mature and self-sufficient at birth. Examples of *r*-selected species are marine invertebrates, such as jellyfish, and plants, such as the dandelion (**Figure 36.14b**). Dandelions have small seeds that are wind dispersed long distances. Many seeds are produced simultaneously to ensure that at least some of them reach a hospitable environment. Seeds that land in inhospitable environments have little chance for survival since their seeds are low in energy content. Note that survival is not necessarily a function of energy stored in the seed itself.

Characteristics of *K*-selected and *r*-selected species

Characteristics of *K*-selected species	Characteristics of *r*-selected species
Mature late	Mature early
Greater longevity	Lower longevity
Increased parental care	Decreased parental care
Increased competition	Decreased competition
Fewer offspring	More offspring
Larger offspring	Smaller offspring

Table 36.2

(a) K-selected species

(b) r-selected species

Figure 36.14 (a) Elephants are considered K-selected species as they live long, mature late, and provide long-term parental care to few offspring. Oak trees produce many offspring that do not receive parental care, but are considered K-selected species based on longevity and late maturation. (b) Dandelions and jellyfish are both considered r-selected species as they mature early, have short lifespans, and produce many offspring that receive no parental care.

Modern Theories of Life History

The *r*- and *K*-selection theory, although accepted for decades and used for much groundbreaking research, has now been reconsidered, and many population biologists have abandoned or modified it. Over the years, several studies attempted to confirm the theory, but these attempts have largely failed. Many species were identified that did not follow the theory's predictions. Furthermore, the theory ignored the age-specific mortality of the populations which scientists now know is very important. New **demographic-based models** of life history evolution have been developed which incorporate many ecological concepts included in *r*- and *K*-selection theory as well as population age structure and mortality factors.

Section Summary

Populations are regulated by a variety of density-dependent and density-independent factors. Species are divided into two categories based on a variety of features of their life history patterns: *r*-selected species, which have large numbers of offspring, and *K*-selected species, which have few offspring. The *r*- and *K*-selection theory has fallen out of use; however, many of its key features are still used in newer, demographically-based models of population dynamics.

36.5 | Human Population Growth

In this section, you will investigate the following questions:

- How can human population growth be exponential?
- How have humans expanded the carrying capacity of their habitat?
- How do population growth and age structure relate to the level of economic development in different countries?
- What are the long-term implications of unchecked human population growth?

Connection for AP® Courses

The methods used to look at animal population dynamics can also be used to look at the human populations. Like animals, humans are affected by abiotic and biotic factors. Unlike animals, humans have the ability to manipulate the factors affecting the growth of their population. As a result, additional factors come into play when studying human population dynamics. When studying projections of human population growth, ethical questions can also come to light.

Information presented and the examples highlighted in the section support concepts outlined in Big Idea 4 of the AP® Biology Curriculum Framework. The AP® Learning Objectives listed in the Curriculum Framework provide a transparent foundation for the AP® Biology course, an inquiry-based laboratory experience, instructional activities, and AP® exam questions. A learning objective merges required content with one or more of the seven science practices.

Big Idea 4	Biological systems interact, and these systems and their interactions possess complex properties.
Enduring Understanding 4.A	Interactions within biological systems lead to complex properties.
Essential Knowledge	**4.A.6** Interactions among living systems and with their environment result in the movement of matter and energy.
Science Practice	**1.4** The student can use representations and models to analyze situations or solve problems qualitatively and quantitatively.
Science Practice	**4.1** The student is able to justify the selection of the kind of data needed to answer scientific questions about the interaction of populations within communities.
Learning Objective	**4.11** The student is able to justify the selection of the kind of data needed to answer scientific questions about the interaction of populations within communities.
Essential Knowledge	**4.A.6** Interactions among living systems and with their environment result in the movement of matter and energy.
Science Practice	**2.2** The student can apply mathematical routines to quantities that describe natural phenomena.
Learning Objective	**4.12** The student is able to apply mathematical routines to quantities that describe communities composed of populations of organisms that interact in complex ways.
Essential Knowledge	**4.A.6** Interactions among living systems and with their environment result in the movement of matter and energy.
Science Practice	**6.4** The student can make claims and predictions about natural phenomena based on scientific theories and models.
Learning Objective	**4.13** The student is able to predict the effects of a change in the community's populations on the community.
Essential Knowledge	**4.A.6** Interactions among living systems and with their environment result in the movement of matter and energy.
Science Practice	**6.4** The student can make claims and predictions about natural phenomena based on scientific theories and models.
Learning Objective	**4.16** The student is able to predict the effects of a change of matter or energy availability on communities.

Concepts of animal population dynamics can be applied to human population growth. Humans are not unique in their ability to alter their environment. For example, beaver dams alter the stream environment where they are built. Humans, however, have the ability to alter their environment to increase its carrying capacity sometimes to the detriment of other species (e.g., via artificial selection for crops that have a higher yield). Earth's human population is growing rapidly, to the extent that some worry about the ability of the earth's environment to sustain this population, as long-term exponential growth carries the potential risks of famine, disease, and large-scale death.

Although humans have increased the carrying capacity of their environment, the technologies used to achieve this transformation have caused unprecedented changes to Earth's environment, altering ecosystems to the point where some may be in danger of collapse. The depletion of the ozone layer, erosion due to acid rain, and damage from global climate change are caused by human activities. The ultimate effect of these changes on our carrying capacity is unknown. As some point out, it is likely that the negative effects of increasing carrying capacity will outweigh the positive ones—the carrying capacity of the world for human beings might actually decrease.

The world's human population is currently experiencing exponential growth even though human reproduction is far below its biotic potential (**Figure 36.15**). To reach its biotic potential, all females would have to become pregnant every nine months or so during their reproductive years. Also, resources would have to be such that the environment would support such growth. Neither of these two conditions exists. In spite of this fact, human population is still growing exponentially.

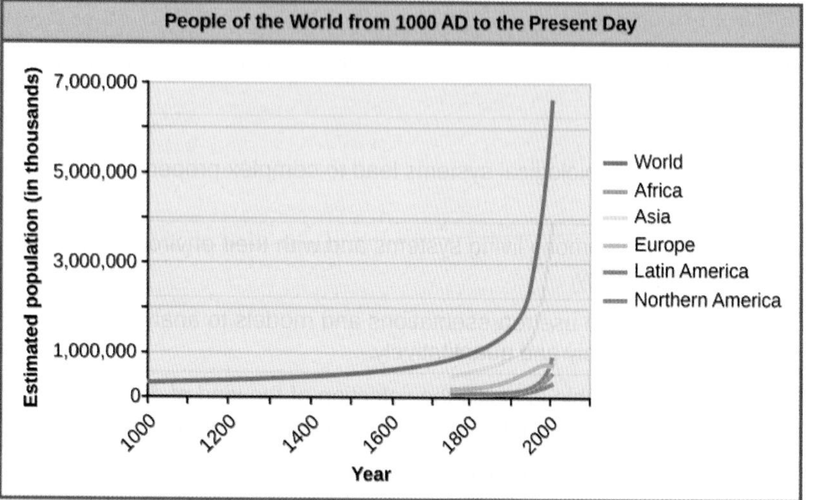

Figure 36.15 Human population growth since 1000 AD is exponential (dark blue line). Notice that while the population in Asia (yellow line), which has many economically underdeveloped countries, is increasing exponentially, the population in Europe (light blue line), where most of the countries are economically developed, is growing much more slowly.

A consequence of exponential human population growth is the time that it takes to add a particular number of humans to the Earth is becoming shorter. **Figure 36.16** shows that 123 years were necessary to add 1 billion humans in 1930, but it only took 24 years to add two billion people between 1975 and 1999. As already discussed, at some point it would appear that our ability to increase our carrying capacity indefinitely on a finite world is uncertain. Without new technological advances, the human growth rate has been predicted to slow in the coming decades. However, the population will still be increasing and the threat of overpopulation remains.

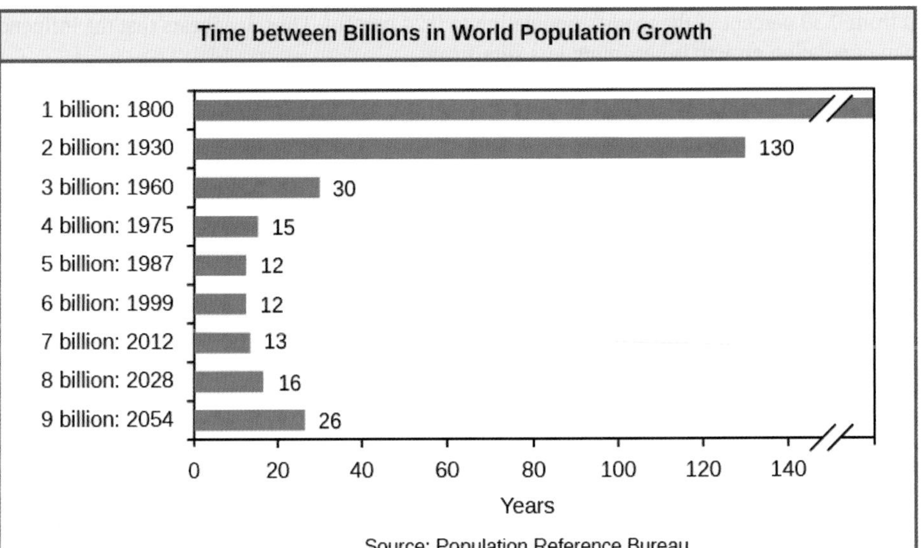

Figure 36.16 The time between the addition of each billion human beings to Earth decreases over time. (credit: modification of work by Ryan T. Cragun)

Click through this interactive view (http://openstaxcollege.org/l/human_growth) of how human populations have changed over time.

Based on the interactive, how would you describe human population growth?

a. a decline in human population growth

b. a lag in human population growth

c. logistic growth

d. exponential growth

Overcoming Density-Dependent Regulation

Humans are unique in their ability to alter their environment with the conscious purpose of increasing its carrying capacity. This ability is a major factor responsible for human population growth and a way of overcoming density-dependent growth regulation. Much of this ability is related to human intelligence, society, and communication. Humans can construct shelter to protect them from the elements and have developed agriculture and domesticated animals to increase their food supplies. In addition, humans use language to communicate this technology to new generations, allowing them to improve upon previous accomplishments.

Other factors in human population growth are migration and public health. Humans originated in Africa, but have since migrated to nearly all inhabitable land on the Earth. Public health, sanitation, and the use of antibiotics and vaccines have decreased the ability of infectious disease to limit human population growth. In the past, diseases such as the bubonic plaque of the fourteenth century killed between 30 and 60 percent of Europe's population and reduced the overall world population by as many as 100 million people. Today, the threat of infectious disease, while not gone, is certainly less severe. According to the World Health Organization, global death from infectious disease declined from 16.4 million in 1993 to 14.7 million in 2002. To compare to some of the epidemics of the past, the percentage of the world's population killed between 1993 and

2002 decreased from 0.30 percent of the world's population to 0.24 percent. Thus, it appears that the influence of infectious disease on human population growth is becoming less significant.

Age Structure, Population Growth, and Economic Development

The age structure of a population is an important factor in population dynamics. **Age structure** is the proportion of a population at different age ranges. Age structure allows better prediction of population growth, plus the ability to associate this growth with the level of economic development in the region. Countries with rapid growth have a pyramidal shape in their age structure diagrams, showing a preponderance of younger individuals, many of whom are of reproductive age or will be soon (Figure 36.17). This pattern is most often observed in underdeveloped countries where individuals do not live to old age because of less-than-optimal living conditions. Age structures of areas with slow growth, including developed countries such as the United States, still have a pyramidal structure, but with many fewer young and reproductive-aged individuals and a greater proportion of older individuals. Other developed countries, such as Italy, have zero population growth. The age structure of these populations is more conical, with an even greater percentage of middle-aged and older individuals. The actual growth rates in different countries are shown in Figure 36.18, with the highest rates tending to be in the less economically developed countries of Africa and Asia.

visual CONNECTION

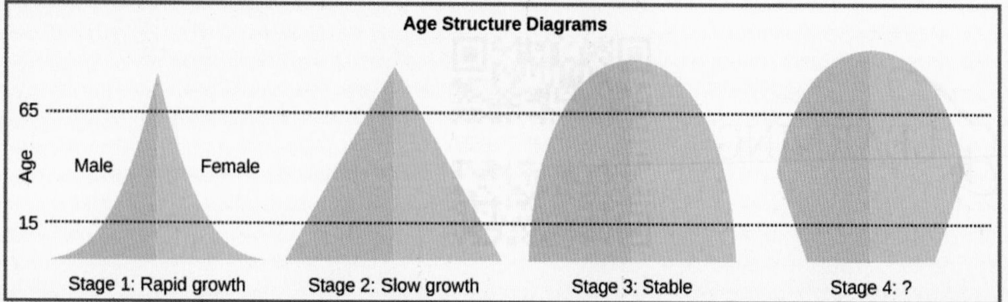

Figure 36.17 Typical age structure diagrams are shown. The rapid growth diagram narrows to a point, indicating that the number of individuals decreases rapidly with age. In the slow growth model, the number of individuals decreases steadily with age. Stable population diagrams are rounded on the top, showing that the number of individuals per age group decreases gradually, and then increases for the older part of the population.

Compare the age structure for Stage 4 to that of Stage 3. What changes in population growth would have to occur for a shift from Stage 3 to Stage 4?

a. Birth rates and death rates remains same in both Stage 3 and Stage 4.
b. Birth rates and death rates decline in Stage 4 compared to Stage 3.
c. Death rates decline in Stage 4 compared to Stage 3, but birth rates remain the same.
d. Birth rates decline in Stage 4 compared to Stage 3, but death rates remain the same.

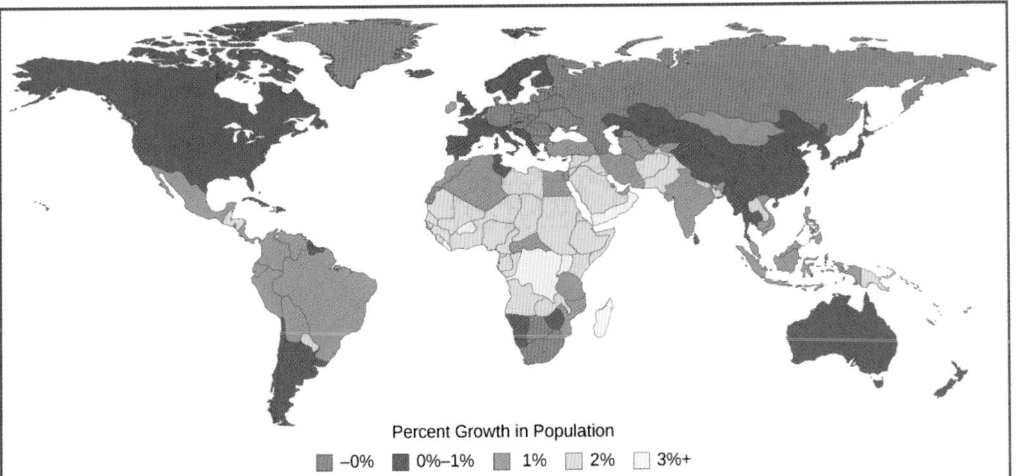

Figure 36.18 The percent growth rate of population in different countries is shown. Notice that the highest growth is occurring in less economically developed countries in Africa and Asia.

Long-Term Consequences of Exponential Human Population Growth

Many dire predictions have been made about the world's population leading to a major crisis called the "population explosion." In the 1968 book *The Population Bomb*, biologist Dr. Paul R. Ehrlich wrote, "The battle to feed all of humanity is over. In the 1970s hundreds of millions of people will starve to death in spite of any crash programs embarked upon now. At this late date nothing can prevent a substantial increase in the world death rate."[8] While many critics view this statement as an exaggeration, the laws of exponential population growth are still in effect, and unchecked human population growth cannot continue indefinitely.

Efforts to control population growth led to the **one-child policy** in China, which used to include more severe consequences, but now imposes fines on urban couples who have more than one child. Due to the fact that some couples wish to have a male heir, many Chinese couples continue to have more than one child. The policy itself, its social impacts, and the effectiveness of limiting overall population growth are controversial. In spite of population control policies, the human population continues to grow. At some point the food supply may run out because of the subsequent need to produce more and more food to feed our population. The United Nations estimates that future world population growth may vary from 6 billion (a decrease) to 16 billion people by the year 2100. There is no way to know whether human population growth will moderate to the point where the crisis described by Dr. Ehrlich will be averted.

Another result of population growth is the endangerment of the natural environment. Many countries have attempted to reduce the human impact on climate change by reducing their emission of the greenhouse gas carbon dioxide. However, these treaties have not been ratified by every country, and many underdeveloped countries trying to improve their economic condition may be less likely to agree with such provisions if it means slower economic development. Furthermore, the role of human activity in causing climate change has become a hotly debated socio-political issue in some developed countries, including the United States. Thus, we enter the future with considerable uncertainty about our ability to curb human population growth and protect our environment.

science practices CONNECTION for AP® Courses

Think About It

Describe the age structures in rapidly growing countries, slowly growing countries, and countries with zero population growth.

8. Paul R. Erlich, prologue to *The Population Bomb*, (1968; repr., New York: Ballantine, 1970).

Visit this website (http://openstaxcollege.org/l/populations) and select “Launch movie” for an animation discussing the global impacts of human population growth.

Section Summary

The world’s human population is growing at an exponential rate. Humans have increased the world’s carrying capacity through migration, agriculture, medical advances, and communication. The age structure of a population allows us to predict population growth. Unchecked human population growth could have dire long-term effects on our environment.

36.6 | Community Ecology

In this section, you will explore the following questions:

- What is the predator-prey cycle?
- What are examples of defenses against predation and herbivory?
- What is the competitive exclusion principle?
- What are examples of symbiotic relationship among species?
- What is community structure and succession?

Connection for AP® Courses

Topics explored in this section that are in scope for AP® include mimicry, the competitive exclusion principle, symbiosis, keystone and foundation species, and primary and secondary succession. Species interact in many ways, the classical example of species interaction being the hunting of prey by its predator. In most cases, populations of predators and prey vary in cycles. Beyond predation, because resources are often limited in an environment, multiple species may compete to obtain them. Communities are complex entities defined by the types and number of species and the dynamics of how they change over time. Like populations, communities change in structure and composition, often by environmental disturbances such as fire or hurricanes.

Information presented and the examples highlighted in the section support concepts outlined in Big Idea 2 and Big Idea 4 of the AP® Biology Curriculum Framework. The learning objectives listed in the Curriculum Framework provide a transparent foundation for the AP® Biology course, an inquiry-based laboratory experience, instructional activities, and AP® exam questions. A learning objective merges required content with one or more of the seven science practices.

Big Idea 2	Biological systems utilize free energy and molecular building blocks to grow, to reproduce, and to maintain dynamic homeostasis.
Enduring Understanding 2.D	Growth and dynamic homeostasis of a biological system are influenced by changes in the system’s environment.
Essential Knowledge	**2.D.1** All biological systems from cells and organisms to populations, communities and ecosystems are affected by complex biotic and abiotic interactions involving exchange of matter and free energy.

Science Practice	**1.3** The student can refine representations and models of natural or man-made phenomena and systems in the domain.
Science Practice	**3.2** The student can refine scientific questions.
Learning Objective	**2.22** The student is able to refine scientific models and questions about the effect of complex biotic and abiotic interactions on all biological systems, from cells and organisms to populations, communities, and ecosystems.
Essential Knowledge	**2.D.1** All biological systems from cells and organisms to populations, communities and ecosystems are affected by complex biotic and abiotic interactions involving exchange of matter and free energy.
Science Practice	**4.2** The student can design a plan for collecting data to answer a particular scientific question.
Science Practice	**7.2** The student can connect concepts in and across domain(s) to generalize or extrapolate in and/or across enduring understandings and/or big ideas.
Learning Objective	**2.23** The student is able to design a plan for collecting data to show that all biological systems are affected by complex biotic and abiotic interactions.
Essential Knowledge	**2.D.1** All biological systems from cells and organisms to populations, communities and ecosystems are affected by complex biotic and abiotic interactions involving exchange of matter and free energy.
Science Practice	**5.1** The student can analyze data to identify patterns or relationships.
Learning Objective	**2.24** The student is able to analyze data to identify possible patterns and relationships between a biotic or abiotic factor and a biological system.
Big Idea 4	Biological systems interact, and these systems and their interactions possess complex properties.
Enduring Understanding 4.A	Interactions within biological systems lead to complex properties.
Essential Knowledge	**4.A.5** Communities are composed of populations of organisms that interact in complex ways.
Science Practice	**1.4** The student can use representations and models to analyze situations or solve problems qualitatively and quantitatively.
Science Practice	**4.1** The student can justify the selection of the kind of data needed to answer a particular scientific question.
Learning Objective	**4.11** The student is able to justify the selection of the kind of data needed to answer scientific questions about the interaction of populations within communities.
Essential Knowledge	**4.A.5** Communities are composed of populations of organisms that interact in complex ways.
Science Practice	**2.2** The student can apply mathematical routines to quantities that describe natural phenomena.
Learning Objective	**4.12** The student is able to apply mathematical routines to quantities that describe communities composed of populations of organisms that interact in complex ways.
Essential Knowledge	**4.A.5** Communities are composed of populations of organisms that interact in complex ways.
Science Practice	**6.4** The student can make claims and predictions about natural phenomena based on scientific theories and models.

Learning Objective	**4.13** The student is able to predict the effects of a change in the community's populations on the community.
Essential Knowledge	**4.A.6** Interactions among living systems and with their environment result in the movement of matter and energy.
Science Practice	**6.4** The student can make claims and predictions about natural phenomena based on scientific theories and models.
Learning Objective	**4.15** The student is able to predict the effects of a change of matter or energy availability on communities.

Populations rarely, if ever, live in isolation from populations of other species. In most cases, numerous species share a habitat. The interactions between these populations play a major role in regulating population growth and abundance. All populations occupying the same habitat form a community: populations inhabiting a specific area at the same time. The number of species occupying the same habitat and their relative abundance is known as species diversity. Areas with low diversity, such as the glaciers of Antarctica, still contain a wide variety of living things, whereas the diversity of tropical rainforests is so great that it cannot be counted. Ecology is studied at the community level to understand how species interact with each other and compete for the same resources.

Predation and Herbivory

Perhaps the classical example of species interaction is predation: the hunting of prey by its predator. Nature shows on television highlight the drama of one living organism killing another. Populations of predators and prey in a community are not constant over time: in most cases, they vary in cycles that appear to be related. The most often cited example of predator-prey dynamics is seen in the cycling of the lynx (predator) and the snowshoe hare (prey), using nearly 200 year-old trapping data from North American forests (**Figure 36.19**). This cycle of predator and prey lasts approximately 10 years, with the predator population lagging 1–2 years behind that of the prey population. As the hare numbers increase, there is more food available for the lynx, allowing the lynx population to increase as well. When the lynx population grows to a threshold level, however, they kill so many hares that hare population begins to decline, followed by a decline in the lynx population because of scarcity of food. When the lynx population is low, the hare population size begins to increase due, at least in part, to low predation pressure, starting the cycle anew.

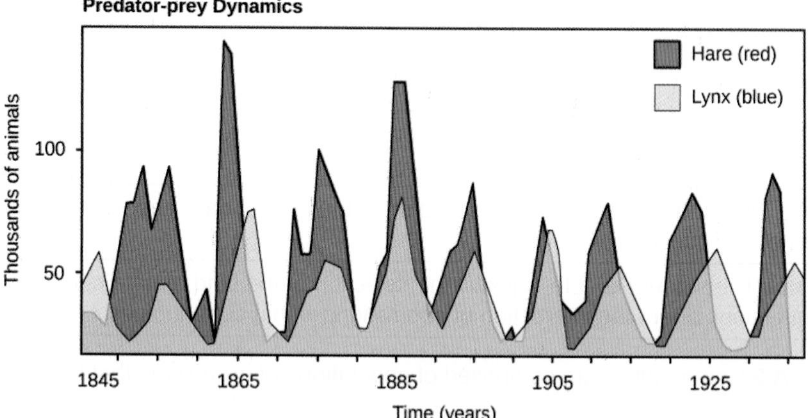

Figure 36.19 The cycling of lynx and snowshoe hare populations in Northern Ontario is an example of predator-prey dynamics.

The idea that the population cycling of the two species is entirely controlled by predation models has come under question. More recent studies have pointed to undefined density-dependent factors as being important in the cycling, in addition to predation. One possibility is that the cycling is inherent in the hare population due to density-dependent effects such as lower fecundity (maternal stress) caused by crowding when the hare population gets too dense. The hare cycling would then induce the cycling of the lynx because it is the lynxes' major food source. The more we study communities, the more complexities we find, allowing ecologists to derive more accurate and sophisticated models of population dynamics.

Herbivory describes the consumption of plants by insects and other animals, and it is another interspecific relationship that affects populations. Unlike animals, most plants cannot outrun predators or use mimicry to hide from hungry animals. Some plants have developed mechanisms to defend against herbivory. Other species have developed mutualistic relationships; for example, herbivory provides a mechanism of seed distribution that aids in plant reproduction.

Defense Mechanisms against Predation and Herbivory

The study of communities must consider evolutionary forces that act on the members of the various populations contained within it. Species are not static, but slowly changing and adapting to their environment by natural selection and other evolutionary forces. Species have evolved numerous mechanisms to escape predation and herbivory. These defenses may be mechanical, chemical, physical, or behavioral.

Mechanical defenses, such as the presence of thorns on plants or the hard shell on turtles, discourage animal predation and herbivory by causing physical pain to the predator or by physically preventing the predator from being able to eat the prey. Chemical defenses are produced by many animals as well as plants, such as the foxglove which is extremely toxic when eaten. Figure 36.20 shows some organisms' defenses against predation and herbivory.

Figure 36.20 The (a) honey locust tree (*Gleditsia triacanthos*) uses thorns, a mechanical defense, against herbivores, while the (b) Florida red-bellied turtle (*Pseudemys nelsoni)* uses its shell as a mechanical defense against predators. (c) Foxglove (*Digitalis* sp.) uses a chemical defense: toxins produced by the plant can cause nausea, vomiting, hallucinations, convulsions, or death when consumed. (d) The North American millipede (*Narceus americanus*) uses both mechanical and chemical defenses: when threatened, the millipede curls into a defensive ball and produces a noxious substance that irritates eyes and skin. (credit a: modification of work by Huw Williams; credit b: modification of work by "JamieS93"/Flickr; credit c: modification of work by Philip Jägenstedt; credit d: modification of work by Cory Zanker)

Many species use their body shape and coloration to avoid being detected by predators. The tropical walking stick is an insect with the coloration and body shape of a twig which makes it very hard to see when stationary against a background of real twigs (Figure 36.21**a**). In another example, the chameleon can change its color to match its surroundings (Figure 36.21**b**). Both of these are examples of **camouflage**, or avoiding detection by blending in with the background.

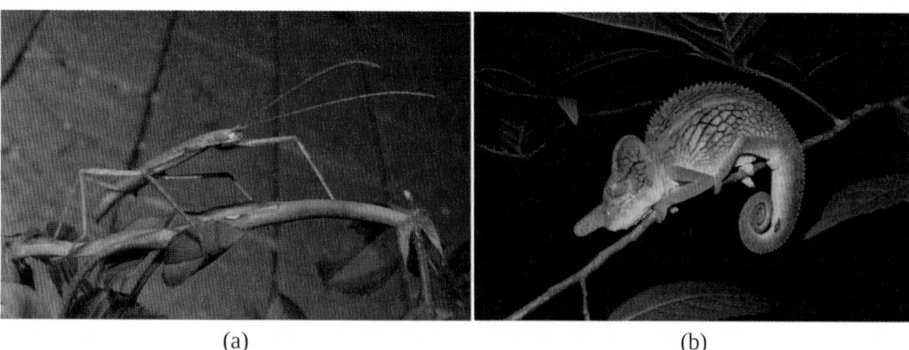

(a) (b)

Figure 36.21 (a) The tropical walking stick and (b) the chameleon use body shape and/or coloration to prevent detection by predators. (credit a: modification of work by Linda Tanner; credit b: modification of work by Frank Vassen)

Some species use coloration as a way of warning predators that they are not good to eat. For example, the cinnabar moth caterpillar, the fire-bellied toad, and many species of beetle have bright colors that warn of a foul taste, the presence of toxic chemical, and/or the ability to sting or bite, respectively. Predators that ignore this coloration and eat the organisms will experience their unpleasant taste or presence of toxic chemicals and learn not to eat them in the future. This type of defensive mechanism is called **aposematic coloration**, or warning coloration (Figure 36.22).

(a) (b)

Figure 36.22 (a) The strawberry poison dart frog (*Oophaga pumilio*) uses aposematic coloration to warn predators that it is toxic, while the (b) striped skunk (*Mephitis mephitis*) uses aposematic coloration to warn predators of the unpleasant odor it produces. (credit a: modification of work by Jay Iwasaki; credit b: modification of work by Dan Dzurisin)

While some predators learn to avoid eating certain potential prey because of their coloration, other species have evolved mechanisms to mimic this coloration to avoid being eaten, even though they themselves may not be unpleasant to eat or contain toxic chemicals. In **Batesian mimicry**, a harmless species imitates the warning coloration of a harmful one. Assuming they share the same predators, this coloration then protects the harmless ones, even though they do not have the same level of physical or chemical defenses against predation as the organism they mimic. Many insect species mimic the coloration of wasps or bees, which are stinging, venomous insects, thereby discouraging predation (Figure 36.23).

(a) (b)

Figure 36.23 Batesian mimicry occurs when a harmless species mimics the coloration of a harmful species, as is seen with the (a) bumblebee and (b) bee-like robber fly. (credit a, b: modification of work by Cory Zanker)

In **Müllerian mimicry**, multiple species share the same warning coloration, but all of them actually have defenses. Figure 36.24 shows a variety of foul-tasting butterflies with similar coloration. In **Emsleyan/Mertensian mimicry**, a deadly prey mimics a less dangerous one, such as the venomous coral snake mimicking the non-venomous milk snake. This type of mimicry is extremely rare and more difficult to understand than the previous two types. For this type of mimicry to work, it is essential that eating the milk snake has unpleasant but not fatal consequences. Then, these predators learn not to eat snakes with this coloration, protecting the coral snake as well. If the snake were fatal to the predator, there would be no opportunity for the predator to learn not to eat it, and the benefit for the less toxic species would disappear.

Figure 36.24 Several unpleasant-tasting *Heliconius* butterfly species share a similar color pattern with better-tasting varieties, an example of Müllerian mimicry. (credit: Joron M, Papa R, Beltrán M, Chamberlain N, Mavárez J, et al.)

Go to this website (http://openstaxcollege.org/l/find_the_mimic) to view stunning examples of mimicry.

Explain the most important reason why mimicry and camouflage are so important in the animal world.

a. Mimicry and camouflage are adaptations that give these animals a advantage in finding prey over others that do not have these adaptations.

b. Mimicry and camouflage are adaptations that give these animals a survival advantage over others that do not have these adaptations.

c. Mimicry and camouflage are aposematic defense mechanisms that give these animals a survival advantage over others that do not have these mechanisms.

d. Mimicry and camouflage are aposematic defense mechanisms that give these animals a reproductive advantage over others that do not have these mechanisms.

Competitive Exclusion Principle

Resources are often limited within a habitat and multiple species may compete to obtain them. All species have an ecological niche in the ecosystem, which describes how they acquire the resources they need and how they interact with other species in the community. The **competitive exclusion principle** states that two species cannot occupy the same niche in a habitat. In other words, different species cannot coexist in a community if they are competing for all the same resources. An example of this principle is shown in Figure 36.25, with two protozoan species, *Paramecium aurelia* and *Paramecium caudatum*. When grown individually in the laboratory, they both thrive. But when they are placed together in the same test tube (habitat), *P. aurelia* outcompetes *P. caudatum* for food, leading to the latter's eventual extinction.

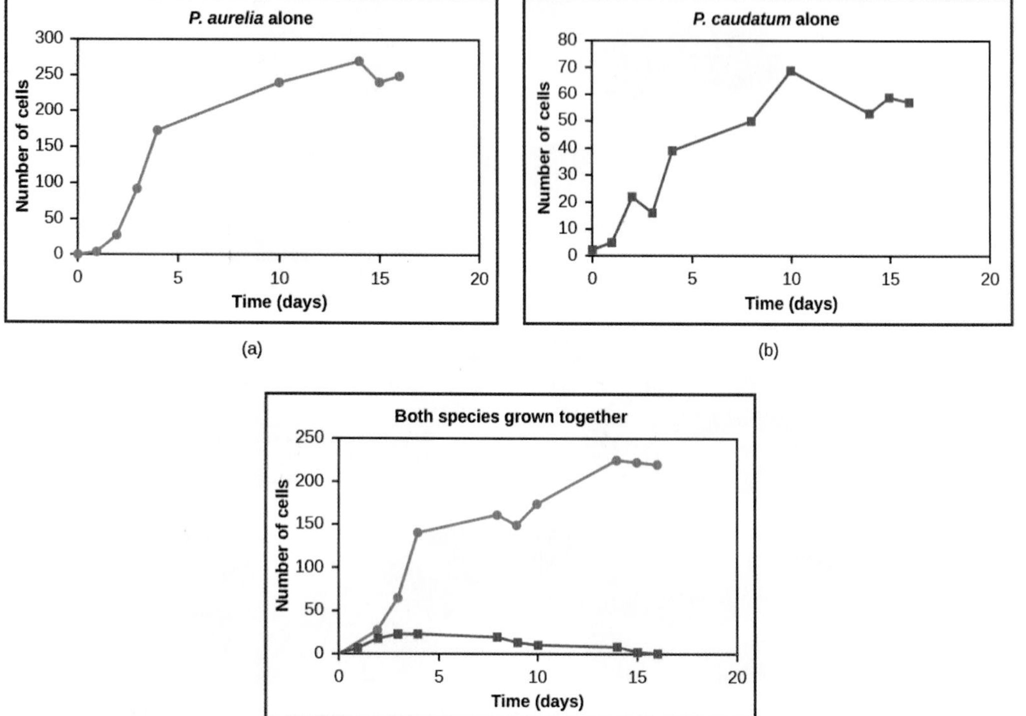

Figure 36.25 *Paramecium aurelia* and *Paramecium caudatum* grow well individually, but when they compete for the same resources, the *P. aurelia* outcompetes the *P. caudatum*.

This exclusion may be avoided if a population evolves to make use of a different resource, a different area of the habitat, or feeds during a different time of day, called resource partitioning. The two organisms are then said to occupy different microniches. These organisms coexist by minimizing direct competition.

Symbiosis

Symbiotic relationships, or **symbioses** (plural), are close interactions between individuals of different species over an extended period of time which impact the abundance and distribution of the associating populations. Most scientists accept this definition, but some restrict the term to only those species that are mutualistic, where both individuals benefit from the interaction. In this discussion, the broader definition will be used.

Commensalism

A **commensal** relationship occurs when one species benefits from the close, prolonged interaction, while the other neither benefits nor is harmed. Birds nesting in trees provide an example of a commensal relationship (Figure 36.26). The tree is not harmed by the presence of the nest among its branches. The nests are light and produce little strain on the structural integrity of the branch, and most of the leaves, which the tree uses to get energy by photosynthesis, are above the nest so they are unaffected. The bird, on the other hand, benefits greatly. If the bird had to nest in the open, its eggs and young would be vulnerable to predators. Another example of a commensal relationship is the clown fish and the sea anemone. The sea anemone is not harmed by the fish, and the fish benefits with protection from predators who would be stung upon nearing the sea anemone.

Figure 36.26 The southern masked-weaver bird is starting to make a nest in a tree in Zambezi Valley, Zambia. This is an example of a commensal relationship, in which one species (the bird) benefits, while the other (the tree) neither benefits nor is harmed. (credit: "Hanay"/Wikimedia Commons)

Mutualism

A second type of symbiotic relationship is called **mutualism**, where two species benefit from their interaction. Some scientists believe that these are the only true examples of symbiosis. For example, termites have a mutualistic relationship with protozoa that live in the insect's gut (Figure 36.27**a**). The termite benefits from the ability of bacterial symbionts within the protozoa to digest cellulose. The termite itself cannot do this, and without the protozoa, it would not be able to obtain energy from its food (cellulose from the wood it chews and eats). The protozoa and the bacterial symbionts benefit by having a protective environment and a constant supply of food from the wood chewing actions of the termite. Lichens have a mutualistic relationship between fungus and photosynthetic algae or bacteria (Figure 36.27**b**). As these symbionts grow together, the glucose produced by the algae provides nourishment for both organisms, whereas the physical structure of the lichen protects the algae from the elements and makes certain nutrients in the atmosphere more available to the algae.

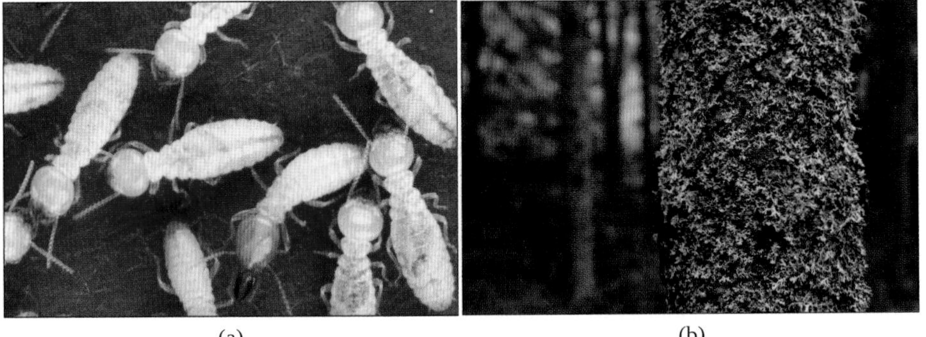

Figure 36.27 (a) Termites form a mutualistic relationship with symbiotic protozoa in their guts, which allow both organisms to obtain energy from the cellulose the termite consumes. (b) Lichen is a fungus that has symbiotic photosynthetic algae living inside its cells. (credit a: modification of work by Scott Bauer, USDA; credit b: modification of work by Cory Zanker)

Parasitism

A **parasite** is an organism that lives in or on another living organism and derives nutrients from it. In this relationship, the parasite benefits, but the organism being fed upon, the **host** is harmed. The host is usually weakened by the parasite as it siphons resources the host would normally use to maintain itself. The parasite, however, is unlikely to kill the host, especially not quickly, because this would allow no time for the organism to complete its reproductive cycle by spreading to another host.

The reproductive cycles of parasites are often very complex, sometimes requiring more than one host species. A tapeworm is a parasite that causes disease in humans when contaminated, undercooked meat such as pork, fish, or beef is consumed (Figure 36.28). The tapeworm can live inside the intestine of the host for several years, benefiting from the food the host is bringing into its gut by eating, and may grow to be over 50 ft long by adding segments. The parasite moves from species to species in a cycle, making two hosts necessary to complete its life cycle. Another common parasite is *Plasmodium falciparum*, the protozoan cause of malaria, a significant disease in many parts of the world. Living in human liver and red blood cells, the organism reproduces asexually in the gut of blood-feeding mosquitoes to complete its life cycle. Thus malaria is spread from human to human by mosquitoes, one of many arthropod-borne infectious diseases.

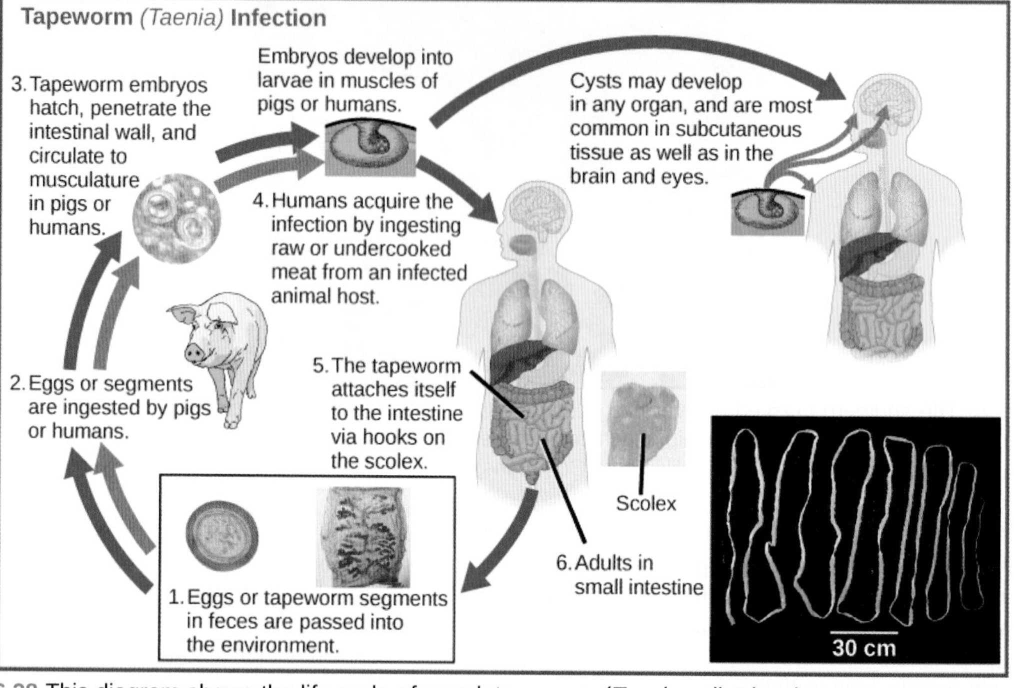

Figure 36.28 This diagram shows the life cycle of a pork tapeworm (*Taenia solium*), a human worm parasite. (credit: modification of work by CDC)

Characteristics of Communities

Communities are complex entities that can be characterized by their structure (the types and numbers of species present) and dynamics (how communities change over time). Understanding community structure and dynamics enables community ecologists to manage ecosystems more effectively.

Foundation Species

Foundation species are considered the "base" or "bedrock" of a community, having the greatest influence on its overall structure. They are usually the primary producers: organisms that bring most of the energy into the community. Kelp, brown algae, is a foundation species, forming the basis of the kelp forests off the coast of California.

Foundation species may physically modify the environment to produce and maintain habitats that benefit the other organisms that use them. An example is the photosynthetic corals of the coral reef (Figure 36.29). Corals themselves are not photosynthetic, but harbor symbionts within their body tissues (dinoflagellates called zooxanthellae) that perform photosynthesis; this is another example of a mutualism. The exoskeletons of living and dead coral make up most of the reef structure, which protects many other species from waves and ocean currents.

Figure 36.29 Coral is the foundation species of coral reef ecosystems. (credit: Jim E. Maragos, USFWS)

Biodiversity, Species Richness, and Relative Species Abundance

Biodiversity describes a community's biological complexity: it is measured by the number of different species (species richness) in a particular area and their relative abundance (species evenness). The area in question could be a habitat, a biome, or the entire biosphere. **Species richness** is the term that is used to describe the number of species living in a habitat or biome. Species richness varies across the globe (Figure 36.30). One factor in determining species richness is latitude, with the greatest species richness occurring in ecosystems near the equator, which often have warmer temperatures, large amounts of rainfall, and low seasonality. The lowest species richness occurs near the poles, which are much colder, drier, and thus less conducive to life in Geologic time (time since glaciations). The predictability of climate or productivity is also an important factor. Other factors influence species richness as well. For example, the study of **island biogeography** attempts to explain the relatively high species richness found in certain isolated island chains, including the Galápagos Islands that inspired the young Darwin. **Relative species abundance** is the number of individuals in a species relative to the total number of individuals in all species within a habitat, ecosystem, or biome. Foundation species often have the highest relative abundance of species.

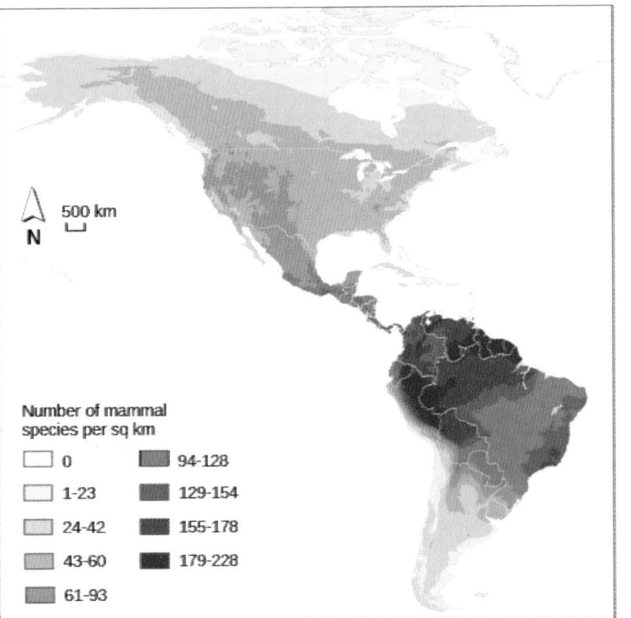

Figure 36.30 The greatest species richness for mammals in North and South America is associated with the equatorial latitudes. (credit: modification of work by NASA, CIESIN, Columbia University)

Keystone Species

A **keystone species** is one whose presence is key to maintaining biodiversity within an ecosystem and to upholding an ecological community's structure. The intertidal sea star, *Pisaster ochraceus*, of the northwestern United States is a keystone species (Figure 36.31). Studies have shown that when this organism is removed from communities, populations of their natural prey (mussels) increase, completely altering the species composition and reducing biodiversity. Another keystone species is the banded tetra, a fish in tropical streams, which supplies nearly all of the phosphorus, a necessary inorganic nutrient, to the rest of the community. If these fish were to become extinct, the community would be greatly affected.

Figure 36.31 The *Pisaster ochraceus* sea star is a keystone species. (credit: Jerry Kirkhart)

everyday CONNECTION

Invasive Species

Invasive species are non-native organisms that, when introduced to an area out of their native range, threaten the ecosystem balance of that habitat. Many such species exist in the United States, as shown in Figure 36.32. Whether enjoying a forest hike, taking a summer boat trip, or simply walking down an urban street, you have likely encountered an invasive species.

Figure 36.32 In the United States, invasive species like (a) purple loosestrife (*Lythrum salicaria*) and the (b) zebra mussel (*Dreissena polymorpha*) threaten certain aquatic ecosystems. Some forests are threatened by the spread of (c) common buckthorn (*Rhamnus cathartica*), (d) garlic mustard (*Alliaria petiolata*), and (e) the emerald ash borer (*Agrilus planipennis*). The (f) European starling (*Sturnus vulgaris*) may compete with native bird species for nest holes. (credit a: modification of work by Liz West; credit b: modification of work by M. McCormick, NOAA; credit c: modification of work by E. Dronkert; credit d: modification of work by Dan Davison; credit e: modification of work by USDA; credit f: modification of work by Don DeBold)

One of the many recent proliferations of an invasive species concerns the growth of Asian carp populations. Asian carp were introduced to the United States in the 1970s by fisheries and sewage treatment facilities that used the fish's excellent filter feeding capabilities to clean their ponds of excess plankton. Some of the fish escaped, however, and by the 1980s they had colonized many waterways of the Mississippi River basin, including the Illinois and Missouri Rivers.

Voracious eaters and rapid reproducers, Asian carp may outcompete native species for food, potentially leading to their extinction. For example, black carp are voracious eaters of native mussels and snails, limiting this food source for native fish species. Silver carp eat plankton that native mussels and snails feed on, reducing this food source by a different alteration of the food web. In some areas of the Mississippi River, Asian carp species have become the most predominant, effectively outcompeting native fishes for habitat. In some parts of the Illinois River, Asian carp constitute 95 percent of the community's biomass. Although edible, the fish is bony and not a desired food in the United States. Moreover, their presence threatens the native fish and fisheries of the Great Lakes, which are important to local economies and recreational anglers. Asian carp have even injured humans. The fish, frightened by the sound of approaching motorboats, thrust themselves into the air, often landing in the boat or directly hitting the boaters.

The Great Lakes and their prized salmon and lake trout fisheries are also being threatened by these invasive fish. Asian carp have already colonized rivers and canals that lead into Lake Michigan. One infested waterway of particular importance is the Chicago Sanitary and Ship Channel, the major supply waterway linking the Great Lakes to the Mississippi River. To prevent the Asian carp from leaving the canal, a series of electric barriers have been successfully used to discourage their migration; however, the threat is significant enough that several states and Canada have sued to have the Chicago channel permanently cut off from Lake Michigan. Local and national politicians have weighed in on how to solve the problem, but no one knows whether the Asian carp will ultimately be considered a nuisance, like other invasive species such as the water hyacinth and zebra mussel, or whether it will be the destroyer of the largest freshwater fishery of the world.

The issues associated with Asian carp show how population and community ecology, fisheries management, and politics intersect on issues of vital importance to the human food supply and economy. Socio-political issues like this make extensive use of the sciences of population ecology (the study of members of a particular species occupying a particular area known as a habitat) and community ecology (the study of the interaction of all species within a habitat).

Why are invasive species such as the Asian carp such a problem in North America?

a. They release some chemicals into the water which are toxic to the flora and fauna of the freshwater habitats in North America.
b. They kill the natural fish population native to freshwater habitats in North America by obtaining food from them. The invasive species will then reproduce rapidly.
c. They provide food and other resources to the native fish population, resulting in an over increase in their population. This decreases the amount of dissolved oxygen in the freshwater habitats of North America.
d. They are not native to freshwater habitats in North America and have no natural predators to keep their population in check. As a result, they will reproduce rapidly competing with native fish for space, food, and other resources.

Community Dynamics

Community dynamics are the changes in community structure and composition over time. Sometimes these changes are induced by **environmental disturbances** such as volcanoes, earthquakes, storms, fires, and climate change. Communities with a stable structure are said to be at equilibrium. Following a disturbance, the community may or may not return to the equilibrium state.

Succession describes the sequential appearance and disappearance of species in a community over time. In **primary succession**, newly exposed or newly formed land is colonized by living things; in **secondary succession**, part of an ecosystem is disturbed and remnants of the previous community remain.

Primary Succession and Pioneer Species

Primary succession occurs when new land is formed or rock is exposed: for example, following the eruption of volcanoes, such as those on the Big Island of Hawaii. As lava flows into the ocean, new land is continually being formed. On the Big Island, approximately 32 acres of land is added each year. First, weathering and other natural forces break down the substrate enough for the establishment of certain hearty plants and lichens with few soil requirements, known as **pioneer species** (Figure 36.33). These species help to further break down the mineral rich lava into soil where other, less hardy species will grow and eventually replace the pioneer species. In addition, as these early species grow and die, they add to an ever-growing layer of decomposing organic material and contribute to soil formation. Over time the area will reach an equilibrium state, with a set of organisms quite different from the pioneer species.

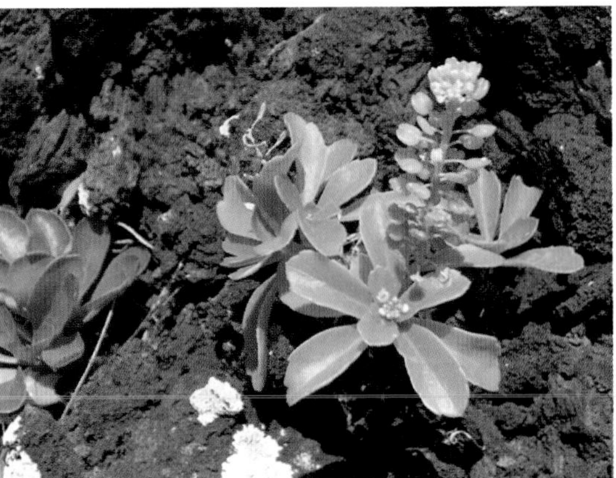

Figure 36.33 During primary succession in lava on Maui, Hawaii, succulent plants are the pioneer species. (credit: Forest and Kim Starr)

Secondary Succession

A classic example of secondary succession occurs in oak and hickory forests cleared by wildfire (Figure 36.34). Wildfires will burn most vegetation and kill those animals unable to flee the area. Their nutrients, however, are returned to the ground in the form of ash. Thus, even when areas are devoid of life due to severe fires, the area will soon be ready for new life to take hold.

Before the fire, the vegetation was dominated by tall trees with access to the major plant energy resource: sunlight. Their height gave them access to sunlight while also shading the ground and other low-lying species. After the fire, though, these trees are no longer dominant. Thus, the first plants to grow back are usually annual plants followed within a few years by quickly growing and spreading grasses and other pioneer species. Due to, at least in part, changes in the environment brought on by the growth of the grasses and other species, over many years, shrubs will emerge along with small pine, oak, and hickory trees. These organisms are called intermediate species. Eventually, over 150 years, the forest will reach its equilibrium point where species composition is no longer changing and resembles the community before the fire. This equilibrium state is referred to as the **climax community**, which will remain stable until the next disturbance.

Secondary Succession of an Oak and Hickory Forest
Pioneer species
Annual plants grow and are succeeded by grasses and perennials.
Intermediate species
Shrubs, then pines, and young oak and hickory begin to grow.
Climax community
The mature oak and hickory forest remains stable until the next disturbance.

Figure 36.34 Secondary succession is shown in an oak and hickory forest after a forest fire.

science practices CONNECTION for AP® Courses

Activity

Don't Trash the Campus. Design and implement a plan to investigate the impact of school litter on a surrounding community. Based on collected data, create a proposal of short- and long-term solutions to the trash problem on campus and submit the proposal to the student council for consideration. Describes ways in which communities/ecosystems can recover from modern levels of local environmental disturbances.

Section Summary

Communities include all the different species living in a given area. The variety of these species is called species richness. Many organisms have developed defenses against predation and herbivory, including mechanical defenses, warning coloration, and mimicry, as a result of evolution and the interaction with other members of the community. Two species cannot exist in the same habitat competing directly for the same resources. Species may form symbiotic relationships such as commensalism or mutualism. Community structure is described by its foundation and keystone species. Communities respond to environmental disturbances by succession (the predictable appearance of different types of plant species) until a stable community structure is established.

36.7 | Behavioral Biology: Proximate and Ultimate Causes of Behavior

In this section, you will explore the following questions:

- What is the difference between innate and learned behavior?
- How are movement and migration behaviors a result of natural selection?
- What are different ways members of a population communicate with each other?
- What are examples of how species use energy for mating displays and other courtship behaviors?
- What are examples of various mating systems?
- What are different ways that species learn?

Connection for AP® Courses

Behavior is the change in activity of an organism in response to a stimulus. **Innate behaviors** have a strong genetic component and are largely independent of environmental influences. In other words, these instinctive behaviors are "hard wired." Examples of innate behaviors include a human baby grabbing her mother's finger and the stork using its long beak to forage. **Learned behaviors** result from environmental conditioning and are modified by learning. For example, you likely have learned by now that reading these AP® Connections help you digest the information and that studying for a test improves your grade.

Information presented and the examples highlighted in the section support concepts outlined in Big Idea 2 and Big Idea 3 of the AP® Biology Curriculum Framework. The AP® Learning Objective listed in the Curriculum Framework provide a transparent foundation for the AP® Biology course, an inquiry-based laboratory experience, instructional activities, and AP® exam questions. A learning objective merges required content with one or more of the seven science practices.

Big Idea 2	Biological systems utilize free energy and molecular building blocks to grow, to reproduce, and to maintain dynamic homeostasis.
Enduring Understanding 2.C	Organisms use feedback mechanisms to regulate growth and reproduction, and to maintain dynamic homeostasis.
Essential Knowledge	**2.C.2** Organisms respond to changes in their external environments.
Science Practice	**6.4** The student can make claims and predictions about natural phenomena based on scientific theories and models.
Learning Objective	**4.13** The student is able to predict the effects of a change in the community's populations on the community.

Enduring Understanding 2.E	Many biological processes involved in growth, reproduction and dynamic homeostasis include temporal regulation and coordination.
Essential Knowledge	**2.E.3** Timing and coordination of behavior are regulated by various mechanisms and are important in natural selection.
Science Practice	**4.1** The student can justify the selection of the kind of data needed to answer a particular scientific question.
Learning Objective	**2.21** The student is able to justify the selection of the kind of data needed to answer scientific questions about the relevant mechanism that organisms use to respond to changes in their external environment.
Essential Knowledge	**2.E.3** Timing and coordination of behavior are regulated by various mechanisms and are important in natural selection.
Science Practice	**5.1** The student can analyze data to identify patterns or relationships.
Learning Objective	**2.38** The student is able to analyze data to support the claim that responses to information and communication of information affect natural selection.
Essential Knowledge	**2.E.3** Timing and coordination of behavior are regulated by various mechanisms and are important in natural selection.
Science Practice	**6.1** The student can justify claims with evidence.
Learning Objective	**2.39** The student is able to justify scientific claims, using evidence, to describe how timing and coordination of behavioral events in organisms are regulated by several mechanisms.
Essential Knowledge	**2.E.3** Timing and coordination of behavior are regulated by various mechanisms and are important in natural selection.
Science Practice	**7.2** The student can connect concepts in and across domain(s) to generalize or extrapolate in and/or across enduring understandings and/or big ideas.
Learning Objective	**2.40** The student is able to connect concepts in and across domain(s) to predict how environmental factors affect response to information and change behavior.
Big Idea 3	Living systems store, retrieve, transmit and respond to information essential to life processes.
Enduring Understanding 3.E	Transmission of information results in changes within and between biological systems.
Essential Knowledge	**3.E.1** Individuals can act on information and communicate it to others.
Science Practice	**5.1** The student can analyze data to identify patterns or relationships.
Learning Objective	**3.40** The student is able to analyze data that indicate how organisms exchange information in response to internal changes and external cues, and which can change behavior.
Essential Knowledge	**3.E.1** Individuals can act on information and communicate it to others.
Science Practice	**1.1** The student can create representations and models of natural or man-made phenomena and systems in the domain.
Learning Objective	**3.41** The student is able to create a representation that describes how organisms exchange information in response to internal changes and external cues, and which can result in changes in behavior.

Essential Knowledge	**3.E.1** Individuals can act on information and communicate it to others.
Science Practice	**7.1** The student can connect phenomena and models across spatial and temporal scales.
Learning Objective	**3.42** The student is able to describe how organisms exchange information in response to internal changes or environmental cues.

Behavioral biology is the study of the biological and evolutionary bases for such changes. The idea that behaviors evolved as a result of the pressures of natural selection is not new. Animal behavior has been studied for decades, by biologists in the science of **ethology**, by psychologists in the science of comparative psychology, and by scientists of many disciplines in the study of neurobiology. Although there is overlap between these disciplines, scientists in these behavioral fields take different approaches. Comparative psychology is an extension of work done in human and behavioral psychology. Ethology is an extension of genetics, evolution, anatomy, physiology, and other biological disciplines. Still, one cannot study behavioral biology without touching on both comparative psychology and ethology.

One goal of behavioral biology is to dissect out the innate behaviors, which have a strong genetic component and are largely independent of environmental influences, from the learned behaviors, which result from environmental conditioning. Innate behavior, or instinct, is important because there is no risk of an incorrect behavior being learned. They are “hard wired” into the system. On the other hand, learned behaviors, although riskier, are flexible, dynamic, and can be altered according to changes in the environment.

Innate Behaviors: Movement and Migration

Innate or instinctual behaviors rely on response to stimuli. The simplest example of this is a **reflex action**, an involuntary and rapid response to stimulus. To test the “knee-jerk” reflex, a doctor taps the patellar tendon below the kneecap with a rubber hammer. The stimulation of the nerves there leads to the reflex of extending the leg at the knee. This is similar to the reaction of someone who touches a hot stove and instinctually pulls his or her hand away. Even humans, with our great capacity to learn, still exhibit a variety of innate behaviors.

Kinesis and Taxis

Another activity or movement of innate behavior is **kinesis**, or the undirected movement in response to a stimulus. Orthokinesis is the increased or decreased speed of movement of an organism in response to a stimulus. Woodlice, for example, increase their speed of movement when exposed to high or low temperatures. This movement, although random, increases the probability that the insect spends less time in the unfavorable environment. Another example is klinokinesis, an increase in turning behaviors. It is exhibited by bacteria such as *E. coli* which, in association with orthokinesis, helps the organisms randomly find a more hospitable environment.

A similar, but more directed version of kinesis is **taxis**: the directed movement towards or away from a stimulus. This movement can be in response to light (phototaxis), chemical signals (chemotaxis), or gravity (geotaxis) and can be directed toward (positive) or away (negative) from the source of the stimulus. An example of a positive chemotaxis is exhibited by the unicellular protozoan *Tetrahymena thermophila*. This organism swims using its cilia, at times moving in a straight line, and at other times making turns. The attracting chemotactic agent alters the frequency of turning as the organism moves directly toward the source, following the increasing concentration gradient.

Fixed Action Patterns

A **fixed action pattern** is a series of movements elicited by a stimulus such that even when the stimulus is removed, the pattern goes on to completion. An example of such a behavior occurs in the three-spined stickleback, a small freshwater fish (**Figure 36.35**). Males of this species develop a red belly during breeding season and show instinctual aggressiveness to other males during this time. In laboratory experiments, researchers exposed such fish to objects that in no way resemble a fish in their shape, but which were painted red on their lower halves. The male sticklebacks responded aggressively to the objects just as if they were real male sticklebacks.

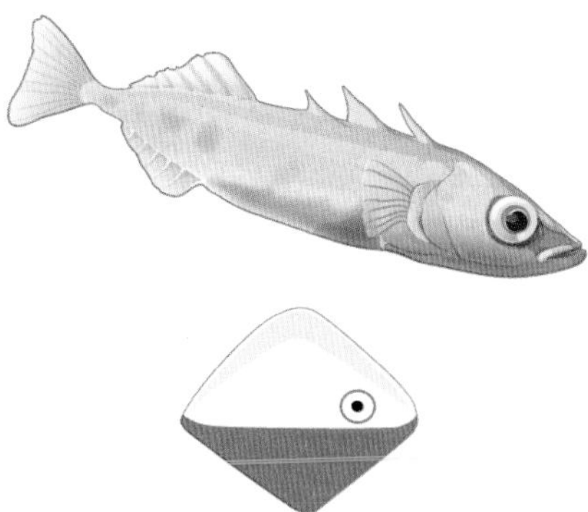

Figure 36.35 Male three-spined stickleback fish exhibit a fixed action pattern. During mating season, the males, which develop a bright red belly, react strongly to red-bottomed objects that in no way resemble fish.

Migration

Migration is the long-range seasonal movement of animals. It is an evolved, adapted response to variation in resource availability, and it is a common phenomenon found in all major groups of animals. Birds fly south for the winter to get to warmer climates with sufficient food, and salmon migrate to their spawning grounds. The popular 2005 documentary *March of the Penguins* followed the 62-mile migration of emperor penguins through Antarctica to bring food back to their breeding site and to their young. Wildebeests (Figure 36.36) migrate over 1800 miles each year in search of new grasslands.

Figure 36.36 Wildebeests migrate in a clockwise fashion over 1800 miles each year in search of rain-ripened grass. (credit: Eric Inafuku)

Although migration is thought of as innate behavior, only some migrating species always migrate (obligate migration). Animals that exhibit facultative migration can choose to migrate or not. Additionally, in some animals, only a portion of the population migrates, whereas the rest does not migrate (incomplete migration). For example, owls that live in the tundra may migrate in years when their food source, small rodents, is relatively scarce, but not migrate during the years when rodents are plentiful.

Foraging

Foraging is the act of searching for and exploiting food resources. Feeding behaviors that maximize energy gain and minimize energy expenditure are called optimal foraging behaviors, and these are favored by natural section. The painted stork, for example, uses its long beak to search the bottom of a freshwater marshland for crabs and other food (Figure 36.37).

Figure 36.37 The painted stork uses its long beak to forage. (credit: J.M. Garg)

Innate Behaviors: Living in Groups

Not all animals live in groups, but even those that live relatively solitary lives, with the exception of those that can reproduce asexually, must mate. Mating usually involves one animal signaling another so as to communicate the desire to mate. There are several types of energy-intensive behaviors or displays associated with mating, called mating rituals. Other behaviors found in populations that live in groups are described in terms of which animal benefits from the behavior. In selfish behavior, only the animal in question benefits; in altruistic behavior, one animal's actions benefit another animal; cooperative behavior describes when both animals benefit. All of these behaviors involve some sort of communication between population members.

Communication within a Species

Animals communicate with each other using stimuli known as **signals**. An example of this is seen in the three-spined stickleback, where the visual signal of a red region in the lower half of a fish signals males to become aggressive and signals females to mate. Other signals are chemical (pheromones), aural (sound), visual (courtship and aggressive displays), or tactile (touch). These types of communication may be instinctual or learned or a combination of both. These are not the same as the communication we associate with language, which has been observed only in humans and perhaps in some species of primates and cetaceans.

A pheromone is a secreted chemical signal used to obtain a response from another individual of the same species. The purpose of pheromones is to elicit a specific behavior from the receiving individual. Pheromones are especially common among social insects, but they are used by many species to attract the opposite sex, to sound alarms, to mark food trails, and to elicit other, more complex behaviors. Even humans are thought to respond to certain pheromones called axillary steroids. These chemicals influence human perception of other people, and in one study were responsible for a group of women synchronizing their menstrual cycles. The role of pheromones in human-to-human communication is still somewhat controversial and continues to be researched.

Songs are an example of an aural signal, one that needs to be heard by the recipient. Perhaps the best known of these are songs of birds, which identify the species and are used to attract mates. Other well-known songs are those of whales, which are of such low frequency that they can travel long distances underwater. Dolphins communicate with each other using a wide variety of vocalizations. Male crickets make chirping sounds using a specialized organ to attract a mate, repel other males, and to announce a successful mating.

Courtship displays are a series of ritualized visual behaviors (signals) designed to attract and convince a member of the opposite sex to mate. These displays are ubiquitous in the animal kingdom. Often these displays involve a series of steps, including an initial display by one member followed by a response from the other. If at any point, the display is performed incorrectly or a proper response is not given, the mating ritual is abandoned and the mating attempt will be unsuccessful. The mating display of the common stork is shown in Figure 36.38.

Aggressive displays are also common in the animal kingdom. An example is when a dog bares its teeth when it wants another dog to back down. Presumably, these displays communicate not only the willingness of the animal to fight, but also its fighting ability. Although these displays do signal aggression on the part of the sender, it is thought that these displays are actually a mechanism to reduce the amount of actual fighting that occurs between members of the same species: they allow individuals to assess the fighting ability of their opponent and thus decide whether it is "worth the fight." The testing of certain hypotheses using game theory has led to the conclusion that some of these displays may overstate an animal's actual fighting ability and are used to "bluff" the opponent. This type of interaction, even if "dishonest," would be favored by natural selection if it is successful more times than not.

Figure 36.38 This stork's courtship display is designed to attract potential mates. (credit: Linda "jinterwas"/Flickr)

Distraction displays are seen in birds and some fish. They are designed to attract a predator away from the nest that contains their young. This is an example of an altruistic behavior: it benefits the young more than the individual performing the display, which is putting itself at risk by doing so.

Many animals, especially primates, communicate with other members in the group through touch. Activities such as grooming, touching the shoulder or root of the tail, embracing, lip contact, and greeting ceremonies have all been observed in the Indian langur, an Old World monkey. Similar behaviors are found in other primates, especially in the great apes.

The killdeer bird distracts predators from its eggs by faking a broken wing display in this **video (http://openstaxcollege.org/l/killdeer_bird)** taken in Boise, Idaho.

Explain why the behavior shown in the video represents both a distraction display and an altruistic type of behavior.

a. The parent creates a distraction to attract the predator away from young fledgling by pretending to have a broken wing. It is an altruistic behavior as the parent runs the risk of getting killed or harmed by predator.

b. The parent creates a distraction by being more aggressive and showing its willingness to fight. Altruistic behavior is seen as the parent runs the risk of getting attacked, killed, or harmed by the predator.

c. Parent creates distraction to attract the predator away from young fledgling by pretending to have a broken wing. It is exhibiting an altruistic behavior as in saving its fledgling; it is increasing its own fitness along with the fitness of the young bird.

d. Parent creates distraction by being more aggressive and showing its willingness to fight. It is exhibiting an altruistic behavior by saving its fledgling; it is decreasing its own fitness along with the fitness of the young bird.

Altruistic Behaviors

Behaviors that lower the fitness of the individual but increase the fitness of another individual are termed altruistic. Examples of such behaviors are seen widely across the animal kingdom. Social insects such as worker bees have no ability to reproduce, yet they maintain the queen so she can populate the hive with her offspring. Meerkats keep a sentry standing guard to warn the rest of the colony about intruders, even though the sentry is putting itself at risk. Wolves and wild dogs bring meat to pack members not present during a hunt. Lemurs take care of infants unrelated to them. Although on the surface, these behaviors appear to be altruistic, it may not be so simple.

There has been much discussion over why altruistic behaviors exist. Do these behaviors lead to overall evolutionary advantages for their species? Do they help the altruistic individual pass on its own genes? And what about such activities between unrelated individuals? One explanation for altruistic-type behaviors is found in the genetics of natural selection. In the 1976 book, *The Selfish Gene*, scientist Richard Dawkins attempted to explain many seemingly altruistic behaviors from the viewpoint of the gene itself. Although a gene obviously cannot be selfish in the human sense, it may appear that way if the sacrifice of an individual benefits related individuals that share genes that are identical by descent (present in relatives because of common lineage). Mammal parents make this sacrifice to take care of their offspring. Emperor penguins migrate miles in harsh conditions to bring food back for their young. Selfish gene theory has been controversial over the years and is still discussed among scientists in related fields.

Even less-related individuals, those with less genetic identity than that shared by parent and offspring, benefit from seemingly altruistic behavior. The activities of social insects such as bees, wasps, ants, and termites are good examples. Sterile workers in these societies take care of the queen because they are closely related to it, and as the queen has offspring, she is passing on genes from the workers indirectly. Thus, it is of fitness benefit for the worker to maintain the queen without having any direct chance of passing on its genes due to its sterility. The lowering of individual fitness to enhance the reproductive fitness of a relative and thus one's inclusive fitness evolves through **kin selection**. This phenomenon can explain many superficially altruistic behaviors seen in animals. However, these behaviors may not be truly defined as altruism in these cases because the actor is actually increasing its own fitness either directly (through its own offspring) or indirectly (through the inclusive fitness it gains through relatives that share genes with it).

Unrelated individuals may also act altruistically to each other, and this seems to defy the "selfish gene" explanation. An example of this observed in many monkey species where a monkey will present its back to an unrelated monkey to have that individual pick the parasites from its fur. After a certain amount of time, the roles are reversed and the first monkey now grooms the second monkey. Thus, there is reciprocity in the behavior. Both benefit from the interaction and their fitness is raised more than if neither cooperated nor if one cooperated and the other did not cooperate. This behavior is still not necessarily altruism, as the "giving" behavior of the actor is based on the expectation that it will be the "receiver" of the behavior in the future, termed reciprocal altruism. Reciprocal altruism requires that individuals repeatedly encounter each other, often the result of living in the same social group, and that cheaters (those that never "give back") are punished.

Evolutionary game theory, a modification of classical game theory in mathematics, has shown that many of these so-called "altruistic behaviors" are not altruistic at all. The definition of "pure" altruism, based on human behavior, is an action that benefits another without any direct benefit to oneself. Most of the behaviors previously described do not seem to satisfy this definition, and game theorists are good at finding "selfish" components in them. Others have argued that the terms "selfish" and "altruistic" should be dropped completely when discussing animal behavior, as they describe human behavior and may not be directly applicable to instinctual animal activity. What is clear, though, is that heritable behaviors that improve the chances of passing on one's genes or a portion of one's genes are favored by natural selection and will be retained in future generations as long as those behaviors convey a fitness advantage. These instinctual behaviors may then be applied, in special circumstances, to other species, as long as it doesn't lower the animal's fitness.

Finding Sex Partners

Not all animals reproduce sexually, but many that do have the same challenge: they need to find a suitable mate and often have to compete with other individuals to obtain one. Significant energy is spent in the process of locating, attracting, and mating with the sex partner. Two types of selection occur during this process and can lead to traits that are important to reproduction called secondary sexual characteristics: **intersexual selection**, the choosing of a mate where individuals of one sex choose mates of the other sex, and **intrasexual selection**, the competition for mates between species members of the same sex. Intersexual selection is often complex because choosing a mate may be based on a variety of visual, aural, tactile, and chemical cues. An example of intersexual selection is when female peacocks choose to mate with the male with the brightest plumage. This type of selection often leads to traits in the chosen sex that do not enhance survival, but are those traits most attractive to the opposite sex (often at the expense of survival). Intrasexual selection involves mating displays and aggressive mating rituals such as rams butting heads—the winner of these battles is the one that is able to mate. Many of these rituals use up considerable energy but result in the selection of the healthiest, strongest, and/or most dominant individuals for mating. Three general mating systems, all involving innate as opposed to learned behaviors, are seen in animal populations: monogamous, polygynous, and polyandrous.

Visit this website (http://openstaxcollege.org/l/sex_selection) for informative videos on sexual selection.

The greater sage grouse uses a mating system in which one male mates with many females. Name this mating system.

a. polyandrous

b. monogamous

c. intrasexual selection

d. polygynous

science practices CONNECTION for AP® Courses

Activity

In 1980, John Endler published his investigation into natural selection in Trinidad guppies (*Poecilia reticulata*). Some of these guppies have brighter coloration than others. Endler hypothesized that guppies with less predation have brighter colors due to sexual selection because females prefer more brightly-colored males. He then on to hypothesized that male guppies that experience greater predation become more drab-colored to camouflage themselves from predators.. In addition to a laboratory study, he tested this using a field experiment involving four areas. Area 1 had no guppies while area 2 had guppies but no predators. Area 3 had guppies and a predator (*Crenicichla alta*). Endler introduced guppies from area 3 (which were drab because of predation) to area 1 (which had no guppies). The guppies that were relocated to area 1 developed brighter colors over 2 years (enough for several guppy generations) and eventually resembled the guppies in area 2. Make a diagram showing each of the locations, all of the fish species present at the start, and the fish present at the end. Label the fish as "more conspicuous colors" or "less conspicuous colors."

Think About It

Describe how this experiment shows that there is genetic variability in the original population. How do you know that there was genetic variability in the fish taken from area 1? Explain the tradeoff between bright colors that are attractive to female guppies and the risk of predation. What would you expect to happen if you moved fish from area 2 back to area 3? What would you expect to happen in each area if female fish began to prefer larger fish rather than more brightly colored fish?

In **monogamous** systems, one male and one female are paired for at least one breeding season. In some animals, such as the gray wolf, these associations can last much longer, even a lifetime. Several explanations have been proposed for this type of mating system. The "mate-guarding hypothesis" states that males stay with the female to prevent other males from mating with her. This behavior is advantageous in such situations where mates are scarce and difficult to find. Another explanation is the "male-assistance hypothesis," where males that remain with a female to help guard and rear their young will have more and healthier offspring. Monogamy is observed in many bird populations where, in addition to the parental care from the female, the male is also a major provider of parental care for the chicks. A third explanation for the evolutionary advantages of monogamy is the "female-enforcement hypothesis." In this scenario, the female ensures that the male does not have other offspring that might compete with her own, so she actively interferes with the male's signaling to attract other mates.

Polygynous mating refers to one male mating with multiple females. In these situations, the female must be responsible for most of the parental care as the single male is not capable of providing care to that many offspring. In resourced-based polygyny, males compete for territories with the best resources, and then mate with females that enter the territory, drawn to its resource richness. The female benefits by mating with a dominant, genetically fit male; however, it is at the cost of having no male help in caring for the offspring. An example is seen in the yellow-rumped honeyguide, a bird whose males defend beehives because the females feed on their wax. As the females approach, the male defending the nest will mate with them. Harem mating structures are a type of polygynous system where certain males dominate mating while controlling a territory with resources. Elephant seals, where the alpha male dominates the mating within the group are an example. A third type of polygyny is a lek system. Here there is a communal courting area where several males perform elaborate displays for females, and the females choose their mate from this group. This behavior is observed in several bird species including the sage grouse and the prairie chicken.

In **polyandrous** mating systems, one female mates with many males. These types of systems are much rarer than monogamous and polygynous mating systems. In pipefishes and seahorses, males receive the eggs from the female, fertilize them, protect them within a pouch, and give birth to the offspring (Figure 36.39). Therefore, the female is able to provide eggs to several males without the burden of carrying the fertilized eggs.

(a) (b)

Figure 36.39 Polyandrous mating, in which one female mates with many males, occurs in the (a) seahorse and the (b) pipefish. (credit a: modification of work by Brian Gratwicke; credit b: modification of work by Stephen Childs)

Simple Learned Behaviors

The majority of the behaviors previously discussed were innate or at least have an innate component (variations on the innate behaviors may be learned). They are inherited and the behaviors do not change in response to signals from the environment. Conversely, learned behaviors, even though they may have instinctive components, allow an organism to adapt to changes in the environment and are modified by previous experiences. Simple learned behaviors include habituation and imprinting—both are important to the maturation process of young animals.

Habituation

Habituation is a simple form of learning in which an animal stops responding to a stimulus after a period of repeated exposure. This is a form of non-associative learning, as the stimulus is not associated with any punishment or reward. Prairie dogs typically sound an alarm call when threatened by a predator, but they become habituated to the sound of human footsteps when no harm is associated with this sound, therefore, they no longer respond to them with an alarm call. In this example, habituation is specific to the sound of human footsteps, as the animals still respond to the sounds of potential predators.

Imprinting

Imprinting is a type of learning that occurs at a particular age or a life stage that is rapid and independent of the species involved. Hatchling ducks recognize the first adult they see, their mother, and make a bond with her. A familiar sight is ducklings walking or swimming after their mothers (Figure 36.40). This is another type of non-associative learning, but is very important in the maturation process of these animals as it encourages them to stay near their mother so they will be protected, greatly increasing their chances of survival. However, if newborn ducks see a human before they see their mother, they will imprint on the human and follow it in just the same manner as they would follow their real mother.

Figure 36.40 The attachment of ducklings to their mother is an example of imprinting. (credit: modification of work by Mark Harkin)

The International Crane Foundation has helped raise the world's population of whooping cranes from 21 individuals to about 600. Imprinting hatchlings has been a key to success: biologists wear full crane costumes so the birds never "see" humans. Watch this video (http://openstaxcollege.org/l/whooping_crane) to learn more.

Workers wear a special costume when interacting with whooping crane chicks. Justify the need for this process.

a. Whooping crane chicks undergo habituation in which the chicks make a bond with the objects they see in the environment. Therefore, workers must wear a special costume to fool the chick into thinking it is associating with an adult whooping crane.

b. Whooping crane chicks undergo imprinting with the first object they see. Therefore, workers must wear a special costume to fool the chick into thinking it is associating with an adult whooping crane to avoid creating the expectation it will mate with a human.

c. Whooping crane chicks undergo imprinting with the first few objects they see. Therefore, workers must wear a special costume to fool the chick into thinking it is associating with an adult whooping crane to avoid creating the expectation that it will mate with a human.

d. Whooping crane undergoes habituation in which the chicks only make a bond with the first object they see. The young chicks only trust that first object to feed them. Thus workers must wear a special costume to fool the chick into thinking it is associating with an adult whooping crane.

Conditioned Behavior

Conditioned behaviors are types of associative learning, where a stimulus becomes associated with a consequence. During operant conditioning, the behavioral response is modified by its consequences, with regards to its form, strength, or frequency.

Classical Conditioning

In **classical conditioning**, a response called the conditioned response is associated with a stimulus that it had previously not been associated with, the conditioned stimulus. The response to the original, unconditioned stimulus is called the unconditioned response. The most cited example of classical conditioning is Ivan Pavlov's experiments with dogs (Figure 36.41). In Pavlov's experiments, the unconditioned response was the salivation of dogs in response to the unconditioned stimulus of seeing or smelling their food. The conditioning stimulus that researchers associated with the unconditioned response was the ringing of a bell. During conditioning, every time the animal was given food, the bell was rung. This was repeated during several trials. After some time, the dog learned to associate the ringing of the bell with food and to respond by salivating. After the conditioning period was finished, the dog would respond by salivating when the bell was rung, even when the unconditioned stimulus, the food, was absent. Thus, the ringing of the bell became the conditioned stimulus and the salivation became the conditioned response. Although it is thought by some scientists that the unconditioned and conditioned responses are identical, even Pavlov discovered that the saliva in the conditioned dogs had characteristic differences when compared to the unconditioned dog.

Figure 36.41 In the classic Pavlovian response, the dog becomes conditioned to associate the ringing of the bell with food.

It had been thought by some scientists that this type of conditioning required multiple exposures to the paired stimulus and response, but it is now known that this is not necessary in all cases, and that some conditioning can be learned in a single pairing experiment. Classical conditioning is a major tenet of behaviorism, a branch of psychological philosophy that proposes that all actions, thoughts, and emotions of living things are behaviors that can be treated by behavior modification and changes in the environment.

Operant Conditioning

In **operant conditioning**, the conditioned behavior is gradually modified by its consequences as the animal responds to the stimulus. A major proponent of such conditioning was psychologist B.F. Skinner, the inventor of the Skinner box. Skinner put rats in his boxes that contained a lever that would dispense food to the rat when depressed. While initially the rat would push the lever a few times by accident, it eventually associated pushing the lever with getting the food. This type of learning is an example of operant conditioning. Operant learning is the basis of most animal training. The conditioned behavior is continually modified by positive or negative reinforcement, often a reward such as food or some type of punishment, respectively. In this way, the animal is conditioned to associate a type of behavior with the punishment or reward, and, over time, can be induced to perform behaviors that they would not have done in the wild, such as the "tricks" dolphins perform at marine amusement park shows (**Figure 36.42**).

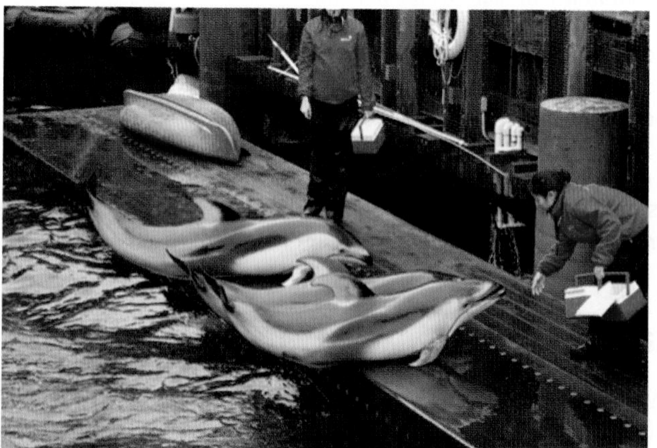

Figure 36.42 The training of dolphins by rewarding them with food is an example of positive reinforcement operant conditioning. (credit: Roland Tanglao)

Cognitive Learning

Classical and operant conditioning are inefficient ways for humans and other intelligent animals to learn. Some primates, including humans, are able to learn by imitating the behavior of others and by taking instructions. The development of complex language by humans has made **cognitive learning**, the manipulation of information using the mind, the most prominent method of human learning. In fact, that is how students are learning right now by reading this book. As students read, they can make mental images of objects or organisms and imagine changes to them, or behaviors by them, and anticipate the consequences. In addition to visual processing, cognitive learning is also enhanced by remembering past experiences, touching physical objects, hearing sounds, tasting food, and a variety of other sensory-based inputs. Cognitive learning is so powerful that it can be used to understand conditioning in detail. In the reverse scenario, conditioning cannot help someone learn about cognition.

Classic work on cognitive learning was done by Wolfgang Köhler with chimpanzees. He demonstrated that these animals were capable of abstract thought by showing that they could learn how to solve a puzzle. When a banana was hung in their cage too high for them to reach, and several boxes were placed randomly on the floor, some of the chimps were able to stack the boxes one on top of the other, climb on top of them, and get the banana. This implies that they could visualize the result of stacking the boxes even before they had performed the action. This type of learning is much more powerful and versatile than conditioning.

Cognitive learning is not limited to primates, although they are the most efficient in using it. Maze running experiments done with rats by H.C. Blodgett in the 1920s were the first to show cognitive skills in a simple mammal. The motivation for the animals to work their way through the maze was a piece of food at its end. In these studies, the animals in Group I were run in one trial per day and had food available to them each day on completion of the run (Figure 36.43). Group II rats were not fed in the maze for the first six days and then subsequent runs were done with food for several days after. Group III rats had food available on the third day and every day thereafter. The results were that the control rats, Group I, learned quickly, and figured out how to run the maze in seven days. Group III did not learn much during the three days without food, but rapidly caught up to the control group when given the food reward. Group II learned very slowly for the six days with no reward to motivate them, and they did not begin to catch up to the control group until the day food was given, and then it took two days longer to learn the maze.

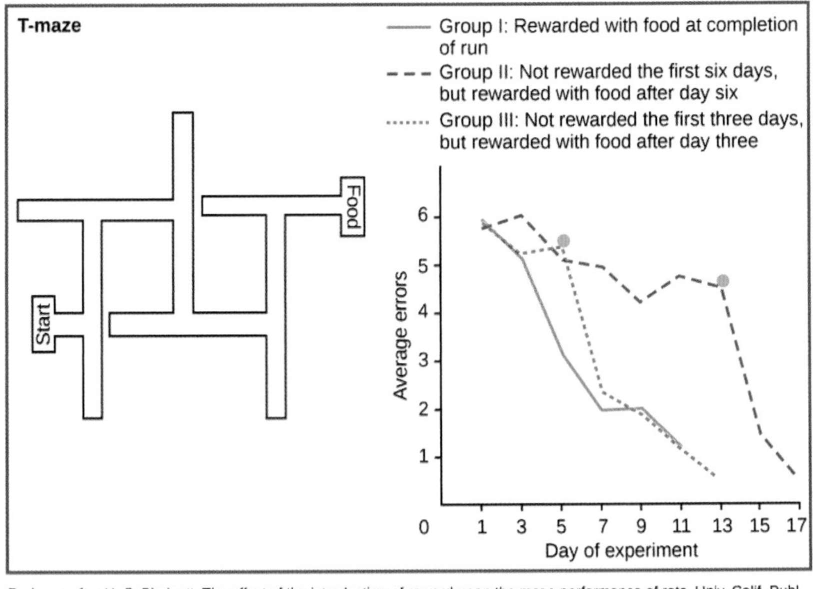

Redrawn after H. C. Blodgett, The effect of the introduction of reward upon the maze performance of rats. Univ. Calif. Publ. Psychol., 1929, 4, No. 8, pages 117 and 120.

Figure 36.43 Group I (the green solid line) found food at the end of each trial, group II (the blue dashed line) did not find food for the first 6 days, and group III (the red dotted line) did not find food during runs on the first three days. Notice that rats given food earlier learned faster and eventually caught up to the control group. The orange dots on the group II and III lines show the days when food rewards were added to the mazes.

It may not be immediately obvious that this type of learning is different than conditioning. Although one might be tempted to believe that the rats simply learned how to find their way through a conditioned series of right and left turns, E.C. Tolman proved a decade later that the rats were making a representation of the maze in their minds, which he called a "cognitive map." This was an early demonstration of the power of cognitive learning and how these abilities were not just limited to humans.

Sociobiology

Sociobiology is an interdisciplinary science originally popularized by social insect researcher E.O. Wilson in the 1970s. Wilson defined the science as "the extension of population biology and evolutionary theory to social organization."[9] The

9. Edward O. Wilson. *On Human Nature* (1978; repr., Cambridge: Harvard University Press, 2004), xx.

main thrust of sociobiology is that animal and human behavior, including aggressiveness and other social interactions, can be explained almost solely in terms of genetics and natural selection. This science is controversial; noted scientists such as the late Stephen Jay Gould criticized the approach for ignoring the environmental effects on behavior. This is another example of the "nature versus nurture" debate of the role of genetics versus the role of environment in determining an organism's characteristics.

Sociobiology also links genes with behaviors and has been associated with "biological determinism," the belief that all behaviors are hardwired into our genes. No one disputes that certain behaviors can be inherited and that natural selection plays a role retaining them. It is the application of such principles to human behavior that sparks this controversy, which remains active today.

science practices CONNECTION for AP® Courses

Lab Investigation

AP® Biology Investigative Labs: Inquiry-Based Approach, Investigation 12: Fruit Fly Behavior. This inquiry-based investigation provides an opportunity for you to design and implement a series of experiments using choice chambers to investigate behaviors that underlie directed movement (taxis) towards or away from environmental stimuli, including chemical signals, light, and temperature, in a small population of *Drosophila*.

Activity

Animal Behavior Field Study

Animal behavior can be studied in nearly every environment. Visit a local park, zoo, athletic field, or even a location on your school campus and observe the behaviors and interactions among different animals and with their environment. Consider the following questions in your study: How do animals exchange information and alter behavior in response to stimuli? What mechanisms do animals use to communicate information? What examples of innate and learned behaviors did you observe? What predictions can you make about observed behavior(s) if environmental conditions change?

Think About It

Describe how Pavlov's dog experiments are an example of classical conditioning. How does operant conditioning that you use to train a pet to do a trick differ from classical conditioning? What type of conditioning describes how you learned that studying likely will improve your grade on an AP® test?

Section Summary

Behaviors are responses to stimuli. They can either be instinctual/innate behaviors, which are not influenced by the environment, or learned behaviors, which are influenced by environmental changes. Instinctual behaviors include mating systems and methods of communication. Learned behaviors include imprinting and habituation, conditioning, and, most powerfully, cognitive learning. Although the connection between behavior, genetics, and evolution is well established, the explanation of human behavior as entirely genetic is controversial.

KEY TERMS

age structure proportion of population members at specific age ranges

aggressive display visual display by a species member to discourage other members of the same species or different species

aposematic coloration warning coloration used as a defensive mechanism against predation

Batesian mimicry type of mimicry where a non-harmful species takes on the warning colorations of a harmful one

behavior change in an organism's activities in response to a stimulus

behavioral biology study of the biology and evolution of behavior

biotic potential (r_{max}) maximal potential growth rate of a species

birth rate (*B*) number of births within a population at a specific point in time

camouflage avoid detection by blending in with the background.

carrying capacity (*K*) number of individuals of a species that can be supported by the limited resources of a habitat

classical conditioning association of a specific stimulus and response through conditioning

climax community final stage of succession, where a stable community is formed by a characteristic assortment of plant and animal species

cognitive learning knowledge and skills acquired by the manipulation of information in the mind

commensalism relationship between species wherein one species benefits from the close, prolonged interaction, while the other species neither benefits nor is harmed

competitive exclusion principle no two species within a habitat can coexist when they compete for the same resources at the same place and time

conditioned behavior behavior that becomes associated with a specific stimulus through conditioning

courtship display visual display used to attract a mate

death rate (*D*) number of deaths within a population at a specific point in time

demographic-based population model modern model of population dynamics incorporating many features of the *r*- and *K*-selection theory

demography statistical study of changes in populations over time

density-dependent regulation regulation of population that is influenced by population density, such as crowding effects; usually involves biotic factors

density-independent regulation regulation of populations by factors that operate independent of population density, such as forest fires and volcanic eruptions; usually involves abiotic factors

distraction display visual display used to distract predators away from a nesting site

Emsleyan/Mertensian mimicry type of mimicry where a harmful species resembles a less harmful one

energy budget allocation of energy resources for body maintenance, reproduction, and parental care

environmental disturbance change in the environment caused by natural disasters or human activities

ethology biological study of animal behavior

exponential growth accelerating growth pattern seen in species under conditions where resources are not limiting

fecundity potential reproductive capacity of an individual

fixed action pattern series of instinctual behaviors that, once initiated, always goes to completion regardless of changes in the environment

foraging behaviors species use to find food

foundation species species which often forms the major structural portion of the habitat

habituation ability of a species to ignore repeated stimuli that have no consequence

host organism a parasite lives on

imprinting identification of parents by newborns as the first organism they see after birth

innate behavior instinctual behavior that is not altered by changes in the environment

intersexual selection selection of a desirable mate of the opposite sex

interspecific competition competition between species for resources in a shared habitat or environment

intrasexual selection competition between members of the same sex for a mate

intraspecific competition competition between members of the same species

island biogeography study of life on island chains and how their geography interacts with the diversity of species found there

iteroparity life history strategy characterized by multiple reproductive events during the lifetime of a species

J-shaped growth curve shape of an exponential growth curve

***K*-selected species** species suited to stable environments that produce a few, relatively large offspring and provide parental care

keystone species species whose presence is key to maintaining biodiversity in an ecosystem and to upholding an ecological community's structure

kin selection sacrificing one's own life so that one's genes will be passed on to future generations by relatives

kinesis undirected movement of an organism in response to a stimulus

learned behavior behavior that responds to changes in the environment

life history inherited pattern of resource allocation under the influence of natural selection and other evolutionary forces

life table table showing the life expectancy of a population member based on its age

logistic growth leveling off of exponential growth due to limiting resources

mark and recapture technique used to determine population size in mobile organisms

migration long-range seasonal movement of animal species

monogamy mating system whereby one male and one female remain coupled for at least one mating season

mortality rate proportion of population surviving to the beginning of an age interval that die during the age interval

mutualism symbiotic relationship between two species where both species benefit

Müllerian mimicry type of mimicry where species share warning coloration and all are harmful to predators

one-child policy China's policy to limit population growth by limiting urban couples to have only one child or face the penalty of a fine

operant conditioning learned behaviors in response to positive and/or negative reinforcement

parasite organism that uses resources from another species, the host

pioneer species first species to appear in primary and secondary succession

polyandry mating system where one female mates with many males

polygyny mating system where one male mates with many females

population density number of population members divided by the area or volume being measured

population growth rate number of organisms added in each reproductive generation

population size (*N*) number of population members in a habitat at the same time

primary succession succession on land that previously has had no life

quadrat square made of various materials used to determine population size and density in slow moving or stationary organisms

***r*-selected species** species suited to changing environments that produce many offspring and provide little or no parental care

reflex action action in response to direct physical stimulation of a nerve

relative species abundance absolute population size of a particular species relative to the population sizes of other species within the community

S-shaped growth curve shape of a logistic growth curve

secondary succession succession in response to environmental disturbances that move a community away from its equilibrium

semelparity life history strategy characterized by a single reproductive event followed by death

signal method of communication between animals including those obtained by the senses of smell, hearing, sight, or touch

species dispersion pattern (also, species distribution pattern) spatial location of individuals of a given species within a habitat at a particular point in time

species richness number of different species in a community

survivorship curve graph of the number of surviving population members versus the relative age of the member

symbiosis close interaction between individuals of different species over an extended period of time that impacts the abundance and distribution of the associating populations

taxis directed movement in response to a stimulus

zero population growth steady population size where birth rates and death rates are equal

CHAPTER SUMMARY

36.1 Population Demography

Populations are individuals of a species that live in a particular habitat. Ecologists measure characteristics of populations: size, density, dispersion pattern, age structure, and sex ratio. Life tables are useful to calculate life expectancies of individual population members. Survivorship curves show the number of individuals surviving at each age interval plotted versus time.

36.2 Life Histories and Natural Selection

All species have evolved a pattern of living, called a life history strategy, in which they partition energy for growth, maintenance, and reproduction. These patterns evolve through natural selection; they allow species to adapt to their environment to obtain the resources they need to successfully reproduce. There is an inverse relationship between fecundity and parental care. A species may reproduce early in life to ensure surviving to a reproductive age or reproduce later in life to become larger and healthier and better able to give parental care. A species may reproduce once (semelparity) or many times (iteroparity) in its life.

36.3 Environmental Limits to Population Growth

Populations with unlimited resources grow exponentially, with an accelerating growth rate. When resources become limiting, populations follow a logistic growth curve. The population of a species will level off at the carrying capacity of its environment.

36.4 Population Dynamics and Regulation

Populations are regulated by a variety of density-dependent and density-independent factors. Species are divided into two categories based on a variety of features of their life history patterns: *r*-selected species, which have large numbers of offspring, and *K*-selected species, which have few offspring. The *r*- and *K*-selection theory has fallen out of use; however, many of its key features are still used in newer, demographically-based models of population dynamics.

36.5 Human Population Growth

The world's human population is growing at an exponential rate. Humans have increased the world's carrying capacity through migration, agriculture, medical advances, and communication. The age structure of a population allows us to predict population growth. Unchecked human population growth could have dire long-term effects on our environment.

36.6 Community Ecology

Communities include all the different species living in a given area. The variety of these species is called species richness. Many organisms have developed defenses against predation and herbivory, including mechanical defenses, warning coloration, and mimicry, as a result of evolution and the interaction with other members of the community. Two species cannot exist in the same habitat competing directly for the same resources. Species may form symbiotic relationships such as commensalism or mutualism. Community structure is described by its foundation and keystone species. Communities respond to environmental disturbances by succession (the predictable appearance of different types of plant species) until a stable community structure is established.

36.7 Behavioral Biology: Proximate and Ultimate Causes of Behavior

Behaviors are responses to stimuli. They can either be instinctual/innate behaviors, which are not influenced by the environment, or learned behaviors, which are influenced by environmental changes. Instinctual behaviors include mating systems and methods of communication. Learned behaviors include imprinting and habituation, conditioning, and, most powerfully, cognitive learning. Although the connection between behavior, genetics, and evolution is well established, the explanation of human behavior as entirely genetic is controversial.

REVIEW QUESTIONS

1. An ecologist is planning to measure both the size and density of a population. Identify the experimental method that can best provide these data.

a. mark and recapture

b. mark and release

c. quadrat

d. life table

2. Which of the following statements can be made about the mark and recapture method of counting population numbers?

a. Using quadrats for counting individuals in a population increases the accuracy of the mark and recapture method.
b. The greater the number of individuals captured during the first round of mark and recapture, the greater is the overall population size.
c. The mark and recapture method is useful for mammals and birds, but of little use for other organisms.
d. An underestimate of population size would tend to be observed in cases of studies involving animals that learn to seek out bait.

3. Which type of dispersal pattern is characterized by even spacing between individuals in the population?

a. random
b. uniform
c. sparse
d. clumped

4. Identify the best method to show the life expectancy of an individual within a population.

a. mark and recapture
b. mark and release
c. quadrat
d. life table

5. Describe how a researcher would best collect data in order to calculate mortality rates within a population.

a. For various age groups, count the number of individuals that died and the number that survived within a defined time period.
b. For various age groups, count the number of individuals that were born and the number that died within a defined time period.
c. For each sex, count the number of individuals that were born and the number that survived within a defined time period.
d. For each sex, count the number of individuals that died and the number that were born within a defined time period.

6. What survivorship pattern can be used to describe humans?

a. by a type I survivorship curve
b. by a type II survivorship curve
c. by a type III survivorship curve
d. by a type IV survivorship curve

7. Different species have different survival curves. A Type III survival curve would most likely be observed for _____.

a. whales
b. seals
c. salmon
d. polar bears

8. Which of the following is associated with long-term parental care?

a. few offspring
b. many offspring
c. semelparity
d. fecundity

9. Which of the following conditions is inversely related with fecundity?

a. number of offspring
b. energy budget of parent
c. amount of parental care
d. age of parent

10. When studying a squash beetle native to the Everglades, scientists collected data to compare the squash beetle to another beetle native to the Great Lakes region. What data would be used to compare the beetles' reproductive potential?

a. few offspring
b. many offspring
c. semelparity
d. fecundity

11. Albatrosses are birds that can live to age 60 and older. They usually do not start breeding until they reach age 8 or 9, which is relatively late compared to other bird species. Based on this information, explain conditions that might be a risk to the survival of albatrosses.

a. increased chance of individuals dying before reproducing
b. decreased life spans of individuals
c. increased chance of offspring dying
d. decreased chances of mating between individuals

12. Frogs are animals with high fecundity. Based on this information, frogs should also have which of the following characteristics?

a. high energy budget
b. extensive energy storage for offspring
c. small numbers of offspring
d. little or no parental care

13. Species with limited resources usually exhibit a(n) ____ growth curve.

a. logistic
b. logical
c. experimental
d. exponential

14. Give an example of exponential population growth.

a. salamanders adapting to fungal infections
b. polar bears living in a warming habitat
c. bacteria growing in enriched medium in a lab
d. feral cats being trapped and neutered in a suburb

15. If the major food source of seals declines due to pollution or overfishing, how would the seal population be affected?

a. The carrying capacity of seals would decrease, as would the seal population.
b. The carrying capacity of seals would decrease, but the seal population would remain the same.
c. The number of seal deaths would increase but the number of births would also increase, so the population size would remain the same.
d. The carrying capacity of seals would remain the same, but the population of seals would decrease.

16. Define carrying capacity of a population and explain whether it changes or remains fixed for a population.

a. Carrying capacity is the amount of land needed to support a population, and it is fixed for each population.
b. Carrying capacity is the amount of water and food resources required to support a population and it is fixed for each population.
c. Carrying capacity is the maximum size of a population that can survive using the available resources and it can vary up or down.
d. Carrying capacity is the time needed for a population to reach its maximum size and it can vary up or down.

17. Suppose a pesticide used by farmers wipes out the insect population that feeds a population of bats. Predict the effects of this change on the bat population.

a. The carrying capacity of the population will increase.
b. The carrying capacity of the population will decrease.
c. The carrying capacity of the population will not change.
d. The carrying capacity of the population cannot be predicted.

18. Which explanation best defines density-dependent growth regulation?

a. a factor that affects population density but not population size
b. a factor that affects population size but not population density
c. a factor that affects population size regardless of population density
d. a factor that affects population size in ways related to population density

19. A forest fire is an example of ____ regulation.

a. density-dependent
b. density-independent
c. r-selected
d. K-selected

20. Species that have many offspring at one time are usually _______.

a. r-selected
b. K-selected
c. both r- and K-selected
d. not selected

21. The following statements compare r-selected and K-selected species. Identify the statement that makes an accurate comparison.

a. r-selected and K-selected species both have limitations in the amount of energy they can invest in reproduction, so they both use similar strategies.
b. r-selected and K-selected species both have limitations in the amount of energy they can invest in reproduction, but they use completely different strategies.
c. r-selected and K-selected species use similar reproductive strategies but r-selected species require less energy to reproduce than K-selected species.
d. r-selected and K-selected species use different reproductive strategies because r-selected species require less energy to reproduce than K-selected species.

22. If a population moves to a new environment rich in resources, what type of growth curve will it exhibit?

a. logistic
b. logical
c. experimental
d. exponential

23. Humans have altered environmental factors that have allowed the human population to grow exponentially. State an example of such a factor.

a. interspecific competition
b. age structure
c. carrying capacity
d. reproductive strategies

24. Humans have altered their own carrying capacity. Explain how humans have changed their carrying capacity and the consequences of this change.

a. By limiting their own carrying capacity, humans have enabled their population to grow rapidly.
b. By decreasing their own carrying capacity, humans have enabled their population to grow slowly.
c. By stabilizing their own carrying capacity, humans have enabled their population to grow steadily.
d. By increasing their own carrying capacity, humans have enabled their population to grow exponentially.

25. Humans have influenced their own carrying capacity in several ways. Some human activities increase carrying capacity while others decrease it. Identify a human activity that has decreased the human carrying capacity of the environment.

a. agriculture
b. using large amounts of natural resources
c. domestication of animals
d. use of language

26. Humans began developing oil as an energy source in the early part of the twentieth century. Explain the relationship between this development and the human carrying capacity of Earth.

a. Drilling for oil enabled humans to increase food production through the use of machinery, which increased the human carrying capacity of the Earth.
b. Oil production allowed new transportation methods faster than methods using animals, which decreased the human carrying capacity of the Earth.
c. Accessing oil as an energy source created increased greenhouse gas emissions, which increased the human carrying capacity of the Earth.
d. Oil as an energy source enabled humans to enjoy more recreational activities, which decreased the human carrying capacity of the Earth.

27. The greatest proportion of young individuals can be found in ___.

a. economically developed countries
b. economically underdeveloped countries
c. countries with zero population growth
d. countries in Europe

28. Explain the correlation between age structure and the level of economic development observed in many countries.

a. There is no correlation between the characteristics of age structures and the level of economic development.
b. Countries that are more economically developed tend to have fewer middle-aged individuals and more young individuals than undeveloped countries.
c. A larger ratio of very young individuals to very old individuals characterizes the age structures of countries with the highest economic development.
d. Age structures of economically undeveloped countries show greater proportions of children and fewer proportions of elderly people.

29. Which environmental characteristic is likely to increase if the human population continues growing unchecked?

a. wilderness areas
b. fresh water supplies
c. fossil fuel reserves
d. atmospheric carbon dioxide

30. Predict and explain the effects of human population on biodiversity many years in the future.

a. Biodiversity will decline as human population increases because of habitat loss, increased pollution, and climate change.
b. Biodiversity will decline as human population increases because of enhanced food supplies, medical advances, and development of renewable energy sources.
c. Biodiversity will increase as human population increases because of habitat loss, increased pollution, and climate change.
d. Biodiversity will increase as human population increases because of enhanced food supplies, medical advances, and development of renewable energy sources.

31. Analyze the predator-prey graphs to identify the graph that correctly depicts a predator-prey cycle.

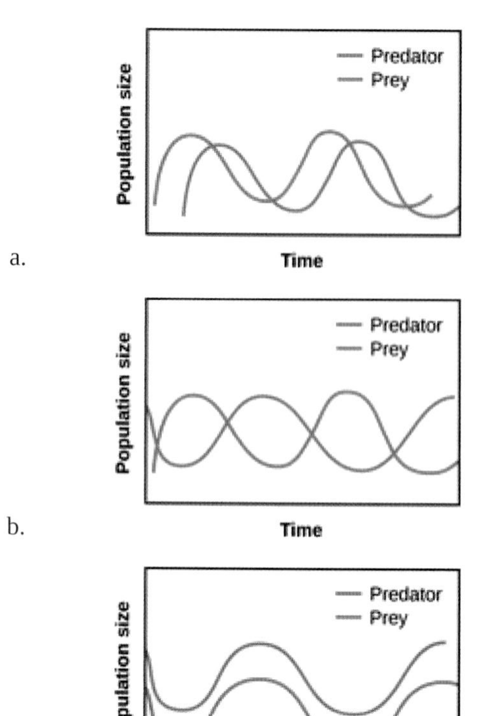

a.

b.

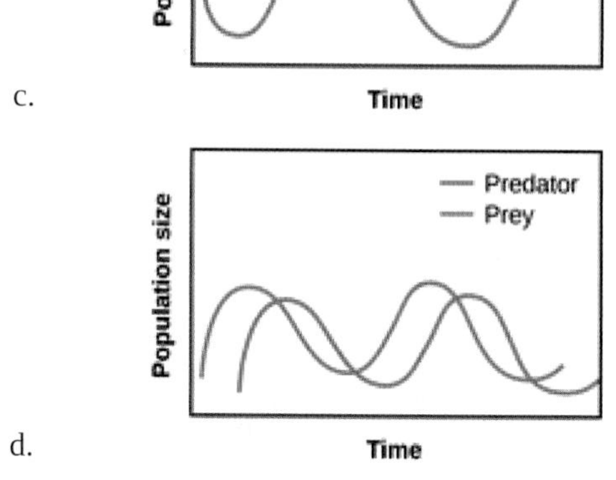

c.

d.

32. Construct a statement to describe a predator-prey cycle.

a. Prey increase in numbers, causing an increase in the predator population, which, in turn, causes a downturn in prey numbers, and leads to a downturn in predator numbers, and then the cycle repeats.

b. The number of prey is directly related to the number of predators so that the two populations remain at the same ratio even though the total population numbers fluctuate.

c. Increasing prey numbers trigger decreases in predator numbers, which eventually causes a decrease in prey numbers as predators become too sparse, and then the cycle repeats.

d. A prey population undergoes a cyclic increasing and decreasing fluctuation in size as its predator population undergoes the same cycle but in a mirror image relationship.

33. In a region in Texas, biologists observed that two highly venomous snakes with similar markings deter owl predators. Upon closer inspection, the snakes were determined to belong to different genera and species. How would these biologists describe the mimicry in this case?

a. Batesian mimicry, because it involves nontoxic species that resembles a toxic species.

b. Emsleyan/Mertensian mimicry because an extremely toxic species resembles a less toxic species.

c. Batesian mimicry because it involves an extremely toxic species that resembles a less toxic species.

d. Mullerian mimicry because it involves different species that both produce toxins and display similar warning coloration.

34. Explain what would happen to an animal species classified as a Batesian mimic if it did not have its mimicry attributes.

a. The animal species would suffer increased loss through predation because its predators would not learn to avoid eating it.

b. The animal species would suffer decreased loss through predation because it still produces harmful toxins that would kill its predators.

c. The animal species would suffer no long-term loss through predation because it still produces foul tasting compounds that its predators would learn to avoid.

d. The animal species would suffer increased loss through predation because predators would not be deterred by its appearance and would find it to be tasty.

35. Explain how two different species can coexist in the same habitat according to the competitive exclusion principle.

a. Two species can coexist in the same habitat as long as they do not share the same trophic level.

b. Two species can coexist in the same habitat as long as they do not share the same mates.

c. Two species can coexist in the same habitat as long as they do not share the same resources.

d. Two species can coexist in the same habitat as long as they do not share the same life span.

36. Explain what would happen if the competitive exclusion principle were violated.

a. One species will prey on another species and drive it to extinction.
b. One species will adapt to another species invading its habitat.
c. One species will block another species' access to a critical resource.
d. One species will contend with another species for the same resources.

37. Describe the symbiotic relationship of mutualism.

a. Only one species benefits and the other derives no benefit or harm from the relationship.
b. One species benefits and the other is harmed by the relationship.
c. Both species benefit from the relationship.
d. Neither species benefits nor is either species harmed.

38. Construct a sentence that describes the symbiotic relationships of mutualism, commensalism, and parasitism.

a. Symbiotic relationships always benefit both species involved.
b. Symbiotic relationships never harm either of the species involved.
c. Symbiotic relationships always benefit at least one of the species involved.
d. Symbiotic relationships always harm at least one of the species involved.

39. Identify the statement that best describes a pioneer species.

a. A pioneer species is a species that is transported out of its native habitat into a non-native habitat, where there are few or no natural predators to keep the population in check.
b. A pioneer species is a species that maintains the community structure in an ecosystem, and whose loss causes the ecosystem to fail.
c. A pioneer species is a species that has the greatest influence over the ecosystem usually by bringing most of the energy into the system.
d. A pioneer species is a species that can colonize landscapes that are devoid of soil and begin the process of succession.

40. Explain what happens to a forest community after a forest fire.

a. The same community is quickly re-established just as it existed before the disturbance.
b. Another mature community with different species grows quickly in place of the original community.
c. Groups of species grow and then are replaced by other groups through a sequential series of changes as the community matures over time.
d. The landscape remains barren for many years until trees grow large enough to provide the shade needed for smaller plants to grow.

41. What is innate behavior?

a. Innate behavior results from practice and conditioning.
b. Innate behavior occurs spontaneously without any learning component.
c. Innate behavior results from thought processes.
d. Innate behavior results from interactions within a social group.

42. What is the difference between innate and learned behaviors?

a. Innate behaviors can change based on previous experiences, whereas learned behaviors remain the same throughout an organism's life.
b. Innate behaviors are controlled by genes, whereas genes play no role in learned behaviors.
c. Innate behaviors allow an organism to adapt to new situations by applying previous experiences, whereas learned behaviors allow an organism to respond quickly.
d. Innate behaviors are involuntary responses to stimuli, whereas learned behaviors change based on an organism's experiences.

43. Describe phototaxis.

a. Phototaxis is the directed movement of an organism in response to gravity.
b. Phototaxis is the long-range movement of an organism in response to a change in season.
c. Phototaxis is the movement of an organism in search of food.
d. Phototaxis is the directed movement of an organism in response to light.

44. Monarch butterflies in the eastern regions of North America migrate thousands of miles to an area in Mexico in the fall and then back to northern regions in the spring. Explain how this migration behavior came to be established in this species.

a. Each new generation learned the migration behavior by observing older generations and mimicking their behavior patterns.
b. In very early generations of this species, a few individuals found that migration improved their chances for survival and taught their young to carry on the behavior.
c. Individuals that migrated survived through the winter, whereas individuals that did not migrate died, leading to selection for migration in later generations.
d. When this butterfly emerged as a new species, by chance it inherited the genetic material that underlies long-distance migration behavior from its ancestor.

45. Pheromones are used in communication between some organisms. What is a pheromone?

a. A pheromone is a type of chemical compound.
b. A pheromone is a type of display.
c. A pheromone is a type of language.
d. A pheromone is a type of song.

46. Construct a statement to describe the type of signal used by birds to communicate the presence of a predator to other birds.

a. Birds release chemical compounds into the air that other birds rapidly recognize as signals of the presence of a predator.
b. Birds flash visual signals such as wing flapping to communicate warnings to other birds whenever a predator is present.
c. Birds physically touch other birds using tactile signals when they observe a predator entering their location.
d. Birds make aural signals such as calls that other birds can hear and learn about a predator that has been observed in the area.

47. The sacrifice of the life of an individual so that the genes of relatives may be passed on is called ____.

a. operant conditioning
b. kin selection
c. kinesis
d. imprinting

48. Cite an example that describes how an animal expends energy in finding, selecting, or winning a mate.

a. Female swallows engage in aggressive harassment of a hawk during breeding season.
b. Male cardinals harass and peck at other male cardinals in their territory.
c. Both male and female squirrels build nests out of leaves, twigs, and other plant material.
d. Female black widow spiders eat males following copulation.

49. The term polyandry comes from the Greek words for 'many' and 'man.' Based on these word origins, describe a polyandrous mating system.

a. One male mates with many females.
b. One female mates with one male.
c. One female mates with many males.
d. Many females mate with one male.

50. Describe an advantage of a monogamous relationship.

a. Having a lot of males around to provide assistance with protecting and feeding offspring ensures that offspring have the best chance of surviving.
b. When very few males are available in a population, this mating system makes sure that each male has a mating partner.
c. In populations where very few females are available, this mating system ensures that no eggs are wasted.
d. The constant presence of one male throughout the offspring rearing process makes it more likely that offspring will survive and be healthier.

51. The ability of rats to learn how to run a maze is an example of cognitive learning. Describe what happens during cognitive learning.

a. Cognitive learning is a type of learning that occurs early in an animal's development when it learns to bond to an object or animal.
b. Cognitive learning occurs when an animal learns to associate a stimulus with a behavior not normally associated with that stimulus.
c. Cognitive learning occurs when an animal learns a behavior in response to a positive stimulus or negative stimulus.
d. Cognitive learning is the most complex type of learning that involves multiple types of brain processes to carry out.

52. Contrast classical conditioning and operant conditioning.

a. In operant conditioning, the animal learns to associate a voluntary behavior with its consequences, whereas in classical conditioning, the animal learns to associate a non-voluntary behavior with an unusual stimulus.
b. In operant conditioning, the animal does not learn a new behavior in response to a stimulus, whereas in classical conditioning, the animal learns to associate a non-voluntary behavior with an unusual stimulus.
c. In operant conditioning, the animal learns to associate a voluntary behavior with its consequences, whereas in classical conditioning, the animal does not learn a new behavior in response to a stimulus.
d. In operant conditioning, the animal learns to associate a non-voluntary behavior with an unusual stimulus, whereas in classical conditioning, the animal learns to associate a voluntary behavior with its consequences.

CRITICAL THINKING QUESTIONS

53. Describe how a researcher could determine the population size and density of a bird population on one of the Hawaiian islands.

a. Population size can be determined by life tables. The area of the island in square kilometers is divided by the population size to determine the density of the bird population.
b. Population size can be determined by the mark and recapture method. The population size is divided by the area of the island in square kilometers to determine the density of the bird population.
c. Population size can be determined by life tables. The population size is divided by the area of the island in square kilometers to determine the density of the bird population.
d. Population size can be determined by the mark and recapture method. The area of the island in square kilometers is divided by the population size to determine the density of the bird population.

54. Give examples of how two different populations of organisms might have the same population density, but different dispersal patterns.

a. Two populations could occupy the same range with the same number of individuals, giving different dispersal patterns. However, both the populations may be dispersed randomly throughout the range, giving identical population densities.
b. Two populations could occupy the different range with the different number of individuals, giving different dispersal patterns. However, both the populations may move over this range in a herd, giving identical population densities.
c. Two populations could occupy the same range with the different number of individuals, giving identical population densities. However, one population may move over this range in a herd while the other population may be dispersed randomly throughout the range.
d. Two populations could occupy the same range with the same number of individuals, giving identical population densities. However, one population may move over this range in a herd while the other population may be dispersed randomly throughout the range.

55. A population is observed to have very large numbers of very young individuals, but very low numbers of sexually mature individuals. What hypothesis might a researcher propose about mortality patterns in this population and how would a researcher follow up to test their hypothesis?

a. A researcher might propose the mortality rate of this species is very high during the developmental period after sexual maturity is reached. This hypothesis can be tested by constructing a life table and calculating mortality rates at different age intervals.
b. A researcher might propose the mortality rate of this species is very high during the developmental period before sexual maturity is reached. This hypothesis can be tested by using the mark and recapture method and calculating population densities.
c. A researcher might propose the mortality rate of this species is very high during the developmental period before sexual maturity is reached. This hypothesis can be tested by constructing a life table and calculating mortality rates at different age intervals.
d. A researcher might propose the mortality rate of this species is very low during the developmental period before sexual maturity is reached. This hypothesis can be tested by constructing a quadrat and calculating mortality rates at different age intervals.

56. An organism, such as an elephant, that invests in long-term care of its offspring faces risks to its survival as a result of this investment. Explain those risks.

a. Organisms that invest in long-term parental care have many offspring. Having many offspring means there is greater risk of rapid increase in population.
b. Organisms that invest in long-term parental care have few offspring. Having a limited number of offspring means there is greater risk to the survival of the species when a single offspring dies.
c. Organisms that invest in long-term parental care have many offspring. Having many offspring means there is greater risk to the survival of the species when a single offspring dies.
d. Organisms that invest in long-term parental care have few offspring. Having a limited number of offspring means there is greater risk of rapid increase in population.

57. A honey bee colony contains one queen, hundreds of drones, and many thousands of worker bees. The queen produces eggs, the drones produce sperm, and the workers are sterile. Explain how the reproductive strategy of honey bees benefits the survival of the species. (credit: Food and Agriculture Organization of the United Nations)

a. The fertile queen and drones produce many offspring while sterile worker bees do not benefit the survival of the species.
b. Worker bees produce many offspring while the sterile queen and drones do not benefit the survival of the species.
c. The sterile queen and drones use the energy taken in by them for their own growth, growth and maintenance of the hive, and protection and nurturing of offspring.
d. Sterile worker bees use the energy taken in by them for their own growth, growth and maintenance of the hive, and protection and nurturing of offspring.

58. Two different plant species expend approximately the same amount of energy on reproduction, yet one produces many seeds in a season and the other produces very few. Explain what is likely to be true of the seeds of these two species.

a. In the plant species that produces many seeds, most of the energy is used to produce seeds, of which only a few will germinate and produce another plant. In the species that produces few seeds, most of the energy is used to increase the chances of seeds produced to germinate and grow into an adult plant.
b. In a plant species that produces many seeds, most of the energy is used to produce seeds, most of which will germinate and produce another plant. In a species that produces few seeds, most of the energy is used to increase the chances of seeds produced to germinate and grow into an adult plant.
c. In a plant species that produces many seeds, most of the energy is used to produce seeds, of which only a few will germinate and produce another plant. In a species that produces few seeds, most of the energy is used to reduce the chances of seeds produced to germinate and grow into an adult plant.
d. In a plant species that produces many seeds, most of the energy is used to increase the chances of seeds produced to germinate and grow into an adult plant. In a species that produces few seeds, most of the energy is used to produce those seeds, which will germinate and produce another plant.

59. Explain how rmax would be expected to differ for an elephant and a flea, and how that changes the time scale over which populations of these two animals would be studied.

a. rmax would be greater for an elephant as elephant reproduces at a faster rate than flea. A shorter time scale would be used to study changes over several elephant generations.
b. rmax would be greater for a flea as flea reproduces at a faster rate than elephant. A shorter time scale would be used to study changes over several flea generations than over several elephant generations.
c. rmax would be greater for a flea as flea reproduces at a faster rate than elephant. A longer time scale would be used to study changes over several flea generations than over several elephant generations.
d. rmax would be greater for an elephant as the elephants grow at an exponential rate so the population growth rate is greatly increased. A shorter time scale would be used to study changes over several elephant generations.

60.

Date	*N*
5/1/12	56
6/1/12	98
7/2/12	203
8/10/12	421

These data were collected on a population of beetles in Florida. Based on the data, how would you describe population growth in this case and what do you predict about growth of this population in the future? Explain your reasoning.

a. Population shows logistic growth, as number of individuals doubles every month and will likely continue to grow logistically until its resources become depleted. At that point, the population growth rate will slow down and level off to zero.
b. The population shows exponential growth, as the number of individuals doubles every month and will likely grow logistically in the future when the resources become limited. At that point, the population growth rate will slow down and level off to zero.
c. The population shows exponential growth, as number of individuals doubles every month and will likely continue to grow exponentially until its resources become limited. At that point, the growth will become logistic; the population growth rate will slow down and level off to zero.
d. The population shows logistic growth and is likely to grow exponentially as the resources are probably increasing. The population growth rate will increase in the future as well.

61. Explain how climate change might lead to a decrease in one population's carrying capacity and an increase in the carrying capacity of a different population.

a. Plant species that are drought-resistant would decline in warm temperatures whereas other species would thrive in number in such a climate.
b. Plant species that are pest-resistant would thrive in warm temperatures whereas other species would decline in number in such a climate.
c. Plant species that are drought-resistant would decline in cold temperatures whereas other species would thrive in number in such a climate.
d. Plant species that are drought-resistant would thrive in warm temperatures whereas other species would decline in number in such a climate.

62. Compare and contrast density-dependent growth regulation with density-independent growth regulation. Give an example of each as they might affect a caterpillar population.

a. Both are environmental conditions that result in changes in population numbers. Density-independent factors have different effects on population densities whereas density-dependent factors have the same effect. An example of the former is a caterpillar population being kept low by a pesticide because it kills them regardless of their numbers. In the case of the latter, a large caterpillar population leads to a decrease in food availability, which will cause the caterpillar population to decline.

b. Both are environmental conditions that result in changes in population numbers. Density-independent factors have the same effect at all population densities whereas density-dependent factors have different effects. An example of the former is of a caterpillar population being kept low by a pesticide because it kills them regardless of their numbers. In the case of the latter, a large caterpillar population leads to a decrease in food availability, which will cause the caterpillar population to decline.

c. Both are environmental conditions that result in changes in population numbers. Density-independent factors have the same effect at all population densities whereas density-dependent factors have different effects. An example of the former is of a caterpillar population being kept low by a pesticide because it kills them when their numbers are low. In the case of the latter, a large caterpillar population leads to a decrease in food availability, which will cause the caterpillar population to decline.

d. Both are environmental conditions that result in changes in population numbers. Density-independent factors have the same effect at all population densities whereas density-dependent factors have different effects. An example of the former is of a caterpillar population being kept low by a pesticide because it kills them regardless of their numbers. In the case of the latter, a large caterpillar population leads to a decrease in food availability, which will cause the caterpillar population to increase.

63. Why doesn't a frog, which is an r-selected species, care for its offspring in the way a wolf, which is a K-selected species, cares for its offspring?

a. Frogs have been selected by stable, predictable environments, therefore they do not feel the need to care for their offspring like wolves.

b. Frogs use very little energy to produce large numbers of offspring, therefore they do not have enough remaining to nurture them.

c. Smaller animals like frogs do not care for their offspring as a lot of them are produced whereas larger animals like wolves only produce a few.

d. Frogs expend a lot of energy to produce large numbers of offspring, therefore they do not have enough to nurture them.

64. Explain which features of a logistic growth curve are the same for every population exhibiting logistic growth and which features might vary from one population to another.

a. The overall S-shape would be the same for all populations. The actual x-y values on the graphs, population numbers corresponding to starting populations, and the ending carrying capacities could differ.

b. The overall carrying capacities would be the same for all populations. The actual x-y values on the graph and population numbers corresponding to the starting populations could differ.

c. The overall S-shape would be the same for all populations showing logistic growth. The only factor that could differ is the actual x-y values on the graphs indicating the time frames for the growth curves.

d. The x-y values on the graphs indicating the time frames for the growth curves would be the same. Overall S shape and population numbers corresponding to the starting populations could differ.

65. Explain why the concept of carrying capacity is important when discussing human population growth.

a. Humans can decrease the carrying capacity of their environment by developing food production methods and engineering high quality shelters, which enables more people to live than would otherwise be possible.

b. Humans have been able to change the carrying capacity of their environment, which enables more people survive. By decreasing their own carrying capacity, humans are responsible for their population boom.

c. Humans have been able to change the carrying capacity of their environment, which enables more people to live. By increasing their own carrying capacity, humans are responsible for their population boom.

d. Humans can increase the carrying capacity of their environment by developing food production methods and engineering high quality shelters, which enables fewer people to live than would otherwise be possible. This would result in population collapse.

66. The Industrial Revolution began with the invention of the steam engine. At about the same time, human population began increasing exponentially. Explain how these two events are linked to the idea that humans are able to change the carrying capacity of their environment.

a. The invention of the steam engine enabled people to use machines to carry out farming activities. The amount of available resources needed to sustain human life increased with the invention of machines. This increase in resources spurred exponential population growth.

b. The invention of the steam engine enabled people to develop pest-resistant crop varieties. The amount of available resources needed to sustain human life increased with the invention of machines. This increase in resources spurred exponential population growth.

c. The amount of available resources needed to sustain human life decreased with the invention of machines, but the carrying capacity increased. This increase in carrying capacity spurred exponential population growth.

d. The invention of the steam engine enables the environment to be changed according to the needs of the people. This regulation of environmental conditions spurred exponential population growth.

67.

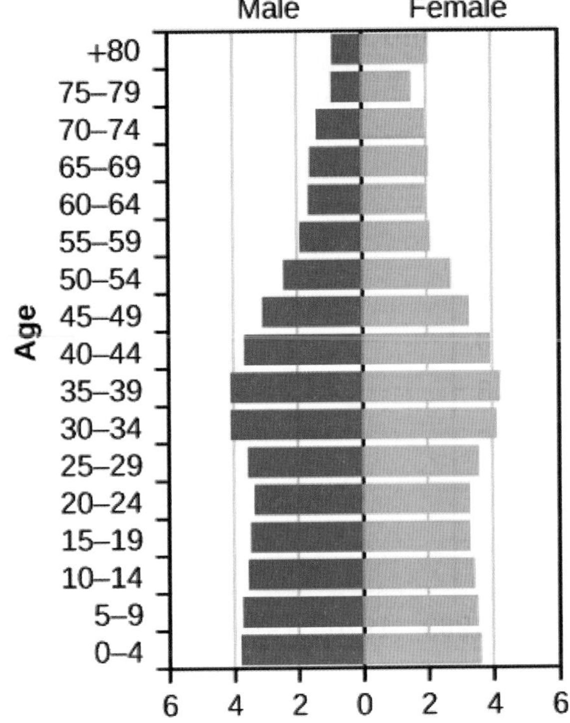

(credit: Quia)

This diagram shows the age structure for a country. Analyze the age structure and use it to predict the economic status of this country. Explain your reasoning.

a. This country is likely to be an economically developing country because it has a fairly even distribution of individuals in all age groups.

b. This country is likely to be an economically developed country because it has many more very young people and very few old people.

c. This country is likely to be an economically developed country because it has a fairly even distribution of individuals in all age groups.

d. This country is likely to be an economically undeveloped country because it has many more very young people and very few old people.

68.

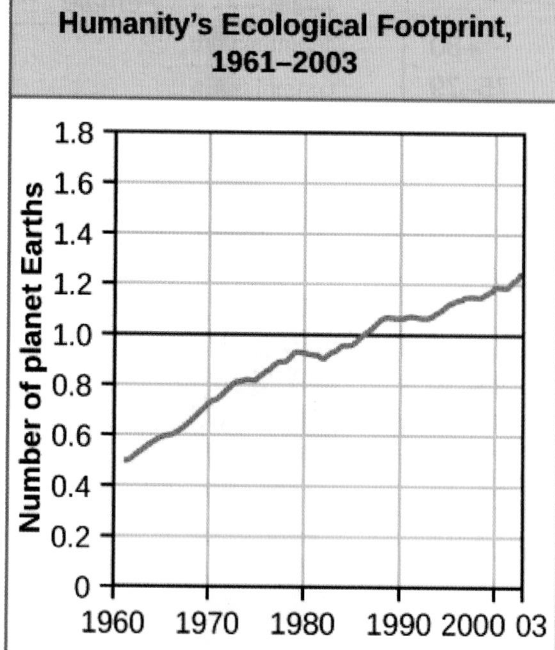

(credit: EPA Victoria)

The global ecological footprint is defined as the total land area needed to supply all of the resources consumed by all humans. This graph shows the relationship between time and the global human footprint measured in number of planet Earths. Analyze the graph, and use it to explain what has been the consequence of human population change so far. Then, predict the consequences of continued population change in the future.

a. The water resources present on Earth has been exceeded by the human population. If the human population keeps increasing, the ecological footprint of humans will increase far beyond the ability of Earth to support human population and our population could crash.

b. The land area present on Earth to supply our resources has been exceeded by the human population. If the human population keeps increasing, the ecological footprint of humans will increase far beyond the ability of Earth to support human population and our population could crash.

c. The land area present on Earth to supply our resources has been exceeded by the human population. If the human population keeps increasing, the birth and death rates will decrease and our population could crash.

d. The water resources present on Earth has been exceeded by the human population. If the human population keeps increasing, the birth and death rates will decrease and our population could crash.

69.

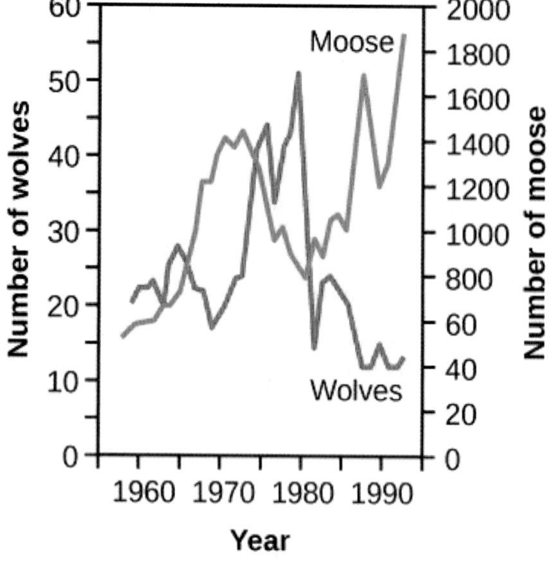

This graph shows a predator-prey cycle for wolves and moose. Explain why the graphs do not resemble the idealized graphs used as models of the predator-prey cycle.

a. This graph reflects all of the influences on both populations in addition to the predator-prey influences.

b. This graph reflects all of the influences on both populations, but not the predator-prey influences.

c. This graph reflects just the influence of predator-prey interactions on both populations.

d. This graph reflects some of the influences on both populations other than the predator-prey influences.

70. Suppose a population of lizards becomes divided into two groups on two different islands after a devastating tsunami. No predators of the lizard are present on one island, and on the other island is a fierce predator that uses the lizard as its primary source of food. Assuming both populations encounter similar environments in every other way, and both survive and grow over the next 100 years, how do you predict any of the characteristics of the two lizard populations to differ at the end of that time? Give specific examples to explain your prediction.

a. The lizards on the island with no predators will likely evolve adaptations such as camouflaged coloration, sharp spines, or toxins to defend against this predator. These adaptations will likely be absent in the other population because they are adapted to other predators.

b. The lizards that survive the fierce predator will likely evolve adaptations such as camouflaged coloration, sharp spines, or toxins to defend against this predator. These adaptations will likely be absent in the other population because they are adapted to other predators.

c. The lizards that survive the fierce predator will likely evolve adaptations such as camouflaged coloration, sharp spines, or toxins to defend against this predator. These adaptations will likely be absent in the other population because this predator is not a factor in their survival.

d. The lizards on the island with no predators will likely evolve adaptations such as camouflaged coloration, sharp spines, or toxins to defend against this predator. These adaptations will likely be absent in the other population because they have survived this predator.

71. The downy woodpecker and the hairy woodpecker are two species that live in the same habitats. The downy woodpecker is slightly smaller and has a smaller beak than the hairy woodpecker. The downy woodpecker uses its bill to search for food on small twigs and branches while the hairy woodpecker is most often observed searching for food on tree trunks. Explain how the competitive exclusion principle relates to this example.

a. Both woodpeckers have identical bill structure, but do not access their food from the same places in the habitat. They do not directly compete with one another for food and thus, can coexist in the same habitat.

b. Both live in the same habitat and have some similarities, but access their food from the same places in the habitat. In this way, the two species can coexist in the same habitat.

c. Both woodpeckers share similarities in their bill structures. So, they directly compete with one another for food. This directly relates to competitive exclusion principle.

d. Both live in the same habitat and have some similarities, but do not access their food from the same places in the habitat. In this way, the two species can coexist in the same habitat.

72. Honey bees are pollinators. Identify the type of symbiotic relationship that exists between honey bees and flowering plants, and explain why your reasoning.

a. This is commensalism because bees help plants pollinate and, in turn, obtain nectar from the plants.

b. This is a mutualistic relationship, because bees obtain nectar from the plants, but do not provide any benefits to the plants.

c. This is commensalism, because bees obtain nectar from the plants, but do not provide any benefits to the plants.

d. This is a mutualistic relationship, because bees help plants pollinate and, in turn, obtain nectar from the plants.

73. Prairie dogs are considered a keystone species in the western U.S. because of their extensive burrowing activities and their role as a prey animal. Explain why these characteristics would result in the keystone role of prairie dogs in their ecosystem.

a. Prairie dogs provide protection and shelter for small animals and harm predator animals in the ecosystem.

b. Without the prairie dogs, the ecosystem might collapse due to lack of protection and shelter for small animals and lack of prey to sustain large predator animals.

c. Prairie dogs dig underground burrows, reducing aeration in the soil and preventing excessive growth of plants above ground.

d. The burrows prairie dogs dig underground provide shelter for other species of animals as well as protection from predators, but prevent growth of plants above ground.

74.

Raised by parents of species A	Contact calls made to other members of the flock	Alarm calls made in response to predator sighting
Species A chicks	Species A call	Species A call
Species B chicks	Species A call	Species B call

Mating pairs of two different species of parrots sometimes lay their eggs in the same nest. When this happens, only one mating pair ends up parenting the chicks even though chicks of both species may be present. The chicks in such mixed nesting groups displayed some interesting behaviors summarized in the table. Classify these behaviors as innate or learned, and explain how they compare.

a. An alarm call is an innate behavior and a contact call is a learned behavior. Innate behavior comes out automatically in response to a stimulus whereas learned behavior develops over time after observing other birds carrying out the behavior.
b. The alarm call is a learned behavior and contact call is an innate behavior. Learned behavior develops over time after observing birds carrying out the behavior whereas innate behavior comes out automatically in response to a certain stimulus.
c. The alarm call is an innate behavior and contact call is a learned behavior. Innate behavior develops over time in response to stimulus after continuous exposure. Learned behavior develops over time after observing other birds carrying out their behavior.
d. The alarm call is a learned behavior and contact call is an innate behavior. Learned behavior comes out automatically whereas innate behavior develops over time in response to stimulus after continuous exposure.

75. Mammals such as humans show a behavior known as the flight or fight response. Explain how natural selection was likely involved in the development of this behavior that can be observed in humans today.

a. Individuals showing fight or flight behavior was more likely to survive than individuals lacking the trait. This trait got randomly selected by natural selection, thus became preferentially incorporated into the human lineage.
b. Individuals showing fight or flight behavior were more likely to survive than individuals lacking the trait. Sudden, inheritable changes were naturally selected, which included the fight or flight behavior. Thus, this response was incorporated into the human lineage.
c. Individuals showing fight or flight behavior were more likely to survive than individuals lacking this trait. Therefore surviving individuals passed on their trait to offspring while non-surviving individuals do not. Thus, this response became incorporated into human lineage.
d. Individuals showing fight or flight behavior were not more fit than individuals lacking this trait. However, the trait was selected by natural selection due to a random chance event in the gene frequency of individuals showing fight or flight behavior.

76. A researcher studying minnows, a type of fish, kept two groups of 20 fish in separate containers. The containers were linked by a pair of small tubes outfitted with a pump that constantly circulated water between both tanks. The researcher observed both groups of fish after placing a larger fish known to be a predator of minnows into one of the tanks. Fish in both tanks demonstrated alarm behavior. How can you explain these observations?

a. Fish in the tank that received the predator released alarm signals in chemical form. These compounds circulated and reached the other tank, eliciting an alarm response from the fish there nonetheless.
b. Fish in the tank that received the predator released alarm signals in the form of electrical signals. These compounds circulated and reached the other tank, eliciting an alarm response from the fish there nonetheless.
c. The predator introduced in one tank of fish released alarm signals in chemical form. These compounds circulated and reached the other tank, eliciting an alarm response from the fish there nonetheless.
d. Fish in the tank that did not receive the predator released alarm signals in the chemical form. These compounds circulated and reached the other tank and elicited an alarm response from the fish.

77. In some species, males expend a lot of energy in courtship rituals, whereas in other species, males expend much less energy in other ways of attracting mates such as producing colorful plumage. What does this mean for any energy that left over males of these species might have to devote to care for offspring?

a. Males of species carrying out courtship rituals assist in parental care whereas males that use colorful plumage to attract mates do not assist with the parental care.
b. Males of species carrying out courtship rituals do not assist in parental care whereas males that use colorful plumage to attract mates have energy available to assist with parental care.
c. Males of species carrying out courtship rituals as well as species of males that use colorful plumage to attract mates, both would assist with the parental care.
d. Males of species carrying out courtship rituals as well as species of males that use colorful plumage to attract mates would not assist in parental care as the females would be involved.

78. Female spotted sandpipers fight each other for resource-rich territories on their beach breeding grounds. Based on this, which mating type would most likely be operating in this species? Explain your reasoning.

a. Polyandrous mating is most likely operating as the females are establishing territories apart from other females. The females will then attract males to the resources they control which will result in many males attracted to few females with the richest territories.
b. Polygynous mating is most likely operating as the females are establishing territories apart from other females. The females from all territories would attract males to the resources they control, which would result in few males attracted to many females in each territory.
c. Polyandrous mating is most likely operating as the females are establishing territories apart from other females. The females from all territories would attract males to the resources they control, which would result in few males attracted to many females in each territory.
d. Polygynous mating is most likely operating as the females are establishing territories apart from other females. The females will then attract males to the resources they control which would result in many males attracted to few females with the richest territories.

79. Describe Pavlov's dog experiments as an example of classical conditioning.

a. Pavlov demonstrated classical conditioning through a maze running experiment with the dog. The motivation for the dog to work its way through the maze was a piece of food at the end of the maze. The dog ran in one trial per day and had food available at the end of the run.
b. Pavlov hung a chicken piece in a cage too high for the dog to reach and several boxes were placed randomly on the floor. Eventually the dog was able to stack the boxes and climb on top to get the chicken piece through classical conditioning.
c. Pavlov put a dog in a large box that contained a lever that would dispense food to the dog when pressed. While initially the dog would push the lever a few times by accident, it eventually associated pushing the lever with getting the food through classical conditioning.
d. Pavlov sounded a bell whenever food was presented to a dog, which produced saliva in response to the sight or smell of the food. Through classical conditioning, the dog started responding to the bell ringing with salivation as the dog came to associate the bell sound with the arrival of food.

TEST PREP FOR AP® COURSES

80. A researcher has been tracking a population of turtles. The researcher marked 200 young turtles just after hatching. A year later, collection data reveal that about 80% survived. A year after that, collection data revealed that about 60% of the original group was still living. After a third year, about 40% could be found alive. What do these data say about the survivorship curve that would best describe this population? Explain your reasoning.

a. Type II survivorship curve because the number of survivors decreases by the same value (20%) every year.
b. Type I survivorship curve because the number of survivors decreases by the same value (20%) every year.
c. Type II survivorship curve because the number of survivors increases by the same value (20%) every year.
d. Type IV survivorship curve because the number of survivors decreases by the same value (20%) every year.

81. After discovering a new species of salamander in a forest ecosystem, a researcher set traps at many different locations within the forest and collects data from his traps. The researcher's goal was to determine which types of environments within the forest the salamander is most likely to be found. Construct another scientific question the researcher can answer using the data he has already collected to further refine his study of this species.

a. What is the population distribution of this salamander species in this ecosystem?
b. What is the rate of population growth of this salamander species in this ecosystem?
c. Which animal species prey on this salamander species in this ecosystem?
d. What abiotic resources are essential for the survival of this salamander species in this ecosystem?

82.

Parous females number
Temperature (°C)
× Observed — Maximum number

(a)

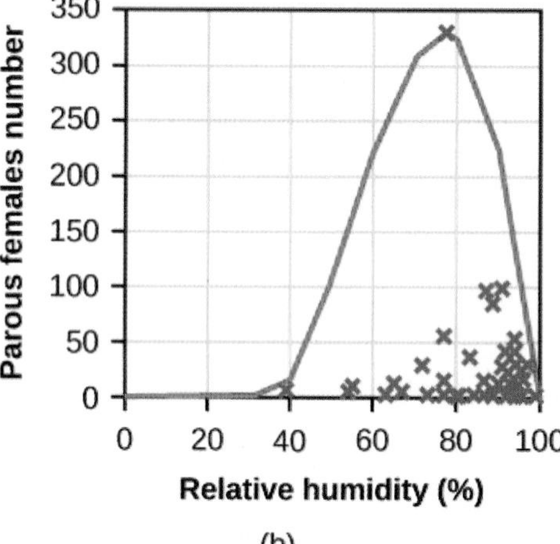

(b)

(credit: Revista da Sociedade Brasileira de Medicina Tropical)

These graphs summarize data collected in an area of Brazil between 2005 and 2006. Researchers captured mosquitos and counted the number of parous females. Parous females are females that produced viable offspring. Based on the information given, how would mosquito populations change in Brazil if the climate shifted to very hot (above 30°C) and very dry (below 60% humidity) conditions for an extended period of time? Explain your reasoning.

a. The mosquito populations would decrease at temperatures above 30°C, as this is the upper limit for parous females, leading to a drop in offspring production. Below 60% humidity not much change would be seen in the population of mosquitoes.

b. The mosquito populations would decrease, possibly reaching zero. As temperatures above 30°C are the upper limit for parous females, offspring production would drop. Drier conditions would do the same.

c. The mosquito populations would stay the same. This would be because temperature above 30°C and humidity below 60% is close to the favorable conditions of offspring production by parous females.

d. The mosquito populations would stay the same at temperatures above 30°C as higher temperatures will not affect the production of viable offspring by parous females. Drier conditions, below 60% humidity, would cause a drop in the population, as it is the lower limit for offspring production.

83.

All birds

Density (*n* per km²)

Control Low High

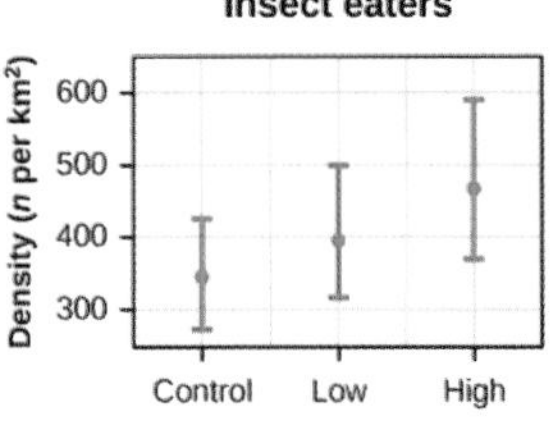

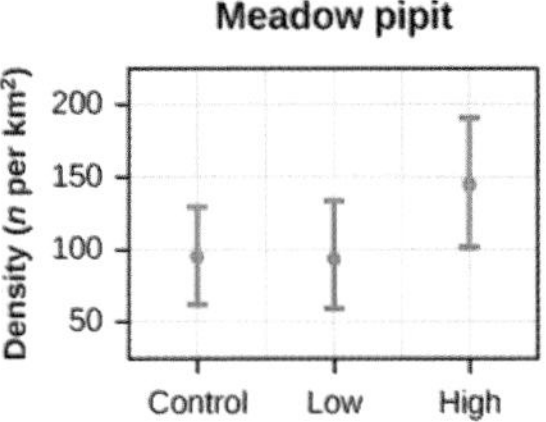

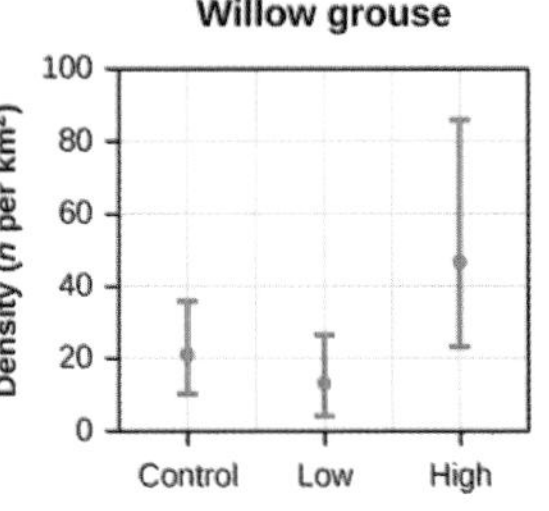

(credit: The Royal Society Publishing: Biology Letters)

Researchers were interested in answering the question, "How does sheep grazing affect the population densities of wild mountain birds?" To answer this question, the researchers counted population numbers of various birds in areas of low intensity sheep grazing and in areas of high intensity sheep grazing. A third set of data was collected from control areas in which no sheep grazing occurred. The results of this study are shown in these graphs. All of the bird species eat insects as their primary source of nutrition. The group labeled "insect eaters" combines many species because the numbers for individual species were too small to show separately as shown for the meadow pipit and willow grouse, which are both highly abundant. Because all of the birds are insect eaters, construct a scientific question related to this fact that the researchers could ask to refine their study even further. Explain your reasoning.

a. Does sheep grazing make insects more available to birds? This question refines the question about how sheep grazing affects bird populations because it asks more specifically how sheep grazing changes the food availability for the birds.
b. How does sheep grazing make insects more available to birds? This question refines the question about how sheep grazing affects insect populations because it asks more specifically how sheep grazing changes the food availability for the insects.
c. Does sheep grazing make insects more available to birds? This question refines the question about how sheep grazing affects bird populations because it asks more specifically how sheep grazing changes the food availability for the insects.
d. How does sheep grazing make insects more available to birds? This question refines the question about how sheep grazing affects bird populations because it asks more specifically how sheep grazing changes the food availability for the insects.

84. A pond ecosystem in an open field begins to be shaded by the growth of trees around its perimeter. Predict changes in this pond after the trees grow large enough to completely shade the pond.

a. The population sizes of all organisms will decrease in response to lower energy flowing into the pond.
b. The population densities of all organisms will increase in response to lower temperatures in the pond.
c. The population distributions of large organisms will shift from clumped to random in response to lower energy flowing into the pond.
d. The population distributions of small organisms will shift from uniform to clumped in response to lower temperatures in the pond.

85. A researcher has been studying a wildflower population growing in a large meadow. The researcher counted individual plants and mapped their locations. Analysis of the data revealed that the wildflower has a uniform population distribution. This result prompts the researcher to ask a new scientific question to further refine his understanding of the ecology of this plant species. Construct a scientific question the researcher might ask that is directly prompted by his first set of findings.

a. When does this plant species flower and how does it attract pollinators?
b. Does this wildflower species have any adaptations that function to defend the plant against herbivores?
c. Which species of insects and/or birds are pollinators for this wildflower species?
d. Does this wildflower species secrete any chemical compounds that inhibit growth of others of its species?

86. Fruit flies are found in many different areas in the world. Fruit flies that are resistant to cold temperatures tend to have decreased fecundity at early ages compared to flies that are not capable of surviving the cold. Explain a likely reason for why this set of traits is observed. (credit: Anthony Zera Publications)

a. Flies having traits that traded early reproductive energy for greater storage of energy in their bodies were favored via natural selection because they survived the cold better than flies that did not have these traits.
b. In cold conditions, flies have less need for reproduction than in warm conditions and so energy normally used for reproduction is diverted to other survival functions.
c. Flies respond to weather conditions to shift their energy resources to either storage in their bodies in the cold or to reproduction when conditions become warm again.
d. All fruit flies have the same genetic makeup, but express different patterns of genes under different conditions, which results in expression of certain genes for cold conditions and others for warm conditions.

87.

	% Females laying eggs in host	% Viability of young	Longevity of female parent (days)
Species A			
Mated females without food	23.5	92.5	2.6
Mated females with food	83.5	95.2	7.8
Species B			
Mated females without food	0.0	–	2.0
Mated females with food	68.9	95.3	6.9

(credit: Brazilian Archives of Biology and Technology)

Female parasitoid wasps lay their eggs inside the bodies of caterpillars. The caterpillars die when the eggs hatch, and the young wasps feed on the body of the caterpillar. Egg-laying females of two species of parasitoid wasps were studied in special growth chambers in which a food source was either provided or omitted. This table summarizes some of the data collected. Identify the statement most consistent with these data.

a. When energy availability is low, females put more energy than normal into producing offspring.
b. When energy availability is high, females produce offspring with higher viability.
c. When energy availability is low, females shift energy away from reproduction and toward their own survival.
d. When energy availability is high, females cannot both produce viable offspring and maintain their own survival.

88. During breeding season, many female elk mate with males, but not all mated females become pregnant. Female elk having body fat less than 6% were found to have greatly reduced chances of becoming pregnant than female elk having body fat above 10%. Explain how natural selection was likely involved in establishing this trait in elk. (credit: USGS Northern Prairie Wildlife Research Center)

a. Through natural selection, female elk that did not have the energy reserves to carry a pregnancy to term and did not become pregnant died whereas those which became pregnant anyway were favored.

b. Natural selection favored the selection of traits preventing pregnancies in female elk with low fat reserves, so this trait has become predominant in natural elk herds observed today.

c. Natural selection randomly changes the frequency of genes allowing traits preventing pregnancies in female elk with low fat reserves to be favored.

d. Natural selection leads to a sudden inheritable change in the genome of the female elk, ensuring female elk with very high fat reserves to effectively carry out pregnancy.

89. Research on elk in Yellowstone National Park was conducted to determine how body condition affects survival of the elk over the winter months. It was found that the probability of survival of female elk is greater when they have accumulated 15% or more body fat by the end of fall. Female elk with body fat less than 10% in late fall were found to be at high risk of not surviving the winter. Explain why this pattern is likely to be observed. (credit: USGS Northern Prairie Wildlife Research Center)

a. In winter, the availability of food decreases. So, there needs to be a certain threshold level of energy their bodies store in the form of fat to ensure their survival.

b. In winter, the availability of food increases. So, there should be a certain threshold level of energy in their bodies stored in the form of fat to ensure their survival.

c. In winter, elk's requirement for food increases due to increase in metabolic activities. So, there should be a certain threshold level of energy in their bodies stored in the form of fat to ensure their survival.

d. Elk release more energy in winter. So, there should be a certain threshold level of energy in their bodies stored in the form of fat to ensure their survival.

90.

Species	Birth rate (*N*/year)	Death rate (*N*/year)
A	1845	1467
B	43	79
C	2800	2115
D	16	16
E	933	1351

The table contains birth rates and death rates for populations of several species living in the same ecosystem. Analyze the data to identify the population(s) experiencing a negative change in population size.

a. species A only

b. species A and species C

c. species B and species D

d. species B and species E

91.

Year after flood	Number of individuals
1	5
2	10
3	16
4	25
5	36
6	58
7	82
8	99
9	110
10	116
11	120
12	122
13	121
14	122

These data were collected on the population size of a species of plant growing in a region during the years after a flood destroyed the area. Explain what the data indicate about this population.

a. The plant population grew exponentially throughout the years as the numbers of individuals increased at an exponential rate. The population eventually became stable after reaching a maximum number of 120 individuals, which could be the carrying capacity of the environment.
b. The population grew exponentially in the first few years and later became logistic as the rate slowed down. The population eventually became stable after reaching a maximum number of 120 individuals, which could be the carrying capacity of the local environment.
c. The plant population grew logistically throughout the years as the growth rate of the population slowed down. The population eventually became stable after reaching a maximum number of 120 individuals, which could be the carrying capacity of the environment.
d. The population grew exponentially in the first few years and later became logistic as the rate slowed down. The population eventually became stable after reaching a number of 116 individuals, which could be the carrying capacity of the environment.

92. It has been suggested a population of a flowering plant is being jeopardized by population declines in a butterfly species thought to be the primary pollinator of the plant. Identify data that could best be used to either justify or refute this suggestion.

a. nectar energy provided to the butterfly species per visit to a flower of the plant species in a field
b. number of fruits produced per flower of plants in a section of a field screened off from access by the butterfly species
c. number of butterfly visits per flower per day in various fields throughout the growing range of the plant
d. species of flowers visited by individual butterflies in a field and frequency of visits to each flower species

93. A conservation group has claimed that the introduction of logging into a forest ecosystem will decrease the carrying capacity of trout living in a stream within the ecosystem. Describe data that could be used to either justify or refute this claim. Explain your reasoning.

a. The growth rate of trout in the stream before and after logging will give an indication as to whether the claim is justified or not.

b. Evaluate the death rate of trout in the stream after the introduction of logging, which will be used to justify or refute the claim.

c. Collect data on number of trout in the stream after the introduction of logging, which will give an indication as to whether the claim is justified or not.

d. Collect data on the number of trout in the stream before and after logging, which will give an indication as to whether the claim is justified or not.

94. Predict how human population change in the next 50 years is likely to affect marine ecosystems.

a. Humans will decrease their own carrying capacity, which will also decrease the carrying capacities of marine ecosystems.

b. Decreased fishing can be expected, which will lead to rebounds in fish populations and healthier marine ecosystems.

c. Increases in greenhouse gas emissions are likely, with increases in ocean temperatures that trigger shifts in marine populations.

d. Biodiversity of marine ecosystems will increase as humans use engineering to increase food production in the oceans.

95. Describe how the quantity of waste from human activities can be expected to change in the next 50 years and why. Explain how that change could impact a specific ecosystem.

a. The amount of waste generated by human activities will increase exponentially as the human population continues to increase exponentially. Removal of waste would require a decrease in habitats, which will lead to decrease in populations of species dependent on those habitats.

b. The amount of waste generated by human activities will increase exponentially as the human population continues to increase exponentially. Removal of waste will require an increase in habitats, which will lead to exponential increase in populations of species dependent on those habitats.

c. The amount of waste generated by human activities will decrease exponentially as the human population continues to increase exponentially. Removal of waste would require an increase in habitats, which will lead to exponential increase in populations of species dependent on those habitats.

d. The amount of waste generated by human activities will decrease exponentially as the human population continues to increase exponentially. Removal of waste will require a decrease in habitats, which will lead to decrease in populations of species dependent on those habitats.

96. A company wants to establish suspended cultures of mussels in a natural estuary from which they can farm mussels in a sustainable enterprise. The suspended cultures would keep the mussels contained for easy capture, but would allow free flow of estuary waters in and out of the cultures. The company wants to know the maximum number of mussels they can farm each month and maintain a sustainable system. A biologist has suggested that the limiting factor for mussels is the amount of phytoplankton that the mussels feed on. Identify data that could best be used to either justify or refute this suggestion.

a. rates of growth of newly established mussel cultures in a lab under different phytoplankton concentrations

b. phytoplankton population changes in the estuary as a function of intensity and duration of sunlight exposure

c. biomasses of natural mussel populations and phytoplankton populations in the estuary determined at many different times

d. lab measurements of phytoplankton biomass in response to added mussel population numbers

97. A non-venomous species of snake has a wide geographical range. In one region, the species has dull coloration and in another region, the species exhibits bright coloration that resembles a local venomous species of snake. A hypothesis has been proposed that the bright coloration is an adaptation to defend against predation, an example of Batesian mimicry. Describe an experimental design that could be used to test this hypothesis.

a. Run field tests in which dull individuals and brightly colored individuals are captured and switched into the other's territory to see how many of each survive.
b. Run field tests in which video cameras are set up to record predators capturing dull individuals and brightly colored individuals in their native territories.
c. Run laboratory tests in which predators familiar with the poisonous snake are offered dull individuals and brightly colored individuals to see if the predators show a preference.
d. Run laboratory tests in which predators familiar with the dull colored non-poisonous snake are offered poisonous brightly colored individuals and non-poisonous brightly colored individuals to see if the predators show a preference.

98. Frogs are amphibians and spend time both on land and in water. Female frogs are vulnerable to predation by fish when they enter the water to lay eggs. A hypothesis has been proposed that frogs rely on chemical detection of predators in addition to visual detection. In other words, frogs detect the presence of predator fish by chemicals released by fish into the water. Design an experiment to test this hypothesis.

a. Arrange containers of water in which water can be freely shared between two compartments. Fish are contained within one compartment and frogs in another such that the frogs on one side cannot see or hear fish on other side. Observe and compare the egg laying behavior of female frogs in the presence and absence of predator fish in the fish tank.
b. Arrange containers of water in which water can be freely shared between two compartments. Fish and frogs are contained within one compartment such that frogs cannot see or hear fish. Observe and compare the egg laying behavior of female frogs in the presence and absence of predator fish.
c. Arrange containers of water in which water can be freely shared between two compartments. Fish and frogs are contained within one compartment such that frogs can see or hear fish. Observe and compare the egg laying behavior of female frogs in the presence and absence of predator fish in the fish tank.
d. Arrange containers of water in which water can be freely shared between two compartments. Fish are contained within one compartment and frogs in another such that frogs on one side can see or hear fish on other side. Observe and compare the egg laying behavior of female frogs in the presence and absence of predator fish in the fish tank.

99.

	Unspotted males	Spotted males
1998		
Upstream	244	742
Downstream	368	1165
2008		
Upstream	298	791
Downstream	1086	205

A biologist studied two populations of the same species of a small fish living in different locations in the same tropical stream. He noticed that adult male fish were either spotted or unspotted and made careful counts of the two variants in the two stream locations in 1998. He repeated his population studies ten years later. Construct a hypothesis that accounts for these data.

a. A new prey species of the fish established itself only in the downstream portion of the stream between 1998 and 2008.

b. A new prey species of the fish established itself only in the upstream portion of the stream between 1998 and 2008.

c. A new predator of the fish established itself only in the downstream portion of the stream between 1998 and 2008.

d. A new predator of the fish established itself in both the upstream and downstream portions of the stream between 1998 and 2008.

100.

	Survival Rate	
	Released into mottled snail region	Released into solid snail region
Mottled snails	95%	5%
Solid snails	22%	93%

A species of marine snail is found in shallow waters near coastlines. This snail feeds on detritus on the ocean bottom. Researchers noticed that snails in one area had a mottled appearance, while snails in another area were solid in color. The researchers set up areas in each region for study and then released both mottled and solid snails into the solid snail region and released both mottled and solid snails into the mottled snail region. The survival rate of each variant was measured. Results are summarized in this table. Construct a possible hypothesis that accounts for these data. Explain your reasoning.

a. A possible hypothesis is that the coloration of the snail is dependent on environmental conditions. Camouflage in both mottled and solid snails is best during optimum environmental conditions and does not change according to the region in which they are placed.

b. A possible hypothesis is that the coloration of the snail is an adaptation in the form of camouflage to protect the snail from predators in the region it is invading. Mottled snails are best camouflaged in the solid snail region and stand out to predators and suffer greater predation when placed in their native region.

c. A possible hypothesis is that the coloration of the snail is an adaptation in the form of camouflage to protect the snail from predators in its native region. Mottled snails are best camouflaged in their native region and stand out to predators and suffer greater predation when placed in the region normally occupied by solid snails.

d. A possible hypothesis is that the coloration of the snail is an adaptation in the form of camouflage to protect the snail from predators in its native region. Solid snails are best camouflaged in mottled snail region and are more obvious to predators when placed in their native region.

101.

The graph summarizes data concerning four different species of lizards that inhabit tropical habitats. Predict how these species will be able to coexist if they inhabit the same region of a tropical habitat.

a. All species will coexist with one another because they consume the same amounts of food.
b. Species A, B, and C will best coexist because of their similarities in amount and type of food eaten.
c. Species A and B will best coexist because they have the most overlap in diet.
d. Species D will best coexist with any one of the other species because this species eats completely different types of food.

102.

	Insects	Nectar	Worms
Species A	95%	5%	0%
Species B	92%	3%	5%

Warblers are a group of small songbirds consisting of many species. The table summarizes data collected on the diets of two species of warblers. In addition, both species A and B use the same types of nesting materials and sites for building nests.

A biologist observes that Species A and Species B primarily inhabit different regions of a forest in western Canada. During a forest fire that wiped out the region it inhabited, Species B fled to the region inhabited by Species A. Predict what is likely to happen to these two species in the future. Explain your reasoning.

a. Both the species will survive because of difference in needs for food and nesting space.
b. Species A will increase in population whereas species B will remain same due to the overlapping needs for food and nesting space.
c. Only one of these species will survive in this region due to the difference in needs for food and nesting space. The species that loses will either die off or migrate to another region.
d. Only one of these species will survive in this region due to the overlapping needs for food and nesting space. The species that loses will either die off or migrate to another region.

103. Himalayan blackberries are an invasive species that has spread in the forest of the Pacific Northwest. The plants develop thick tangles of cane covered with thorns that cover ground with a tight mat. Ecologists hypothesized that Himalayan blackberries displace native species of shrubs by reproducing faster and reducing areas available for growth. They recorded the density of blackberries and native salmonberries, a native shrub, along a creek for several years. The percentage areas of ground covered by blackberries and native shrubs were plotted over time. Based on the graph, what statement best explain the role of blackberries on the ecosystem studied?

a. Blackberries promote the growth of salmonberry shrubs.
b. Blackberries and salmonberry shrubs do not interfere with each other's growth.
c. Salmonberry shrubs prevent the growth of blackberries.
d. Blackberries displaced salmonberry shrubs.

104. Predict how ecosystems in the northernmost land regions will be affected by human population change in the next 50 years.

a. Biodiversity of these northernmost regions will remain constant as humans will find other more habitable locations to house their growing numbers.
b. The populations of organisms presently inhabiting these regions will shift as global warming causes many species to decline and new species to move in.
c. The carrying capacity of these regions for humans will decrease as the human population increases exponentially.
d. Ecosystems can be expected to remain untouched by humans as new technologies are developed to sustain a growing population.

105. A researcher is interested in investigating whether the croaking pattern produced by males in a frog species is a learned behavior or an innate behavior. Which of the following would best help the researcher answer this question?

a. genetic analyses of adult male frogs raised in isolation and in multigenerational frog communities
b. field observations of adult frogs in their native habitat during mating season
c. video recordings of individual frogs raised in large multigenerational frog communities
d. audio recordings of individual frogs at sexual maturity after being raised in total isolation

106. A biologist hypothesizes birds of various species recognize the predator warning calls of other bird species. The biologist has established several feeders in a forest where birds come to feed regularly. They are spread out over a wide area, making it difficult to observe all of the boxes at the same time. Describe how the biologist can use this site to collect data to test his hypothesis.

a. The biologist can use video cameras to record the behavior of birds coming to the feeders.

b. The biologist can leave an audio recorder near the feeders.

c. The biologist can record the behavior of birds by comparing them with other birds using video cameras.

d. The biologist could observe the birds continually for one month.

107.

	Yellow bunting encountered and fled	Yellow bunting encountered and attacked	Total encounters
Butterflies with eyespot	9	19	28
Butterflies without eyespot	0	18	18

Yellow buntings are birds that feed on butterflies, including Aglaisurticae, a species of butterfly that has bright circular coloring on its wing called an eyespot. Biologists have hypothesized that eyespots mimic owl eyes. Owls are predators of yellow buntings.

In laboratory experiments using yellow buntings captured from the wild and held in captivity, individual birds were observed during sessions in which they were given butterflies that had either not be treated or had been treated to remove their eyespots. Yellow buntings were scored according to whether they showed fleeing behavior when they encountered butterflies of both types. The data were compiled into a table. How do these data support the claim that one species' response to information can affect natural selection in another species?

a. Comparison of the total number of encounters shows that more birds responded to the eyespot, a trait that will likely be selected against in natural populations of the butterfly.

b. Comparison of the number of birds attacking butterflies with and without eyespots suggests that the presence of an eyespot makes butterflies more visible to predators resulting in selection against the trait.

c. Comparison of the number of birds fleeing from butterflies with and without eyespots indicates that the eyespot trait has been disfavored because this trait makes the butterflies stand out to predators.

d. Comparison of the number of birds fleeing from butterflies with and without eyespots suggests that selection has occurred in butterflies in favor of the eyespot trait, which mimics a predator of the bird.

108.

Calls made by small bird	Call sound frequency	Small bird hearing range (1–10 kHz)	Large bird hearing range (1–4 kHz)
Mobbing call	4.5 kHz	Yes	Yes
Scolding call	4 kHz	Yes	Yes
Warning call	7–8 kHz	Yes	No

(credit: Behavioral Ecology and Sociobiology)

Biologists analyzed the sound frequencies of different calls made by a small bird species that serve as prey for a much larger predator bird species. The small bird makes three different kinds of calls: a mobbing call that a group of adults make when mobbing a single predator bird in defense of their nests, a scolding call that a single bird makes to scold a predator bird perched nearby, and a warning call that a single bird makes to warn other birds when a predator bird flies into the vicinity. A table was created to summarize the data from this analysis and also show the range of sound frequencies audible to the prey and predator species. Explain how these data support the claim that communication of information affects natural selection in the small bird species.

a. A scolding call made by small birds can be heard by large predator birds, which is required to scold away the birds; therefore, this trait is favorable and has been naturally selected.

b. As the mobbing call made by small birds can be heard by large predator birds, therefore small birds cannot defend their nests without the predators knowing. This unfavorable trait is thus naturally selected.

c. The warning call made by small birds cannot be heard by large predator birds, giving the small birds an advanced warning. This is an unfavorable trait that gives birds a survival disadvantage.

d. The warning call made by small birds cannot be heard by large predator birds, giving the small birds an advanced warning. This is a favorable trait that gives birds a survival advantage.

109. Which of the following statements most directly supports the claim that Monarch butterfly migration is a regulated event?

a. Monarch butterflies fly up to 3,000 miles from their summer habitat in North America to their winter habitat in Mexico.

b. Because the life span of a Monarch butterfly is so short, not every generation of Monarchs migrates.

c. Monarch caterpillars feed on milkweed while adult butterflies feed on flower nectar.

d. Changes in day length trigger hormonal and nervous system changes in Monarchs that result in behavioral changes.

110. What evidence can you cite to support the claim that the timing of entry into hibernation by grizzly bears is regulated? Justify why this evidence supports the claim.

a. Grizzly bears go into hibernation at the end of winters. This observation provides evidence that there is some environmental cue that triggers physiological changes in bears.

b. Grizzly bears do not go into hibernation at the beginning of autumn. This observation provides evidence that there is some environmental cue that triggers physiological changes in bears.

c. Grizzly bears go into hibernation at random times during the year. This observation provides evidence that there is some environmental cue that triggers physiological changes in bears.

d. Grizzly bears do not go into hibernation at random times during the year. This observation provides evidence that there is some environmental cue that triggers physiological changes in bears.

111. Some animal behaviors can be modified by experience. Which of the following accurately predicts how an experiential factor is likely to affect an animal's behavior?

a. A species of salmon will migrate up the same river regardless of increases in predators that visit these waterways from one year to the next.

b. Female elk that had difficult deliveries of calves will continue to mate with males in succeeding mating seasons.

c. Bears that receive food from humans are later more likely to break into human habitations than bears that are not approached by humans.

d. A bird raised from an egg isolated in a lab environment will give the same alarm call as birds of the same species raised in the wild.

112. Estivation is a type of dormancy that some animals enter during hot, dry periods. Typically, the metabolisms of these animals slow down, their bodies retain water and some shift to altered nitrogen metabolism. Predict how the behavior of an animal such as a lizard would change in response to environmental factors that trigger the lizard into entering estivation.

a. The lizard would sit on a rock to remain protected from predation and water loss. The breathing and heart rate would slow as it begins estivating. Then it would only do critical activities needed to sustain its living state.

b. The lizard would live in a shaded spot to remain protected from predation and water loss. The breathing and heart rate would slow as it begins estivating. This way a lizard can perform all activities.

c. The lizard would stay in a shaded spot to remain protected from predation and water loss. Its breathing and heart rate would slow as it begins estivating. Then it would only do critical activities needed to sustain its living state.

d. The lizard would live in a shaded spot to remain protected from predation and water loss. The breathing and heart rate would increase as it begins estivating. Then it would only do critical activities needed to sustain its living state.

113.

	Number of trials where test animals spent the majority of time		
Treatment of paper towels	**Stimulus**	**Control**	***P***
Non-injured	12	8	0.504
Injured	3	17	0.002

Many animals produce chemical compounds that function as alarm cues. Researchers interested in determining whether salamanders fall into this group performed the following experiment. Long-toed salamanders were captured from the wild. A few were injured and tissue from their injuries was collected and ground up with water. This solution was used to moisten a paper towel. Others were not injured and placed on moistened paper towels for 48 hours. The moistened paper towels were placed at one end of a rectangular box (stimulus end) and a paper towel moistened with water was placed at the other end (control end). In each test, a salamander was placed in the center and the researchers observed the direction in which the salamander moved. Multiple trials were performed using paper towels moistened with chemicals from injured and non-injured salamanders and the data was compiled into a table. Which of the following statements is an accurate analysis of the data?

a. This salamander releases chemical compounds during injury that elicit avoidance behavior in members of its own species.
b. Chemical compounds released from this salamander species during injury elicit attractant behavior in members of its own species.
c. Both injured and non-injured salamanders produce chemical compounds that elicit avoidance behavior in non-injured salamanders.
d. There was a significant difference between stimulus and control results from treatment involving non-injured salamanders.

114.

Food dispersion	Presence of species B	Number of species A giving alarm calls	Number of species A not giving alarm calls
Concentrated	Present	10	2
Concentrated	Absent	1	11
Dispersed	Present	2	10
Dispersed	Absent	0	12

(credit: Ethology)

Biologists have observed some animal species making predator warning calls when no predator is in the area. In one species of bird, for example, individuals appeared to perform this behavior as a means for deceiving other birds into fleeing from a food source that the bird making the call was then better able to access.

In investigating the possibility that this bird species uses false alarm calls to improve its access to food, the following experiment was conducted. Researchers set up a bird feeding table in a protected area to attract two species of birds, species A and B. They either clumped food in one concentrated pile on the table or dispersed the food in a much wider area under and around the table. They then observed the number of times an individual in species A gave a predator warning call when no predator was in sight as well as the presence or absence of species B at the feeding table. The data collected by the researchers are shown here. What do the data suggest about the use of deception by species A? Explain your reasoning.

a. Species A uses deception in cases when food is plentiful, but concentrated, so access is limited to a small group of birds. A bird that had restricted access to the food has open access because of the alarm. Only in cases where it's necessary does the bird carry out this deceptive behavior.
b. Species A uses deception in cases when food is plentiful, but concentrated, so that access is limited to a large group of birds. A bird that had restricted access to the food has open access because of the alarm. Only in cases where it's necessary does the bird carry out this deceptive behavior.
c. Species A uses deception in cases when food is plentiful, but dispersed, so that access is limited to a small group of birds. A bird that had restricted access to the food has open access because of the alarm. Only in cases where it's necessary does the bird carry out this deceptive behavior.
d. Species A uses deception in cases when food is plentiful, but concentrated, so that access is limited to a small group of birds. A bird that had unrestricted access to the food has open access because of the alarm. Deceptive behavior is carried out regardless of whether it is needed or not.

115.

Footsteps → Greeting behavior
Loud noise → Hiding behavior
Many trials of footsteps followed by loud noise → Hiding behavior
Footsteps → Hiding behavior

This representation was created to describe how the behavior of a cat was affected as it was exposed to different stimuli. Identify the term that should be used for the process represented by this diagram.

a. innate behavior
b. classical conditioning
c. operant conditioning
d. cognitive learning

116. Elk migrate from summer feeding grounds in high mountain meadows down into lower valleys during winter. Using the words behavioral changes, physiological changes, seasonal changes, and migration, write the order of events that occur to bring about this migration.

a. seasonal changes, physiological changes, migration, and behavioral changes, respectively
b. physiological changes, seasonal changes, behavioral changes, and migration, respectively
c. seasonal changes, behavioral changes, physiological changes, and migration, respectively
d. seasonal changes, physiological changes, behavioral changes, and migration, respectively

117. Some fish swim in schools, which can respond rapidly by moving quickly away from predator threats. In schools, fish swim in a coordinated pattern without moving chaotically and bumping into one another. Which type of communication between individuals could account for the precisely coordinated movements of all of the fish in a school in response to a threat?

a. aural signals
b. pheromone signals
c. tactile signals
d. visual signals

118. Describe a situation in which animals of the same species exchange information in response to an approaching predator. Include a description of how the information flows between individuals.

a. Herring gulls have a brightly colored bill. When a predator approaches, the parent gull stands over its chick and taps the bill on the ground in front of it, which elicits a begging response from a hungry chick.
b. Prairie dogs live in underground burrows. If a look-out observes an approaching predator, they give an aural alarm cry communicating the information to the foraging individuals who then run back to safety.
c. Herring gulls have a brightly colored bill. When a predator approaches, the parent gull stands over its nest and taps the bill on the ground, thus exchanging information of the approaching predator.
d. Prairie dogs live inside the bark of trees. If a look-out observes an approaching predator, they give an aural alarm cry communicating the information to the foraging individuals who then run back to safety.

SCIENCE PRACTICE CHALLENGE QUESTIONS

119. A flask of nutrient broth, buffered to maintain pH, is inoculated with a strain of *E. coli*. The flask is placed in a constant temperature environment where it is aerated by shaking.

A. **Predict** the effect of a change in energy availability over time.

B. **Represent** the change graphically in terms of the number of cells as a function of time.

C. In your graph as time progresses there is a change in the growth rate of the population. Add annotation to your graph to **describe** the time interval during which the growth rate is increasing linearly in proportion to the number of cells. Add annotation to your graph to **describe** another time interval during which the growth rate is decreasing in proportion to the square of the number of cells. Add a third annotation to **describe** an interval of time where the rate of growth is zero.

D. **Select and justify** two measurements of the *E. coli* population that could be made at two different points in time during growth that would be sufficient to answer questions about the population size at any time.

E. **Describe** the population of *E. coli* if the environment was continuously supplement by additional nutrient broth.

120. The following problem extends the Hardy-Weinberg model of population dynamics that was covered in Chapter 19. It applies mathematics that would be appropriate after a second course in Algebra. While the concept applied in this problem are within the scope of the Exam the mathematical representations are not and the item is provided to allow students who are able another look at the concepts.

The Hardy-Weinberg model of population dynamics is an algebraic representation of the relationships among genotype frequencies, F, and the probability of the dominant allele A, p, and the recessive allele a, q. The Hardy-Weinberg model of population dynamics is based on several assumptions. One of these assumptions is “random mating.” If all genes in a population are equally able to reproduce, this means that all genes are equally fit and equally fertile. Consequently, the population never evolves.

Populations do evolve and the Hardy-Weinberg model can be modified slightly to allow evolution to occur. Suppose that there is an initial population at generation zero and the probability of the dominant allele at that time is p_0. Later, at population k the probability is different. But if the frequencies of the three different combinations of alleles is known then the probabilities p_k and q_k can be calculated at generation k

(1) $p_k = F_k(AA) + ½F_k(Aa)\ q_k = F_k(aa) + ½F_k(Aa)$

And since p and q are probabilities for a case where only two alleles exist, p+q=1. Then also $(p+q)^2=1$, leading the Hardy-Weinberg equation

$$p^2{}_k + 2p_k q_k + q^2{}_k = 1$$

The gene distribution never changes and $p_k=p_{k-1}$.

The equations of the Hardy-Weinberg model were modified (Haldane, 1924) to create a model in which evolution occurs:

(2)

$$F_k(AA) = p^2{}_k w_{AA} \big/ W\ F_k(Aa) = 2p_k q_k w_{Aa} \big/ W\ F_k =$$

$$q^2{}_k w_{aa} \big/ W\ W = p^2 w_{AA} + 2pqw_{Aa} \big/ q^2 w_{aa}$$

Haldane divides by the factor $W=F_k(AA)+F_k(Aa)+F_k(aa)$ so that the probabilities that are still calculated with equation (1) to continue to satisfy the condition for p and q to represent probabilities: $(p+q)^2=1$.

A. **Justify** Haldane’s model in terms of what the factors w_{AA}, w_{Aa}, and w_{aa} mean.

B. Suppose that $w_{AA} = w_{Aa} = 1$, but that $w_{aa} = 0.8$. **Predict** what will happen to the population over time.

Fitness is determined by the environment. Moree (*The American Naturalist*, 86, 1952) measured the relative fitness in *Drosophila melanogaster* of a recessive allele that imparts black eye color as population density increases. A varying number of flies with an equal number of males and females were placed in a pint jar and progeny counted. In each experiment the population was initially heterozygous.

Number of females x Number of males	w_{aa}
1 x 1	0
10 x 10	0.06
50 x 50	0.11
150 x 150	0.46

Table 36.3

C. Apply Haldane’s approach to **calculate** the probability p in the first generation after mating 150 female and 150 male flies that are heterozygous using $w_{AA} = w_{Aa} = 1$.

Rendel (Evolution, 5, 1951) conducted an investigation of the dependence of fecundity (fertility) on light in ebony-eyed *D. melanogaster*. A summary of some of the data that he reported is shown in the table below:

	Fraction females inseminated	
Phenotype of male	Light condition	Dark condition
Ebony	0.215	0.607
Wild type	0.494	0.466

Table 36.4

D. **Pose two scientific questions** concerning the behavioral response indicated by the data that can be tested experimentally.

E. Is there a question you can add here to wrap up this set with this LO from the list? In this case "light" is the single environmental factor, and they two phenotypes are ebony and wild type that result from different genotypes within the population of flies.

37 | ECOSYSTEMS

Figure 37.1 In the southwestern United States, rainy weather causes an increase in production of pinyon nuts, causing the deer mouse population to explode. Deer mice may carry a virus called *Sin Nombre* (a hantavirus) that causes respiratory disease in humans and has a high fatality rate. In 1992–1993, wet *El Niño* weather caused a *Sin Nombre* epidemic. Navajo healers, who were aware of the link between this disease and weather, predicted the outbreak. (credit "highway": modification of work by Phillip Capper; credit "mouse": modification of work by USFWS)

Chapter Outline

Introduction

In 1993, an interesting example of ecosystem dynamics occurred when a rare lung disease struck inhabitants of the southwestern United States. This disease had an alarming rate of fatalities, killing more than half of early patients, many of whom were Native Americans. These formerly healthy young adults died from complete respiratory failure. The disease was unknown, and the Centers for Disease Control (CDC), the United States government agency responsible for managing potential epidemics, was brought in to investigate. The scientists could have learned about the disease had they known to talk with the Navajo healers who lived in the area and who had observed the connection between rainfall and mice populations, thereby predicting the 1993 outbreak.

The cause of the disease, determined within a few weeks by the CDC investigators, was the hantavirus known as *Sin Nombre*, the virus with "no name." With insights from traditional Navajo medicine, scientists were able to characterize the disease and rapidly and institute effective health measures to prevent its spread. Though not as common any more, infections from hantavirus still occur. You can read more about hantavirus in this **CDC article (http://openstaxcollege.org/l/32hanta)** .

37.1 | Ecology for Ecosystems

In this section, you will explore the following questions:

- What are the basic types of ecosystems on Earth?
- What are methods that ecologists use to study ecosystem structure and dynamics?
- What are the different methods of ecosystem modeling?
- What is the difference between a food chain and a food web, and what is the importance of each?

Connection for AP® Courses

Life in an ecosystem is often about the competition for limited resources, a characteristic of the theory of natural selection. Competition in communities (all living things within a specific habitat) is observed both within species and among different species. The resources for which organisms compete include organic material from living or previously living organisms, sunlight, and mineral nutrients, which provide the energy for living processes and the matter to make up organisms' physical structures. Other critical factors influencing community dynamics are the components of its physical and geographic environment: a habitat's latitude, amount of rainfall, topography (elevation), and available species. These are all important environmental variables that determine which organisms can exist within a particular area.

Information presented and the examples highlighted in the section support concepts outlined in Big Idea 2 and Big Idea 4 of the AP® Biology Curriculum Framework. The AP® Learning Objectives listed in the Curriculum Framework provide a transparent foundation for the AP® Biology course, an inquiry-based laboratory experience, instructional activities, and AP® exam questions. A learning objective merges required content with one or more of the seven science practices.

Big Idea 2	Biological systems utilize free energy and molecular building blocks to grow, to reproduce, and to maintain dynamic homeostasis.
Enduring Understanding 2.A	Growth, reproduction and maintenance of living systems require free energy and matter.
Essential Knowledge	**2.A.1** All living systems require constant input of free energy.
Science Practice	**6.4** The student can make claims and predictions about natural phenomena based on scientific theories and models.
Learning Objective	**2.3** The student is able to predict how changes in free energy availability affect organisms, populations, and ecosystems.
Enduring Understanding 2.D	Growth and dynamic homeostasis of a biological system are influenced by changes in the system's environment.
Essential Knowledge	**2.D.1** All biological systems from cells and organisms to populations, communities and ecosystems are affected by complex biotic and abiotic interactions involving exchange of matter and free energy.
Science Practice	**5.1** The student can analyze data to identify patterns or relationships.
Learning Objective	**2.24** The student is able to analyze data to identify possible patterns and relationships between a biotic or abiotic factor and a biological system, including an ecosystem.
Big Idea 4	Biological systems interact, and these systems and their interactions possess complex properties.
Enduring Understanding 4.A	Interactions within biological systems lead to complex properties.
Essential Knowledge	**4.A.6** Interactions among living systems and with their environment result in the movement of matter and energy.
Science Practice	**2.2** The student can apply mathematical routines to quantities that describe natural phenomena.
Learning Objective	**4.14** The student is able to apply mathematical routines to quantities that describe interactions among living systems and their environment, which result in the movement of matter and energy.
Essential Knowledge	**4.A.6** Interactions among living systems and with their environment result in the movement of matter and energy.

Science Practice	**1.4** The student can use representations and models to analyze situations or solve problems qualitatively and quantitatively.
Learning Objective	**4.15** The student is able to use visual representations to analyze situations or solve problems qualitatively to illustrate how interactions among living systems and with their environment result in the movement of matter and energy.
Essential Knowledge	**4.A.6** Interactions among living systems and with their environment result in the movement of matter and energy.
Science Practice	**6.4** The student can make claims and predictions about natural phenomena based on scientific theories and models.
Learning Objective	**4.16** The student is able to predict the effects of a change of matter or energy availability on communities and ecosystems.

An **ecosystem** is a community of living organisms and their interactions with their abiotic (non-living) environment. Ecosystems can be small, such as the tide pools found near the rocky shores of many oceans, or large, such as the Amazon Rainforest in Brazil (Figure 37.2).

(a)

(b)

Figure 37.2 A (a) tidal pool ecosystem in Matinicus Island in Maine is a small ecosystem, while the (b) Amazon Rainforest in Brazil is a large ecosystem. (credit a: modification of work by "takomabibelot"/Flickr; credit b: modification of work by Ivan Mlinaric)

There are three broad categories of ecosystems based on their general environment: freshwater, ocean water, and terrestrial. Within these broad categories are individual ecosystem types based on the organisms present and the type of environmental habitat.

Ocean ecosystems are the most common, comprising 75 percent of the Earth's surface and consisting of three basic types: shallow ocean, deep ocean water, and deep ocean surfaces (the low depth areas of the deep oceans). The shallow ocean ecosystems include extremely biodiverse coral reef ecosystems, and the deep ocean surface is known for its large numbers of plankton and krill (small crustaceans) that support it. These two environments are especially important to aerobic respirators worldwide as the phytoplankton perform 40 percent of all photosynthesis on Earth. Although not as diverse as the other two, deep ocean ecosystems contain a wide variety of marine organisms. Such ecosystems exist even at the bottom of the ocean where light is unable to penetrate through the water.

Freshwater ecosystems are the rarest, occurring on only 1.8 percent of the Earth's surface. Lakes, rivers, streams, and springs comprise these systems; they are quite diverse, and they support a variety of fish, amphibians, reptiles, insects, phytoplankton, fungi, and bacteria.

Terrestrial ecosystems, also known for their diversity, are grouped into large categories called biomes, such as tropical rain forests, savannas, deserts, coniferous forests, deciduous forests, and tundra. Grouping these ecosystems into just a few biome categories obscures the great diversity of the individual ecosystems within them. For example, there is great variation in desert vegetation: the saguaro cacti and other plant life in the Sonoran Desert, in the United States, are relatively abundant compared to the desolate rocky desert of Boa Vista, an island off the coast of Western Africa (Figure 37.3).

(a)

(b)

Figure 37.3 Desert ecosystems, like all ecosystems, can vary greatly. The desert in (a) Saguaro National Park, Arizona, has abundant plant life, while the rocky desert of (b) Boa Vista island, Cape Verde, Africa, is devoid of plant life. (credit a: modification of work by Jay Galvin; credit b: modification of work by Ingo Wölbern)

Ecosystems are complex with many interacting parts. They are routinely exposed to various disturbances, or changes in the environment that effect their compositions: yearly variations in rainfall and temperature and the slower processes of plant growth, which may take several years. Many of these disturbances are a result of natural processes. For example, when lightning causes a forest fire and destroys part of a forest ecosystem, the ground is eventually populated by grasses, then by bushes and shrubs, and later by mature trees, restoring the forest to its former state. The impact of environmental disturbances caused by human activities is as important as the changes wrought by natural processes. Human agricultural practices, air pollution, acid rain, global deforestation, overfishing, eutrophication, oil spills, and illegal dumping on land and into the ocean are all issues of concern to conservationists.

Equilibrium is the steady state of an ecosystem where all organisms are in balance with their environment and with each other. In ecology, two parameters are used to measure changes in ecosystems: resistance and resilience. The ability of an ecosystem to remain at equilibrium in spite of disturbances is called **resistance**. The speed at which an ecosystem recovers equilibrium after being disturbed, called its **resilience**. Ecosystem resistance and resilience are especially important when considering human impact. The nature of an ecosystem may change to such a degree that it can lose its resilience entirely. This process can lead to the complete destruction or irreversible altering of the ecosystem.

Food Chains and Food Webs

The term "food chain" is sometimes used metaphorically to describe human social situations. In this sense, food chains are thought of as a competition for survival, such as "who eats whom?" Someone eats and someone is eaten. Therefore, it is not surprising that in our competitive "dog-eat-dog" society, individuals who are considered successful are seen as being at the top of the food chain, consuming all others for their benefit, whereas the less successful are seen as being at the bottom.

The scientific understanding of a food chain is more precise than in its everyday usage. In ecology, a **food chain** is a linear sequence of organisms through which nutrients and energy pass: primary producers, primary consumers, and higher-level consumers are used to describe ecosystem structure and dynamics. There is a single path through the chain. Each organism in a food chain occupies what is called a **trophic level**. Depending on their role as producers or consumers, species or groups of species can be assigned to various trophic levels.

In many ecosystems, the bottom of the food chain consists of photosynthetic organisms (plants and/or phytoplankton), which are called **primary producers**. The organisms that consume the primary producers are herbivores: the **primary consumers**. **Secondary consumers** are usually carnivores that eat the primary consumers. **Tertiary consumers** are carnivores that eat other carnivores. Higher-level consumers feed on the next lower tropic levels, and so on, up to the organisms at the top of the food chain: the **apex consumers**. In the Lake Ontario food chain shown in Figure 37.4, the Chinook salmon is the apex consumer at the top of this food chain.

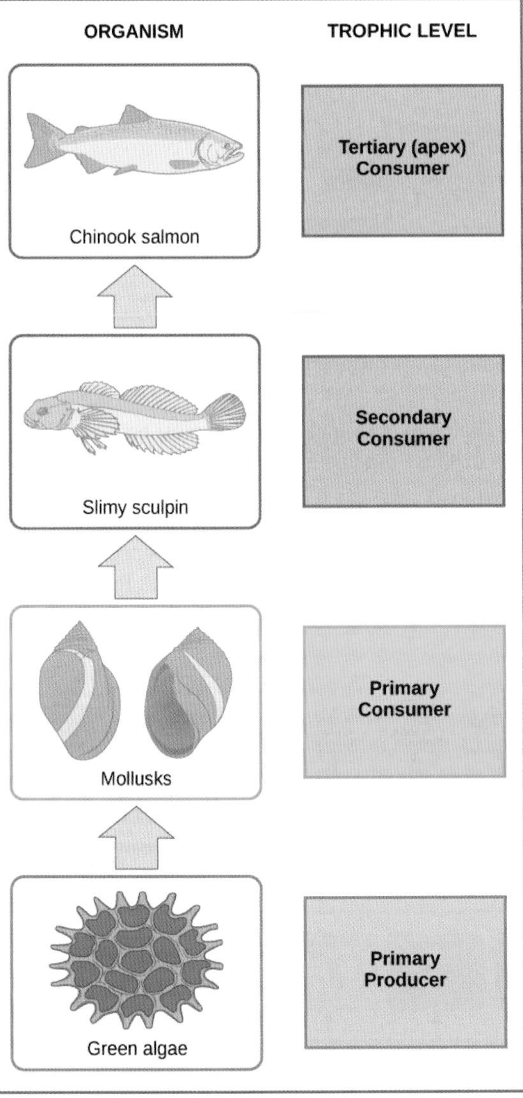

Figure 37.4 These are the trophic levels of a food chain in Lake Ontario at the United States-Canada border. Energy and nutrients flow from photosynthetic green algae at the bottom to the top of the food chain: the Chinook salmon.

One major factor that limits the length of food chains is energy. Energy is lost as heat between each trophic level due to the second law of thermodynamics. Thus, after a limited number of trophic energy transfers, the amount of energy remaining in the food chain may not be great enough to support viable populations at yet a higher trophic level.

The loss of energy between trophic levels is illustrated by the pioneering studies of Howard T. Odum in the Silver Springs, Florida, ecosystem in the 1940s (**Figure 37.5**). The primary producers generated 20,819 kcal/m^2/yr (kilocalories per square meter per year), the primary consumers generated 3368 kcal/m^2/yr, the secondary consumers generated 383 kcal/m^2/yr, and the tertiary consumers only generated 21 kcal/m^2/yr. Thus, there is little energy remaining for another level of consumers in this ecosystem.

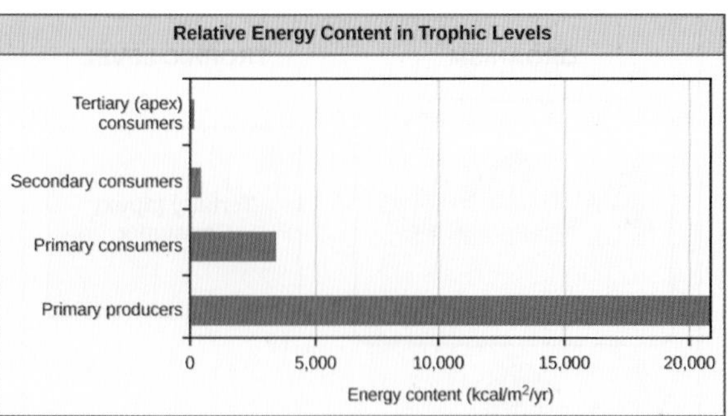

Figure 37.5 The relative energy in trophic levels in a Silver Springs, Florida, ecosystem is shown. Each trophic level has less energy available and supports fewer organisms at the next level.

There is a problem when using food chains to accurately describe most ecosystems. Even when all organisms are grouped into appropriate trophic levels, some of these organisms can feed on species from more than one trophic level; likewise, some of these organisms can be eaten by species from multiple trophic levels. In other words, the linear model of ecosystems, the food chain, is not completely descriptive of ecosystem structure. A holistic model—which accounts for all the interactions between different species and their complex interconnected relationships with each other and with the environment—is a more accurate and descriptive model for ecosystems. A **food web** is a graphic representation of a holistic, non-linear web of primary producers, primary consumers, and higher-level consumers used to describe ecosystem structure and dynamics (Figure 37.6).

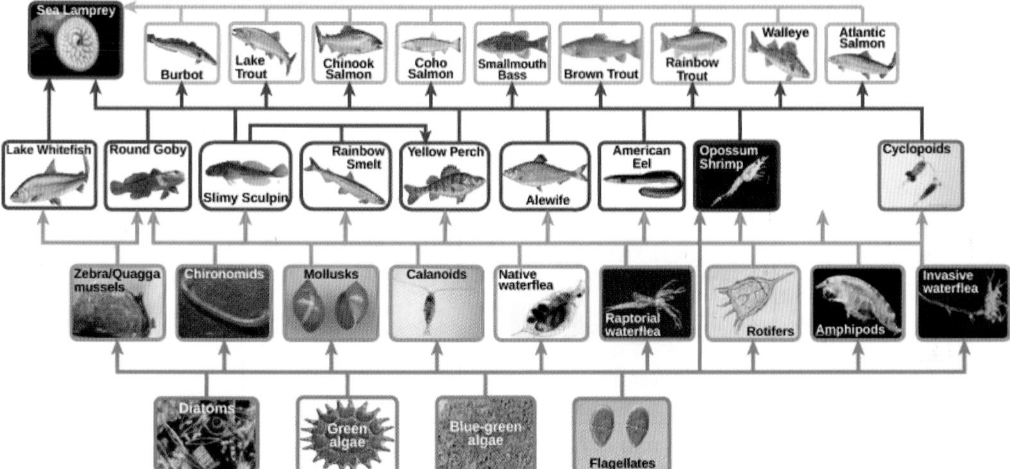

Figure 37.6 This food web shows the interactions between organisms across trophic levels in the Lake Ontario ecosystem. Primary producers are outlined in green, primary consumers in orange, secondary consumers in blue, and tertiary (apex) consumers in purple. Arrows point from an organism that is consumed to the organism that consumes it. Notice how some lines point to more than one trophic level. For example, the opossum shrimp eats both primary producers and primary consumers. (credit: NOAA, GLERL)

A comparison of the two types of structural ecosystem models shows strength in both. Food chains are more flexible for analytical modeling, are easier to follow, and are easier to experiment with, whereas food web models more accurately represent ecosystem structure and dynamics, and data can be directly used as input for simulation modeling.

Head to this online interactive simulator (http://openstaxcollege.org/l/food_web) to investigate food web function. In the *Interactive Labs* box, under Food Web, click **Step 1**. Read the instructions first, and then click **Step 2** for additional instructions. When you are ready to create a simulation, in the upper-right corner of the *Interactive Labs* box, click **OPEN SIMULATOR**.

What happens to a food web in the absence of primary producers such as plants? Why?

a. A food web will be produced, but position of some organisms will vary in the food web as their diet will vary.

b. Some primary consumers will perform the function of primary producers in the food web or chain.

c. A food web is unable to be produced as there is no basal energy source for consumers to obtain energy from.

d. A food web is unable to be produced because very less amount of basal energy source is available for consumers to obtain energy from.

Two general types of food webs are often shown interacting within a single ecosystem. A **grazing food web** (such as the Lake Ontario food web in Figure 37.6) has plants or other photosynthetic organisms at its base, followed by herbivores and various carnivores. A **detrital food web** consists of a base of organisms that feed on decaying organic matter (dead organisms), called decomposers or detritivores. These organisms are usually bacteria or fungi that recycle organic material back into the biotic part of the ecosystem as they themselves are consumed by other organisms. As all ecosystems require a method to recycle material from dead organisms, most grazing food webs have an associated detrital food web. For example, in a meadow ecosystem, plants may support a grazing food web of different organisms, primary and other levels of consumers, while at the same time supporting a detrital food web of bacteria, fungi, and detrivorous invertebrates feeding off dead plants and animals.

Three-spined Stickleback

It is well established by the theory of natural selection that changes in the environment play a major role in the evolution of species within an ecosystem. However, little is known about how the evolution of species within an ecosystem can alter the ecosystem environment. In 2009, Dr. Luke Harmon, from the University of Idaho in Moscow, published a paper that for the first time showed[1] that the evolution of organisms into subspecies can have direct effects on their ecosystem environment.

The three-spined stickleback (*Gasterosteus aculeatus*) is a freshwater fish that evolved from a saltwater fish to live in freshwater lakes about 10,000 years ago, which is considered a recent development in evolutionary time (Figure 37.7). Over the last 10,000 years, these freshwater fish then became isolated from each other in different lakes. Depending on which lake population was studied, findings showed that these sticklebacks then either remained as one species or evolved into two species. The divergence of species was made possible by their use of different areas of the pond for feeding called micro niches.

Dr. Harmon and his team created artificial pond microcosms in 250-gallon tanks and added muck from freshwater ponds as a source of zooplankton and other invertebrates to sustain the fish. In different experimental tanks they introduced one species of stickleback from either a single-species or double-species lake.

Over time, the team observed that some of the tanks bloomed with algae while others did not. This puzzled the scientists, and they decided to measure the water's dissolved organic carbon (DOC), which consists of mostly large molecules of decaying organic matter that give pond-water its slightly brownish color. It turned out that the water from the tanks with two-species fish contained larger particles of DOC (and hence darker water) than water with single-species fish. This increase in DOC blocked the sunlight and prevented algal blooming. Conversely, the water from the single-species tank contained smaller DOC particles, allowing more sunlight penetration to fuel the algal blooms.

This change in the environment, which is due to the different feeding habits of the stickleback species in each lake type, probably has a great impact on the survival of other species in these ecosystems, especially other photosynthetic organisms. Thus, the study shows that, at least in these ecosystems, the environment and the evolution of populations have reciprocal effects that may now be factored into simulation models.

Figure 37.7 The three-spined stickleback evolved from a saltwater fish to freshwater fish. (credit: Barrett Paul, USFWS)

In the lake microcosms, why were algal blooms possible in the presence of one, but not two stickleback species?

a. Because there were larger molecules of dissolved organic content in the presence of two species versus one species.
b. Because two stickleback species consume all of the nutrients required by the algae to bloom.
c. Because one species had more dissolved organic matter available in their habitat than the other species.
d. Because more algae is consumed in the presence of two stickleback species versus only one species.

Research into Ecosystem Dynamics: Ecosystem Experimentation and Modeling

The study of the changes in ecosystem structure caused by changes in the environment (disturbances) or by internal forces is called **ecosystem dynamics**. Ecosystems are characterized using a variety of research methodologies. Some ecologists study ecosystems using controlled experimental systems, while some study entire ecosystems in their natural state, and others use both approaches.

A **holistic ecosystem model** attempts to quantify the composition, interaction, and dynamics of entire ecosystems; it is the most representative of the ecosystem in its natural state. A food web is an example of a holistic ecosystem model. However, this type of study is limited by time and expense, as well as the fact that it is neither feasible nor ethical to do experiments on large natural ecosystems. To quantify all different species in an ecosystem and the dynamics in their habitat is difficult, especially when studying large habitats such as the Amazon Rainforest, which covers 1.4 billion acres (5.5 million km^2) of the Earth's surface.

For these reasons, scientists study ecosystems under more controlled conditions. Experimental systems usually involve either partitioning a part of a natural ecosystem that can be used for experiments, termed a **mesocosm**, or by re-creating an ecosystem entirely in an indoor or outdoor laboratory environment, which is referred to as a **microcosm**. A major limitation to these approaches is that removing individual organisms from their natural ecosystem or altering a natural ecosystem through partitioning may change the dynamics of the ecosystem. These changes are often due to differences in species numbers and diversity and also to environment alterations caused by partitioning (mesocosm) or re-creating (microcosm) the natural habitat. Thus, these types of experiments are not totally predictive of changes that would occur in the ecosystem from which they were gathered.

As both of these approaches have their limitations, some ecologists suggest that results from these experimental systems should be used only in conjunction with holistic ecosystem studies to obtain the most representative data about ecosystem structure, function, and dynamics.

Scientists use the data generated by these experimental studies to develop ecosystem models that demonstrate the structure and dynamics of ecosystems. Three basic types of ecosystem modeling are routinely used in research and ecosystem management: a conceptual model, an analytical model, and a simulation model. A **conceptual model** is an ecosystem model that consists of flow charts to show interactions of different compartments of the living and nonliving components of the ecosystem. A conceptual model describes ecosystem structure and dynamics and shows how environmental disturbances affect the ecosystem; however, its ability to predict the effects of these disturbances is limited. Analytical and simulation models, in contrast, are mathematical methods of describing ecosystems that are indeed capable of predicting the effects of potential environmental changes without direct experimentation, although with some limitations as to accuracy. An **analytical model** is an ecosystem model that is created using simple mathematical formulas to predict the effects of environmental disturbances on ecosystem structure and dynamics. A **simulation model** is an ecosystem model that is created using complex computer algorithms to holistically model ecosystems and to predict the effects of environmental disturbances on ecosystem structure and dynamics. Ideally, these models are accurate enough to determine which components of the ecosystem are particularly sensitive to disturbances, and they can serve as a guide to ecosystem managers (such as conservation ecologists or fisheries biologists) in the practical maintenance of ecosystem health.

Conceptual Models

Conceptual models are useful for describing ecosystem structure and dynamics and for demonstrating the relationships between different organisms in a community and their environment. Conceptual models are usually depicted graphically as flow charts. The organisms and their resources are grouped into specific compartments with arrows showing the relationship and transfer of energy or nutrients between them. Thus, these diagrams are sometimes called compartment models.

To model the cycling of mineral nutrients, organic and inorganic nutrients are subdivided into those that are bioavailable (ready to be incorporated into biological macromolecules) and those that are not. For example, in a terrestrial ecosystem near a deposit of coal, carbon will be available to the plants of this ecosystem as carbon dioxide gas in a short-term period, not from the carbon-rich coal itself. However, over a longer period, microorganisms capable of digesting coal will incorporate its carbon or release it as natural gas (methane, CH_4), changing this unavailable organic source into an available one. This conversion is greatly accelerated by the combustion of fossil fuels by humans, which releases large amounts of carbon dioxide into the atmosphere. This is thought to be a major factor in the rise of the atmospheric carbon dioxide levels in the industrial age. The carbon dioxide released from burning fossil fuels is produced faster than photosynthetic organisms can use it. This process is intensified by the reduction of photosynthetic trees because of worldwide deforestation. Most scientists agree that high atmospheric carbon dioxide is a major cause of global climate change.

Conceptual models are also used to show the flow of energy through particular ecosystems. Figure 37.8 is based on Howard

1. *Nature* (Vol. 458, April 1, 2009)

T. Odum's classical study of the Silver Springs, Florida, holistic ecosystem in the mid-twentieth century.[2] This study shows the energy content and transfer between various ecosystem compartments.

2. Howard T. Odum, "Trophic Structure and Productivity of Silver Springs, Florida," *Ecological Monographs* 27, no. 1 (1957): 47–112.

visual CONNECTION

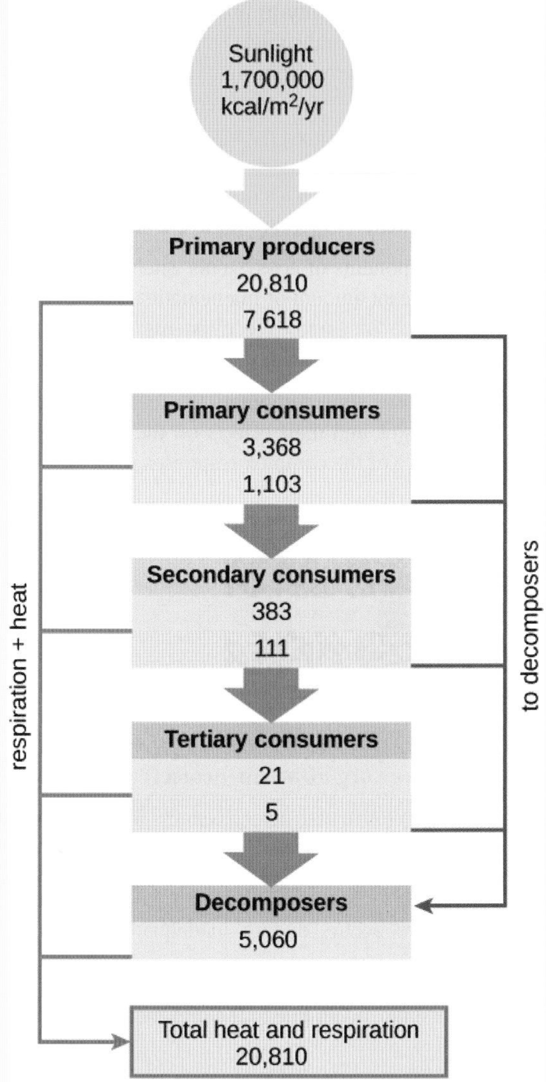

Figure 37.8 This conceptual model shows the flow of energy through a spring ecosystem in Silver Springs, Florida. Notice that the energy decreases with each increase in trophic level.

Why do you think the value for gross productivity of the primary producers is the same as the value for total heat and respiration ($20,810\ kcal/m^2/yr$)?

a. Total heat and respiration refers to the energy used by all trophic levels and the energy provided by the primary producers is more than the energy provided by primary consumers to these levels.

b. Gross productivity of primary producers is the same as the value for total heat and respiration because of the high efficiency of conversion of solar energy to energy used by all trophic levels by primary producers.

c. The value for gross productivity of primary producers and total heat and respiration is same as primary producers provide energy to primary consumers and secondary consumers only.

d. Total heat and respiration refers to energy used by all trophic levels and the only accessible energy to these levels is provided by primary producers.

Analytical and Simulation Models

The major limitation of conceptual models is their inability to predict the consequences of changes in ecosystem species and/or environment. Ecosystems are dynamic entities and subject to a variety of abiotic and biotic disturbances caused by natural forces and/or human activity. Ecosystems altered from their initial equilibrium state can often recover from such disturbances and return to a state of equilibrium. As most ecosystems are subject to periodic disturbances and are often in a state of change, they are usually either moving toward or away from their equilibrium state. There are many of these equilibrium states among the various components of an ecosystem, which affects the ecosystem overall. Furthermore, as humans have the ability to greatly and rapidly alter the species content and habitat of an ecosystem, the need for predictive models that enable understanding of how ecosystems respond to these changes becomes more crucial.

Analytical models often use simple, linear components of ecosystems, such as food chains, and are known to be complex mathematically; therefore, they require a significant amount of mathematical knowledge and expertise. Although analytical models have great potential, their simplification of complex ecosystems is thought to limit their accuracy. Simulation models that use computer programs are better able to deal with the complexities of ecosystem structure.

A recent development in simulation modeling uses supercomputers to create and run individual-based simulations, which accounts for the behavior of individual organisms and their effects on the ecosystem as a whole. These simulations are considered to be the most accurate and predictive of the complex responses of ecosystems to disturbances.

Visit **The Darwin Project (http://openstaxcollege.org/l/Darwin_project)** to view a variety of ecosystem models.

Why doesn’t an increased number of prey species in marine ecosystems lead to maximal feeding of predators?

a. Because there may not be enough predators that can eat each of the prey species.

b. Non-maximal feeding of predators occurs due to inadequate dispersal of prey species in the marine ecosystems.

c. Non maximal feeding of predators may occur due to the presence of new prey species with effective defenses that are inherited.

d. Because of natural selection, non-maximal feeding of predators occurs.

science practices CONNECTION for AP® Courses

Activity

Investigate a food web in an aquatic or terrestrial ecosystem of your choice, for example, coral reef. Create a diagram of the food web and describe the role of each organism in the web. Then arbitrarily remove one organism from the food web and predict how this will affect the ecosystem with respect to the movement of matter and energy. Put that organism back in your food web and remove a different organism. Predict how the ecosystem will be affected. Was your prediction the same as it was for the first organism?

Think About It

What are the differences and similarities between food chains and food webs? How are both used to describe an ecosystem with respect to the movement of matter and energy through the ecosystem?

37.2 | Energy Flow through Ecosystems

In this section, you will explore the following questions:

- How do organisms acquire energy in a food web and associated food chains?
- How does the efficiency of energy transfer between trophic levels affect ecosystem structure and dynamics?
- What are the characteristics of each trophic level in an ecosystem, and how can ecological pyramids be used to model them?

Connection for AP® Courses

As we learned when we explored concepts in earlier chapters, all living organisms require energy in one form or another, usually ATP, to carry out cellular processes. It is important to understand how organisms in an ecosystem acquire free energy and how that energy is passed among organisms through food webs and their constituent food chains. Energy takes a one-way path through ecosystems because energy conversions result in a loss of usable (free) energy through the release of heat. In addition, matter cycles and recycles as it moves from organism to organism. We also have learned that the biotic and abiotic components of an ecosystem interact. Autotrophs, chemoautotrophs, heterotrophs and decomposers comprise the living components, whereas abiotic factors include nutrients, temperature, pH, availability of sunlight, and type of soil. In this section, a variety of ways to depict this movement of energy through an ecosystem will be presented. Utilizing multiple representations of data as well as understanding the movement of matter and energy through systems are significant concepts in the AP® Biology course.

Information presented and the examples highlighted in the section support concepts outlined in Big Idea 4 of the AP® Biology Curriculum Framework. The AP® Learning Objectives listed in the Curriculum Framework provide a transparent foundation for the AP® Biology course, an inquiry-based laboratory experience, instructional activities, and AP® exam questions. A learning objective merges required content with one or more of the seven science practices.

Big Idea 4	Biological systems interact, and these systems and their interactions possess complex properties.
Enduring Understanding 4.A	Interactions within biological systems lead to complex properties.
Essential Knowledge	**4.A.6** Interactions among living systems and with their environment result in the movement of matter and energy.

Science Practice	**2.2** The student can apply mathematical routines to quantities that describe natural phenomena.
Learning Objective	**4.14** The student is able to apply mathematical routines to quantities that describe interactions among living systems and their environment, which result in the movement of matter and energy.
Essential Knowledge	**4.A.6** Interactions among living systems and with their environment result in the movement of matter and energy.
Science Practice	**1.4** The student can use representations and models to analyze situations or solve problems qualitatively and quantitatively.
Learning Objective	**4.15** The student is able to use visual representations to analyze situations or solve problems qualitatively to illustrate how interactions among living systems and with their environment result in the movement of matter and energy.

All living things require energy in one form or another. Energy is required by most complex metabolic pathways (often in the form of adenosine triphosphate, ATP), especially those responsible for building large molecules from smaller compounds, and life itself is an energy-driven process. Living organisms would not be able to assemble macromolecules (proteins, lipids, nucleic acids, and complex carbohydrates) from their monomeric subunits without a constant energy input.

It is important to understand how organisms acquire energy and how that energy is passed from one organism to another through food webs and their constituent food chains. Food webs illustrate how energy flows directionally through ecosystems, including how efficiently organisms acquire it, use it, and how much remains for use by other organisms of the food web.

How Organisms Acquire Energy in a Food Web

Energy is acquired by living things in three ways: photosynthesis, chemosynthesis, and the consumption and digestion of other living or previously living organisms by heterotrophs.

Photosynthetic and chemosynthetic organisms are both grouped into a category known as autotrophs: organisms capable of synthesizing their own food (more specifically, capable of using inorganic carbon as a carbon source). Photosynthetic autotrophs (photoautotrophs) use sunlight as an energy source, whereas chemosynthetic autotrophs (chemoautotrophs) use inorganic molecules as an energy source. Autotrophs are critical for all ecosystems. Without these organisms, energy would not be available to other living organisms and life itself would not be possible.

Photoautotrophs, such as plants, algae, and photosynthetic bacteria, serve as the energy source for a majority of the world's ecosystems. These ecosystems are often described by grazing food webs. Photoautotrophs harness the solar energy of the sun by converting it to chemical energy in the form of ATP (and NADP). The energy stored in ATP is used to synthesize complex organic molecules, such as glucose.

Chemoautotrophs are primarily bacteria that are found in rare ecosystems where sunlight is not available, such as in those associated with dark caves or hydrothermal vents at the bottom of the ocean (**Figure 37.9**). Many chemoautotrophs in hydrothermal vents use hydrogen sulfide (H_2S), which is released from the vents as a source of chemical energy. This allows chemoautotrophs to synthesize complex organic molecules, such as glucose, for their own energy and in turn supplies energy to the rest of the ecosystem.

Figure 37.9 Swimming shrimp, a few squat lobsters, and hundreds of vent mussels are seen at a hydrothermal vent at the bottom of the ocean. As no sunlight penetrates to this depth, the ecosystem is supported by chemoautotrophic bacteria and organic material that sinks from the ocean's surface. This picture was taken in 2006 at the submerged NW Eifuku volcano off the coast of Japan by the National Oceanic and Atmospheric Administration (NOAA). The summit of this highly active volcano lies 1535 m below the surface.

Productivity within Trophic Levels

Productivity within an ecosystem can be defined as the percentage of energy entering the ecosystem incorporated into biomass in a particular trophic level. **Biomass** is the total mass, in a unit area at the time of measurement, of living or previously living organisms within a trophic level. Ecosystems have characteristic amounts of biomass at each trophic level. For example, in the English Channel ecosystem the primary producers account for a biomass of 4 g/m^2 (grams per meter squared), while the primary consumers exhibit a biomass of 21 g/m^2.

The productivity of the primary producers is especially important in any ecosystem because these organisms bring energy to other living organisms by photoautotrophy or chemoautotrophy. The rate at which photosynthetic primary producers incorporate energy from the sun is called **gross primary productivity**. An example of gross primary productivity is shown in the compartment diagram of energy flow within the Silver Springs aquatic ecosystem as shown (Figure 37.8). In this ecosystem, the total energy accumulated by the primary producers (gross primary productivity) was shown to be 20,810 $kcal/m^2/yr$.

Because all organisms need to use some of this energy for their own functions (like respiration and resulting metabolic heat loss) scientists often refer to the net primary productivity of an ecosystem. **Net primary productivity** is the energy that remains in the primary producers after accounting for the organisms' respiration and heat loss. The net productivity is then available to the primary consumers at the next trophic level. In our Silver Spring example, 13,187 of the 20,810 $kcal/m^2/yr$ were used for respiration or were lost as heat, leaving 7,632 $kcal/m^2/yr$ of energy for use by the primary consumers.

Ecological Efficiency: The Transfer of Energy between Trophic Levels

As illustrated in Figure 37.8, large amounts of energy are lost from the ecosystem from one trophic level to the next level as energy flows from the primary producers through the various trophic levels of consumers and decomposers. The main reason for this loss is the second law of thermodynamics, which states that whenever energy is converted from one form to another, there is a tendency toward disorder (entropy) in the system. In biologic systems, this means a great deal of energy is lost as metabolic heat when the organisms from one trophic level consume the next level. In the Silver Springs ecosystem example (Figure 37.8), we see that the primary consumers produced 1103 $kcal/m^2/yr$ from the 7618 $kcal/m^2/yr$ of energy available to them from the primary producers. The measurement of energy transfer efficiency between two successive trophic levels is termed the **trophic level transfer efficiency (TLTE)** and is defined by the formula:

$$\text{TLTE} = \frac{\text{production at present trophic level}}{\text{production at previous trophic level}} \times 100$$

In Silver Springs, the TLTE between the first two trophic levels was approximately 14.8 percent. The low efficiency of energy transfer between trophic levels is usually the major factor that limits the length of food chains observed in a food web. The fact is, after four to six energy transfers, there is not enough energy left to support another trophic level. In the Lake Ontario example shown in Ecology of Ecosystems, only three energy transfers occurred between the primary producer, (green algae), and the apex consumer (Chinook salmon).

Ecologists have many different methods of measuring energy transfers within ecosystems. Some transfers are easier or more difficult to measure depending on the complexity of the ecosystem and how much access scientists have to observe the ecosystem. In other words, some ecosystems are more difficult to study than others, and sometimes the quantification of energy transfers has to be estimated.

Another main parameter that is important in characterizing energy flow within an ecosystem is the net production efficiency. **Net production efficiency (NPE)** allows ecologists to quantify how efficiently organisms of a particular trophic level incorporate the energy they receive into biomass; it is calculated using the following formula:

$$\text{NPE} = \frac{\text{net consumer productivity}}{\text{assimilation}} \times 100$$

Net consumer productivity is the energy content available to the organisms of the next trophic level. **Assimilation** is the biomass (energy content generated per unit area) of the present trophic level after accounting for the energy lost due to incomplete ingestion of food, energy used for respiration, and energy lost as waste. Incomplete ingestion refers to the fact that some consumers eat only a part of their food. For example, when a lion kills an antelope, it will eat everything except the hide and bones. The lion is missing the energy-rich bone marrow inside the bone, so the lion does not make use of all the calories its prey could provide.

Thus, NPE measures how efficiently each trophic level uses and incorporates the energy from its food into biomass to fuel the next trophic level. In general, cold-blooded animals (ectotherms), such as invertebrates, fish, amphibians, and reptiles, use less of the energy they obtain for respiration and heat than warm-blooded animals (endotherms), such as birds and mammals. The extra heat generated in endotherms, although an advantage in terms of the activity of these organisms in colder environments, is a major disadvantage in terms of NPE. Therefore, many endotherms have to eat more often than ectotherms to get the energy they need for survival. In general, NPE for ectotherms is an order of magnitude (10x) higher than for endotherms. For example, the NPE for a caterpillar eating leaves has been measured at 18 percent, whereas the NPE for a squirrel eating acorns may be as low as 1.6 percent.

The inefficiency of energy use by warm-blooded animals has broad implications for the world's food supply. It is widely accepted that the meat industry uses large amounts of crops to feed livestock, and because the NPE is low, much of the energy from animal feed is lost. For example, it costs about $0.01 to produce 1000 dietary calories (kcal) of corn or soybeans, but approximately $0.19 to produce a similar number of calories growing cattle for beef consumption. The same energy content of milk from cattle is also costly, at approximately $0.16 per 1000 kcal. Much of this difference is due to the low NPE of cattle. Thus, there has been a growing movement worldwide to promote the consumption of non-meat and non-dairy foods so that less energy is wasted feeding animals for the meat industry.

Modeling Ecosystems Energy Flow: Ecological Pyramids

The structure of ecosystems can be visualized with ecological pyramids, which were first described by the pioneering studies of Charles Elton in the 1920s. **Ecological pyramids** show the relative amounts of various parameters (such as number of organisms, energy, and biomass) across trophic levels.

Pyramids of numbers can be either upright or inverted, depending on the ecosystem. As shown in Figure 37.10, typical grassland during the summer has a base of many plants and the numbers of organisms decrease at each trophic level. However, during the summer in a temperate forest, the base of the pyramid consists of few trees compared with the number of primary consumers, mostly insects. Because trees are large, they have great photosynthetic capability, and dominate other plants in this ecosystem to obtain sunlight. Even in smaller numbers, primary producers in forests are still capable of supporting other trophic levels.

Another way to visualize ecosystem structure is with pyramids of biomass. This pyramid measures the amount of energy converted into living tissue at the different trophic levels. Using the Silver Springs ecosystem example, this data exhibits an upright biomass pyramid (Figure 37.10), whereas the pyramid from the English Channel example is inverted. The plants (primary producers) of the Silver Springs ecosystem make up a large percentage of the biomass found there. However, the phytoplankton in the English Channel example make up less biomass than the primary consumers, the zooplankton. As with inverted pyramids of numbers, this inverted pyramid is not due to a lack of productivity from the primary producers, but results from the high turnover rate of the phytoplankton. The phytoplankton are consumed rapidly by the primary consumers, thus, minimizing their biomass at any particular point in time. However, phytoplankton reproduce quickly, thus they are able to support the rest of the ecosystem.

Pyramid ecosystem modeling can also be used to show energy flow through the trophic levels. Notice that these numbers are the same as those used in the energy flow compartment diagram in Figure 37.8. Pyramids of energy are always upright, and an ecosystem without sufficient primary productivity cannot be supported. All types of ecological pyramids are useful for characterizing ecosystem structure. However, in the study of energy flow through the ecosystem, pyramids of energy are the most consistent and representative models of ecosystem structure (Figure 37.10).

visual CONNECTION

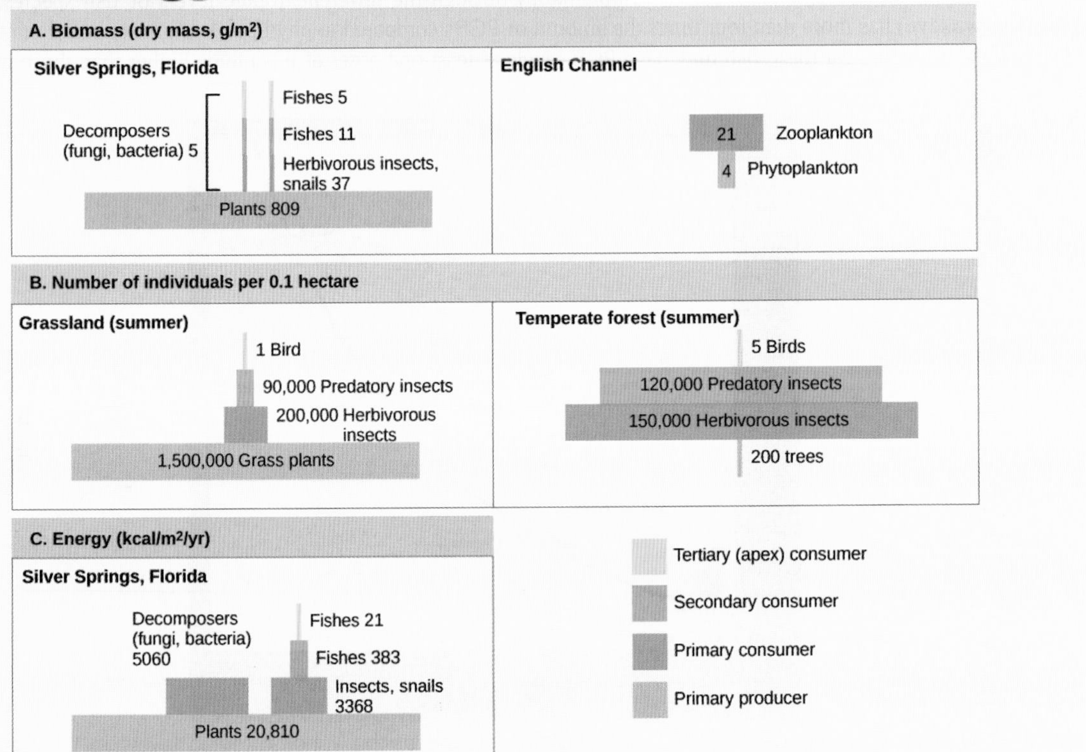

Figure 37.10 Ecological pyramids depict the (a) biomass, (b) number of organisms, and (c) energy in each trophic level.

Pyramids depicting the number of organisms or biomass may be inverted, upright, or even diamond-shaped. Which type of pyramid is always upright and why?

a. Pyramid of biomass, as biomass will always be found at the base and there is loss and not gain of biomass through the trophic levels.
b. Pyramid of number, as the numbers of producers is always more than the number of consumers in every ecosystem.
c. Pyramid of energy, as energy will always be found at the base and there is loss and not gain of energy through the trophic levels.
d. Pyramid of predators, as predators are always fewer in an ecosystem than the producers for the ecosystem to work efficiently.

Consequences of Food Webs: Biological Magnification

One of the most important environmental consequences of ecosystem dynamics is biomagnification. **Biomagnification** is the increasing concentration of persistent, toxic substances in organisms at each trophic level, from the primary producers to the apex consumers. Many substances have been shown to bioaccumulate, including classical studies with the pesticide **d**ichloro**d**iphenyl**t**richloroethane (DDT), which was published in the 1960s bestseller, *Silent Spring*, by Rachel Carson. DDT was a commonly used pesticide before its dangers became known. In some aquatic ecosystems, organisms from each trophic level consumed many organisms of the lower level, which caused DDT to increase in birds (apex consumers) that ate fish. Thus, the birds accumulated sufficient amounts of DDT to cause fragility in their eggshells. This effect increased egg breakage during nesting and was shown to have adverse effects on these bird populations. The use of DDT was banned in the United States in the 1970s.

Other substances that biomagnify are polychlorinated biphenyls (PCBs), which were used in coolant liquids in the United States until their use was banned in 1979, and heavy metals, such as mercury, lead, and cadmium. These substances were best studied in aquatic ecosystems, where fish species at different trophic levels accumulate toxic substances brought through the ecosystem by the primary producers. As illustrated in a study performed by the National Oceanic and Atmospheric Administration (NOAA) in the Saginaw Bay of Lake Huron (Figure 37.11), PCB concentrations increased from the ecosystem's primary producers (phytoplankton) through the different trophic levels of fish species. The apex consumer (walleye) has more than four times the amount of PCBs compared to phytoplankton. Also, based on results from other studies, birds that eat these fish may have PCB levels at least one order of magnitude higher than those found in the lake fish.

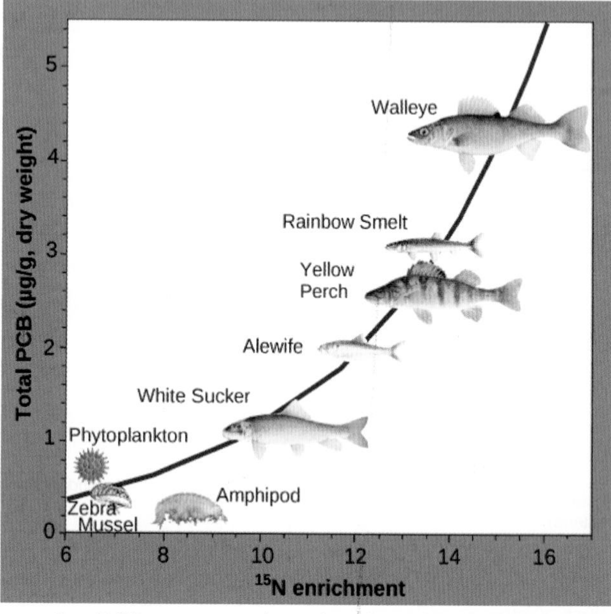

Figure 37.11 This chart shows the PCB concentrations found at the various trophic levels in the Saginaw Bay ecosystem of Lake Huron. Numbers on the x-axis reflect enrichment with heavy isotopes of nitrogen (^{15}N), which is a marker for increasing trophic level. Notice that the fish in the higher trophic levels accumulate more PCBs than those in lower trophic levels. (credit: Patricia Van Hoof, NOAA, GLERL)

Other concerns have been raised by the accumulation of heavy metals, such as mercury and cadmium, in certain types of seafood. The United States Environmental Protection Agency (EPA) recommends that pregnant women and young children should not consume any swordfish, shark, king mackerel, or tilefish because of their high mercury content. These individuals are advised to eat fish low in mercury: salmon, tilapia, shrimp, pollock, and catfish. Biomagnification is a good example of how ecosystem dynamics can affect our everyday lives, even influencing the food we eat.

everyday CONNECTION for AP® Courses

Many people enjoy eating swordfish, but pregnant women and young children should avoid it due to its high mercury content resulting from biomagnification.

Figure 37.12

Why does biomagnification render larger, predatory species such as swordfish more toxic to humans than smaller, planktivorous species such as anchovies?

a. Larger animals consume many small organisms, which leads to accumulation of oxygen in their body over time.
b. Larger animals consume many small organisms, which leads to accumulation of mercury in their body over time.
c. Larger animals consume many small organisms, which leads to accumulation of hydrogen in their body over time.
d. Larger animals consume many small organisms, which leads to accumulation of polyglucose in their body over time.

science practices CONNECTION for AP® Courses

Lab Investigation

AP® Biology Investigation Labs: Inquiry-Based Approach, Investigation 10: Energy Dynamics. This inquiry-based investigation provides an opportunity for you to explore factors that govern energy capture, allocation, storage, and transfer between producers and consumers in a terrestrial ecosystem composed of Wisconsin Fast Plants (producers) and cabbage white butterfly (*Pieris rapae*) larvae.

Activity

An ecosystem consists of earthworms, heterotrophic soil bacteria, grass, deer, beetles, and a lion. Create a mini-poster to describe the trophic structure of the ecosystem, how each organism receives inputs of energy and nutrients, where outputs (e.g., wastes) go, and the effect(s) each organisms has on the others. Include all energy transformations and transfers based on the hypothetical assumption that 9,500 J of net energy is available at the producer level.

37.3 | Biogeochemical Cycles

In this section, you will explore the following questions:

- What are the basic stages in the biogeochemical cycles of water, nitrogen, phosphorus, and sulfur?
- How have human activities impacted these biogeochemical cycles, and what are the potential consequences for Earth?

Connection for AP® Courses

As we learned in Energy Flow through Ecosystems, energy takes a one-way path (flows directionally) through the trophic levels in an ecosystem. However, the matter that comprises living organisms is conserved and recycled through what are referred to as **biogeochemical cycles**. The six most common elements associated with organic molecules—carbon, nitrogen, hydrogen, oxygen, phosphorus, and sulfur—take a variety of chemical forms and may exist for long periods in Earth's atmosphere, on land, in water, or beneath our planet's surface. Geologic processes, including weathering and erosion, play a role in this recycling of materials from the environment to living organisms. For the purpose of AP®, you do *not* need to know the details of every biogeochemical cycle, though some details of those cycles are covered in this section.

Information presented and the examples highlighted in the section support concepts outlined in Big Idea 2 and Big Idea 4 of the AP® Biology Curriculum Framework. The AP® Learning Objectives listed in the Curriculum Framework provide a transparent foundation for the AP® Biology course, an inquiry-based laboratory experience, instructional activities, and AP® exam questions. A learning objective merges required content with one or more of the seven science practices.

Big Idea 2	Biological systems utilize free energy and molecular building blocks to grow, to reproduce, and to maintain dynamic homeostasis.
Enduring Understanding 2.A	Growth, reproduction and maintenance of living systems require free energy and matter.
Essential Knowledge	**2.A.3** Organisms must exchange matter with the environment to grow, reproduce and maintain organization.
Science Practice	**1.1** The student can create representations and models of natural or man-made phenomena and systems in the domain.
Science Practice	**1.4** The student can use representations and models to analyze situations or solve problems qualitatively and quantitatively.
Learning Objective	**2.9** The student is able to represent graphically or model quantitatively the exchange of molecules between an organism and its environment, and the subsequent use of these molecules to build new molecules that facilitate dynamic homeostasis, growth and reproduction.
Big Idea 4	Biological systems interact, and these systems and their interactions possess complex properties.
Enduring Understanding 4.A	Interactions within biological systems lead to complex properties.
Essential Knowledge	**4.A.6** Interactions among living systems and with their environment result in the movement of matter and energy.
Science Practice	**1.4** The student can use representations and models to analyze situations or solve problems qualitatively and quantitatively.

Learning Objective	**4.15** The student is able to use visual representations to analyze situations or solve problems qualitatively to illustrate how interactions among living systems and with their environment results in the movement of matter and energy.

Water contains hydrogen and oxygen, which is essential to all living processes. The **hydrosphere** is the area of the Earth where water movement and storage occurs: as liquid water on the surface and beneath the surface or frozen (rivers, lakes, oceans, groundwater, polar ice caps, and glaciers), and as water vapor in the atmosphere. Carbon is found in all organic macromolecules and is an important constituent of fossil fuels. Nitrogen is a major component of our nucleic acids and proteins and is critical to human agriculture. Phosphorus, a major component of nucleic acid (along with nitrogen), is one of the main ingredients in artificial fertilizers used in agriculture and their associated environmental impacts on our surface water. Sulfur, critical to the 3–D folding of proteins (as in disulfide binding), is released into the atmosphere by the burning of fossil fuels, such as coal.

The cycling of these elements is interconnected. For example, the movement of water is critical for the leaching of nitrogen and phosphate into rivers, lakes, and oceans. Furthermore, the ocean itself is a major reservoir for carbon. Thus, mineral nutrients are cycled, either rapidly or slowly, through the entire biosphere, from one living organism to another, and between the biotic and abiotic world.

Head to this website (http://openstaxcollege.org/l/biogeochemical) to learn more about biogeochemical cycles.

What is true of geochemical cycles?

a. There is a variable amount of each element on Earth.

b. A reservoir is where elements remain through time.

c. Only external energy sources drive movement of elements.

d. Geochemical cycles are characterized by the movement of elements.

The Water (Hydrologic) Cycle

Water is the basis of all living processes. The human body is more than 1/2 water and human cells are more than 70 percent water. Thus, most land animals need a supply of fresh water to survive. However, when examining the stores of water on Earth, 97.5 percent of it is non-potable salt water (Figure 37.13). Of the remaining water, 99 percent is locked underground as water or as ice. Thus, less than 1 percent of fresh water is easily accessible from lakes and rivers. Many living things, such as plants, animals, and fungi, are dependent on the small amount of fresh surface water supply, a lack of which can have massive effects on ecosystem dynamics. Humans, of course, have developed technologies to increase water availability, such as digging wells to harvest groundwater, storing rainwater, and using desalination to obtain drinkable water from the ocean. Although this pursuit of drinkable water has been ongoing throughout human history, the supply of fresh water is still a major issue in modern times.

Freshwater 2.5%
(35,000,000 km³)
Lakes and rivers 0.3%
Groundwater (soil moisture, swamp water, permafrost) 30.8%
Glaciers and permanent snow cover 68.9%
Saltwater 97.5%
(1,365,000,000 km³)

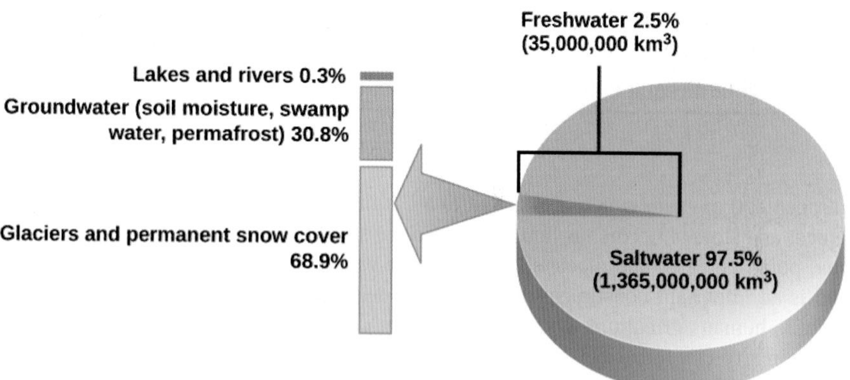

Figure 37.13 Only 2.5 percent of water on Earth is fresh water, and less than 1 percent of fresh water is easily accessible to living things.

Water cycling is extremely important to ecosystem dynamics. Water has a major influence on climate and, thus, on the environments of ecosystems, some located on distant parts of the Earth. Most of the water on Earth is stored for long periods in the oceans, underground, and as ice. Figure 37.14 illustrates the average time that an individual water molecule may spend in the Earth's major water reservoirs. **Residence time** is a measure of the average time an individual water molecule stays in a particular reservoir. A large amount of the Earth's water is locked in place in these reservoirs as ice, beneath the ground, and in the ocean, and, thus, is unavailable for short-term cycling (only surface water can evaporate).

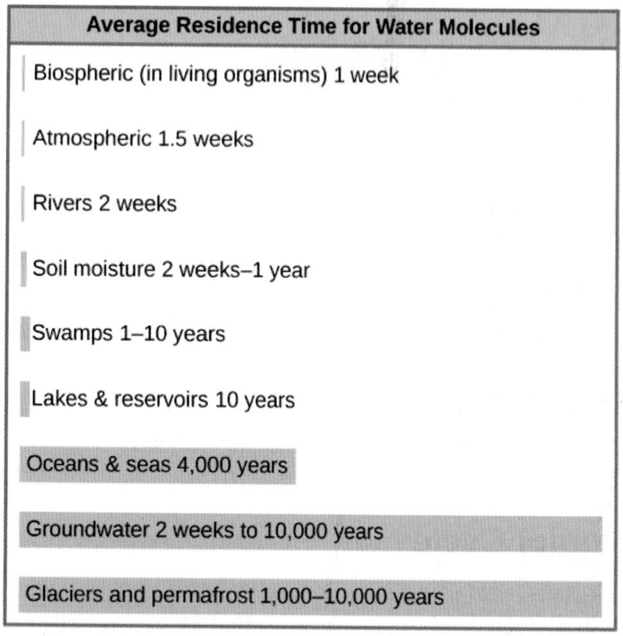

Average Residence Time for Water Molecules
Biospheric (in living organisms) 1 week
Atmospheric 1.5 weeks
Rivers 2 weeks
Soil moisture 2 weeks–1 year
Swamps 1–10 years
Lakes & reservoirs 10 years
Oceans & seas 4,000 years
Groundwater 2 weeks to 10,000 years
Glaciers and permafrost 1,000–10,000 years

Figure 37.14 This graph shows the average residence time for water molecules in the Earth's water reservoirs.

There are various processes that occur during the cycling of water, shown in Figure 37.15. These processes include the following:

- evaporation/sublimation
- condensation/precipitation
- subsurface water flow
- surface runoff/snowmelt
- streamflow

The water cycle is driven by the sun's energy as it warms the oceans and other surface waters. This leads to the evaporation (water to water vapor) of liquid surface water and the sublimation (ice to water vapor) of frozen water, which deposits large amounts of water vapor into the atmosphere. Over time, this water vapor condenses into clouds as liquid or frozen droplets and is eventually followed by precipitation (rain or snow), which returns water to the Earth's surface. Rain eventually permeates into the ground, where it may evaporate again if it is near the surface, flow beneath the surface, or be stored for long periods. More easily observed is surface runoff: the flow of fresh water either from rain or melting ice. Runoff can then make its way through streams and lakes to the oceans or flow directly to the oceans themselves.

Head to this website (http://openstaxcollege.org/l/freshwater) to learn more about the world's fresh water supply.

Water characterizes the most common and the most rare ecosystems worldwide. Why is it essential to find ways to manage water resources for human populations?

a. Humans utilize water from oceans, which is the most common ecosystem.

b. Humans utilize freshwater, which is the rarest ecosystem.

c. Humans utilize freshwater, which is the most common ecosystem.

d. Humans utilize water from oceans, which is the rarest ecosystem.

Rain and surface runoff are major ways in which minerals, including carbon, nitrogen, phosphorus, and sulfur, are cycled from land to water. The environmental effects of runoff will be discussed later as these cycles are described.

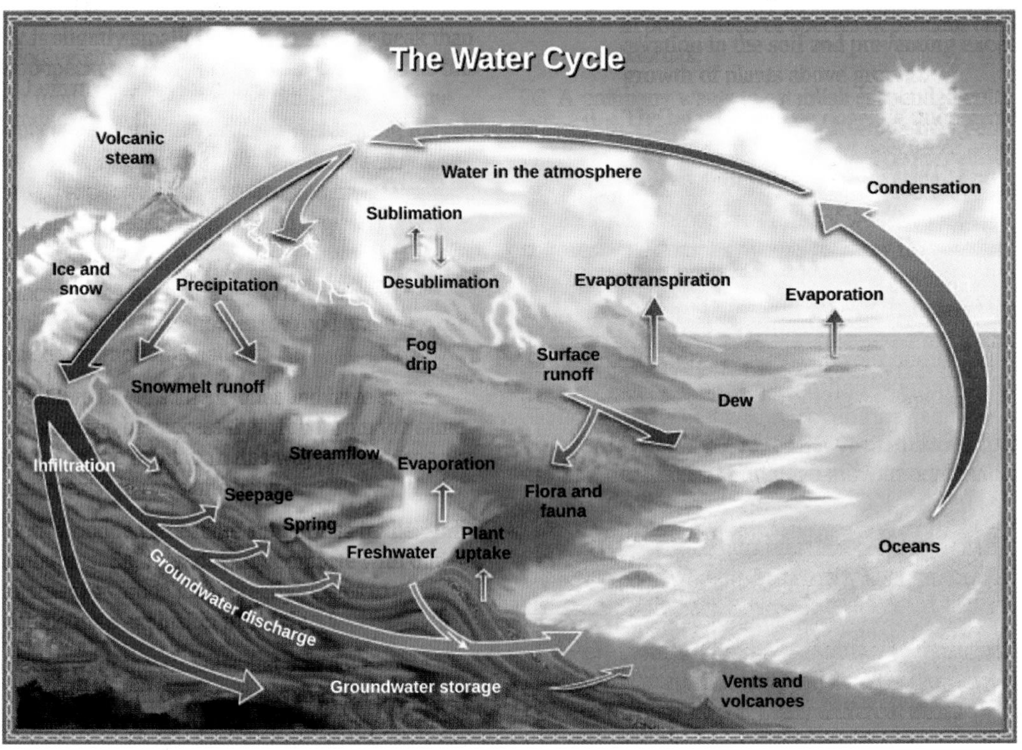

Figure 37.15 Water from the land and oceans enters the atmosphere by evaporation or sublimation, where it condenses into clouds and falls as rain or snow. Precipitated water may enter freshwater bodies or infiltrate the soil. The cycle is complete when surface or groundwater reenters the ocean. (credit: modification of work by John M. Evans and Howard Perlman, USGS)

The Carbon Cycle

Carbon is the second most abundant element in living organisms. Carbon is present in all organic molecules, and its role in the structure of macromolecules is of primary importance to living organisms. Carbon compounds contain especially high energy, particularly those derived from fossilized organisms, mainly plants, which humans use as fuel. Since the 1800s, the number of countries using massive amounts of fossil fuels has increased. Since the beginning of the Industrial Revolution, global demand for the Earth's limited fossil fuel supplies has risen; therefore, the amount of carbon dioxide in our atmosphere has increased. This increase in carbon dioxide has been associated with climate change and other disturbances of the Earth's ecosystems and is a major environmental concern worldwide. Thus, the "carbon footprint" is based on how much carbon dioxide is produced and how much fossil fuel countries consume.

The carbon cycle is most easily studied as two interconnected sub-cycles: one dealing with rapid carbon exchange among living organisms and the other dealing with the long-term cycling of carbon through geologic processes. The entire carbon cycle is shown in Figure 37.16.

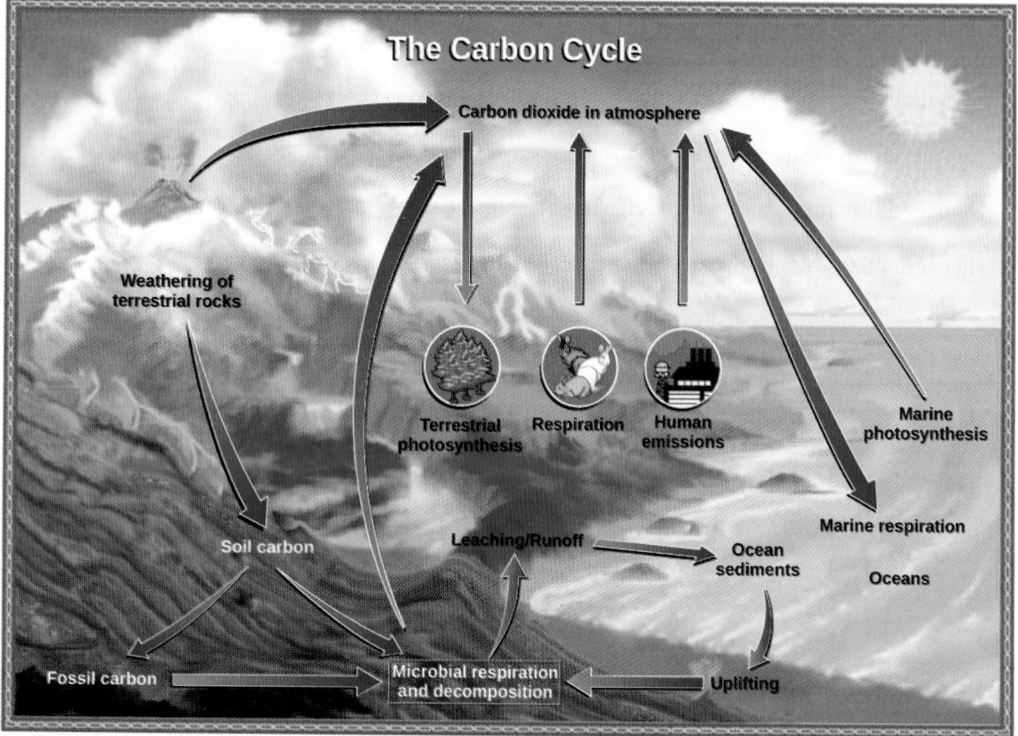

Figure 37.16 Carbon dioxide gas exists in the atmosphere and is dissolved in water. Photosynthesis converts carbon dioxide gas to organic carbon, and respiration cycles the organic carbon back into carbon dioxide gas. Long-term storage of organic carbon occurs when matter from living organisms is buried deep underground and becomes fossilized. Volcanic activity and, more recently, human emissions, bring this stored carbon back into the carbon cycle. (credit: modification of work by John M. Evans and Howard Perlman, USGS)

Click this link (http://openstaxcollege.org/l/themecarbon) to read information about the United States Carbon Cycle Science Program.

Compare and contrast carbon sources and sinks, and provide one example of each.

a. Carbon sources, such as burning fossil fuels, produce carbon while carbon sinks, such as oceans, absorb carbon.

b. Carbon sources, such as volcanic activity, absorb carbon while carbon sinks, such as vegetation, produce carbon.

c. Carbon sources, such as vegetation, produce carbon while carbon sinks, such as volcanic activity, absorb carbon.

d. Carbon sources, such as volcanic activity, produce carbon while carbon sinks, such as burning fossil fuels, absorb carbon.

The Biological Carbon Cycle

Living organisms are connected in many ways, even between ecosystems. A good example of this connection is the exchange of carbon between autotrophs and heterotrophs within and between ecosystems by way of atmospheric carbon dioxide. Carbon dioxide is the basic building block that most autotrophs use to build multi-carbon, high energy compounds, such as glucose. The energy harnessed from the sun is used by these organisms to form the covalent bonds that link carbon atoms together. These chemical bonds thereby store this energy for later use in the process of respiration. Most terrestrial autotrophs obtain their carbon dioxide directly from the atmosphere, while marine autotrophs acquire it in the dissolved form (carbonic acid, $H_2CO_3^-$). However carbon dioxide is acquired, a by-product of the process is oxygen. The photosynthetic organisms are responsible for depositing approximately 21 percent oxygen content of the atmosphere that we observe today.

Heterotrophs and autotrophs are partners in biological carbon exchange (especially the primary consumers, largely herbivores). Heterotrophs acquire the high-energy carbon compounds from the autotrophs by consuming them, and breaking them down by respiration to obtain cellular energy, such as ATP. The most efficient type of respiration, aerobic respiration, requires oxygen obtained from the atmosphere or dissolved in water. Thus, there is a constant exchange of oxygen and carbon dioxide between the autotrophs (which need the carbon) and the heterotrophs (which need the oxygen). Gas exchange through the atmosphere and water is one way that the carbon cycle connects all living organisms on Earth.

The Biogeochemical Carbon Cycle

The movement of carbon through the land, water, and air is complex, and in many cases, it occurs much more slowly geologically than as seen between living organisms. Carbon is stored for long periods in what are known as carbon reservoirs, which include the atmosphere, bodies of liquid water (mostly oceans), ocean sediment, soil, land sediments (including fossil fuels), and the Earth's interior.

As stated, the atmosphere is a major reservoir of carbon in the form of carbon dioxide and is essential to the process of photosynthesis. The level of carbon dioxide in the atmosphere is greatly influenced by the reservoir of carbon in the oceans. The exchange of carbon between the atmosphere and water reservoirs influences how much carbon is found in each location, and each one affects the other reciprocally. Carbon dioxide (CO_2) from the atmosphere dissolves in water and combines with water molecules to form carbonic acid, and then it ionizes to carbonate and bicarbonate ions (Figure 37.17)

Step 1: CO_2 (atmospheric) ⇌ CO_2 (dissolved)
Step 2: CO_2 (dissolved) + H_2O ⇌ H_2CO_3 (carbonic acid)
Step 3: H_2CO_3 ⇌ + H^+ + HCO_3^- (biocarbonate ion)
Step 4: HCO_3^- ⇌ H^+ + CO_3^{2-} (carbonate ion)

Figure 37.17 Carbon dioxide reacts with water to form bicarbonate and carbonate ions.

The equilibrium coefficients are such that more than 90 percent of the carbon in the ocean is found as bicarbonate ions. Some of these ions combine with seawater calcium to form calcium carbonate ($CaCO_3$), a major component of marine organism shells. These organisms eventually form sediments on the ocean floor. Over geologic time, the calcium carbonate forms limestone, which comprises the largest carbon reservoir on Earth.

On land, carbon is stored in soil as a result of the decomposition of living organisms (by decomposers) or from weathering of terrestrial rock and minerals. This carbon can be leached into the water reservoirs by surface runoff. Deeper underground, on land and at sea, are fossil fuels: the anaerobically decomposed remains of plants that take millions of years to form. Fossil fuels are considered a non-renewable resource because their use far exceeds their rate of formation. A **non-renewable resource**, such as fossil fuel, is either regenerated very slowly or not at all. Another way for carbon to enter the atmosphere is from land (including land beneath the surface of the ocean) by the eruption of volcanoes and other geothermal systems. Carbon sediments from the ocean floor are taken deep within the Earth by the process of **subduction**: the movement of one tectonic plate beneath another. Carbon is released as carbon dioxide when a volcano erupts or from volcanic hydrothermal vents.

Carbon dioxide is also added to the atmosphere by the animal husbandry practices of humans. The large numbers of land animals raised to feed the Earth's growing population results in increased carbon dioxide levels in the atmosphere due to farming practices and the respiration and methane production. This is another example of how human activity indirectly affects biogeochemical cycles in a significant way. Although much of the debate about the future effects of increasing atmospheric carbon on climate change focuses on fossils fuels, scientists take natural processes, such as volcanoes and respiration, into account as they model and predict the future impact of this increase.

The Nitrogen Cycle

Getting nitrogen into the living world is difficult. Plants and phytoplankton are not equipped to incorporate nitrogen from the atmosphere (which exists as tightly bonded, triple covalent N_2) even though this molecule comprises approximately 78 percent of the atmosphere. Nitrogen enters the living world via free-living and symbiotic bacteria, which incorporate nitrogen into their macromolecules through nitrogen fixation (conversion of N_2). Cyanobacteria live in most aquatic ecosystems where sunlight is present; they play a key role in nitrogen fixation. Cyanobacteria are able to use inorganic sources of nitrogen to "fix" nitrogen. *Rhizobium* bacteria live symbiotically in the root nodules of legumes (such as peas, beans, and peanuts) and provide them with the organic nitrogen they need. Free-living bacteria, such as *Azotobacter*, are also important nitrogen fixers.

Organic nitrogen is especially important to the study of ecosystem dynamics since many ecosystem processes, such as primary production and decomposition, are limited by the available supply of nitrogen. As shown in Figure 37.18, the nitrogen that enters living systems by nitrogen fixation is successively converted from organic nitrogen back into nitrogen gas by bacteria. This process occurs in three steps in terrestrial systems: ammonification, nitrification, and denitrification. First, the ammonification process converts nitrogenous waste from living animals or from the remains of dead animals into ammonium (NH_4^+) by certain bacteria and fungi. Second, the ammonium is converted to nitrites (NO_2^-) by nitrifying bacteria, such as *Nitrosomonas*, through nitrification. Subsequently, nitrites are converted to nitrates (NO_3^-) by similar organisms. Third, the process of denitrification occurs, whereby bacteria, such as *Pseudomonas* and *Clostridium*, convert the nitrates into nitrogen gas, allowing it to re-enter the atmosphere.

visual CONNECTION

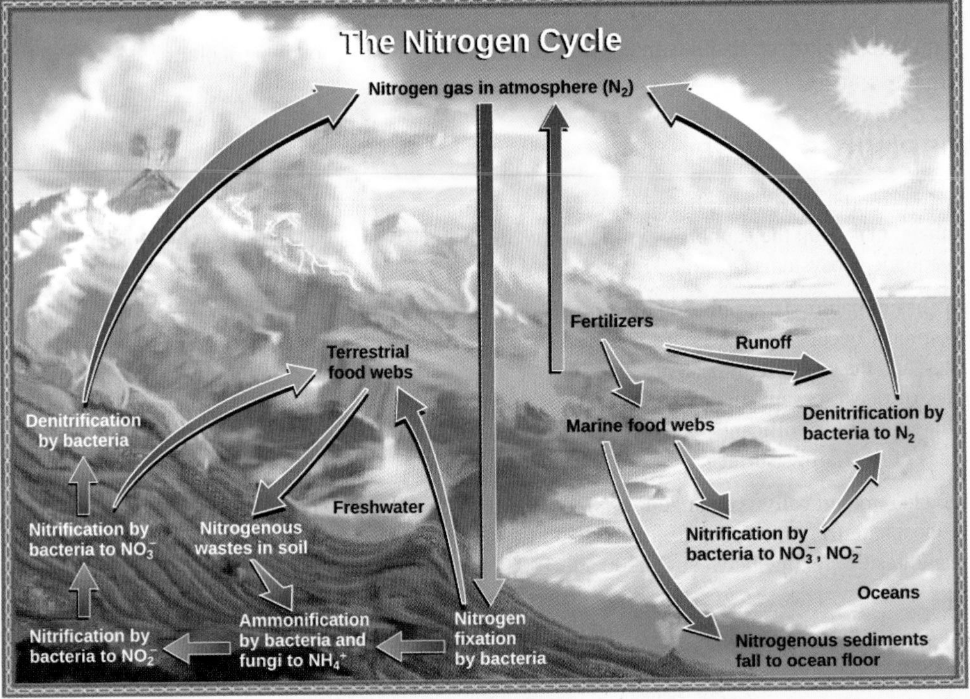

Figure 37.18 Nitrogen enters the living world from the atmosphere via nitrogen-fixing bacteria. This nitrogen and nitrogenous waste from animals is then processed back into gaseous nitrogen by soil bacteria, which also supply terrestrial food webs with the organic nitrogen they need. (credit: modification of work by John M. Evans and Howard Perlman, USGS)

Which of the following statements about the nitrogen cycle is false?

a. Ammonification converts organic nitrogenous matter from living organisms into ammonium ($NH4^+$).
b. Denitrification by bacteria converts nitrates ($NO3^-$) to nitrogen gas (N2).
c. Nitrification by bacteria converts nitrates ($NO3^-$) to nitrites ($NO2^-$).
d. Nitrogen fixing bacteria convert nitrogen gas (N2) into organic compounds.

Human activity can release nitrogen into the environment by two primary means: the combustion of fossil fuels, which releases different nitrogen oxides, and by the use of artificial fertilizers in agriculture, which are then washed into lakes, streams, and rivers by surface runoff. Atmospheric nitrogen is associated with several effects on Earth's ecosystems including the production of acid rain (as nitric acid, HNO_3) and greenhouse gas (as nitrous oxide, N_2O) potentially causing climate change. A major effect from fertilizer runoff is saltwater and freshwater **eutrophication**, a process whereby nutrient runoff causes the excess growth of microorganisms, depleting dissolved oxygen levels and killing ecosystem fauna.

A similar process occurs in the marine nitrogen cycle, where the ammonification, nitrification, and denitrification processes are performed by marine bacteria. Some of this nitrogen falls to the ocean floor as sediment, which can then be moved to land in geologic time by uplift of the Earth's surface and thereby incorporated into terrestrial rock. Although the movement of nitrogen from rock directly into living systems has been traditionally seen as insignificant compared with nitrogen fixed from the atmosphere, a recent[3] study showed that this process may indeed be significant and should be included in any study of the global nitrogen cycle.

3. Scott L. Morford, Benjamin Z. Houlton, and Randy A. Dahlgren, "Increased Forest Ecosystem Carbon and Nitrogen Storage from Nitrogen Rich Bedrock," *Nature* 477, no. 7362 (2011): 78–81.

science practices CONNECTION for AP® Courses

Think About It

What is the process of nitrogen fixation and how does it relate to crop rotation in agriculture?

The Phosphorus Cycle

Phosphorus is an essential nutrient for living processes; it is a major component of nucleic acid and phospholipids, and, as calcium phosphate, makes up the supportive components of our bones. Phosphorus is often the limiting nutrient (necessary for growth) in aquatic ecosystems (Figure 37.19).

Phosphorus occurs in nature as the phosphate ion (PO_4^{3-}). In addition to phosphate runoff as a result of human activity, natural surface runoff occurs when it is leached from phosphate-containing rock by weathering, thus sending phosphates into rivers, lakes, and the ocean. This rock has its origins in the ocean. Phosphate-containing ocean sediments form primarily from the bodies of ocean organisms and from their excretions. However, in remote regions, volcanic ash, aerosols, and mineral dust may also be significant phosphate sources. This sediment then is moved to land over geologic time by the uplifting of areas of the Earth's surface.

Phosphorus is also reciprocally exchanged between phosphate dissolved in the ocean and marine ecosystems. The movement of phosphate from the ocean to the land and through the soil is extremely slow, with the average phosphate ion having an oceanic residence time between 20,000 and 100,000 years.

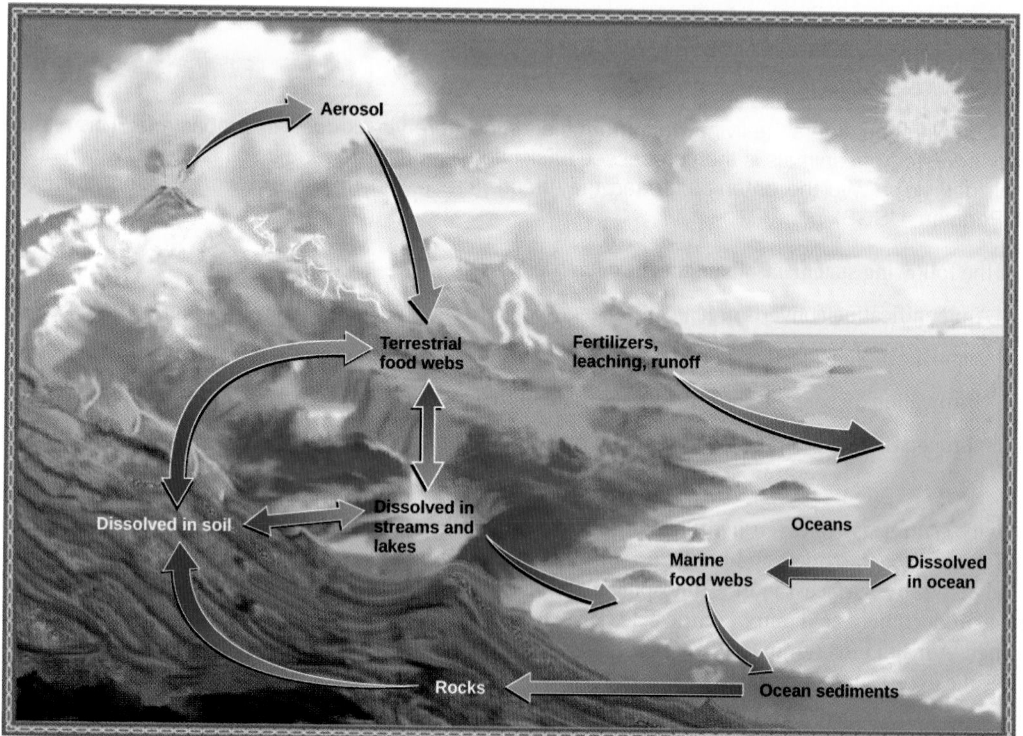

Figure 37.19 In nature, phosphorus exists as the phosphate ion (PO_4^{3-}). Weathering of rocks and volcanic activity releases phosphate into the soil, water, and air, where it becomes available to terrestrial food webs. Phosphate enters the oceans via surface runoff, groundwater flow, and river flow. Phosphate dissolved in ocean water cycles into marine food webs. Some phosphate from the marine food webs falls to the ocean floor, where it forms sediment. (credit: modification of work by John M. Evans and Howard Perlman, USGS)

Excess phosphorus and nitrogen that enters these ecosystems from fertilizer runoff and from sewage causes excessive growth of microorganisms and depletes the dissolved oxygen, which leads to the death of many ecosystem fauna, such as shellfish and finfish. This process is responsible for dead zones in lakes and at the mouths of many major rivers (Figure 37.19).

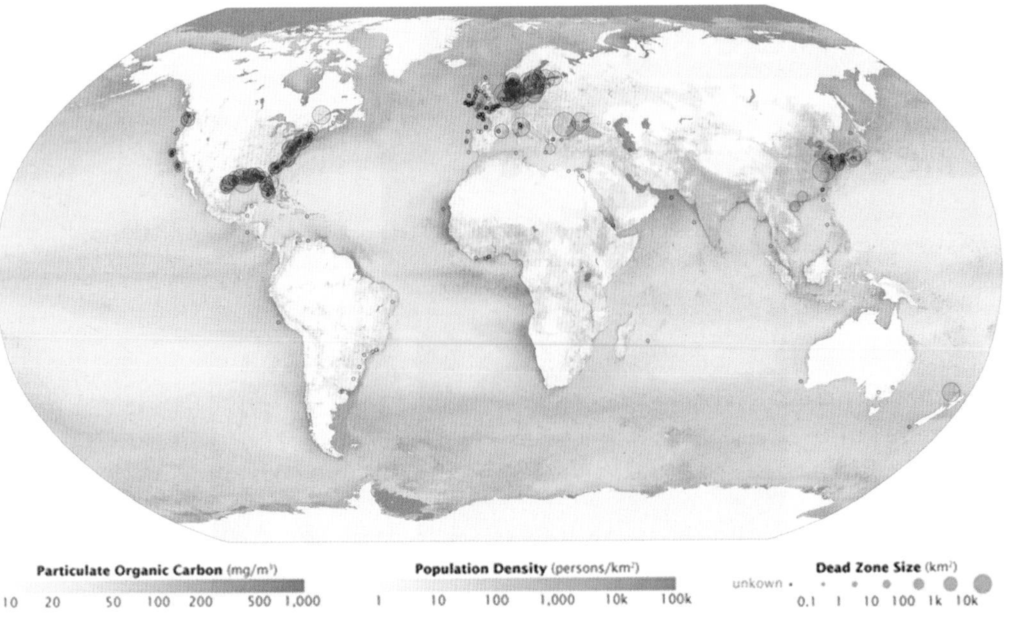

Figure 37.20 Dead zones occur when phosphorus and nitrogen from fertilizers cause excessive growth of microorganisms, which depletes oxygen and kills fauna. Worldwide, large dead zones are found in coastal areas of high population density. (credit: NASA Earth Observatory)

A **dead zone** is an area within a freshwater or marine ecosystem where large areas are depleted of their normal flora and fauna; these zones can be caused by eutrophication, oil spills, dumping of toxic chemicals, and other human activities. The number of dead zones has been increasing for several years, and more than 400 of these zones were present as of 2008. One of the worst dead zones is off the coast of the United States in the Gulf of Mexico, where fertilizer runoff from the Mississippi River basin has created a dead zone of over 8463 square miles. Phosphate and nitrate runoff from fertilizers also negatively affect several lake and bay ecosystems including the Chesapeake Bay in the eastern United States.

everyday CONNECTION

Chesapeake Bay

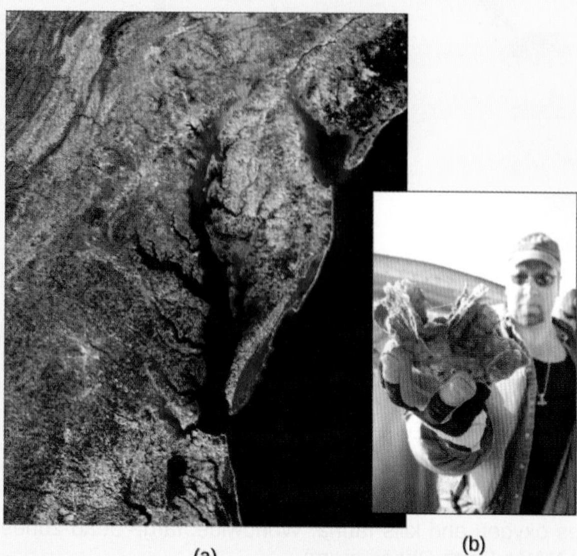

Figure 37.21 This (a) satellite image shows the Chesapeake Bay, an ecosystem affected by phosphate and nitrate runoff. A (b) member of the Army Corps of Engineers holds a clump of oysters being used as a part of the oyster restoration effort in the bay. (credit a: modification of work by NASA/MODIS; credit b: modification of work by U.S. Army)

The Chesapeake Bay has long been valued as one of the most scenic areas on Earth; it is now in distress and is recognized as a declining ecosystem. In the 1970s, the Chesapeake Bay was one of the first ecosystems to have identified dead zones, which continue to kill many fish and bottom-dwelling species, such as clams, oysters, and worms. Several species have declined in the Chesapeake Bay due to surface water runoff containing excess nutrients from artificial fertilizer used on land. The source of the fertilizers (with high nitrogen and phosphate content) is not limited to agricultural practices. There are many nearby urban areas and more than 150 rivers and streams empty into the bay that are carrying fertilizer runoff from lawns and gardens. Thus, the decline of the Chesapeake Bay is a complex issue and requires the cooperation of industry, agriculture, and everyday homeowners.

Of particular interest to conservationists is the oyster population; it is estimated that more than 200,000 acres of oyster reefs existed in the bay in the 1700s, but that number has now declined to only 36,000 acres. Oyster harvesting was once a major industry for Chesapeake Bay, but it declined 88 percent between 1982 and 2007. This decline was due not only to fertilizer runoff and dead zones but also to overharvesting. Oysters require a certain minimum population density because they must be in close proximity to reproduce. Human activity has altered the oyster population and locations, greatly disrupting the ecosystem.

The restoration of the oyster population in the Chesapeake Bay has been ongoing for several years with mixed success. Not only do many people find oysters good to eat, but they also clean up the bay. Oysters are filter feeders, and as they eat, they clean the water around them. In the 1700s, it was estimated that it took only a few days for the oyster population to filter the entire volume of the bay. Today, with changed water conditions, it is estimated that the present population would take nearly a year to do the same job.

Restoration efforts have been ongoing for several years by non-profit organizations, such as the Chesapeake Bay Foundation. The restoration goal is to find a way to increase population density so the oysters can reproduce more efficiently. Many disease-resistant varieties (developed at the Virginia Institute of Marine Science for the College of William and Mary) are now available and have been used in the construction of experimental oyster reefs. Efforts to clean and restore the bay by Virginia and Delaware have been hampered because much of the pollution entering the bay comes from other states, which stresses the need for inter-state cooperation to gain successful restoration.

The new, hearty oyster strains have also spawned a new and economically viable industry—oyster aquaculture—which not only supplies oysters for food and profit, but also has the added benefit of cleaning the bay.

How did fertilizer runoff produce a dead zone in the Chesapeake Bay?

a. Excess nitrogen from fertilizer decreases microbial growth, depleting dissolved oxygen in water, thereby killing the fauna of the ecosystem.
b. Fertilizer runoff decreases the carbon dioxide concentration in water, thereby killing fauna of the ecosystem.
c. Fertilizer runoff produces a dead zone in the Chesapeake Bay by increasing oxygen concentration in the ecosystem.
d. Excess nitrogen from fertilizer increases microbial growth, depleting dissolved oxygen in water, thereby killing the fauna of the ecosystem.

The Sulfur Cycle

Sulfur is an essential element for the macromolecules of living things. As a part of the amino acid cysteine, it is involved in the formation of disulfide bonds within proteins, which help to determine their 3-D folding patterns, and hence their functions. As shown in Figure 37.21, sulfur cycles between the oceans, land, and atmosphere. Atmospheric sulfur is found in the form of sulfur dioxide (SO_2) and enters the atmosphere in three ways: from the decomposition of organic molecules, from volcanic activity and geothermal vents, and from the burning of fossil fuels by humans.

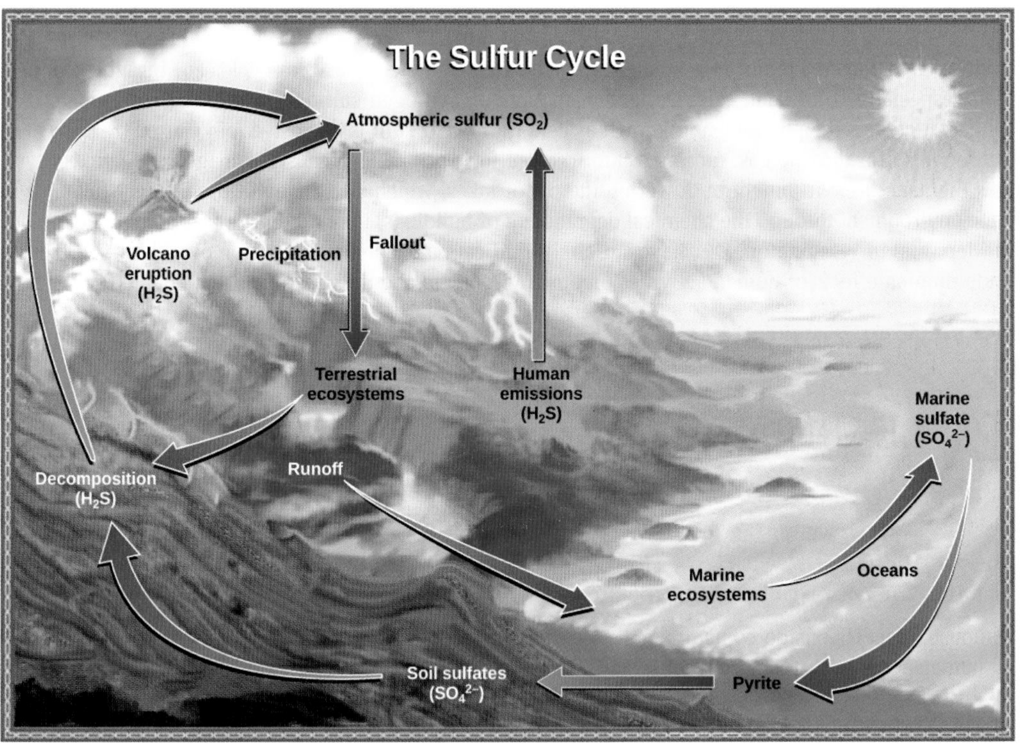

Figure 37.22 Sulfur dioxide from the atmosphere becomes available to terrestrial and marine ecosystems when it is dissolved in precipitation as weak sulfuric acid or when it falls directly to the Earth as fallout. Weathering of rocks also makes sulfates available to terrestrial ecosystems. Decomposition of living organisms returns sulfates to the ocean, soil and atmosphere. (credit: modification of work by John M. Evans and Howard Perlman, USGS)

On land, sulfur is deposited in four major ways: precipitation, direct fallout from the atmosphere, rock weathering, and geothermal vents (Figure 37.22). Atmospheric sulfur is found in the form of sulfur dioxide (SO_2), and as rain falls through the atmosphere, sulfur is dissolved in the form of weak sulfuric acid (H_2SO_4). Sulfur can also fall directly from the atmosphere in a process called **fallout**. Also, the weathering of sulfur-containing rocks releases sulfur into the soil. These rocks originate from ocean sediments that are moved to land by the geologic uplifting of ocean sediments. Terrestrial ecosystems can then make use of these soil sulfates (SO_4-), and upon the death and decomposition of these organisms, release the sulfur back into the atmosphere as hydrogen sulfide (H_2S) gas.

Figure 37.23 At this sulfur vent in Lassen Volcanic National Park in northeastern California, the yellowish sulfur deposits are visible near the mouth of the vent.

Sulfur enters the ocean via runoff from land, from atmospheric fallout, and from underwater geothermal vents. Some ecosystems (Figure 37.9) rely on chemoautotrophs using sulfur as a biological energy source. This sulfur then supports marine ecosystems in the form of sulfates.

Human activities have played a major role in altering the balance of the global sulfur cycle. The burning of large quantities of fossil fuels, especially from coal, releases larger amounts of hydrogen sulfide gas into the atmosphere. As rain falls through this gas, it creates the phenomenon known as acid rain. **Acid rain** is corrosive rain caused by rainwater falling to the ground through sulfur dioxide gas, turning it into weak sulfuric acid, which causes damage to aquatic ecosystems. Acid rain damages the natural environment by lowering the pH of lakes, which kills many of the resident fauna; it also affects the man-made environment through the chemical degradation of buildings. For example, many marble monuments, such as the Lincoln Memorial in Washington, DC, have suffered significant damage from acid rain over the years. These examples show the wide-ranging effects of human activities on our environment and the challenges that remain for our future.

Click this link (http://openstaxcollege.org/l/climate_change) to learn more about global climate change.

The greenhouse effect is considered natural and essential to human survival. Why, then, is society concerned about the impact of human activities on the greenhouse gas effect?

a. The greenhouse effect is reduced due to human activities.

b. Human activities strengthen the greenhouse effect by trapping more heat in the atmosphere.

c. Human activities decrease the release of carbon dioxide gas, thereby strengthening the greenhouse effect.

d. Human activities cause less heat to be trapped in the atmosphere and decrease the temperature.

KEY TERMS

acid rain corrosive rain caused by rainwater falling to the ground through sulfur dioxide gas, turning it into weak sulfuric acid; can damage structures and ecosystems

analytical model ecosystem model that is created with mathematical formulas to predict the effects of environmental disturbances on ecosystem structure and dynamics

apex consumer organism at the top of the food chain

assimilation biomass consumed and assimilated from the previous trophic level after accounting for the energy lost due to incomplete ingestion of food, energy used for respiration, and energy lost as waste

biogeochemical cycle cycling of mineral nutrients through ecosystems and through the non-living world

biomagnification increasing concentrations of persistent, toxic substances in organisms at each trophic level, from the primary producers to the apex consumers

biomass total weight, at the time of measurement, of living or previously living organisms in a unit area within a trophic level

chemoautotroph organism capable of synthesizing its own food using energy from inorganic molecules

conceptual model (also, compartment models) ecosystem model that consists of flow charts that show the interactions of different compartments of the living and non-living components of the ecosystem

dead zone area within an ecosystem in lakes and near the mouths of rivers where large areas of ecosystems are depleted of their normal flora and fauna; these zones can be caused by eutrophication, oil spills, dumping of toxic chemicals, and other human activities

detrital food web type of food web in which the primary consumers consist of decomposers; these are often associated with grazing food webs within the same ecosystem

ecological pyramid (also, Eltonian pyramid) graphical representation of different trophic levels in an ecosystem based of organism numbers, biomass, or energy content

ecosystem community of living organisms and their interactions with their abiotic environment

ecosystem dynamics study of the changes in ecosystem structure caused by changes in the environment or internal forces

equilibrium steady state of an ecosystem where all organisms are in balance with their environment and each other

eutrophication process whereby nutrient runoff causes the excess growth of microorganisms, depleting dissolved oxygen levels and killing ecosystem fauna

fallout direct deposit of solid minerals on land or in the ocean from the atmosphere

food chain linear representation of a chain of primary producers, primary consumers, and higher-level consumers used to describe ecosystem structure and dynamics

food web graphic representation of a holistic, non-linear web of primary producers, primary consumers, and higher-level consumers used to describe ecosystem structure and dynamics

grazing food web type of food web in which the primary producers are either plants on land or phytoplankton in the water; often associated with a detrital food web within the same ecosystem

gross primary productivity rate at which photosynthetic primary producers incorporate energy from the sun

holistic ecosystem model study that attempts to quantify the composition, interactions, and dynamics of entire ecosystems; often limited by economic and logistical difficulties, depending on the ecosystem

hydrosphere area of the Earth where water movement and storage occurs

mesocosm portion of a natural ecosystem to be used for experiments

microcosm re-creation of natural ecosystems entirely in a laboratory environment to be used for experiments

net consumer productivity energy content available to the organisms of the next trophic level

net primary productivity energy that remains in the primary producers after accounting for the organisms' respiration and heat loss

net production efficiency (NPE) measure of the ability of a trophic level to convert the energy it receives from the previous trophic level into biomass

non-renewable resource resource, such as fossil fuel, that is either regenerated very slowly or not at all

primary consumer trophic level that obtains its energy from the primary producers of an ecosystem

primary producer trophic level that obtains its energy from sunlight, inorganic chemicals, or dead and/or decaying organic material

residence time measure of the average time an individual water molecule stays in a particular reservoir

resilience (ecological) speed at which an ecosystem recovers equilibrium after being disturbed

resistance (ecological) ability of an ecosystem to remain at equilibrium in spite of disturbances

secondary consumer usually a carnivore that eat primary consumers

simulation model ecosystem model that is created with computer programs to holistically model ecosystems and to predict the effects of environmental disturbances on ecosystem structure and dynamics

subduction movement of one tectonic plate beneath another

tertiary consumer carnivore that eat other carnivores

trophic level position of a species or group of species in a food chain or a food web

trophic level transfer efficiency (TLTE) energy transfer efficiency between two successive trophic levels

CHAPTER SUMMARY

37.1 Ecology for Ecosystems

Ecosystems exist on land, at sea, in the air, and underground. Different ways of modeling ecosystems are necessary to understand how environmental disturbances will affect ecosystem structure and dynamics. Conceptual models are useful to show the general relationships between organisms and the flow of materials or energy between them. Analytical models are used to describe linear food chains, and simulation models work best with holistic food webs.

37.2 Energy Flow through Ecosystems

Organisms in an ecosystem acquire energy in a variety of ways, which is transferred between trophic levels as the energy flows from the bottom to the top of the food web, with energy being lost at each transfer. The efficiency of these transfers is important for understanding the different behaviors and eating habits of warm-blooded versus cold-blooded animals. Modeling of ecosystem energy is best done with ecological pyramids of energy, although other ecological pyramids provide other vital information about ecosystem structure.

37.3 Biogeochemical Cycles

Mineral nutrients are cycled through ecosystems and their environment. Of particular importance are water, carbon, nitrogen, phosphorus, and sulfur. All of these cycles have major impacts on ecosystem structure and function. As human activities have caused major disturbances to these cycles, their study and modeling is especially important. A variety of human activities, such as pollution, oil spills, and events) have damaged ecosystems, potentially causing global climate change. The health of Earth depends on understanding these cycles and how to protect the environment from irreversible damage.

REVIEW QUESTIONS

1. What type of ecosystem is the rarest on Earth, among both terrestrial and aquatic exosystems?

a. ocean
b. freshwater
c. grasslands
d. tundra

2. If an ecosystem is considered to be highly resilient, what can be inferred about that ecosystem?

a. The ecosystem is in a steady state.
b. The ecosystem has the ability to remain in equilibrium despite disturbance.
c. The ecosystem recovers quickly from disturbance.
d. The ecosystem is exposed to disturbances.

3. What is a re-created ecosystem in a laboratory environment known as?

a. mesocosm
b. simulation
c. microcosm
d. duplication

4. A scientist wants to analyze how deer grazing alters plant species composition in a forest and sections off a portion of the forest for observation and analysis. What type of system is the scientist using?

a. mesocosm
b. simulation
c. microcosm
d. duplication

5. What term describes the use of mathematical equations in the modeling of linear aspects of ecosystems?

a. analytical modeling
b. simulation modeling
c. conceptual modeling
d. microcosm modeling

6. If a scientist constructs a flow chart to depict the interactions among species in an estuary, what kind of model is she creating?

a. analytical model
b. stimulation model
c. conceptual model
d. microcosm model

7. What are usually the primary producers in an ocean grazing food web?

a. plants
b. animals
c. fungi
d. phytoplankton

8. Which of the following statements is true of trophic levels in an ecosystem?

a. Food chains are accurate representations of dynamics in an ecosystem.
b. In terrestrial ecosystems, primary producers commonly eat plants.
c. Food webs are easier to interpret than food chains.
d. The least amount of energy is available at the top of a food chain.

9. Where are coral reefs found?

a. shallow ocean water
b. deep ocean water
c. deep ocean surfaces
d. shallow freshwater

10. What is the weight of living organisms in an ecosystem at a particular point in time known as?

a. energy
b. productivity
c. entropy
d. biomass

11. If you wanted to measure gross primary productivity in a terrestrial ecosystem, what would you measure?

a. rate of energy incorporation by plants
b. energy available after a plant incorporates energy for its own biological functions
c. amount of energy from plants entering the trophic level of deer
d. total mass of plants and animals in an area at a given point in time

12. What law of chemistry determines how much energy can be transferred when it is converted from one form to another?

a. the first law of thermodynamics
b. the second law of thermodynamics
c. the conservation of matter
d. the conservation of energy

13. What is the primary factor that limits the length of food chains in ecosystems?

a. low energy transfer efficiency between trophic levels
b. too much net primary productivity
c. excess assimilation
d. low gross primary productivity

14. What type of pyramid is considered the most representative of ecosystem structure?

a. biomass
b. energy
c. number of organisms
d. number of species

15. Why are the numbers of primary producers smaller than the number of primary consumers in the English Channel ecosystem?

a. The primary consumers have a high turnover rate.
b. The primary producers have a low turnover rate.
c. The apex consumers have a low turnover rate.
d. The primary producers have a high turnover rate.

16. What forms of life are found in areas where sunlight is unavailable and use inorganic molecules as an energy source?

a. photoautotrophs
b. chemoautotrophs
c. primary consumers
d. secondary consumers

17. What is the process whereby nitrogen is brought into organic molecules called?

a. nitrification
b. denitrification
c. nitrogen fixation
d. nitrogen cycling

18. Which of the following is a mechanism by which phosphorus is released into the environment?

a. rock weathering
b. decomposition of organic molecules
c. volcanic activity
d. geothermal vent activity

19. What is produced by eutrophication via excess nitrogen where a hydrologic reservoir lacks normal flora and fauna?

a. fixation
b. acid rain
c. dead zones
d. nitrification

20. What is a potential consequence of excess phosphorus and nitrogen in an ecosystem?

a. This could result in increased global temperatures.
b. Subduction can be promoted.
c. These elements might be fixed in excess.
d. A dead zone could be produced from depleted oxygen.

21. What term is given for freshwater that flows from rain or melting ice in the hydrologic cycle?

a. residence time
b. surface runoff
c. evaporation
d. sublimation

22. What most strongly influences how much carbon is present in a given location?

a. number of bacteria
b. runoff
c. eutrophication
d. atmosphere and water exchange

CRITICAL THINKING QUESTIONS

23. Why does grouping terrestrial organisms into biomes obscure diversity?

a. Biomes groups terrestrial organisms only on the basis of similar habitat conditions.
b. Organisms belonging to a similar biome have dissimilarities in their makeup.
c. There is variation within different types of biomes that biome categorization does not capture.
d. Terrestrial biomes are defined based only on the growth form of the dominant vegetation.

24. Why are mesocosm and microcosm experiments not considered to represent the true nature of ecosystems?

a. The ecosystem is either recreated or partitioned in both the experiments, which may alter the dynamics of the ecosystem the experiments are aiming to analyze.
b. In both the experiments, dynamics of the ecosystem may get altered due to differences in species numbers and diversity although there are no alterations in the environment.
c. In both the experiments, the ecosystem is recreated which may alter the dynamics of the ecosystem the experiments are aiming to analyze.
d. Altering a natural ecosystem through partitioning, which occurs in both the experiments may change its dynamics due to differences in species numbers and diversity.

25. If a scientist wanted to monitor a desert food chain, what type of model might they develop and why?

a. An analytical model would be ideal because they can address simple, linear ecosystem components that are mathematically complex.
b. A simulation model would be ideal because they can address simple, linear systems that are mathematically complex.
c. An analytical model would be ideal as they are considered ecologically more realistic than any other model.
d. A simulation model would be ideal because it uses numerical techniques to solve problems and visualize the complex relationships that exist in the ecosystem.

26. Compare and contrast food chains and food webs. What are the strengths of each concept in describing ecosystems?

a. Both food chain and food web follow a single path as energy is transferred in an ecosystem. Food chains are easier to follow and experiment with but less accurate whereas food webs are more holistic and complex.
b. Both food web and food chain describe energy transfer dynamics in an ecosystem. Food chains are non-linear systems which are easier to follow and experiment with whereas food webs are linear, holistic and can be directly used as input for simulation models.
c. Both food chain and food web follow a single path as energy is transferred in an ecosystem. Food chains are linear systems, easier to follow and used directly as input for simulation models, whereas food webs are non-linear, accurate, holistic and flexible for analytical modeling.
d. Both food web and food chain describe energy transfer dynamics in an ecosystem. Food chains are linear systems, easier to follow and experiment with whereas food webs are non-linear, accurate and holistic and can be directly used as input for simulation models.

27. Name one natural and one human-related type of disturbance. Why are they of concern to conservationists?

a. Lightening is a type of natural disturbance whereas pollution is a human related disturbance. Both are of concern to conservationists because they affect the entire ecosystem.
b. Fire is a type of natural disturbances whereas agriculture is a human related disturbance. Both types are of concern to conservationists because ecosystems cannot bounce back from a disturbance.
c. Pollution is a type of natural disturbance whereas lightening is a human related disturbance. Both are of concern to conservationists because they alter ecosystems.
d. Lightening is a type of natural disturbance whereas pollution is a human related disturbance. Both are of concern to conservationists because they alter ecosystems.

28. Compare grazing and detrital food webs. Why would they both be present in the same ecosystem?

a. The primary producers of detrital food webs are decomposers whereas those of grazing food webs are non-photosynthetic. Both primary producers support different components of the ecosystem.
b. The primary producers of detrital food webs are photosynthetic whereas those of grazing food webs are decomposers. Both primary producers support different components of the ecosystem.
c. The primary producers of detrital food webs are decomposers whereas those of grazing food webs are photosynthetic. Both primary producers support different components of the ecosystem.
d. The primary producers of detrital food webs are chemoautotrophs whereas those of grazing food webs are photosynthetic. Both primary producers support different components of the ecosystem.

29. How does the amount of food that endotherms and ectotherms consume compare with their net production efficiency (NPE)?

a. The amount of food eaten by an animal does not affect its net production efficiency (NPE).
b. Endotherms use more energy compared to ectotherms due to energy loss by respiration and heat.
c. Both endotherms and ectotherms use the same energy from food.
d. Ectotherms use more energy compared to endotherms due to energy loss by respiration and heat.

30. Compare the three types of ecosystem pyramids and how well they describe ecosystem structure. Identify which ones can be inverted and give a specific example of an inverted pyramid for each.

a. The three types of ecosystem pyramids are pyramids of energy, number and biomass out of which number and energy pyramids can be inverted. Examples of inverted pyramids of number and energy are temperate forests in summer and phytoplankton in the English Channel respectively.
b. The three types of ecosystem pyramids are pyramids of energy, number and biomass out of which number and biomass pyramids can be inverted. Examples of inverted pyramids of number and biomass are temperate forests in summer and phytoplankton in the English Channel respectively.
c. The three types of ecosystem pyramids are pyramids of energy, number and biomass out of which number and biomass pyramids can be inverted. Examples of inverted pyramids of number and biomass are temperate forests in summer and Silver Springs ecosystem in Florida respectively.
d. The three types of ecosystem pyramids are pyramids of energy, number and biomass out of which number and biomass pyramids can be inverted. Examples of inverted pyramids of number and biomass are grasslands in summer and phytoplankton in the English Channel respectively.

31. Why do scientists more commonly analyze net primary productivity compared with gross primary productivity?

a. Net primary productivity incorporates features like production at present and next trophic levels, whereas gross primary productivity does not.
b. Net primary productivity is the rate at which photosynthetic primary producers incorporate energy from the sun.
c. As net primary productivity is the energy content available to the organisms of the next trophic level.
d. As respiration and heat loss uses energy of the primary producer, therefore, net primary productivity is what is actually available to primary consumers.

32. Describe nitrogen fixation and why it is important to agriculture.

a. The process of nitrate formation from ammonia is called nitrogen fixation. It improves agricultural production as nitrogen is required by plants for nucleotide and protein formation.

b. The process of nitrogen being bonded to organic molecule is called nitrogen fixation. It improves the crop yield by allowing the plants to compete with weeds.

c. The reduction of nitrates back to nitrogen gas is called nitrogen fixation. It improves agricultural production as nitrogen is required by plants for nucleotide and protein formation.

d. The process of nitrogen being bonded into organic molecules is called nitrogen fixation. It improves agricultural production as nitrogen is required by plants for nucleotide and protein formation.

33. How do agricultural animals such as cattle raise atmospheric carbon levels? What is a side effect?

a. Cattle produce carbon monoxide, which when inhaled can cause death.

b. Cattle produce carbon monoxide, which is a major contributor to global warming.

c. Agricultural animals increase the amount of greenhouse gases by producing carbon dioxide and methane, so they contribute to global warming.

d. Agricultural animals increase the amount of greenhouse gases by producing ozone, which contributes to global warming.

34. What form of sulfur is found in the atmosphere and how does it leave the atmosphere?

a. hydrogen sulfide, which leaves the atmosphere as weak sulfur dioxide rain

b. sulfur dioxide, which leaves the atmosphere as weak sulfur dioxide rain

c. hydrogen sulfide, which leaves the atmosphere as weak sulfuric acid rain

d. sulfur dioxide, which leaves the atmosphere as weak sulfuric acid rain

TEST PREP FOR AP® COURSES

35. Producers and consumers are necessary for ecosystem function and for energy to pass through an ecosystem. What might happen in an aquatic system with excess producers relative to consumers?

a. Oxygen depletion would result in dieoff.

b. There would be no basal energy source.

c. Carbon cannot be sequestered.

d. There would be more undigestable animal parts.

36. Energy is a fundamental component in an ecosystem and is contributed by the primary producers. Describe how light energy can, in turn, support the consumers of an ecosystem.

a. Light energy is converted by primary producers and primary consumers. Consumers belonging to higher trophic levels feed on them to gain energy.

b. Primary producers can only obtain energy from sunlight by photosynthesis and gain energy by feeding on them or other consumers which have consumed these producers.

c. Primary producers convert light energy by photosynthesis and consumers gain energy by feeding on them or other consumers which have consumed these producers.

d. Primary producers convert light energy through chemosynthesis and consumers gain energy by feeding on them or other consumers which have consumed these producers.

37. In a microcosm experiment using fish tanks to mimic a lake environment, an increase in the number of stickleback species would increase the dissolved organic carbon particle size. How could this affect primary producers in the ecosystem?

a. enhance growth rate

b. increase abundance

c. decrease abundance

d. maintain growth rate

38. Studies on stickleback fish revealed that the presence of two species of stickleback reduced the amount of algal blooms relative to the presence of one species of stickleback in a microcosm experiment. How does this occur?

a. This occurred as the presence of two species caused an increase in dissolved organic carbon molecule size, which blocked the penetration of light in water and prevented algal photosynthesis.
b. This occurred because two stickleback species consumed all the nutrients which prevented algae from being able to grow.
c. This occurred because dissolved organic carbon molecule size increased in the presence of one fish species which increased the amount of algal blooms.
d. This occurred as algae are consumed in more amounts in the presence of two stickleback species.

39. This figure depicts energy exchange through trophic levels. Which level represents the primary producers?

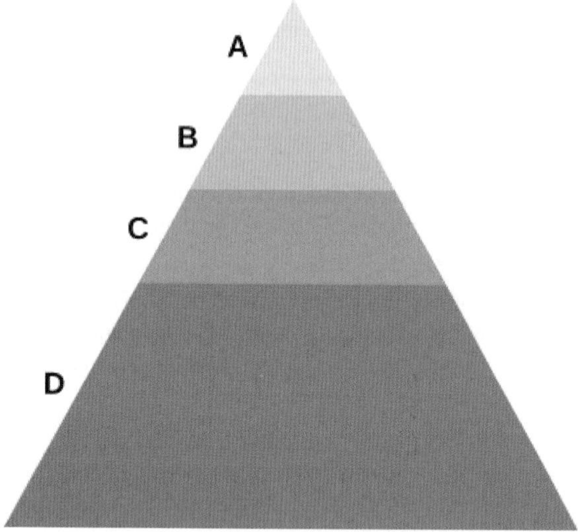

a. A
b. B
c. C
d. D

40.

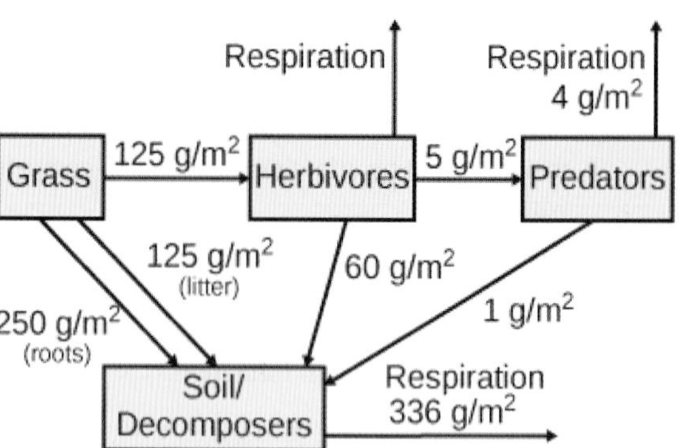

How much carbon (g/m^2) is released into the atmosphere as a result of the metabolic activity of herbivores? Give your answer to the nearest whole number.

a. 125 g/m^2 carbon is released into the atmosphere as a result of the metabolic activity of herbivores.
b. 65 g/m^2 carbon is released into the atmosphere as a result of the metabolic activity of herbivores.
c. 60 g/m^2 carbon is released into the atmosphere as a result of the metabolic activity of herbivores.
d. 5 g/m^2 carbon is released into the atmosphere as a result of the metabolic activity of herbivores.

41. The following is a food web for a meadow habitat that occupies 25.6 km^2. The primary producers' biomass is uniformly distributed throughout the habitat and totals 1,500 kg/km^2. Developers have approved a project that will permanently reduce the primary producers' biomass by 50 percent and remove all rabbits and deer. Which of the following is the most likely result at the completion of the project?

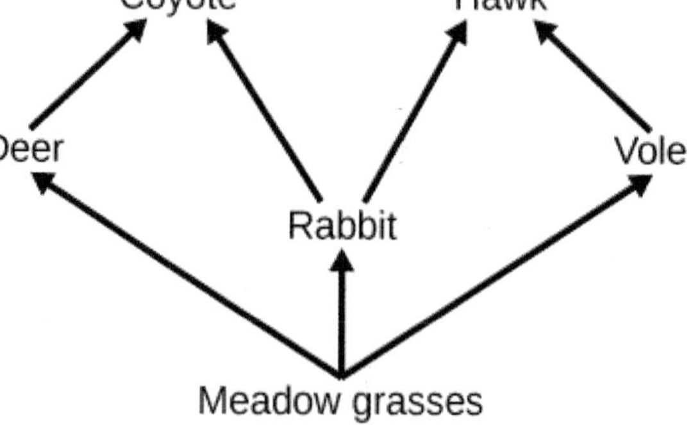

a. The biomass of coyotes will be 6 kg, and the biomass of hawks will be 0.5 kg.
b. The biomass of coyotes will be dramatically reduced.
c. The coyotes will switch prey preferences and outcompete the hawks.
d. There will be 50 percent fewer voles and 90 percent fewer hawks.

42.

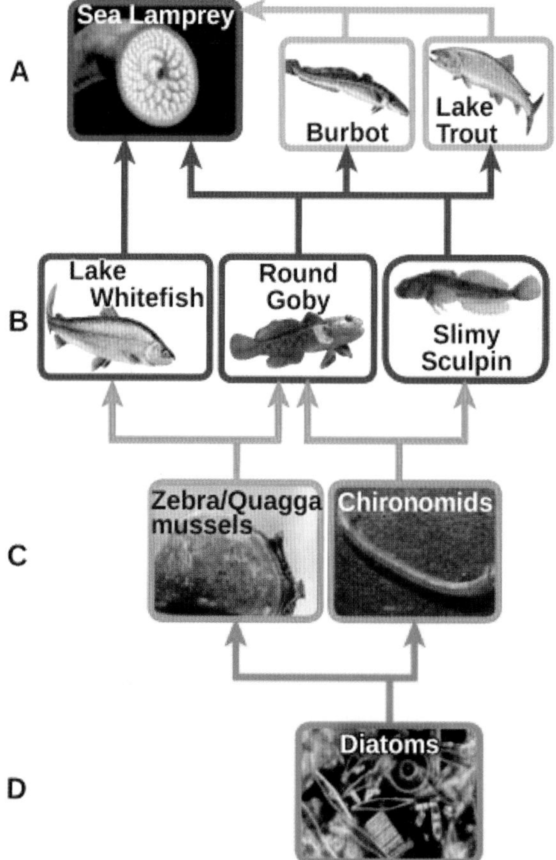

This figure shows a food web of an ecosystem. What would happen to the food web if all of the species of the entire row B was wiped out by a natural disaster such as an oil spill? Why?

a. The producers may die out, causing the food web to collapse.
b. The food web would not be affected as the secondary and tertiary consumers would become primary and secondary consumers, respectively.
c. The tertiary consumers would die out due to lack of food and this could potentially lead to collapse of the entire food web.
d. The food web might suffer from loss of primary producers for a while which would then recover quickly, thus, reviving the ecosystem.

43. Humans are very active in modifying ecosystems worldwide. If a new set of buildings on the edge of a forest block sunlight from reaching the majority of one part of the forest, what might happen to that part of the forest?

a. Herbivores would occur in high abundance.
b. Plants would occur in high abundance.
c. Everything would remain the same.
d. Herbivores would occur in low abundance.

44. If you examined predator-prey relationships within an ecosystem and noticed that the removal of predators also resulted in the die-off of herbivores, what would you suspect occurred?

a. Removal of predators would directly lower the number of herbivores.
b. The lack of predators could mean that too much primary production occurred.
c. Herbivores from another region may have entered the ecosystem and consumed the primary producers, causing death of the original herbivores species.
d. Overeating by herbivores could have caused depletion of the primary producers, leaving the herbivores without enough food.

45. Although producers are essential for energy to flow into an ecosystem, consumers also have important roles. What might happen in an aquatic system with excess consumers relative to producers?

a. Oxygen depletion would result in dieoff.
b. There would be an excess of the basal energy source.
c. Consumers would deplete the abundance of producers.
d. There would be more undigestable animal parts.

46. The following is the equation for trophic level transfer efficiency: (production at present trophic level/production at past trophic level)×100. If primary producers produce 1600 kcal/m^2, and primary consumers have 900 kcal/m^2, what is the trophic level transfer efficiency?

a. 50
b. 200
c. 800
d. 1600

47. There are four trophic levels in a food chain and the amount of energy at the trophic level of the primary producer is 33,000 kcal/m^2. Which of the following represents the amount of energy of the tertiary consumer?

a. 75 kcal/m^2
b. 500 kcal/m^2
c. 11,000 kcal/m^2
d. 33,000 kcal/m^2

48. Why does this figure show a higher value of gross productivity for the decomposers than the tertiary consumers?

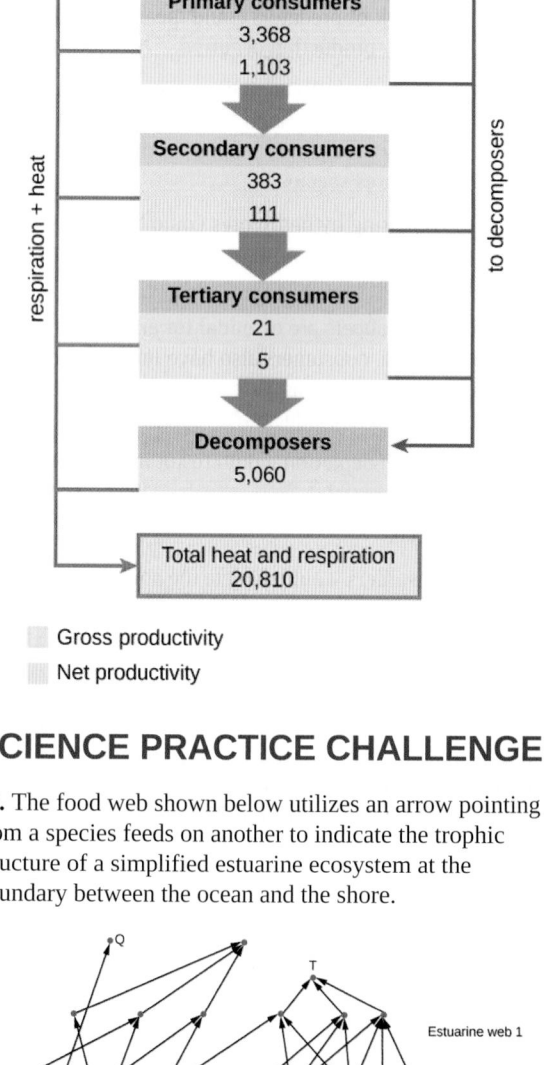

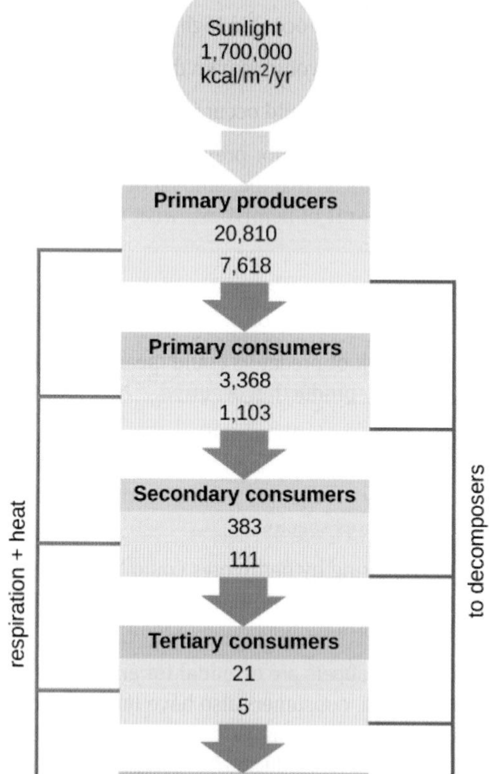

a. Due to the difference in conversion efficiencies of decomposers and tertiary consumers.
b. Because large animals are tertiary consumers whereas small microorganisms are decomposers.
c. Because tertiary consumers only consume secondary consumers whereas decomposers consume dead components of each trophic level.
d. Because tertiary consumers only consume primary consumers whereas decomposers consume dead components of each trophic level.

49. One of the key concerns about global climate change is excess amounts of carbon being released into the atmosphere. There are, however, some ways in which carbon can be sequestered from the atmosphere. Which of the following is a natural process that promotes carbon sequestration?

a. burning fossil fuels
b. methane from cattle
c. photosynthesis by plants
d. volcanic eruption

SCIENCE PRACTICE CHALLENGE QUESTIONS

50. The food web shown below utilizes an arrow pointing from a species feeds on another to indicate the trophic structure of a simplified estuarine ecosystem at the boundary between the ocean and the shore.

Figure 37.24

A. **Analyze** the interactions among species and indicate primary producers by circling the node in the food web. **Identify** the primary producers by circling the nodes in the food web.

B. **Predict** quantitatively how free energy availability for a top species such as the one designated as T in the web changes if it feeds directly on S, assuming the abundance of species S is limited only by radiant energy input.

C. Consider the consequences of the dietary shift described in B if the abundance of species becomes depleted due to consumption by species T. Under those circumstances **refine** your analysis of the food web to describe the potential effect on species Q and R.

D. Based on the preceding analyses, **construct a claim** regarding the effect of the structure, in terms of biodiversity and number of interactions among species, on ecosystem stability.

38 | CONSERVATION BIOLOGY AND BIODIVERSITY

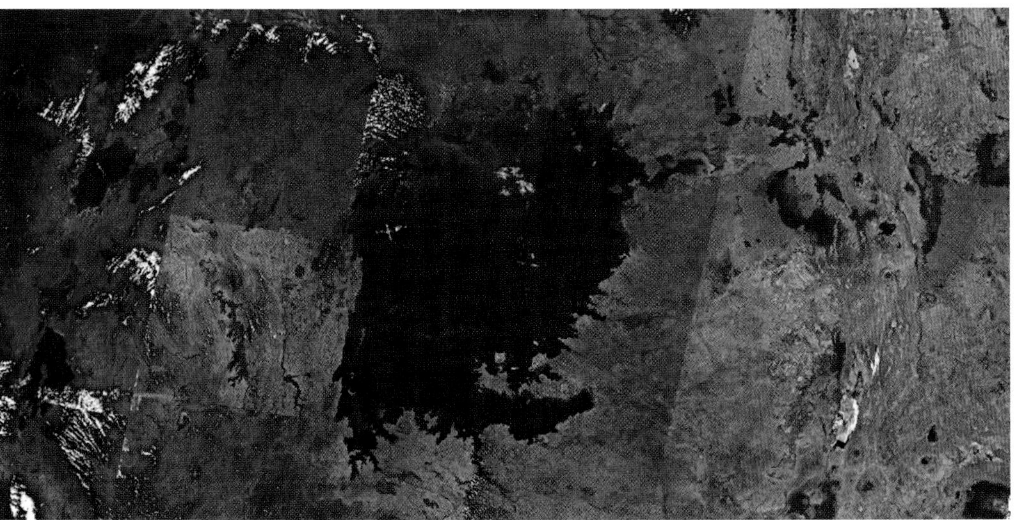

Figure 38.1 Lake Victoria in Africa, shown in this satellite image, was the site of one of the most extraordinary evolutionary findings on the planet, as well as a casualty of devastating biodiversity loss. (credit: modification of work by Rishabh Tatiraju, using NASA World Wind software)

Chapter Outline

Introduction

In the 1980s, biologists working in Lake Victoria in Africa discovered one of the most extraordinary products of evolution on the planet. Located in the Great Rift Valley, Lake Victoria is a large lake about 68,900 km^2 in area (larger than Lake Huron, the second largest of North America's Great Lakes). Biologists were studying species of a family of fish called cichlids. They found that as they sampled for fish in different locations of the lake, they never stopped finding new species, and they identified nearly 500 evolved types of cichlids. But while studying these variations, they quickly discovered that the invasive Nile Perch was destroying the lake's cichlid population, bringing hundreds of cichlid species to extinction with devastating rapidity. You can read more about the new species of cichlids at the **Science Daily website (http://openstaxcollege.org/l/32dreampond)** .

38.1 | The Biodiversity Crisis

In this section, you will explore the following questions:

- What are the different types of biodiversity?
- Why can biodiversity be described as the equilibrium of naturally fluctuating rates of extinction and speciation?
- What are examples of historical causes of high extinction rates in Earth's history?

Connection for AP® Courses

We have come to the last chapter in the text, and the journey has taken us from the origin of life on Earth to the exploration of the myriad and diverse organisms that currently inhabit our planet. Although some information in this chapter is not in scope for AP®, we must recognize how the activities of our own species, *Home sapiens*, impact ecosystems and the species inhabiting them. By appreciating and protecting other species, we preserve our own. The inverse is also true.

The exact number and kinds of species on Earth is unknown, but scientists estimate that there are about 8.7 million eukaryotic species, with only 1.5 million identified, named, and studied. The number of prokaryotes far exceeds these numbers. **Biodiversity** describes the number and variety of organisms in the biosphere.

We have learned that evolution and speciation continue to occur, but Earth has experienced five mass **extinctions**—the elimination of major groups of species. For AP® you do not need to know the names, dates and causes of these extinctions; however understanding them will help you understand how biodiversity has changed over time.

Information presented and the examples highlighted in the section support concepts outlined in Big Idea 1 and Big Idea 4 of the AP® Biology Curriculum Framework. The AP® Learning Objectives listed in the Curriculum Framework provide a transparent foundation for the AP® Biology course, an inquiry-based laboratory experience, instructional activities, and AP® exam questions. A learning objective merges required content with one or more of the seven science practices.

Big Idea 1	The process of evolution drives the diversity and unity of life.
Enduring Understanding 1.C	Life continues to evolve within a changing environment.
Essential Knowledge	**1.C.1** Speciation and extinction have occurred throughout Earth's history.
Science Practice	**5.1** The student can analyze data to identify patterns or relationships.
Learning Objective	**1.20** The student is able to analyze data related to questions of speciation and extinction throughout the Earth's history.
Essential Knowledge	**1.C.1** Speciation and extinction have occurred throughout Earth's history.
Science Practice	**4.2** The student can design a plan for collecting data to answer a particular scientific question.
Learning Objective	**1.21** The student is able to design a plan for collecting data to investigate the scientific claim that speciation and extinction have occurred throughout the Earth's history.
Big Idea 4	Biological systems interact, and these systems and their interactions possess complex properties.
Enduring Understanding 4.B	Competition and cooperation are important aspects of biological systems.

Essential Knowledge	**4.B.4** Distribution of local and global ecosystems changes over time.
Science Practice	**6.3** The student can articulate the reasons that scientific explanations and theories are refined or replaced.
Learning Objective	**4.20** The student is able to explain how the distribution of ecosystems changes over time by identifying large-scale events that have resulted in these changes in the past.

Traditionally, ecologists have measured biodiversity by taking into account both the number of species and their commonness. Biodiversity can be estimated at a number of levels of organization of living things. These estimation indexes, which came from information theory, are most useful as a first step in quantifying biodiversity between and within ecosystems; they are less useful when the main concern among conservation biologists is simply the loss of biodiversity. However, biologists recognize that measures of biodiversity, in terms of species diversity, may help focus efforts to preserve the biologically or technologically important elements of biodiversity.

The Lake Victoria cichlids provide an example through which we can begin to understand biodiversity. The biologists studying cichlids in the 1980s discovered hundreds of cichlid species representing a variety of specializations to particular habitat types and specific feeding strategies: eating plankton floating in the water, scraping and then eating algae from rocks, eating insect larvae from the bottom, and eating the eggs of other species of cichlid. The cichlids of Lake Victoria are the product of an **adaptive radiation**. An adaptive radiation is a rapid (less than three million years in the case of the Lake Victoria cichlids) branching through speciation of a phylogenetic tree into many closely related species; typically, the species "radiate" into different habitats and niches. The Galápagos finches are an example of a modest adaptive radiation with 15 species. The cichlids of Lake Victoria are an example of a spectacular adaptive radiation that includes about 500 species.

At the time biologists were making this discovery, some species began to quickly disappear. A culprit in these declines was a species of large fish that was introduced to Lake Victoria by fisheries to feed the people living around the lake. The Nile perch was introduced in 1963, but lay low until the 1980s when its populations began to surge. The Nile perch population grew by consuming cichlids, driving species after species to the point of extinction (the disappearance of a species). In fact, there were several factors that played a role in the extinction of perhaps 200 cichlid species in Lake Victoria: the Nile perch, declining lake water quality due to agriculture and land clearing on the shores of Lake Victoria, and increased fishing pressure. Scientists had not even catalogued all of the species present—so many were lost that were never named. The diversity is now a shadow of what it once was.

The cichlids of Lake Victoria are a thumbnail sketch of contemporary rapid species loss that occurs all over Earth and is caused by human activity. Extinction is a natural process of macroevolution that occurs at the rate of about one out of 1 million species becoming extinct per year. The fossil record reveals that there have been five periods of mass extinction in history with much higher rates of species loss, and the rate of species loss today is comparable to those periods of mass extinction. However, there is a major difference between the previous mass extinctions and the current extinction we are experiencing: human activity. Specifically, three human activities have a major impact: destruction of habitat, introduction of exotic species, and over-harvesting. Predictions of species loss within the next century, a tiny amount of time on geological timescales, range from 10 percent to 50 percent. Extinctions on this scale have only happened five other times in the history of the planet, and they have been caused by cataclysmic events that changed the course of the history of life in each instance. Earth is now in one of those times.

Types of Biodiversity

Scientists generally accept that the term biodiversity describes the number and kinds of species in a location or on the planet. Species can be difficult to define, but most biologists still feel comfortable with the concept and are able to identify and count eukaryotic species in most contexts. Biologists have also identified alternate measures of biodiversity, some of which are important for planning how to preserve biodiversity.

Genetic diversity is one of those alternate concepts. Genetic diversity or variation is the raw material for adaptation in a species. A species' future potential for adaptation depends on the genetic diversity held in the genomes of the individuals in populations that make up the species. The same is true for higher taxonomic categories. A genus with very different types of species will have more genetic diversity than a genus with species that look alike and have similar ecologies. If there were a choice between one of these genera of species being preserved, the one with the greatest potential for subsequent evolution is the most genetically diverse one. It would be ideal not to have to make such choices, but increasingly this may be the norm.

Many genes code for proteins, which in turn carry out the metabolic processes that keep organisms alive and reproducing. Genetic diversity can be measured as **chemical diversity** in that different species produce a variety of chemicals in their cells, both the proteins as well as the products and byproducts of metabolism. This chemical diversity has potential benefit for humans as a source of pharmaceuticals, so it provides one way to measure diversity that is important to human health and welfare.

Humans have generated diversity in domestic animals, plants, and fungi. This diversity is also suffering losses because of migration, market forces, and increasing globalism in agriculture, especially in heavily populated regions such as China, India, and Japan. The human population directly depends on this diversity as a stable food source, and its decline is troubling biologists and agricultural scientists.

It is also useful to define **ecosystem diversity**, meaning the number of different ecosystems on the planet or in a given geographic area (Figure 38.2). Whole ecosystems can disappear even if some of the species might survive by adapting to other ecosystems. The loss of an ecosystem means the loss of interactions between species, the loss of unique features of coadaptation, and the loss of biological productivity that an ecosystem is able to create. An example of a largely extinct ecosystem in North America is the prairie ecosystem. Prairies once spanned central North America from the boreal forest in northern Canada down into Mexico. They are now all but gone, replaced by crop fields, pasture lands, and suburban sprawl. Many of the species survive, but the hugely productive ecosystem that was responsible for creating the most productive agricultural soils is now gone. As a consequence, soils are disappearing or must be maintained at greater expense.

(a)

(b)

Figure 38.2 The variety of ecosystems on Earth—from (a) coral reef to (b) prairie—enables a great diversity of species to exist. (credit a: modification of work by Jim Maragos, USFWS; credit b: modification of work by Jim Minnerath, USFWS)

Current Species Diversity

Despite considerable effort, knowledge of the species that inhabit the planet is limited. A recent estimate suggests that the eukaryote species for which science has names, about 1.5 million species, account for less than 20 percent of the total number of eukaryote species present on the planet (8.7 million species, by one estimate). Estimates of numbers of prokaryotic species are largely guesses, but biologists agree that science has only begun to catalog their diversity. Even with what is known, there is no central repository of names or samples of the described species; therefore, there is no way to be sure that the 1.5 million descriptions is an accurate number. It is a best guess based on the opinions of experts in different taxonomic groups. Given that Earth is losing species at an accelerating pace, science is very much in the place it was with the Lake Victoria cichlids: knowing little about what is being lost. Table 38.1 presents recent estimates of biodiversity in different groups.

Estimates of the Numbers of Described and Predicted Species by Taxonomic Group

	Mora et al. 2011[1]		Chapman 2009[2]		Groombridge & Jenkins 2002[3]	
	Described	Predicted	Described	Predicted	Described	Predicted
Animalia	1,124,516	9,920,000	1,424,153	6,836,330	1,225,500	10,820,000
Chromista	17,892	34,900	25,044	200,500	—	—
Fungi	44,368	616,320	98,998	1,500,000	72,000	1,500,000
Plantae	224,244	314,600	310,129	390,800	270,000	320,000
Protozoa	16,236	72,800	28,871	1,000,000	80,000	600,000
Prokaryotes	—	—	10,307	1,000,000	10,175	—
Total	1,438,769	10,960,000	1,897,502	10,897,630	1,657,675	13,240,000

Table 38.1

There are various initiatives to catalog described species in accessible ways, and the internet is facilitating that effort. Nevertheless, it has been pointed out that at the current rate of species description, which according to the State of Observed Species Report is 17,000 to 20,000 new species per year, it will take close to 500 years to finish describing life on this planet.[4] Over time, the task becomes both increasingly impossible and increasingly easier as extinction removes species from the planet.

Naming and counting species may seem an unimportant pursuit given the other needs of humanity, but it is not simply an accounting. Describing species is a complex process by which biologists determine an organism's unique characteristics and whether or not that organism belongs to any other described species. It allows biologists to find and recognize the species after the initial discovery, and allows them to follow up on questions about its biology. In addition, the unique characteristics of each species make it potentially valuable to humans or other species on which humans depend. Understanding these characteristics is the value of finding and naming species.

Patterns of Biodiversity

Biodiversity is not evenly distributed on Earth. Lake Victoria contained almost 500 species of cichlids alone, ignoring the other fish families present in the lake. All of these species were found only in Lake Victoria; therefore, the 500 species of cichlids were endemic. **Endemic species** are found in only one location. Endemics with highly restricted distributions are particularly vulnerable to extinction. Higher taxonomic levels, such as genera and families, can also be endemic. Lake Huron contains about 79 species of fish, all of which are found in many other lakes in North America. What accounts for the difference in fish diversity in these two lakes? Lake Victoria is a tropical lake, while Lake Huron is a temperate lake. Lake Huron in its present form is only about 7,000 years old, while Lake Victoria in its present form is about 15,000 years old. Biogeographers have suggested these two factors, latitude and age, are two of several hypotheses to explain biodiversity patterns on the planet.

---

1. Mora Camilo et al., "How Many Species Are There on Earth and in the Ocean?" *PLoS Biology* (2011), doi:10.1371/journal.pbio.1001127.
2. Arthur D. Chapman, *Numbers of Living Species in Australia and the World*, 2nd ed. (Canberra, AU: Australian Biological Resources Study, 2009). http://www.environment.gov.au/biodiversity/abrs/publications/other/species-numbers/2009/pubs/nlsaw-2nd-complete.pdf.
3. Brian Groombridge and Martin D. Jenkins. *World Atlas of Biodiversity: Earth's Living Resources in the 21st Century*. Berkeley: University of California Press, 2002.
4. International Institute for Species Exploration (IISE), *2011 State of Observed Species (SOS)*. Tempe, AZ: IISE, 2011. Accessed May, 20, 2012. http://species.asu.edu/SOS.

Biogeographer

Biogeography is the study of the distribution of the world's species—both in the past and in the present. The work of biogeographers is critical to understanding our physical environment, how the environment affects species, and how environmental changes impact the distribution of a species; it has also been critical to developing evolutionary theory. Biogeographers need to understand both biology and ecology. They also need to be well-versed in evolutionary studies, soil science, and climatology.

There are three main fields of study under the heading of biogeography: ecological biogeography, historical biogeography (called paleobiogeography), and conservation biogeography. Ecological biogeography studies the current factors affecting the distribution of plants and animals. Historical biogeography, as the name implies, studies the past distribution of species. Conservation biogeography, on the other hand, is focused on the protection and restoration of species based upon known historical and current ecological information. Each of these fields considers both zoogeography and phytogeography—the past and present distribution of animals and plants.

One of the oldest observed patterns in ecology is that species biodiversity in almost every taxonomic group increases as latitude declines. In other words, biodiversity increases closer to the equator (Figure 38.3).

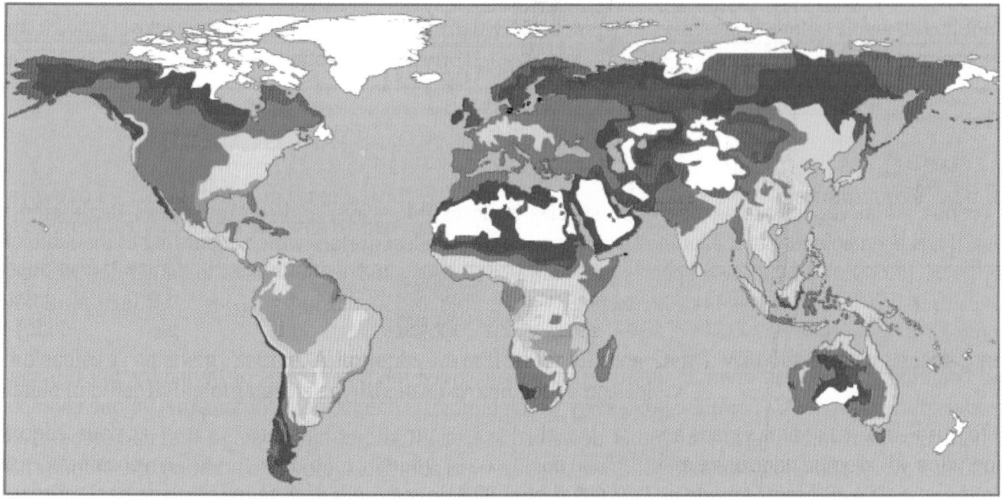

Figure 38.3 This map illustrates the number of amphibian species across the globe and shows the trend toward higher biodiversity at lower latitudes. A similar pattern is observed for most taxonomic groups.

It is not yet clear why biodiversity increases closer to the equator, but hypotheses include the greater age of the ecosystems in the tropics versus temperate regions that were largely devoid of life or drastically impoverished during the last glaciation. The idea is that greater age provides more time for speciation. Another possible explanation is the increased energy the tropics receive from the sun versus the decreased energy that temperate and polar regions receive. It is not entirely clear how greater energy input could translate into more species. The complexity of tropical ecosystems may promote speciation by increasing the **heterogeneity**, or number of ecological niches, in the tropics relative to higher latitudes. The greater heterogeneity provides more opportunities for coevolution, specialization, and perhaps greater selection pressures leading to population differentiation. However, this hypothesis suffers from some circularity—ecosystems with more species encourage speciation, but how did they get more species to begin with? The tropics have been perceived as being more stable than temperate regions, which have a pronounced climate and day-length seasonality. The tropics have their own forms of seasonality, such as rainfall, but they are generally assumed to be more stable environments and this stability might promote speciation.

Regardless of the mechanisms, it is certainly true that all levels of biodiversity are greatest in the tropics. Additionally, the rate of endemism is highest, and there are more biodiversity hotspots. However, this richness of diversity also means that knowledge of species is lowest, and there is a high potential for biodiversity loss.

Conservation of Biodiversity

In 1988, British environmentalist Norman Myers developed a conservation concept to identify areas rich in species and at significant risk for species loss: biodiversity hotspots. **Biodiversity hotspots** are geographical areas that contain high numbers of endemic species. The purpose of the concept was to identify important locations on the planet for conservation efforts, a kind of conservation triage. By protecting hotspots, governments are able to protect a larger number of species. The original criteria for a hotspot included the presence of 1500 or more endemic plant species and 70 percent of the area disturbed by human activity. There are now 34 biodiversity hotspots (**Figure 38.4**) containing large numbers of endemic species, which include half of Earth's endemic plants.

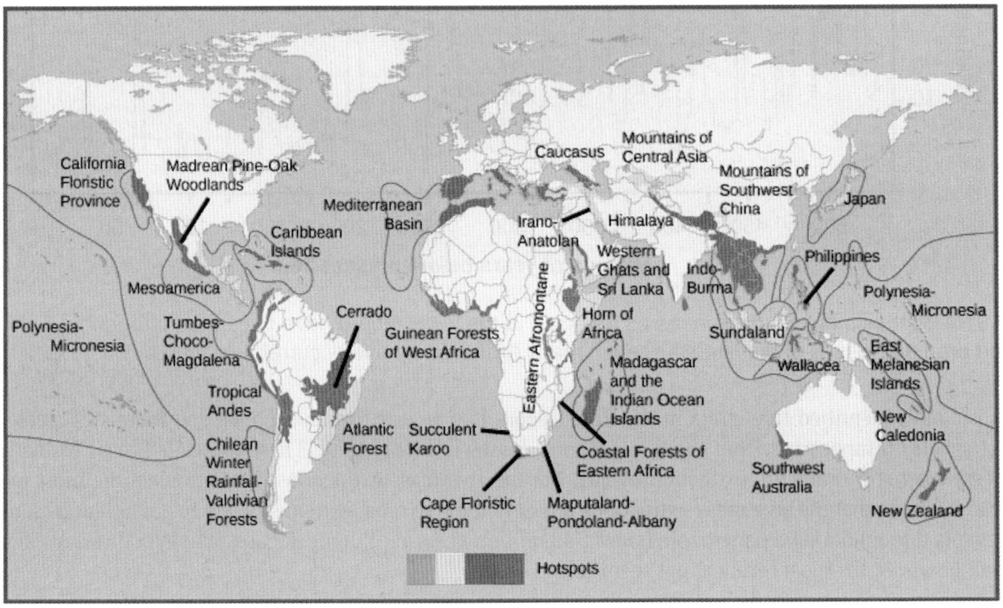

Figure 38.4 Conservation International has identified 34 biodiversity hotspots, which cover only 2.3 percent of the Earth's surface but have endemic to them 42 percent of the terrestrial vertebrate species and 50 percent of the world's plants.

Biodiversity Change through Geological Time

The number of species on the planet, or in any geographical area, is the result of an equilibrium of two evolutionary processes that are ongoing: speciation and extinction. Both are natural "birth" and "death" processes of macroevolution. When speciation rates begin to outstrip extinction rates, the number of species will increase; likewise, the number of species will decrease when extinction rates begin to overtake speciation rates. Throughout Earth's history, these two processes have fluctuated—sometimes leading to dramatic changes in the number of species on Earth as reflected in the fossil record (**Figure 38.5**).

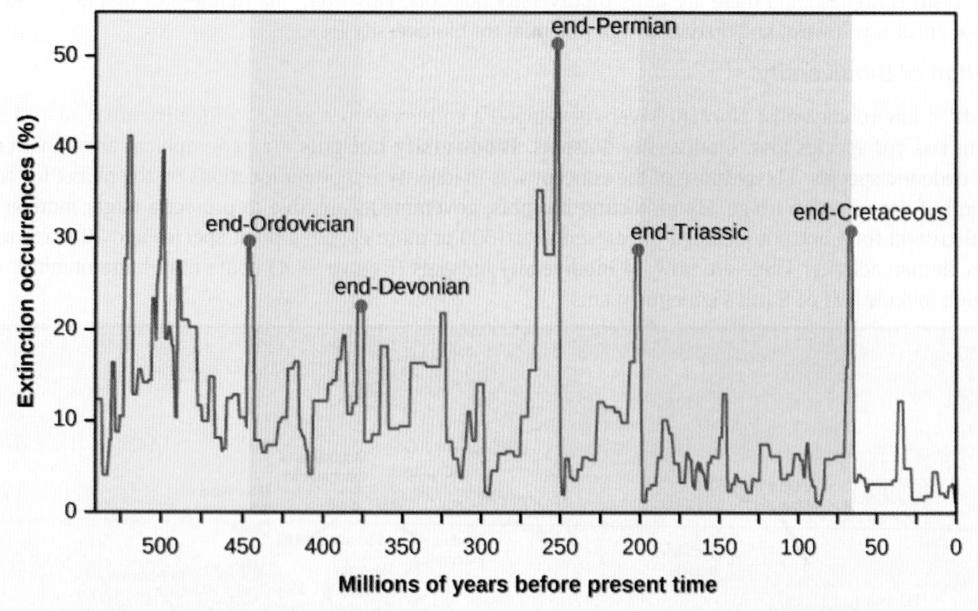

Figure 38.5 Percent extinction occurrences as reflected in the fossil record have fluctuated throughout Earth's history. Sudden and dramatic losses of biodiversity, called mass extinctions, have occurred five times.

Paleontologists have identified five strata in the fossil record that appear to show sudden and dramatic (greater than half of all extant species disappearing from the fossil record) losses in biodiversity. These are called mass extinctions. There are many lesser, yet still dramatic, extinction events, but the five mass extinctions have attracted the most research. An argument can be made that the five mass extinctions are only the five most extreme events in a continuous series of large extinction events throughout the Phanerozoic (since 542 million years ago). In most cases, the hypothesized causes are still controversial; however, the most recent event seems clear.

The Five Mass Extinctions

The fossil record of the mass extinctions was the basis for defining periods of geological history, so they typically occur at the transition point between geological periods. The transition in fossils from one period to another reflects the dramatic loss of species and the gradual origin of new species. These transitions can be seen in the rock strata. Table 38.2 provides data on the five mass extinctions.

Mass Extinctions

Geological Period	Mass Extinction Name	Time (millions of years ago)
Ordovician–Silurian	end-Ordovician O–S	450–440
Late Devonian	end-Devonian	375–360
Permian–Triassic	end-Permian	251
Triassic–Jurassic	end-Triassic	205
Cretaceous–Paleogene	end-Cretaceous K–Pg (K–T)	65.5

Table 38.2 This table shows the names and dates for the five mass extinctions in Earth's history.

The Ordovician-Silurian extinction event is the first recorded mass extinction and the second largest. During this period, about 85 percent of marine species (few species lived outside the oceans) became extinct. The main hypothesis for its cause is a period of glaciation and then warming. The extinction event actually consists of two extinction events separated by about 1 million years. The first event was caused by cooling, and the second event was due to the subsequent warming. The climate changes affected temperatures and sea levels. Some researchers have suggested that a gamma-ray burst, caused by a nearby supernova, is a possible cause of the Ordovician-Silurian extinction. The gamma-ray burst would have stripped away the Earth's ozone layer causing intense ultraviolet radiation from the sun and may account for climate changes observed at the time. The hypothesis is speculative, but extraterrestrial influences on Earth's history are an active line of research. Recovery of biodiversity after the mass extinction took from 5 to 20 million years, depending on the location.

The late Devonian extinction may have occurred over a relatively long period of time. It appears to have affected marine species and not the plants or animals inhabiting terrestrial habitats. The causes of this extinction are poorly understood.

The end-Permian extinction was the largest in the history of life. Indeed, an argument could be made that Earth nearly became devoid of life during this extinction event. The planet looked very different before and after this event. Estimates are that 96 percent of all marine species and 70 percent of all terrestrial species were lost. It was at this time, for example, that the trilobites, a group that survived the Ordovician–Silurian extinction, became extinct. The causes for this mass extinction are not clear, but the leading suspect is extended and widespread volcanic activity that led to a runaway global-warming event. The oceans became largely anoxic, suffocating marine life. Terrestrial tetrapod diversity took 30 million years to recover after the end-Permian extinction. The Permian extinction dramatically altered Earth's biodiversity makeup and the course of evolution.

The causes of the Triassic–Jurassic extinction event are not clear and hypotheses of climate change, asteroid impact, and volcanic eruptions have been argued. The extinction event occurred just before the breakup of the supercontinent Pangaea, although recent scholarship suggests that the extinctions may have occurred more gradually throughout the Triassic.

The causes of the end-Cretaceous extinction event are the ones that are best understood. It was during this extinction event about 65 million years ago that the dinosaurs, the dominant vertebrate group for millions of years, disappeared from the planet (with the exception of a theropod clade that gave rise to birds). Indeed, every land animal that weighed more then 25 kg became extinct. The cause of this extinction is now understood to be the result of a cataclysmic impact of a large meteorite, or asteroid, off the coast of what is now the Yucatán Peninsula. This hypothesis, proposed first in 1980, was a radical explanation based on a sharp spike in the levels of iridium (which rains down from space in meteors at a fairly constant rate but is otherwise absent on Earth's surface) at the rock stratum that marks the boundary between the Cretaceous and Paleogene periods (**Figure 38.6**). This boundary marked the disappearance of the dinosaurs in fossils as well as many other taxa. The researchers who discovered the iridium spike interpreted it as a rapid influx of iridium from space to the atmosphere (in the form of a large asteroid) rather than a slowing in the deposition of sediments during that period. It was a radical explanation, but the report of an appropriately aged and sized impact crater in 1991 made the hypothesis more believable. Now an abundance of geological evidence supports the theory. Recovery times for biodiversity after the end-Cretaceous extinction are shorter, in geological time, than for the end-Permian extinction, on the order of 10 million years.

visual CONNECTION

Figure 38.6 In 1980, Luis and Walter Alvarez, Frank Asaro, and Helen Michels discovered, across the world, a spike in the concentration of iridium within the sedimentary layer at the K–Pg boundary. These researchers hypothesized that this iridium spike was caused by an asteroid impact that resulted in the K–Pg mass extinction. In the photo, the iridium layer is the light band. (credit: USGS)

Scientists measured the relative abundance of fern spores above and below the Cretaceous-Paleogene boundary in a rock sample. Which of the following statements most likely represents their findings?

a. An abundance of fern spores from several species was found above the Cretaceous-Paleogene boundary, but none were found below.

b. Fern spores were found both above and below the Cretaceous-Paleogene boundary, but the spores were more abundant below the boundary than above the boundary.

c. Many species of fern spores were found both above and below the boundary, but the total number of spores was greater above the boundary.

d. An abundance of fern spores from several species was found below the Cretaceous-Paleogene boundary, but none were found above.

Explore this **interactive website (http://openstaxcollege.org/l/extinctions)** about mass extinctions.

Why did the dinosaurs that survived the immediate impact of the meteorite also die off?

a. The Earth became unbearably hot.

b. Prolonged drought resulted from the meteorite impact.

c. Debris in the atmosphere formed a thick cloud, which blocked the sun. Plants and animals died.

d. A giant tsunami wiped out all the dinosaurs from the surface of the Earth.

The Pleistocene Extinction

The Pleistocene Extinction is one of the lesser extinctions, and a recent one. It is well known that the North American, and to some degree Eurasian, **megafauna**, or large animals, disappeared toward the end of the last glaciation period. The extinction appears to have happened in a relatively restricted time period of 10,000–12,000 years ago. In North America, the losses were quite dramatic and included the woolly mammoths (last dated about 4,000 years ago in an isolated population), mastodon, giant beavers, giant ground sloths, saber-toothed cats, and the North American camel, just to name a few. The possibility that the rapid extinction of these large animals was caused by over-hunting was first suggested in the 1900s. Research into this hypothesis continues today. It seems likely that over-hunting caused many pre-written history extinctions in many regions of the world.

In general, the timing of the Pleistocene extinctions correlated with the arrival of humans and not with climate-change events, which is the main competing hypothesis for these extinctions. The extinctions began in Australia about 40,000 to 50,000 years ago, just after the arrival of humans in the area: a marsupial lion, a giant one-ton wombat, and several giant kangaroo species disappeared. In North America, the extinctions of almost all of the large mammals occurred 10,000–12,000 years ago. All that are left are the smaller mammals such as bears, elk, moose, and cougars. Finally, on many remote oceanic islands, the extinctions of many species occurred coincident with human arrivals. Not all of the islands had large animals, but when there were large animals, they were lost. Madagascar was colonized about 2,000 years ago and the large mammals that lived there became extinct. Eurasia and Africa do not show this pattern, but they also did not experience a recent arrival of humans. Humans arrived in Eurasia hundreds of thousands of years ago after the origin of the species in Africa. This topic remains an area of active research and hypothesizing. It seems clear that even if climate played a role, in most cases human hunting precipitated the extinctions.

Present-Time Extinctions

The sixth, or Holocene, mass extinction appears to have begun earlier than previously believed and has mostly to do with the activities of *Homo sapiens*. Since the beginning of the Holocene period, there are numerous recent extinctions of individual species that are recorded in human writings. Most of these are coincident with the expansion of the European colonies since the 1500s.

One of the earlier and popularly known examples is the dodo bird. The dodo bird lived in the forests of Mauritius, an island in the Indian Ocean. The dodo bird became extinct around 1662. It was hunted for its meat by sailors and was easy prey because the dodo, which did not evolve with humans, would approach people without fear. Introduced pigs, rats, and dogs brought to the island by European ships also killed dodo young and eggs.

Steller's sea cow became extinct in 1768; it was related to the manatee and probably once lived along the northwest coast of North America. Steller's sea cow was first discovered by Europeans in 1741 and was hunted for meat and oil. The last sea cow was killed in 1768. That amounts to 27 years between the sea cow's first contact with Europeans and extinction of the species.

In 1914, the last living passenger pigeon died in a zoo in Cincinnati, Ohio. This species had once darkened the skies of North America during its migrations, but it was hunted and suffered from habitat loss through the clearing of forests for farmland. In 1918, the last living Carolina parakeet died in captivity. This species was once common in the eastern United States, but it suffered from habitat loss. The species was also hunted because it ate orchard fruit when its native foods were destroyed to make way for farmland. The Japanese sea lion, which inhabited a broad area around Japan and the coast of Korea, became extinct in the 1950s due to fishermen. The Caribbean monk seal was distributed throughout the Caribbean Sea but was driven to extinction via hunting by 1952.

These are only a few of the recorded extinctions in the past 500 years. The International Union for Conservation of Nature (IUCN) keeps a list of extinct and endangered species called the Red List. The list is not complete, but it describes 380 extinct species of vertebrates after 1500 AD, 86 of which were driven extinct by overhunting or overfishing.

Estimates of Present-Time Extinction Rates

Estimates of **extinction rates** are hampered by the fact that most extinctions are probably happening without observation. The extinction of a bird or mammal is likely to be noticed by humans, especially if it has been hunted or used in some other way. But there are many organisms that are of less interest to humans (not necessarily of less value) and many that are undescribed.

The background extinction rate is estimated to be about one per million species per year (E/MSY). For example, assuming there are about ten million species in existence, the expectation is that ten species would become extinct each year (each year represents ten million species per year).

One contemporary extinction rate estimate uses the extinctions in the written record since the year 1500. For birds alone this method yields an estimate of 26 E/MSY. However, this value may be underestimated for three reasons. First, many species would not have been described until much later in the time period, so their loss would have gone unnoticed. Second, the number of recently extinct species is increasing because extinct species now are being described from skeletal remains. And third, some species are probably already extinct even though conservationists are reluctant to name them as such. Taking these factors into account raises the estimated extinction rate closer to 100 E/MSY. The predicted rate by the end of the century is 1500 E/MSY.

A second approach to estimating present-time extinction rates is to correlate species loss with habitat loss by measuring forest-area loss and understanding species-area relationships. The **species-area relationship** is the rate at which new species are seen when the area surveyed is increased. Studies have shown that the number of species present increases as the size of the island increases. This phenomenon has also been shown to hold true in other habitats as well. Turning this relationship around, if the habitat area is reduced, the number of species living there will also decline. Estimates of extinction rates based on habitat loss and species-area relationships have suggested that with about 90 percent habitat loss an expected 50 percent of species would become extinct. Species-area estimates have led to species extinction rate calculations of about 1000 E/MSY and higher. In general, actual observations do not show this amount of loss and suggestions have been made that there is a delay in extinction. Recent work has also called into question the applicability of the species-area relationship when estimating the loss of species. This work argues that the species-area relationship leads to an overestimate of extinction rates. A better relationship to use may be the endemics-area relationship. Using this method would bring estimates down to around 500 E/MSY in the coming century. Note that this value is still 500 times the background rate.

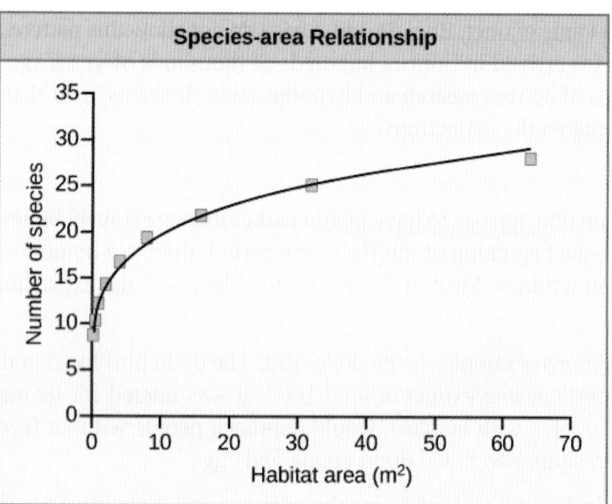

Figure 38.7 Studies have shown that the number of species present increases with the size of the habitat. (credit: modification of work by Adam B. Smith)

Check out this **interactive exploration (http://openstaxcollege.org/l/what_is_missing)** of endangered and extinct species, their ecosystems, and the causes of the endangerment or extinction.

Choose "What you can do" from the navigation menu at the left of the home page and answer the question: Why would eating less meat lead to biodiversity preservation?

a. because livestock farming accounts for 40% of all deforestation, which reduces habitats for numerous species, leads to building up of greenhouse gases, soil erosion and increase in rainfall

b. because livestock farming accounts for 40% of all deforestation, which reduces habitats for numerous species, leads to building up of greenhouse gases, soil erosion and decrease in rainfall

c. because livestock farming accounts for 63% of all deforestation, which reduces habitats for numerous species, leads to building up of greenhouse gases, soil erosion and increase in rainfall

d. because livestock farming accounts for 63% of all deforestation, which reduces habitats for numerous species and leads to a build up of greenhouse gases, soil erosion and decrease in rainfall

science practices CONNECTION for AP® Courses

Think About It

How have large-scale events results in changes in ecosystem dynamics? What are some hypotheses about the causes of mass extinctions? What types of evidence do scientists use to support these hypotheses? What particular evidence supports a specific event's occurrence?

38.2 | The Importance of Biodiversity to Human Life

In this section, you will explore the following questions:

- How does chemical diversity benefit humans?
- What are components of biodiversity that support human agriculture?
- What are ecosystem services?

Connection for AP® Courses

The information in this section does not directly apply to the concepts and content required for AP®. However, as students of biology, we need to understand the importance of preserving species and ecosystems before addressing why we should be concerned about the negative impacts of human activity on biodiversity (**Threats to Biodiversity**)

The loss of an individual species, such as the passenger pigeon, dodo bird, or woolly mammoth, seems unimportant to the "big picture," unless it's the loss of a keystone species (see the chapter that discusses population and community ecology). Extinction is a normal part of macroevolution. However, accelerated extinction rates accompanied by the loss of tens of thousands of species and the collapse of ecosystems can affect human welfare. With respect to health, many medicines, including aspirin, codeine, digoxin, atropine, and vincristine, are derived from plants. In recent years, animal venoms and toxins have excited researchers because of their pharmaceutical potential. Agricultural diversity is a requirement for food security, and the loss of wild relatives to crops threatens our ability to create new varieties that can grow in areas with previously impossible climates and soil conditions. Since 1990, global fish production has declined, and for approximately one billion of us, aquatic resources provide the main source of animal protein. Furthermore, who can put a number or monetary value on the psychological benefits of the natural landscapes we enjoy while vacationing and artists use for inspiration?

Information presented and examples highlighted in this section are not within the scope for AP® and do not align to the Curriculum Framework.

Agriculture began after early hunter-gatherer societies first settled in one place and heavily modified their immediate environment. This cultural transition has made it difficult for humans to recognize their dependence on undomesticated living things on the planet. Biologists recognize the human species is embedded in ecosystems and is dependent on them, just as every other species on the planet is dependent. Technology smoothes out the extremes of existence, but ultimately the human species cannot exist without its ecosystem.

Human Health

Contemporary societies that live close to the land often have a broad knowledge of the medicinal uses of plants growing in their area. Most plants produce **secondary plant compounds**, which are toxins used to protect the plant from insects and other animals that eat them, but some of which also work as medication. For centuries in Europe, older knowledge about the medical uses of plants was compiled in herbals—books that identified plants and their uses. Humans are not the only species to use plants for medicinal reasons: the great apes, orangutans, chimpanzees, bonobos, and gorillas have all been observed self-medicating with plants.

Modern pharmaceutical science also recognizes the importance of these plant compounds. Examples of significant medicines derived from plant compounds include aspirin, codeine, digoxin, atropine, and vincristine (**Figure 38.8**). Many medicines were once derived from plant extracts but are now synthesized. It is estimated that, at one time, 25 percent of modern drugs contained at least one plant extract. That number has probably decreased to about 10 percent as natural plant ingredients are replaced by synthetic versions. Antibiotics, which are responsible for extraordinary improvements in health and lifespans in developed countries, are compounds largely derived from fungi and bacteria.

Figure 38.8 *Catharanthus roseus*, the Madagascar periwinkle, has various medicinal properties. Among other uses, it is a source of vincristine, a drug used in the treatment of lymphomas. (credit: Forest and Kim Starr)

In recent years, animal venoms and poisons have excited intense research for their medicinal potential. By 2007, the FDA had approved five drugs based on animal toxins to treat diseases such as hypertension, chronic pain, and diabetes. Another five drugs are undergoing clinical trials, and at least six drugs are being used in other countries. Other toxins under investigation come from mammals, snakes, lizards, various amphibians, fish, snails, octopuses, and scorpions.

Aside from representing billions of dollars in profits, these medicines improve people's lives. Pharmaceutical companies are actively looking for new compounds synthesized by living organisms that can function as medicine. It is estimated that 1/3 of pharmaceutical research and development is spent on natural compounds and that about 35 percent of new drugs brought to market between 1981 and 2002 were from natural compounds. The opportunities for new medications will be reduced in direct proportion to the disappearance of species.

Agricultural Diversity

Since the beginning of human agriculture more than 10,000 years ago, human groups have been breeding and selecting crop varieties. This crop diversity matched the cultural diversity of highly subdivided populations of humans. For example, potatoes were domesticated beginning around 7,000 years ago in the central Andes of Peru and Bolivia. The potatoes grown in that region belong to seven species and the number of varieties likely is in the thousands. Each variety has been bred to thrive at particular elevations and soil and climate conditions. The diversity is driven by the diverse demands of the topography, the limited movement of people, and the demands created by crop rotation for different varieties that will do well in different fields.

Potatoes are only one example of human-generated diversity. Every plant, animal, and fungus that has been cultivated by humans has been bred from original wild ancestor species into diverse varieties arising from the demands for food value, adaptation to growing conditions, and resistance to pests. The potato demonstrates a well-known example of the risks of low crop diversity: the tragic Irish potato famine when the single variety grown in Ireland became susceptible to a potato blight, wiping out the crop. The loss of the crop led to famine, death, and mass emigration. Resistance to disease is a chief benefit to maintaining crop biodiversity, and lack of diversity in contemporary crop species carries similar risks. Seed companies, which are the source of most crop varieties in developed countries, must continually breed new varieties to keep up with evolving pest organisms. These same seed companies, however, have participated in the decline of the number of varieties available as they focus on selling fewer varieties in more areas of the world.

The ability to create new crop varieties relies on the diversity of varieties available and the accessibility of wild forms related to the crop plant. These wild forms are often the source of new gene variants that can be bred with existing varieties to create varieties with new attributes. Loss of wild species related to a crop will mean the loss of potential in crop improvement. Maintaining the genetic diversity of wild species related to domesticated species ensures our continued food supply.

Since the 1920s, government agriculture departments have maintained seed banks of crop varieties as a way to maintain crop diversity. This system has flaws because, over time, seed banks are lost through accidents, and there is no way to replace them. In 2008, the Svalbard Global Seed Vault (**Figure 38.9**) began storing seeds from around the world as a backup system to the regional seed banks. If a regional seed bank stores varieties in Svalbard, losses can be replaced from Svalbard. The seed vault is located deep into the rock of an arctic island. Conditions within the vault are maintained at ideal temperature and humidity for seed survival, but the deep underground location of the vault in the arctic means that failure of the vault's systems will not compromise the climatic conditions inside the vault.

visual CONNECTION

Figure 38.9 The Svalbard Global Seed Vault is a storage facility for seeds of Earth's diverse crops. (credit: Mari Tefre, Svalbard Global Seed Vault)

The Svalbard Global Seed Vault is located on Spitsbergen island in Norway, which has an arctic climate. Why might an arctic climate be good for seed storage?

a. Such severe climatic conditions don't let seeds dry out; they retain water and remain viable.
b. The ground is permanently frozen, so the seeds will be kept at 10°C even if the electricity fails.
c. Because such a climate extends the dormancy periods of seeds to more than what is normal.
d. Because the ground is permanently frozen, the seeds will be kept below 0°C even if electricity fails.

Crop success is largely dependent on the quality of the soil. Although some agricultural soils are rendered sterile using controversial cultivation and chemical treatments, most contain a huge diversity of organisms that maintain nutrient cycles—breaking down organic matter into nutrient compounds that crops need for growth. These organisms also maintain soil texture that affects water and oxygen dynamics in the soil that are necessary for plant growth. If farmers had to maintain arable soil using alternate means, the cost of food would be much higher than it is now. These kinds of processes are called ecosystem services. They occur within ecosystems, such as soil ecosystems, as a result of the diverse metabolic activities of the organisms living there, but they provide benefits to human food production, drinking water availability, and breathable air.

Other key ecosystem services related to food production are plant pollination and crop pest control. Over 150 crops in the United States require pollination to produce. One estimate of the benefit of honeybee pollination within the United States is $1.6 billion per year; other pollinators contribute up to $6.7 billion more.

Many honeybee populations are managed by apiarists who rent out their hives' services to farmers. Honeybee populations in North America have been suffering large losses caused by a syndrome known as colony collapse disorder, whose cause is unclear. Other pollinators include a diverse array of other bee species and various insects and birds. Loss of these species would make growing crops requiring pollination impossible, increasing dependence on other crops.

Finally, humans compete for their food with crop pests, most of which are insects. Pesticides control these competitors; however, pesticides are costly and lose their effectiveness over time as pest populations adapt. They also lead to collateral damage by killing non-pest species and risking the health of consumers and agricultural workers. Ecologists believe that the bulk of the work in removing pests is actually done by predators and parasites of those pests, but the impact has not been well studied. A review found that in 74 percent of studies that looked for an effect of landscape complexity on natural enemies of pests, the greater the complexity, the greater the effect of pest-suppressing organisms. An experimental study found that introducing multiple enemies of pea aphids (an important alfalfa pest) increased the yield of alfalfa significantly. This study shows the importance of landscape diversity via the question of whether a diversity of pests is more effective at control than one single pest; the results showed this to be the case. Loss of diversity in pest enemies will inevitably make it more difficult and costly to grow food.

Wild Food Sources

In addition to growing crops and raising animals for food, humans obtain food resources from wild populations, primarily fish populations. For approximately 1 billion people, aquatic resources provide the main source of animal protein. But since 1990, global fish production has declined. Despite considerable effort, few fisheries on the planet are managed for sustainability.

Fishery extinctions rarely lead to complete extinction of the harvested species, but rather to a radical restructuring of the marine ecosystem in which a dominant species is so over-harvested that it becomes a minor player, ecologically. In addition to humans losing the food source, these alterations affect many other species in ways that are difficult or impossible to predict. The collapse of fisheries has dramatic and long-lasting effects on local populations that work in the fishery. In addition, the loss of an inexpensive protein source to populations that cannot afford to replace it will increase the cost of living and limit societies in other ways. In general, the fish taken from fisheries have shifted to smaller species as larger species are fished to extinction. The ultimate outcome could clearly be the loss of aquatic systems as food sources.

View a **brief video (http://openstaxcollege.org/l/declining_fish)** discussing declining fish stocks.

What would be the most effective approach to reversing the damage of overfishing?

a. Ban all fishing in the oceans of the world for ten years.

b. The damage is irreparable and no measure will reverse the loss.

c. Fish only overabundant invasive species.

d. Set aside 40% of the world's oceans as no-fishing zones with international cooperation for enforcement.

Psychological and Moral Value

Finally, it has been argued that humans benefit psychologically from living in a biodiverse world. A chief proponent of this idea is entomologist E. O. Wilson. He argues that human evolutionary history has adapted us to live in a natural environment and that built environments generate stressors that affect human health and well-being. There is considerable research into the psychological regenerative benefits of natural landscapes that suggests the hypothesis may hold some truth. In addition, there is a moral argument that humans have a responsibility to inflict as little harm as possible on other species.

38.3 | Threats to Biodiversity

In this section, you will explore the following questions:

- What are significant threats to biodiversity?
- What are the impacts of habitat loss, exotic species, and hunting on biodiversity?
- What are examples of early and predicted effects of climate change on biodiversity?

Connection for AP® Courses

The core threats to biodiversity include human population growth and the unsustainable removable of resources from the environment. The three greatest proximate threats to biodiversity are habitat loss, overharvesting, and introduction of exotic species. A fourth major cause of species extinction—climate change—is becoming increasingly more significant.

The burning of fossil fuels raises levels of carbon dioxide in the atmosphere, and this “greenhouse effect” results in global climate change.

Information presented and the examples highlighted in the section support concepts outlined in Big Idea 1 and Big Idea 4 of the AP® Biology Curriculum Framework. The AP® Learning Objectives listed in the Curriculum Framework provide a transparent foundation for the AP® Biology course, an inquiry-based laboratory experience, instructional activities, and AP® exam questions. A learning objective merges required content with one or more of the seven science practices.

Big Idea 1	The process of evolution drives the diversity and unity of life.
Enduring Understanding 1.C	Life continues to evolve within a changing environment.
Essential Knowledge	**1.C.1** Speciation and extinction have occurred throughout Earth’s history.
Science Practice	**5.1** The student can analyze data to identify patterns or relationships.
Learning Objective	**1.20** The student is able to analyze data related to questions of speciation and extinction throughout the Earth’s history.
Essential Knowledge	**1.C.1** Speciation and extinction have occurred throughout Earth’s history.
Science Practice	**4.2** The student can design a plan for collecting data to answer a particular scientific question.
Learning Objective	**1.21** The student is able to design a plan for collecting data to investigate the scientific claim that speciation and extinction have occurred throughout the Earth’s history.
Big Idea 4	Biological systems interact, and these systems and their interaction possess complex properties.
Enduring Understanding 4.A	Interactions within biological systems lead to complex properties.
Essential Knowledge	**4.A.6** Interactions among living systems and with their environment result in the movement of matter and energy.
Science Practice	**6.4** The student can make claims and predictions about natural phenomena based on scientific theories and models.
Learning Objective	**4.16** The student is able to predict the effects of a change of matter or energy availability on communities.
Big Idea 4	Biological systems interact, and these systems and their interaction possess complex properties.
Enduring Understanding 4.B	Competition and cooperation are important aspects of biological systems.
Essential Knowledge	**4.B.4** Distribution of local and global ecosystems changes over time.
Science Practice	**6.4** The student can make claims and predictions about natural phenomena based on scientific theories and models.
Learning Objective	**4.21** The student is able to predict consequences of human actions on both local and global ecosystems.

The human population requires resources to survive and grow, and those resources are being removed unsustainably from the environment. As mentioned, the three greatest proximate threats to biodiversity are habitat loss, overharvesting, and introduction of exotic species. The first two of these are a direct result of human population growth and resource use. The third results from increased mobility and trade. A fourth major cause of extinction, anthropogenic climate change, has not yet had a large impact, but it is predicted to become significant during this century. Global climate change is also a consequence of human population needs for energy and the use of fossil fuels to meet those needs (Figure 38.10). Environmental issues, such as toxic pollution, have specific targeted effects on species, but they are not generally seen as threats at the magnitude of the others.

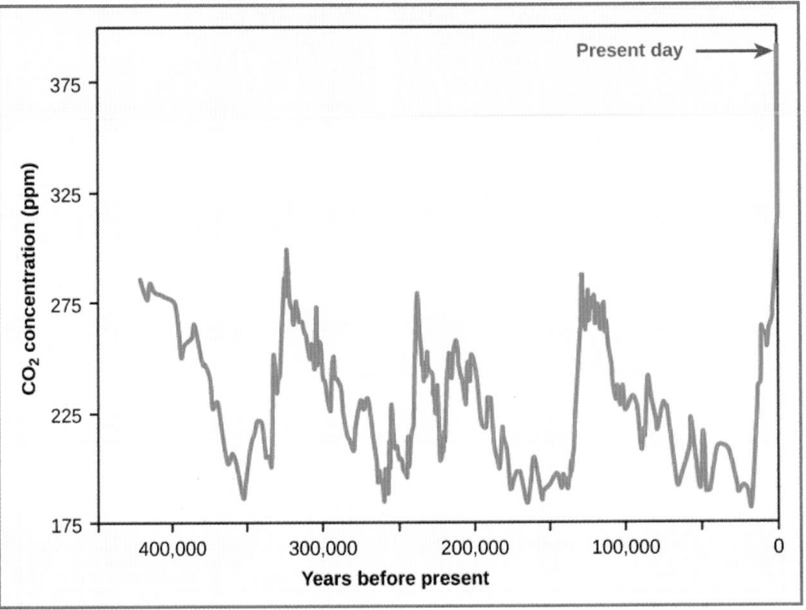

Figure 38.10 Atmospheric carbon dioxide levels fluctuate in a cyclical manner. However, the burning of fossil fuels in recent history has caused a dramatic increase in the levels of carbon dioxide in the Earth's atmosphere, which have now reached levels never before seen in human history. Scientists predict that the addition of this "greenhouse gas" to the atmosphere is resulting in climate change that will significantly impact biodiversity in the coming century.

Habitat Loss

Humans rely on technology to modify their environment and replace certain functions that were once performed by the natural ecosystem. Other species cannot do this. Elimination of their ecosystem—whether it is a forest, a desert, a grassland, a freshwater estuarine, or a marine environment—will kill the individuals in the species. Remove the entire habitat within the range of a species and, unless they are one of the few species that do well in human-built environments, the species will become extinct. Human destruction of habitats accelerated in the latter half of the twentieth century. Consider the exceptional biodiversity of Sumatra: it is home to one species of orangutan, a species of critically endangered elephant, and the Sumatran tiger, but half of Sumatra's forest is now gone. The neighboring island of Borneo, home to the other species of orangutan, has lost a similar area of forest. Forest loss continues in protected areas of Borneo. The orangutan in Borneo is listed as endangered by the International Union for Conservation of Nature (IUCN), but it is simply the most visible of thousands of species that will not survive the disappearance of the forests of Borneo. The forests are removed for timber and to plant palm oil plantations (Figure 38.11). Palm oil is used in many products including food products, cosmetics, and biodiesel in Europe. A five-year estimate of global forest cover loss for the years 2000–2005 was 3.1 percent. In the humid tropics where forest loss is primarily from timber extraction, 272,000 km^2 was lost out of a global total of 11,564,000 km^2 (or 2.4 percent). In the tropics, these losses certainly also represent the extinction of species because of high levels of endemism.

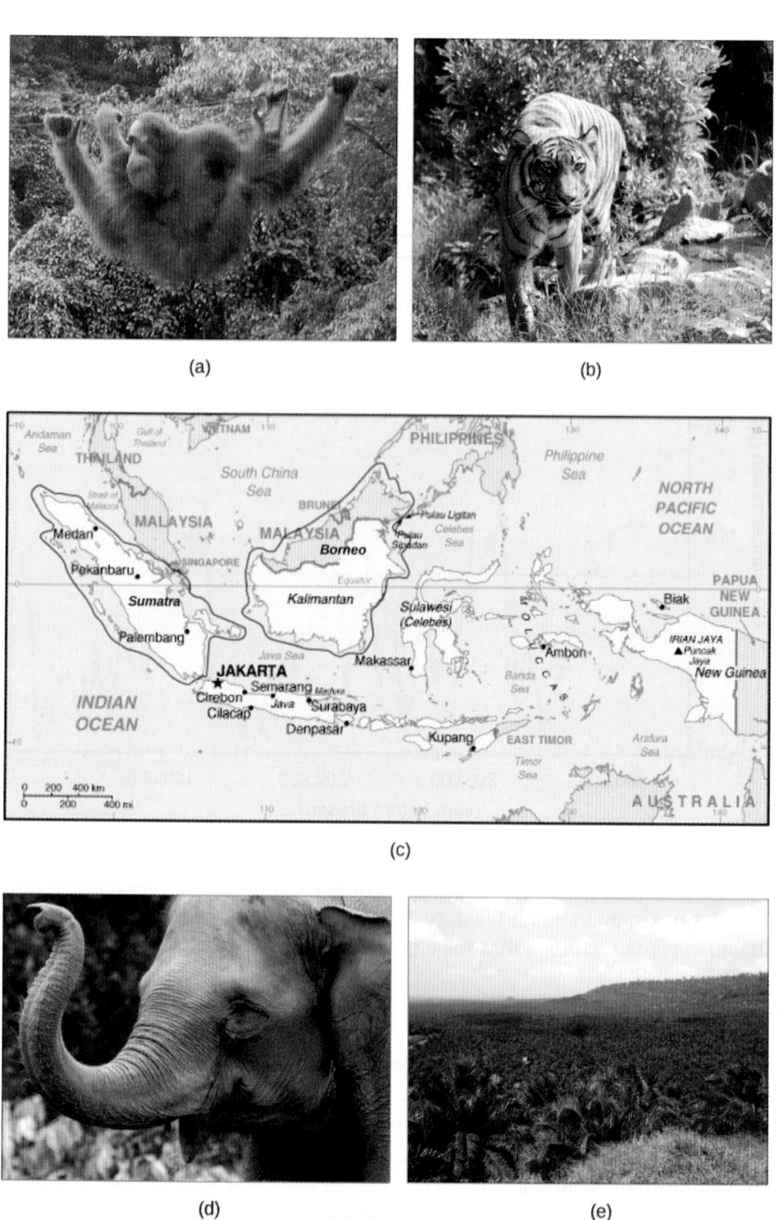

Figure 38.11 (a) One species of orangutan, *Pongo pygmaeus,* is found only in the rainforests of Borneo, and the other species of orangutan (*Pongo abelii*) is found only in the rainforests of Sumatra. These animals are examples of the exceptional biodiversity of (c) the islands of Sumatra and Borneo. Other species include the (b) Sumatran tiger (*Panthera tigris sumatrae*) and the (d) Sumatran elephant (*Elephas maximus sumatranus*), both critically endangered species. Rainforest habitat is being removed to make way for (e) oil palm plantations such as this one in Borneo's Sabah Province. (credit a: modification of work by Thorsten Bachner; credit b: modification of work by Dick Mudde; credit c: modification of work by U.S. CIA World Factbook; credit d: modification of work by "Nonprofit Organizations"/Flickr; credit e: modification of work by Dr. Lian Pin Koh)

everyday CONNECTION

Preventing Habitat Destruction with Wise Wood Choices

Most consumers do not imagine that the home improvement products they buy might be contributing to habitat loss and species extinctions. Yet the market for illegally harvested tropical timber is huge, and the wood products often find themselves in building supply stores in the United States. One estimate is that 10 percent of the imported timber stream in the United States, which is the world's largest consumer of wood products, is potentially illegally logged. In 2006, this amounted to $3.6 billion in wood products. Most of the illegal products are imported from countries that act as intermediaries and are not the originators of the wood.

How is it possible to determine if a wood product, such as flooring, was harvested sustainably or even legally? The Forest Stewardship Council (FSC) certifies sustainably harvested forest products, therefore, looking for their certification on flooring and other hardwood products is one way to ensure that the wood has not been taken illegally from a tropical forest. Certification applies to specific products, not to a producer; some producers' products may not have certification while other products are certified. While there are other industry-backed certifications other than the FSC, these are unreliable due to lack of independence from the industry. Another approach is to buy domestic wood species. While it would be great if there was a list of legal versus illegal wood products, it is not that simple. Logging and forest management laws vary from country to country; what is illegal in one country may be legal in another. Where and how a product is harvested and whether the forest from which it comes is being maintained sustainably all factor into whether a wood product will be certified by the FSC. It is always a good idea to ask questions about where a wood product came from and how the supplier knows that it was harvested legally.

Which of the following woods was most likely legally harvested?

a. unknown wood stacked in a corner of the store
b. bird-eye maple from Vermont with a FSC certificate
c. teak imported from Thailand
d. purpleheart wood from the Amazon forest

Habitat destruction can affect ecosystems other than forests. Rivers and streams are important ecosystems and are frequently modified through land development and from damming or water removal. Damming of rivers affects the water flow and access to all parts of a river. Differing flow regimes can reduce or eliminate populations that are adapted to these changes in flow patterns. For example, an estimated 91percent of river lengths in the United States have been developed: they have modifications like dams, to create energy or store water; levees, to prevent flooding; or dredging or rerouting, to create land that is more suitable for human development. Many fish species in the United States, especially rare species or species with restricted distributions, have seen declines caused by river damming and habitat loss. Research has confirmed that species of amphibians that must carry out parts of their life cycles in both aquatic and terrestrial habitats have a greater chance of suffering population declines and extinction because of the increased likelihood that one of their habitats or access between them will be lost.

Overharvesting

Overharvesting is a serious threat to many species, but particularly to aquatic species. There are many examples of regulated commercial fisheries monitored by fisheries scientists that have nevertheless collapsed. The western Atlantic cod fishery is the most spectacular recent collapse. While it was a hugely productive fishery for 400 years, the introduction of modern factory trawlers in the 1980s and the pressure on the fishery led to it becoming unsustainable. The causes of fishery collapse are both economic and political in nature. Most fisheries are managed as a common (shared) resource even when the fishing territory lies within a country's territorial waters. Common resources are subject to an economic pressure known as the **tragedy of the commons** in which essentially no fisher has a motivation to exercise restraint in harvesting a fishery when it is not owned by that fisher. The natural outcome of harvests of resources held in common is their overexploitation. While large fisheries are regulated to attempt to avoid this pressure, it still exists in the background. This overexploitation is exacerbated when access to the fishery is open and unregulated and when technology gives fishers the ability to overfish. In a few fisheries, the biological growth of the resource is less than the potential growth of the profits made from fishing if that time and money were invested elsewhere. In these cases—whales are an example—economic forces will always drive toward fishing the population to extinction.

Explore a U.S. Fish & Wildlife Service **interactive map (http://openstaxcollege.org/l/habitat_map)** of critical habitat for endangered and threatened species in the United States. To begin, select "Visit the online mapper."

For the most part, fishery extinction is not equivalent to biological extinction—the last fish of a species is rarely fished out of the ocean. At the same time, fishery extinction is still harmful to fish species and their ecosystems. There are some instances in which true extinction is a possibility. Whales have slow-growing populations and are at risk of complete extinction through hunting. There are some species of sharks with restricted distributions that are at risk of extinction. The groupers are another population of generally slow-growing fishes that, in the Caribbean, includes a number of species that are at risk of extinction from overfishing.

Coral reefs are extremely diverse marine ecosystems that face peril from several processes. Reefs are home to 1/3 of the world's marine fish species—about 4,000 species—despite making up only 1 percent of marine habitat. Most home marine aquaria are stocked with wild-caught organisms, not cultured organisms. Although no species is known to have been driven extinct by the pet trade in marine species, there are studies showing that populations of some species have declined in response to harvesting, indicating that the harvest is not sustainable at those levels. There are concerns about the effect of the pet trade on some terrestrial species such as turtles, amphibians, birds, plants, and even the orangutan.

View a **brief video (http://openstaxcollege.org/l/ocean_matters)** discussing the role of marine ecosystems in supporting human welfare and the decline of ocean ecosystems.

The ocean is home to many organisms. How are some of the smallest species connected to human breathing?

a. Phytoplankton release over 50% of the oxygen produced on Earth through chemosynthesis.

b. Phytoplankton release over 50% of the carbon dioxide produced on Earth through photosynthesis.

c. Phytoplankton release over 20% of the oxygen produced on Earth through photosynthesis.

d. Phytoplankton release over 50% of the oxygen produced on Earth through photosynthesis.

Bush meat is the generic term used for wild animals killed for food. Hunting is practiced throughout the world, but hunting practices, particularly in equatorial Africa and parts of Asia, are believed to threaten several species with extinction. Traditionally, bush meat in Africa was hunted to feed families directly; however, recent commercialization of the practice now has bush meat available in grocery stores, which has increased harvest rates to the level of unsustainability. Additionally, human population growth has increased the need for protein foods that are not being met from agriculture. Species threatened by the bush meat trade are mostly mammals including many primates living in the Congo basin.

Exotic Species

Exotic species are species that have been intentionally or unintentionally introduced by humans into an ecosystem in which they did not evolve. Such introductions likely occur frequently as natural phenomena. For example, Kudzu (*Pueraria lobata*), which is native to Japan, was introduced in the United States in 1876. It was later planted for soil conservation.

Problematically, it grows too well in the southeastern United States—up to a foot a day. It is now a pest species and covers over 7 million acres in the southeastern United States. If an introduced species is able to survive in its new habitat, that introduction is now reflected in the observed range of the species. Human transportation of people and goods, including the intentional transport of organisms for trade, has dramatically increased the introduction of species into new ecosystems, sometimes at distances that are well beyond the capacity of the species to ever travel itself and outside the range of the species' natural predators.

Most exotic species introductions probably fail because of the low number of individuals introduced or poor adaptation to the ecosystem they enter. Some species, however, possess preadaptations that can make them especially successful in a new ecosystem. These exotic species often undergo dramatic population increases in their new habitat and reset the ecological conditions in the new environment, threatening the species that exist there. For this reason, exotic species are also called invasive species. Exotic species can threaten other species through competition for resources, predation, or disease.

Explore an **interactive global database (http://openstaxcollege.org/l/exotic_invasive)** of exotic or invasive species.

How do iguanas propagate themselves and other invasive species?

a. Iguanas interbreed with invasive species and their offspring continue to breed.

b. Iguanas consume other exotic animal and seed species.

c. Iguanas reproduce in urban settings and defecate the seeds of invasive plants.

d. Iguanas reproduce in settings where other invasive species thrive.

Lakes and islands are particularly vulnerable to extinction threats from introduced species. In Lake Victoria, as mentioned earlier, the intentional introduction of the Nile perch was largely responsible for the extinction of about 200 species of cichlids. The accidental introduction of the brown tree snake via aircraft (**Figure 38.12**) from the Solomon Islands to Guam in 1950 has led to the extinction of three species of birds and three to five species of reptiles endemic to the island. Several other species are still threatened. The brown tree snake is adept at exploiting human transportation as a means to migrate; one was even found on an aircraft arriving in Corpus Christi, Texas. Constant vigilance on the part of airport, military, and commercial aircraft personnel is required to prevent the snake from moving from Guam to other islands in the Pacific, especially Hawaii. Islands do not make up a large area of land on the globe, but they do contain a disproportionate number of endemic species because of their isolation from mainland ancestors.

Figure 38.12 The brown tree snake, *Boiga irregularis*, is an exotic species that has caused numerous extinctions on the island of Guam since its accidental introduction in 1950. (credit: NPS)

It now appears that the global decline in amphibian species recognized in the 1990s is, in some part, caused by the fungus *Batrachochytrium dendrobatidis*, which causes the disease **chytridiomycosis** (Figure 38.13). There is evidence that the fungus is native to Africa and may have been spread throughout the world by transport of a commonly used laboratory and pet species: the African clawed toad (*Xenopus laevis*). It may well be that biologists themselves are responsible for spreading this disease worldwide. The North American bullfrog, *Rana catesbeiana*, which has also been widely introduced as a food animal but which easily escapes captivity, survives most infections of *Batrachochytrium dendrobatidis* and can act as a reservoir for the disease.

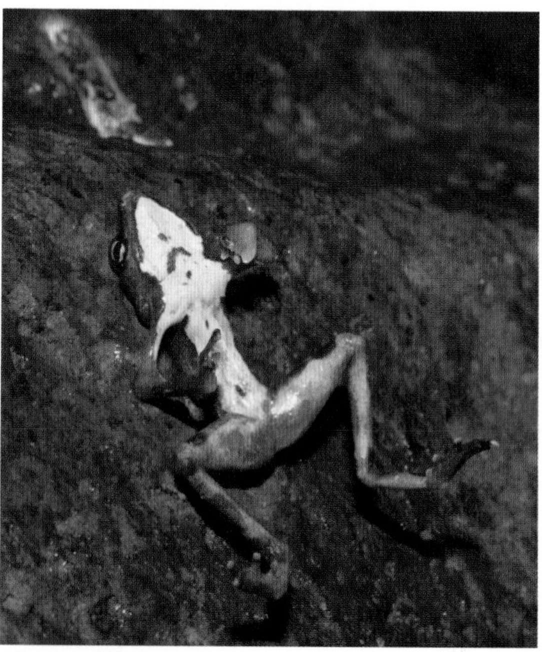

Figure 38.13 This Limosa Harlequin Frog (*Atelopus limosus*), an endangered species from Panama, died from a fungal disease called chytridiomycosis. The red lesions are symptomatic of the disease. (credit: Brian Gratwicke)

Early evidence suggests that another fungal pathogen, *Pseudogymnoascus destructans*, introduced from Europe is responsible for **white-nose syndrome**, which infects cave-hibernating bats in eastern North America and has spread from a point of origin in western New York State (Figure 38.14). The disease has decimated bat populations and threatens extinction of species already listed as endangered: the Indiana bat, *Myotis sodalis*, and potentially the Virginia big-eared bat, *Corynorhinus townsendii virginianus*. How the fungus was introduced is unclear, but one logical presumption would be that recreational cavers unintentionally brought the fungus on clothes or equipment from Europe.

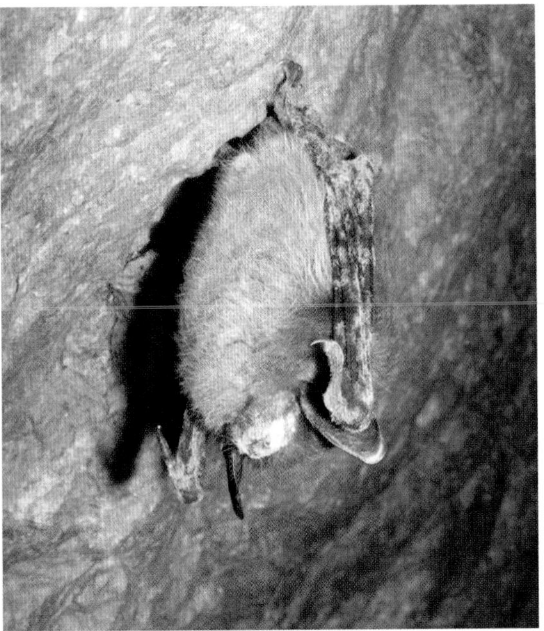

Figure 38.14 This little brown bat in Greeley Mine, Vermont, March 26, 2009, was found to have white-nose syndrome. (credit: Marvin Moriarty, USFWS)

everyday CONNECTION for AP® Courses

Invasive plants can also destroy native habitats. The Brazilian pepper tree pictured below was brought in to Florida in the 1800s. Now widespread throughout Florida, it produces a dense canopy, creating too much shade for native plant species to thrive.

Figure 38.15 (credit: Forest Starr & Kim Starr)

Populations of bats in many habitats are declining because of an infection referred to as white-nose syndrome. The pathogen forms mycelia, fuzzy tangles of white filaments, on the nose of the bats. When scraped from the nose of bats and observed under the light microscope, the filaments display cells with a nucleus and cell walls. Which of the following organisms is the most probable cause of the white-nose syndrome of bats?

a. a bacterium
b. a fungus
c. a helminth
d. a virus

science practices CONNECTION for AP® Courses

Activity

Importing of Exotic Species. Introducing a non-native species into an established community can have a number of possible effects. Using your local environment for inspiration, predict some of these effects. What factors should be considered before the importation of non-native or invasive species? Design a campaign that highlights the dangers of importing a specific non–native or invasive species into your local environment.

Climate Change

Climate change, and specifically the anthropogenic (meaning, caused by humans) warming trend presently underway, is recognized as a major extinction threat, particularly when combined with other threats such as habitat loss. Scientists disagree about the likely magnitude of the effects, with extinction rate estimates ranging from 15 percent to 40 percent of species committed to extinction by 2050. Scientists do agree, however, that climate change will alter regional climates, including rainfall and snowfall patterns, making habitats less hospitable to the species living in them. The warming trend will shift colder climates toward the north and south poles, forcing species to move with their adapted climate norms while facing habitat gaps along the way. The shifting ranges will impose new competitive regimes on species as they find themselves in contact with other species not present in their historic range. One such unexpected species contact is between polar bears and grizzly bears. Previously, these two species had separate ranges. Now, their ranges are overlapping and there are documented cases of these two species mating and producing viable offspring. Changing climates also throw off species' delicate timing adaptations to seasonal food resources and breeding times. Many contemporary mismatches to shifts in resource availability and timing have already been documented.

Figure 38.16 Since 2008, grizzly bears (*Ursus arctos horribilis*) have been spotted farther north than their historic range, a possible consequence of climate change. As a result, grizzly bear habitat now overlaps polar bear (*Ursus maritimus*) habitat. The two kinds of bears, which are capable of mating and producing viable offspring, are considered separate species as historically they lived in different habitats and never met. However, in 2006 a hunter shot a wild grizzly-polar bear hybrid known as a grolar bear, the first wild hybrid ever found.

Range shifts are already being observed: for example, some European bird species ranges have moved 91 km northward. The same study suggested that the optimal shift based on warming trends was double that distance, suggesting that the populations are not moving quickly enough. Range shifts have also been observed in plants, butterflies, other insects, freshwater fishes, reptiles, and mammals.

Climate gradients will also move up mountains, eventually crowding species higher in altitude and eliminating the habitat for those species adapted to the highest elevations. Some climates will completely disappear. The rate of warming appears to be accelerated in the arctic, which is recognized as a serious threat to polar bear populations that require sea ice to hunt seals during the winter months: seals are the only source of protein available to polar bears. A trend to decreasing sea ice coverage has occurred since observations began in the mid-twentieth century. The rate of decline observed in recent years is far greater than previously predicted by climate models.

Finally, global warming will raise ocean levels due to melt water from glaciers and the greater volume of warmer water. Shorelines will be inundated, reducing island size, which will have an effect on some species, and a number of islands will disappear entirely. Additionally, the gradual melting and subsequent refreezing of the poles, glaciers, and higher elevation mountains—a cycle that has provided freshwater to environments for centuries—will also be jeopardized. This could result in an overabundance of salt water and a shortage of fresh water.

38.4 | Preserving Biodiversity

In this section, you will explore the following questions:

- What are examples of new technologies for measuring biodiversity and legislative framework for conservation?
- What are the principles and challenges of conservation preserve design?
- What are examples of the effects of habitat restoration and the roles of zoos in biodiversity conservation

Connection for AP® Courses

The information in this section does not directly apply to concepts and content required for AP®. However, as a student of biology and traveler through the amazing world of Earth's living organisms, you have learned why it is important to protect ecosystems and preserve species. When we think of saving species through conservation efforts, we typically target endangered animals—despite the fact that most of the world's food supply comes from plants, not animals. The challenges associated with preserving biodiversity must be met with understanding biodiversity itself, changes in human behavior and beliefs, and various preservation strategies.

Modern technologies, such as DNA analysis, allow researchers to catalogue species and track genetic and evolutionary changes. Global legislation has been enacted to protect species. The approach to protect individual species alone is insufficient to address the negative impacts of human activities. More effective and widespread conservative efforts, such as the establishment of wildlife and ecosystem preserves, can be implemented. Preserves are areas of land set aside with varying degrees of protection for the organisms that inhabit them. Habitat restoration is another tool for protecting ecosystems and can improve the biodiversity of degraded ecosystems. Conservation has shown that ecosystems and the species that inhabit them, including *Homo sapiens*, can persist and thrive when we recognize the benefits of preserving Earth's habitats.

Information presented and examples highlighted in this section are not within the scope for AP® and do not align to the Curriculum Framework.

Measuring Biodiversity

The technology of molecular genetics and data processing and storage are maturing to the point where cataloguing the planet's species in an accessible way is close to feasible. **DNA barcoding** is one molecular genetic method, which takes advantage of rapid evolution in a mitochondrial gene present in eukaryotes, excepting the plants, to identify species using the sequence of portions of the gene. Plants may be barcoded using a combination of chloroplast genes. Rapid mass sequencing machines make the molecular genetics portion of the work relatively inexpensive and quick. Computer resources store and make available the large volumes of data. Projects are currently underway to use DNA barcoding to catalog museum specimens, which have already been named and studied, as well as testing the method on less studied groups. As of mid 2012, close to 150,000 named species had been barcoded. Early studies suggest there are significant numbers of undescribed species that looked too much like sibling species to previously be recognized as different. These now can be identified with DNA barcoding.

Numerous computer databases now provide information about named species and a framework for adding new species. However, as already noted, at the present rate of description of new species, it will take close to 500 years before the complete catalog of life is known. Many, perhaps most, species on the planet do not have that much time.

There is also the problem of understanding which species known to science are threatened and to what degree they are threatened. This task is carried out by the non-profit IUCN which, as previously mentioned, maintains the Red List—an online listing of endangered species categorized by taxonomy, type of threat, and other criteria (Figure 38.17). The Red List is supported by scientific research. In 2011, the list contained 61,000 species, all with supporting documentation.

visual CONNECTION

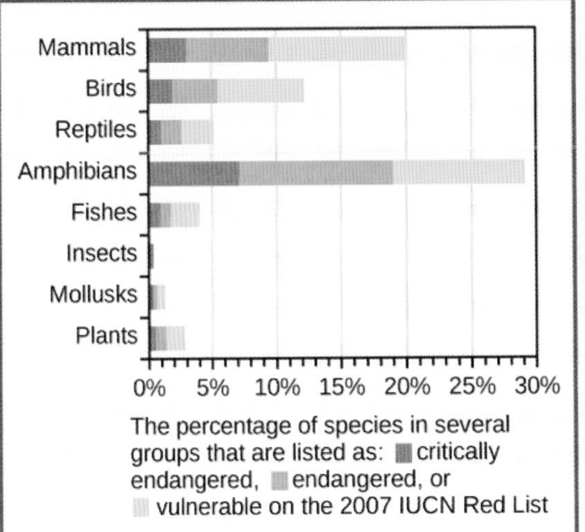

Figure 38.17 This chart shows the percentage of various animal species, by group, on the IUCN Red List as of 2007.

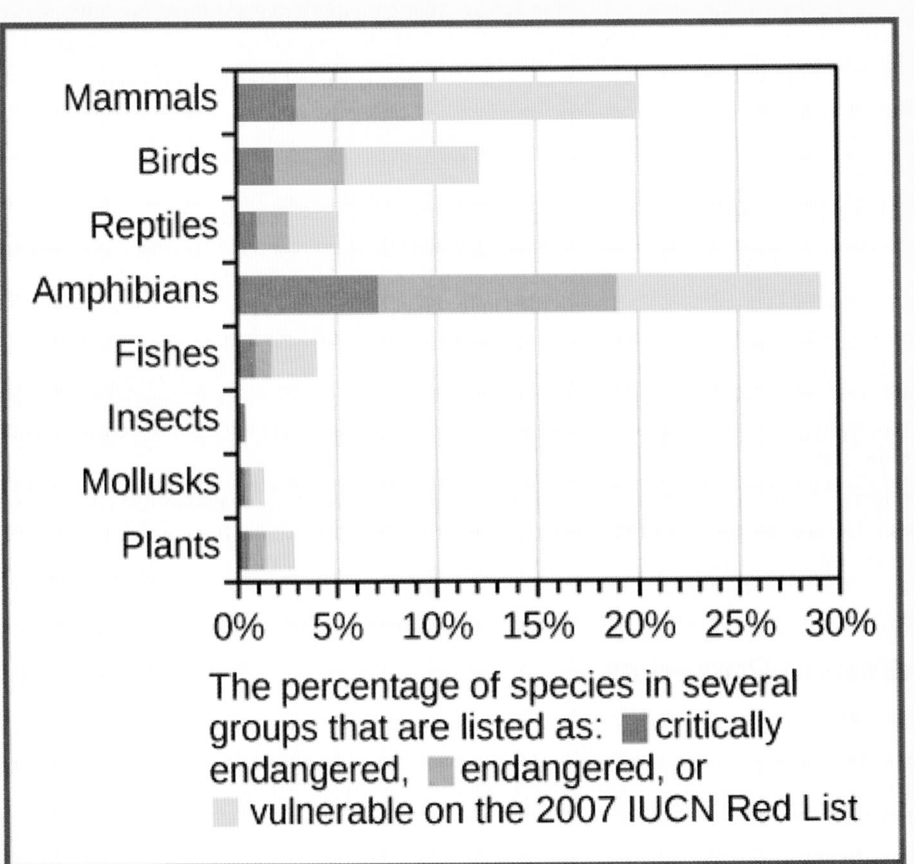

Which of the following statements is not supported by the graph?

a. There are more vulnerable fishes than critically endangered and endangered fishes combined.

b. There are more critically endangered amphibians than vulnerable, endangered and critically endangered reptiles combined.

c. Within each group, there are more critically endangered species than vulnerable species.

d. A greater percentage of bird species are critically endangered than mollusk species.

Changing Human Behavior

Legislation throughout the world has been enacted to protect species. The legislation includes international treaties as well as national and state laws. The Convention on International Trade in Endangered Species of Wild Fauna and Flora (CITES) treaty came into force in 1975. The treaty, and the national legislation that supports it, provides a legal framework for preventing approximately 33,000 listed species from being transported across nations' borders, thus protecting them from being caught or killed when international trade is involved. The treaty is limited in its reach because it only deals with international movement of organisms or their parts. It is also limited by various countries' ability or willingness to enforce the treaty and supporting legislation. The illegal trade in organisms and their parts is probably a market in the hundreds of millions of dollars. Illegal wildlife trade is monitored by another non-profit: Trade Records Analysis of Flora and Fauna in Commerce (TRAFFIC).

Within many countries there are laws that protect endangered species and regulate hunting and fishing. In the United States, the Endangered Species Act (ESA) was enacted in 1973. Species at risk are listed by the Act; the U.S. Fish & Wildlife Service is required by law to develop management plans that protect the listed species and bring them back to sustainable numbers. The Act, and others like it in other countries, is a useful tool, but it suffers because it is often difficult to get a species listed, or to get an effective management plan in place once it is listed. Additionally, species may be controversially taken off the list without necessarily having had a change in their situation. More fundamentally, the approach to protecting individual species rather than entire ecosystems is both inefficient and focuses efforts on a few highly visible and often charismatic species, perhaps at the expense of other species that go unprotected. At the same time, the Act has a critical habitat provision outlined in the recovery mechanism that may benefit species other than the one targeted for management.

The Migratory Bird Treaty Act (MBTA) is an agreement between the United States and Canada that was signed into law in 1918 in response to declines in North American bird species caused by hunting. The Act now lists over 800 protected species. It makes it illegal to disturb or kill the protected species or distribute their parts (much of the hunting of birds in the past was for their feathers).

The international response to global warming has been mixed. The Kyoto Protocol, an international agreement that came out of the United Nations Framework Convention on Climate Change that committed countries to reducing greenhouse gas emissions by 2012, was ratified by some countries, but spurned by others. Two important countries in terms of their potential impact that did not ratify the Kyoto Protocol were the United States and China. The United States rejected it as a result of a powerful fossil fuel industry and China because of a concern it would stifle the nation's growth. Some goals for reduction in greenhouse gasses were met and exceeded by individual countries, but worldwide, the effort to limit greenhouse gas production is not succeeding. The intended replacement for the Kyoto Protocol has not materialized because governments cannot agree on timelines and benchmarks. Meanwhile, climate scientists predict the resulting costs to human societies and biodiversity will be high.

As already mentioned, the private non-profit sector plays a large role in the conservation effort both in North America and around the world. The approaches range from species-specific organizations to the broadly focused IUCN and TRAFFIC. The Nature Conservancy takes a novel approach. It purchases land and protects it in an attempt to set up preserves for ecosystems. Ultimately, human behavior will change when human values change. At present, the growing urbanization of the human population is a force that poses challenges to the valuing of biodiversity.

Conservation in Preserves

Establishment of wildlife and ecosystem preserves is one of the key tools in conservation efforts. A preserve is an area of land set aside with varying degrees of protection for the organisms that exist within the boundaries of the preserve. Preserves can be effective in the short term for protecting both species and ecosystems, but they face challenges that scientists are still exploring to strengthen their viability as long-term solutions.

How Much Area to Preserve?

Due to the way protected lands are allocated (they tend to contain less economically valuable resources rather than being set aside specifically for the species or ecosystems at risk) and the way biodiversity is distributed, determining a target percentage of land or marine habitat that should be protected to maintain biodiversity levels is challenging. The IUCN World Parks Congress estimated that 11.5 percent of Earth's land surface was covered by preserves of various kinds in 2003. This area is greater than previous goals; however, it only represents 9 out of 14 recognized major biomes. Research has shown that 12 percent of all species live only outside preserves; these percentages are much higher when only threatened species and high quality preserves are considered. For example, high quality preserves include only about 50 percent of threatened amphibian species. The conclusion must be that either the percentage of area protected must increase, or the percentage of high quality preserves must increase, or preserves must be targeted with greater attention to biodiversity protection. Researchers argue that more attention to the latter solution is required.

Preserve Design

There has been extensive research into optimal preserve designs for maintaining biodiversity. The fundamental principle behind much of the research has been the seminal theoretical work of Robert H. MacArthur and Edward O. Wilson published in 1967 on island biogeography.[5] This work sought to understand the factors affecting biodiversity on islands. The fundamental conclusion was that biodiversity on an island was a function of the origin of species through migration, speciation, and extinction on that island. Islands farther from a mainland are harder to get to, so migration is lower and the equilibrium number of species is lower. Within island populations, evidence suggests that the number of species gradually increases to a level similar to the numbers on the mainland from which the species is suspected to have migrated. In addition, smaller islands are harder to find, so their immigration rates for new species are lower. Smaller islands are also less geographically diverse so there are fewer niches to promote speciation. And finally, smaller islands support smaller populations, so the probability of extinction is higher.

As islands get larger, the number of species accelerates, although the effect of island area on species numbers is not a direct correlation. Conservation preserves can be seen as "islands" of habitat within "an ocean" of non-habitat. For a species to persist in a preserve, the preserve must be large enough. The critical size depends, in part, on the home range that is characteristic of the species. A preserve for wolves, which range hundreds of kilometers, must be much larger than a preserve for butterflies, which might range within ten kilometers during its lifetime. But larger preserves have more core area of optimal habitat for individual species, they have more niches to support more species, and they attract more species because they can be found and reached more easily.

Preserves perform better when there are buffer zones around them of suboptimal habitat. The buffer allows organisms to exit the boundaries of the preserve without immediate negative consequences from predation or lack of resources. One large preserve is better than the same area of several smaller preserves because there is more core habitat unaffected by edges. For this same reason, preserves in the shape of a square or circle will be better than a preserve with many thin "arms." If preserves must be smaller, then providing wildlife corridors between them so that individuals and their genes can move between the preserves, for example along rivers and streams, will make the smaller preserves behave more like a large one. All of these factors are taken into consideration when planning the nature of a preserve before the land is set aside.

In addition to the physical, biological, and ecological specifications of a preserve, there are a variety of policy, legislative, and enforcement specifications related to uses of the preserve for functions other than protection of species. These can include anything from timber extraction, mineral extraction, regulated hunting, human habitation, and nondestructive human recreation. Many of these policy decisions are made based on political pressures rather than conservation considerations. In some cases, wildlife protection policies have been so strict that subsistence-living indigenous populations have been forced from ancestral lands that fell within a preserve. In other cases, even if a preserve is designed to protect wildlife, if the protections are not or cannot be enforced, the preserve status will have little meaning in the face of illegal poaching and timber extraction. This is a widespread problem with preserves in areas of the tropics.

Limitations on Preserves

Some of the limitations on preserves as conservation tools are evident from the discussion of preserve design. Political and economic pressures typically make preserves smaller, never larger, so setting aside areas that are large enough is difficult. If the area set aside is sufficiently large, there may not be sufficient area to create a buffer around the preserve. In this case, an area on the outer edges of the preserve inevitably becomes a riskier suboptimal habitat for the species in the preserve. Enforcement of protections is also a significant issue in countries without the resources or political will to prevent poaching and illegal resource extraction.

Climate change will create inevitable problems with the location of preserves. The species within them will migrate to higher latitudes as the habitat of the preserve becomes less favorable. Scientists are planning for the effects of global warming on future preserves and striving to predict the need for new preserves to accommodate anticipated changes to habitats; however, the end effectiveness is tenuous since these efforts are prediction based.

Finally, an argument can be made that conservation preserves reinforce the cultural perception that humans are separate from nature, can exist outside of it, and can only operate in ways that do damage to biodiversity. Creating preserves reduces the pressure on human activities outside the preserves to be sustainable and non-damaging to biodiversity. Ultimately, the political, economic, and human demographic pressures will degrade and reduce the size of conservation preserves if the activities outside them are not altered to be less damaging to biodiversity.

---

5. Robert H. MacArthur and Edward O. Wilson, E. O., *The Theory of Island Biogeography* (Princeton, N.J.: Princeton University Press, 1967).

An **interactive global data system (http://openstaxcollege.org/l/protected_areas)** of protected areas can be found at website. Review data about individual protected areas by location or study statistics on protected areas by country or region.

Access the website in this link and answer the following question.Which country has the largest percentage of its land protected?

a. Costa Rica

b. Madagascar

c. United States

d. Germany

Habitat Restoration

Habitat restoration holds considerable promise as a mechanism for restoring and maintaining biodiversity. Of course once a species has become extinct, its restoration is impossible. However, restoration can improve the biodiversity of degraded ecosystems. Reintroducing wolves, a top predator, to Yellowstone National Park in 1995 led to dramatic changes in the ecosystem that increased biodiversity. The wolves (**Figure 38.18**) function to suppress elk and coyote populations and provide more abundant resources to the guild of carrion eaters. Reducing elk populations has allowed revegetation of riparian areas, which has increased the diversity of species in that habitat. Decreasing the coyote population has increased the populations of species that were previously suppressed by this predator. The number of species of carrion eaters has increased because of the predatory activities of the wolves. In this habitat, the wolf is a keystone species, meaning a species that is instrumental in maintaining diversity in an ecosystem. Removing a keystone species from an ecological community may cause a collapse in diversity. The results from the Yellowstone experiment suggest that restoring a keystone species can have the effect of restoring biodiversity in the community. Ecologists have argued for the identification of keystone species where possible and for focusing protection efforts on those species; likewise, it also makes sense to attempt to return them to their ecosystem if they have been removed.

Figure 38.18 (a) The Gibbon wolf pack in Yellowstone National Park, March 1, 2007, represents a keystone species. The reintroduction of wolves into Yellowstone National Park in 1995 led to a change in the grazing behavior of (b) elk. To avoid predation, the elk no longer grazed exposed stream and riverbeds, such as (c) the Lamar Riverbed in Yellowstone. This allowed willow and cottonwood seedlings to grow. The seedlings decreased erosion and provided shading to the creek, which improved fish habitat. A new colony of (d) beaver may also have benefited from the habitat change. (credit a: modification of work by Doug Smith, NPS; credit c: modification of work by Jim Peaco, NPS; credit d: modification of work by "Shiny Things"/Flickr)

Other large-scale restoration experiments underway involve dam removal. In the United States, since the mid-1980s, many aging dams are being considered for removal rather than replacement because of shifting beliefs about the ecological value of free-flowing rivers and because many dams no longer provide the benefit and functions that they did when they were first built. The measured benefits of dam removal include restoration of naturally fluctuating water levels (the purpose of dams is frequently to reduce variation in river flows), which leads to increased fish diversity and improved water quality. In the Pacific Northwest, dam removal projects are expected to increase populations of salmon, which is considered a keystone species because it transports key nutrients to inland ecosystems during its annual spawning migrations. In other regions such as the Atlantic coast, dam removal has allowed the return of spawning anadromous fish species (species that are born in fresh water, live most of their lives in salt water, and return to fresh water to spawn). Some of the largest dam removal projects have yet to occur or have happened too recently for the consequences to be measured. The large-scale ecological experiments that these removal projects constitute will provide valuable data for other dam projects slated either for removal or construction.

The Role of Captive Breeding

Zoos have sought to play a role in conservation efforts both through captive breeding programs and education. The transformation of the missions of zoos from collection and exhibition facilities to organizations that are dedicated to conservation is ongoing. In general, it has been recognized that, except in some specific targeted cases, captive breeding programs for endangered species are inefficient and often prone to failure when the species are reintroduced to the wild. Zoo facilities are far too limited to contemplate captive breeding programs for the numbers of species that are now at risk. Education is another potential positive impact of zoos on conservation efforts, particularly given the global trend to urbanization and the consequent reduction in contacts between people and wildlife. A number of studies have been performed to look at the effectiveness of zoos on people's attitudes and actions regarding conservation; at present, the results tend to be mixed.

KEY TERMS

adaptive radiation rapid branching through speciation of a phylogenetic tree into many closely related species

biodiversity variety of a biological system, typically conceived as the number of species, but also applying to genes, biochemistry, and ecosystems

biodiversity hotspot concept originated by Norman Myers to describe a geographical region with a large number of endemic species and a large percentage of degraded habitat

bush meat wild-caught animal used as food (typically mammals, birds, and reptiles); usually referring to hunting in the tropics of sub-Saharan Africa, Asia, and the Americas

chemical diversity variety of metabolic compounds in an ecosystem

chytridiomycosis disease of amphibians caused by the fungus *Batrachochytrium dendrobatidis;* thought to be a major cause of the global amphibian decline

DNA barcoding molecular genetic method for identifying a unique genetic sequence to associate with a species

ecosystem diversity variety of ecosystems

endemic species species native to one place

exotic species (also, invasive species) species that has been introduced to an ecosystem in which it did not evolve

extinction disappearance of a species from Earth; local extinction is the disappearance of a species from a region

extinction rate number of species becoming extinct over time, sometimes defined as extinctions per million species–years to make numbers manageable (E/MSY)

genetic diversity variety of genes in a species or other taxonomic group or ecosystem, the term can refer to allelic diversity or genome-wide diversity

heterogeneity number of ecological niches

megafauna large animals

secondary plant compound compound produced as byproducts of plant metabolic processes that is usually toxic, but is sequestered by the plant to defend against herbivores

species-area relationship relationship between area surveyed and number of species encountered; typically measured by incrementally increasing the area of a survey and determining the cumulative numbers of species

tragedy of the commons economic principle that resources held in common will inevitably be overexploited

white-nose syndrome disease of cave-hibernating bats in the eastern United States and Canada associated with the fungus *Pseudogymnoascus destructans*

CHAPTER SUMMARY

38.1 The Biodiversity Crisis

Biodiversity exists at multiple levels of organization and is measured in different ways depending on the goals of those taking the measurements. These measurements include numbers of species, genetic diversity, chemical diversity, and ecosystem diversity. The number of described species is estimated to be 1.5 million with about 17,000 new species being described each year. Estimates for the total number of species on Earth vary but are on the order of 10 million. Biodiversity is negatively correlated with latitude for most taxa, meaning that biodiversity is higher in the tropics. The mechanism for this pattern is not known with certainty, but several plausible hypotheses have been advanced.

Five mass extinctions with losses of more than 50 percent of extant species are observable in the fossil record. Biodiversity recovery times after mass extinctions vary, but have been up to 30 million years. Recent extinctions are recorded in written history and are the basis for one method of estimating contemporary extinction rates. The other method uses measures of habitat loss and species-area relationships. Estimates of contemporary extinction rates vary, but some rates are as high as 500 times the background rate, as determined from the fossil record, and are predicted to rise.

38.2 The Importance of Biodiversity to Human Life

Humans use many compounds that were first discovered or derived from living organisms as medicines: secondary plant compounds, animal toxins, and antibiotics produced by bacteria and fungi. More medicines are expected to be discovered in nature. Loss of biodiversity will impact the number of pharmaceuticals available to humans.

Crop diversity is a requirement for food security, and it is being lost. The loss of wild relatives to crops also threatens breeders' abilities to create new varieties. Ecosystems provide ecosystem services that support human agriculture: pollination, nutrient cycling, pest control, and soil development and maintenance. Loss of biodiversity threatens these ecosystem services and risks making food production more expensive or impossible. Wild food sources are mainly aquatic, but few are being managed for sustainability. Fisheries' ability to provide protein to human populations is threatened when extinction occurs.

Biodiversity may provide important psychological benefits to humans. Additionally, there are moral arguments for the maintenance of biodiversity.

38.3 Threats to Biodiversity

The core threats to biodiversity are human population growth and unsustainable resource use. To date, the most significant causes of extinctions are habitat loss, introduction of exotic species, and overharvesting. Climate change is predicted to be a significant cause of extinctions in the coming century. Habitat loss occurs through deforestation, damming of rivers, and other activities. Overharvesting is a threat particularly to aquatic species, while the taking of bush meat in the humid tropics threatens many species in Asia, Africa, and the Americas. Exotic species have been the cause of a number of extinctions and are especially damaging to islands and lakes. Exotic species' introductions are increasing because of the increased mobility of human populations and growing global trade and transportation. Climate change is forcing range changes that may lead to extinction. It is also affecting adaptations to the timing of resource availability that negatively affects species in seasonal environments. The impacts of climate change are greatest in the arctic. Global warming will also raise sea levels, eliminating some islands and reducing the area of all others.

38.4 Preserving Biodiversity

New technological methods such as DNA barcoding and information processing and accessibility are facilitating the cataloging of the planet's biodiversity. There is also a legislative framework for biodiversity protection. International treaties such as CITES regulate the transportation of endangered species across international borders. Legislation within individual countries protecting species and agreements on global warming have had limited success; there is at present no international agreement on targets for greenhouse gas emissions. In the United States, the Endangered Species Act protects listed species but is hampered by procedural difficulties and a focus on individual species. The Migratory Bird Act is an agreement between Canada and the United States to protect migratory birds. The non-profit sector is also very active in conservation efforts in a variety of ways.

Conservation preserves are a major tool in biodiversity protection. Presently, 11percent of Earth's land surface is protected in some way. The science of island biogeography has informed the optimal design of preserves; however, preserves have limitations imposed by political and economic forces. In addition, climate change will limit the effectiveness of preserves in the future. A downside of preserves is that they may lessen the pressure on human societies to function more sustainably outside the preserves.

Habitat restoration has the potential to restore ecosystems to previous biodiversity levels before species become extinct. Examples of restoration include reintroduction of keystone species and removal of dams on rivers. Zoos have attempted to take a more active role in conservation and can have a limited role in captive breeding programs. Zoos also may have a useful role in education.

REVIEW QUESTIONS

1. In an effort to enter all identified species on Earth into a digital catalog, scientists are preparing a unique tag for each species. The following algorithms have been generated to create unique tags. Estimate which algorithm is best suited for the task.

a. an algorithm that creates 15,000 to 20,000 unique tags

b. an algorithm that creates 150,000 to 200,000 unique tags

c. an algorithm that creates 1.5 million to 2 million unique tags

d. an algorithm that creates 10 million to 20 million unique tags

2. Two genera of birds exist side-by-side on an island. Genus A is characterized by a few species of similar, genetic material. Genus B contains different species of birds with a wide variety of genetic traits. After a volcanic explosion changes the ecosystem, which genus has the highest probability of surviving the disaster?

a. Genus A, which contains well adapted species.

b. Genus B, which has greater genetic diversity and is more likely to have traits that confer an advantage in the new environment.

c. Genus A, which can serve as ancestors for the new species.

d. Genus B, because these species likely evolved from Genus A species in the past.

3. A report describes the biodiversity of an island in a remote archipelago in the Pacific Ocean having a larger number of species of birds than neighboring islands. The biologists that investigated the ecosystem of the island described it as an example of adaptive radiation. Their conclusion is based on the fact that they observed _____.

a. a burst of speciation

b. the presence of of invasive species

c. a hypothesized cause of a mass extinction

d. evidence of an apex predator

4. Findings from layers dating to the Cambrian geological period show an appearance of many new organisms in addition to older forms of life. The Cambrian explosion corresponds to a time where _____.

a. New species radiated from existing species.

b. New species appeared due to spontaneous mutations.

c. Ancient species were replaced by newly evolved species.

d. A massive die-out freed ecosystems for new species.

5. Paleontologists are analyzing fossils from a newly excavated site with layers dating from several geological periods. They established a particular layer probably correlates to a mass extinction. Which of the following is the most likely reason for their conclusion?

a. Over 95 percent of species present in older layers have disappeared in this particular layer.

b. An asteroid impact altered the geological terrain significantly.

c. All of the fossils observed were of larger sized organisms.

d. A loss of over 50 percent of species was observed.

6. What is a likely reason that small animals survived the cataclysmic impact of a large meteorite that caused the massive extinction at the Cretaceous-Paleocene?

a. Small animals stopped being hunted by dinosaurs.

b. Small animals do not depend on plants for food.

c. Small animals needed less food for survival and reproduce rapidly.

d. Small animals fed on the dead dinosaurs.

7. Scientists are evaluating an island ecosystem to be upgraded to a hot spot of biodiversity. They conduct field research on the species that populate the area. Their final assessment on the biodiversity of the ecosystem will be based on which estimate?

a. the total number of species in an ecosystem

b. the total number of organisms in an ecosystem

c. the total number of species divided by the area of the ecosystem

d. the total number of endangered species in an ecosystem

8. A secondary plant compound might be used for which of the following?

a. a new crop variety

b. a new drug

c. a soil nutrient

d. a new species

9. A component of snake venom kills the prey by preventing blood from clotting. Which of the following is the most likely medical application for the active component?

a. promoting scab formation

b. speeding healing of wounds

c. relaxing muscle pain

d. a blood thinner

10. Different varieties of potatoes are known to thrive at different altitudes. What could be the related benefit of maintaining the diversity of potato plants?

a. Diverse types of pollinators can be involved.
b. The range of usable land is extended.
c. The taste of potatoes when fried is improved.
d. Resistance to pests can be introduced if necessary.

11. Which of the following agricultural crops is most likely to survive a catastrophic event?

a. monoculture of a crop on a large surface
b. diverse varieties of a crop surrounded by a diverse ecosystem
c. single crop surrounded by a diverse ecosystem
d. diverse varieties of a crop in a simple ecosystem

12. Which factor is present in an ecosystem that performs the same role as a pesticide?

a. pollination
b. plant resistance to chemicals
c. asexual reproduction
d. presence of insect predators

13. Urban designers included wetlands and lagoons connected to a water treatment plant to a new subdivision of homes. The designers would have most likely applied which principle of conservation to their plans?

a. ecosystem service
b. biodiversity preservation
c. habitat restoration
d. chemical diversity

14. Most antibiotics in use today are prepared or derived from____.

a. secondary compounds from microorganisms
b. secondary compounds from viruses
c. fully synthetic chemical compounds
d. compounds synthesized by plants

15. Loss of biodiversity and accelerations of extinction rates have several causes. Which of the following situations causes direct loss of biodiversity owing to loss of habitat?

a. fishing cod at a rate that is greater than natural replacement
b. converting a prairie to a farm field
c. introduction of an invasive ornamental plant in a new ecosystem
d. emission of greenhouse gases increasing the average temperatures of an area

16. Which of the following activities will result in major habitat loss?

a. picking wild flowers in a meadow
b. cutting a tree in one's backyard
c. a farmer switching from wheat to soy crop
d. building a dam that will flood a large plain

17. Exotic predator species are especially threatening to what kind of ecosystem?

a. deserts
b. marine ecosystems
c. islands
d. tropical forests

18. Backpackers returning from a long trip abroad are stopped by customs and asked whether they brought back plants, flowers or fruit from their trip location. Their fruit bought at a local market is confiscated. Why was the fruit confiscated?

a. The hikers are supposed to pay duty on imported fruit.
b. The fruit can be processed to produce illicit drugs.
c. The fruit seed could be planted and could eliminate all local species.
d. The fruit may introduce new exotic pests that threaten local plants.

19. Grizzly bears and black bears have a varied diet and hunting grounds. On the other hand, polar bears feed mostly on seals. They walk on the sea ice and wait by breathing holes for seals to emerge from the water for fresh air. Which of the following animals would be most affected by the melting of sea ice in Alaska?

a. grizzly bears
b. polar bears
c. koalas
d. black bears

20.

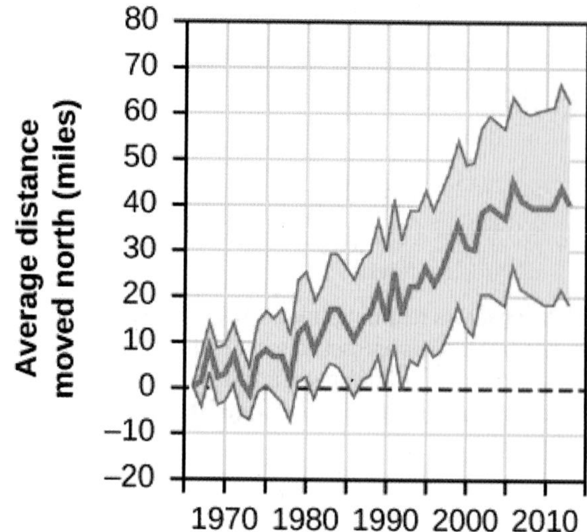

This graph shows the movement northward of wintering grounds of North American bird species. The trend closely mirrors the increase in average winter temperatures. What is one problem that could develop from birds using farther north areas?

a. Abandoned wintering grounds are left with a poorer ecosystem.
b. Movement northward leads to overcrowding of reproductive grounds.
c. Food competition increases with birds that do not migrate.
d. All of the above.

21. The method of DNA barcoding allows cataloguing of an organism using rapid sequencing methods. The choice of which gene to use for barcoding is guided by its rate of evolution. Which genes are most useful for barcoding eukaryotes with the exception of plants?

a. nuclear genes
b. chloroplast genes
c. plasmids
d. mitochondrial

22. The choice of using a mitochondrial gene for barcoding of genes depends on _____.

a. the fact that suitable primers for sequencing are not available for nuclear genes
b. Any gene can be used.
c. the slow rate of evolution in mitochondrial genes
d. that there is less variability between individuals of a same species than between individuals of different species

23. While planning an ecological preserve, conservationists plan for an area limited in size with highly diversified niches, which provide habitats to a rich diversity of species. With these constraints in mind, decide which of the following ecosystems is the foundation of the preserve design?

a. desert
b. islands
c. the tropical rain forest
d. the temperate rain forest

24. A marine preserve is designed off the coast of the Northwest of the US. The coast is dotted by several Native American reservations where the traditional occupation is catching and processing fish. Which parties must be involved in the design of the preserve?

a. marine biologists only
b. marine biologists and oceanographers
c. marine biologists, oceanographers, and policy makers
d. marine biologists, oceanographers, policy makers, and representatives of the tribes

25. Loss of wetlands has a great impact both on the biotic and abiotic parts of an ecosystem. Wetlands provide rich habitats and act as a filter for pollution. Some loss of wetland is due to silt and invasive species clogging water flow.To restore these wetlands, it is often enough to _____.

a. Open new waterways.
b. Restore the water supply.
c. Re-introduce endangered animals.
d. Introduce water adapted plants.

26. Acid mining pollutes nearby streams by acidifying water and discharging highly toxic by-products. Bacteria have been used to neutralize the pH and detoxify chemical compounds making the stream suitable for animals and plants. This approach to restoration of habitat is an example of _____.

a. keystone species introduction
b. bioremediation
c. ecosystem preservation
d. biological control

27. What was the name of the first international agreement

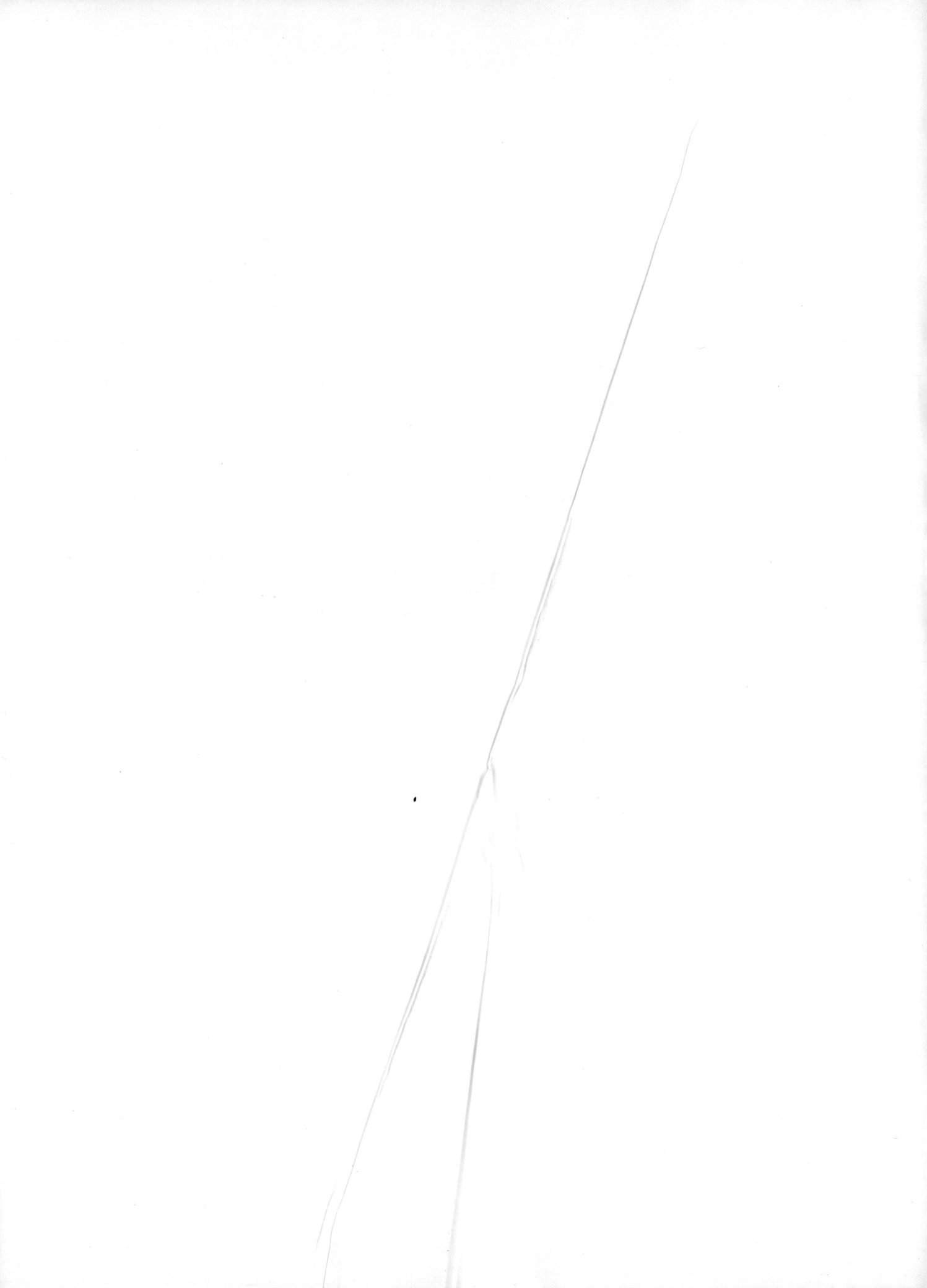